Showing Why Math Matters

Rockswold teaches algebra in context, answering the question, "Why am I learning this?"

Creating a Social Network

Although it may not be obvious, math is essential for social networks to operate properly. Matrices are used to keep track of relationships between people on Facebook, Twitter, or Spotify. Also, a matrix can be used to describe links to and from websites on the Internet. (See the Chapter 6 opener on page 480, Section 6.5, Example 2 on page 538, and Example 9 page 545.)

Starting Up Your Own Company

If you are starting up a small business, you might be interested in a payment startup called Square that allows businesses to swipe credit cards on iPhones and Android devices. Square's dramatic growth during recent years can be analyzed with the aid of a linear inequality. (See the Introduction to Section 2.3 on page 112 and Example 3 on pages 115–116.)

Getting the Jitters?

The side effects of caffeine include either headaches or the jitters. However, with the aid of a system of linear inequalities, we can identify the levels of caffeine intake where neither side effect occurs. (See the Introduction to Section 6.2 on page 499.)

Determining a Margin of Error

Whether a person is being shot out of cannon or manufacturing an iPhone, the concept of a margin of error is essential. To determine accurate margins of error, we need the concept of an absolute value inequality. (See the Introduction to Section 2.5 on page 142 and Example 7 on page 148.)

Modeling Half-Life of a Facebook Link

A typical Facebook link experiences half of its engagements, or hits, during the first 3 hours. By using exponential functions we can estimate how many hits a Facebook link might experience in a given period of time. (See the Chapter 5 opener on page 360.)

Classifying Tornados

The intensity of a tornado is often classified using the Fujita scale: the greater the wind speed of a tornado, the greater its Fujita number. To use this scale we need the concept of a piecewise-constant function. (See the discussion in Section 2.4 on page 129.)

Diminishing Returns and Overfishing

If there are only a few fishing boats in a large body of water, each boat might catch its limit. However, as the number of boats increases, there is a point of diminishing returns, where each boat starts to catch fewer and fewer fish. We can analyze this situation with a piecewise-polynomial function. (See Example 7 in Section 4.2 on page 259.)

Understanding Size in Biology

Larger animals tend to have slower heart rates and larger birds tend to have bigger wings. To understand size and physical characteristics in nature, we need to study power functions. (See the discussion and Example 10 in Section 4.8 on pages 335–336.)

PEARSON ALWAYS LEARN

Gary K. Rockswold

College Algebra with Modeling & Visualization

Second Custom Edition for Santa Fe College

Taken from:
College Algebra with Modeling & Visualization, Fifth Edition
by Gary K. Rockswold

Cover Art: Courtesy of Corbis

College Algebra with Modeling & Visualization, Fifth Edition
by Gary K. Rockswold

Pearson Learning Solutions, 501 Boylston Street, Suite 900,
Boston, MA 02116
A Pearson Education Company
www.pearsoned.com

Printed in the United States of America

3 4 5 6 7 8 9 10 V092 18 17 16 15 14

000200010271785215

ML

ISBN 10: 1-269-35866-9
ISBN 13: 978-1-269-35866-8

Welcome Students!

MyMathLab is an interactive website where you can:

- Self-test & work through practice exercises with step-by-step help to improve your math skills.
- Study more efficiently with a personalized study plan and exercises that match your book.
- Get help when YOU need it. MyMathLab includes multimedia learning aids, videos, animations, and live tutorial help.

Before You Begin:

To register for MyMathLab you will need:

☑ A **MyMathLab student access code** (packaged with your new text, standalone at your bookstore, or available for purchase with a major credit card at www.coursecompass.com)

☑ **Your instructors' Course ID number:** ____________________

☑ **Your school's zip code:** __________________

☑ **A valid email address**

Student Registration:

- Go to http.//www.coursecompass.com and click the **Student** button under Register.
- Review the **Before You Start** information to ensure you have everything you need to register; click Next.
- On the Course ID page:
  - Enter the Course ID and click on Find Course
  - Choose your enrollment method
    - If your student access code came packaged with your textbook, select Access Code. *(Select "Buy Now" to purchase online access using your credit card)*
    - Enter your student access code as displayed; use the tab key to move from box to box and use all **CAPITAL LETTERS** when entering the access code. Click Next.
- Please read all information in the License Agreement and Privacy Policy. Click on Accept if you agree to the terms.
- On the Access Information screen:
  - **If you have registered for other Pearson online products** and already have a login name and password, **select Yes.** Boxes will appear for you to enter your login information.
  - **If this is the first time you have registered for a Pearson online product, select No.** Boxes will appear for you to enter your desired login name and password. You may want to use your email address as your login name. If you do not use your email address, be prepared with a second login name choice if the one you first selected is already in use. Your login name must be at least 4 characters and cannot be the same as your password.
  - **If you aren't sure whether you have a Pearson account or not, select Not Sure**. Enter your email address and click Search. If you have an account, your login information will be sent to your email address within a few moments. Change your selection to Yes, and enter your login name and password as directed.
- On the Account Information page, enter your first and last name and email address. Re-type your email address to make sure it is correct.
- In the School Location section, select United States from the School Country drop-down menu. Enter your **school zip code**, and then select your school from the drop-down list.

- Select a security question and answer to ensure the privacy of your account Click Next.
- When your registration process is complete you will see a confirmation screen. Click Log In Now to reach CourseCompass, and click Log In. Enter your login name and password and click Log In.

Logging In:

- Go to www.coursecompass.com and click on Log In. Enter your login name and password and click Log in.
- On the MyCourseCompass page, click on the course name to enter your instructor's course.
- The first time you enter your course from your own computer and any time you use a new computer click the **Installation Wizard** on the announcements page or navigational button at the bottom left of the screen. The wizard (or Browser Check) will detect and then help you install the plug-ins and players you need to access the math exercises and multimedia content in your MyMathLab course. Follow the screen instructions to complete this process. NOTE: Check with your instructor to ensure all plug-ins are installed in the college computer labs.
- After completing the installation process and closing the wizard you will be on your course home page and ready to begin exploring your **MyMathLab** course.

Need help?

Contact Product Support at http://www.mymathlab.com/contactus.htm for live CHAT, email or phone support.

Tips for using MyMathLab on your Mac computer and Windows Vista Operating System

Tips for configuring your browser on your Mac computer

- To use MyMathLab, you must set your browser to accept cookies.

To enable cookies in Firefox:

1. From the Firefox menu, choose **Firefox > Preferences**
2. At the top of the window, click the **Privacy** icon.
3. In the Cookies section of the window:
   - Check "**Accept cookies from sites**"
   - Check "**Accept third-party cookies**" (Firefox 3 only)
4. From the **Keep until** dropdown list, choose either "**they expire**" or "**I close Firefox**".
5. Close the Preferences window.

To enable cookies in Safari:

1. From the Safari menu, choose **Safari > Preferences.**
2. At the top of the window, click the **Security** lock icon.
3. Under Accept Cookies, make sure **Always** is selected.
4. Close the Preferences window.

If you have set additional security options (site filters, script controls, and the like) and encounter problems using MyMathLab, please contact Product Support to get additional help at **888.883.1299** or email **helpdesk@mylabs.ecollege.com**

Tips for using the TestGen plug-in

- If your course includes TestGen tests, you must use **Safari** when taking these tests. Although the TestGen test will open in Firefox, certain features such as the navigation buttons do not work.
- To install the TestGen plug-in, you need StuffIt Expander. If you do not have this program, you can download it for **free** from this site: http://my.smithmicro.com/mac/stuffitexpander/download-html.
- After you have installed the TestGen plug-in, you need to quit and then reopen Safari to verify the installation.
- If you are using an Intel-based Mac, you will also need to enable Rosetta to use the TestGen plug-in.

  To check if your Mac is Intel-based:
  1. From the Apple icon menu, select **About this Mac**.
  2. Review the **Processor** information.
  3. Intel-based Macs will have **Intel** in the processor description.

  To enable Rosetta for Safari:
  1. From the **Finder**, navigate to your **Applications** folder.
  2. Select your web browser (do not open the application).
  3. From the **File** menu, choose **Get Info**.
  4. Check the box that says "**Open using Rosetta**".
  5. Close the window to save your settings.

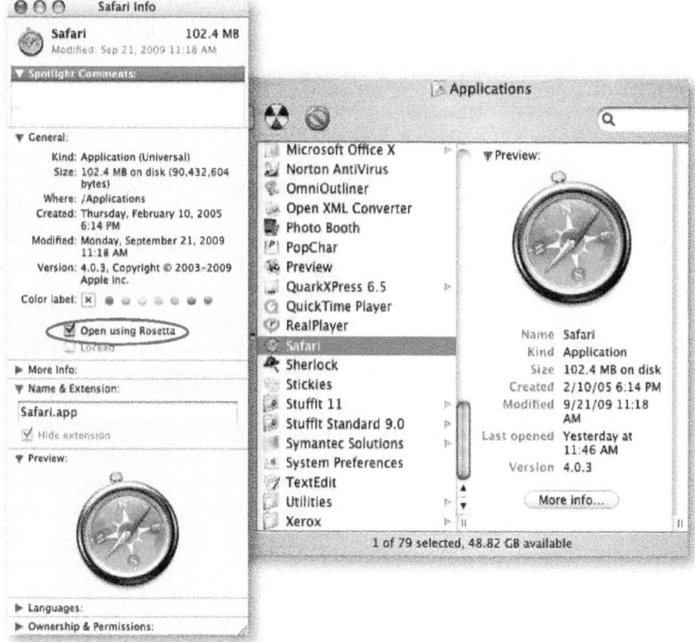

Tips for using MyMathLab on Windows Vista Operating System

- Go to: Tool>Internet Options>Privacy Tab
- Students must key in these sites and hit allow after they key in each one: www.mathxl.com, www.mylabsenterprise.com, www.pearsoncmg.com
- Then go to: Tools>Phishing Filter>Turn off filter
- Reboot

Dear Santa Fe student,

We are so glad to have you enrolled in College Algebra at Santa Fe College! In this course, we want to share with you some of the beauty and utility of Mathematics. You will see numerous applications of Algebra to the real world and have opportunity to apply what you learn in real world scenarios. This semester, you will approach problems from multiple viewpoints and learn how technology can aid you with some of the intricacies of problem solving. You will collaborate with your classmates as you utilize critical thinking skills necessary for achieving professional success in any career.

This textbook was selected because we believe it will be especially valuable to you as you meet the challenges of College Algebra. There are many examples for you to follow, clear explanations and plenty of exercises to give you practice applying concepts and to help you refine your skills. With MyMathLab, the accompanying online learning system, you'll have all the help you need 24/7 while you practice problem solving.

At Santa Fe College, we value YOU, and greatly desire to give you a valuable experience in College Algebra. May your mathematical experiences be rich and rewarding!

Best wishes from the College Algebra Redesign Team,
Warren Bernard
Bettina Capuano
Teklay Fessahaye
Heather Holley
Laura Trefry
Laura Younts, College Algebra Coordinator

In memory of a kind man who said to me,

"Have joy wherever you go."

Marvin, 1914–2010

Foreword

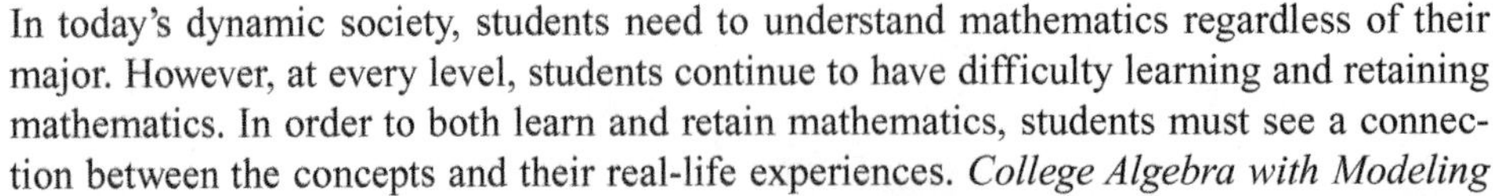

In today's dynamic society, students need to understand mathematics regardless of their major. However, at every level, students continue to have difficulty learning and retaining mathematics. In order to both learn and retain mathematics, students must see a connection between the concepts and their real-life experiences. *College Algebra with Modeling and Visualization,* Fifth Edition, addresses these issues by appropriately connecting applications, modeling, and visualization to mathematical concepts and skills. This text consistently gives meaning to the equations and demonstrates that mathematics *is* relevant. It allows students to learn mathematics in the context of their experiences. Students learn mathematics more fully when concepts are presented not only symbolically but also visually. By complementing a symbolic approach with an emphasis on visual presentations, this text allows students to absorb information faster and more intuitively.

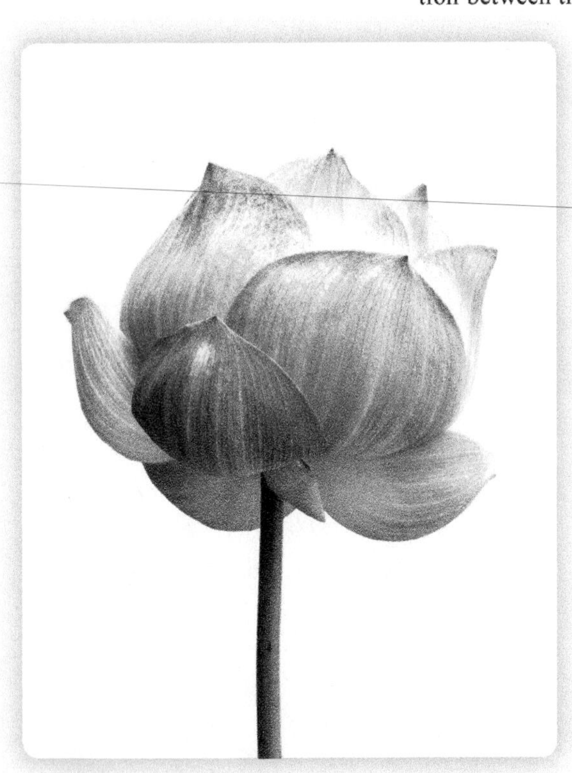

The concept of a function is the unifying theme in this text with an emphasis on the rule of four (verbal, graphical, numerical, and symbolic representations). A flexible approach allows instructors to strike their own balance of skills, rule of four, applications, modeling, and technology. Rather than reviewing all of the necessary intermediate algebra skills in the first chapter, this text integrates required math skills seamlessly by referring students "just in time" to Chapter R, "Basic Concepts from Algebra and Geometry." Instructors are free to assign supplemental homework from this chapter. Students also have additional opportunities to review their skills in the MyMathLab® course when needed. Here personalized homework and quizzes are readily available on a wide variety of review topics.

Students frequently do not realize that mathematics is transforming our society. To communicate this fact, the author has established a website at www.garyrockswold.net. Here, several resources are available, including a number of invited addresses given by the author. These presentations are accessible to students and allow them to understand the big picture of how mathematics influences everyone's life.

Contents

Preface

Changes to the Fifth Edition

The Fifth Edition has an exciting new look that makes mathematics more visual and easier for students to understand. The following changes are the result of suggestions made by students, instructors, and reviewers.

- Several features have been added that allow graphs and tables to be labeled in a way that explains topics visually with fewer words.
- Hundreds of new real-world applications that relate to students' lives have been added.
- Approximately 1000 examples and exercises have been replaced or modified to better meet student needs.
- Real-world data has been added and updated to be more current and meaningful to students.
- Chapter 1 has been streamlined from five to four sections at the request of reviewers. As a result, the first two chapters can be covered more efficiently. Also at the request of reviewers, the definition of increasing and decreasing has been modified.
- Chapter 2 has been reorganized so that it begins with equations of lines in Section 2.1. Now additional modeling with linear functions occurs in Section 2.4.
- Chapter 3 includes new visual presentations and explanations for solving quadratic equations, quadratic inequalities, and transformations of graphs. Rules for the order of transformations have also been included.
- Chapter 4 includes a new subsection covering radical functions and their transformations. Several visuals have been added to help students understand polynomial behavior and graphs of rational functions.
- Chapter 5 has increased emphasis on transformations of exponential and logarithmic functions. It includes more visual explanations of logarithms.
- Chapter 6 has a new subsection on social networks and matrices. Several application topics that relate to student's lives, such as the Internet, have been included.
- Appendix C is new and explains how percentages, constant percent change, and exponential functions are related. These topics are important to students in their everyday lives.

Features

NEW!

- **See the Concept**

  This new and exciting feature allows students to make important connections by walking them through detailed visualizations. Students use graphs, tables, and diagrams to learn new concepts in a concise and efficient way. This feature also promotes multiple learning styles and deepens every student's understanding of mathematics. (See pages 32, 117, 241, 298, and 385.)

NEW!

- **Comment Boxes**

  This new feature allows graphs, tables, and symbolic explanations to be labeled in such a way that a *concept is easier to understand.* The explanation is now tied closely to a graph, table, or equation. (See pages 26, 81, 222, 279, and 302.)

- **Chapter and Section Introductions**

  Many college algebra students have little or no understanding of mathematics beyond basic computation. To motivate students, chapter and section introductions explain some of the reasons for studying mathematics. (See pages 1, 75, 142, and 240.)

- **Now Try**

  This feature occurs after each example. It suggests a similar exercise students can work to see if they understand the concept presented in the example. (See pages 17, 82, and 114.)

- **Getting Started**

  This feature occurs in selected examples that require multistep solutions. Getting Started helps students develop an overall problem-solving strategy before they begin writing a detailed solution. (See pages 6 and 79.)

- **Algebra and Geometry Review Notes**

  Throughout the text, Algebra and Geometry Review Notes, located in the margins, direct students "just in time" to Chapter R, where important topics in algebra and geometry are reviewed. Instructors can use this chapter for extra review or refer students to it as needed. This feature *frees* instructors from having to frequently review material from intermediate algebra and geometry. (See pages 105 and 168.) In addition, quizzes and personalized homework on review skills are now embedded in MyMathLab.

- **Calculator Help Notes**

  The Calculator Help Notes in the margins direct students "just in time" to Appendix A, "Using the Graphing Calculator." This appendix shows students the keystrokes necessary to complete specific examples from the text. This feature *frees* instructors from having to teach the specifics of the graphing calculator and gives students a convenient reference written specifically for this text. (See pages 6, 20, and 101.)

- **Class Discussion**

  This feature, included in most sections, poses a question that can be used for either classroom discussion or homework. (See pages 49, 165, and 244.)

- **Making Connections**

  This feature, which occurs throughout the text, shows students how concepts covered previously are related to new concepts being presented. (See pages 29, 102, 118, 144, and 183.)

- **Putting It All Together**

  This helpful feature at the end of each section summarizes techniques and reinforces the mathematical concepts presented in the section. It is given in an easy-to-follow grid. (See pages 106, 107, and 339–340.)

- **Checking Basic Concepts**

  This feature, included after every two sections, provides a small set of exercises that can be used as mixed review. These exercises require about 15 or 20 minutes to complete and can be used for collaborative learning exercises if time permits. (See pages 112, 141, and 196.)

- **Exercise Sets**

  The exercise sets are the heart of any mathematics text, and this text includes a large variety of instructive exercises. Each set of exercises covers skill building, mathematical concepts, and applications. Graphical interpretation and tables of data are often used to extend students understanding of mathematical concepts. The exercise sets are graded carefully and categorized according to topic, making it easy for an instructor to select appropriate assignments. (See pages 88–93 and 191–196.)

- **Chapter Summaries**

  Chapter summaries are presented in an easy-to-read grid. They allow students to quickly review key concepts from the chapter. (See pages 232–235 and 349–353.)

- **Chapter Review Exercises**

  This exercise set contains both skill-building and applied exercises. These exercises stress different techniques for solving problems and provide students with the review necessary to pass a chapter test. (See pages 70–74 and 353–357).

- **Extended and Discovery Exercises**

  Extended and Discovery Exercises occur at the end of selected sections and at the end of every chapter. These exercises are usually more complex and challenging than the rest of the exercises and often require extension of a topic presented or exploration of a new topic. They can be used for either collaborative learning or extra homework assignments. (See pages 73–74, 238, and 356–357.)

- **Cumulative Review Exercises**

  These comprehensive exercise sets, which occur after every two chapters, give students an opportunity to review previous material. (See pages 160–162 and 357–359.)

Instructor Supplements

ANNOTATED INSTRUCTOR'S EDITION

- Includes sample homework assignments indicated by problem numbers underlined in blue within each end-of-section exercise set.
- Sample homework assignments assignable in MyMathLab.
- Includes Teaching Examples, an extra set of examples for instructors to present in class, doubling the number of examples available for instructors. Solutions and Power Point Slides are available for these.
- Includes Teaching Tips, helpful ideas about presenting topics or teaching from the text
- Includes all the answers to the exercise sets, usually right on the page where the exercise appears

ISBN: 0-321-83678-2 / 978-0-321-83678-6

INSTRUCTOR'S SOLUTIONS MANUAL

- By David Atwood, *Rochester Community and Technical College*
- Provides complete solutions to all text exercises, excluding Writing about Mathematics

ISBN: 0-321-82652-3 / 978-0-321-82652-7

INSTRUCTOR'S TESTING MANUAL (DOWNLOAD ONLY)

- By David Atwood, *Rochester Community and Technical College*
- Provides prepared tests for each chapter of the text, as well as answers
- Available in MyMathLab or downloadable from Pearson Education's online catalog.

TESTGEN® (DOWNLOAD ONLY)

- Enables instructors to build, edit, print, and administer tests using a computerized bank of questions that cover all the objectives of the text
- Using algorithmically based questions, allows instructors to create multiple but equivalent versions of the same question or test with the click of a button
- Lets instructors modify test bank questions or add new questions
- Provides printable or online tests
- Available in MyMathLab or downloadable from Pearson Education's online catalog

INSIDER'S GUIDE

- Includes resources to help faculty with course preparation and classroom management
- Provides helpful teaching tips correlated to the sections of text, as well as general teaching advice

ISBN: 0-321-57706-X / 978-0-321-57706-1

POWERPOINT PRESENTATION (DOWNLOAD ONLY)

- Classroom presentation software correlated specifically to this textbook sequence
- Available for download within MyMathLab or from Pearson Education's online catalog

Student Supplements

STUDENT'S SOLUTIONS MANUAL

- By David Atwood, *Rochester Community and Technical College*
- Provides complete solutions to all odd-numbered text exercises, excluding Writing about Mathematics and Extended and Discovery Exercises

ISBN: 0-321-82618-3 / 978-0-321-82618-3

Technology Resources

MyMathLab®

MyMathLab Online Course (access code required)

MyMathLab delivers **proven results** in helping individual students succeed.

- MyMathLab has a consistently positive impact on the quality of learning in higher education math instruction. MyMathLab can be successfully implemented in any environment—lab-based, hybrid, fully online, traditional—and demonstrates the quantifiable difference that integrated usage has on student retention, subsequent success, and overall achievement.
- MyMathLab's comprehensive online gradebook automatically tracks your students' results on tests, quizzes, homework, and in the study plan. You can use the gradebook to quickly intervene if your students have trouble or to provide positive feedback on a job well done. The data within MyMathLab is easily exported to a variety of spreadsheet programs, such as Microsoft Excel. You can determine which points of data you want to export and then analyze the results to determine success.

MyMathLab provides **engaging experiences** that personalize, stimulate, and measure learning for each student.

- **Exercises:** The homework and practice exercises in MyMathLab are correlated to the exercises in the textbook, and they regenerate algorithmically to give students unlimited opportunity for practice and mastery. The software offers immediate, helpful feedback when students enter incorrect answers.
- **Multimedia Learning Aids:** Exercises include guided solutions, sample problems, videos, and eText clips for extra help at point-of-use.
- **Expert Tutoring:** Although many students describe the whole of MyMathLab as "like having your own personal tutor," students using MyMathLab do have access to live tutoring from Pearson, from qualified math and statistics instructors.

And, MyMathLab comes from a **trusted partner** with educational expertise and an eye on the future.

- Knowing that you are using a Pearson product means knowing that you are using quality content. That means that our eTexts are accurate and our assessment tools work. Whether you are just getting started with MyMathLab, or have a question along the way, we're here to help you learn about our technologies and how to incorporate them into your course.

Rockswold's MyMathLab course engages students and keeps them thinking.

- Author designated preassigned homework assignments are provided.
- Integrated Review provides optional quizzes throughout the course that test prerequisite knowledge. After taking each quiz, students receive a personalized, just-in-time review assignment to help them refresh forgotten skills.
- Interactive figures are available, enabling users to manipulate figures to bring hard-to-convey math concepts to life.
- Section-Lecture Videos provide lectures for each section of the text to help students review important concepts and procedures 24/7. Assignable questions are available to check students' video comprehension.

To learn more about how MyMathLab combines proven learning applications with powerful assessment, visit www.mymathlab.com or contact your Pearson representative.

MyMathLab Ready to Go Course (access code required)

These new Ready to Go courses provide students with all the same great MyMathLab features, but make it easier for instructors to get started. Each course includes pre-assigned homework and quizzes to make creating a course even simpler.

Ask your Pearson representative about the details for this particular course or to see a copy of this course.

MyMathLab Plus/MyLabsPlus

MyLabsPlus combines proven results and engaging experiences from MyMathLab with convenient management tools and a dedicated services team. Designed to support growing math and statistics programs, it includes additional features such as

- **Batch Enrollment:** Your school can create the login name and password for every student and instructor, so everyone can be ready to start class on the first day. Automation of this process is also possible through integration with your school's Student Information System.
- **Login from your campus portal:** You and your students can link directly from your campus portal into your MyLabsPlus courses. A Pearson service team works with your institution to create a single sign-on experience for instructors and students.
- **Advanced Reporting:** MyLabsPlus's advanced reporting allows instructors to review and analyze students' strengths and weaknesses by tracking their performance on tests, assignments, and tutorials. Administrators can review grades and assignments across all courses on your MyLabsPlus campus for a broad overview of program performance.
- **24/7 Support:** Students and instructors receive 24/7 support, 365 days a year, by email or online chat.

MyLabsPlus is available to qualified adopters. For more information, visit our website at www.mylabsplus.com or contact your Pearson representative.

MathXL®

MathXL Online Course (access code required)

MathXL is the homework and assessment engine that runs MyMathLab. (MyMathLab is MathXL plus a learning management system.)

With MathXL, instructors can

- Create, edit, and assign online homework and tests using algorithmically generated exercises correlated at the objective level to the textbook.
- Create and assign their own online exercises and import TestGen tests for added flexibility.
- Maintain records of all student work tracked in MathXL's online gradebook.

With MathXL, students can:

- Take chapter tests in MathXL and receive personalized study plans and/or personalized homework assignments based on their test results.
- Use the study plan and/or the homework to link directly to tutorial exercises for the objectives they need to study.
- Access supplemental animations and video clips directly from selected exercises.

MathXL is available to qualified adopters. For more information, visit our website at www.mathxl.com or contact your Pearson representative.

Acknowledgments

Many individuals contributed to the development of this textbook. I would like to thank the following reviewers, whose comments and suggestions were invaluable in preparing this edition of the text.

Dawit Aberra	*Fort Valley State University*
Dr. Josephine D. Davis	*Fort Valley State University*
Christy Dittmar	*Austin Community College*
Chi Giang	*Westchester Community College*
Christian Mason	*Virginia Commonwealth University*
Val Mohanakumar	*Hillsborough Community College*
Nancy Pevey	*Pellissippi State Community College*
Carolynn Reed	*Austin Community College*
Tracy Romesser	*Erie Community College North*
Jeffrey Saikali	*San Diego Miramar College*
Meredith Watts	*Massachusetts Bay Community College*
Cathleen Zucco-Teveloff	*Rowan University*

I would like to welcome Terry Krieger and Jessica Rockswold to the team for the fifth edition. They have provided invaluable help with developing new applications, visualizations, examples, and exercises. Terry and Jessica have contributed at all levels in the development of this new and exciting edition.

I would like to thank Paul Lorczak, Lynn Baker, Namyong Lee at Minnesota State University, Mankato, Mark Rockswold at Denver Community College, and David Atwood at Rochester Community and Technical College for their superb work with proofreading and accuracy checking.

Without the excellent cooperation from the professional staff at Pearson, this project would have been impossible. They are, without a doubt, the best. Thanks go to Greg Tobin for his support of this project. Particular recognition is due Anne Kelly and Christine O'Brien, who gave advice, support, assistance, and encouragement. The outstanding contributions of Sheila Spinney, Judith Garber, Heather Scott, Peggy Sue Lucas, Justine Goulart, and Joe Vetere are much appreciated. The outstanding work of Kathy Diamond was instrumental to the success of this project.

Thanks go to Wendy Rockswold, who gave invaluable assistance and encouragement throughout the project. She also supplied several of the photographs found throughout the text.

A special thank you goes to the many students and instructors who used the first four editions of this text. Their suggestions were insightful. Please feel free to contact me at either *gary.rockswold@mnsu.edu* or www.garyrockswold.net with your comments. Your opinion is important.

Gary Rockswold

1 Introduction to Functions and Graphs

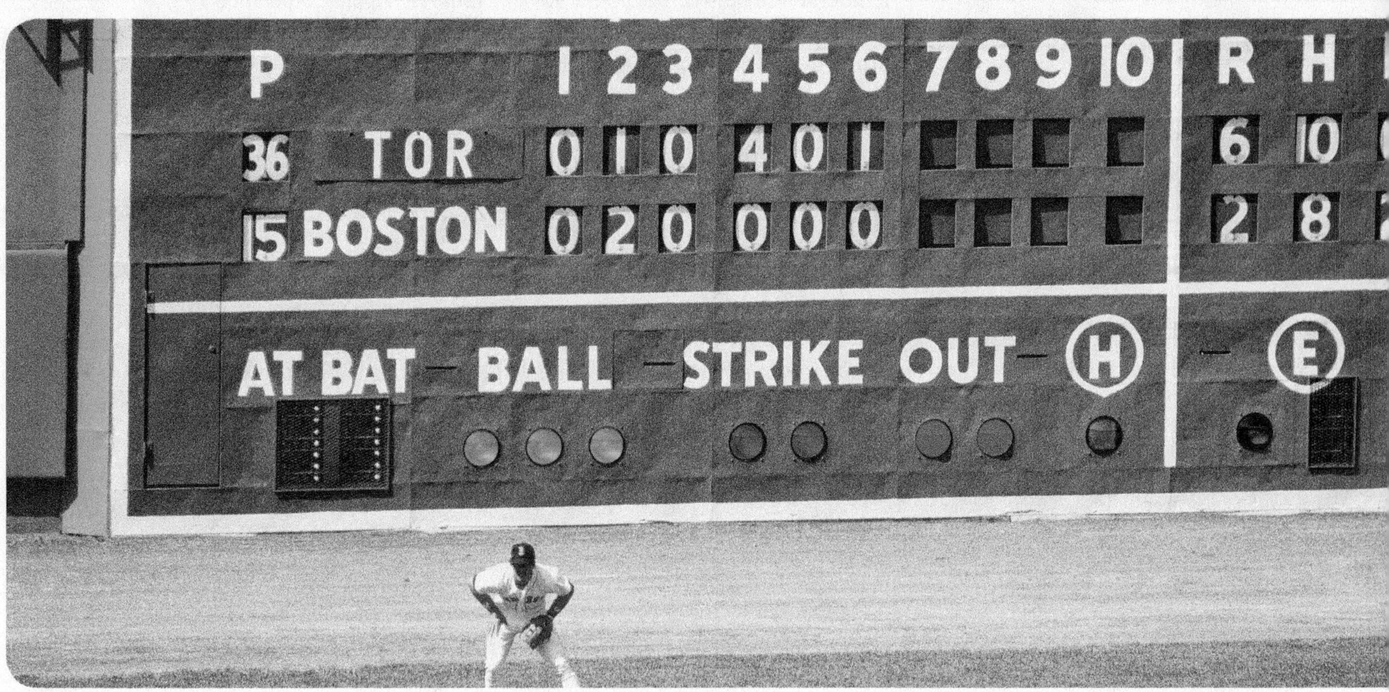

> The essence of mathematics is not to make simple things complicated, but to make complicated things simple.
>
> —Stanley Gudder

Have you ever thought about how we "live by the numbers"? Money, sports, digital televisions, speed limits, grade point averages, gas mileages, and temperatures are all based on numbers. When we are told what our weight, blood pressure, body mass index, and cholesterol levels are, it can even affect how we feel about ourselves. Numbers permeate our society.

Numbers are part of mathematics, but mathematics is *much more* than numbers. Mathematics also includes techniques to analyze these numbers and to guide our decisions about the future. Mathematics is used not only in science and technology; it is also used to describe almost every facet of life, including consumer behavior, social networks, and the Internet. Mathematics gives people the reasoning skills to solve problems from work and life.

In this chapter we discuss numbers and how functions are used to do computations with these numbers. Understanding numbers and mathematical concepts is essential to understanding and dealing with the many changes that will occur in our lifetimes. Mathematics makes life easier!

1.1 Numbers, Data, and Problem Solving

- **Recognize common sets of numbers**
- **Evaluate expressions by applying the order of operations**
- **Learn scientific notation and use it in applications**
- **Apply problem-solving strategies**

Introduction

Because society is becoming more complex and diverse, our need for mathematics is increasing dramatically each year. Numbers are essential to our everyday lives. For example, the iPhone 4Gs is 4.5 inches in height, 2.31 inches in width, and 0.37 inch in thickness. It has an 8-gigabyte flash drive and a 5-megapixel camera, and it can operate at temperatures between 32° and 95°F. (***Source:*** Apple Corporation.)

Mathematics not only provides numbers to describe new products but also gives us problem-solving strategies. This section discusses basic sets of numbers and introduces some essential problem-solving strategies.

Sets of Numbers

One important set of numbers is the set of **natural numbers**. This set comprises the *counting numbers* $N = \{1, 2, 3, 4, \dots\}$.

The **integers** $I = \{\dots, -3, -2, -1, 0, 1, 2, 3, \dots\}$ are a set of numbers that contains the natural numbers, their additive inverses (negatives), and 0.

A **rational number** can be expressed as the *ratio* of two integers $\frac{p}{q}$, where $q \neq 0$. A rational number results when an integer is divided by a nonzero integer. Thus rational numbers include fractions and the integers. Examples of rational numbers are

$$\frac{2}{1}, \frac{1}{3}, -\frac{1}{4}, \frac{-50}{2}, \frac{22}{7}, 0, \sqrt{25}, \text{ and } 1.2.$$

Rational Numbers

Note that 0 and 1.2 are both rational numbers. They can be represented by the fractions $\frac{0}{1}$ and $\frac{12}{10}$. Because two fractions that look different can be equivalent, rational numbers have more than one form. A rational number can always be expressed in a decimal form that either *repeats* or *terminates*. For example, $\frac{2}{3} = 0.\overline{6}$, a repeating decimal, and $\frac{1}{4} = 0.25$, a terminating decimal. The overbar indicates that $0.\overline{6} = 0.6666666\dots$.

CLASS DISCUSSION

The number 0 was invented well after the natural numbers. Many societies did not have a zero—for example, there is no Roman numeral for 0. Discuss some possible reasons for this.

Real numbers can be represented by decimal numbers. Since every rational number has a decimal form, real numbers include rational numbers. However, some real numbers cannot be expressed as a ratio of two integers. These numbers are called **irrational numbers**. The numbers $\sqrt{2}$, $\sqrt{15}$, and π are examples of irrational numbers. They can be represented by nonrepeating, nonterminating decimals. Note that for any positive integer a, if $\sqrt{a}$ is not an integer, then $\sqrt{a}$ is an irrational number.

Real numbers are either rational or irrational numbers and can always be *approximated* by a terminating decimal. Examples of real numbers include

$$2, -10, -131.3337, \frac{1}{3} = 0.\overline{3}, -\sqrt{5} \approx -2.2361, \text{ and } \sqrt{11} \approx 3.3166.$$

Real Numbers

NOTE The symbol $\approx$ means **approximately equal**. This symbol is used in place of an equals sign whenever two unequal quantities are close in value. For example, $\frac{1}{2} = 0.5$, whereas $\frac{1}{3} \approx 0.3333$.

Figure 1.1 illustrates how the different sets of numbers are related.

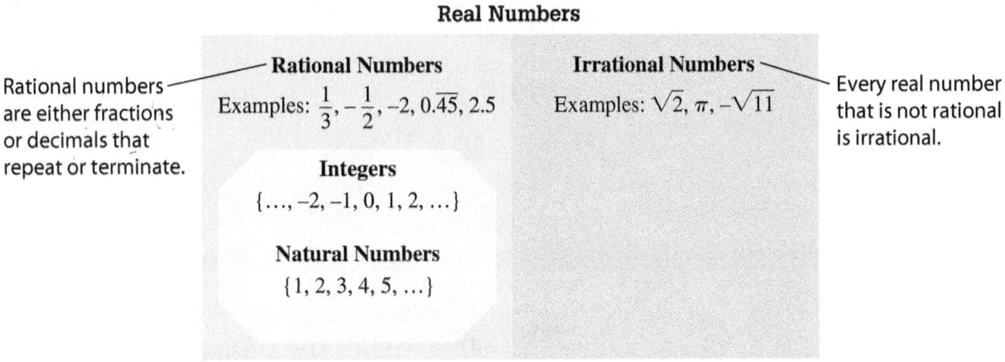

Real Numbers

Rational numbers are either fractions or decimals that repeat or terminate.

Rational Numbers

Examples: $\frac{1}{3}, -\frac{1}{2}, -2, 0.\overline{45}, 2.5$

Integers

$\{\ldots, -2, -1, 0, 1, 2, \ldots\}$

Natural Numbers

$\{1, 2, 3, 4, 5, \ldots\}$

Irrational Numbers

Examples: $\sqrt{2}, \pi, -\sqrt{11}$

Every real number that is not rational is irrational.

Figure 1.1

EXAMPLE 1 Classifying numbers

Classify each real number as one or more of the following: natural number, integer, rational number, or irrational number.

$$5, -1.2, \frac{13}{7}, -\sqrt{7}, -12, \sqrt{16}$$

SOLUTION

5: natural number, integer, and rational number

-1.2: rational number

$\frac{13}{7}$: rational number

$-\sqrt{7}$: irrational number

-12: integer and rational number

$\sqrt{16} = 4$: natural number, integer, and rational number

Now Try Exercise 7

Order of Operations

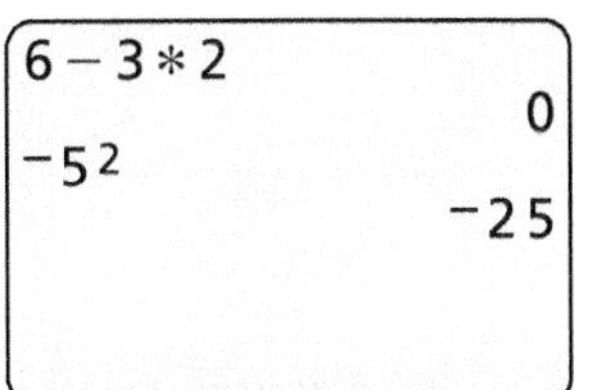

Figure 1.2

Does $6 - 3 \cdot 2$ equal 0 or 6? Does -5^2 equal 25 or -25? Figure 1.2 correctly shows that $6 - 3 \cdot 2 = 0$ and that $-5^2 = -25$. Because multiplication is performed before subtraction, $6 - 3 \cdot 2 = 0$. Similarly, because exponents are evaluated before performing negation, $-5^2 = -25$. It is essential that algebraic expressions be evaluated consistently, so the following rules have been established.

ORDER OF OPERATIONS

Using the following order of operations, perform all calculations within parentheses, square roots, and absolute value bars and above and below fraction bars. Then use the same order of operations to perform any remaining calculations.

1. Evaluate all exponents. Then do any negation *after* evaluating exponents.
2. Do all multiplication and division from *left to right.*
3. Do all addition and subtraction from *left to right.*

EXAMPLE 2 Evaluating arithmetic expressions by hand

Evaluate each expression by hand.

(a) $3(1 - 5)^2 - 4^2$ **(b)** $\frac{10 - 6}{5 - 3} - 4 - |7 - 2|$

SOLUTION

(a) $3(1 - 5)^2 - 4^2 = 3(-4)^2 - 4^2$
$= 3(16) - 16$
$= 48 - 16$
$= 32$

(b) $\frac{10 - 6}{5 - 3} - 4 - |7 - 2| = \frac{4}{2} - 4 - |5|$
$= 2 - 4 - 5$
$= -2 - 5$
$= -7$

NOTE $(-4)^2 = (-4)(-4) = 16$ and $-4^2 = -(4)(4) = -16$.

Now Try Exercises 19 and 21

Scientific Notation

Numbers that are large or small in absolute value are often expressed in scientific notation. Table 1.1 lists examples of numbers in **standard (decimal) form** and in **scientific notation**.

Applications of Scientific Notation

Standard Form	Scientific Notation	Application
93,000,000 mi	9.3×10^7 mi	Distance to the sun
256,000	2.56×10^5	Number of cell towers in 2010
9,000,000,000	9×10^9	Estimated world population in 2050
0.00000538 sec	5.38×10^{-6} sec	Time for light to travel 1 mile
0.000005 cm	5×10^{-6} cm	Size of a typical virus

Table 1.1

EXAMPLE 3 Writing a number in scientific notation

Write 0.000578 in scientific notation.

SOLUTION

To write 0.000578 in scientific notation, start by moving the decimal point to the right of the first nonzero digit, 5, to obtain 5.78.

Decimal Form		*Scientific Notation*	
0 . 0 0 0 5 . 7 8 (1 2 3 4)	→	5.78×10^{-4}	Move the decimal point right.

Since the decimal point was moved four places to the *right*, the exponent of 10 is *negative* 4, or -4. If the decimal point had been moved to the *left*, the exponent of 10 would be *positive* 4.

Now Try Exercise 35

Here is a formal definition of scientific notation.

SCIENTIFIC NOTATION

A real number r is in **scientific notation** when r is written as $c \times 10^n$, where $1 \le |c| < 10$ and n is an integer.

Calculator Help

To display numbers in scientific notation, see Appendix A (page AP-2).

An Application The next example demonstrates how scientific notation appears in the description of a new technology.

EXAMPLE 4 **Analyzing the energy produced by your body**

Nanotechnology is a technology of the very small: on the order of one billionth of a meter. Researchers are using nanotechnology to power tiny devices with energy from the human body. (***Source:*** Z. Wang, "Self-Powered Nanotech," *Scientific American*, January 2008.)

(a) Write one billionth in scientific notation.

(b) While typing, a person's fingers generate about 2.2×10^{-3} watt of electrical energy. Write this number in standard (decimal) form.

SOLUTION

(a) One billionth can be written as $\frac{1}{1{,}000{,}000{,}000} = \frac{1}{10^9} = 1 \times 10^{-9}$.

(b) Move the decimal point in 2.2 three places to the left: $2.2 \times 10^{-3} = 0.0022$.

Now Try Exercise 77

The next example illustrates how to evaluate expressions in scientific notation.

EXAMPLE 5 **Evaluating expressions by hand**

Evaluate each expression. Write your result in scientific notation and standard form.

(a) $(3 \times 10^3)(2 \times 10^4)$ **(b)** $(5 \times 10^{-3})(6 \times 10^5)$ **(c)** $\dfrac{4.6 \times 10^{-1}}{2 \times 10^2}$

SOLUTION

(a)
$$\begin{aligned}(3 \times 10^3)(2 \times 10^4) &= 3 \times 2 \times 10^3 \times 10^4 && \text{Commutative property}\\ &= 6 \times 10^{3+4} && \text{Add exponents.}\\ &= 6 \times 10^7 && \text{Scientific notation}\\ &= 60{,}000{,}000 && \text{Standard form}\end{aligned}$$

(b)
$$\begin{aligned}(5 \times 10^{-3})(6 \times 10^5) &= 5 \times 6 \times 10^{-3} \times 10^5 && \text{Commutative property}\\ &= 30 \times 10^2 && \text{Add exponents.}\\ &= 3 \times 10^3 && \text{Scientific notation}\\ &= 3000 && \text{Standard form}\end{aligned}$$

Algebra Review
To review exponents, see Chapter R (page R-8).

(c)
$$\begin{aligned}\frac{4.6 \times 10^{-1}}{2 \times 10^2} &= \frac{4.6}{2} \times \frac{10^{-1}}{10^2} && \text{Multiplication of fractions}\\ &= 2.3 \times 10^{-1-2} && \text{Subtract exponents.}\\ &= 2.3 \times 10^{-3} && \text{Scientific notation}\\ &= 0.0023 && \text{Standard form}\end{aligned}$$

Now Try Exercises 53, 55, and 57

Calculators Calculators often use E to express powers of 10. For example, 4.2×10^{-3} might be displayed as 4.2E–3. On some calculators, numbers can be entered in scientific notation with the (EE) key, which you can find by pressing (2nd) (,).

EXAMPLE 6 **Computing in scientific notation with a calculator**

Approximate each expression. Write your answer in scientific notation.

(a) $\left(\dfrac{6 \times 10^3}{4 \times 10^6}\right)(1.2 \times 10^2)$ **(b)** $\sqrt{4500\pi}\left(\dfrac{103 + 450}{0.233}\right)^3$

```
(6*10^3)/(4*10^6
)*(1.2*10^2)
                .18
(6E3)/(4E6)*(1.2
E2)
                .18
```

Figure 1.3

SOLUTION

(a) The given expression is entered in two ways in Figure 1.3. Note that in both cases

$$\left(\frac{6 \times 10^3}{4 \times 10^6}\right)(1.2 \times 10^2) = 0.18 = 1.8 \times 10^{-1}.$$

Calculator Help
To enter numbers in scientific notation, see Appendix A (page AP-2).

(b) Be sure to insert parentheses around 4500π and around the numerator, $103 + 450$, in the expression $\sqrt{4500\pi}\left(\frac{103 + 450}{0.233}\right)^3$. From Figure 1.4 we can see that the result is approximately 1.59×10^{12}.

```
√(4500π)*((103+4
50)/.233)^3
      1.58960355E12
```

Figure 1.4

Now Try Exercises 61 and 63

EXAMPLE 7 Computing with a calculator

Use a calculator to evaluate each expression. Round answers to the nearest thousandth.

(a) $\sqrt[3]{131}$ **(b)** $\pi^3 + 1.2^2$ **(c)** $\frac{1 + \sqrt{2}}{3.7 + 9.8}$ **(d)** $|\sqrt{3} - 6|$

SOLUTION

(a) On some calculators the cube root can be found by using the MATH menu. If your calculator does not have a cube root key, enter 131^(1/3). From the first two lines in Figure 1.5, we see that $\sqrt[3]{131} \approx 5.079$.

(b) Do *not* use 3.14 for the value of π. Instead, use the built-in key to obtain a more accurate value of π. From the bottom two lines in Figure 1.5, $\pi^3 + 1.2^2 \approx 32.446$.

(c) When evaluating this expression be sure to include parentheses around the numerator and around the denominator. Most calculators have a special square root key that can be used to evaluate $\sqrt{2}$. From the first three lines in Figure 1.6, $\frac{1 + \sqrt{2}}{3.7 + 9.8} \approx 0.179$.

Algebra Review
To review cube roots, see Chapter R (page R-37).

(d) The absolute value can be found on some calculators by using the MATH NUM menus. From the bottom two lines in Figure 1.6, $|\sqrt{3} - 6| \approx 4.268$.

Calculator Help
To enter expressions such as $\sqrt[3]{131}$, $\sqrt{2}$, π, and $|\sqrt{3} - 6|$, see Appendix A (page AP-2).

```
3√(131)
         5.078753078
π^3+1.2²
         32.44627668
```

Figure 1.5

```
(1+√(2))/(3.7+9.
8)
        .1788306342
abs(√(3)-6)
        4.267949192
```

Figure 1.6

Now Try Exercises 67, 69, 71, and 73

Problem Solving

Many problem-solving strategies are used in algebra. However, in this subsection we focus on two important strategies that are used frequently: making a sketch and applying one or more formulas. These strategies are illustrated in the next two examples.

EXAMPLE 8 Finding the speed of Earth

Earth travels around the sun in an approximately circular orbit with an average radius of 93 million miles. If Earth takes 1 year, or about 365 days, to complete one orbit, estimate the orbital speed of Earth in miles per hour.

SOLUTION

Getting Started Speed S equals distance D divided by time T, $S = \frac{D}{T}$. We need to find the number of miles Earth travels in 1 year and then divide it by the number of hours in 1 year. ▶

Geometry Review
To find the circumference of a circle, see Chapter R (page R-2).

Distance Traveled Make a sketch of Earth orbiting the sun, as shown in Figure 1.7. In 1 year Earth travels the circumference of a circle with a radius of 93 million miles. The circumference of a circle is $2\pi r$, where r is the radius, so the distance D is

$$D = 2\pi r = 2\pi(93{,}000{,}000) \approx 584{,}300{,}000 \text{ miles.}$$

Hours in 1 Year The number of hours T in 1 year, or 365 days, equals

$$T = 365 \times 24 = 8760 \text{ hours.}$$

Speed of Earth $S = \frac{D}{T} = \frac{584{,}300{,}000}{8760} \approx 66{,}700$ miles per hour.

Now Try Exercise 79

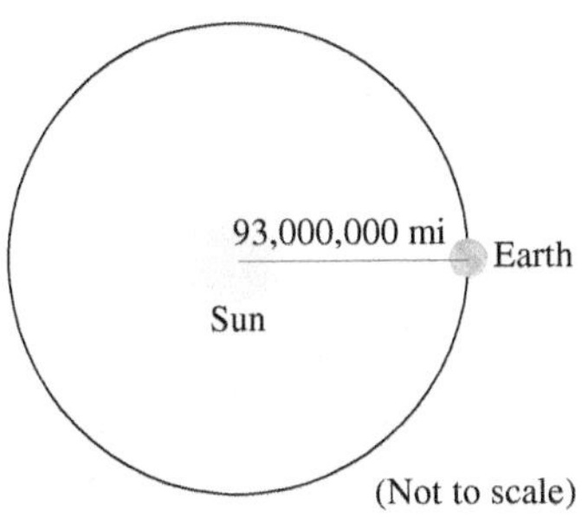

Figure 1.7

Many times in geometry we evaluate formulas to determine quantities, such as perimeter, area, and volume. In the next example we use a formula to determine the number of fluid ounces in a soda can.

EXAMPLE 9 **Finding the volume of a soda can**

The volume V of the cylindrical soda can in Figure 1.8 is given by $V = \pi r^2 h$, where r is its radius and h is its height.

(a) If $r = 1.4$ inches and $h = 5$ inches, find the volume of the can in cubic inches.

(b) Could this can hold 16 fluid ounces? (*Hint:* 1 cubic inch equals 0.55 fluid ounce.)

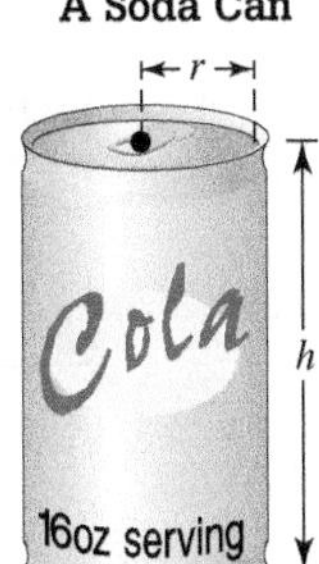

Figure 1.8

SOLUTION

(a) $V = \pi r^2 h = \pi(1.4)^2(5) = 9.8\pi \approx 30.8$ cubic inches.

(b) To find the number of fluid ounces, multiply the number of cubic inches by 0.55.

$$30.8 \times 0.55 = 16.94$$

Yes, the can could hold 16 fluid ounces.

Now Try Exercise 85

1.1 Putting It All Together

Numbers play a central role in our society. Without numbers, data could be described qualitatively but not quantitatively. For example, we could say that the day seems hot but would not be able to give an actual number for the temperature. Mathematics provides problem-solving strategies that are used in almost every facet of our lives.

CONCEPT	COMMENTS	EXAMPLES
Natural numbers	Sometimes referred to as the *counting numbers*	1, 2, 3, 4, 5, . . .
Integers	Include the natural numbers, their opposites, and 0	. . . , −2, −1, 0, 1, 2, . . .
Rational numbers	Include integers; all fractions $\frac{p}{q}$, where p and q are integers with $q \neq 0$; all repeating and all terminating decimals	$\frac{1}{2}, -3, \frac{128}{6}, -0.335, 0,$ $0.25 = \frac{1}{4}, 0.\overline{33} = \frac{1}{3}$

continued on next page

CONCEPT	COMMENTS	EXAMPLES
Irrational numbers	Can be written as nonrepeating, nonterminating decimals; cannot be a rational number; if a square root of a positive integer is not an integer, it is an irrational number.	$\pi, \sqrt{2}, -\sqrt{5}, \sqrt[3]{7}, \pi^4$
Real numbers	Any number that can be expressed in standard (decimal) form Include the rational numbers and irrational numbers	$\pi, \sqrt{7}, -\frac{4}{7}, 0, -10, 1.237$ $0.\overline{6} = \frac{2}{3}, 1000, \sqrt{15}, -\sqrt{5}$
Order of operations	Using the following order of operations, perform all calculations within parentheses, square roots, and absolute value bars and above and below fraction bars. Then perform any remaining calculations. 1. Evaluate all exponents. Then do any negation *after* evaluating exponents. 2. Do all multiplication and division from *left to right.* 3. Do all addition and subtraction from *left to right.*	$-4^2 - 12 \div 2 - 2 = -16 - 12 \div 2 - 2$ $= -16 - 6 - 2$ $= -22 - 2$ $= -24$ $\frac{2 + 4^2}{3 - 3 \cdot 5} = \frac{2 + 16}{3 - 15}$ $= \frac{18}{-12}$ $= -\frac{3}{2}$
Scientific notation	A number in the form $c \times 10^n$, where $1 \leq \lvert c \rvert < 10$ and n is an integer Used to represent numbers that are large or small in absolute value	$3.12 \times 10^4 = 31{,}200$ $-1.4521 \times 10^{-2} = -0.014521$ $5 \times 10^9 = 5{,}000{,}000{,}000$ $1.5987 \times 10^{-6} = 0.0000015987$

1.1 Exercises

Classifying Numbers

Exercises 1–6: Classify the number as one or more of the following: natural number, integer, rational number, or real number.

1. $\frac{21}{24}$ (Fraction of people in the United States completing at least 4 years of high school)
2. 695,000 (Number of Facebook status updates every 60 seconds)
3. 7.5 (Average number of gallons of water used each minute while taking a shower)
4. 8.4 (Neilsen rating of the TV show *Modern Family* the week of January 2, 2012)
5. $90\sqrt{2}$ (Distance in feet from home plate to second base on a baseball field)
6. -71 (Wind chill when the temperature is -30°F and the wind speed is 40 mi/hr)

Exercises 7–10: Classify each number as one or more of the following: natural number, integer, rational number, or irrational number.

7. $\pi, -3, \frac{2}{9}, \sqrt{9}, 1.\overline{3}, -\sqrt{2}$
8. $\frac{3}{1}, -\frac{5}{8}, \sqrt{7}, 0.\overline{45}, 0, 5.6 \times 10^3$
9. $\sqrt{13}, \frac{1}{3}, 5.1 \times 10^{-6}, -2.33, 0.\overline{7}, -\sqrt{4}$
10. $-103, \frac{21}{25}, \sqrt{100}, -\frac{5.7}{10}, \frac{2}{9}, -1.457, \sqrt{3}$

Exercises 11–16: For the measured quantity, state the set of numbers that most appropriately describes it. Choose from the natural numbers, integers, and rational numbers. Explain your answer.

11. Shoe sizes
12. Populations of states
13. Speed limits
14. Gallons of gasoline

15. Temperatures in a winter weather forecast in Montana

16. Numbers of compact disc sales

Order of Operations

Exercises 17–28: Evaluate by hand.

17. $|5 - 8 \cdot 7|$

18. $-2(16 - 3 \cdot 5) \div 2$

19. $-6^2 - 3(2 - 4)^4$

20. $(4 - 5)^2 - 3^2 - 3\sqrt{9}$

21. $\sqrt{9 - 5} - \dfrac{8 - 4}{4 - 2}$

22. $\dfrac{6 - 4^2 \div 2^3}{3 - 4}$

23. $\sqrt{13^2 - 12^2}$

24. $\dfrac{13 - \sqrt{9 + 16}}{|5 - 7|^2}$

25. $\dfrac{4 + 9}{2 + 3} - \dfrac{-3^2 \cdot 3}{5}$

26. $10 \div 2 \div \dfrac{5 + 10}{5}$

27. $-5^2 - 20 \div 4 - 2$

28. $5 - (-4)^3 - (4)^3$

Scientific Notation

Exercises 29–40: Write the number in scientific notation.

29. 40 (Percent of smartphones that run the Android operating system in 2012)

30. 11,700,000 (Number of U. S. cancer survivors in 2007)

31. 0.00365 (Proportion of cosmetic surgeries performed on 13–19 year olds)

32. 0.62 (Number of miles in 1 kilometer)

33. 2450

34. 105.6

35. 0.56

36. −0.00456

37. −0.0087

38. 1,250,000

39. 206.8

40. 0.00007

Exercises 41–52: Write the number in standard form.

41. 1×10^{-6} (Wavelength of visible light in meters)

42. 9.11×10^{-31} (Weight of an electron in kilograms)

43. 2×10^8 (Years required for the sun to orbit our galaxy)

44. 8×10^9 (Annual dollars spent in the United States on cosmetics)

45. 1.567×10^2

46. -5.68×10^{-1}

47. 5×10^5

48. 3.5×10^3

49. 0.045×10^5

50. -5.4×10^{-5}

51. 67×10^3

52. 0.0032×10^{-1}

Exercises 53–60: Evaluate the expression by hand. Write your result in scientific notation and standard form.

53. $(4 \times 10^3)(2 \times 10^5)$

54. $(3 \times 10^1)(3 \times 10^4)$

55. $(5 \times 10^2)(7 \times 10^{-4})$

56. $(8 \times 10^{-3})(7 \times 10^1)$

57. $\dfrac{6.3 \times 10^{-2}}{3 \times 10^1}$

58. $\dfrac{8.2 \times 10^2}{2 \times 10^{-2}}$

59. $\dfrac{4 \times 10^{-3}}{8 \times 10^{-1}}$

60. $\dfrac{2.4 \times 10^{-5}}{4.8 \times 10^{-7}}$

Exercises 61–66: Use a calculator to approximate the expression. Write your result in scientific notation.

61. $\dfrac{8.947 \times 10^7}{0.00095}(4.5 \times 10^8)$

62. $(9.87 \times 10^6)(3.4 \times 10^{12})$

63. $\left(\dfrac{101 + 23}{0.42}\right)^2 + \sqrt{3.4 \times 10^{-2}}$

64. $\sqrt[3]{(2.5 \times 10^{-8}) + 10^{-7}}$

65. $(8.5 \times 10^{-5})(-9.5 \times 10^7)^2$

66. $\sqrt{\pi(4.56 \times 10^4) + (3.1 \times 10^{-2})}$

Exercises 67–76: Use a calculator to evaluate the expression. Round your result to the nearest thousandth.

67. $\sqrt[3]{192}$

68. $\sqrt{(32 + \pi^3)}$

69. $|\pi - 3.2|$

70. $\dfrac{1.72 - 5.98}{35.6 + 1.02}$

71. $\dfrac{0.3 + 1.5}{5.5 - 1.2}$

72. $3.2(1.1)^2 - 4(1.1) + 2$

73. $\dfrac{1.5^3}{\sqrt{2} + \pi - 5}$

74. $4.3^2 - \dfrac{5}{17}$

75. $15 + \dfrac{4 + \sqrt{3}}{7}$

76. $\dfrac{5 + \sqrt{5}}{2}$

Applications

77. Nanotechnology (Refer to Example 4.) During inhalation, the typical body generates 0.14 watt of electrical power, which could be used to power tiny electrical circuits. Write this number in scientific notation. (***Source:*** *Scientific American,* January 2008.)

78. **Movement of the Pacific Plate** The Pacific plate (the floor of the Pacific Ocean) near Hawaii is moving at about 0.000071 kilometer per year. This is about the speed at which a fingernail grows. Use scientific notation to determine how many kilometers the Pacific plate travels in 1 million years.

79. **Orbital Speed** (Refer to Example 8.) The planet Mars travels around the sun in a nearly circular orbit with a radius of 141 million miles. If it takes 1.88 years for Mars to complete one orbit, estimate the orbital speed of Mars in miles per hour.

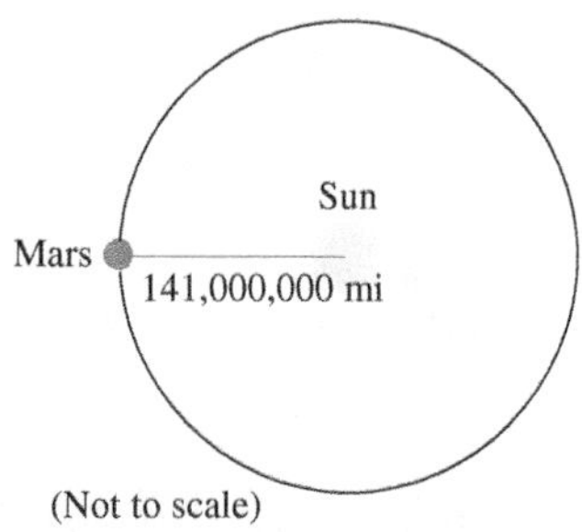

80. **Size of the Milky Way** The speed of light is about 186,000 miles per second. The Milky Way galaxy has an approximate diameter of 6×10^{17} miles. Estimate, to the nearest thousand, the number of years it takes for light to travel across the Milky Way. (***Source:*** C. Ronan, *The Natural History of the Universe.*)

81. **Living with Cancer** The number of people living with cancer (cancer survivors) has increased dramatically from 1971 to 2007. (***Source:*** CDC.)
   (a) In 1971 the population of the United States was 208 million and the number living with cancer was 3,000,000. To the nearest tenth, approximate the percentage of the population living with cancer in 1971.
   (b) In 2007 the population of the United States was 300 million and the number living with cancer was 11,700,000. To the nearest tenth, approximate the percentage of the population living with cancer in 2007.

82. **Discharge of Water** The Amazon River discharges water into the Atlantic Ocean at an average rate of 4,200,000 cubic feet per second, the highest rate of any river in the world. Is this more or less than 1 cubic mile of water per day? Explain your calculations. (***Source:*** *The Guinness Book of Records 1993.*)

83. **Analyzing Debt** A 1-inch-high stack of \$100 bills contains about 250 bills. In 2010 the gross federal debt was approximately 13.5 trillion dollars.
   (a) If the entire federal debt were converted into a stack of \$100 bills, how many feet high would it be?
   (b) The distance between Los Angeles and New York is approximately 2500 miles. Could this stack of \$100 bills reach between these two cities?

84. **Volume of a Cone** The volume V of a cone is given by $V = \frac{1}{3}\pi r^2 h$, where r is its radius and h is its height. Find V when $r = 4$ inches and $h = 1$ foot. Round your answer to the nearest hundredth.

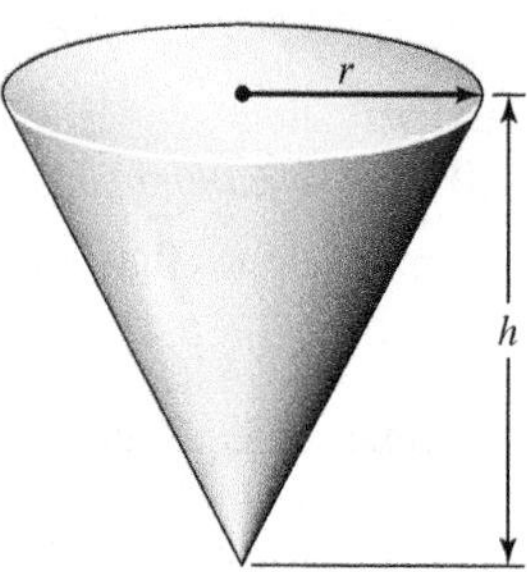

85. **Size of a Soda Can** (Refer to Example 9.) The volume V of a cylindrical soda can is given by $V = \pi r^2 h$, where r is its radius and h is its height.
   (a) If $r = 1.3$ inches and $h = 4.4$ inches, find the volume of the can in cubic inches.
   (b) Could this can hold 12 fluid ounces? (*Hint:* 1 cubic inch equals about 0.55 fluid ounce.)

86. **Volume of a Sphere** The volume of a sphere is given by $V = \frac{4}{3}\pi r^3$, where r is the radius of the sphere. Calculate the volume if the radius is 3 feet. Approximate your answer to the nearest tenth.

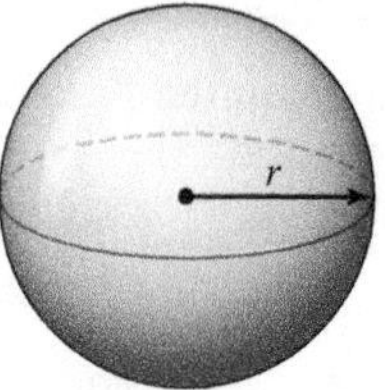

Writing about Mathematics

87. Describe some basic sets of numbers that are used in mathematics and where you find them in everyday life.

88. Suppose that a positive number a is written in scientific notation as $a = c \times 10^n$, where n is an integer and $1 \leq c < 10$. Explain what n indicates about the size of a.

Extended and Discovery Exercise

Exercises 1–4: Measuring the thickness of a very thin layer of material can be difficult to do directly. For example, it would be difficult to measure the thickness of an oil film on water or a coat of paint with a ruler. However, it can be done indirectly using the following formula.

$$\text{Thickness} = \frac{\text{Volume}}{\text{Area}}$$

That is, the thickness of a thin layer equals the volume of the substance divided by the area that it covers. For example, if a volume of 1 cubic inch of paint is spread over an area of 100 square inches, then the thickness of the paint equals $\frac{1}{100}$ *inch. Use this formula in the following exercises.*

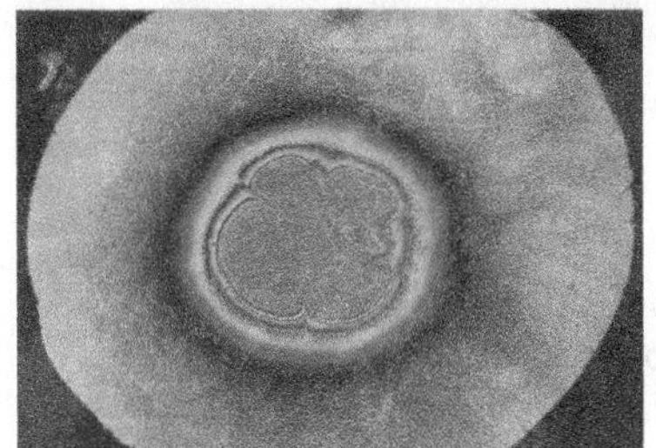

1. **Thickness of an Oil Film** A drop of oil measuring 0.12 cubic centimeter in volume is spilled onto a lake. The oil spreads out in a circular shape having a *diameter* of 23 centimeters. Approximate the thickness of the oil film.

2. **Thickness of Gold Foil** A flat, rectangular sheet of gold foil measures 20 centimeters by 30 centimeters and has a mass of 23.16 grams. If 1 cubic centimeter of gold has a mass of 19.3 grams, find the thickness of the gold foil. (***Source:*** U. Haber-Schaim, *Introductory Physical Science*.)

3. **Thickness of Cement** A 100-foot-long sidewalk is 5 feet wide. If 125 cubic feet of cement are evenly poured to form the sidewalk, find the thickness of the sidewalk.

4. **Depth of a Lake** A lake covers 2.5×10^7 square feet and contains 7.5×10^8 cubic feet of water. Find the average depth of the lake.

1.2 Visualizing and Graphing Data

- **Analyze one-variable data**
- **Find the domain and range of a relation**
- **Graph in the *xy*-plane**
- **Calculate distance**
- **Find the midpoint**
- **Learn the standard equation of a circle**
- **Learn to graph equations with a calculator (optional)**

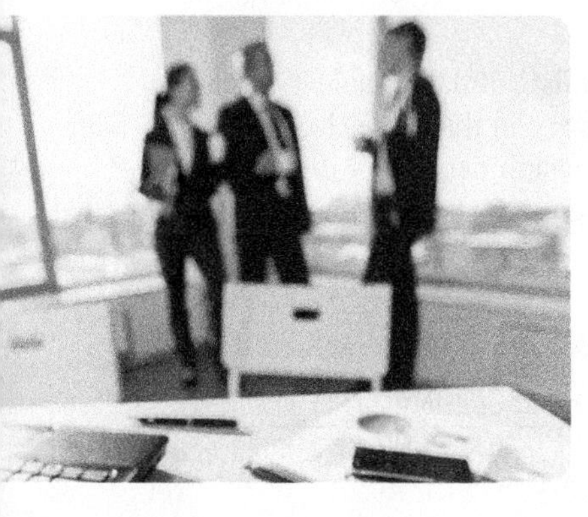

Introduction

There is a wealth of information in data, but the challenge is to convert data into meaningful information that can be used to solve problems. Visualization can be a powerful tool to analyze data, as pictures and graphs are often easier to understand than a list of numbers. For example, looking at Table 1.2, it is difficult to identify trends in the data for *Popular Science* iPad subscriptions. On the other hand, the *line graph* in Figure 1.9 makes it easy to see that there is a sudden increase in subscriptions in October 2011. This increase could be an indicator for Apple that its new product Newsstand, which makes it easier to subscribe to magazines, is a success. Insights like this are important to businesses and therefore visualization is an effective business strategy.

Popular Science iPad Subscription Sales 2011

Date	Subscriptions
27 Feb	7,100
24 Apr	15,400
19 Jun	20,100
14 Aug	25,000
9 Oct	28,700
30 Oct	36,000
27 Nov	40,700

Table 1.2

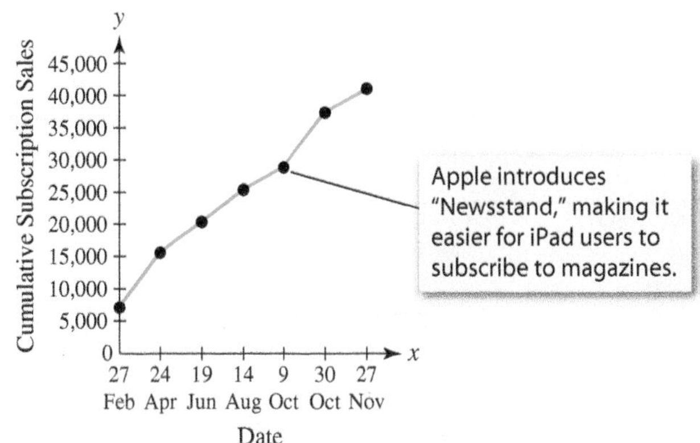

Figure 1.9

One-Variable Data

Data often occur in the form of a list. A list of test scores without names is an example; the only variable is the score. Data of this type are referred to as **one-variable data.** If the values in a list are unique, they can be represented visually on a number line.

Means and medians can be found for one-variable data sets. To calculate the **mean** (or **average**) of a set of n numbers, we add the n numbers and then divide the sum by n. The **median** is equal to the value that is located in the middle of a *sorted* list. If there is an odd number of data items, the median is the middle data item. If there is an even number of data items, the median is the average of the two middle items.

EXAMPLE 1 Analyzing a list of temperatures

Table 1.3 lists the low temperatures T in degrees Fahrenheit that occurred in Minneapolis, Minnesota, for six consecutive nights during January 2012.

Low Temperatures in Minneapolis for Six Nights

T	−12	−4	−8	21	18	9

Table 1.3

(a) Plot these temperatures on a number line.
(b) Find the maximum and minimum of these temperatures.
(c) Determine the mean of these six temperatures.
(d) Find the median and interpret the result.

SOLUTION
(a) In Figure 1.10 the numbers in Table 1.3 are plotted on a number line.

Number Line Graph of Low Temperatures

−30 −20 −10 0 10 20 30

Figure 1.10

(b) The maximum is 21°F and the minimum is −12°F.
(c) The mean temperature is calculated as follows:

$$\frac{-12 + (-4) + (-8) + 21 + 18 + 9}{6} = \frac{24}{6} = 4.$$

Thus the average low temperature was 4°F.
(d) In the ordered list −12, −8, −4, 9, 18, 21, the median is the average of the two middle temperatures, −4°F and 9°F. The median is $\frac{-4 + 9}{2} = 2.5$°F. This means that half of the temperatures are above 2.5°F and half are below.

Now Try Exercises 1 and 5

Two-Variable Data

Relations Sometimes a relationship exists between two lists of data. Table 1.4 lists the monthly average precipitation in inches for Portland, Oregon. In this table, 1 corresponds to January, 2 to February, and so on. We show the relationship between a month and its average precipitation by combining the two lists so that corresponding months and precipitations are visually paired.

This table forms a relation with ordered pairs in the form (month, precipitation).

Average Precipitation for Portland, Oregon

Month	1	2	3	4	5	6	7	8	9	10	11	12
Precipitation (inches)	6.2	3.9	3.6	2.3	2.0	1.5	0.5	1.1	1.6	3.1	5.2	6.4

Table 1.4

If x is the month and y is the precipitation in inches, then the **ordered pair** (x, y) represents the average amount of precipitation y during month x. For example, the ordered pair (5, 2.0) indicates that the average precipitation in May is 2.0 inches, whereas the ordered pair (2, 3.9) indicates that the average precipitation in February is 3.9 inches. *Order is important* in an ordered pair.

Since the data in Table 1.4 involve two variables, the month and precipitation, we refer to them as **two-variable data**. It is important to realize that a relation established by two-variable data is between two lists rather than within a single list. January is not related to August, and 6.2 inches of precipitation is not associated with 1.1 inches of precipitation. Instead, January is paired with 6.2 inches, and August is paired with 1.1 inches. We now define the mathematical concept of a relation.

RELATION

A **relation** is a set of ordered pairs.

If we denote the ordered pairs in a relation by (x, y), then the set of all x-values is called the **domain** of the relation and the set of all y-values is called the **range**. The relation shown in Table 1.4 has domain

$$D = \{1, 2, 3, 4, 5, 6, 7, 8, 9, 10, 11, 12\}$$ x-values

The domain is the set of months.

and range

$$R = \{0.5, 1.1, 1.5, 1.6, 2.0, 2.3, 3.1, 3.6, 3.9, 5.2, 6.2, 6.4\}.$$ y-values

The range is the set of average precipitations.

EXAMPLE 2 Finding the domain and range of a relation

A physics class measured the time y that it takes for an object to fall x feet, as shown in Table 1.5. The object was dropped twice from each height.

Falling Object

x (feet)	20	20	40	40
y (seconds)	1.2	1.1	1.5	1.6

Table 1.5

(a) Express the data as a relation S.
(b) Find the domain and range of S.

SOLUTION

(a) A relation is a set of ordered pairs, so we can write

$$S = \{(20, 1.2), (20, 1.1), (40, 1.5), (40, 1.6)\}.$$

(b) The domain is the set of x-values of the ordered pairs, or $D = \{20, 40\}$. The range is the set of y-values of the ordered pairs, or $R = \{1.1, 1.2, 1.5, 1.6\}$.

NOTE If an element in the domain or range occurs more than once in a data table, it is listed only once in the set for the domain or the range.

Now Try Exercise 13

Graphing Relations To visualize a relation, we often use the **Cartesian (rectangular) coordinate plane**, or ***xy*-plane**. The horizontal axis is the ***x*-axis** and the vertical axis is the ***y*-axis**. The axes intersect at the **origin** and determine four regions called **quadrants**, numbered I, II, III, and IV, counterclockwise, as shown in Figure 1.11. We can plot the ordered pair (x, y) using the x- and y-axes. A grid is sometimes helpful when plotting points, as shown in Figure 1.12. A point lying on the x-axis or y-axis does not belong to any quadrant. The point $(-3, 0)$ is located on the x-axis, whereas the point $(0, -3)$ lies on the y-axis. Neither point belongs to a quadrant.

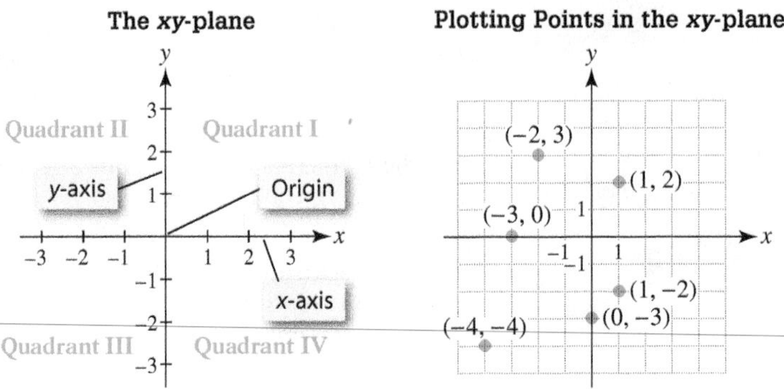

Figure 1.11

Figure 1.12

The term **scatterplot** is given to a graph in the xy-plane where distinct points are plotted. Figure 1.12 is an example of a scatterplot.

EXAMPLE 3 Graphing a relation

Complete the following for the relation

$$S = \{(5, 10), (5, -5), (-10, 10), (0, 15), (-15, -10)\}.$$

(a) Find the domain and range of the relation.
(b) Determine the maximum and minimum of the x-values and then of the y-values.
(c) Label appropriate scales on the xy-axes.
(d) Plot the relation as a scatterplot.

SOLUTION

(a) The elements of the domain D correspond to the first number in each ordered pair.

$$D = \{-15, -10, 0, 5\}$$

The elements of the range R correspond to the second number in each ordered pair.

$$R = \{-10, -5, 10, 15\}$$

(b) x-minimum: -15; x-maximum: 5; y-minimum: -10; y-maximum: 15

(c) An appropriate scale for both the x-axis and the y-axis might be -20 to 20, with each tick mark representing a distance of 5. This scale is shown in Figure 1.13.

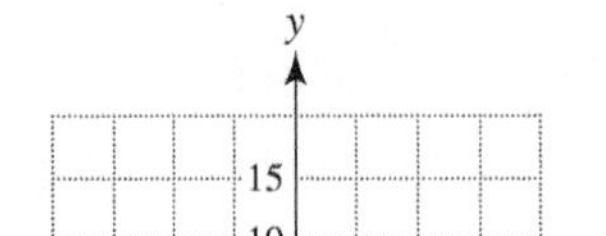

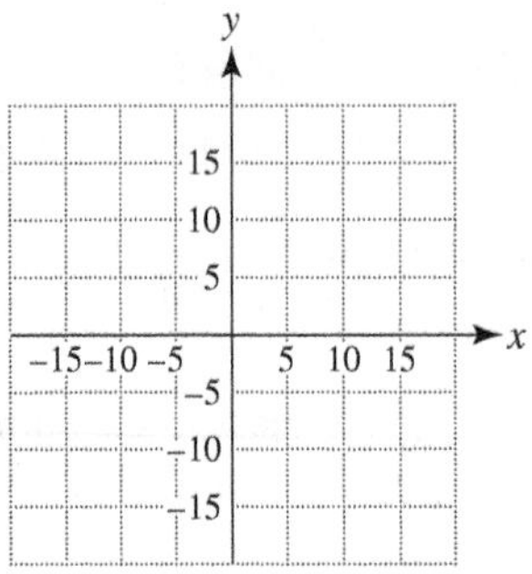

Figure 1.13

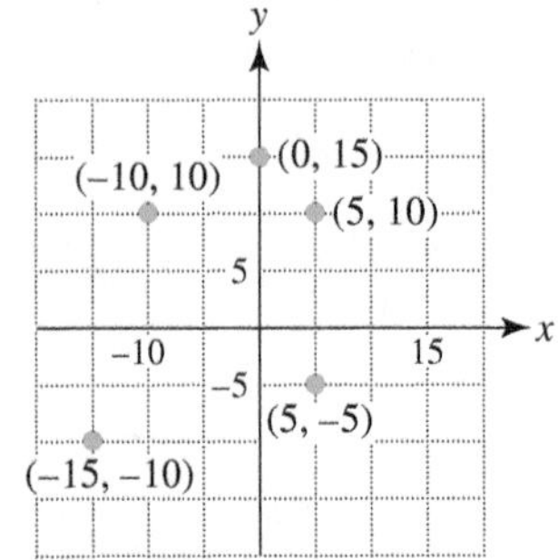

Figure 1.14

(d) The points in S are plotted in Figure 1.14.

Now Try Exercise 17

Sometimes it is helpful to connect consecutive data points in a scatterplot with straight-line segments. This type of graph, which visually emphasizes changes in the data, is called a **line graph**.

EXAMPLE 4 Making a scatterplot and a line graph

Use Table 1.4 on page 12 to make a scatterplot of average monthly precipitation in Portland, Oregon. Then make a line graph.

SOLUTION

Use the x-axis for the months and the y-axis for the precipitation amounts. To make a scatterplot, simply graph the ordered pairs (1, 6.2), (2, 3.9), (3, 3.6), (4, 2.3), (5, 2.0), (6, 1.5), (7, 0.5), (8, 1.1), (9, 1.6), (10, 3.1), (11, 5.2), and (12, 6.4) in the xy-plane, as shown in Figure 1.15. Then connect consecutive data points to make a line graph, as shown in Figure 1.16.

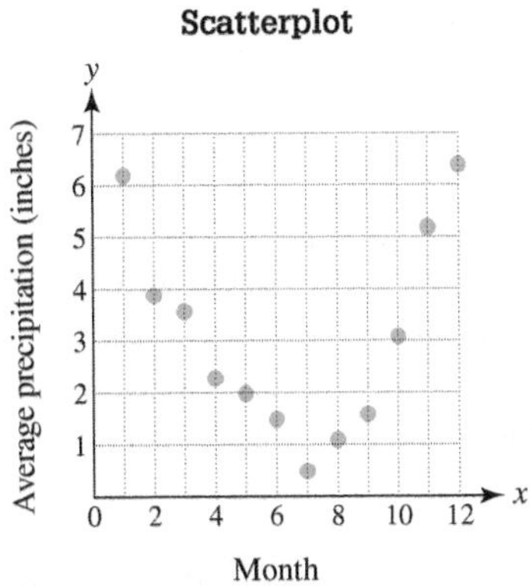

Figure 1.15 Monthly Average Precipitation

Line Graph

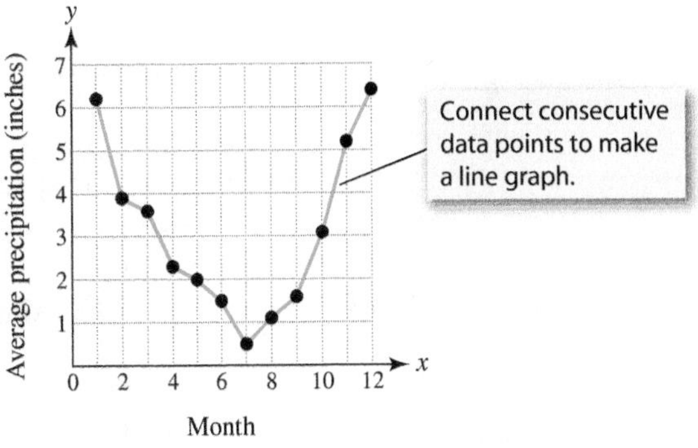

Connect consecutive data points to make a line graph.

Figure 1.16

Now Try Exercise 23

Geometry Review
To review the Pythagorean theorem, see Chapter R (page R-2).

Distance Between Two Points

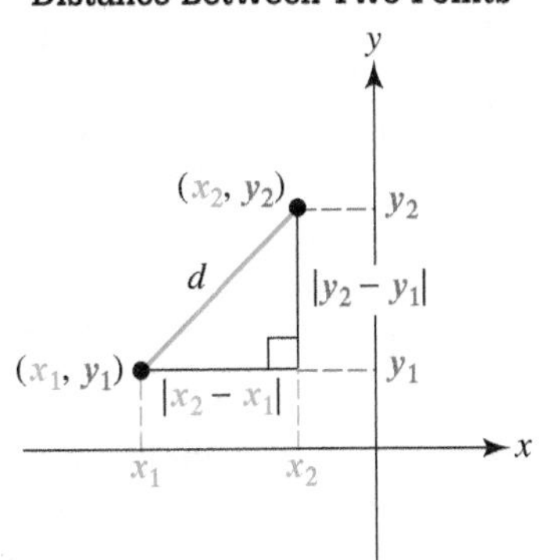

Figure 1.17

The Distance Formula

In the xy-plane, the length of a line segment with endpoints (x_1, y_1) and (x_2, y_2) can be calculated by using the **Pythagorean theorem**. See Figure 1.17.

The lengths of the legs of the right triangle are $|x_2 - x_1|$ and $|y_2 - y_1|$. The distance d is the hypotenuse of the right triangle. Applying the Pythagorean theorem to this triangle gives $d^2 = (x_2 - x_1)^2 + (y_2 - y_1)^2$. Because distance is nonnegative, we can solve this equation for d to get $d = \sqrt{(x_2 - x_1)^2 + (y_2 - y_1)^2}$.

DISTANCE FORMULA

The **distance** d between the points (x_1, y_1) and (x_2, y_2) in the xy-plane is

$$d = \sqrt{(x_2 - x_1)^2 + (y_2 - y_1)^2}.$$

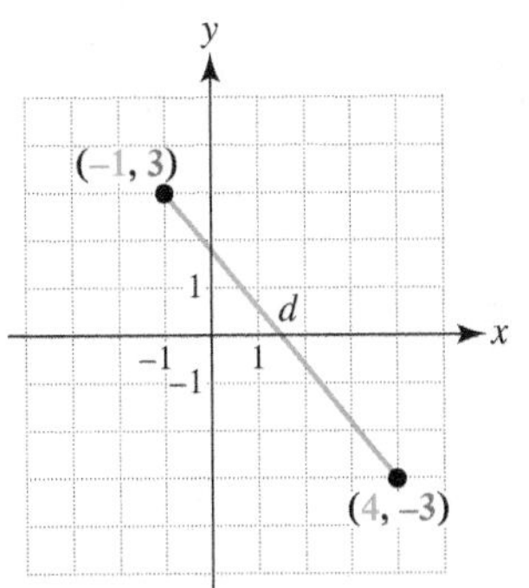

Figure 1.18

Figure 1.18 shows a line segment connecting the points $(-1, 3)$ and $(4, -3)$. Its length is

$$\begin{aligned} d &= \sqrt{(4 - (-1))^2 + (-3 - 3)^2} && \text{Distance formula} \\ &= \sqrt{61} && \text{Exact length} \\ &\approx 7.81. && \text{Approximate.} \end{aligned}$$

EXAMPLE 5 **Finding the distance between two points**

Find the exact distance between $(3, -4)$ and $(-2, 7)$. Then approximate this distance to the nearest hundredth.

SOLUTION

In the distance formula, let (x_1, y_1) be $(3, -4)$ and (x_2, y_2) be $(-2, 7)$.

$$\begin{aligned} \sqrt{(x_2 - x_1)^2 + (y_2 - y_1)^2} &= \sqrt{(-2 - 3)^2 + (7 - (-4))^2} && \text{Distance formula} \\ &= \sqrt{(-5)^2 + 11^2} && \text{Subtract.} \\ &= \sqrt{146} && \text{Simplify.} \\ &\approx 12.08 && \text{Approximate.} \end{aligned}$$

The *exact* distance is $\sqrt{146}$, and the *approximate* distance, rounded to the nearest hundredth, is 12.08. Note that we would obtain the same answer if we let (x_1, y_1) be $(-2, 7)$ and (x_2, y_2) be $(3, -4)$.

Now Try Exercise 27

In the next example the distance between two moving cars is found.

EXAMPLE 6 **Finding the distance between two moving cars**

Suppose that at noon car A is traveling south at 20 miles per hour and is located 80 miles north of car B. Car B is traveling east at 40 miles per hour.

(a) Let (0, 0) be the initial coordinates of car B in the *xy*-plane, where units are in miles. Plot the location of each car at noon and at 1:30 P.M.

(b) Approximate the distance between the cars at 1:30 P.M.

Distance Between Two Cars

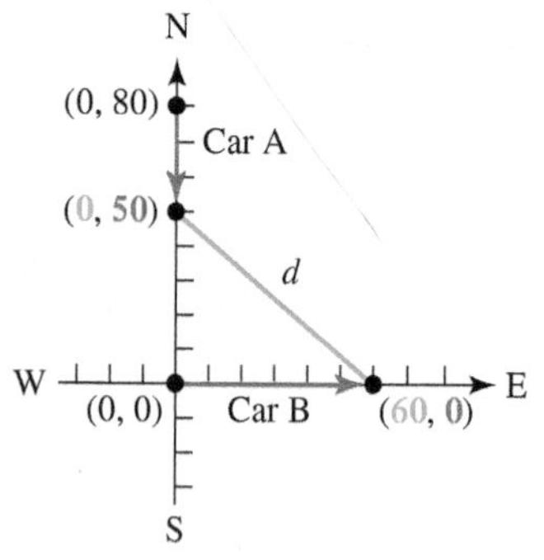

Figure 1.19

SOLUTION

(a) If the initial coordinates of car B are (0, 0), then the initial coordinates of car A are (0, 80), because car A is 80 miles north of car B. After 1 hour and 30 minutes, or 1.5 hours, car A has traveled $1.5 \times 20 = 30$ miles south, and so it is located 50 miles north of the initial location of car B. Thus its coordinates are (0, 50) at 1:30 PM. Car B traveled $1.5 \times 40 = 60$ miles east, so its coordinates are (60, 0) at 1:30 PM. See Figure 1.19, where these points are plotted.

(b) To find the distance between the cars at 1:30 P.M. we must find the distance *d* between the points (0, 50) and (60, 0).

$$d = \sqrt{(60 - 0)^2 + (0 - 50)^2} = \sqrt{6100} \approx 78.1 \text{ miles}$$

Now Try Exercise 43

The Midpoint Formula

A common way to make estimations is to average data values. For example, in 1995 the average cost of tuition and fees at public colleges and universities was about \$4000, whereas in 2005 it was about \$6000. One might estimate the cost of tuition and fees in 2000 to be \$5000. This type of averaging is referred to as finding the midpoint. If a line segment is drawn between two data points, then its *midpoint* is the unique point on the line segment that is equidistant from the endpoints.

On a real number line, the midpoint M of two data points x_1 and x_2 is calculated by averaging their coordinates, as shown in Figure 1.20. For example, the midpoint of -3 and 5 is $M = \frac{-3 + 5}{2} = 1$.

Finding the Midpoint on a Number Line

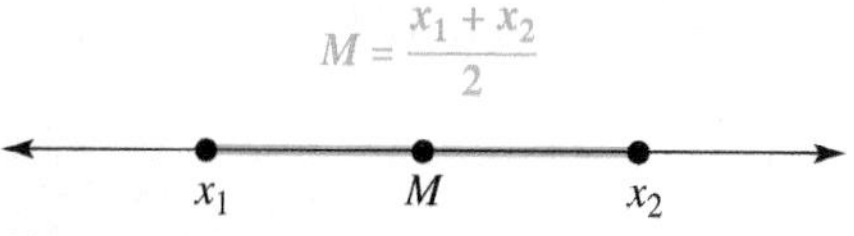

Figure 1.20

Finding the Midpoint

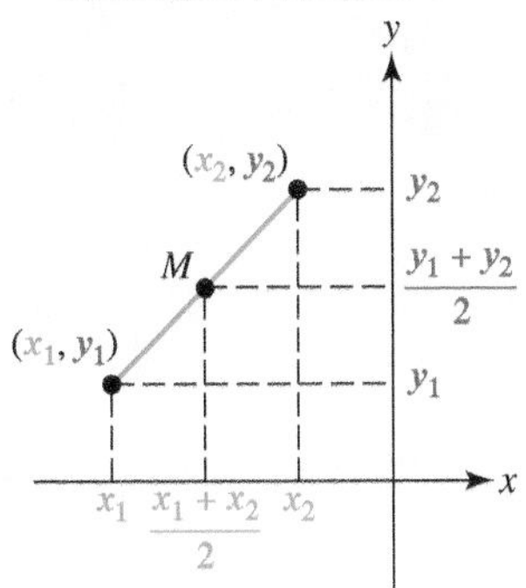

Figure 1.21

The midpoint formula in the xy-plane is similar to the formula for the real number line, except that both coordinates are averaged. Figure 1.21 shows midpoint M located on the line segment connecting the two data points (x_1, y_1) and (x_2, y_2). The x-coordinate of the midpoint M is located halfway between x_1 and x_2 and is $\frac{x_1 + x_2}{2}$. Similarly, the y-coordinate of M is the average of y_1 and y_2. For example, if we let (x_1, y_1) be $(-3, 1)$ and (x_2, y_2) be $(-1, 3)$ in Figure 1.21, then the midpoint is computed by

$$\left(\frac{-3 + -1}{2}, \frac{1 + 3}{2}\right) = (-2, 2).$$

MIDPOINT FORMULA IN THE XY-PLANE

The **midpoint** of the line segment with endpoints (x_1, y_1) and (x_2, y_2) in the xy-plane is

$$\left(\frac{x_1 + x_2}{2}, \frac{y_1 + y_2}{2}\right).$$

EXAMPLE 7 **Finding the midpoint**

Find the midpoint of the line segment connecting the points $(6, -7)$ and $(-4, 6)$.

SOLUTION

In the midpoint formula, let (x_1, y_1) be $(6, -7)$ and (x_2, y_2) be $(-4, 6)$. Then the midpoint M can be found as follows.

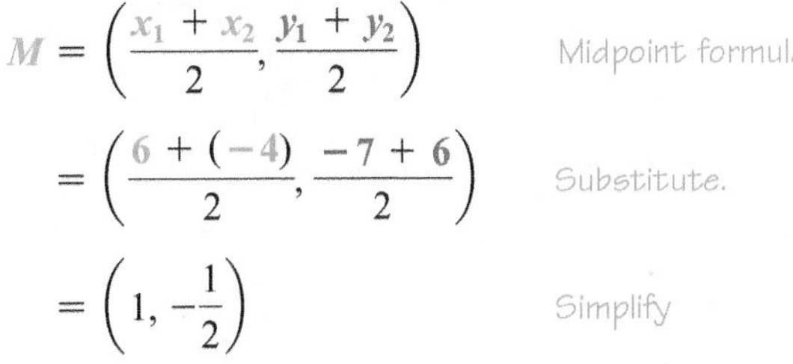

$$M = \left(\frac{x_1 + x_2}{2}, \frac{y_1 + y_2}{2}\right) \quad \text{Midpoint formula}$$

$$= \left(\frac{6 + (-4)}{2}, \frac{-7 + 6}{2}\right) \quad \text{Substitute.}$$

$$= \left(1, -\frac{1}{2}\right) \quad \text{Simplify}$$

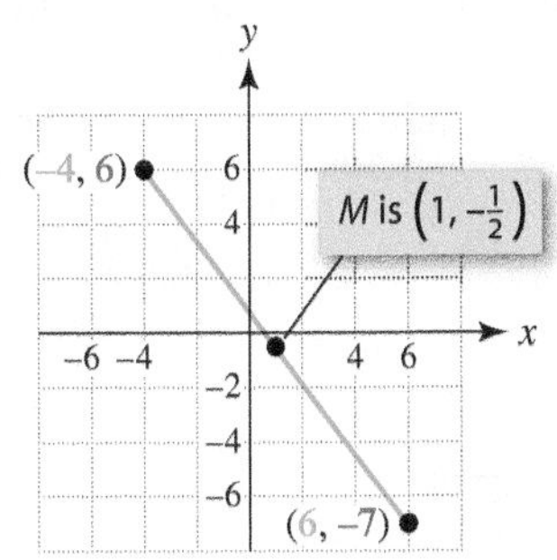

Figure 1.22

The midpoint M of this line segment is shown in Figure 1.22

Now Try Exercise 49

EXAMPLE 8 **Estimating U.S. population**

In 1990 the population of the United States was 249 million, and by 2010 it had increased to 308 million. Use the midpoint formula to estimate the population in 2000. (***Source:*** Bureau of the Census.)

SOLUTION

The U.S. populations in 1990 and 2010 are given by the points $(1990, 249)$ and $(2010, 308)$. The midpoint M of the line segment connecting these points is

$$M = \left(\frac{1990 + 2010}{2}, \frac{249 + 308}{2}\right) = (2000, 278.5).$$

The midpoint formula estimates a population of 278.5 million in 2000 (The actual population was 281 million.)

Now Try Exercise 45

Circles

Applying the Distance Formula to Circles A **circle** consists of the set of points in a plane that are equidistant from a fixed point. The distance is called the **radius** of the circle, and the fixed point is called the **center**. If we let the center of the circle be (h, k), the radius be r, and (x, y) be any point on the circle, then the distance between (x, y) and (h, k) must equal r. See Figure 1.23. By the distance formula we have

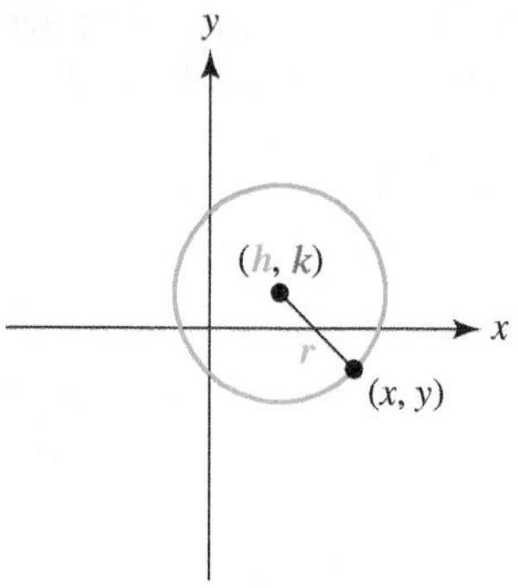

$$\sqrt{(x - h)^2 + (y - k)^2} = r.$$

Squaring each side gives

$$(x - h)^2 + (y - k)^2 = r^2.$$

Figure 1.23

STANDARD EQUATION OF A CIRCLE

The circle with center (h, k) and radius r has equation

$$(x - h)^2 + (y - k)^2 = r^2.$$

NOTE If the center of a circle is (0, 0), then the equation simplifies to $x^2 + y^2 = r^2$. For example, the equation of the circle with center (0, 0) and radius 7 is $x^2 + y^2 = 49$.

EXAMPLE 9 Finding the center and radius of a circle

Find the center and radius of the circle with the given equation. Graph each circle.
(a) $x^2 + y^2 = 9$ **(b)** $(x - 1)^2 + (y + 2)^2 = 4$

SOLUTION

(a) Because the equation $x^2 + y^2 = 9$ can be written as $(x - 0)^2 + (y - 0)^2 = 3^2$, the center is (0, 0) and the radius is $\sqrt{9}$, or 3. The graph of this circle is shown in Figure 1.24.

(b) For $(x - 1)^2 + (y + 2)^2 = 4$, the center is $(1, -2)$ and the radius is $\sqrt{4}$, or 2. The graph is shown in Figure 1.25.

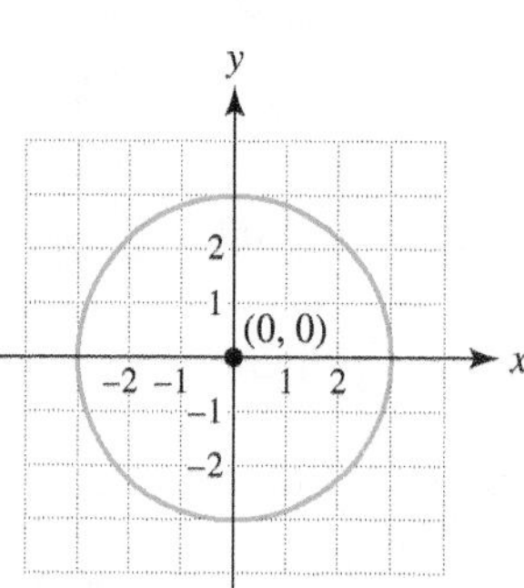

Figure 1.24

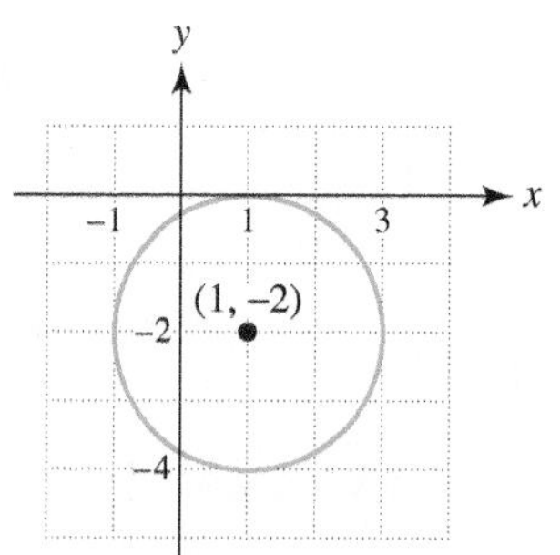

Figure 1.25

Now Try Exercises 59, 63, 81, and 83

EXAMPLE 10 Finding the equation of a circle

Find the equation of the circle that satisfies the conditions. Graph each circle.
(a) Radius 4, center $(-3, 5)$
(b) Center $(6, -3)$ with the point $(1, 2)$ on the circle

SOLUTION

(a) Let $r = 4$ and $(h, k) = (-3, 5)$. The equation of this circle is

$$(x - (-3))^2 + (y - 5)^2 = 4^2 \quad \text{or} \quad (x + 3)^2 + (y - 5)^2 = 16.$$

A graph of the circle is shown in Figure 1.26.

(b) First we must find the distance between the points $(6, -3)$ and $(1, 2)$ to determine r.

$$r = \sqrt{(6 - 1)^2 + (-3 - 2)^2} = \sqrt{50} \approx 7.1$$

Since $r^2 = 50$, the equation of the circle is $(x - 6)^2 + (y + 3)^2 = 50$. Its graph is shown in Figure 1.27.

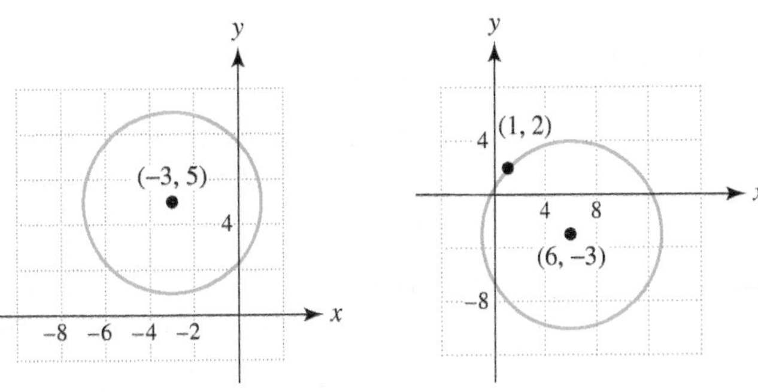

Figure 1.26

Figure 1.27

Now Try Exercises 71, 75, 85, and 87

EXAMPLE 11 Finding the equation of a circle

The diameter of a circle is shown in Figure 1.28. Find the standard equation of the circle.

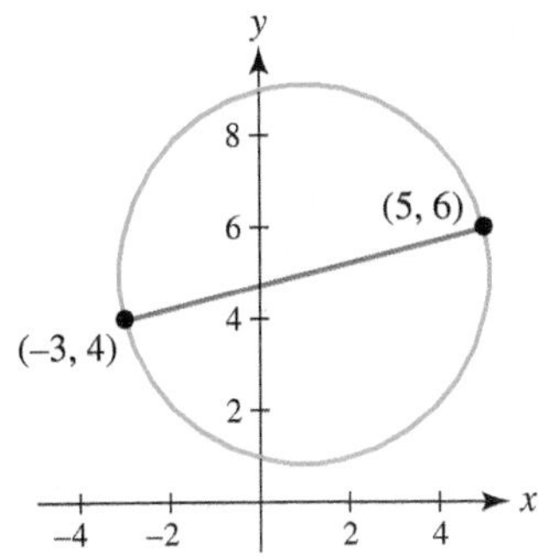

Figure 1.28

SOLUTION

Getting Started First find the center of the circle, which is the midpoint of a diameter. Then find the radius by calculating the distance between the center and one of the given endpoints of the diameter. ▶

Find the center C of the circle by applying the midpoint formula to the endpoints of the diameter $(-3, 4)$ and $(5, 6)$.

$$C = \left(\frac{-3 + 5}{2}, \frac{4 + 6}{2}\right) = (1, 5)$$

Use the distance formula to find the radius, which equals the distance from the center $(1, 5)$ to the endpoint $(5, 6)$.

$$r = \sqrt{(5 - 1)^2 + (6 - 5)^2} = \sqrt{17}$$

Thus r^2 equals 17, and the standard equation is $(x - 1)^2 + (y - 5)^2 = 17$.

Now Try Exercise 79

Graphing with a Calculator (Optional)

Graphing calculators can be used to create tables, scatterplots, line graphs, and other types of graphs. The **viewing rectangle**, or **window**, on a graphing calculator is similar to the view finder in a camera. A camera cannot take a picture of an entire scene; it must be centered on a portion of the available scenery and then it can capture different views of the same scene by zooming in and out. Graphing calculators have similar capabilities. The calculator screen can show only a finite, rectangular region of the xy-plane, which is infinite. The viewing rectangle must be specified by setting minimum and maximum values for both the x- and y-axes before a graph can be drawn.

We will use the following terminology to describe a viewing rectangle. **Xmin** is the minimum x-value and **Xmax** is the maximum x-value along the x-axis. Similarly, **Ymin** is the minimum y-value and **Ymax** is the maximum y-value along the y-axis. Most graphs show an x-scale and a y-scale using tick marks on the respective axes. The distance represented by consecutive tick marks on the x-axis is called **Xscl**, and the distance represented by consecutive tick marks on the y-axis is called **Yscl**. See Figure 1.29. This information can be written concisely as

$$[\text{Xmin, Xmax, Xscl}] \text{ by } [\text{Ymin, Ymax, Yscl}].$$

Identifying the Window Size

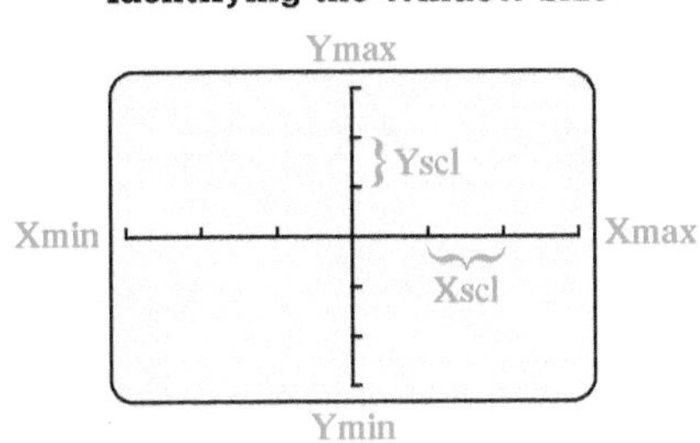

Figure 1.29

For example, $[-10, 10, 1]$ by $[-10, 10, 1]$ means that Xmin $= -10$, Xmax $= 10$, Xscl $= 1$, Ymin $= -10$, Ymax $= 10$, and Yscl $= 1$. This setting is referred to as the **standard viewing rectangle.**

EXAMPLE 12 Setting the viewing rectangle

Show the standard viewing rectangle and the viewing rectangle given by $[-30, 40, 10]$ by $[-400, 800, 100]$ on your calculator.

SOLUTION

The required window settings and viewing rectangles are displayed in Figures 1.30–1.33. Notice that in Figure 1.31, there are 10 tick marks on the positive x-axis, since its length is 10 and the distance between consecutive tick marks is 1. Note that **Xres** is usually equal to 1.

Calculator Help
To set a viewing rectangle or window, see Appendix A (page AP-3).

The Standard Viewing Rectangle

WINDOW
Xmin=−10
Xmax=10
Xscl=1
Ymin=−10
Ymax=10
Yscl=1
Xres=1

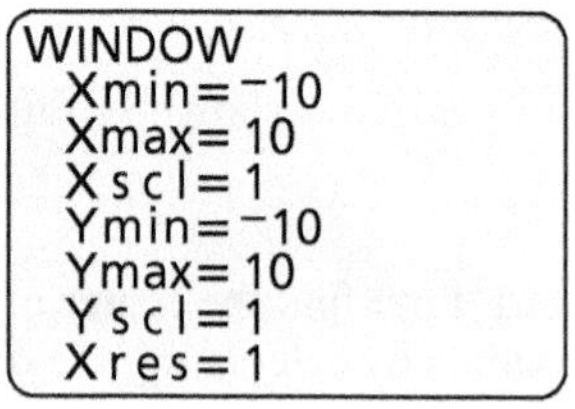

Figure 1.30

$[-10, 10, 1]$ by $[-10, 10, 1]$

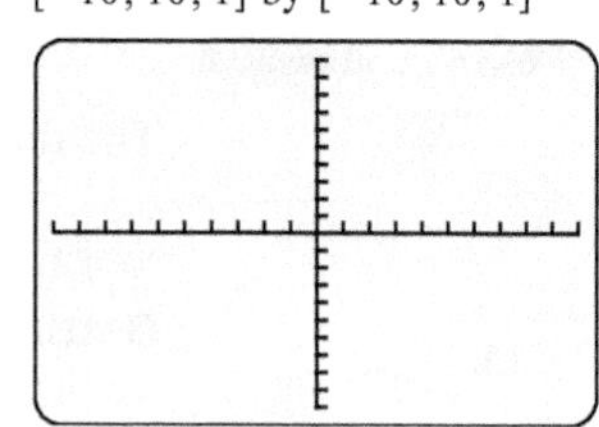

Figure 1.31

Setting a Different Window

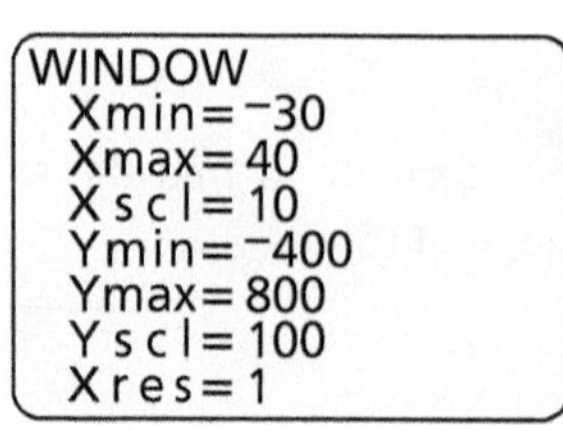

WINDOW
Xmin=−30
Xmax=40
Xscl=10
Ymin=−400
Ymax=800
Yscl=100
Xres=1

Figure 1.32

$[-30, 40, 10]$ by $[-400, 800, 100]$

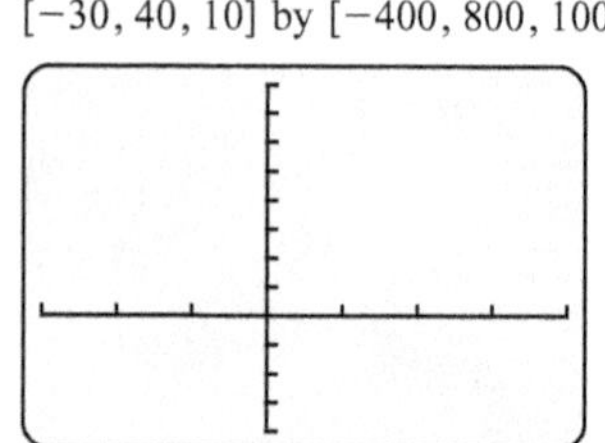

Figure 1.33

Now Try Exercise 93

EXAMPLE 13 Making a scatterplot with a graphing calculator

Plot the points $(-5, -5)$, $(-2, 3)$, $(1, -7)$, and $(4, 8)$ in the standard viewing rectangle.

SOLUTION

The standard viewing rectangle is given by $[-10, 10, 1]$ by $[-10, 10, 1]$. The points $(-5, -5)$, $(-2, 3)$, $(1, -7)$, and $(4, 8)$ are plotted in Figure 1.34.

$[-10, 10, 1]$ by $[-10, 10, 1]$

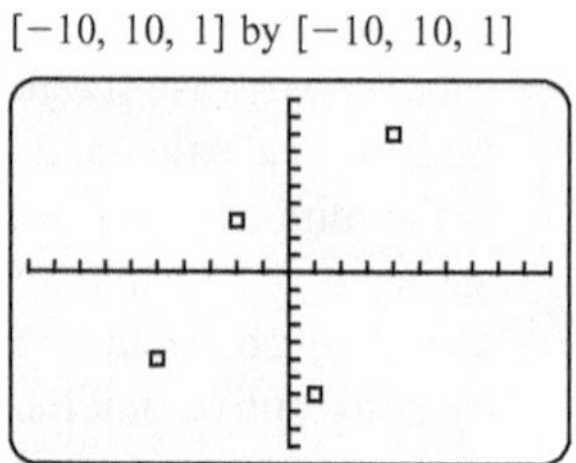

Figure 1.34

Calculator Help
To make the scatterplot in Figure 1.34, see Appendix A (page AP-3).

Now Try Exercise 101

EXAMPLE 14 **Creating a line graph with a graphing calculator**

Table 1.6 lists the percentage of music album sales accounted for by compact discs (CDs) from 1990 to 2010. Make a line graph of these sales in [1988, 2012, 2] by [0, 100, 20].

CD Album Sales

Year	1990	1995	2000	2005	2010
CDs (% share)	31	65	89	90	74

Source: Recording Industry Association of America.

Table 1.6

SOLUTION

Enter the data points (1990, 31), (1995, 65), (2000, 89), (2005, 90), and (2010, 74). A line graph can be created by selecting this option on your graphing calculator. The graph is shown in Figure 1.35.

Calculator Help

To make a line graph, see Appendix A (page AP-3).

[1988, 2012, 2] by [0, 100, 20]

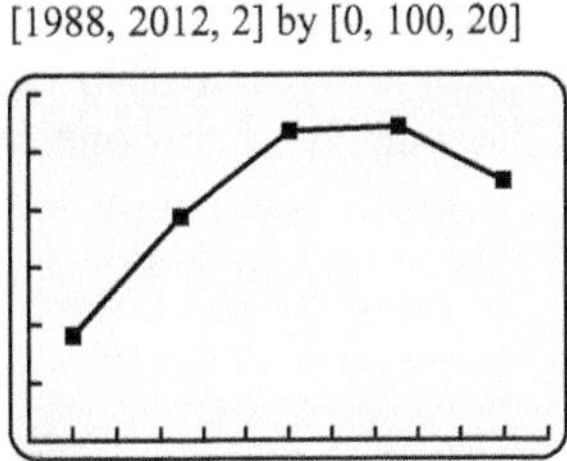

Figure 1.35

Now Try Exercise 105

1.2 Putting It All Together

CONCEPT	EXPLANATION	EXAMPLES
Mean, or average	To find the mean, or average, of n numbers, divide their sum by n.	The mean of the four numbers $-3, 5, 6, 9$ is $$\frac{-3 + 5 + 6 + 9}{4} = 4.25.$$
Median	The median of a sorted list of numbers equals the value that is located in the middle of the list. Half the data are greater than or equal to the median, and half the data are less than or equal to the median.	The median of 2, 3, 6, 9, 11 is 6, the middle data item. The median of 2, 3, 6, 9 is the average of the two middle values: 3 and 6. Therefore the median is $\frac{3 + 6}{2} = 4.5$.
Relation, domain, and range	A relation is a set of ordered pairs (x, y). The set of x-values is called the domain, and the set of y-values is called the range.	The relation $S = \{(1, 3), (2, 5), (1, 6)\}$ has domain $D = \{1, 2\}$ and range $R = \{3, 5, 6\}$.
Distance formula	The distance between (x_1, y_1) and (x_2, y_2) is $$d = \sqrt{(x_2 - x_1)^2 + (y_2 - y_1)^2}.$$	The distance between $(2, -1)$ and $(-1, 3)$ is $$d = \sqrt{(-1 - 2)^2 + (3 - (-1))^2} = 5.$$

continued on next page

CONCEPT	EXPLANATION	EXAMPLES
Midpoint formula	The midpoint of the line segment connecting (x_1, y_1) and (x_2, y_2) is $$M = \left(\frac{x_1 + x_2}{2}, \frac{y_1 + y_2}{2}\right).$$	The midpoint of the line segment connecting (4, 3) and (−2, 5) is $$M = \left(\frac{4 + (-2)}{2}, \frac{3 + 5}{2}\right) = (1, 4).$$
Standard equation of a circle	The circle with center (h, k) and radius r has the equation $$(x - h)^2 + (y - k)^2 = r^2.$$	The circle with center (−3, 4) and radius 5 has the equation $$(x + 3)^2 + (y - 4)^2 = 25.$$

The next table summarizes some basic concepts related to one-variable and two-variable data.

TYPE OF DATA	METHODS OF VISUALIZATION	COMMENTS
One-variable data	Number line, list, one-column or one-row table	The data items are the same type and can be described using x-values. Computations of the mean and median are performed on one-variable data.
Two-variable data	Two-column or two-row table, scatterplot, line graph or other type of graph in the xy-plane	Two types of data are related, can be described by using ordered pairs (x, y), and are often called a relation.

1.2 Exercises

Data Involving One Variable

Exercises 1–4: For the table of data, complete the following.

(a) Plot the numbers on a number line.
(b) Find the maximum and minimum of the data.
(c) Determine the mean of the data.

1.

3	−2	5	0	6	−1

2.

5	−3	4	−2	1	6

3.

−10	20	30	−20	0	10

4.

0.5	−1.5	2.0	4.5	−3.5	−1.0

Exercises 5–8: Sort the list of numbers from smallest to largest and display the result in a table.

(a) Determine the maximum and minimum values.
(b) Calculate the mean and median. Round each result to the nearest hundredth when appropriate.

5. −10, 25, 15, −30, 55, 61, −30, 45, 5

6. −1.25, 4.75, −3.5, 1.5, 2.5, 4.75, 1.5

7. $\sqrt{15}, 2^{2.3}, \sqrt[3]{69}, \pi^2, 2^{\pi}, 4.1$

8. $\frac{22}{7}, 3.14, \sqrt[3]{28}, \sqrt{9.4}, 4^{0.9}, 3^{1.2}$

Exercises 9 and 10: **Geography** *The set of numbers contains data about geographic features of the world.*

(a) Plot the numbers on a number line.
(b) Calculate the mean and median for the set of numbers. Interpret your results.
(c) Try to identify the geographic feature associated with the largest number in the set.

9. {31.7, 22.3, 12.3, 26.8, 24.9, 23.0} (Areas of largest freshwater lakes in thousands of square miles) (***Source:*** U.S. National Oceanic and Atmospheric Administration.)

10. {19.3, 18.5, 29.0, 7.31, 16.1, 22.8, 20.3} (Highest elevations of the continents in thousands of feet) (***Source:*** *National Geographic Atlas of the World.*)

11. Designing a Data Set Find a set of three numbers with a mean of 20 and a median of 18. Is your answer unique?

12. Designing a Data Set Find a set of five numbers with a mean of 10 and a median of 9. Is your answer unique?

Data Involving Two Variables

Exercises 13–16: For the table of data, complete the following.

(a) Express the data as a relation S.
(b) Find the domain and range of S.

13.

x	-1	2	3	5	9
y	5	2	-1	-4	-5

14.

x	-2	0	2	4	6
y	-4	-2	-1	0	4

15.

x	1	4	5	4	1
y	5	5	6	6	5

16.

x	-1	0	3	-1	-2
y	$\frac{1}{2}$	1	$\frac{3}{4}$	3	$-\frac{5}{6}$

Exercises 17–22: Complete the following.

(a) Find the domain and range of the relation.
(b) Determine the maximum and minimum of the x-values and then of the y-values.
(c) Label appropriate scales on the xy-axes.
(d) Plot the relation.

17. $\{(0, 5), (-3, 4), (-2, -5), (7, -3), (0, 0)\}$

18. $\{(1, 1), (3, 0), (-5, -5), (8, -2), (0, 3)\}$

19. $\{(2, 2), (-3, 1), (-4, -1), (-1, 3), (0, -2)\}$

20. $\{(1, 1), (2, -3), (-1, -1), (-1, 2), (-1, 0)\}$

21. $\{(10, 50), (-35, 45), (0, -55), (75, 25), (-25, -25)\}$

22. $\{(-1.2, 1.5), (1.0, 0.5), (-0.3, 1.1), (-0.8, -1.3)\}$

Exercises 23 and 24: **Plotting Real Data** *Use the table to make a scatterplot and line graph of the data.*

23. Global Cell Phone Subscribers (millions)

Year	1990	1995	2000	2005	2011
Subscribers	5	34	109	208	324

Source: CTIA–The Wireless Association.

24. Atmospheric CO_2 Levels (parts per million)

Year	1958	1975	1990	2005	2011
CO_2 Amounts	315	335	355	380	392

Source: Mauna Loa Observatory.

Distance Formula

Exercises 25–40: Find the exact distance between the two points. Where appropriate, also give approximate results to the nearest hundredth.

25. $(2, -2), (5, 2)$

26. $(0, -3), (12, -8)$

27. $(7, -4), (9, 1)$

28. $(-1, -6), (-8, -5)$

29. $(3.6, 5.7), (-2.1, 8.7)$

30. $(-6.5, 2.7), (3.6, -2.9)$

31. $(-3, 2), (-3, 10)$

32. $(7, 9), (-1, 9)$

33. $\left(\frac{1}{2}, -\frac{1}{2}\right), \left(\frac{3}{4}, \frac{1}{2}\right)$

34. $\left(-\frac{1}{3}, \frac{2}{3}\right), \left(\frac{1}{3}, -\frac{4}{3}\right)$

35. $\left(\frac{2}{5}, \frac{3}{10}\right), \left(-\frac{1}{10}, \frac{4}{5}\right)$

36. $\left(-\frac{1}{2}, \frac{2}{3}\right), \left(\frac{1}{3}, -\frac{5}{2}\right)$

37. $(20, 30), (-30, -90)$

38. $(40, 6), (-20, 17)$

39. $(a, 0), (0, -b)$

40. $(x, y), (1, 2)$

41. Geometry An **isosceles triangle** has at least two sides of equal length. Determine whether the triangle with vertices $(0, 0)$, $(3, 4)$, $(7, 1)$ is isosceles.

42. Geometry An **equilateral triangle** has sides of equal length. Determine whether the triangle with vertices $(-1, -1)$, $(2, 3)$, $(-4, 3)$ is equilateral.

43. Distance between Cars (Refer to Example 6.) At 9:00 A.M. car A is traveling north at 50 miles per hour and is located 50 miles south of car B. Car B is traveling west at 20 miles per hour.

(a) Let $(0, 0)$ be the initial coordinates of car B in the *xy*-plane, where units are in miles. Plot the locations of each car at 9:00 A.M. and at 11:00 A.M.

(b) Find the distance d between the cars at 11:00 A.M.

44. Distance between Ships Two ships leave a harbor at the same time. The first ship heads north at 20 miles per hour, and the second ship heads west at 15 miles per hour. Write an expression that gives the distance d between the ships after t hours.

Midpoint Formula

Exercises 45–48: Use the midpoint formula for the following.

45. Nintendo Wii Six months after Nintendo Wii was introduced it had sold 10 million units, and after 24 months it had sold 44 million units. Estimate the number of units sold 15 months after the Nintendo Wii was introduced. (The actual value was 25 million units.) (***Source:*** Company Reports.)

46. World Population In 1874 the world population was 1.24 billion. By 2050 this number is expected to be 9 billion. Estimate the world population in 1962. (The actual value was 3.14 billion.) (***Source:*** United Nations Data.)

47. Olympic Times In the Olympic Games, the 200-meter dash is run in approximately 19 seconds. Estimate the time to run the 100-meter dash.

48. Real Numbers Between any two real numbers a and b there is always another real number. How could such a number be found?

Exercises 49–58: Find the midpoint of the line segment connecting the points.

49. $(1, 2), (5, -3)$ **50.** $(-6, 7), (9, -4)$

51. $(-30, 50), (50, -30)$ **52.** $(28, -33), (52, 38)$

53. $(1.5, 2.9), (-5.7, -3.6)$ **54.** $(9.4, -4.5), (-7.7, 9.5)$

55. $(\sqrt{2}, \sqrt{5}), (\sqrt{2}, -\sqrt{5})$

56. $(\sqrt{7}, 3\sqrt{3}), (-\sqrt{7}, -\sqrt{3})$

57. $(a, b), (-a, 3b)$ **58.** $(-a, b), (3a, b)$

Circles

Exercises 59–66: Find the center and radius of the circle.

59. $x^2 + y^2 = 25$ **60.** $x^2 + y^2 = 100$

61. $x^2 + y^2 = 7$ **62.** $x^2 + y^2 = 20$

63. $(x - 2)^2 + (y + 3)^2 = 9$

64. $(x + 1)^2 + (y - 1)^2 = 16$

65. $x^2 + (y + 1)^2 = 100$ **66.** $(x - 5)^2 + y^2 = 19$

Exercises 67–70: Find the standard equation of the circle.

67.

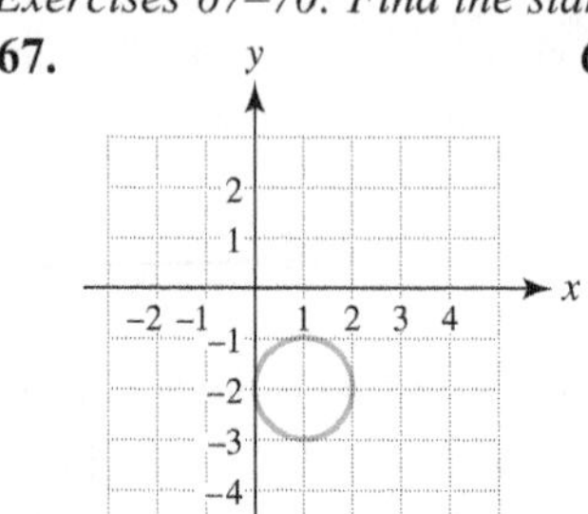

68.

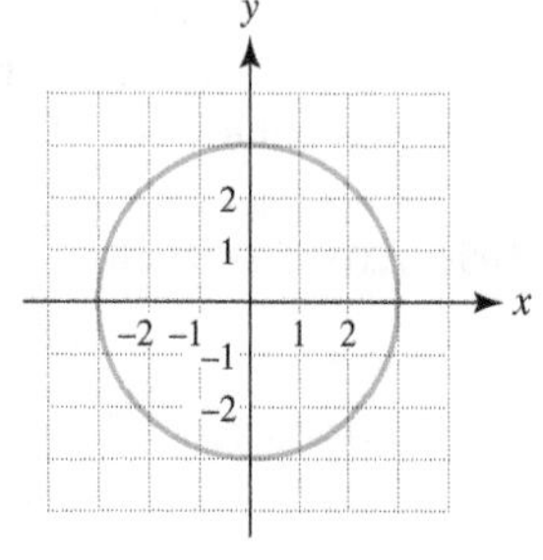

69.

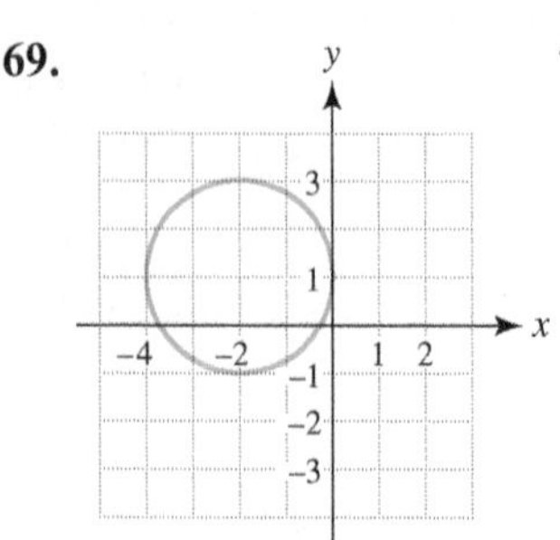

70.

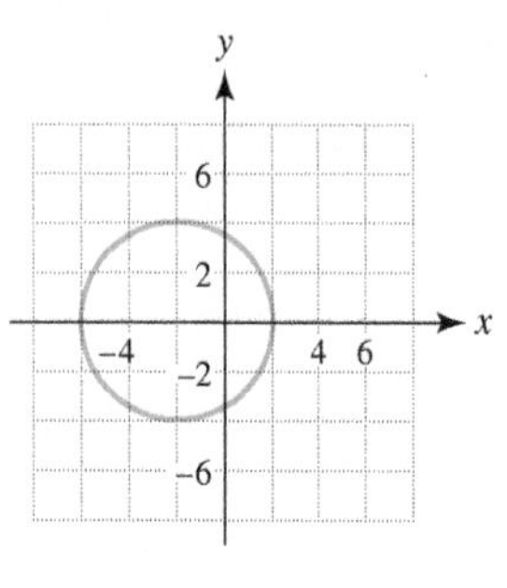

Exercises 71–78: Find the standard equation of a circle that satisfies the conditions.

71. Radius 8, center $(3, -5)$

72. Radius 5, center $(-1, 4)$

73. Radius 7, center $(3, 0)$

74. Radius 1, center $(0, 0)$

75. Center $(3, -5)$ with the point $(4, 2)$ on the circle

76. Center $(0, 0)$ with the point $(-3, -1)$ on the circle

77. Endpoints of a diameter $(-5, -7)$ and $(1, 1)$

78. Endpoints of a diameter $(-3, -2)$ and $(1, -4)$

Exercises 79 and 80: (Refer to Example 11.) Use the diameter to find the standard equation of the circle shown.

79.

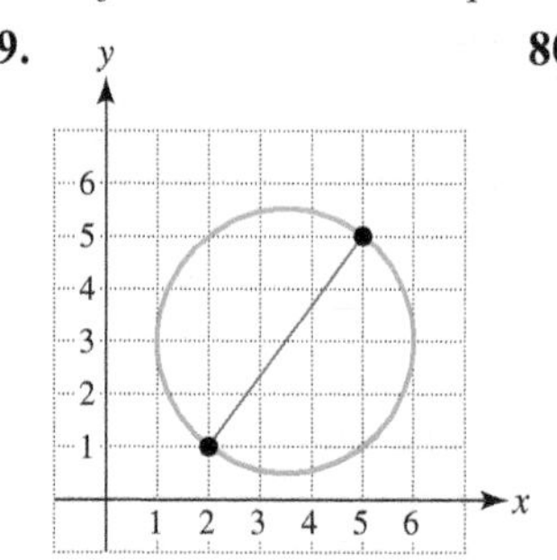

80.

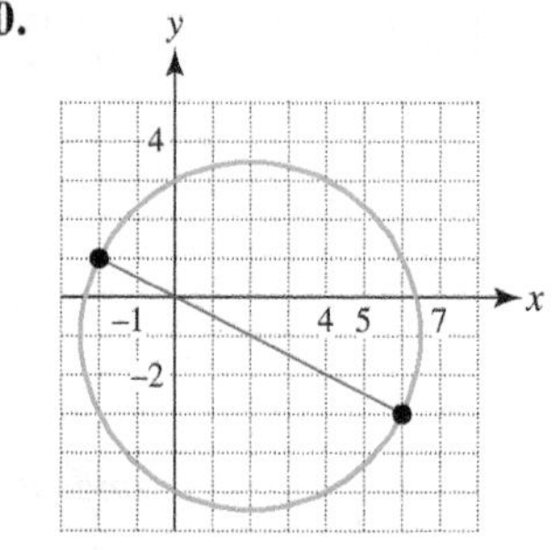

Exercises 81–90: Graph the equation.

81. $x^2 + y^2 = 25$ **82.** $x^2 + y^2 = 1$

83. $(x - 2)^2 + (y + 1)^2 = 25$

84. $(x + 2)^2 + (y + 3)^2 = 1$

85. $(x + 2)^2 + y^2 = 16$ **86.** $x^2 + (y - 2)^2 = 9$

87. $(x + 3)^2 + (y + 1)^2 = 9$

88. $(x - 1)^2 + (y - 2)^2 = 4$

89. $\left(x - \frac{1}{2}\right)^2 + (y - 1)^2 = 10$

90. $(x + 1)^2 + \left(y + \frac{3}{2}\right)^2 = 6$

Graphing Calculators

Exercises 91–96: Predict the number of tick marks on the positive x-axis and the positive y-axis. Then show the viewing rectangle on your graphing calculator.

91. Standard viewing rectangle

92. $[-4.7, 4.7, 1]$ by $[-3.1, 3.1, 1]$

93. $[0, 100, 10]$ by $[-50, 50, 10]$

94. $[-30, 30, 5]$ by $[-20, 20, 5]$

95. $[1980, 1995, 1]$ by $[12000, 16000, 1000]$

96. $[1800, 2000, 20]$ by $[5, 20, 5]$

Exercises 97–100: Match the settings for a viewing rectangle with the correct figure (a–d).

97. $[-9, 9, 1]$ by $[-6, 6, 1]$

98. $[-6, 6, 1]$ by $[-9, 9, 1]$

99. $[-2, 2, 0.5]$ by $[-4.5, 4.5, 0.5]$

100. $[-4, 8, 1]$ by $[-600, 600, 100]$

a.

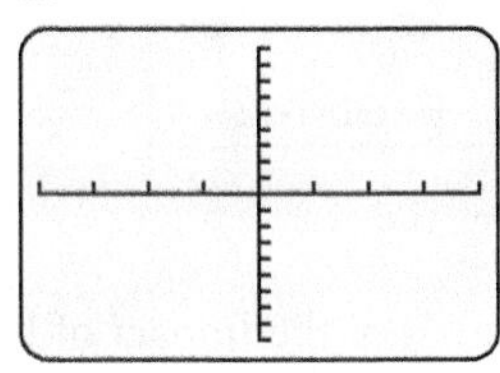

b.

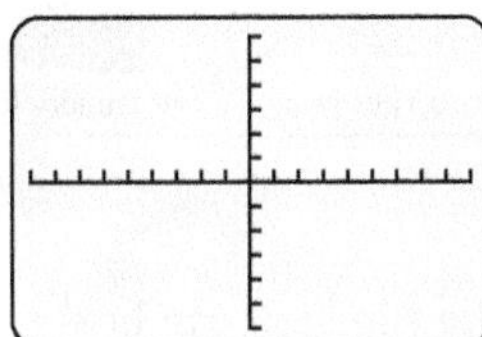

c.

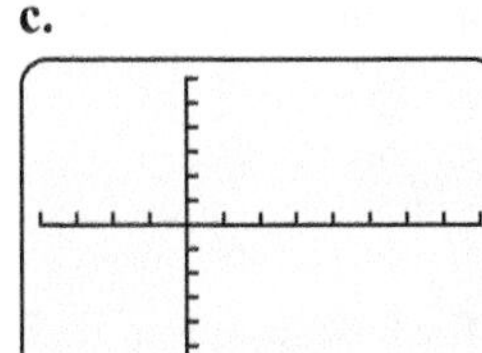

d.

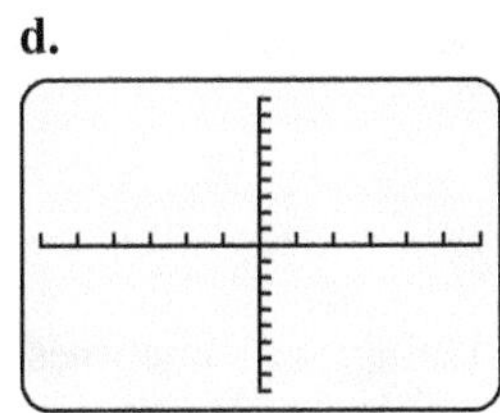

Exercises 101–104: Make a scatterplot of the relation.

101. $\{(1, 3), (-2, 2), (-4, 1), (-2, -4), (0, 2)\}$

102. $\{(6, 8), (-4, -10), (-2, -6), (2, -5)\}$

103. $\{(10, -20), (-40, 50), (30, 60), (-50, -80), (70, 0)\}$

104. $\{(-1.2, 0.6), (1.0, -0.5), (0.4, 0.2), (-2.8, 1.4)\}$

Exercises 105–108: The table contains real data.

(a) Determine the maximum and minimum values for each variable in the table.

(b) Use your results from part (a) to find an appropriate viewing rectangle.

(c) Make a scatterplot of the data.

(d) Make a line graph of the data.

105. Netflix Subscriptions (millions)

x	2006	2007	2008	2009	2010
y	6.1	7.3	9.1	11.9	19.4

Source: Company Reports.

106. Global Vehicle Sales That Are Electric/Hybrid

x	2011	2015	2019	2022	2025
y	0%	1%	2%	4.5%	8%

Source: *Business Insider* (projected).

107. MySpace U.S. Advertising Revenue ($ millions)

x	2006	2007	2008	2009	2010	2011
y	225	475	590	430	270	180

Source: eMarketer.

108. U.S. College Students Who Study Chinese (thousands)

x	1995	1998	2002	2006	2009
y	26	29	34	51	60

Source: Institute of International Education.

Writing about Mathematics

109. Give an example of a relation that has meaning in the real world. Give an example of an ordered pair (x, y) that is in your relation. Does the ordered pair (y, x) also have meaning? Explain your answers.

110. Do the mean and median represent the same thing? Explain your answer and give an example.

CHECKING BASIC CONCEPTS FOR SECTIONS 1.1 AND 1.2

1. Approximate each expression to the nearest hundredth.

(a) $\sqrt{4.2(23.1 + 0.5^3)}$ **(b)** $\dfrac{23 + 44}{85.1 - 32.9}$

2. Evaluate the expression by hand.

(a) $5 - (-4)^2 \cdot 3$ **(b)** $5 \div 5\sqrt{2 + 2}$

3. Write each number using scientific notation.

(a) 348,500,000 **(b)** -1237.4

(c) 0.00198

4. Find the exact distance between the points $(-3, 1)$ and $(3, -5)$. Then round this distance to the nearest hundredth.

5. Find the midpoint of the line segment connecting the points $(-2, 3)$ and $(4, 2)$.

6. Find the standard equation of a circle with center $(-4, 5)$ and radius 8.

7. The average depths in feet of four oceans are 13,215, 12,881, 13,002, and 3953. Calculate the mean and median of these depths.

8. Make a scatterplot and a line graph with the four points $(-5, -4), (-1, 2), (2, -2)$, and $(3, 6)$. State the quadrant in which each point lies.

1.3 Functions and Their Representations

- Learn function notation
- Represent a function four different ways
- Define a function formally
- Identify the domain and range of a function
- Use calculators to represent functions (optional)
- Identify functions
- Represent functions with diagrams and equations

Introduction

Because there are more than 300 million people in the United States who consume many natural resources, *going green* has become an important social and environmental issue. Figure 1.36 gives some information about U.S. consumption.

Population and Consumption in the United States

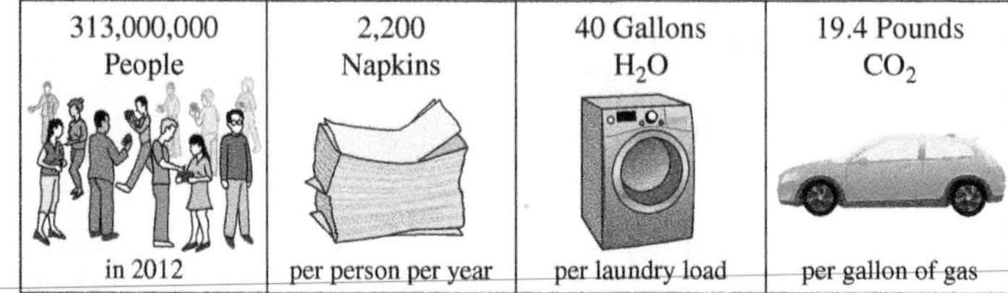

313,000,000
People
in 2012
2,200
Napkins
per person per year
40 Gallons
H_2O
per laundry load
19.4 Pounds
CO_2
per gallon of gas

Figure 1.36

The mathematical concept of a function can be used to analyze the impact of human consumption (see Exercises 101 and 102) and also to describe natural phenomena, such as lightning. This section introduces the important concept of a function, which is used throughout the course.

Basic Concepts

Although thunder is caused by lightning, we sometimes see a flash of lightning before we hear the thunder. The farther away lightning is, the greater the time lapse between seeing the flash of lightning and hearing the thunder. Table 1.7 lists the *approximate* distance y in miles between a person and a bolt of lightning when there is a time lapse of x seconds between seeing the lightning and hearing the thunder.

Distance from Lightning

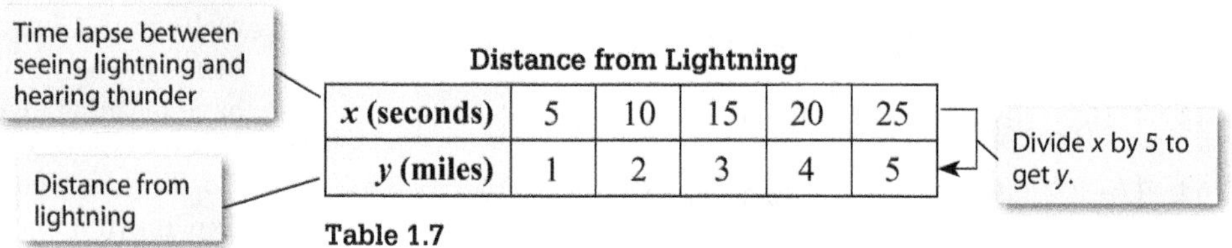

x (seconds)	5	10	15	20	25
y (miles)	1	2	3	4	5

Table 1.7

Table 1.7 established a special type of relation between x and y, called a *function*.

- Each x determines *exactly* one y, so we say that Table 1.7 *represents* or *defines* a function f.
- Function f *computes* the distance y between an observer and a lightning bolt, given the time lapse x. We say that y is a function of x.
- This computation is denoted $y = f(x)$, which is called **function notation** and is read "y equals f of x." It means that function f with **input** x produces **output** y. That is,

$$f(\textbf{Input}) = \textbf{Output}$$

or

$$f(\textbf{Time lapse in seconds}) = \textbf{Miles from lightning}.$$

We can represent the five values in Table 1.7 in function notation as

$$f(5) = 1,\ f(10) = 2,\ f(15) = 3,\ f(20) = 4,\ f(25) = 5,$$

A 5 second delay means the lightning bolt was about 1 mile away.

or more generally as,

$$f(x) = y.$$

The expression $f(x)$ represents the ***output*** y from f when the **input** is x.

Function f calculates a set of ordered pairs (x, y), where $y = f(x)$. From Table 1.7, the five ordered pairs (5, 1), (10, 2), (15, 3), (20, 4), and (25, 5) belong to the relation computed by f. We can think of these ordered pairs as input-output pairs in the form (**input**, **output**).

A given x-value determines exactly one y-value. For example, if x equals 30 seconds, then y equals $\frac{30}{5} = 6$ miles. Thus the y-values (outputs) *depend* on the x-values (inputs). We call x the **independent variable** and y the **dependent variable**.

Computation Performed by Function f

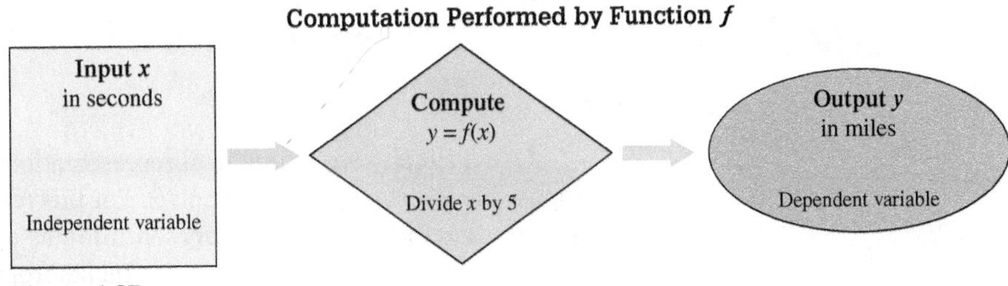

Figure 1.37

In Section 1.2 we discussed the domain and range of a relation. For a function, the set of valid or meaningful inputs x is called the **domain**, and the set of corresponding outputs y is the **range**. For example, suppose that a function f computes the height after x seconds of a ball that was thrown into the air. Then the domain of f consists of all times that the ball was in flight, and the range includes all heights attained by the ball.

This discussion about function notation is summarized as follows.

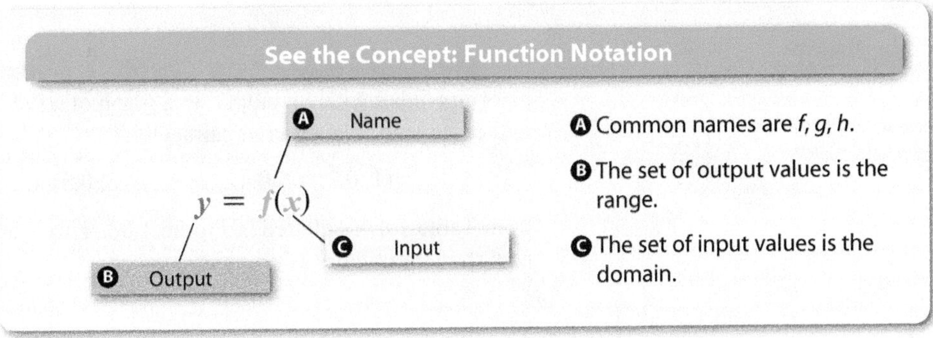

See the Concept: Function Notation
A Name
y = f(x)
B Output
C Input
A Common names are f, g, h.
B The set of output values is the range.
C The set of input values is the domain.

NOTE Every function is a *relation* that calculates *exactly* one output for each valid input.

Representations of Functions

Functions can be represented by verbal descriptions, tables, symbols, and graphs.

Verbal Representation (Words) If function f gives the distance between an observer and a bolt of lightning, then we can verbally describe f with the following sentence: "Divide x seconds by 5 to obtain y miles." We call this a **verbal representation** of f.

Sometimes when the computation performed by a function has meaning, we can interpret this computation verbally. For example, a verbal description of function f is "f calculates the number of miles from a lightning bolt when the delay between thunder and lightning is x seconds."

Numerical Representation (Table of Values) Table 1.7 gave a numerical representation for the function f that calculates the distance between a lightning bolt and an observer. A **numerical representation** is a *table of values* that lists input-output pairs for a function. A different numerical representation for f is shown in Table 1.8.

Distance from a Bolt of Lightning

x (seconds)	1	2	3	4	5	6	7
y (miles)	0.2	0.4	0.6	0.8	1.0	1.2	1.4

Table 1.8

One difficulty with numerical representations is that it is often either inconvenient or impossible to list all possible inputs x. For this reason we sometimes refer to a table of this type as a **partial numerical representation** as opposed to a **complete numerical representation**, which would include all elements from the domain of a function. For example, many valid inputs do not appear in Table 1.8, such as $x = 11$ or $x = 0.75$.

Symbolic Representation (Formula) A formula gives a **symbolic representation** of a function. The computation performed by f is expressed by

$$f(x) = \frac{x}{5},$$ Formula for f

where $y = f(x)$. We say that function f is *represented by*, *defined by*, or *given by* $f(x) = \frac{x}{5}$. For example, if the elapsed time is 6 seconds, we write $f(6) = \frac{6}{5} = 1.2$ miles. A formula is an efficient and complete, but less visual, way to define a function.

Graphical Representation (Graph) A **graphical representation**, or **graph**, visually pairs an x-input with a y-output. In a graph of a function, the ordered pairs (x, y) are plotted in the xy-plane. The ordered pairs

$$(1, 0.2), (2, 0.4), (3, 0.6), (4, 0.8), (5, 1.0), (6, 1.2), \text{and } (7, 1.4)$$

from Table 1.8 are plotted in Figure 1.38. This scatterplot suggests a line for the graph of f, as shown in Figure 1.39.

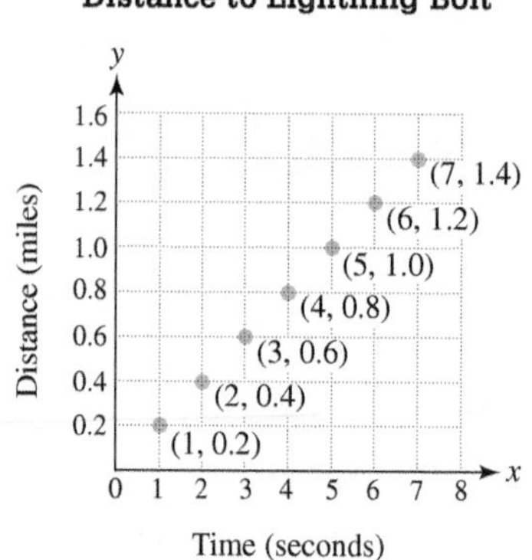

Figure 1.38

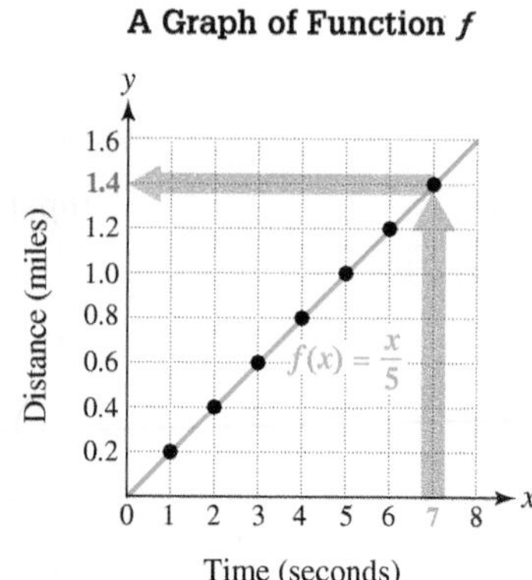

Figure 1.39

Evaluating $f(a)$ Graphically

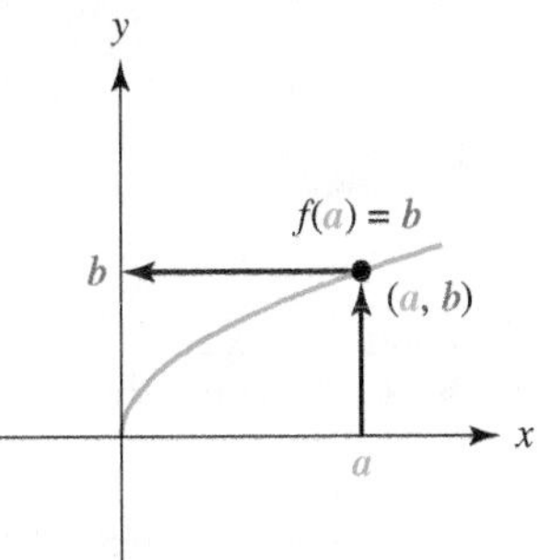

Figure 1.40

From Table 1.8 $f(5) = 1$, so the point (5, 1) lies on the graph of f. Similarly, since (7, 1.4) lies on the graph of f, it follows that $f(7) = 1.4$. See Figure 1.39 where the red arrows illustrate that $f(7) = 1.4$ because the point (7, 1.4) lies on the graph of f.

MAKING CONNECTIONS

Functions, Points, and Graphs If $f(a) = b$, then the point (a, b) lies on the graph of f. Conversely, if the point (a, b) lies on the graph of f, then $f(a) = b$. Thus each point on the graph of f can be written in the form $(a, f(a))$. See Figure 1.40.

The next example shows how we often use symbolic and numerical representations (formulas and tables) to graph a function by hand.

EXAMPLE 1 **Graphing the absolute value function by hand**

Graph $f(x) = |x|$ by hand.

SOLUTION

Getting Started Unless you already know what the graph of a given function looks like, a good technique to use when graphing by hand is to first make a table of values. Then plot the points in the table and sketch a smooth curve (or line) between these points. ▶

Start by selecting convenient x-values and then substitute them into $f(x) = |x|$, as shown in Table 1.9. For example, when $x = -2$, then $f(-2) = |-2| = 2$, so the point $(-2, 2)$ is located on the graph of $y = f(x)$.

Next, plot the points as shown in Figure 1.41. The points appear to be V-shaped, and the graph of f shown in Figure 1.42 results if all possible real number ordered pairs $(x, |x|)$ are plotted.

Make a Table

x	$\|x\|$
−2	2
−1	1
0	0
1	1
2	2

Table 1.9

Plot Points

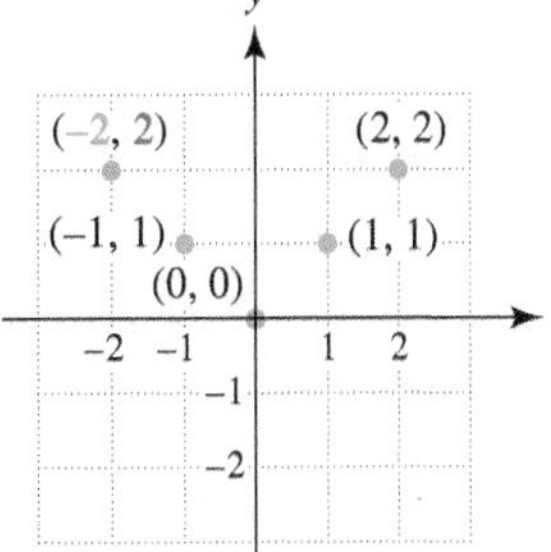

Figure 1.41

Sketch a Graph

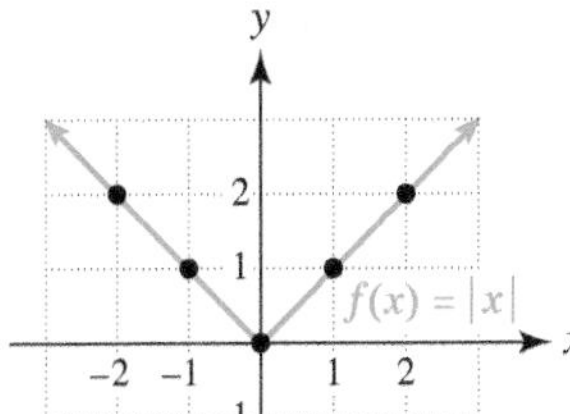

Figure 1.42

Now Try Exercise 13

MAKING CONNECTIONS

The Expressions f and $f(x)$ The italic letter f represents the *name* of a function, whereas the expression $f(x)$ represents the function f evaluated for input x. That is, $f(x)$ typically represents a formula for function f that can be used to evaluate f for various values of x.

The following See the Concept illustrates four representations for a function.

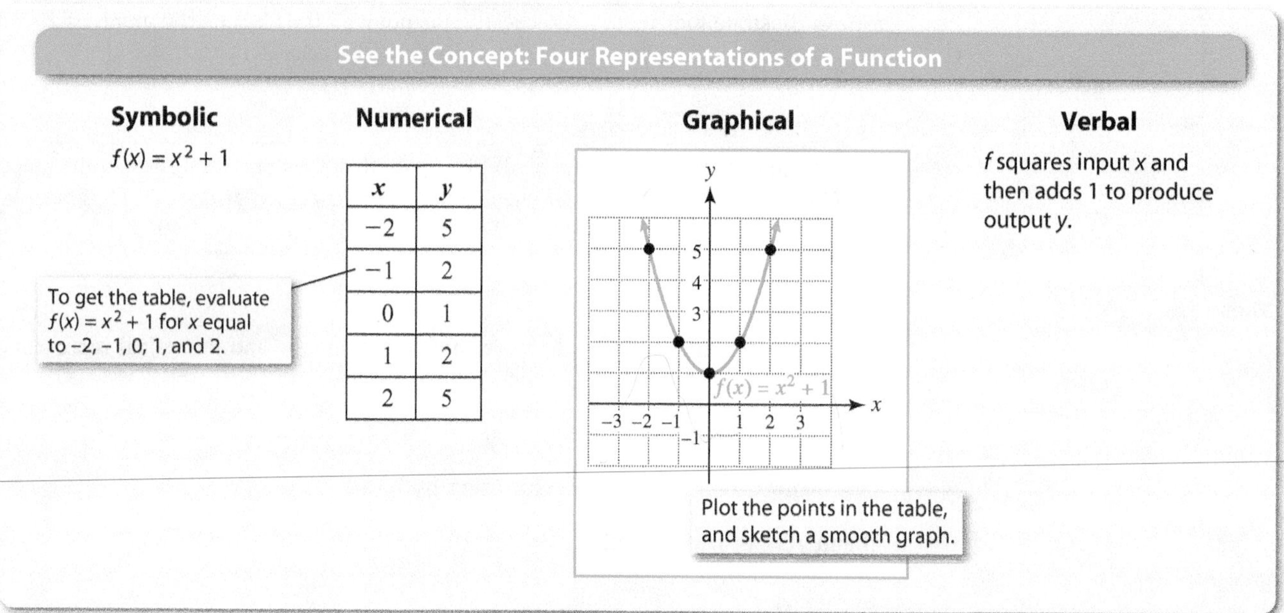

See the Concept: Four Representations of a Function
Symbolic
f(x) = x² + 1
Numerical
x | y
−2 | 5
−1 | 2
0 | 1
1 | 2
2 | 5
To get the table, evaluate f(x) = x² + 1 for x equal to −2, −1, 0, 1, and 2.
Graphical
y
x
f(x) = x² + 1
Plot the points in the table, and sketch a smooth graph.
Verbal
f squares input x and then adds 1 to produce output y.

Formal Definition of a Function

Because the idea of a function is a fundamental concept in mathematics, it is important that we define a function precisely. This definition should allow for *all* representations of a function. The commonality among representations is the concept of an ordered pair. A relation is a set of ordered pairs, and a function is a special type of relation.

FUNCTION

A **function** is a relation in which *each* element in the domain corresponds to *exactly one* element in the range.

The set of ordered pairs for a function can be either finite or infinite.

$$f = \{(-3, 5), (0, 6), (3, 2)\} \quad \text{Finite Set}$$
$$h = \{(1, 2), (2, 4), (3, 6), (4, 8), \dots\} \quad \text{Infinite Set}$$

A function given by $g(x) = x^2$, where x can be any real number, is another infinite set of ordered pairs of the form (x, x^2). Examples include $(-3, 9)$, $(4, 16)$, and $\left(\frac{1}{2}, \frac{1}{4}\right)$.

EXAMPLE 2 Finding the domain and range

Let a function f be defined by $f(-1) = 4$, $f(0) = 3$, $f(1) = 4$, and $f(2) = -2$. Write f as a set of ordered pairs. Give the domain and range.

SOLUTION

Because $f(-1) = 4$, the ordered pair $(-1, 4)$ is in the set. It follows that

$$f = \{(-1, 4), (0, 3), (1, 4), (2, -2)\}.$$

The domain D of f is the set of x-values, and the range R of f is the set of y-values. Thus

$$D = \{-1, 0, 1, 2\} \quad \text{and} \quad R = \{-2, 3, 4\}.$$

Now Try Exercise 21

EXAMPLE 3 **Computing revenue of technology companies**

The function f computes the revenue in dollars per unique user for different technology companies. This function is defined by $f(A) = 189$, $f(G) = 24$, $f(Y) = 8$, $f(F) = 4$, where A is Amazon, G is Google, Y is Yahoo, and F is Facebook. (***Source:*** *Business Insider*.)

(a) Write f as a set of ordered pairs.

(b) Give the domain and range of f.

SOLUTION

(a) $f = \{(A, 189), (G, 24), (Y, 8), (F, 4)\}$

(b) The domain D and range R of f are

$$D = \{A, F, G, Y\} \quad \text{and} \quad R = \{4, 8, 24, 189\}.$$

Now Try Exercise 97

MAKING CONNECTIONS

Relations and Functions Every function is a relation, whereas not every relation is a function. A function has exactly one output for each valid input.

Finding Domain, Range, and Function Values

Implied Domain Unless stated otherwise, the domain of a function f is the set of all *real* numbers for which its symbolic representation (formula) is defined. The domain can be thought of as the set of all valid inputs that make sense in the expression for $f(x)$. In this case the domain is sometimes referred to as the **implied domain.**

When determining the domain of a function we must exclude values of x that result in division by 0. Division by 0 is *always* undefined. Also, unless stated otherwise, we will exclude values of x that result in taking the square root of a negative number. Examples of three functions and their domains D are the following.

The Domains D of Three Functions

1. $f(x) = 2x$ — D is all real numbers because $2x$ is defined for all real numbers x.
2. $g(x) = \frac{1}{x}$ — D is all real numbers except 0 ($x \neq 0$).
3. $h(x) = \sqrt{x}$ — D is all nonnegative real numbers ($x \geq 0$).

EXAMPLE 4 **Evaluating a function and finding its domain**

Let $f(x) = \frac{x}{x - 1}$.

(a) If possible, evaluate $f(2)$, $f(1)$, and $f(a + 1)$. **(b)** Find the domain of f.

SOLUTION

(a) To evaluate $f(2)$, substitute 2 for x in the formula $f(x) = \frac{x}{x - 1}$.

$$f(2) = \frac{2}{2 - 1} = 2 \qquad \text{Let } x = 2.$$

To evaluate $f(1)$, let x be 1 in the formula.

$$f(1) = \frac{1}{1 - 1} = \frac{1}{0}, \qquad \text{Division by 0 is undefined.}$$

which is undefined. Thus 1 is not in the domain of f.

To evaluate $f(a + 1)$, let x be $a + 1$ in the formula.

$$f(a + 1) = \frac{a + 1}{a + 1 - 1} = \frac{a + 1}{a} \qquad \text{Let } x = a + 1.$$

(b) The formula $f(x) = \frac{x}{x - 1}$ is undefined whenever $x - 1$ equals 0. Thus we exclude 1 from the domain $(x \neq 1)$. In *set-builder notation* the domain is written $\{x \mid x \neq 1\}$.

Now Try Exercise 31

SET-BUILDER NOTATION

The expression $\{x \mid x \neq 1\}$ is written in **set-builder notation** and represents the set of all real numbers x such that x does not equal 1. Another example is $\{y \mid 1 < y < 5\}$, which represents the set of all real numbers y such that y is greater than 1 *and* less than 5.

EXAMPLE 5 **Evaluating a function symbolically and graphically**

A function g is given by $g(x) = x^2 - 2x$, and its graph is shown in Figure 1.43.

(a) Find the domain and range of g.
(b) Use $g(x)$ to evaluate $g(-1)$.
(c) Use the graph of g to evaluate $g(-1)$.

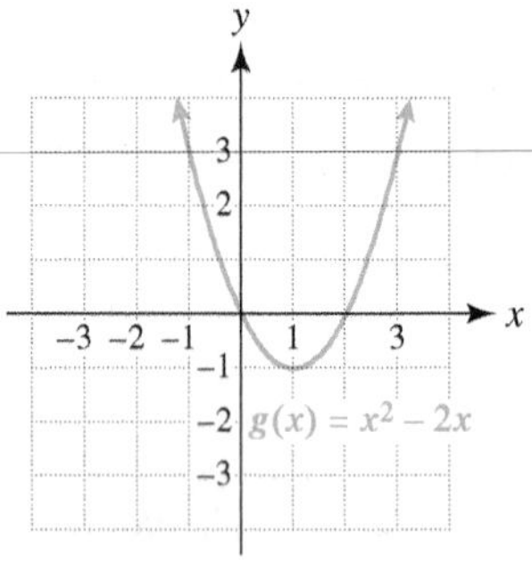

Figure 1.43

SOLUTION

(a) The domain for $g(x) = x^2 - 2x$ includes all real numbers because the formula is defined for all real number inputs x.

The minimum y-value on the graph is -1. The arrows on the graph point upward, so there is no maximum y-value. The range is all real numbers greater than or equal to -1, or $\{y \mid y \geq -1\}$.

(b) To evaluate $g(-1)$, substitute -1 for x in $g(x) = x^2 - 2x$.

$$g(-1) = (-1)^2 - 2(-1) = 1 + 2 = 3$$

(c) Refer to Figure 1.44 in the following See the Concept where $g(-1) = 3$.

See the Concept: Evaluating $g(-1) = 3$ Graphically

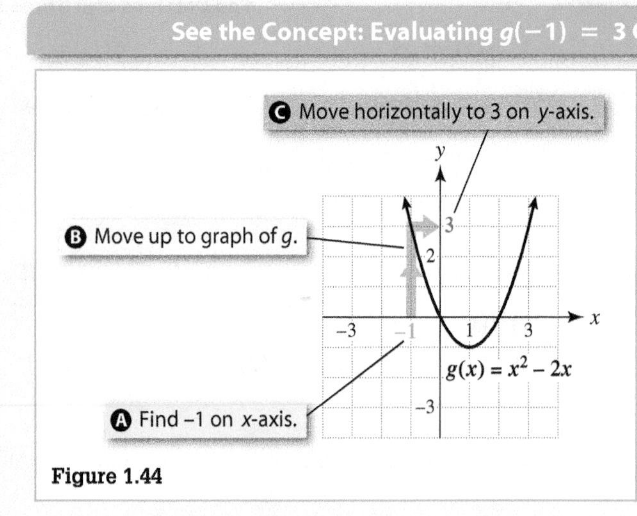
C Move horizontally to 3 on y-axis.
B Move up to graph of g.
A Find –1 on x-axis.
g(x) = x² – 2x

Figure 1.44

A To evaluate $g(-1)$, begin by finding $x = -1$ on the x-axis.

B Next, move upward until the graph of g is reached.

C Finally, move to the right until the y-axis is reached. The y-value corresponding to an x-value of -1 is 3. Thus $g(-1) = 3$.

Now Try Exercise 37

EXAMPLE 6 **Finding the domain and range graphically**

A graph of $f(x) = \sqrt{x - 2}$ is shown in Figure 1.45.

(a) Evaluate $f(1)$.
(b) Find the domain and range of f.

SOLUTION

(a) Start by finding 1 on the x-axis. Move up and down on the grid. Note that we do not intersect the graph of f. See Figure 1.46. Thus $f(1)$ is *undefined.*

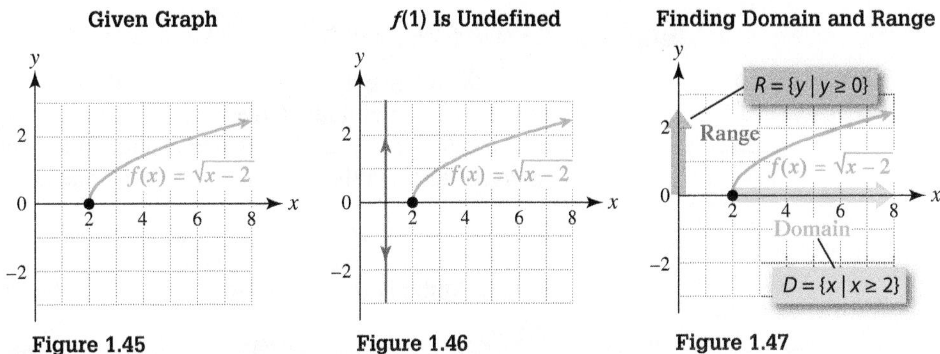

Figure 1.45 Figure 1.46 Figure 1.47

(b) In Figure 1.45 the arrow on the graph of f indicates that both the x-values and the y-values increase without reaching a maximum value. In Figure 1.47 the domain and range of f have been labeled by an arrow on each axis. Note that points appear on the graph for all x greater than or equal to 2. Thus the domain is $D = \{x \mid x \geq 2\}$. The minimum y-value on the graph of f is 0 and it occurs at the point (2, 0). There is no maximum y-value on the graph, so the range is $R = \{y \mid y \geq 0\}$.

Now Try Exercise 45

Graphing Calculators and Functions (Optional)

Graphing calculators can be used to create graphs and tables of a function—usually more efficiently and reliably than pencil-and-paper techniques. However, a graphing calculator uses the same basic method that we might use to draw a graph. For example, one way to sketch a graph of $y = x^2$ is to first make a table of values, such as Table 1.10.

Making a Table for $y = x^2$

x	−3	−2	−1	0	1	2	3
y	9	4	1	0	1	4	9

Table 1.10

We can plot these points in the xy-plane, as shown in Figure 1.48. Next we might connect the points with a smooth curve, as shown in Figure 1.49. A graphing calculator typically plots numerous points and connects them to make a graph. In Figure 1.50, a graphing calculator has been used to graph $y = x^2$.

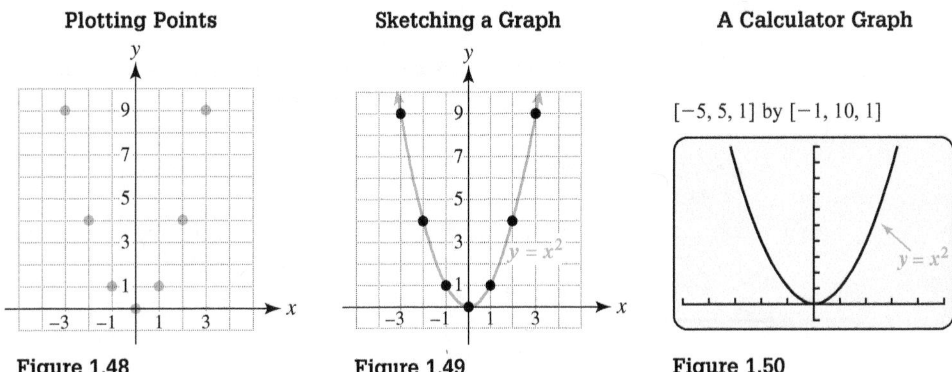

Figure 1.48 Figure 1.49 Figure 1.50

An Application In the next example we use a graphing calculator to represent a function that computes the decrease in air temperature as altitude increases.

EXAMPLE 7 Representing a function

When the relative humidity is less than 100%, air cools at a rate of 3.6°F for every 1000-foot increase in altitude. Give verbal, symbolic, graphical, and numerical representations of a function f that computes this change in temperature for an increase in altitude of x thousand feet. Let the domain of f be $0 \leq x \leq 6$. (***Source:*** L. Battan, *Weather in Your Life.*)

SOLUTION

Verbal Multiply the input x by -3.6 to obtain the change y in temperature.

Symbolic Let $f(x) = -3.6x$.

Graphical Since $f(x) = -3.6x$, enter $y_1 = -3.6x$, as shown in Figure 1.51. Graph y_1 in a viewing rectangle such as [0, 6, 1] by [−25, 10, 5], used in Figure 1.52.

Calculator Help
To enter a formula and create a graph, see Appendix A (pages AP-4 and AP-5).

Graphing with a Calculator

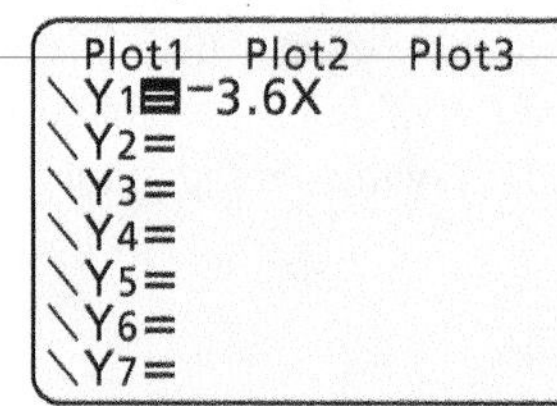

Figure 1.51

[0, 6, 1] by [−25, 10, 5]

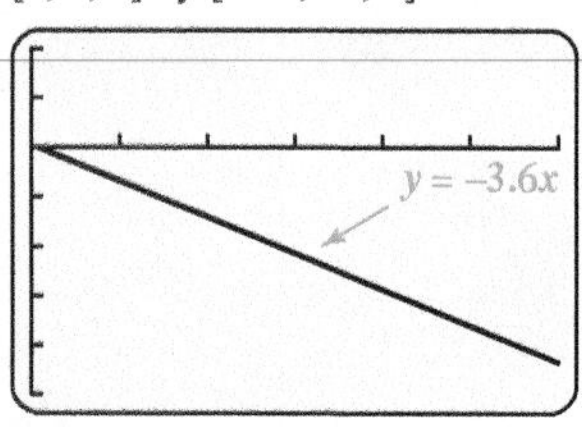

Figure 1.52

Numerical It is impossible to list all inputs x, since $0 \leq x \leq 6$. However, Figures 1.53 and 1.54 show how to create a table for $y_1 = -3.6x$ with $x = 0, 1, 2, 3, 4, 5, 6$. Other values for x in the domain of f are possible.

Calculator Help
To create a table similar to Figure 1.54, see Appendix A (page AP-5).

Making a Table of Values

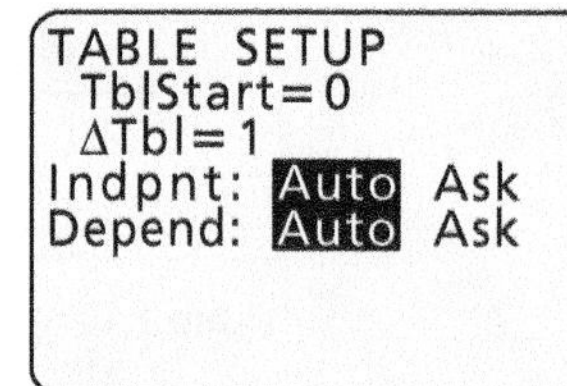

Figure 1.53

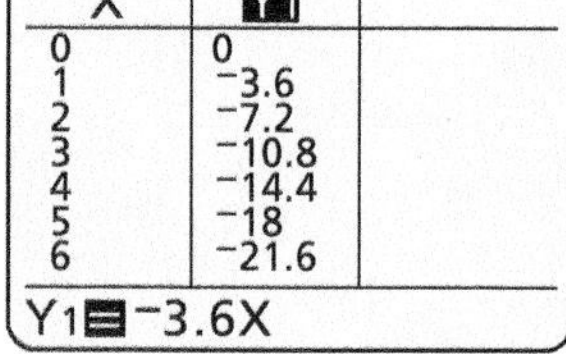

X	Y1
0	0
1	-3.6
2	-7.2
3	-10.8
4	-14.4
5	-18
6	-21.6

Y1=-3.6X

Figure 1.54

Now Try Exercise 103

NOTE Each of the four representations presented in Example 7 represent the *same* function f.

Identifying Functions

A function is a special type of relation where each valid input (x-value) produces exactly one output (y-value). We can use this concept to identify functions.

EXAMPLE 8 Determining if a set of ordered pairs is a function

Determine if each set of ordered pairs represents a function.

(a) $A = \{(-2, 3), (-1, 2), (0, -3), (-2, 4)\}$
(b) $B = \{(1, 4), (2, 5), (-3, -4), (-1, 7), (0, 4)\}$

SOLUTION

(a) Set A does not represent a function because input -2 results in two outputs: 3 and 4.
(b) Inputs 1 and 0 have the same output 4. However, set B represents a function because each input (x-value) results in one output (y-value).

Now Try Exercises 77 and 79

The following operations can be carried out by functions because they result in *one* output for each valid input.

- Calculating the square of a number x
- Finding the sale price when an item with regular price x is discounted 25%
- Naming the biological mother of person x

NOTE Not all computations can be done by functions. Suppose that we were given an eye color as an input and asked to output the name of each person in the class having this eye color. Typically we would *not* be computing a function. If, for example, several people in the class had brown eyes, there would not be a unique output (name) for each input (eye color).

Some tables do not represent a function. For example, Table 1.11 represents a relation but *not a function* because input 1 produces two outputs, 3 and 12.

Points on a Vertical Line Have the Same x-Values

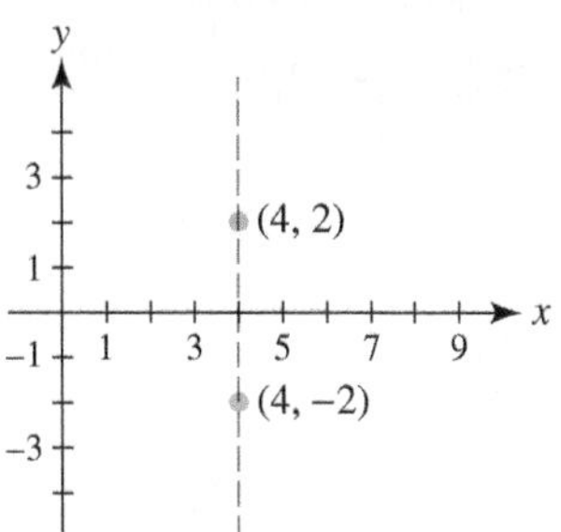

Figure 1.55

Not a Function

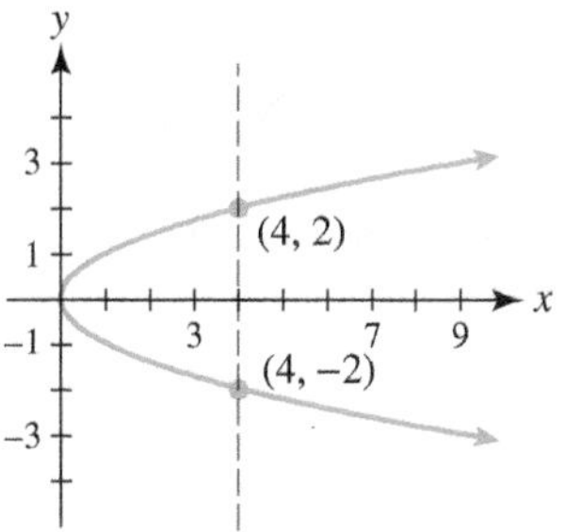

Figure 1.56

A Relation That Is Not a Function

x	1	2	3	1	4
y	3	6	9	12	2

Table 1.11

Vertical Line Test To conclude that a graph represents a function, we must be convinced that it is impossible for two distinct points with the same x-coordinate to lie on the graph. For example, the ordered pairs (4, 2) and (4, −2) are distinct points with the same x-coordinate. These two points could not lie on the graph of the same function because input 4 would result in two outputs: 2 and −2. When the points (4, 2) and (4, −2) are plotted, they lie on the same vertical line, as shown in Figure 1.55. A graph passing through these points intersects the line twice, as illustrated in Figure 1.56. Therefore the graph in Figure 1.56 does *not* represent a function.

To determine if a graph represents a function, simply visualize vertical lines in the xy-plane. If every vertical line intersects a graph at no more than one point, then it is a graph of a function. This procedure is called the **vertical line test** for a function.

VERTICAL LINE TEST

If every vertical line intersects a graph at no more than one point, then the graph represents a function.

NOTE If a vertical line intersects a graph more than once, then the graph does *not* represent a function.

EXAMPLE 9 Identifying a function graphically

Use the vertical line test to determine if the graph represents a function.

(a)

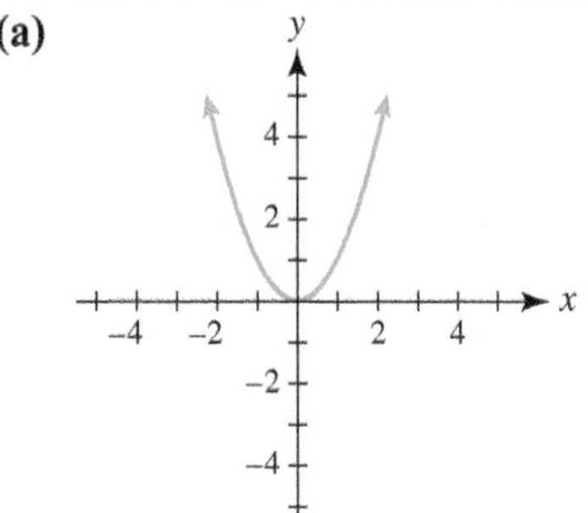

(b)

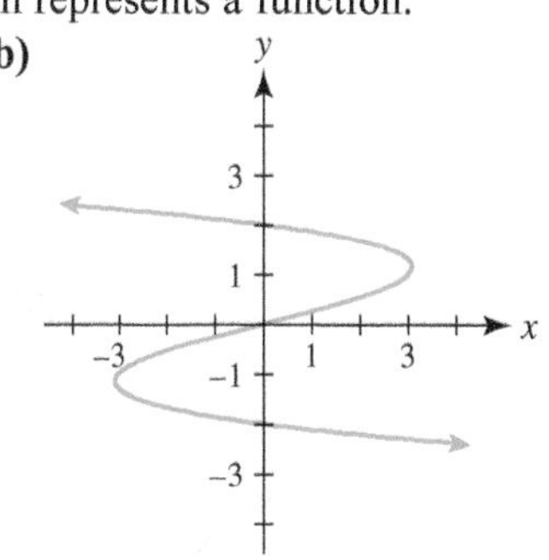

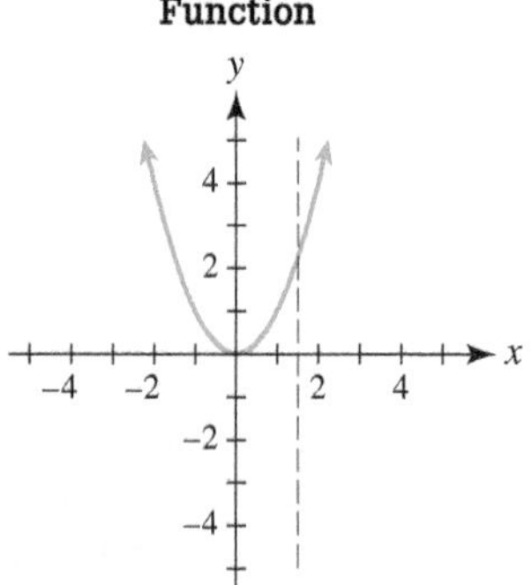

Figure 1.57

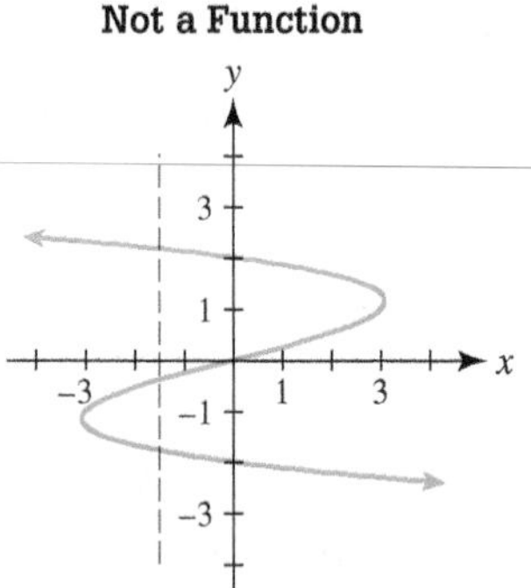

Figure 1.58

SOLUTION

(a) Note in Figure 1.57 that every vertical line that could be visualized would intersect the graph at most once. Therefore the graph represents a function.

(b) The graph in Figure 1.58 does not represent a function because it is possible for a vertical line to intersect the graph more than once.

Now Try Exercises 65 and 67

Functions Represented by Diagrams and Equations

Thus far we have discussed four representations of a function: verbal, numerical, symbolic, and graphical. Two other ways that we can represent, or define, a function are with diagrams and equations.

Diagrammatic Representation (Diagram) Functions are sometimes represented using **diagrammatic representations,** or **diagrams.** Figure 1.59 is a diagram of a function with domain $D = \{5, 10, 15, 20\}$ and range $R = \{1, 2, 3,\}$. An arrow is used to show that input x produces output y. For example, in Figure 1.59 an arrow points from 5 to 1, so $f(5) = 1$ and the point $(5, 1)$ lies on the graph of f. Figure 1.60 shows a relation, but not a function.

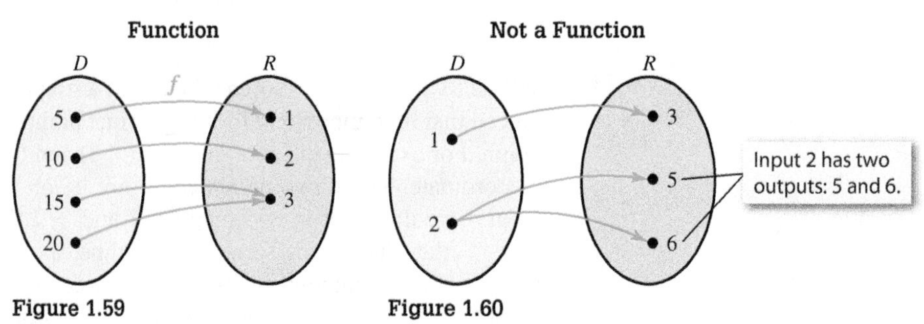

Figure 1.59 Figure 1.60

> **MAKING CONNECTIONS**
>
> **Functions as Mappings** Functions are sometimes referred to as **mappings** between the domain and the range. If $f(5) = 1$, then we say that the range value 1 is the **image** of 5 and that the domain value 5 is the **preimage** of 1.

Functions Defined by Equations Equations can sometimes define functions. For example, the equation $x + y = 1$ defines a function f given by $f(x) = 1 - x$, where $y = f(x)$. Notice that for each input x, there is exactly one y output determined by $y = 1 - x$. In Figure 1.61 the graph passes the vertical line test. However, the graph of the equation $x^2 + y^2 = 4$ is a circle with center $(0, 0)$ and radius 2. Because a circle does not pass the vertical line test, this equation does not represent a function. See Figure 1.62.

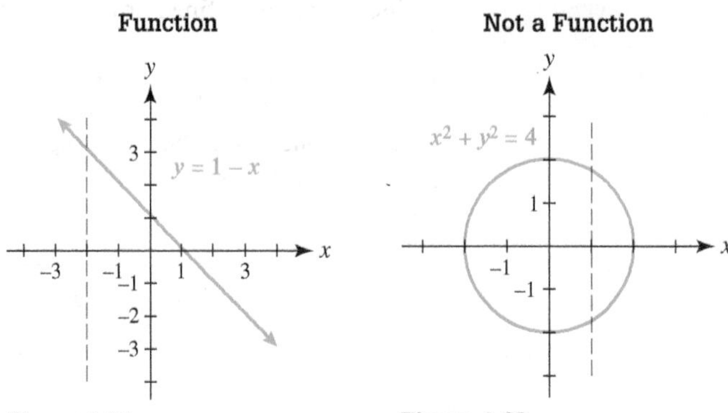

Figure 1.61 Figure 1.62

EXAMPLE 10 Identifying a function

Determine if y is a function of x.

(a) $x = y^2$

(b) $y = x^2 - 2$

SOLUTION

(a) For y to be a function of x in the equation $x = y^2$, each valid x-value must result in one y-value. If we let $x = 4$, then y could be either -2 or 2 since

$$4 = (-2)^2 \quad \text{and} \quad 4 = (2)^2. \qquad x = y^2$$

Therefore y is not a function of x. A graph of $x = y^2$ is shown in Figure 1.63. Note that this graph fails the vertical line test.

(b) In the equation $y = x^2 - 2$ each x-value determines exactly one y-value, and so y is a function of x. A graph of this equation is shown in Figure 1.64. This graph passes the vertical line test.

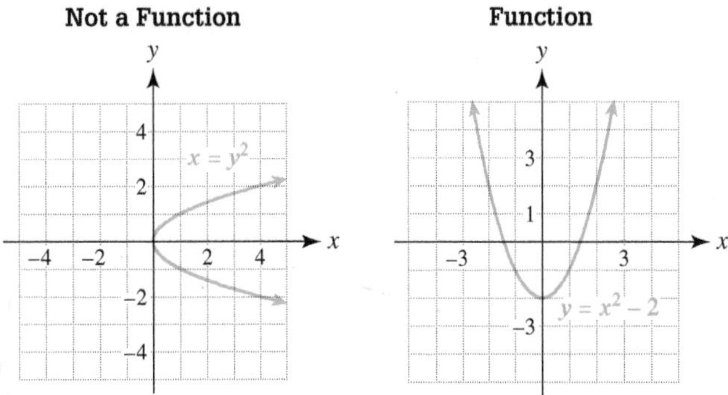

Figure 1.63

Figure 1.64

Now Try Exercises 83 and 89

1.3 Putting It All Together

CONCEPT	EXPLANATION	EXAMPLES
Function	A function is a *relation* in which each valid input results in one output. The *domain* of a function is the set of valid inputs (x-values), and the *range* is the set of resulting outputs (y-values).	$f = \{(1, 3), (2, 6), (3, 9), (4, 9)\}$ The domain is $D = \{1, 2, 3, 4\}$, and the range is $R = \{3, 6, 9\}$.
Implied domain	When a function is represented by a formula, its domain, unless otherwise stated, is the set of all valid inputs (x-values) that are defined or make sense in the formula.	$f(x) = \dfrac{1}{x + 4}$ Domain of f: $\{x \mid x \neq -4\}$
Identifying graphs of functions	*Vertical Line Test*: If every vertical line intersects a graph at no more than one point, then the graph represents a function. (Otherwise the graph does not represent a function.)	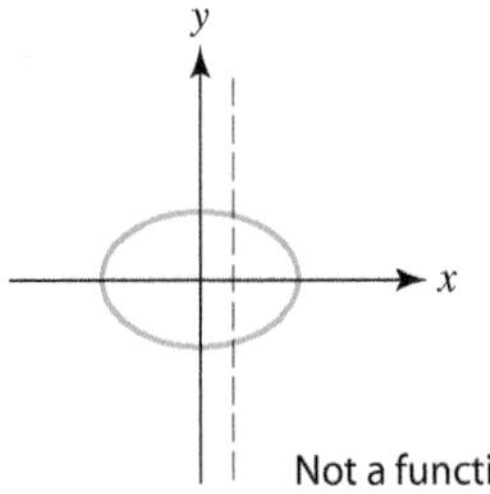 y x Not a function

continued on next page

CONCEPT	EXPLANATION	EXAMPLES
Verbal representation of a function	Words describe precisely what is computed.	A verbal representation of $f(x) = x^2$ is "Square the input x to obtain the output."
Symbolic representation of a function	Mathematical formula	The squaring function is given by $f(x) = x^2$, and the square root function is given by $g(x) = \sqrt{x}$.
Numerical representation of a function	Table of values	A *partial* numerical representation of $f(x) = 3x$ is shown. **x**: 0, 1, 2, 3 **f(x)**: 0, 3, 6, 9
Graphical representation of a function	Graph of ordered pairs (x, y) that satisfy $y = f(x)$	Each point on the graph satisfies $y = 2x$. 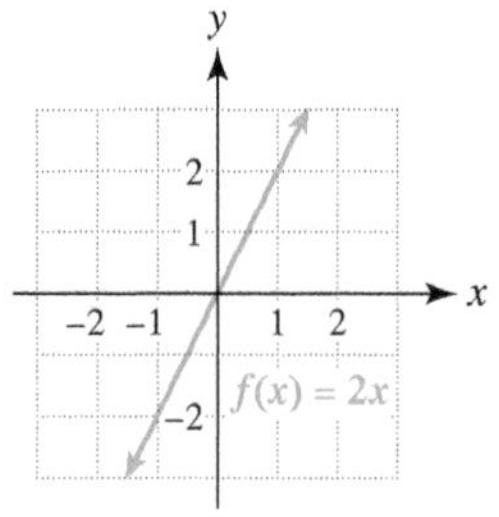

1.3 Exercises

Evaluating and Representing Functions

1. If $f(-2) = 3$, identify a point on the graph of f.

2. If $f(3) = -9.7$, identify a point on the graph of f.

3. If $(7, 8)$ lies on the graph of f, then $f(__) = __$.

4. If $(-3, 2)$ lies on the graph of f, then $f(___) = __$.

Exercises 5–20: Graph $y = f(x)$ by hand by first plotting points to determine the shape of the graph.

5. $f(x) = 3$ **6.** $f(x) = -2$

7. $f(x) = 2x$ **8.** $f(x) = x + 1$

9. $f(x) = 4 - x$ **10.** $f(x) = 3 + 2x$

11. $f(x) = \frac{1}{2}x - 2$ **12.** $f(x) = 2 - 2x$

13. $f(x) = |x - 1|$ **14.** $f(x) = |0.5x|$

15. $f(x) = |3x|$ **16.** $f(x) = |2x - 1|$

17. $f(x) = \frac{1}{2}x^2$ **18.** $f(x) = 2x^2$

19. $f(x) = x^2 - 2$ **20.** $f(x) = x^2 + 1$

Exercises 21–26: A function g is defined.

(a) Write g as a set of ordered pairs.

(b) Give the domain and range of g.

21. $g(-1) = 0, g(2) = -2, g(5) = 7$

22. $g(-2) = 5, g(3) = 9, g(4) = -4$

23. $g(1) = 8, g(2) = 8, g(3) = 8$

24. $g(-5) = 0, g(0) = -5, g(5) = 0$

25. $g(-1) = 2, g(0) = 4, g(1) = -3, g(2) = 2$

26. $g(-4) = 5, g(0) = -5, g(4) = 5, g(8) = 0$

Exercises 27–36: Complete the following.

(a) Find $f(x)$ for the indicated values of x, if possible.
(b) Find the domain of f.

27. $f(x) = x^3$ for $x = -2, 5$

28. $f(x) = 2x - 1$ for $x = 8, -1$

29. $f(x) = \sqrt{x}$ for $x = -1, a + 1$

30. $f(x) = \sqrt{1 - x}$ for $x = -2, a + 2$

31. $f(x) = 6 - 3x$ for $x = -1, a + 1$

32. $f(x) = -7$ for $x = 6, a - 1$

33. $f(x) = \dfrac{3x - 5}{x + 5}$ for $x = -1, a$

34. $f(x) = x^2 - x + 1$ for $x = 1, -2$

35. $f(x) = \dfrac{1}{x^2}$ for $x = 4, -7$

36. $f(x) = \dfrac{1}{x - 9}$ for $x = 4, a + 9$

Exercises 37–42: (Refer to Example 5.) Use the graph to complete the following.

(a) Estimate the domain and range of g.
(b) Use the formula to evaluate $g(-1)$ and $g(2)$.
(c) Use the graph of g to evaluate $g(-1)$ and $g(2)$.

37.

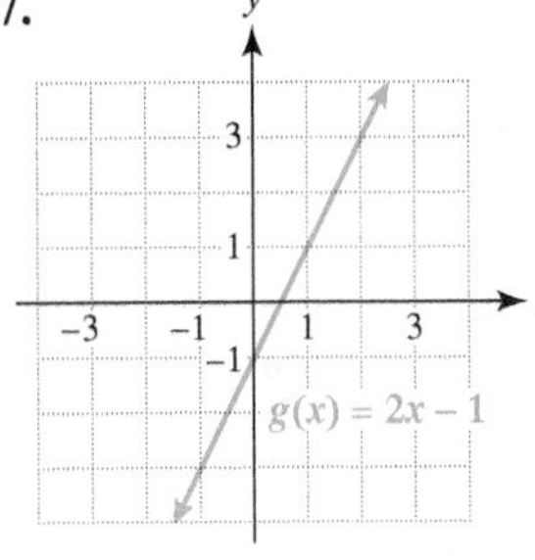

38.

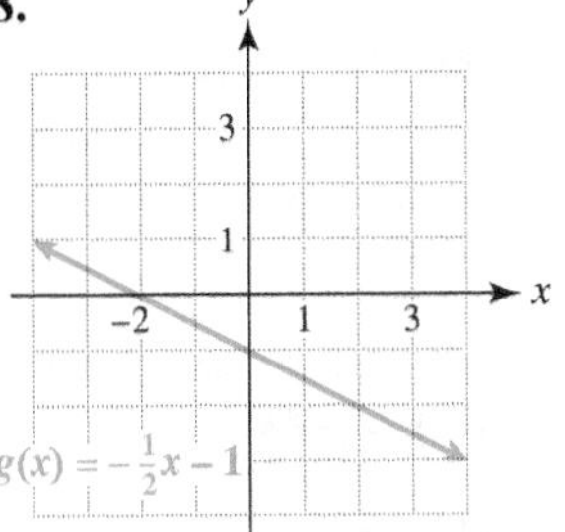

39.

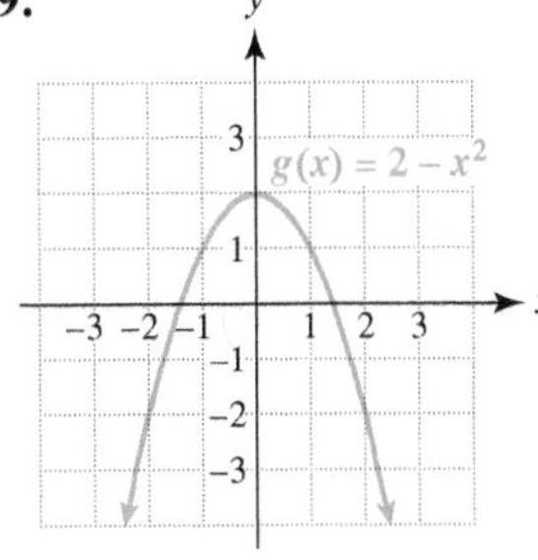

40.

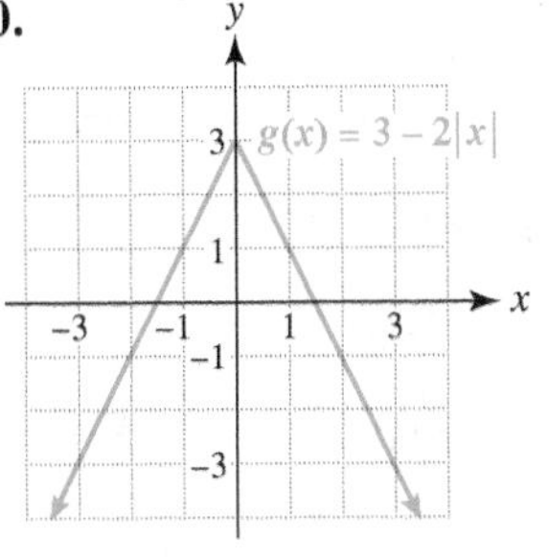

41.

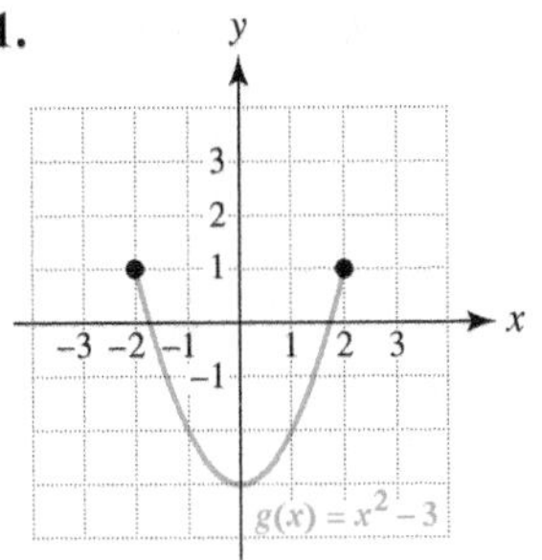

42.

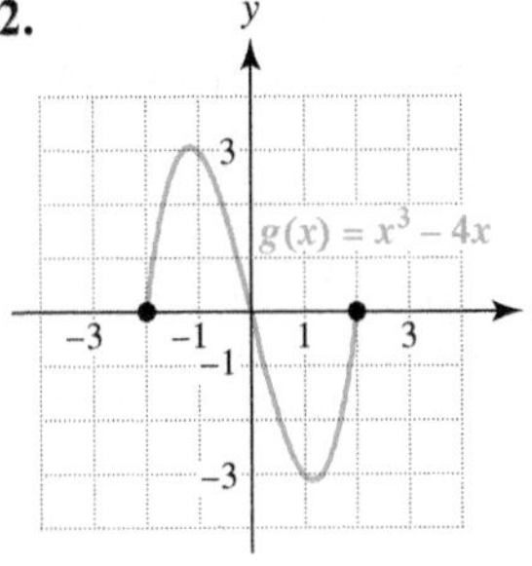

Exercises 43–48: Use the graph of the function f to estimate its domain and range. Evaluate $f(0)$.

43.

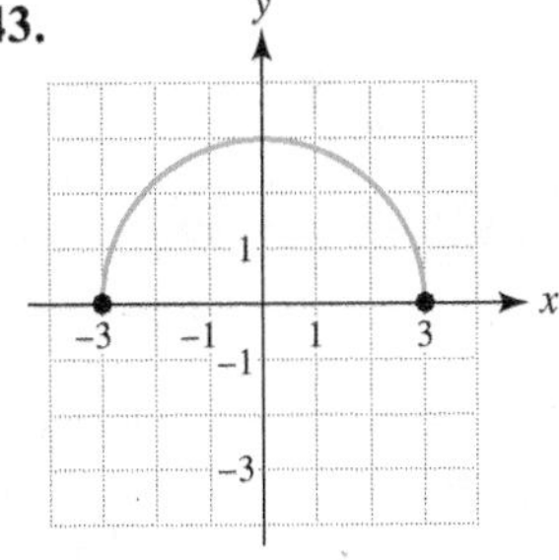

44.

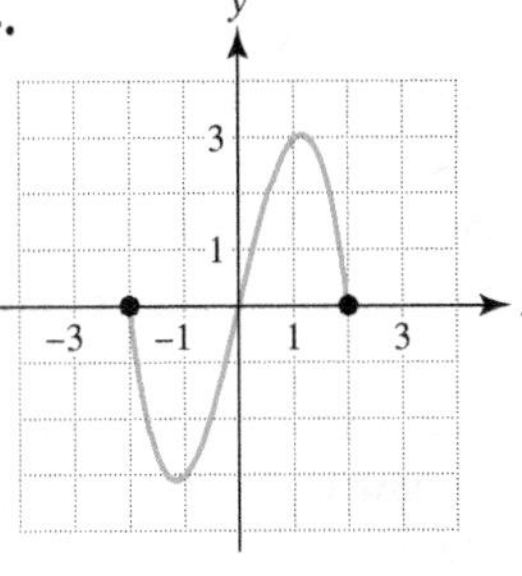

45.

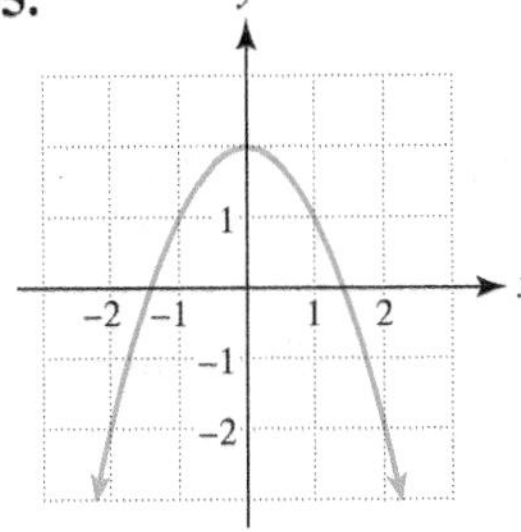

46.

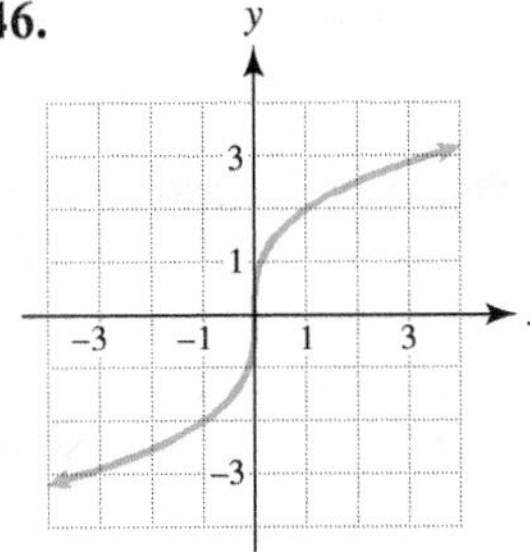

47.

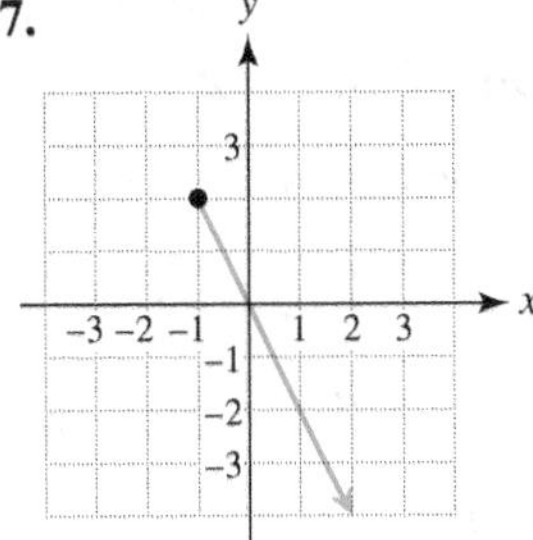

48.

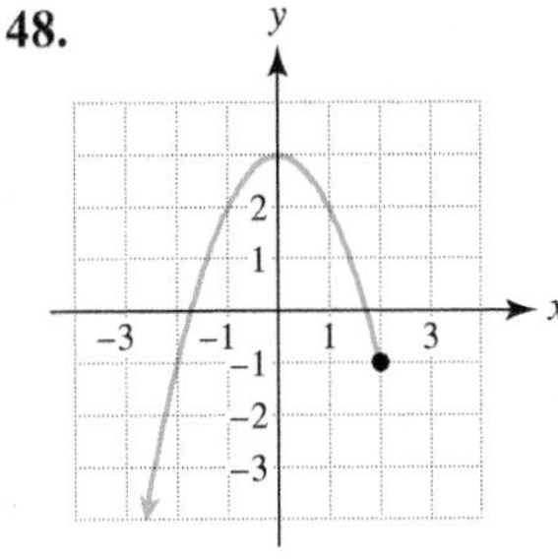

Exercises 49 and 50: **Diagrams** *Complete the following.*

(a) Evaluate $f(2)$.
(b) Write f as a set of ordered pairs.
(c) Find the domain and range of f.

49.

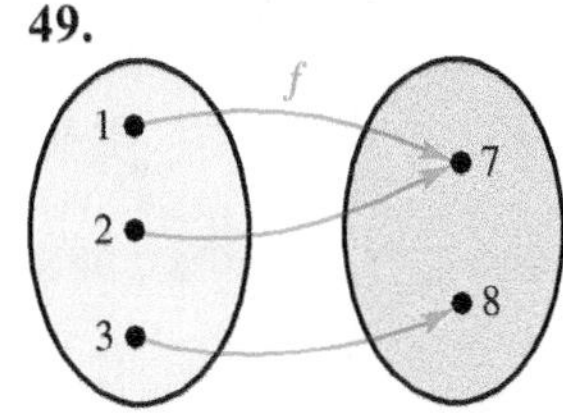

50.

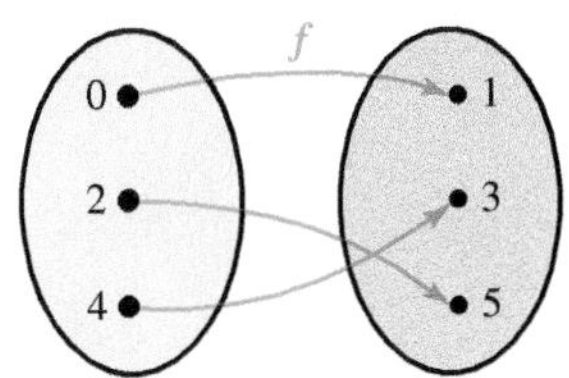

Exercises 51–54: Graph $y = f(x)$ in the viewing rectangle $[-4.7, 4.7, 1]$ by $[-3.1, 3.1, 1]$.

(a) Use the graph to evaluate $f(2)$.
(b) Evaluate $f(2)$ symbolically.
(c) Let $x = -3, -2, -1, 0, 1, 2, 3$ and make a table of values for $f(x)$.

51. $f(x) = 0.25x^2$ **52.** $f(x) = 3 - 1.5x^2$

53. $f(x) = \sqrt{x + 2}$ **54.** $f(x) = |1.6x - 2|$

Exercises 55–62: Use $f(x)$ to determine verbal, graphical, and numerical representations. For the numerical representation use a table with $x = -2, -1, 0, 1, 2$. Evaluate $f(2)$.

55. $f(x) = x^2$ **56.** $f(x) = 2x - 5$

57. $f(x) = |2x + 1|$ **58.** $f(x) = 8$

59. $f(x) = 5 - x$ **60.** $f(x) = |x|$

61. $f(x) = \sqrt{x + 1}$ **62.** $f(x) = x^2 - 1$

63. Cost of Driving In 2012 the average cost of driving a new car was about 50 cents per mile. Give symbolic, graphical, and numerical representations of the cost in dollars of driving x miles. For the numerical representation use a table with $x = 1, 2, 3, 4, 5, 6$. (***Source:*** Associated Press.)

64. Counterfeit Money It is estimated that nine out of every one million bills are counterfeit. Give a numerical representation (table) of the predicted number of counterfeit bills in a sample of x million bills where $x = 0, 1, 2, \ldots, 6$. (***Source:*** Department of the Treasury.)

Identifying Functions

Exercises 65–70: Does the graph represent a function? If so, determine the function's domain and range.

65.

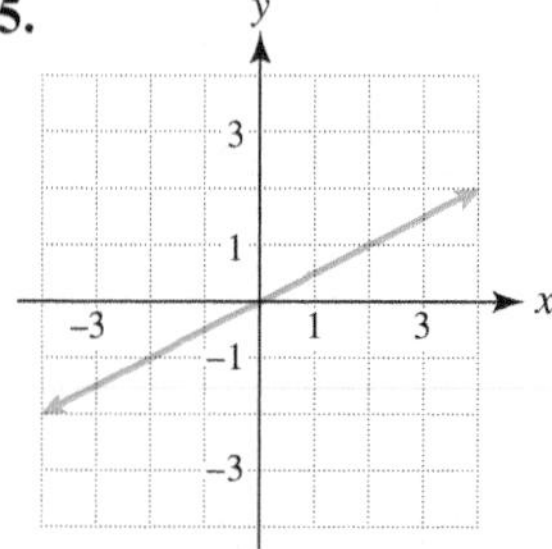

66.

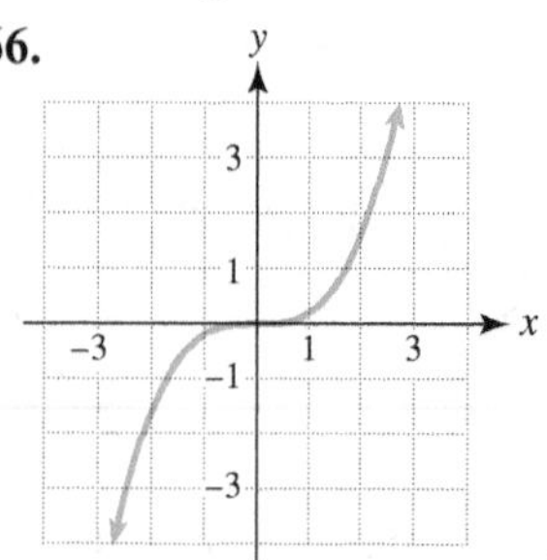

67.

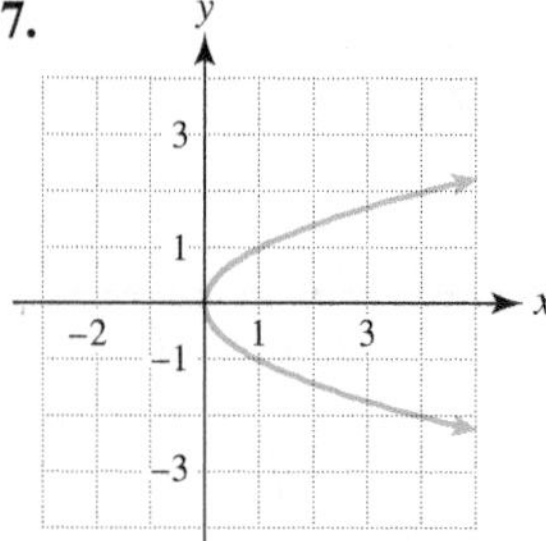

68.

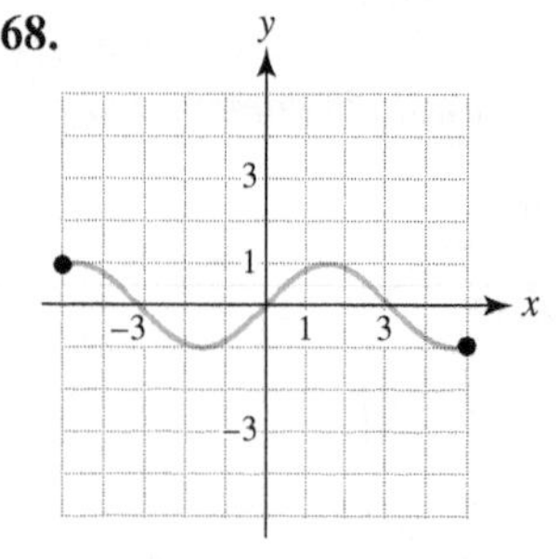

69. **70.**

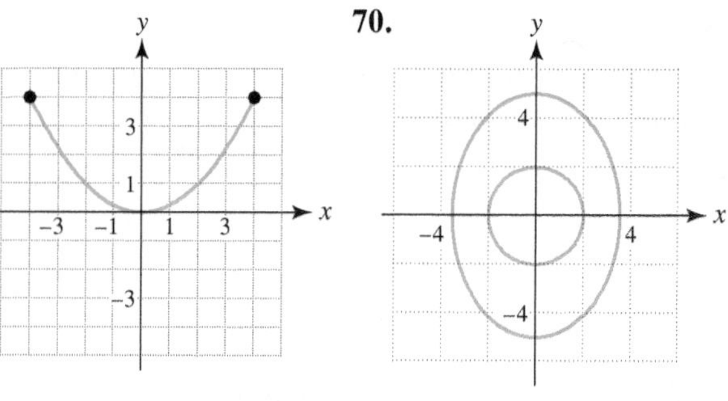

Exercises 71–74: Complete the following.

(a) Determine if the following can be calculated with a function.
(b) Explain your answer.

71. Input is a real number x; output is its real cube root.

72. Input is a Social Security number x; output is the age of the person with Social Security number x.

73. Input x is a score on a math exam; output is the ID numbers for all students having score x.

74. Input is a Social Security number x; output is the full names of the children of the person with Social Security number x.

75. Identification Numbers A relation takes a student's identification number at your college as input and outputs the student's name. Does this relation compute a function? Explain.

76. Heights A relation takes a height rounded to the nearest inch as input and outputs the name of a student with that height. Does this relation typically compute a function? Explain.

Exercises 77–82: Determine if S is a function.

77. $S = \{(1, 2), (2, 3), (4, 5), (1, 3)\}$

78. $S = \{(-3, 7), (-1, 7), (3, 9), (6, 7), (10, 0)\}$

79. $S = \{(a, 2), (b, 3), (c, 3), (d, 3), (e, 2)\}$

80. $S = \{(a, 2), (a, 3), (b, 5), (-b, 7)\}$

81. S is given by the table.

x	1	3	1
y	10.5	2	−0.5

82. S is given by the table.

x	1	2	3
y	1	1	1

Exercises 83–90: Determine if y is a function of x.

83. $x = y^4$

84. $y^2 = x + 1$

85. $\sqrt{x + 1} = y$

86. $x^2 = y - 7$

87. $x^2 + y^2 = 70$

88. $(x - 1)^2 + y^2 = 1$

89. $x + y = 2$

90. $y = |x|$

Exercises 91–96: **Formulas** *Write a symbolic representation (formula) for a function g that calculates the given quantity. Then evaluate g(10) and interpret the result.*

91. The number of inches in x feet

92. The number of quarts in x gallons

93. The number of dollars in x quarters

94. The number of quarters in x dollars

95. The number of seconds in x days

96. The number of feet in x miles

Applications

97. DVD Video Rentals (Refer to Example 3.) The function V computes the percent share of disc DVD rentals accounted for by various companies. This function is defined by $V(R) = 37$, $V(N) = 30$, and $V(S) = 17$, where R is Redbox, N is Netflix, and S is rental stores. (*Source: Business Insider.*)

(a) Write V as a set of ordered pairs.

(b) Give the domain and range of V.

98. Food Insecurity Function P computes the percentage of U.S. households that were food insecure during a selected year. This function is defined by $P(2006) = 10.9$, $P(2007) = 11.1$, $P(2008) = 14.6$, $P(2009) = 14.7$, and $P(2010) = 14.5$. (*Source:* U.S. Census Bureau.)

(a) Write P as a set of ordered pairs.

(b) Give the domain and range of P.

99. Electronic Waste As technology advances there are more and more obsolete electronic devices that need to be disposed of. The function $f(x) = 40x$ estimates the millions of tons of electronic waste that will accumulate worldwide after x years. Evaluate $f(5)$ and interpret the result. (*Source: Environmental Protection Agency.*)

100. Portion Size If the average American always ordered the larger portion while eating out, then $W(x) = 8x$ would estimate the resulting weight gain in pounds after x years. Evaluate $W(3)$ and interpret the result. (*Source:* FDA.)

101. Going Green The average person uses 2200 paper napkins in one year. Write the formula for a function N that calculates the number of paper napkins that the average person uses in x years. Evaluate $N(3)$ and interpret your result.

102. Going Green The average top-loading washing machine uses about 40 gallons of water per load of clothes. Write the formula for a function W that calculates the number of gallons of water used while washing x loads of clothes. Evaluate $W(30)$ and interpret your result.

103. Air Temperature When the relative humidity is 100%, air cools 5.8°F for every 1-mile increase in altitude. Give verbal, symbolic, graphical, and numerical representations of a function f that computes this change in temperature for an increase in altitude of x miles for $0 \le x \le 3$. (*Source:* L. Battan.)

104. Crutch Length Each year 15 million people have foot and ankle problems. Many times they need crutches. The formula $f(x) = 0.72x + 2$ calculates the appropriate crutch length in inches for a person with a height of x inches. (*Source: Journal of the American Physical Therapy Association.*)

(a) Find the crutch length for a person 6 feet 3 inches tall.

(b) For each 1-inch increase in height, by how much does the recommended crutch length increase?

Writing about Mathematics

105. Explain how you could use a complete numerical representation (table) for a function to determine its domain and range.

106. Explain in your own words what a function is. How is a function different from a relation?

Domain and Range in Context

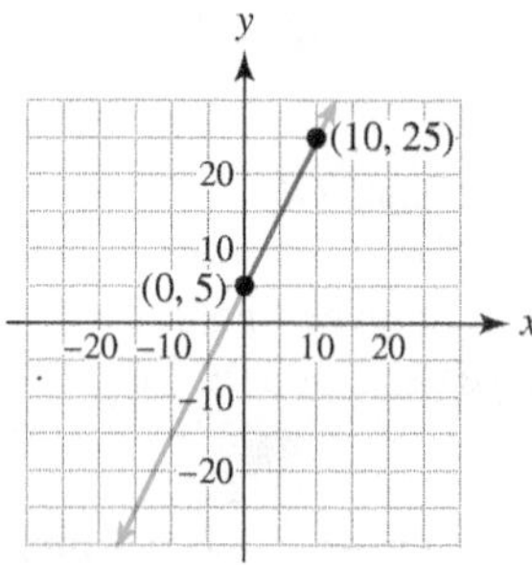

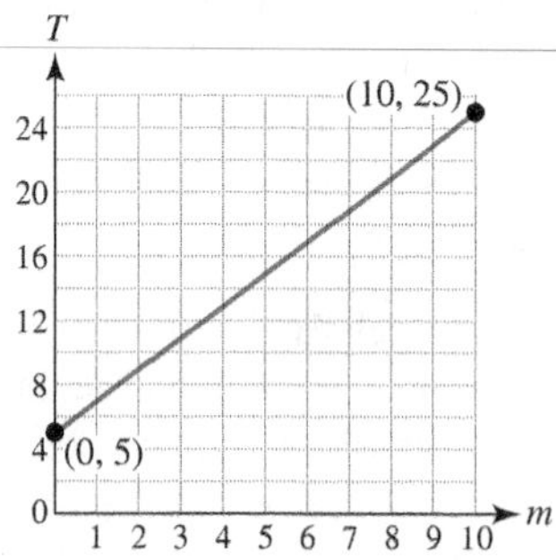

We define a function $y = f(x)$ as being a relationship that assigns to each input (x) one and only one output (y). An important characteristic of any function is its domain and range.

The domain of a function is the set of all possible input values, and the range of a function is the set of all resulting output values. When determining these sets it may be necessary to consider the context in which a formula exists. If no context is given, then the equation represents an abstract formula whose domain is simply the set of input values that can be used to get a result, and the range is the set of those results.

Consider the function defined by the formula $f(x) = 5 + 2x$. The domain would be the set of numbers that can be doubled and the result added to 5. Because this can be done to any number, the domain is the set of all real numbers, and so is the range. If we examine the graph of this function (shown on the left above), we see that the graph extends infinitely to the left and right, so the domain is the set of all real numbers, and infinitely up and down, so the range is also the set of all real numbers.

If we define the function $T(m) = 5 + 2m$ as computing the temperature of a sample of water during a ten minute experiment, then the graph has a specific beginning and end point which limit the domain and range (shown on the left below). Therefore the domain of this function in context is now $0 \leq m \leq 10$ and the range is $5 \leq T \leq 25$. Using interval notation we can write the domain as $[0, 10]$ and the range as $[5, 25]$.

NOTE The graph on the bottom appears on the top as a line segment connecting points (0, 5) and (10, 25).

EXERCISES

Find the relevant domains and ranges for the following functions.

1. The function $P(t) = 25{,}000 + 2000t$ computes the population of a city from years 1980–2005, with $t = 0$ representing 1980.

2. A sample of water is being heated until it boils (**212°F**) so the temperature increases at a constant rate. The relevant formula is given by $T(m) = 35.2 + 2.6m$, where m represents the number of minutes the heat is applied, and T measures the corresponding temperature in degrees Fahrenheit.

3. A rocket is shot upward from an initial height of 100 feet, reaches a peak height, and falls back to the ground. The formula that represents the height of this object as a function of the number of seconds **t** the rocket has been in the air is given by $H(t) = -16t^2 + 320t + 100$. This formula is valid only from the time the rocket is first shot upward until the time the rocket returns to the ground.
   (a) Given that a relevant graph of this function is shown, determine the domain and range for this function as it is defined in this exercise.

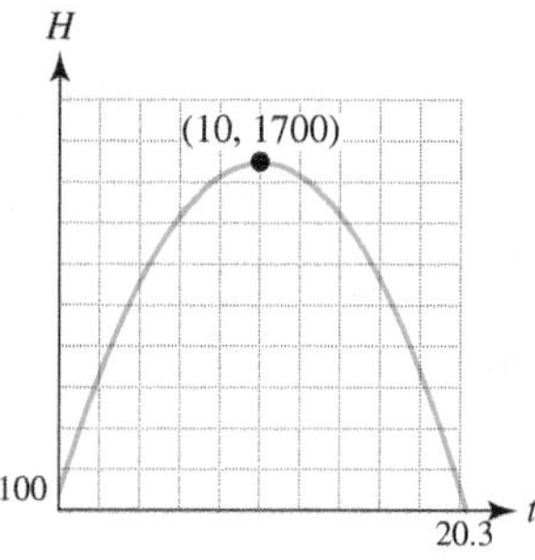

   (b) What is the domain and range of the abstract quadratic function $y = -16x^2 + 320x + 100$?

4. A national society held its convention every two years during the 1990's. The following table lists the budget in dollars for the convention's opening night festivities. The budget can be thought of as a function of the given year as defined by this table.

Year	1990	1992	1994	1996	1998
Budget	10,000	12,000	15,000	15,000	20,000

Determine the relevant domain and range for this function.

Solutions to Exercises

1. As stated, the function $P(t) = 25{,}000 + 2000t$ is valid for the years 1980–2005, which is a 25 year period. Because the input variable t represents the number of years (as opposed to the year itself), the domain is set of numbers satisfying $0 \le t \le 25$, which is the interval $[0, 25]$. Because the population is always increasing, the range can be found by evaluating the function at the beginning and end of this time period. $P(0) = 25{,}000$ and $P(25) = 75{,}000$, so the range is given by $25{,}000 \le P \le 75{,}000$, which is interval $[25{,}000, 75000]$. The relevant graph is shown below on the left.

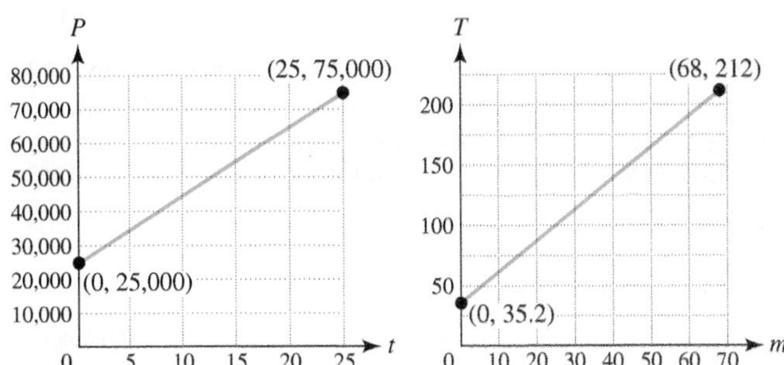

2. As stated, the function $T(m) = 35.2 + 2.6m$ measures the temperature of a sample of water, with m representing the number of minutes the water is heated. Therefore the initial value for the domain is $m = 0$, and the initial value for the range is $T(0) = 35.2$. The temperature keeps increasing, and is left on until the water reaches a temperature of **212°F**. So that is the end value for the range. In order to determine the end value for the domain, we need to figure out how many minutes it will take for the water to boil. We therefore need to solve the equation $T(m) = 212$ for m.

$$35.2 + 2.6m = 212$$
$$2.6m = 212 - 35.2$$
$$2.6m = 176.8$$
$$m = \frac{176.8}{2.6}$$
$$m = 68$$

This tells us the water needs to be heated for 68 minutes in order to boil.

Domain: [0, 68]
Range: [35.2, 212]

This graph is shown above on the right.

3. (a) Given that the formula $H(t) = -16t^2 + 320t + 100$ is only relevant from the time the rocket was first shot until the time it lands, we can see from the graph that $0 \le t \le 20.3$. So the domain is the interval $[0, 20.3]$. When the rocket lands the height is 0, and when it peaks the height is 1700 feet. So the range is given by $0 \le H(t) \le 1700$, which is the interval $[0, 1700]$. Note that this result is different from the previous two exercises in the sense that the height was not always increasing. Therefore while the domain restrictions are still determined by the first and last input values as they always are, the range restrictions arise in this exercise from the last point having the lowest output value and the maximum point having the largest output value. It is important to realize that the range restrictions do not have to come from the same data points as those that define the domain.

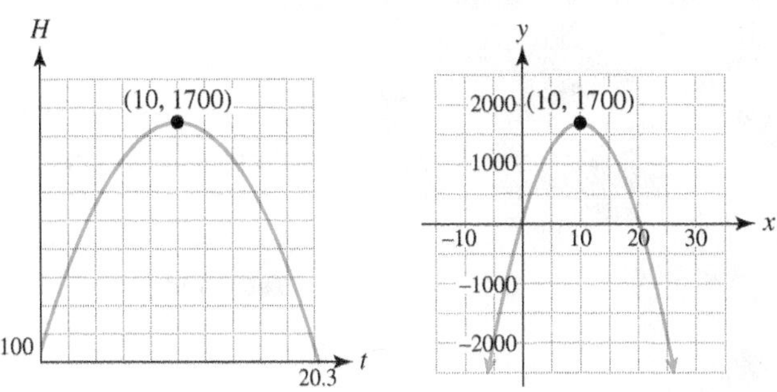

(b) The graph of the quadratic function $y = -16x^2 + 320x + 100$ is a downward opening parabola whose graph is the same as that of the rocket's, except that as an abstract function the arms of the parabola continue outward and downward on either end without having a first or last point. Therefore the domain is the set of all real numbers $(-\infty, +\infty)$ and the range is the set $y \le 1700$, $(-\infty, 1700]$

Year	1990	1992	1994	1996	1998
Budget	10,000	12,000	15,000	15,000	20,000

Given that the entire function is defined by the values given in the table, the domain is the set of years **{1990, 1992, 1994, 1996, 1998}** and the range is the corresponding set of budgets from those years **{10000, 12000, 15000, 20000}**. Note that the repeated range value of 15,000 does not have to be listed twice. Once a number is in a set, it may be used as many times as necessary.

1.4 Types of Functions and Their Rates of Change

- Identify linear functions
- Interpret slope as a rate of change
- Identify nonlinear functions
- Identify where a function is increasing or decreasing
- Use interval notation
- Use and interpret average rate of change
- Calculate the difference quotient

Introduction

Functions are used to describe, or ***model***, everything from weather to new product "specs," global warming, and U.S. population. New functions are created each day in the *dynamic field* of mathematics. Finding new functions, such as one that calculates memory requirements for an iPod (Example 3), requires creativity. This section discusses two basic types of functions: *linear* and *nonlinear*. We also discuss *constant* functions, which are a special type of linear function.

Linear Functions

A car is initially located 30 miles north of the Texas border and is traveling north on Interstate 35 at 60 miles per hour. The distances between the automobile and the border are listed in Table 1.12 for various times. A scatterplot of the data is shown in Figure 1.65. It suggests that a line that rises from left to right might model these data.

Distance from Texas Border

Elapsed time (hours)	0	1	2	3	4	5
Distance (miles)	30	90	150	210	270	330

Increases by 60 miles each hour

Table 1.12

A Scatterplot of Table 1.12

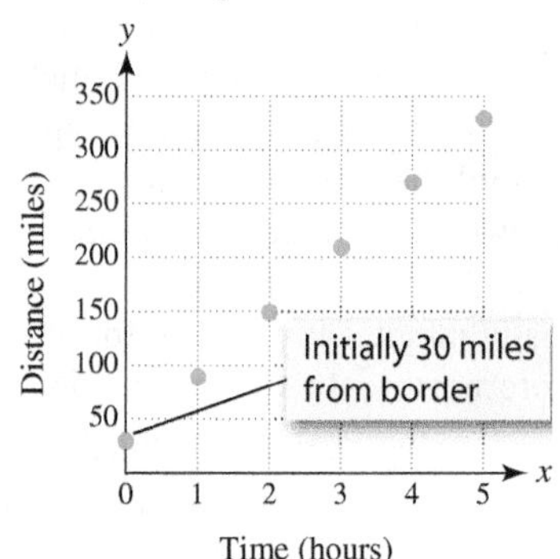

Figure 1.65

If the car travels for x hours, the distance traveled can be found by multiplying 60 times x and adding the initial distance of 30 miles. This computation can be expressed as $f(x) = 60x + 30$. For example, $f(1.5) = 60(1.5) + 30 = 120$ means that the car is 120 miles from the border after 1.5 hours. The formula is valid for nonnegative x. The graph of $f(x) = 60x + 30$ is a *line* (ray), shown in Figure 1.66. We call f a *linear function.*

A Linear Model

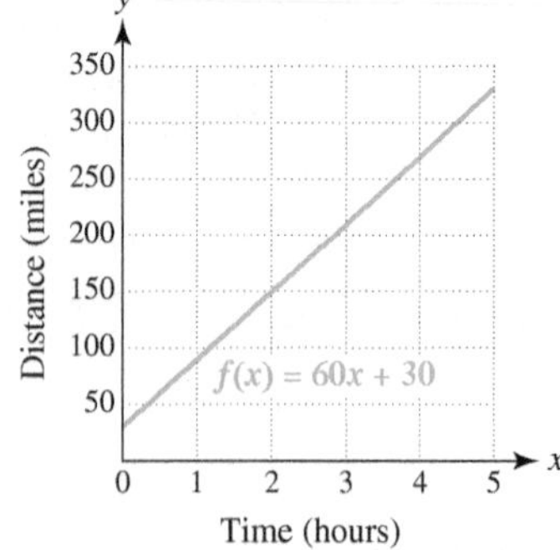

Figure 1.66

LINEAR FUNCTION

A function f represented by $f(x) = mx + b$, where m and b are constants, is a **linear function.**

Recognizing Linear Functions In the example of the moving car, $f(x) = 60x + 30$, so $m = 60$ and $b = 30$. The value of m represents the **speed** of the car, and b is the **initial distance** of the car from the border.

A distinguishing feature of a linear function f is that each time x increases by one unit, the value of $f(x)$ always changes by an amount equal to m. That is, a linear function has a **constant rate of change**. (The constant rate of change m is equal to the slope of the graph of f.) The following applications are modeled by linear functions. Try to determine the value of the constant m in each case.

- The wages earned by an individual working x hours at \$9.25 per hour
- The amount of tuition and fees due when registering for x credits if each credit costs \$350 and the fees are fixed at \$560

Constant Functions If $m = 0$, then a linear function can be written as $f(x) = b$. In this case, f is a *constant function.*

CONSTANT FUNCTION

A function f represented by $f(x) = b$, where b is a constant (fixed number), is a **constant function.**

For example, if $f(x) = 2$, then every input x always results in an output of 2. Thus every point on the graph of f has a y-coordinate of 2 and its graph is a horizontal line. See Table 1.13 and Figure 1.67.

A Constant Function

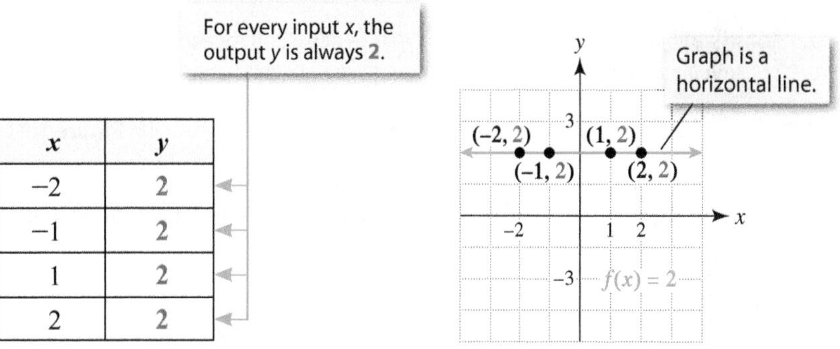

x	y
−2	2
−1	2
1	2
2	2

Table 1.13

Figure 1.67

Slope as a Rate of Change

The graph of a linear function is a line. The slope m is a real number that measures the "tilt" of a line in the xy-plane. If the input x to a linear function increases by 1 unit, then the output y changes by a constant amount that is equal to the slope of its graph. In Figure 1.68 a line passes through the points (x_1, y_1) and (x_2, y_2). The *change in* y is $y_2 - y_1$, and the *change in* x is $x_2 - x_1$. The ratio of the change in y to the change in x is called the *slope.* We sometimes denote the change in y by Δy (delta y) and the change in x by Δx (delta x). That is, $\Delta y = y_2 - y_1$ and $\Delta x = x_2 - x_1$.

Finding Slope Given Two Points

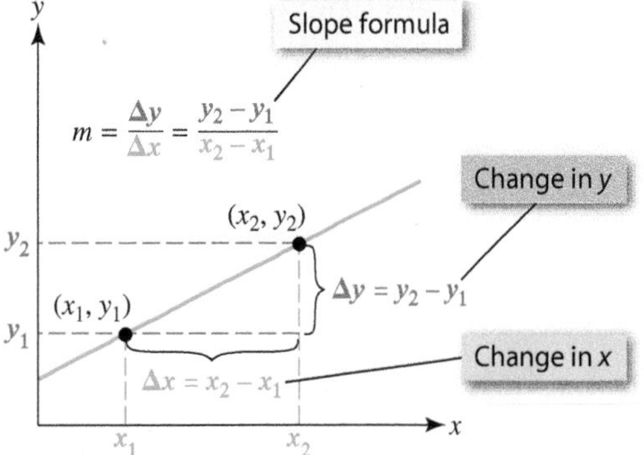

Figure 1.68

The following is a definition of slope.

SLOPE

The **slope** m of the line passing through the points (x_1, y_1) and (x_2, y_2) is

$$m = \frac{\Delta y}{\Delta x} = \frac{y_2 - y_1}{x_2 - x_1}, \qquad \text{where } x_1 \neq x_2.$$

Figures 1.69–1.72 summarize some basic concepts about slope.

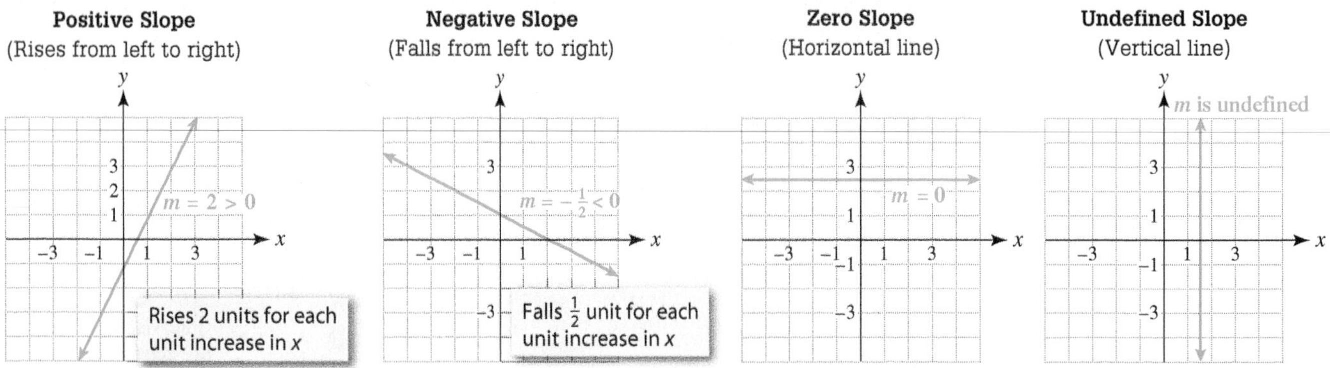

Figure 1.69 Figure 1.70 Figure 1.71 Figure 1.72

Given two points on a line we can calculate the slope of the line, as illustrated in Example 1.

EXAMPLE 1 **Calculating the slope of a line**

Find the slope of the line passing through the points $(-2, 3)$ and $(1, -2)$. Plot these points together with the line. Explain what the slope indicates about the line.

SOLUTION

Let $(x_1, y_1) = (-2, 3)$ and $(x_2, y_2) = (1, -2)$. The slope is

$$m = \frac{y_2 - y_1}{x_2 - x_1} = \frac{-2 - 3}{1 - (-2)} = -\frac{5}{3}.$$

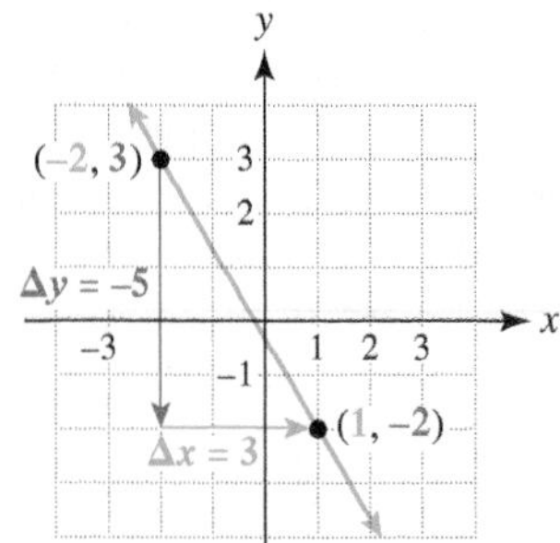

Figure 1.73

A line passing through these two points is shown in Figure 1.73. The change in y is $\Delta y = -5$ and the change in x is $\Delta x = 3$, so $m = \frac{\Delta y}{\Delta x} = -\frac{5}{3}$ indicates that the line falls $\frac{5}{3}$ units for each unit increase in x, or equivalently, the line falls 5 units for each 3-unit increase in x.

Now Try Exercise 5

Linear Functions and Slope The graph of $f(x) = mx + b$ is a line that has slope m. We can verify this as follows. Since $f(0) = b$ and $f(1) = m + b$, the graph of f passes through the points $(0, b)$ and $(1, m + b)$. The slope of this line is

$$\frac{y_2 - y_1}{x_2 - x_1} = \frac{m + b - b}{1 - 0} = \frac{m}{1} = m.$$

Interpreting Slope In applications involving linear functions, slope sometimes is interpreted as a *(constant) rate of change* as in the next two examples.

EXAMPLE 2 Interpreting slope and going green

The function given by $P(x) = 19.4x$ calculates the pounds of CO_2 (carbon dioxide) released into the atmosphere by a car burning x gallons of gasoline.

(a) Calculate $P(5)$ and interpret the result.

(b) Find the slope of the graph of P. Interpret this slope as a rate of change.

SOLUTION

(a) $P(5) = 19.4(5) = 97$, so burning 5 gallons of gasoline releases 97 pounds of CO_2.

(b) The slope of the graph of P is 19.4. This means that 19.4 pounds of CO_2 are released for every gallon of gasoline burned by a car.

Now Try Exercise 27

EXAMPLE 3 Interpreting slope and iPod memory

Figure 1.74 shows the (approximate) number of songs that can be stored on x gigabytes of Classic iPod memory. (***Source:*** Apple Corporation.)

(a) Why is it reasonable for the graph to pass through the origin?

(b) Find the slope of the line segment.

(c) Interpret the slope as a rate of change.

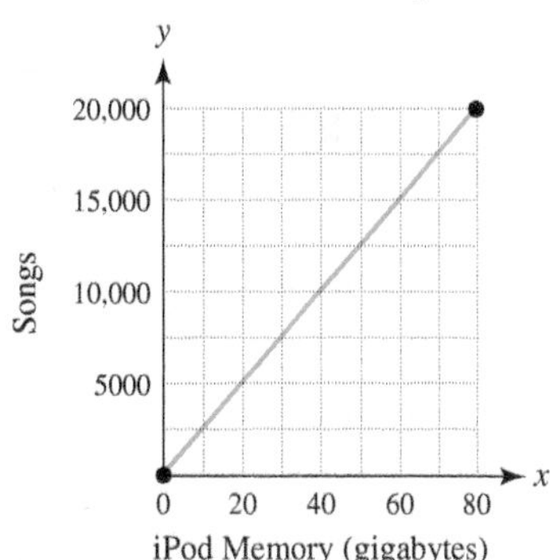

Figure 1.74

SOLUTION

(a) Because 0 songs require no memory, the graph passes through the point (0, 0).

(b) The graph passes through the points (0, 0) and (80, 20,000). The slope of the line is

$$m = \frac{20{,}000 - 0}{80 - 0} = 250.$$

(c) An iPod holds 250 songs per gigabyte.

Now Try Exercise 25

MAKING CONNECTIONS

Units for Rates of Change The units for a rate of change can be found from a graph by placing the units from the vertical axis over the units from the horizontal axis. For example, in Figure 1.74 the units on the y-axis are *songs* and the units on the x-axis are *gigabytes*. Thus the units for the slope, or rate of change, are *songs per gigabyte*.

Representations of Linear Functions Any linear function can be written as $f(x) = mx + b$, where m equals the slope of the graph of f. Also, because $f(0) = m(0) + b = b$, the point $(0, b)$ lies on the graph of f and the value of b is the **y-intercept** of the graph of f. A function can have at most one y-intercept because $f(0)$ can have at most one value.

Linear Function with $m = \frac{3}{2}$ and $b = 3$

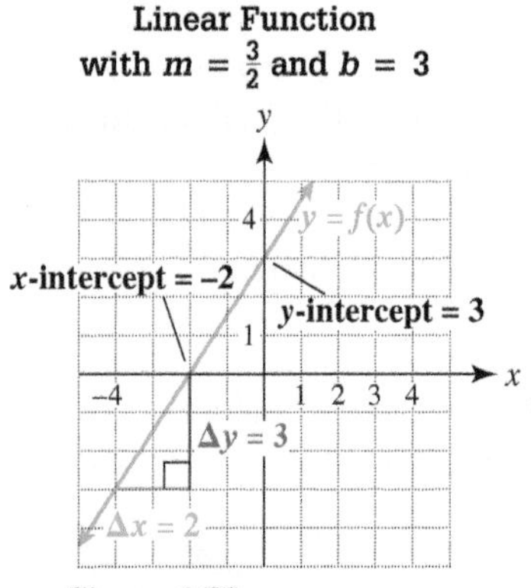

Figure 1.75

Consider the graph of the linear function f shown in Figure 1.75. The graph is a line that intersects each axis once. From the graph we can see that when y increases by 3 units, x increases by 2 units. Thus the change in y is $\Delta y = 3$, the change in x is $\Delta x = 2$, and the slope is $\frac{\Delta y}{\Delta x} = \frac{3}{2}$. The graph f intersects the y-axis at the point $(0, 3)$, and so the y-intercept is 3. We can write the formula for f as:

$$f(x) = \frac{3}{2}x + 3.$$

slope y-intercept

The graph of f in Figure 1.75 intersects the x-axis at the point $(-2, 0)$. We say that the ***x*-intercept** on the graph of f is -2. When we evaluate $f(-2)$, we obtain

$$f(-2) = \frac{3}{2}(-2) + 3 = 0.$$

An x-intercept corresponds to an input that results in an output of 0. We also say that -2 is a *zero* of the function f, since $f(-2) = 0$. A **zero** of a function f corresponds to an x-intercept on the graph of f. If the slope of the graph of a linear function f is not 0, then the graph of f has exactly one x-intercept.

The following See the Concept shows four representations of a linear function.

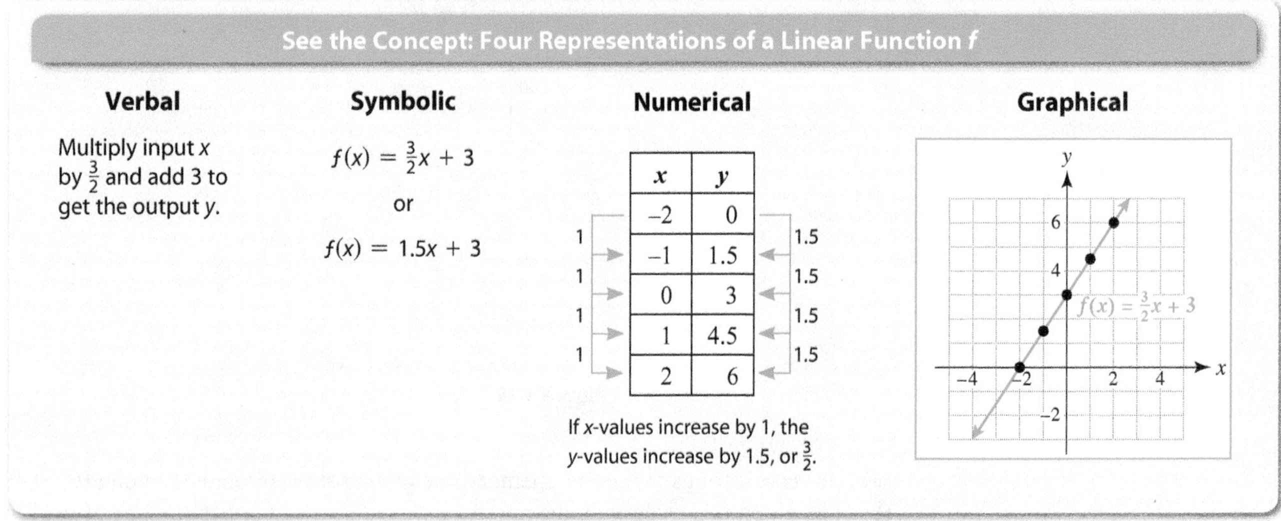

See the Concept: Four Representations of a Linear Function f
Verbal
Multiply input x by 3/2 and add 3 to get the output y.
Symbolic
f(x) = 3/2 x + 3
or
f(x) = 1.5x + 3
Numerical
x y
−2 0
−1 1.5
0 3
1 4.5
2 6
1 1 1 1
1.5 1.5 1.5 1.5
If x-values increase by 1, the y-values increase by 1.5, or 3/2.
Graphical
y
6
4
f(x) = 3/2 x + 3
−4 −2 2 4
−2
x

EXAMPLE 4 Finding a formula from a graph

Use the graph of a linear function f in Figure 1.76 to complete the following.

(a) Find the slope, y-intercept, and x-intercept.

(b) Write a formula for f.

(c) Find any zeros of f.

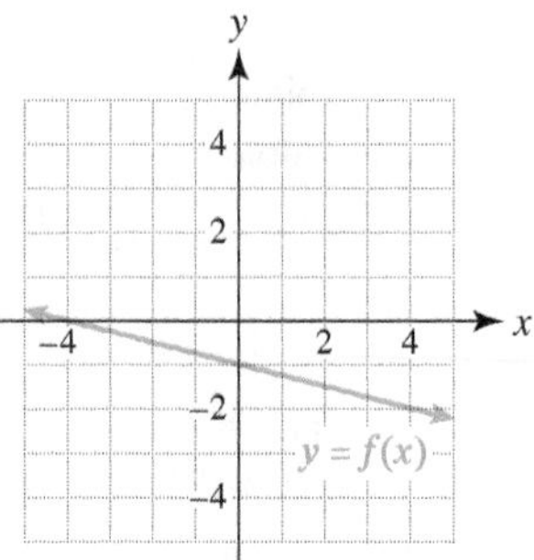

Figure 1.76

SOLUTION

(a) The line **falls 1** unit each time the x-values increase by 4 units. Therefore the slope is $-\frac{1}{4}$. The graph intersects the y-axis at the point $(0, -1)$ and intersects the x-axis at the point $(-4, 0)$. Therefore the y-intercept is -1, and the x-intercept is -4.

(b) Because the slope is $-\frac{1}{4}$ and the y-intercept is -1, it follows that

$$f(x) = -\frac{1}{4}x - 1.$$

(c) Zeros of f correspond to x-intercepts, so the only zero is -4.

Now Try Exercise 43

Nonlinear Functions

We have discussed linear and constant functions. *Nonlinear functions* are another type of function.

Recognizing Nonlinear Functions If a function is not linear, then it is called a **nonlinear function.** *The graph of a nonlinear function is not a (straight) line.* With a nonlinear function, it is possible for the input x to increase by 1 unit and the output y to change by different amounts. Nonlinear functions *cannot* be written in the form $f(x) = mx + b$.

One example of a nonlinear function is $f(x) = x^2$. In Figure 1.77 (below), its graph is *not* a line. In Table 1.14 we see that $f(x)$ does not increase by a constant amount for each unit increase in x.

The Function $f(x) = x^2$

x	0	1	2	3	4
$f(x)$	0	1	4	9	16

Table 1.14

Increases: 1, 3, 5, 7

Increase is not constant.

The increase in $f(x)$ is not the same for each unit increase in x, so $f(x) = x^2$ is nonlinear.

CLASS DISCUSSION

The time required to drive 100 miles depends on the average speed x. Let $f(x)$ compute this time, given x as input. For example, $f(50) = 2$, because it would take 2 hours to travel 100 miles at an average speed of 50 miles per hour. Find a formula for f. Is f linear or nonlinear?

Real-world phenomena often are modeled by using nonlinear functions. The following are two examples of quantities that can be described by nonlinear functions.

- The monthly average temperature in Chicago (Monthly average temperatures increase and decrease throughout the year.)
- The height of a child between the ages of 2 and 18 (A child grows faster at certain ages.)

Graphs of Nonlinear Functions There are many nonlinear functions. In Figures 1.77–1.80 graphs and formulas are given for four common nonlinear functions. Note that each graph is not a line. See Appendix B for more examples of functions.

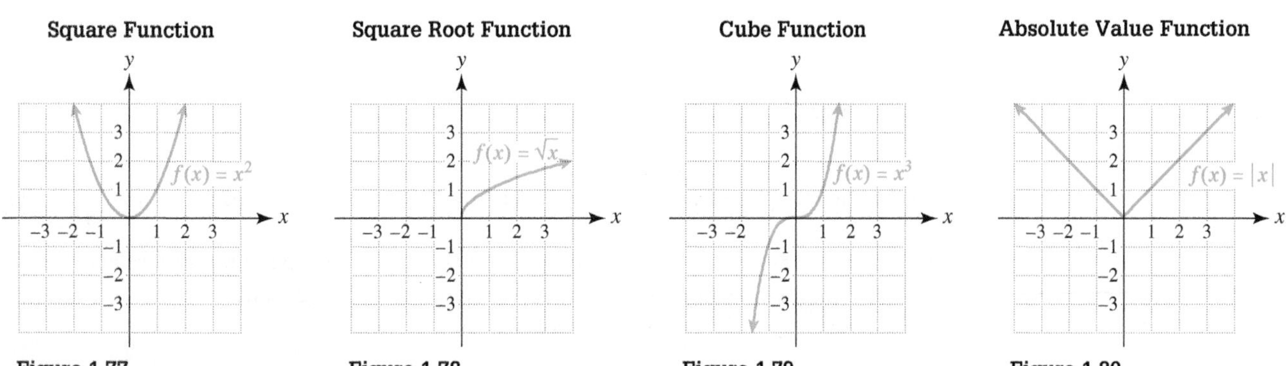

Figure 1.77 **Figure 1.78** **Figure 1.79** **Figure 1.80**

Increasing and Decreasing Functions

Sales of rock music have not remained constant during the past two decades. In 1990, rock music accounted for 36% of all U.S. music sales. This percentage decreased to a low of 24% in 2001 and then increased to 34% in 2006. (***Source:*** Recording Industry Association of America.)

A linear function cannot be used to describe these data because the graph of a (nonconstant) linear function either always rises or always falls. The concepts of increasing and decreasing are important to nonlinear functions. Figure 1.81 illustrates the concepts of an increasing and decreasing function f that models rock music sales.

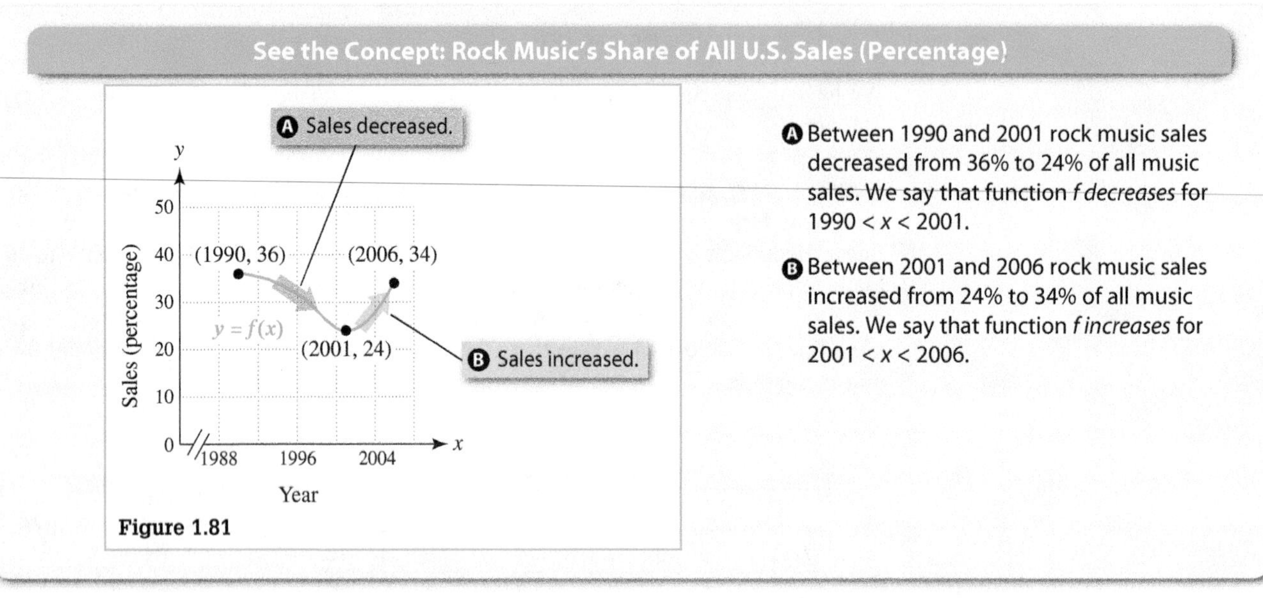

See the Concept: Rock Music's Share of All U.S. Sales (Percentage)
A Sales decreased.
B Sales increased.
(1990, 36)
(2006, 34)
(2001, 24)
y = f(x)
Sales (percentage)
Year
1988
1996
2004
A Between 1990 and 2001 rock music sales decreased from 36% to 24% of all music sales. We say that function f decreases for 1990 < x < 2001.
B Between 2001 and 2006 rock music sales increased from 24% to 34% of all music sales. We say that function f increases for 2001 < x < 2006.

Figure 1.81

NOTE The inequality $a < x < b$ means that $x > a$ *and* $x < b$.

EXAMPLE 5 **Recognizing increasing and decreasing graphs**

The graphs of three functions are shown in Figure 1.82. Determine intervals where each function is increasing or decreasing.

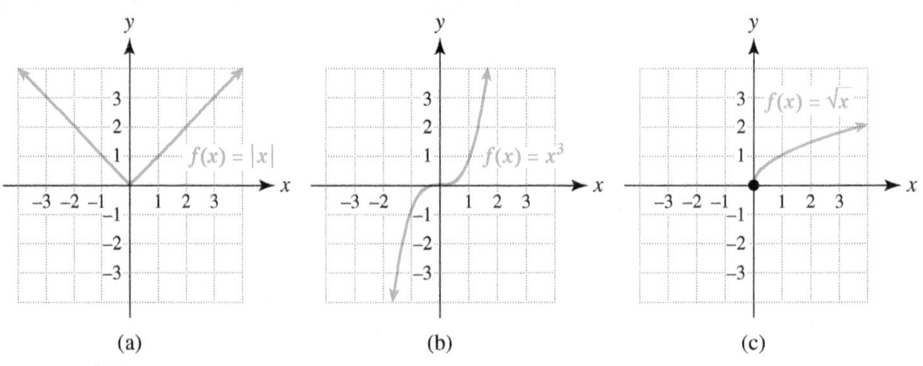

Figure 1.82

SOLUTION

(a) Moving from *left to right*, the graph of $f(x) = |x|$ is decreasing for $x < 0$ and increasing for $x > 0$.

(b) Moving from *left to right*, the graph of $f(x) = x^3$ is increasing for all real numbers x. Note that the y-values always increase as the x-values increase.

(c) The graph of $f(x) = \sqrt{x}$ is increasing for $x > 0$.

Now Try Exercises 65, 66, and 67

The concepts of increasing and decreasing are defined as follows.

INCREASING AND DECREASING FUNCTIONS

Suppose that a function f is defined over an *open* interval I on the number line. If x_1 and x_2 are in I,

(a) f **increases** on I if, whenever $x_1 < x_2$, $f(x_1) < f(x_2)$;

(b) f **decreases** on I if, whenever $x_1 < x_2$, $f(x_1) > f(x_2)$.

Figures 1.83–1.85 in See the Concept illustrate increasing and decreasing functions.

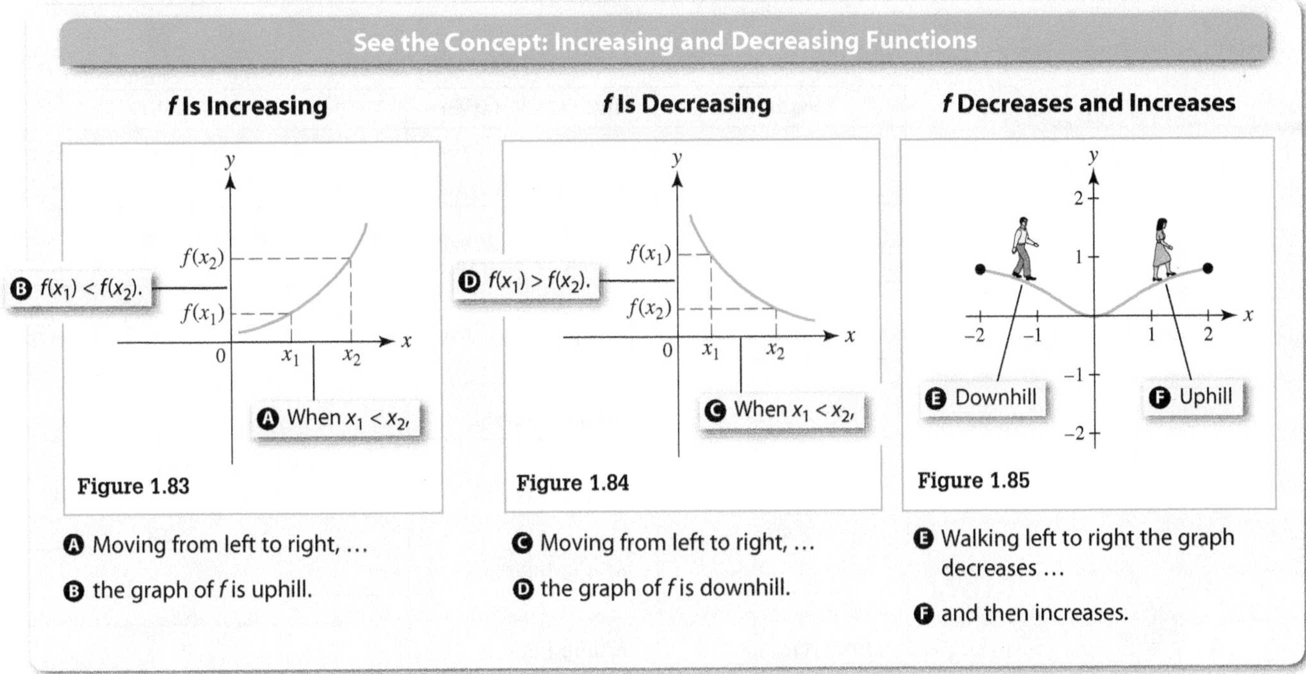

NOTE When stating where a function is increasing and where it is decreasing, it is important to give x-intervals and not y-intervals. These x-intervals do *not* include the endpoints.

Interval Notation

To describe intervals where functions are increasing or decreasing, a number line graph is sometimes used. The set $\{x \mid x > 2\}$, which includes all real numbers greater than 2, is graphed in Figure 1.86. Note that a parenthesis at $x = 2$ indicates that the endpoint *is not included*. The set $\{x \mid -1 \le x \le 4\}$ is shown in Figure 1.87 and the set $\{x \mid -\frac{7}{2} < x < -\frac{1}{2}\}$ is shown in Figure 1.88. Note that brackets, either [or], are used when endpoints *are included*.

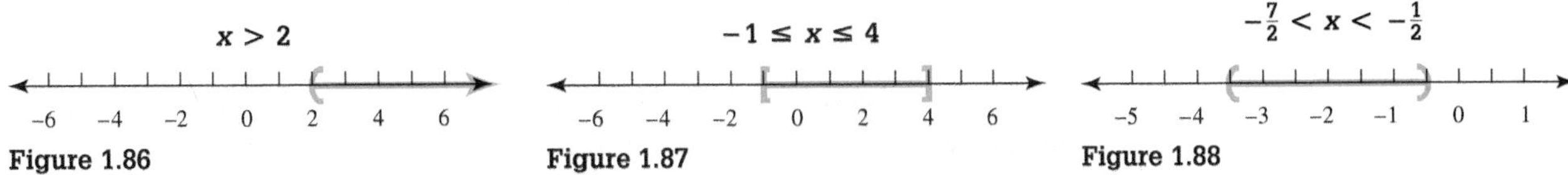

Figure 1.86 Figure 1.87 Figure 1.88

A convenient notation is called **interval notation**. Instead of drawing the entire number line, as in Figure 1.87, we can express this set of real numbers as $[-1, 4]$. Because

MAKING CONNECTIONS

Points and Intervals The expression (2, 5) has two possible meanings. It may represent the ordered pair (2, 5), which can be plotted as a point on the xy-plane, or it may represent the open interval $2 < x < 5$. To alleviate confusion, phrases like "the point (2, 5)" or "the interval (2, 5)" may be used.

the set includes the endpoints -1 and 4, the interval is a **closed interval** and brackets are used. A set that included all real numbers satisfying $-\frac{7}{2} < x < -\frac{1}{2}$ would be expressed as the **open interval** $\left(-\frac{7}{2}, -\frac{1}{2}\right)$. Parentheses indicate that the endpoints are not included in the set. An example of a **half-open interval** is $[0, 4)$, which represents the set of real numbers satisfying $0 \leq x < 4$.

Table 1.15 provides some examples of interval notation. The symbol ∞ refers to **infinity**; it does not represent a real number. The notation $(1, \infty)$ means $\{x \mid x > 1\}$, or simply $x > 1$. Since this interval has no maximum x-value, ∞ is used in the position of the right endpoint. A similar interpretation holds for the symbol $-\infty$, which represents **negative infinity**.

NOTE An inequality in the form $x < 1$ *or* $x > 3$ indicates the set of real numbers that are either less than 1 or greater than 3. The **union symbol** $\cup$ can be used to write this inequality in interval notation as $(-\infty, 1) \cup (3, \infty)$.

Interval Notation

Inequality	Interval Notation	Graph
$-2 < x < 2$	$(-2, 2)$ open interval	-5 -4 -3 -2 -1 0 1 2 3 4 5
$-1 < x \leq 3$	$(-1, 3]$ half-open interval	-5 -4 -3 -2 -1 0 1 2 3 4 5
$-3 \leq x \leq 2$	$[-3, 2]$ closed interval	-5 -4 -3 -2 -1 0 1 2 3 4 5
$x > -3$	$(-3, \infty)$ infinite interval	-5 -4 -3 -2 -1 0 1 2 3 4 5
$x \leq 1$	$(-\infty, 1]$ infinite interval	-5 -4 -3 -2 -1 0 1 2 3 4 5
$x \leq -2$ or $x > 1$	$(-\infty, -2] \cup (1, \infty)$ infinite intervals	-5 -4 -3 -2 -1 0 1 2 3 4 5
$-\infty < x < \infty$ (entire number line)	$(-\infty, \infty)$ infinite interval	-5 -4 -3 -2 -1 0 1 2 3 4 5

Table 1.15

EXAMPLE 6 **Determining where a function is increasing or decreasing**

Use the graph of $f(x) = 4x - \frac{1}{3}x^3$ (shown in Figure 1.89) and interval notation to identify where f is increasing or decreasing.

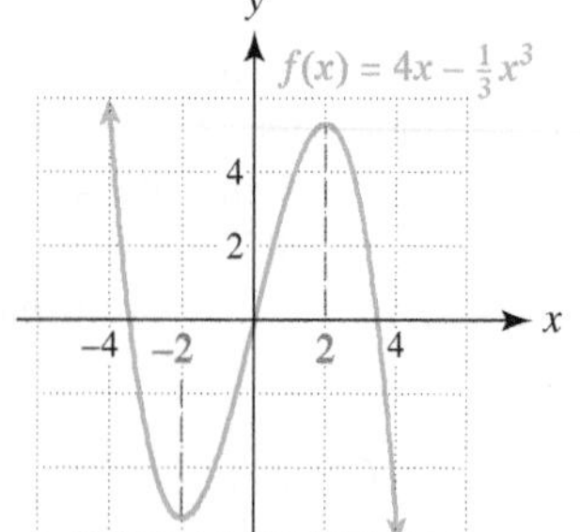

Figure 1.89

SOLUTION Moving from left to right on the graph of f, the y-values decrease until $x = -2$, increase until $x = 2$, and decrease thereafter. Thus $f(x) = 4x - \frac{1}{3}x^3$ is decreasing on $(-\infty, -2)$, increasing on $(-2, 2)$, and decreasing again on $(2, \infty)$.

Now Try Exercise 69

Average Rate of Change

The graphs of nonlinear functions are not lines, so there is no notion of a single slope. The slope of the graph of a linear function gives its constant rate of change. With a nonlinear function, we speak instead of an *average* rate of change. Suppose that the points (x_1, y_1) and (x_2, y_2) lie on the graph of a nonlinear function f. See Figure 1.90. The slope of the line L passing through these two points represents the *average rate of change of f from x_1 to x_2*. The line L is referred to as a **secant line**. If different values for x_1 and x_2 are selected, then a different secant line and a different average rate of change (slope) usually result.

Slope of L Is Average Rate of Change

The average rate of change of f from x_1 to x_2 equals the slope of red secant line L.

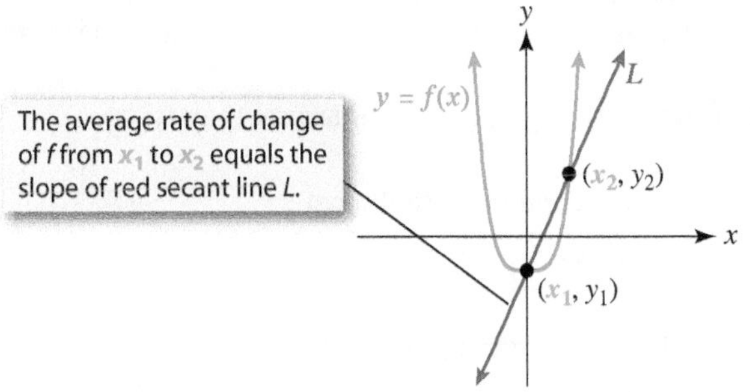

Figure 1.90

Distance Traveled by a Car

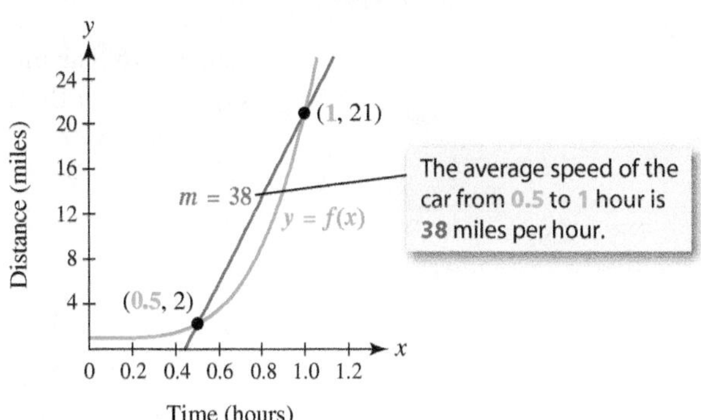

Figure 1.91

In applications the average rate of change measures how fast a quantity is changing over an interval of its domain, *on average*. For example, suppose the graph of the function f in Figure 1.91 represents the distance y in miles that a car has traveled on a straight highway (under construction) after x hours. The points $(0.5, \mathbf{2})$ and $(1, \mathbf{21})$ lie on this graph. Thus after 0.5 hour the car has traveled 2 miles and after 1 hour the car has traveled 21 miles. The slope of the red line passing through these two points is

$$m = \frac{y_2 - y_1}{x_2 - x_1} = \frac{21 - 2}{1 - 0.5} = 38.$$

This means that during the half hour from 0.5 to 1 hour the average rate of change, or average *speed*, is 38 miles per hour.

AVERAGE RATE OF CHANGE

Let (x_1, y_1) and (x_2, y_2) be distinct points on the graph of a function f. The **average rate of change of f from x_1 to x_2** is

$$\frac{y_2 - y_1}{x_2 - x_1}.$$

That is, the average rate of change from x_1 to x_2 equals the slope of the line passing through (x_1, y_1) and (x_2, y_2).

NOTE If $y = f(x)$, then average rate of change equals $\frac{f(x_2) - f(x_1)}{x_2 - x_1}$.

EXAMPLE 7 **Finding an average rate of change**

Let $f(x) = 2x^2$. Find the average rate of change from $x = 1$ to $x = 3$.

SOLUTION First calculate $f(1) = 2(1)^2 = \mathbf{2}$ and $f(3) = 2(3)^2 = \mathbf{18}$. The average rate of change equals the slope of the line passing through the points $(1, \mathbf{2})$ and $(3, \mathbf{18})$.

$$\text{Average rate of change} = \frac{18 - 2}{3 - 1} = \frac{16}{2} = 8.$$

The average rate of change from $x = 1$ to $x = 3$ is 8.

Now Try Exercise 97

NOTE If f is a constant function, its average rate of change is always 0. For a linear function defined by $f(x) = mx + b$, the average rate of change is always m, the slope of its graph. The average rate of change for a nonlinear function varies.

EXAMPLE 8 **Calculating and interpreting average rates of change**

Table 1.16 lists the U.S. population in millions for selected years.

(a) Calculate the average rates of change in the U.S. population from 1800 to 1840 and from 1900 to 1940.

(b) Illustrate your results from part (a) graphically. Interpret the results.

U.S. Population (millions)

Year	Population
1800	5
1840	17
1900	76
1940	132

Table 1.16

SOLUTION

(a) In 1800 the population was **5** million, and in 1840 it was **17** million. Therefore the average rate of change in the population from 1800 to 1840 was

$$\frac{\mathbf{17} - \mathbf{5}}{1840 - 1800} = 0.3.$$

In 1900 the population was **76** million, and in 1940 it was **132** million. Therefore the average rate of change in the population from 1900 to 1940 was

$$\frac{\mathbf{132} - \mathbf{76}}{1940 - 1900} = 1.4.$$

(b) These average rates of change are illustrated graphically and interpreted in Figure 1.92.

Interpreting Average Rate of Change

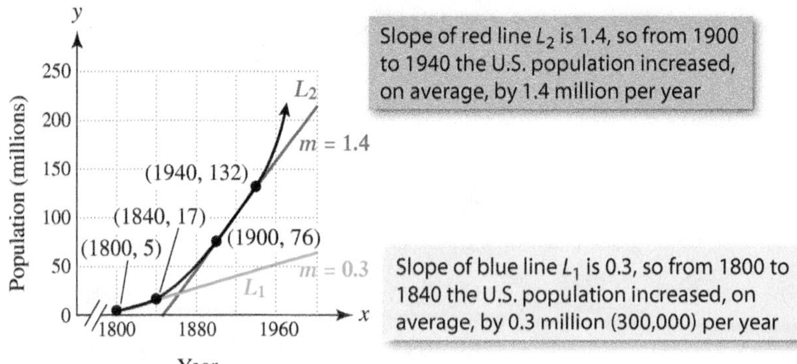
y
250
200
150
100
50
0
Population (millions)
L_2
$m = 1.4$
(1940, 132)
(1840, 17)
(1800, 5)
(1900, 76)
$m = 0.3$
L_1
1800
1880
1960
x
Year
Slope of red line L_2 is 1.4, so from 1900 to 1940 the U.S. population increased, on average, by 1.4 million per year
Slope of blue line L_1 is 0.3, so from 1800 to 1840 the U.S. population increased, on average, by 0.3 million (300,000) per year

Figure 1.92

Now Try Exercise 99

The Difference Quotient

The difference quotient is often used in calculus to calculate rates of change and is explained in the following See the Concept. In Figure 1.93, the red secant line L passes through two points, $(x, f(x))$ and $(x + h, f(x + h))$, on the graph of $y = f(x)$. (In Figure 1.93, we assume that $h > 0$.)

See the Concept: Understanding the Difference Quotient

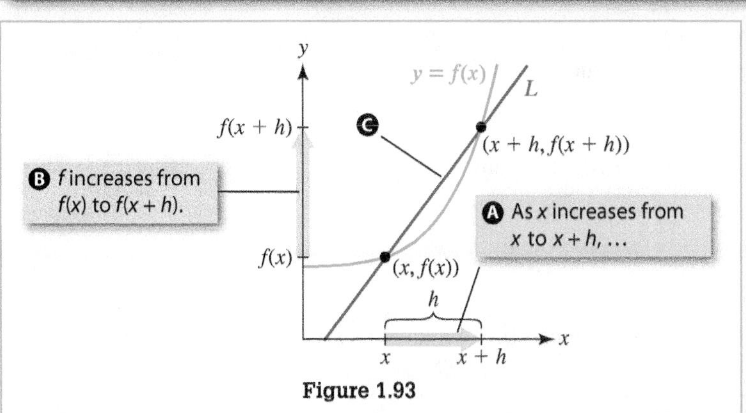

Figure 1.93

C The slope of the red line L represents the average rate of change of f from x to $x + h$.

The slope of L is $\dfrac{f(x+h) - f(x)}{(x+h) - x}$ and this formula simplifies to the *difference quotient* of f.

The following box gives a definition of the difference quotient.

DIFFERENCE QUOTIENT

The **difference quotient of a function *f*** is an expression of the form

$$\frac{f(x+h) - f(x)}{h}, \qquad \text{where } h \neq 0.$$

EXAMPLE 9 Finding a difference quotient

Let $f(x) = 3x - 2$.

(a) Find $f(x + h)$.

(b) Find the difference quotient of f and simplify the result.

SOLUTION

(a) To find $f(x + h)$, substitute $(x + h)$ for x in the expression $3x - 2$.

$$\begin{aligned} f(x+h) &= 3(x+h) - 2 && f(x) = 3x - 2 \\ &= 3x + 3h - 2 && \text{Distributive property} \end{aligned}$$

(b) The difference quotient can be calculated as follows.

Include parentheses when $f(x)$ is more than one term.

$$\begin{aligned} \frac{f(x+h) - f(x)}{h} &= \frac{(3x + 3h - 2) - (3x - 2)}{h} && \text{Substitute.} \\ &= \frac{3x + 3h - 2 - 3x + 2}{h} && \text{Distributive property} \\ &= \frac{3h}{h} && \text{Combine like terms.} \\ &= 3 && \text{Simplify.} \end{aligned}$$

Difference quotient

NOTE The difference quotient for a linear function $f(x) = mx + b$ always equals the slope m of the graph of f.

Now Try Exercise 107

EXAMPLE 10 **Calculating a difference quotient**

Let $f(x) = x^2 - 2x$.
(a) Find $f(x + h)$.
(b) Find the difference quotient of f and simplify the result.

SOLUTION
(a) To calculate $f(x + h)$, substitute $(x + h)$ for x in the expression $x^2 - 2x$.

$$f(x + h) = (x + h)^2 - 2(x + h) \qquad f(x) = x^2 - 2x$$
$$= x^2 + 2xh + h^2 - 2x - 2h \qquad \text{Square the binomial; distributive property.}$$

Algebra Review
To square a binomial, see Chapter R (page R-17)

(b) The difference quotient can be calculated as follows.

$$\frac{f(x + h) - f(x)}{h} = \frac{x^2 + 2xh + h^2 - 2x - 2h - (x^2 - 2x)}{h} \qquad \text{Substitute.}$$
$$= \frac{2xh + h^2 - 2h}{h} \qquad \text{Combine like terms.}$$
$$= \frac{h(2x + h - 2)}{h} \qquad \text{Factor out } h.$$
$$= 2x + h - 2 \qquad \text{Simplify.}$$

Now Try Exercise 109

1.4 Putting It All Together

CONCEPT	FORMULA	EXAMPLES
Slope of a line passing through (x_1, y_1) and (x_2, y_2)	$m = \frac{\Delta y}{\Delta x} = \frac{y_2 - y_1}{x_2 - x_1}$ $\Delta y = y_2 - y_1$ denotes the change in y. $\Delta x = x_2 - x_1$ denotes the change in x.	A line passing through $(-1, 3)$ and $(1, 7)$ has slope $m = \frac{7 - 3}{1 - (-1)} = \frac{4}{2} = 2$. This slope indicates that the line rises 2 units for each unit increase in x.
Constant function	$f(x) = b$, where b is a fixed number, or constant.	$f(x) = 12$, $g(x) = -2.5$, and $h(x) = 0$. Every constant function is also linear.
Linear function	$f(x) = mx + b$, where m and b are constants. The graph of f has slope m.	$f(x) = 3x - 1$, $g(x) = -5$, and $h(x) = \frac{1}{2} - \frac{3}{4}x$. Their graphs have slopes 3, 0, and $-\frac{3}{4}$.
Nonlinear function	A nonlinear function cannot be expressed in the form $f(x) = mx + b$.	$f(x) = \sqrt{x} + 1$, $g(x) = 4x^3$, and $h(x) = x^{1.01} + 2$.

CONCEPT	CONSTANT FUNCTION	LINEAR FUNCTION	NONLINEAR FUNCTION
Slope of graph	Always zero	Always constant	No notion of one slope
Graph	Horizontal line	Nonvertical line	Not a line
Examples			

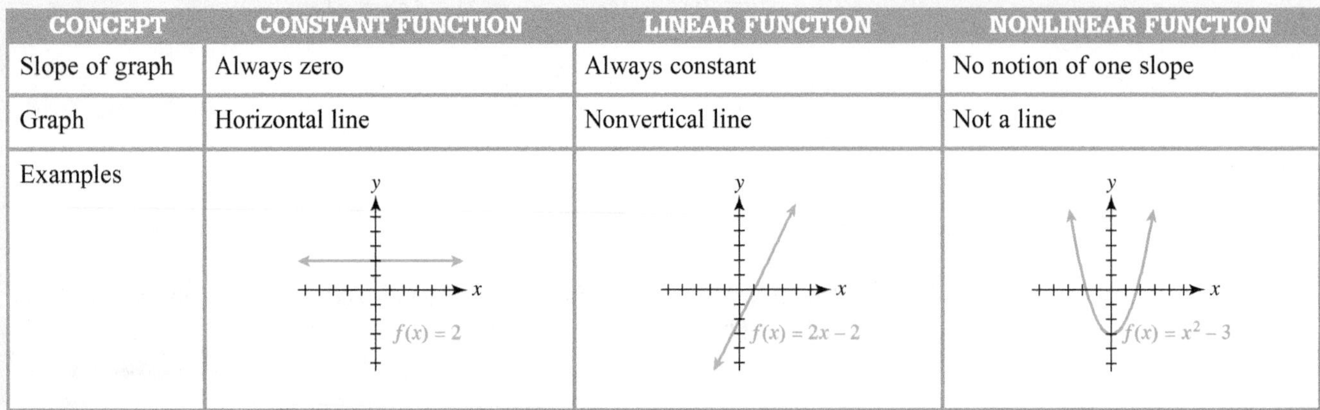

CONCEPT	EXPLANATION	EXAMPLES
Interval notation	An efficient notation for writing inequalities	$x \le 6$ is equivalent to $(-\infty, 6]$. $x > 3$ is equivalent to $(3, \infty)$. $2 < x \le 5$ is equivalent to $(2, 5]$.
Increasing and decreasing	f increases on an *open* interval if, whenever $x_1 < x_2$, then $f(x_1) < f(x_2)$. f decreases on an *open* interval if, whenever $x_1 < x_2$, then $f(x_1) > f(x_2)$.	f is increasing on $(-\infty, -2)$ and on $(2, \infty)$. f is decreasing on $(-2, 2)$.
Average rate of change of f from x_1 to x_2	If (x_1, y_1) and (x_2, y_2) are distinct points on the graph of f, then the average rate of change from x_1 to x_2 equals $$\frac{y_2 - y_1}{x_2 - x_1}.$$	If $f(x) = 3x^2$, then the average rate of change from $x = 1$ to $x = 3$ is $$\frac{27 - 3}{3 - 1} = 12$$ because $f(3) = 27$ and $f(1) = 3$. This means that, on average, $f(x)$ increases by 12 units for each unit increase in x from 1 to 3.
Difference quotient	Calculates average rate of change of f from x to $x + h$. $$\frac{f(x + h) - f(x)}{h}, h \neq 0$$	If $f(x) = 2x$, then the difference quotient equals $$\frac{2(x + h) - 2x}{h} = \frac{2h}{h} = 2.$$

1.4 Exercises

Formulas for Linear Functions

Exercises 1–4: A linear function f can be written in the form $f(x) = mx + b$. Identify m and b for the given $f(x)$.

1. $f(x) = 5 - 2x$
2. $f(x) = 3 - 4x$
3. $f(x) = -8x$
4. $f(x) = -6$

Slope

Exercises 5–18: If possible, find the slope of the line passing through each pair of points.

5. $(4, 6), (2, 5)$
6. $(-8, 5), (-3, -7)$
7. $(-1, 4), (5, -2)$
8. $(10, -4), (-15, 7)$
9. $(12, -8), (7, -8)$
10. $(8, -5), (8, 2)$
11. $(0.2, -0.1), (-0.3, 0.4)$
12. $(-0.3, 0.6), (-0.2, 1.1)$
13. $(-0.5, 9.2), (-0.3, 7.6)$
14. $(1.6, 12), (1.6, 5)$
15. $(-5, 6), (-5, 8)$
16. $(17, 7), (19, 7)$
17. $\left(\frac{1}{3}, -\frac{3}{5}\right), \left(-\frac{5}{6}, \frac{7}{10}\right)$
18. $\left(-\frac{13}{15}, -\frac{7}{8}\right), \left(\frac{1}{10}, \frac{3}{16}\right)$

Exercises 19–24: State the slope of the graph of f. Explain what the slope indicates about the graph.

19. $f(x) = 2x + 7$
20. $f(x) = 6 - x$
21. $f(x) = -\frac{3}{4}x$
22. $f(x) = \frac{2}{3}x$
23. $f(x) = 9 - x$
24. $f(x) = 23$

Slope as a Rate of Change

25. Price of Carpet The graph shows the price of x square feet of carpeting.

(a) Why is it reasonable for the graph to pass through the origin?

(b) Find the slope of the graph.

(c) Interpret the slope as a rate of change.

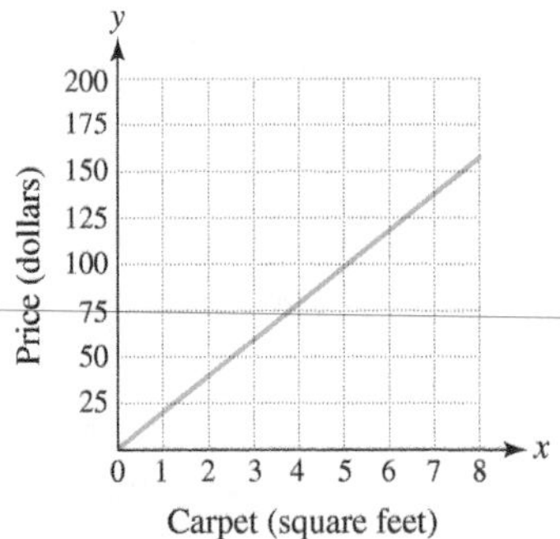

26. Landscape Rock The figure shows the price of x tons of landscape rock.

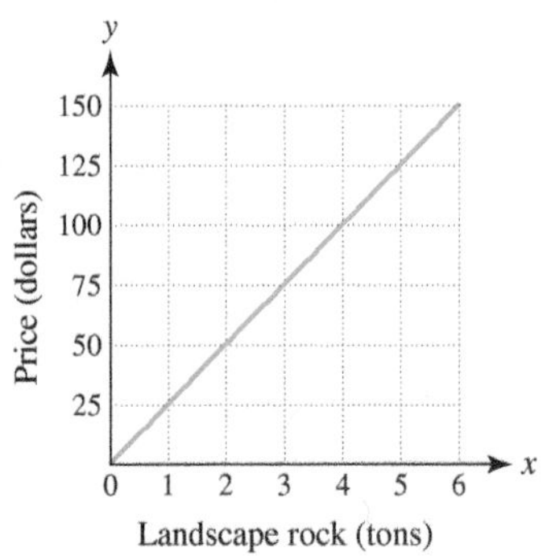

(a) Why is it reasonable for the graph to pass through the origin?

(b) Find the slope of the graph.

(c) Interpret the slope as a rate of change.

27. Velocity of a Train The distance D in miles that a train is from a station after x hours is given by the formula $D(x) = 150 - 20x$.

(a) Calculate $D(5)$ and interpret the result.

(b) Find the slope of the graph of D. Interpret this slope as a rate of change.

28. Cost of Paint The cost C in dollars of purchasing x gallons of paint is given by $C(x) = 29x$.

(a) Evaluate $C(5)$ and interpret your result.

(b) Find the slope of the graph of C. Interpret this slope as a rate of change.

29. Velocity of a Car A driver's distance D in miles from a rest stop after x hours is given by $D(x) = 75x$.

(a) How far is the driver from the rest stop after 2 hours?

(b) Find the slope of the graph of D. Interpret this slope as a rate of change.

30. Age in the United States The median age of the U.S. population for each year t between 1970 and 2010 can be approximated by the formula $A(t) = 0.243t - 450.8$. (***Source:*** Bureau of the Census.)

(a) Compute the median ages in 1980 and 2000.

(b) What is the slope of the graph of A? Interpret the slope.

Linear and Nonlinear Functions

Exercises 31–38: Determine if f is a linear or nonlinear function. If f is a linear function, determine if f is a constant function. Support your answer by graphing f.

31. $f(x) = -2x + 5$

32. $f(x) = 3x - 2$

33. $f(x) = 1$

34. $f(x) = -2$

35. $f(x) = |x + 1|$

36. $f(x) = |2x - 1|$

37. $f(x) = x^2 - 1$

38. $f(x) = \sqrt{x - 1}$

Recognizing Linear Data

Exercises 39–42: Decide whether a line can pass through the data points. If it can, determine the slope of the line.

39.

x	0	1	2	3	4
y	−1	3	7	11	15

40.

x	−4	−2	0	2	4
y	1	$-\frac{1}{2}$	−2	$-\frac{7}{2}$	−5

41.

x	−5	−3	1	3	5
y	−5	−2	1	4	7

42.

x	10	20	25	35	40
y	40	190	300	600	790

Linear Functions

Exercises 43–46: The graph of a linear function f is shown.

(a) Identify the slope, y-intercept, and x-intercept.
(b) Write a formula for f.
(c) Estimate the zero of f.

43.

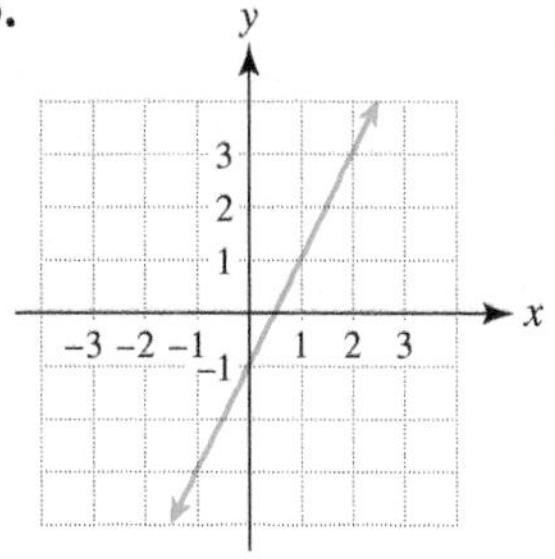

44.

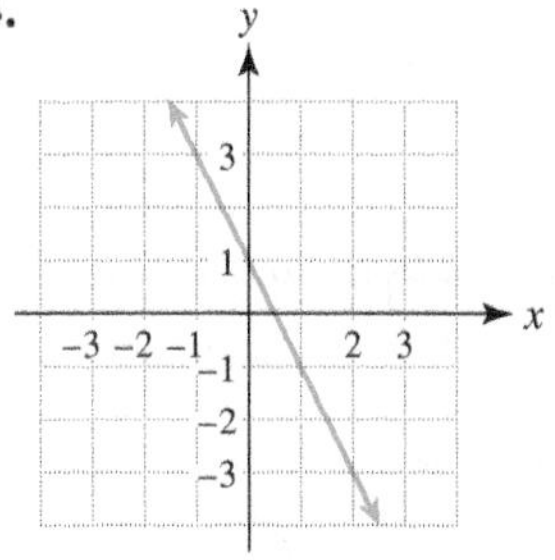

45.

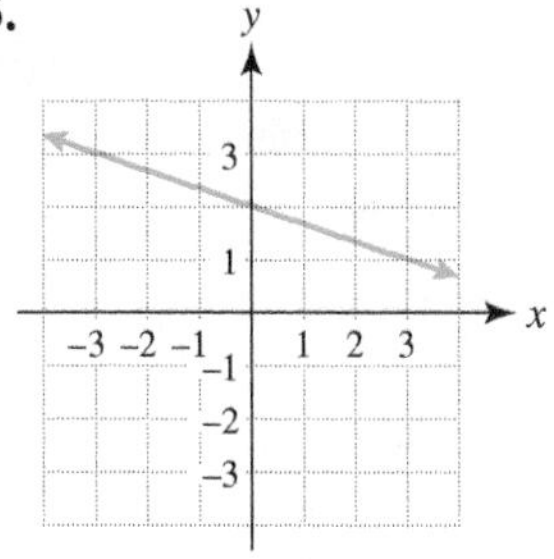

46.

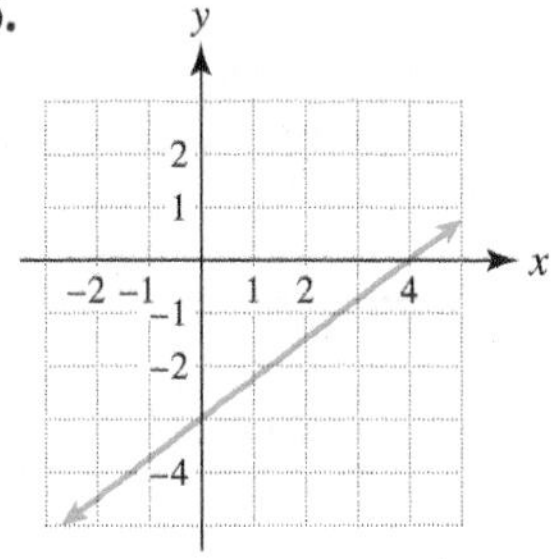

Exercises 47–50: Write a formula for a linear function f whose graph satisfies the conditions.

47. Slope $-\frac{3}{4}$, y-intercept $\frac{1}{3}$

48. Slope -122, y-intercept 805

49. Slope 15, passing through the origin

50. Slope 1.68, passing through (0, 1.23)

Interval Notation

Exercises 51–64: Express each of the following in interval notation.

51. $x \geq 5$

52. $x < 100$

53. $4 \leq x < 19$

54. $-4 < x < -1$

55. $\{x \mid -1 \leq x\}$

56. $\{x \mid x \leq -3\}$

57. $\{x \mid x < 1 \text{ or } x \geq 3\}$

58. $\{x \mid x \leq -2 \text{ or } x \geq 0\}$

59.

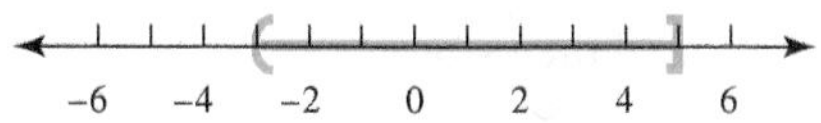

60.

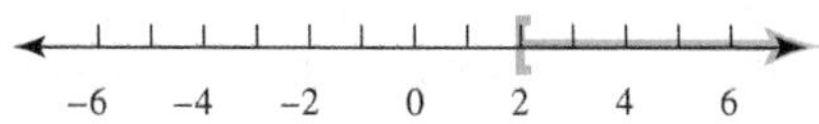

61.

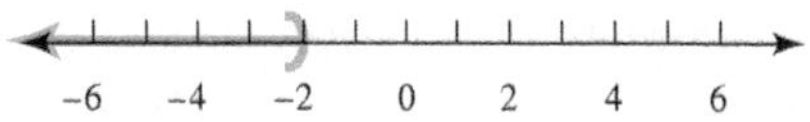

62.

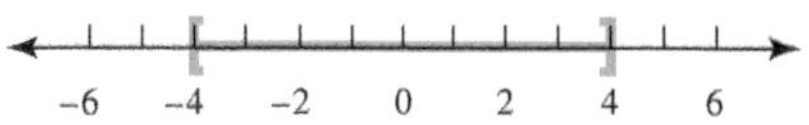

63.

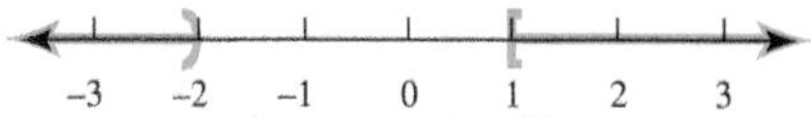

64.

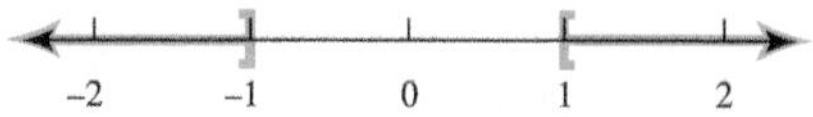

Increasing and Decreasing Functions

Exercises 65–72: Use the graph of f to determine intervals where f is increasing and where f is decreasing.

65.

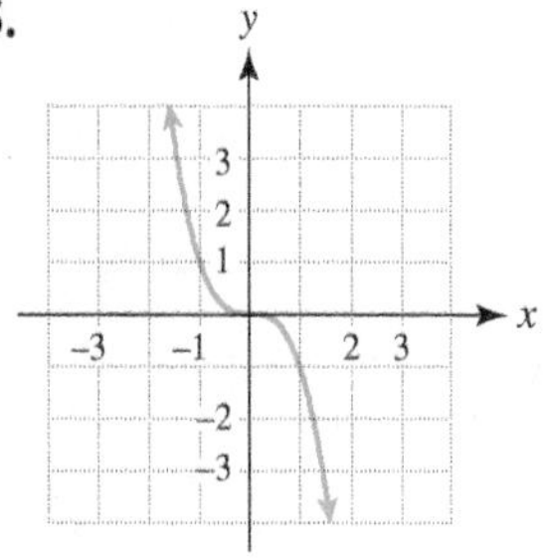

66.

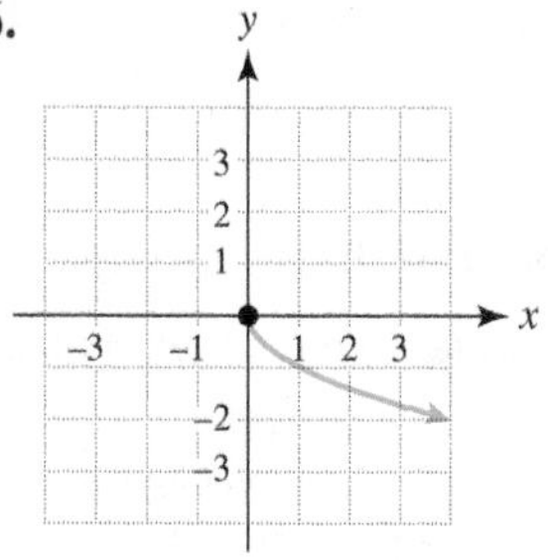

67.

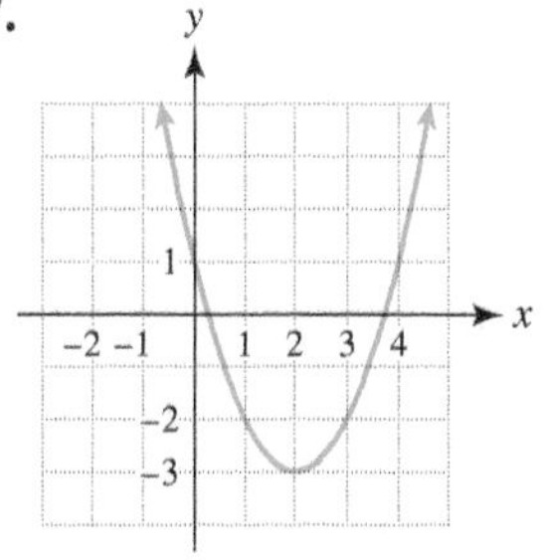

68.

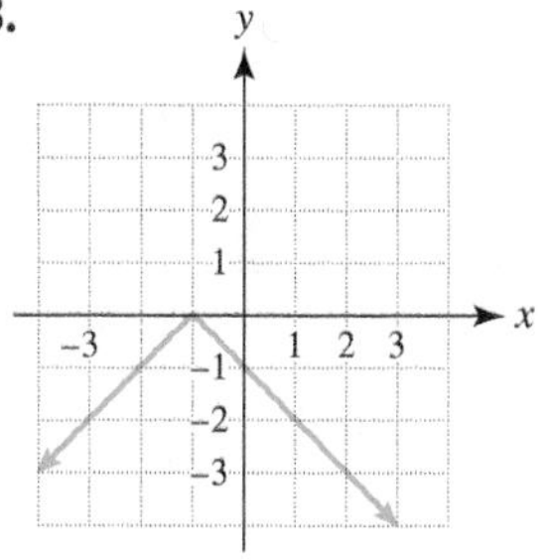

69.

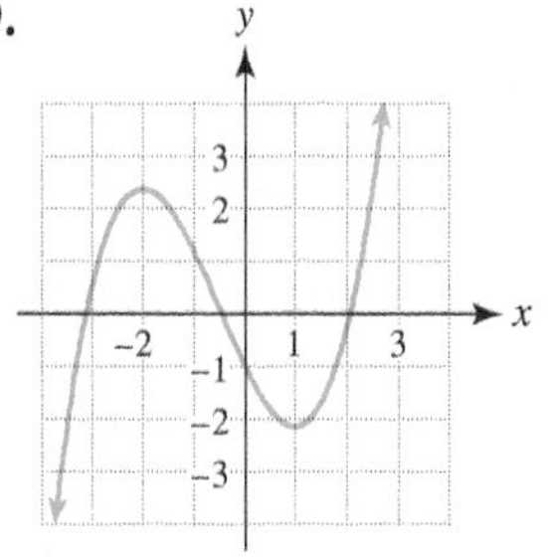

70.

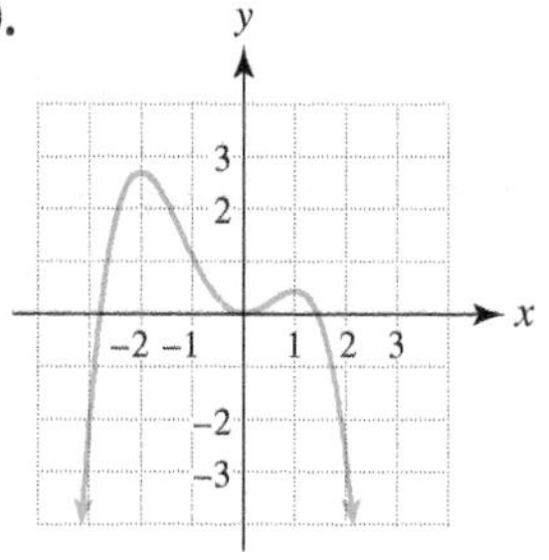

71.

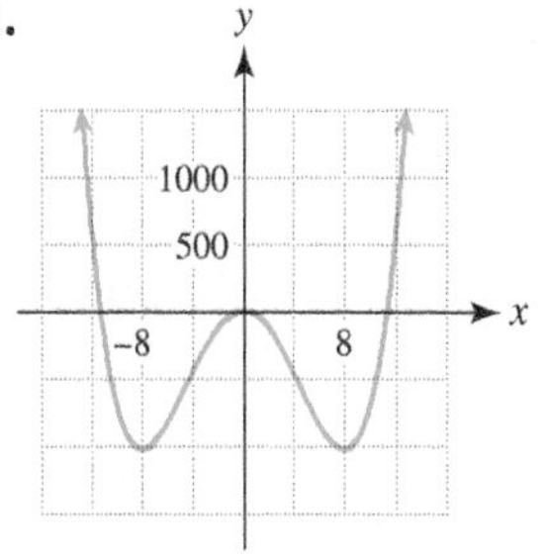

72.

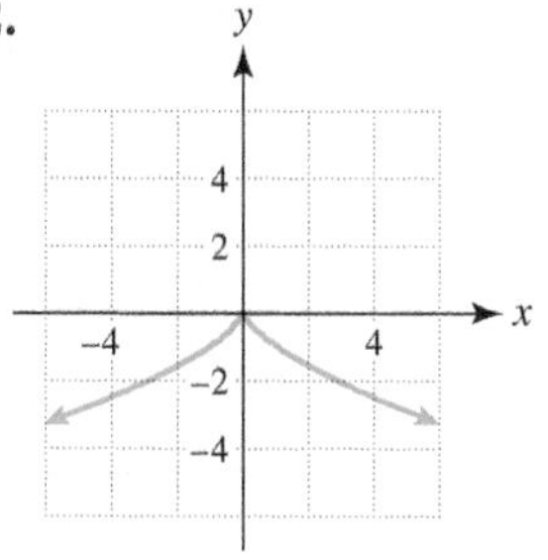

Exercises 73–88: Identify where f is increasing and where f is decreasing. (Hint: Consider the graph $y = f(x)$.)

73. $f(x) = 2x - 1$

74. $f(x) = 4 - x$

75. $f(x) = x^2 - 2$

76. $f(x) = -\frac{1}{2}x^2$

77. $f(x) = 2x - x^2$

78. $f(x) = x^2 - 4x$

79. $f(x) = \sqrt{x - 1}$

80. $f(x) = -\sqrt{x + 1}$

81. $f(x) = |x + 3|$

82. $f(x) = |x - 1|$

83. $f(x) = x^3$

84. $f(x) = \sqrt[3]{x}$

85. $f(x) = \frac{1}{3}x^3 - 4x$

86. $f(x) = x^3 - 3x$

87. $f(x) = -\frac{1}{4}x^4 + \frac{1}{3}x^3 + x^2$

88. $f(x) = \frac{1}{4}x^4 - 2x^2$

Exercises 89 and 90: **Tides** *The graph gives the tides at Clearwater Beach, Florida, x hours after midnight on a particular day, where $0 \le x \le 27$.* (*Source:* Tide/Current Predictor.)

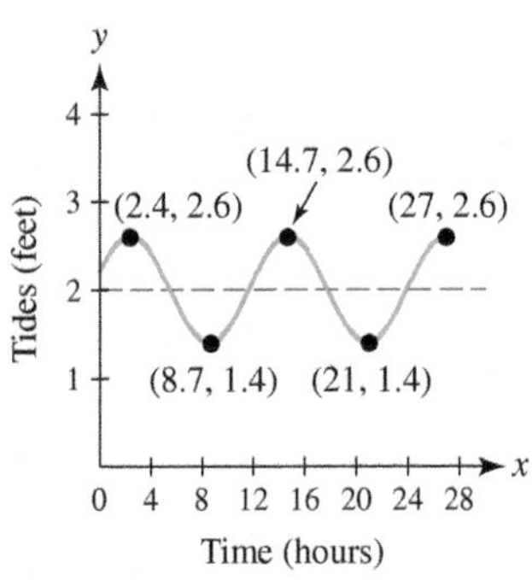

89. When were water levels increasing?

90. When were water levels decreasing?

Average Rates of Change

Exercises 91 and 92: Find the average rates of change of f from −3 to −1 and from 1 to 3.

91. $f(x) = -0.3x^2 + 4$

92. $f(x) = 0.3x^2 - 4$

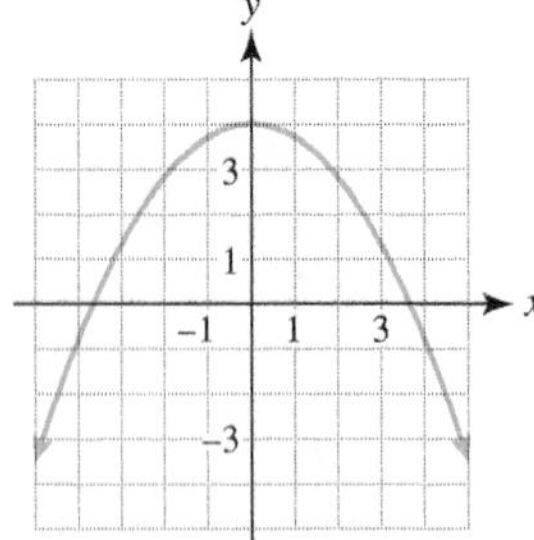

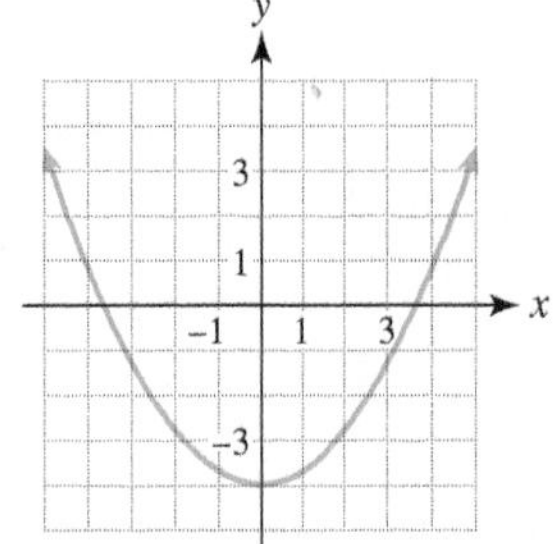

Exercises 93 and 94: (Refer to Examples 7 and 8.) Use the given f(x) to complete the following.

(a) Calculate the average rate of change of f from $x = 1$ to $x = 2$.

(b) Illustrate your result from part (a) graphically.

93. $f(x) = x^2$

94. $f(x) = 4 - x^2$

Exercises 95–98: Compute the average rate of change of f from x_1 to x_2. Round your answer to two decimal places when appropriate.

95. $f(x) = 7x - 2, x_1 = 1$, and $x_2 = 4$

96. $f(x) = -8x + 5, x_1 = -2$, and $x_2 = 0$

97. $f(x) = \sqrt{2x - 1}, x_1 = 1$, and $x_2 = 3$

98. $f(x) = 0.5x^2 - 5, x_1 = -1$, and $x_2 = 4$

99. **U.S. Cigarette Consumption** The following table lists the number of cigarettes in billions consumed in the United States for selected years.

Year	1900	1940	1980	2010
Cigarettes	3	182	632	315

Source: Department of Health and Human Services.

(a) Find the average rate of change during each time period.

(b) Interpret the results.

100. **Torricelli's Law** A cylindrical tank contains 100 gallons of water. A plug is pulled from the bottom of the tank and the amount of water in gallons remaining in the tank after x minutes is given by

$$A(x) = 100\left(1 - \frac{x}{5}\right)^2.$$

(a) Calculate the average rate of change of A from 1 to 1.5 and from 2 to 2.5. Interpret your results.

(b) Are the two average rates of change the same or different? Explain why.

Curve Sketching

Exercises 101 and 102: Sketch a graph that illustrates the motion of the person described. Let the x-axis represent time and the y-axis represent distance from home. Be sure to label each axis.

101. A person drives a car away from home for 2 hours at 50 miles per hour and then stops for 1 hour.

102. A person drives to a nearby park at 25 miles per hour for 1 hour, rests at the park for 2 hours, and then drives home at 50 miles per hour.

Exercises 103 and 104: **Critical Thinking** *Do not use a graphing calculator.*

103. On the same coordinate axes, sketch the graphs of a constant function f and a nonlinear function g that intersect exactly twice.

104. Sketch a graph of a function that has only positive average rates of change for $x \geq 1$ and only negative average rates of change for $x \leq 1$.

The Difference Quotient

Exercises 105–116: (Refer to Examples 9 and 10.) Complete the following for the given $f(x)$.

(a) Find $f(x + h)$.

(b) Find the difference quotient of f and simplify.

105. $f(x) = 3$ **106.** $f(x) = -5$

107. $f(x) = 2x + 1$ **108.** $f(x) = -3x + 4$

109. $f(x) = 3x^2 + 1$ **110.** $f(x) = x^2 - 2$

111. $f(x) = -x^2 + 2x$ **112.** $f(x) = -4x^2 + 1$

113. $f(x) = 2x^2 - x + 1$ **114.** $f(x) = x^2 + 3x - 2$

115. $f(x) = x^3$ **116.** $f(x) = 1 - x^3$

117. Speed of a Car Let the distance in feet that a car travels in t seconds be given by $d(t) = 8t^2$ for $0 \leq t \leq 6$.

(a) Find $d(t + h)$.

(b) Find the difference quotient for d and simplify.

(c) Evaluate the difference quotient when $t = 4$ and $h = 0.05$. Interpret your result.

118. Draining a Pool Let the number of gallons G of water in a pool after t hours be given by $G(t) = 4000 - 100t$ for $0 \leq t \leq 40$.

(a) Find $G(t + h)$.

(b) Find the difference quotient. Interpret your result.

Writing about Mathematics

119. What does the average rate of change represent for a linear function? What does it represent for a nonlinear function? Explain your answers.

120. Suppose you are given a graphical representation of a function f. Explain how you would determine whether f is constant, linear, or nonlinear. How would you determine the type if you were given a numerical or symbolic representation? Give examples.

121. Suppose that a function f has a positive average rate of change from 1 to 4. Is it correct to assume that function f only increases on the interval $(1, 4)$? Make a sketch to support your answer.

122. If $f(x) = mx + b$, what does the difference quotient for function f equal? Explain your reasoning.

Extended and Discovery Exercise

1. Geometry Suppose that the radius of a circle on a computer monitor is increasing at a constant rate of 1 inch per second.

(a) Does the circumference of the circle increase at a constant rate? If it does, find this rate.

(b) Does the area of the circle increase at a constant rate? Explain.

2. Velocity If the distance in feet run by a racehorse in t seconds is given by $d(t) = 2t^2$, then the difference quotient for d is $4t + 2h$. How could you estimate the velocity of the racehorse at exactly 7 seconds?

CHECKING BASIC CONCEPTS FOR SECTIONS 1.3 AND 1.4

1. Give symbolic, numerical, and graphical representations of a function f that computes the number of feet in x miles. For the numerical representation use a table and let $x = 1, 2, 3, 4, 5$.

2. Let $f(x) = \frac{2x}{x - 4}$.

(a) Find $f(2)$ and $f(a + 4)$.

(b) Find the domain of f.

3. Find the slope of the line passing through the points $(-2, 4)$ and $(4, -5)$.

4. Identify each function f as constant, linear, or nonlinear.

(a) $f(x) = -1.4x + 5.1$

(b) $f(x) = 25$

(c) $f(x) = 2x^2 - 5$

5. Write each expression in interval notation.

(a) $x \leq 5$ **(b)** $1 \leq x < 6$

6. Determine where $f(x) = x^2 - 2$ is increasing and where it is decreasing.

7. Find the average rate of change of $f(x) = x^2 - 3x$ from $x = -3$ to $x = -1$.

8. Find the difference quotient for $f(x) = 4x^2$.

When Rates of Change are Increasing, Decreasing, or Constant

The rate at which a function changes is an important tool for analyzing the behavior of that function. Consider the six graphs shown, which are meant to represent the population of a country measured over a period of time.

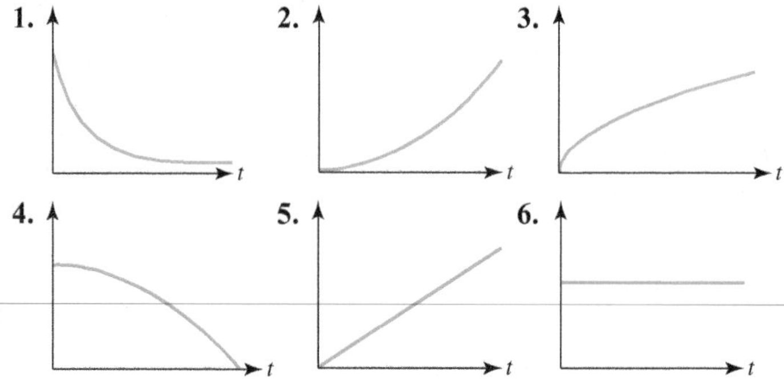

Graphs 2, 3, and 5 are rising, so those three graphs represent an increasing population. Graphs 1 and 4 are falling, so those two graphs represent a decreasing population. Graph 6 is horizontal, so this represents a population that is staying constant. These results are obtained by observing whether the graphs are rising, falling, or staying level. But if we want information about the ***rates*** at which these populations were changing, we need to determine whether the slopes of the graphs are getting larger (moving to the right on a number line), smaller (moving to the left on a number line), or remaining constant. This is determined by the **concavity** of the graphs.

Graphs 1 and 2 are sections of graphs that are **concave up**. As graph 1 proceeds from left to right, the slopes are getting less negative. As graph 2 proceeds from left to right, the slopes are getting more positive. Either way these numbers are increasing, so both of these graphs represent **increasing rates of change**.

Graphs 3 and 4 are sections of graphs that are **concave down**. As graph 3 proceeds from left to right, the slopes are getting less positive. As graph 4 proceeds from left to right, the slopes are getting more negative. Either way these numbers are decreasing, so both of these graphs represent **decreasing rates of change**.

Graphs 5 and 6 are **linear**. This means that the rate at which these populations are changing is staying constant. For graph 5, this constant rate of change would be the slope of the line. The same is true of graph 6, but because the slope of a horizontal line is 0, that is also the constant rate at which that population is changing.

NOTE An important distinction should be made between the discussion above and what it means when expressed in everyday language. Look again at graph **4**. Because this graph is concave down, as the graph proceeds from left to right the slopes are getting more negative, hence this graph is said to exhibit a decreasing rate of change. But because the population at any time **t** is measured by the vertical location of the graph, as a graph gets steeper the population is in fact changing at a faster and faster rate. This seems to contradict the fact that the rate of change is described mathematically as decreasing.

The problem is in the language. Mathematics is a very precise language, whereas the everyday words we use to describe the real world can be interpreted in many ways. The decreasing rate of change is a mathematical measure of how the slopes are changing as the graph proceeds from left to right. In this case the slopes get more and more negative, so they are decreasing. But when we say the population is changing at a faster and faster rate, we are talking about the magnitude of the rate of change, that is, the absolute value of the number we assign to the slope. So even though these numbers are getting more negative they are increasing in absolute value. This means the decrease is indeed happening faster and faster. When we use everyday language to describe rates of change we are generally talking about the magnitude of the rate of change. In this sense, as a graph gets steeper it always represents an increasing magnitude, and as a graph levels off it always represents a decreasing magnitude.

In the same way, a rate of change can be thought of as velocity or speed. Velocity is equivalent to slope, which can be negative if a function decreases. Speed is equivalent to the magnitude of the slope, which is never negative.

This is generally not a source of confusion if the function itself is increasing. In this case the rate of change is the same as the magnitude of the rate (a positive number always equals its own absolute value). But if a function is decreasing, the graph getting steeper represents decreasing slopes with an increasing magnitude of those slopes, and the opposite is true if a decreasing graph levels off.

EXERCISES

Answer the following from a mathematical perspective, not an everyday language perspective.

1. Match the description with the best graph shape. In each case the independent variable represents time.

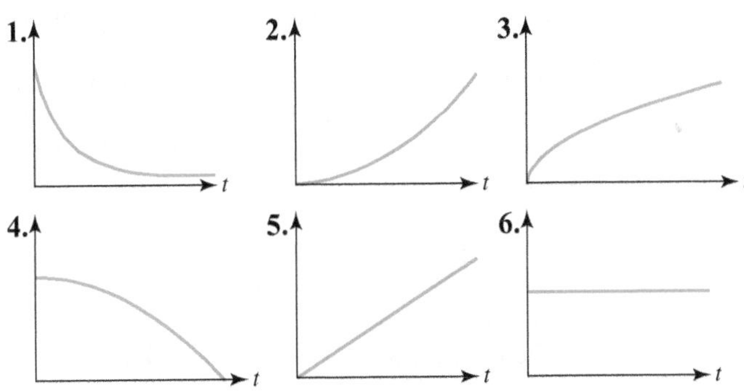

(a) A hot cup of coffee is left on a table to cool down to room temperature. The coffee cools quickly at first, but cools slower and slower as the temperature gets closer to room temperature. The dependent variable represents the temperature of the coffee (from the time the cup is placed on the table until the time it reaches room temperature). This is graph ______.

(b) The number of internet users has been increasing over the years, but at a slower and slower rate as the years go by. The dependent variable represents the number of internet users. This is graph ______.

(c) A car travels a distance of 100 miles with cruise control keeping the speed constant. The dependent variable represents the speed of the car. This is graph ______.

(d) A car travels a distance of 100 miles with cruise control keeping the speed constant. The dependent variable represents the distance the car travels. This is graph ______.

(e) A ball is dropped from the top of a building and falls faster and faster until it hits the ground. The dependent variable represents the distance the ball falls until it hits the ground. This is graph ______.

(f) The same ball is dropped from the same building, but now the dependent variable represents the height of the ball until it reaches the ground. This is graph ______.

2. The total sales of plasma TV's increased faster and faster between the years 2000 and 2005, and slower and slower between the years 2005 and 2010 as LCD TVs became more popular. Draw a graph shape that represents the total sales of plasma TV's between the years 2000 and 2010. What can you say about the concavity of your graph on either side of 2005?

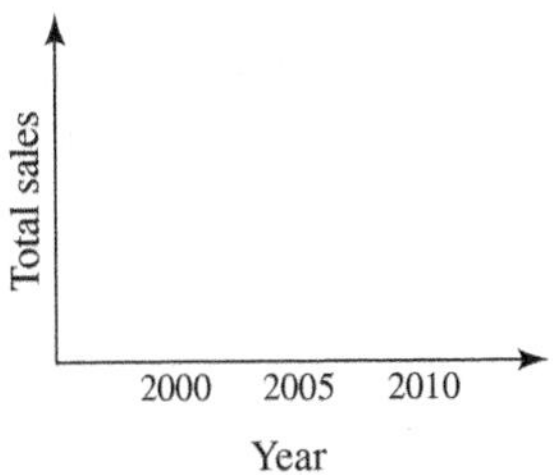

3. Use information from the following tables to determine whether the rates of change are increasing, decreasing, or staying constant. (Note that you are not being asked about the magnitudes of these rates, nor whether these rates themselves are positive or negative. The first three tables have positive rates of change because the outputs are increasing. The last three tables represent negative rates of change because the outputs are decreasing.)

(a)

x	y
0	25
1	37
2	50
3	65
4	85

(b)

t	$P(t)$
0	5
2	15
4	25
5	30
8	45

(c)

x	$F(x)$
5	65
10	75
17	85
25	95
35	105

(d)

r	$T(r)$
3	100
8	90
10	86
20	66
30	46

(e)

p	$C(p)$
2	50
4	44
6	39
8	35
10	33

(f)

s	$V(s)$
0	800
4	700
6	630
12	390
16	190

4. (a) Which of the tables on the previous page has no corresponding graph shape represented at the top of the previous page?

   (b) Which of the graph shapes does not correspond to the type of information represented by any of the tables?

5. Given the following functions, use tables or graphs to determine whether the rates of change are increasing, decreasing, or staying constant as $x \to +\infty$.

   (a) $f(x) = \dfrac{2 - 9x}{10}$

   (b) $g(x) = \sqrt{3x + 25}$

   (c) $h(x) = \dfrac{x^5 + 5}{x^3 + 1}$

Solutions to Exercises

1. (a) The coffee is cooling down, so this graph must be decreasing. The rate of cooling is getting less negative, hence increasing, so this graph must be concave up. This is graph **1**.

   (b) The number of internet users has been rising, so this graph must be increasing. The rate of increase has been slowing up, so this graph must be concave down. This is graph **3**.

   (c) The car is on cruise control and the dependent variable measures speed. Because the speed stays constant, this graph stays horizontal. This is graph **6**.

   (d) The car is still on cruise control so the speed is still constant, but now the dependent variable represents distance traveled. Because the distance is growing the graph is increasing, but because the speed is constant this graph will be linear. This is graph **5**.

   (e) As the ball drops the distance it falls will be getting larger, so this graph must be increasing. Due to gravity the distance the ball falls increases faster and faster, so the graph must be concave up. This is graph **2**.

   (f) The height gets less as the ball falls, so this graph is decreasing. As the ball falls faster and faster the slopes will be getting more negative, so this graph must be concave down. This is graph **4**.

2. The sales have been rising throughout the decade, so the graph is always increasing. For the first five years the rate of increase was increasing, so that portion of the graph is concave up. For the next five years the rate of increase was decreasing, so that portion of the graph is concave down. The point at 2005 where the concavity changes is called an **inflection point** of the graph.

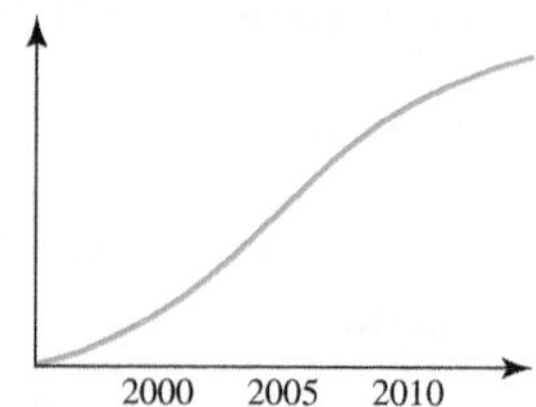

3. A rate of change column has been added to each table. If the numbers in this column are getting larger, either more positive or less negative, the rates of change are increasing. If the numbers are getting smaller, either less positive or more negative, the rates of change are decreasing. If the numbers are staying the same, the rates of change are constant.

(a) increasing ROC (more positive)

x	y	*ROC*
0	25	NA
1	37	12
2	50	13
3	65	15
4	85	20

(b) constant ROC (no change)

t	$P(t)$	*ROC*
0	5	NA
2	15	5
4	25	5
5	30	5
8	45	5

(c) decreasing ROC (less positive)

x	$F(x)$	*ROC*
5	65	NA
10	75	2
17	85	1.43
25	95	1.25
35	105	1

(d) constant ROC (no change)

r	$T(r)$	*ROC*
3	100	NA
8	90	−2
10	86	−2
20	66	−2
30	46	−2

(e) increasing ROC (less negative)

p	$C(p)$	*ROC*
2	50	NA
4	44	−3
6	39	−2.5
8	35	−2
10	33	−1

(f) decreasing ROC (more negative)

s	$V(s)$	*ROC*
0	800	NA
4	700	−25
6	630	−35
12	390	−40
16	190	−50

4. (a) Table d is linear and decreasing, and there is no corresponding graph.

(b) Graph 6 has constant outputs, and there is no corresponding table.

5. (a) $f(x) = \frac{2 - 9x}{10}$. This is a linear function, so the rate of change is constant. No other computations are necessary.

(b) $g(x) = \sqrt{3x + 25}$. If we create a small table of values we can see that the outputs are increasing at a slower and slower rate. The rate of change is getting less positive, hence decreasing. The graph is concave down.

x	$g(x)$	*ROC*
0	5	NA
10	7.42	0.242
20	9.22	0.180
30	10.72	0.150
40	12.04	0.132

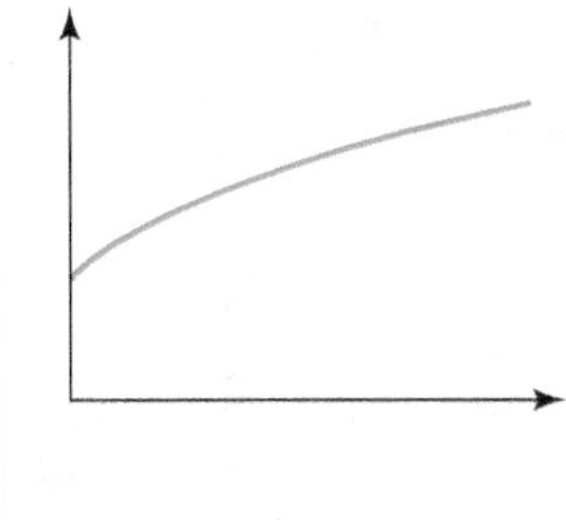

(c) $h(x) = \frac{x^5 + 5}{x^3 + 1}$. If we create a small table of values we can see that the outputs are increasing at a faster and faster rate. The rate of change is getting more positive, hence increasing. The graph is concave up.

x	$h(x)$	*ROC*
0	5	NA
10	99.91	9.491
20	399.95	30.004
30	899.97	50.002
40	1600	70.007

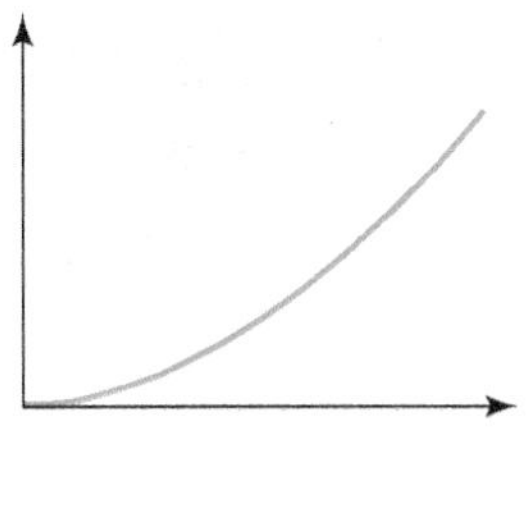

When Functions are Positive, Negative, or Zero

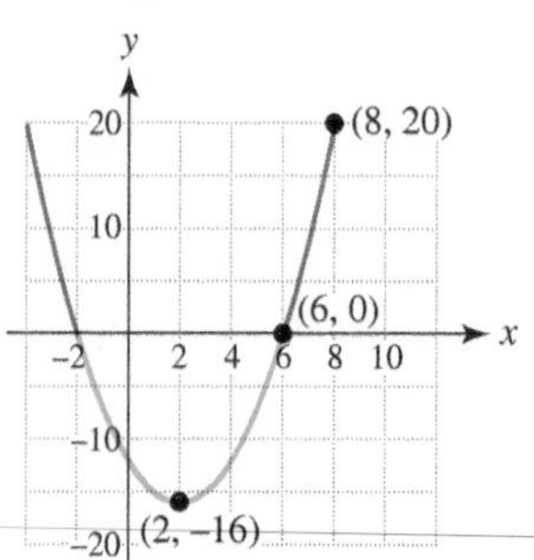

Recall that the graph of the function $y = f(x)$ represents a mathematical picture of the points (x, y) that would satisfy the formula. When we refer to the function f as having a certain value, we are referring to the value for the output variable, in this case y.

So, for example, if we are given the function $y = f(x) = x^2 - 4x - 12$, we would say that f is positive at $x = 8$ because $f(8) = 20$, f is negative at $x = 2$ because $f(2) = -16$, and f is zero at $x = 6$ because $f(6) = 0$.

On the graph, we can visually determine whether f is positive, negative, or zero by observing where the graph lies relative to the horizontal axis (generically called the x-axis). If the graph lies above the axis the output variable has a positive value, if the graph lies below the axis the output variable has a negative value, and if the graph lies on the axis itself the output variable has a value of zero. In this case the input value is a horizontal intercept (x-intercept) of the graph, and the specific input value at which this occurs is called a **zero** of the function.

EXERCISES

Under certain conditions, the graph shown represents the profit ***P*** *in dollars per week of this company as a function of the price, x dollars, at which it sells its product. The shape of the graph is determined by market principles. The less the company charges, the more units of product will be sold at a smaller margin of profit per unit. As the price rises, more profit is made for each unit sold, but fewer people will buy the product at the higher price. Therefore, there tends to be an optimum price, generally determined by appropriate market research, which represents a compromise between setting the price too low or too high. At this price, the profit will be maximized.*

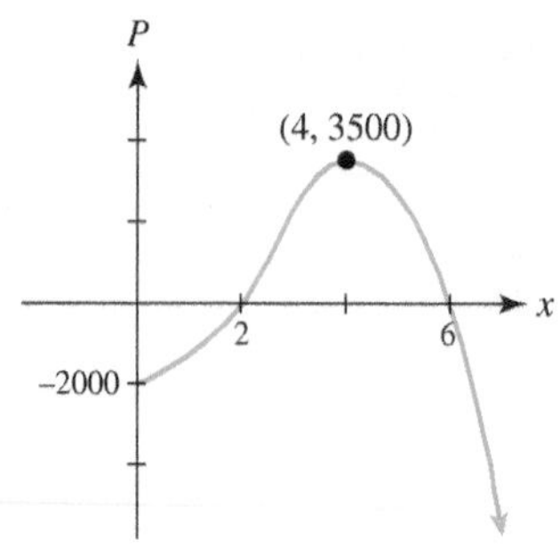

(a) At what price(s) for the product will the company break even? That is, when will profit equal 0?
(b) At what price for the product will the company maximize its profit?
(c) What will this profit be over a ten week period?
(d) What are the fixed costs per week for this company to operate?
(e) A negative profit is considered a loss. At what interval of values for x would the company suffer a loss?
(f) At what interval of values for x would the company make a profit?

Solutions to Exercises

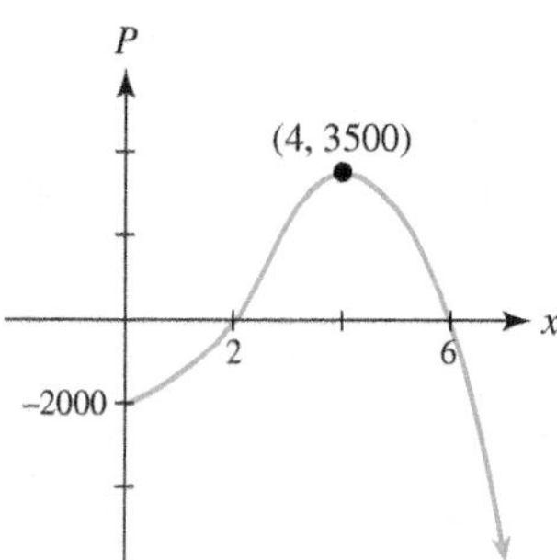

(a) The company will break even when the profit function equals 0. According to the graph this happens if the company charges either \$2 or \$6 per unit of product.
(b) The company will maximize its profit when the graph has an absolute maximum. In this case the maximum point will occur if the company charges \$4 per unit of product.
(c) Because the units for the profit graph are dollars per week, we can determine from the graph that at a price of \$4 per unit, the company will earn \$3500 per week. Therefore over a 10 week period, the company's profit would be $10 \times \$3500 = \$35{,}000$.
(d) The fixed costs on a profit graph are represented by the (negative) starting point of the graph. We can determine from the graph that the fixed costs per week are \$2000.
(e) The company will incur a loss whenever the profit curve has a negative value for the output. We can see from the graph above that this occurs when $0 \le x < 2$ and $x > 6$. In interval notation this would be represented by $[0, 2) \cup (6, +\infty)$.
(f) The company will make a profit whenever the profit curve has a positive value for the output. We can see from the graph that this occurs when $2 < x < 6$, which is the interval $(2, 6)$.

1 Summary

CONCEPT	EXPLANATION AND EXAMPLES
Section 1.1 Numbers, Data, and Problem Solving	
Sets of Numbers	*Natural numbers:* $N = \{1, 2, 3, 4, \dots\}$ *Integers:* $I = \{\dots, -3, -2, -1, 0, 1, 2, 3, \dots\}$ *Rational numbers:* $\frac{p}{q}$, where p and q are integers with $q \neq 0$; includes fractions, repeating and terminating decimals *Irrational numbers:* Includes nonrepeating, nonterminating decimals *Real numbers:* Any number that can be expressed in decimal form; includes rational and irrational numbers
Order of Operations	Using the following order of operations, perform all calculations within parentheses, square roots, and absolute value bars and above and below fraction bars. Then use the same order of operations to perform any remaining calculations. **1.** Evaluate all exponents. Then do any negation *after* evaluating exponents. **2.** Do all multiplication and division from *left to right.* **3.** Do all addition and subtraction from *left to right.* **Example:** $5 + 3 \cdot 2^3 = 5 + 3 \cdot 8 = 5 + 24 = 29$
Scientific Notation	A real number r is written as $c \times 10^n$, where $1 \leq \lvert c \rvert < 10$. **Examples:** $1234 = 1.234 \times 10^3$ $0.054 = 5.4 \times 10^{-2}$
Section 1.2 Visualizing and Graphing Data	
Mean (Average) and Median	The mean represents the average of a set of numbers, and the median represents the middle of a sorted list. **Example:** 4, 6, 9, 13, 15; Mean $= \frac{4 + 6 + 9 + 13 + 15}{5} = 9.4$; Median $= 9$
Relation, Domain, and Range	A relation S is a set of ordered pairs. The domain D is the set of x-values, and the range R is the set of y-values. **Example:** $S = \{(-1, 2), (4, -5), (5, 9)\}$; $D = \{-1, 4, 5,\}, R = \{-5, 2, 9\}$
Cartesian (Rectangular) Coordinate System, or *xy*-Plane	The xy-plane has four quadrants and is used to graph ordered pairs. 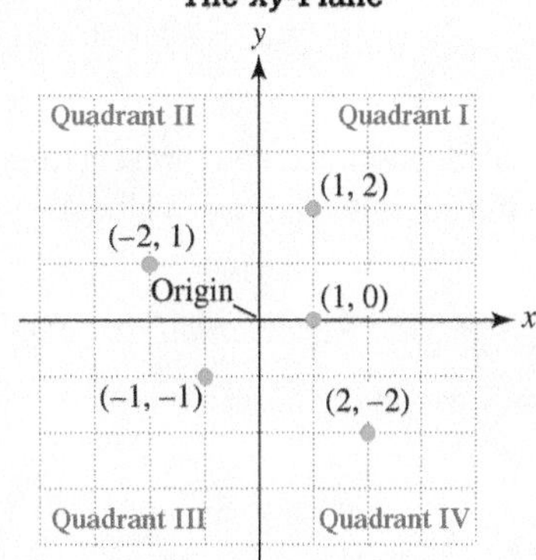

CONCEPT	EXPLANATION AND EXAMPLES
Section 1.2 Visualizing and Graphing Data (CONTINUED)	
Distance Formula	The distance d between the points (x_1, y_1) and (x_2, y_2) is $$d = \sqrt{(x_2 - x_1)^2 + (y_2 - y_1)^2}.$$ **Example:** The distance between $(-3, 5)$ and $(2, -7)$ is $$d = \sqrt{(2 - (-3))^2 + (-7 - 5)^2} = \sqrt{5^2 + (-12)^2} = 13.$$
Midpoint Formula	The midpoint M of the line segment with endpoints (x_1, y_1) and (x_2, y_2) is $$M = \left(\frac{x_1 + x_2}{2}, \frac{y_1 + y_2}{2}\right).$$ **Example:** The midpoint of the line segment connecting $(1, 2)$ and $(-3, 5)$ is $$M = \left(\frac{1 + (-3)}{2}, \frac{2 + 5}{2}\right) = \left(-1, \frac{7}{2}\right).$$
Standard Equation of a Circle	The circle with center (h, k) and radius r has the equation $$(x - h)^2 + (y - k)^2 = r^2.$$ **Example:** A circle with center $(-2, 5)$ and radius 6 has the equation $$(x + 2)^2 + (y - 5)^2 = 36.$$
Scatterplot and Line Graph	A scatterplot consists of a set of ordered pairs plotted in the xy-plane. When consecutive points are connected with line segments, a line graph results.
Section 1.3 Functions and Their Representations	
Function	A function computes exactly one output for each valid input. The set of valid inputs is called the domain D, and the set of outputs is called the range R. **Examples:** $f(x) = \sqrt{1 - x}$ $D = \{x \mid x \le 1\}, R = \{y \mid y \ge 0\}$ $g = \{(-1, 0.5), (0, 4), (2, 4), (6, \pi)\}$ $D = \{-1, 0, 2, 6\}, R = \{0.5, \pi, 4\}$
Function Notation	**Examples:** $f(x) = x^2 - 4$; $f(3) = 3^2 - 4 = 5$ and $f(a + 1) = (a + 1)^2 - 4 = a^2 + 2a - 3$
Representations of Functions	A function can be represented symbolically (formula), graphically (graph), numerically (table of values), and verbally (words). Other representations are possible. ***Symbolic Representation*** $f(x) = x^2 - 1$

CONCEPT	EXPLANATION AND EXAMPLES

Section 1.3 Functions and Their Representations (CONTINUED)

Representations of Functions

Numerical Representation

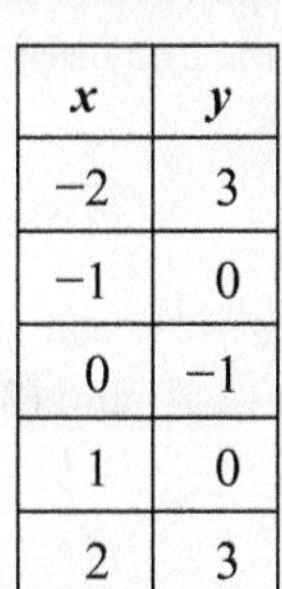

x	y
-2	3
-1	0
0	-1
1	0
2	3

Graphical Representation

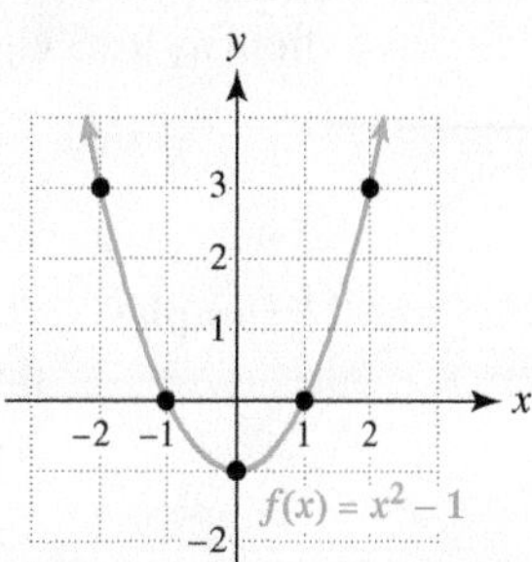

Verbal Representation f computes the square of the input x and then subtracts 1.

Vertical Line Test

If every vertical line intersects a graph at most once, then the graph represents a function.

Section 1.4 Types of Functions and Their Rates of Change

Slope

The slope m of the line passing through (x_1, y_1) and (x_2, y_2) is

$$m = \frac{\Delta y}{\Delta x} = \frac{y_2 - y_1}{x_2 - x_1}.$$

Example: The slope of the line passing through $(1, -1)$ and $(-2, 3)$ is

$$m = \frac{3 - (-1)}{-2 - 1} = -\frac{4}{3}.$$

Constant Function

Given by $f(x) = b$, where b is a constant; its graph is a horizontal line.

Linear Function

Given by $f(x) = mx + b$; its graph is a nonvertical line; the slope of its graph is equal to m, which is also equal to its constant rate of change.

Examples: The graph of $f(x) = -8x + 100$ has slope -8.
If $G(t) = -8t + 100$ calculates the number of gallons of water in a tank after t minutes, then water is *leaving* the tank at 8 gallons per minute.

Nonlinear Function

A nonlinear function *cannot* be written as $f(x) = mx + b$ and its graph is not a line.

Examples: $f(x) = x^2 - 4$; $g(x) = \sqrt[3]{x} - 2$; $h(t) = \frac{1}{t + 1}$

Interval Notation

A concise way to express intervals on the number line

Example: $x < 4$ is expressed as $(-\infty, 4)$.
$-3 \le x < 1$ is expressed as $[-3, 1)$.
$x \le 2$ or $x \ge 5$ is expressed as $(-\infty, 2] \cup [5, \infty)$.

Increasing/Decreasing

f increases on an *open* interval I if, whenever $x_1 < x_2$, $f(x_1) < f(x_2)$.
f decreases on an *open* interval I if, whenever $x_1 < x_2$, $f(x_1) > f(x_2)$.

Example: $f(x) = |x|$ increases on $(0, \infty)$ and decreases on $(-\infty, 0)$.

CONCEPT	EXPLANATION AND EXAMPLES
Section 1.4 Types of Functions and Their Rates of Change (CONTINUED)	
Average Rate of Change	If (x_1, y_1) and (x_2, y_2) are distinct points on the graph of f, then the average rate of change from x_1 to x_2 equals the slope of the line passing through these two points, given by $$\frac{y_2 - y_1}{x_2 - x_1}.$$ **Example:** $f(x) = x^2$; because $f(2) = 4$ and $f(3) = 9$, the graph of f passes through the points $(2, 4)$ and $(3, 9)$, and the average rate of change from 2 to 3 is given by $\frac{9-4}{3-2} = 5$.
Difference Quotient	The difference quotient of a function f is an expression of the form $$\frac{f(x+h) - f(x)}{h}, \quad \text{where } h \neq 0,$$ and is the average rate of change from x to $x + h$. **Example:** Let $f(x) = x^2$. The difference quotient of f is $$\frac{(x+h)^2 - x^2}{h} = \frac{x^2 + 2xh + h^2 - x^2}{h} = 2x + h.$$

1 Review Exercises

Exercises 1 and 2: Classify each number listed as one or more of the following: natural number, integer, rational number, or real number.

1. $-2, \frac{1}{2}, 0, 1.23, \sqrt{7}, \sqrt{16}$

2. $55, 1.5, \frac{104}{17}, 2^3, \sqrt{3}, -1000$

Exercises 3 and 4: Write each number in scientific notation.

3. 1,891,000 **4.** 0.0001001

Exercises 5 and 6: Write each number in standard form.

5. 1.52×10^4 **6.** -7.2×10^{-3}

7. Evaluate each expression with a calculator. Round answers to the nearest hundredth.

(a) $\sqrt[3]{1.2} + \pi^3$ **(b)** $\frac{3.2 + 5.7}{7.9 - 4.5}$

(c) $\sqrt{5^2 + 2.1}$ **(d)** $1.2(6.3)^2 + \frac{3.2}{\pi - 1}$

8. Evaluate each expression. Write your answer in scientific notation and in standard form.

(a) $(4 \times 10^3)(5 \times 10^{-5})$ **(b)** $\frac{3 \times 10^{-5}}{6 \times 10^{-2}}$

Exercises 9 and 10: Evaluate by hand.

9. $4 - 3^2 \cdot 5$ **10.** $3 \cdot 3^2 \div \frac{3 - 5}{6 + 2}$

Exercises 11 and 12: Sort the list of numbers from smallest to largest and display the result in a table.

(a) Determine the maximum and minimum values.
(b) Calculate the mean and median.

11. $-5, 8, 19, 24, -23$

12. $8.9, -1.2, -3.8, 0.8, 1.7, 1.7$

Exercises 13 and 14: Complete the following.

(a) Express the data as a relation S.
(b) Find the domain and range of S.

13.

x	-15	-10	0	5	20
y	-3	-1	1	3	5

14.

x	-0.6	-0.2	0.1	0.5	1.2
y	10	20	25	30	80

Exercises 15 and 16: Make a scatterplot of the relation. Determine if the relation is a function.

15. $\{(10, 13), (-12, 40), (-30, -23), (25, -22), (10, 20)\}$

16. $\{(1.5, 2.5), (0, 2.1), (-2.3, 3.1), (0.5, -0.8), (-1.1, 0)\}$

Exercises 17 and 18: Find the distance between the points.

17. $(-4, 5), (2, -3)$

18. $(1.2, -4), (0.2, 6)$

Exercises 19 and 20: Find the midpoint of the line segment with the given endpoints.

19. $(24, -16), (-20, 13)$

20. $\left(\frac{1}{2}, \frac{5}{4}\right)\left(\frac{1}{2}, -\frac{5}{2}\right)$

21. Determine if the triangle with vertices $(1, 2)$, $(-3, 5)$, and $(0, 9)$ is isosceles.

22. Find the standard equation of a circle with center $(-5, 3)$ and radius 9.

23. A diameter of a circle has endpoints $(-2, 4)$ and $(6, 6)$. Find the standard equation of the circle.

24. Use the graph to determine the domain and range of each function. Evaluate $f(-2)$.

(a) **(b)**

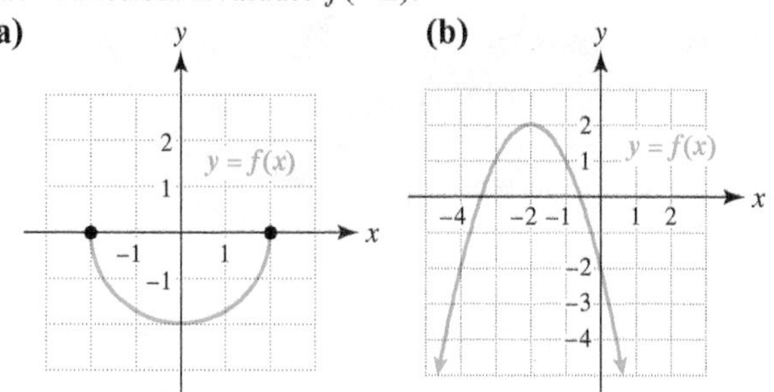

Exercises 25–32: Graph $y = f(x)$ by first plotting points to determine the shape of the graph.

25. $f(x) = -2$

26. $f(x) = 3x$

27. $f(x) = -x + 1$

28. $f(x) = 2x - 3$

29. $f(x) = 4 - 2x^2$

30. $f(x) = \frac{1}{2}x^2 - 1$

31. $f(x) = |x + 3|$

32. $f(x) = \sqrt{3 - x}$

Exercises 33 and 34: Use the verbal representation to express the function f symbolically, graphically, and numerically. Let $y = f(x)$ with $0 \leq x \leq 100$. For the numerical representation, use a table with $x = 0, 25, 50, 75, 100$.

33. To convert x pounds to y ounces, multiply x by 16.

34. To find the area y of a square, multiply the length x of a side by itself.

Exercises 35–40: Complete the following for the function f.

(a) Evaluate f(x) at the indicated values of x.

(b) Find the domain of f.

35. $f(x) = 5$ for $x = -3, 1.5$

36. $f(x) = 4 - 5x$ for $x = -5, 6$

37. $f(x) = x^2 - 3$ for $x = -10, a + 2$

38. $f(x) = x^3 - 3x$ for $x = -10, a + 1$

39. $f(x) = \frac{1}{x - 4}$ for $x = -3, a + 1$

40. $f(x) = \sqrt{x + 3}$ for $x = 1, a - 3$

41. Determine if y is a function of x in $x = y^2 + 5$.

42. Write $5 \leq x < 10$ in interval notation.

Exercises 43 and 44: The graph of a linear function f is shown.

(a) Identify the slope, y-intercept, and x-intercept.

(b) Write a formula for f.

(c) Find any zeros of f.

43. **44.**

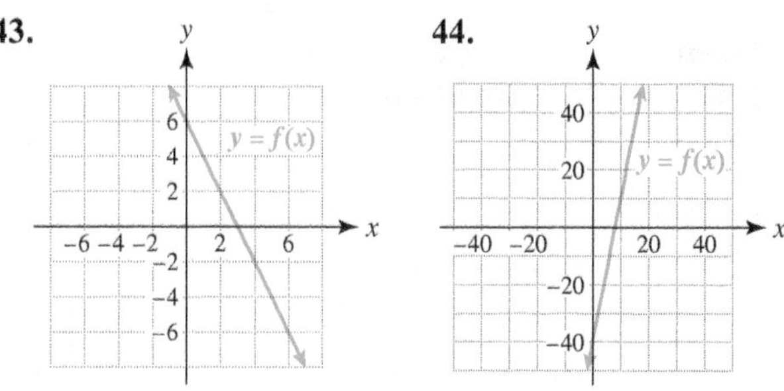

Exercises 45 and 46: Determine if the graph represents a function.

45. **46.**

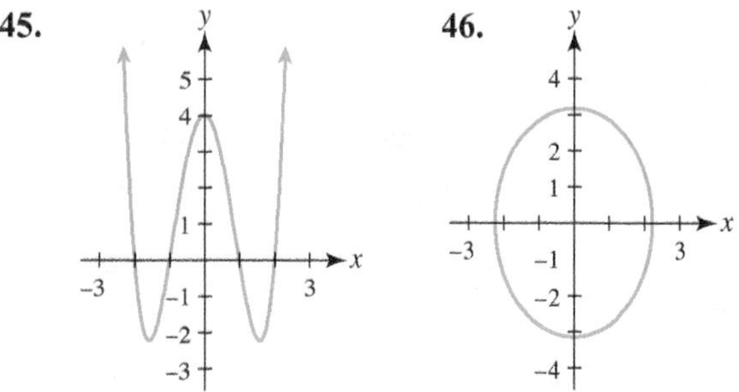

Exercises 47 and 48: Determine if S represents a function.

47. $S = \{(-3, 4), (-1, 2), (3, -5), (4, 2)\}$

48. $S = \{(-1, 3), (0, 2), (-1, 7), (3, -3)\}$

Exercises 49 and 50: State the slope of the graph of f.

49. $f(x) = 7$

50. $f(x) = \frac{1}{3}x - \frac{2}{3}$

Exercises 51–54: If possible, find the slope of the line passing through each pair of points.

51. $(-1, 7), (3, 4)$

52. $(1, -4), (2, 10)$

53. $(8, 4), (-2, 4)$

54. $\left(-\frac{1}{3}, \frac{2}{3}\right), \left(-\frac{1}{3}, -\frac{5}{6}\right)$

Exercises 55–58: Decide whether the function f is constant, linear, or nonlinear.

55. $f(x) = 8 - 3x$

56. $f(x) = 2x^2 - 3x - 8$

57. $f(x) = |x + 2|$

58. $f(x) = 6$

59. Sketch a graph for a 2-hour period showing the distance between two cars meeting on a straight highway, each traveling 60 miles per hour. Assume that the cars are initially 120 miles apart.

60. Determine where the graph of $f(x) = |x - 3|$ is increasing and where it is decreasing.

61. Determine if a line passes through every point in the table. If it does, give its slope.

x	−2	0	2	4
y	50	42	34	26

62. Find the average rate of change of $f(x) = x^2 - x + 1$ from $x_1 = 1$ to $x_2 = 3$.

Exercises 63 and 64: Find the difference quotient for $f(x)$.

63. $f(x) = 5x + 1$

64. $f(x) = 3x^2 - 2$

Applications

65. Speed of Light The average distance between the planet Mars and the sun is approximately 228 million kilometers. Estimate the time required for sunlight, traveling at 300,000 kilometers per second, to reach Mars. (***Source:*** C. Ronan, *The Natural History of the Universe.*)

66. Geometry Suppose that 0.25 cubic inch of paint is applied to a circular piece of plastic with a diameter of 20 inches. Estimate the thickness of the paint. (*Hint:* Thickness equals volume divided by area.)

67. Enclosing a Pool A rectangular swimming pool that is 25 feet by 50 feet has a 6-foot-wide sidewalk around it.

(a) How much fencing would be needed to enclose the sidewalk?

(b) Find the area of the sidewalk.

68. Distance A driver's distance D in miles from a rest stop after t hours is given by $D(t) = 280 - 70t$.

(a) How far is the driver from the rest stop after 2 hours?

(b) Find the slope of the graph of D. Interpret this slope as a rate of change.

69. Survival Rates The survival rates for song sparrows are shown in the table. The values listed are the numbers of song sparrows that attain a given age from 100 eggs. For example, 6 sparrows reach an age of 2 years from 100 eggs laid in the wild. (***Source:*** S. Kress, *Bird Life.*)

Age	0	1	2	3	4
Number	100	10	6	3	2

(a) Make a line graph of the data. Interpret the data.

(b) Does this line graph represent a function?

(c) Calculate and interpret the average rate of change for each 1-year period.

70. Cost of Tuition The graph shows the cost of taking x credits at a university.

(a) Why is it reasonable for the graph to pass through the origin?

(b) Find the slope of the graph.

(c) Interpret the slope as a rate of change.

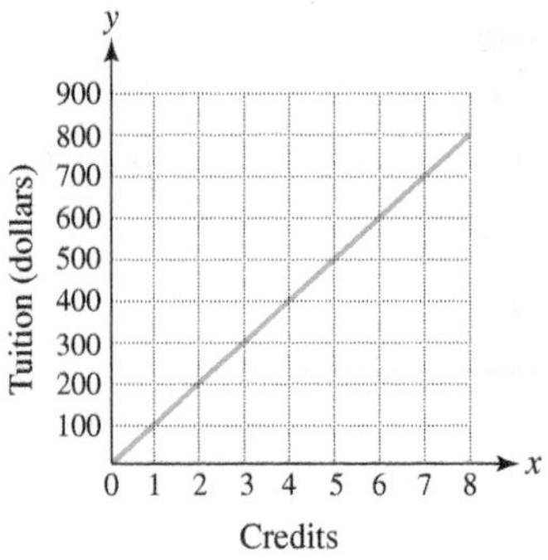

71. Average Rate of Change Let $f(x) = 0.5x^2 + 50$ represent the outside temperature in degrees Fahrenheit at x P.M., where $1 \le x \le 5$.

(a) Graph f. Is f linear or nonlinear?

(b) Calculate the average rate of change of f from 1 P.M. to 4 P.M.

(c) Interpret this average rate of change.

72. Distance At noon car A is traveling north at 30 miles per hour and is located 20 miles north of car B. Car B is traveling west at 50 miles per hour. Approximate the distance between the cars at 12:45 P.M. to the nearest mile.

Extended and Discovery Exercises

Because a parabolic curve becomes sharp gradually, as shown in the first figure on the next page, curves designed by engineers for highways and railroads frequently have parabolic, rather than circular, shapes. If railroad tracks changed abruptly from straight to circular, the momentum of the locomotive could cause a derailment. The second figure below illustrates straight tracks connecting to a circular curve. (***Source:*** F. Mannering and W. Kilareski, *Principles of Highway Engineering and Traffic Analysis.*)

In order to design a curve and estimate its cost, engineers determine the distance around the curve before it is built. In the third figure on the next page the distance along a parabolic curve from A to C is approximated by two line segments AB and BC. The distance formula can be used to calculate the length of each segment. The sum of these two lengths gives a crude estimate of the length of the curve.

A better estimate can be made using four line segments, as shown in the fourth figure. As the number of segments increases, so does the accuracy of the approximation.

A Parabolic Curve

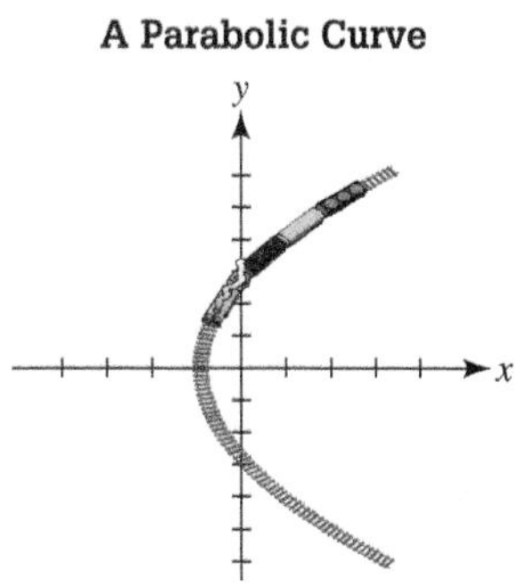

A Circular Curve

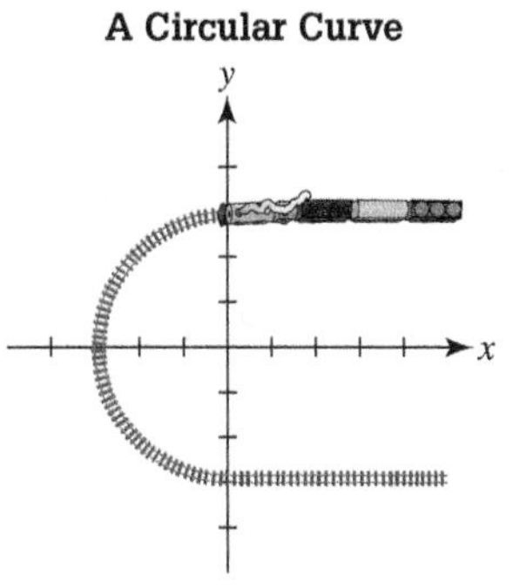

An Estimate of Curve Length

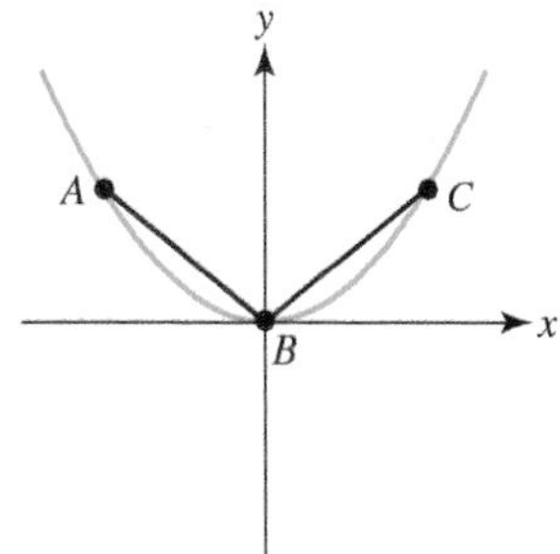

A Better Estimate

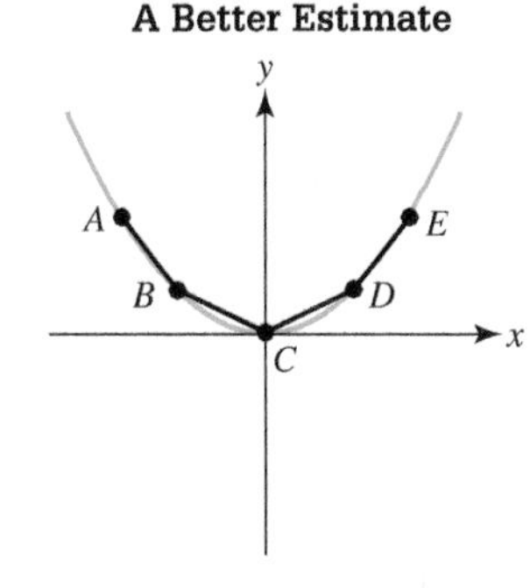

1. **Curve Length** Suppose that a curve designed for railroad tracks is represented by the equation $y = 0.2x^2$, where the units are in kilometers. The points $(-3, 1.8)$, $(-1.5, 0.45)$, $(0, 0)$, $(1.5, 0.45)$, and $(3, 1.8)$ lie on the graph of $y = 0.2x^2$. Approximate the length of the curve from $x = -3$ to $x = 3$ by using line segments connecting these points.

Exercises 2–5: **Curve Length** *Use three line segments connecting the four points to estimate the length of the curve on the graph of f from x = −1 to x = 2. Graph f and a line graph of the four points in the indicated viewing rectangle.*

2. $f(x) = x^2$; $(-1, 1)$, $(0, 0)$, $(1, 1)$, $(2, 4)$; $[-4.5, 4.5, 1]$ by $[-1, 5, 1]$

3. $f(x) = \sqrt[3]{x}$; $(-1, -1)$, $(0, 0)$, $(1, 1)$, $(2, \sqrt[3]{2})$; $[-3, 3, 1]$ by $[-2, 2, 1]$

4. $f(x) = 0.5x^3 + 2$; $(-1, 1.5)$, $(0, 2)$, $(1, 2.5)$, $(2, 6)$; $[-4.5, 4.5, 1]$ by $[0, 6, 1]$

5. $f(x) = 2 - 0.5x^2$; $(-1, 1.5)$, $(0, 2)$, $(1, 1.5)$, $(2, 0)$; $[-3, 3, 1]$ by $[-1, 3, 1]$

6. The distance along the curve of $y = x^2$ from $(0, 0)$ to $(3, 9)$ is about 9.747. Use this fact to estimate the distance along the curve of $y = 9 - x^2$ from $(0, 9)$ to $(3, 0)$.

7. Estimate the distance along the curve of $y = \sqrt{x}$ from $(1, 1)$ to $(4, 2)$. (The actual value is approximately 3.168.)

8. **Endangered Species** The Florida scrub-jay is an endangered species that prefers to live in open landscape with short vegetation. NASA has attempted to create a habitat for these birds near Kennedy Space Center. The following table lists their population for selected years, where $x = 0$ corresponds to 1980, $x = 1$ to 1981, $x = 2$ to 1982, and so on.

x (1980 ↔ 0)	0	5	9
y (population)	3697	2512	2176

x (1980 ↔ 0)	11	15	19
y (population)	2100	1689	1127

Source: *Mathematics Explorations II*, NASA–AMATYC–NSF.

(a) Make a scatterplot of the data.

(b) Find a linear function f that models the data.

(c) Graph the data and f in the same viewing rectangle.

(d) Estimate the scrub-jay population in 1987 and in 2003.

9. **Rise in Sea Level** If the global climate were to warm significantly, the Arctic ice cap would melt. It is estimated that this ice cap contains the equivalent of 680,000 cubic miles of water. Over 200 million people currently live on soil that is less than 3 feet above sea level. In the United

States, several large cities have low average elevations, such as Boston (14 feet), New Orleans (4 feet), and San Diego (13 feet). (***Sources:*** Department of the Interior, Geological Survey.)

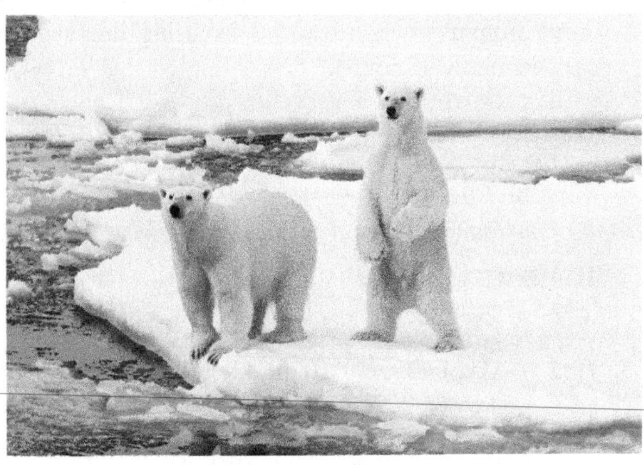

(a) Devise a plan to determine how much sea level would rise if the Arctic cap melted. (*Hint:* The radius of Earth is 3960 miles and 71% of its surface is covered by oceans.)

(b) Use your plan to estimate this rise in sea level.

(c) Discuss the implications of your calculation.

(d) Estimate how much sea level would rise if the 6,300,000 cubic miles of water in the Antarctic ice cap melted.

10. Prove that $\sqrt{2}$ is irrational by assuming that $\sqrt{2}$ is rational and arriving at a contradiction.

2 Linear Functions and Equations

For over two centuries people have been transferring carbon from below the surface of the earth into the atmosphere. In 2006, the burning of coal, oil, and natural gas released 7 billion tons of carbon into the atmosphere. If the rate of growth continues, the amount could double to 14 billion tons by 2056. This increase is modeled by a linear function C in the figure on the left below. The green horizontal line $y = 7$ represents the 2006 level of emissions, and the red horizontal line $y = 14$ represents a doubling of carbon emissions. Their points of intersection with the graph of C represent when these levels of emission could

> The human mind has never invented a labor-saving device greater than algebra.
>
> —J.W. Gibbs

No Restrictions on Carbon Emissions

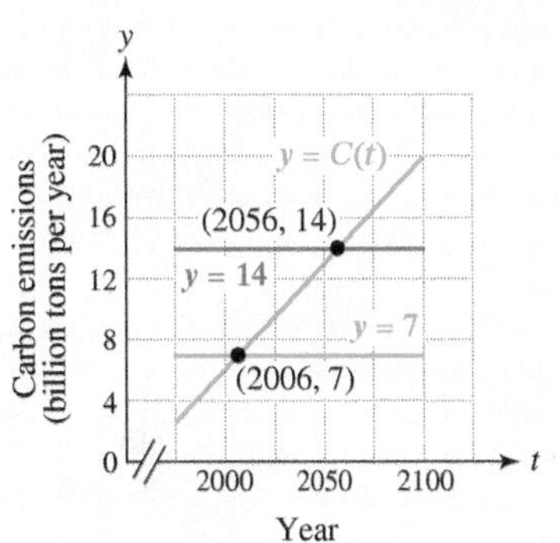

Restrictions on Carbon Emissions

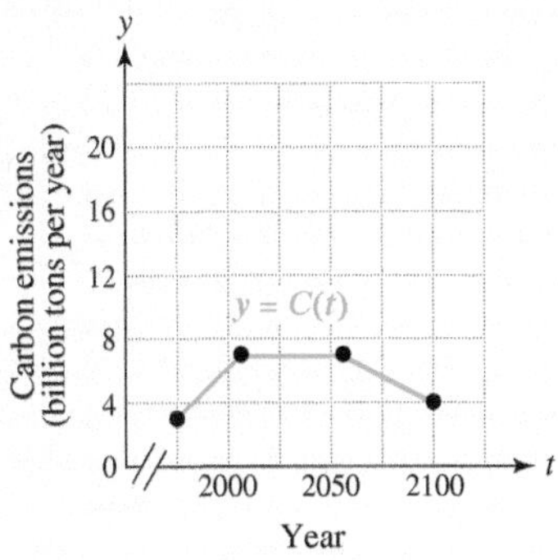

occur. The figure on the right illustrates what might happen if levels of carbon emission could be held at 7 billion tons per year for the next 50 years. In this case, emissions are expected to decline after 50 years. This graph, made up of line segments, is called a *piecewise-linear function.*

Whatever your point of view, mathematics plays an essential role in understanding the future of carbon emissions; without mathematical support, predictions lack credibility. To model carbon emissions, we need constant, linear, and piecewise-defined functions. All of these important concepts are discussed in this chapter.

Source: R. Socolow and S. Pacala, "A Plan to Keep Carbon in Check," *Scientific American*, September, 2006.

2.1 Equations of Lines

- **Write the point-slope and slope-intercept forms**
- **Find the intercepts of a line**
- **Write equations for horizontal, vertical, parallel, and perpendicular lines**
- **Model data with lines and linear functions (optional)**
- **Use linear regression to model data (optional)**

Introduction

The graph of a linear function is a line. One way to determine a linear function is to find the equation of this line. Once this equation is known, we can easily write the symbolic representation for the linear function.

For example, Apple Corporation sold approximately 55 million iPods in fiscal 2008, making the iPod the fastest-selling music player in history. However, sales then decreased to about 43 million in 2011. (***Source:*** Apple Corporation.) This decline can be modeled by a line. The equation of this line determines a linear function that we can use to estimate iPod sales for other years. See Example 4. This section discusses how to use data points to find equations of lines and linear functions.

Forms for Equations of Lines

Point-Slope Form Suppose that a nonvertical line with slope m passes through the point (x_1, y_1). If (x, y) is any point on this *nonvertical* line with $x \neq x_1$, then the change in y is $\Delta y = y - y_1$, the change in x is $\Delta x = x - x_1$, and the slope is $m = \frac{\Delta y}{\Delta x} = \frac{y - y_1}{x - x_1}$, as illustrated in Figure 2.1.

Two Points Determine a Line

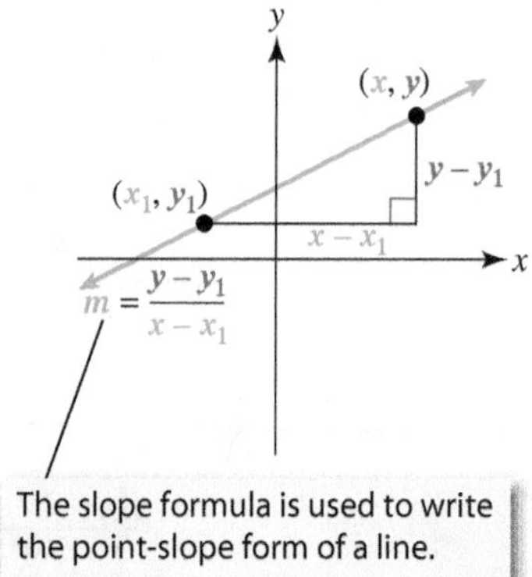

Figure 2.1

With this slope formula, the equation of the line can be found.

$$m = \frac{y - y_1}{x - x_1} \qquad \text{Slope formula}$$

$$y - y_1 = m(x - x_1) \qquad \text{Cross multiply.}$$

$$y = m(x - x_1) + y_1 \qquad \text{Add } y_1 \text{ to each side.}$$

The equation $y - y_1 = m(x - x_1)$ is traditionally called the *point-slope form* of the equation of a line. Since we think of y as being a function of x, written $y = f(x)$, the equivalent form $y = m(x - x_1) + y_1$ will also be referred to as the point-slope form. The point-slope form is not unique, as any point on the line can be used for (x_1, y_1). However, these point-slope forms are *equivalent*, meaning their graphs are identical.

POINT-SLOPE FORM

The line with slope m passing through the point (x_1, y_1) has an equation

$$y = m(x - x_1) + y_1, \quad \text{or} \quad y - y_1 = m(x - x_1),$$

the **point-slope form** of the equation of a line.

In the next example we find the equation of a line given two points.

EXAMPLE 1 **Determining a point-slope form**

Find an equation of the line passing through the points $(-2, -3)$ and $(1, 3)$. Plot the points and graph the line by hand.

SOLUTION Begin by finding the slope of the line.

$$m = \frac{3 - (-3)}{1 - (-2)} = \frac{6}{3} = 2$$

Substituting $(x_1, y_1) = (1, 3)$ and $m = 2$ into the point-slope form results in

First point-slope form $\quad y = 2(x - 1) + 3. \qquad y = m(x - x_1) + y_1$

If we use the point $(-2, -3)$, the point-slope form is

Second point-slope form $\quad y = 2(x + 2) - 3. \qquad \text{Note that } (x - (-2)) = (x + 2).$

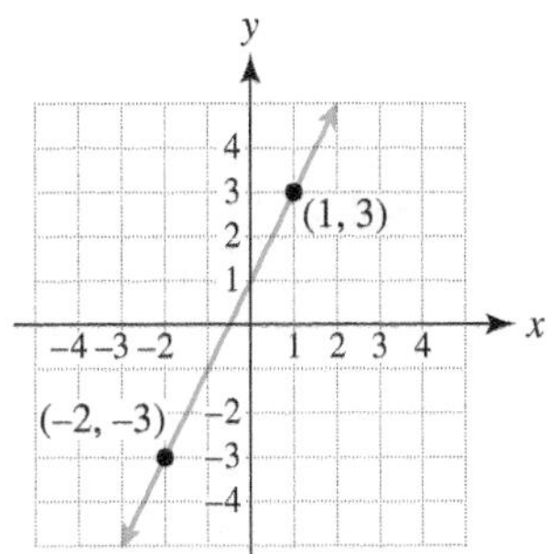

Figure 2.2

This line and the two points are shown in Figure 2.2.

Now Try Exercise 1

Slope-Intercept Form The two point-slope forms found in Example 1 are equivalent.

First point-slope form	**Second point-slope form**	
$y = 2(x - 1) + 3$	$y = 2(x + 2) - 3$	Point-slope form
$y = 2x - 2 + 3$	$y = 2x + 4 - 3$	Distributive property
$y = 2x + 1$	$y = 2x + 1$	Simplify.

Slope-Intercept Form
$y = mx + b$

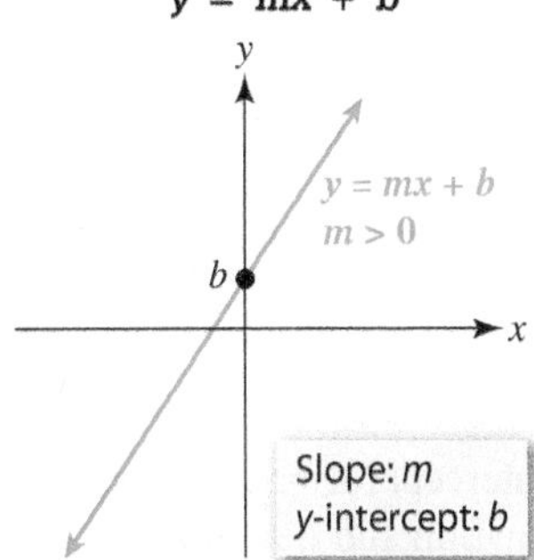

Figure 2.3

Both point-slope forms simplify to the same equation.

The form $y = mx + b$ is called the *slope-intercept form*. Unlike the point-slope form, the slope-intercept form is *unique*. The real number m represents the slope and the real number b represents the y-intercept, as illustrated in Figure 2.3.

SLOPE-INTERCEPT FORM

The line with slope m and y-intercept b is given by

$$y = mx + b,$$

the **slope-intercept form** of the equation of a line.

EXAMPLE 2 Finding equations of lines

Find the point-slope form for the line that satisfies the conditions. Then convert this equation into slope-intercept form and write the formula for a function f whose graph is the line.
(a) Slope $-\frac{1}{2}$, passing through the point $(-3, -7)$
(b) x-intercept -4, y-intercept 2

SOLUTION
(a) Let $m = -\frac{1}{2}$ and $(x_1, y_1) = (-3, -7)$ in the point-slope form.

$$y = m(x - x_1) + y_1 \qquad \text{Point-slope form}$$

$$y = -\frac{1}{2}(x + 3) - 7 \qquad \text{Substitute.}$$

The slope-intercept form can be found by simplifying.

$$y = -\frac{1}{2}(x + 3) - 7 \qquad \text{Point-slope form}$$

$$y = -\frac{1}{2}x - \frac{3}{2} - 7 \qquad \text{Distributive property}$$

$$y = -\frac{1}{2}x - \frac{17}{2} \qquad \text{Slope-intercept form}$$

Thus $f(x) = -\frac{1}{2}x - \frac{17}{2}$ is the formula for the function whose graph is this line.

(b) The line passes through the points $(-4, 0)$ and $(0, 2)$. Its slope is

$$m = \frac{2 - 0}{0 - (-4)} = \frac{1}{2}.$$

Thus a point-slope form for the line is $y = \frac{1}{2}(x + 4) + 0$, where the point $(-4, 0)$ is used for (x_1, y_1). The slope-intercept form is $y = \frac{1}{2}x + 2$ and $f(x) = \frac{1}{2}x + 2$ is the formula for the function whose graph is this line.

Now Try Exercises 5 and 9

The next example demonstrates how to find the slope-intercept form of a line without first finding the point-slope form.

EXAMPLE 3 Finding slope-intercept form

Find the slope-intercept form of the line passing through the points $(-2, 1)$ and $(2, 3)$.

SOLUTION
Getting Started We need to determine m and b in the slope-intercept form, $y = mx + b$. First find the slope m. Then substitute *either* point into the equation and determine b. ▶

$$m = \frac{3 - 1}{2 - (-2)} = \frac{2}{4} = \frac{1}{2}$$

Thus $y = \frac{1}{2}x + b$. To find b, we substitute $(2, 3)$ in this equation.

$$3 = \frac{1}{2}(2) + b \quad \text{Let } x = 2 \text{ and } y = 3.$$
$$3 = 1 + b \quad \text{Multiply.}$$
$$2 = b \quad \text{Determine } b.$$

Thus $y = \frac{1}{2}x + 2$.

Now Try Exercise 21

An Application In the next example we model the data about iPods discussed in the introduction to this section.

EXAMPLE 4 **Estimating iPod sales**

Apple Corporation sold approximately 55 million iPods in fiscal 2008 and 43 million iPods in fiscal 2011.

(a) Find the point-slope form of the line passing through (2008, 55) and (2011, 43). Interpret the slope of the line as a rate of change.

(b) Sketch a graph of the data and the line connecting these points.

(c) Estimate sales in 2010 and compare the estimate to the true value of 50 million.

(d) Estimate sales in 2023. Discuss the accuracy of your answers.

SOLUTION

Getting Started First find the slope m of the line connecting the data points, and then substitute this value for m and either of the two data points in the point-slope form. We can use this equation to estimate sales by substituting the required year for x in the equation. ▶

(a) The slope of the line passing through (2008, 55) and (2011, 43) is

$$m = \frac{43 - 55}{2011 - 2008} = -4.$$

Thus sales of iPods decreased, on average, by 4 million iPods per year from 2008 to 2011. If we substitute -4 for m and (2008, 55) for (x_1, y_1), the point-slope form is

$$y = -4(x - 2008) + 55.$$

(b) The requested line passing through the data points is shown in Figure 2.4.

(c) If $x = 2010$, then $y = -4(2010 - 2008) + 55 = 47$ million. This estimated value is 3 million lower than the true value of 50 million.

(d) We can use the equation to estimate 2023 sales as follows.

$$y = -4(2023 - 2008) + 55 = -5 \text{ million} \quad \text{Let } x = 2023.$$

The 2023 value is clearly incorrect because sales cannot be negative.

Now Try Exercise 81

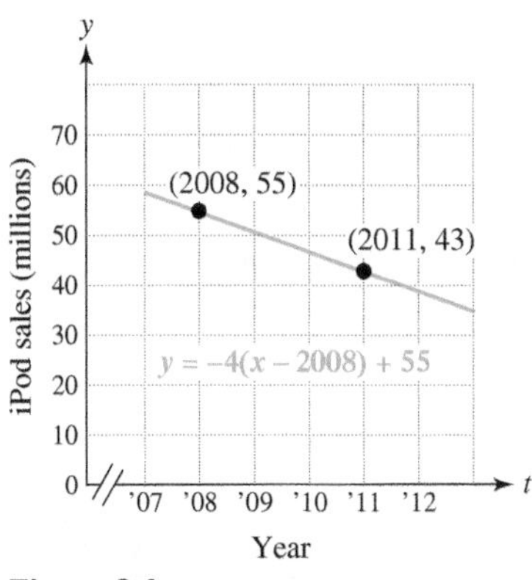

Figure 2.4

Finding Intercepts

The point-slope form and the slope-intercept form are not the only forms for the equation of a line. An equation of a line is in **standard form** when it is written as

$$ax + by = c,$$

where a, b, and c are constants and a and b are not *both* zero. By using standard form, we can write the equation of any line, including vertical lines (which are discussed later in this section). Examples of equations of lines in standard form include the following.

Equations in Standard Form: $ax + by = c$

$$2x - 3y = -6, \quad y = \frac{1}{4}, \quad x = -3, \quad \text{and} \quad -3x + y = \frac{1}{2}$$

$a = 0$ | $b = 0$

The following box gives an example of how to find the intercepts for a line given in standard form.

See the Concept : Finding Intercepts for $3x + 4y = 12$

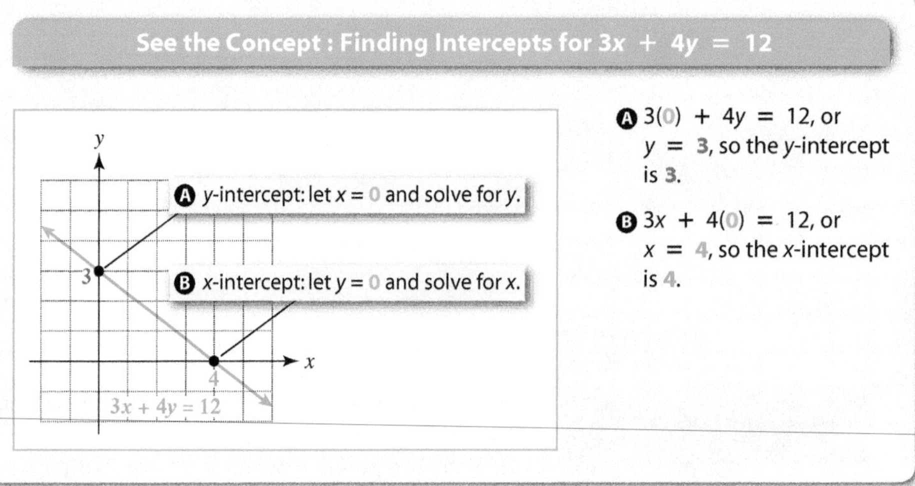

A $3(0) + 4y = 12$, or $y = 3$, so the y-intercept is 3.

B $3x + 4(0) = 12$, or $x = 4$, so the x-intercept is 4.

NOTE To solve $ax = b$, divide each side by a to obtain $x = \frac{b}{a}$. Thus $3x = 12$ implies that $x = \frac{12}{3} = 4$. Linear equations are solved in general in the next section.

FINDING INTERCEPTS

To find any x-intercepts, let $y = 0$ in the equation and solve for x.
To find any y-intercepts, let $x = 0$ in the equation and solve for y.

EXAMPLE 5 **Finding intercepts**

Locate the x- and y-intercepts for the line whose equation is $4x + 3y = 6$. Use the intercepts to graph the equation.

SOLUTION To locate the x-intercept, let $y = 0$ in the equation.

$$4x + 3(0) = 6 \quad \text{Let } y = 0.$$
$$x = 1.5 \quad \text{Divide each side by 4.}$$

The x-intercept is 1.5. To find the y-intercept, substitute $x = 0$ into the equation.

$$4(0) + 3y = 6 \quad \text{Let } x = 0.$$
$$y = 2 \quad \text{Divide each side by 3.}$$

The y-intercept is 2. Therefore the line passes through the points $(1.5, 0)$ and $(0, 2)$, as shown in Figure 2.5.

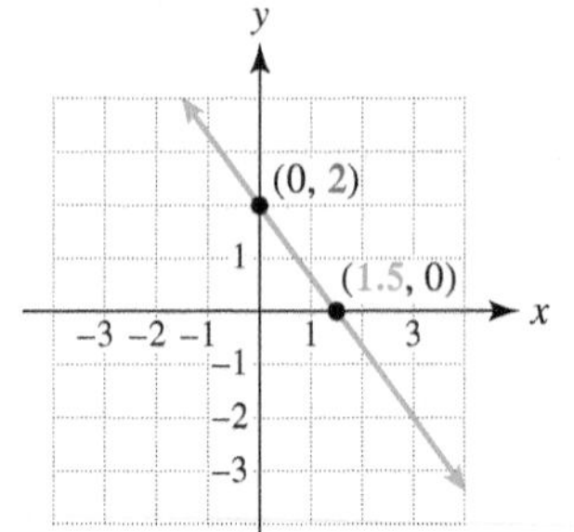

Figure 2.5

Now Try Exercise 57

Horizontal, Vertical, Parallel, and Perpendicular Lines

Horizontal and Vertical Lines The graph of a constant function f, defined by the formula $f(x) = b$, is a *horizontal line* having slope 0 and y-intercept b.

A *vertical line* cannot be represented by a function because distinct points on a vertical line have the same x-coordinate. In fact, this is the distinguishing feature of points on a vertical line—they all have the same x-coordinate. See Figures 2.6 and 2.7.

CLASS DISCUSSION

Why do you think that a vertical line sometimes is said to have “infinite slope?” What are some problems with taking this phrase too literally?

Equations of Vertical Lines

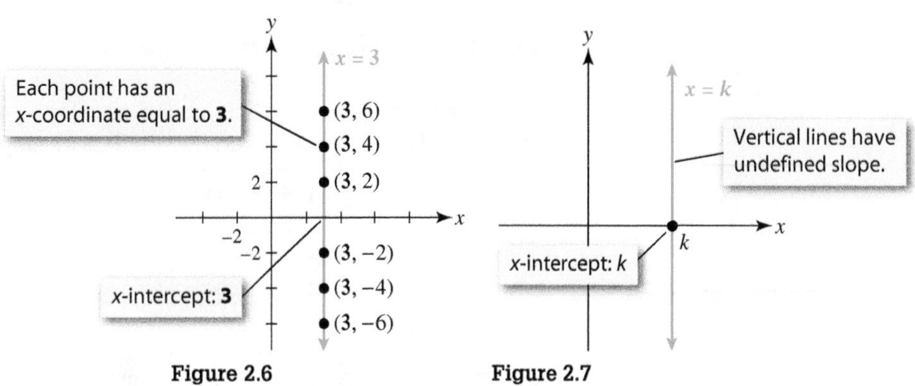

Figure 2.6 **Figure 2.7**

EQUATIONS OF HORIZONTAL AND VERTICAL LINES

An equation of the horizontal line with y-intercept b is $y = b$. An equation of the vertical line with x-intercept k is $x = k$.

EXAMPLE 6 **Finding equations of horizontal and vertical lines**

Find equations of vertical and horizontal lines passing through the point (8, 5). If possible, for each line write a formula for a linear function whose graph is the line.

SOLUTION The x-coordinate of the point (8, 5) is 8. The vertical line $x = 8$ passes through every point in the xy-plane with an x-coordinate of 8, including the point (8, 5). Similarly, the horizontal line $y = 5$ passes through every point with a y-coordinate of 5, including (8, 5). See Figure 2.8, where each line is shown.

Vertical and Horizontal Lines

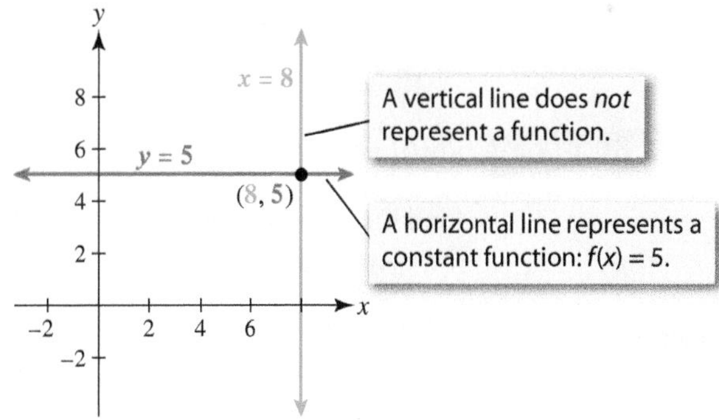

Figure 2.8

The horizontal line $y = 5$ represents the constant function $f(x) = 5$. The vertical line $x = 8$ does *not* represent a function because it does *not* pass the vertical line test.

Now Try Exercises 49 and 51

Parallel Lines Two nonvertical parallel lines have equal slopes.

PARALLEL LINES

Two lines with slopes m_1 and m_2, neither of which is vertical, are parallel if and only if their slopes are equal; that is, $m_1 = m_2$.

NOTE The phrase "if and only if" is used when two statements are mathematically equivalent. If two nonvertical lines are parallel, then $m_1 = m_2$. Conversely, if two nonvertical lines have equal slopes, then they are parallel. Either condition implies the other.

EXAMPLE 7 Finding parallel lines

Find the slope-intercept form of a line parallel to $y = -2x + 5$, passing through $(4, 3)$.

SOLUTION The line $y = -2x + 5$ has slope -2, so any parallel line also has slope $m = -2$. The line passing through $(4, 3)$ with slope -2 is determined as follows.

$$y = -2(x - 4) + 3 \quad \text{Point-slope form}$$
$$y = -2x + 8 + 3 \quad \text{Distributive property}$$
$$y = -2x + 11 \quad \text{Slope-intercept form}$$

Now Try Exercise 35

Perpendicular Lines Two lines are perpendicular if the product of their slopes is equal to -1.

PERPENDICULAR LINES

Two lines with nonzero slopes m_1 and m_2 are perpendicular if and only if their slopes have product -1; that is, $m_1 m_2 = -1$.

For perpendicular lines, m_1 and m_2 are *negative reciprocals*. That is, $m_1 = -\frac{1}{m_2}$ and $m_2 = -\frac{1}{m_1}$. Table 2.1 shows some slopes of perpendicular lines.

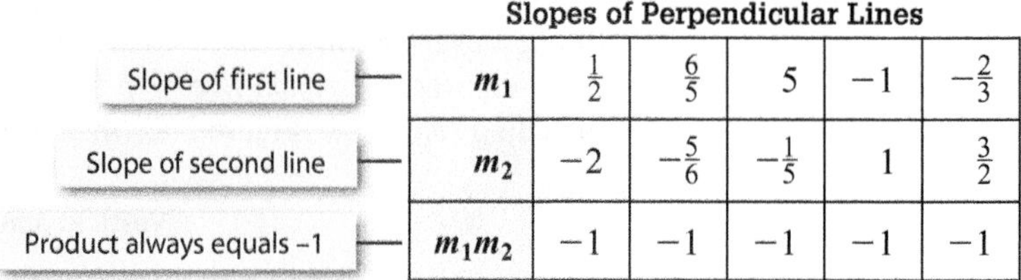

Slopes of Perpendicular Lines

Slope of first line	m_1	$\frac{1}{2}$	$\frac{6}{5}$	5	-1	$-\frac{2}{3}$
Slope of second line	m_2	-2	$-\frac{5}{6}$	$-\frac{1}{5}$	1	$\frac{3}{2}$
Product always equals −1	$m_1 m_2$	-1	-1	-1	-1	-1

Table 2.1

EXAMPLE 8 Finding perpendicular lines

Find the slope-intercept form of the line perpendicular to $y = -\frac{2}{3}x + 2$, passing through the point $(-2, 1)$. Graph the lines.

SOLUTION The line $y = -\frac{2}{3}x + 2$ has slope $-\frac{2}{3}$. The negative reciprocal of $m_1 = -\frac{2}{3}$ is $m_2 = \frac{3}{2}$. The slope-intercept form of a line having slope $\frac{3}{2}$ and passing through $(-2, 1)$ can be found as follows.

$$y = m(x - x_1) + y_1 \quad \text{Point-slope form}$$
$$y = \frac{3}{2}(x + 2) + 1 \quad \text{Let } m = \tfrac{3}{2},\ x_1 = -2, \text{ and } y_1 = 1.$$
$$y = \frac{3}{2}x + 3 + 1 \quad \text{Distributive property}$$
$$y = \frac{3}{2}x + 4 \quad \text{Slope-intercept form}$$

Perpendicular Lines

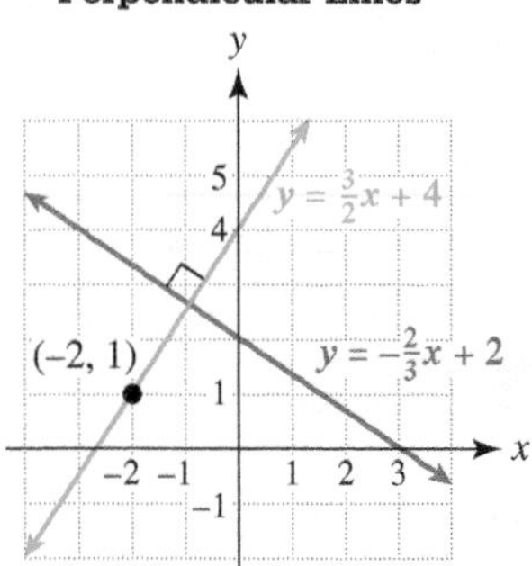

Figure 2.9

Figure 2.9 shows graphs of these perpendicular lines.

Now Try Exercise 41

Calculator Help
To set a square viewing rectangle, see Appendix A (page AP-5).

NOTE If a graphing calculator is used to graph these lines, a square viewing rectangle must be used for the lines to appear perpendicular.

EXAMPLE 9 **Determining a rectangle**

In Figure 2.10 a rectangle is outlined by four lines denoted y_1, y_2, y_3, and y_4. Find the equation of each line.

CLASS DISCUSSION

Check the results from Example 9 by graphing the four equations in the same viewing rectangle. How does your graph compare with Figure 2.10? Why is it important to use a square viewing rectangle?

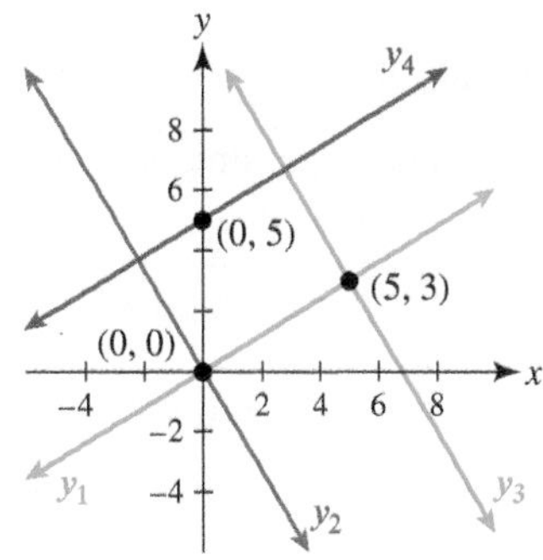

Figure 2.10

SOLUTION

Line y_1: This line passes through the points (0, 0) and (5, 3), so $m = \frac{3}{5}$ and the y-intercept is 0. Its equation is $y_1 = \frac{3}{5}x$.

Line y_2: This line passes through the point (0, 0) and is perpendicular to y_1, so its slope is given by $m = -\frac{5}{3}$ and the y-intercept is 0. Its equation is $y_2 = -\frac{5}{3}x$.

Line y_3: This line passes through the point (5, 3) and is parallel to y_2, so its slope is given by $m = -\frac{5}{3}$. In a point-slope form, its equation is $y_3 = -\frac{5}{3}(x - 5) + 3$, which is equivalent to $y_3 = -\frac{5}{3}x + \frac{34}{3}$.

Line y_4: This line passes through the point (0, 5), so its y-intercept is 5. It is parallel to y_1, so its slope is given by $m = \frac{3}{5}$. Its equation is $y_4 = \frac{3}{5}x + 5$.

Now Try Exercise 95

Interpolation and Extrapolation

In 2005 about **$350** million was spent on U.S. digital music single downloads. This amount reached **$1350** million in 2010. (***Source:*** RIAA.) These data can be modeled with a line, and the slope of this line is

$$m = \frac{1350 - 350}{2010 - 2005} = 200.$$

This value means that the increase in the amount spent on U.S. music downloads was, on average, $200 million per year from 2005 to 2010.

A point-slope form of the line passing through (2005, **350**) with slope 200 is

$$y = 200(x - 2005) + 350.$$

We can easily write a formula for a linear function

$$D(x) = 200(x - 2005) + 350,$$

whose graph is this line. See Figure 2.11.

U.S. Digital Single Download Sales

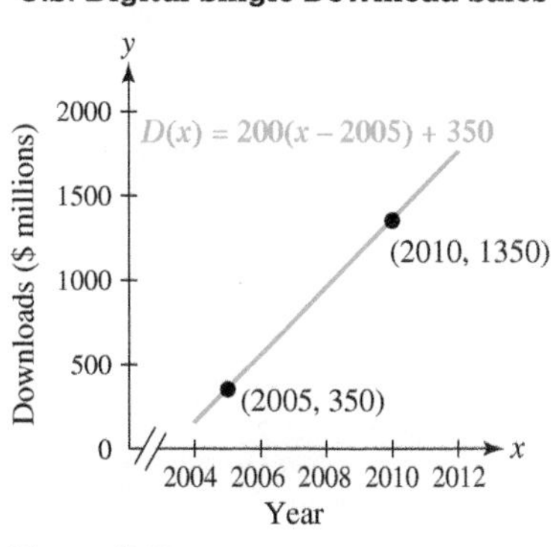

Figure 2.11

This formula can be used to estimate the value of downloads in 2008 as follows.

$$D(2008) = 200(2008 - 2005) + 350 = 950$$

Thus $D(x)$ estimates that the value of digital music single downloads was $950 million in 2008. (The actual value was $1000 million.) Because 2008 is *between* 2005 and 2010, we say that this estimation involves **interpolation.** Interpolation occurs when we estimate between given data points. However, if we use $D(x)$ to estimate this value in 2003 we obtain the following.

$$D(2003) = 200(2003 - 2005) + 350 = -50$$

This estimate is incorrect because sales cannot be negative. Because 2003 is *not between* 2005 and 2010, we say that this estimation involves **extrapolation.** Extrapolation occurs when we estimate "outside" of the given data. Interpolation is usually more accurate than extrapolation.

Modeling Data (Optional)

Point-slope form can sometimes be useful when modeling real data. In the next example we model how investments in cloud computing have increased. Cloud computing allows people to use files and applications on the Internet.

EXAMPLE 10 Modeling investments for cloud computing

Table 2.2 lists the investments in billions of dollars for cloud computing for selected years.

Investments in Cloud Computing ($ billions)

Year	2005	2006	2007	2008	2009
Investments	26	113	195	299	374

Source: Thomson Reuters.

Table 2.2

(a) Make a scatterplot of the data.
(b) Find a formula in point-slope form for a linear function f that models the data.
(c) Graph the data and $y = f(x)$ in the same xy-plane.
(d) Interpret the slope of the graph of $y = f(x)$.
(e) Estimate the investment in cloud computing in 2014. Does your answer involve interpolation or extrapolation?

Calculator Help
To make a scatterplot, see Appendix A (page AP-3). To plot data and graph an equation, see Appendix A (page AP-6).

SOLUTION

(a) See Figure 2.12

[2004, 2010, 1] by [0, 500, 100]

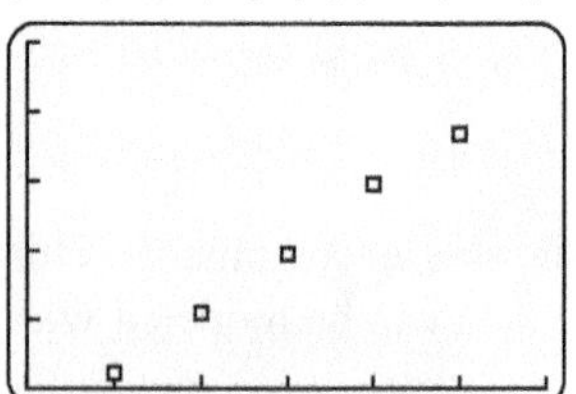

Figure 2.12

(b) Because the data are nearly linear, we could require that the line pass through the first data point (2005, 26) and the last data point (2009, 374). The slope of this line is

$$m = \frac{374 - 26}{2009 - 2005} = 87. \qquad \text{Slope} = \frac{y_2 - y_1}{x_2 - x_1}$$

Thus we can write a formula for f as

$$f(x) = 87(x - 2005) + 26.$$

NOTE When modeling real data, answers for $f(x)$ may vary, depending on the points that are used to determine the line.

(c) See Figure 2.13

Modeling Cloud Investments

[2004, 2010, 1] by [0, 500, 100]

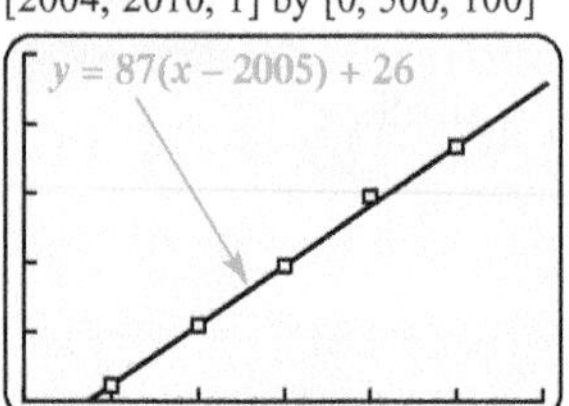

Figure 2.13

(d) Slope 87 indicates that investments increased, on average, by \$87 billion per year between 2005 and 2009.
(e) To estimate the investment amount in 2014, we can evaluate $f(2014)$.

$$f(2014) = 87(2014 - 2005) + 26 = 809$$

This model predicts an \$809 billion investment in cloud computing during 2014. This result involves extrapolation because 2014 is "outside" of 2005 and 2009.

Now Try Exercise 87

Linear Regression (Optional)

We have used linear functions to model data involving the variables x and y. Problems where one variable is used to predict the behavior of a second variable are called **regression** problems. If a linear function or line is used to approximate the data, then the technique is referred to as **linear regression**.

We have already solved problems by selecting a line that *visually* fits the data in a scatterplot. See Example 10. However, this technique has some disadvantages. First, it does not produce a unique line. Different people may arrive at different lines to fit the same data. Second, the line is not determined automatically by a calculator or computer. A statistical method used to determine a unique linear function or line is based on the method of **least squares.**

Correlation Coefficient Most graphing calculators have the capability to calculate the least-squares regression line automatically. When determining the least-squares line, calculators often compute a real number r, called the **correlation coefficient**, where $-1 \leq r \leq 1$. When r is positive and near 1, low x-values correspond to low y-values and high x-values correspond to high y-values. For example, there is a positive correlation between years of education x and income y. More years of education correlate with higher income. When r is near -1, the reverse is true. Low x-values correspond to high y-values and high x-values correspond to low y-values. If $r \approx 0$, then there is little or no correlation between the data points. In this case, a linear function does not provide a suitable model. A summary of these concepts is shown in the following.

Correlation Coefficient r ($-1 \leq r \leq 1$)

Value of r	Comments	Sample Scatterplot
$r = 1$	There is an exact linear fit. The line passes through all data points and has a positive slope.	y, x
$r = -1$	There is an exact linear fit. The line passes through all data points and has a negative slope.	y, x
$0 < r < 1$	There is a positive correlation. As the x-values increase, so do the y-values. The fit is not exact.	y, x
$-1 < r < 0$	There is a negative correlation. As the x-values increase, the y-values decrease. The fit is not exact.	y, x
$r = 0$	There is no correlation. The data has no tendency toward being linear. A regression line predicts poorly.	y, x

MAKING CONNECTIONS

Correlation and Causation

When geese begin to fly north, summer is coming and the weather becomes warmer. Geese flying north correlate with warmer weather. However, geese flying north clearly do not *cause* warmer weather. It is important to remember that correlation does not always indicate causation.

Calculator Help
To find a line of least-squares fit, see Appendix A (page AP-6).

In the next example we use a graphing calculator to find the line of least-squares fit that models three data points.

EXAMPLE 11 **Determining a line of least-squares fit**

Find the line of least-squares fit for the data points (1, 1), (2, 3), and (3, 4). What is the correlation coefficient? Plot the data and graph the line.

SOLUTION Begin by entering the three data points into the STAT EDIT menu. Refer to Figures 2.14–2.17. Select the LinReg (ax + b) option from the STAT CALC menu. From the home screen we can see that the line (linear function) of least squares is given by the formula $y = \frac{3}{2}x - \frac{1}{3}$. The correlation coefficient is $r \approx 0.98$. Since $r \neq 1$, the line does not provide an *exact* model of the data.

Enter Data into Two Lists

L1 L2 L3 1
1 1
2 3
3 4
L1(1)=1

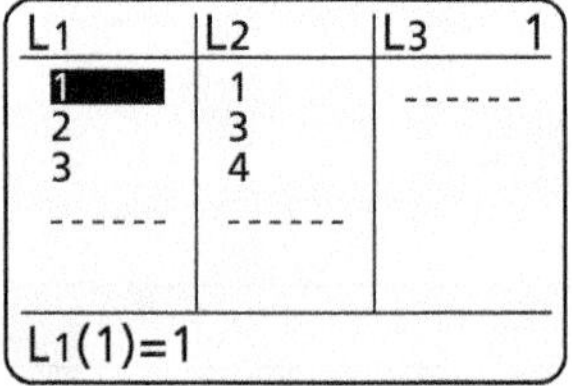

Figure 2.14

Select Linear Regression

EDIT CALC TESTS
1:1-Var Stats
2:2-Var Stats
3:Med-Med
4:LinReg(ax+b)
5:QuadReg
6:CubicReg
7:↓QuartReg

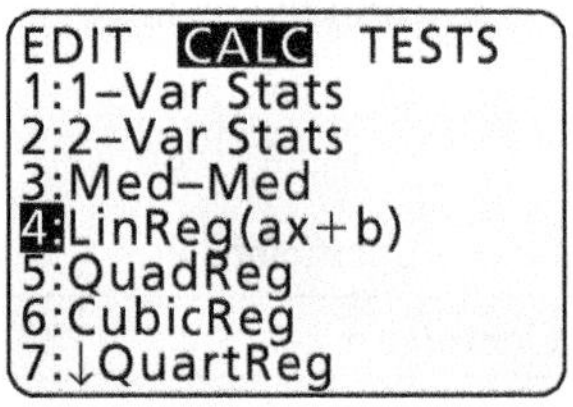

Figure 2.15

Equation for Regression Line

LinReg
y=ax+b
a=1.5
b=⁻.3333333333
r2=.9642857143
r =.9819805061

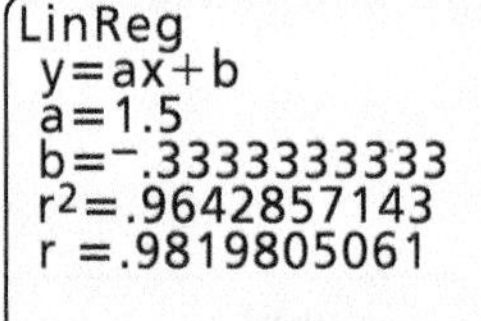

Figure 2.16

Data and Regression Line
[0, 5, 1] by [0, 5, 1]

$y = \frac{3}{2}x - \frac{1}{3}$

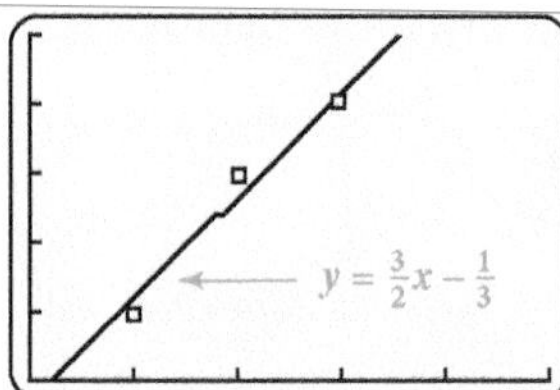

Figure 2.17

Now Try Exercise 99

An Application In the next example, we find the regression line that models the cloud computing data found in Example 10.

EXAMPLE 12 **Modeling data with a regression line**

Refer to the data from Table 2.2 in Example 10.

(a) Find the least-squares regression line that models this data.

(b) Compare the regression line with the one that was found in Example 10 by writing both lines in slope-intercept form.

SOLUTION

(a) Figures 2.18–2.21 show how to find this regression line. Its equation is

$$y = 88.2x - 176{,}816.$$

Enter Data into Two Lists

L1 L2 L3 1
2005 26
2006 113
2007 195
2008 299
2009 374
L1(1)=2005

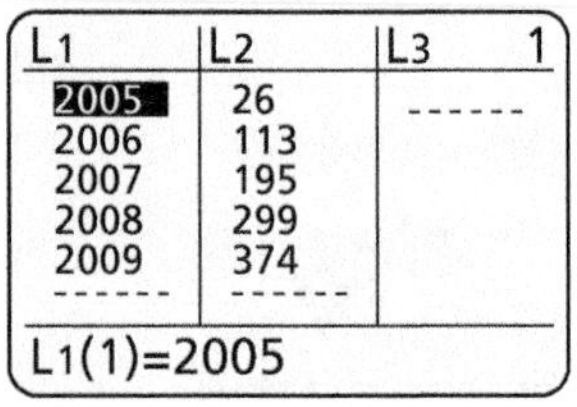

Figure 2.18

Select Linear Regression

EDIT CALC TESTS
1:1-Var Stats
2:2-Var Stats
3:Med-Med
4:LinReg(ax+b)
5:QuadReg
6:CubicReg
7:↓QuartReg

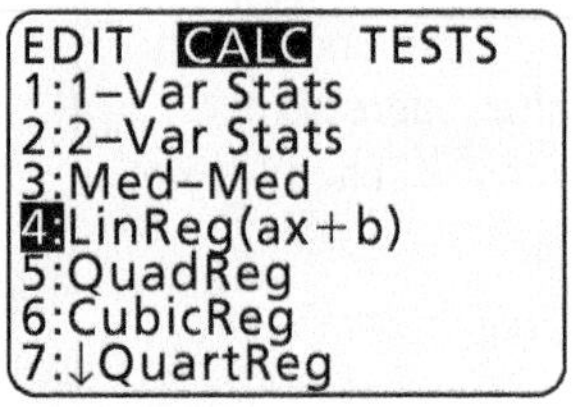

Figure 2.19

Equation for Regression Line

LinReg
y=ax+b
a=88.2
b=⁻176816
r2=.9981420939
r=.9990706151

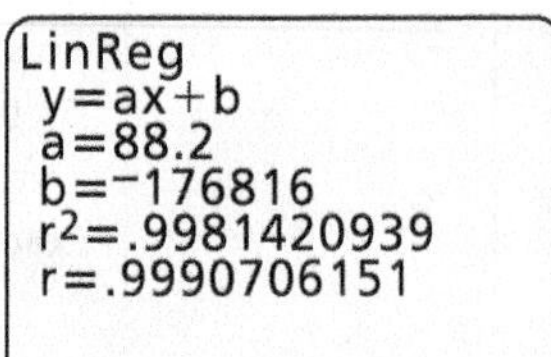

Figure 2.20

Data and Regression Line
[2004, 2010, 1] by [0, 500, 100]

y = 88.2x – 176,816

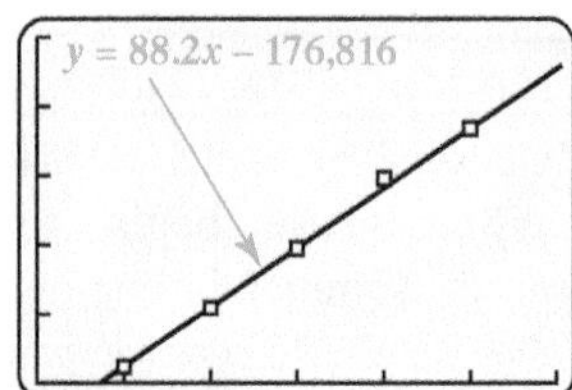

Figure 2.21

(b) The equation of the line found in Example 10 can be written in slope-intercept form as follows.

$y = 87(x - 2005) + 26$ Example 10 equation

$y = 87x - 174{,}435 + 26$ Distributive property

$y = 87x - 174{,}409$

Calculator Help
To copy the regression equation directly into Y_1, see Appendix A (page AP-11).

Notice that the slope-intercept forms for these two lines are not exactly alike. However, both lines model the data reasonably well, as shown in Figures 2.13 and 2.21.

Now Try Exercise 107

2.1 Putting It All Together

The following table summarizes three forms for equations of a line and how to find the intercepts.

CONCEPT	COMMENTS	EXAMPLES
Point-slope form $y = m(x - x_1) + y_1$ or $y - y_1 = m(x - x_1)$	Used to find the equation of a line, given two points or one point and the slope	Given two points (5, 1) and (4, 3), first compute $m = \frac{3 - 1}{4 - 5} = -2$. An equation of this line is $y = -2(x - 5) + 1$.
Slope-intercept form $y = mx + b$	A unique equation for a line, determined by the slope m and the y-intercept b	An equation of the line with slope 5 and y-intercept -4 is $y = 5x - 4$.
Standard form $ax + by = c$	Any line can be written in this form.	$3x + 5y = 15$ $x = -4$ Vertical line $y = 7$ Horizontal line
Finding intercepts	**1.** To find x-intercepts, let $y = 0$ and solve for x. **2.** To find y-intercepts, let $x = 0$ and solve for y.	**1.** In $3x + 5y = 15$ let $y = 0$ to obtain $3x = 15$, or $x = 5$. The x-intercept is 5. **2.** In $3x + 5y = 15$ let $x = 0$ to obtain $5y = 15$, or $y = 3$. The y-intercept is 3.

The following table summarizes special types of lines.

CONCEPT	EQUATION(S)	EXAMPLES
Horizontal line	$y = b$, where b is a constant	A horizontal line with y-intercept 7 has the equation $y = 7$.
Vertical line	$x = k$, where k is a constant	A vertical line with x-intercept -8 has the equation $x = -8$.
Parallel lines	$y = m_1x + b_1$ and $y = m_2x + b_2$, where $m_1 = m_2$	The lines given by $y = -3x - 1$ and $y = -3x + 5$ are parallel because they both have slope -3.
Perpendicular lines	$y = m_1x + b_1$ and $y = m_2x + b_2$, where $m_1m_2 = -1$	The lines $y = 2x - 5$ and $y = -\frac{1}{2}x + 2$ are perpendicular because $m_1m_2 = 2\left(-\frac{1}{2}\right) = -1$.

continued on next page

The following table summarizes linear regression.

CONCEPT	DESCRIPTION
Correlation coefficient r	The values of r satisfy $-1 \le r \le 1$, where a line fits the data better if r is near -1 or 1. A value near 0 indicates a poor fit.
Least-squares regression line	The line of least-squares fit for the points (1, 3), (2, 5), and (3, 6) is $y = \frac{3}{2}x + \frac{5}{3}$ and $r \approx 0.98$. Try verifying this with a calculator.

2.1 Exercises

Equations of Lines

Exercises 1–4: Find the point-slope form of the line passing through the given points. Use the first point as (x_1, y_1). Plot the points and graph the line by hand.

1. $(1, 2), (3, -2)$

2. $(-2, 3), (1, 0)$

3. $(-3, -1), (1, 2)$

4. $(-1, 2), (-2, -3)$

Exercises 5–10: Find a point-slope form of the line satisfying the conditions. Use the first point given for (x_1, y_1). Then convert the equation to slope-intercept form, and write the formula for a function f whose graph is the line.

5. Slope -2.4, passing through $(4, 5)$

6. Slope 1.7, passing through $(-8, 10)$

7. Passing through $(1, -2)$ and $(-9, 3)$

8. Passing through $(-6, 10)$ and $(5, -12)$

9. x-intercept 4, y-intercept -3

10. x-intercept -2, y-intercept 5

Exercises 11–14: Find the slope-intercept form for the line in the figure.

11.

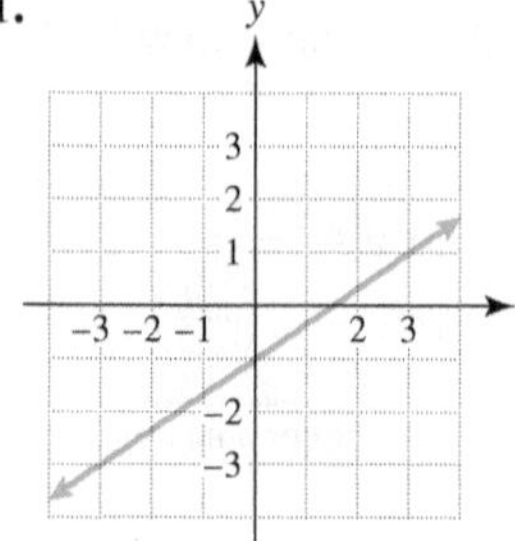

12.

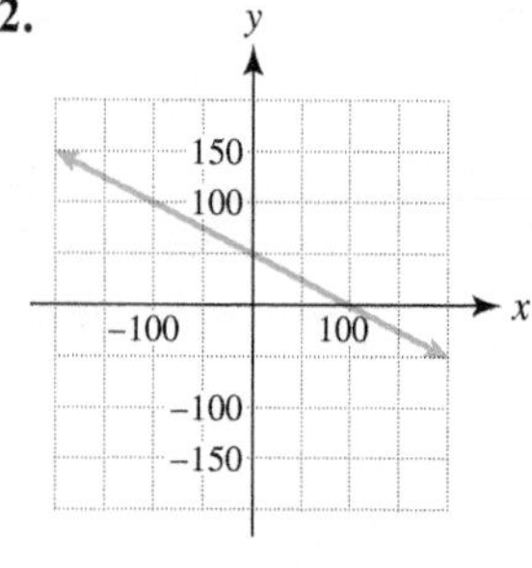

13.

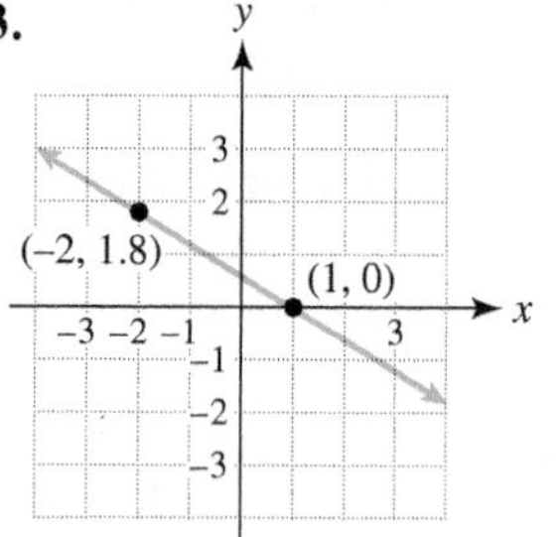

14.

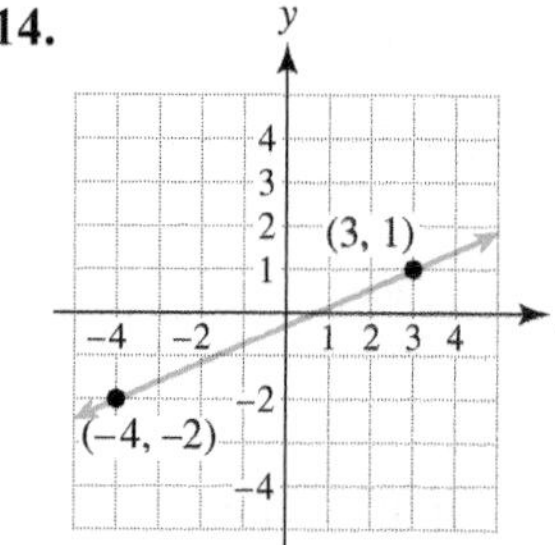

Exercises 15–20: **Concepts** *Match the given equation to its graph (a–f) shown.*

15. $y = m(x - x_1) + y_1, m > 0$

16. $y = m(x - x_1) + y_1, m < 0$

17. $y = mx, m > 0$

18. $y = mx + b, m < 0$ and $b > 0$

19. $x = k, k > 0$

20. $y = b, b < 0$

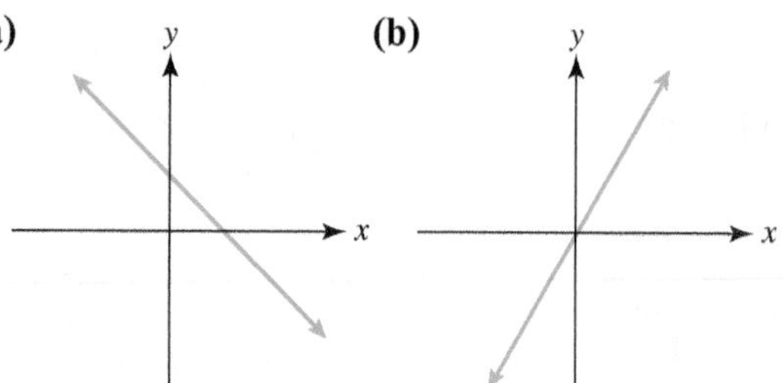

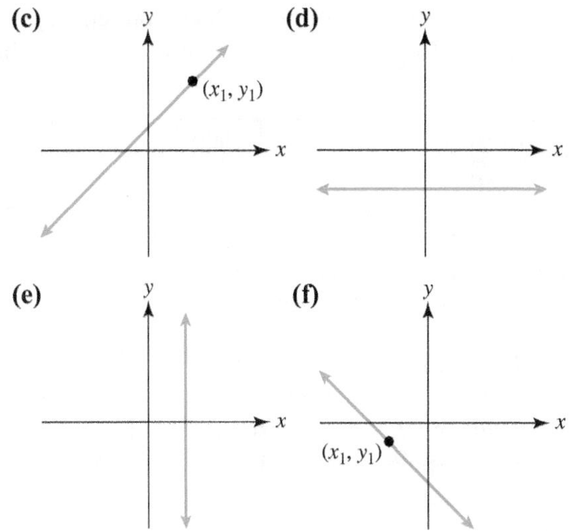

Exercises 21–48: Find the slope-intercept form for the line satisfying the conditions.

21. Passing through $(-1, -4)$ and $(1, 2)$

22. Passing through $(-1, 6)$ and $(2, -3)$

23. Passing through $(4, 5)$ and $(1, -3)$

24. Passing through $(8, -2)$ and $(-2, 3)$

25. y-intercept 5, slope -7.8

26. y-intercept -155, slope 5.6

27. y-intercept 45, x-intercept 90

28. x-intercept -6, y-intercept -8

29. Slope -3, passing through $(0, 5)$

30. Slope $\frac{1}{3}$, passing through $\left(\frac{1}{2}, -2\right)$

31. Passing through $(0, -6)$ and $(4, 0)$

32. Passing through $\left(\frac{3}{4}, -\frac{1}{4}\right)$ and $\left(\frac{5}{4}, \frac{7}{4}\right)$

33. Passing through $\left(\frac{1}{2}, \frac{3}{4}\right)$ and $\left(\frac{1}{5}, \frac{2}{3}\right)$

34. Passing through $\left(-\frac{7}{3}, \frac{5}{3}\right)$ and $\left(\frac{5}{6}, -\frac{7}{6}\right)$

35. Parallel to $y = 4x + 16$, passing through $(-4, -7)$

36. Parallel to the line $y = -\frac{3}{4}(x - 100) - 99$, passing through $(1, 3)$

37. Perpendicular to the line $y = -\frac{2}{3}(x - 1980) + 5$, passing through $(1980, 10)$

38. Perpendicular to $y = 6x - 10$, passing through $(15, -7)$

39. Parallel to $y = \frac{2}{3}x + 3$, passing through $(0, -2.1)$

40. Parallel to $y = -4x - \frac{1}{4}$, passing through $(2, -5)$

41. Perpendicular to $y = -2x$, passing through $(-2, 5)$

42. Perpendicular to $y = -\frac{6}{7}x + \frac{3}{7}$, passing through $(3, 8)$

43. Perpendicular to $x + y = 4$, passing through $(15, -5)$

44. Parallel to $2x - 3y = -6$, passing through $(4, -9)$

45. Passing through $(5, 7)$ and parallel to the line passing through $(1, 3)$ and $(-3, 1)$

46. Passing through $(1990, 4)$ and parallel to the line passing through $(1980, 3)$ and $(2000, 8)$

47. Passing through $(-2, 4)$ and perpendicular to the line passing through $\left(-5, \frac{1}{2}\right)$ and $\left(-3, \frac{2}{3}\right)$

48. Passing through $\left(\frac{3}{4}, \frac{1}{4}\right)$ and perpendicular to the line passing through $(-3, -5)$ and $(-4, 0)$

Horizontal and Vertical Lines

Exercises 49–56: Find an equation of the line satisfying the conditions. If possible, for each line write a formula for a linear function whose graph is the line.

49. Vertical, passing through $(-5, 6)$

50. Vertical, passing through $(1.95, 10.7)$

51. Horizontal, passing through $(-5, 6)$

52. Horizontal, passing through $(1.95, 10.7)$

53. Perpendicular to $y = 15$, passing through $(4, -9)$

54. Perpendicular to $x = 15$, passing through $(1.6, -9.5)$

55. Parallel to $x = 4.5$, passing through $(19, 5.5)$

56. Parallel to $y = -2.5$, passing through $(1985, 67)$

Finding Intercepts

Exercises 57–68: Determine the x- and y-intercepts on the graph of the equation. Graph the equation.

57. $4x - 5y = 20$

58. $-3x - 5y = 15$

59. $x - y = 7$

60. $15x - y = 30$

61. $6x - 7y = -42$

62. $5x + 2y = -20$

63. $y - 3x = 7$

64. $4x - 3y = 6$

65. $0.2x + 0.4y = 0.8$

66. $\frac{2}{3}y - x = 1$

67. $y = 8x - 5$

68. $y = -1.5x + 15$

Exercises 69–72: The ***intercept form of a line*** *is* $\frac{x}{a} + \frac{y}{b} = 1$. *Determine the x- and y-intercepts on the graph of the equation. Draw a conclusion about what the constants a and b represent in this form.*

69. $\frac{x}{5} + \frac{y}{7} = 1$

70. $\frac{x}{2} + \frac{y}{3} = 1$

71. $\frac{2x}{3} + \frac{4y}{5} = 1$

72. $\frac{5x}{6} - \frac{y}{2} = 1$

Exercises 73 and 74: (Refer to Exercises 69–72.) Write the intercept form for the line with the given intercepts.

73. x-intercept 5, y-intercept 9

74. x-intercept $\frac{2}{3}$, y-intercept $-\frac{5}{4}$

Interpolation and Extrapolation

Exercises 75–78: The table lists data that are exactly linear.

(a) Find the slope-intercept form of the line that passes through these data points.

(b) Predict y when x = −2.7 and 6.3. Decide if these calculations involve interpolation or extrapolation.

75.

x	−3	−2	−1	0	1
y	−7.7	−6.2	−4.7	−3.2	−1.7

76.

x	−2	−1	0	1	2
y	10.2	8.5	6.8	5.1	3.4

77.

x	5	23	32	55	61
y	94.7	56.9	38	−10.3	−22.9

78.

x	−11	−8	−7	−3	2
y	−16.1	−10.4	−8.5	−0.9	8.6

79. iPhone Revenues The percentage of smartphone revenues that were due to iPhones is shown in the table.

Year	2008	2009	2010	2011
Percentage	3	10	16	24

Source: Business Insider.

(a) Find a linear function f that models these data. Does f model these data exactly or approximately?

(b) Use f to estimate this percentage in 2007.

(c) Did your answer use interpolation or extrapolation? Comment on your result.

80. Deaths on School Grounds Deaths on school grounds nationwide for school years ending in year x are shown in the table.

x (year)	1998	1999	2000
y (deaths)	43	26	9

Source: FBI.

(a) Find a linear function f that models these data. Is f exact or approximate?

(b) Use f to estimate the number of deaths on school grounds in 2003. Compare your answer to the actual value of 49. Did your estimate involve interpolation or extrapolation?

Applications

81. Projected Cost of College In 2003 the average annual cost of attending a private college or university, including tuition, fees, room, and board, was $25,000. This cost rose to about $37,000 in 2010, as illustrated in the figure. (*Source:* Cerulli Associates.)

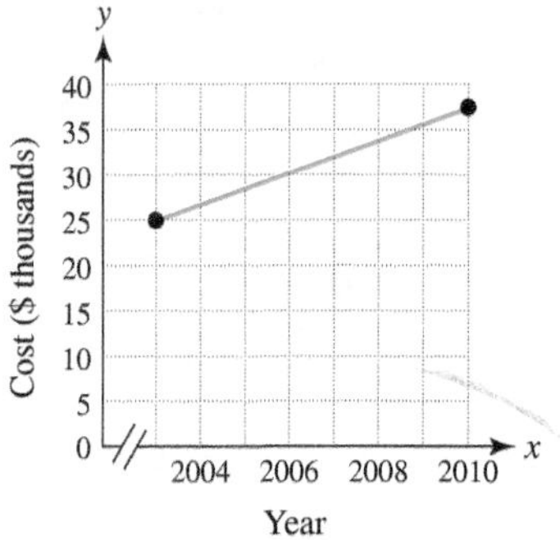

(a) Find a point-slope form of the line passing through the points (2003, 25,000) and (2010, 37,000). Interpret the slope.

(b) Use the equation to estimate the cost of attending a private college in 2007.

82. Distance A person is riding a bicycle. The graph shows the rider's distance y in miles from an interstate highway after x hours.

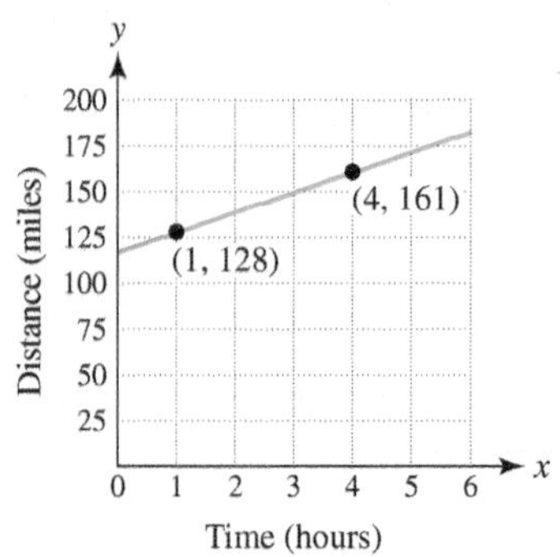

(a) How fast is the bicyclist traveling?

(b) Find the slope-intercept form of the line.

(c) How far was the bicyclist from the interstate highway initially?

(d) How far was the bicyclist from the interstate highway after 1 hour and 15 minutes?

83. Water in a Tank The graph shows the amount of water in a 100-gallon tank after x minutes have elapsed.

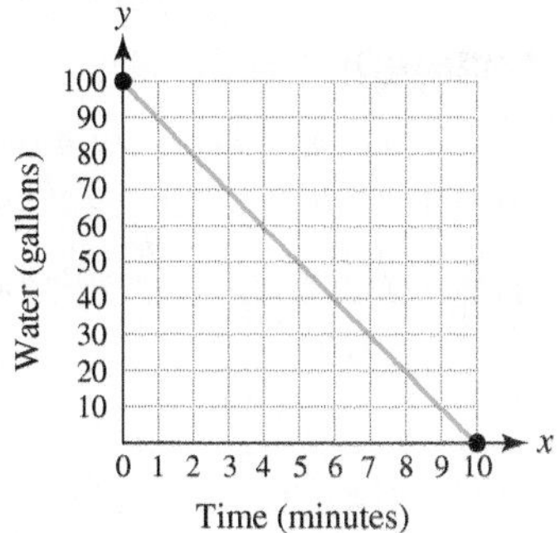

(a) Is water entering or leaving the tank? How much water is in the tank after 3 minutes?

(b) Find the x- and y-intercepts. Interpret each intercept.

(c) Find the slope-intercept form of the equation of the line. Interpret the slope.

(d) Use the graph to estimate the x-coordinate of the point $(x, 50)$ that lies on the line.

84. Cost of Driving The cost of driving a car includes both fixed costs and mileage costs. Assume that insurance and car payments cost \$350 per month and gasoline, oil, and routine maintenance cost \$0.29 per mile.

(a) Find a linear function f that gives the *annual* cost of driving this car x miles.

(b) What does the y-intercept on the graph of f represent?

85. U.S. Music Sales In 1999 music sales from vinyl, CDs, and downloads were \$15 billion and in 2013 they were \$9 billion. (*Source:* RIAA.)

(a) Find the point-slope form for a line passing through the points (1999, 15) and (2013, 9).

(b) Interpret the slope of this line.

(c) Estimate sales in 2008 and compare them with the true value of \$10.4 billion. Did your answer use interpolation or extrapolation?

86. Toyota Vehicle Sales In 1998 Toyota sold 1.4 million vehicles and in 2007 it sold 2.3 million vehicles. (*Source:* Toyota Motor Division.)

(a) Find the point-slope form for a line passing through the points (1998, 1.4) and (2007, 2.3).

(b) Interpret the slope of this line.

(c) Estimate sales in 2004 and compare them with the true value of 2.0 million vehicles. Did your answer use interpolation or extrapolation?

87. Bankruptcies The table lists the number of bankruptcies filed in thousands for selected years.

Year	2006	2007	2008	2009	2010
Bankruptcies	160	220	290	380	425

Source: Administrative Office of the United States.

(a) Make a scatterplot of the data.

(b) Find a formula in point-slope form for a linear function f that models the data.

(c) Graph the data and $y = f(x)$ in the same xy-plane.

(d) Interpret the slope of the graph of $y = f(x)$.

(e) Estimate the number of bankruptcies in 2014. Did your answer involve interpolation or extrapolation?

88. College Tuition The table lists average tuition and fees in dollars at private colleges for selected years.

Year	1995	2000	2005	2010
Cost	12,432	16,233	21,235	26,273

Source: The College Board.

(a) Make a scatterplot of the data.

(b) Find a formula in point-slope form for a linear function f that models the data.

(c) Graph the data and $y = f(x)$ in the same xy-plane.

(d) Interpret the slope of the graph of $y = f(x)$.

(e) Estimate the cost in 2014. Did your answers involve interpolation or extrapolation?

89. Hours Worked in Europe The table lists the annual hours worked by the average worker in Europe for selected years.

Year	1970	1980	1990	2000	2010
Hours	2000	1860	1750	1690	1590

Source: Gallup Research.

continued on next page

(a) Let x represent the number of years *after* 1970. Find a formula in slope-intercept form for a linear function f that models the data.

(b) Interpret the slope of the graph of $y = f(x)$.

(c) Estimate the annual hours worked in 2014.

90. Green Building Material The table lists U.S. demand for green building materials in billions of dollars for selected years.

Year	2010	2011	2012	2013
Demand	65	70	75	80

Source: Freedonia Group.

(a) Let x represent the number of years *after* 2010. Find a formula in slope-intercept form for a linear function f that models the data.

(b) Interpret the slope of the graph of $y = f(x)$.

(c) Estimate the demand in 2020.

Perspectives and Viewing Rectangles

91. Graph $y = \frac{1}{1024}x + 1$ in $[0, 3, 1]$ by $[-2, 2, 1]$.
(a) Is the graph a horizontal line?

(b) Why does the calculator screen appear as it does?

92. Graph $y = 1000x + 1000$ in the standard window.
(a) Is the graph a vertical line?

(b) Explain why the calculator screen appears as it does.

93. Square Viewing Rectangle Graph the lines $y = 2x$ and $y = -\frac{1}{2}x$ in the standard viewing rectangle.
(a) Do the lines appear to be perpendicular?

(b) Graph the lines in the following viewing rectangles.
i. $[-15, 15, 1]$ by $[-10, 10, 1]$
ii. $[-10, 10, 1]$ by $[-3, 3, 1]$
iii. $[-3, 3, 1]$ by $[-2, 2, 1]$
Do the lines appear to be perpendicular in any of these viewing rectangles?

(c) Determine the viewing rectangles where perpendicular lines will appear perpendicular. (Answers may vary.)

94. Square Viewing Rectangle Continuing with Exercise 93, make a conjecture about which viewing rectangles result in the graph of a circle with radius 5 and center at the origin appearing circular.
i. $[-9, 9, 1]$ by $[-6, 6, 1]$
ii. $[-5, 5, 1]$ by $[-10, 10, 1]$
iii. $[-5, 5, 1]$ by $[-5, 5, 1]$
iv. $[-18, 18, 1]$ by $[-12, 12, 1]$
Test your conjecture by graphing this circle in each viewing rectangle. (*Hint:* Graph $y_1 = \sqrt{25 - x^2}$ and $y_2 = -\sqrt{25 - x^2}$ to create the circle.)

Finding a Rectangle

Exercises 95–98: (Refer to Example 9.) A rectangle is determined by the stated conditions. Find the slope-intercept form of the four lines that outline the rectangle.

95. Vertices (0, 0), (2, 2), and (1, 3)

96. Vertices (1, 1), (5, 1), and (5, 5)

97. Vertices (4, 0), (0, 4), (0, −4), and (−4, 0)

98. Vertices (1, 1) and (2, 3); the point (3.5, 1) lies on a side of the rectangle.

Linear Regression

Exercises 99 and 100: Find the line of least-squares fit for the given data points. What is the correlation coefficient? Plot the data and graph the line.

99. (−2, 2), (1, 0), (3, −2)

100. (−1, −1), (1, 4), (2, 6)

Exercises 101–104: Complete the following.
(a) Conjecture whether the correlation coefficient r for the data will be positive, negative, or zero.
(b) Use a calculator to find the equation of the least-squares regression line and the value of r.
(c) Use the regression line to predict y when x = 2.4.

101.

x	−1	0	1	2	3
y	−5.7	−2.6	1.1	3.9	7.3

102.

x	−4	−2	0	2	4
y	1.2	2.8	5.3	6.7	9.1

103.

x	1	3	5	7	10
y	5.8	−2.4	−10.7	−17.8	−29.3

104.

x	−4	−3	−1	3	5
y	37.2	33.7	27.5	16.4	9.8

105. **Distant Galaxies** In the late 1920s Edwin P. Hubble (1889–1953) determined both the distance to several galaxies and the velocity at which they were receding from Earth. Four galaxies with their distances in light-years and velocities in miles per second are listed in the table.

Galaxy	Distance	Velocity
Virgo	50	990
Ursa Minor	650	9,300
Corona Borealis	950	15,000
Bootes	1700	25,000

Source: A. Sharov and I. Novikov, *Edwin Hubble: The Discoverer of the Big Bang Universe.*

(a) Let x be distance and y be velocity. Plot the points in $[-100, 1800, 100]$ by $[-1000, 28000, 1000]$.

(b) Find the least-squares regression line.

(c) If the galaxy Hydra is receding at a speed of 37,000 miles per second, estimate its distance.

106. **Airline Travel** The table at the top of the next column lists the numbers of airline passengers in millions at some of the largest airports in the United States during 2002 and 2006.

(a) Graph the data by using the 2002 data for x-values and the corresponding 2006 data for y-values. Predict whether the correlation coefficient will be positive or negative.

(b) Use a calculator to find the linear function f based on least-squares regression that models the data. Graph $y = f(x)$ and the data in the same viewing rectangle.

(c) In 2002 Newark International Airport had 29.0 million passengers. Assuming that this airport followed a trend similar to that of the five airports listed in the table, use $f(x)$ to estimate the number of passengers at Newark International in 2006. Compare this result to the actual value of 36.7 million passengers.

Airport	2002	2006
Atlanta (Hartsfield)	76.9	84.4
Chicago (O'Hare)	66.5	77.0
Los Angeles (LAX)	56.2	61.0
Dallas/Fort Worth	52.8	60.2
Denver	35.7	47.3

Source: Airports Association Council International.

107. **Passenger Travel** The table shows the number of miles (in trillions) traveled by passengers of all types x years after 1970.

Year (1970 ↔ 0)	0	10	20	30	40
Miles (trillions)	2.2	2.8	3.7	4.7	5.5

Source: Department of Transportation.

(a) Make a scatterplot of the data. Predict whether the correlation coefficient will be positive or negative.

(b) Use least-squares regression to find $f(x) = ax + b$ so that f models the data.

(c) Graph f and the data. Interpret the slope.

(d) Predict the number of passenger miles in 2015.

108. **High School Enrollment** The table lists the number of students (in millions) attending U.S. public school (grades 9–12) x years after 2000.

x (year)	0	3	5	7
y (students)	13.5	14.3	14.8	15.1

Source: National Center for Education Statistics.

(a) Use least-squares regression to find $f(x) = ax + b$ so that f models the data.

(b) Graph f and the data. Interpret the slope.

(c) Estimate enrollment in 2002 and compare the estimate to the actual value of 14.1 million.

Writing about Mathematics

109. Compare the slope-intercept form with the point-slope form. Give examples of each.

110. Explain how you would find the equation of a line passing through two points. Give an example.

2.2 Linear Equations

- Learn about equations and recognize a linear equation
- Solve linear equations symbolically
- Solve linear equations graphically and numerically
- Solve problems involving percentages
- Apply problem-solving strategies

Introduction

In Example 4 of Section 2.1, we modeled iPod sales y in millions during year x with the equation of a line, or *linear function*, given by

$$f(x) = -4(x - 2008) + 55.$$

To predict the year when iPod sales might decrease to 27 million, we could set the formula for $f(x)$ equal to 27 and solve the following *linear equation* for x.

$$27 = -4(x - 2008) + 55 \quad \text{Linear equation}$$

This section discusses linear equations and their solutions. See Example 5 in this section.

Equations

An **equation** is a statement that two mathematical expressions are equal. Equations always contain an equals sign.

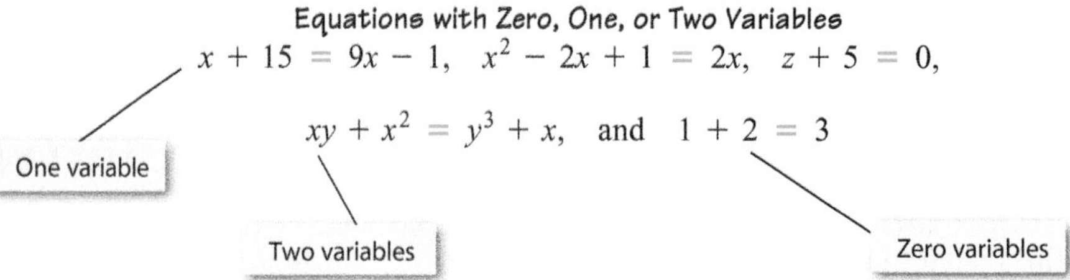

Equations with Zero, One, or Two Variables
$x + 15 = 9x - 1,\quad x^2 - 2x + 1 = 2x,\quad z + 5 = 0,$
$xy + x^2 = y^3 + x,\quad \text{and} \quad 1 + 2 = 3$
One variable
Two variables
Zero variables

We will concentrate on equations with one variable.

To **solve** an equation means to find all values for the variable that make the equation a true statement. Such values are called **solutions.** The set of all solutions is the **solution set**. For example, the solutions to the equation $x^2 - 1 = 0$ are 1 or -1, written as ± 1. Either value for x **satisfies** the equation. The solution set is $\{-1, 1\}$. Two equations are **equivalent** if they have the same solution set. For example, the equations $x + 2 = 5$ and $x = 3$ are equivalent.

If an equation has no solutions, then its solution set is empty and the equation is called a **contradiction**. The equation $x + 2 = x$ has no solutions and is a contradiction. However, if every (meaningful) value for the variable is a solution, then the equation is an **identity**. The equation $x + x = 2x$ is an identity because every value for x makes the equation true. Any equation that is satisfied by some but not all values of the variable is a **conditional equation.** The equation $x^2 - 1 = 0$ is a conditional equation. Only the values -1 and 1 for x make this equation a true statement.

Like functions, equations can be either *linear* or *nonlinear.* A linear equation is one of the simplest types of equations.

LINEAR EQUATION IN ONE VARIABLE

A **linear equation** in one variable is an equation that can be written in the form

$$ax + b = 0,$$

where a and b are constants with $a \neq 0$.

If an equation is not linear, then we say that it is a **nonlinear equation**. The following gives examples of linear and nonlinear equations.

Example	Explanation
$2x + 5 = 0$	*Linear:* Is written as $ax + b = 0$ with $a = 2$ and $b = 5$
$3x = -7$	*Linear:* Can be written as $3x + 7 = 0$
$5(x - 1) = 4$	*Linear:* Can be written as $5x - 9 = 0$
$x^2 + 2x = 1$	*Nonlinear:* Contains x^2
$\sqrt{x} = 7$	*Nonlinear:* Contains $\sqrt{x}$

Symbolic Solutions

A linear equation can be solved symbolically, and the solution is *always exact.* To solve a linear equation symbolically, we usually apply the *properties of equality* to the given equation and transform it into an equivalent equation that is simpler.

PROPERTIES OF EQUALITY

Addition Property of Equality

If a, b, and c are real numbers, then

$$a = b \quad \text{is equivalent to} \quad a + c = b + c.$$

Multiplication Property of Equality

If a, b, and c are real numbers with $c \neq 0$, then

$$a = b \quad \text{is equivalent to} \quad ac = bc.$$

Loosely speaking, the addition property states that "if equals are added to equals, the results are equal." For example, if $x + 5 = 15$, then we can add -5 to each side of the equation, or equivalently subtract 5 from each side, to obtain the following.

Equivalent equations

$$x + 5 = 15 \qquad \text{Given equation}$$

$$x + 5 - 5 = 15 - 5 \qquad \text{Subtract 5 from each side.}$$

$$x = 10 \qquad \text{Simplify.}$$

Similarly, the multiplication property states that "if equals are multiplied by nonzero equals, the results are equal." For example, if $5x = 20$, then we can multiply each side by $\frac{1}{5}$, or equivalently divide each side by 5, to obtain the following.

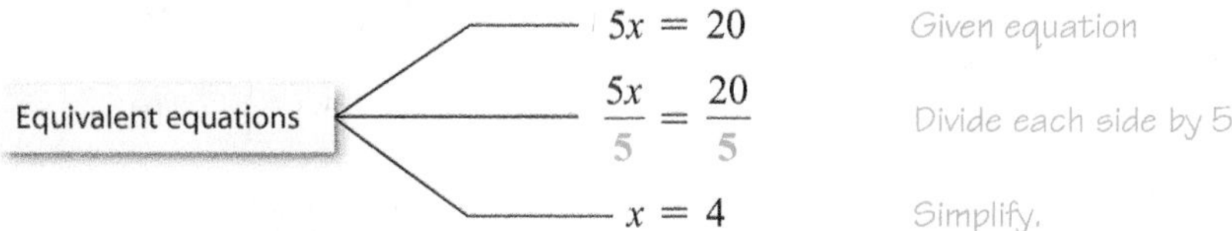
Equivalent equations
5x = 20
Given equation
5x/5 = 20/5
Divide each side by 5.
x = 4
Simplify.

These two properties along with the distributive property are applied in the next two examples. We also check our answers.

EXAMPLE 1 **Solving a linear equation symbolically**

Solve the equation $3(x - 4) = 2x - 1$. Check your answer.

SOLUTION

Getting Started First we apply the distributive property: $a(b - c) = ab - ac$. Thus

$$3(x - 4) = 3 \cdot x - 3 \cdot 4 = 3x - 12. \blacktriangleright$$

Algebra Review
To review the distributive properties, see Chapter R (page R-15).

Solving the given equation results in the following.

$$3(x - 4) = 2x - 1 \quad \text{Given equation}$$
$$3x - 12 = 2x - 1 \quad \text{Distributive property}$$
$$3x - 2x - 12 + 12 = 2x - 2x - 1 + 12 \quad \text{Subtract 2x and add 12.}$$
$$3x - 2x = 12 - 1 \quad \text{Simplify.}$$
$$x = 11 \quad \text{Simplify.}$$

The solution is 11. We can check our answer as follows.

$$3(x - 4) = 2x - 1 \quad \text{Given equation}$$
$$3(11 - 4) \stackrel{?}{=} 2 \cdot 11 - 1 \quad \text{Let } x = 11.$$
$$21 = 21 \checkmark \quad \text{The answer checks.}$$

Now Try Exercise 23

EXAMPLE 2 **Solving a linear equation symbolically**

Solve $3(2x - 5) = 10 - (x + 5)$. Check your answer.

SOLUTION

Getting Started In this problem subtraction must be distributed over the quantity $(x + 5)$. Thus

$$10 - (x + 5) = 10 - 1(x + 5) = 10 - x - 5. ▶$$

Solving the given equation results in the following.

$$3(2x - 5) = 10 - (x + 5) \quad \text{Given equation}$$
$$6x - 15 = 10 - x - 5 \quad \text{Distributive property}$$
$$6x - 15 = 5 - x \quad \text{Simplify.}$$
$$7x - 15 = 5 \quad \text{Add x to each side.}$$
$$7x = 20 \quad \text{Add 15 to each side.}$$
$$x = \frac{20}{7} \quad \text{Divide each side by 7.}$$

The solution is $\frac{20}{7}$. To check this answer, let $x = \frac{20}{7}$ and simplify.

$$3(2x - 5) = 10 - (x + 5) \quad \text{Given equation}$$
$$3\left(2 \cdot \frac{20}{7} - 5\right) \stackrel{?}{=} 10 - \left(\frac{20}{7} + 5\right) \quad \text{Let } x = \tfrac{20}{7}.$$
$$3\left(\frac{5}{7}\right) \stackrel{?}{=} 10 - \frac{55}{7} \quad \text{Simplify.}$$
$$\frac{15}{7} = \frac{15}{7} \checkmark \quad \text{The answer checks.}$$

Now Try Exercise 27

Fractions and Decimals When fractions or decimals appear in an equation, we sometimes can make our work simpler by multiplying each side of the equation by the least common denominator (LCD) or a common denominator of all fractions in the equation. This method is illustrated in the next two examples.

EXAMPLE 3 **Eliminating fractions**

Solve each linear equation.

(a) $\frac{x}{3} + 1 = \frac{2}{3}$ **(b)** $\frac{t-2}{4} - \frac{1}{3}t = 5 - \frac{1}{12}(3 - t)$

SOLUTION

(a) To eliminate fractions, multiply each side (or term in the equation) by the LCD, 3.

$$\frac{x}{3} + 1 = \frac{2}{3} \quad \text{Given equation}$$

$$3 \cdot \frac{x}{3} + 3 \cdot 1 = 3 \cdot \frac{2}{3} \quad \text{Multiply each side (term) by 3.}$$

$$x + 3 = 2 \quad \text{Simplify.}$$

$$x + 3 - 3 = 2 - 3 \quad \text{Subtract 3 from each side.}$$

$$x = -1 \quad \text{Simplify.}$$

The solution is -1.

Algebra Review
To review least common multiples and least common denominators, see Chapter R (page R-30).

(b) To eliminate fractions, multiply each side (or term in the equation) by the LCD, 12.

$$\frac{t-2}{4} - \frac{1}{3}t = 5 - \frac{1}{12}(3 - t) \quad \text{Given equation}$$

$$\frac{12(t-2)}{4} - \frac{12}{3}t = 12(5) - \frac{12}{12}(3 - t) \quad \text{Multiply each side (term) by 12.}$$

$$3(t - 2) - 4t = 60 - (3 - t) \quad \text{Simplify.}$$

$$3t - 6 - 4t = 60 - 3 + t \quad \text{Distributive property}$$

$$-t - 6 = 57 + t \quad \text{Combine like terms on each side.}$$

$$-2t = 63 \quad \text{Add } -t \text{ and 6 to each side.}$$

$$t = -\frac{63}{2} \quad \text{Divide each side by } -2.$$

The solution is $-\frac{63}{2}$.

Now Try Exercises 29 and 33

EXAMPLE 4 **Eliminating decimals**

Solve each linear equation.

(a) $5.1x - 2 = 3.7$ **(b)** $0.03(z - 3) - 0.5(2z + 1) = 0.23$

SOLUTION

(a) To eliminate decimals, multiply each side (or term in the equation) by 10.

$$5.1x - 2 = 3.7 \quad \text{Given equation}$$

$$10(5.1x) - 10(2) = 10(3.7) \quad \text{Multiply each side (term) by 10.}$$

$$51x - 20 = 37 \quad \text{Simplify.}$$

$$51x - 20 + 20 = 37 + 20 \quad \text{Add 20 to each side.}$$

$$51x = 57 \quad \text{Simplify.}$$

$$x = \frac{57}{51} \text{ or } \frac{19}{17} \quad \text{Divide each side by 51; simplify.}$$

The solution is $\frac{19}{17}$.

(b) To eliminate decimals, multiply each side (or term in the equation) by 100.

$$\begin{aligned} 0.03(z-3) - 0.5(2z+1) &= 0.23 && \text{Given equation} \\ 3(z-3) - 50(2z+1) &= 23 && \text{Multiply each side (term) by 100.} \\ 3z - 9 - 100z - 50 &= 23 && \text{Distributive property} \\ -97z - 59 &= 23 && \text{Combine like terms.} \\ -97z &= 82 && \text{Add 59 to each side.} \\ z &= -\frac{82}{97} && \text{Divide each side by } -97. \end{aligned}$$

The solution is $-\frac{82}{97}$.

Now Try Exercises 35 and 37

An Application In the next example we solve the equation presented in the introduction to this section.

EXAMPLE 5 Analyzing iPod sales

The linear function defined by $f(x) = -4(x - 2008) + 55$ estimates iPod sales (in millions of units) during fiscal year x. Use $f(x)$ to estimate when iPod sales could reach 27 million.

SOLUTION We need to find the year x when iPod sales, given by $f(x)$, equal 27 million.

$$\begin{aligned} -4(x-2008) + 55 &= 27 && \text{Given equation} \\ -4(x-2008) + 55 - 55 &= 27 - 55 && \text{Subtract 55 from each side.} \\ -4(x-2008) &= -28 && \text{Simplify.} \\ \frac{-4(x-2008)}{-4} &= \frac{-28}{-4} && \text{Divide each side by } -4. \\ x - 2008 &= 7 && \text{Simplify.} \\ x &= 2015 && \text{Add 2008 to each side.} \end{aligned}$$

Rather than dividing by −4, the distributive property could be used.

This model predicts that iPod sales could decrease to 27 million in 2015.

Now Try Exercise 97

Contradictions, Identities, and Conditional Equations The next example illustrates how an equation can have no solutions (contradiction), one solution (conditional equation), or infinitely many solutions (identity).

EXAMPLE 6 Identifying contradictions, identities, and conditional equations

Identify each equation as a contradiction, identity, or conditional equation.

(a) $7 + 6x = 2(3x + 1)$ **(b)** $2x - 5 = 3 - (1 + 2x)$

(c) $2(5 - x) - 25 = 3(x - 5) - 5x$

SOLUTION

(a)

$$\begin{aligned} 7 + 6x &= 2(3x+1) && \text{Given equation} \\ 7 + 6x &= 6x + 2 && \text{Distributive property} \\ 7 &= 2 && \text{Subtract } 6x \text{ from each side.} \end{aligned}$$

The statement $7 = 2$ is false and there are *no* solutions. The equation is a contradiction.

(b)

$$\begin{aligned} 2x - 5 &= 3 - (1 + 2x) && \text{Given equation} \\ 2x - 5 &= 3 - 1 - 2x && \text{Distributive property} \\ 4x &= 7 && \text{Add } 2x \text{ and } 5 \text{ to each side.} \\ x &= \frac{7}{4} && \text{Divide each side by 4.} \end{aligned}$$

There is one solution: $\frac{7}{4}$. This is a conditional equation.

(c)

$$\begin{aligned} 2(5 - x) - 25 &= 3(x - 5) - 5x && \text{Given equation} \\ 10 - 2x - 25 &= 3x - 15 - 5x && \text{Distributive property} \\ -2x - 15 &= -2x - 15 && \text{Simplify each side.} \\ 0 &= 0 && \text{Add } 2x \text{ and } 15 \text{ to each side.} \end{aligned}$$

The statement $0 = 0$ is true and the solution set includes *all real numbers*. The equation is an identity.

Now Try Exercises 39, 41, and 43

Graphical and Numerical Solutions

Graphical Solutions The equation $f(x) = g(x)$ results whenever the formulas for two functions f and g are set equal to each other. A solution to this equation corresponds to the x-coordinate of a point where the graphs of f and g intersect. We call this graphical technique the **intersection-of-graphs** method and it is used to solve the linear equation $2x + 1 = -x + 4$ in the following box.

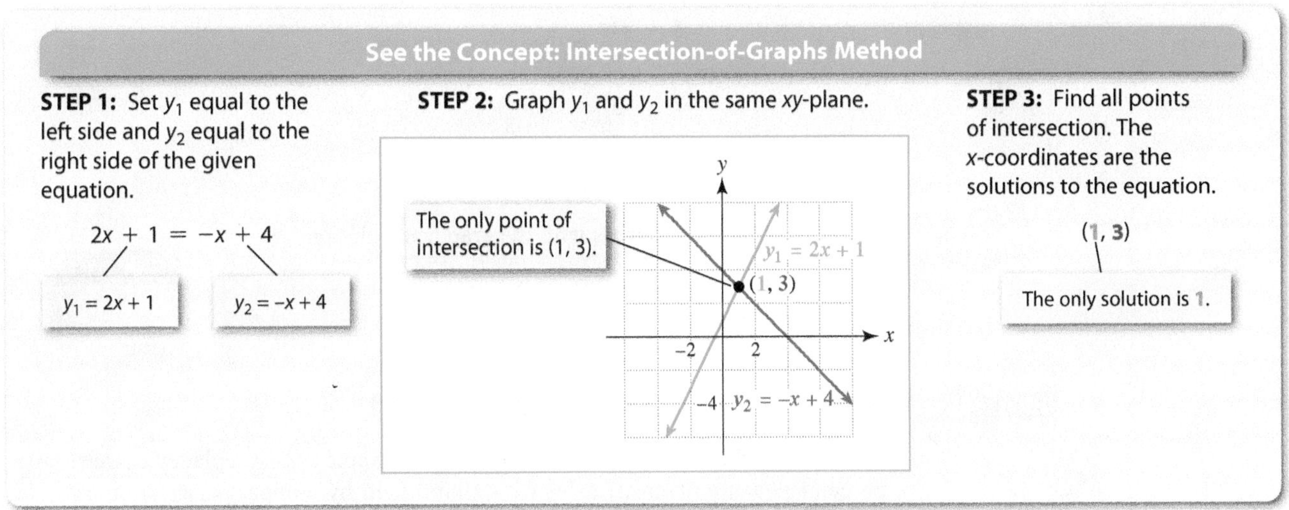

See the Concept: Intersection-of-Graphs Method
STEP 1: Set y_1 equal to the left side and y_2 equal to the right side of the given equation.
$2x + 1 = -x + 4$
$y_1 = 2x + 1$
$y_2 = -x + 4$
STEP 2: Graph y_1 and y_2 in the same xy-plane.
The only point of intersection is (1, 3).
$y_1 = 2x + 1$
(1, 3)
$y_2 = -x + 4$
y
x
−2
2
−4
STEP 3: Find all points of intersection. The x-coordinates are the solutions to the equation.
(1, 3)
The only solution is 1.

We can check our work from the example above by substituting 1 for x in the given equation.

$$\begin{aligned} 2x + 1 &= -x + 4 && \text{Given equation} \\ 2(1) + 1 &\stackrel{?}{=} -(1) + 4 && \text{Let } x = 1. \\ 3 &= 3 \checkmark && \text{It checks.} \end{aligned}$$

Notice that the point of intersection is (1, 3), and that when we substitute 1 for x, each side of the equation evaluates to 3.

EXAMPLE 7 **Solving an equation graphically and symbolically**

Solve $2x - 1 = \frac{1}{2}x + 2$ graphically and symbolically.

SOLUTION

Graphical Solution Graph $y_1 = 2x - 1$ and $y_2 = \frac{1}{2}x + 2$. Their graphs intersect at the point (2, 3), as shown in Figure 2.22, so the solution is 2. Figure 2.23 shows these graphs as created by a graphing calculator.

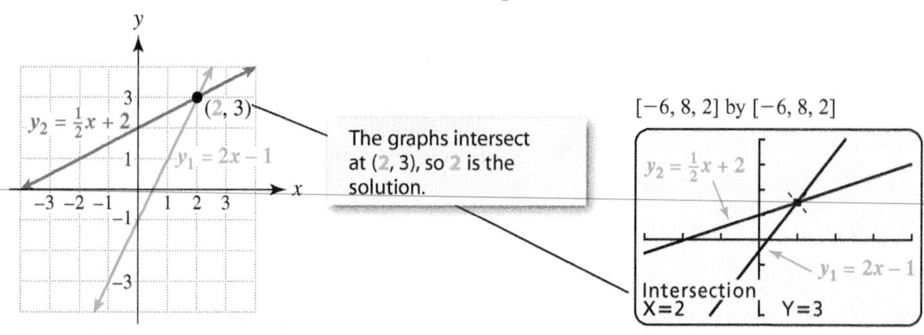

Figure 2.22

Figure 2.23

Symbolic Solution

$$2x - 1 = \frac{1}{2}x + 2 \qquad \text{Given equation}$$

$$2x = \frac{1}{2}x + 3 \qquad \text{Add 1 to each side.}$$

$$\frac{3}{2}x = 3 \qquad \text{Subtract } \tfrac{1}{2}x \text{ from each side.}$$

$$\frac{2}{3} \cdot \frac{3}{2}x = \frac{2}{3} \cdot 3 \qquad \text{Multiply each side by } \tfrac{2}{3}.$$

$$x = 2 \qquad \text{Multiply fractions.}$$

The solution is 2 and agrees with the graphical solution.

Now Try Exercise 53

EXAMPLE 8 **Applying the intersection-of-graphs method**

During the 1990s, compact discs were a new technology that replaced cassette tapes. The percentage share of music sales (in dollars) held by compact discs from 1987 to 1998 could be modeled by $f(x) = 5.91x + 13.7$. During the same time period the percentage share of music sales held by cassette tapes could be modeled by $g(x) = -4.71x + 64.7$. In these formulas $x = 0$ corresponds to 1987, $x = 1$ to 1988, and so on. Use the intersection-of-graphs method to estimate the year when the percentage share of CDs equaled the percentage share of cassettes. (***Source:*** Recording Industry Association of America.)

SOLUTION We must solve the linear equation $f(x) = g(x)$, or equivalently,

$$5.91x + 13.7 = -4.71x + 64.7.$$

Graph $y_1 = 5.91x + 13.7$ and $y_2 = -4.71x + 64.7$, as in Figure 2.24. In Figure 2.25 their graphs intersect near the point (4.8, **42.1**). Since $x = 0$ corresponds to 1987 and $1987 + 4.8 \approx 1992$, it follows that in 1992 sales of CDs and cassette tapes were approximately equal. Each had about **42.1%** of the sales in 1992.

Calculator Help
To find the point of intersection in Figure 2.25, see Appendix A (page AP-7).

Determining When Sales Were Equal

[0, 12, 2] by [0, 100, 10]

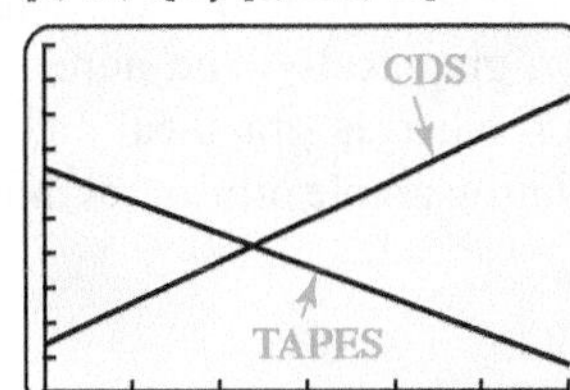

Figure 2.24

[0, 12, 2] by [0, 100, 10]

CDS = TAPES

Intersection
X=4.8022599 Y=42.081356

Figure 2.25

Now Try Exercise 99

Numerical Solutions Sometimes it is also possible to find a numerical solution to an equation by using a table of values. When the solution is an integer or a convenient fraction, we can usually find it by using the table feature on a graphing calculator. However, when the solution is a fraction with a repeating decimal representation or an irrational number, a numerical method gives only an approximate solution. The formula

$$f(x) = 755.7(x - 1985) + 6121 \quad \text{Tuitions and fees after 1985}$$

can be used to model tuition and fees at private colleges and universities during year x. See Exercise 98. To determine when tuition and fees were about \$23,500, we could solve the equation

$$755.7(x - 1985) + 6121 = 23,500$$

for x by making a table of values for $f(x)$, as shown in Figure 2.26. By scrolling through the x-values, we can see that tuition and fees at private schools were about \$23,500 in 2008.

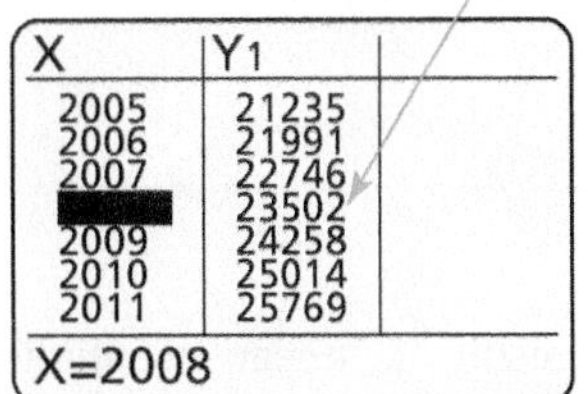

X Y1
2005 21235
2006 21991
2007 22746
23502
2009 24258
2010 25014
2011 25769
X=2008

Figure 2.26

Calculator Help
To make a table of values, see Appendix A (page AP-5).

NOTE Regardless of whether we use a symbolic, graphical, or numerical method to solve an equation, we should find the same solution set. However, our answers may differ slightly because of rounding.

A numerical technique is used in the next example, where a sequence of tables are generated to obtain an increasingly accurate answer.

EXAMPLE 9 **Solving an equation numerically**

Solve $\sqrt{3}(2x - \pi) + \frac{1}{3}x = 0$ numerically to the nearest tenth.

SOLUTION Make a table of $y_1 = \sqrt{3}(2x - \pi) + \frac{1}{3}x$, incrementing x, as shown in Figures 2.27–2.29. The solution to $y_1 = 0$, lies between x-values where y_1 changes from negative to positive. This process shows that the solution is 1.4 (to the nearest tenth).

Increment x by 1

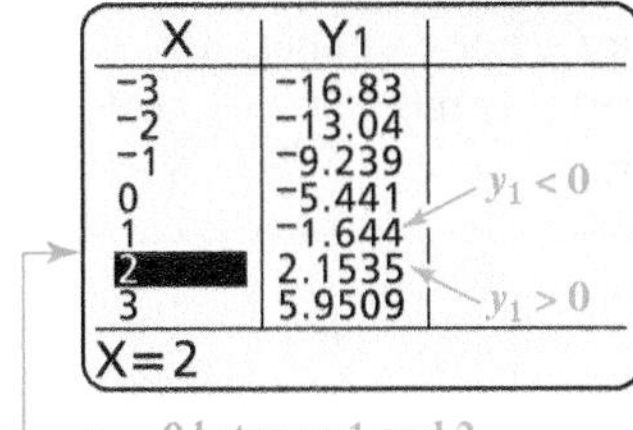

Figure 2.27

Increment x by 0.1

X	Y1
1	-1.644
1.1	-1.264
1.2	-.8845
1.3	-.5047
1.4	-.125
1.5	.25475
1.6	.6345

X=1.5

$y_1 < 0$; $y_1 > 0$

$y_1 = 0$ between 1.4 and 1.5.

Figure 2.28

Increment x by 0.01

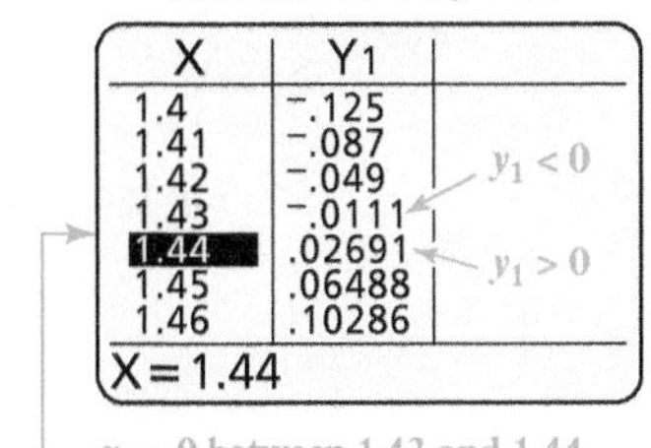

Figure 2.29

Now Try Exercise 71

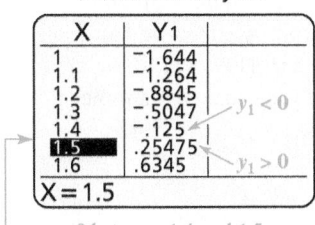

MAKING CONNECTIONS

Symbolic, Graphical, and Numerical Solutions Linear equations can be solved symbolically, graphically, and numerically. Symbolic solutions to linear equations are *always exact*, whereas graphical and numerical solutions are *sometimes approximate*. The following example illustrates how to solve the equation $2x - 1 = 3$ with each method.

Symbolic Solution

$$2x - 1 = 3$$
$$2x = 4$$
$$x = 2$$

Check:

$$2(2) - 1 \stackrel{?}{=} 3$$
$$3 = 3 \checkmark$$

It checks.

Graphical Solution

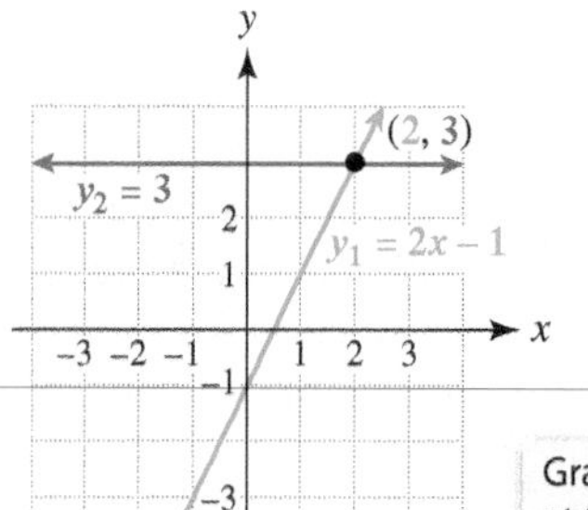

Graphs intersect at (2, 3).

The solution is 2.

Numerical Solution

x	0	1	2	3
$2x - 1$	-1	1	3	5

Because $2x - 1$ equals 3 when $x = 2$, the solution to $2x - 1 = 3$ is 2.

Percentages Applications involving percentages often result in linear equations because percentages can be computed by linear functions. A function for taking P percent of x is given by $f(x) = \frac{P}{100}x$, where $\frac{P}{100}$ is the decimal form for P percent. For example, to calculate 35% of x, let $f(x) = 0.35x$. Then 35% of \$150 is $f(150) = 0.35(150) = 52.5$, or \$52.50.

EXAMPLE 10 **Solving an application involving percentages**

A survey found that 76% of bicycle riders do not wear helmets. (***Source:*** Opinion Research Corporation for Glaxo Wellcome, Inc.)

(a) Find a formula $f(x)$ for a function that computes the number of people who do not wear helmets among x bicycle riders.

(b) There are approximately 38.7 million riders of all ages who do not wear helmets. Find the total number of bicycle riders.

SOLUTION

(a) A function f that computes 76% of x is given by $f(x) = 0.76x$.

(b) We must find the x-value for which $f(x) = 38.7$ million, or solve the equation $0.76x = 38.7$. Solving gives $x = \frac{38.7}{0.76} \approx 50.9$ million bike riders.

Now Try Exercise 105

Solving for a Variable

The circumference C of a circle is given by $C = 2\pi r$, where r is the radius. This equation is *solved* for C. That is, given r, we can easily calculate C. For example, if $r = 4$, then $C = 2\pi(4)$, or $C = 8\pi$. However, if we are given C, then it is more work to calculate r. Solving the equation for r makes it simpler to calculate r.

$$C = 2\pi r \qquad \text{Given equation}$$
$$\frac{C}{2\pi} = r \qquad \text{Divide each side by } 2\pi.$$

The equation $r = \frac{C}{2\pi}$ is solved for r.

EXAMPLE 11 Solving for a variable

The area of a trapezoid with bases a and b and height h is given by $A = \frac{1}{2}h(a + b)$. Solve this equation for b.

SOLUTION

Getting Started If we multiply each side by 2 and divide each side by h, the right side of the equation becomes $a + b$. Subtracting a from each side isolates b. ▶

$$A = \frac{1}{2}h(a + b) \quad \text{Given equation}$$

$$2A = h(a + b) \quad \text{Multiply each side by 2.}$$

$$\frac{2A}{h} = a + b \quad \text{Divide each side by } h.$$

$$\frac{2A}{h} - a = b \quad \text{Subtract } a \text{ from each side.}$$

The equation $b = \frac{2A}{h} - a$ is solved for b.

Now Try Exercise 85

Problem-Solving Strategies

To become more proficient at solving problems, we need to establish a procedure to guide our thinking. The following steps may be helpful in solving application problems.

SOLVING APPLICATION PROBLEMS

STEP 1: Read the problem and make sure you understand it. Assign a variable to what you are being asked to find. If necessary, write other quantities in terms of this variable.

STEP 2: Write an equation that relates the quantities described in the problem. You may need to sketch a diagram and refer to known formulas.

STEP 3: Solve the equation and determine the solution.

STEP 4: Look back and check your solution. Does it seem reasonable?

These steps are applied in the next four examples.

EXAMPLE 12 Working together

A large pump can empty a tank of gasoline in 5 hours, and a smaller pump can empty the same tank in 9 hours. If both pumps are used to empty the tank, how long will it take?

SOLUTION

STEP 1: We are asked to find the time it takes for *both* pumps to empty the tank. Let this time be t.

t: Time to empty the tank

STEP 2: In 1 hour the large pump will empty $\frac{1}{5}$ of the tank and the smaller pump will empty $\frac{1}{9}$ of the tank. The fraction of the tank that they will empty together in 1 hour is given by $\frac{1}{5} + \frac{1}{9}$. In 2 hours the large pump will empty $\frac{2}{5}$ of the tank and the smaller pump will empty $\frac{2}{9}$ of the tank. The fraction of the tank that they will empty together in 2 hours is $\frac{2}{5} + \frac{2}{9}$. Similarly, in t hours the fraction of the tank that the two pumps can empty is $\frac{t}{5} + \frac{t}{9}$. Since the tank is empty when this fraction reaches 1, we must solve the following equation.

$$\frac{t}{5} + \frac{t}{9} = 1$$

STEP 3: Multiply by the LCD, 45, to eliminate fractions.

$$\frac{45t}{5} + \frac{45t}{9} = 45 \quad \text{Multiply by LCD.}$$
$$9t + 5t = 45 \quad \text{Simplify.}$$
$$14t = 45 \quad \text{Add like terms.}$$
$$t = \frac{45}{14} \approx 3.21 \quad \text{Divide by 14 and approximate.}$$

Working together, the two pumps can empty the tank in about 3.21 hours.

STEP 4: This sounds reasonable. Working together the two pumps should be able to empty the tank faster than the large pump working alone, but not twice as fast. Note that $\frac{3.21}{5} + \frac{3.21}{9} \approx 1$.

Now Try Exercise 107

EXAMPLE 13 **Solving an application involving motion**

In 1 hour an athlete traveled 10.1 miles by running first at 8 miles per hour and then at 11 miles per hour. How long did the athlete run at each speed?

SOLUTION

STEP 1: We are asked to find the time spent running at each speed. If we let x represent the time in hours spent running at 8 miles per hour, then $1 - x$ represents the time spent running at 11 miles per hour because the total running time was 1 hour.

x: Time spent running at 8 miles per hour

$1 - x$: Time spent running at 11 miles per hour

STEP 2: Distance d equals rate r times time t, that is, $d = rt$. In this example we have two rates (or speeds) and two times. The total distance must sum to 10.1 miles.

$$d = r_1t_1 + r_2t_2 \quad \text{General equation}$$
$$10.1 = 8x + 11(1 - x) \quad \text{Substitute.}$$

STEP 3: We can solve this equation symbolically.

$$10.1 = 8x + 11 - 11x \quad \text{Distributive property}$$
$$10.1 = 11 - 3x \quad \text{Combine like terms.}$$
$$3x = 0.9 \quad \text{Add } 3x\text{; subtract 10.1.}$$
$$x = 0.3 \quad \text{Divide by 3.}$$

The athlete runs 0.3 hour (18 minutes) at 8 miles per hour and 0.7 hour (42 minutes) at 11 miles per hour.

STEP 4: We can check this solution as follows.

$$8(0.3) + 11(0.7) = 10.1 \checkmark \quad \text{It checks.}$$

This sounds reasonable. The runner's average speed was 10.1 miles per hour, so the runner must have run longer at 11 miles per hour than at 8 miles per hour.

Now Try Exercise 109

Geometry Review
To review similar triangles, see Chapter R (page R-5).

Similar triangles are often used in applications involving geometry and are used to solve the next application.

EXAMPLE 14 Solving an application involving similar triangles

A person 6 feet tall stands 17 feet from the base of a streetlight, as illustrated in Figure 2.30. If the person's shadow is 8 feet, estimate the height of the streetlight.

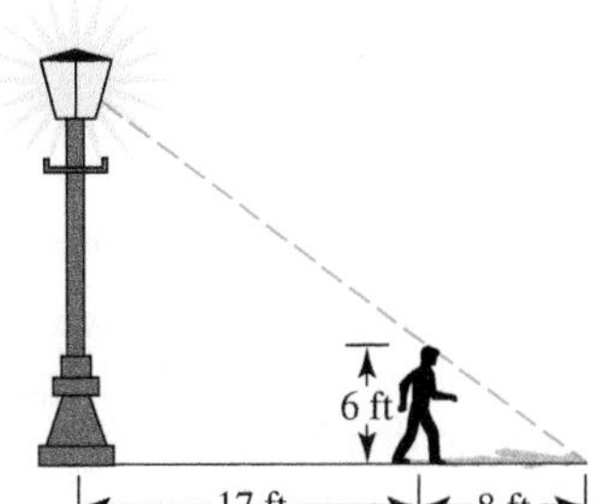

Figure 2.30

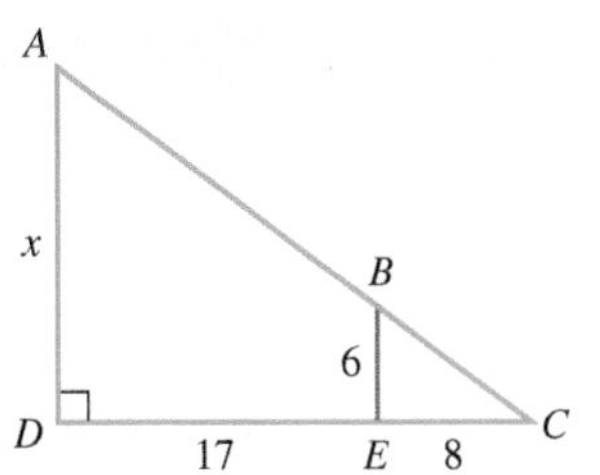

Figure 2.31

SOLUTION

STEP 1: We are asked to find the height of the streetlight in Figure 2.30. Let x represent this height.

x: Height of the streetlight

STEP 2: In Figure 2.31, triangle ACD is similar to triangle BCE. Thus ratios of corresponding sides are equal.

$$\frac{AD}{BE} = \frac{DC}{EC} \quad \text{Similar triangles}$$

$$\frac{x}{6} = \frac{17 + 8}{8}$$

STEP 3: We can solve this equation symbolically.

$$\frac{x}{6} = \frac{25}{8} \quad \text{Simplify.}$$

$$x = \frac{6 \cdot 25}{8} \quad \text{Multiply by 6.}$$

$$x = 18.75 \quad \text{Simplify.}$$

The height of the streetlight is 18.75 feet.

STEP 4: One way to check this answer is to form a different proportion. Note that x is to $17 + 8$ in triangle ADC as 6 is to 8 in triangle BEC. If $x = 18.75$, then $\frac{18.75}{25} = \frac{6}{8}$, which is true, and our answer checks.

Now Try Exercise 113

EXAMPLE 15 Mixing acid in chemistry

Pure water is being added to 153 milliliters of a 30% solution of hydrochloric acid. How much water should be added to dilute the solution to a 13% mixture?

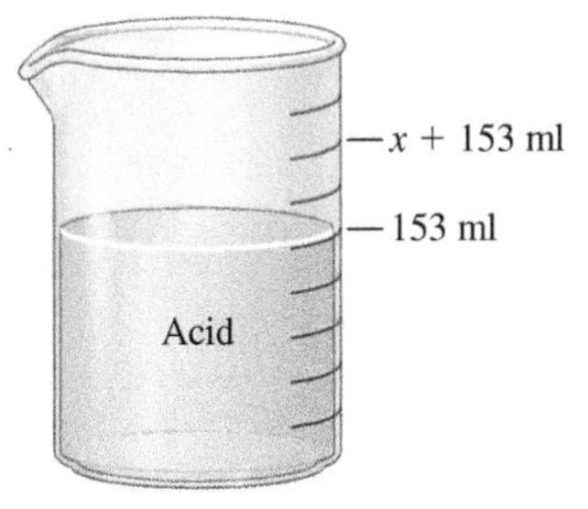

Figure 2.32

SOLUTION

STEP 1: We are asked to find the amount of water that should be added to 153 milliliters of 30% acid to make a 13% solution. Let this amount of water be equal to x. See Figure 2.32.

x: Amount of pure water to be added

$x + 153$: Final volume of 13% solution

STEP 2: Since only water is added, the total amount of acid in the solution after the water is added must equal the amount of acid before the water is added. The volume of pure acid after the water is added equals 13% of $x + 153$ milliliters, and the volume of pure acid before the water is added equals 30% of 153 milliliters. We must solve the following equation.

$$0.13(x + 153) = 0.30(153) \quad \text{Pure acid after equals pure acid before.}$$

STEP 3: Begin by dividing each side by 0.13.

$$0.13(x + 153) = 0.30(153) \quad \text{Equation to solve}$$

$$x + 153 = \frac{0.30(153)}{0.13} \quad \text{Divide by 0.13.}$$

$$x = \frac{0.30(153)}{0.13} - 153 \quad \text{Subtract 153.}$$

$$x \approx 200.08 \quad \text{Approximate.}$$

We should add about 200 milliliters of pure water.

STEP 4: Initially the solution contains $0.30(153) = 45.9$ milliliters of pure acid. If we add 200 milliliters of water to the 153 milliliters, the final solution is 353 milliliters, which includes 45.9 milliliters of pure acid. Its concentration is $\frac{45.9}{353} \approx 0.13$, or about 13%.

Now Try Exercise 117

2.2 Putting It All Together

A general four-step procedure for solving applications is given in this section. The following table summarizes some of the important concepts.

CONCEPT	EXPLANATION	EXAMPLES
Linear equation	A linear equation can be written as $ax + b = 0,\ a \neq 0.$	$4x + 5 = 0$ $3x - 1 = x + 2$
Addition property	$a = b$ is equivalent to $a + c = b + c.$	$x - 7 = 25$ $x - 7 + 7 = 25 + 7$ $x = 32$
Multiplication property	$a = b$ is equivalent to $ac = bc,\ c \neq 0.$	$\frac{1}{2}x = 4$ $2 \cdot \frac{1}{2}x = 4 \cdot 2$ $x = 8$
Distributive property	$a(b + c) = ab + ac$ $a(b - c) = ab - ac$	$2(5 + x) = 10 + 2x$ $-(2 - x) = -1(2 - x) = -2 + x$
Identity	An equation that is true for all (meaningful) values of the variable	$3(x - 2) = 3x - 6$ $2x + 3x = (2 + 3)x = 5x$
Contradiction	An equation that has no solutions	$x + 5 = x$ $2x - 2x = 5$
Conditional equation	An equation that is satisfied by some, but not all, of the values of the variable	$2x - 1 = 5$ Given equation $2x = 6$ Add 1. $x = 3$ Divide by 2.
Percentages	P percent of x equals $\frac{P}{100}x$, where $\frac{P}{100}$ is the decimal form for P percent.	35% of x is calculated by $f(x) = \frac{35}{100}x$, or $f(x) = 0.35x$.

The following example illustrates three ways to solve $5x - 1 = 3$.

Symbolic Solution

$$5x - 1 = 3$$
$$5x = 4$$
$$x = \frac{4}{5}$$

Check:

$$5\left(\frac{4}{5}\right) - 1 \stackrel{?}{=} 3$$
$$4 - 1 \stackrel{?}{=} 3$$
$$3 \stackrel{?}{=} 3 \checkmark$$

It checks.

Graphical Solution

$[-9, 9, 1]$ by $[-6, 6, 1]$

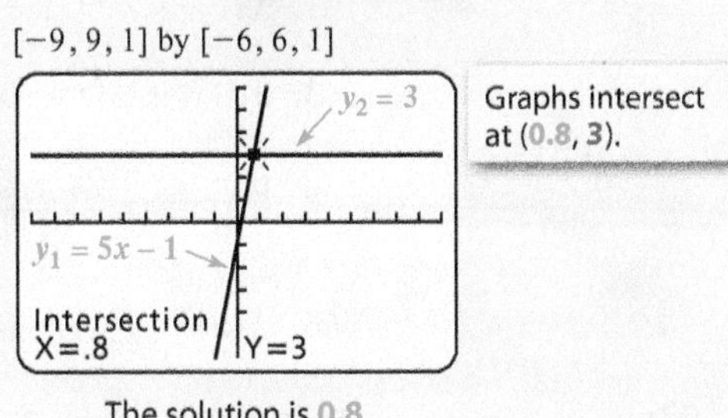

The solution is 0.8.

Numerical Solution

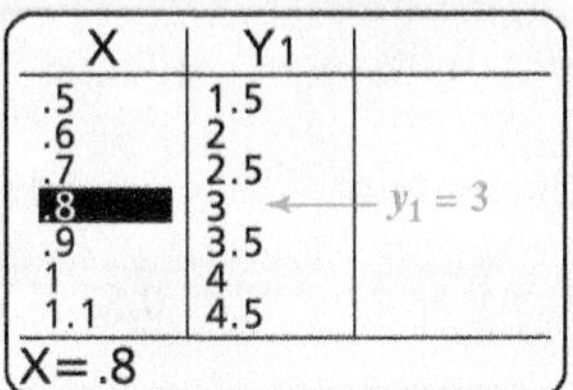

X	Y1
.5	1.5
.6	2
.7	2.5
.8	3
.9	3.5
1	4
1.1	4.5

In the table, $y_1 = 3$ when $x = 0.8$.

2.2 Exercises

Concepts about Linear Equations

1. How many solutions are there to $ax + b = 0$ with $a \neq 0$?

2. How many times does the graph of $y = ax + b$ with $a \neq 0$ intersect the x-axis?

3. Apply the distributive property to $4 - (5 - 4x)$.

4. What property is used to solve $15x = 5$?

5. If $f(x) = ax + b$ with $a \neq 0$, how are the zero of f and the x-intercept of the graph of f related?

6. Distinguish between a contradiction and an identity.

Identifying Linear and Nonlinear Equations

Exercises 7–12: Determine whether the equation is linear or nonlinear by trying to write it in the form $ax + b = 0$.

7. $3x - 1.5 = 7$
8. $100 - 23x = 20x$
9. $2\sqrt{x} + 2 = 1$
10. $4x^3 - 7 = 0$
11. $7x - 5 = 3(x - 8)$
12. $2(x - 3) = 4 - 5x$

Solving Linear Equations Symbolically

Exercises 13–38: Solve the equation and check your answer.

13. $2x - 8 = 0$
14. $4x - 8 = 0$
15. $-5x + 3 = 23$
16. $-9x - 3 = 24$
17. $4(z - 8) = z$
18. $-3(2z - 1) = 2z$
19. $-5(3 - 4t) = 65$
20. $6(5 - 3t) = 66$
21. $k + 8 = 5k - 4$
22. $2k - 3 = k + 3$
23. $2(1 - 3x) + 1 = 3x$
24. $5(x - 2) = -2(1 - x)$
25. $-5(3 - 2x) - (1 - x) = 4(x - 3)$
26. $-3(5 - x) - (x - 2) = 7x - 2$
27. $-4(5x - 1) = 8 - (x + 2)$
28. $6(3 - 2x) = 1 - (2x - 1)$
29. $\frac{2}{7}n + 2 = \frac{4}{7}$
30. $\frac{6}{11} - \frac{2}{33}n = \frac{5}{11}n$
31. $\frac{1}{2}(d - 3) - \frac{2}{3}(2d - 5) = \frac{5}{12}$
32. $\frac{7}{3}(2d - 1) - \frac{2}{5}(4 - 3d) = \frac{1}{5}d$
33. $\frac{x - 5}{3} + \frac{3 - 2x}{2} = \frac{5}{4} - 2(1 - x)$
34. $\frac{3x - 1}{5} - 2 = \frac{2 - x}{3}$
35. $0.1z - 0.05 = -0.07z$
36. $1.1z - 2.5 = 0.3(z - 2)$
37. $0.15t + 0.85(100 - t) = 0.45(100)$
38. $0.35t + 0.65(10 - t) = 0.55(10)$

Exercises 39–48: Complete the following.

(a) Solve the equation symbolically.

(b) Classify the equation as a contradiction, an identity, or a conditional equation.

39. $5x - 1 = 5x + 4$

40. $7 - 9z = 2(3 - 4z) - z$

41. $3(x - 1) = 5$

42. $22 = -2(2x + 1.4)$

43. $0.5(x - 2) + 5 = 0.5x + 4$

44. $\frac{1}{2}x - 2(x - 1) = -\frac{3}{2}x + 2$

45. $\frac{t + 1}{2} = \frac{3t - 2}{6}$

46. $\frac{2x + 1}{3} = \frac{2x - 1}{3}$

47. $\frac{1 - 2x}{4} = \frac{3x - 1.5}{-6}$

48. $0.5(3x - 1) + 0.5x = 2x - 0.5$

Solving Linear Equations Graphically

Exercises 49 and 50: A linear equation is solved by using the intersection-of-graphs method. Find the solution by interpreting the graph. Assume that the solution is an integer.

49.

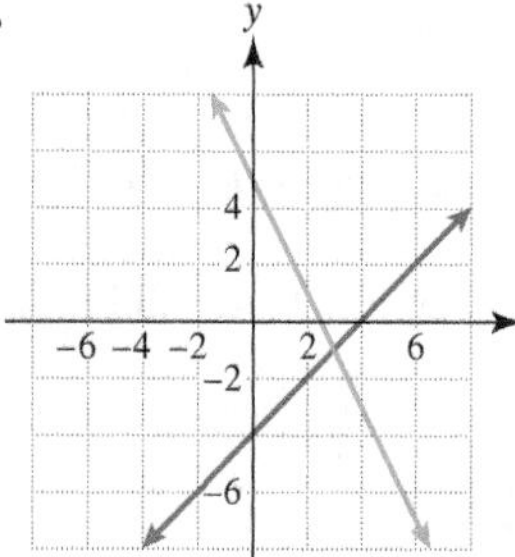

50.

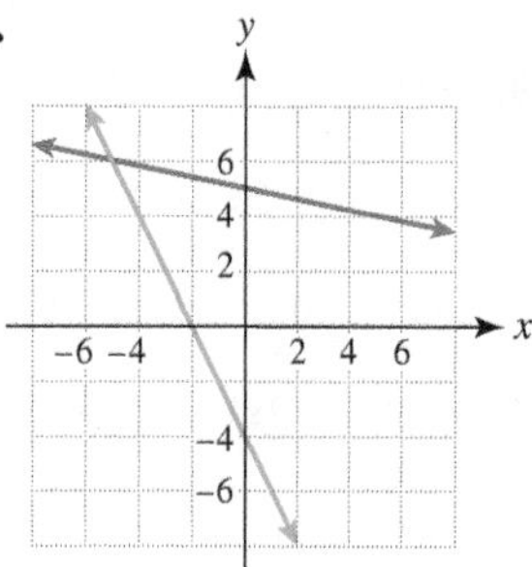

Exercises 51 and 52: Use the graph of $y = f(x)$ to solve each equation.

(a) $f(x) = -1$ *(b)* $f(x) = 0$ *(c)* $f(x) = 2$

51.

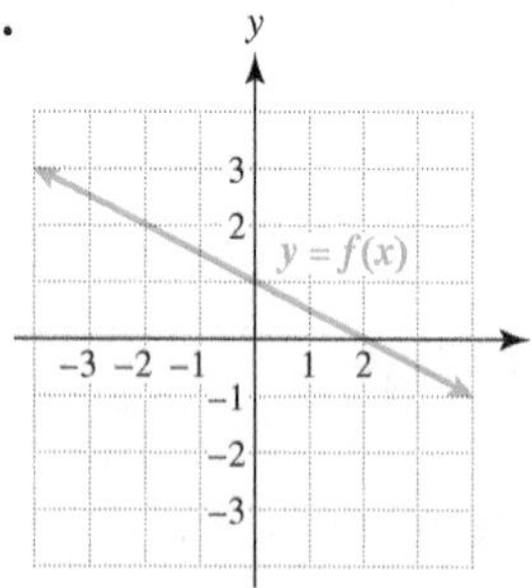

52.

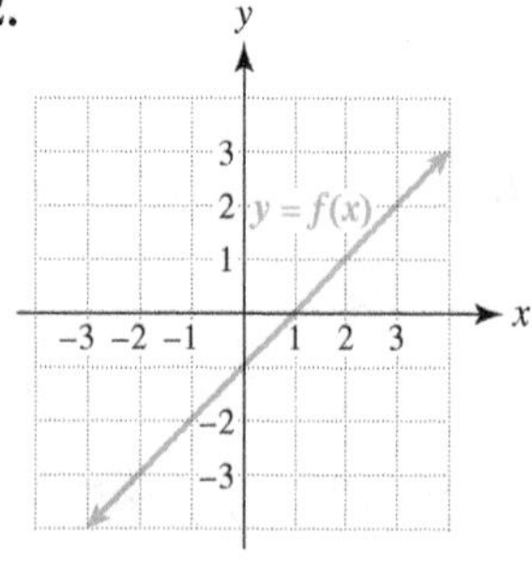

Exercises 53–58: Use the intersection-of-graphs method to solve the equation. Then solve symbolically.

53. $x + 4 = 1 - 2x$

54. $2x = 3x - 1$

55. $-x + 4 = 3x$

56. $1 - 2x = x + 4$

57. $2(x - 1) - 2 = x$

58. $-(x + 1) - 2 = 2x$

Exercises 59–66: Solve the linear equation with the intersection-of-graphs method. Approximate the solution to the nearest thousandth whenever appropriate.

59. $5x - 1.5 = 5$

60. $8 - 2x = 1.6$

61. $3x - 1.7 = 1 - x$

62. $\sqrt{2}x = 4x - 6$

63. $3.1(x - 5) = \frac{1}{5}x - 5$

64. $65 = 8(x - 6) - 5.5$

65. $\frac{6 - x}{7} = \frac{2x - 3}{3}$

66. $\pi(x - \sqrt{2}) = 1.07x - 6.1$

Solving Linear Equations Numerically

Exercises 67–74: Use tables to solve the equation numerically to the nearest tenth.

67. $2x - 7 = -1$

68. $1 - 6x = 7$

69. $2x - 7.2 = 10$

70. $5.8x - 8.7 = 0$

71. $\sqrt{2}(4x - 1) + \pi x = 0$

72. $\pi(0.3x - 2) + \sqrt{2}x = 0$

73. $0.5 - 0.1(\sqrt{2} - 3x) = 0$

74. $\sqrt{5} - \pi(\pi + 0.3x) = 0$

Solving Linear Equations by More Than One Method

Exercises 75–82: Solve the equation (to the nearest tenth)

(a) symbolically,

(b) graphically, and

(c) numerically.

75. $5 - (x + 1) = 3$

76. $7 - (3 - 2x) = 1$

77. $x - 3 = 2x + 1$

78. $3(x - 1) = 2x - 1$

79. $\sqrt{3}(2 - \pi x) + x = 0$

80. $3(\pi - x) + \sqrt{2} = 0$

81. $6x - 8 = -7x + 18$

82. $5 - 8x = 3(x - 7) + 37$

Solving for a Variable

Exercises 83–90: Solve the equation for the specified variable.

83. $A = LW$ for W

84. $E = IR + 2$ for R

85. $P = 2L + 2W$ for L

86. $V = 2\pi rh + \pi r^2$ for h

87. $3x + 2y = 8$ for y

88. $5x - 4y = 20$ for y

89. $y = 3(x - 2) + x$ for x

90. $y = 4 - (8 - 2x)$ for x

Exercises 91–96: The equation of a line is written in standard form.

(a) Solve the equation for y.
(b) Write a formula f(x) for a function whose graph is the given line.

91. $2x + y = 8$ **92.** $3x - y = 5$

93. $2x - 4y = -1$ **94.** $7x + 3y = -4$

95. $-9x + 8y = 9$ **96.** $-2x - 6y = 3$

Applications

97. Income The per capita (per person) income from 1980 to 2010 can be modeled by

$$f(x) = 1000(x - 1980) + 10{,}000,$$

where x is the year. Determine the year when the per capita income was \$19,000. (***Source:*** Bureau of the Census.)

98. Tuition and Fees Tuition and fees during year x at private colleges can be modeled by

$$f(x) = 755.7(x - 1985) + 6121.$$

Use $f(x)$ to determine when tuition and fees might reach \$28,000.

99. Vinyl and CD Sales During the 1980s, sales of compact discs surpassed vinyl record sales. From 1985 to 1990, sales of compact discs in millions can be modeled by the formula $f(x) = 51.6(x - 1985) + 9.1$, whereas sales of vinyl LP records in millions can be modeled by $g(x) = -31.9(x - 1985) + 167.7$. Approximate the year x when sales of LP records and compact discs were equal by using the intersection-of-graphs method. (***Source:*** Recording Industry Association of America.)

100. Median Age The median age A in the United States during year x, where $2000 \le x \le 2050$, is projected to be

$$A(x) = 0.07(x - 2000) + 35.3.$$

Use $A(x)$ to estimate when the median age may reach 37 years. (***Source:*** Bureau of the Census.)

101. Legalize of Not? The attitudes toward legalization of marijuana changed between 1995 and 2012. The formula $A(x) = -1.6x + 3265$ gives the percentage of people in year x who were against legalization, and the formula $F(x) = 1.5x - 2968$ gives the percentage of people in year x who were in favor of legalization. (***Source:*** Gallup Poll.)

(a) Interpret the slope of the graphs of A and F.

(b) Estimate the year when the percentages for and against were equal.

102. Population Density In 2000 the population density of the United States was 80 people per square mile, and in 2011 it was 88 people per square mile. Use a linear function to estimate when the U.S. population density will reach 91 people per square mile.

103. Sale Price A store is discounting all regularly priced merchandise by 25%. Find a function f that computes the sale price of an item having a regular price of x. If an item normally costs \$56.24, what is its sale price?

104. Sale Price Continuing Exercise 103, use f to find the regular price of an item that costs \$19.62 on sale.

105. Skin Cancer Approximately 4.8% of all cancer cases diagnosed in 2011 were skin cancer. (***Source:*** American Cancer Society.)

(a) If x cases of cancer were diagnosed, how many of these were skin cancer?

(b) There were 76,000 cases of skin cancer diagnosed in 2011. Find the total number of cancer cases in 2011.

106. Grades In order to receive an A in a college course it is necessary to obtain an average of 90% correct on three 1-hour exams of 100 points each and on one final exam of 200 points. If a student scores 82, 88, and 91 on the 1-hour exams, what is the minimum score that the person can receive on the final exam and still earn an A?

107. Working Together Suppose that a lawn can be raked by one gardener in 3 hours and by a second gardener in 5 hours.

(a) Mentally estimate how long it will take the two gardeners to rake the lawn working together.

(b) Solve part (a) symbolically.

108. Pumping Water Suppose that a large pump can empty a swimming pool in 50 hours and a small pump can empty the pool in 80 hours. How long will it take to empty the pool if both pumps are used?

109. Motion A car went 372 miles in 6 hours, traveling part of the time at 55 miles per hour and part of the time at 70 miles per hour. How long did the car travel at each speed?

110. Mixing Candy Two types of candy sell for \$2.50 per pound and \$4.00 per pound. A store clerk is trying to make a 5-pound mixture worth \$17.60. How much of each type of candy should be included in the mixture?

111. **Running** At 2:00 P.M. a runner heads north on a highway, jogging at 10 miles per hour. At 2:30 P.M. a driver heads north on the same highway to pick up the runner. If the car travels at 55 miles per hour, how long will it take the driver to catch the runner?

112. **Investments** A total of \$5000 was invested in two accounts. One pays 5% annual interest, and the second pays 7% annual interest. If the first-year interest is \$325, how much was invested in each account?

113. **Height of a Tree** In the accompanying figure, a person 5 feet tall casts a shadow 4 feet long. A nearby tree casts a shadow 33 feet long. Find the height of the tree by solving a linear equation.

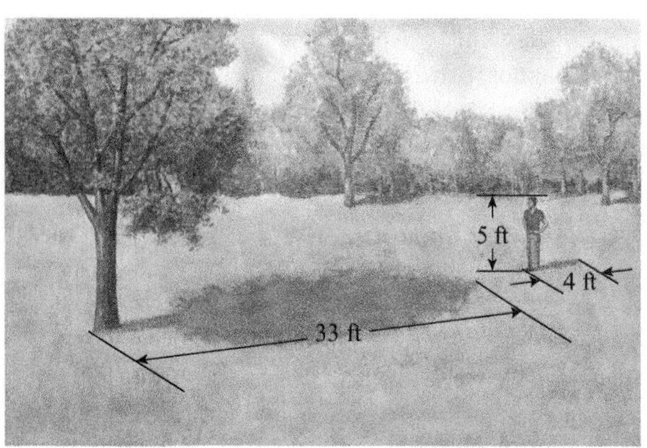

114. **Shadow Length** A person 66 inches tall is standing 15 feet from a streetlight. If the person casts a shadow 84 inches long, how tall is the streetlight?

115. **Conical Water Tank** A water tank in the shape of an inverted cone has a height of 11 feet and a radius of 3.5 feet, as illustrated in the figure. If the volume of the cone is $V = \frac{1}{3}\pi r^2 h$, find the volume of the water in the tank when the water is 7 feet deep. (*Hint:* Consider using similar triangles.)

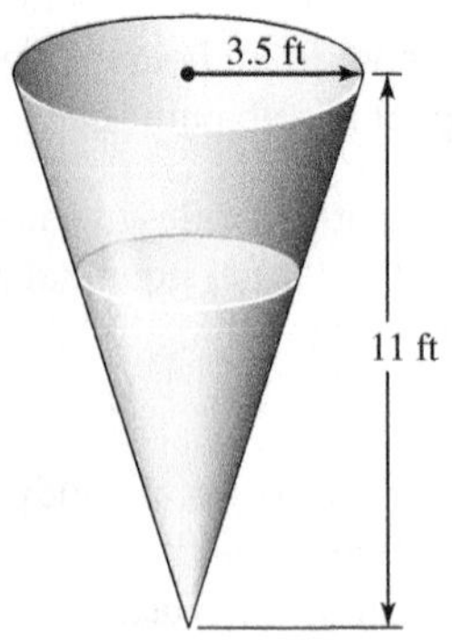

116. **Dimension of a Cone** (Refer to Exercise 115.) A conical water tank holds 100 cubic feet of water and has a diameter of 6 feet. Estimate its height to the nearest tenth of a foot.

117. **Chemistry** Determine how much pure water should be mixed with 5 liters of a 40% solution of sulfuric acid to make a 15% solution of sulfuric acid.

118. **Mixing Antifreeze** A radiator holds 5 gallons of fluid. If it is full with a 15% solution, how much fluid should be drained and replaced with a 65% antifreeze mixture to result in a 40% antifreeze mixture?

119. **Window Dimensions** A rectangular window has a length that is 18 inches more than its width. If its perimeter is 180 inches, find its dimensions.

120. **Sales of CRT and LCD Screens** In 2002, 75 million CRT (cathode ray tube) monitors were sold and 29 million flat LCD (liquid crystal display) monitors were sold. In 2006 the numbers were 45 million for CRT monitors and 88 million for LCD monitors. (***Source:*** International Data Corporation.)

(a) Find a linear function C that models these data for CRT monitors and another linear function L that models these data for LCD monitors. Let x be the year.

(b) Interpret the slopes of the graphs of C and of L.

(c) Determine graphically the year when sales of these two types of monitors were equal.

(d) Solve part (c) symbolically.

(e) Solve part (c) numerically.

121. **Online Shopping** In 2011 online sales were \$192 billion, and in 2014 they are predicted to be \$249 billion. (***Source:*** Forrestor Forecast.)

(a) Find a linear function S that models these data. Write $S(x)$ in slope-intercept form.

(b) Interpret the slope of the graph of S.

(c) Determine when online sales were \$230 billion.

122. **Geometry** A 174-foot-long fence is being placed around the perimeter of a rectangular swimming pool that has a 3-foot-wide sidewalk around it. The actual swimming pool without the sidewalk is twice as long as it is wide. Find the dimensions of the pool without the sidewalk.

123. **Temperature Scales** The Celsius and Fahrenheit scales are related by the equation $C = \frac{5}{9}(F - 32)$. These scales have the same temperature reading at a unique value where $F = C$. Find this temperature.

124. Business A company manufactures compact discs with recorded music. The master disc costs $2000 to produce and copies cost $0.45 each. If a company spent $2990 producing compact discs, how many copies did the company manufacture?

125. Two-Cycle Engines Two-cycle engines, used in snowmobiles, chain saws, and outboard motors, require a mixture of gasoline and oil. For certain engines the amount of oil in pints that should be added to x gallons of gasoline is computed by $f(x) = 0.16x$. (***Source:*** Johnson Outboard Motor Company.)

(a) Why is it reasonable to expect f to be linear?

(b) Evaluate $f(3)$ and interpret the answer.

(c) How much gasoline should be mixed with 2 pints of oil?

126. Perimeter Find the length of the longest side of the rectangle if its perimeter is 25 feet.

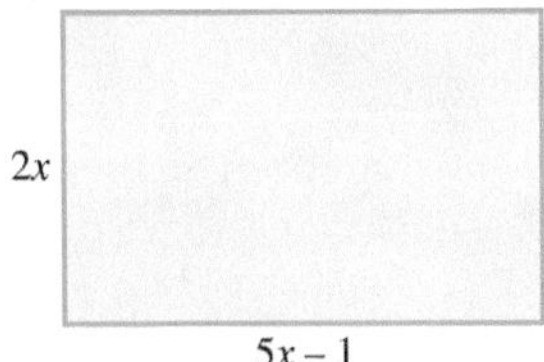

Modeling Data with Linear Functions

Exercises 127 and 128: The following data can be modeled by a linear function. Estimate the value of x when $y = 2.99$.

127.

x	2	4	6	8
y	0.51	1.23	1.95	2.67

128.

x	1	2	3	4
y	−1.66	2.06	5.78	9.50

Writing about Mathematics

129. Describe a basic graphical method used to solve a linear equation. Give an example.

130. Describe verbally how to solve $ax + b = 0$. What assumptions have you made about the value of a?

Extended and Discovery Exercises

1. Geometry Suppose that two rectangles are similar and the sides of the first rectangle are twice as long as the corresponding sides of the second rectangle.

(a) Is the perimeter of the first rectangle twice the perimeter of the second rectangle? Explain.

(b) Is the area of the first rectangle twice the area of the second rectangle? Explain.

2. Geometry Repeat the previous exercise for an equilateral triangle. Try to make a generalization. (*Hint:* The area of an equilateral triangle is $A = \frac{\sqrt{3}}{4}x^2$, where x is the length of a side.) What will happen to the circumference of a circle if the radius is doubled? What will happen to its area?

3. Indoor Air Pollution Formaldehyde is an indoor air pollutant formerly found in plywood, foam insulation, and carpeting. When concentrations in the air reach 33 micrograms per cubic foot ($\mu g/ft^3$), eye irritation can occur. One square foot of new plywood could emit 140 μg per hour. (***Source:*** A. Hines, *Indoor Air Quality & Control.*)

(a) A room has 100 square feet of new plywood flooring. Find a linear function f that computes the amount of formaldehyde in micrograms that could be emitted in x hours.

(b) The room contains 800 cubic feet of air and has no ventilation. Determine how long it would take for concentrations to reach 33 $\mu g/ft^3$.

4. Temperature and Volume The table shows the relationship between the temperature of a sample of helium and its volume.

Temperature (°C)	0	25	50	75	100
Volume (in³)	30	32.7	35.4	38.1	40.8

(a) Make a scatterplot of the data.

(b) Write a formula for a function f that receives the temperature x as input and outputs the volume y of the helium.

(c) Find the volume when the temperature is 65°C.

(d) Find the temperature if the volume is 25 cubic inches. Did your answer involve interpolation or extrapolation? Do you believe that your answer is accurate?

CHECKING BASIC CONCEPTS FOR SECTIONS 2.1 AND 2.2

1. Find an equation of the line passing through the points $(-3, 4)$ and $(5, -2)$. Give equations of lines that are parallel and perpendicular to this line.

2. Find equations of horizontal and vertical lines that pass through the point $(-4, 7)$.

3. Write the slope-intercept form of the line.

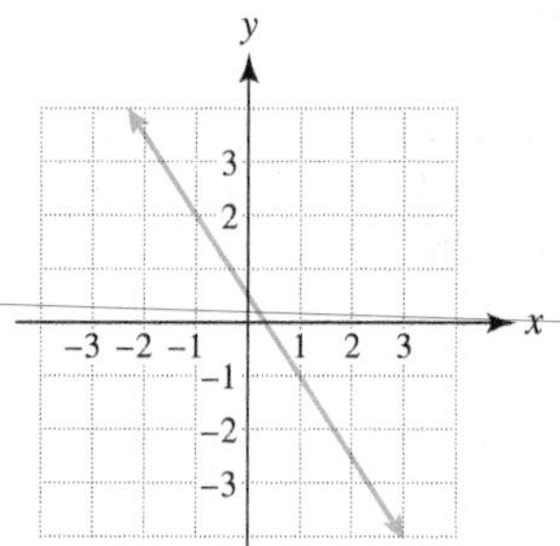

4. Find the x- and y-intercepts of the graph of the equation $-3x + 2y = -18$.

5. Solve $5x + 2 = 2x - 3$ and check your answer.

6. Solve each equation.
   (a) $\frac{3x}{4} + 2 = \frac{2x}{3}$
   (b) $-4.1x + 5.45 = 1.05(5 - 2x)$

7. Solve the linear equation $4(x - 2) = 2(5 - x) - 3$ by using each method. Compare your results.
   (a) Graphical
   (b) Numerical
   (c) Symbolic

2.3 Linear Inequalities

- **Understand basic terminology related to inequalities**
- **Solve linear inequalities symbolically**
- **Solve linear inequalities graphically and numerically**
- **Solve compound inequalities**

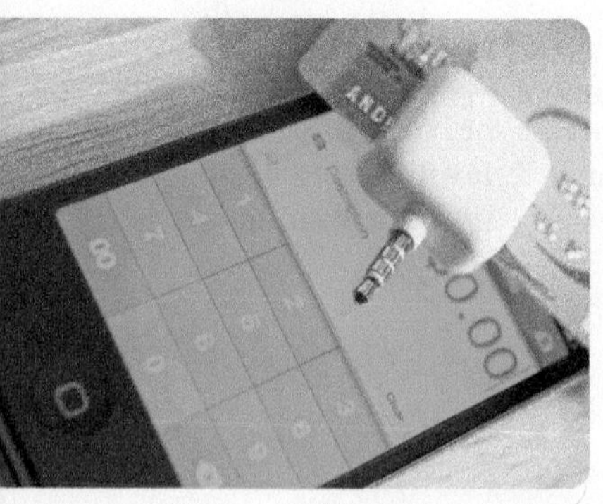

Introduction

Twitter cofounder Jack Dorsey has started another company called Square. Square is a payment startup that allows businesses to swipe credit cards on their iPhones and Android devices. During a 12-month period from March 2011 to March 2012, Square's *daily* payment volume grew from \$1 million to \$11 million. In Example 3 we make estimations about this growth by using linear inqualities. (***Source:*** Business Insider.)

Inequalities

Inequalities result whenever the equals sign in an equation is replaced with any one of the symbols $<$, $\leq$, $>$, or $\geq$.

Inequalities with Zero, One, and Two Variables

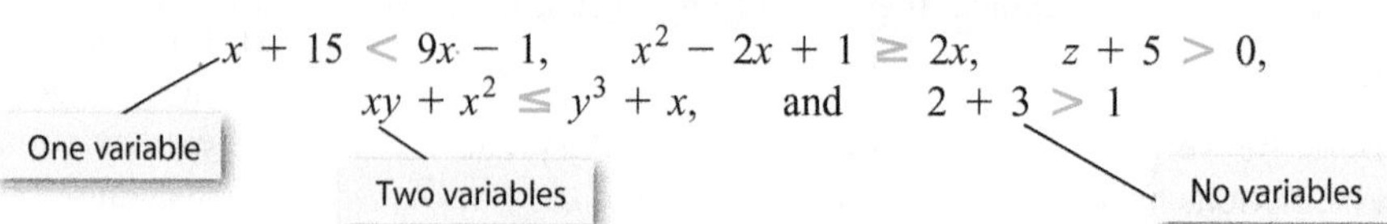

$$x + 15 < 9x - 1, \quad x^2 - 2x + 1 \geq 2x, \quad z + 5 > 0,$$
$$xy + x^2 \leq y^3 + x, \quad \text{and} \quad 2 + 3 > 1$$

We will concentrate on inequalities with one variable.

To **solve** an inequality means to find all values for the variable that make the inequality a true statement. Such values are **solutions**, and the set of all solutions is the **solution set** to the inequality. Two inequalities are **equivalent** if they have the same solution set. It is common for an inequality to have infinitely many solutions. For instance, the inequality $x - 1 > 0$ has infinitely many solutions because any real number x satisfying $x > 1$ is a solution. The solution set is $\{x \mid x > 1\}$.

Like functions and equations, inequalities in one variable can be classified as *linear* or *nonlinear*.

LINEAR INEQUALITY IN ONE VARIABLE

A **linear inequality** in one variable is an inequality that can be written in the form

$$ax + b > 0,$$

where $a \neq 0$. (The symbol $>$ may be replaced by $\geq$, $<$, or $\leq$.)

Linear Inequalities

$3x - 4 < 0$, $7x + 5 \geq x$, $x + 6 > 23$, and $7x + 2 \leq -3x + 6$.

Using techniques from algebra, we can transform these inequalities into one of the forms $ax + b > 0$, $ax + b \geq 0$, $ax + b < 0$, or $ax + b \leq 0$. For example, by subtracting x from each side of $7x + 5 \geq x$, we obtain the equivalent inequality $6x + 5 \geq 0$. If an inequality is not a linear inequality, it is called a **nonlinear inequality**.

PROPERTIES OF INEQUALITIES

Let a, b, and c be real numbers.

1. $a < b$ and $a + c < b + c$ are equivalent.
   (The same number may be added to or subtracted from each side of an inequality.)
2. If $c > 0$, then $a < b$ and $ac < bc$ are equivalent.
   (Each side of an inequality may be multiplied or divided by the same *positive* number.)
3. If $c < 0$, then $a < b$ and $ac > bc$ are equivalent.
   (Each side of an inequality may be multiplied or divided by the same *negative* number provided the inequality symbol is *reversed*.)

Replacing $<$ with $\leq$ and $>$ with $\geq$ results in similar properties.

The following examples illustrate each property.

Property 1: To solve $x - 5 < 6$, add 5 to each side to obtain $x < 11$.
Property 2: To solve $5x < 10$, divide each side by 5 to obtain $x < 2$.
Property 3: To solve $-5x < 10$, divide each side by -5 to obtain $x > -2$. (Whenever you multiply or divide an inequality by a *negative* number, *reverse* the inequality symbol.)

MAKING CONNECTIONS

Linear Functions, Equations, and Inequalities These concepts are closely related.

$f(x) = ax + b$	Linear function ($a = m$)
$ax + b = 0, a \neq 0$	Linear equation
$ax + b > 0, a \neq 0$	Linear inequality

Review of Interval Notation In Section 1.4 interval notation was introduced as an efficient way to express intervals on the real number line. For example, the interval $3 \leq x \leq 5$ is written as $[3, 5]$, whereas the interval $3 < x < 5$ is written as $(3, 5)$. A bracket, [or], is used when an endpoint is included, and a parenthesis, (or), is used when an endpoint is not included. The interval $x \geq 2$ is written as $[2, \infty)$, where ∞ denotes infinity, and the interval $x < 2$ is written as $(-\infty, 2)$

Symbolic Solutions In the next example we solve linear inequalities symbolically and express the solution set in both set-builder and interval notation.

EXAMPLE 1 **Solving linear inequalities symbolically**

Solve each inequality. Write the solution set in set-builder and interval notation.

(a) $2x - 3 < \dfrac{x + 2}{-3}$

(b) $-3(4z - 4) \ge 4 - (z - 1)$

SOLUTION

(a) Use Property 3 by multiplying each side by -3 to clear fractions.

$2x - 3 < \dfrac{x + 2}{-3}$	Given inequality
$-3(2x - 3) > -3\left(\dfrac{x + 2}{-3}\right)$	Property 3: Multiply by -3 and reverse the inequality symbol.
$-6x + 9 > x + 2$	Distributive property; simplify.
$9 < 7x + 2$	Property 1: Add $6x$.
$7 > 7x$	Property 1: Add -2 (or subtract 2).
$1 > x$	Property 2: Divide by 7.

Reverse $<$ to $>$ when multiplying by a negative.

The solution set is $\{x \mid x < 1\}$, and in interval notation it is written as $(-\infty, 1)$.

(b) Begin by applying the distributive property.

$-3(4z - 4) \ge 4 - (z - 1)$	Given inequality
$-12z + 12 \ge 4 - z + 1$	Distributive property
$-12z + 12 \ge -z + 5$	Simplify.
$-12z + z \ge 5 - 12$	Property 1: Add z and -12.
$-11z \ge -7$	Simplify.
$z \le \dfrac{7}{11}$	Property 3: Divide by -11 and reverse inequality symbol.

The solution set is $\left\{z \mid z \le \frac{7}{11}\right\}$, and in interval notation it is written as $\left(-\infty, \frac{7}{11}\right]$.

Now Try Exercises 15 and 17

Graphical Solutions The intersections-of-graphs method can be extended to solve inequalities. The following box shows the actual and projected percentages of college degrees conferred to females F and to males M. (*Source:* Bureau of Labor Statistics.)

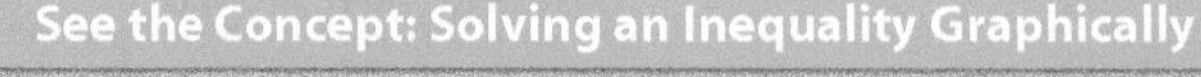

College Degrees Conferred, 1975–2017 (Female versus Male)

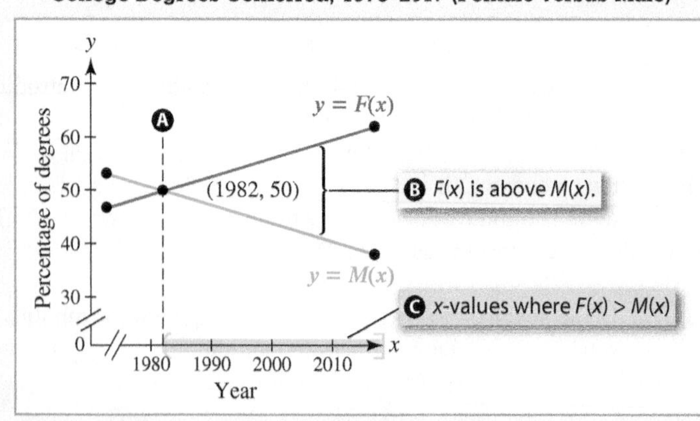

A In 1982 half, or 50%, of all college degrees conferred were given to females.

B There are more female graduates after 1982.

C $F(x) > M(x)$ when $1982 < x \le 2017$.

The preceding box illustrates how we can solve the inequality $F(x) > M(x)$ graphically. This graphical technique is used in the next example.

EXAMPLE 2 **Solving a linear inequality graphically**

Graph $y_1 = \frac{1}{2}x + 2$ and $y_2 = 2x - 1$ by hand. Use the graph to solve the linear inequality $\frac{1}{2}x + 2 > 2x - 1$.

SOLUTION The graphs of $y_1 = \frac{1}{2}x + 2$ and $y_2 = 2x - 1$ are shown in Figure 2.33. The graphs intersect at the point (2, 3). The graph of $y_1 = \frac{1}{2}x + 2$ is above the graph of $y_2 = 2x - 1$ to the left of the point of intersection, or when $x < 2$. Thus the solution set to the inequality $\frac{1}{2}x + 2 > 2x - 1$ is $\{x \mid x < 2\}$, or $(-\infty, 2)$.

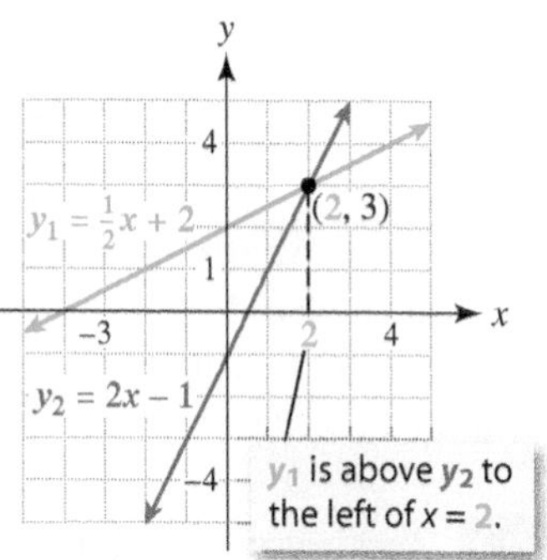

Figure 2.33

Now Try Exercise 39

An Application In the next example we use graphical and symbolic techniques to analyze the growth of Square, which is discussed in the introduction to this section.

EXAMPLE 3 **Analyzing the growth of Square**

The *daily* payment processing volume for the company Square grew from \$1 million in March 2011 to \$11 million in March 2012. Its growth was approximately linear.

(a) Write a formula $S(x)$ for a linear function that models this growth in millions of dollars, where x represents months after March 2011. Assume that $0 \le x \le 12$.

(b) Determine symbolically and graphically when Square's daily volume was \$8.5 million or less.

SOLUTION

(a) The graph of S must pass through the point (0, 1) and (12, 11). The slope of this graph is

$$m = \frac{11 - 1}{12 - 0} = \frac{10}{12} = \frac{5}{6}.$$

The graph passes through (0, 1), so the y-intercept is 1. Thus $S(x) = \frac{5}{6}x + 1$.

(b) ***Symbolic Solution*** We must determine when $S(x) \le 8.5$.

$$\frac{5}{6}x + 1 \le 8.5 \quad \text{Substitute for } S(x).$$

$$\frac{5}{6}x \le 7.5 \quad \text{Subtract 1 from each side.}$$

$$x \le 9 \quad \text{Multiply each side by } \tfrac{6}{5}, \text{ or } 1.2.$$

The daily payment processing volume for Square was \$8.5 million or less from March 2011 to December 2011. (Note that $x = 0$ corresponds to March 2011.)

Graphical Solution A graphical solution to $\frac{5}{6}x + 1 \leq 8.5$ is shown in Figure 2.34.

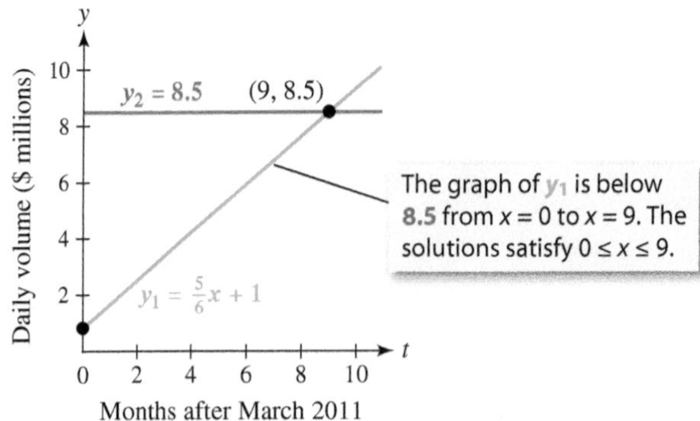

Figure 2.34

Now Try Exercise 89

x-Intercept Method If a linear inequality can be written as $y_1 > 0$, where $>$ may be replaced by $\geq$, $\leq$, or $<$, then we can solve this inequality by using the ***x*-intercept method**. To apply this method for $y_1 > 0$, graph y_1 and find the x-intercept. The solution set includes x-values where the graph of y_1 is above the x-axis.

EXAMPLE 4 Applying the x-intercept method

Solve the inequality $1 - x > \frac{1}{2}x - 2$ by using the x-intercept method. Write the solution set in set-builder and interval notation.

SOLUTION

Graphing by Hand First, use properties of inequalities to rewrite the given inequality so that 0 is on the right side.

$$1 - x > \frac{1}{2}x - 2 \qquad \text{Given inequality}$$

$$1 - x - \frac{1}{2}x + 2 > 0 \qquad \text{Subtract } \tfrac{1}{2}x \text{ and add 2.}$$

$$3 - \frac{3}{2}x > 0 \qquad \text{Simplify.}$$

Next, graph $y_1 = 3 - \frac{3}{2}x$ and locate the x-intercept 2. From Figure 2.35(a), $y_1 > 0$ when $x < 2$ and the solution set is $\{x \mid x < 2\}$, or $(-\infty, 2)$.

Graphing with a Calculator With a calculator graph $y_1 = 1 - x - \frac{1}{2}x + 2$ without simplifying further, as shown in Figure 2.35(b). The calculator can locate the zero, or x-intercept, of 2.

Calculator Help
To locate a zero or x-intercept on the graph of a function, see Appendix A (page AP-7).

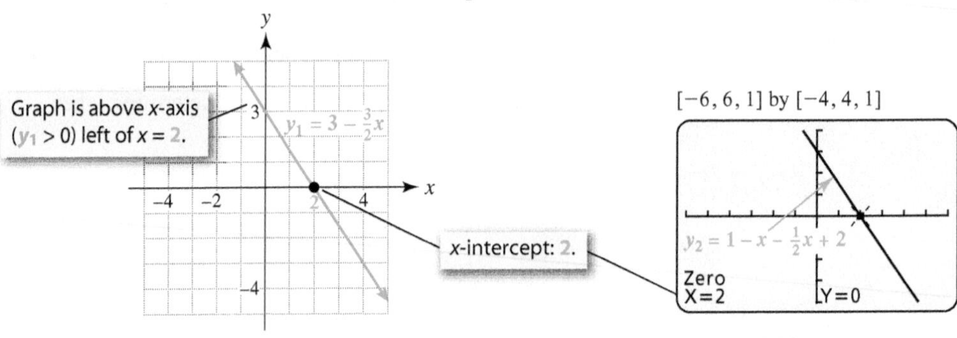

Figure 2.35(a) **Figure 2.35(b)**

Now Try Exercise 51

MAKING CONNECTIONS

Equations and Inequalities In mathematics a lot of time is spent solving equations and determining equality. One reason is that equality is frequently a boundary between *greater than* and *less than.* The solution set to an inequality often can be found by first locating where two expressions are equal. Since equality and inequality are closely connected, many of the techniques used to solve equations can also be applied to inequalities.

Visualizing Solutions We can visualize the solution set to the linear inequality $ax + b > 0$ with $a \neq 0$, as shown in the following See the Concept. (The inequality $ax + b < 0$ can be solved similarly.)

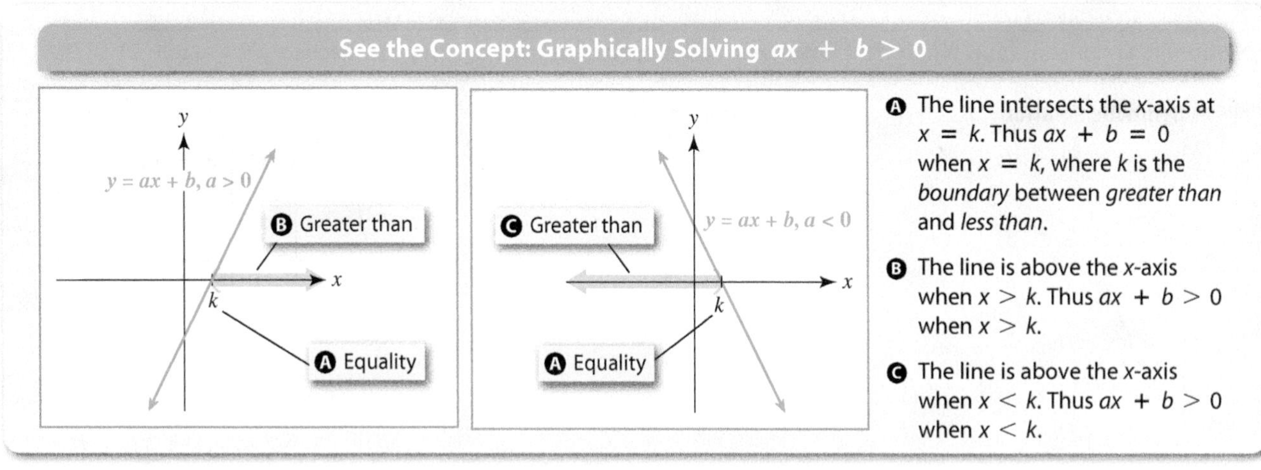

See the Concept: Graphically Solving ax + b > 0
y
y = ax + b, a > 0
B Greater than
x
k
A Equality
y
C Greater than
y = ax + b, a < 0
x
k
A Equality
A The line intersects the x-axis at x = k. Thus ax + b = 0 when x = k, where k is the boundary between greater than and less than.
B The line is above the x-axis when x > k. Thus ax + b > 0 when x > k.
C The line is above the x-axis when x < k. Thus ax + b > 0 when x < k.

Numerical Solutions Suppose that it costs a company $5x + 200$ dollars to produce x earbuds and the company receives $15x$ dollars for selling x earbuds. Then the profit P from selling x earbuds is $P = 15x - (5x + 200) = 10x - 200$. A value of $x = 20$ results in $P = 0$, and so $x = 20$ is called the **boundary number** because selling 20 earbuds represents the boundary between making money and losing money (the break-even point). To make money, the profit P must be positive, and the inequality

$$10x - 200 > 0$$

must be satisfied. The table of values for $y_1 = 10x - 200$ in Table 2.3 shows the boundary number $x = 20$ along with several **test values**. The test values of $x = 17$, 18, and 19 result in a loss. The test values of $x = 21$, 22, and 23 result in a profit. Therefore the solution set to $10x - 200 > 0$ is $\{x \mid x > 20\}$.

Profit from Sales

x	17	18	19	20	21	22	23
$10x - 200$	−30	−20	−10	0	10	20	30

Table 2.3 Less than 0 (for 17–19); Boundary number (20); Greater than 0 (for 21–23)

EXAMPLE 5 **Solving a linear inequality with test values**

Solve $3(6 - x) + 5 - 2x < 0$ numerically.

SOLUTION Make a table of $y_1 = 3(6 - x) + 5 - 2x$ as shown in Figure 2.36 on the next page. The boundary number for this inequality lies between $x = 4$ and $x = 5$. Changing the increment from 1 to 0.1 in Figure 2.37 shows that the boundary number for the inequality is $x = 4.6$. The test values of $x = 4.7, 4.8$, and 4.9 indicate that when $x > 4.6$, the inequality $y_1 < 0$ is true. The solution set to $3(6 - x) + 5 - 2x < 0$ is $\{x | x > 4.6\}$.

Incrementing x by 1

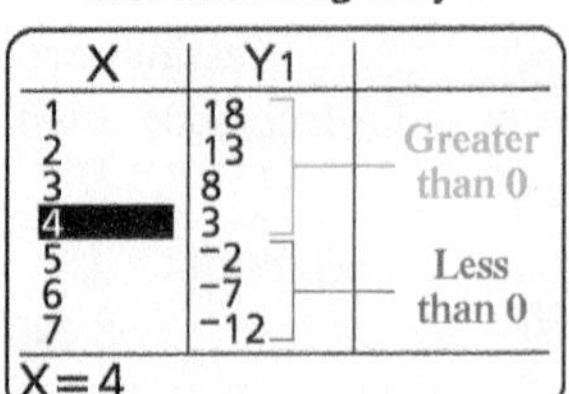

Figure 2.36

Incrementing x by 0.1

X	Y1	
4.3	1.5	Greater than 0
4.4	1	
4.5	.5	
4.6	0	
4.7	−.5	Less than 0
4.8	−1	
4.9	−1.5	

X=4.6

Figure 2.37

Now Try Exercise 71

MAKING CONNECTIONS

Symbolic, Graphical, and Numerical Solutions Each method is used to solve the inequality $3 - (x + 2) > 0$.

Symbolic Solution

$$3 - (x + 2) > 0$$
$$-(x + 2) > -3$$
$$x + 2 < 3$$
$$x < 1$$

Graphical Solution

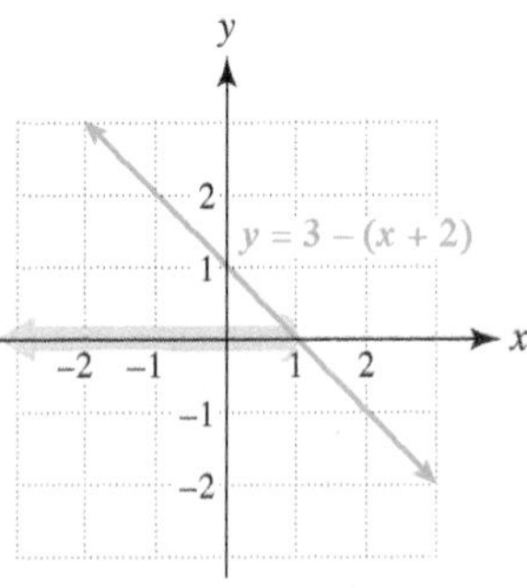

The graph of $y = 3 - (x + 2)$ is above the x-axis when $x < 1$.

Numerical Solution

x	$3 - (x + 2)$	
−2	3	Greater than 0
−1	2	
0	1	
1	0	Equals 0
2	−1	Less than 0
3	−2	

The values of $3 - (x + 2)$ are greater than 0 when $x < 1$.

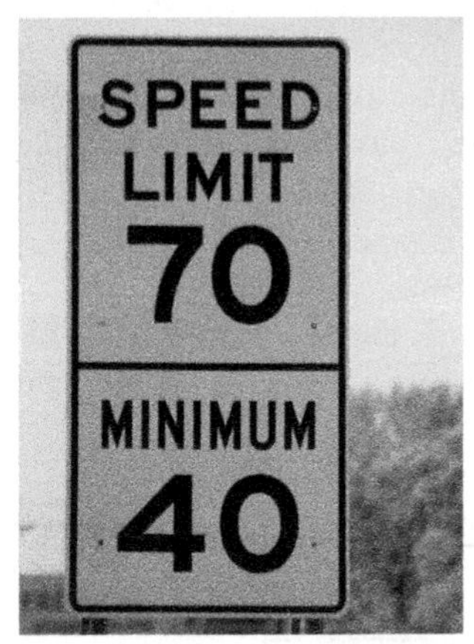

Compound Inequalities

Sometimes a variable must satisfy two inequalities. For example, on a freeway there may be a minimum speed limit of 40 miles per hour and a maximum speed limit of 70 miles per hour. If x represents the speed of a vehicle, then x must satisfy the compound inequality

$$x \geq 40 \quad \text{and} \quad x \leq 70.$$

A **compound inequality** occurs when two inequalities are connected by the word *and* or *or*. When the word *and* connects two inequalities, the two inequalities can sometimes be written as a **three-part inequality**. For example, the previous compound inequality may be written as the three-part inequality

$$40 \leq x \leq 70.$$

Compound inequalities involving the word *or* are discussed in the next section.

EXAMPLE 6 **Solving a three-part inequality symbolically**

Solve the inequality. Write the solution set in set-builder and interval notation.

(a) $-4 \leq 5x + 1 < 21$ **(b)** $\frac{1}{2} < \frac{1 - 2t}{4} < 2$

SOLUTION

(a) Use properties of inequalities to simplify the three-part inequality.

$$-4 \leq 5x + 1 < 21 \quad \text{Given inequality}$$
$$-5 \leq 5x < 20 \quad \text{Add } -1 \text{ to each part.}$$
$$-1 \leq x < 4 \quad \text{Divide each part by 5.}$$

The solution set is $\{x | -1 \leq x < 4\}$, or $[-1, 4)$.

(b) Begin by multiplying each part by 4 to clear fractions.

$$\frac{1}{2} < \frac{1-2t}{4} < 2 \qquad \text{Given inequality}$$

$$2 < 1 - 2t < 8 \qquad \text{Multiply each part by 4.}$$

$$1 < -2t < 7 \qquad \text{Add } -1 \text{ to each part.}$$

$$-\frac{1}{2} > t > -\frac{7}{2} \qquad \text{Divide by } -2\text{; reverse inequalities.}$$

$$-\frac{7}{2} < t < -\frac{1}{2} \qquad \text{Rewrite the inequality.}$$

The solution set is $\left\{t \mid -\frac{7}{2} < t < -\frac{1}{2}\right\}$, or $\left(-\frac{7}{2}, -\frac{1}{2}\right)$.

Now Try Exercises 23 and 35

NOTE In Example 6, it is correct to write a three-part inequality as either $-\frac{1}{2} > t > -\frac{7}{2}$ or $-\frac{7}{2} < t < -\frac{1}{2}$. However, we usually write the smaller number on the left side and the larger number on the right side.

Three-part inequalities occur in many applications and can often be solved symbolically and graphically. This is demonstrated in the next example.

EXAMPLE 7 Modeling sunset times

In Boston, on the 82nd day (March 22) the sun set at 7:00 P.M., and on the 136th day (May 15) the sun set at 8:00 P.M. Use a linear function S to estimate the days when the sun set between 7:15 P.M. and 7:45 P.M., inclusive. Do not consider any days of the year after May 15. (***Source:*** R. Thomas, *The Old Farmer's 2012 Almanac.*)

SOLUTION

Getting Started First find a linear function S whose graph passes through the points (82, 7) and (136, 8). Then solve the compound inequality $7.25 \le S(x) \le 7.75$. Note that 7.25 hours past noon corresponds to 7:15 P.M. and 7.75 hours past noon corresponds to 7:45 P.M. ▶

Symbolic Solution The slope of the line passing through (82, 7) and (136, 8) is given by $\frac{8-7}{136-82} = \frac{1}{54}$. The point-slope form of the line passing through (82, 7) with slope $\frac{1}{54}$ is

$$S(x) = \frac{1}{54}(x - 82) + 7. \qquad \text{Point-slope form}$$

Now solve the following compound inequality.

$$7.25 \le \frac{1}{54}(x - 82) + 7 \le 7.75 \qquad \text{Given inequality}$$

$$0.25 \le \frac{1}{54}(x - 82) \le 0.75 \qquad \text{Subtract 7 from each part.}$$

$$13.5 \le x - 82 \le 40.5 \qquad \text{Multiply each part by 54.}$$

$$95.5 \le x \le 122.5 \qquad \text{Add 82 to each part.}$$

If we round 95.5 and 122.5 up to 96 and 123, then this model predicts that the sun set between 7:15 P.M. and 7:45 P.M. from the 96th day (April 5) to the 123rd day (May 2). (Note that the actual days were April 5 and May 1.)

[80, 150, 10] by [6.5, 8.5, 1]

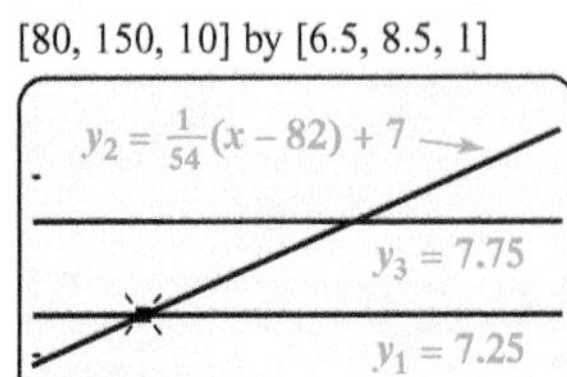

Figure 2.38

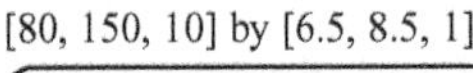

[80, 150, 10] by [6.5, 8.5, 1]

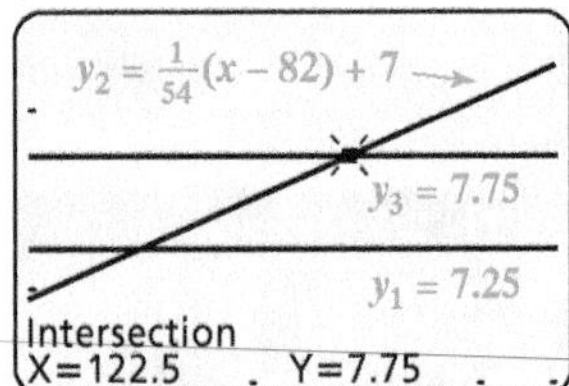

Figure 2.39

Graphical Solution Graph $y_1 = 7.25$, $y_2 = \frac{1}{54}(x - 82) + 7$, and $y_3 = 7.75$ and determine their points of intersection, (95.5, 7.25) and (122.5, 7.75), as shown in Figures 2.38 and 2.39. The graph of y_2 is between the graphs of y_1 and y_3 for $95.5 \le x \le 122.5$. This agrees with the symbolic solution. A different graph showing this solution appears in Figure 2.40.

Modeling Sunset Times in Boston

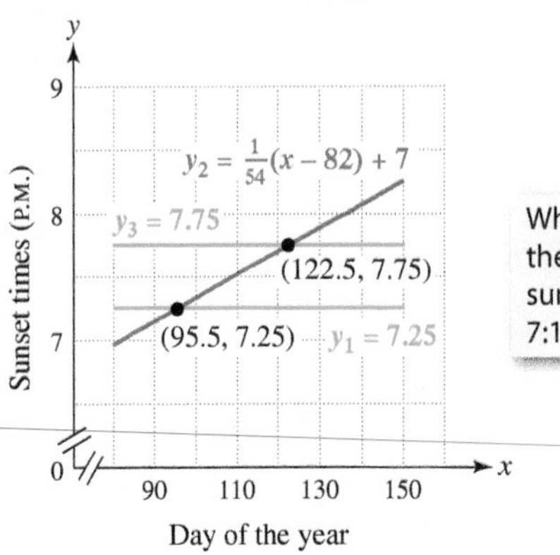

Figure 2.40

Now Try Exercise 93

EXAMPLE 8 **Solving inequalities symbolically**

Solve the linear inequalities symbolically. Express the solution set using interval notation.

(a) $-\frac{x}{2} + 1 \le 3$ **(b)** $-8 < \frac{3x - 1}{2} \le 5$ **(c)** $5(x - 6) < 2x - 2(1 - x)$

SOLUTION

(a) Simplify the inequality as follows.

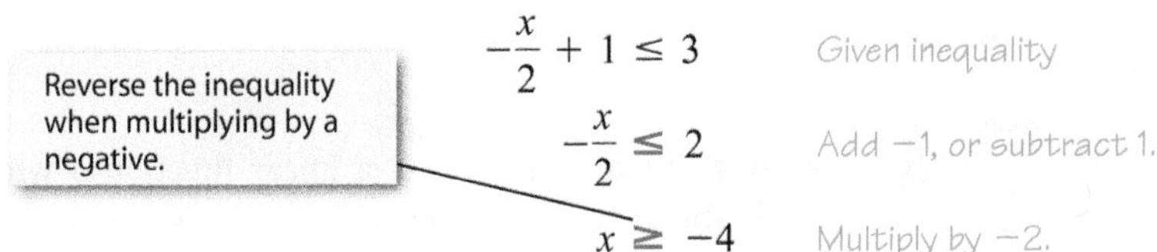

$$-\frac{x}{2} + 1 \le 3 \quad \text{Given inequality}$$

$$-\frac{x}{2} \le 2 \quad \text{Add } -1 \text{, or subtract 1.}$$

$$x \ge -4 \quad \text{Multiply by } -2.$$

In interval notation the solution set is $[-4, \infty)$.

(b) The parts of this compound inequality can be solved simultaneously.

$$-8 < \frac{3x - 1}{2} \le 5 \quad \text{Given inequality}$$

$$-16 < 3x - 1 \le 10 \quad \text{Multiply by 2.}$$

$$-15 < 3x \le 11 \quad \text{Add 1.}$$

$$-5 < x \le \frac{11}{3} \quad \text{Divide by 3.}$$

The solution set is $\left(-5, \frac{11}{3}\right]$.

(c) Start by applying the distributive property to each side of the inequality.

$$5(x - 6) < 2x - 2(1 - x) \quad \text{Given inequality}$$

$$5x - 30 < 2x - 2 + 2x \quad \text{Distributive property}$$

$$5x - 30 < 4x - 2 \quad \text{Simplify.}$$

$$x - 30 < -2 \quad \text{Subtract } 4x.$$

$$x < 28 \quad \text{Add 30.}$$

The solution set is $(-\infty, 28)$.

Now Try Exercises 13, 27, and 33

2.3 Putting It All Together

Any linear inequality can be written as $ax + b > 0$ with $a \neq 0$, where $>$ can be replaced by $\geq$, $<$, or $\leq$. The following table includes methods for solving linear inequalities.

CONCEPT	EXPLANATION	EXAMPLES
Compound inequality	Two inequalities connected by the word *and* or *or*	$x \leq 4$ or $x \geq 10$ $x \geq -3$ and $x < 4$ $x > 5$ and $x \leq 20$ can be written as the three-part inequality $5 < x \leq 20$.
Symbolic method	Use properties of inequalities to simplify $f(x) > g(x)$ to either $x > k$ or $x < k$ for some real number k.	$\frac{1}{2}x + 1 > 3 - \frac{3}{2}x$ Given inequality $2x + 1 > 3$ Add $\frac{3}{2}x$. $2x > 2$ Subtract 1. $x > 1$ Divide by 2.
Intersection-of-graphs method	To solve $f(x) > g(x)$, graph $y_1 = f(x)$ and $y_2 = g(x)$. Find the point of intersection. The solution set includes x-values where the graph of y_1 is above the graph of y_2.	$\frac{1}{2}x + 1 > 3 - \frac{3}{2}x$ Graph $y_1 = \frac{1}{2}x + 1$ and $y_2 = 3 - \frac{3}{2}x$. The solution set for $y_1 > y_2$ is $\{x \mid x > 1\}$. 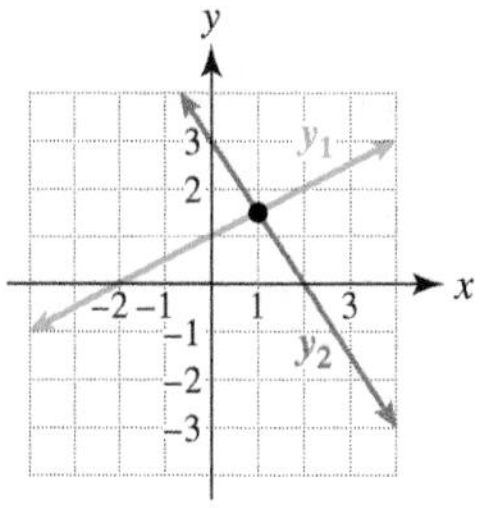
The x-intercept method	Write the inequality as $h(x) > 0$. Graph $y_1 = h(x)$. Solutions occur where the graph is above the x-axis.	$\frac{1}{2}x + 1 > 3 - \frac{3}{2}x$ Graph $y_1 = \frac{1}{2}x + 1 - \left(3 - \frac{3}{2}x\right)$. The solution set for $y_1 > 0$ is $\{x \mid x > 1\}$. 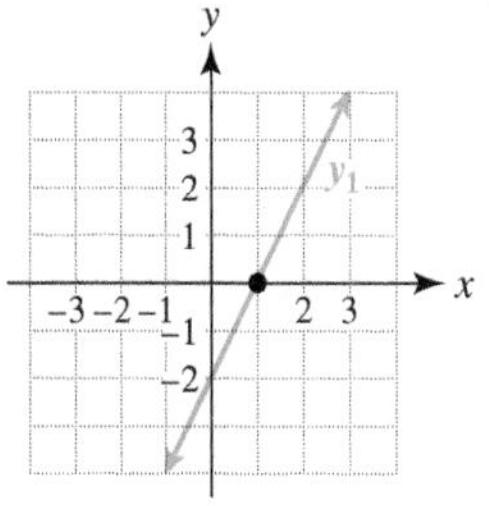
Numerical method	Write the inequality as $h(x) > 0$. Create a table for $y_1 = h(x)$ and find the boundary number $x = k$ such that $h(k) = 0$. Use the test values in the table to determine if the solution set is $x > k$ or $x < k$.	$\frac{1}{2}x + 1 > 3 - \frac{3}{2}x$ Table $y_1 = \frac{1}{2}x + 1 - \left(3 - \frac{3}{2}x\right)$. The solution set for $y_1 > 0$ is $\{x \mid x > 1\}$.

x	−1	0	1	2	3
y_1	−4	−2	0	2	4

Less than 0   Greater than 0

2.3 Exercises

Review of Interval Notation

Exercises 1–8: Express the following in interval notation.

1. $x < 2$
2. $x > -3$
3. $x \geq -1$
4. $x \leq 7$
5. $\{x \mid 1 \leq x < 8\}$
6. $\{x \mid -2 < x \leq 4\}$
7. $\{x \mid x \leq 1\}$
8. $\{x \mid x > 5\}$

Solving Linear Inequalities Symbolically

Exercises 9–38: Solve the inequality symbolically. Express the solution set in set-builder or interval notation.

9. $2x + 6 \geq 10$
10. $-4x - 3 < 5$
11. $-2(x - 10) + 1 > 0$
12. $3(x + 5) \leq 0$
13. $\dfrac{t + 2}{3} \geq 5$
14. $\dfrac{2 - t}{6} < 0$
15. $4x - 1 < \dfrac{3 - x}{-3}$
16. $\dfrac{x + 5}{-10} > 2x + 3$
17. $-3(z - 4) \geq 2(1 - 2z)$
18. $-\frac{1}{4}(2z - 6) + z \geq 5$
19. $\dfrac{1 - x}{4} < \dfrac{2x - 2}{3}$
20. $\dfrac{3x}{4} < x - \dfrac{x + 2}{2}$
21. $2x - 3 > \frac{1}{2}(x + 1)$
22. $5 - (2 - 3x) \leq -5x$
23. $5 < 4t - 1 \leq 11$
24. $-1 \leq 2t \leq 4$
25. $3 \leq 4 - x \leq 20$
26. $-5 < 1 - 2x < 40$
27. $-7 \leq \dfrac{1 - 4x}{7} < 12$
28. $0 < \dfrac{7x - 5}{3} \leq 4$
29. $5 > 2(x + 4) - 5 > -5$
30. $\frac{8}{3} \geq \frac{4}{3} - (x + 3) \geq \frac{2}{3}$
31. $3 \leq \frac{1}{2}x + \frac{3}{4} \leq 6$
32. $-4 \leq 5 - \frac{4}{5}x < 6$
33. $5x - 2(x + 3) \geq 4 - 3x$
34. $3x - 1 < 2(x - 3) + 1$
35. $\dfrac{1}{2} \leq \dfrac{1 - 2t}{3} < \dfrac{2}{3}$
36. $-\dfrac{3}{4} < \dfrac{2 - t}{5} < \dfrac{3}{4}$
37. $\frac{1}{2}z + \frac{2}{3}(3 - z) - \frac{5}{4}z \geq \frac{3}{4}(z - 2) + z$
38. $\dfrac{2}{3}(1 - 2z) - \dfrac{3}{2}z + \dfrac{5}{6}z \geq \dfrac{2z - 1}{3} + 1$

Solving Linear Inequalities Graphically

Exercises 39–46: (Refer to Example 2.) Solve the inequality graphically. Use set-builder notation.

39. $x + 2 \geq 2x$
40. $2x - 1 \leq x$
41. $\frac{2}{3}x - 2 > -\frac{4}{3}x + 4$
42. $-2x \geq -\frac{5}{3}x + 1$
43. $-1 \leq 2x - 1 \leq 3$
44. $-2 < 1 - x < 2$
45. $-3 < x - 2 \leq 2$
46. $-1 \leq 1 - 2x < 5$

Exercises 47–50: Use the given graph of $y = ax + b$ to solve each equation and inequality. Write the solution set to each inequality in set-builder or interval notation.

(a) $ax + b = 0$ (b) $ax + b < 0$ (c) $ax + b \geq 0$

47.

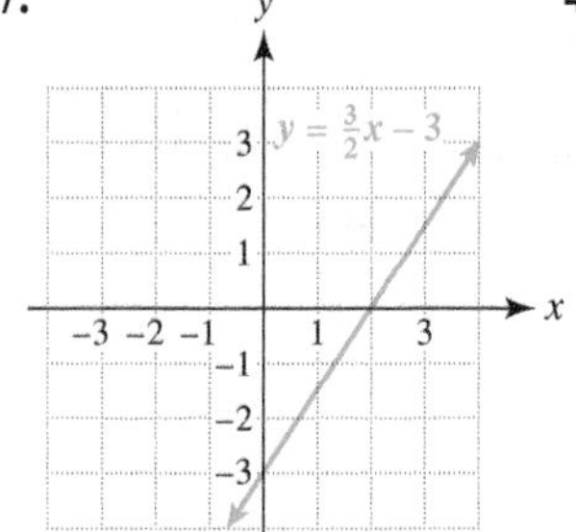

48.

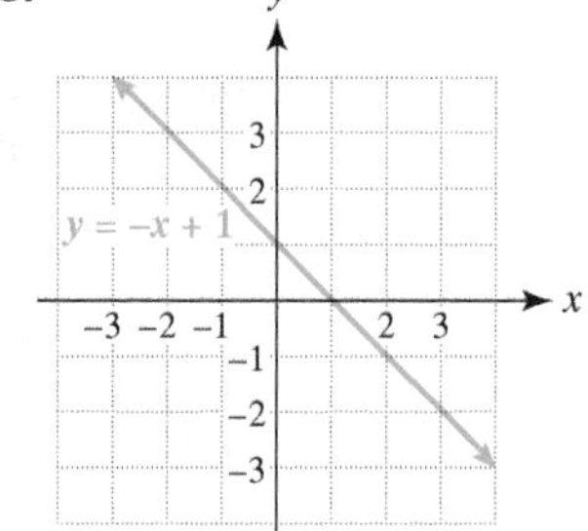

49.

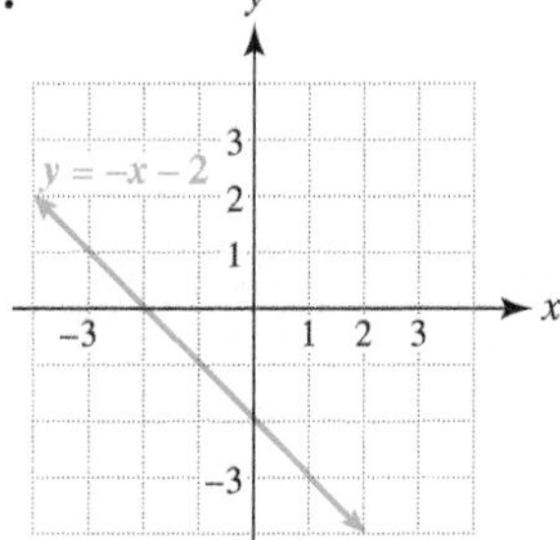

50.

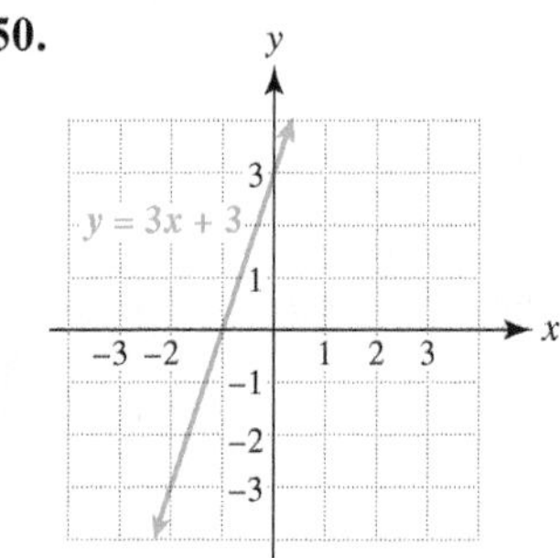

Exercises 51–54: **x-Intercept Method** *(Refer to Example 4.) Use the x-intercept method to solve the inequality. Write the solution set in set-builder or interval notation. Then check your answer by solving the inequality symbolically.*

51. $x - 3 \leq \frac{1}{2}x - 2$
52. $x - 2 \leq \frac{1}{3}x$
53. $2 - x < 3x - 2$
54. $\frac{1}{2}x + 1 > \frac{3}{2}x - 1$

Exercises 55–60: Solve the linear inequality graphically. Write the solution set in set-builder notation. Approximate endpoints to the nearest hundredth whenever appropriate.

55. $5x - 4 > 10$
56. $-3x + 6 \leq 9$
57. $-2(x - 1990) + 55 \geq 60$
58. $\sqrt{2}x > 10.5 - 13.7x$

59. $\sqrt{5}(x - 1.2) - \sqrt{3}x < 5(x + 1.1)$

60. $1.238x + 0.998 \leq 1.23(3.987 - 2.1x)$

Exercises 61–66: Solve the compound linear inequality graphically. Write the solution set in set-builder or interval notation, and approximate endpoints to the nearest tenth whenever appropriate.

61. $3 \leq 5x - 17 < 15$ 62. $-4 < \dfrac{55 - 3.1x}{4} < 17$

63. $1.5 \leq 9.1 - 0.5x \leq 6.8$ 64. $0.2x < \dfrac{2x - 5}{3} < 8$

65. $x - 4 < 2x - 5 < 6$ 66. $-3 \leq 1 - x \leq 2x$

67. The graphs of two linear functions f and g are shown.
(a) Solve the equation $g(x) = f(x)$.
(b) Solve the inequality $g(x) > f(x)$.

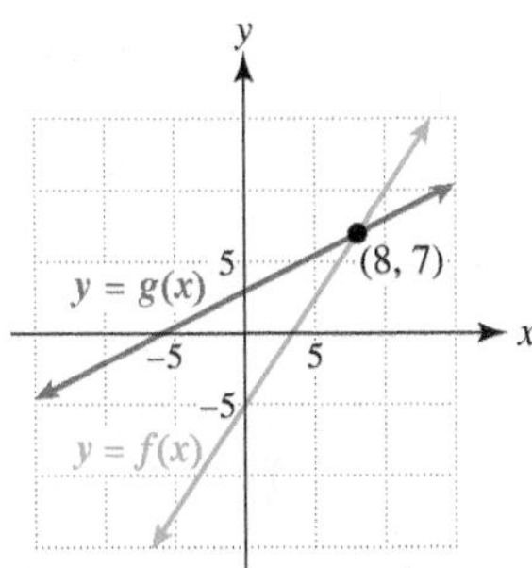

68. Use the figure to solve each equation or inequality.
(a) $f(x) = g(x)$ (b) $g(x) = h(x)$
(c) $f(x) < g(x) < h(x)$ (d) $g(x) > h(x)$

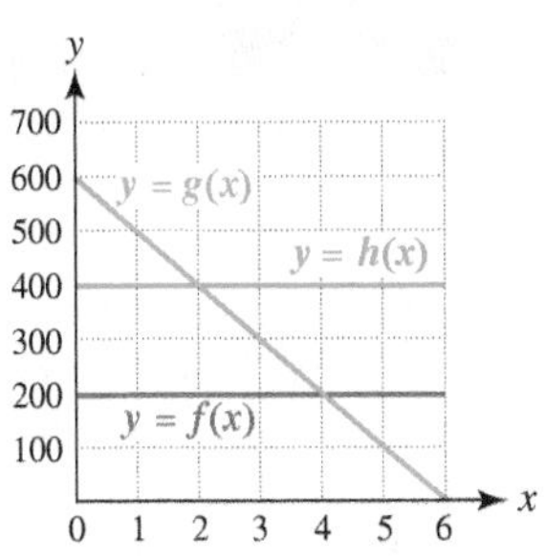

Solving Linear Inequalities Numerically

Exercises 69 and 70: Assume y_1 represents a linear function with the set of real numbers for its domain. Use the table to solve the inequalities. Use set-builder notation.

69. $y_1 > 0, y_1 \leq 0$ 70. $y_1 < 0, y_1 \geq 0$

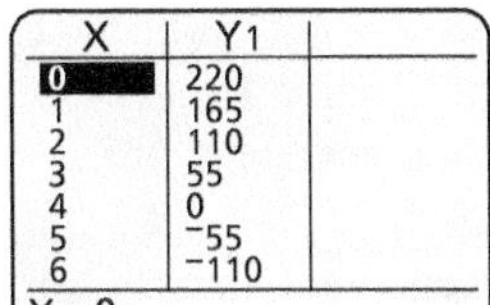

X	Y1
0	220
1	165
2	110
3	55
4	0
5	−55
6	−110

X=0

X	Y1
−5	−32
−4	−16
−3	0
−2	16
−1	32
0	48
1	64

X=−5

Exercises 71–78: Solve each inequality numerically. Write the solution set in set-builder or interval notation, and approximate endpoints to the nearest tenth when appropriate.

71. $-4x - 6 > 0$ 72. $1 - 2x \geq 9$

73. $1 \leq 3x - 2 \leq 10$ 74. $-5 < 2x - 1 < 15$

75. $-\dfrac{3}{4} < \dfrac{2 - 5x}{3} \leq \dfrac{3}{4}$ 76. $\dfrac{3x - 1}{5} < 15$

77. $(\sqrt{11} - \pi)x - 5.5 \leq 0$

78. $1.5(x - 0.7) + 1.5x < 1$

You Decide the Method

Exercises 79–82: Solve the inequality. Approximate the endpoints to the nearest thousandth when appropriate.

79. $2x - 8 > 5$ 80. $5 < 4x - 2.5$

81. $\pi x - 5.12 \leq \sqrt{2}x - 5.7(x - 1.1)$

82. $5.1x - \pi \geq \sqrt{3} - 1.7x$

Applications

83. **Distance Between Cars** Cars A and B are both traveling in the same direction. Their distances in miles north of St. Louis after x hours are computed by the functions f_A and f_B, respectively. The graphs of f_A and f_B are shown in the figure for $0 \leq x \leq 10$.
(a) Which car is traveling faster? Explain.
(b) How many hours elapse before the two cars are the same distance from St. Louis? How far are they from St. Louis when this occurs?
(c) During what time interval is car B farther from St. Louis than car A?

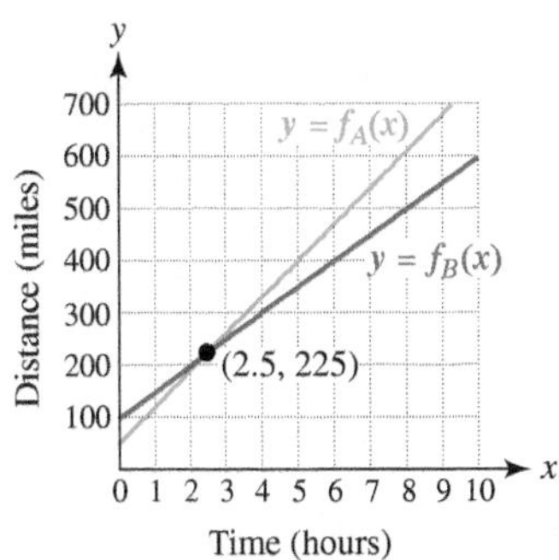

84. **Distance** Function f computes the distance y in miles between a car and the city of Omaha after x hours, where $0 \leq x \leq 6$. The graphs of f and the horizontal lines $y = 100$ and $y = 200$ are shown in the figure on the next page.
(a) Is the car moving toward or away from Omaha? Explain.
(b) Determine the times when the car is 100 miles and 200 miles from Omaha.

(c) Determine when the car is from 100 to 200 miles from Omaha.

(d) When is the car's distance from Omaha greater than 100 miles?

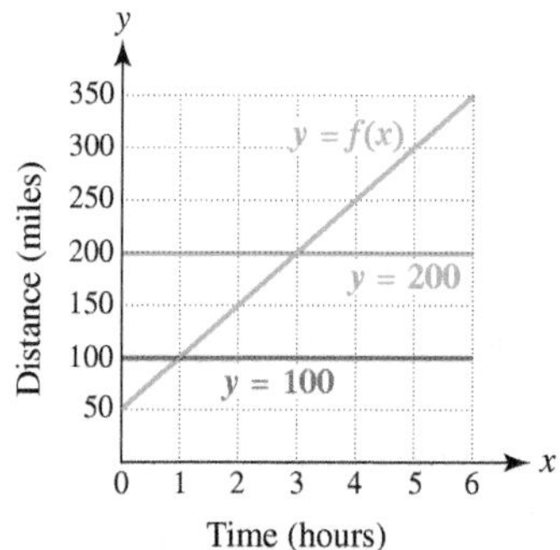

85. Clouds and Temperature As the altitude increases, both the air temperature and the dew point decrease. As long as the air temperature is greater than the dew point, clouds will not form. Typically, the air temperature T cools at 19°F for each 1-mile increase in altitude and the dew point D decreases by 5.8°F for each 1-mile increase in altitude. (***Source:*** A. Miller and R. Anthes, *Meteorology*.)

(a) Suppose the air temperature at ground level is 65°F. Write a formula for a linear function T that gives the air temperature at x miles high.

(b) Suppose the dew point at ground level is 50°F. Write a formula for a linear function D that gives the dew point at x miles high.

(c) Determine symbolically altitudes where clouds will not form.

(d) Solve part (c) graphically.

86. Temperature and Altitude Suppose the Fahrenheit temperature x miles above ground level is given by the formula $T(x) = 85 - 19x$.

(a) Use the intersection-of-graphs method to estimate the altitudes where the temperature is below freezing. Assume that the domain of T is $0 \le x \le 6$.

(b) What does the x-intercept on the graph of $y = T(x)$ represent?

(c) Solve part (a) symbolically.

87. U.S. Social Gaming Social gaming revenues (via the Internet) in billions of dollars from 2010 to 2015 are projected to be modeled by $R(x) = 0.86x + 1.2$, where x represents years after 2010. (***Source:*** BI Intelligence.)

(a) Interpret the slope of the graph of R.

(b) Estimate when this revenue is expected to be more than \$3 billion.

88. Overweight Americans If trends continue, the past and future percentages of the population who are overweight can be estimated by $W(x) = x + 45$, where x represents years after 1980. (***Source:*** *New York Times*.)

(a) Interpret the slope of the graph of W.

(b) Estimate when this percentage was between 70% and 77%.

89. Facebook Users The number of active Facebook users increased from 100 million in 2008 to 1 billion in 2012. (***Source:*** *Business Insider*.)

(a) Find a formula for a linear function U that models this growth in millions of users, where x is years after 2008.

(b) Estimate when the number of users was 550 million or more.

90. Cost of Education The cost of K–12 education per student was \$2200 in 1978 and increased to \$10,300 in 2008. (***Source:*** *Department of Education*.)

(a) Find a formula for a linear function C that models this cost in dollars, where x is years after 1978.

(b) Estimate when this cost was from \$4900 to \$7600.

91. Video Sharing In 2006 about 33% of Americans reported watching online videos via sharing sites such as YouTube and Vimeo. By 2011 this number increased to 71% (***Source:*** Column Five.)

(a) Find a formula for a linear function V that models the data, where x represents the year.

(b) Estimate when this percentage was between 40% and 55%.

92. Consumer Spending In 2005 consumers used credit and debit cards to pay for 40% of all purchases. This percentage was 55% in 2011. (***Source:*** Bloomburg.)

(a) Find a linear function P that models the data.

(b) Estimate when this percentage was between 45% and 50%.

93. Modeling Sunrise Times In Boston, on the 90th day (March 30) the sun rose at 6:30 A.M., and on the 129th day (May 8) the sun rose at 5:30 A.M. Use a linear function to estimate the days when the sun rose between 5:45 A.M. and 6:00 A.M. Do not consider days after May 8. (***Source:*** R Thomas.)

94. Modeling Sunrise Times In Denver, on the 77th day (March 17) the sun rose at 7:00 A.M., and on the 112th day (April 21) the sun rose at 6:00 A.M. Use a linear function to estimate the days when the sun rose between 6:10 A.M. and 6:40 A.M. Do not consider days after April 21. (***Source:*** R. Thomas.)

95. Error Tolerances Suppose that an aluminum can is manufactured so that its radius r can vary from 1.99 inches to 2.01 inches. What range of values is possible for the circumference C of the can? Express your answer by using a three-part inequality.

96. Error Tolerances Suppose that a square picture frame has sides that vary between 9.9 inches and 10.1 inches. What range of values is possible for the perimeter P of the picture frame? Express your answer by using a three-part inequality.

97. Modeling Data The following data are exactly linear.

x	0	2	4	6
y	−1.5	4.5	10.5	16.5

(a) Find a linear function f that models the data.

(b) Solve the inequality $f(x) > 2.25$.

98. Modeling Data The following data are exactly linear.

x	1	2	3	4	5
y	0.4	3.5	6.6	9.7	12.8

(a) Find a linear function f that models the data.

(b) Solve the inequality $2 \leq f(x) \leq 8$.

Linear Regression

99. Female College Graduates The table in the next column lists the percentage P of the female population who had college degrees in selected years.

x	1980	1990	2000	2010
$P(\%)$	12.8	18.4	23.6	33.0

Source: Bureau of the Census.

(a) Find a linear function P that models the data.

(b) Estimate when this percentage was between 18% and 28.5%.

(c) Did your estimate involve interpolation or extrapolation?

100. Tablet Sales The table lists the actual and projected number N of tablets, such as the iPad, sold worldwide in millions for selected years x.

x	2011	2012	2013	2014	2015
N	90	165	250	340	470

Source: Business Insider.

(a) Find a linear function N that models the data.

(b) Estimate when this number is expected to be more than 637 million.

(c) Did your estimate involve interpolation or extrapolation?

Writing about Mathematics

101. Suppose the solution to the equation $ax + b = 0$ with $a > 0$ is $x = k$. Discuss how the value of k can be used to help solve the linear inequalities $ax + b > 0$ and $ax + b < 0$. Illustrate this process graphically. How would the solution sets change if $a < 0$?

102. Describe how to numerically solve the linear inequality $ax + b \leq 0$. Give an example.

103. If you multiply each part of a three-part inequality by the same negative number, what must you make sure to do? Explain by using an example.

104. Explain how a linear function, a linear equation, and a linear inequality are related. Give an example.

Extended and Discovery Exercises

1. Arithmetic Mean The **arithmetic mean** of two numbers a and b is given by $\frac{a+b}{2}$. Use properties of inequalities to show that if $a < b$, then $a < \frac{a+b}{2} < b$.

2. Geometric Mean The **geometric mean** of two numbers a and b is given by $\sqrt{ab}$. Use properties of inequalities to show that if $0 < a < b$, then $a < \sqrt{ab} < b$.

2.4 More Modeling with Functions

- Model data with a linear function
- Evaluate and graph piecewise-defined functions
- Evaluate and graph the greatest integer function
- Use direct variation to solve problems

Introduction

Throughout history, people have attempted to explain the world around them by creating models. A model is based on observations. It can be a diagram, a graph, an equation, a verbal expression, or some other form of communication. Models are used in diverse areas such as economics, chemistry, astronomy, religion, and mathematics. Regardless of where it is used, a **model** is an *abstraction* with the following two characteristics:

1. A model is able to explain present phenomena. It should not contradict data and information already known to be correct.
2. A model is able to make predictions about data or results. It should use current information to forecast phenomena or create new information.

Mathematical models are used to forecast business trends, design social networks, estimate ecological trends, control highway traffic, describe the Internet, predict weather, and discover new information when human knowledge is inadequate.

Modeling with Linear Functions

Linear functions can be used to model things that change at a constant rate. For example, the distance traveled by a car can be modeled by a linear function *if* the car is traveling at a constant speed.

MODELING WITH A LINEAR FUNCTION

To model a quantity that is changing at a constant rate with $f(x) = mx + b$, the following formula may be used.

$$f(x) = (\text{constant rate of change})\,x + (\text{initial amount})$$

The constant rate of change corresponds to the slope of the graph of f, and the initial amount corresponds to the y-intercept.

This method is illustrated in the next two examples.

EXAMPLE 1 Writing formulas for functions

Write the formula for a linear function that models each situation. Choose both an appropriate name and an appropriate variable for the function. State what the input variable represents and the domain of the function.

(a) In 2011 the average cost of attending a public college was \$8200, and it is projected to increase, on average, by \$600 per year until 2014. (***Source:*** The College Board.)

(b) A car's speed is 50 miles per hour, and it begins to slow down at a constant rate of 10 miles per hour each second.

SOLUTION

(a) Getting Started To model cost with a linear function, we need to find two quantities: the initial amount and the rate of change. In this example the initial amount is \$8200 and the rate of change is \$600 per year. ▶

Let C be the name of the function and x be the number of years after 2011. Then

$$\begin{aligned} C(x) &= (\text{constant rate of change})x + (\textbf{initial amount}) \\ &= 600x + \mathbf{8200} \end{aligned}$$

models the cost in dollars of attending a public college x years after 2011. Because this projection is valid only until 2014, or for 3 years past 2011, the domain D of function C is

$$D = \{x | x = 0, 1, 2, \text{ or } 3\}.$$

Note that x represents a year, so it may be most appropriate to restrict the domain to integer values for x.

(b) Let S be the name of the function and t be the elapsed time in seconds that the car has been slowing down. Then

$$\begin{aligned} S(t) &= (\text{constant rate of change})t + (\textbf{initial speed}) \\ &= -10t + 50 \end{aligned}$$

models the speed of the car after an elapsed time of t seconds. Because the car's initial speed is 50 miles per hour and it slows at 10 miles per hour per second, the car can slow down for at most 5 seconds before it comes to a stop. Thus the domain D of S is

$$D = \{t | 0 \le t \le 5\}.$$

Note that t represents time in seconds and does not need to be restricted to an integer.

Now Try Exercises 11 and 13

EXAMPLE 2 **Finding a symbolic representation**

A 100-gallon tank, initially full of water, is being drained at a rate of 5 gallons per minute.

(a) Write a formula for a linear function f that models the number of gallons of water in the tank after x minutes.

(b) How much water is in the tank after 4 minutes?

(c) Graph f. Identify the x- and y-intercepts and interpret each.

(d) Discuss the domain of f.

SOLUTION

(a) The amount of water in the tank is *decreasing* at 5 gallons per minute, so the constant rate of change is -5. The initial amount of water is 100 gallons.

$$\begin{aligned} f(x) &= (\text{constant rate of change})x + (\textbf{initial amount}) \\ &= -5x + 100 \end{aligned}$$

(b) After 4 minutes the tank contains $f(4) = -5(4) + 100 = 80$ gallons.

(c) $f(x) = -5x + 100$, so the graph has y-intercept 100 and slope -5. See Figure 2.41.

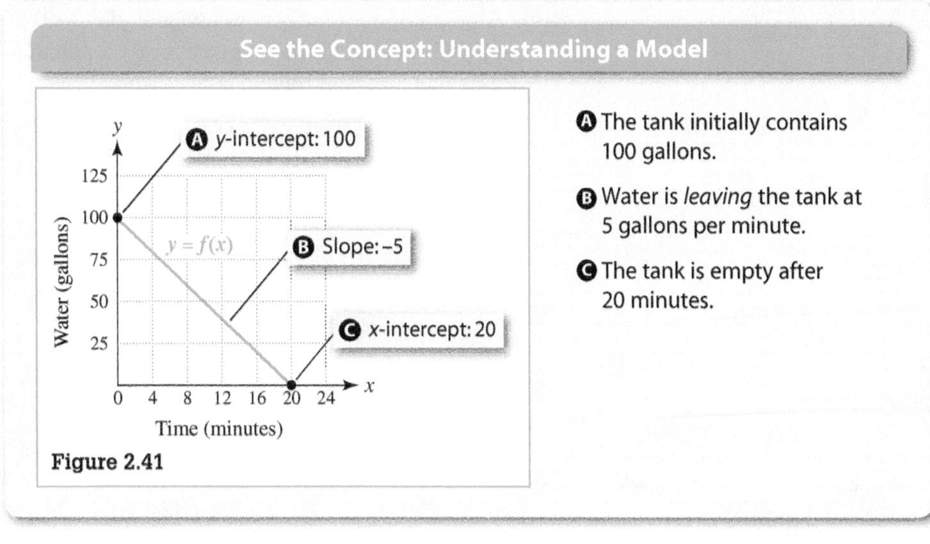

Figure 2.41

(d) From the graph we see that the domain of f must be restricted to $0 \le x \le 20$. For example, 21 is not in the domain of f because $f(21) = -5(21) + 100 = -5$; the tank cannot hold -5 gallons. Similarly, -1 is not in the domain of f because $f(-1) = -5(-1) + 100 = 105$; the tank holds *at most* 100 gallons.

Now Try Exercise 17

If the slopes between consecutive pairs of data points are always the same, the data can be modeled exactly by a linear function. If the slopes between consecutive pairs of data points are nearly the same, then the data can be modeled approximately by a linear function. In the next example we model data approximately.

EXAMPLE 3 Modeling airliner CO_2 emissions

Airliners emit carbon dioxide into the atmosphere when they burn jet fuel. Table 2.4 shows the *average* number y of pounds of carbon dioxide (CO_2) emitted by an airliner for each passenger who flies a distance of x miles.

Carbon Dioxide Emissions

x (miles)	240	360	680	800
y (pounds)	150	230	435	510

Source: E. Rogers and T. Kostigen, *The Green Book.*

Table 2.4

(a) Calculate the slopes of the line segments that connect consecutive data points.
(b) Find a linear function f that models the data.
(c) Graph f and the data. What does the slope of the graph of f indicate?
(d) Calculate $f(1000)$ and interpret the result.

SOLUTION

(a) The slopes of the lines passing through the points (240, 150), (360, 230), (680, 435), and (800, 510) are as follows.

$$m_1 = \frac{230 - 150}{360 - 240} \approx 0.67, \quad m_2 = \frac{435 - 230}{680 - 360} \approx 0.64, \quad \text{and}$$

$$m_3 = \frac{510 - 435}{800 - 680} \approx 0.63$$

(b) One possibility for m is to find the average of m_1, m_2, and m_3. The average of 0.67, 0.64, and 0.63 is 0.65, rounded to the nearest hundredth. Because traveling 0 miles produces 0 pounds of carbon dioxide, let the graph of f pass through (0, 0). Thus the y-intercept is 0 and $f(x) = 0.65x + 0$.

(c) A graph of the four data points and $f(x) = 0.65x$ is shown in Figure 2.42. The slope of 0.65 indicates that, on average, 0.65 pound of carbon dioxide is produced for each mile that a person travels in an airliner.

Modeling CO_2 Emissions

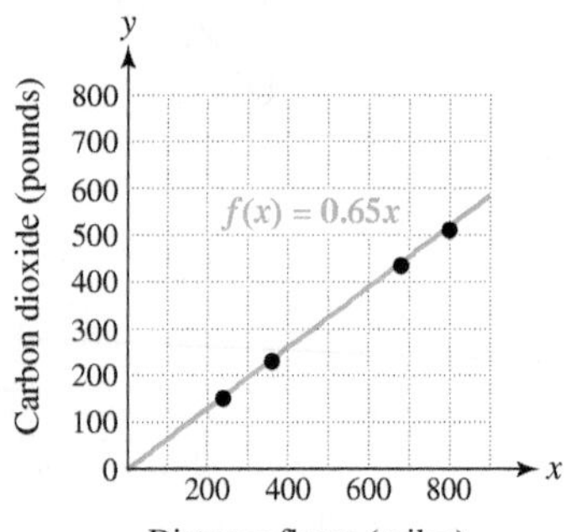

Figure 2.42

Calculator Help
To make a scatterplot, see Appendix A (page AP-3). To plot data and graph an equation in the same viewing rectangle, see Appendix A (page AP-6).

(d) $f(1000) = 0.65(1000) = 650$; thus 650 pounds of carbon dioxide are emitted into the atmosphere, on average, when a person flies 1000 miles.

Now Try Exercise 23

MAKING CONNECTIONS

Slope and Approximately Linear Data Another way to obtain an initial value for m is to calculate the slope between the first and last data point in the table. The value for m can then be adjusted visually by graphing f and the data. In Example 3 this would have resulted in

$$m = \frac{510 - 150}{800 - 240} \approx 0.64,$$

which compares favorably with our decision to let $m = 0.65$.

Piecewise-Defined Functions

When a function f models data, there may not be one formula for $f(x)$ that works. In this case, the function is sometimes defined on pieces of its domain and is therefore called a **piecewise-defined function**. If each piece is linear, the function is a **piecewise-linear function.** An example of a piecewise-defined function is the *Fujita scale,* which classifies tornadoes by intensity. If a tornado has wind speeds between 40 and 72 miles per hour, it is an F1 tornado. Tornadoes with wind speeds *greater than* 72 miles per hour but not more than 112 miles per hour are F2 tornadoes. The Fujita scale is represented by the following function F, where the input x represents the maximum wind speed of a tornado and the output is the F-scale number from 1 to 5.

Fujita Scale (F1 → F5)

$$F(x) = \begin{cases} 1 & \text{if } 40 \le x \le 72 \\ 2 & \text{if } 72 < x \le 112 \\ 3 & \text{if } 112 < x \le 157 \\ 4 & \text{if } 157 < x \le 206 \\ 5 & \text{if } 206 < x \le 260 \end{cases}$$

F is defined in five pieces over intervals of its domain.

F(180) = 4

For example, if the maximum wind speed is 180 miles per hour, then $F(180) = 4$ because 180 is between 157 and 206; that is, $157 < 180 \le 206$. Thus a tornado with a maximum wind speed of 180 miles per hour is an F4 tornado.

A graph of $y = f(x)$ is shown in Figure 2.43. It is composed of horizontal line segments. Because each piece is constant, F is sometimes called a **piecewise-constant function** or a **step function**. A solid dot occurs at the point (72, 1) and an open circle occurs at the point (72, 2), because technically a tornado with 72-mile-per-hour winds is an F1 tornado, not an F2 tornado.

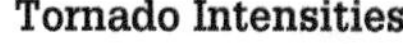

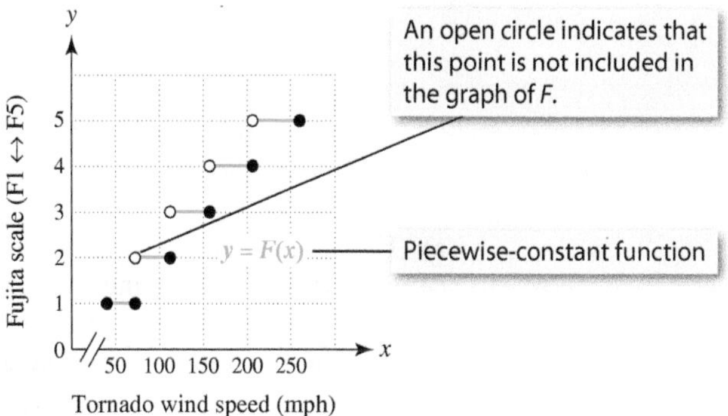

Figure 2.43

Continuous Functions The graph of a **continuous function** can be sketched without picking up the pencil. There are no breaks in the graph of a continuous function. Because there are breaks in the graph shown in Figure 2.43, function F is not continuous; rather it is **discontinuous** at $x = 72, 112, 157,$ and 206.

An Application The housing market peaked in 2005. Shortly after, the housing bubble burst and continued to plummet, hitting a low in 2011. In the next example we use a piecewise-defined function to model housing starts from 2005 to 2011.

EXAMPLE 4 Analyzing housing starts

Table 2.5 lists numbers of single residential homes built during selected years.

Housing Starts in Millions

Year	2000	2005	2011	2012
Homes	1.3	1.7	0.4	0.5

Source: Bureau of the Census.

Table 2.5

(a) Plot a line graph of these data. Let this graph define a function H.
(b) Find and interpret the slope of each line segment.
(c) Is H continuous on its domain?
(d) Identify where H is increasing, decreasing, or constant.
(e) Write a piecewise-defined formula for H.

SOLUTION

(a) Plot the points (2000, 1.3), (2005, 1.7), (2011, 0.4), and (2012, 0.5). Connect these points with three line segments as shown in Figure 2.44. (*Source:* Bureau of the Census.)

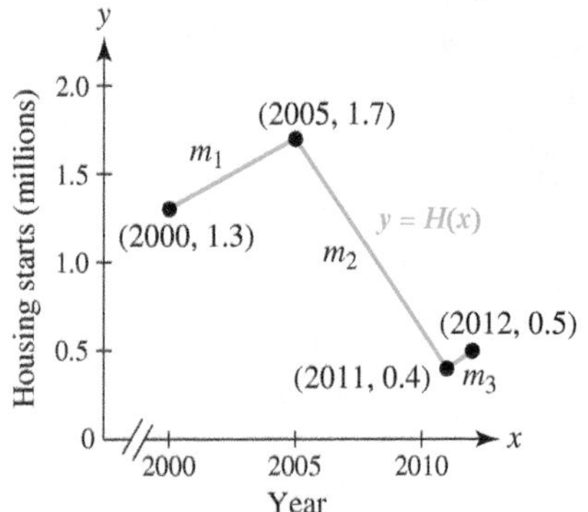

Figure 2.44

(b) The first line segment passes through (2000, 1.3) and (2005, 1.7) with slope

$$m_1 = \frac{1.7 - 1.3}{2005 - 2000} = \frac{0.4}{5} = \frac{2}{25} = 0.08.$$

Housing starts increased, on average, by 0.08 million (80,000) per year from 2000 to 2005. The other two slopes are $m_2 = -\frac{13}{60} \approx -0.22$ and $m_3 = \frac{1}{10}$ and can be interpreted similarly.

(c) There are no breaks in the graph so H is continuous on its domain, [2000, 2012].

(d) Function H is increasing on the intervals (2000, 2005) and (2011, 2012). It is decreasing on (2005, 2011) and is never constant.

(e) **Getting Started** We must determine three equations for the lines that represent the three line segments. Given the slope and one point we can write the point-slope form of each line. ▶

The first line segment passes through (2000, 1.3) and has slope $\frac{2}{25}$. Therefore $H(x) = \frac{2}{25}(x - 2000) + 1.3$, if $2000 \le x \le 2005$. Continuing in this manner, we can write a piecewise-defined formula for $H(x)$.

$$H(x) = \begin{cases} \frac{2}{25}(x - 2000) + 1.3, & \text{if } 2000 \le x \le 2005 \\ -\frac{13}{60}(x - 2005) + 1.7, & \text{if } 2005 < x \le 2011 \\ \frac{1}{10}(x - 2011) + 0.4, & \text{if } 2011 < x \le 2012 \end{cases}$$

Now Try Exercise 43

EXAMPLE 5 **Evaluating and graphing a piecewise-defined function**

Use $f(x)$ to complete the following.

$$f(x) = \begin{cases} x - 1 & \text{if } -4 \le x < 2 \\ -2x & \text{if } \ 2 \le x \le 4 \end{cases}$$

(a) What is the domain of f?
(b) Evaluate $f(-3)$, $f(2)$, $f(4)$, and $f(5)$.
(c) Sketch a graph of f.
(d) Is f a continuous function on its domain?

SOLUTION

(a) Function f is defined for x-values satisfying either $-4 \le x < 2$ or $2 \le x \le 4$. Thus the domain of f is $D = \{x \mid -4 \le x \le 4\}$, or $[-4, 4]$.

(b) For x-values satisfying $-4 \le x < 2$, $f(x) = x - 1$ and so $f(-3) = -4$. Similarly, if $2 \le x \le 4$, then $f(x) = -2x$. Thus $f(2) = -4$ and $f(4) = -8$. The expression $f(5)$ is undefined because 5 is not in the domain of f.

(c) **Getting Started** Because each piece of $f(x)$ is linear, the graph of $y = f(x)$ consists of two line segments. Therefore we can find the endpoints of each line segment and then sketch the graph. ▶

Graph the First Piece

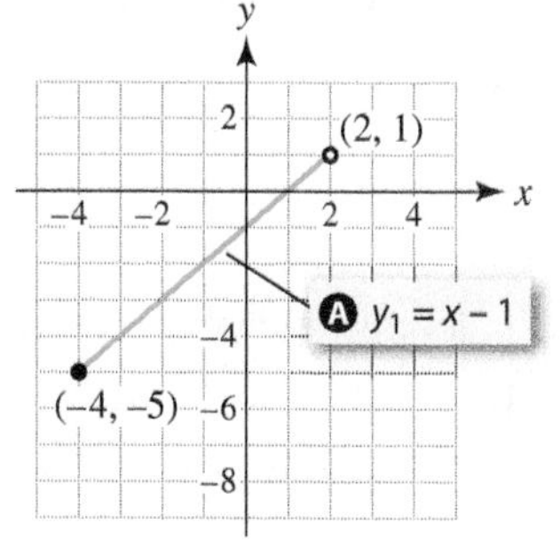

Figure 2.45

Graph the Second Piece

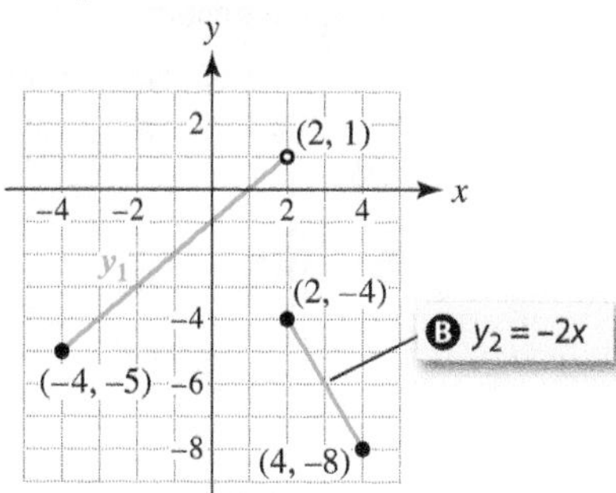

Figure 2.46

A Evaluate $y_1 = x - 1$ at $x = -4$ and $x = 2$. Place a dot at $(-4, -5)$ and an open circle at $(2, 1)$, because $y_1 = x - 1$ applies for $x < 2$. Sketch a line segment between these points.

B Evaluate $y_2 = -2x$ at $x = 2$ and $x = 4$. Place dots at $(2, -4)$ and $(4, -8)$. Sketch a line segment between these points.

(d) The function f is *not* continuous because in Figure 2.46 there is a break in its graph at $x = 2$.

Now Try Exercise 33

The Greatest Integer Function

A common piecewise-defined function used in mathematics is the greatest integer function, denoted $f(x) = [\![x]\!]$. The **greatest integer function** is defined as follows.

$[\![x]\!]$ is the greatest integer less than or equal to x.

Some examples of the evaluation of $[\![x]\!]$ include

$$[\![6.7]\!] = 6, \quad [\![3]\!] = 3, \quad [\![-2.3]\!] = -3, \quad [\![-10]\!] = -10, \quad \text{and} \quad [\![-\pi]\!] = -4.$$

The graph of $y = [\![x]\!]$ is shown in Figure 2.47. The greatest integer function is both a piecewise-constant function and a step function.

The Greatest Integer Function

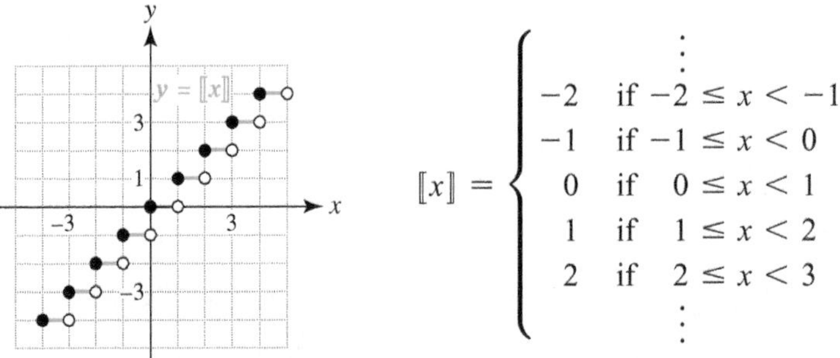

$$[\![x]\!] = \begin{cases} \vdots \\ -2 & \text{if } -2 \le x < -1 \\ -1 & \text{if } -1 \le x < 0 \\ 0 & \text{if } \ \ 0 \le x < 1 \\ 1 & \text{if } \ \ 1 \le x < 2 \\ 2 & \text{if } \ \ 2 \le x < 3 \\ \vdots \end{cases}$$

Figure 2.47

Calculator Help
To access the greatest integer function or to set a calculator in dot mode, see Appendix A (pages AP-6 and AP-8).

In some applications, fractional parts are either not allowed or ignored. Framing lumber for houses is measured in 2-foot multiples, and mileage charges for rental cars may be calculated to the mile.

Suppose a car rental company charges \$31.50 per day plus \$0.25 for each mile driven, where fractions of a mile are ignored. The function given by $f(x) = 0.25[\![x]\!] + 31.50$ calculates the cost of driving x miles in one day. For example, the cost of driving 100.4 miles is

$$f(100.4) = 0.25[\![100.4]\!] + 31.50 = 0.25(100) + 31.50 = \$56.50.$$

Dot Mode
[0, 10, 1] by [31, 35, 1]

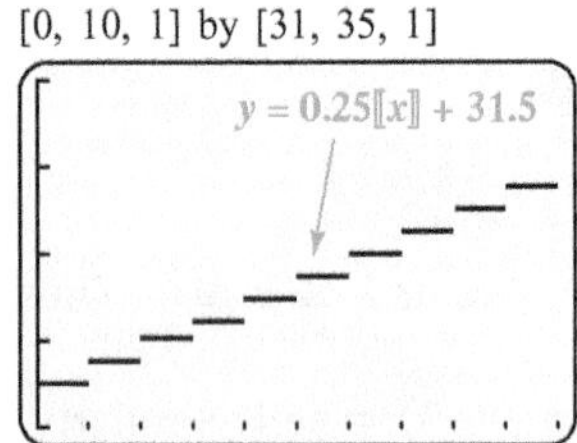

Figure 2.48

On some calculators and computers, the greatest integer function is denoted int(X). A graph of $Y_1 = 0.25*\text{int}(X) + 31.5$ is shown in Figure 2.48.

MAKING CONNECTIONS

Connected and Dot Modes Graphing calculators often connect points to make a graph look continuous. However, if a graph has breaks in it, a graphing calculator may connect points where there should be breaks. In *dot mode*, points are plotted but not connected. Figure 2.49 is the same graph shown in Figure 2.48, except that it is plotted in *connected mode.* Note that connected mode generates an inaccurate graph of this step function.

Connected Mode
[0, 10, 1] by [31, 35, 1]

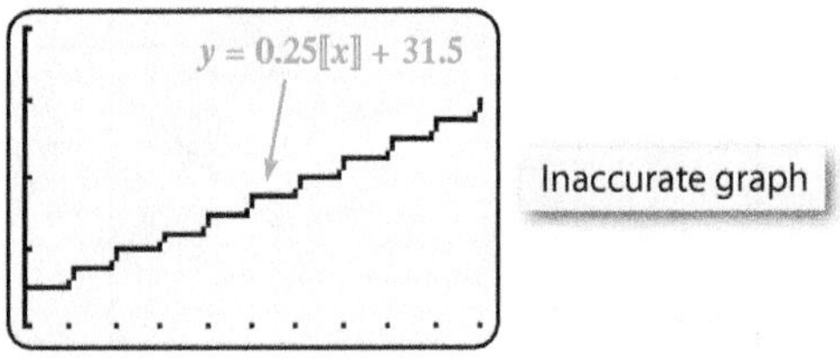

y = 0.25[[x]] + 31.5

Inaccurate graph

Figure 2.49

Direct Variation

When a change in one quantity causes a proportional change in another quantity, the two quantities are said to *vary directly* or to *be directly proportional.* For example, if we work for \$8 per hour, our pay is proportional to the number of hours that we work. Doubling the hours doubles the pay, tripling the hours triples the pay, and so on.

DIRECT VARIATION

Let x and y denote two quantities. Then y is **directly proportional** to x, or y **varies directly** with x, if there exists a nonzero number k such that

$$y = kx.$$

The number k is called the **constant of proportionality** or the **constant of variation.**

If a person earns \$57.75 working for 7 hours, the constant of proportionality k is the hourly pay rate. If y represents the pay in dollars and x the hours worked, then k is found by substituting values for x and y into the equation $y = kx$ and solving for k. That is,

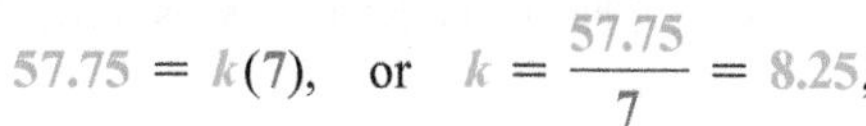

$$57.75 = k(7), \quad \text{or} \quad k = \frac{57.75}{7} = 8.25,$$

so the hourly pay rate is \$8.25 and, in general, $y = 8.25x$.

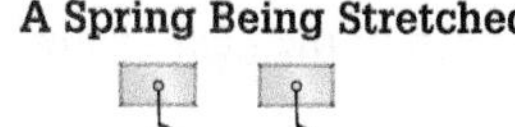

A Spring Being Stretched

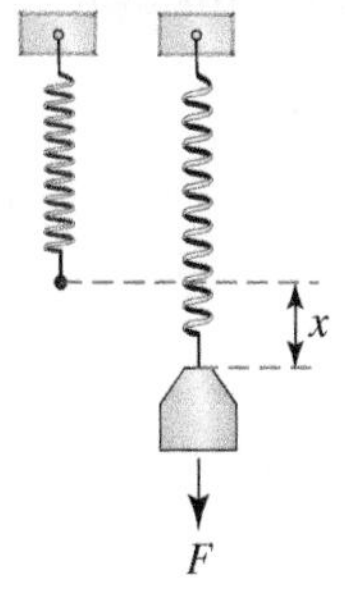

Figure 2.50

An Application Hooke's law states that the distance that an elastic spring stretches beyond its natural length is *directly proportional* to the amount of weight hung on the spring, as illustrated in Figure 2.50. This law is valid whether the spring is stretched or compressed. The constant of proportionality is called the **spring constant**. Thus if a weight or force F is applied and the spring stretches a distance x beyond its natural length, then the equation $F = kx$ models this situation, where k is the spring constant.

EXAMPLE 6 Working with Hooke's law

A 12-pound weight is hung on a spring, and it stretches 2 inches.

(a) Find the spring constant.

(b) Determine how far the spring will stretch when a 19-pound weight is hung on it.

SOLUTION

(a) Let $F = kx$, given that $F = 12$ pounds and $x = 2$ inches. Thus

$$12 = k(2), \quad \text{or} \quad k = 6,$$

and the spring constant equals 6.

(b) If $F = 19$ and $F = 6x$, then $19 = 6x$, or $x = \frac{19}{6} \approx 3.17$ inches.

Now Try Exercise 63

The following four-step method can often be used to solve variation problems.

SOLVING A VARIATION PROBLEM

When solving a variation problem, the following steps can be used.

STEP 1: Write the general equation for the type of variation problem that you are solving.

STEP 2: Substitute given values in this equation so the constant of variation k is the only unknown value in the equation. Solve for k.

STEP 3: Substitute the value of k in the general equation in Step 1.

STEP 4: Use this equation to find the requested quantity.

EXAMPLE 7 Solving a direct variation problem

Let T vary directly with x, and suppose that $T = 33$ when $x = 5$. Find T when $x = 31$.

SOLUTION

STEP 1: The equation for direct variation is $T = kx$.

STEP 2: Substitute 33 for T and 5 for x. Then solve for k.

$$\begin{aligned} T &= kx && \text{Direct variation equation} \\ 33 &= k(5) && \text{Let } T = 33 \text{ and } x = 5. \\ \frac{33}{5} &= k && \text{Divide each side by 5.} \end{aligned}$$

STEP 3: Thus $T = \frac{33}{5}x$, or $T = 6.6x$.

STEP 4: When $x = 31$, we have $T = 6.6(31) = 204.6$.

Now Try Exercise 51

Suppose that, for each point (x, y) in a data set, the ratios $\frac{y}{x}$ are equal to some constant k. That is, $\frac{y}{x} = k$ for each data point. Then $y = kx$, so y varies directly with x and the constant of variation is k. In addition, the data points (x, y) all lie on the line $y = kx$, which has slope k and passes through the origin. These concepts are used in the next example.

EXAMPLE 8 **Modeling memory requirements**

Table 2.6 lists the megabytes (MB) x needed to record y seconds of music.

Recording Digital Music

x (MB)	0.23	0.49	1.16	1.27
y (sec)	10.7	22.8	55.2	60.2

Table 2.6

(a) Compute the ratios $\frac{y}{x}$ for the four data points. Does y vary directly with x? If it does, what is the constant of variation k?
(b) Estimate the seconds of music that can be stored on 5 megabytes.
(c) Graph the data in Table 2.6 and the line $y = kx$.

SOLUTION

(a) The four ratios $\frac{y}{x}$ from Table 2.6 are

$$\frac{10.7}{0.23} \approx 46.5, \quad \frac{22.8}{0.49} \approx 46.5, \quad \frac{55.2}{1.16} \approx 47.6, \quad \text{and} \quad \frac{60.2}{1.27} \approx 47.4.$$

Because the ratios are nearly equal, it is reasonable to say that y is directly proportional to x. The constant of proportionality is about 47, the average of the four ratios. This means that $y = 47x$ and we can store about 47 seconds of music per megabyte.

(b) Let $x = 5$ in the equation $y = 47x$, to obtain $y = 47(5) = 235$ seconds.

(c) Graphs of the data and the line $y = 47x$ are shown in Figure 2.51.

Music and Memory Requirements

[0, 1.5, 0.5] by [0, 70, 10]

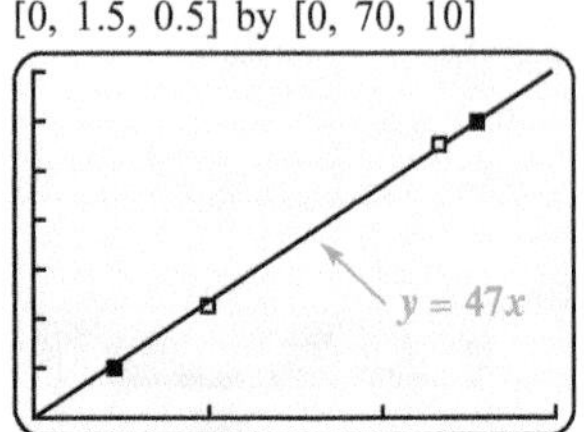

Figure 2.51

Now Try Exercise 65

2.4 Putting It All Together

The following table summarizes important concepts.

CONCEPT	DESCRIPTION
Models	A good model describes and explains current data. It should also make predictions and forecast phenomena.
Linear model	If a quantity experiences a constant rate of change, then it can be modeled by a linear function in the form $f(x) = mx + b$. $f(x) = $ (constant rate of change)x + (**initial value**)
Piecewise-defined function	A function is piecewise-defined if it has different formulas on different intervals of its domain. Many times the domain is restricted. $f(x) = \begin{cases} 2x - 3 & \text{if } -3 \le x < 1 \\ x + 5 & \text{if } 1 \le x \le 5 \end{cases}$ When $x = 2$ then $f(x) = x + 5$, so $f(2) = 2 + 5 = 7$. The domain of f is $[-3, 5]$.

CONCEPT	DESCRIPTION
The greatest integer function	$[\![x]\!]$ is the greatest integer less than or equal to x. $[\![-5.9]\!] = -6$, $[\![8.7]\!] = 8$, and $[\![-5]\!] = -5$
Direct variation	The variable y is directly proportional to x or varies directly with x if $y = kx$ for some nonzero constant k. Constant k is the constant of proportionality or the constant of variation.

2.4 Exercises

Modeling with Linear Functions

Exercises 1 and 2: Write a symbolic representation (formula) for a function f that computes the following.

1. **(a)** The number of pounds in x ounces

(b) The number of dimes in x dollars

(c) The monthly electric bill in dollars if x kilowatt-hours are used at 6 cents per kilowatt-hour and there is a fee of \$6.50

(d) The cost of skiing x times with a \$500 season pass

2. **(a)** The distance traveled by a car moving at 50 miles per hour for x hours

(b) The total number of hours in day x

(c) The distance in miles between a runner and home after x hours if the runner starts 1 mile from home and jogs *away* from home at 6 miles per hour

(d) A car's speed in feet per second after x seconds if its tires are 2 feet in diameter and rotating 14 times per second

Exercises 3–6: Find the formula for a linear function f that models the data in the table exactly.

3.

x	−2	0	4
$f(x)$	4	3	1

4.

x	−6	0	3
$f(x)$	−5	−1	1

5.

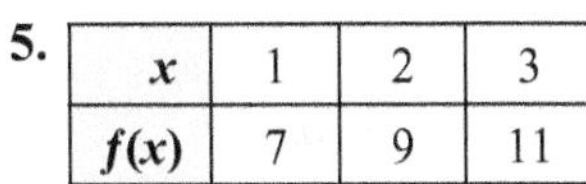

x	1	2	3
$f(x)$	7	9	11

6.

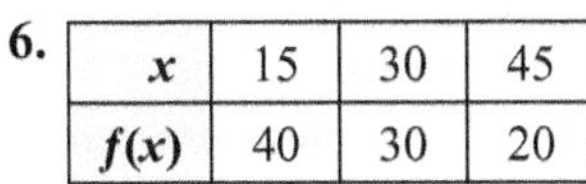

x	15	30	45
$f(x)$	40	30	20

Exercises 7–10: Match the situation with the graph (a–d) that models it best, where x-values represent time.

7. Height of the Empire State Building from 1990 to 2010

8. Average cost of a new car from 1980 to 2010

9. Distance between a runner in a race and the finish line

10. Amount of money earned after x hours when working at an hourly rate of pay

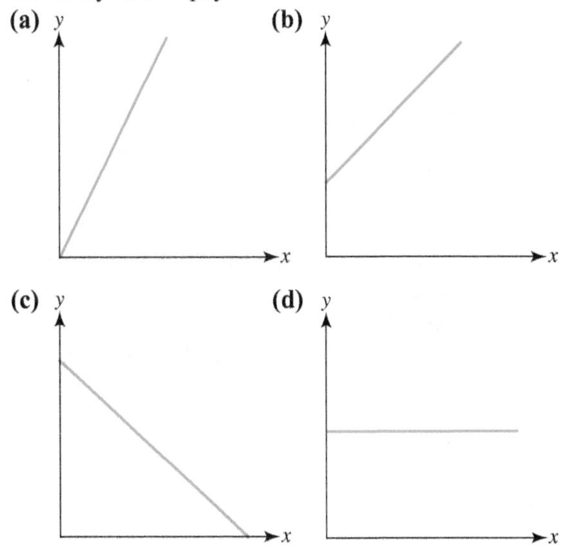

Exercises 11–16: Write a formula for a linear function that models the situation. Choose both an appropriate name and an appropriate variable for the function. State what the input variable represents and the domain of the function. Assume that the domain is an interval of the real numbers.

11. **U.S. Homes with Broadband** In 2010 about 27% of U.S. homes had broadband Internet access. This percentage is expected to increase, on average, by 1.2 percentage points per year for the next 4 years. (***Source:*** Bureau of the Census.)

12. **Velocity of a Falling Object** A stone is dropped from a water tower and its velocity increases at a rate of 32 feet per second. The stone hits the ground with a velocity of 96 feet per second.

13. **Text Messages** In the first month of 2010 about 0.4 trillion text messages were sent. The number of text messages being sent during 2010 grew by 0.5 trillion per month. (***Source:*** CTIA.)

14. **Speed of a Car** A car is traveling at 30 miles per hour, and then it begins to slow down at a constant rate of 6 miles per hour every 4 seconds.

15. **Population Density** In 1900 the average number of people per square mile in the United States was 21.5, and it increased, on average, by 6 people every 10 years until 2011. (***Source:*** Bureau of the Census.)

16. **Injury Rate** In 1992 the number of injury cases recorded in private industry per 100 full-time workers was 8.3, and it decreased, on average, by 0.27 injury every year until 2010. (***Source:*** Bureau of Labor Statistics.)

17. **Draining a Water Tank** A 300-gallon tank is initially full of water and is being drained at a rate of 10 gallons per minute.
    (a) Write a formula for a function W that gives the number of gallons of water in the tank after t minutes.
    (b) How much water is in the tank after 7 minutes?
    (c) Graph W and identify and interpret the intercepts.
    (d) Find the domain of W.

18. **Filling a Tank** A 500-gallon tank initially contains 200 gallons of fuel oil. A pump is filling the tank at a rate of 6 gallons per minute.
    (a) Write a formula for a linear function f that models the number of gallons of fuel oil in the tank after x minutes.
    (b) Graph f. What is an appropriate domain for f?
    (c) Identify the y-intercept and interpret it.
    (d) Does the x-intercept of the graph of f have any physical meaning in this problem? Explain.

19. **Living with HIV/AIDS** In 2007 there were 1.2 million people in the United States who had been infected with HIV. At that time the infection rate was 40,000 people per year. (***Source:*** CDC.)
    (a) Write a formula for a linear function f that models the total number of people in millions who were living with HIV/AIDS x years after 2007.
    (b) Estimate the number of people who may have been infected by the year 2014.

20. **Birth Rate** In 1990 the number of births per 1000 people in the United States was 16.7 and decreasing, on average, at 0.136 birth per 1000 people each year. (***Source:*** National Center for Health Statistics.)
    (a) Write a formula for a linear function f that models the birth rate x years after 1990.
    (b) Estimate the birth rate in 2012 and compare this estimate to the actual value of 13.7.

21. **Ice Deposits** A roof has a 0.5-inch layer of ice on it from a previous storm. Another ice storm begins to deposit ice at a rate of 0.25 inch per hour.
    (a) Find a formula for a linear function f that models the thickness of the ice on the roof x hours after the second ice storm started.
    (b) How thick is the ice after 2.5 hours?

22. **Rainfall** Suppose that during a storm rain is falling at a rate of 1 inch per hour. The water coming from a circular roof with a radius of 20 feet is running down a downspout that can accommodate 400 gallons of water per hour. See the figure.
    (a) Determine the number of cubic inches of water falling on the roof in 1 hour.
    (b) One gallon equals about 231 cubic inches. Write a formula for a function g that computes the gallons of water landing on the roof in x hours.
    (c) How many gallons of water land on the roof during a 2.5-hour rain storm?
    (d) Will one downspout be sufficient to handle this type of rainfall? How many downspouts should there be?

Exercises 23 and 24: **Modeling Fuel Consumption** *The table shows the distance y in miles traveled by a vehicle using x gallons of gasoline.*

(a) Calculate the slopes of the line segments that connect consecutive points.
(b) Find a linear function that models the data.
(c) Graph f and the data together. What does the slope indicate?
(d) Evaluate f(30) and interpret the result.

23.

x (gallons)	5	10	15	20
y (miles)	84	169	255	338

24.

x (gallons)	5	10	15	20
y (miles)	194	392	580	781

Piecewise-Defined Functions

25. **Speed Limits** The graph of $y = f(x)$ gives the speed limit y along a rural highway x miles from its starting point.
(a) What are the maximum and minimum speed limits along this stretch of highway?
(b) Estimate the miles of highway with a speed limit of 55 miles per hour.
(c) Evaluate $f(4)$, $f(12)$, and $f(18)$.
(d) At what x-values is the graph discontinuous? Interpret each discontinuity.

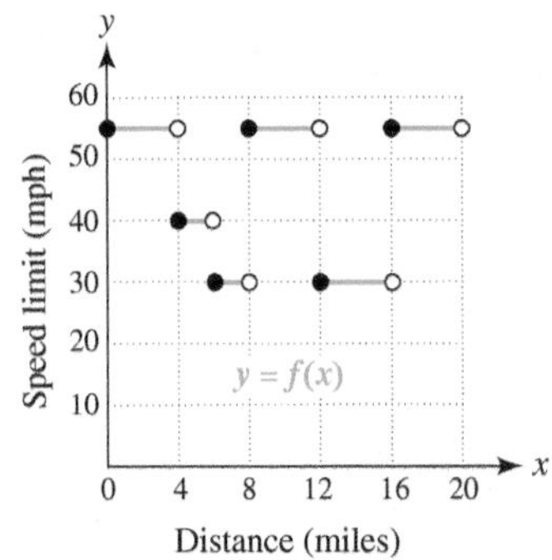

26. **ATM** The graph of $y = f(x)$ depicts the amount of money y in dollars in an automatic teller machine (ATM) after x minutes.
(a) Determine the initial and final amounts of money in the ATM.
(b) Evaluate $f(10)$ and $f(50)$. Is f continuous?
(c) How many *withdrawals* occurred?
(d) When did the largest withdrawal occur? How much was it?
(e) How much was deposited into the machine?

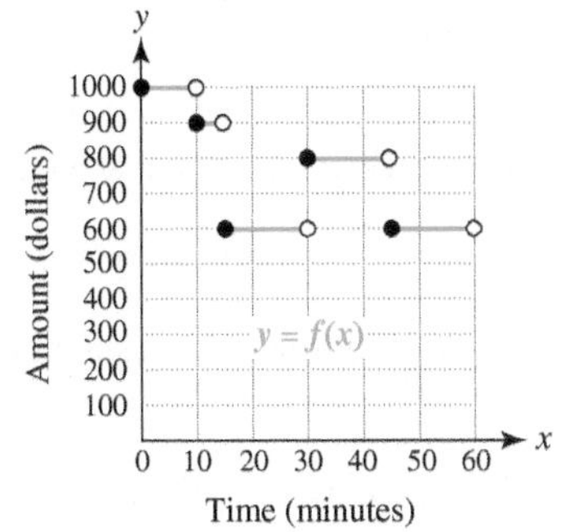

27. **First-Class Mail** In January 2012, the retail flat rate in dollars for first-class mail weighing up to 5 ounces could be computed by the piecewise-constant function P, where x is the number of ounces.

$$P(x) = \begin{cases} 0.90 & \text{if } 0 < x \le 1 \\ 1.10 & \text{if } 1 < x \le 2 \\ 1.30 & \text{if } 2 < x \le 3 \\ 1.50 & \text{if } 3 < x \le 4 \\ 1.70 & \text{if } 4 < x \le 5 \end{cases}$$

(a) Evaluate $P(1.5)$ and $P(3)$. Interpret your results.
(b) Sketch a graph of P. What is the domain of P?
(c) Where is P discontinuous on its domain?

28. **Swimming Pool Levels** The graph of $y = f(x)$ shows the amount of water y in thousands of gallons remaining in a swimming pool after x days.
(a) Estimate the initial and final amounts of water in the pool.
(b) When did the amount of water in the pool remain constant?
(c) Approximate $f(2)$ and $f(4)$.
(d) At what rate was water being drained from the pool when $1 \le x \le 3$?

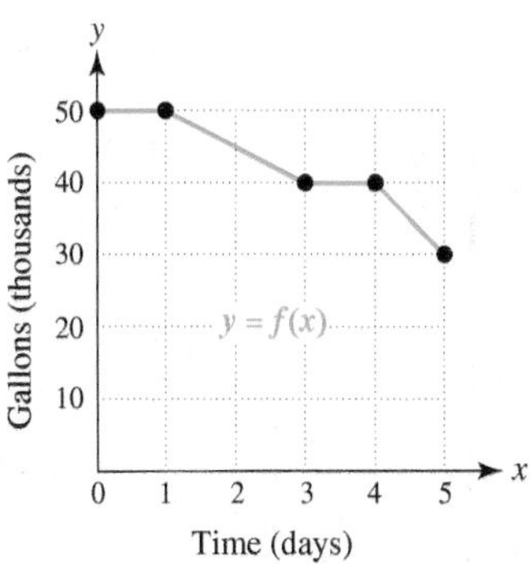

Exercises 29 and 30: An individual is driving a car along a straight road. The graph shows the driver's distance from home after x hours.
(a) Use the graph to evaluate $f(1.5)$ and $f(4)$.
(b) Interpret the slope of each line segment.
(c) Describe the motion of the car.
(d) Identify where f is increasing, decreasing, or constant.

29.

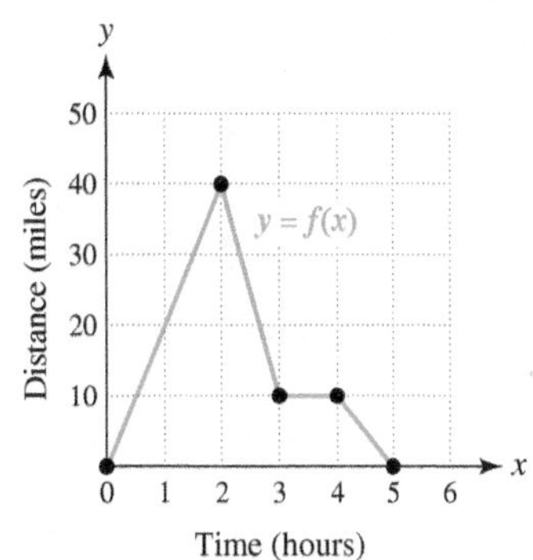

30.

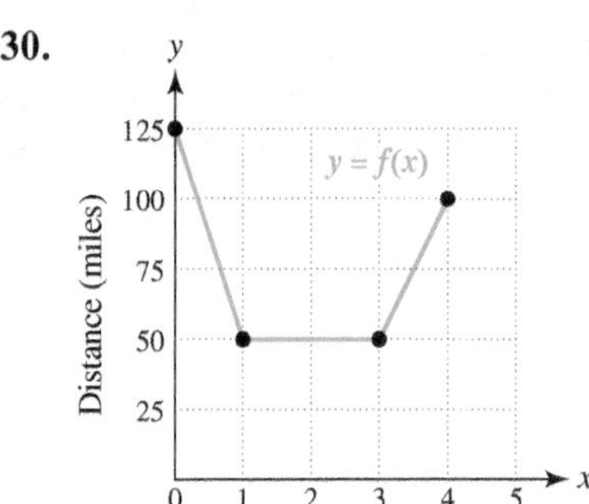

Exercises 31–36: Complete the following for $f(x)$.

(a) Determine the domain of f.
(b) Evaluate $f(-2)$, $f(0)$, and $f(3)$.
(c) Graph f.
(d) Is f continuous on its domain?

31. $f(x) = \begin{cases} 2 & \text{if } -5 \le x \le -1 \\ x + 3 & \text{if } -1 < x \le 5 \end{cases}$

32. $f(x) = \begin{cases} 2x + 1 & \text{if } -3 \le x < 0 \\ x - 1 & \text{if } 0 \le x \le 3 \end{cases}$

33. $f(x) = \begin{cases} 3x & \text{if } -1 \le x < 1 \\ x + 1 & \text{if } 1 \le x \le 2 \end{cases}$

34. $f(x) = \begin{cases} -2 & \text{if } -6 \le x < -2 \\ 0 & \text{if } -2 \le x < 0 \\ 3x & \text{if } 0 \le x \le 4 \end{cases}$

35. $f(x) = \begin{cases} x & \text{if } -3 \le x \le -1 \\ 1 & \text{if } -1 < x < 1 \\ 2 - x & \text{if } 1 \le x \le 3 \end{cases}$

36. $f(x) = \begin{cases} 3 & \text{if } -4 \le x \le -1 \\ x - 2 & \text{if } -1 < x \le 2 \\ 0.5x & \text{if } 2 < x \le 4 \end{cases}$

Exercises 37 and 38: Graph f.

37. $f(x) = \begin{cases} -\frac{1}{2}x + 1 & \text{if } -4 \le x \le -2 \\ 1 - 2x & \text{if } -2 < x \le 1 \\ \frac{2}{3}x + \frac{4}{3} & \text{if } 1 < x \le 4 \end{cases}$

38. $f(x) = \begin{cases} \frac{3}{2} - \frac{1}{2}x & \text{if } -3 \le x < -1 \\ -2x & \text{if } -1 \le x \le 2 \\ \frac{1}{2}x - 5 & \text{if } 2 < x \le 3 \end{cases}$

39. Use $f(x)$ to complete the following.

$$f(x) = \begin{cases} 3x - 1 & \text{if } -5 \le x < 1 \\ 4 & \text{if } 1 \le x \le 3 \\ 6 - x & \text{if } 3 < x \le 5 \end{cases}$$

(a) Evaluate f at $x = -3, 1, 2,$ and 5.

(b) On what interval is f constant?

(c) Sketch a graph of f. Is f continuous on its domain?

40. Use $g(x)$ to complete the following.

$$g(x) = \begin{cases} -2x - 6 & \text{if } -8 \le x \le -2 \\ x & \text{if } -2 < x < 2 \\ 0.5x + 1 & \text{if } 2 \le x \le 8 \end{cases}$$

(a) Evaluate g at $x = -8, -2, 2,$ and 8.

(b) For what x-values is g increasing?

(c) Sketch a graph of g. Is g continuous on its domain?

Exercises 41 and 42: Use the graph of $y = f(x)$ to write a piecewise-defined formula for f. Write each piece in slope-intercept form.

41.

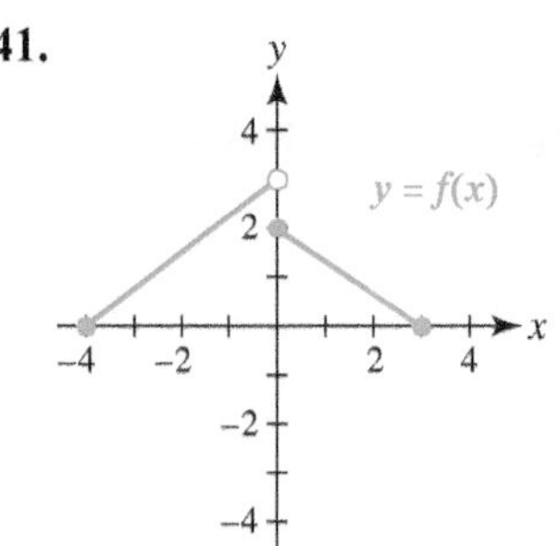

42.

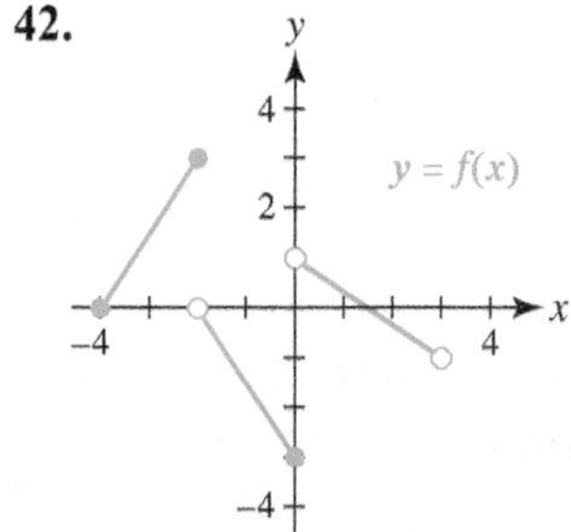

43. Housing Market One way to describe the housing market is to divide the population of the United States by the number of new housing starts. This ratio is listed in the following table for selected years.

Year	2000	2005	2009	2011
Ratio	225	180	700	727

Source: Bureau of the Census.

(a) Plot a line graph of these data. Let this graph be function R.

(b) Evaluate $R(2009)$ and interpret the result. Do small or large values indicate a strong housing market?

(c) Is R continuous on its domain?

(d) Identify where R is increasing, decreasing, or constant.

(e) Write a piecewise-defined formula for R.

44. **High School Dropouts** The table lists the percentage of the population that did not have a high school diploma for selected years.

Year	1960	1980	2000	2010
Percentage	28	14	11	8

Source: Bureau of the Census.

(a) Plot a line graph of these data. Let this graph be function D.

(b) Interpret the slope of each line segment.

(c) Is D continuous on its domain?

(d) Identify where D is increasing, decreasing, or constant.

(e) Write a piecewise-defined formula for D.

Greatest Integer Function

Exercises 45–48: Complete the following.

(a) Use dot mode to graph the function f in the standard viewing rectangle.

(b) Evaluate $f(-3.1)$ and $f(1.7)$.

45. $f(x) = [\![2x - 1]\!]$

46. $f(x) = [\![x + 1]\!]$

47. $f(x) = 2[\![x]\!] + 1$

48. $f(x) = [\![-x]\!]$

49. **Lumber Costs** The lumber used to frame walls of houses is frequently sold in multiples of 2 feet. If the length of a board is not exactly a multiple of 2 feet, there is often no charge for the additional length. For example, if a board measures at least 8 feet but less than 10 feet, then the consumer is charged for only 8 feet.

(a) Suppose that the cost of lumber is $0.80 for every 2 feet. Find a formula for a function f that computes the cost of a board x feet long for $6 \leq x \leq 18$.

(b) Graph f.

(c) Determine the costs of boards with lengths of 8.5 feet and 15.2 feet.

50. **Cost of Carpet** Each foot of carpet purchased from a 12-foot-wide roll costs $36. If a fraction of a foot is purchased, a customer does not pay for the extra amount. For example, if a customer wants 14 feet of carpet and the salesperson cuts off 14 feet 4 inches, the customer does not pay for the extra 4 inches.

(a) How much does 9 feet 8 inches of carpet from this roll cost?

(b) Using the greatest integer function, write a formula for the price P of x feet of carpet.

Direct Variation

Exercises 51–54: Let y be directly proportional to x. Complete the following.

51. Find y when $x = 5$, if $y = 7$ when $x = 14$.

52. Find y when $x = 2.5$, if $y = 13$ when $x = 10$.

53. Find y when $x = \frac{1}{2}$, if $y = \frac{3}{2}$ when $x = \frac{2}{3}$.

54. Find y when $x = 1.3$, if $y = 7.2$ when $x = 5.2$.

Exercises 55–58: Find the constant of proportionality k and the undetermined value in the table if y is directly proportional to x.

55.

x	3	5	6	8
y	7.5	12.5	15	?

56.

x	1.2	4.3	5.7	?
y	3.96	14.19	18.81	23.43

57. Sales tax y on a purchase of x dollars

x	$25	$55	?
y	$1.50	$3.30	$5.10

58. Cost y of buying x compact discs at the same price

x	3	4	5
y	$41.97	$55.96	?

59. **Cost of Tuition** The cost of tuition is directly proportional to the number of credits taken. If 11 credits cost $720.50, find the cost of taking 16 credits. What is the constant of proportionality?

60. **Strength of a Beam** The maximum load that a horizontal beam can carry is directly proportional to its width. If a beam 1.5 inches wide can support a load of 250 pounds, find the load that a beam of the same type can support if its width is 3.5 inches.

61. **Antarctic Ozone Layer** Stratospheric ozone occurs in the atmosphere between altitudes of 12 and 18 miles. Ozone in the stratosphere is frequently measured in Dobson units, where 300 Dobson units corresponds to an ozone layer 3 millimeters thick. In 1991 the reported minimum in the Antarctic *ozone hole* was about 110 Dobson units. (***Source:*** R. Huffman, *Atmospheric Ultraviolet Remote Sensing.*)

(a) The thickness y of the ozone layer is directly proportional to the number of Dobson units x. Find the constant of proportionality k.

(b) How thick was the ozone layer in 1991?

62. **Weight on Mars** The weight of an object on Earth is directly proportional to the weight of an object on Mars. If a 25-pound object on Earth weighs 10 pounds on Mars, how much would a 195-pound astronaut weigh on Mars?

63. **Hooke's Law** Suppose a 15-pound weight stretches a spring 8 inches, as shown in the figure.

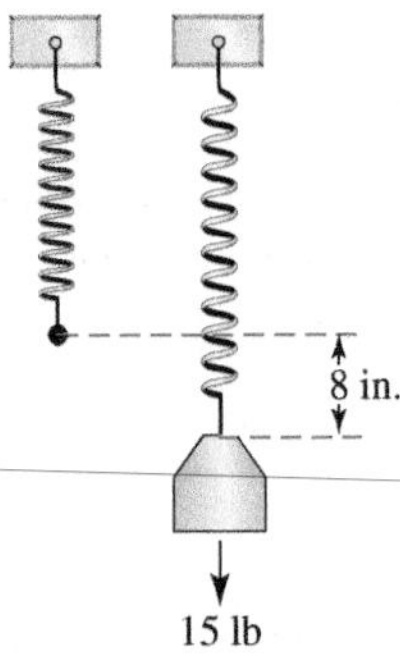

(a) Find the spring constant.

(b) How far will a 25-pound weight stretch this spring?

64. **Hooke's Law** If an 80-pound force compresses a spring 3 inches, how much force must be applied to compress the spring 7 inches?

65. **Force of Friction** The table lists the force F needed to push a cargo box weighing x pounds on a wood floor.

x (lb)	150	180	210	320
F (lb)	26	31	36	54

(a) Compute the ratio $\frac{F}{x}$ for each data pair in the table. Interpret these ratios.

(b) Approximate a constant of proportionality k satisfying $F = kx$. (k is the *coefficient of friction*.)

(c) Graph the data and the equation together.

(d) Estimate the force needed to push a 275-pound cargo box on the floor.

66. **Electrical Resistance** The electrical resistance of a wire varies directly with its length. If a 255-foot wire has a resistance of 1.2 ohms, find the resistance of 135 feet of the same type of wire. Interpret the constant of proportionality in this situation.

Linear Regression

67. **Ring Size** The table lists ring size S for a finger with circumference x in centimeters.

x (cm)	4.65	5.40	5.66	6.41
S (size)	4	7	8	11

Source: Overstock.

(a) Find a linear function S that models the data.

(b) Find the circumference of a finger with a ring size of 6.

68. **Hat Size** The table lists hat size H for a head with circumference x in inches.

x (in.)	$21\frac{1}{8}$	$21\frac{7}{8}$	$22\frac{5}{8}$	25
S (size)	$6\frac{3}{4}$	7	$7\frac{1}{4}$	8

(a) Find a linear function S that models the data.

(b) Find the circumference of a head with a hat size of $7\frac{1}{2}$.

69. **Super Bowl Ads** The table lists the cost in millions of dollars for a 30-second Super Bowl commercial for selected years.

Year	1994	1998	2004	2008	2012
Cost	1.2	1.6	2.3	2.7	3.5

Source: MSNBC.

(a) Find a linear function f that models the data.

(b) Estimate the cost in 2009 and compare the estimate to the actual value of \$3.0 million. Did your estimate involve interpolation or extrapolation?

(c) Use f to predict the year when the cost could reach \$4.0 million.

70. **Women in Politics** The table lists the percentage P of women in state legislatures during year x.

x	1993	1997	2001	2005	2007
P	20.5	21.6	22.4	22.7	23.5

Source: National Women's Political Caucus.

(a) Find a linear function P that models the data.

(b) Estimate this percentage in 2003 and compare the estimate to the actual value of 22.4%. Did your estimate involve interpolation or extrapolation?

(c) Use P to predict the year when this percentage could reach 25%.

Writing about Mathematics

71. Explain what a piecewise-defined function is and why it is used. Sketch a graph of a continuous piecewise-linear function f that increases, decreases, and is constant. Let the domain of f be $-4 \le x \le 4$.

72. Find a real data set on the Internet that can be modeled by a linear function. Find the linear modeling function. Is your model exact or approximate? Explain.

73. How can you recognize a symbolic representation (formula) of a linear function? How can you recognize a graph or table of values of a linear function?

74. Explain how you determine whether a linear function is increasing, decreasing, or constant. Give an example of each.

Extended and Discovery Exercises

Exercises 1 and 2: **Estimating Populations** *Biologists sometimes use direct variation to estimate the number of fish in small lakes. They start by tagging a small number of fish and then releasing them. They assume that over a period of time, the tagged fish distribute themselves evenly throughout the lake. Later, they collect a second sample. The total number of fish and the number of tagged fish in the second sample are counted. To determine the total population of fish in the lake, biologists assume that the proportion of tagged fish in the second sample is equal to the proportion of tagged fish in the entire lake. This technique can also be used to count other types of animals, such as birds, when they are not migrating.*

1. Eighty-five fish are tagged and released into a pond. A later sample of 94 fish from the pond contains 13 tagged fish. Estimate the number of fish in the pond.

2. Sixty-three blackbirds are tagged and released. Later it is estimated that out of a sample of 32 blackbirds, only 8 are tagged. Estimate the population of blackbirds in the area.

3. **Height and Shoe Size** In this exercise you will determine if there is a relationship between height and shoe size.
   (a) Have classmates write their sex, shoe size, and height in inches on a slip of paper. When you have enough information, complete the following table—one for adult males and one for adult females.

Height (inches)					
Shoe size					

   (b) Make a scatterplot of each table, with height on the x-axis and shoe size on the y-axis. Is there any relationship between height and shoe size? Explain.

   (c) Try to find a linear function that models each data set.

Exercises 4 and 5: **Linear Approximation** *Graph the function f in the standard viewing rectangle.*
(a) Choose any curved portion of the graph of f and repeatedly zoom in. Describe how the graph appears. Repeat this process on different portions of the graph.
(b) Under what circumstances could a linear function be used to accurately model a nonlinear graph?

4. $f(x) = 4x - x^3$

5. $f(x) = x^4 - 5x^2$

CHECKING BASIC CONCEPTS FOR SECTIONS 2.3 AND 2.4

1. Solve the inequality $2(x - 4) > 1 - x$. Express the solution set in set-builder notation.

2. Solve the compound inequality $-2 \leq 1 - 2x \leq 3$. Use set-builder or interval notation.

3. Use the graph to solve each equation and inequality. Then solve each part symbolically. Use set-builder or interval notation when possible.

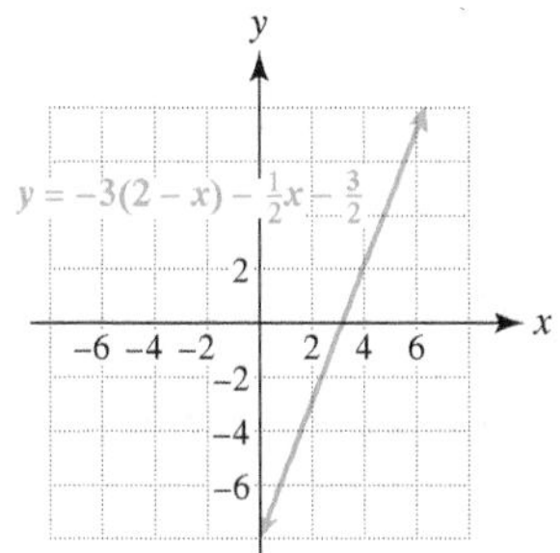

   (a) $-3(2 - x) - \frac{1}{2}x - \frac{3}{2} = 0$

   (b) $-3(2 - x) - \frac{1}{2}x - \frac{3}{2} > 0$

   (c) $-3(2 - x) - \frac{1}{2}x - \frac{3}{2} \leq 0$

4. The death rate from heart disease for people ages 15 through 24 is 2.7 per 100,000 people.
   (a) Write a function f that models the number of deaths in a population of x million people 15 to 24 years old.
   (b) There are about 39 million people in the United States who are 15 to 24 years old. Estimate the number of deaths from heart disease in this age group.

5. A driver of a car is initially 50 miles south of home, driving 60 miles per hour south. Write a function f that models the distance between the driver and home.

2.5 Absolute Value Equations and Inequalities

- Evaluate and graph the absolute value function
- Solve absolute value equations
- Solve absolute value inequalities

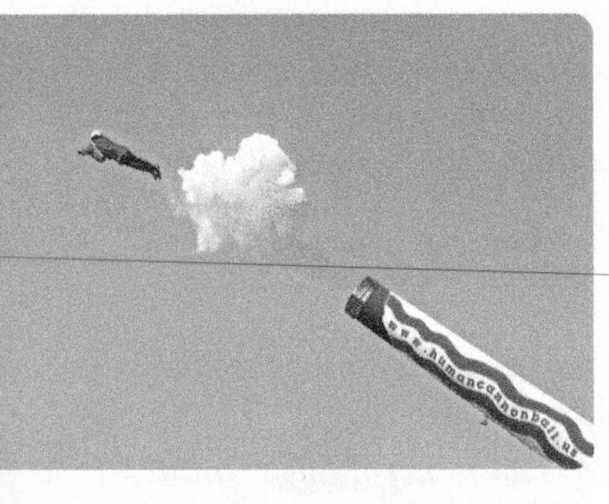

Introduction

A margin of error can be very important in many aspects of life, including being fired out of a cannon. The most dangerous part of the feat, first done by a human in 1875, is to land squarely on a net. For a human cannonball who wants to fly 180 feet in the air and then land in the center of a net with a 60-foot-long safe zone, there is a margin of error of ± 30 feet. That is, the horizontal distance D traveled by the human cannonball can vary between $180 - 30 = 150$ feet and $180 + 30 = 210$ feet. (***Source:*** Ontario Science Center.)

This margin of error can be expressed mathematically by using the *absolute value inequality*

$$|D - 180| \le 30.$$

The absolute value is necessary because D can be either less than or greater than 180, but by not more than 30 feet.

The Absolute Value Function

The absolute value function is defined by $f(x) = |x|$. The following See the Concept describes many of the properties of this function.

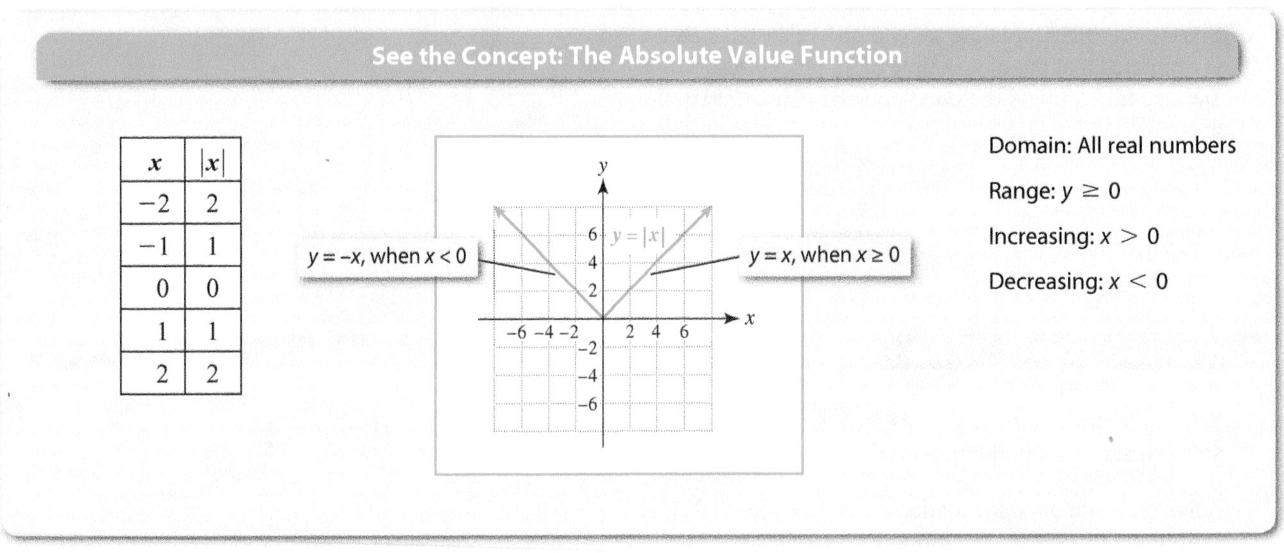

x	$\lvert x\rvert$
−2	2
−1	1
0	0
1	1
2	2

Symbolic Representations (Formulas) The graph of the absolute value function suggests that the absolute value function can be defined symbolically using the following piecewise-linear function.

$$|x| = \begin{cases} -x & \text{if } x < 0 \\ x & \text{if } x \ge 0 \end{cases} \qquad \text{Piecewise-linear function}$$

There is another formula for $|x|$. Consider the following examples.

$$\sqrt{3^2} = \sqrt{9} = 3 \quad \text{and} \quad \sqrt{(-3)^2} = \sqrt{9} = 3$$
$$\sqrt{7^2} = \sqrt{49} = 7 \quad \text{and} \quad \sqrt{(-7)^2} = \sqrt{49} = 7$$

That is, regardless of whether a real number x is positive or negative, the expression $\sqrt{x^2}$ equals the *absolute value* of x. This statement is summarized by

Calculator Help
To access the absolute value function, see Appendix A (page AP-8).

$$\sqrt{x^2} = |x| \quad \text{for all real numbers } x.$$

For example, $\sqrt{y^2} = |y|$, $\sqrt{(x-1)^2} = |x-1|$, and $\sqrt{(2x)^2} = |2x|$.

EXAMPLE 1 **Analyzing the graph of $y = |ax + b|$**

Graph $y = f(x)$ and $y = |f(x)|$ separately. Discuss how the absolute value affects the graph of f.

(a) $f(x) = x + 2$ **(b)** $f(x) = -2x + 4$

SOLUTION

(a) The line $y = x + 2$ is shown in Figure 2.52. The graph of $y = |x + 2|$ in Figure 2.53 is V-shaped and *never* dips below the x-axis because an absolute value is *never* negative.

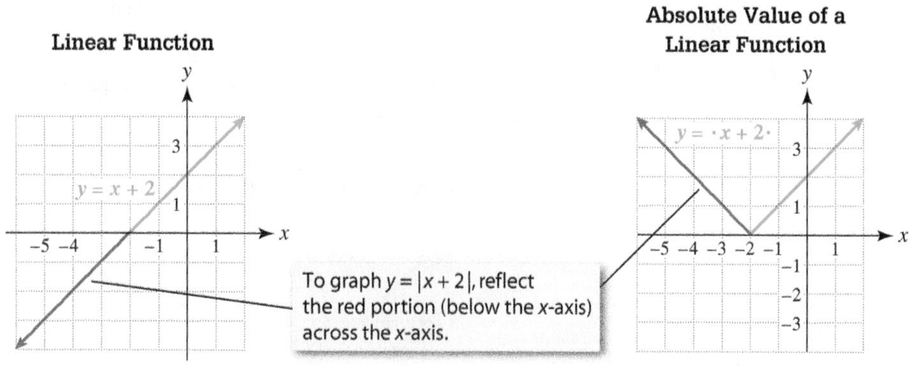

Figure 2.52

Figure 2.53

(b) The graphs of $y_1 = -2x + 4$ and $y_2 = |-2x + 4|$ are shown in Figures 2.54 and 2.55, respectively.

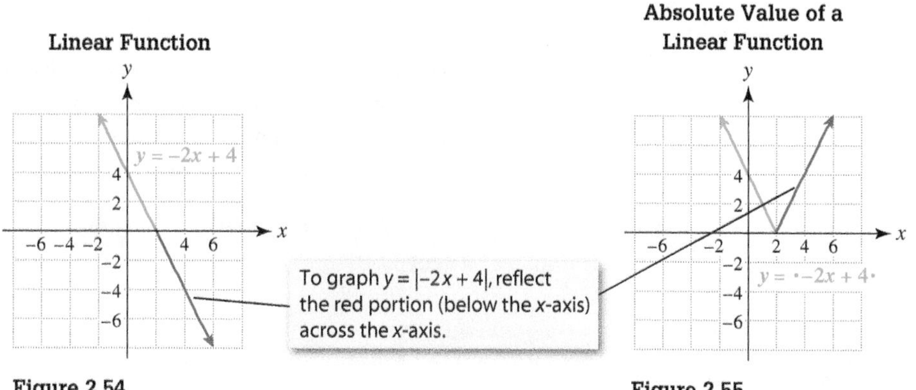

Figure 2.54

Figure 2.55

Now Try Exercises 13 and 17

NOTE Example 1 illustrates the fact that the graph of $y = |ax + b|$ with $a \neq 0$ is V-shaped and is never located below the x-axis. The vertex (or point) of the V-shaped graph corresponds to the x-intercept, which can be found by solving the linear equation $ax + b = 0$.

MAKING CONNECTIONS

Graphs and the Absolute Value In general, the graph of $y = |f(x)|$ is a reflection of the graph of $y = f(x)$ across the x-axis whenever $f(x) < 0$. Otherwise (whenever $f(x) > 0$), their graphs are identical. The following graphs illustrate this connection.

The Effect of the Absolute Value on a Graph

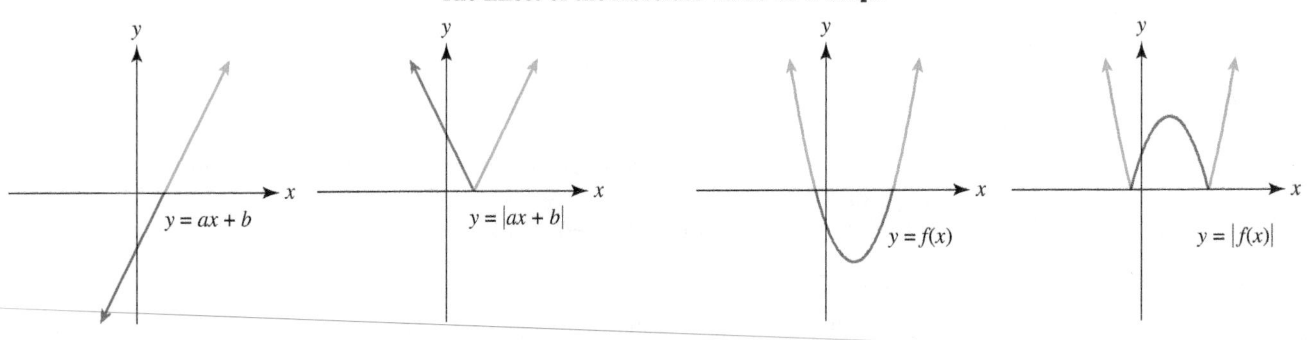

Absolute Value Equations

The equation $|x| = 5$ has two solutions: ± 5. This fact is shown visually in Figure 2.56, where the graph of $y = |x|$ intersects the horizontal line $y = 5$ at the points $(\pm 5, 5)$. In general, the solutions to $|x| = k$ with $k > 0$ are given by $x = \pm k$. See Figure 2.57.

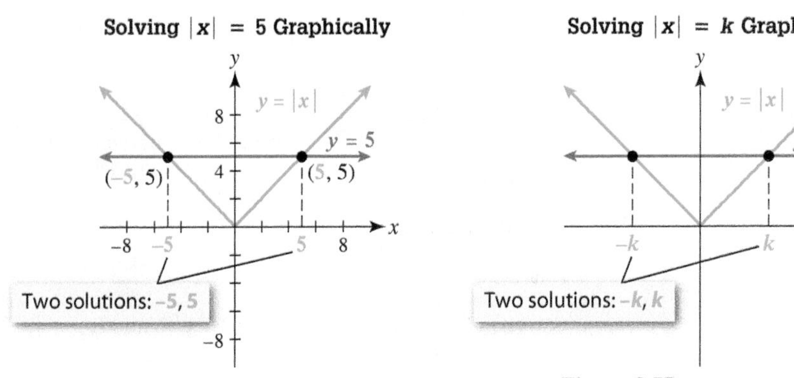

Figure 2.56 **Figure 2.57**

The absolute value equation $|ax + b| = k$ can be solved graphically. In the following box, the V-shaped graph of $y = |ax + b|$ intersects the horizontal line ($y = k$) two, one, or zero times, depending on the value of k.

See the Concept: Solving $|ax + b| = k$ Graphically

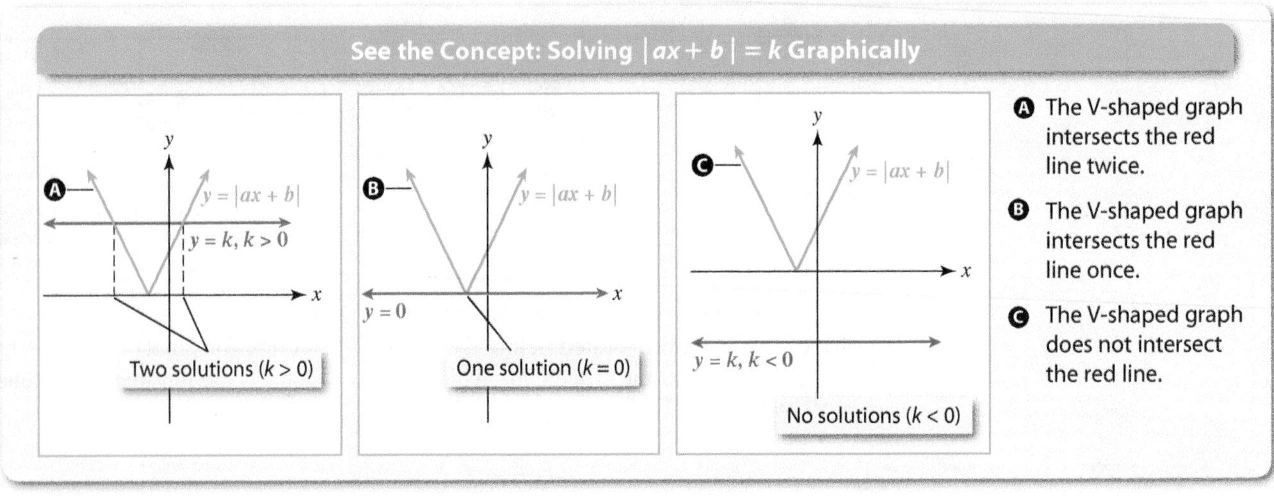

- **A** The V-shaped graph intersects the red line twice.
- **B** The V-shaped graph intersects the red line once.
- **C** The V-shaped graph does not intersect the red line.

Because the solution to $|x| = k$ are given by $x = \pm k$, it follows that the solutions to $|ax + b| = k$ are given by $ax + b = \pm k$. This concept is used to solve absolute value equations symbolically.

ABSOLUTE VALUE EQUATIONS

Let k be a positive number. Then

$$|ax + b| = k \quad \text{is equivalent to} \quad ax + b = \pm k.$$

EXAMPLE 2 **Solving absolute value equations**

Solve each equation.

(a) $\left|\frac{3}{4}x - 6\right| = 15$ **(b)** $|1 - 2x| = -3$ **(c)** $|3x - 2| - 5 = -2$

SOLUTION

(a) The equation $\left|\frac{3}{4}x - 6\right| = 15$ is satisfied when $\frac{3}{4}x - 6 = \pm 15$.

$\frac{3}{4}x - 6 = 15$	or	$\frac{3}{4}x - 6 = -15$	Equations to solve
$\frac{3}{4}x = 21$	or	$\frac{3}{4}x = -9$	Add 6 to each side.
$x = 28$	or	$x = -12$	Multiply by $\frac{4}{3}$.

The solutions are -12 and 28.

No Solutions

y
x
3
1
−3 −2 −1
1 2 3
−1
−2
y = |1 − 2x|
y = −3

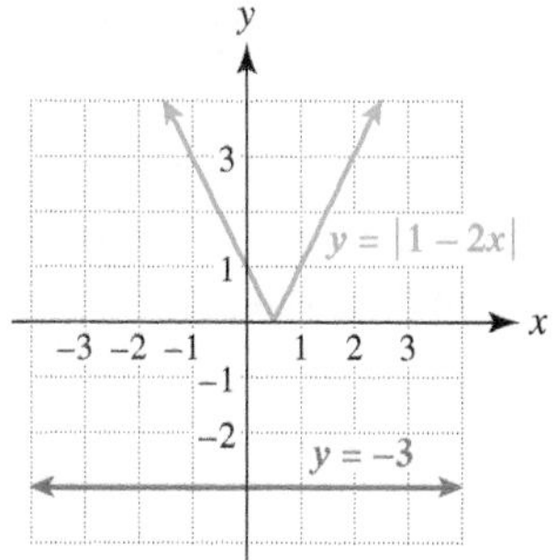

Figure 2.58

(b) Because an absolute value is never negative, $|1 - 2x| \geq 0$ for all x and can never equal -3. There are no solutions. This is illustrated graphically in Figure 2.58.

(c) Because the right side of the equation is a negative number, it might appear at first glance that there were no solutions. However, if we add 5 to each side of the equation,

$$|3x - 2| - 5 = -2 \quad \text{becomes} \quad |3x - 2| = 3.$$

This equation is equivalent to $3x - 2 = \pm 3$ and has two solutions.

$3x - 2 = 3$	or	$3x - 2 = -3$	Equations to solve
$3x = 5$	or	$3x = -1$	Add 2 to each side.
$x = \frac{5}{3}$	or	$x = -\frac{1}{3}$	Divide by 3.

The solutions are $-\frac{1}{3}$ and $\frac{5}{3}$.

Now Try Exercises 21, 29, and 31

EXAMPLE 3 **Solving an equation with technology**

Solve the equation $|2x + 5| = 2$ graphically, numerically, and symbolically.

SOLUTION

Graphical Solution Graph $y_1 = |2x + 5|$ and $y_2 = 2$. The V-shaped graph of y_1 intersects the horizontal line at the points $(-3.5, 2)$ and $(-1.5, 2)$, as shown in Figures 2.59 and 2.60. The solutions are -3.5 and -1.5.

Numerical Solution Table y_1 and y_2, as shown in Figure 2.61. The solutions to $y_1 = y_2$ are -3.5 and -1.5.

Calculator Help
To find a point of intersection, see Appendix A (page AP-7).

First Graphical Solution

$[-9, 9, 1]$ by $[-6, 6, 1]$

y₁ = |2x + 5|
y₂ = 2
Intersection
X=⁻3.5
Y=2

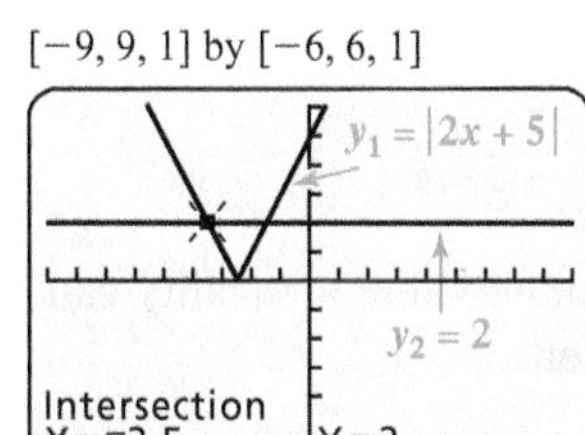

Figure 2.59

Second Graphical Solution

$[-9, 9, 1]$ by $[-6, 6, 1]$

y₁ = |2x + 5|
y₂ = 2
Intersection
X=⁻1.5
Y=2

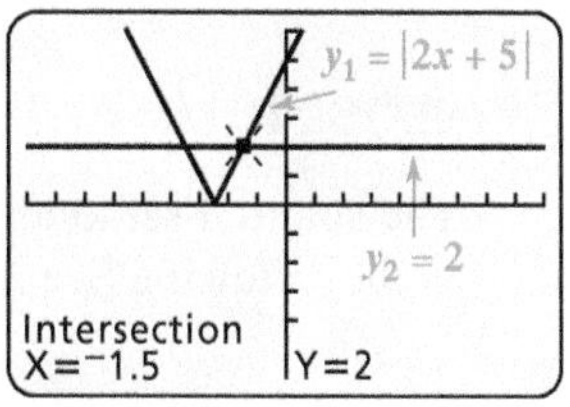

Figure 2.60

Numerical Solutions

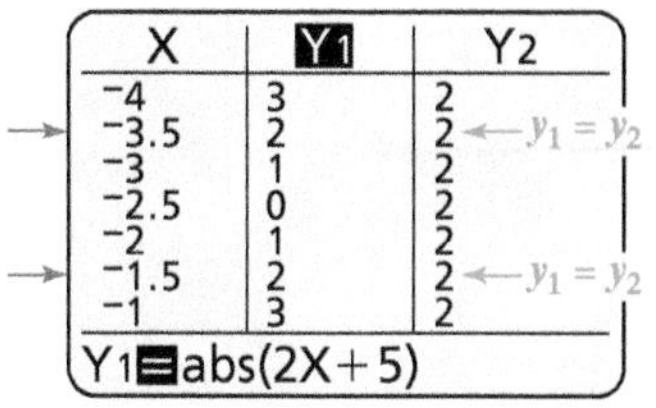

X Y1 Y2
−4 3 2
−3.5 2 2
−3 1 2
−2.5 0 2
−2 1 2
−1.5 2 2
−1 3 2
Y1=abs(2X+5)
y₁ = y₂
y₁ = y₂

Figure 2.61

Symbolic Solution The equation $|2x + 5| = 2$ is satisfied when $2x + 5 = \pm 2$.

$$
\begin{array}{rclcrcll}
2x + 5 &=& 2 & \text{or} & 2x + 5 &=& -2 & \text{Equations to solve} \\
2x &=& -3 & \text{or} & 2x &=& -7 & \text{Subtract 5 from each side.} \\
x &=& -\frac{3}{2} & \text{or} & x &=& -\frac{7}{2} & \text{Divide by 2.}
\end{array}
$$

Now Try Exercises 45(a), (b), (c)

EXAMPLE 4 **Describing speed limits with absolute values**

The maximum and minimum lawful speeds S on an interstate highway satisfy the equation $|S - 55| = 15$. Find the maximum and minimum speed limits.

SOLUTION The equation $|S - 55| = 15$ is equivalent to $S - 55 = \pm 15$.

$$
\begin{array}{rclcrcll}
S - 55 &=& 15 & \text{or} & S - 55 &=& -15 & \text{Equations to solve} \\
S &=& 70 & \text{or} & S &=& 40 & \text{Add 55 to each side.}
\end{array}
$$

The maximum speed limit is 70 miles per hour and the minimum is 40 miles per hour.

Now Try Exercise 73

An Equation with Two Absolute Values Sometimes more than one absolute value sign occurs in an equation. For example, an equation might be in the form

$$|ax + b| = |cx + d|.$$

In this case there are two possibilities:

$$\text{either} \quad ax + b = cx + d \quad \text{or} \quad ax + b = -(cx + d).$$

This symbolic technique is demonstrated in the next example.

EXAMPLE 5 **Solving an equation involving two absolute values**

Solve the equation $|x - 2| = |1 - 2x|$.

SOLUTION We must solve both of the following equations.

$$
\begin{array}{rclcrcl}
x - 2 &=& 1 - 2x & \text{or} & x - 2 &=& -(1 - 2x) \\
3x &=& 3 & \text{or} & x - 2 &=& -1 + 2x \\
x &=& 1 & \text{or} & -1 &=& x
\end{array}
$$

There are two solutions: -1 and 1.

Now Try Exercise 35

Absolute Value Inequalities

The solution set to an absolute value inequality can be understood graphically, as shown in the following See the Concept.

See the Concept: Solving |ax + b| < k and |ax + b| > k Graphically

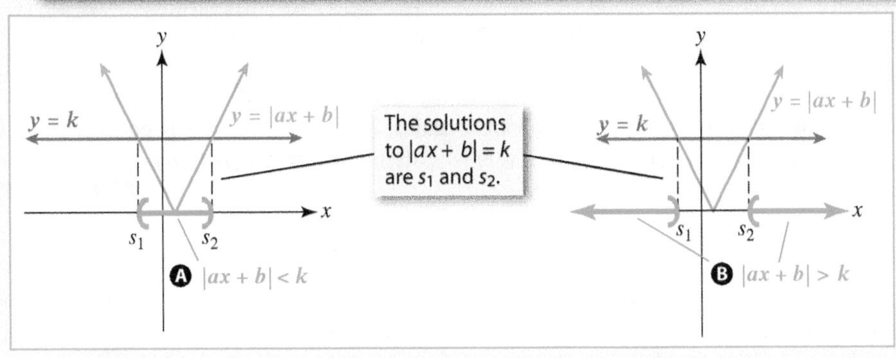

A The V-shaped graph is *below* the red line between s_1 and s_2. The solutions to $|ax + b| < k$ satisfy $s_1 < x < s_2$.

B The V-shaped graph is *above* the red line to the left of s_1 and to the right of s_2. The solutions to $|ax + b| > k$ satisfy $x < s_1$ or $x > s_2$.

NOTE In both of the above figures, equality (determined by s_1 and s_2) is the boundary between *greater than* and *less than*. For this reason, s_1 and s_2 are called *boundary numbers*.

ABSOLUTE VALUE INEQUALITIES

Let the solutions to $|ax + b| = k$ be s_1 and s_2, where $s_1 < s_2$ and $k > 0$.

1. $|ax + b| < k$ is equivalent to $s_1 < x < s_2$.
2. $|ax + b| > k$ is equivalent to $x < s_1$ or $x > s_2$.

Similar statements can be made for inequalities involving $\le$ or $\ge$.

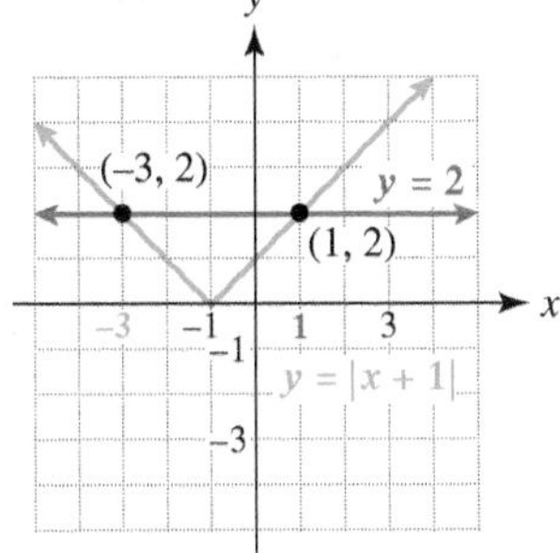

Figure 2.62

For example, the graphs of $y = |x + 1|$ and $y = 2$ are shown in Figure 2.62. These graphs intersect at the points $(-3, 2)$ and $(1, 2)$. It follows that the two solutions to

$$|x + 1| = 2$$

are $s_1 = -3$ and $s_2 = 1$. The solutions to $|x + 1| < 2$ lie between $s_1 = -3$ and $s_2 = 1$, which can be written as $-3 < x < 1$. Furthermore, the solutions to $|x + 1| > 2$ lie "outside" $s_1 = -3$ and $s_2 = 1$. This can be written as $x < -3$ or $x > 1$.

NOTE The **union symbol** $\cup$ may be used to write $x < s_1$ or $x > s_2$ in interval notation. For example, $x < -3$ or $x > 1$ is written as $(-\infty, -3) \cup (1, \infty)$ in interval notation. This indicates that the solution set includes all real numbers in either $(-\infty, -3)$ or $(1, \infty)$.

EXAMPLE 6 **Solving inequalities involving absolute values symbolically**

Solve each inequality symbolically. Write the solution set in interval notation.

(a) $|2x - 5| \le 6$ **(b)** $|5 - x| > 3$

SOLUTION

(a) Begin by solving $|2x - 5| = 6$, or equivalently, $2x - 5 = \pm 6$.

$$2x - 5 = 6 \quad \text{or} \quad 2x - 5 = -6$$

$$2x = 11 \quad \text{or} \quad 2x = -1$$

$$x = \frac{11}{2} \quad \text{or} \quad x = -\frac{1}{2}$$

The solutions to $|2x - 5| = 6$ are $-\frac{1}{2}$ and $\frac{11}{2}$. The solution set for the inequality $|2x - 5| \le 6$ includes all real numbers x satisfying $-\frac{1}{2} \le x \le \frac{11}{2}$. In interval notation this is written as $\left[-\frac{1}{2}, \frac{11}{2}\right]$.

(b) To solve $|5 - x| > 3$, begin by solving $|5 - x| = 3$, or equivalently, $5 - x = \pm 3$.

$$\begin{aligned} 5 - x &= 3 \quad &\text{or} \quad 5 - x &= -3 \\ -x &= -2 \quad &\text{or} \quad -x &= -8 \\ x &= 2 \quad &\text{or} \quad x &= 8 \end{aligned}$$

The solutions to $|5 - x| = 3$ are 2 and 8. Thus $|5 - x| > 3$ is equivalent to $x < 2$ or $x > 8$. In interval notation this is written as $(-\infty, 2) \cup (8, \infty)$.

Now Try Exercises 55 and 63

Error Tolerances The iPhone 4s is 4.5 inches in height. However, it would be impossible to make every iPhone 4s *exactly* 4.5 inches high. Instead there is typically an error tolerance, where the height of an actual iPhone must be within a certain range.

Suppose that the actual height of a particular phone is A inches, but it is specified that this phone should be S inches high. If the maximum error tolerance is E, then Figure 2.63 illustrates this situation.

Distance Between A and S Must Be Less Than E

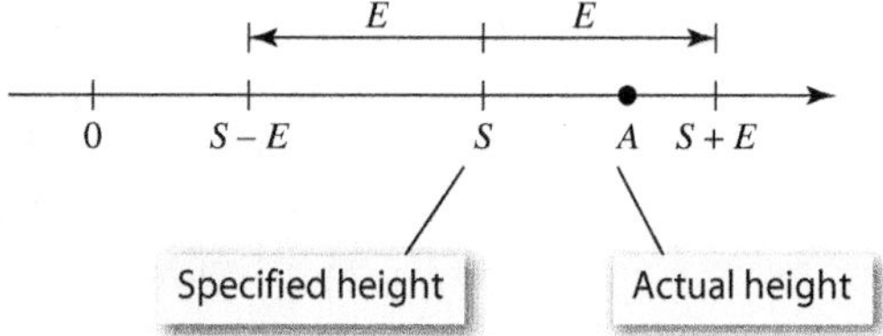

Figure 2.63

The value of A must be located between $S - E$ and $S + E$ on the number line. That is, the distance between A and S must be less than the error tolerance E, and this statement can be written as $|A - S| < E$.

EXAMPLE 7 **Finding error tolerances on the iPhone 4s**

The iPhone 4s is 4.5 inches high. Suppose that the actual height A of any particular iPhone has a maximum error tolerance that is less than 0.005 inch.

(a) Write an absolute value statement that describes this situation.

(b) Solve this inequality for A and interpret your result.

SOLUTION

(a) The distance between A and 4.5 on the number line must be less than 0.005. This statement can be written as $|A - 4.5| < 0.005$.

(b) To solve this inequality, we first solve $|A - 4.5| = 0.005$.

$$\begin{aligned} A - 4.5 &= -0.005 \quad \text{or} \quad A - 4.5 = 0.005 \qquad &\text{First solve equality.} \\ A &= 4.495 \quad \text{or} \quad A = 4.505 \qquad &\text{Add 4.5 to each side.} \end{aligned}$$

Thus $4.495 < A < 4.505$. The actual height must be greater than 4.495 inches *and* less than 4.505 inches.

Now Try Exercise 83

An Alternative Method There is a second symbolic method that can be used to solve absolute value inequalities. This method is often used in advanced mathematics courses, such as calculus. It is based on the following two properties.

ABSOLUTE VALUE INEQUALITIES (ALTERNATIVE METHOD)

Let k be a positive number.

1. $|ax + b| < k$ is equivalent to $-k < ax + b < k$.
2. $|ax + b| > k$ is equivalent to $ax + b < -k$ or $ax + b > k$.

Similar statements can be made for inequalities involving $\leq$ or $\geq$.

EXAMPLE 8 Using an alternative method

Solve each absolute value inequality. Write your answer in interval notation.

(a) $|4 - 5x| \leq 3$

(b) $|-4x - 6| > 2$

SOLUTION

(a) $|4 - 5x| \leq 3$ is equivalent to the following three-part inequality.

$$-3 \leq 4 - 5x \leq 3 \quad \text{Equivalent inequality}$$

$$-7 \leq -5x \leq -1 \quad \text{Subtract 4 from each part.}$$

$$\frac{7}{5} \geq x \geq \frac{1}{5} \quad \text{Divide each part by } -5\text{; reverse the inequality.}$$

In interval notation the solution is $\left[\frac{1}{5}, \frac{7}{5}\right]$.

(b) $|-4x - 6| > 2$ is equivalent to the following compound inequality.

$$-4x - 6 < -2 \quad \text{or} \quad -4x - 6 > 2 \quad \text{Equivalent compound inequality}$$

$$-4x < 4 \quad \text{or} \quad -4x > 8 \quad \text{Add 6 to each side.}$$

$$x > -1 \quad \text{or} \quad x < -2 \quad \text{Divide each by } -4\text{; reverse the inequality.}$$

In interval notation the solution set is $(-\infty, -2) \cup (-1, \infty)$.

Now Try Exercises 57 and 61

CLASS DISCUSSION

Sketch the graphs of $y = ax + b$, $y = |ax + b|$, $y = -k$, and $y = k$ on one xy-plane. Now use these graphs to explain why the alternative method for solving absolute value inequalities is correct.

2.5 Putting It All Together

The following table summarizes some important concepts from this section.

CONCEPT	EXPLANATION	EXAMPLES
Absolute value function	$f(x) = \|x\|$: The output from the absolute value function is never negative. $\|x\|$ is equivalent to $\sqrt{x^2}$. $\|x\| = \begin{cases} -x & \text{if } x < 0 \\ x & \text{if } x \geq 0 \end{cases}$	$f(-2) = \|-2\| = 2$ y, x, 3, 2, 1, -1, -2, -3, -3 -2 -1, 1 2 3, $f(x) = \|x\|$

continued on next page

CONCEPT	EXPLANATION	EXAMPLES
Absolute value equations	**1.** If $k > 0$, then $\lvert ax + b \rvert = k$ has two solutions, given by $ax + b = \pm k$. **2.** If $k = 0$, then $\lvert ax + b \rvert = k$ has one solution, given by $ax + b = 0$. **3.** If $k < 0$, then $\lvert ax + b \rvert = k$ has no solutions.	**1.** Solve $\lvert 3x - 5 \rvert = 4$. $3x - 5 = -4$ or $3x - 5 = 4$ $3x = 1$ or $3x = 9$ $x = \frac{1}{3}$ or $x = 3$ **2.** Solve $\lvert x - 1 \rvert = 0$. $x - 1 = 0$ implies $x = 1$. **3.** $\lvert 4x - 9 \rvert = -2$ has no solutions.
Absolute value inequalities	To solve $\lvert ax + b \rvert < k$ or $\lvert ax + b \rvert > k$ with $k > 0$, first solve $\lvert ax + b \rvert = k$. Let these solutions be s_1 and s_2, where $s_1 < s_2$.	To solve $\lvert x - 5 \rvert < 4$ or $\lvert x - 5 \rvert > 4$, first solve $\lvert x - 5 \rvert = 4$ to obtain the solutions $s_1 = 1$ and $s_2 = 9$.
	1. $\lvert ax + b \rvert < k$ is equivalent to $s_1 < x < s_2$. **2.** $\lvert ax + b \rvert > k$ is equivalent to $x < s_1$ or $x > s_2$.	**1.** $\lvert x - 5 \rvert < 4$ is equivalent to $1 < x < 9$. **2.** $\lvert x - 5 \rvert > 4$ is equivalent to $x < 1$ or $x > 9$.
Alternative method	**1.** $\lvert ax + b \rvert < k$ with $k > 0$ is equivalent to $-k < ax + b < k$. **2.** $\lvert ax + b \rvert > k$ with $k > 0$ is equivalent to $ax + b < -k$ or $ax + b > k$.	**1.** $\lvert x - 1 \rvert < 5$ is solved as follows. $-5 < x - 1 < 5$ $-4 < x < 6$ **2.** $\lvert x - 1 \rvert > 5$ is solved as follows. $x - 1 < -5$ or $x - 1 > 5$ $x < -4$ or $x > 6$

2.5 Exercises

Basic Concepts

Exercises 1–8: Let $a \neq 0$.

1. Solve $\lvert x \rvert = 3$.

2. Solve $\lvert x \rvert \leq 3$.

3. Solve $\lvert x \rvert > 3$.

4. Solve $\lvert ax + b \rvert \leq -2$.

5. Describe the graph of $y = \lvert ax + b \rvert$.

6. Solve $\lvert ax + b \rvert = 0$.

7. Rewrite $\sqrt{36a^2}$ by using an absolute value.

8. Rewrite $\sqrt{(ax + b)^2}$ by using an absolute value.

Absolute Value Graphs

Exercises 9–12: Graph by hand.
(a) Find the x-intercept.
(b) Determine where the graph is increasing and where it is decreasing.

9. $y = \lvert x + 1 \rvert$

10. $y = \lvert 1 - x \rvert$

11. $y = \lvert 2x - 3 \rvert$

12. $y = \lvert \frac{1}{2}x + 1 \rvert$

Exercises 13–18: (Refer to Example 1.) Do the following.
(a) Graph $y = f(x)$.
(b) Use the graph of $y = f(x)$ to sketch a graph of the equation $y = \lvert f(x) \rvert$.
(c) Determine the x-intercept for the graph of $y = \lvert f(x) \rvert$.

13. $y = 2x$

14. $y = \frac{1}{2}x$

15. $y = 3x - 3$

16. $y = 2x - 4$

17. $y = 6 - 2x$

18. $y = 2 - 4x$

Absolute Value Equations and Inequalities

Exercises 19–40: Solve the absolute value equation.

19. $|-2x| = 4$

20. $|3x| = -6$

21. $|5x - 7| = 2$

22. $|-3x - 2| = 5$

23. $|3 - 4x| = 5$

24. $|2 - 3x| = 1$

25. $|-6x - 2| = 0$

26. $|6x - 9| = 0$

27. $|7 - 16x| = 0$

28. $|-x - 4| = 0$

29. $|17x - 6| = -3$

30. $|-8x - 11| = -7$

31. $|1.2x - 1.7| - 5 = -1$

32. $|3 - 3x| - 2 = 2$

33. $|4x - 5| + 3 = 2$

34. $|4.5 - 2x| + 1.1 = 9.7$

35. $|2x - 9| = |8 - 3x|$

36. $|x - 3| = |8 - x|$

37. $\left|\frac{3}{4}x - \frac{1}{4}\right| = \left|\frac{3}{4} - \frac{1}{4}x\right|$

38. $\left|\frac{1}{2}x + \frac{3}{2}\right| = \left|\frac{3}{2}x - \frac{7}{2}\right|$

39. $|15x - 5| = |35 - 5x|$

40. $|20x - 40| = |80x - 20|$

Exercises 41 and 42. The graphs of f and g are shown. Solve each equation and inequality.

41. **(a)** $f(x) = g(x)$

(b) $f(x) < g(x)$

(c) $f(x) > g(x)$

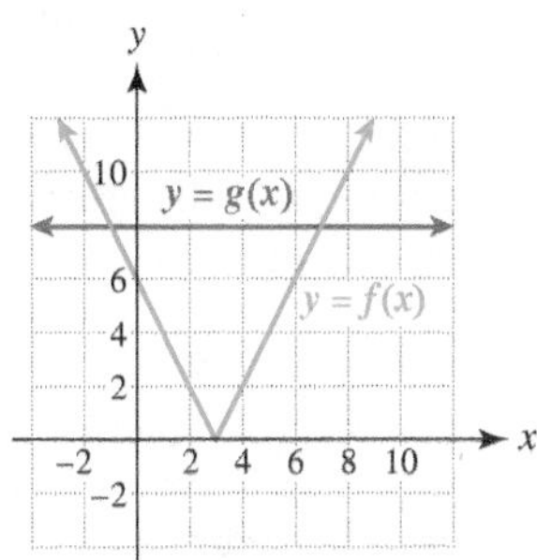

42. **(a)** $f(x) = g(x)$

(b) $f(x) \leq g(x)$

(c) $f(x) \geq g(x)$

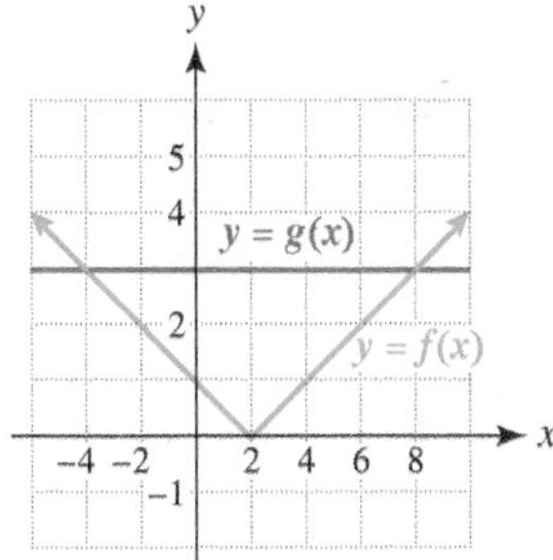

Exercises 43 and 44: Solve each equation or inequality.

43. **(a)** $|2x - 3| = 1$

(b) $|2x - 3| < 1$

(c) $|2x - 3| > 1$

44. **(a)** $|5 - x| = 2$

(b) $|5 - x| \leq 2$

(c) $|5 - x| \geq 2$

Exercises 45–48: Solve the equation
(a) graphically,
(b) numerically, and
(c) symbolically.
Then solve the related inequality.

45. $|2x - 5| = 10, \quad |2x - 5| < 10$

46. $|3x - 4| = 8, \quad |3x - 4| \leq 8$

47. $|5 - 3x| = 2, \quad |5 - 3x| > 2$

48. $|4x - 7| = 5, \quad |4x - 7| \geq 5$

Exercises 49–54: Solve the equation symbolically. Then solve the related inequality.

49. $|2.1x - 0.7| = 2.4, \quad |2.1x - 0.7| \geq 2.4$

50. $\left|\frac{1}{2}x - \frac{3}{4}\right| = \frac{7}{4}, \quad \left|\frac{1}{2}x - \frac{3}{4}\right| \leq \frac{7}{4}$

51. $|3x| + 5 = 6, \quad |3x| + 5 > 6$

52. $|x| - 10 = 25, \quad |x| - 10 < 25$

53. $\left|\frac{2}{3}x - \frac{1}{2}\right| = -\frac{1}{4}, \quad \left|\frac{2}{3}x - \frac{1}{2}\right| \leq -\frac{1}{4}$

54. $|5x - 0.3| = -4, \quad |5x - 0.3| > -4$

You Decide the Method

Exercises 55–66: Solve the inequality. Write the solution in interval notation.

55. $|3x - 1| < 8$

56. $|15 - x| < 7$

57. $|7 - 4x| \leq 11$

58. $|-3x + 1| \leq 5$

59. $|0.5x - 0.75| < 2$

60. $|2.1x - 5| \leq 8$

61. $|2x - 3| > 1$

62. $|5x - 7| > 2$

63. $|-3x + 8| \geq 3$

64. $|-7x - 3| \geq 5$

65. $|0.25x - 1| > 3$

66. $|-0.5x + 5| \geq 4$

Domain and Range

67. If $f(k) = -6$, what is the value of $|f(k)|$?

68. If $f(k) = 17$, what is the value of $|f(k)|$?

69. If the domain of $f(x)$ is given by $[-2, 4]$, what is the domain of $|f(x)|$?

70. If the domain of $f(x)$ is given by $(-\infty, 0]$, what is the domain of $|f(x)|$?

71. If the range of $f(x)$ is given by $(-\infty, 0]$, what is the range of $|f(x)|$?

72. If the range of $f(x)$ is given by $(-4, 5)$, what is the range of $|f(x)|$?

Applications

73. Speed Limits The maximum and minimum lawful speeds S on an interstate highway satisfy the equation $|S - 57.5| = 17.5$. Find the maximum and minimum speed limits.

74. Human Cannonball A human cannonball plans to travel 180 feet and land squarely on a net with a 70-foot-long safe zone.

(a) What distances D can this performer travel and still land safely on the net?

(b) Use an absolute value inequality to describe the restrictions on D.

75. Temperature and Altitude Air temperature decreases as altitude increases. If the ground temperature is 80°F, then the air temperature x miles high is $T = 80 - 19x$.

(a) Determine the altitudes x where the air temperature T is between 0°F and 32°F, inclusive.

(b) Use an absolute value inequality to describe these altitudes.

76. Dew Point and Altitude The dew point decreases as altitude increases. If the dew point on the ground is 80°F, then the dew point x miles high is $D = 80 - \frac{29}{5}x$.

(a) Determine the altitudes x where the dew point D is between 50°F and 60°F, inclusive.

(b) Use an absolute value inequality to describe these altitudes.

Exercises 77–82: **Average Temperatures** *The inequality describes the range of monthly average temperatures T in degrees Fahrenheit at a certain location.*

(a) Solve the inequality.

(b) If the high and low monthly average temperatures satisfy equality, interpret the inequality.

77. $|T - 43| \leq 24$, Marquette, Michigan

78. $|T - 62| \leq 19$, Memphis, Tennessee

79. $|T - 50| \leq 22$, Boston, Massachusetts

80. $|T - 10| \leq 36$, Chesterfield, Canada

81. $|T - 61.5| \leq 12.5$, Buenos Aires, Argentina

82. $|T - 43.5| \leq 8.5$, Punta Arenas, Chile

83. Classic iPod Dimensions The classic iPod is 10.5 millimeters thick. Suppose that the actual thickness T of any particular iPod has a maximum error tolerance that is less than 0.05 millimeter.

(a) Write an absolute value statement that describes this situation.

(b) Solve this inequality for T and interpret your result.

84. Error In Measurements An aluminum can should have a diameter D of 3 inches with a maximum error tolerance that is less than 0.004 inch.

(a) Write an absolute value statement that describes this situation.

(b) Solve this inequality for D and interpret your result.

85. Machine Parts A part for a machine must fit into a hole and must have a diameter D that is less than or equal to 2.125 inches. The diameter D cannot be less than this maximum diameter of 2.125 inches by more than 0.014 inch.

(a) Write an absolute value statement that describes this situation.

(b) Solve this inequality for D and interpret your result.

86. Error in Measurements Suppose that a 12-inch ruler must have the correct length L to within 0.0002 inch.

(a) Write an absolute value inequality for L that describes this requirement.

(b) Solve this inequality and interpret the results.

87. Relative Error If a quantity is measured to be Q and its exact value is A, then the relative error in Q is

$$\left|\frac{Q - A}{A}\right|.$$

If the exact value is $A = 35$ and you want the relative error in Q to be less than or equal to 0.02 (or 2%), what values for Q are possible?

88. Relative Error (Refer to Exercise 87.) The exact perimeter P of a square is 50 feet. What measured lengths are possible for the side S of the square to have relative error in the perimeter that is less than or equal to 0.04 (or 4%)?

Writing about Mathematics

89. Explain how to solve $|ax + b| = k$ with $k > 0$ symbolically. Give an example.

90. Explain how you can use the solutions to $|ax + b| = k$ with $k > 0$ to solve the inequalities $|ax + b| < k$ and $|ax + b| > k$. Give an example.

Extended and Discovery Exercises

1. Let δ be a positive number and let x and c be real numbers. Write an absolute value inequality that expresses that the distance between x and c on the number line is less than δ.

2. Let ε be a positive number, L be a real number, and f be a function. Write an absolute value inequality that expresses that the distance between $f(x)$ and L on the number line is less than ε.

CHECKING BASIC CONCEPTS FOR SECTION 2.5

1. Rewrite $\sqrt{4x^2}$ by using an absolute value.
2. Graph $y = |3x - 2|$ by hand.
3. (a) Solve the equation $|2x - 1| = 5$.
   (b) Use part (a) to solve the absolute value inequalities $|2x - 1| \leq 5$ and $|2x - 1| > 5$.
4. Solve each equation or inequality. For each inequality, write the solution set in interval notation.
   (a) $|2 - 5x| - 4 = -1$
   (b) $|3x - 5| \leq 4$
   (c) $|\frac{1}{2}x - 3| > 5$
5. Solve $|x + 1| = |2x|$.

2 Summary

CONCEPT	EXPLANATION AND EXAMPLES
Section 2.1 Equations of Lines	
Point-Slope Form	If a line with slope m passes through (x_1, y_1), then $$y = m(x - x_1) + y_1 \quad \text{or} \quad y - y_1 = m(x - x_1).$$ **Example:** $y = -\frac{3}{4}(x + 4) + 5$ has slope $-\frac{3}{4}$ and passes through $(-4, 5)$.
Slope-Intercept Form	If a line has slope m and y-intercept b, then $y = mx + b$. **Example:** $y = 3x - 4$ has slope 3 and y-intercept -4.
Determining Intercepts	To find the x-intercept(s), let $y = 0$ in the equation and solve for x. To find the y-intercept(s), let $x = 0$ in the equation and solve for y. **Examples:** The x-intercept on the graph of $3x - 4y = 12$ is 4 because $3x - 4(0) = 12$ implies that $x = 4$. The y-intercept on the graph of $3x - 4y = 12$ is -3 because $3(0) - 4y = 12$ implies that $y = -3$.
Horizontal and Vertical Lines	A horizontal line passing through the point (a, b) is given by $y = b$, and a vertical line passing through (a, b) is given by $x = a$. **Examples:** The horizontal line $y = -3$ passes through $(6, -3)$. The vertical line $x = 4$ passes through $(4, -2)$.
Parallel and Perpendicular Lines	Parallel lines have equal slopes satisfying $m_1 = m_2$, and perpendicular lines have slopes satisfying $m_1 m_2 = -1$, provided neither line is vertical. **Examples:** The lines $y_1 = 3x - 1$ and $y_2 = 3x + 4$ are parallel. The lines $y_1 = 3x - 1$ and $y_2 = -\frac{1}{3}x + 4$ are perpendicular.

CONCEPT	EXPLANATION AND EXAMPLES

Section 2.1 Equations of Lines (CONTINUED)

Linear Regression

One way to determine a linear function or a line that models data is to use the method of least squares. This method determines a unique line that can be found with a calculator. The correlation coefficient r $(-1 \leq r \leq 1)$ measures how well a line fits the data.

Example: The line of least squares modeling the data (1, 1), (3, 4), and (4, 6) is given by $y \approx 1.643x - 0.714$, with $r \approx 0.997$.

Section 2.2 Linear Equations

Linear Equation

Can be written as $ax + b = 0$ with $a \neq 0$ and has one solution

Example: The solution to $2x - 4 = 0$ is 2 because $2(2) - 4 = 0$.

Properties of Equality

Addition: $a = b$ is equivalent to $a + c = b + c$.
Multiplication: $a = b$ is equivalent to $ac = bc$, provided $c \neq 0$.

Example:

$\frac{1}{2}x - 4 = 3$ Given equation

$\frac{1}{2}x = 7$ Addition property; add 4.

$x = 14$ Multiplication property; multiply by 2.

Contradiction, Identity, and Conditional Equation

A contradiction has no solutions, an identity is true for all (meaningful) values of the variable, and a conditional equation is true for some, but not all, values of the variable.

Examples:

$3(1 - 2x) = 3 - 6x$ Identity

$x + 5 = x$ Contradiction

$x - 1 = 4$ Conditional equation

Intersection-of-Graphs and x-Intercept Methods

Intersection-of-graphs method: Set y_1 equal to the left side of the equation and set y_2 equal to the right side. The x-coordinate of a point of intersection is a solution.

Example: The graphs of $y_1 = 2x$ and $y_2 = x + 1$ intersect at (1, 2), so the solution to the linear equation $2x = x + 1$ is 1. See the figure below on the left.

x-intercept method: Move all terms to the left side of the equation. Set y_1 equal to the left side of the equation. The solutions are the x-intercepts. (See Section 2.3.)

Example: Write $2x = x + 1$ as $2x - (x + 1) = 0$. Graph $y_1 = 2x - (x + 1)$. The only x-intercept is 1, as shown in the figure on the right.

Point of Intersection (1, 2)

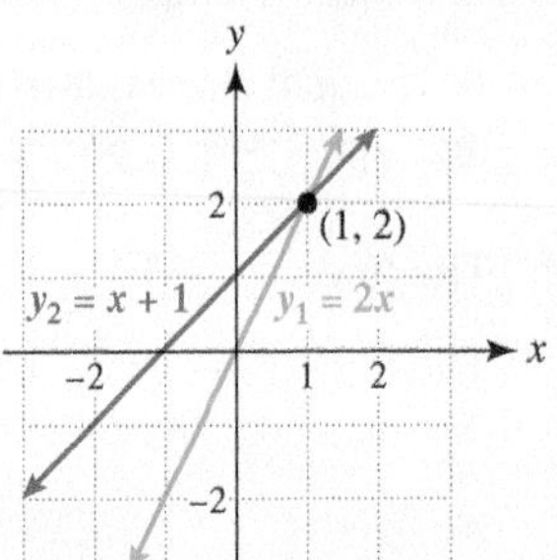

x-intercept: 1

CONCEPT	EXPLANATION AND EXAMPLES
Section 2.2 Linear Equations (CONTINUED)	
Problem-Solving Strategies	STEP 1: Read the problem and make sure you understand it. Assign a variable to what you are being asked to find. If necessary, write other quantities in terms of this variable. STEP 2: Write an equation that relates the quantities described in the problem. You may need to sketch a diagram and refer to known formulas. STEP 3: Solve the equation and determine the solution. STEP 4: Look back and check your solution. Does it seem reasonable?
Section 2.3 Linear Inequalities	
Linear Inequality	Can be written as $ax + b > 0$ with $a \neq 0$, where $>$ can be replaced by $<$, $\leq$, or $\geq$. If the solution to $ax + b = 0$ is k, then the solution to the linear inequality $ax + b > 0$ is either the interval $(-\infty, k)$ or the interval (k, ∞). **Example:** $3x - 1 < 2$ is linear since it can be written as $3x - 3 < 0$. The solution set is $\{x \mid x < 1\}$, or $(-\infty, 1)$.
Properties of Inequalities	*Addition:* $a < b$ is equivalent to $a + c < b + c$. *Multiplication:* $a < b$ is equivalent to $ac < bc$ when $c > 0$. $a < b$ is equivalent to $ac > bc$ when $c < 0$. **Example:** $-3x - 4 < 14$ Given equation $-3x < 18$ Addition property; add 4. $x > -6$ Multiplication property; divide by -3. Reverse the inequality symbol.
Compound Inequality	**Example:** $x \geq -2$ and $x \leq 4$ is equivalent to $-2 \leq x \leq 4$. This is called a three-part inequality.
Section 2.4 More Modeling with Functions	
Linear Model	If a quantity increases or decreases by a constant amount for each unit increase in x, then it can be modeled by a linear function given by $f(x) = (\text{constant rate of change})x + (\text{initial amount})$. **Example:** If water is pumped from a full 100-gallon tank at 7 gallons per minute, then $A(t) = 100 - 7t$ gives the gallons of water in the tank after t minutes.
Piecewise-Defined Function	A function defined by more than one formula on its domain **Examples:** Step function, greatest integer function, absolute value function, and $f(x) = \begin{cases} 4 - x & \text{if } -4 \leq x < 1 \\ 3x & \text{if } 1 \leq x \leq 5 \end{cases}$ It follows that $f(2) = 6$ because if $1 \leq x \leq 5$ then $f(x) = 3x$. Note that f is continuous on its domain of $[-4, 5]$.

CONCEPT	EXPLANATION AND EXAMPLES
Section 2.4 More Modeling with Functions (CONTINUED)	
Direct Variation	A quantity y is directly proportional to a quantity x, or y varies directly with x, if $y = kx$, where $k \neq 0$. If data vary directly, the ratios $\frac{y}{x}$ are equal to the constant of variation k. **Example:** If a person works for \$8 per hour, then that person's pay P is directly proportional to, or varies directly with, the number of hours H that the person works by the equation $P = 8H$, where the constant of variation is $k = 8$.
Section 2.5 Absolute Value Equations and Inequalities	
Absolute Value Function	An absolute value function is defined by $f(x) = \|x\|$. Its graph is V-shaped. An equivalent formula is $f(x) = \sqrt{x^2}$. **Examples:** $f(-9) = \|-9\| = 9$; $\sqrt{(2x + 1)^2} = \|2x + 1\|$
Absolute Value Equations	$\|ax + b\| = k$ with $k > 0$ is equivalent to $ax + b = \pm k$. **Example:** $\|2x - 3\| = 4$ is equivalent to $2x - 3 = 4$ or $2x - 3 = -4$. The solutions are $\frac{7}{2}$ and $-\frac{1}{2}$.
Absolute Value Inequalities	Let the solutions to $\|ax + b\| = k$ be s_1 and s_2, where $s_1 < s_2$ and $k > 0$. **1.** $\|ax + b\| < k$ is equivalent to $s_1 < x < s_2$. **2.** $\|ax + b\| > k$ is equivalent to $x < s_1$ or $x > s_2$. Similar statements can be made for inequalities involving $\leq$ or $\geq$. **Example:** The solutions to $\|2x + 1\| = 5$ are given by $x = -3$ and $x = 2$. The solutions to $\|2x + 1\| < 5$ are given by $-3 < x < 2$. The solutions to $\|2x + 1\| > 5$ are given by $x < -3$ or $x > 2$.

2 Review Exercises

Exercises 1 and 2: Find the point-slope form of the line passing through the given points. Use the first point as (x_1, y_1).

1. $(-3, 4)$, $(2, 5)$

2. $(1, -6)$, $(-7, 5)$

Exercises 3–6: Find the point-slope form of the line passing through the given points. Use the first point as (x_1, y_1). Then convert the equation to slope-intercept form and write a formula for a function f whose graph is the line.

3. Slope $-\frac{7}{5}$, passing through $(-5, 6)$

4. Passing through $(-4, -7)$ and $(-2, 3)$

5. x-intercept 5, y-intercept -2

6. y-intercept 6, passing through $(8, -2)$

7. Write a formula for a linear function f whose graph has slope -2 and passes through $(-2, 3)$.

8. Find the average rate of change of $f(x) = -3x + 8$ from -2 to 3.

Exercises 9–14: Find the slope-intercept form of the equation of a line satisfying the conditions.

9. Slope 7, passing through $(-3, 9)$

10. Passing through $(2, -4)$ and $(7, -3)$

11. Passing through $(1, -1)$, parallel to $y = -3x + 1$

12. Passing through the point $(-2, 1)$, perpendicular to the line $y = 2(x + 5) - 22$

13. Parallel to the line segment connecting $(0, 3.1)$ and $(5.7, 0)$, passing through $(1, -7)$

14. Perpendicular to $y = -\frac{5}{7}x$, passing through $\left(\frac{6}{7}, 0\right)$

Exercises 15–20: Find an equation of the specified line.

15. Parallel to the y-axis, passing through $(6, -7)$

16. Parallel to the x-axis, passing through $(-3, 4)$

17. Horizontal, passing through $(1, 3)$

18. Vertical, passing through $(1.5, 1.9)$

19. Vertical with x-intercept 2.7

20. Horizontal with y-intercept -8

Exercises 21 and 22: Determine the x- and y-intercepts for the graph of the equation. Graph the equation.

21. $5x - 4y = 20$

22. $\dfrac{x}{3} - \dfrac{y}{2} = 1$

Exercises 23–28: Solve the linear equation either symbolically or graphically.

23. $5x - 22 = 10$

24. $5(4 - 2x) = 16$

25. $-2(3x - 7) + x = 2x - 1$

26. $5x - \frac{1}{2}(4 - 3x) = \frac{3}{2} - (2x + 3)$

27. $\pi x + 1 = 6$

28. $\dfrac{x - 4}{2} = x + \dfrac{1 - 2x}{3}$

Exercises 29 and 30: Use a table to solve each linear equation numerically to the nearest tenth.

29. $3.1x - 0.2 - 2(x - 1.7) = 0$

30. $\sqrt{7} - 3x - 2.1(1 + x) = 0$

Exercises 31–34: Complete the following.

(a) Solve the equation symbolically.

(b) Classify the equation as a contradiction, an identity, or a conditional equation.

31. $4(6 - x) = -4x + 24$

32. $\frac{1}{2}(4x - 3) + 2 = 3x - (1 + x)$

33. $5 - 2(4 - 3x) + x = 4(x - 3)$

34. $\dfrac{x - 3}{4} + \dfrac{3}{4}x - 5(2 - 7x) = 36x - \dfrac{43}{4}$

Exercises 35–38: Express the inequality in interval notation.

35. $x > -3$

36. $x \leq 4$

37. $-2 \leq x < \frac{3}{4}$

38. $x \leq -2$ or $x > 3$

Exercises 39–44: Solve the linear inequality. Write the solution set in set-builder or interval notation.

39. $3x - 4 \leq 2 + x$

40. $-2x + 6 \leq -3x$

41. $\dfrac{2x - 5}{2} < \dfrac{5x + 1}{5}$

42. $-5(1 - x) > 3(x - 3) + \frac{1}{2}x$

43. $-2 \leq 5 - 2x < 7$

44. $-1 < \dfrac{3x - 5}{-3} < 3$

Exercises 45 and 46: Solve the inequality graphically.

45. $2x > x - 1$

46. $-1 \leq 1 + x \leq 2$

47. The graphs of two linear functions f and g are shown in the figure. Solve each equation or inequality.

(a) $f(x) = g(x)$

(b) $f(x) < g(x)$

(c) $f(x) > g(x)$

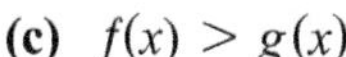

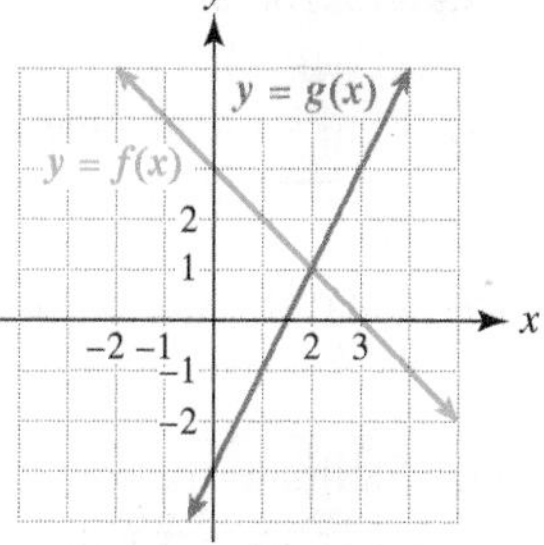

48. The graphs of three linear functions f, g, and h with domains $D = \{x | 0 \leq x \leq 7\}$ are shown in the figure. Solve each equation or inequality.

(a) $f(x) = g(x)$

(b) $g(x) = h(x)$

(c) $f(x) < g(x) < h(x)$

(d) $g(x) > h(x)$

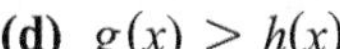

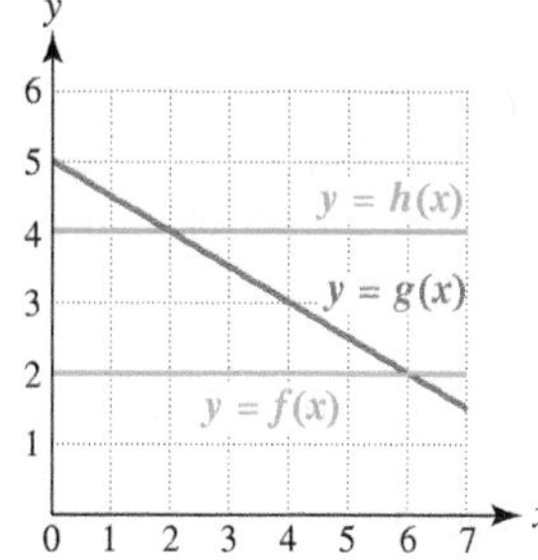

49. Use $f(x)$ to complete the following.

$$f(x) = \begin{cases} 8 + 2x & \text{if } -3 \leq x \leq -1 \\ 5 - x & \text{if } -1 < x \leq 2 \\ x + 1 & \text{if } \ 2 < x \leq 5 \end{cases}$$

(a) Evaluate f at $x = -2, -1, 2$, and 3.

(b) Sketch a graph of f. Is f continuous on its domain?

(c) Determine the x-value(s) where $f(x) = 3$.

50. If $f(x) = [\![2x - 1]\!]$, evaluate $f(-3.1)$ and $f(2.5)$.

Exercises 51–54: Solve the equation.

51. $|2x - 5| - 1 = 8$ **52.** $|3 - 7x| = 10$

53. $|6 - 4x| = -2$ **54.** $|9 + x| = |3 - 2x|$

Exercises 55–58: Solve the equation. Use the solutions to help solve the related inequality.

55. $|x| = 3,\quad |x| > 3$

56. $|-3x + 1| = 2, |-3x + 1| < 2$

57. $|3x - 7| = 10,\ |3x - 7| > 10$

58. $|4 - x| = 6,\quad |4 - x| \leq 6$

Exercises 59–62: Solve the inequality.

59. $|3 - 2x| < 9$ **60.** $|-2x - 3| > 3$

61. $|\frac{1}{3}x - \frac{1}{6}| \geq 1$ **62.** $|\frac{1}{2}x| - 3 \leq 5$

Applications

63. U.S. Median Income In 1980 the median family income was \$17,700 and in 2010 it was \$49,500. (***Source:*** Bureau of the Census.)

(a) Find a linear function f that models these data. Let x represent the number of years after 1980.

(b) Interpret the slope and y-intercept for the graph of f.

(c) Estimate the median income in 1992 and compare your answer with the true value of \$30,600.

(d) Predict the year when median income might reach \$60,000. Did your answer involve interpolation or extrapolation?

64. Course Grades In order to receive a B grade in a college course, it is necessary to have an overall average of 80% correct on two 1-hour exams of 75 points each and one final exam of 150 points. If a person scores 55 and 72 on the 1-hour exams, what is the minimum score that the person can receive on the final exam and still earn a B?

65. Medicare Spending In 2010 Medicare spending was \$524 billion and in 2020 it is projected to be \$949 billion. (***Source:*** Congressional Budget Office.)

(a) Find a linear function f that models these data. Let x represent the number of years after 2010.

(b) Interpret the slope and y-intercept for the graph of f.

(c) Estimate Medicare spending in 2016. Did your answer involve interpolation or extrapolation?

(d) Predict the years when Medicare spending could be between \$694 billion and \$864 billion.

66. Temperature Scales The table shows equivalent temperatures in degrees Celsius and degrees Fahrenheit.

°F	−40	32	59	95	212
°C	−40	0	15	35	100

(a) Plot the data with Fahrenheit temperature on the x-axis and Celsius temperature on the y-axis. What type of relation exists between the data?

(b) Find a function C that receives the Fahrenheit temperature x as input and outputs the corresponding Celsius temperature. Interpret the slope.

(c) If the temperature is 83°F, what is it in degrees Celsius?

67. Distance from Home The graph depicts the distance y that a person driving a car on a straight road is from home after x hours. Interpret the graph. What speeds did the car travel?

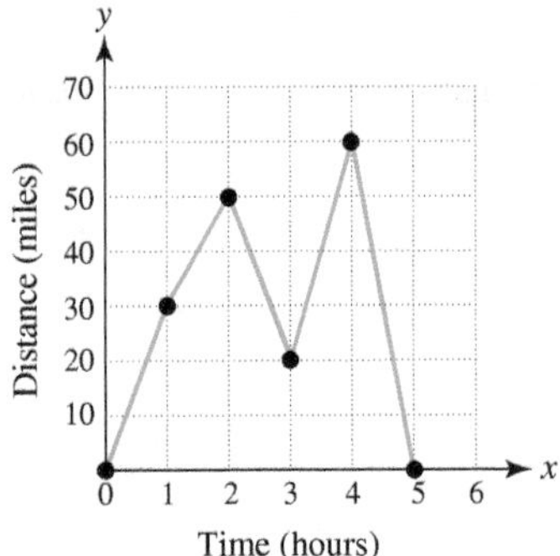

68. Piecewise-Linear Function Given the data points (1, 2), (4, 9), and (6, 3), complete the following.

(a) Write the formula for a piecewise-linear function f that passes through these data points whose domain is $1 \leq x \leq 6$.

(b) Evaluate $f(5)$.

(c) Is f continuous on its domain?

69. Population Estimates In 2008 the population of a city was 143,247, and in 2012 it was 167,933. Estimate the population in 2010.

70. Distance A driver of a car is initially 455 miles from home, traveling toward home on a straight freeway at 70 miles per hour.

(a) Write a formula for a linear function f that models the distance between the driver and home after x hours.

(b) Graph f. What is an appropriate domain?

(c) Identify the x- and y-intercepts. Interpret each.

71. Working Together Suppose that one worker can shovel snow from a storefront sidewalk in 50 minutes and another worker can shovel it in 30 minutes. How long will it take if they work together?

72. Antifreeze Initially, a tank contains 20 gallons of a 30% antifreeze solution. How many gallons of an 80% antifreeze solution should be added to the tank in order to increase the concentration of the antifreeze in the tank to 50%?

73. Running An athlete traveled 13.5 miles in 1 hour and 48 minutes, jogging at 7 miles per hour and then at 8 miles per hour. How long did the runner jog at each speed?

74. Least-Squares Fit The table lists the actual annual cost y to drive a midsize car 15,000 miles per year for selected years x.

x	1970	1980	1990	2000	2010
y	\$1763	\$3176	\$5136	\$6880	\$8595

Source: Runzheimer International.

(a) Predict whether the correlation coefficient is positive, negative, or zero.

(b) Find a least-squares regression line that models these data. What is the correlation coefficient?

(c) Estimate the cost of driving a midsize car in 2005.

(d) Estimate the year when the cost to drive a car could reach \$10,000.

75. Modeling The table lists data that are exactly linear.

x	−3	−2	−1	1	2
y	6.6	5.4	4.2	1.8	0.6

(a) Determine the slope-intercept form of the line that passes through these data points.

(b) Predict y when $x = -1.5$ and 3.5. State whether these calculations involve interpolation or extrapolation.

(c) Predict x when $y = 1.3$.

76. Geometry A rectangle is twice as long as it is wide and has a perimeter of 78 inches. Find the width and length of this rectangle.

77. Flow Rates A water tank has an inlet pipe with a flow rate of 5 gallons per minute and an outlet pipe with a flow rate of 3 gallons per minute. A pipe can be either closed or completely open. The graph shows the number of gallons of water in the tank after x minutes have elapsed. Use the concept of slope to interpret each piece of this graph.

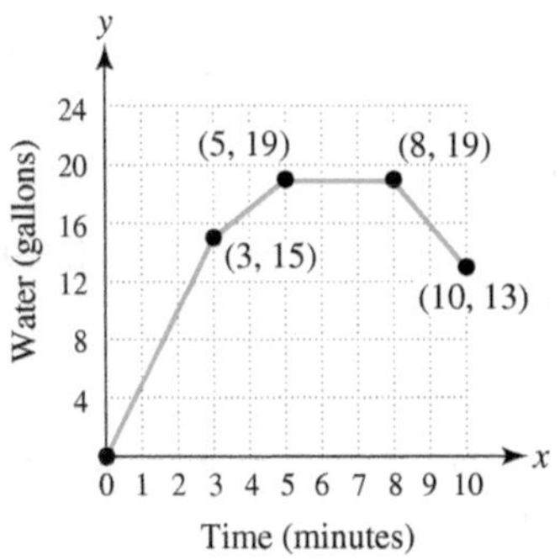

78. Flow Rates (Refer to Exercise 77.) Suppose the tank is modified so that it has a second inlet pipe, which flows at a rate of 2 gallons per minute. Interpret the graph by determining when each inlet and outlet pipe is open or closed.

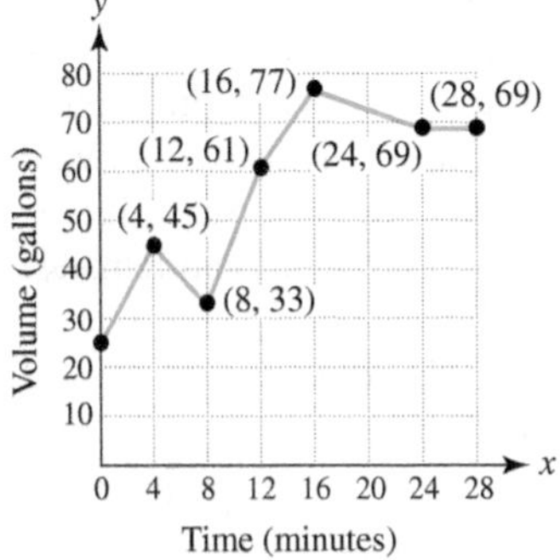

79. Air Temperature For altitudes up to 4 kilometers, moist air will cool at a rate of about 6°C per kilometer. If the ground temperature is 25°C, at what altitudes would the air temperature be from 5°C to 15°C? (***Source:*** A. Miller and R. Anthes, *Meteorology.*)

80. Water Pollution At one time the Thames River in England supported an abundant community of fish. Pollution then destroyed all the fish in a 40-mile stretch near its mouth for a 45-year period beginning in 1915. Since then, improvement of sewage treatment facilities and other ecological steps have resulted in a dramatic increase in the number of different fish present. The number of species present from 1967 to 1978 can be modeled by $f(x) = 6.15x - 12{,}059$, where x is the year.

(a) Estimate the year when the number of species first exceeded 70.

(b) Estimate the years when the number of species was between 50 and 100.

81. Relative Error The actual length of a side of a building is 52.3 feet. How accurately must an apprentice carpenter measure this side to have the relative error in the measurement be less than 0.003 (0.3%)? (*Hint:* Use $\left|\frac{C - A}{A}\right|$, where C is the carpenter's measurement and A is the actual length.)

82. Brown Trout Due to acid rain, the percentage of lakes in Scandinavia that lost their population of brown trout increased dramatically between 1940 and 1975. Based on a sample of 2850 lakes, this percentage can be approximated by the following piecewise-linear function. (***Source:*** C. Mason, *Biology of Freshwater Pollution.*)

$$f(x) = \begin{cases} \frac{11}{20}(x - 1940) + 7 & \text{if } 1940 \le x < 1960 \\ \frac{32}{15}(x - 1960) + 18 & \text{if } 1960 \le x \le 1975 \end{cases}$$

(a) Determine the percentage of lakes that lost brown trout by 1947 and by 1972.

(b) Sketch a graph of f.

(c) Is f a continuous function on its domain?

Extended and Discovery Exercises

1. Archeology It is possible for archeologists to estimate the height of an adult based only on the length of the humerus, a bone located between the elbow and the shoulder. The approximate relationship between the height y of an individual and the length x of the humerus is shown in the table for both males and females. All measurements are in inches. Although individual values may vary, tables like this are the result of measuring bones from many skeletons.

x	8	9	10	11
y **(females)**	50.4	53.5	56.6	59.7
y **(males)**	53.0	56.0	59.0	62.0

x	12	13	14
y **(females)**	62.8	65.9	69.0
y **(males)**	65.0	68.0	71.0

(a) Find the estimated height of a female with a 12-inch humerus.

(b) Plot the ordered pairs (x, y) for both sexes. What type of relation exists between the data?

(c) For each 1-inch increase in the length of the humerus, what are the corresponding increases in the heights of females and of males?

(d) Determine linear functions f and g that model these data for females and males, respectively.

(e) Suppose a humerus from a person of unknown sex is estimated to be between 9.7 and 10.1 inches long. Use f and g to approximate the range for the height of a female and a male.

2. Archeology Continuing with Exercise 1, have members of the class measure their heights and the lengths of their humeri (plural of *humerus*) in inches.

(a) Make a table of the results.

(b) Find regression lines that fit the data points for males and females.

(c) Compare your results with the table in Exercise 1.

3. A Puzzle Three people leave for a city 15 miles away. The first person walks 4 miles per hour, and the other two people ride in a car that travels 28 miles per hour. After some time, the second person gets out of the car and walks 4 miles per hour to the city while the driver goes back and picks up the first person. The driver takes the first person to the city. If all three people arrive in the city at the same time, how far did each person walk?

4. Limit Notation Let ε and δ be positive numbers; let x, c, and L be real numbers; and let f be a function. Consider the following: "If the distance between x and c is less than δ, then the distance between $f(x)$ and L is less than ε." Rewrite this sentence by using two absolute value inequalities.

1–2 Cumulative Review Exercises

1. Write 123,000 and 0.0051 in scientific notation.

2. Write 6.7×10^6 and 1.45×10^{-4} in standard form.

3. Evaluate $\frac{4 + \sqrt{2}}{4 - \sqrt{2}}$. Round your answer to the nearest hundredth.

4. The table represents a relation S.

x	−1	0	1	2	3
y	6	4	3	0	0

(a) Does S represent a function?

(b) Determine the domain and range of S.

5. Find the standard equation of a circle with center $(-2, 3)$ and radius 7.

6. Evaluate $-5^2 - 2 - \frac{10 - 2}{5 - 1}$ by hand.

7. Find the exact distance between $(-3, 5)$ and $(2, -3)$.

8. Find the midpoint of the line segment with endpoints $(5, -2)$ and $(-3, 1)$.

9. Find the domain and range of the function shown in the graph. Evaluate $f(-1)$.

(a)

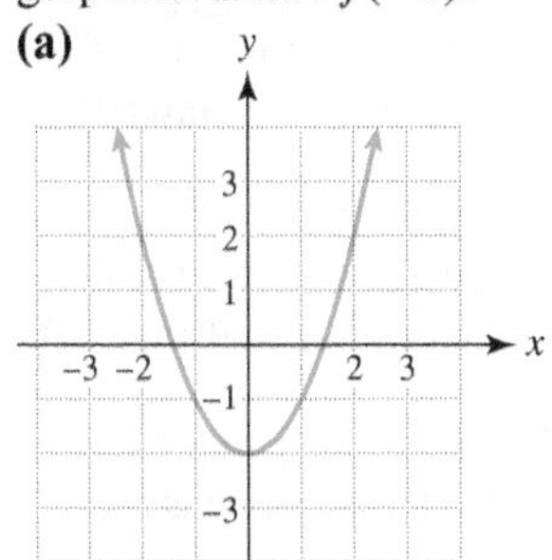

(b)

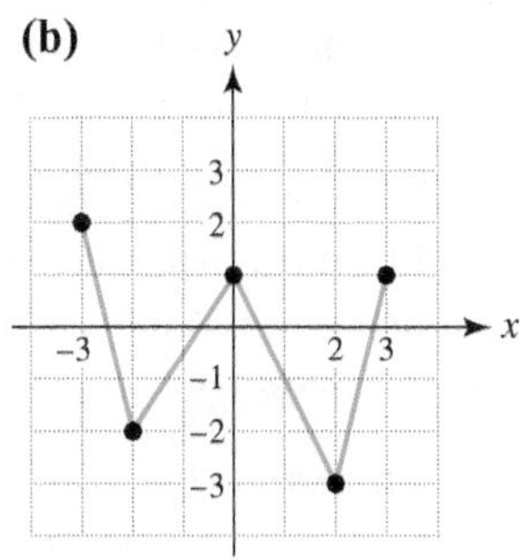

10. Graph f by hand.
(a) $f(x) = 3 - 2x$ (b) $f(x) = |x + 1|$

Exercises 11 and 12: Complete the following.

(a) Evaluate $f(2)$ and $f(a - 1)$.
(b) Determine the domain of f.

11. $f(x) = 5x - 3$

12. $f(x) = \sqrt{2x - 1}$

13. Determine if the graph represents a function. Explain your answer.

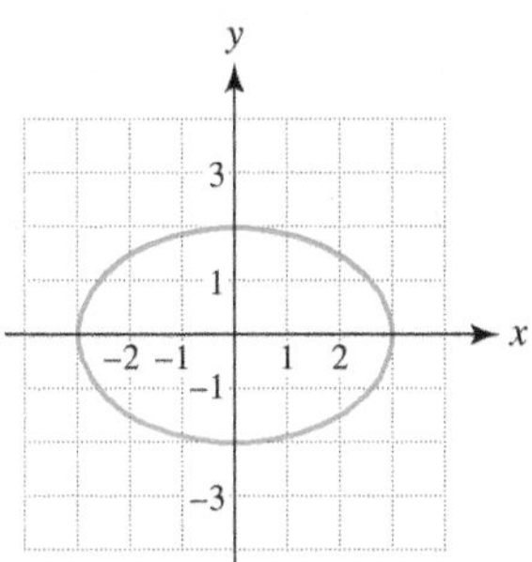

14. Write a formula for a function f that computes the cost of taking x credits if credits cost \$80 each and fees are fixed at \$89.

15. Find the average rate of change of $f(x) = x^2 - 2x + 1$ from $x = 1$ to $x = 2$.

16. Find the difference quotient for $f(x) = 2x^2 - x$.

Exercises 17 and 18: The graph of a linear function f is shown.

(a) Identify the slope, y-intercept, and x-intercept.
(b) Write a formula for f.
(c) Find any zeros of f.

17. 18.

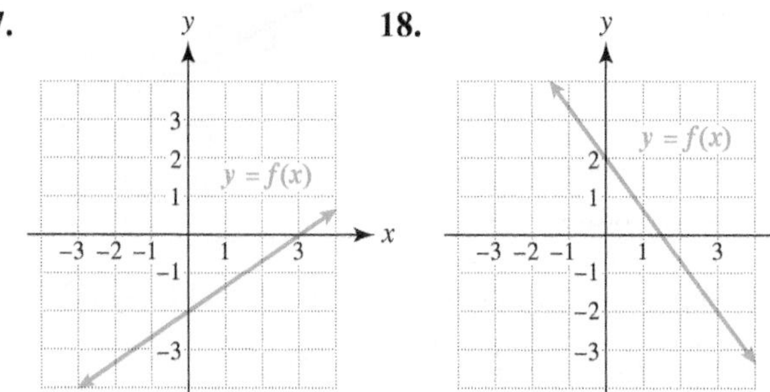

Exercises 19–24: Write an equation of a line satisfying the given conditions. Use slope-intercept form whenever possible.

19. Passing through $(1, -5)$ and $\left(-3, \frac{1}{2}\right)$

20. Passing through the point $(-3, 2)$ and perpendicular to the line $y = \frac{2}{3}x - 7$

21. Parallel to the y-axis and passing through $(-1, 3)$

22. Slope 30, passing through (2002, 50)

23. Passing through $(-3, 5)$ and parallel to the line segment connecting (2.4, 5.6) and (3.9, 8.6)

24. Perpendicular to the y-axis and passing through the origin

Exercises 25 and 26: Determine the x- and y-intercepts on the graph of the equation. Graph the equation.

25. $-2x + 3y = 6$ 26. $x = 2y - 3$

Exercises 27–30: Solve the equation.

27. $4x - 5 = 1 - 2x$ 28. $\frac{2x - 4}{2} = \frac{3x}{7} - 1$

29. $\frac{2}{3}(x - 2) - \frac{4}{5}x = \frac{4}{15} + x$

30. $-0.3(1 - x) - 0.1(2x - 3) = 0.4$

31. Solve $x + 1 = 2x - 2$ graphically and numerically.

32. Solve $2x - (5 - x) = \frac{1 - 4x}{2} + 5(x - 2)$. Is this equation either an identity or a contradiction?

Exercises 33–36: Express each inequality in interval notation.

33. $x < 5$ 34. $-2 \le x \le 5$

35. $x < -2$ or $x > 2$ 36. $x \ge -3$

Exercises 37 and 38: Solve the inequality. Write the solution set in set-builder or interval notation.

37. $-3(1 - 2x) + x \le 4 - (x + 2)$

38. $\frac{1}{3} \le \frac{2 - 3x}{2} < \frac{4}{3}$

39. The graphs of two linear functions f and g are shown. Solve each equation or inequality.

(a) $f(x) = g(x)$

(b) $f(x) > g(x)$

(c) $f(x) \leq g(x)$

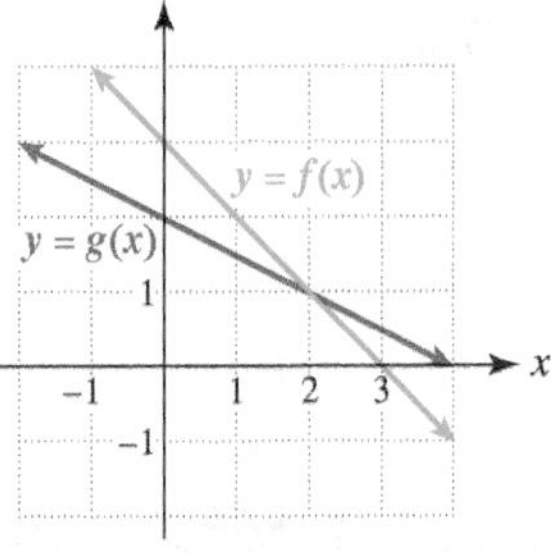

40. Graph f. Is f continuous on the interval $[-4, 4]$?

$$f(x) = \begin{cases} 2 - x & \text{if } -4 \leq x < -2 \\ \frac{1}{2}x + 5 & \text{if } -2 \leq x < 2 \\ 2x + 1 & \text{if } \quad 2 \leq x \leq 4 \end{cases}$$

Exercises 41–44: Solve the equation.

41. $|d + 1| = 5$

42. $|3 - 2x| = 7$

43. $|2t| - 4 = 10$

44. $|11 - 2x| = |3x + 1|$

Exercises 45 and 46: Solve the inequality.

45. $|2t - 5| \leq 5$

46. $|5 - 5t| > 7$

Applications

47. Cost A company's cost C in dollars for making x computers is $C(x) = 500x + 20{,}000$.

(a) Evaluate $C(1500)$. Interpret the result.

(b) Find the slope of the graph of C. Interpret the slope and y-intercept.

48. Distance At midnight car A is traveling north at 60 miles per hour and is located 40 miles south of car B. Car B is traveling west at 70 miles per hour. Approximate the distance between the cars at 1:15 A.M. to the nearest tenth of a mile.

49. Average Rate of Change On a warm summer day the Fahrenheit temperature x hours past noon is given by the formula $T(x) = 70 + \frac{3}{2}x^2$.

(a) Find the average rate of change of T from 2:00 P.M. to 4:00 P.M.

(b) Interpret this average rate of change.

50. Distance from Home A driver is initially 270 miles from home, traveling toward home on a straight interstate at 72 miles per hour.

(a) Write a formula for a function D that models the distance between the driver and home after x hours.

(b) What is an appropriate domain for D? Graph D.

(c) Identify the x- and y-intercepts. Interpret each.

51. Working Together Suppose one person can mow a large lawn in 5 hours with a riding mower and it takes another person 12 hours to mow the lawn with a push mower. How long will it take to mow the lawn if the two people work together?

52. Running An athlete traveled 15 miles in 1 hour and 45 minutes, running at 8 miles per hour and then 10 miles per hour. How long did the athlete run at each speed?

53. Chicken Consumption In 2001 Americans ate, on average, 56 pounds of chicken annually. This amount increased to 84 pounds in 2010. (*Source:* Department of Agriculture.)

(a) Determine a formula

$$f(x) = m(x - x_1) + y_1$$

that models these data. Let x be the year.

(b) Estimate the annual chicken consumption in 2015.

54. Income The table lists per capita income.

Year	1980	1990	2000	2010
Income	\$10,183	\$19,572	\$29,760	\$40,584

Source: Bureau of Economic Analysis.

(a) Find the least-squares regression line for the data.

(b) Estimate the per capita income in 1995. Did this calculation involve interpolation or extrapolation?

3 Quadratic Functions and Equations

> The work of mathematicians from even a millennium ago is still routinely used today, and the work of mathematicians from today will be part of the math of the future.
>
> —Terry Tao, Fields Medal 2006

The last basketball player in the NBA to shoot foul shots underhand was Rick Barry, who retired in 1980. On average, he was able to make about 9 out of 10 shots. Since then, every NBA player has used the overhand style of shooting foul shots—even though this style has often resulted in lower free-throw percentages.

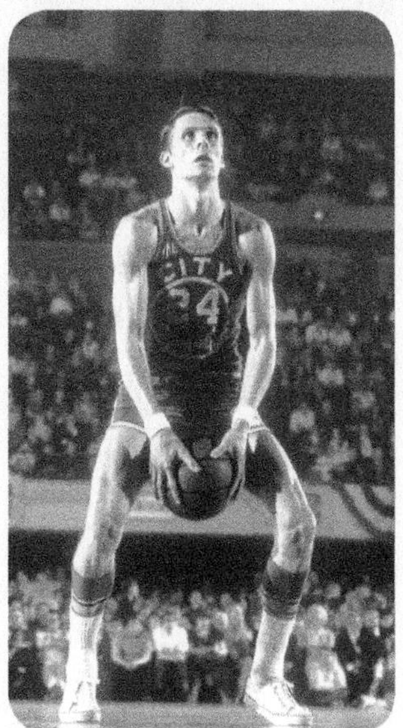

Rick Barry

According to Dr. Peter Brancazio, a physics professor emeritus from Brooklyn College and author of *Sports Science*, there are good reasons for shooting underhand. An underhand shot obtains a higher arc, and as the ball approaches the hoop, it has a better chance of going through the hoop than does a ball with a flatter arc. Lower release points require steeper arcs and increase the chances of the ball passing through the hoop. (See the Extended and Discovery Exercise at the end of this chapter to model the arc of a basketball.)

Mathematics plays an important role in analyzing applied problems such as shooting foul shots. Whether NBA players choose to listen to Professor Brancazio is another question, but mathematics tells us that steeper arcs are necessary for accurate foul shooting.

Source: Curtis Rist, "The Physics of Foul Shots," *Discover*, October 2000. (Photograph reprinted with permission.)

3.1 Quadratic Functions and Models

- **Learn basic concepts about quadratic functions and their graphs**
- **Complete the square and apply the vertex formula**
- **Graph a quadratic function by hand**
- **Solve applications and model data**
- **Use quadratic regression to model data (optional)**

Introduction

Sometimes when data lie on or nearly on a line, they can be modeled with a linear function ($f(x) = mx + b$) and are called *linear data*. Data that are not linear are called **nonlinear data** and must be modeled with a nonlinear function. One of the simplest types of nonlinear functions is a *quadratic function,* which can be used to model the flight of a baseball, an athlete's heart rate, or MySpace advertising revenue. Figures 3.1–3.3 illustrate three sets of nonlinear data that can be modeled by a quadratic function. Although the complete graph of a quadratic function is either ∪-shaped or ∩-shaped, we often use only one side or a portion of the graph to model real-world data.

Data Modeled with a Parabola

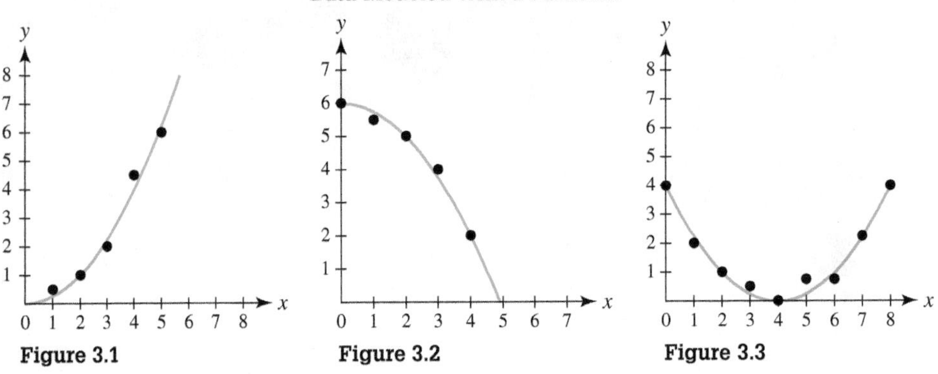

Figure 3.1 **Figure 3.2** **Figure 3.3**

Basic Concepts

The formula for a quadratic function is different from that of a linear function because it contains an x^2-term. Examples of quadratic functions include the following.

Quadratic Functions

$$f(x) = 2x^2 - 4x - 1, \quad g(x) = 4 - x^2, \quad \textit{and} \quad h(x) = \frac{1}{3}x^2 + \frac{2}{3}x + 1$$

The following box defines a *general form* for a quadratic function.

QUADRATIC FUNCTION

Let a, b, and c be constants with $a \neq 0$. A function represented by

$$f(x) = ax^2 + bx + c$$

is a **quadratic function.**

The following are some basics of quadratic functions.

- The domain is *all* real numbers.
- The leading coefficient is a: $f(x) = ax^2 + bx + c$.

Examples: $f(x) = 2x^2 - 4x - 1$, $g(x) = 4 - 1x^2$, $h(x) = \frac{1}{3}x^2 + \frac{2}{3}x + 1$

$a = 2$ $a = -1$ $a = \frac{1}{3}$

- The graph is a **parabola**, or ∪-shaped, that opens upward if a is positive, and opens downward if a is negative.

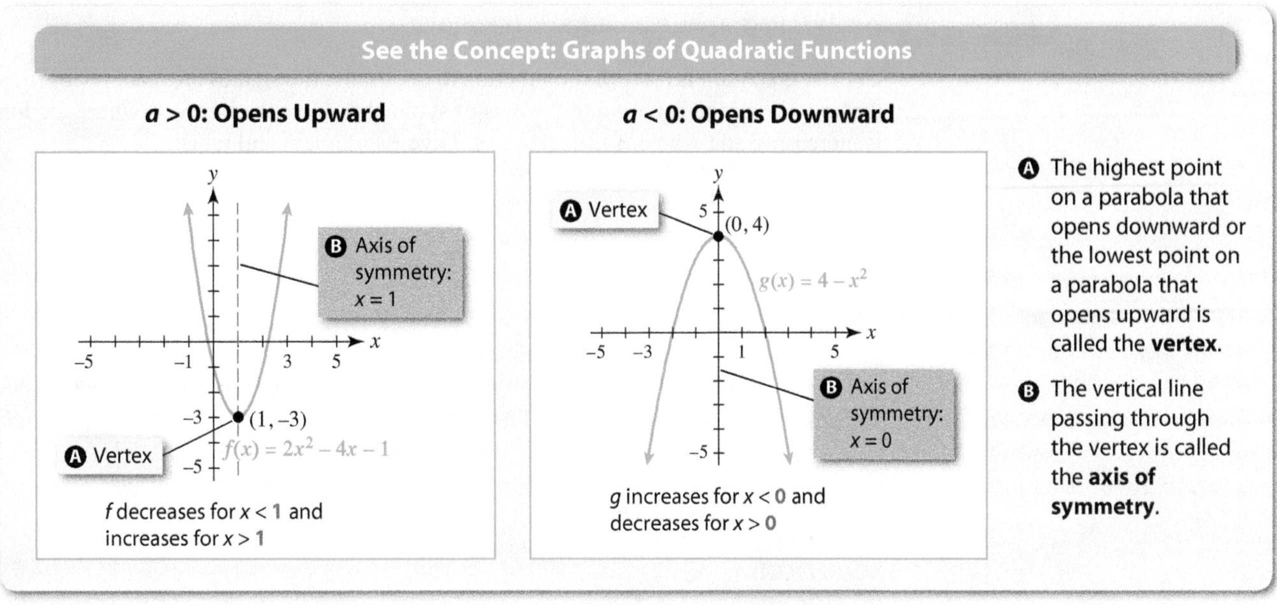

The leading coefficient a of a quadratic function not only determines whether its graph opens upward or downward but also controls the width of the parabola. This concept is illustrated in Figures 3.4 and 3.5.

CLASS DISCUSSION

What does the graph of a quadratic function resemble if its leading coefficient is nearly 0?

The Effect of a on the Graph of $y = ax^2$

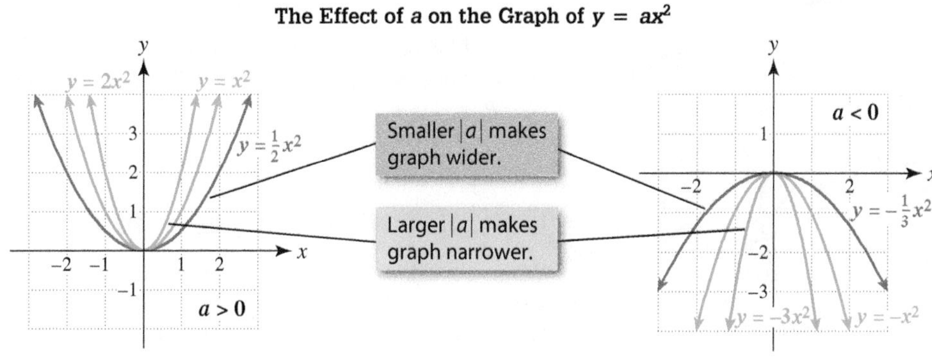

Figure 3.4

Figure 3.5

EXAMPLE 1 Identifying quadratic functions

Identify the function as linear, quadratic, or neither. If it is quadratic, identify the leading coefficient and evaluate the function at $x = 2$.

(a) $f(x) = 3 - 2^2x$ **(b)** $g(x) = 5 + x - 3x^2$ **(c)** $h(x) = \dfrac{3}{x^2 + 1}$

SOLUTION

Getting Started The formula for a quadratic function always has an x^2-term and may have an x-term and a constant. It does not have a variable raised to any other power or a variable in a denominator. ▶

(a) Because $f(x) = 3 - 2^2x$ can be written as $f(x) = -4x + 3$, f is linear.

(b) Because $g(x) = 5 + x - 3x^2$ can be written as $g(x) = -3x^2 + x + 5$, g is a quadratic function with $a = -3$, $b = 1$, and $c = 5$. The leading coefficient is $a = -3$ and

$$g(2) = 5 + 2 - 3(2)^2 = -5.$$

(c) $h(x) = \frac{3}{x^2 + 1}$ cannot be written as $h(x) = ax + b$ or as $h(x) = ax^2 + bx + c$, so h is neither a linear nor a quadratic function.

Now Try Exercises 1, 3, and 5

EXAMPLE 2 **Analyzing graphs of quadratic functions**

Use the graph of each quadratic function to determine the sign of the leading coefficient a, the vertex, and the equation of the axis of symmetry. Give the intervals where the function is increasing and where it is decreasing. Give the domain and range.

(a)

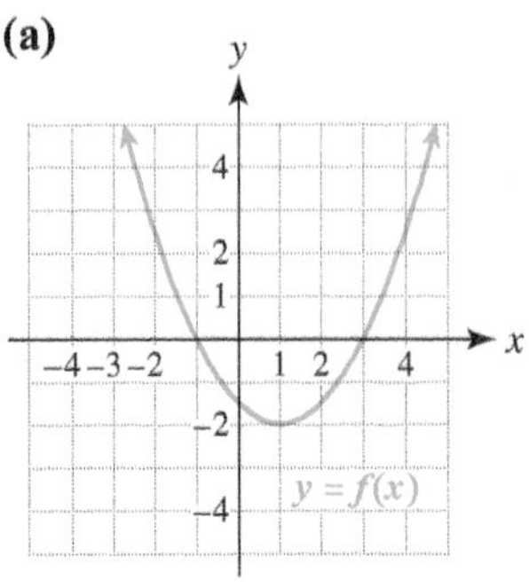

Figure 3.6

(b)

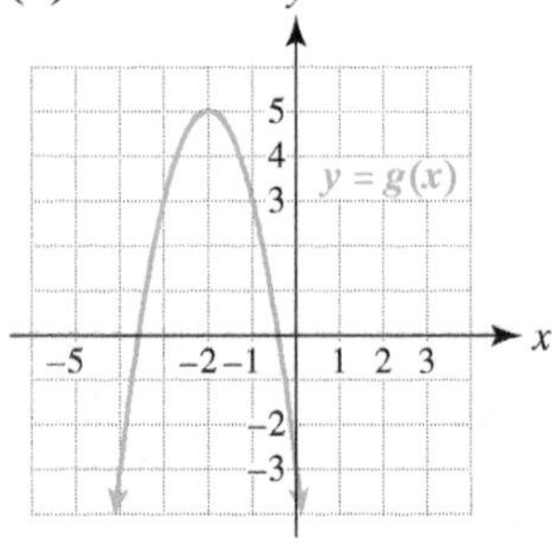

Figure 3.7

SOLUTION

(a) The graph of f in Figure 3.6 opens upward, so a is positive. The vertex is the lowest point on the graph and is $(1, -2)$. The axis of symmetry is a vertical line passing through the vertex with equation $x = 1$. Function f increases to the right of the vertex and decreases to the left of the vertex. Thus f is increasing for $x > 1$ and decreasing for $x < 1$. The domain includes all real numbers and the range is $R = \{y \mid y \geq -2\}$.

(b) The graph of g in Figure 3.7 opens downward, so a is negative. The vertex is $(-2, 5)$, and the axis of symmetry is given by $x = -2$. Function g is increasing for $x < -2$ and decreasing for $x > -2$. The domain includes all real numbers and the range is $R = \{y \mid y \leq 5\}$.

Now Try Exercises 7 and 9

Completing the Square and the Vertex Formula

When a quadratic function f is expressed as $f(x) = ax^2 + bx + c$, the coordinates of the vertex are not apparent. However, if f is written as $f(x) = a(x - h)^2 + k$, then the vertex is located at (h, k), as illustrated in Figure 3.8. For example, in Figure 3.9 the graph of $f(x) = -2(x - 1)^2 + 2$ opens downward with vertex $(1, 2)$.

A Parabola with Vertex (h, k)

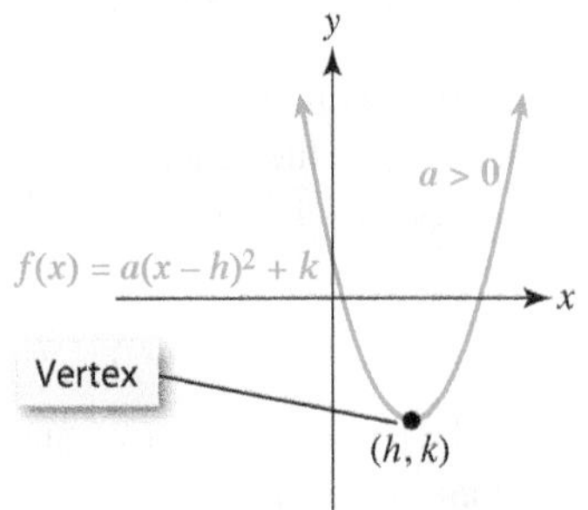

Figure 3.8

A Parabola with Vertex (1, 2)

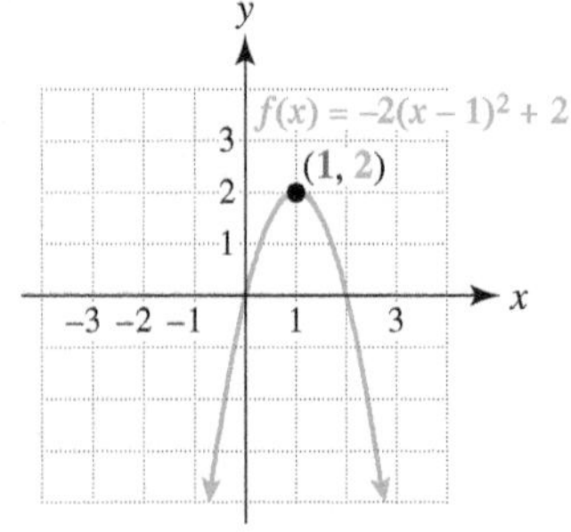

Figure 3.9

To justify that the vertex is indeed (h, k), consider the following. If $a > 0$ in the form $f(x) = a(x - h)^2 + k$, then the term $a(x - h)^2$ is never negative and the minimum value of $f(x)$ is k. This value occurs when $x = h$ because

$$f(h) = a(h - h)^2 + k = 0 + k = k.$$

Thus the lowest point on the graph of $f(x) = a(x - h)^2 + k$ with $a > 0$ is (h, k), and because this graph is a parabola that opens upward, the vertex must be (h, k). A similar discussion can be used to justify that (h, k) is the vertex when $a < 0$.

The formula $f(x) = a(x - h)^2 + k$ is sometimes called the **standard form for a parabola with a vertical axis**. Because the vertex is apparent in this formula, we will call it simply the **vertex form**.

VERTEX FORM

The parabolic graph of $f(x) = a(x - h)^2 + k$ with $a \neq 0$ has vertex (h, k). Its graph opens upward when $a > 0$ and opens downward when $a < 0$.

The next example illustrates how to determine the vertex form given the graph of a parabola.

EXAMPLE 3 Writing the equation of a parabola

Find the vertex form for the graph shown in Figure 3.10.

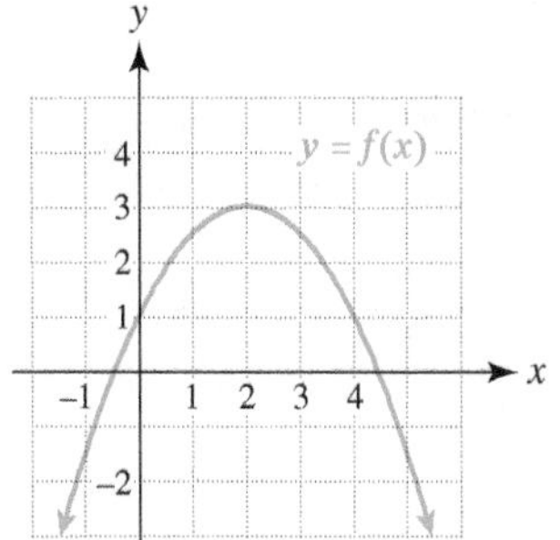

Figure 3.10

SOLUTION

Getting Started We must determine a, h, and k in $f(x) = a(x - h)^2 + k$. The coordinates of the vertex correspond to the values of h and k. To find a, substitute the coordinates of a point on the graph in the equation and solve for a. ▶

From Figure 3.10, the vertex is $(2, 3)$. Thus $h = 2$ and $k = 3$ and $f(x) = a(x - 2)^2 + 3$. The point $(0, 1)$ lies on the graph, so $f(0) = 1$. (Any point on the graph of f other than the vertex could be used.)

$$f(x) = a(x - 2)^2 + 3 \quad \text{Vertex form}$$
$$1 = a(0 - 2)^2 + 3 \quad \text{Let } x = 0 \text{ and } f(0) = 1. \text{ Solve for } a.$$
$$1 = 4a + 3 \quad \text{Simplify.}$$
$$-2 = 4a \quad \text{Subtract 3 from each side.}$$
$$a = -\frac{1}{2} \quad \text{Divide by 4 and rewrite equation.}$$

Thus $f(x) = -\frac{1}{2}(x - 2)^2 + 3$. **Now Try Exercise 25**

EXAMPLE 4 Converting to $f(x) = ax^2 + bx + c$

Write $f(x) = 2(x - 1)^2 + 4$ in the form $f(x) = ax^2 + bx + c$.

SOLUTION Begin by expanding the expression $(x - 1)^2$.

$$2(x - 1)^2 + 4 = 2(x^2 - 2x + 1) + 4 \quad \text{Square binomial.}$$
$$= 2x^2 - 4x + 2 + 4 \quad \text{Distributive property}$$
$$= 2x^2 - 4x + 6 \quad \text{Add terms.}$$

Algebra Review
To review squaring a binomial, see Chapter R (page R-17).

Thus $f(x) = 2x^2 - 4x + 6$. **Now Try Exercise 15**

Completing the Square We can convert the general form $f(x) = ax^2 + bx + c$ to vertex form by **completing the square**. If a quadratic expression can be written as $x^2 + kx + \left(\frac{k}{2}\right)^2$, then it is a perfect square trinomial and can be factored as

$$x^2 + kx + \left(\frac{k}{2}\right)^2 = \left(x + \frac{k}{2}\right)^2.$$

Note that the k used to complete the square is different from the k found in the vertex form. (A variable can have different meanings in different situations.)

This technique of converting to vertex form by completing the square is illustrated in the next example.

EXAMPLE 5 **Converting to vertex form**

Write each formula in vertex form by completing the square. Identify the vertex.

(a) $f(x) = x^2 + 6x - 3$ **(b)** $f(x) = \frac{1}{3}x^2 - x + 2$

SOLUTION

(a) Start by letting $y = f(x)$.

Algebra Review
To review perfect square trinomials, see Chapter R (page R-25).

$$y = x^2 + 6x - 3 \qquad \text{Given formula}$$
$$y + 3 = x^2 + 6x \qquad \text{Add 3 to each side.}$$
$$y + 3 + 9 = x^2 + 6x + 9 \qquad \text{Let } k = 6\text{; add } \left(\tfrac{k}{2}\right)^2 = \left(\tfrac{6}{2}\right)^2 = 9.$$
$$y + 12 = (x + 3)^2 \qquad \text{Factor perfect square trinomial.}$$
$$y = (x + 3)^2 - 12 \qquad \text{Subtract 12.}$$

The required form is $f(x) = (x + 3)^2 - 12$. The vertex is $(-3, -12)$.

(b) Start by letting $y = f(x)$.

$$y = \frac{1}{3}x^2 - x + 2 \qquad \text{Given formula}$$

Multiply each side by 3.

$$3y = x^2 - 3x + 6 \qquad \text{Make leading coefficient 1.}$$
$$3y - 6 = x^2 - 3x \qquad \text{Subtract 6 from each side.}$$
$$3y - 6 + \frac{9}{4} = x^2 - 3x + \frac{9}{4} \qquad \text{Let } k = -3\text{; add} \left(\tfrac{k}{2}\right)^2 = \left(\tfrac{-3}{2}\right)^2 = \tfrac{9}{4}.$$
$$3y - \frac{15}{4} = \left(x - \frac{3}{2}\right)^2 \qquad \text{Factor perfect square trinomial.}$$
$$3y = \left(x - \frac{3}{2}\right)^2 + \frac{15}{4} \qquad \text{Add } \tfrac{15}{4} \text{ to each side.}$$
$$y = \frac{1}{3}\left(x - \frac{3}{2}\right)^2 + \frac{5}{4} \qquad \text{Multiply each side by } \tfrac{1}{3}.$$

The required form is $f(x) = \frac{1}{3}\left(x - \frac{3}{2}\right)^2 + \frac{5}{4}$. The vertex is $\left(\frac{3}{2}, \frac{5}{4}\right)$.

Now Try Exercises 29 and 35

Derivation of the Vertex Formula The procedure above of completing the square can be done in general to derive a formula for determining the vertex of any parabola.

$$y = ax^2 + bx + c \qquad \text{General equation for a parabola}$$
$$\frac{y}{a} = x^2 + \frac{b}{a}x + \frac{c}{a} \qquad \text{Divide each side by } a \text{ to make leading coefficient 1.}$$
$$\frac{y}{a} - \frac{c}{a} = x^2 + \frac{b}{a}x \qquad \text{Subtract } \tfrac{c}{a} \text{ from each side.}$$
$$\frac{y}{a} - \frac{c}{a} + \frac{b^2}{4a^2} = x^2 + \frac{b}{a}x + \frac{b^2}{4a^2} \qquad \text{Add } \left(\tfrac{b/a}{2}\right)^2 = \tfrac{b^2}{4a^2}.$$
$$\frac{y}{a} + \frac{b^2 - 4ac}{4a^2} = \left(x + \frac{b}{2a}\right)^2 \qquad \text{Combine left terms; factor perfect square trinomial.}$$
$$\frac{y}{a} = \left(x + \frac{b}{2a}\right)^2 - \frac{b^2 - 4ac}{4a^2} \qquad \text{Isolate } y\text{-term on the left side.}$$
$$y = a\left(x + \frac{b}{2a}\right)^2 - \frac{b^2 - 4ac}{4a} \qquad \text{Multiply by } a.$$
$$y = a\Big(x - \underbrace{\left(-\frac{b}{2a}\right)}_{h}\Big)^2 + \underbrace{\frac{4ac - b^2}{4a}}_{k} \qquad \text{Write } y = a(x - h)^2 + k.$$

Because the coordinates of the vertex are (h, k), the x-coordinate is $-\frac{b}{2a}$. Note that it is *not* necessary to memorize the expression for k, because the y-coordinate can be found by evaluating $y = f(x)$ for $x = -\frac{b}{2a}$. This derivation of the *vertex formula* is now summarized.

VERTEX FORMULA

The *vertex* of the graph of $f(x) = ax^2 + bx + c$ with $a \neq 0$ is the point $\left(-\frac{b}{2a}, f\left(-\frac{b}{2a}\right)\right)$.

NOTE If a parabola has two x-intercepts, then the x-coordinate of the vertex is equal to the midpoint of these two x-intercepts. For example, the x-intercepts in Figure 3.9 on page 166 are 0 and 2. Their midpoint is $\frac{0 + 2}{2} = 1$, which is the x-coordinate of the vertex.

EXAMPLE 6 **Converting to $f(x) = a(x - h)^2 + k$**

Use the vertex formula to write $f(x) = 3x^2 + 12x + 7$ in vertex form.

SOLUTION Begin by finding the vertex. Let $a = 3$ and $b = 12$.

$$x = -\frac{b}{2a} = -\frac{12}{2(3)} = -2$$

Since $f(-2) = 3(-2)^2 + 12(-2) + 7 = -5$, the vertex is $(-2, -5)$. Because $a = 3$, $f(x)$ can be written as $f(x) = 3(x + 2)^2 - 5$.

Now Try Exercise 37

Graphing Quadratic Functions When sketching a parabola, it is important to determine the vertex, the axis of symmetry, and whether the parabola opens upward or downward. In the next example we sketch the graphs of two quadratic functions by hand.

EXAMPLE 7 **Graphing quadratic functions by hand**

Graph each quadratic function. Find the intervals where the function is increasing and where it is decreasing.

(a) $g(x) = 2(x - 1)^2 - 3$ **(b)** $h(x) = -\frac{1}{2}x^2 - x + 2$

SOLUTION

(a) The vertex is $(1, -3)$ and the axis of symmetry is $x = 1$. The parabola opens upward because $a = 2$ is positive. In Table 3.1 we list the vertex and a few other points located on either side of the vertex. Note the symmetry of the y-values on each side of the vertex. These points and a smooth ∪-shaped curve are plotted in Figure 3.11. When $x = 0$, $y = -1$, and so the y-intercept is -1. Function g is decreasing when $x < 1$ and increasing when $x > 1$.

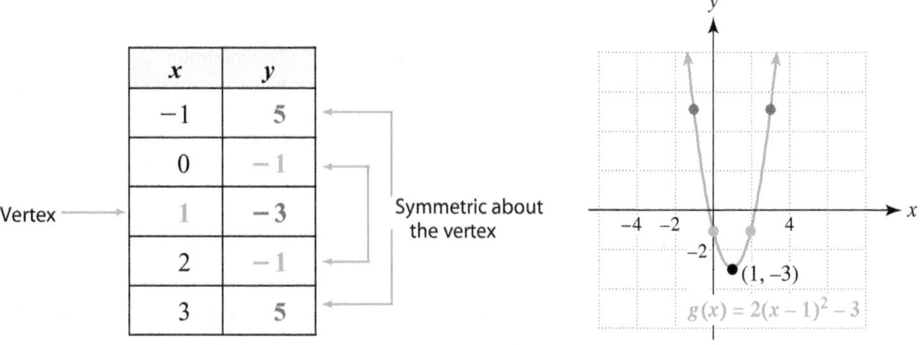

x	y
-1	5
0	-1
1	-3
2	-1
3	5

Table 3.1

Figure 3.11

(b) The formula $h(x) = -\frac{1}{2}x^2 - x + 2$ is not in vertex form, but we can find the vertex.

$$x = -\frac{b}{2a} = -\frac{-1}{2\left(-\frac{1}{2}\right)} = -1$$

The y-coordinate of the vertex is $h(-1) = -\frac{1}{2}(-1)^2 - (-1) + 2 = \frac{5}{2}$. Thus the vertex is $\left(-1, \frac{5}{2}\right)$, the axis of symmetry is $x = -1$, and the parabola opens downward because $a = -\frac{1}{2}$ is negative. In Table 3.2 we list the vertex and a few other points located on either side of the vertex. These points and a smooth ∩-shaped curve are plotted in Figure 3.12. When $x = 0$, $y = 2$, and so the y-intercept is 2. Function h is increasing when $x < -1$ and decreasing when $x > -1$.

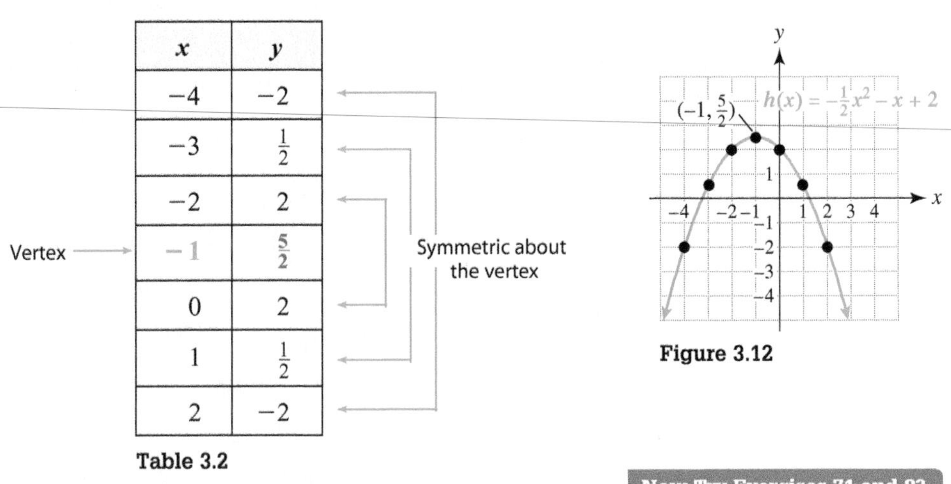

x	y
-4	-2
-3	$\frac{1}{2}$
-2	2
-1	$\frac{5}{2}$
0	2
1	$\frac{1}{2}$
2	-2

Table 3.2

Figure 3.12

Now Try Exercises 71 and 83

Applications and Models

Min-Max Values Sometimes when a quadratic function f is used in applications, the vertex provides important information. The reason is that the y-coordinate of the vertex is the minimum value of $f(x)$ when its graph opens upward and is the maximum value of $f(x)$ when its graph opens downward. See Figure 3.13 and 3.14.

Minimum or Maximum y-Value of a Parabola

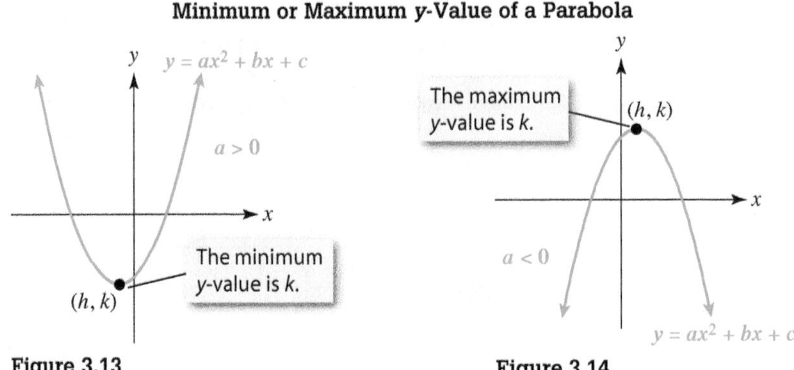

Figure 3.13

Figure 3.14

The process for finding a maximum for a quadratic function is applied in the next example.

EXAMPLE 8 Maximizing area

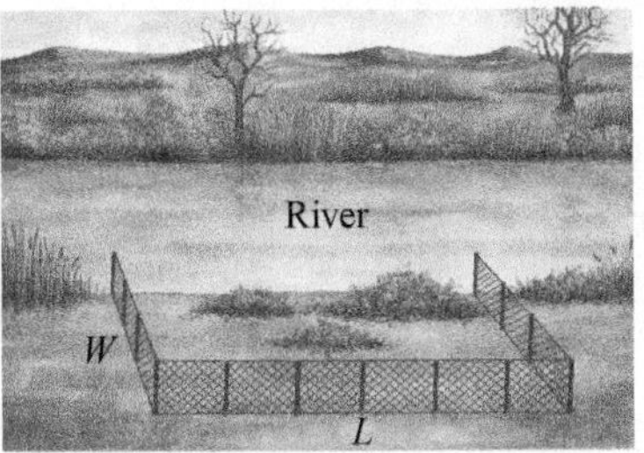

Figure 3.15

A rancher is fencing a rectangular area for cattle using the straight portion of a river as one side of the rectangle, as illustrated in Figure 3.15. If the rancher has 2400 feet of fence, find the dimensions of the rectangle that give the maximum area for the cattle.

SOLUTION

Getting Started Because the goal is to maximize the area, first write a formula for the area. If the formula is quadratic with $a < 0$ (parabola opening downward), then the maximum area will be the y-coordinate of the vertex. ▶

Let W be the width and L be the length of the rectangle. Because the 2400-foot fence does not go along the river, it follows that

$$W + L + W = 2400, \quad \text{or} \quad L = 2400 - 2W.$$

Area A of a rectangle equals length times width, so

$$\begin{aligned} A &= LW && \text{Area of rectangle} \\ &= (2400 - 2W)W && \text{Substitute for } L. \\ &= 2400W - 2W^2. && \text{Distributive property} \end{aligned}$$

Thus the graph of $A = -2W^2 + 2400W$ is a parabola opening downward, and by the vertex formula, maximum area occurs when

$$W = -\frac{b}{2a} = -\frac{2400}{2(-2)} = 600 \text{ feet.}$$

The corresponding length is $L = 2400 - 2W = 2400 - 2(600) = 1200$ feet. The dimensions that maximize area are 600 feet by 1200 feet. The maximum area is 720,000 square feet.

Now Try Exercise 105

Modeling Another application of quadratic functions occurs in projectile motion, such as when a baseball is hit up in the air. If air resistance is ignored, then the formula

$$s(t) = -16t^2 + v_0t + h_0$$

calculates the height s of the object above the ground in feet after t seconds. In this formula h_0 represents the initial height of the object in feet and v_0 represents its initial *vertical* velocity in feet per second. If the initial velocity is upward, then $v_0 > 0$, and if the initial velocity is downward, then $v_0 < 0$.

EXAMPLE 9 Modeling the flight of a baseball

A baseball is hit straight up with an initial velocity of $v_0 = 80$ feet per second (or about 55 miles per hour) and leaves the bat with an initial height of $h_0 = 3$ feet, as shown in Figure 3.16.

(a) Write a formula $s(t)$ that models the height of the baseball after t seconds.

(b) How high is the baseball after 2 seconds?

(c) Find the maximum height of the baseball. Support your answer graphically.

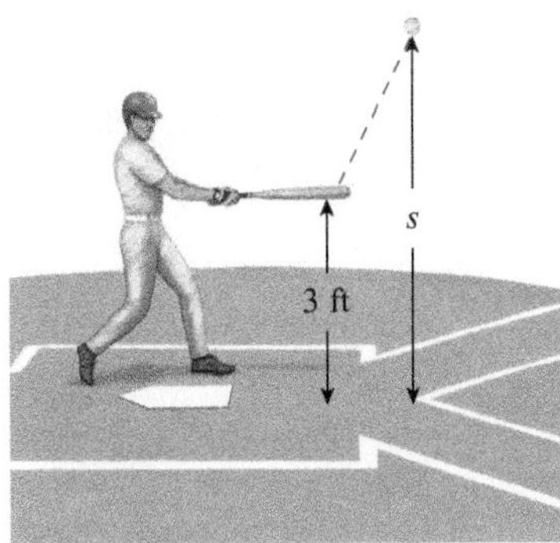

Figure 3.16

Calculator Help

To find a maximum or minimum point on a graph, see Appendix A (page AP-8).

SOLUTION

(a) Because $v_0 = 80$ and the initial height is $h_0 = 3$,

$$s(t) = -16t^2 + v_0t + h_0 = -16t^2 + 80t + 3.$$

(b) $s(2) = -16(2)^2 + 80(2) + 3 = 99$, so the baseball is 99 feet high after 2 seconds.

(c) Because $a = -16$, the graph of s is a parabola opening downward. The vertex is the highest point on the graph, with a t-coordinate of

$$t = -\frac{b}{2a} = -\frac{80}{2(-16)} = 2.5.$$

The corresponding y-coordinate of the vertex is

$$s(2.5) = -16(2.5)^2 + 80(2.5) + 3 = 103 \text{ feet}.$$

Thus the vertex is (2.5, 103) and the maximum height of the baseball is 103 feet after 2.5 seconds. Graphical support is shown in Figure 3.17, where the vertex is (2.5, 103).

Height of a Baseball

[0, 5, 1] by [−20, 120, 20]

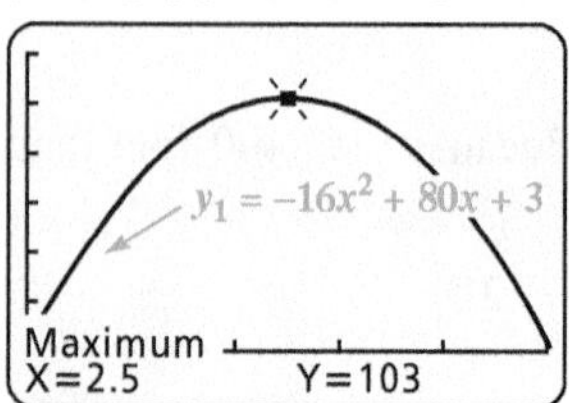

Figure 3.17

Now Try Exercise 101

A well-conditioned athlete's heart rate can reach 200 beats per minute (bpm) during strenuous physical activity. Upon stopping an activity, a typical heart rate decreases rapidly at first and then gradually levels off, as shown in Table 3.3.

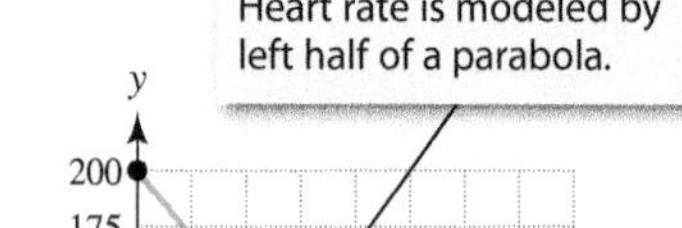

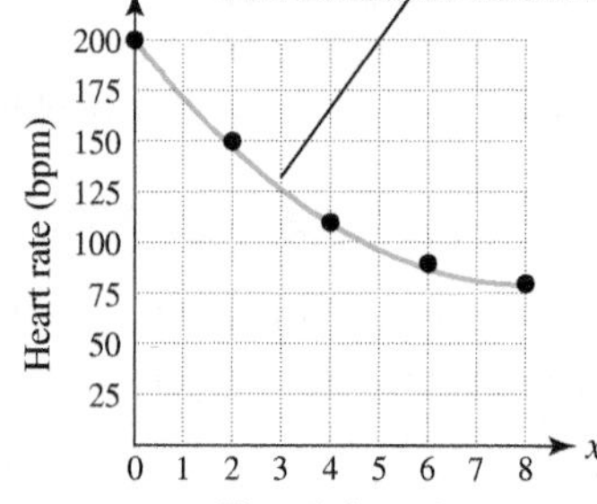

Figure 3.18

Athlete's Heart Rate After Exercise

Time (min)	0	2	4	6	8
Heart rate (bpm)	200	150	110	90	80

Source: Adapted from: V. Thomas, *Science and Sport.*

Table 3.3

The data are not linear because for each 2-minute interval the heart rate does not decrease by a fixed amount. In Figure 3.18 the data are modeled with a nonlinear function. Note that the graph resembles the left half of a parabola that opens upward.

EXAMPLE 10 Modeling an athlete's heart rate

Find a quadratic function f expressed in vertex form that models the data in Table 3.3. Support your result by graphing f and the data in the same xy-plane. What is the domain of your function?

SOLUTION To model the data we use the left half of a parabola. Since the minimum heart rate of 80 beats per minute occurs when $x = 8$, let (8, 80) be the vertex and write

$$f(x) = a(x - 8)^2 + 80.$$

Next we must determine a value for the leading coefficient a. One possibility is to have the graph of f pass through the first data point (0, 200), or equivalently, let $f(0) = 200$.

$$f(0) = 200 \qquad \text{Have the graph pass through (0, 200).}$$

$$a(0 - 8)^2 + 80 = 200 \qquad \text{Let } x = 0 \text{ in } f(x)\text{. Solve for } a.$$

$$a(0 - 8)^2 = 120 \qquad \text{Subtract 80.}$$

$$a = \frac{120}{64} \qquad \text{Divide by } (0 - 8)^2 = 64.$$

$$a = 1.875 \qquad \text{Write as a decimal.}$$

Thus $f(x) = 1.875(x - 8)^2 + 80$ can be used to model the athlete's heart rate. A graph of f and the data are shown in Figure 3.19, which is similar to Figure 3.18. Figure 3.20 shows a table of $f(x)$. Although the table in Figure 3.20 does not match Table 3.3 exactly, it gives reasonable approximations. (Note that formulas for $f(x)$ may vary. For example, if we had selected the point (2, 150) rather than (0, 200), then $a \approx 1.94$. You may wish to verify this result.)

The domain D of $f(x) = 1.875(x - 8)^2 + 80$ needs to be restricted to $0 \le x \le 8$ because this interval corresponds to the domain of the data in Table 3.3.

Calculator Help
To create a table similar to Figure 3.20, see Appendix A (page AP-9).

Modeling an Athlete's Heart Rate

[−0.5, 8.5, 2] by [0, 220, 20]

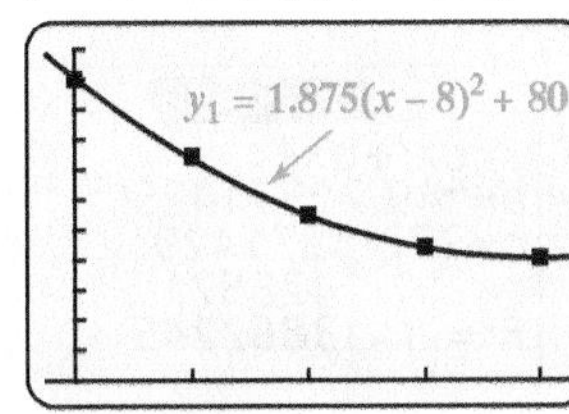

Figure 3.19

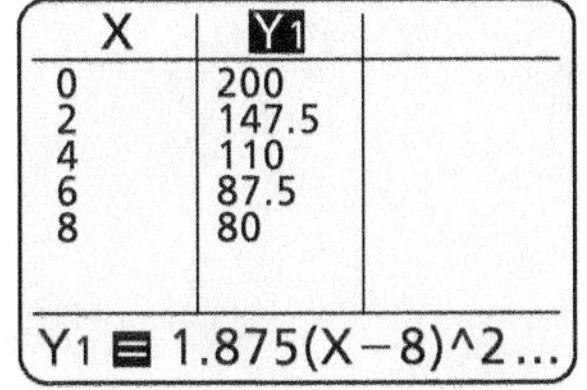

X
Y1
0
2
4
6
8
200
147.5
110
87.5
80
Y1 = 1.875(X−8)^2...

Figure 3.20

Now Try Exercise 115

MAKING CONNECTIONS

General Form, Vertex Form, and Modeling When modeling quadratic data by hand, it is often easier to use the vertex form, $f(x) = a(x - h)^2 + k$, rather than the general form, $f(x) = ax^2 + bx + c$. Because (h, k) corresponds to the vertex of a parabola, it may be appropriate to let (h, k) correspond to either the highest data point or the lowest data point in the scatterplot. Then a value for a can be found by substituting a data point into the formula for $f(x)$. In the next subsection least-squares regression provides a quadratic modeling function in general form.

Quadratic Regression (Optional)

In Chapter 2 we discussed how a regression line could be found by the method of least squares. This method can also be applied to quadratic data; the process is illustrated next.

EXAMPLE 11 **Finding a quadratic regression model**

Table 3.4 lists MySpace U.S. advertising revenue in millions of dollars for 2006 through 2011, where x corresponds to years after 2006.

(a) Plot the data. Discuss reasons why a quadratic function might model the data.
(b) Find a least-squares function f given by $f(x) = ax^2 + bx + c$ that models the data.
(c) Graph f and the data in [−2, 7, 1] by [0, 1000, 100]. Discuss the fit.

MySpace Ad Revenue ($ millions)

Year	0	1	2	3	4	5
Revenue	225	450	590	435	285	190

Table 3.4

[−2, 7, 1] by [0, 1000, 100]

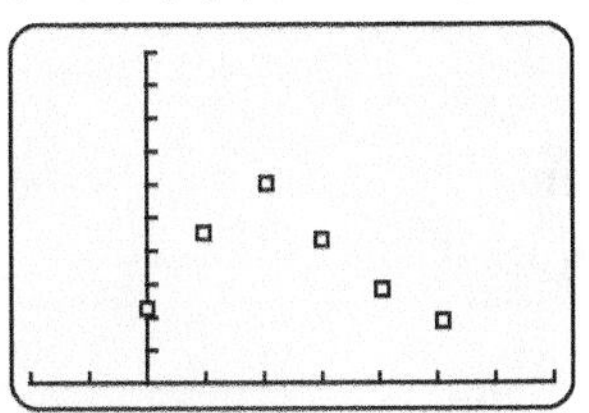

Figure 3.21

SOLUTION

(a) A plot of the data is shown in Figure 3.21. The y-values (ad revenue) first increase and then decrease as the year x increases. The data suggest a parabolic shape opening downward.

(b) Enter the data into your calculator, and then select quadratic regression from the menu, as shown in Figure 3.22 and Figure 3.23. In Figure 3.24 the modeling function f is given (approximately) by $f(x) = -49.29x^2 + 222.9x + 257$.

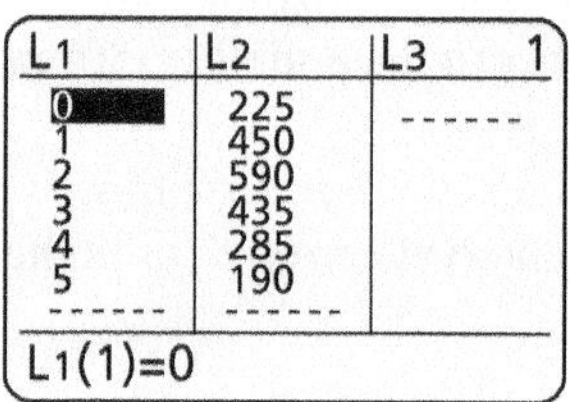

Figure 3.22

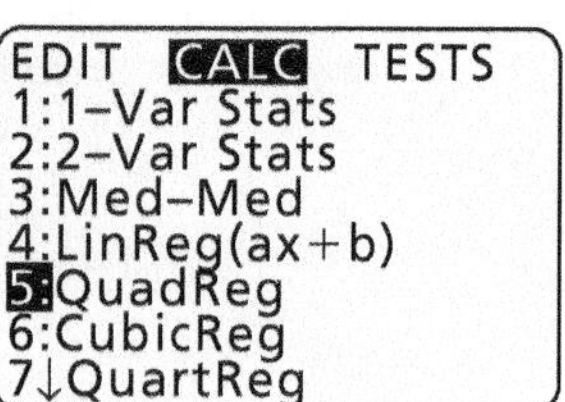

Figure 3.23

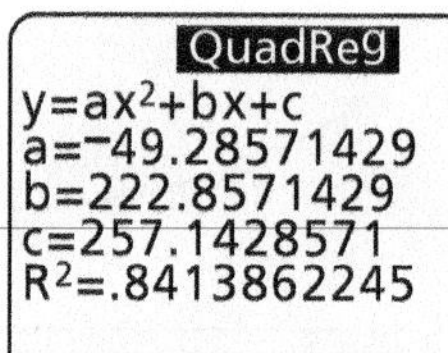

Figure 3.24

[−2, 7, 1] by [0, 1000, 100]

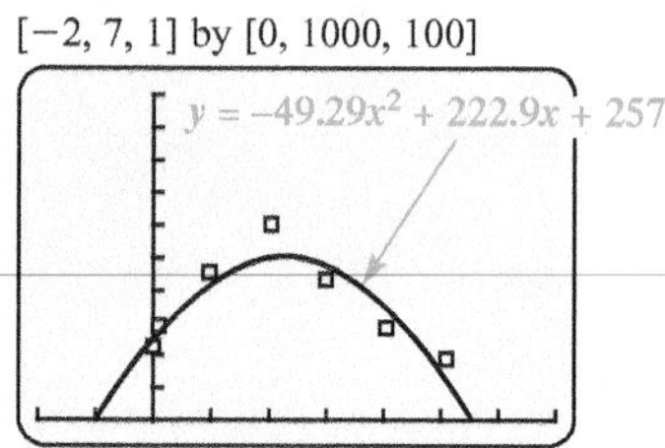

Figure 3.25

Calculator Help
To find an equation of least-squares fit, see Appendix A (page AP-9).

(c) The graph of $y_1 = -49.29x^2 + 222.9x + 257$ with the data is shown in Figure 3.25. Although the model is not exact, the parabola describes the general trend in the data. The parabola opens downward because $a = -49.29$ is negative.

Now Try Exercise 125

3.1 Putting It All Together

The following table summarizes some important topics from this section.

CONCEPT	SYMBOLIC REPRESENTATION	COMMENTS AND EXAMPLES
Quadratic function	$f(x) = ax^2 + bx + c$, where a, b, and c are constants with $a \neq 0$ (general form)	It models data that are not linear. Its graph is a parabola (∪-shaped) that opens either upward ($a > 0$) or downward ($a < 0$).
Parabola	The graph of $y = ax^2 + bx + c$, $a \neq 0$, is a parabola.	y; Maximum: k; (h, k); x; $a < 0$; $x = h$ Vertex: (h, k); axis of symmetry: $x = h$ Maximum (or minimum) y-value: k

CONCEPT	SYMBOLIC REPRESENTATION	COMMENTS AND EXAMPLES
Completing the square to find vertex form	To complete the square for $x^2 + kx$, add $\left(\frac{k}{2}\right)^2$ to make a perfect square trinomial.	$y = x^2 - 2x + 3$ $y - 3 = x^2 - 2x$ $k = -2$ $y - 3 + 1 = x^2 - 2x + 1$ Add $\left(\frac{-2}{2}\right)^2 = 1$. $y - 2 = (x - 1)^2$ $y = (x - 1)^2 + 2$
Vertex formula	The vertex for $f(x) = ax^2 + bx + c$ is the point $\left(-\frac{b}{2a}, f\left(-\frac{b}{2a}\right)\right)$.	If $f(x) = x^2 - 2x + 3$, then $x = -\frac{-2}{2(1)} = 1$. y-value of vertex: $f(1) = 2$ Vertex: (1, 2); axis of symmetry: $x = 1$
Vertex form (standard form for a parabola with vertical axis)	The vertex form for a quadratic function is $f(x) = a(x - h)^2 + k$, with vertex (h, k).	Let $f(x) = 2(x + 3)^2 - 5$. Parabola opens upward: $a > 0$ $a = 2$ Vertex: $(-3, -5)$ Axis of symmetry: $x = -3$ Minimum y-value on graph: -5

3.1 Exercises

Basics of Quadratic Functions

Exercises 1–6: Identify f as being linear, quadratic, or neither. If f is quadratic, identify the leading coefficient a and evaluate f(−2).

1. $f(x) = 1 - 2x + 3x^2$

2. $f(x) = -5x + 11$

3. $f(x) = \dfrac{1}{x^2 - 1}$

4. $f(x) = (x^2 + 1)^2$

5. $f(x) = \frac{1}{2} - \frac{3}{10}x$

6. $f(x) = \frac{1}{5}x^2$

Exercises 7–10: Use the graph to find the following.

(a) Sign of the leading coefficient
(b) Vertex
(c) Axis of symmetry
(d) Intervals where f is increasing and where f is decreasing
(e) Domain and range

7.

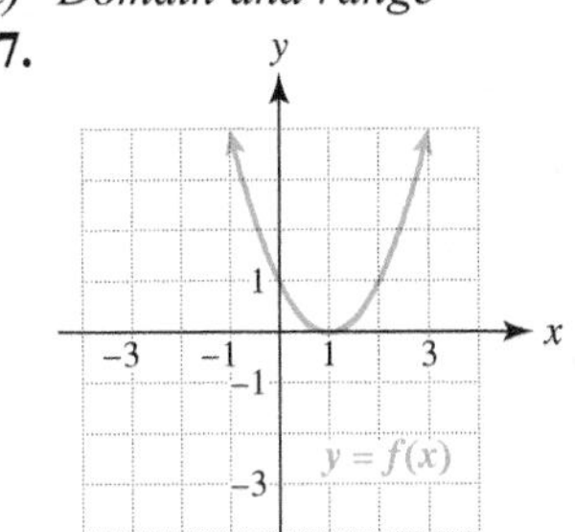

8.

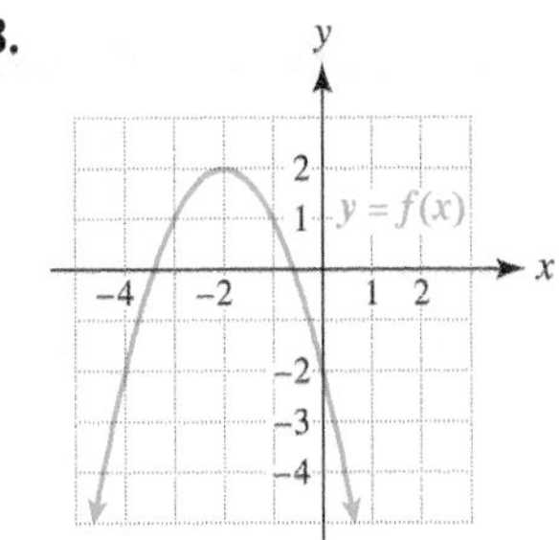

9.

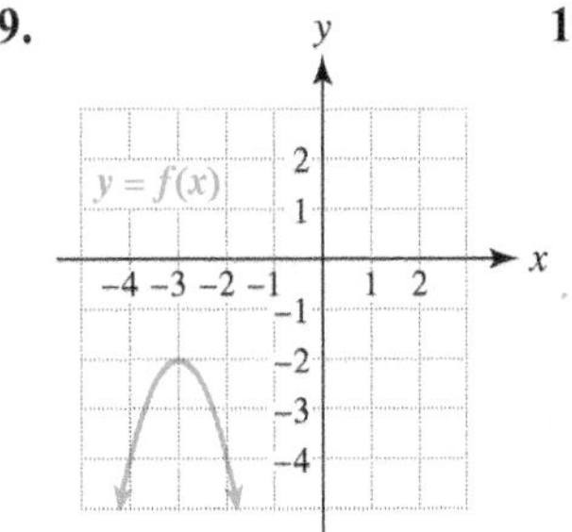

10.

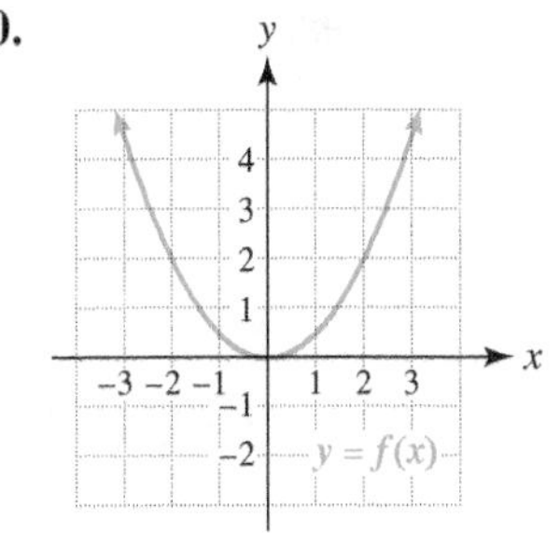

Exercises 11–14: The formulas for f(x) and g(x) are identical except for their leading coefficients a. Compare the graphs of f and g. You may want to support your answers by graphing f and g together.

11. $f(x) = x^2$, $g(x) = 2x^2$

12. $f(x) = \frac{1}{2}x^2$, $g(x) = -\frac{1}{2}x^2$

13. $f(x) = 2x^2 + 1$, $g(x) = -\frac{1}{3}x^2 + 1$

14. $f(x) = x^2 + x$, $g(x) = \frac{1}{4}x^2 + x$

Vertex Formula

Exercises 15–20: Identify the vertex and leading coefficient. Then write the expression as $f(x) = ax^2 + bx + c$.

15. $f(x) = -3(x - 1)^2 + 2$

16. $f(x) = 5(x + 2)^2 - 5$

17. $f(x) = 5 - 2(x - 4)^2$ **18.** $f(x) = \frac{1}{2}(x + 3)^2 - 5$

19. $f(x) = \frac{3}{4}(x + 5)^2 - \frac{7}{4}$ **20.** $f(x) = -5(x - 4)^2$

Exercises 21–28: Use the graph of the quadratic function f to write its formula as $f(x) = a(x - h)^2 + k$.

21.

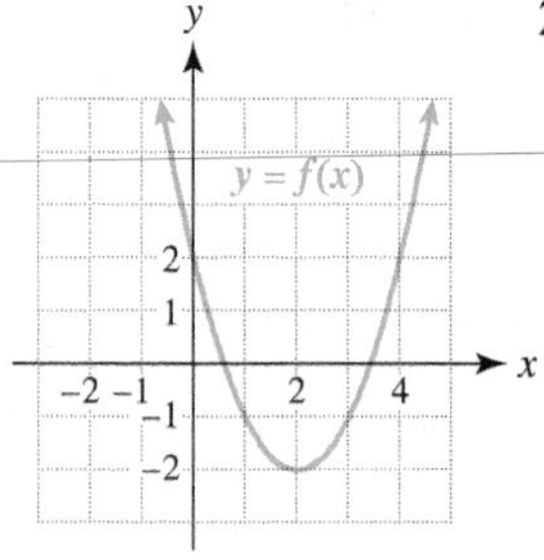

22.

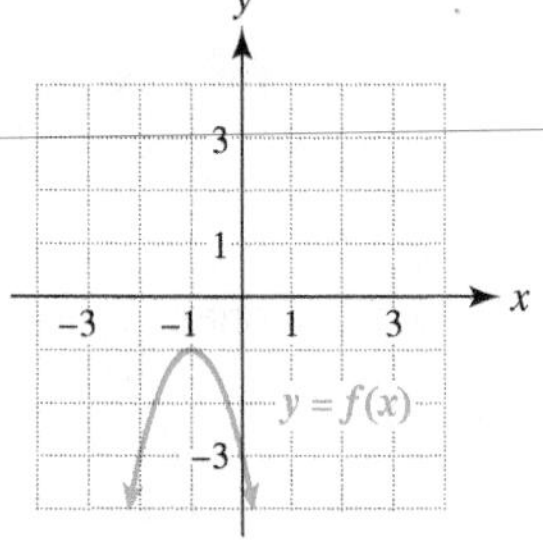

23.

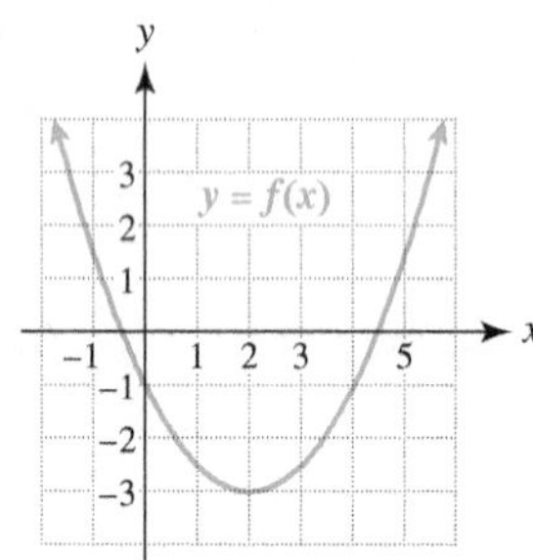

24.

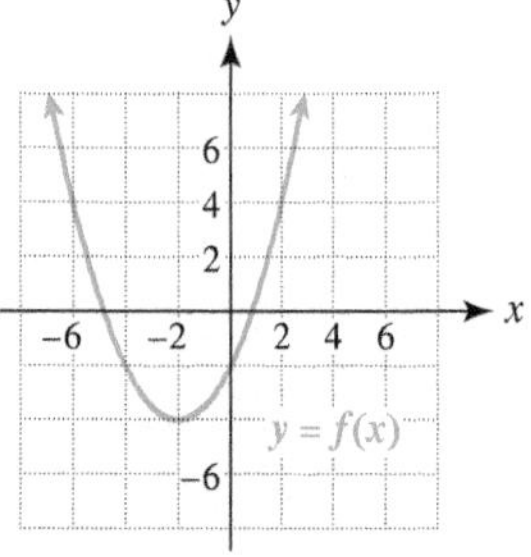

25.

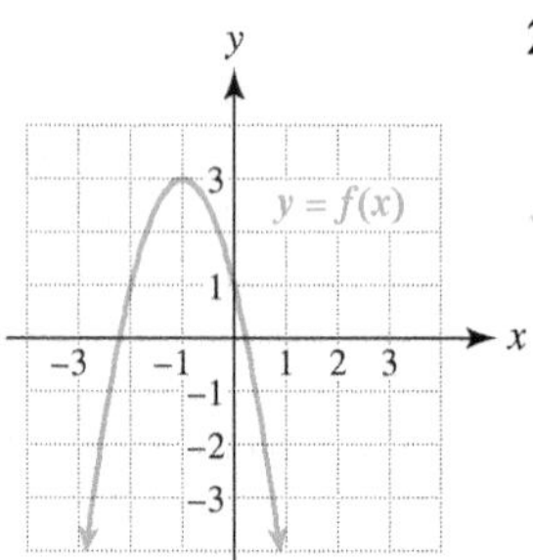

26.

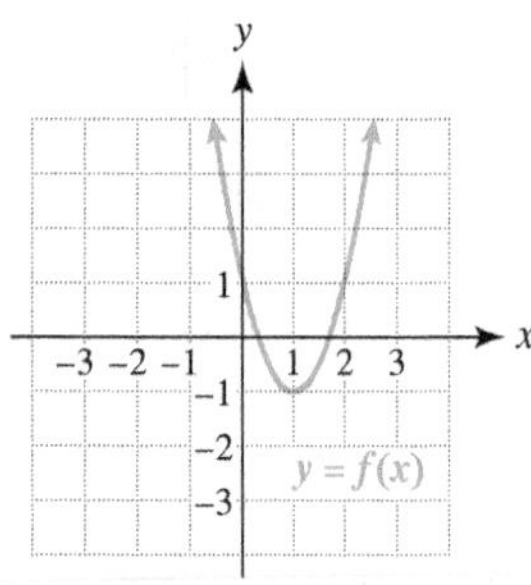

27.

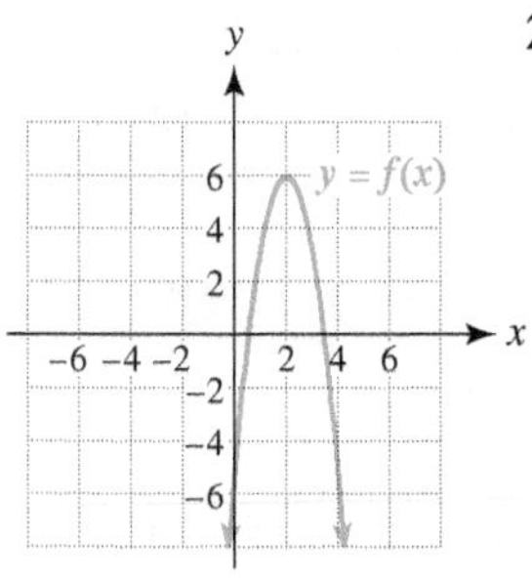

28.

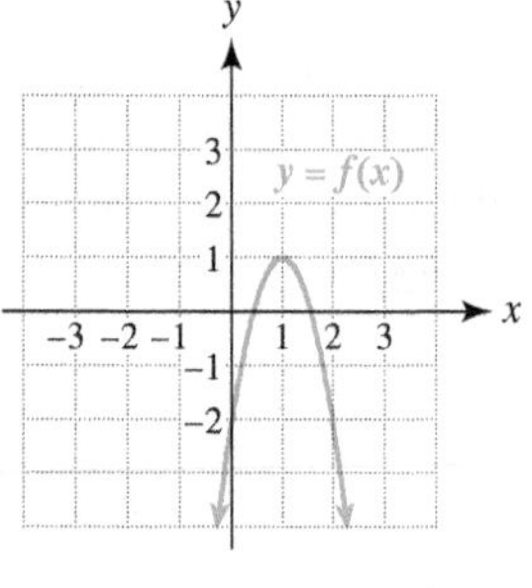

Exercises 29–40: Write the given expression in the form $f(x) = a(x - h)^2 + k$. Identify the vertex.

29. $f(x) = x^2 + 4x - 5$ **30.** $f(x) = x^2 + 10x + 7$

31. $f(x) = x^2 - 3x$ **32.** $f(x) = x^2 - 7x + 5$

33. $f(x) = 2x^2 - 5x + 3$ **34.** $f(x) = 3x^2 + 6x + 2$

35. $f(x) = \frac{1}{3}x^2 + x + 1$ **36.** $f(x) = -\frac{1}{2}x^2 - \frac{3}{2}x + 1$

37. $f(x) = 2x^2 - 8x - 1$ **38.** $f(x) = -\frac{1}{2}x^2 - x$

39. $f(x) = 2 - 9x - 3x^2$

40. $f(x) = 6 + 5x - 10x^2$

Exercises 41–52: Complete the following.

(a) Use the vertex formula to find the vertex.
(b) Find the intervals where f is increasing and where f is decreasing.

41. $f(x) = 6 - x^2$ **42.** $f(x) = 2x^2 - 2x + 1$

43. $f(x) = x^2 - 6x$ **44.** $f(x) = -2x^2 + 4x + 5$

45. $f(x) = 2x^2 - 4x + 1$ **46.** $f(x) = -3x^2 + x - 2$

47. $f(x) = \frac{1}{2}x^2 + 10$ **48.** $f(x) = \frac{9}{10}x^2 - 12$

49. $f(x) = -\frac{3}{4}x^2 + \frac{1}{2}x - 3$ **50.** $f(x) = -\frac{4}{5}x^2 - \frac{1}{5}x + 1$

51. $f(x) = 1.5 - 3x - 6x^2$ **52.** $f(x) = -4x^2 + 16x$

Min-Max

Exercises 53–58: Find the minimum y-value on the graph of $y = f(x)$.

53. $f(x) = x^2 + 4x - 2$ **54.** $f(x) = x^2 - 6x$

55. $f(x) = 3x^2 - 4x + 2$ **56.** $f(x) = 2x^2 + 6x$

57. $f(x) = x^2 + 3x + 5$ **58.** $f(x) = 2x^2 - x + 1$

Exercises 59–64: Find the maximum y-value on the graph of $y = f(x)$.

59. $f(x) = -x^2 + 3x - 2$ **60.** $f(x) = -x^2 + 4x + 5$

61. $f(x) = 5x - x^2$ **62.** $f(x) = -2x^2 - 2x - 5$

63. $f(x) = 2x - 3x^2$ **64.** $f(x) = -4x^2 + 6x - 9$

Graphing Quadratic Functions

Exercises 65–84: Sketch a graph of f.

65. $f(x) = x^2$ **66.** $f(x) = -2x^2$

67. $f(x) = -\frac{1}{2}x^2$ **68.** $f(x) = 4 - x^2$

69. $f(x) = x^2 - 3$ **70.** $f(x) = x^2 + 2$

71. $f(x) = (x - 2)^2 + 1$ **72.** $f(x) = (x + 1)^2 - 2$

73. $f(x) = -3(x + 1)^2 + 3$

74. $f(x) = -2(x - 1)^2 + 1$

75. $f(x) = x^2 - 2x - 2$ **76.** $f(x) = x^2 - 4x$

77. $f(x) = -x^2 + 4x - 2$ **78.** $f(x) = -x^2 + 2x + 1$

79. $f(x) = 2x^2 - 4x - 1$ **80.** $f(x) = 3x^2 + 6x$

81. $f(x) = -3x^2 - 6x + 1$ **82.** $f(x) = -2x^2 + 4x - 1$

83. $f(x) = -\frac{1}{2}x^2 + x + 1$ **84.** $f(x) = \frac{1}{2}x^2 - 2x + 2$

Exercises 85 and 86: **Average Rate of Change** *Find the average rate of change of f from 1 to 3.*

85. $f(x) = -3x^2 + 5x$ **86.** $f(x) = 4x^2 - 3x + 1$

Exercises 87 and 88: **Difference Quotient** *Find the difference quotient of f.*

87. $f(x) = 3x^2 - 2x$ **88.** $f(x) = 5 - 4x^2$

Exercises 89 and 90: Find the formula for a quadratic function that satisfies the given conditions.

89. Axis of symmetry $x = 3$, passing through the points $(3, 1)$ and $(1, 9)$

90. Vertex $(-3, 4)$, passing through $(-2, 1)$

Graphs and Models

Exercises 91–94: Match the situation with the graph of the quadratic function (a–d) that models it best.

91. The height y of a stone thrown from ground level after x seconds

92. The number of people attending a popular movie x weeks after its opening

93. The temperature after x hours in a house where the furnace quits and a repair person fixes it

94. The cumulative number of reported AIDS cases in year x, where $1982 \le x \le 1994$

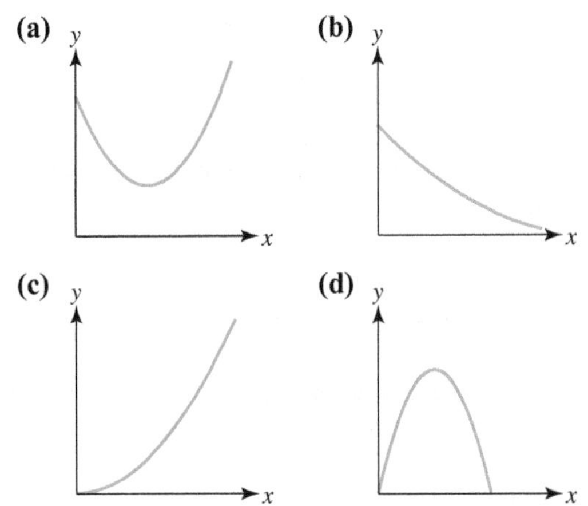

Applications and Models

95. Maximizing Area A farmer has 1000 feet of fence to enclose a rectangular area. What dimensions for the rectangle result in the maximum area enclosed by the fence?

96. Maximizing Area A homeowner has 80 feet of fence to enclose a rectangular garden. What dimensions for the garden give the maximum area?

97. Maximizing Revenue Suppose the revenue R in thousands of dollars that a company receives from producing x thousand DVD players is given by the formula $R(x) = x(40 - 2x)$.

(a) Evaluate $R(2)$ and interpret the result.

(b) How many DVD players should the company produce to maximize its revenue?

(c) What is the maximum revenue?

98. Maximizing Revenue A large hotel is considering giving the following group discount on room rates: the regular price of \$120 decreases by \$2 for each room rented. For example, one room costs \$118, two rooms cost $\$116 \times 2 = \$232$, three rooms cost $\$114 \times 3 = \$342$, and so on.

(a) Write a formula for a function R that gives the revenue for renting x rooms.

(b) Sketch a graph of R. What is a reasonable domain?

(c) Determine the maximum revenue and the corresponding number of rooms rented.

99. Minimizing Cost A business that produces color copies is trying to minimize its average cost per copy (total cost divided by the number of copies). This average cost in cents is given by

$$f(x) = 0.00000093x^2 - 0.0145x + 60,$$

where x represents the total number of copies produced.

(a) Describe the graph of f.

(b) Find the minimum average cost per copy and the corresponding number of copies made.

100. Minimizing Cost A publisher is trying to minimize its average cost per book printed (total cost divided by the number of books printed). This average cost in dollars is given by

$$f(x) = 0.000000015x^2 - 0.0007x + 26,$$

where x represents the total number of books printed.

(a) Describe the graph of f.

(b) Find the minimum average cost per book and the corresponding number of books printed.

101. **Hitting a Baseball** A baseball is hit so that its height in feet after t seconds is $s(t) = -16t^2 + 44t + 4$.
(a) How high is the baseball after 1 second?

(b) Find the maximum height of the baseball. Support your answer graphically.

102. **Flight of a Baseball** (Refer to Example 9.) A baseball is hit straight up with an initial velocity of $v_0 = 96$ feet per second (about 65 miles per hour) and leaves the bat with an initial height of $h_0 = 2.5$ feet.
(a) Write a formula $s(t)$ that models the height after t seconds.

(b) How high is the baseball after 4 seconds?

(c) Find the maximum height of the baseball. Support your answer graphically.

103. **Throwing a Stone** (Refer to Example 9.) A stone is thrown *downward* with a velocity of 66 feet per second (45 miles per hour) from a bridge that is 120 feet above a river, as illustrated in the figure.
(a) Write a formula $s(t)$ that models the height of the stone after t seconds.

(b) Does the stone hit the water within the first 2 seconds? Explain.

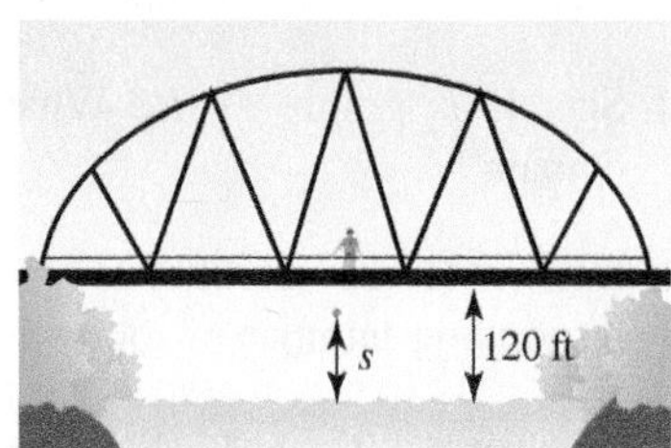

104. **Hitting a Golf Ball** A golf ball is hit so that its height h in feet after t seconds is $h(t) = -16t^2 + 60t$.
(a) What is the initial height of the golf ball?

(b) How high is the golf ball after 1.5 seconds?

(c) Find the maximum height of the golf ball.

105. **Maximizing Area** (Refer to Example 8.) A farmer wants to fence a rectangular area by using the wall of a barn as one side of the rectangle and then enclosing the other three sides with 160 feet of fence. Find the dimensions of the rectangle that give the maximum area inside.

106. **Maximizing Area** A rancher plans to fence a rectangular area for cattle using the straight portion of a river as one side of the rectangle. If the farmer has P feet of fence, find the dimensions of the rectangle that give the maximum area for the cattle.

Exercises 107–110: **Maximizing Altitude** *If air resistance is ignored, the height h of a projectile above the ground after x seconds is given by* $h(x) = -\frac{1}{2}gx^2 + v_0x + h_0$, *where g is the acceleration due to gravity. This formula is also valid for other celestial bodies. Suppose a ball is thrown straight up at 88 feet per second from a height of 25 feet.*

(a) For the given g, graphically estimate both the maximum height and the time when it occurs.

(b) Solve part (a) symbolically.

107. $g = 32$ (Earth)
108. $g = 5.1$ (Moon)
109. $g = 13$ (Mars)
110. $g = 88$ (Jupiter)

111. **Suspension Bridge** The cables that support a suspension bridge, such as the Golden Gate Bridge, can be modeled by parabolas. Suppose that a 300-foot-long suspension bridge has at each end a tower that is 120 feet tall, as shown in the figure. If the cable comes within 20 feet of the road at the center of the bridge, find a function that models the height of the cable above the road a distance of x feet from the center of the bridge.

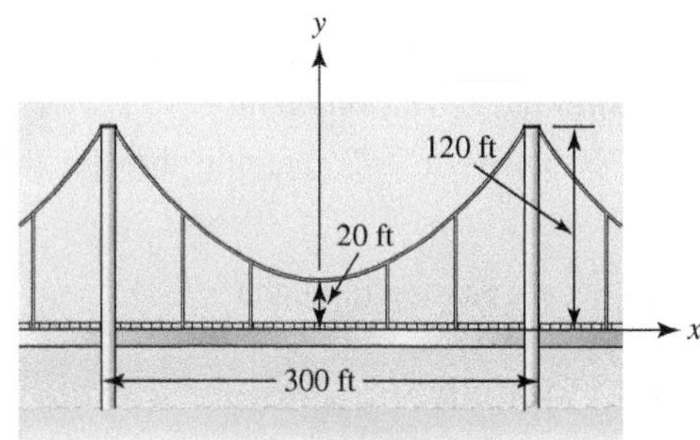

112. **Suspension Bridge** Repeat Exercise 111 for a suspension bridge that has 100-foot towers, a length of 200 feet, and a cable that comes within 15 feet of the road at the center of the bridge.

Exercises 113 and 114: Find $f(x) = a(x - h)^2 + k$ *so that f models the data exactly.*

113.

x	-1	0	1	2	3
y	5	-1	-3	-1	5

114.

x	-2	-1	0	1	2
y	2	4	2	-4	-14

115. **Heart Rate** The table shows the heart rate of an athlete upon stopping a moderate activity.

Time (min)	0	1	2	3	4
Heart rate (bpm)	122	108	98	92	90

(a) Model the data with $H(t) = a(t - h)^2 + k$. What is the domain of H?

(b) Approximate the athlete's heart rate for $t = 1.5$ minutes.

116. Heart Rate The heart rate of an athlete while weight training is recorded for 4 minutes. The table lists the heart rate after x minutes.

Time (min)	0	1	2	3	4
Heart rate (bpm)	84	111	120	110	85

(a) Explain why the data are not linear.

(b) Find a quadratic function f that models the data.

(c) What is the domain of your function?

117. Slideshare Slideshare is a social sharing site where users share professional materials such as PowerPoint presentations. The table shows the number of Slideshare visitors in millions for selected years, where x represents years after 2007.

Year	0	1	2	3	4
Visitors	1.5	6.1	17	33.2	60.1

Source: *Business Insider.*

(a) Model the data with $V(x) = a(x - h)^2 + k$.

(b) Approximate the number of visitors to Slideshare in 2012 if trends were to continue.

118. iPhone Sales The table lists the number of iPhones sold in millions in the first 5 years on the market. Find a quadratic function f that models the data.

Year	1	2	3	4	5
Units sold	1	20	50	100	180

Source: Business Insider.

Exercises 119 and 120: **AIDS in America (1982–1994)** *In the early years of AIDS, the numbers of both AIDS cases and AIDS deaths could be modeled with quadratic functions. The tables list cumulative numbers for selected years.*

(a) Find a quadratic function f that models the data.
(b) Graph the data and f together.
(c) Evaluate $f(1991)$ and interpret the result.

119. Cumulative AIDS cases in thousands

Year	1982	1986	1990	1994
Cases	1.6	41.9	197	442

Source: Department of Health and Human Services.

120. Cumulative AIDS deaths in thousands

Year	1982	1986	1990	1994
Deaths	0.6	24.8	122	298

Source: Department of Health and Human Services.

Quadratic Regression

Exercises 121 and 122: **Quadratic Models** *Use least-squares regression to find a quadratic function f that models the data given in the table. Estimate $f(3.5)$ to the nearest hundredth.*

121.

x	0	2	4	6
$f(x)$	-1	16	57	124

122.

x	10	20	30	40
$f(x)$	4.2	24.3	84.1	184

123. China's Rise The economic rise of China has greatly increased American interest in learning Chinese. The following table lists the U.S. college and university enrollments in thousands to study Chinese.

Year	1980	1986	1995	2002	2009
Enrollment	11	17	27	34	61

Source: The Economist

(a) Find a quadratic function that models the data. Support your result graphically.

(b) Estimate the enrollment to study Chinese in 2006 and compare to the actual value of 51 thousand.

124. MySpace Visitors The table lists the number of unique MySpace visitors per month in millions for various years.

Year	2006	2007	2008	2009	2010	2011
Visitors	55	70	77	65	55	35

Source: comScore

(a) Find a quadratic function that models the data. Support your result graphically.

(b) Estimate the number of MySpace visitors in 2012 if trends continued.

125. Head Start Enrollment Head Start provides a wide range of services to children of low-income families. The table lists Head Start participation in thousands.

Year	1970	1980	1990	2006
Enrollment	447	376	541	909

Source: Department of Health and Human Services.

(a) Find a quadratic function that models the data.

(b) Estimate enrollment in 1985.

126. Photosynthesis In one study the efficiency of photosynthesis in an Antarctic species of grass was investigated. The table lists results for various temperatures. The temperature x is in degrees Celsius and the efficiency y is given as a percent. (***Source:*** D. Brown and P. Rothery, *Models in Biology: Mathematics, Statistics and Computing.*)

x (°C)	−1.5	0	2.5	5	7	10	12
y (%)	33	46	55	80	87	93	95

x (°C)	15	17	20	22	25	27	30
y (%)	91	89	77	72	54	46	34

(a) Plot the data. Discuss reasons why a quadratic function might model the data.

(b) Find a least-squares quadratic function f given by $f(x) = ax^2 + bx + c$ that models the data.

(c) Graph f and the data in the window $[-5, 35, 5]$ by $[20, 110, 10]$. Discuss the fit.

Writing about Mathematics

127. How do the values of a, h, and k affect the graph of $f(x) = a(x - h)^2 + k$?

128. Explain why the vertex is important when you are trying to find either the maximum y-value or the minimum y-value on the graph of a quadratic function.

Extended and Discovery Exercises

Exercises 1–4: **Difference Quotient** *Complete the following.*

(a) Evaluate $f(x)$ for each x-value in the table.

x	1	2	3	4	5
$f(x)$					

(b) Calculate the average rate of change of f between consecutive data points in the table.

(c) Find the difference quotient for $f(x)$. Then let $h = 1$ in the difference quotient.

(d) Evaluate this difference quotient for $x = 1, 2, 3,$ and 4. Compare these results to your results in part (b).

1. $f(x) = x^2 - 3$

2. $f(x) = 2x - x^2$

3. $f(x) = -2x^2 + 3x - 1$

4. $f(x) = 3x^2 + x + 2$

3.2 Quadratic Equations and Problem Solving

- **Understand basic concepts about quadratic equations**
- **Use factoring, the square root property, completing the square, and the quadratic formula to solve quadratic equations**
- **Understand the discriminant**
- **Solve problems involving quadratic equations**

Introduction

In Example 10 of Section 3.1 we modeled an athlete's heart rate x minutes after exercise stopped by using $f(x) = 1.875(x - 8)^2 + 80$. This vertex form can easily be changed to *general form.*

$$f(x) = 1.875(x - 8)^2 + 80 \quad \text{Vertex form}$$
$$= 1.875(x^2 - 16x + 64) + 80 \quad \text{Square the binomial.}$$
$$= 1.875x^2 - 30x + 200 \quad \text{General form}$$

To determine the length of time needed for the athlete's heart rate to slow from **200** beats per minute to **110** beats per minute, we can solve the *quadratic equation*

$$1.875x^2 - 30x + 200 = 110, \quad \text{or} \quad \text{Quadratic equation}$$
$$1.875x^2 - 30x + 90 = 0 \quad \text{Subtract 110 from each side.}$$

(See Example 7.) A quadratic equation results when the formula for a quadratic function is set equal to a constant.

Quadratic Equations

A quadratic equation can be defined as follows.

QUADRATIC EQUATION

A **quadratic equation** in one variable is an equation that can be written in the form

$$ax^2 + bx + c = 0,$$

where a, b, and c are constants with $a \neq 0$.

Examples of quadratic equations include

$$2x^2 - 3x - 4 = 0, \quad x^2 = 3, \quad -5x^2 + x = 0, \quad \text{and} \quad 3x + 1 = x^2.$$

The following See the Concept explains that quadratic equations can have zero, one, or two *real* solutions by showing that a parabola can intersect the x-axis zero, one, or two times. (Complex solutions are discussed in the next section.)

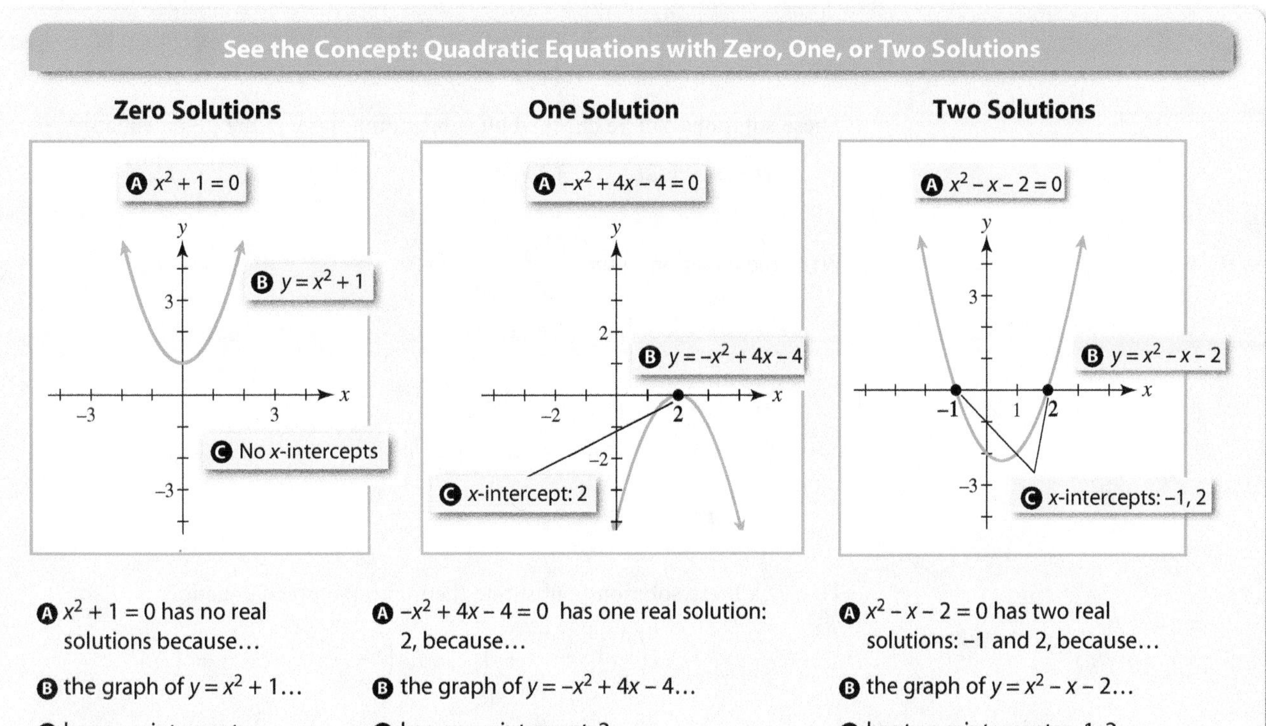

Quadratic equations can be solved symbolically by a variety of methods: factoring, the square root property, completing the square, and the quadratic formula. They can also be solved graphically and numerically; however, the exact solution can *always* be obtained symbolically.

Factoring

Factoring to solve an equation is based on the **zero-product property**, which states that if $ab = 0$, then $a = 0$ or $b = 0$ or both. It is important to remember that this property works only for 0. For example, if $ab = 1$, then this equation does *not* imply that either $a = 1$ or $b = 1$. For example, $a = \frac{1}{2}$ and $b = 2$ also satisfies $ab = 1$ and neither a nor b is 1.

EXAMPLE 1 Solving quadratic equations with factoring

Solve each quadratic equation. Check your results.

(a) $x^2 - 2x + 1 = 0$ **(b)** $2x^2 + 2x - 11 = 1$ **(c)** $12t^2 = t + 1$

SOLUTION

(a) Begin by factoring and applying the zero-product property.

$x^2 - 2x + 1 = 0$		Given equation
$(x - 1)(x - 1) = 0$		Factor.
$x - 1 = 0$ or	$x - 1 = 0$	Zero-product property
$x = 1$ or	$x = 1$	Solve.

The only solution is 1. We can check our answer.

$(1)^2 - 2(1) + 1 = 0$	Let $x = 1$.
$0 = 0$ ✓	It checks.

Algebra Review
To review factoring trinomials, see Chapter R (pages R-22–R-23).

(b) Start by writing the equation in the form $ax^2 + bx + c = 0$.

$$2x^2 + 2x - 11 = 1 \quad \text{Given equation}$$
$$2x^2 + 2x - 12 = 0 \quad \text{Subtract 1 from each side.}$$
$$x^2 + x - 6 = 0 \quad \text{Divide each side by 2.}$$
$$(x + 3)(x - 2) = 0 \quad \text{Factor.}$$
$$x + 3 = 0 \quad \text{or} \quad x - 2 = 0 \quad \text{Zero-product property}$$
$$x = -3 \quad \text{or} \quad x = 2 \quad \text{Solve.}$$

These solutions can be checked by substituting them in the given equation.

$$2(-3)^2 + 2(-3) - 11 \stackrel{?}{=} 1 \qquad 2(2)^2 + 2(2) - 11 \stackrel{?}{=} 1$$
$$1 = 1 \checkmark \qquad 1 = 1 \checkmark$$

(c) Write the equation in the form $at^2 + bt + c = 0$.

$$12t^2 = t + 1 \quad \text{Given equation}$$
$$12t^2 - t - 1 = 0 \quad \text{Subtract } t \text{ and 1.}$$
$$(3t - 1)(4t + 1) = 0 \quad \text{Factor.}$$
$$3t - 1 = 0 \quad \text{or} \quad 4t + 1 = 0 \quad \text{Zero-product property}$$
$$t = \frac{1}{3} \quad \text{or} \quad t = -\frac{1}{4} \quad \text{Solve.}$$

To check these solutions, substitute them into the given equation.

$$12\left(\frac{1}{3}\right)^2 = \frac{1}{3} + 1 \qquad 12\left(-\frac{1}{4}\right)^2 = -\frac{1}{4} + 1$$
$$\frac{4}{3} = \frac{4}{3} \checkmark \qquad \frac{3}{4} = \frac{3}{4} \checkmark$$

Now Try Exercises 1, 7, and 9

We can also use factoring to find the x-intercepts of the graph of a quadratic function, because the x-intercepts of the graph of $y = ax^2 + bx + c$ correspond to the solutions to $ax^2 + bx + c = 0$. The y-intercept is c, the value of y when $x = 0$.

EXAMPLE 2 Finding intercepts

Find the exact values for both the x-intercepts and the y-intercept shown in Figure 3.26.

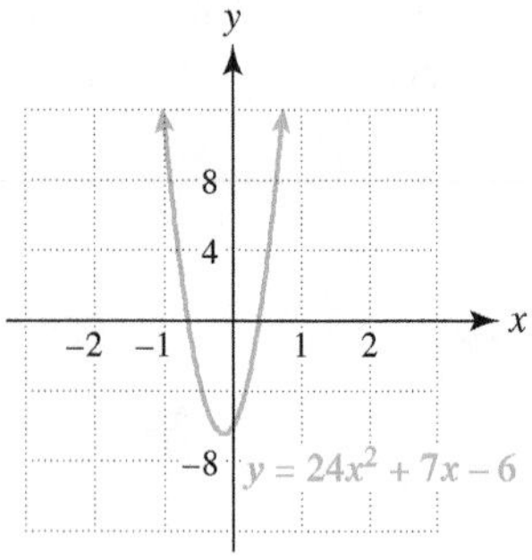

Figure 3.26

SOLUTION From the graph it is difficult to determine the *exact* x-intercepts. However, they can be determined symbolically.

$$24x^2 + 7x - 6 = 0 \quad \text{Set expression equal to 0.}$$
$$(3x + 2)(8x - 3) = 0 \quad \text{Factor.}$$
$$3x + 2 = 0 \quad \text{or} \quad 8x - 3 = 0 \quad \text{Zero-product property}$$
$$x = -\frac{2}{3} \quad \text{or} \quad x = \frac{3}{8} \quad \text{Solve.}$$

The x-intercepts are $-\frac{2}{3}$ and $\frac{3}{8}$.

To find the y-intercept, let $x = 0$ in $y = 24x^2 + 7x - 6$.

$$24(0)^2 + 7(0) - 6 = -6$$

The y-intercept is -6.

Now Try Exercise 33

MAKING CONNECTIONS

Symbolic, Numerical, and Graphical Solutions Quadratic equations can be solved symbolically, numerically, and graphically. The following example illustrates each technique for the equation $x(x - 2) = 3$. (Also, see Example 7.)

Symbolic Solution

$$x(x - 2) = 3$$
$$x^2 - 2x = 3$$
$$x^2 - 2x - 3 = 0$$
$$(x + 1)(x - 3) = 0$$

The solutions are -1 and 3.

Numerical Solution

x	$x(x - 2)$
-2	8
-1	3
0	0
1	-1
2	0
3	3
4	8

Let $y = x(x - 2)$. In the table $y = 3$ when $x = -1$ or $x = 3$.

Graphical Solution

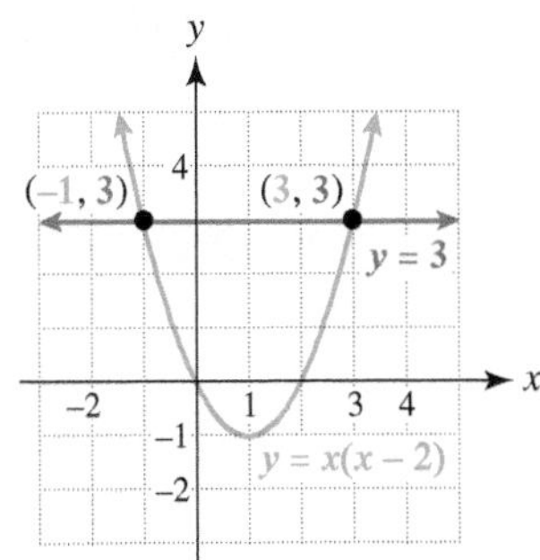

The graph of $y = x(x - 2)$ intersects the graph of $y = 3$ at $(-1, 3)$ and $(3, 3)$. The solutions are -1 and 3.

The Square Root Property

Algebra Review
To review square roots, see Chapter R (Page R-37).

Some quadratic equations can be written as $x^2 = k$, where k is a nonnegative number. The solutions are $\pm\sqrt{k}$. (Recall that the symbol $\pm$ represents *plus or minus*.) For example, $x^2 = 16$ has two solutions: ± 4. We refer to this as the **square root property**. See Extended and Discovery Exercise 7 in this section for a justification of this property.

SQUARE ROOT PROPERTY

Let k be a nonnegative number. Then the solutions to the equation

$$x^2 = k$$

are given by $x = \pm\sqrt{k}$.

EXAMPLE 3 Using the square root property

If a metal ball is dropped 100 feet from a water tower, its height h in feet above the ground after t seconds is given by $h(t) = 100 - 16t^2$. Determine how long it takes the ball to hit the ground.

SOLUTION The ball strikes the ground when the equation $100 - 16t^2 = 0$ is satisfied.

$$100 - 16t^2 = 0$$

$$100 = 16t^2 \quad \text{Add } 16t^2 \text{ to each side.}$$

$$t^2 = \frac{100}{16} \quad \text{Divide each side by 16. Rewrite.}$$

$$t = \pm\sqrt{\frac{100}{16}} \quad \text{Square root property}$$

$$t = \pm\frac{10}{4} \quad \text{Simplify.}$$

In this example only positive values for time are valid, so the ball strikes the ground after $\frac{10}{4}$, or 2.5, seconds.

Now Try Exercise 105

Functions can be defined by formulas, graphs, tables, and diagrams. Functions can also be defined by equations. In the next example we use the square root property to solve equations for y and then determine if y is a function of x, where $y = f(x)$.

EXAMPLE 4 **Determining if equations represent functions**

Solve each equation for y. Determine if y is a function of x.

(a) $x^2 + (y - 1)^2 = 4$ **(b)** $2y = \frac{x + y}{2}$

SOLUTION

(a) Start by subtracting x^2 from each side of the equation.

$$(y - 1)^2 = 4 - x^2 \quad \text{Subtract } x^2 \text{ from each side.}$$
$$y - 1 = \pm\sqrt{4 - x^2} \quad \text{Square root property}$$
$$y = 1 \pm \sqrt{4 - x^2} \quad \text{Add 1 to each side.}$$

There are two formulas, $y = 1 + \sqrt{4 - x^2}$ and $y = 1 - \sqrt{4 - x^2}$, which indicates that y is *not* a function of x. That is, one x-input can produce two y-outputs.

NOTE The equation $x^2 + (y - 1)^2 = 4$ is in standard form for a circle that has center (0, 1) and radius 2. A circle does not pass the vertical line test, so the equation does not represent a function.

Algebra Review
To clear fractions, see Chapter R (page R-33).

(b) Clear fractions by multiplying each side of $2y = \frac{x + y}{2}$ by 2.

$$4y = x + y \quad \text{Multiply each side by 2.}$$
$$3y = x \quad \text{Subtract } y \text{ from each side.}$$
$$y = \frac{x}{3} \quad \text{Divide each side by 3.}$$

The equation $y = \frac{x}{3}$ defines a linear function, $f(x) = \frac{1}{3}x$, so y is a function of x.

Now Try Exercises 71 and 73

Completing the Square

Another technique that can be used to solve a quadratic equation is *completing the square.* If a quadratic equation is written in the form $x^2 + kx = d$, where k and d are constants, then the equation can be solved using

$$x^2 + kx + \left(\frac{k}{2}\right)^2 = \left(x + \frac{k}{2}\right)^2.$$

Algebra Review
To review factoring perfect square trinomials, see Chapter R (page R-25)

For example, $k = 6$ in $x^2 + 6x = 7$, so add $\left(\frac{k}{2}\right)^2 = \left(\frac{6}{2}\right)^2 = 9$ to each side.

$$x^2 + 6x = 7 \quad \text{Given equation}$$
$$x^2 + 6x + 9 = 7 + 9 \quad \text{Add 9 to each side.}$$
$$(x + 3)^2 = 16 \quad \text{Factor the perfect square.}$$
$$x + 3 = \pm 4 \quad \text{Square root property}$$
$$x = -3 \pm 4 \quad \text{Add } -3 \text{ to each side.}$$
$$x = 1 \quad \text{or} \quad x = -7 \quad \text{Simplify.}$$

NOTE If the coefficient a of the x^2-term is not 1, we can divide each side of the equation by a so that it becomes 1. See Example 5(b).

Completing the square is useful when solving quadratic equations that do not factor easily.

EXAMPLE 5 **Completing the square**

Solve each equation.

(a) $x^2 - 8x + 9 = 0$ **(b)** $2x^2 - 8x = 7$

SOLUTION

(a) Start by writing the equation in the form $x^2 + kx = d$ with $k = -8$ and $d = -9$.

$$x^2 - 8x + 9 = 0 \quad \text{Given equation}$$
$$x^2 - 8x = -9 \quad \text{Subtract 9 from each side.}$$
$$x^2 - 8x + 16 = -9 + 16 \quad \text{Add } \left(\tfrac{k}{2}\right)^2 = \left(\tfrac{-8}{2}\right)^2 = 16.$$
$$(x - 4)^2 = 7 \quad \text{Factor the perfect square.}$$
$$x - 4 = \pm\sqrt{7} \quad \text{Square root property}$$
$$x = 4 \pm \sqrt{7} \quad \text{Add 4 to each side.}$$

(b) Divide each side by 2 to obtain a 1 for the leading coefficient.

$$2x^2 - 8x = 7 \quad \text{Given equation}$$
$$x^2 - 4x = \tfrac{7}{2} \quad \text{Divide each side by 2.}$$
$$x^2 - 4x + 4 = \tfrac{7}{2} + 4 \quad \text{Add } \left(\tfrac{-4}{2}\right)^2 = 4 \text{ to each side.}$$
$$(x - 2)^2 = \tfrac{15}{2} \quad \text{Factor the perfect square.}$$
$$x - 2 = \pm\sqrt{\tfrac{15}{2}} \quad \text{Square root property}$$
$$x = 2 \pm \sqrt{\tfrac{15}{2}} \quad \text{Add 2 to each side.}$$

Now Try Exercises 53 and 55

The Quadratic Formula

The quadratic formula can be used to find the solutions to *any* quadratic equation.

QUADRATIC FORMULA

The solutions to the quadratic equation $ax^2 + bx + c = 0$, where $a \neq 0$, are given by

$$x = \frac{-b \pm \sqrt{b^2 - 4ac}}{2a}.$$

EXAMPLE 6 **Using the quadratic formula**

Solve the equation $3x^2 - 6x + 2 = 0$.

SOLUTION Let $a = 3$, $b = -6$, and $c = 2$.

$$x = \frac{-b \pm \sqrt{b^2 - 4ac}}{2a} \quad \text{Quadratic formula}$$
$$x = \frac{-(-6) \pm \sqrt{(-6)^2 - 4(3)(2)}}{2(3)} \quad \text{Substitute for } a, b, \text{ and } c.$$
$$x = \frac{6 \pm \sqrt{12}}{6} \quad \text{Simplify.}$$
$$x = 1 \pm \frac{1}{6}\sqrt{12} \quad \text{Divide: } \tfrac{a \pm b}{c} = \tfrac{a}{c} \pm \tfrac{b}{c}.$$

Algebra Review
To review simplifying square roots, see Chapter R (page R-43).

NOTE Because $\sqrt{12} = \sqrt{4} \cdot \sqrt{3} = 2\sqrt{3}$, we can write $1 \pm \frac{1}{6}\sqrt{12}$ as $1 \pm \frac{1}{3}\sqrt{3}$.

Now Try Exercise 25

NOTE When solving quadratic equations, a common strategy is to first write the equation in the form $ax^2 + bx + c = 0$ and to then try to factor the left side of the equation. If the factors are not easily found, the quadratic formula is used.

EXAMPLE 7 **Estimating an athlete's heart rate**

An athlete's heart rate is given by $1.875x^2 - 30x + 200$. Determine when the heart rate was 110 beats per minute by solving the quadratic equation $1.875x^2 - 30x + 90 = 0$ symbolically, graphically, and numerically, where $0 \le x \le 8$. (This equation was discussed in the introduction to this section.)

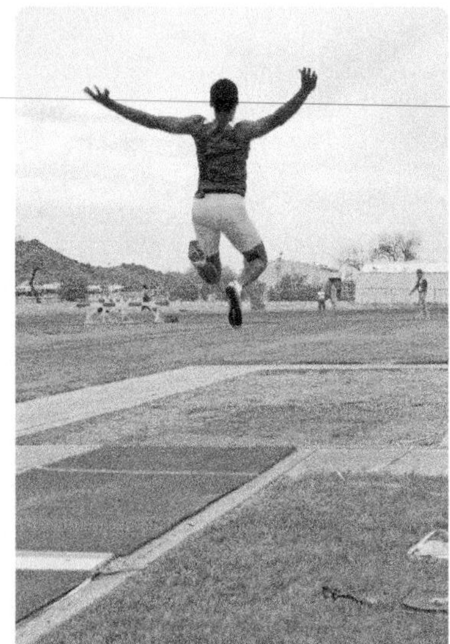

SOLUTION

Symbolic Solution Let $a = 1.875$, $b = -30$, and $c = 90$ in the quadratic formula.

$$
\begin{aligned}
x &= \frac{-b \pm \sqrt{b^2 - 4ac}}{2a} && \text{Quadratic formula} \\
&= \frac{-(-30) \pm \sqrt{(-30)^2 - 4(1.875)(90)}}{2(1.875)} && a = 1.875,\ b = -30, \text{ and } c = 90 \\
&= \frac{30 \pm \sqrt{225}}{3.75} && \text{Simplify.} \\
&= 12 \text{ or } 4 && \text{Simplify.}
\end{aligned}
$$

The x-values are restricted to $0 \le x \le 8$, so the only valid solution is 4. Thus the athlete's heart rate reached 110 beats per minute 4 minutes after the athlete stopped exercising.

Graphical Solution To use the *x-intercept method* to solve this quadratic equation, graph $y_1 = 1.875x^2 - 30x + 90$ and locate the x-intercepts, as shown in Figures 3.27 and 3.28. The x-intercepts are 4 and 12, in agreement with the symbolic solution.

Numerical Solution Make a table of $y_1 = 1.875x^2 - 30x + 90$, as shown in Figure 3.29. The numerical solution agrees with the symbolic and graphical solutions because $y_1 = 0$ when $x = 4$ or $x = 12$.

Calculator Help
To find a zero, or x-intercept, see Appendix A (page AP-7).

Graphical Solutions

[0, 16, 4] by [−125, 125, 25]

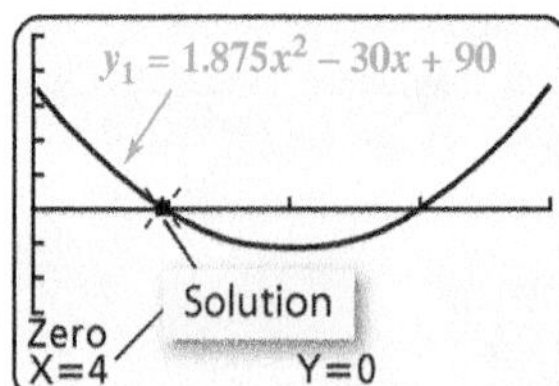

Figure 3.27

[0, 16, 4] by [−125, 125, 25]

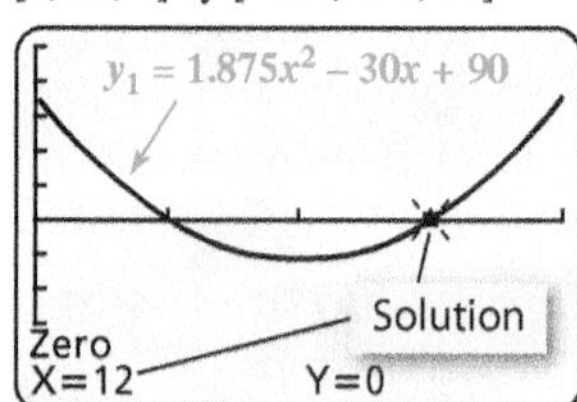

Figure 3.28

Numerical Solutions

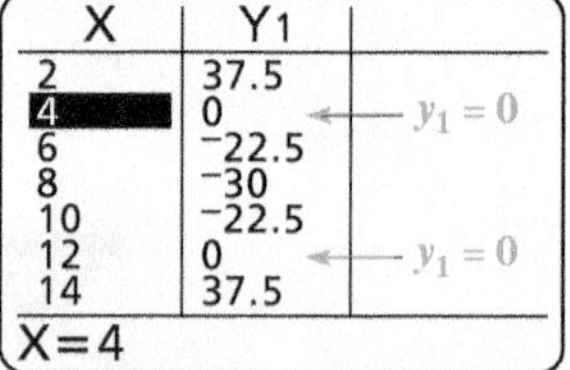

X	Y1
2	37.5
4	0
6	−22.5
8	−30
10	−22.5
12	0
14	37.5

X=4

Figure 3.29

Now Try Exercise 107

The Discriminant

The quantity $b^2 - 4ac$ in the quadratic formula is called the **discriminant.** It provides information about the number of real solutions to a quadratic equation.

QUADRATIC EQUATIONS AND THE DISCRIMINANT

To determine the number of real solutions to $ax^2 + bx + c = 0$ with $a \neq 0$, evaluate the discriminant $b^2 - 4ac$.

1. If $b^2 - 4ac > 0$, there are two real solutions.
2. If $b^2 - 4ac = 0$, there is one real solution.
3. If $b^2 - 4ac < 0$, there are no real solutions.

NOTE When $b^2 - 4ac < 0$, the solutions to a quadratic equation may be expressed as two complex numbers. Complex numbers are discussed in the next section.

In Example 6 the discriminant is $b^2 - 4ac = (-6)^2 - 4(3)(2) = 12$. Because the discriminant is positive, there are two real solutions.

EXAMPLE 8 **Using the discriminant**

Use the discriminant to find the number of solutions to $4x^2 - 12x + 9 = 0$. Then solve the equation by using the quadratic formula. Support your result graphically.

SOLUTION

Symbolic Solution Let $a = 4$, $b = -12$, and $c = 9$. The discriminant is given by

$$b^2 - 4ac = (-12)^2 - 4(4)(9) = 0.$$

Since the discriminant is 0, there is one solution.

$$x = \frac{-b \pm \sqrt{b^2 - 4ac}}{2a} \qquad \text{Quadratic formula}$$

$$x = \frac{-(-12) \pm \sqrt{0}}{8} \qquad \text{Substitute.}$$

$$x = \frac{3}{2} \qquad \text{Simplify.}$$

The only solution is $\frac{3}{2}$.

Graphical Solution A graph of $y = 4x^2 - 12x + 9$ is shown in Figure 3.30. The graph suggests that there is one solution because there is one x-intercept: $\frac{3}{2}$.

One Solution: $b^2 - 4ac = 0$

x-intercept: $\frac{3}{2}$

$y = 4x^2 - 12x + 9$

Figure 3.30

Now Try Exercise 87

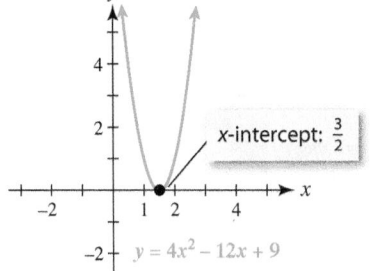

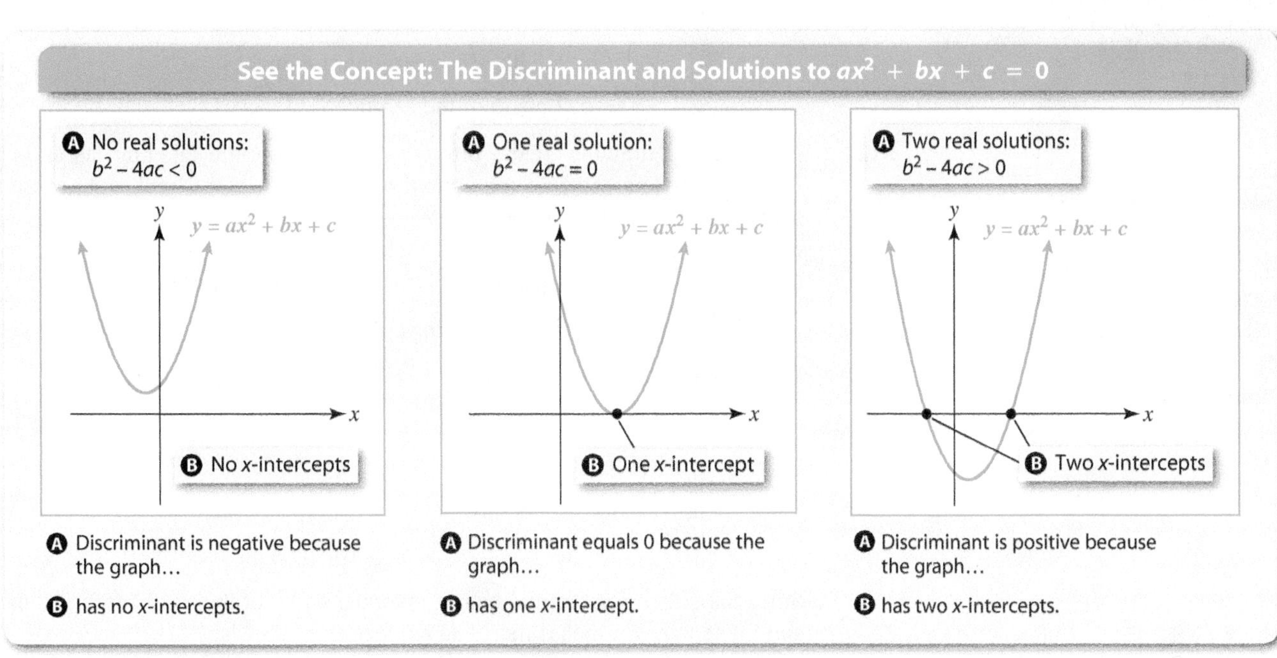

See the Concept: The Discriminant and Solutions to $ax^2 + bx + c = 0$
A No real solutions: $b^2 - 4ac < 0$
$y = ax^2 + bx + c$
B No x-intercepts
A Discriminant is negative because the graph...
B has no x-intercepts.
A One real solution: $b^2 - 4ac = 0$
$y = ax^2 + bx + c$
B One x-intercept
A Discriminant equals 0 because the graph...
B has one x-intercept.
A Two real solutions: $b^2 - 4ac > 0$
$y = ax^2 + bx + c$
B Two x-intercepts
A Discriminant is positive because the graph...
B has two x-intercepts.

Factoring and the Discriminant If a, b, and c are *integers* and $b^2 - 4ac$ is a perfect square, then the trinomial $ax^2 + bx + c$ can be factored using only integer coefficients. For example, if $6x^2 + x - 2 = 0$, then

$$b^2 - 4ac = 1^2 - 4(6)(-2) = 49,$$

which *is* a perfect square ($49 = 7^2$). Thus we can factor $6x^2 + x - 2$ as $(2x - 1)(3x + 2)$ to solve $6x^2 + x - 2 = 0$. However, if $3x^2 - x - 1 = 0$, then $b^2 - 4ac = 13$, which is *not* a perfect square. This trinomial cannot be factored (by using traditional methods with integer coefficients), so either the quadratic formula or completing the square should be used to solve $3x^2 - x - 1 = 0$. See Extended and Discovery Exercises 1–4 at the end of this section.

Problem Solving and Modeling

Many types of applications involve quadratic equations. To solve the next two problems, we use the steps for "Solving Application Problems" from Section 2.2.

EXAMPLE 9 **Solving a construction problem**

A box is being constructed by cutting 2-inch squares from the corners of a rectangular piece of cardboard that is 6 inches longer than it is wide, as illustrated in Figure 3.31. If the box is to have a volume of 224 cubic inches, find the dimensions of the piece of cardboard.

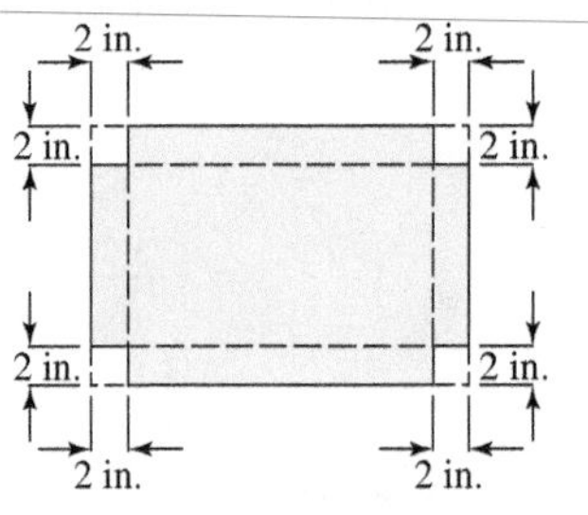

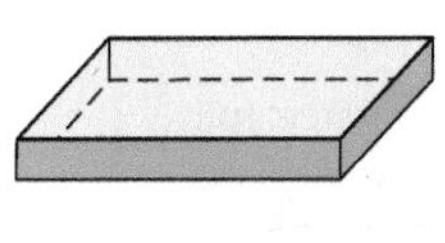

Figure 3.31

SOLUTION

Geometry Review
To review formulas related to boxes, see Chapter R (page R-3).

STEP 1: The rectangular piece of cardboard is 6 inches longer than it is wide. Let x be its width and $x + 6$ be its length.

$$x\text{: Width of the cardboard in inches}$$

$$x + 6\text{: Length of the cardboard in inches}$$

$x - 4$, $x + 2$, x, $x + 6$

Figure 3.32

STEP 2: First make a drawing of the box with the appropriate labeling, as shown in Figure 3.32. The width of the *bottom* of the box is $x - 4$ inches, because two square corners with sides of 2 inches have been removed. Similarly, the length of the bottom of the box is $x + 2$ inches. Because the height times the width times the length must equal the volume, or 224 cubic inches, it follows that

$$2(x - 4)(x + 2) = 224, \quad \text{or} \quad (x - 4)(x + 2) = 112.$$

STEP 3: Write the quadratic equation in the form $ax^2 + bx + c = 0$ and factor.

$$x^2 - 2x - 8 = 112 \qquad \text{Equation to be solved}$$

$$x^2 - 2x - 120 = 0 \qquad \text{Subtract 112.}$$

$$(x - 12)(x + 10) = 0 \qquad \text{Factor.}$$

$$x = 12 \quad \text{or} \quad x = -10 \qquad \text{Zero-product property}$$

Since the dimensions cannot be negative, the width of the cardboard is 12 inches and the length is 6 inches more, or 18 inches.

STEP 4: After the 2-inch-square corners are cut out, the dimensions of the bottom of the box are $12 - 4 = 8$ inches by $18 - 4 = 14$ inches. The volume of the box is then $2 \cdot 8 \cdot 14 = 224$ cubic inches, which checks.

Now Try Exercise 111

When items are sold, a discount is sometimes given to a customer who makes a large order, which affects the revenue that a company receives. We discuss this situation in the next example.

EXAMPLE 10 **Determining revenue**

A company charges \$5 for earbud headphones, but it reduces this cost by \$0.05 for each additional pair ordered, up to a maximum of 50 earbuds. For example, the price for one pair is \$5, the price for two pair is 2(\$4.95) = \$9.90, the price for 3 pair is 3(\$4.90) = \$14.70, and so on. If the total price is \$95, how many earbuds were ordered?

SOLUTION

[0, 100, 10] by [0, 150, 50]

$y_2 = 95$

$y_1 = x(5 - 0.05(x - 1))$

Intersection X=25 Y=95

Figure 3.33

[0, 100, 10] by [0, 150, 50]

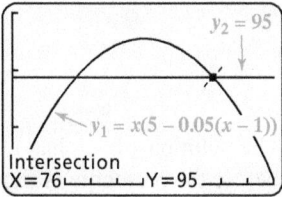

$y_2 = 95$

$y_1 = x(5 - 0.05(x - 1))$

Intersection X=76 Y=95

Figure 3.34

STEP 1: We are asked to find the number of earbuds that results in an order costing \$95. Let this number be x.

x: Number of earbuds ordered

STEP 2: Revenue equals the number of earbuds sold times the price of each pair. If x earbuds are sold, then the price in dollars of each pair is $5 - 0.05(x - 1)$. (Note that when $x = 1$ the price is $5 - 0.05(1 - 1) = \$5$.) The revenue R is given by

$$R(x) = x(5 - 0.05(x - 1)),$$

Revenue = Number Sold × Price

and we must solve the equation

$$x(5 - 0.05(x - 1)) = 95, \quad \text{or} \quad -0.05x^2 + 5.05x - 95 = 0.$$

STEP 3: We can solve $-0.05x^2 + 5.05x - 95$ by using the quadratic formula with $a = -0.05$, $b = 5.05$, and $c = -95$.

$$x = \frac{-5.05 \pm \sqrt{(5.05)^2 - 4(-0.05)(-95)}}{2(-0.05)} \quad \text{Quadratic formula}$$

$$= \frac{-5.05 \pm 2.55}{-0.1} \quad \text{Use a calculator.}$$

$$= 25 \text{ or } 76 \quad \text{Simplify.}$$

This discount only applies to orders of 50 earbuds or fewer, so the answer is 25 earbuds. A graphical solution is shown in Figure 3.33 and 3.34.

STEP 4: If 25 earbuds are ordered, then the cost of each pair is $5 - 0.05(24) = \$3.80$ and the total revenue is $25(3.80) = \$95$.

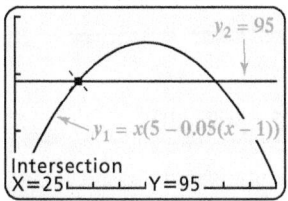

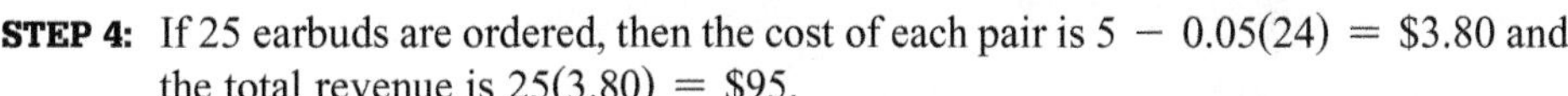

h_0 s

Figure 3.35

A Modeling Application In Section 3.1 we learned that the height s of an object propelled into the air is modeled by $s(t) = -16t^2 + v_0t + h_0$, where v_0 represents the object's initial (vertical) velocity in feet per second and h_0 represents the object's initial height in feet, as illustrated in Figure 3.35. In the next example we model the position of a projectile.

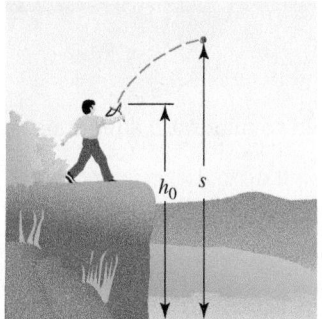

EXAMPLE 11 **Modeling projectile motion**

Table 3.5 shows the height of a projectile shot into the air.

Height of a Projectile

t (seconds)	0	2	4	6	8
$s(t)$ (feet)	96	400	576	624	544

Table 3.5

(a) Use $s(t) = -16t^2 + v_0t + h_0$ to model the data.
(b) After how many seconds did the projectile strike the ground?

t (seconds)	$s(t)$ (feet)
0	96
2	400
4	576
6	624
8	544

Table 3.5 (repeated)

SOLUTION

Getting Started The value for h_0 can be determined by noting that $s(0) = 96$. The value for v_0 can be determined by using any other value in Table 3.5. We use $s(2) = 400$ to determine v_0. ▶

(a) Because $s(0) = 96$, $h_0 = 96$ and $s(t) = -16t^2 + v_0 t + 96$. Substituting $s(2) = 400$ gives the following result.

$$-16(2)^2 + v_0(2) + 96 = 400 \quad s(2) = 400$$
$$2v_0 + 32 = 400 \quad \text{Simplify.}$$
$$2v_0 = 368 \quad \text{Subtract 32 from each side.}$$
$$v_0 = 184 \quad \text{Divide each side by 2.}$$

Thus $s(t) = -16t^2 + 184t + 96$ models the height of the projectile.

(b) The projectile strikes the ground when $s(t) = 0$.

$$-16t^2 + 184t + 96 = 0 \quad s(t) = 0\text{; equation to be solved}$$
$$2t^2 - 23t - 12 = 0 \quad \text{Divide each term by } -8.$$
$$(2t + 1)(t - 12) = 0 \quad \text{Factor the trinomial.}$$
$$t = -\frac{1}{2} \quad \text{or} \quad t = 12 \quad \text{Solve the equation.}$$

Thus the projectile strikes the ground after 12 seconds. The solution of $-\frac{1}{2}$ has no meaning in this problem because it corresponds to a time before the projectile is shot into the air.

Now Try Exercise 119

3.2 Putting It All Together

The following table summarizes important topics related to quadratic equations.

CONCEPT	EXPLANATION	EXAMPLES
Quadratic equation	$ax^2 + bx + c = 0$, where a, b, and c are constants with $a \neq 0$	A quadratic equation can have zero, one, or two real solutions. $x^2 = -5$ No real solutions $(x - 2)^2 = 0$ One real solution: 2 $x^2 - 4 = 0$ Two real solutions: ± 2
Factoring	A symbolic technique for solving equations, based on the zero-product property: if $ab = 0$, then either $a = 0$ or $b = 0$.	$x^2 - 3x = -2$ $x^2 - 3x + 2 = 0$ $(x - 1)(x - 2) = 0$ $x - 1 = 0$ or $x - 2 = 0$ $x = 1$ or $x = 2$

CONCEPT	EXPLANATION	EXAMPLES
Square root property	The solutions to $x^2 = k$ are $x = \pm\sqrt{k}$, where $k \geq 0$.	$x^2 = 9$ is equivalent to $x = \pm 3$. $x^2 = 11$ is equivalent to $x = \pm\sqrt{11}$.
Completing the square	To solve $x^2 + kx = d$ symbolically, add $\left(\frac{k}{2}\right)^2$ to each side to obtain a perfect square trinomial. Then apply the square root property.	$x^2 - 6x = 1$ $x^2 - 6x + 9 = 1 + 9$ $\quad \left(\frac{-6}{2}\right)^2 = 9$ $(x - 3)^2 = 10$ $x - 3 = \pm\sqrt{10}$ $x = 3 \pm \sqrt{10}$
Quadratic formula	The solutions to $ax^2 + bx + c = 0$ are given by $x = \frac{-b \pm \sqrt{b^2 - 4ac}}{2a}$. Always gives the *exact* solutions	To solve $2x^2 - x - 4 = 0$, let $a = 2$, $b = -1$, and $c = -4$. $x = \frac{-(-1) \pm \sqrt{(-1)^2 - 4(2)(-4)}}{2(2)}$ $= \frac{1 \pm \sqrt{33}}{4} \approx 1.69 \text{ or } -1.19$
Graphical solution	To use the *x-intercept method* to solve $ax^2 + bx + c = 0$, let y_1 equal the left side of the equation and graph y_1. The real solutions correspond to the x-intercepts. The *intersection-of-graphs* method can also be used when one side of the equation is *not* equal to 0. Let y_1 equal the left side of the equation and y_2 equal the right side of the equation. The real solutions correspond to the x-coordinates of any points of intersection.	To solve $x^2 + x - 2 = 0$, graph $y = x^2 + x - 2$. The solutions are -2 and 1. Solutions: −2, 1 $y = x^2 + x - 2$
Numerical solution	To solve $ax^2 + bx + c = 0$, let y_1 equal the left side of the equation and create a table for y_1. The zeros of y_1 are the real solutions. May *not* be a good method when solutions are fractions or irrational numbers	To solve $2x^2 + x - 1 = 0$, make a table. The solutions are -1 and 0.5. X: −2, −1.5, −1, −.5, 0, .5, 1 Y1: 5, 2, 0, −1, −1, 0, 2 $y_1 = 0$ (at $x = -1$ and $x = .5$) Y1=2X^2+X−1

3.2 Exercises

Quadratic Equations

Exercises 1–32: Solve the quadratic equation. Check your answers for Exercises 1–16.

1. $x^2 + x - 11 = 1$

2. $x^2 - 9x + 10 = -8$

3. $t^2 = 2t$

4. $t^2 - 7t = 0$

5. $3x^2 - 7x = 0$

6. $5x = 9x^2$

7. $2z^2 = 13z + 15$

8. $4z^2 = 7 - 27z$

9. $x^2 + 6x + 9 = 0$

10. $x^2 - 8x + 16 = 0$

11. $4x^2 + 1 = 4x$

12. $9x^2 + 4 = 12x$

13. $x(3x + 14) = 5$

14. $x(5x + 19) = 4$

15. $6x^2 + \frac{5}{2} = 8x$

16. $8x^2 + 63 = -46x$

17. $(t + 3)^2 = 5$

18. $(t - 2)^2 = 11$

19. $4x^2 - 13 = 0$

20. $9x^2 - 11 = 0$

21. $2(x - 1)^2 + 4 = 0$

22. $-3(x + 5)^2 - 6 = 0$

23. $\frac{1}{2}x^2 - 3x + \frac{1}{2} = 0$

24. $\frac{3}{4}x^2 + \frac{1}{2}x - \frac{1}{2} = 0$

25. $-3z^2 - 2z + 4 = 0$

26. $-4z^2 + z + 1 = 0$

27. $25k^2 + 1 = 10k$

28. $49k^2 + 4 = -28k$

29. $-0.3x^2 + 0.1x = -0.02$

30. $-0.1x^2 + 1 = 0.5x$

31. $2x(x + 2) = (x - 1)(x + 2)$

32. $(2x - 1)(x + 2) = (x + 3)(x + 1)$

Exercises 33–38: Find the exact values of all intercepts.

33.

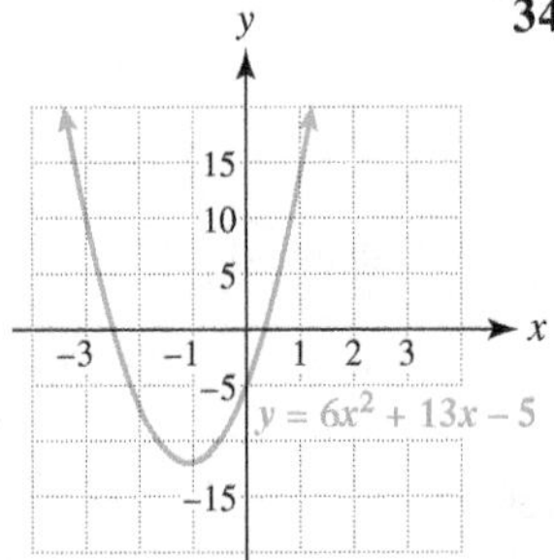

34.

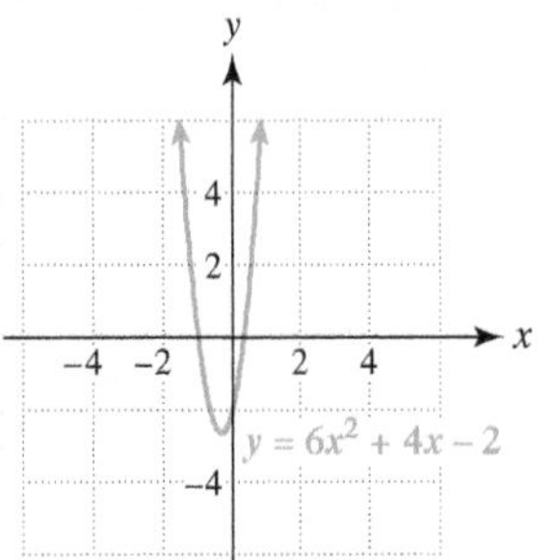

35.

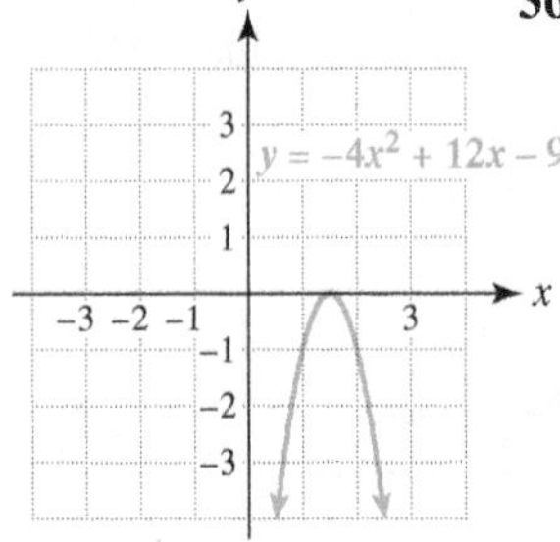

36.

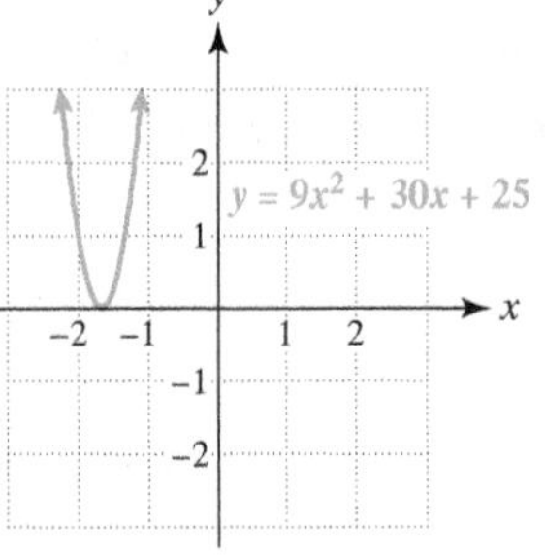

37.

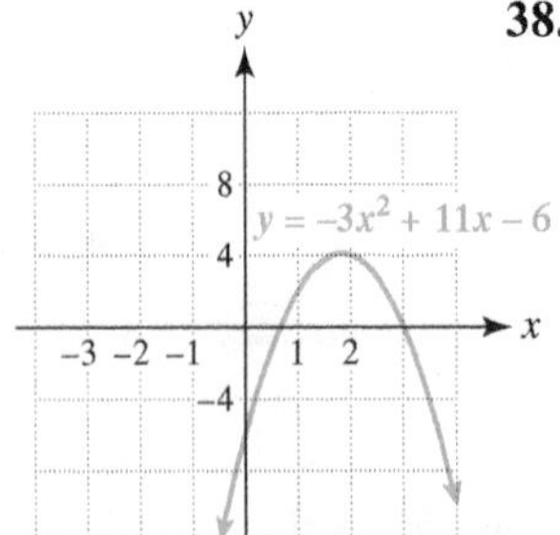

38.

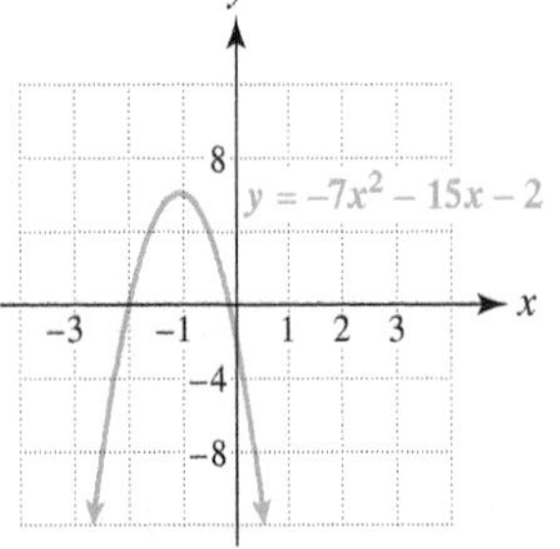

Graphical and Numerical Solutions

Exercises 39–46: Solve each quadratic equation (a) graphically, (b) numerically, and (c) symbolically. Express graphical and numerical solutions to the nearest tenth when appropriate.

39. $x^2 + 2x = 0$

40. $x^2 - 4 = 0$

41. $x^2 - x - 6 = 0$

42. $2x^2 + 5x - 3 = 0$

43. $2x^2 = 6$

44. $x^2 - 225 = 0$

45. $4x(x - 3) = -9$

46. $-4x(x - 1) = 1$

Exercises 47–50: Solve the quadratic equation graphically.

47. $20x^2 + 11x = 3$

48. $-2x^2 + 4x = 1.595$

49. $2.5x^2 = 4.75x - 2.1$

50. $x(x + 24) = 6912$

Completing the Square

Exercises 51–64: Solve the equation by completing the square.

51. $x^2 + 4x - 6 = 0$

52. $x^2 - 10x = 1$

53. $x^2 + 5x = 4$

54. $x^2 + 6x - 5 = 0$

55. $3x^2 - 6x = 2$

56. $2x^2 - 3x + 1 = 0$

57. $x^2 - 8x = 10$

58. $x^2 - 2x = 2$

59. $\frac{1}{2}t^2 - \frac{3}{2}t = 1$

60. $\frac{1}{3}t^2 + \frac{1}{2}t = 2$

61. $-2z^2 + 3z + 1 = 0$

62. $-3z^2 - 5z + 3 = 0$

63. $-\frac{3}{2}z^2 - \frac{1}{4}z + 1 = 0$

64. $-\frac{1}{5}z^2 - \frac{1}{2}z + 2 = 0$

Finding Domains

Exercises 65–68: Find the domain of the function. Write your answer in set-builder notation.

65. $f(x) = \dfrac{1}{x^2 - 5}$

66. $f(x) = \dfrac{4x}{7 - x^2}$

67. $g(t) = \dfrac{5 - t}{t^2 - t - 2}$

68. $g(t) = \dfrac{t + 1}{2t^2 - 11t - 21}$

Solving for a Variable

Exercises 69–76: (Refer to Example 4.) Solve the equation for y. Determine if y is a function of x.

69. $4x^2 + 3y = \dfrac{y + 1}{3}$

70. $\dfrac{x^2 + y}{2} = y - 2$

71. $3y = \dfrac{2x - y}{3}$

72. $\dfrac{5 - y}{3} = \dfrac{x + 3y}{4}$

73. $x^2 + (y - 3)^2 = 9$

74. $(x + 2)^2 + (y + 1)^2 = 1$

75. $3x^2 + 4y^2 = 12$

76. $x - 25y^2 = 50$

Exercises 77–84: Solve for the specified variable.

77. $V = \frac{1}{3}\pi r^2 h$ for r

78. $V = \frac{1}{2}gt^2 + h$ for t

79. $K = \frac{1}{2}mv^2$ for v

80. $W = I^2 R$ for I

81. $a^2 + b^2 = c^2$ for b

82. $S = 4\pi r^2 + x^2$ for r

83. $s = -16t^2 + 100t$ for t

84. $T^2 - kT - k^2 = 0$ for T

The Discriminant

Exercises 85–100: Complete the following.

(a) Write the equation as $ax^2 + bx + c = 0$ with $a > 0$.
(b) Calculate the discriminant $b^2 - 4ac$ and determine the number of real solutions.
(c) Solve the equation.

85. $3x^2 = 12$

86. $8x^2 - 2 = 14$

87. $x^2 - 2x = -1$

88. $6x^2 = 4x$

89. $4x = x^2$

90. $16x^2 + 9 = 24x$

91. $x^2 + 1 = x$

92. $2x^2 + x = 2$

93. $2x^2 + 3x = 12 - 2x$

94. $3x^2 + 3 = 5x$

95. $9x(x - 4) = -36$

96. $\frac{1}{4}x^2 + 3x = x - 4$

97. $x\left(\frac{1}{2}x + 1\right) = -\frac{13}{2}$

98. $4x = 6 + x^2$

99. $3x^2 = 1 - x$

100. $x(5x - 3) = 1$

Exercises 101–104: The graph of $f(x) = ax^2 + bx + c$ is shown in the figure.

(a) State whether $a > 0$ or $a < 0$.
(b) Solve the equation $ax^2 + bx + c = 0$.
(c) Is the discriminant positive, negative, or zero?

101.

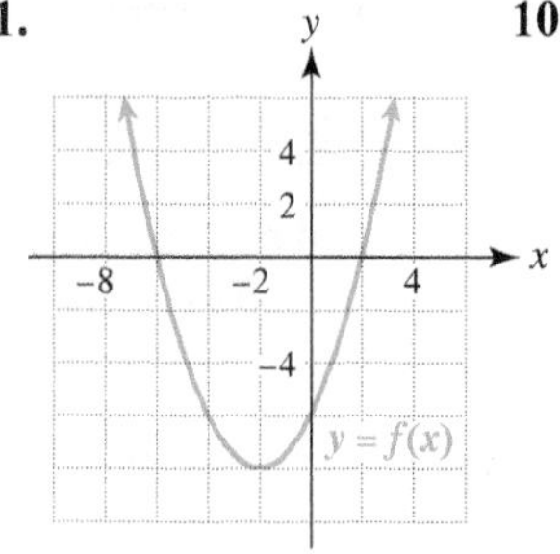

102.

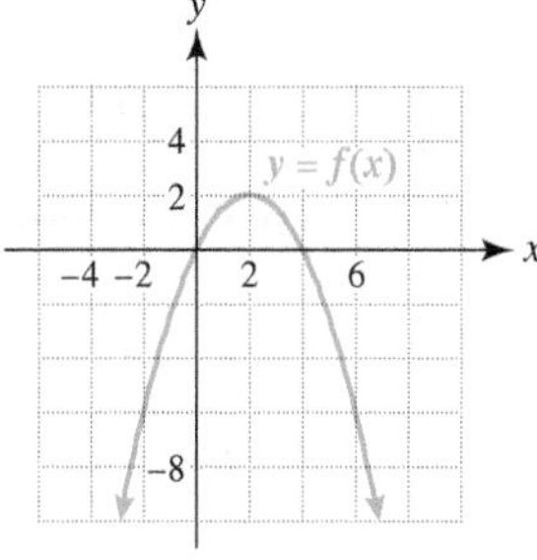

103.

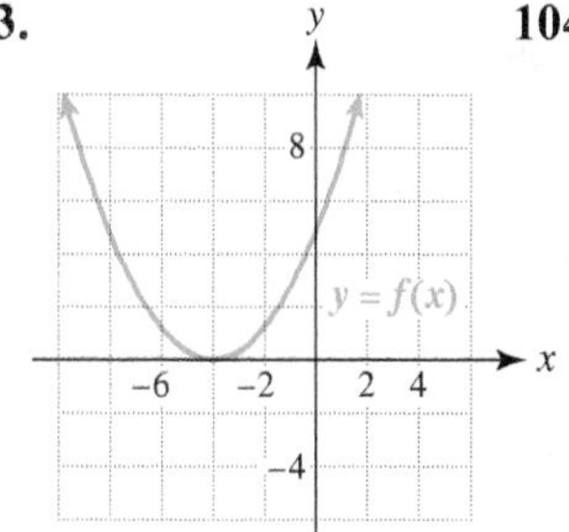

104.

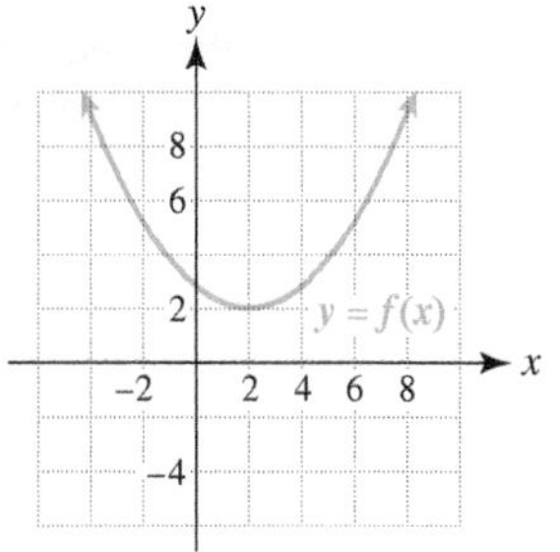

Applications and Models

105. Height of a Baseball A baseball is dropped from a stadium seat that is 75 feet above the ground. Its height s in feet after t seconds is given by $s(t) = 75 - 16t^2$. Estimate to the nearest tenth of a second how long it takes for the baseball to strike the ground.

106. Height of a Baseball A baseball is thrown *downward* with an initial velocity of 30 feet per second from a stadium seat that is 80 feet above the ground. Estimate to the nearest tenth of a second how long it takes for the baseball to strike the ground.

107. Facebook Visitors The number of unique monthly visitors in millions to Facebook can be approximated by

$$V(x) = 16x^2 + 7x + 32,$$

where x is the number of years after 2008. Estimate the year when Facebook averaged 55 million unique monthly visitors.

108. U.S. AIDS Cases From 1984 to 1994 the cumulative number of AIDS cases can be modeled by the equation

$$C(x) = 3034x^2 + 14{,}018x + 6400,$$

where x represents years after 1984. Estimate the year when 200,000 AIDS cases had been diagnosed.

109. Screen Dimensions The width of a rectangular computer screen is 2.5 inches more than its height. If the area of the screen is 93.5 square inches, determine its dimensions symbolically, graphically, and numerically. Do your answers agree?

110. Maximizing Area A rectangular pen for a pet is under construction using 100 feet of fence.

(a) Find the dimensions that give an area of 576 square feet.

(b) Find the dimensions that give maximum area.

111. Construction (Refer to Example 9.) A box is being constructed by cutting 4-inch squares from the corners of a rectangular sheet of metal that is 10 inches longer than it is wide. If the box is to have a volume of 476 cubic inches, find the dimensions of the metal sheet.

112. **Construction** A box is being constructed by cutting 2-inch squares from the corners of a *square* sheet of metal. If the box is to have a volume of 1058 cubic inches, find the dimensions of the metal sheet.

113. **Geometry** A cylindrical aluminum can is being constructed to have a height h of 4 inches. If the can is to have a volume of 28 cubic inches, approximate its radius r. (*Hint:* $V = \pi r^2 h$.)

114. **Braking Distance** Braking distance for cars on level pavement can be approximated by $D(x) = \frac{x^2}{30k}$. The input x is the car's velocity in miles per hour and the output $D(x)$ is the braking distance in feet. The positive constant k is a measure of the traction of the tires. Small values of k indicate a slippery road or worn tires. (***Source:*** L. Haefner, *Introduction to Transportation Systems.*)
   (a) Let $k = 0.3$. Evaluate $D(60)$ and interpret the result.
   (b) If $k = 0.25$, find the velocity x that corresponds to a braking distance of 300 feet.

115. **Window Dimensions** A window comprises a square with sides of length x and a semicircle with diameter x, as shown in the figure. If the total area of the window is 463 square inches, estimate the value of x to the nearest hundredth of an inch.

116. **Picture Frame** A frame for a picture is 2 inches wide. The picture inside the frame is 4 inches longer than it is wide. See the figure. If the area of the picture is 320 square inches, find the outside dimensions of the picture frame.

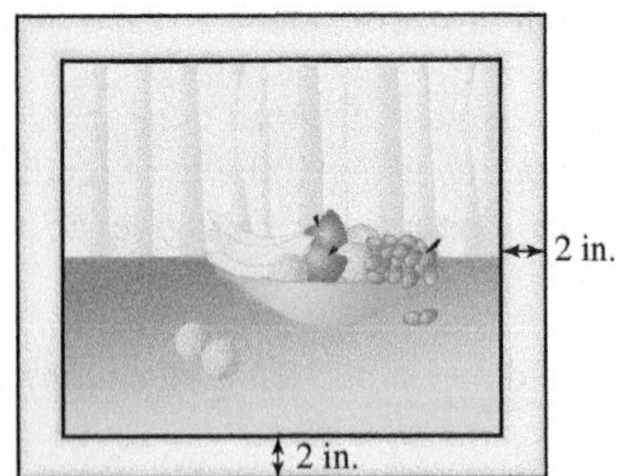

117. **Cost** (Refer to Example 10.) A company charges \$20 to make one monogrammed shirt but reduces this cost by \$0.10 per shirt for each *additional* shirt ordered up to 100 shirts. If the cost of an order is \$989, how many shirts were ordered?

118. **Ticket Prices** The price of one airline ticket is \$250. For each additional ticket sold to a group, the price of every ticket is reduced by \$2. For example, 2 tickets cost $2 \cdot 248 = \$496$ and 3 tickets cost $3 \cdot 246 = \$738$.
   (a) Write a quadratic function that gives the total cost of buying x tickets.
   (b) What is the cost of 5 tickets?
   (c) How many tickets were sold if the cost is \$5200?
   (d) What number of tickets sold gives the greatest cost?

Modeling Quadratic Data

119. **Projectile Motion** The table shows the height of a projectile that is shot into the air.

t (seconds)	0	1	2	3	4
s (feet)	32	176	288	368	416

   (a) Use $s(t) = -16t^2 + v_0 t + h_0$ to model the data.
   (b) After how long did the projectile strike the ground?

120. **Falling Object** The table lists the velocity and distance traveled by a falling object for various elapsed times.

Time (sec)	0	1	2	3	4
Velocity (ft/sec)	0	32	64	96	128
Distance (ft)	0	16	64	144	256

   (a) Make a scatterplot of the ordered pairs determined by (time, velocity) and (time, distance) in the same viewing rectangle $[-1, 5, 1]$ by $[-10, 280, 20]$.
   (b) Find a function v that models the velocity.
   (c) The distance is modeled by $d(x) = ax^2$. Find a.
   (d) Find the time when the distance is 200 feet. Find the velocity at this time.

121. Pedestrian and Bicycle Programs The Department of Transportation's budget for pedestrian and bicycle programs in millions of dollars for selected years is given in the table.

Year	1995	2001	2009
Budget	180	340	1200

Source: DOT.

(a) Determine a quadratic function B whose vertex is (1995, 180) and whose graph passes through the point (2009, 1200). Write $B(x)$ in vertex form.

(b) Use $B(x)$ to determine when the budget was \$700 million.

122. Safe Runway Speed The taxiway used by an aircraft to exit a runway should not have sharp curves. The safe radius for any curve depends on the speed of the airplane. The table lists the minimum radius R of the exit curves, where the taxiing speed of the airplane is x miles per hour.

x(mi/hr)	10	20	30	40	50
R(ft)	50	200	450	800	1250

Source: Federal Aviation Administration.

(a) If the taxiing speed x of the plane doubles, what happens to the minimum radius R of the curve?

(b) The FAA used $R(x) = ax^2$ to compute the values in the table. Determine a.

(c) If $R = 500$, find x. Interpret your results.

Quadratic Regression

123. iPod Sales The table shows the number of iPods sold in millions of units for various years.

Year	2006	2007	2008	2009	2010	2011
Sales	39.4	51.6	54.8	54.1	50.3	42.6

Source: Apple Corporation.

(a) Use regression to find a quadratic function I that models the data. Let $x = 0$ correspond to 2006.

(b) Use I to estimate when sales were 28 million units.

124. Biology Some types of worms have a remarkable capacity to live without moisture. The table shows the number of worms y surviving after x days in one study.

x (days)	0	20	40	80	120	160
y (worms)	50	48	45	36	20	3

Source: D. Brown and P. Rothery, *Models in Biology*.

(a) Use regression to find a quadratic function f that models these data.

(b) Graph f and the data in the same window.

(c) Solve the quadratic equation $f(x) = 0$ graphically. Do both solutions have meaning? Explain.

125. Walmart Employees The table lists numbers of Walmart employees E in millions, x years after 1987.

x	0	5	10	15	20
E	0.20	0.38	0.68	1.4	2.2

Source: Walmart.

(a) Evaluate $E(15)$ and interpret the result.

(b) Find a quadratic function f that models these data.

(c) Graph the data and quadratic function f in the same xy-plane.

(d) Use f to estimate the year when the number of employees reached 3 million.

126. Women in the Workforce The number N of women in millions who were gainfully employed in the workforce in selected years is shown in the table.

Year	1900	1910	1920	1930	1940	1950
N	5.3	7.4	8.6	10.8	12.8	18.4

Year	1960	1970	1980	1990	2000	2010
N	23.2	31.5	45.5	56.6	65.6	74.8

Source: Department of Labor.

(a) Use regression to find a quadratic function f that models the data. Support your result graphically.

(b) Predict the number of women in the labor force in 2020.

Writing about Mathematics

127. Discuss three symbolic methods for solving a quadratic equation. Make up a quadratic equation and use each method to find the solution set.

128. Explain how to solve a quadratic equation graphically.

EXTENDED AND DISCOVERY EXERCISES

Exercises 1–4: **Discriminant and Factoring** *(Refer to pages 187 and 188.) For each equation, calculate the discriminant. Use the discriminant to decide whether the equation can be solved by factoring. If it can, solve the equation by factoring. Otherwise, use the quadratic formula.*

1. $8x^2 + 14x - 15 = 0$ **2.** $15x^2 - 17x - 4 = 0$

3. $5x^2 - 3x - 3 = 0$ **4.** $3x^2 - 2x - 4 = 0$

5. **Quadratic Formula** Prove the quadratic formula by completing the following.
   (a) Write $ax^2 + bx + c = 0$ as $x^2 + \frac{b}{a}x = -\frac{c}{a}$.
   (b) Complete the square to obtain $\left(x + \frac{b}{2a}\right)^2 = \frac{b^2 - 4ac}{4a^2}$.
   (c) Use the square root property and solve for x.

6. **Difference Quotient** If the difference quotient for the function $f(x) = ax^2 - bx + 1$ equals $2x + h - 4$, find values for a and b.

7. **Square Root Property** Use the fact that $\sqrt{x^2} = |x|$ to show that the solutions to $x^2 = k$ with $k > 0$ are given by $x = \pm\sqrt{k}$.

CHECKING BASIC CONCEPTS FOR SECTIONS 3.1 AND 3.2

1. Graph $f(x) = (x - 1)^2 - 4$. Identify the vertex, axis of symmetry, and x-intercepts.

2. A graph of $f(x) = ax^2 + bx + c$ is shown.
   (a) Is a positive, negative, or zero?
   (b) Find the vertex and axis of symmetry.
   (c) Solve $ax^2 + bx + c = 0$.
   (d) Is the discriminant positive, negative, or zero?

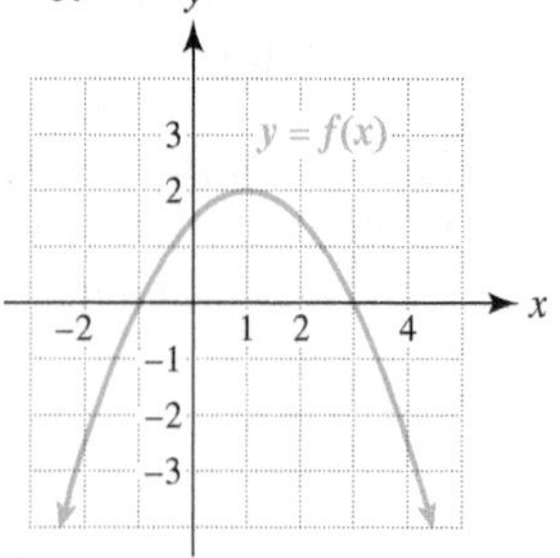

3. Use $f(x) = a(x - h)^2 + k$ to model the data exactly.

x	-3	-2	-1	0	1
$f(x)$	11	5	3	5	11

4. Find the vertex on the graph of $y = 3x^2 - 9x - 2$.

5. Write $f(x) = x^2 + 4x - 3$ as $f(x) = a(x - h)^2 + k$. What are the coordinates of the vertex? What is the minimum y-value of the graph of f?

6. Solve the quadratic equations.
   (a) $16x^2 = 81$
   (b) $2x^2 + 3x = 2$
   (c) $x^2 = x - 3$
   (d) $2x^2 = 3x + 4$

7. **Dimensions of a Rectangle** A rectangle is 4 inches longer than it is wide and has an area of 165 square inches. Find its dimensions.

8. **Height of a Baseball** The height s of a baseball in feet after t seconds is given by $s(t) = -16t^2 + 96t + 2$.
   (a) Find the height of the baseball after 1 second.
   (b) After how long is the baseball 142 feet high?
   (c) Find the maximum height of the baseball.
   (d) How long is the baseball in the air?

3.3 Complex Numbers

- **Perform arithmetic operations on complex numbers**
- **Solve quadratic equations having complex solutions**

Introduction

Throughout history, people have invented (or discovered) new numbers to solve equations and describe data. New numbers were often met with resistance and were seen as imaginary and useless. There was no Roman numeral for 0, as many skeptics probably wondered why a number was needed to represent nothing. Negative numbers also met strong resistance. After all, how could one possibly have -6 apples? Complex numbers were no different. In this section we introduce complex numbers and the "imaginary" unit i. Ultimately, complex numbers are no more imaginary than any other number. Society needs and uses complex numbers just as much as other numbers.

Basic Concepts

Graphing a quadratic equation is helpful only in finding the *real* solutions to the equation. Real solutions to the equation $x^2 + 1 = 0$ correspond to x-intercepts. See Figure 3.36. We can also solve this equation for real solutions symbolically, as shown next to Figure 3.36.

Solving $x^2 + 1 = 0$ Graphically and Symbolically

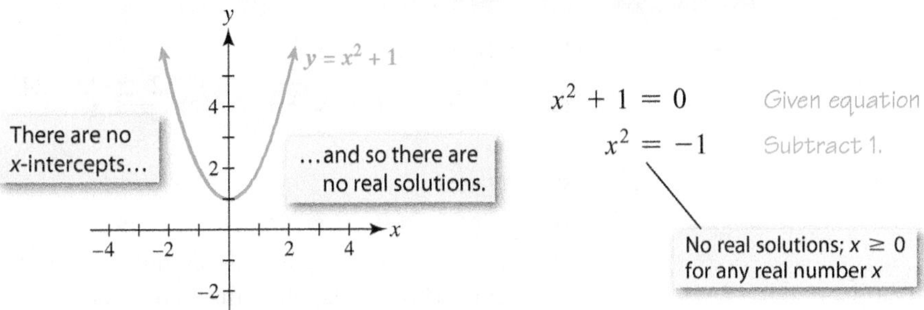
y
$y = x^2 + 1$
There are no x-intercepts...
...and so there are no real solutions.
x
$x^2 + 1 = 0$
$x^2 = -1$
Given equation
Subtract 1.
No real solutions; $x^2 \geq 0$ for any real number x

Figure 3.36

Above we showed that there are no *real* solutions to the equation $x^2 + 1 = 0$. However, we can *invent* two solutions.

$$x^2 = -1, \quad \text{or} \quad x = \pm\sqrt{-1}$$

We now define a new number called the **imaginary unit**, denoted i.

PROPERTIES OF THE IMAGINARY UNIT i

$$i = \sqrt{-1}, \qquad i^2 = -1$$

Solving $x^2 + 1 = 0$ using the imaginary unit

$$x = \pm\sqrt{-1} \quad \text{or}$$
$$x = \pm i$$

Using the real numbers and the imaginary unit i, complex numbers can be defined. A **complex number** can be written in **standard form** as $a + bi$, where a and b are real numbers. The **real part** is a and the **imaginary part** is b. Every real number a is also a complex number because it can be written as $a + 0i$. A complex number $a + bi$ with $b \neq 0$ is an **imaginary number**. A complex number $a + bi$ with $a = 0$ and $b \neq 0$ is sometimes called a **pure imaginary number**. Examples of pure imaginary numbers include $3i$ and $-i$. Table 3.6 lists several complex numbers with their real and imaginary parts.

Complex Numbers

Example	$a + bi$	a	b
5	$5 + 0i$	5	0
$-5 - 2i$	$-5 - 2i$	-5	-2
$-3i$	$0 - 3i$	0	-3
$4 + 6i$	$4 + 6i$	4	6
	Standard form	Real part	Imaginary part

Table 3.6

Using the imaginary unit i, square roots of negative numbers can be written as complex numbers.

THE EXPRESSION $\sqrt{-a}$

If $a > 0$, then $\sqrt{-a} = i\sqrt{a}$.

EXAMPLE 1 **Simplifying the expression $\sqrt{-a}$**

Simplify each expression.

(a) $\sqrt{-16}$ **(b)** $\sqrt{-3}$ **(c)** $\dfrac{2 \pm \sqrt{-24}}{2}$

SOLUTION

(a) When $a > 0$, $\sqrt{-a} = i\sqrt{a}$. Thus $\sqrt{-16} = i\sqrt{16} = 4i$.

(b) $\sqrt{-3} = i\sqrt{3}$; we usually do not write $\sqrt{3i}$ because of the possibility of confusion about whether i is under the square root symbol.

(c) First note that $\sqrt{-24} = i\sqrt{24} = i\sqrt{4} \cdot \sqrt{6} = 2i\sqrt{6}$.

$$\frac{2 \pm \sqrt{-24}}{2} = \frac{2 \pm 2i\sqrt{6}}{2} \qquad \text{Simplify } \sqrt{-24}.$$

$$= \frac{2}{2} \pm \frac{2i\sqrt{6}}{2} \qquad \frac{a \pm b}{c} = \frac{a}{c} \pm \frac{b}{c}$$

$$= 1 \pm i\sqrt{6} \qquad \text{Simplify fractions.}$$

Now Try Exercises 1, 5, and 13

The property $\sqrt{a} \cdot \sqrt{b} = \sqrt{ab}$ is true only when *both* a and b are positive. When simplifying products containing square roots of negative numbers, it is important to first apply the property $\sqrt{-a} = i\sqrt{a}$, where $a > 0$. This technique is illustrated in the next example.

EXAMPLE 2 **Simplifying complex expressions**

Simplify each expression.

(a) $\sqrt{-3} \cdot \sqrt{-3}$ **(b)** $\sqrt{-2} \cdot \sqrt{-8}$

SOLUTION

(a) $\sqrt{-3} \cdot \sqrt{-3} = i\sqrt{3} \cdot i\sqrt{3} = i^2(\sqrt{3})^2 = -1(3) = -3 \qquad i^2 = -1$

NOTE $\sqrt{-3} \cdot \sqrt{-3} \neq \sqrt{(-3) \cdot (-3)} = \sqrt{9} = 3$

(b) $\sqrt{-2} \cdot \sqrt{-8} = i\sqrt{2} \cdot i\sqrt{8} = i^2\sqrt{16} = -1(4) = -4$

Now Try Exercises 15 and 17

Arithmetic Operations on Complex Numbers

Calculator Help
To perform arithmetic on complex numbers, see Appendix A (page AP-10).

Arithmetic operations are also defined for complex numbers.

Addition and Subtraction To add the complex numbers $(-2 + 3i)$ and $(4 - 6i)$, simply combine the real parts and the imaginary parts.

$$(-2 + 3i) + (4 - 6i) = -2 + 4 + 3i - 6i$$
$$= 2 - 3i$$

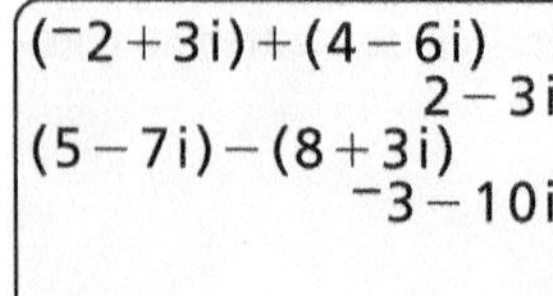

Figure 3.37

This same process works for subtraction.

$$(5 - 7i) - (8 + 3i) = 5 - 8 - 7i - 3i$$
$$= -3 - 10i$$

These operations are performed on a calculator in Figure 3.37.

Algebra Review
Before multiplying complex numbers, you may want to review multiplication of binomials in Chapter R (page R-15).

Multiplication Two complex numbers can be multiplied. The property $i^2 = -1$ is applied when appropriate.

$$\begin{aligned}(-5 + i)(7 - 9i) &= -5(7) + (-5)(-9i) + (i)(7) + (i)(-9i)\\ &= -35 + 45i + 7i - 9i^2\\ &= -35 + 52i - 9(-1)\\ &= -26 + 52i\end{aligned}$$

NOTE Express your results in the standard form $a + bi$.

Division The **conjugate** of $a + bi$ is $a - bi$. To find the conjugate, change the sign of the imaginary part b. Table 3.7 lists examples of complex numbers and their conjugates.

Complex Conjugates

$a + bi$	$2 + 5i$	$6 - 3i$	$-2 + 7i$	$-1 - i$	5	$-4i$
$a - bi$	$2 - 5i$	$6 + 3i$	$-2 - 7i$	$-1 + i$	5	$4i$

Change the sign on *b*.

Table 3.7

To simplify the quotient $\frac{3 + 2i}{5 - i}$, first multiply both the numerator and the denominator by the conjugate of the *denominator*.

$$\begin{aligned}\frac{3 + 2i}{5 - i} &= \frac{(3 + 2i)(5 + i)}{(5 - i)(5 + i)} && \text{Multiply by } \frac{\text{conjugate}}{\text{conjugate}}.\\ &= \frac{3(5) + (3)(i) + (2i)(5) + (2i)(i)}{(5)(5) + (5)(i) + (-i)(5) + (-i)(i)} && \text{Expand.}\\ &= \frac{15 + 3i + 10i + 2i^2}{25 + 5i - 5i - i^2} && \text{Simplify.}\\ &= \frac{15 + 13i + 2(-1)}{25 - (-1)} && i^2 = -1\\ &= \frac{13 + 13i}{26} && \text{Simplify.}\\ &= \frac{1}{2} + \frac{1}{2}i && \frac{a + bi}{c} = \frac{a}{c} + \frac{b}{c}i\end{aligned}$$

The last step expresses the quotient as a complex number in standard form. The evaluation of the previous multiplication and division examples is shown in Figure 3.38.

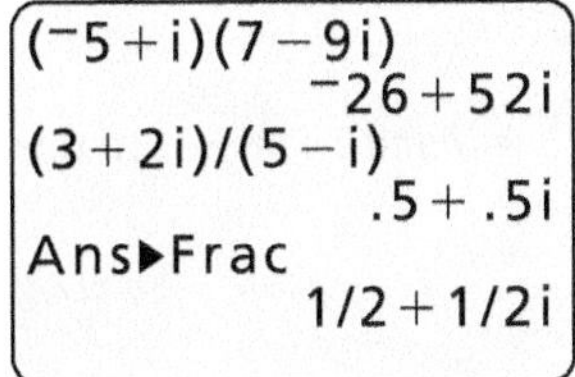

Figure 3.38

EXAMPLE 3 **Performing complex arithmetic**

Write each expression in standard form. Support your results using a calculator.

(a) $(-3 + 4i) + (5 - i)$ **(b)** $(-7i) - (6 - 5i)$

(c) $(-3 + 2i)^2$ **(d)** $\frac{17}{4 + i}$

SOLUTION

(a) $(-3 + 4i) + (5 - i) = -3 + 5 + 4i - i = 2 + 3i$

(b) $(-7i) - (6 - 5i) = -6 - 7i + 5i = -6 - 2i$

(c)
$$\begin{aligned}(-3 + 2i)^2 &= (-3 + 2i)(-3 + 2i)\\ &= 9 - 6i - 6i + 4i^2\\ &= 9 - 12i + 4(-1)\\ &= 5 - 12i\end{aligned}$$

(d) $\dfrac{17}{4+i} = \dfrac{17}{4+i} \cdot \dfrac{4-i}{4-i}$ Multiply by $\dfrac{\text{conjugate}}{\text{conjugate}}$.

$= \dfrac{68-17i}{16-i^2}$

$= \dfrac{68-17i}{17}$ $i^2 = -1$

$= 4 - i$

Standard forms can be found using a calculator. See Figures 3.39 and 3.40.

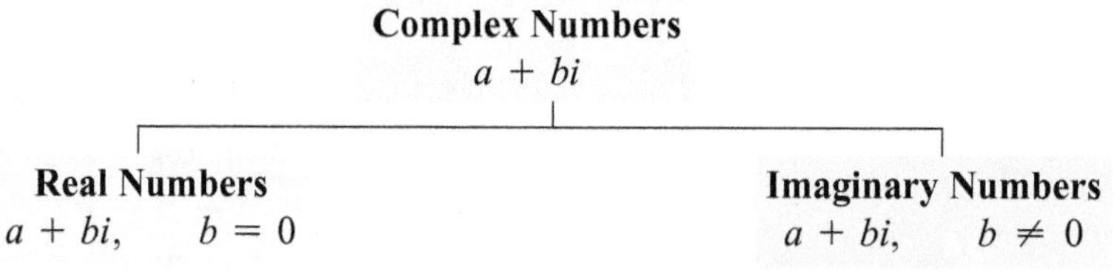

Figure 3.39 Figure 3.40

Now Try Exercises 23, 25, 35, and 39

MAKING CONNECTIONS

Complex, Real, and Imaginary Numbers The following diagram illustrates the relationship among complex, real, and imaginary numbers, where a and b are real numbers. Note that complex numbers comprise two disjoint sets of numbers: the real numbers and the imaginary numbers.

Complex Numbers
$a + bi$

Real Numbers
$a + bi, \quad b = 0$

Imaginary Numbers
$a + bi, \quad b \neq 0$

NOTE *Every* real number is a complex number.

Powers of i We can simplify powers of i using the fact that $i^1 = i$ and $i^2 = -1$. In the next example we use these ideas.

EXAMPLE 4 Simplifying Powers of i

Simplify each power of i.
(a) i^8 **(b)** i^{19}

SOLUTION
(a) $i^8 = (i^2)^4 = (-1)^4 = 1$. Another way to simplify is the following.

$$i^8 = (i^2)(i^2)(i^2)(i^2) = (-1)(-1)(-1)(-1) = 1$$

(b) Write $i^{19} = i^{18} \cdot i$. Then $i^{19} = (i^2)^9 \cdot i = (-1)^9 i = -1 \cdot i = -i$.

Now Try Exercises 61 and 63

NOTE In the Extended and Discovery Exercise in this section we discover a pattern for calculating the powers of i.

Quadratic Equations with Complex Solutions

We can use the quadratic formula to solve any quadratic equation $ax^2 + bx + c = 0$. If the discriminant $b^2 - 4ac$ is negative, then there are no real solutions, and the graph of

$y = ax^2 + bx + c$ does not intersect the x-axis. However, there are solutions that can be expressed as imaginary numbers. This is illustrated in the next example.

EXAMPLE 5 **Solving quadratic equations with imaginary solutions**

Solve the quadratic equation. Support your results graphically.

(a) $x^2 + 3x + 5 = 0$ **(b)** $\frac{1}{2}x^2 + 17 = 5x$ **(c)** $-2x^2 = 3$

SOLUTION

Getting Started Make sure each equation is in the form $ax^2 + bx + c = 0$, and then apply the quadratic formula, which always "works." ▶

(a) Let $a = 1$, $b = 3$, and $c = 5$ and apply the quadratic formula.

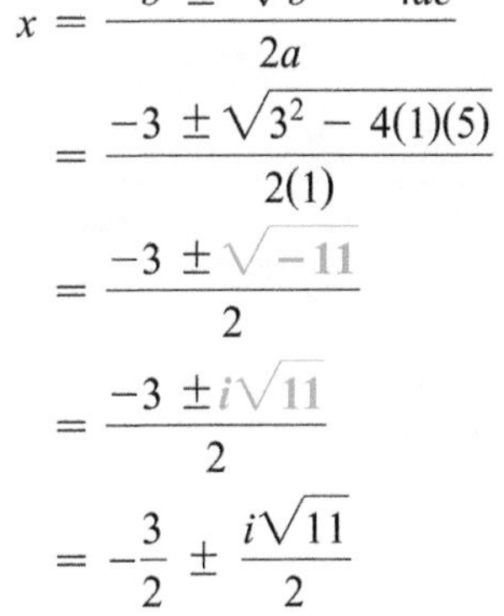

$$x = \frac{-b \pm \sqrt{b^2 - 4ac}}{2a}$$

$$= \frac{-3 \pm \sqrt{3^2 - 4(1)(5)}}{2(1)}$$

$$= \frac{-3 \pm \sqrt{-11}}{2}$$

$$= \frac{-3 \pm i\sqrt{11}}{2}$$

$$= -\frac{3}{2} \pm \frac{i\sqrt{11}}{2}$$

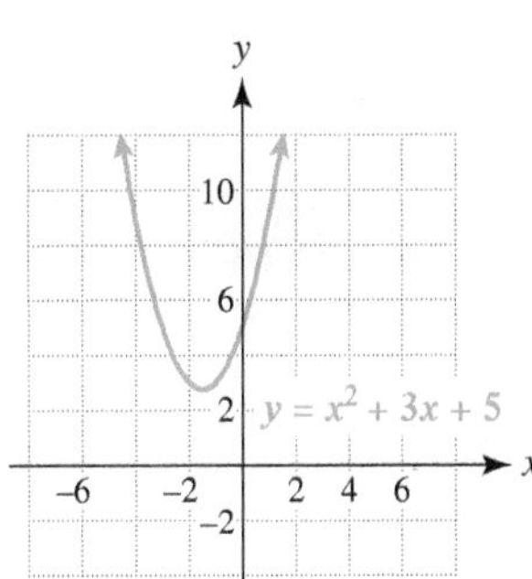

Figure 3.41

In Figure 3.41 the graph of $y_1 = x^2 + 3x + 5$ does not intersect the x-axis, which indicates that the equation $x^2 + 3x + 5 = 0$ has no real solutions. However, there are two complex solutions that are imaginary.

(b) Rewrite the equation as $\frac{1}{2}x^2 - 5x + 17 = 0$, and let $a = \frac{1}{2}$, $b = -5$, and $c = 17$.

$$x = \frac{5 \pm \sqrt{(-5)^2 - 4(0.5)(17)}}{2(0.5)}$$

$$= 5 \pm \sqrt{-9}$$

$$= 5 \pm 3i$$

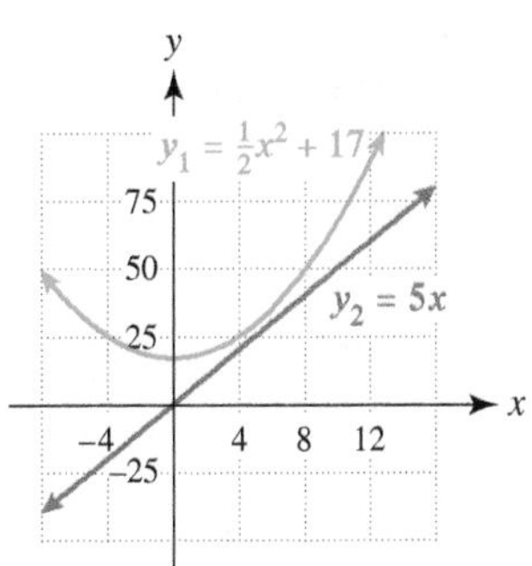

Figure 3.42

In Figure 3.42 the graphs of $y_1 = \frac{1}{2}x^2 + 17$ and $y_2 = 5x$ do not intersect, which indicates that the equation $\frac{1}{2}x^2 + 17 = 5x$ has no real solutions. However, there are two complex solutions that are imaginary.

(c) Rather than use the quadratic formula for this equation, we apply the square root property because the equation contains no x-term.

$$-2x^2 = 3 \quad \text{Given equation}$$

$$x^2 = -\frac{3}{2} \quad \text{Divide each side by } -2.$$

$$x = \pm\sqrt{-\frac{3}{2}} \quad \text{Square root property}$$

$$x = \pm i\sqrt{\frac{3}{2}} \quad \sqrt{-a} = i\sqrt{a}$$

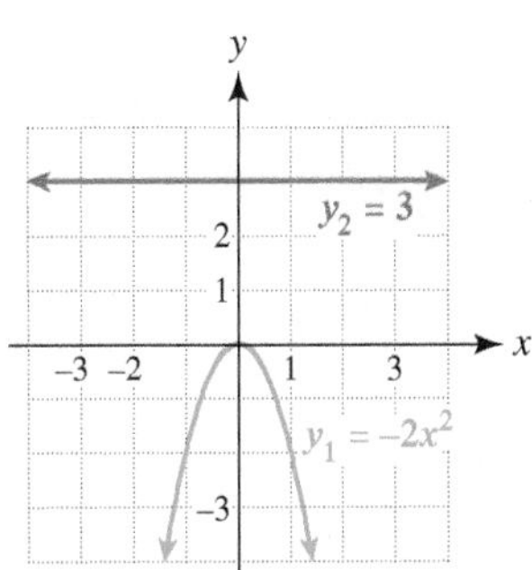

Figure 3.43

In Figure 3.43 the graphs of $y_1 = -2x^2$ and $y_2 = 3$ do not intersect, which indicates that the equation $-2x^2 = 3$ has no real solutions. However, there are two complex solutions that are imaginary.

Now Try Exercises 67, 73, and 75

CLASS DISCUSSION

What is the result if the expression is evaluated? (See Example 5(a).)

$$\left(-\frac{3}{2}+\frac{i\sqrt{11}}{2}\right)^2+3\left(-\frac{3}{2}+\frac{i\sqrt{11}}{2}\right)+5$$

3.3 Putting It All Together

Some of the important topics in this section are summarized in the following table.

CONCEPT	EXPLANATION	COMMENTS AND EXAMPLES
Imaginary unit	$i = \sqrt{-1}$, $i^2 = -1$	The imaginary unit i allows us to define the complex numbers.
The expression $\sqrt{-a}$ with $a > 0$	$\sqrt{-a} = i\sqrt{a}$	$\sqrt{-4} = 2i$ $\sqrt{-5} = i\sqrt{5}$ $\sqrt{-32} = i\sqrt{32} = i\sqrt{16}\sqrt{2} = 4i\sqrt{2}$ $\sqrt{-5}\sqrt{-20} = i\sqrt{5}i\sqrt{20} = i^2\sqrt{100} = -10$
Complex number	$a + bi$, where a and b are real numbers	Every real number is a complex number. $5 - 4i$, 5, $2 + i$, and $-9i$ are examples of complex numbers.
Standard form of a complex number	$a + bi$, where a and b are real numbers	Converting to standard form: $\frac{3 \pm 4i}{2} = \frac{3}{2} + 2i$ or $\frac{3}{2} - 2i$
Conjugates	The conjugate of $a + bi$ is $a - bi$.	*Number* — *Conjugate* $5 - 6i$ — $5 + 6i$ $-12i$ — $12i$ -7 — -7 $2 + 3i$ — $2 - 3i$
Arithmetic operations on complex numbers	Complex numbers may be added, subtracted, multiplied, or divided.	$(2 + 3i) + (-3 - i) = -1 + 2i$ $(5 + i) - (3 - i) = 2 + 2i$ $(1 + i)(5 - i) = 5 - i + 5i - i^2 = 6 + 4i$ $\frac{3 + i}{1 - i} = \frac{(3 + i)(1 + i)}{(1 - i)(1 + i)}$ $= 1 + 2i$
Powers of i	Use the fact that $i^2 = -1$ to simplify powers of i.	$i^{27} = i^{26} \cdot i$ $= (i^2)^{13} \cdot i$ $= (-1)^{13} \cdot i$ $= -i$

CONCEPT	EXPLANATION	COMMENTS AND EXAMPLES
Complex solutions to equations	Complex numbers $a + bi$ with $b \neq 0$ can be solutions to equations that cannot be solved with only real numbers.	$x^2 + 5 = 0$ implies $x^2 = -5$; there are no real solutions, but $x = \pm i\sqrt{5}$ are two complex solutions. Note that the graph of $y = x^2 + 5$ has no x-intercepts. The quadratic formula can be used to find complex solutions.

3.3 Exercises

Complex Numbers

Exercises 1–20: Simplify by using the imaginary unit i.

1. $\sqrt{-4}$

2. $\sqrt{-16}$

3. $\sqrt{-100}$

4. $\sqrt{-49}$

5. $\sqrt{-23}$

6. $\sqrt{-11}$

7. $\sqrt{-12}$

8. $\sqrt{-32}$

9. $\sqrt{-54}$

10. $\sqrt{-28}$

11. $\dfrac{4 \pm \sqrt{-16}}{2}$

12. $\dfrac{-2 \pm \sqrt{-36}}{6}$

13. $\dfrac{-6 \pm \sqrt{-72}}{3}$

14. $\dfrac{2 \pm \sqrt{-8}}{4}$

15. $\sqrt{-5} \cdot \sqrt{-5}$

16. $\sqrt{-8} \cdot \sqrt{-8}$

17. $\sqrt{-18} \cdot \sqrt{-2}$

18. $\sqrt{-20} \cdot \sqrt{-5}$

19. $\sqrt{-3} \cdot \sqrt{-6}$

20. $\sqrt{-15} \cdot \sqrt{-5}$

Exercises 21–48: Write the expression in standard form.

21. $3i + 5i$

22. $-7i + 5i$

23. $(3 + i) + (-5 - 2i)$

24. $(-4 + 2i) + (7 + 35i)$

25. $2i - (-5 + 23i)$

26. $(12 - 7i) - (-1 + 9i)$

27. $3 - (4 - 6i)$

28. $(7 + i) - (-8 + 5i)$

29. $(2)(2 + 4i)$

30. $(-5)(-7 + 3i)$

31. $(1 + i)(2 - 3i)$

32. $(-2 + i)(1 - 2i)$

33. $(-3 + 2i)(-2 + i)$

34. $(2 - 3i)(1 + 4i)$

35. $(-2 + 3i)^2$

36. $(2 - 3i)^2$

37. $2i(1 - i)^2$

38. $-i(5 - 2i)^2$

39. $\dfrac{1}{1 + i}$

40. $\dfrac{1 - i}{2 + 3i}$

41. $\dfrac{4 + i}{5 - i}$

42. $\dfrac{10}{1 - 4i}$

43. $\dfrac{2i}{10 - 5i}$

44. $\dfrac{3 - 2i}{1 + 2i}$

45. $\dfrac{3}{-i}$

46. $\dfrac{4 - 2i}{i}$

47. $\dfrac{-2 + i}{(1 + i)^2}$

48. $\dfrac{3}{(2 - i)^2}$

Exercises 49–54: Evaluate the expression with a calculator.

49. $(23 - 5.6i) + (-41.5 + 93i)$

50. $(-8.05 - 4.67i) + (3.5 + 5.37i)$

51. $(17.1 - 6i) - (8.4 + 0.7i)$

52. $\left(\frac{3}{4} - \frac{1}{10}i\right) - \left(-\frac{1}{8} + \frac{4}{25}i\right)$

53. $(-12.6 - 5.7i)(5.1 - 9.3i)$

54. $(7.8 + 23i)(-1.04 + 2.09i)$

Exercises 55 and 56: Evaluate with a calculator. Round values to the nearest thousandth.

55. $\dfrac{17 - 135i}{18 + 142i}$

56. $\dfrac{141 + 52i}{102 - 31i}$

Powers of *i*

Exercises 57–64: Simplify the powers of i.

57. i^{50}

58. i^{28}

59. i^{31}

60. i^{21}

61. i^{12}

62. i^{103}

63. i^{57}

64. i^{30}

Quadratic Equations with Complex Solutions

Exercises 65–82: Solve. Write answers in standard form.

65. $x^2 + 5 = 0$

66. $4x^2 + 3 = 0$

67. $5x^2 + 1 = 3x^2$

68. $x(3x + 1) = -1$

69. $3x = 5x^2 + 1$

70. $4x^2 = x - 1$

71. $x(x - 4) = -5$

72. $2x^2 + x + 1 = 0$

73. $x^2 = 3x - 5$

74. $3x - x^2 = 5$

75. $x^2 + 2x + 4 = 0$

76. $x(x - 4) = -8$

77. $3x^2 - 4x = x^2 - 3$

78. $2x^2 + 3 = 1 - x$

79. $2x(x - 2) = x - 4$

80. $3x^2 + x = x(5 - x) - 2$

81. $3x(3 - x) - 8 = x(x - 2)$

82. $-x(7 - 2x) = -6 - (3 - x)$

Zeros of Quadratic Functions

Exercises 83–88: The graph of a function is given.

(a) Use the graph to predict the number of real zeros and the number of imaginary zeros.

(b) Find these zeros using the quadratic formula.

83.

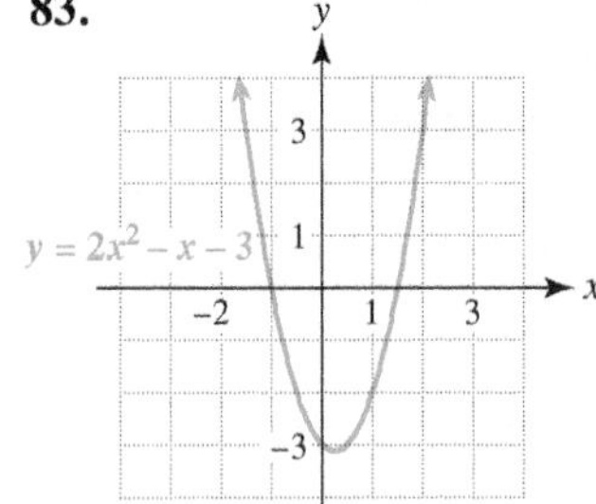

84.

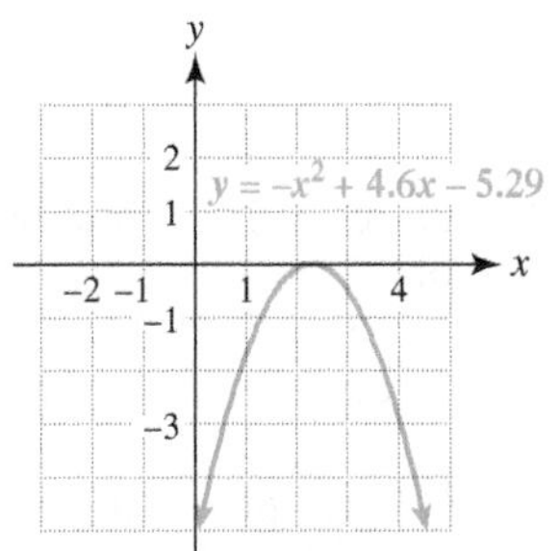

85.

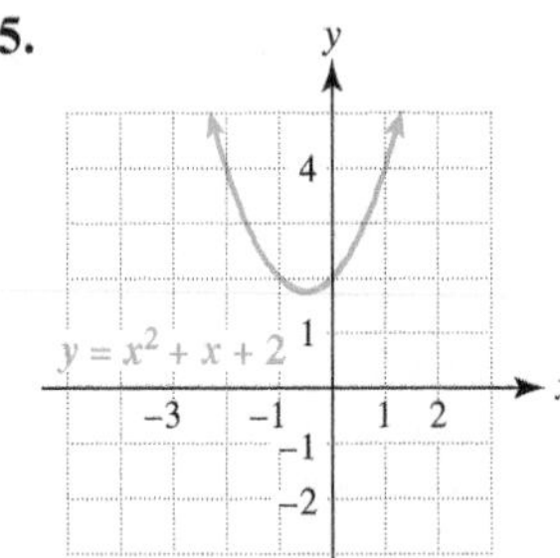

86.

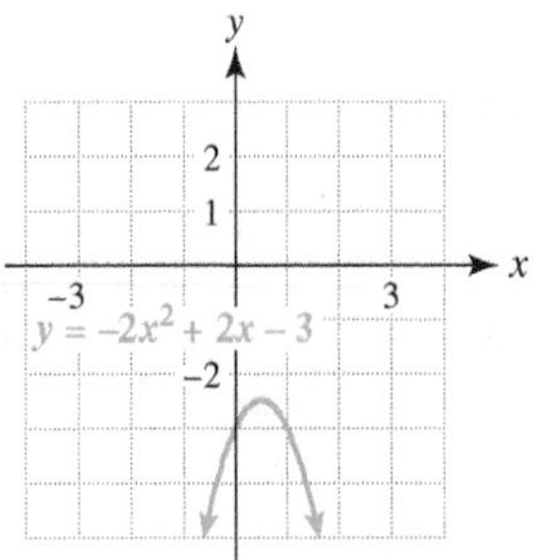

87.

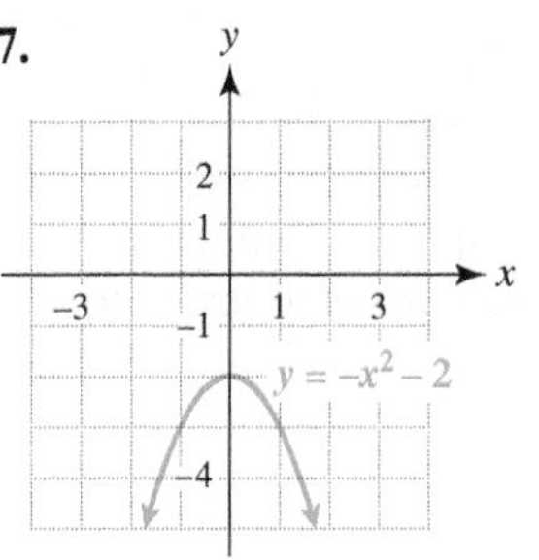

88.

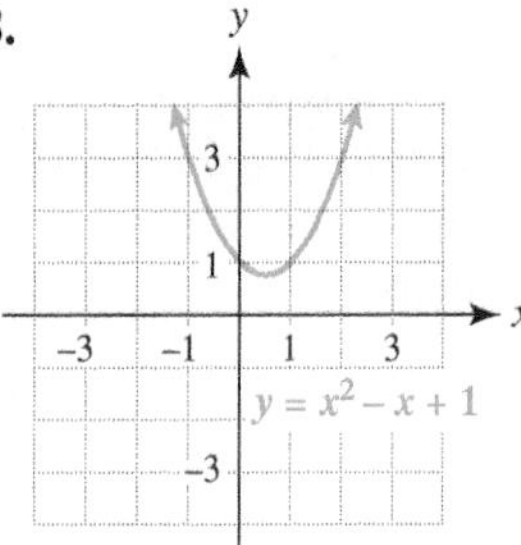

Applications

Exercises 89–94: **Electricity** *Complex numbers are used in the study of electrical circuits. Impedance Z (or the opposition to the flow of electricity), voltage V, and current I can all be represented by complex numbers. They are related by the equation $Z = \frac{V}{I}$. Find the value of the missing variable.*

89. $V = 50 + 98i$ $\quad I = 8 + 5i$

90. $V = 30 + 60i$ $\quad I = 8 + 6i$

91. $I = 1 + 2i$ $\quad Z = 3 - 4i$

92. $I = \frac{1}{2} + \frac{1}{4}i$ $\quad Z = 8 - 9i$

93. $Z = 22 - 5i$ $\quad V = 27 + 17i$

94. $Z = 10 + 5i$ $\quad V = 10 + 8i$

Writing about Mathematics

95. Could a quadratic function have one real zero and one imaginary zero? Explain.

96. Give an example of a quadratic function that has only real zeros and an example of one that has only imaginary zeros. How do their graphs compare? Explain how to determine from a graph whether a quadratic function has real zeros.

Extended and Discovery Exercise

1. Powers of *i* The properties of the imaginary unit are $i = \sqrt{-1}$ and $i^2 = -1$.

(a) Begin simplifying the expressions $i, i^2, i^3, i^4, i^5, \ldots,$ until a simple pattern is discovered. For example, $i^3 = i \cdot i^2 = i \cdot (-1) = -i$.

(b) Summarize your findings by describing how to simplify i^n for any natural number n.

3.4 Quadratic Inequalities

- Understand basic concepts about quadratic inequalities
- Solve quadratic inequalities graphically
- Solve quadratic inequalities symbolically

Introduction

Highway engineers often use quadratic functions to model safe stopping distances for cars. For example, $f(x) = \frac{1}{12}x^2 + \frac{11}{5}x$ is sometimes used to model the stopping distance for a car traveling at x miles per hour on dry, level pavement. If a driver can see only 200 feet ahead on a highway with a sharp curve, then safe driving speeds x satisfy the *quadratic inequality*

$$\frac{1}{12}x^2 + \frac{11}{5}x \leq 200, \qquad \text{Quadratic inequality}$$

or equivalently,

$$\frac{1}{12}x^2 + \frac{11}{5}x - 200 \leq 0. \qquad \text{Subtract 200.}$$

(See Example 4.) This section discusses methods for solving quadratic inequalities.

Basic Concepts

A quadratic equation can be written as $ax^2 + bx + c = 0$ with $a \neq 0$. If the equals sign is replaced by $>$, $\geq$, $<$, or $\leq$, a **quadratic inequality** results. Examples of *quadratic equations* include

$$x^2 + 2x - 1 = 0, \qquad 4x^2 = 1, \qquad 2x^2 = 1 - 3x,$$

and examples of *quadratic inequalities* include

$$x^2 + 2x - 1 \geq 0, \qquad 4x^2 < 1, \quad \text{and} \quad 2x^2 \leq 1 - 3x.$$

MAKING CONNECTIONS

Quadratic Function, Equation, and Inequality The three concepts are closely related.

$f(x) = ax^2 + bx + c, a \neq 0$	Quadratic function
$ax^2 + bx + c = 0, a \neq 0$	Quadratic equation
$ax^2 + bx + c > 0, a \neq 0$	Quadratic inequality

Because equality is (usually) the boundary between *greater than* and *less than*, a first step in solving a quadratic inequality is to determine the x-values where equality occurs. These x-values are *boundary numbers*. We begin by discussing graphical solutions to quadratic inequalities.

Graphical and Numerical Solutions

Quadratic inequalities can be solved graphically, as illustrated in the next example.

EXAMPLE 1 Solving quadratic inequalities graphically

Solve each inequality graphically.
(a) $x^2 - 4 < 0$ **(b)** $x^2 - 4 > 0$

SOLUTION

(a) The graph of $y = x^2 - 4$ opens upward with x-intercepts -2 and 2, as shown in Figure 3.44 on the next page. Because the x-axis represents where $y = 0$, the solutions to $x^2 - 4 < 0$ correspond to the red portion where the graph of $y = x^2 - 4$ is **below** the x-axis, which is between the x-intercepts ± 2. Thus the solution set is $\{x \mid -2 < x < 2\}$ or $(-2, 2)$.

Solving $x^2 - 4 < 0$ and $x^2 - 4 > 0$

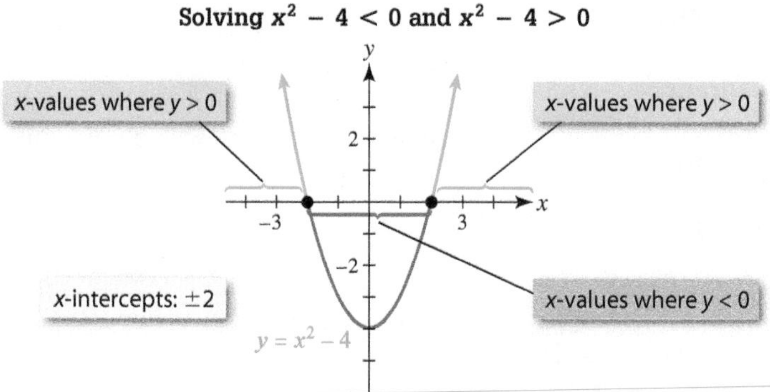

Figure 3.44

(b) From Figure 3.44 the green portions of the graph of $y = x^2 - 4$ are above the x-axis left of x-intercept -2 or right of x-intercept 2. Thus the solution set can be written as $\{x \mid x < -2 \text{ or } x > 2\}$, or $(-\infty, -2) \cup (2, \infty)$.

Now Try Exercise 1

The following steps summarize how to solve a quadratic inequality graphically.

SOLVING QUADRATIC INEQUALITIES GRAPHICALLY

STEP 1: If necessary, rewrite the inequality as $ax^2 + bx + c > 0$, where $>$ may be replaced by $<$, $\leq$, or $\geq$.

STEP 2: Graph $y = ax^2 + bx + c$ and determine any x-intercepts.

STEP 3: Depending on the inequality symbol, locate the x-values where the graph is either above or below the x-axis.

STEP 4: Use the information from Step 3 to solve the inequality.

In the next example we apply these steps to solve a quadratic inequality.

EXAMPLE 2 Solving a quadratic inequality graphically

Solve the inequality $2 + x \geq x^2$ graphically.

SOLUTION

STEP 1: Rewrite $2 + x \geq x^2$ as $-x^2 + x + 2 \geq 0$.

STEP 2: Figure 3.45 shows a graph of $y = -x^2 + x + 2$ where the x-intercepts are $\mathbf{-1}$ and $\mathbf{2}$. When graphing by hand, it may be helpful to locate the x-interecepts symbolically.

$$-x^2 + x + 2 = 0 \quad \text{Let } y = 0 \text{ to find } x\text{-intercepts.}$$
$$x^2 - x - 2 = 0 \quad \text{Multiply each side by } -1.$$
$$(x + 1)(x - 2) = 0 \quad \text{Factor.}$$
$$x = -1 \quad \text{or} \quad x = 2 \quad \text{Zero-product property.}$$

This confirms that the x-intercepts are -1 and 2.

STEP 3: The inequality symbol in $-x^2 + x + 2 \geq 0$ is $\geq$, so locate x-values where the parabola is above the x-axis. This occurs between the x-intercepts: -1, 2.

Solving $-x^2 + x + 2 \geq 0$ Graphically

x-intercepts: −1, 2

$y = -x^2 + x + 2$

x-values where the graph is above the x-axis

Figure 3.45

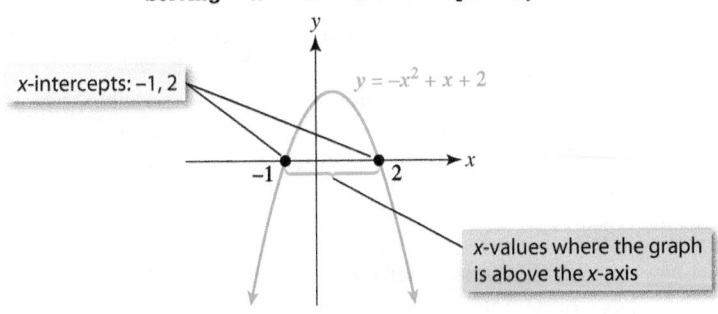

STEP 4: Because $\geq$ includes equality, the solution set includes -1 and 2 and can be written as $[-1, 2]$, or $\{x \mid -1 \leq x \leq 2\}$.

Now Try Exercise 35

In the next example we use symbolic, graphical, and numerical methods.

EXAMPLE 3 Solving quadratic equations and inequalities

Solve each equation or inequality.

(a) $2x^2 - 3x - 2 = 0$ **(b)** $2x^2 - 3x - 2 < 0$ **(c)** $2x^2 - 3x - 2 > 0$

SOLUTION

(a) *Symbolic Solution* The equation $2x^2 - 3x - 2 = 0$ can be solved by factoring.

$$(2x + 1)(x - 2) = 0 \quad \text{Factor trinomial.}$$

$$x = -\frac{1}{2} \quad \text{or} \quad x = 2 \quad \text{Zero-product property}$$

The solutions are $-\frac{1}{2}$ and 2.

(b) *Graphical Solution* The graph of $y = 2x^2 - 3x - 2$ is a parabola opening upward. Its x-intercepts are $-\frac{1}{2}$ and 2. See Figure 3.46. This parabola is below the x-axis ($y < 0$) for x-values between $-\frac{1}{2}$ and 2, so the solution set is $\left(-\frac{1}{2}, 2\right)$, or $\left\{x \mid -\frac{1}{2} < x < 2\right\}$.

(c) *Graphical Solution* In Figure 3.47, the graph of $y = 2x^2 - 3x - 2$ is above the x-axis ($y > 0$) for x-values less than $-\frac{1}{2}$ or greater than 2, so the solution set is $\left(-\infty, -\frac{1}{2}\right) \cup (2, \infty)$, or $\left\{x \mid x < -\frac{1}{2} \text{ or } x > 2\right\}$.

Numerical Solution The table of values in Figure 3.48 supports these graphical results. Note that $y_1 = 0$ for $x = -\frac{1}{2}$ and $x = 2$. For $-\frac{1}{2} < x < 2$, we see that $y_1 < 0$, and for $x < -\frac{1}{2}$ or $x > 2$, we see that $y_1 > 0$.

Graphical Solutions

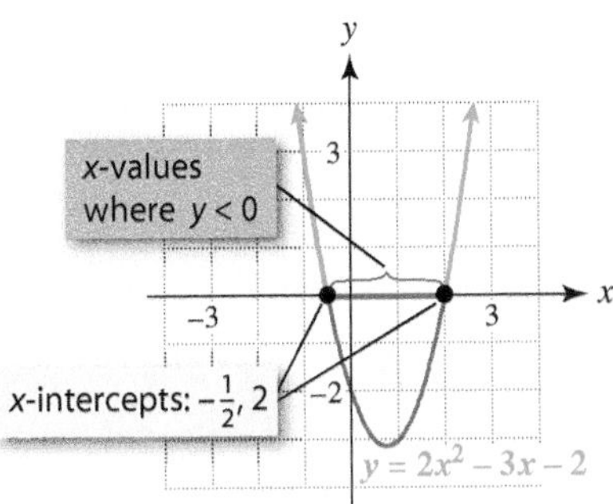

Figure 3.46

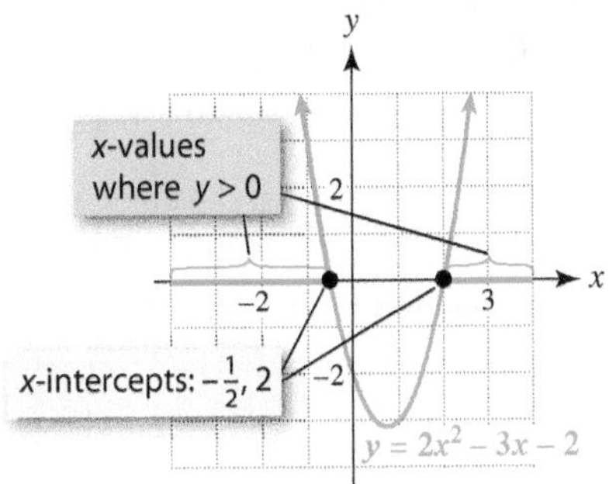

Figure 3.47

Numerical Solutions

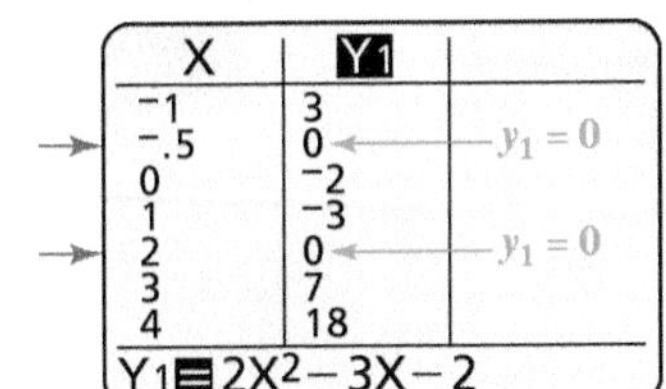

X	Y1
-1	3
-.5	0
0	-2
1	-3
2	0
3	7
4	18

Y1 = 2X² − 3X − 2

Figure 3.48

Now Try Exercise 7

NOTE *For a graphical solution, it is not necessary to graph the parabola precisely.* Instead you can simply *visualize* the parabola opening upward with x-intercepts $-\frac{1}{2}$ and 2.

The following box describes how to use the graph of $y = ax^2 + bx + c$ to solve either $ax^2 + bx + c > 0$ or $ax^2 + bx + c < 0$. The solution set depends on whether the graph opens upward or downward and on whether there are zero, one, or two intercepts.

SOLVING QUADRATIC INEQUALITIES GRAPHICALLY

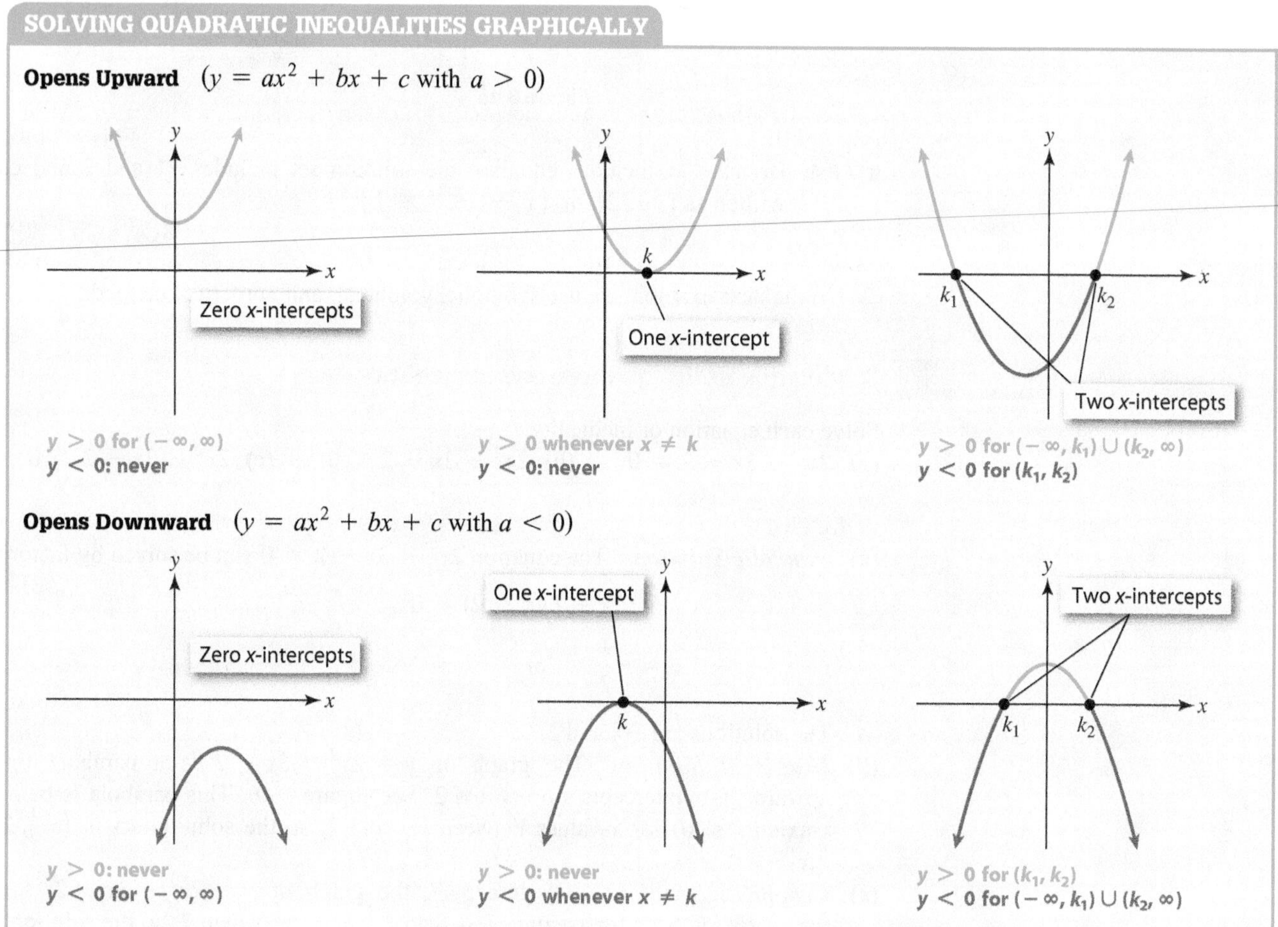

CLASS DISCUSSION

Sketch a graph of $y = ax^2 + bx + c$ if the quadratic inequality $ax^2 + bx + c < 0$ satisfies the following conditions.

(a) $a > 0$, solution set: $\{x \mid -1 < x < 3\}$
(b) $a < 0$, solution set: $\{x \mid x \neq 1\}$
(c) $a < 0$, solution set: $\{x \mid x < -2 \text{ or } x > 2\}$

EXAMPLE 4 **Determining safe speeds**

In the introduction to this section the quadratic inequality

$$\frac{1}{12}x^2 + \frac{11}{5}x \leq 200$$

was explained. Solve this inequality to determine safe speeds on a curve where a driver can see the road ahead for only 200 feet. What might be a safe speed limit for this curve?

[−100, 100, 50] by [−300, 300, 100]

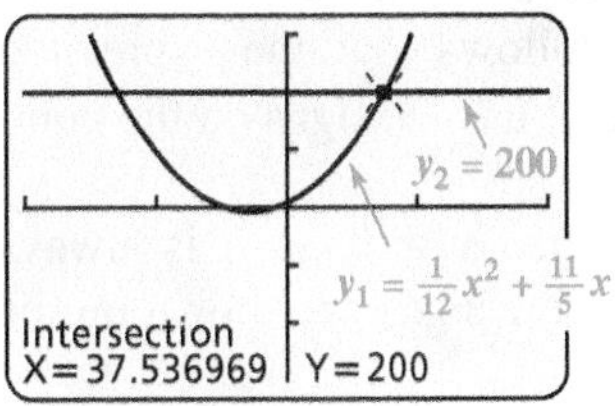

Figure 3.49

SOLUTION Graph $y_1 = \frac{1}{12}x^2 + \frac{11}{5}x$ and $y_2 = 200$, as shown in Figure 3.49. Since we are interested in *positive* speeds, we need to locate only the point of intersection where x is positive. This is where $x \approx 37.5$. For positive x-values to the left of $x \approx 37.5$, $y_1 < 200$. Thus safe speeds are less than 37.5 miles per hour. A reasonable speed limit might be 35 miles per hour.

Now Try Exercise 67

Symbolic Solutions

Although it is usually easier to solve a quadratic inequality graphically by visualizing a parabola and its x-intercepts, we can also solve a quadratic inequality symbolically without the aid of a graph. The symbolic method, which involves a table or a number line, is often used to solve more complicated inequalities. (See Section 4.7.)

SOLVING QUADRATIC INEQUALITIES SYMBOLICALLY

STEP 1: If necessary, write the inequality as $ax^2 + bx + c < 0$, where $<$ may be replaced by $>$, $\leq$, or $\geq$.

STEP 2: Solve the equation $ax^2 + bx + c = 0$. The solutions are called boundary numbers.

STEP 3: Use the boundary numbers to separate the number line into disjoint open intervals. Note that on each open interval, $y = ax^2 + bx + c$ is either always positive or always negative.

STEP 4: To solve the inequality, choose a convenient test value (an x-value) from each disjoint interval in Step 3. Evaluate $y = ax^2 + bx + c$ at each test point. If the result is positive, then $y > 0$ over that interval. If the result is negative, then $y < 0$ over that interval. You may want to use either a number line or a table of values to organize your work.

Algebra Review
To review factoring, see Chapter R (pages R-22–R-23).

NOTE Do not pick a boundary number for a test value, because the result will be $y = 0$.

For example, to solve $2x^2 - 5x - 12 < 0$ symbolically, replace $<$ with $=$ and solve the equation by factoring.

$$2x^2 - 5x - 12 = 0 \quad \text{Quadratic equation}$$
$$(2x + 3)(x - 4) = 0 \quad \text{Factor.}$$
$$2x + 3 = 0 \quad \text{or} \quad x - 4 = 0 \quad \text{Zero-product property}$$
$$x = -\frac{3}{2} \quad \text{or} \quad x = 4 \quad \text{Solve.}$$

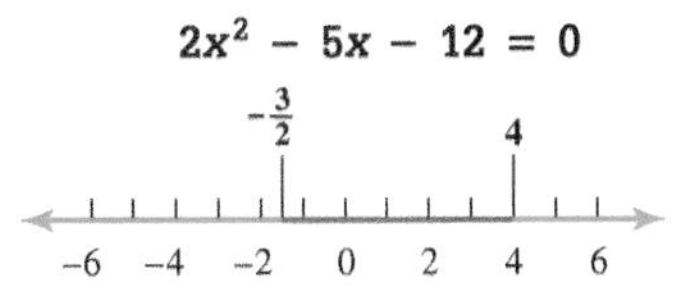

Figure 3.50

The boundary numbers $-\frac{3}{2}$ and 4 separate the number line into three disjoint intervals:

$$\left(-\infty, -\tfrac{3}{2}\right), \left(-\tfrac{3}{2}, 4\right), \text{ and } (4, \infty),$$

as illustrated in Figure 3.50.

The expression $2x^2 - 5x - 12$ is either always positive or always negative on a particular interval. To determine where $2x^2 - 5x - 12 < 0$, we can use the **test values** shown in Table 3.8.

Checking Test Values

Interval	Test Value x	$2x^2 - 5x - 12$	Positive or Negative?
$\left(-\infty, -\frac{3}{2}\right)$	−2	6	Positive
$\left(-\frac{3}{2}, 4\right)$	0	−12	Negative
$(4, \infty)$	6	30	Positive

Table 3.8

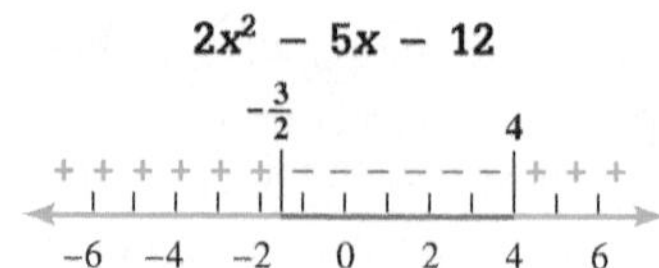

Figure 3.51

For example, since the test value -2 lies in the interval $\left(-\infty, -\frac{3}{2}\right)$ and $2x^2 - 5x - 12$ evaluated at $x = -2$ equals 6, which is greater than 0, it follows that the expression $2x^2 - 5x - 12$ is always positive for $\left(-\infty, -\frac{3}{2}\right)$. This interval has + signs on the number line in Figure 3.51. (See Table 3.8 on the previous page.)

See that the expression $2x^2 - 5x - 12$ equals -12 when $x = 0$, so it is always negative between the boundary numbers of $-\frac{3}{2}$ and 4. Negative signs are shown on the real number line in Figure 3.51 in the interval $\left(-\frac{3}{2}, 4\right)$.

Finally, when $x = 6$, the expression $2x^2 - 5x - 12$ equals 30, which is positive. Thus + signs are placed along the x-axis in Figure 3.51 for $x > 4$. Therefore the solution set for $2x^2 - 5x - 12 < 0$ is $\left(-\frac{3}{2}, 4\right)$.

Note that it is important to choose one test value less than $-\frac{3}{2}$, one test value between $-\frac{3}{2}$ and 4, and one test value greater than 4. You do *not* need to use both a table and a number line.

EXAMPLE 5 **Solving a quadratic inequality**

Solve $x^2 \geq 2 - x$ symbolically. Write the solution set in interval notation.

SOLUTION

STEP 1: Rewrite the inequality as $x^2 + x - 2 \geq 0$.

STEP 2: Solve the quadratic equation $x^2 + x - 2 = 0$.

$$(x + 2)(x - 1) = 0 \qquad \text{Factor.}$$

$$x = -2 \quad \text{or} \quad x = 1 \qquad \text{Zero-product property}$$

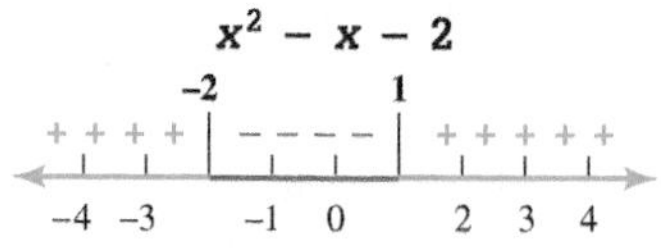

x² − x − 2

-2 1

-4 -3 -1 0 2 3 4

Figure 3.52

STEP 3: These two boundary numbers separate the number line into three disjoint intervals:

$$(-\infty, -2), \quad (-2, 1), \quad \text{and} \quad (1, \infty).$$

STEP 4: We choose the test values $x = -3, x = 0$, and $x = 2$. From Table 3.9 or Figure 3.52 the expression $x^2 + x - 2$ is positive when $x = -3$ and $x = 2$. Thus the solution set is $(-\infty, -2] \cup [1, \infty)$. The boundary numbers, -2 and 1, are included because the inequality involves $\geq$ rather than $>$.

Interval	Test Value x	$x^2 + x - 2$	Positive or Negative?
$(-\infty, -2)$	-3	4	Positive
$(-2, 1)$	0	-2	Negative
$(1, \infty)$	2	4	Positive

Table 3.9

Now Try Exercise 61

3.4 Putting It All Together

The following table summarizes concepts related to solving quadratic inequalities.

CONCEPT	DESCRIPTION
Quadratic inequality	Can be written as $ax^2 + bx + c < 0$, where $<$ may be replaced by $>$, $\leq$, or $\geq$. **Example:** $-x^2 + x < -2$ is a quadratic inequality; it can be written as $-x^2 + x + 2 < 0$.

CONCEPT	DESCRIPTION
Graphical solution	Write the inequality as $ax^2 + bx + c < 0$, where $<$ may be $>$, $\leq$, or $\geq$. Graph $y = ax^2 + bx + c$, and use the x-intercepts, or boundary numbers, to determine x-values where the graph is below (above) the x-axis. In the figure, the inequality $-x^2 + x + 2 < 0$ is satisfied ($y < 0$) when either $x < -1$ or $x > 2$.
Symbolic solution	Write the inequality as $ax^2 + bx + c < 0$, where $<$ may be $>$, $\leq$, or $\geq$. Solve the equation $ax^2 + bx + c = 0$. To determine where $y = ax^2 + bx + c$ is positive or negative, use a table of test values or a number line. **Example:** Solve $-x^2 + x + 2 < 0$. Solving $-x^2 + x + 2 = 0$ results in $x = -1$ or $x = 2$. From the table the solution set is $\{x \mid x < -1 \text{ or } x > 2\}$ or $(-\infty, -1) \cup (2, \infty)$.

Interval	Test Value x	$-x^2 + x + 2$	Positive or Negative?
$(-\infty, -1)$	-2	-4	Negative
$(-1, 2)$	0	2	Positive
$(2, \infty)$	3	-4	Negative

3.4 Exercises

Quadratic Inequalities

Exercises 1–6: Solve each inequality.

1. (a) $x^2 - 1 > 0$ (b) $x^2 - 1 < 0$

2. (a) $x^2 - 9 < 0$ (b) $x^2 - 9 > 0$

3. (a) $x^2 - 16 \leq 0$ (b) $x^2 - 16 \geq 0$

4. (a) $x^2 - 25 \geq 0$ (b) $x^2 - 25 \leq 0$

5. (a) $4 - x^2 > 0$ (b) $4 - x^2 < 0$

6. (a) $\frac{1}{4} - x^2 < 0$ (b) $\frac{1}{4} - x^2 > 0$

Exercises 7–18: Solve each equation and inequality. Use set-builder or interval notation to write solution sets to the inequalities.

7. (a) $x^2 - x - 12 = 0$ (b) $x^2 - x - 12 < 0$ (c) $x^2 - x - 12 > 0$

8. (a) $x^2 - 8x + 12 = 0$ (b) $x^2 - 8x + 12 < 0$ (c) $x^2 - 8x + 12 > 0$

9. (a) $k^2 - 5 = 0$ (b) $k^2 - 5 \leq 0$ (c) $k^2 - 5 \geq 0$

10. (a) $n^2 - 17 = 0$ (b) $n^2 - 17 \leq 0$ (c) $n^2 - 17 \geq 0$

11. (a) $3x^2 + 8x = 0$ (b) $3x^2 + 8x \leq 0$ (c) $3x^2 + 8x \geq 0$

12. (a) $7x^2 - 4x = 0$ (b) $7x^2 - 4x \leq 0$ (c) $7x^2 - 4x \geq 0$

13. (a) $-4x^2 + 12x - 9 = 0$ (b) $-4x^2 + 12x - 9 < 0$ (c) $-4x^2 + 12x - 9 > 0$

14. (a) $x^2 + 2x + 1 = 0$ (b) $x^2 + 2x + 1 < 0$ (c) $x^2 + 2x + 1 > 0$

15. **(a)** $12z^2 - 23z + 10 = 0$

(b) $12z^2 - 23z + 10 \leq 0$

(c) $12z^2 - 23z + 10 \geq 0$

16. **(a)** $18z^2 + 9z - 20 = 0$

(b) $18z^2 + 9z - 20 \leq 0$

(c) $18z^2 + 9z - 20 \geq 0$

17. **(a)** $x^2 + 2x - 1 = 0$

(b) $x^2 + 2x - 1 < 0$

(c) $x^2 + 2x - 1 > 0$

18. **(a)** $x^2 + 4x - 3 = 0$

(b) $x^2 + 4x - 3 < 0$

(c) $x^2 + 4x - 3 > 0$

Exercises 19–24: The graph of $f(x) = ax^2 + bx + c$ is shown in the figure. Solve each inequality.

19. **(a)** $f(x) < 0$

(b) $f(x) \geq 0$

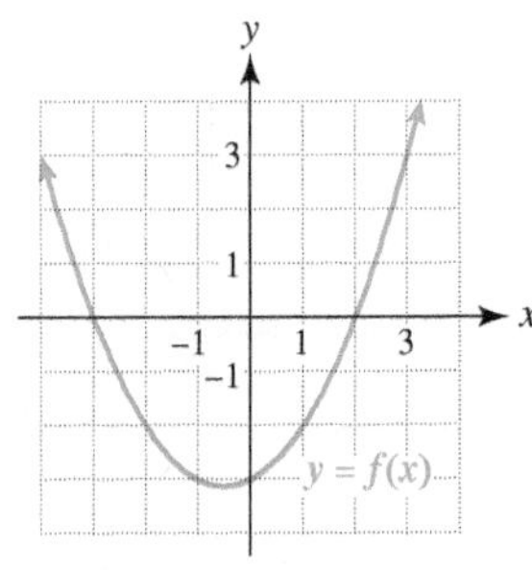

20. **(a)** $f(x) > 0$

(b) $f(x) < 0$

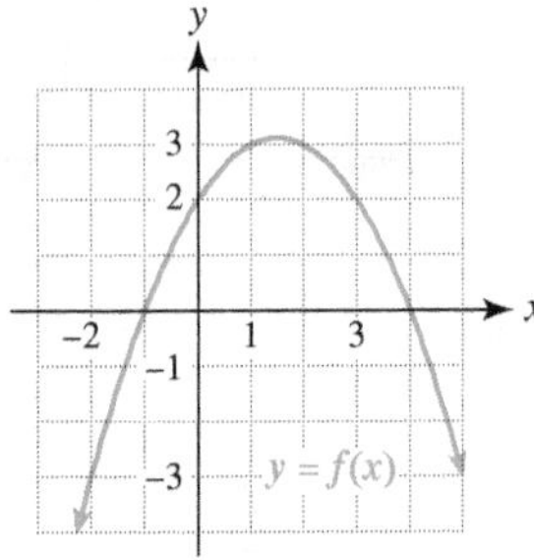

21. **(a)** $f(x) \leq 0$

(b) $f(x) > 0$

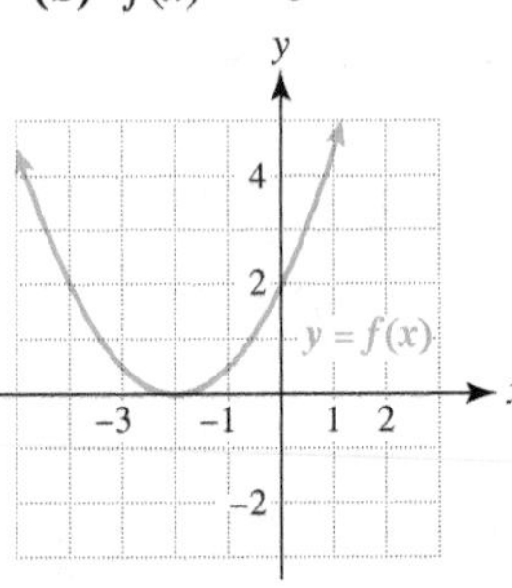

22. **(a)** $f(x) \geq 0$

(b) $f(x) \leq 0$

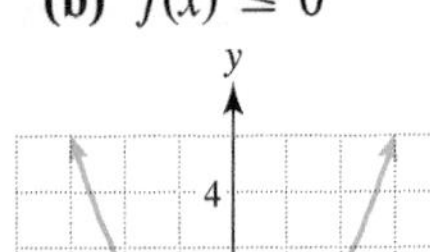

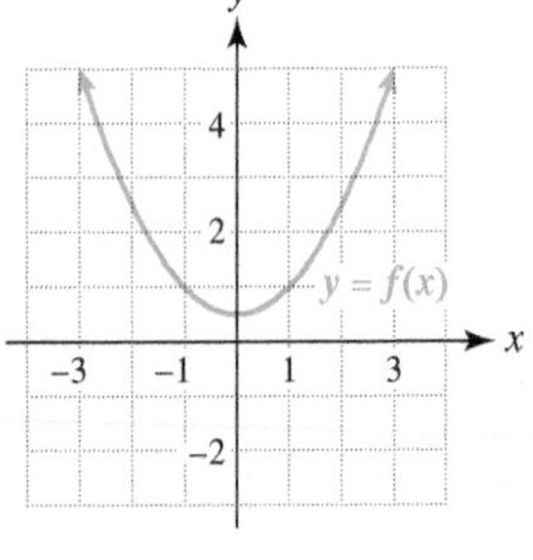

23. **(a)** $f(x) > 0$

(b) $f(x) < 0$

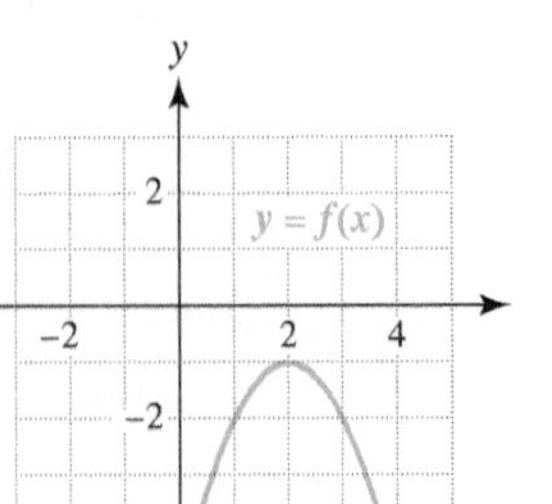

24. **(a)** $f(x) \geq 0$

(b) $f(x) < 0$

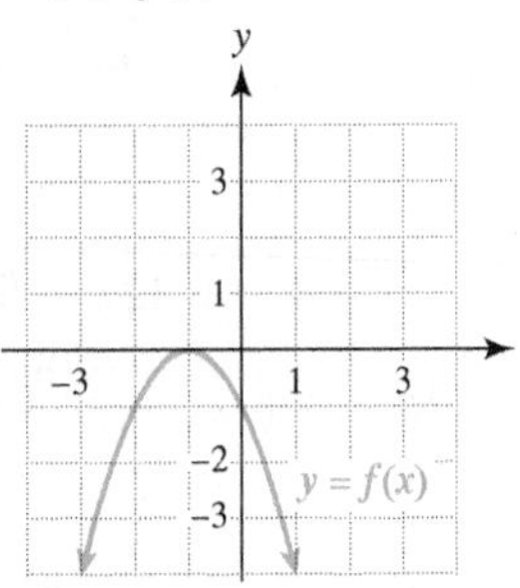

Exercises 25–28: Use the graph of $y = f(x)$ to solve each equation or inequality. Use set-builder or interval notation to write solution sets to the inequalities.

(a) $f(x) = 0$ *(b)* $f(x) < 0$ *(c)* $f(x) > 0$

25.

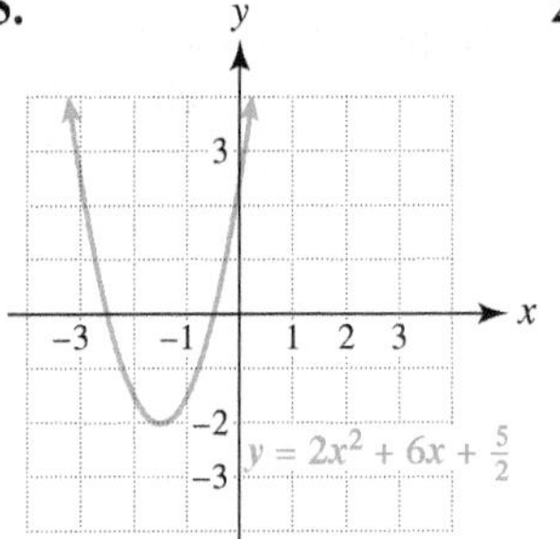

26.

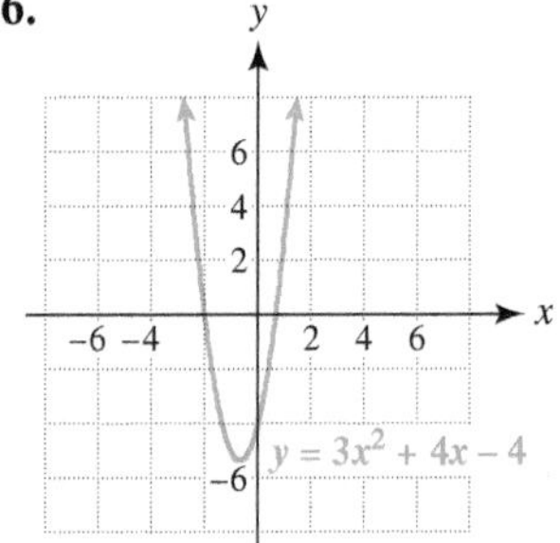

27. **28.**

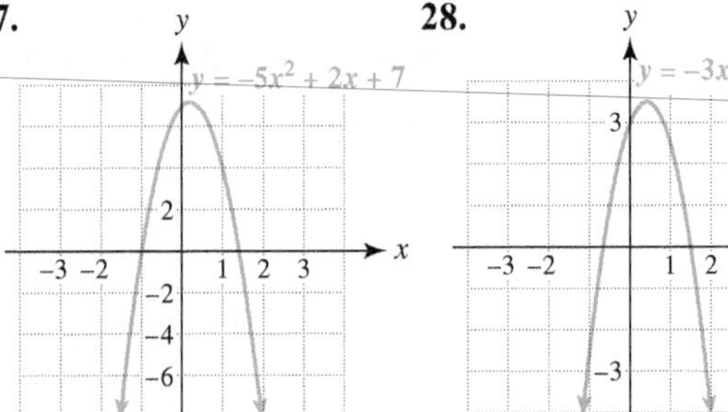

Exercises 29–32: The table contains test values for a quadratic function $f(x) = ax^2 + bx + c$. Solve each inequality.

(a) $f(x) > 0$ *(b)* $f(x) \leq 0$

29.

x	−2	−1	0	1	2
f(x)	3	0	−1	0	3

30.

x	−6	−4	1	5	8
f(x)	−22	0	20	0	−36

31.

x	−6	−4	−2	0	2
f(x)	0	4	0	−12	−32

32.

x	−4	−2	0	2	4
f(x)	16	0	−8	−8	0

Exercises 33–58: Solve the inequality.

33. $2x^2 + 5x + 2 \leq 0$

34. $x^2 - 3x - 4 < 0$

35. $x^2 + x > 6$

36. $-3x \geq 9 - 12x^2$

37. $x^2 \leq 4$

38. $2x^2 > 16$

39. $x(x - 4) \geq -4$

40. $x^2 - 3x - 10 < 0$

41. $-x^2 + x + 6 \leq 0$

42. $-x^2 - 2x + 8 > 0$

43. $6x^2 - x < 1$

44. $5x^2 \leq 10 - 5x$

45. $(x + 4)(x - 10) \leq 0$

46. $(x - 3.1)(x + 2.7) > 0$

47. $2x^2 + 4x + 3 < 0$

48. $2x^2 + x + 4 < 0$

49. $9x^2 + 4 > 12x$

50. $x^2 + 2x \geq 35$

51. $x^2 \geq x$

52. $x^2 \geq -3$

53. $x(x - 1) \geq 6$

54. $x^2 - 9 < 0$

55. $x^2 - 5 \leq 0$

56. $0.5x^2 - 3x > -1$

57. $7x^2 + 515.2 \geq 179.8x$

58. $-10 < 3x - x^2$

Exercises 59–66: (Refer to Example 5.) Use a table to solve.

59. $x^2 - 9x + 14 \leq 0$

60. $x^2 + 10x + 21 > 0$

61. $x^2 \geq 3x + 10$

62. $x^2 < 3x + 4$

63. $\frac{1}{8}x^2 + x + 2 \geq 0$

64. $x^2 - \frac{1}{2}x - 5 < 0$

65. $x^2 > 3 - 4x$

66. $2x^2 \leq 1 - 4x$

Applications

67. **Stopping Distance** The stopping distance D in feet for a car traveling at x miles per hour on *wet* level pavement can be estimated by $D(x) = \frac{1}{9}x^2 + \frac{11}{3}x$. If a driver can see only 300 feet ahead on a curve, find a safe speed limit.

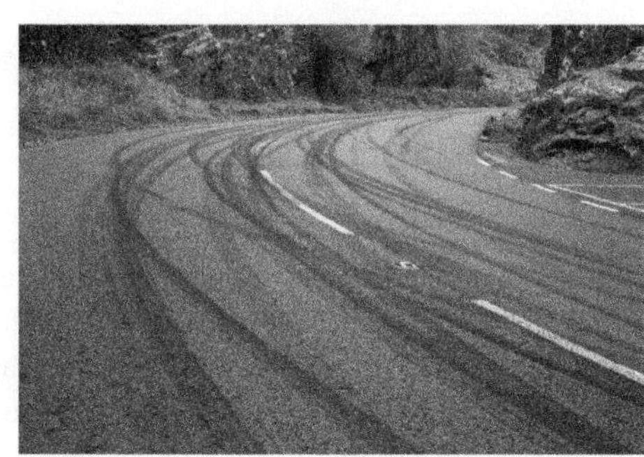

68. **Safe Driving Speeds** The stopping distance d in feet for a car traveling at x miles per hour is given by $d(x) = \frac{1}{12}x^2 + \frac{11}{9}x$. Determine the driving speeds that correspond to stopping distances between 300 and 500 feet, inclusive. Round speeds to the nearest mile per hour.

69. **Geometry** The volume of a cylinder is given by $V = \pi r^2 h$, where r is the radius and h is the height. If the height of a cylindrical can is 6 inches and the volume must be between 24π and 54π cubic inches, inclusive, find the possible values for the radius of the can.

70. **Geometry** A rectangle is 4 feet longer than it is wide. If the area of the rectangle must be less than or equal to 672 square feet, find the possible values for the width x.

71. **Heart Rate** Suppose that a person's heart rate, x minutes after vigorous exercise has stopped, can be modeled by $f(x) = \frac{4}{5}(x - 10)^2 + 80$. The output is in beats per minute, where the domain of f is $0 \leq x \leq 10$.

(a) Evaluate $f(0)$ and $f(2)$. Interpret the result.

(b) Estimate the times when the person's heart rate was between 100 and 120 beats per minute, inclusive.

72. **Carbon Monoxide Exposure** When a person breathes carbon monoxide (CO), it enters the bloodstream to form carboxyhemoglobin (COHb), which reduces the transport of oxygen to tissues. The formula given by $T(x) = 0.0079x^2 - 1.53x + 76$ approximates the number of hours T that it takes for a person's bloodstream to reach the 5% COHb level, where x is the concentration of CO in the air in parts per million (ppm) and $50 \leq x \leq 100$. (Smokers routinely have a 5% concentration.) Estimate the CO concentration x necessary for a person to reach the 5% COHb level in 4–5 hours. (***Source:*** *Indoor Air Quality Environmental Information Handbook.*)

73. **AIDS Deaths** Let $f(x) = 2375x^2 + 5134x + 5020$ estimate the number of U.S. AIDS deaths x years after 1984, where $0 \leq x \leq 10$. Estimate when the number of AIDS deaths was from 90,000 to 200,000.

74. **Air Density** As the altitude increases, air becomes thinner, or less dense. An approximation of the density of air at an altitude of x meters above sea level is given by

$$d(x) = (3.32 \times 10^{-9})x^2 - (1.14 \times 10^{-4})x + 1.22.$$

The output is the density of air in kilograms per cubic meter. The domain of d is $0 \leq x \leq 10{,}000$. (***Source:*** A. Miller and J. Thompson, *Elements of Meteorology.*)

(a) Denver is sometimes referred to as the mile-high city. Compare the density of air at sea level and in Denver. (*Hint:* 1 ft $\approx$ 0.305 m.)

(b) Determine the altitudes where the density is greater than 1 kilogram per cubic meter.

75. **iPod Sales** Sales of iPods in millions x years after 2006 can be modeled by

$$I(x) = -2.277x^2 + 11.71x + 40.4.$$

To the nearest year, estimate when sales were between 50 and 55 million iPods. (***Source:*** Apple Corporation.)

76. **Heart Rate** The table shows a person's heart rate after exercise has stopped.

(a) Find values for the constants a, h, and k so that the formula $f(x) = a(x - h)^2 + k$ models the data, where x represents time and $0 \leq x \leq 4$.

Time (min)	0	2	4
Heart rate (bpm)	154	106	90

(b) Evaluate $f(1)$ and interpret the result.

(c) Estimate the times when the heart rate was from 115 to 125 beats per minute.

Writing about Mathematics

77. Explain how a table of values can be used to help solve a quadratic inequality, provided that the boundary numbers are listed in the table.

78. Explain how to determine the solution set for the inequality $ax^2 + bx + c < 0$, where $a > 0$. How would the solution set change if $a < 0$?

CHECKING BASIC CONCEPTS FOR SECTIONS 3.3 AND 3.4

1. Simplify by using the imaginary unit i.
   (a) $\sqrt{-25}$ (b) $\sqrt{-3} \cdot \sqrt{-18}$
   (c) $\dfrac{7 \pm \sqrt{-98}}{14}$

2. Write each expression in standard form.
   (a) $-3i - (5 - 2i)$ (b) $(6 - 7i) + (-1 + i)$
   (c) $i(1 - i)(1 + i)$ (d) $\dfrac{1 + 2i}{4 - i}$

3. Use the graph of $y = f(x)$ to solve $f(x) \leq 0$ and $f(x) > 0$. Write your answer in set-builder or interval notation.

(a)

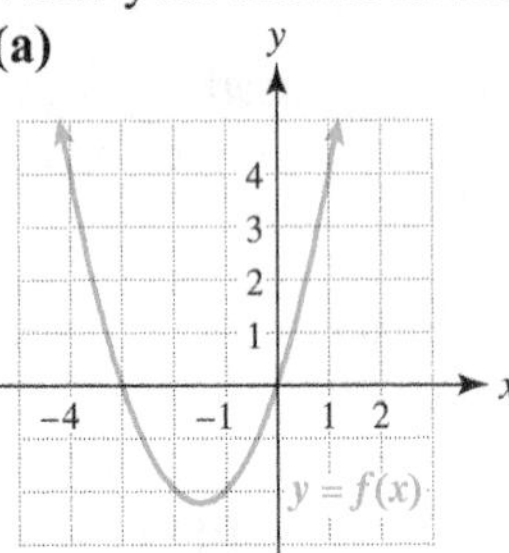

(b)

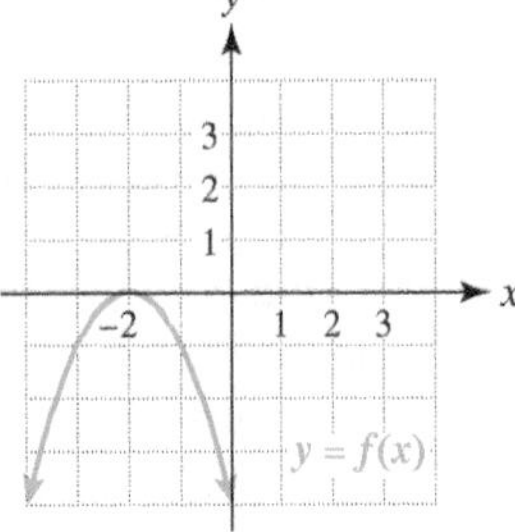

4. Solve each equation and inequality. Write the solution set for each inequality in set-builder or interval notation.
   (a) $2x^2 + 7x - 4 = 0$
   (b) $2x^2 + 7x - 4 < 0$
   (c) $2x^2 + 7x - 4 > 0$

5. Solve each inequality. Use set-builder or interval notation.
   (a) $x^2 - 36 \geq 0$
   (b) $4x^2 + 9 > 9x$
   (c) $2x(x - 1) \leq 2$

6. **Safe Driving Speeds** The stopping distance d in feet for a car traveling x miles per hour on *wet* level pavement can be estimated by $d(x) = \frac{1}{9}x^2 + \frac{11}{3}x$. Determine the driving speeds that correspond to stopping distances between 80 and 180 feet, inclusive.

3.5 Transformations of Graphs

- **Graph functions using vertical and horizontal shifts**
- **Graph functions using stretching and shrinking**
- **Graph functions using reflections**
- **Combine transformations**
- **Model data with transformations (optional)**

Introduction

Graphs are often used to model different types of phenomena. For example, when a cold front moves across the United States, we might use a circular arc on a weather map to describe its shape. (See Exercise 7 in the Extended and Discovery Exercises on page 238.) If the front does not change its shape significantly, we could model the movement of the front on a television weather map by translating the circular arc. Before we can portray a cold front on a weather map, we need to discuss how to transform graphs of functions. (***Sources:*** S. Hoggar, *Mathematics for Computer Graphics;* A. Watt, *3D Computer Graphics*.)

Vertical and Horizontal Shifts

Graphs of $f(x) = x^2$ and $g(x) = \sqrt{x}$ will be used to demonstrate shifts, or translations, in the xy-plane. Basic functions such as these are sometimes referred to as **parent functions**. Symbolic, numerical, and graphical representations of f and g are shown in Figures 3.53 and 3.54, respectively. Points listed in the table are plotted on the graph.

Vertical Shifts If 2 is added to the formula for each parent function, their graphs are shifted upward 2 units. The graphs of $y = x^2 + 2$ and $y = \sqrt{x} + 2$ are shown in Figures 3.55 and 3.56. Notice that the y-values in the graphs and tables increase by 2 units.

If 2 is subtracted from each of the parent formulas, the graphs are shifted downward 2 units. Verify this by graphing $y = x^2 - 2$ and $y = \sqrt{x} - 2$. Translations of this type are called **vertical shifts**, or **vertical translations**. They do not alter the shape of the graph, only its position. The parent and shifted graphs are congruent.

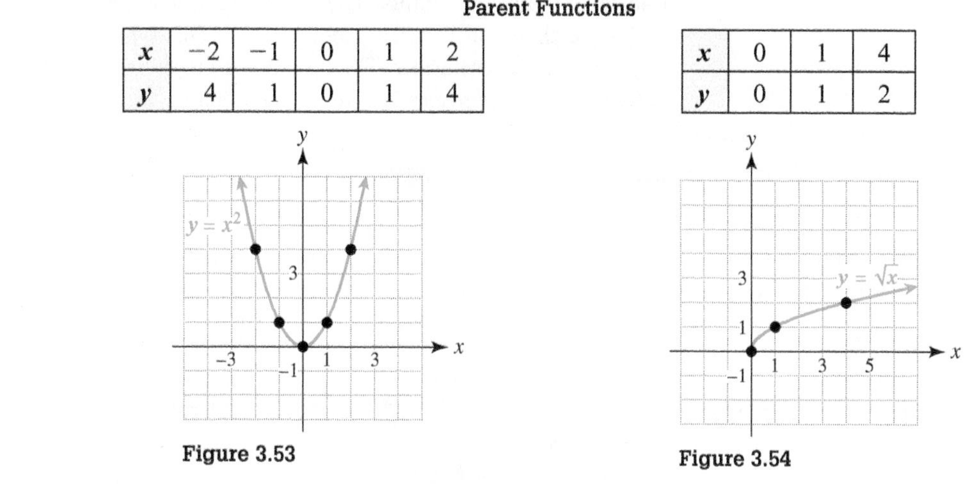

Parent Functions

x	-2	-1	0	1	2
y	4	1	0	1	4

x	0	1	4
y	0	1	2

Figure 3.53

Figure 3.54

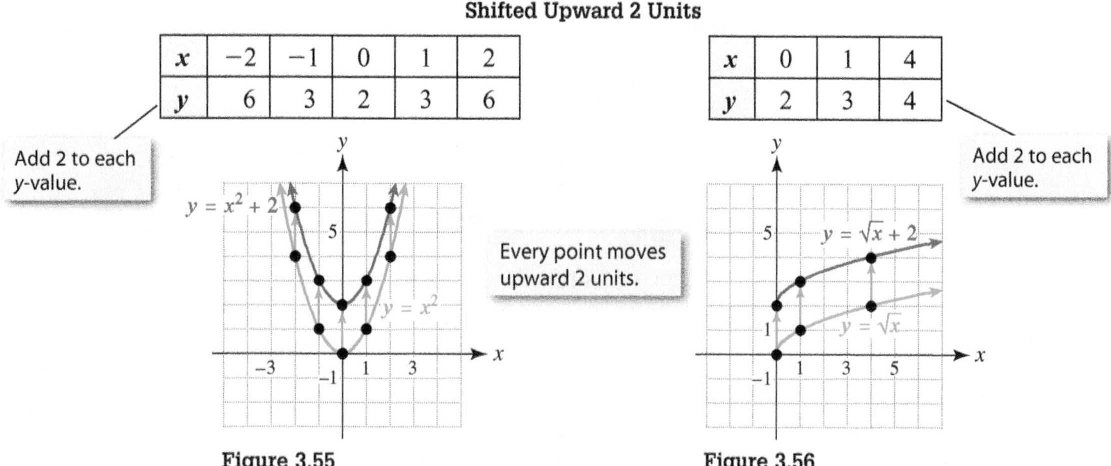

Shifted Upward 2 Units

x	-2	-1	0	1	2
y	6	3	2	3	6

x	0	1	4
y	2	3	4

Figure 3.55

Figure 3.56

Horizontal Shifts If the variable x is replaced by $(x - 2)$ in the formulas for f and g, a different type of shift results. Figures 3.57 and 3.58 show the graphs and tables of $y = (x - 2)^2$ and $y = \sqrt{(x - 2)}$, together with the graphs of the parent functions.

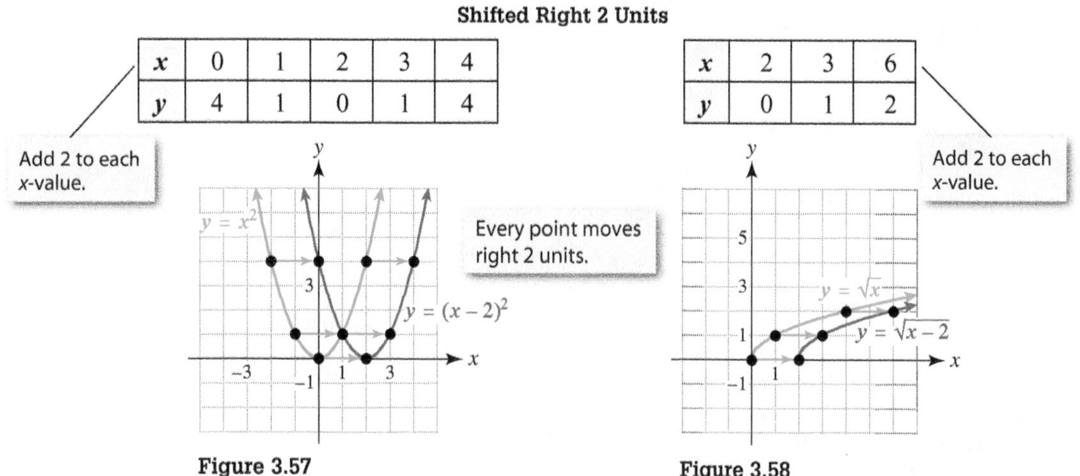

Shifted Right 2 Units

x	0	1	2	3	4
y	4	1	0	1	4

x	2	3	6
y	0	1	2

Figure 3.57

Figure 3.58

Each new graph shows a shift of the parent graph to the *right* by 2 units. Notice that a table for a graph shifted *right* 2 units can be obtained from the parent table by *adding* 2 to each x-value.

If the variable x is replaced by $(x + 3)$ in each equation, the parent graphs are translated to the *left* 3 units. The graphs of $y = (x + 3)^2$ and $y = \sqrt{(x + 3)}$ and their tables are shown in Figures 3.59 and 3.60. This type of translation is a **horizontal shift**, or **horizontal translation**. The table for a graph shifted *left* 3 units is obtained from the parent table by *subtracting* 3 from each x-value.

Shifted Left 3 Units

x	−5	−4	−3	−2	−1
y	4	1	0	1	4

x	−3	−2	1
y	0	1	2

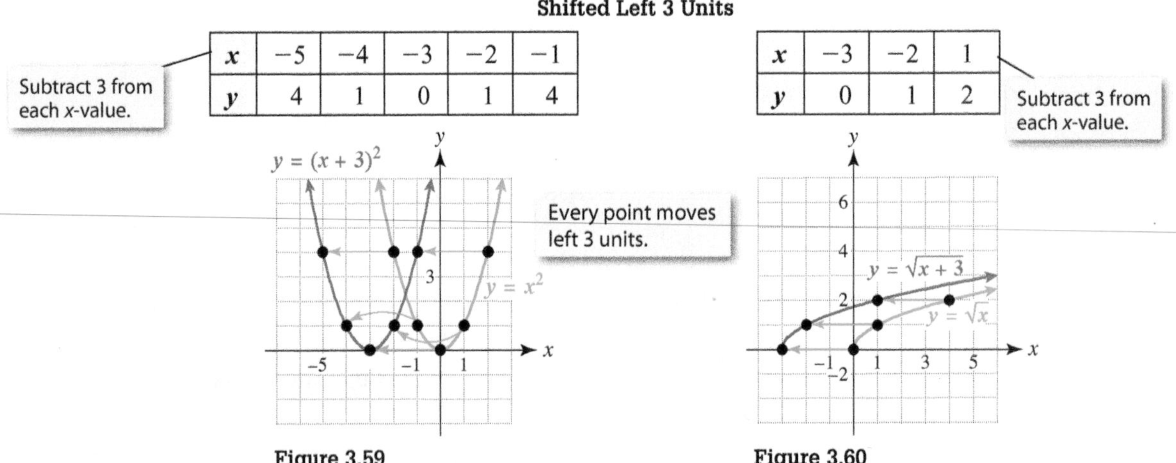

Figure 3.59 **Figure 3.60**

These ideas are summarized in the following box.

VERTICAL AND HORIZONTAL SHIFTS

Let f be a function, and let c be a positive number.

To Graph	Shift the Graph of $y = f(x)$ by c Units
$y = f(x) + c$	upward
$y = f(x) - c$	downward
$y = f(x - c)$	right
$y = f(x + c)$	left

Shifts can be combined to translate a graph of $y = f(x)$. For example, we can shift the graph of $y = |x|$ to the right 2 units and downward 4 units, as follows.

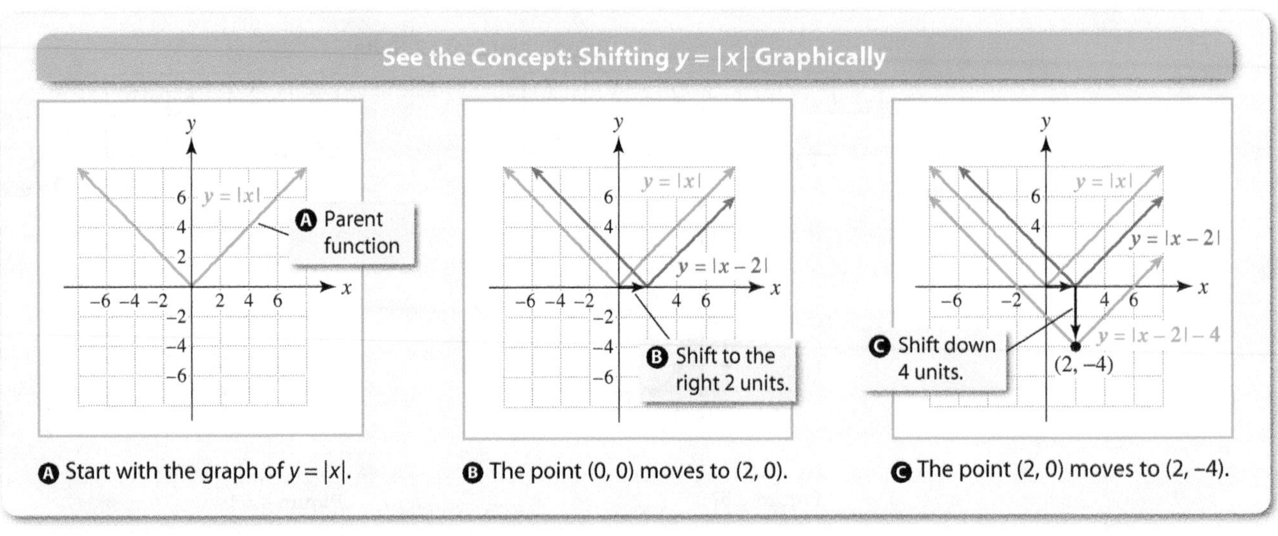

A Start with the graph of $y = |x|$.

B The point (0, 0) moves to (2, 0).

C The point (2, 0) moves to (2, −4).

Shifting $y = |x|$ Symbolically

$$y = |x| \xrightarrow{\text{Shift to the right 2 units}} y = |x - 2| \xrightarrow{\text{Shift down 4 units}} y = |x - 2| - 4$$

EXAMPLE 1 **Combining vertical and horizontal shifts**

Complete the following.

(a) Write an equation that shifts the graph of $f(x) = x^2$ left 2 units. Graph your equation.

(b) Write an equation that shifts the graph of $f(x) = x^2$ left 2 units and downward 3 units. Graph your equation.

SOLUTION

(a) To shift $f(x) = x^2$ left 2 units, replace x with $x + 2$ to obtain $y = f(x + 2)$, or $y = (x + 2)^2$. Its graph is shown in Figure 3.61.

(b) To shift $f(x) = x^2$ left 2 units and downward 3 units, we subtract 3 from the equation found in part (a) to obtain $y = f(x + 2) - 3$, or $y = (x + 2)^2 - 3$. Its graph is shown in Figure 3.62. The graph does not change shape.

Shifting $y = x^2$ Left 2 Units

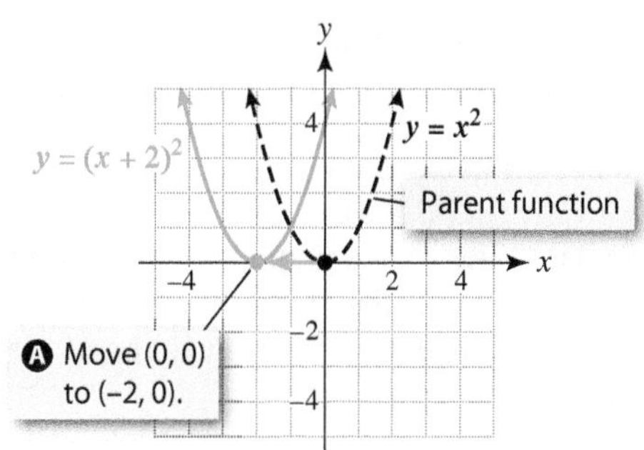

Figure 3.61

Shifting $y = x^2$ Left 2 Units and Downward 3 Units

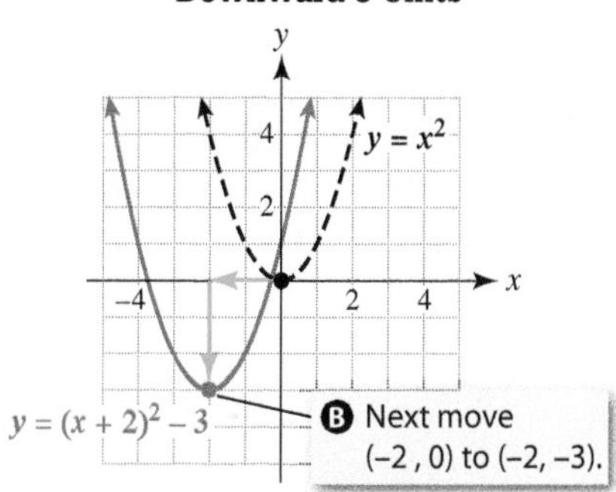

Figure 3.62

Now Try Exercise 9

EXAMPLE 2 **Writing formulas**

Write a formula for a function g whose graph is similar to that of $f(x) = 4x^2 - 2x + 1$ but is shifted right 1980 units and upward 50 units. Do not simplify the formula.

SOLUTION Replace x with $(x - 1980)$ in the formula for $f(x)$ and then add 50.

$$\begin{aligned} g(x) &= f(x - 1980) + 50 \\ &= 4(x - 1980)^2 - 2(x - 1980) + 1 + 50 \\ &= 4(x - 1980)^2 - 2(x - 1980) + 51 \end{aligned}$$

Now Try Exercise 19

In the next example we translate a circle that is centered at the origin.

EXAMPLE 3 **Translating a circle**

The equation of a circle having radius 3 and center (0, 0) is $x^2 + y^2 = 9$. Write an equation that shifts this circle to the right 4 units and upward 2 units. What are the center and radius of this circle? (Note that a circle is not a function.)

SOLUTION

Getting Started The standard equation for a circle with center (h, k) and radius r is

$$(x - h)^2 + (y - k)^2 = r^2.$$

If we determine the new center and radius, we can apply the standard equation. ▶

Translating a Circle

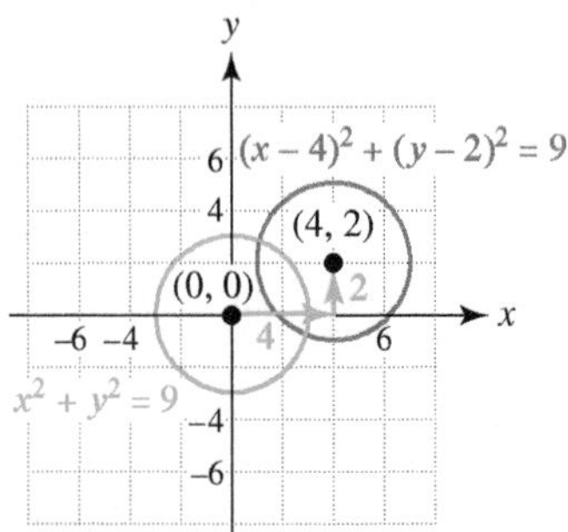

Figure 3.63

If a circle with center (0, 0) and radius 3 is translated to the right 4 units and upward 2 units, then the center of the new circle is (0 + 4, 0 + 2), or (4, 2); the radius remains the same. The standard equation for a circle with center (4, 2) and radius 3 is

$$(x - 4)^2 + (y - 2)^2 = 9.$$

Figure 3.63 illustrates this translation.

Now Try Exercise 23

NOTE Example 3 illustrates that to translate a circle horizontally c units, replace x with $(x - c)$, and to translate a circle vertically c units, replace y with $(y - c)$. If c is positive, the translation is either to the right or upward. If c is negative, the translation is either to the left or downward.

Stretching and Shrinking

Vertical Stretching and Shrinking The graph of a function can be transformed by vertical stretching or shrinking as described next.

VERTICAL STRETCHING AND SHRINKING

If the point (x, y) lies on the graph of $y = f(x)$, then the point (x, cy) lies on the graph of $y = cf(x)$. If $c > 1$, the graph of $y = cf(x)$ is a vertical stretching of the graph of $y = f(x)$, whereas if $0 < c < 1$, the graph of $y = cf(x)$ is a vertical shrinking of the graph of $y = f(x)$.

MAKING CONNECTIONS

Vertical Stretching and Shrinking

Vertical stretching "pulls" the graph away from the x-axis.

Vertical shrinking "pushes" the graph towards the x-axis. In both cases the x-intercepts do not change.

For example, if the point (4, 2) is on the graph of $y = f(x)$, then the point (4, 4) is on the graph of $y = 2f(x)$ and the point (4, 1) is on the graph of $y = \frac{1}{2}f(x)$. The graph of $f(x) = \sqrt{x}$ in Figure 3.64 can be stretched or shrunk *vertically*. In Figure 3.65, the graph of $y = 2f(x)$, or $y = 2\sqrt{x}$, represents a vertical stretching of the graph of $y = \sqrt{x}$. In Figure 3.66, the graph of $y = \frac{1}{2}f(x)$, or $y = \frac{1}{2}\sqrt{x}$, represents a vertical shrinking of the graph of $y = \sqrt{x}$. Compared to the y-values in the table for $y = \sqrt{x}$, the y-values in the tables for $y = 2f(x)$ and $y = \frac{1}{2}f(x)$ have been multiplied by 2 and $\frac{1}{2}$, respectively. The x-values have not changed.

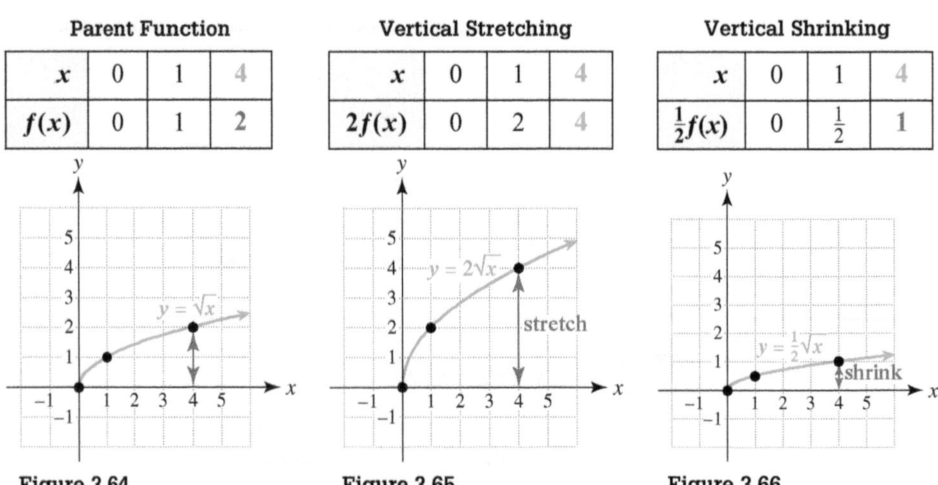

Parent Function

x	0	1	4
$f(x)$	0	1	2

Vertical Stretching

x	0	1	4
$2f(x)$	0	2	4

Vertical Shrinking

x	0	1	4
$\frac{1}{2}f(x)$	0	$\frac{1}{2}$	1

Figure 3.64 Figure 3.65 Figure 3.66

Horizontal Stretching and Shrinking The line graph in Figure 3.67 can be stretched or shrunk *horizontally*. On one hand, if the line graph represents the graph of a function f, then the graph of $y = f\left(\frac{1}{2}x\right)$ in Figure 3.68 is a horizontal stretching of the graph of $y = f(x)$. On the other hand, the graph of $y = f(2x)$ in Figure 3.69 represents a horizontal shrinking of the graph of $y = f(x)$. Compared to the x-values in the table for $y = f(x)$, the x-values in the table for $y = f\left(\frac{1}{2}x\right)$ have been multiplied by 2 and the x-values in the table for $y = f(2x)$ have been multiplied by $\frac{1}{2}$. The y-values have not changed.

Parent Function

x	-2	-1	1	2
$f(x)$	3	-3	3	-3

Horizontal Stretching

x	-4	-2	2	4
$f\left(\frac{1}{2}x\right)$	3	-3	3	-3

Horizontal Shrinking

x	-1	$-\frac{1}{2}$	$\frac{1}{2}$	1
$f(2x)$	3	-3	3	-3

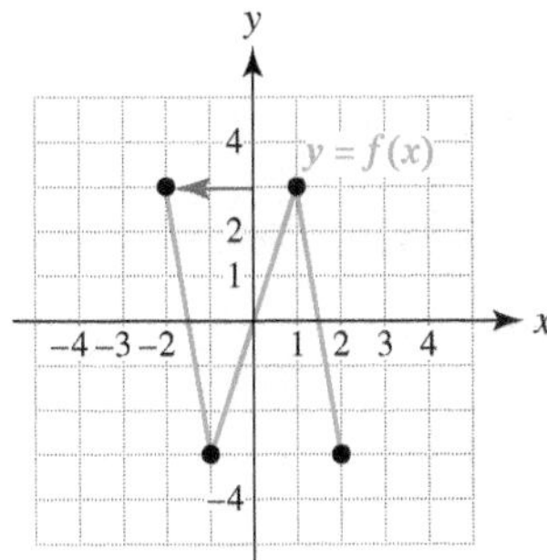

Figure 3.67

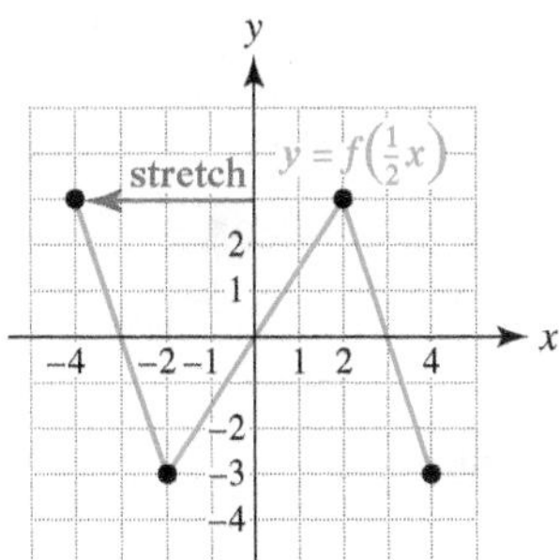

Figure 3.68

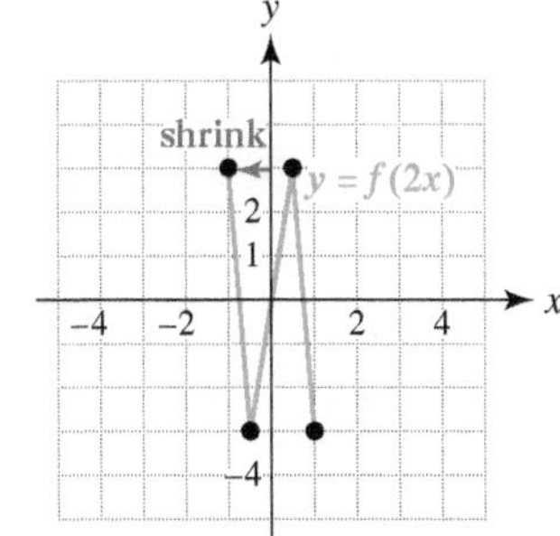

Figure 3.69

NOTE Horizontal stretching or shrinking does not change the height (maximum or minimum y-values) of the graph, nor does it change the y-intercept. Horizontal stretching and shrinking can be generalized for any function f.

HORIZONTAL STRETCHING AND SHRINKING

If the point (x, y) lies on the graph of $y = f(x)$, then the point $\left(\frac{x}{c}, y\right)$ lies on the graph of $y = f(cx)$. If $c > 1$, the graph of $y = f(cx)$ is a horizontal shrinking of the graph of $y = f(x)$, whereas if $0 < c < 1$, the graph of $y = f(cx)$ is a horizontal stretching of the graph of $y = f(x)$.

For example, if the point $(-2, 3)$ is on the graph of $y = f(x)$, then the point $(-1, 3)$ is on the graph of $y = f(2x)$ and the point $(-4, 3)$ is on the graph of $y = f\left(\frac{1}{2}x\right)$.

MAKING CONNECTIONS

Horizontal Stretching and Shrinking

Horizontal stretching "pulls" the graph away from the y-axis.

Horizontal shrinking "pushes" the graph towards the y-axis. In both cases the y-intercepts do not change.

EXAMPLE 4 **Stretching and shrinking of a graph**

Use the graph and table of $y = f(x)$ in Figure 3.70 on the next page to sketch a graph of each equation.

(a) $y = 3f(x)$

(b) $y = f\left(\frac{1}{2}x\right)$

SOLUTION

(a) The graph of $y = 3f(x)$, shown in Figure 3.71, is a vertical stretching of the graph of the given function $y = f(x)$, shown in Figure 3.70, and can be obtained by multiplying each y-coordinate on the graph of $y = f(x)$ by 3.

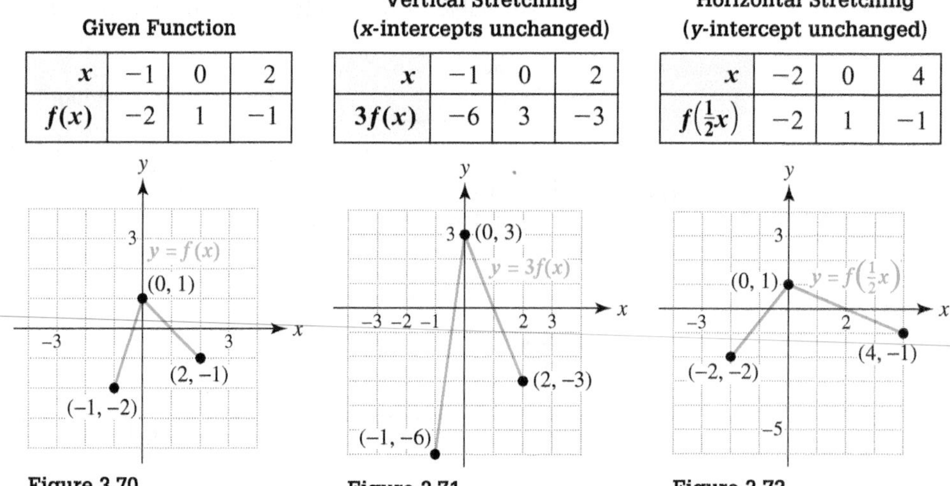

Given Function

x	-1	0	2
$f(x)$	-2	1	-1

Vertical Stretching (x-intercepts unchanged)

x	-1	0	2
$3f(x)$	-6	3	-3

Horizontal Stretching (y-intercept unchanged)

x	-2	0	4
$f\left(\frac{1}{2}x\right)$	-2	1	-1

Figure 3.70 Figure 3.71 Figure 3.72

(b) The graph of $y = f\left(\frac{1}{2}x\right)$, shown in Figure 3.72, is a horizontal stretching of the graph of $y = f(x)$, shown in Figure 3.70, and can be obtained by *dividing* each x-coordinate on the graph of $y = f(x)$ by $\frac{1}{2}$, which is equivalent to multiplying each x-coordinate by 2.

Now Try Exercises 33(a) and (b)

Reflection of Graphs

Another type of translation is called a **reflection**. The reflection of the blue graph of $y = f(x)$ across the x-axis is shown in Figure 3.73 as a red curve. This reflection can be thought of as flipping the graph of $y = f(x)$ across the x-axis.

If (x, y) is a point on the graph of f, then $(x, -y)$ lies on the graph of its reflection across the x-axis, as shown in Figure 3.73. Thus a reflection of $y = f(x)$ is given by the equation $-y = f(x)$, or equivalently, $y = -f(x)$.

If a point (x, y) lies on the graph of a function f, then the point $(-x, y)$ lies on the graph of its reflection across the y-axis, as shown in Figure 3.74. Thus a reflection of $y = f(x)$ across the y-axis is given by $y = f(-x)$. This reflection can be thought of as flipping the graph of $y = f(x)$ across the y-axis. Another example is shown in Figure 3.75.

Reflection Across x-Axis

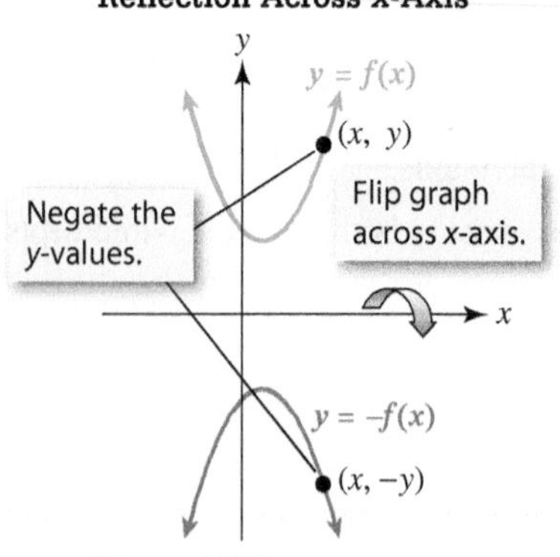

Figure 3.73

Reflections Across y-Axis

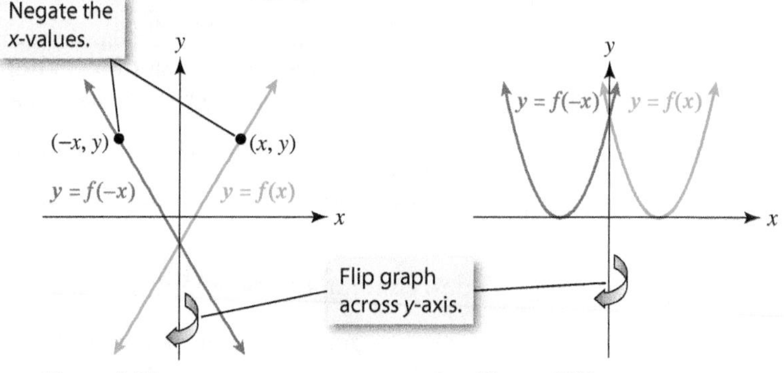

Figure 3.74 Figure 3.75

These results are summarized in the following box.

REFLECTIONS OF GRAPHS ACROSS THE x-AND y-AXES

1. The graph of $y = -f(x)$ is a reflection of the graph of $y = f(x)$ across the x-axis.
2. The graph of $y = f(-x)$ is a reflection of the graph of $y = f(x)$ across the y-axis.

EXAMPLE 5 Reflecting graphs of functions

Complete the following.

(a) Write an equation that reflects the graph of $f(x) = x^2 + 1$ across the x-axis. Graph your equation.

(b) Write an equation that reflects the graph of $f(x) = \sqrt{x}$ across the y-axis. Graph your equation.

SOLUTION

(a) To reflect $f(x) = x^2 + 1$ across the x-axis, replace $f(x)$ with $-f(x)$ to obtain $y = -f(x)$, or $y = -x^2 - 1$. See Figure 3.76.

(b) To reflect $f(x) = \sqrt{x}$ across the y-axis, replace x with $-x$ to obtain $y = f(-x)$, or $y = \sqrt{-x}$. See Figure 3.77.

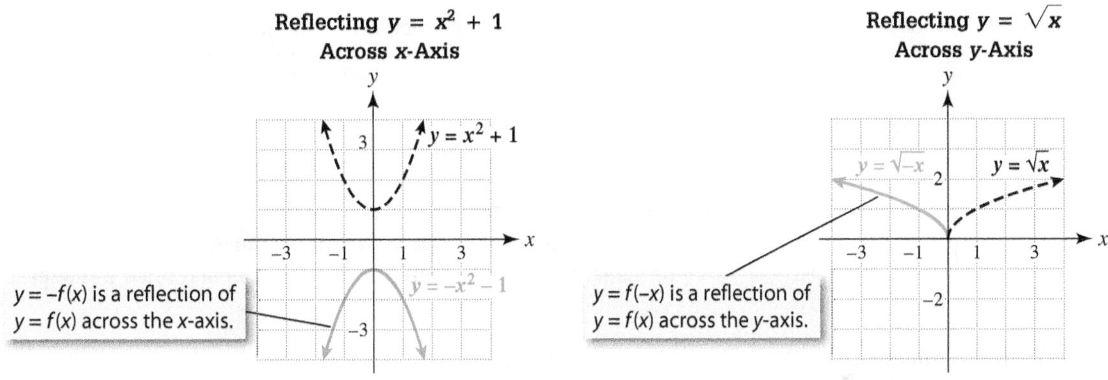

Figure 3.76

Figure 3.77

Now Try Exercises 35 and 37

Calculator Help

To access the variable Y_1 as shown in Figure 3.78, see Appendix A (page AP-10).

Graphing Calculators (Optional) On a graphing calculator capable of using function notation, entering equations for reflections of a function f is easy. For example, if $f(x) = (x - 4)^2$, let $Y_1 = (X - 4)^2$, $Y_2 = -Y_1$, and $Y_3 = Y_1(-X)$. See Figures 3.78 and 3.79.

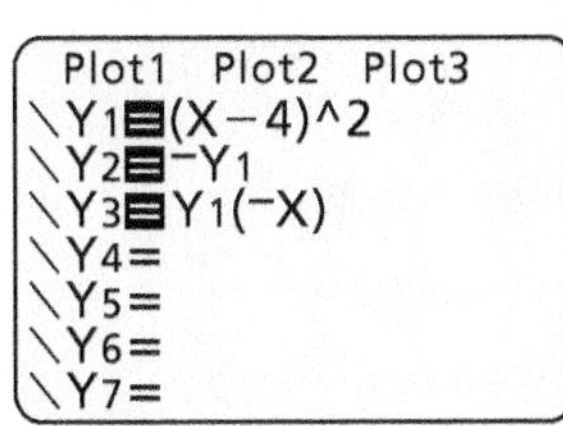

Figure 3.78

[−10, 10, 1] by [−10, 10, 1]

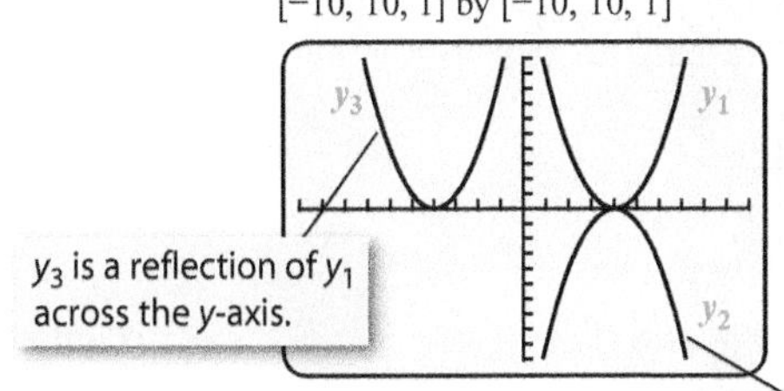

Figure 3.79

EXAMPLE 6 Reflecting graphs of functions

For each representation of f, graph the reflection across the x-axis and across the y-axis.

(a) $f(x) = x^2 + 2x - 3$

(b) The graph of f is a line graph determined by Table 3.10.

x	-2	-1	0	3
$f(x)$	1	-3	-1	2

Table 3.10

SOLUTION

(a) The graph of $f(x) = x^2 + 2x - 3$ is shown in Figure 3.80. To obtain its reflection across the x-axis, graph $y = -f(x)$, or $y = -x^2 - 2x + 3$, as shown in Figure 3.81. The vertex is now $(-1, 4)$.

For the reflection across the y-axis, let $y = f(-x)$, or $y = (-x)^2 + 2(-x) - 3$, and graph, as shown in Figure 3.82. The vertex is now $(1, -4)$.

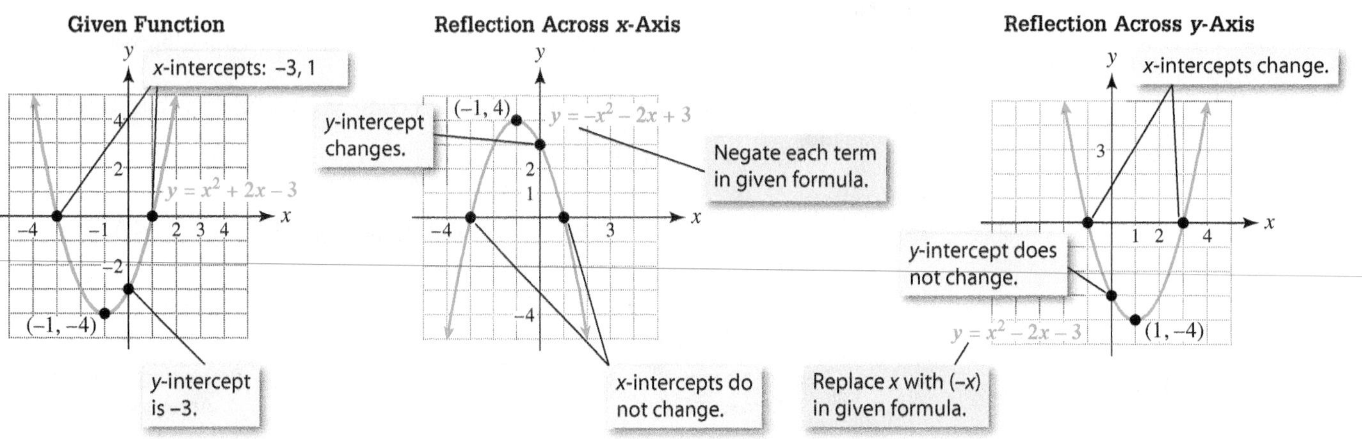

Figure 3.80 $y = f(x)$ **Figure 3.81** $y = -f(x)$ **Figure 3.82** $y = f(-x)$

(b) The graph of $y = f(x)$ is a line graph, shown in Figure 3.83. To graph the reflection of f across the x-axis, make a table of values for $y = -f(x)$ by negating each y-value in the table for $f(x)$. Then plot these points and draw a line graph, as in Figure 3.84.

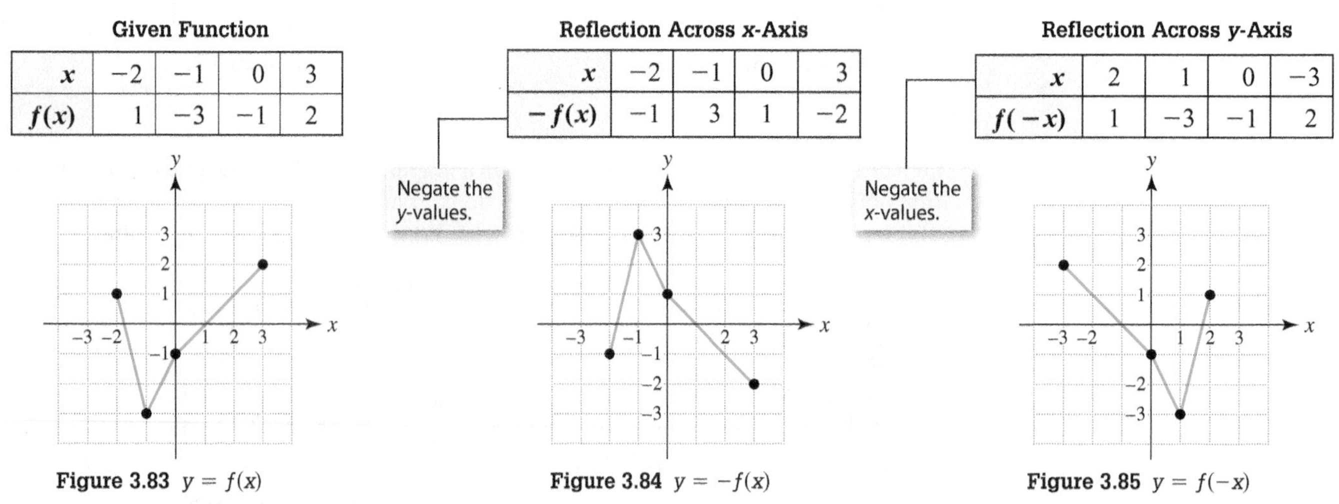

x	-2	-1	0	3
$f(x)$	1	-3	-1	2

x	-2	-1	0	3
$-f(x)$	-1	3	1	-2

x	2	1	0	-3
$f(-x)$	1	-3	-1	2

Figure 3.83 $y = f(x)$ **Figure 3.84** $y = -f(x)$ **Figure 3.85** $y = f(-x)$

To graph the reflection of f across the y-axis, make a table of values for $y = f(-x)$ by negating each x-value in the table for $f(x)$. Then plot these points and draw a line graph, as in Figure 3.85.

Now Try Exercises 39 and 43

NOTE Compared to the y-values in a table of values for $y = f(x)$, the y-values in a table of values for $y = -f(x)$ are negated; the x-values do *not* change. Compared to the x-values in a table of values for $y = f(x)$, the x-values in a table of values for $y = f(-x)$ are negated; the y-values do *not* change.

Combining Transformations

> **CLASS DISCUSSION**
>
> Given a table of values for $y = f(x)$, how would you make a table of values for $y = -f(-x)$?

Transformation of graphs can be combined to create new graphs. For example, the graph of $y = -2(x - 1)^2 + 3$ can be obtained by performing four transformations on the graph of $y = x^2$.

1. Shift the graph of $y = x^2$ to the right 1 unit: $y = (x - 1)^2$.
2. Vertically stretch the graph of $y = (x - 1)^2$ by a factor of 2: $y = 2(x - 1)^2$.
3. Reflect the graph of $y = 2(x - 1)^2$ across the x-axis: $y = -2(x - 1)^2$.
4. Shift the graph of $y = -2(x - 1)^2$ upward 3 units: $y = -2(x - 1)^2 + 3$.

These steps are summarized as follows.

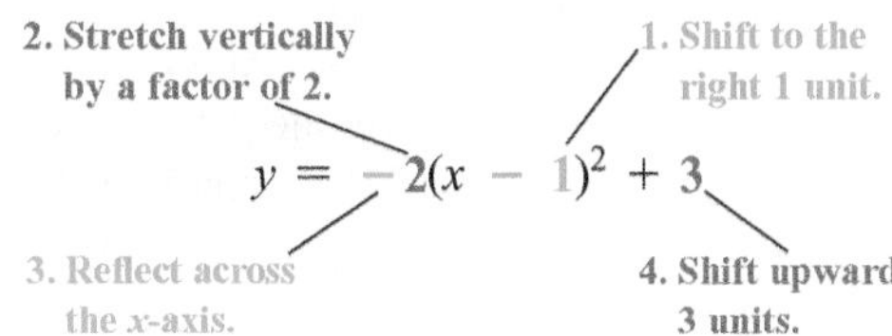

The resulting sequence of graphs is shown in Figures 3.86–3.89.

1. Shift Right

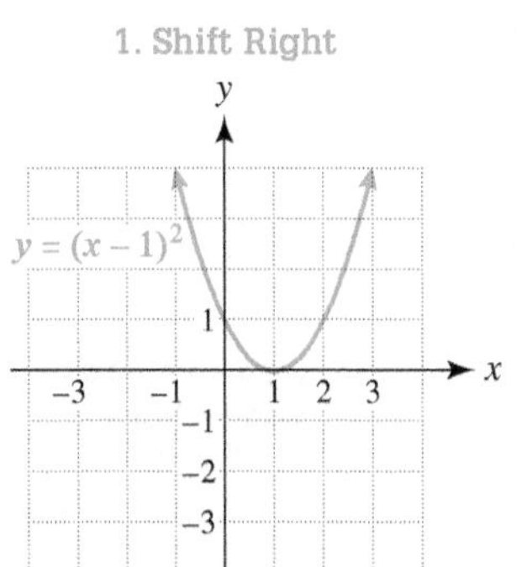

Figure 3.86

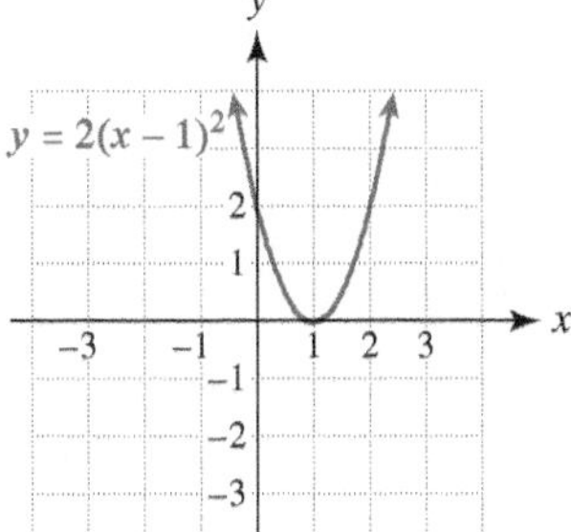

Figure 3.87

3. Reflect Across x-Axis

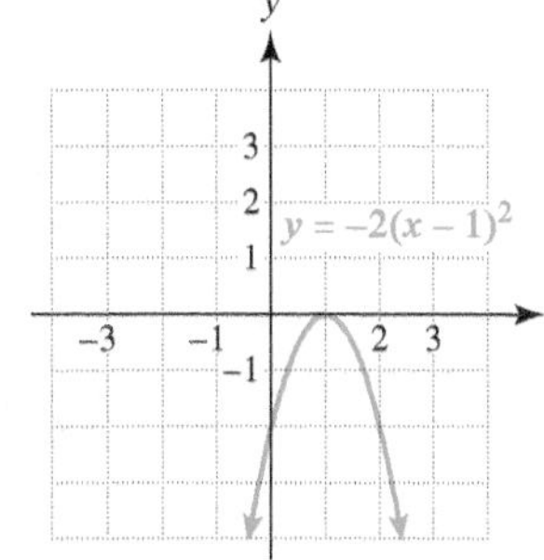

Figure 3.88

4. Shift Upward

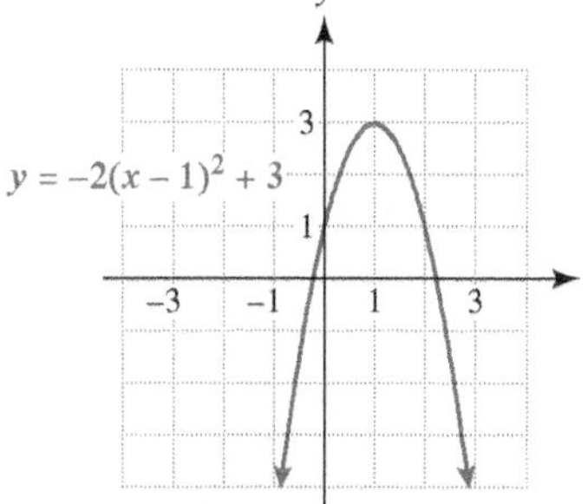

Figure 3.89

NOTE *The order in which transformations are made can be important.* For example, changing the order of a stretch and shift can result in a different equation and graph.

1. Stretch by a factor of 2. 2. Shift 3 units upward.

$$y = 2|x| + 3$$

1. Shift 3 units upward. 2. Stretch by a factor of 2.

$$y = 2(|x| + 3), \text{ or } y = 2|x| + 6$$

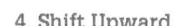

Also be careful when performing reflections and shifts. On the one hand, if we reflect the graph of $y = \sqrt{x}$ across the y-axis to obtain $y = \sqrt{-x}$ and then shift it right 2 units, we obtain $y = \sqrt{-(x - 2)}$. On the other hand, if we shift the graph of $y = \sqrt{x}$ right 2 units to obtain $y = \sqrt{x - 2}$ and then reflect it across the y-axis, we obtain $y = \sqrt{-x - 2}$. The final equations are different and so are their graphs. (Try sketching each graph.)

The following order can be used to graph the functions that we will encounter in this section.

> **COMBINING TRANSFORMATIONS**
>
> To graph a function by applying more than one transformation, use the following order.
>
> 1. Horizontal transformations
> 2. Stretching, shrinking, and reflections
> 3. Vertical transformations

EXAMPLE 7 **Combining transformations of graphs**

Describe how the graph of each equation can be obtained by transforming the parent graph of $y = \sqrt{x}$. Then graph the equation.

(a) $y = -\frac{1}{2}\sqrt{x}$ **(b)** $y = \sqrt{-x - 2} - 1$

SOLUTION

(a) Vertically shrink the graph of $y = \sqrt{x}$ by a factor of $\frac{1}{2}$ and then reflect it across the x-axis. See Figure 3.90.

(b) The following transformations can be used to obtain the graph of the equation $y = \sqrt{-x - 2} - 1$ from $y = \sqrt{x}$.

1. Shift the graph of $y = \sqrt{x}$ right 2 units: $y = \sqrt{x - 2}$.
2. Reflect the graph of $y = \sqrt{x - 2}$ across the y-axis: $y = \sqrt{-x - 2}$.
3. Shift the graph of $y = \sqrt{-x - 2}$ down 1 unit: $y = \sqrt{-x - 2} - 1$.

See Figure 3.91.

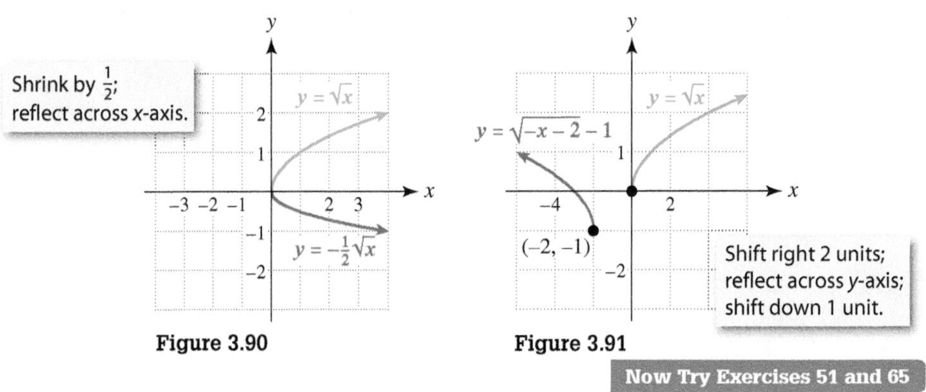

Figure 3.90

Figure 3.91

Now Try Exercises 51 and 65

Modeling with Transformations (Optional)

Transformations of the graph of $y = x^2$ can be used to model some types of nonlinear data. By shifting, stretching, and shrinking this graph, we can transform it into a *portion of a parabola* that has the desired shape and location. In the next example we demonstrate this technique by modeling numbers of Walmart employees.

EXAMPLE 8 **Modeling data with a quadratic function**

Table 3.11 lists numbers of Walmart employees in millions for selected years.

(a) Make a scatterplot of the data.

(b) Use transformations to determine $f(x) = a(x - h)^2 + k$ so that $f(x)$ models the data. Graph $y = f(x)$ together with the data.

(c) Use $f(x)$ to estimate the number of Walmart employees in 2010. Compare it with the actual value of 2.1 million employees.

Walmart Employees (in millions)

Year	Employees
1987	0.20
1992	0.37
1997	0.68
2002	1.4
2007	2.2

Source: Walmart.

Table 3.11

SOLUTION

(a) A scatterplot of the data is shown in Figure 3.92. This plot suggests that the data could be modeled by the *right half* of a parabola that opens upward.

(b) Because the parabola opens upward, it follows that $a > 0$ and the vertex is the lowest point on the parabola. The minimum number of employees is 0.20 million in 1987. One possibility for the vertex (h, k) is (1987, 0.20). Translate the graph of $y = x^2$ right 1987 units and upward 0.20 unit. Thus $f(x) = a(x - 1987)^2 + 0.20$.

To determine a, graph the data and $y = f(x)$ for different values of a. See Figures 3.93 and 3.94. With a little experimentation, a reasonable value for a near 0.005 can be found.

A scatterplot of the data and graph of $f(x) = 0.005(x - 1987)^2 + 0.2$ are shown in Figure 3.94. (Answers may vary.) Note that this equation is in *vertex form*.

Testing Values Graphically

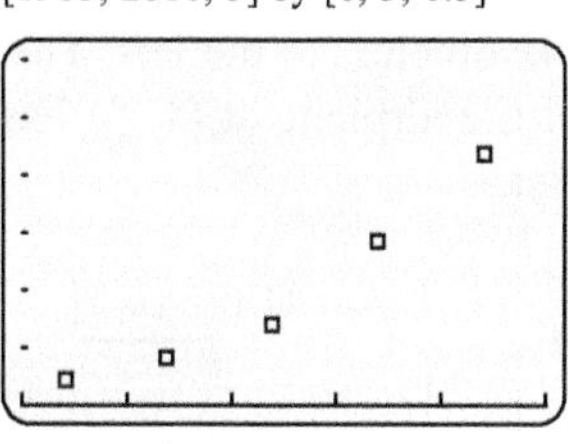

Figure 3.92

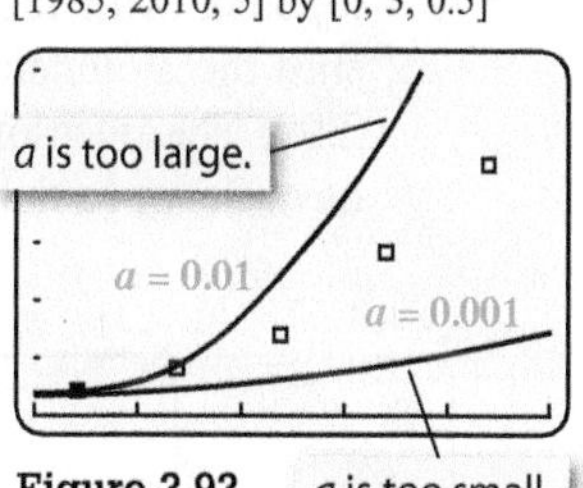

Figure 3.93

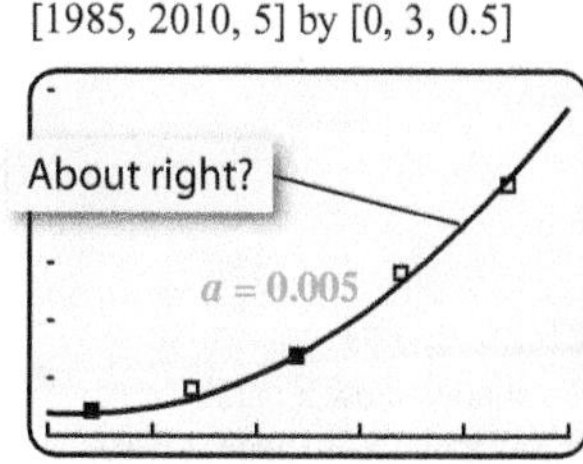

Figure 3.94

(c) To estimate the number of employees in 2010, evaluate $f(2010)$.

$$f(2010) = 0.005(2010 - 1987)^2 + 0.2 = 2.845$$

This model provides an estimate of about 2.8 million Walmart employees in 2010. The calculation involves extrapolation and is not accurate.

Now Try Exercise 95

Translations and Computer Graphics In video games, the background is often translated to give the illusion that the player in the game is moving. A simple scene of a mountain and an airplane is shown in Figure 3.95. To make it appear to the player as though the airplane were flying to the right, the image of the mountain could be translated horizontally to the left, as shown in Figure 3.96. Note that the position of the plane does not change. (***Source:*** C. Pokorny and C. Gerald, *Computer Graphics*.)

Shifting the Background to Show Motion

Figure 3.95

Figure 3.96

EXAMPLE 9 Using translations to model movement

Suppose that the mountain in Figure 3.95 can be described by $f(x) = -0.4x^2 + 4$ and that the airplane is located at the point (1, 5).

(a) Graph f in $[-4, 4, 1]$ by $[0, 6, 1]$, where the units are in kilometers. Plot a point (a scatterplot with one point) to mark the position of the airplane.

(b) Assume that the airplane is moving horizontally to the right at 0.4 kilometer per second. To give a video player the illusion that the airplane is moving, graph the image of the mountain and the position of the airplane after 5 seconds and then after 10 seconds.

SOLUTION

(a) The graph of $y = f(x) = -0.4x^2 + 4$ and the position of the airplane at (1, 5) are shown in Figure 3.97 on the next page. The "mountain" has been shaded to emphasize its position.

(b) Five seconds later, the airplane has moved $5(0.4) = 2$ kilometers right. In 10 seconds it has moved $10(0.4) = 4$ kilometers right. To graph these new positions, translate the graph of the mountain 2 and 4 kilometers (units) to the left. First, shift the mountain 2 kilometers to the left by replacing x with $(x + 2)$ and graphing

$$y = f(x + 2) = -0.4(x + 2)^2 + 4$$

together with the point (1, 5). Next, graph $y = f(x + 4) = -0.4(x + 4)^2 + 4$ to shift the mountain 4 kilometers to the left. The results are shown in Figures 3.98 and 3.99. The position of the airplane at (1, 5) has not changed. However, it appears to have flown to the right.

Calculator Help
To shade below a parabola, see Appendix A (page AP-10).

$[-4, 4, 1]$ by $[0, 6, 1]$

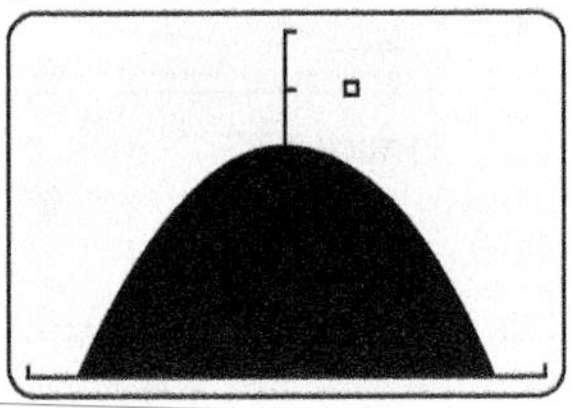

Figure 3.97

$[-4, 4, 1]$ by $[0, 6, 1]$

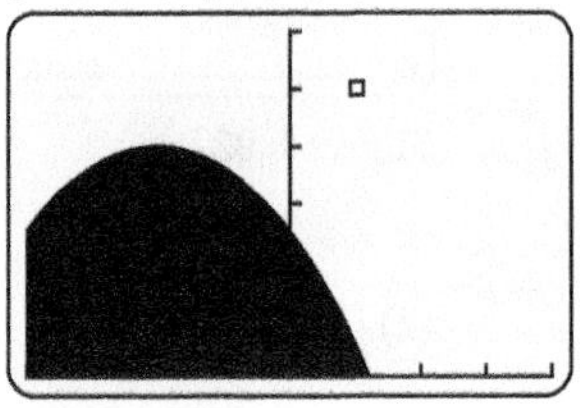

Figure 3.98

$[-4, 4, 1]$ by $[0, 6, 1]$

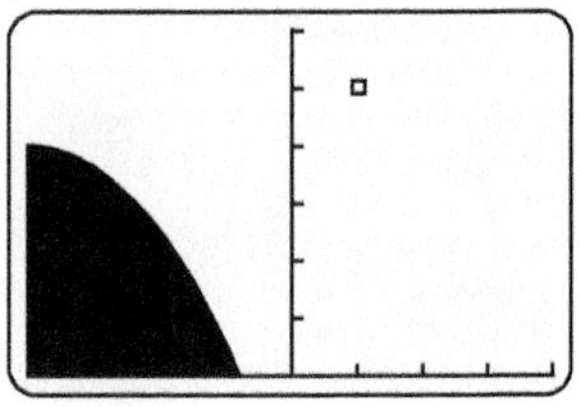

Figure 3.99

Now Try Exercise 101

CLASS DISCUSSION

Discuss how one might create the illusion of the airplane moving to the left and *gaining altitude* as it passes over the mountain.

3.5 Putting It All Together

In this section we discussed several transformations of graphs. The following table summarizes how these transformations affect the graph of $y = f(x)$.

EQUATION	EFFECT ON GRAPH OF $y = f(x)$
Let $c > 0$.	
$y = f(x) + c$	The graph of $y = f(x)$ is shifted upward c units.
$y = f(x) - c$	The graph of $y = f(x)$ is shifted downward c units.
$y = f(x + c)$	The graph of $y = f(x)$ is shifted to the left c units.
$y = f(x - c)$	The graph of $y = f(x)$ is shifted to the right c units.

Examples:

Shifted Down

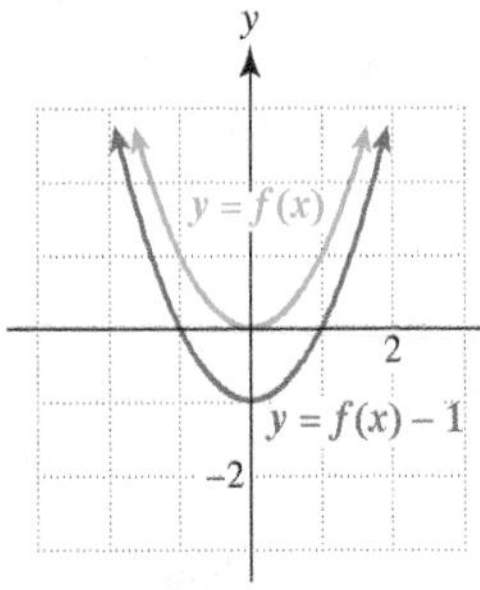

Shifted Left

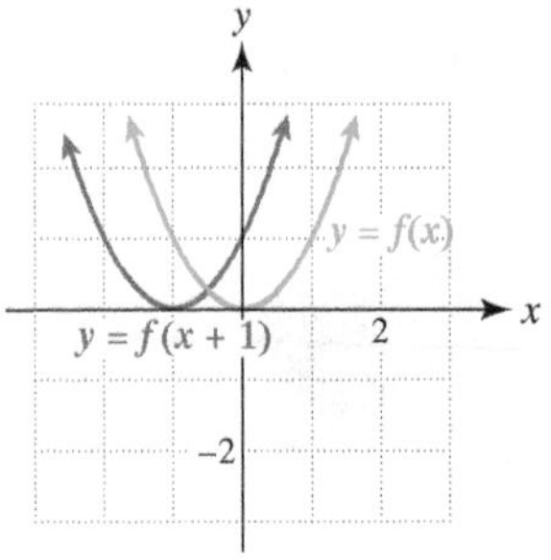

<table>
<tr><th>EQUATION</th><th>EFFECT ON GRAPH OF $y = f(x)$</th></tr>
<tr><td>Let $c > 0$.
$y = cf(x)$</td><td>

If (x, y) lies on the graph of $y = f(x)$, then (x, cy) lies on the graph of $y = cf(x)$. The graph is vertically stretched if $c > 1$ and vertically shrunk if $0 < c < 1$.

Examples:

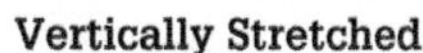

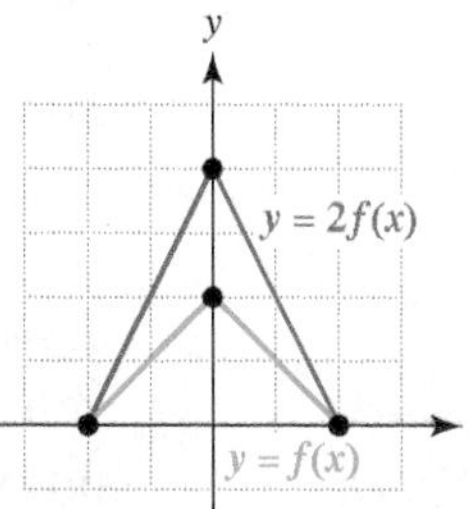

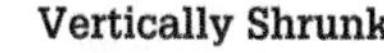

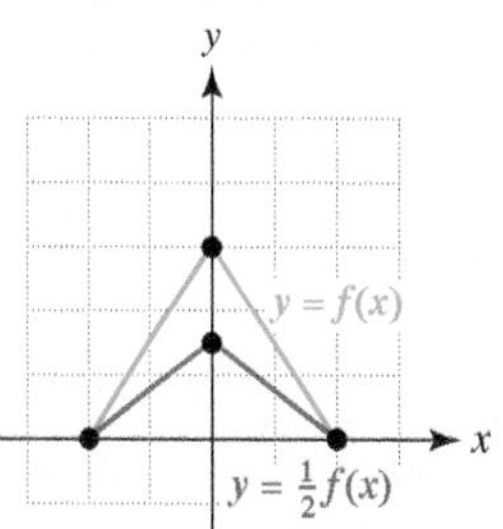

</td></tr>
<tr><td>Let $c > 0$.
$y = f(cx)$</td><td>

If (x, y) lies on the graph of $y = f(x)$, then $\left(\frac{x}{c}, y\right)$ lies on the graph of $y = f(cx)$. The graph is horizontally shrunk if $c > 1$ and horizontally stretched if $0 < c < 1$.

Examples:

Horizontally Shrunk

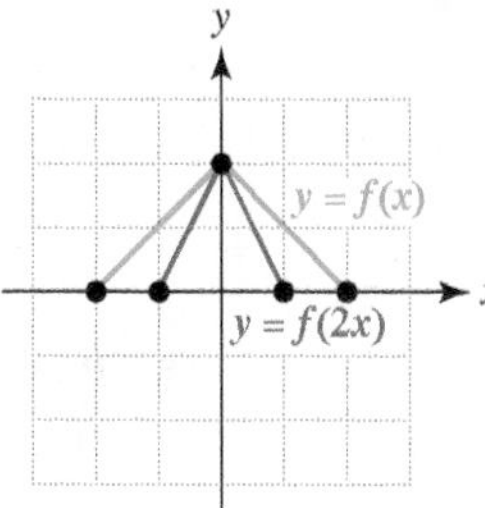

Horizontally Stretched

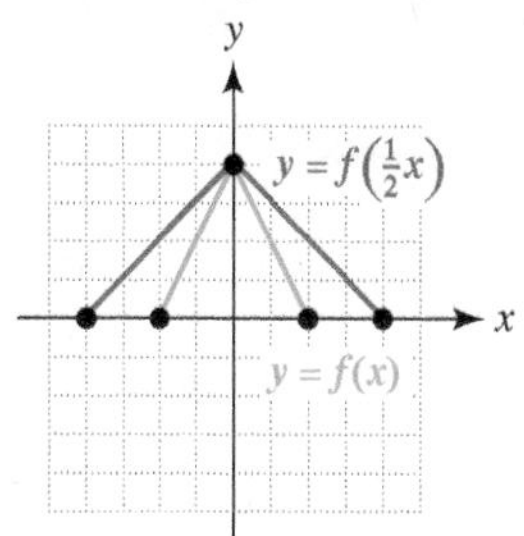

</td></tr>
<tr><td>$y = -f(x)$
$y = f(-x)$</td><td>

The graph of $y = f(x)$ is reflected across the x-axis.
The graph of $y = f(x)$ is reflected across the y-axis.

Examples:

Reflected Across *x*-Axis **Reflected Across *y*-Axis**

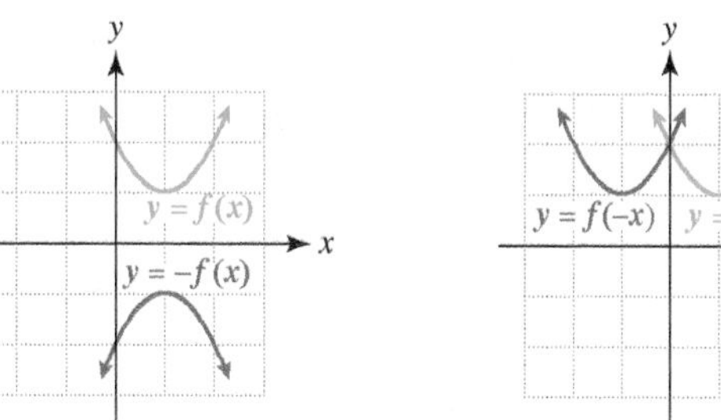

</td></tr>
</table>

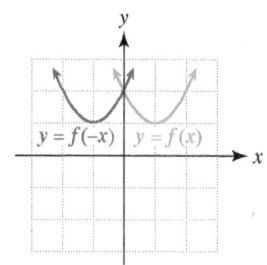

3.5 Exercises

Vertical and Horizontal Translations

Exercises 1–8: Write the equation of the graph. (Note: The given graph is a translation of the graph of one of the following equations: $y = x^2$, $y = \sqrt{x}$, or $y = |x|$.)

1.
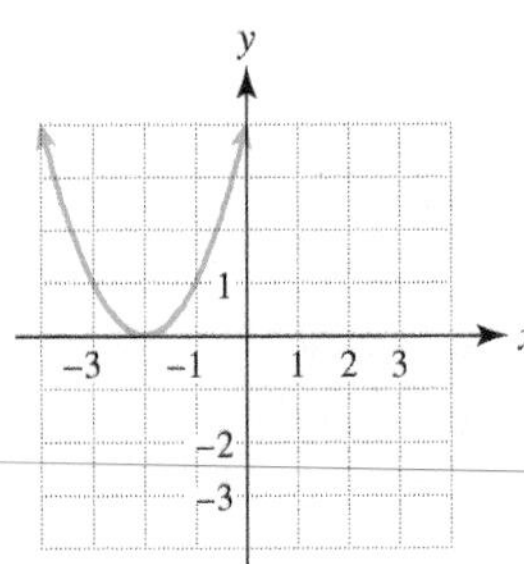

2.
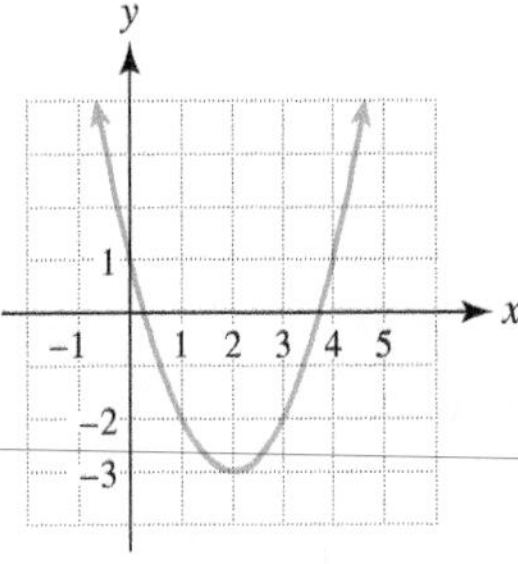

3.
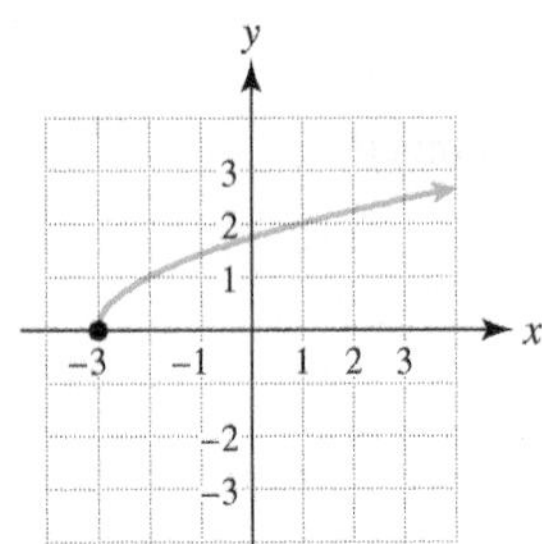

4.
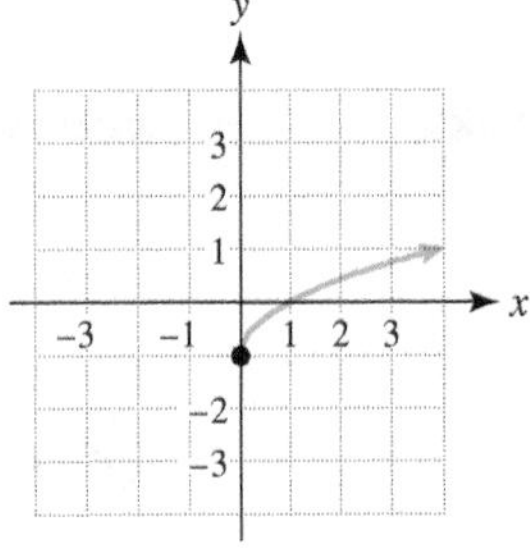

5.
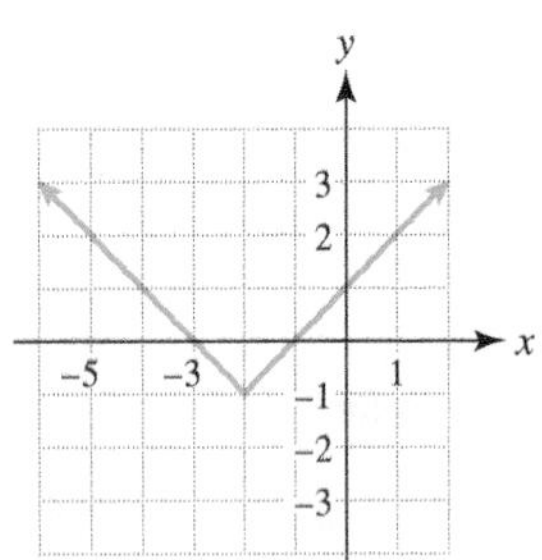

6.
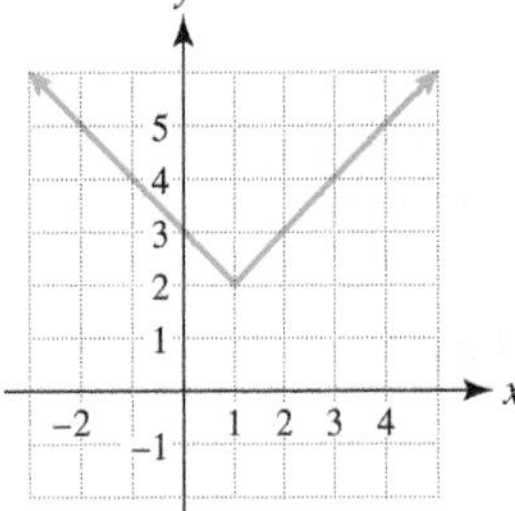

7.
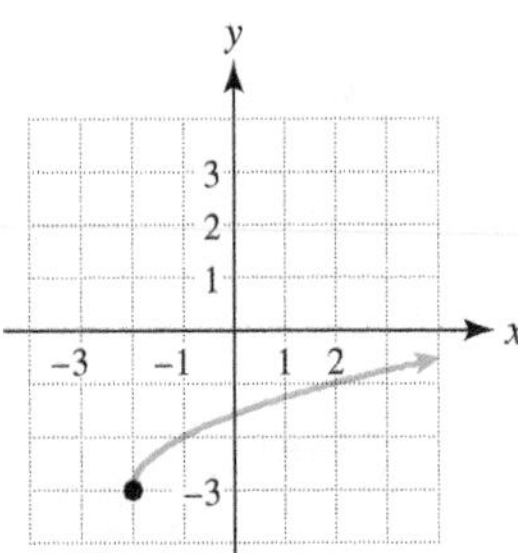

8.
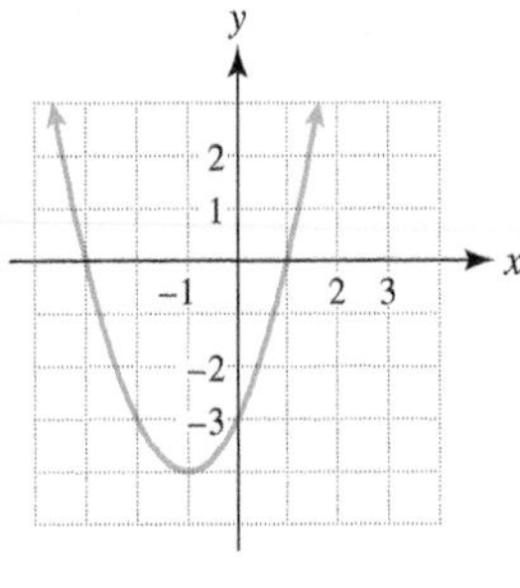

Exercises 9–14: Find an equation that shifts the graph of f by the desired amounts. Do not simplify. Graph f and the shifted graph in the same xy-plane.

9. $f(x) = x^2$; right 2 units, downward 3 units

10. $f(x) = 3x - 4$; left 3 units, upward 1 unit

11. $f(x) = x^2 - 4x + 1$; left 6 units, upward 4 units

12. $f(x) = x^2 - x - 2$; right 2 units, upward 3 units

13. $f(x) = \frac{1}{2}x^2 + 2x - 1$; left 3 units, downward 2 units

14. $f(x) = 5 - 3x - \frac{1}{2}x^2$; right 5 units, downward 8 units

Exercises 15–22: (Refer to Example 2.) Write a formula for a function g whose graph is similar to f(x) but satisfies the given conditions. Do not simplify the formula.

15. $f(x) = 3x^2 + 2x - 5$
   (a) Shifted left 3 units
   (b) Shifted downward 4 units

16. $f(x) = 2x^2 - 3x + 2$
   (a) Shifted right 8 units
   (b) Shifted upward 2 units

17. $f(x) = 2x^2$
   (a) Shifted right 2 units and upward 4 units
   (b) Shifted left 8 units and downward 5 units

18. $f(x) = 5x^2$
   (a) Shifted left 10 units and downward 6 units
   (b) Shifted right 1 unit and upward 10 units

19. $f(x) = 3x^2 - 3x + 2$
   (a) Shifted right 2000 units and upward 70 units
   (b) Shifted left 300 units and downward 30 units

20. $f(x) = |x|$
   (a) Shifted right 4 units and downward 3 units
   (b) Shifted left 5 units and upward 2 units

21. $f(x) = \sqrt{x}$
   (a) Shifted right 4 units, reflected about the x-axis
   (b) Shifted left 2 units, reflected about the y-axis

22. $f(x) = \sqrt{x}$
   (a) Reflected about the x-axis, shifted left 2 units
   (b) Reflected about the y-axis, shifted right 3 units

Exercises 23–26: **Translating Circles** *Write an equation that shifts the given circle in the specified manner. State the center and radius of the translated circle.*

23. $x^2 + y^2 = 4$; right 3 units, downward 4 units

24. $x^2 + y^2 = 9$; right 2 units, downward 6 units

25. $x^2 + y^2 = 5$; left 5 units, upward 3 units

26. $x^2 + y^2 = 7$; left 3 units, downward 7 units

Transforming Graphical Representations

Exercises 27–34: Use the accompanying graph of $y = f(x)$ to sketch a graph of each equation.

27. **(a)** $y = f(x) + 2$
(b) $y = f(x - 2) - 1$
(c) $y = -f(x)$

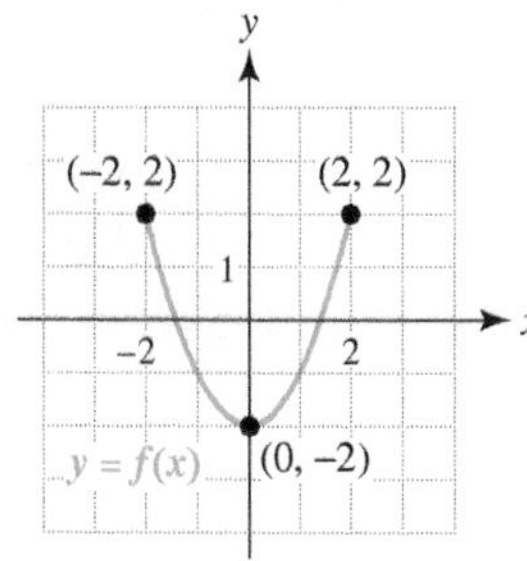

28. **(a)** $y = f(x + 1)$
(b) $y = -f(x)$
(c) $y = 2f(x)$

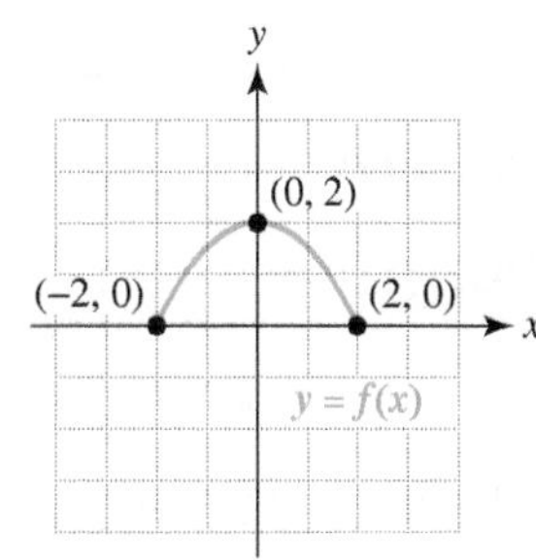

29. **(a)** $y = f(x + 3) - 2$
(b) $y = f(-x)$
(c) $y = \frac{1}{2}f(x)$

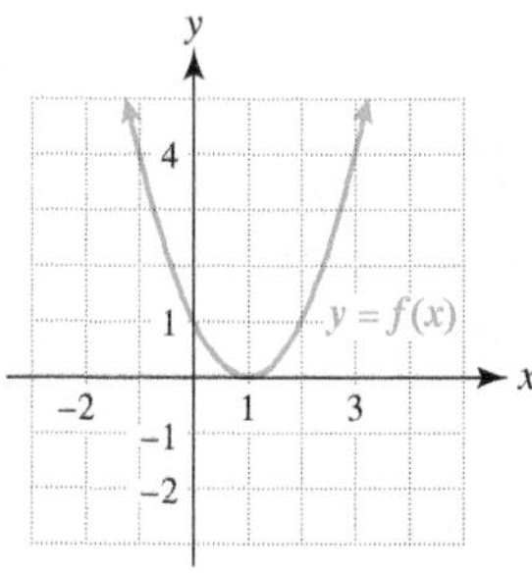

30. **(a)** $y = f(x - 1) - 2$
(b) $y = -f(x) + 1$
(c) $y = f\left(\frac{1}{2}x\right)$

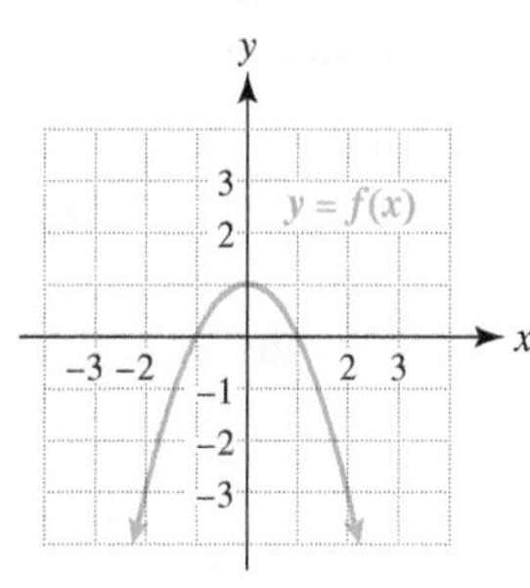

31. **(a)** $y = f(x + 1) + 1$
(b) $y = -f(x) - 1$
(c) $y = \frac{1}{2}f(2x)$

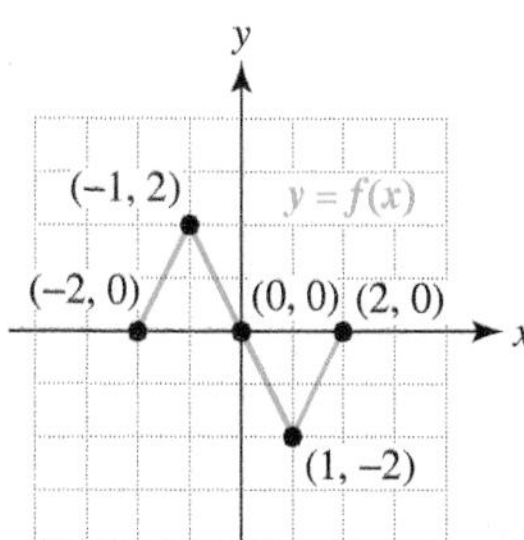

32. **(a)** $y = f(x) - 2$
(b) $y = f(x - 1) + 2$
(c) $y = 2f(-x)$

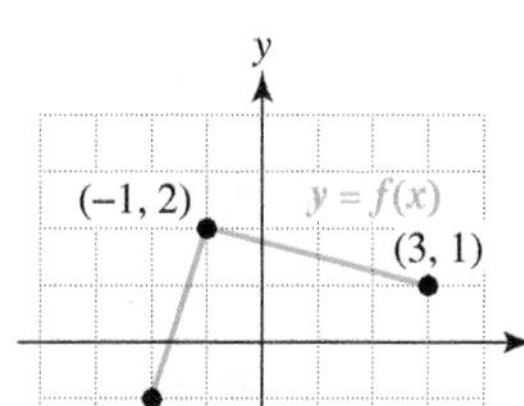

33. **(a)** $y = f(2x) + 1$

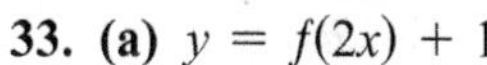

(b) $y = 2f\left(\frac{1}{2}x\right) + 1$
(c) $y = \frac{1}{2}f(2 - x)$

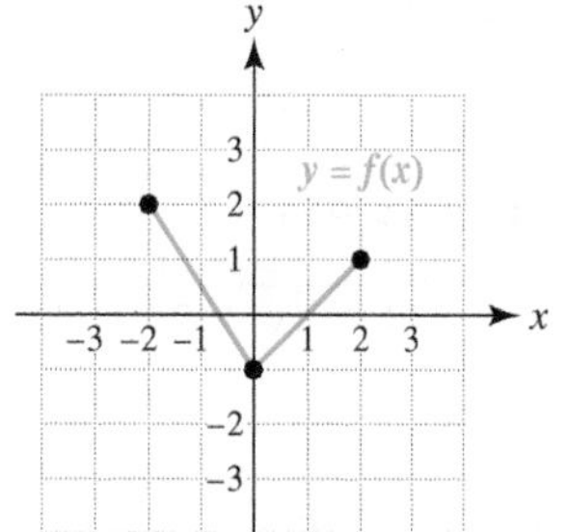

34. **(a)** $y = f(2x)$
(b) $y = f\left(\frac{1}{2}x\right) - 1$
(c) $y = 2f(1 - x)$

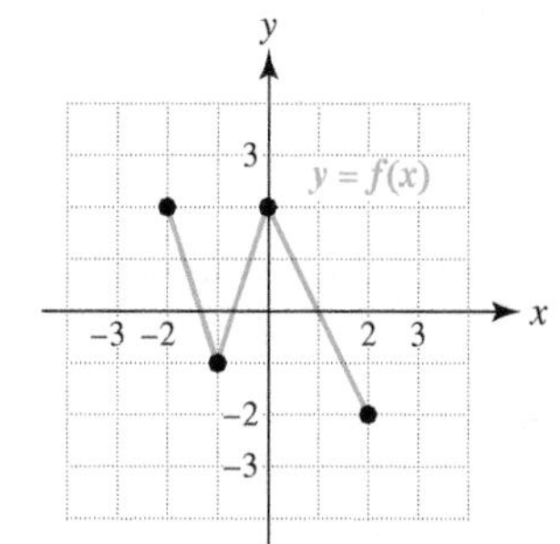

Reflections of Graphs

Exercises 35–38: Write the requested equation. Then graph the given equation and your equation.

35. Reflect $f(x) = \sqrt{x} + 1$ across the x-axis.

36. Reflect $f(x) = |x| - 1$ across the x-axis.

37. Reflect $f(x) = x^2 - x$ across the y-axis.

38. Reflect $f(x) = \sqrt{-x + 1}$ across the y-axis.

Exercises 39–44: (Refer to Example 6.) For the given representation of a function f, graph the reflection across the x-axis and graph the reflection across the y-axis.

39. $f(x) = x^2 - 2x - 3$

40. $f(x) = 4 - 7x - 2x^2$

41. $f(x) = |x + 1| - 1$

42. $f(x) = \frac{1}{2}|x - 2| + 2$

43. Line graph determined by the table

x	−3	−1	1	2
$f(x)$	2	3	−1	−2

44. Line graph determined by the table

x	−4	−2	0	1
$f(x)$	−1	−4	2	2

Graphing Transformations of Functions

Exercises 45–54. Use transformations to explain how the graph of f can be found by using the graph of $y = x^2$, $y = \sqrt{x}$, or $y = |x|$. You do not need to graph $y = f(x)$.

45. $f(x) = (x - 3)^2 + 1$

46. $f(x) = (x + 2)^2 - 3$

47. $f(x) = \frac{1}{4}(x + 1)^2$

48. $f(x) = 2(x - 4)^2$

49. $f(x) = -\sqrt{x + 5}$

50. $f(x) = -\sqrt{x} - 3$

51. $f(x) = 2\sqrt{-x}$

52. $f(x) = \sqrt{-\frac{1}{2}x}$

53. $f(x) = |-(x + 1)|$

54. $f(x) = |4 - x|$

Exercises 55–78: Use transformations to sketch a graph of f.

55. $f(x) = x^2 - 3$
56. $f(x) = -x^2$
57. $f(x) = (x - 5)^2 + 3$
58. $f(x) = (x + 4)^2$
59. $f(x) = -\sqrt{x}$
60. $f(x) = 2(x - 1)^2 + 1$
61. $f(x) = -x^2 + 4$
62. $f(x) = \sqrt{-x}$
63. $f(x) = |x| - 4$
64. $f(x) = \sqrt{x} + 1$
65. $f(x) = \sqrt{x - 3} + 2$
66. $f(x) = |x + 2| - 3$
67. $f(x) = |2x|$
68. $f(x) = \frac{1}{2}|x|$
69. $f(x) = 1 - \sqrt{x}$
70. $f(x) = 2\sqrt{x - 2} - 1$
71. $f(x) = -\sqrt{1 - x}$
72. $f(x) = \sqrt{-x} - 1$
73. $f(x) = \sqrt{-(x + 1)}$
74. $f(x) = 2 + \sqrt{-(x - 3)}$
75. $f(x) = (x - 1)^3$
76. $f(x) = (x + 2)^3$
77. $f(x) = -x^3$
78. $f(x) = (-x)^3 + 1$

Transforming Numerical Representations

Exercises 79–86: Two functions, f and g, are related by the given equation. Use the numerical representation of f to make a numerical representation of g.

79. $g(x) = f(x) + 7$

x	1	2	3	4	5	6
$f(x)$	5	1	6	2	7	9

80. $g(x) = f(x) - 10$

x	0	5	10	15	20
$f(x)$	−5	11	21	32	47

81. $g(x) = f(x - 2)$

x	−4	−2	0	2	4
$f(x)$	5	2	−3	−5	−9

82. $g(x) = f(x + 50)$

x	−100	−50	0	50	100
$f(x)$	25	80	120	150	100

83. $g(x) = f(x + 1) - 2$

x	1	2	3	4	5	6
$f(x)$	2	4	3	7	8	10

84. $g(x) = f(x - 3) + 5$

x	−3	0	3	6	9
$f(x)$	3	8	15	27	31

85. $g(x) = f(-x) + 1$

x	−2	−1	0	1	2
$f(x)$	11	8	5	2	−1

86. $g(x) = -f(x + 2)$

x	−4	−2	0	2	4
$f(x)$	5	8	10	8	5

Exercises 87–94: The points $(-12, 6)$, $(0, 8)$, and $(8, -4)$ lie on the graph of $y = f(x)$. Determine three points that lie on the graph of $y = g(x)$.

87. $g(x) = f(x) + 2$

88. $g(x) = f(x) - 3$

89. $g(x) = f(x - 2) + 1$

90. $g(x) = f(x + 1) - 1$

91. $g(x) = -\frac{1}{2}f(x)$

92. $g(x) = -2f(x)$

93. $g(x) = f(-2x)$

94. $g(x) = f\left(-\frac{1}{2}x\right)$

Applications

Exercises 95–98: (Refer to Example 8.) Use transformations of graphs to model the table of data with the formula $f(x) = a(x - h)^2 + k$. (Answers may vary.)

95. Number of iPhones sold (millions)

Year	2008	2009	2010	2011
iPhones	11.6	20.7	40.0	72.3

Source: Apple Corporation.

96. Apple apps downloaded (billions)

Year	2009	2010	2011
Apps	1.1	2.9	6.5

Source: Apple Corporation.

97. Google revenue ($ billions)

Year	2008	2009	2010	2011
Revenue	22	24	29	38

Source: Google.

98. Average price of a home in thousands of dollars

Year	1970	1980	1990	2000	2005
Price	30	80	150	210	300

Source: Bureau of the Census.

99. U.S. Home Ownership The general trend in the percentage P of homes lived in by owners rather than renters between 1990 and 2006 is modeled by

$$P(x) = 0.00075x^2 + 0.17x + 44,$$

where $x = 0$ corresponds to 1990, $x = 1$ to 1991, and so on. Determine a function g that computes P, where x is the actual year. For example, $P(0) = 44$, so $g(1990) = 44$.

100. U.S. AIDS Deaths The function D defined by

$$D(x) = 2375x^2 + 5134x + 5020$$

models AIDS deaths x years after 1984. Write a formula $g(x)$ that computes AIDS deaths during year x, where x is the actual year.

Using Transformations to Model Motion

101. Computer Graphics (Refer to Example 9.) Suppose that the airplane in Figure 3.95 is flying at 0.2 kilometer per second to the left, rather than to the right. If the position of the airplane is fixed at $(-1, 5)$, graph the image of the mountain and the position of the airplane after 15 seconds.

102. Computer Graphics (Refer to Example 9.) Suppose that the airplane in Figure 3.95 is traveling to the right at 0.1 kilometer per second and gaining altitude at 0.05 kilometer per second. If the airplane's position is fixed at $(-1, 5)$, graph the image of the mountain and the position of the airplane after 20 seconds.

103. Modeling a Weather Front Suppose a cold front passing through the United States at noon, has a shape described by the function $y = \frac{1}{20}x^2$. Each unit represents 100 miles. Des Moines, Iowa, is located at $(0, 0)$, and the positive y-axis points north. See the figure at the top of the next column.

(a) If the cold front moves south at 40 miles per hour and retains its present shape, graph its new location at 4 P.M.

(b) Suppose that by midnight the vertex of the front, which is maintaining the same shape, has moved 250 miles south and 210 miles east of Des Moines. Columbus, Ohio, is located approximately 550 miles east and 80 miles south of Des Moines. Plot the locations of Des Moines and Columbus together with the new position of the cold front. Determine whether the cold front has reached Columbus by midnight.

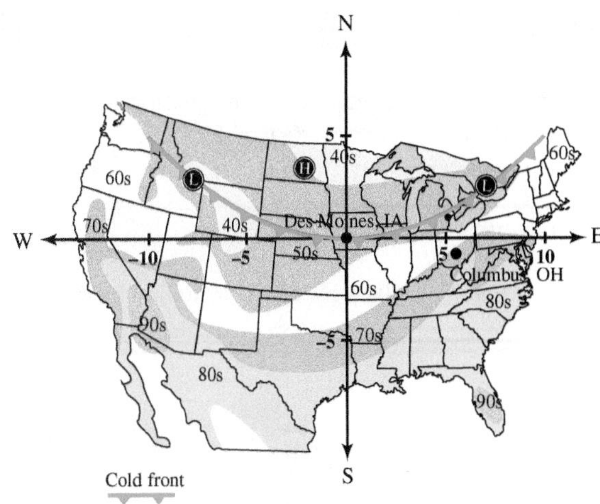

104. Modeling Motion The first figure below is a picture composed of lines and curves. In this exercise we will model only the semicircle that outlines the top of the silo. In order to make it appear that the person is walking to the right, the background must be translated horizontally to the left, as shown in the second figure.

The semicircle at the top of the silo in the first figure is described by $f(x) = \sqrt{9 - x^2} + 12$.

(a) Graph f in the window $[-12, 12, 1]$ by $[0, 16, 1]$.

(b) To give the illusion that the person is walking to the right at 2 units per second, graph the top of the silo after 1 second and after 4 seconds.

Writing about Mathematics

105. Explain how to graph the reflection of $y = f(x)$ across the x-axis. Give an example.

106. Let c be a positive number. Explain how to shift the graph of $y = f(x)$ upward, downward, left, or right c units. Give examples.

107. If the graph of $y = f(x)$ undergoes a vertical stretch or shrink to become the graph of $y = g(x)$, do these two graphs have the same x-intercepts? y-intercepts? Explain your answers.

108. If the graph of $y = f(x)$ undergoes a horizontal stretch or shrink to become the graph of $y = g(x)$, do these two graphs have the same x-intercepts? y-intercepts? Explain your answers.

CHECKING BASIC CONCEPTS FOR SECTION 3.5

1. Predict how the graph of each equation will appear compared to the graph of $f(x) = x^2$.
   (a) $y = (x + 4)^2$ **(b)** $y = x^2 - 3$
   (c) $y = (x - 5)^2 + 3$

2. Use the graph shown to sketch a graph of each equation.

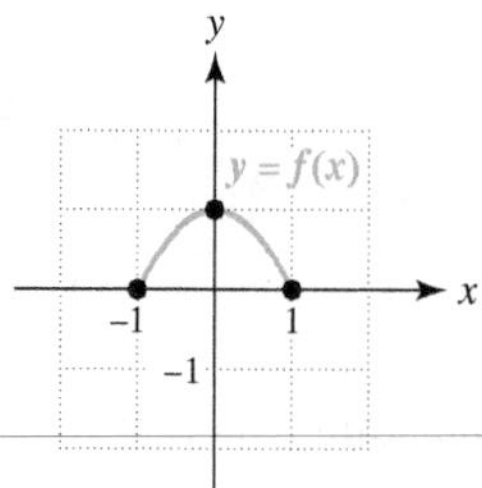

   (a) $y = -2f(x)$ **(b)** $y = f\left(-\frac{1}{2}x\right)$
   (c) $y = f(x - 1) + 1$

3. Write an equation that transforms the graph of $f(x) = x^2$ in the desired ways. Do not simplify.
   (a) Right 3 units, downward 4 units
   (b) Reflected about the x-axis
   (c) Shifted left 6 units, reflected about the y-axis
   (d) Reflected about the y-axis, shifted left 6 units

4. Use transformations to sketch a graph of the equation $y = \sqrt{x + 1} - 2$.

5. Use the table for $f(x)$ to make tables for $g(x)$ and $h(x)$.
   (a) $g(x) = f(x - 2) + 3$ **(b)** $h(x) = -2f(x + 1)$

x	−4	−2	0	2	4
$f(x)$	1	3	6	8	9

3 Summary

CONCEPT	EXPLANATION AND EXAMPLES
Section 3.1 Quadratic Functions and Models	
Quadratic Function	General form: $f(x) = ax^2 + bx + c, \quad a \neq 0$ **Examples:** $f(x) = x^2$ and $f(x) = -3x^2 + x + 5$
Parabola	The graph of a quadratic function is a parabola. *Vertex form*: $f(x) = a(x - h)^2 + k$ (standard form for a parabola with a vertical axis) *Leading coefficient*: a; *vertex*: (h, k); *axis of symmetry*: $x = h$ **Example:** 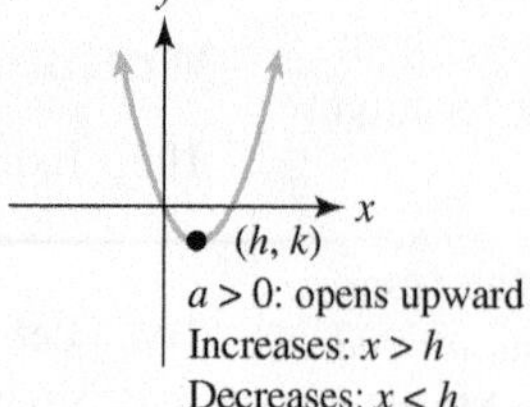 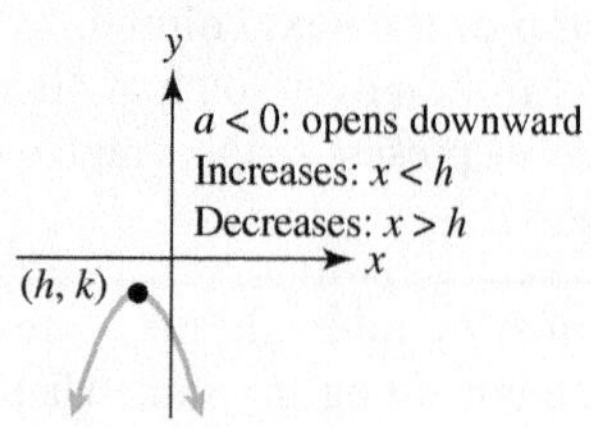
Completing the Square to Find the Vertex	The vertex of a parabola can be found by completing the square. **Example:** $y = x^2 - 4x + 1$ $y - 1 = x^2 - 4x$ Subtract 1. $y - 1 + 4 = x^2 - 4x + 4$ Add $\left(\frac{-4}{2}\right)^2 = 4$. $y + 3 = (x - 2)^2$ Perfect square trinomial $y = (x - 2)^2 - 3$ Subtract 3. The vertex is $(2, -3)$.

CONCEPT	EXPLANATION AND EXAMPLES
Section 3.1 Quadratic Functions and Models (CONTINUED)	
Vertex Formula	x-coordinate: $x = -\frac{b}{2a}$; y-coordinate: $y = f\left(-\frac{b}{2a}\right)$ **Example:** $f(x) = 2x^2 + 4x - 4$ $x = -\frac{4}{2(2)} = -1, \quad y = 2(-1)^2 + 4(-1) - 4 = -6$ Vertex: $(-1, -6)$
Section 3.2 Quadratic Equations and Problem Solving	
Quadratic Equation	Can be written as $ax^2 + bx + c = 0, \quad a \neq 0$ A quadratic equation can have zero, one, or two real solutions. **Examples:** $x^2 + 1 = 0$, (Zero solutions) $x^2 + 2x + 1 = 0$, (One solution) and $x(x - 1) = 20$ (Two solutions)
Factoring	Write an equation in the form $ab = 0$ and apply the zero-product property. **Example:** $x^2 - 3x = -2$ — Given equation $x^2 - 3x + 2 = 0$ — Set equal to 0. $(x - 1)(x - 2) = 0$ — Factor. $x = 1$ or $x = 2$ — Zero-product property
Square Root Property	If $x^2 = k$ and $k \geq 0$, then $x = \pm\sqrt{k}$. **Example:** $x^2 = 16$ implies $x = \pm 4$.
Completing the Square	If $x^2 + kx = d$, then add $\left(\frac{k}{2}\right)^2$ to each side. **Example:** $x^2 - 4x = 2$ — $k = -4$ $x^2 - 4x + 4 = 2 + 4$ — Add $\left(\frac{-4}{2}\right)^2 = 4$. $(x - 2)^2 = 6$ — Perfect square trinomial $x - 2 = \pm\sqrt{6}$ — Square root property $x = 2 \pm \sqrt{6}$ — Add 2.
Quadratic Formula	$x = \frac{-b \pm \sqrt{b^2 - 4ac}}{2a}$ — Always works to solve $ax^2 + bx + c = 0$ **Example:** $2x^2 - 5x - 3 = 0$ $x = \frac{-(-5) \pm \sqrt{(-5)^2 - 4(2)(-3)}}{2(2)} = \frac{5 \pm 7}{4} = 3, -\frac{1}{2}$

CONCEPT	EXPLANATION AND EXAMPLES

Section 3.2 Quadratic Equations and Problem Solving (CONTINUED)

Discriminant

The number of real solutions to $ax^2 + bx + c = 0$ with $a \neq 0$ can be found by evaluating the discriminant, $b^2 - 4ac$.

1. If $b^2 - 4ac > 0$, there are two real solutions.

2. If $b^2 - 4ac = 0$, there is one real solution.

3. If $b^2 - 4ac < 0$, there are no real solutions (two complex solutions).

Section 3.3 Complex Numbers

Imaginary Unit

$i = \sqrt{-1}, \quad i^2 = -1$

Examples: $\sqrt{-4} = 2i$, $\sqrt{-7} = i\sqrt{7}$

$\sqrt{-3} \cdot \sqrt{-27} = i\sqrt{3} \cdot i\sqrt{27} = i^2\sqrt{81} = -9$

Complex Number

$a + bi$, where a and b are real numbers (standard form)

Complex numbers include all real numbers. We can add, subtract, multiply, and divide complex numbers.

Examples:

$(2 - 3i) + (1 + 5i) = (2 + 1) + (-3 + 5)i = 3 + 2i$ (Add)

$3i - (2 + i) = -2 + (3 - 1)i = -2 + 2i$ (Subtract)

$(3 - i)(1 + 2i) = 3(1) + 3(2i) - i(1) - i(2i) = 5 + 5i$ (Multiply)

$\frac{1 - i}{2 + i} = \frac{(1 - i)(2 - i)}{(2 + i)(2 - i)} = \frac{1 - 3i}{5} = \frac{1}{5} - \frac{3}{5}i$ (Divide)

Complex Conjugate

The conjugate of $a + bi$ is $a - bi$.

Examples:

Number	$5 - 2i$	$5i$	-7	$-1 + 4i$
Conjugate	$5 + 2i$	$-5i$	-7	$-1 - 4i$

Complex Solutions

The quadratic formula can be used to solve quadratic equations with complex solutions.

Example: The solutions to $x^2 - x + 2 = 0$ are

$$x = \frac{1 \pm \sqrt{(-1)^2 - 4(1)(2)}}{2(1)} = \frac{1}{2} \pm i\frac{\sqrt{7}}{2}.$$

Section 3.4 Quadratic Inequalities

Quadratic Inequality

$ax^2 + bx + c < 0$ with $a \neq 0$, where $<$ may be replaced by $\leq$, $>$, or $\geq$.

Example: $3x^2 - x + 1 \leq 0$

CONCEPT	EXPLANATION AND EXAMPLES

Section 3.4 Quadratic Inequalities (CONTINUED)

Graphical Solution

Graph $y = ax^2 + bx + c$ and find the x-intercepts; then determine x-values where the inequality is satisfied.

Example: Solve $-x^2 - x + 2 > 0$.

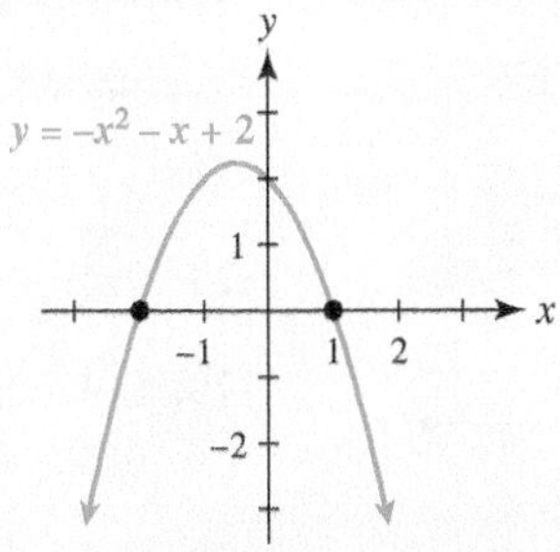

The x-intercepts are -2 and 1.

Solution set is $\{x \mid -2 < x < 1\}$, or $(-2, 1)$ in interval notation.

Symbolic Solution

First solve $ax^2 + bx + c = 0$ and use a table of values or a number line to determine the x-intervals where the inequality is satisfied.

Example: Solve $x^2 - 4 \geq 0$.

$x^2 - 4 = 0$ implies $x = \pm 2$.

Solution set is $\{x \mid x \leq -2 \text{ or } x \geq 2\}$, or $(-\infty, -2] \cup [2, \infty)$.

Interval	Test Value x	$x^2 - 4$	Positive or Negative?
$(-\infty, -2)$	-3	5	Positive
$(-2, 2)$	0	-4	Negative
$(2, \infty)$	3	5	Positive

Section 3.5 Transformations of Graphs

Vertical Shifts with $c > 0$

$y = f(x) + c$ shifts the graph of $y = f(x)$ upward c units.
$y = f(x) - c$ shifts the graph of $y = f(x)$ downward c units.

Horizontal Shifts with $c > 0$

$y = f(x - c)$ shifts the graph of $y = f(x)$ to the right c units.
$y = f(x + c)$ shifts the graph of $y = f(x)$ to the left c units.

Vertical Stretching and Shrinking

$y = cf(x)$ vertically stretches the graph of $y = f(x)$ when $c > 1$ and shrinks the graph when $0 < c < 1$.

Horizontal Stretching and Shrinking

$y = f(cx)$ horizontally shrinks the graph of $y = f(x)$ when $c > 1$ and stretches the graph when $0 < c < 1$.

Reflections

$y = -f(x)$ is a reflection of $y = f(x)$ across the x-axis.
$y = f(-x)$ is a reflection of $y = f(x)$ across the y-axis.

3 Review Exercises

Exercises 1 and 2: Use the graph to find the following.

(a) Sign of the leading coefficient
(b) Vertex
(c) Axis of symmetry
(d) Intervals where f is increasing and where f is decreasing

1.

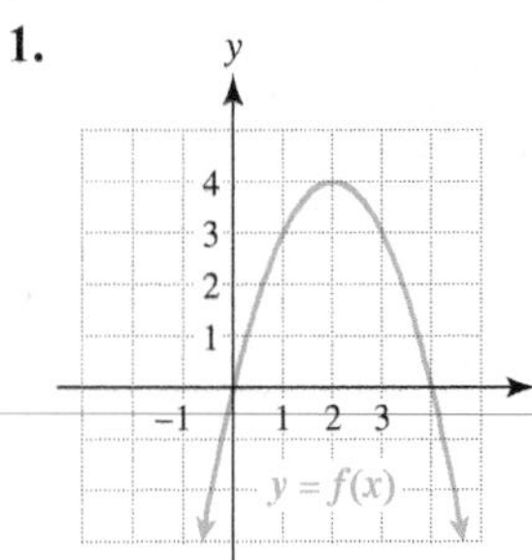

2.

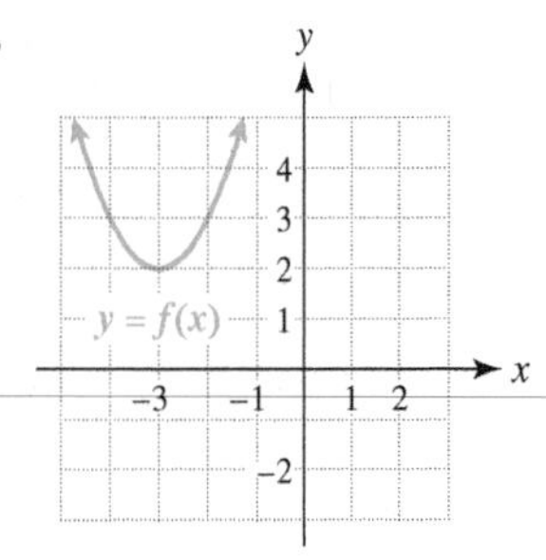

Exercises 3 and 4: Write f(x) in the form $f(x) = ax^2 + bx + c$, and identify the leading coefficient.

3. $f(x) = -2(x - 5)^2 + 1$ **4.** $f(x) = \frac{1}{3}(x + 1)^2 - 2$

Exercises 5 and 6: Use the graph of the quadratic function f to write it as $f(x) = a(x - h)^2 + k$.

5.

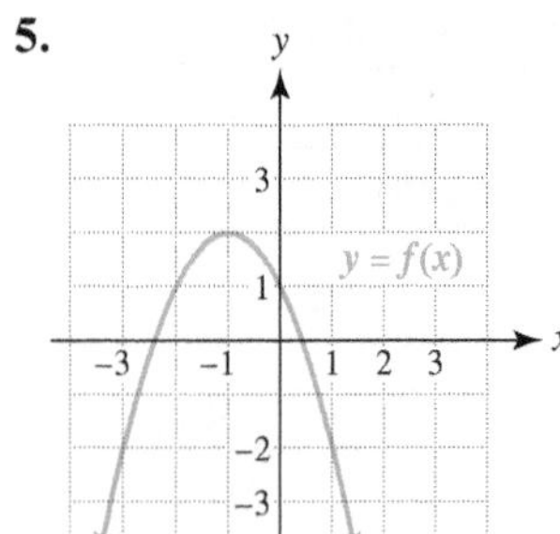

6.

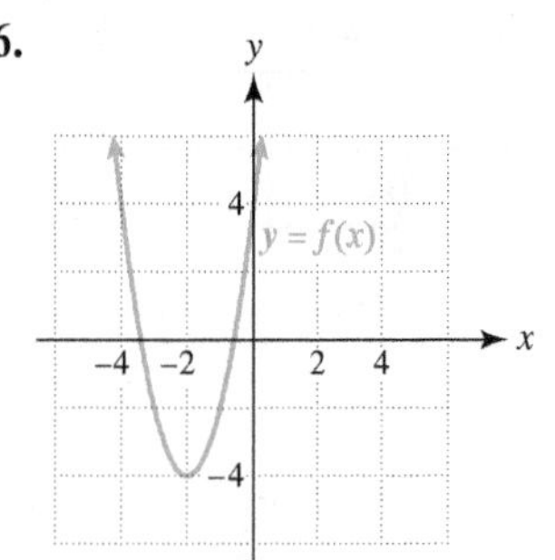

Exercises 7 and 8: Write f(x) in the form $f(x) = a(x - h)^2 + k$, and identify the vertex.

7. $f(x) = x^2 + 6x - 1$ **8.** $f(x) = 2x^2 + 4x - 5$

Exercises 9 and 10: Use the vertex formula to determine the vertex on the graph of f.

9. $f(x) = -3x^2 + 2x - 4$ **10.** $f(x) = x^2 + 8x - 5$

Exercises 11–14: Sketch a graph of the function.

11. $f(x) = -3x^2 + 3$ **12.** $g(x) = 2(x - 1)^2 - 3$

13. $f(x) = -|x + 3|$ **14.** $f(x) = \sqrt{2 - x}$

15. Average Rate of Change Find the average rate of change of $f(x) = -6x^2 + 7x + 5$ from 2 to 4.

16. Difference Quotient Find the difference quotient for $f(x) = x^2 - 2x$.

Exercises 17–24: Solve the quadratic equation.

17. $x^2 - x - 20 = 0$ **18.** $-5x^2 - 3x = 0$

19. $4z^2 - 7 = 0$ **20.** $25z^2 = 9$

21. $-2t^2 - 3t + 14 = 0$ **22.** $x(6 - x) = -16$

23. $0.1x^2 - 0.3x = 1$ **24.** $(k + 2)^2 = 7$

Exercises 25–28: Solve by completing the square.

25. $x^2 + 2x = 5$ **26.** $x^2 - 3x = 3$

27. $2z^2 - 6z - 1 = 0$ **28.** $-\frac{1}{4}x^2 - \frac{1}{2}x + 1 = 0$

29. Solve the equation $2x^2 - 3y^2 = 6$ for y. Is y a function of x?

30. Solve $h = -\frac{1}{2}gt^2 + 100$ for t.

31. Use the imaginary unit i to simplify each expression.
(a) $\sqrt{-16}$ **(b)** $\sqrt{-48}$ **(c)** $\sqrt{-5} \cdot \sqrt{-15}$

32. Write each expression in standard form.
(a) $(2 - 3i) + (-3 + 3i)$ **(c)** $(3 + 2i)(-4 - i)$
(b) $(-5 + 3i) - (-3 - 5i)$ **(d)** $\dfrac{3 + 2i}{2 - i}$

Exercises 33 and 34: Use the graph and the given f(x) to complete the following.

(a) Find any x-intercepts.
(b) Find the complex zeros of f.

33.

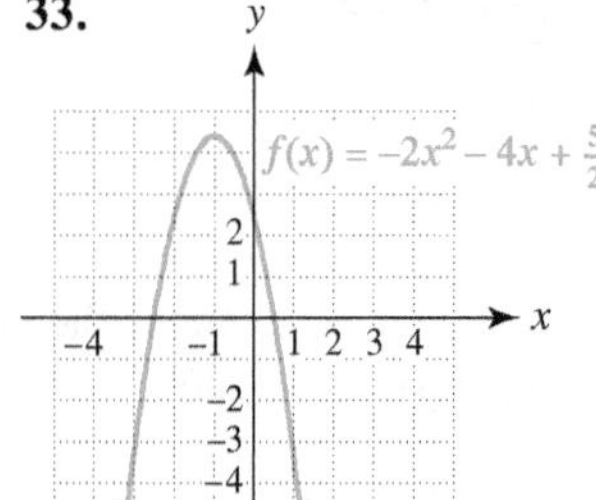

34.

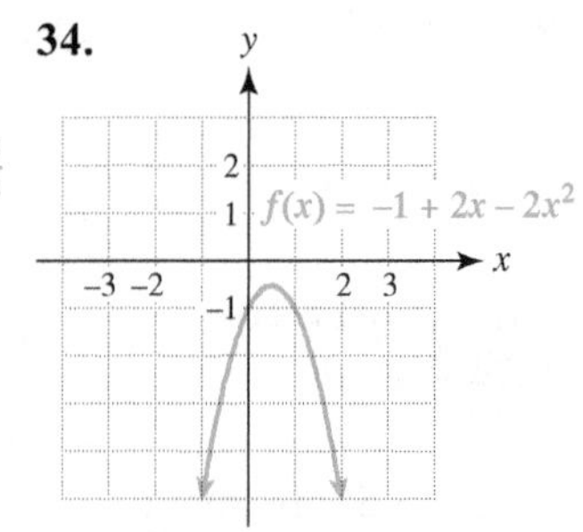

Exercises 35 and 36: Find all complex solutions.

35. $4x^2 + 9 = 0$ **36.** $2x^2 + 3 = 2x$

37. Use the graph of $y = f(x)$ to solve the inequality.
(a) $f(x) > 0$ **(b)** $f(x) \le 0$

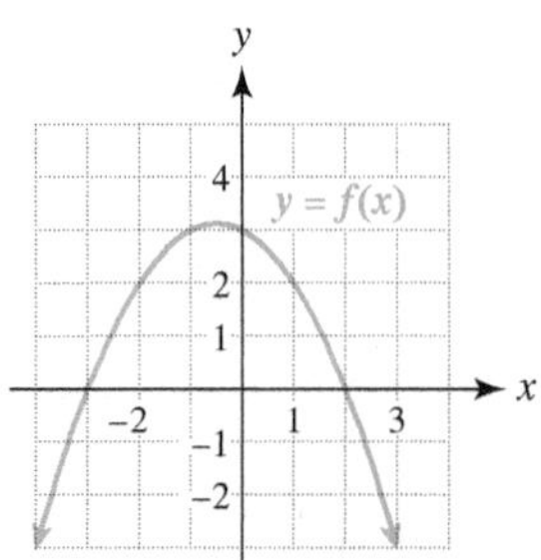

38. Solve the equation or inequality.
(a) $x^2 - 3x + 2 = 0$ **(b)** $x^2 - 3x + 2 < 0$
(c) $x^2 - 3x + 2 > 0$

Exercises 39–42: Solve the inequality. Use set-builder or interval notation to write a solution set to the inequality.

39. $x^2 - 3x + 2 \leq 0$ **40.** $9x^2 - 4 > 0$

41. $n(n - 2) \geq 15$ **42.** $n^2 + 4 \leq 6n$

43. If $f(x) = 2x^2 - 3x + 1$, use transformations to graph $y = -f(x)$ and $y = f(-x)$.

44. Use the given graph of $y = f(x)$ to sketch a graph of each expression.
(a) $y = f(x + 1) - 2$
(b) $y = -2f(x)$
(c) $y = f(2x)$

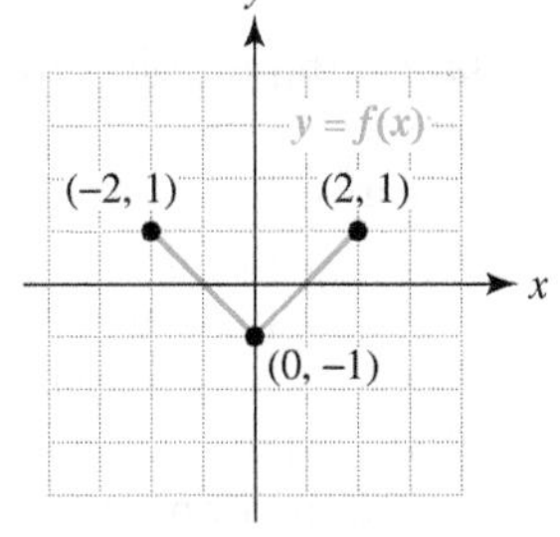

Exercises 45–48: Use transformations to sketch a graph of f.

45. $f(x) = x^2 - 4$ **46.** $f(x) = -4\sqrt{-x}$

47. $f(x) = -2(x - 2)^2 + 3$ **48.** $f(x) = -|x - 3|$

Applications

49. Maximizing Area A homeowner has 44 feet of fence to enclose a rectangular garden. One side of the garden needs no fencing because it is along the wall of the house. What dimensions will maximize area?

50. Maximizing Revenue The revenue R in dollars received from selling x radios is $R(x) = x(90 - x)$.
(a) Evaluate $R(20)$ and interpret the result.
(b) What number of radios sold will maximize revenue?
(c) What is the maximum revenue?
(d) What number of radios should be sold for revenue to be \$2000 or more?

51. Projectile A slingshot is used to propel a stone upward so that its height h in feet after t seconds is given by $h(t) = -16t^2 + 88t + 5$.
(a) Evaluate $h(0)$ and interpret the result.
(b) How high was the stone after 2 seconds?
(c) Find the maximum height of the stone.
(d) At what time(s) was the stone 117 feet high?

52. World Population The function given by the formula $f(x) = 0.000478x^2 - 1.813x + 1720.1$ models world population in billions from 1950 to 2010 during year x.
(a) Evaluate $f(1985)$ and interpret the result.
(b) Estimate world population during the year 2000.
(c) According to this model, when did world population reach 7 billion?

53. Construction A box is being constructed by cutting 3-inch squares from the corners of a rectangular sheet of metal that is 4 inches longer than it is wide. If the box is to have a volume of 135 cubic inches, find the dimensions of the metal sheet.

54. Room Prices Room prices are regularly \$100, but for each additional room rented by a group, the price is reduced by \$3 for each room. For example, 1 room costs \$100, 2 rooms cost 2 × \$97 = \$194, and so on.
(a) Write a quadratic function C that gives the total cost of renting x rooms.
(b) What is the total cost of renting 6 rooms?
(c) How many rooms are rented if the cost is \$730?
(d) What number of rooms rented gives the greatest cost?

55. Minutes Spent on Facebook The following table gives estimates for the total number of minutes in billions spent on Facebook per year. Find a function in the form $M(x) = a(x - h)^2 + k$ that models this data.

Year	2007	2008	2009
Minutes	60	84	184

Source: *Business Insider.*

56. Irrigation and Yield The table shows how irrigation of rice crops affects yield, where x represents the percent of total area that is irrigated and y is the rice yield in tons per hectare. (1 hectare ≈ 2.47 acres.)

x	0	20	40	60	80	100
y	1.6	1.8	2.2	3.0	4.5	6.1

Source: D. Grigg, *The World Food Problem.*

(a) Use least-squares regression to find a quadratic function that models the data.
(b) Solve the equation $f(x) = 3.7$. Interpret the results.

Extended and Discovery Exercises

1. **Shooting a Foul Shot** (Refer to the introduction to this chapter.) When a basketball player shoots a foul shot, the ball follows a parabolic arc. This arc depends on both the angle and velocity with which the basketball is released. If a person shoots the basketball overhand from a position 8 feet above the floor, then the path can sometimes be modeled by the parabola

$$y = \frac{-16x^2}{0.434v^2} + 1.15x + 8,$$

where v is the velocity of the ball in feet per second, as illustrated in the figure. (***Source:*** C. Rist, "The Physics of Foul Shots.")

(a) If the basketball hoop is 10 feet high and located 15 feet away, what initial velocity v should the basketball have?

(b) Check your answer from part (a) graphically. Plot the point (0, 8) where the ball is released and the point (15, 10) where the basketball hoop is. Does your graph pass through both points?

(c) What is the maximum height of the basketball?

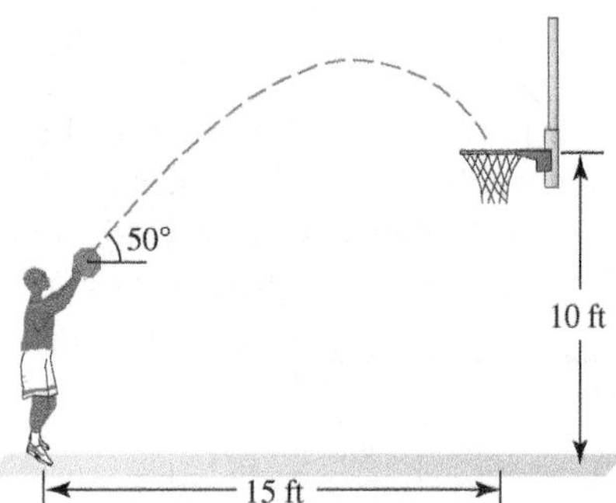

2. **Shooting a Foul Shot** (Continuation of Exercise 1) If a person releases a basketball underhand from a position 3 feet above the floor, it often has a steeper arc than if it is released overhand and the path sometimes may be modeled by

$$y = \frac{-16x^2}{0.117v^2} + 2.75x + 3.$$

See the figure below. Complete parts (a), (b), and (c) from Exercise 1. Then compare the paths for an overhand shot and an underhand shot.

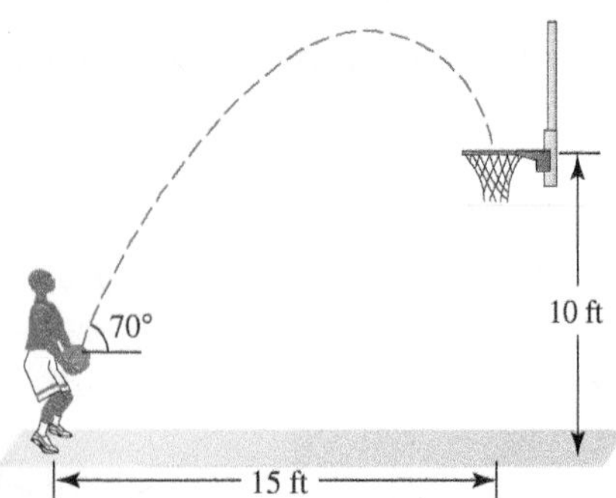

Exercises 3–6: **Reflecting Functions** *Computer graphics frequently use reflections. Reflections can speed up the generation of a picture or create a figure that appears perfectly symmetrical.* (***Source:*** S. Hoggar, *Mathematics for Computer Graphics.*)

(a) For the given $f(x)$, constant k, and viewing rectangle, graph $x = k$, $y = f(x)$, and $y = f(2k - x)$.

(b) Generalize how the graph of $y = f(2k - x)$ compares to the graph of $y = f(x)$.

3. $f(x) = \sqrt{x}$, $k = 2$, $[-1, 8, 1]$ by $[-4, 4, 1]$

4. $f(x) = x^2$, $k = -3$, $[-12, 6, 1]$ by $[-6, 6, 1]$

5. $f(x) = x^4 - 2x^2 + 1$, $k = -6$, $[-15, 3, 1]$ by $[-3, 9, 1]$

6. $f(x) = 4x - x^3$, $k = 5$, $[-6, 18, 1]$ by $[-8, 8, 1]$

7. **Modeling a Cold Front** A weather map of the United States on April 22, 1996, is shown in the figure. There was a cold front roughly in the shape of a circular arc, with a radius of about 750 miles, passing north of Dallas and west of Detroit. The center of the arc was located near Pierre, South Dakota. If Pierre has the coordinates (0, 0) and the positive y-axis points north, then the equation of the front can be modeled by

$$f(x) = -\sqrt{750^2 - x^2},$$

where $0 \le x \le 750$. (***Source:*** AccuWeather, Inc.)

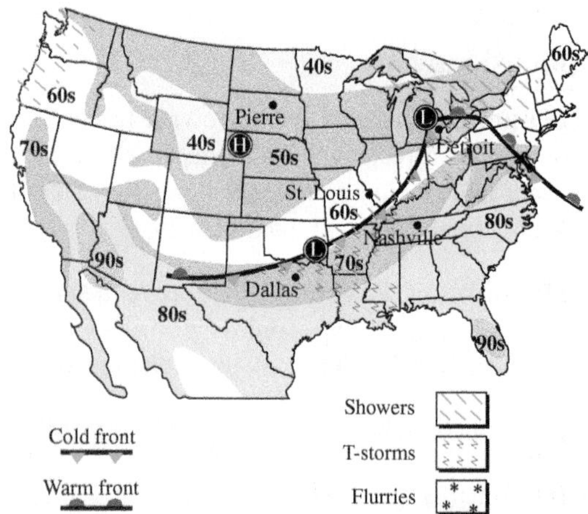

(a) St. Louis is located at $(535, -400)$ and Nashville is at $(730, -570)$, where units are in miles. Plot these points and graph f in the window $[0, 1200, 100]$ by $[-800, 0, 100]$. Did the cold front reach these cities?

(b) During the next 12 hours, the center of the front moved approximately 110 miles south and 160 miles east. Assuming the cold front did not change shape, use transformations of graphs to determine an equation that models its new location.

(c) Use graphing to determine visually if the cold front reached both cities.

4 More Nonlinear Functions and Equations

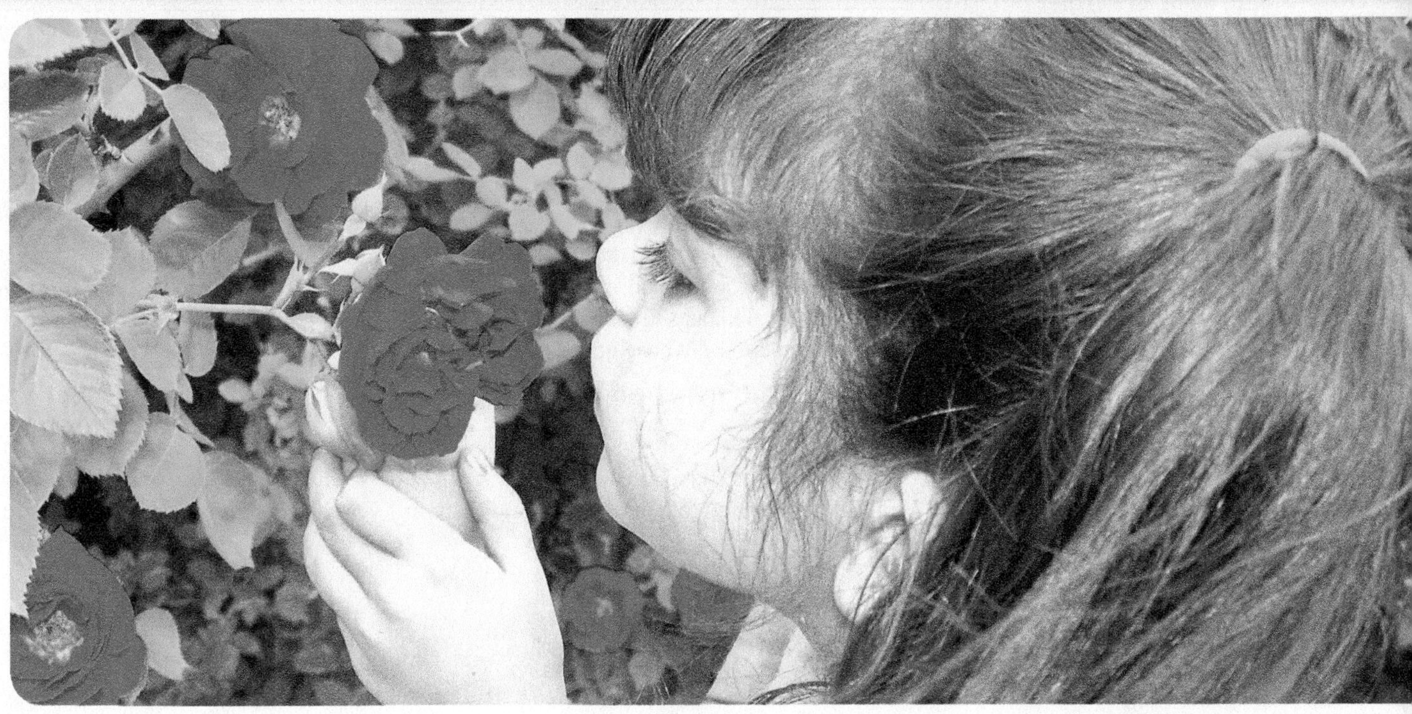

Mathematics can be both abstract and applied. Abstract mathematics is focused on axioms, theorems, and proofs that can be derived independently of empirical evidence. Theorems that were proved centuries ago are still valid today. In this sense, abstract mathematics transcends time. Yet, even though mathematics can be developed in an abstract setting—separate from science and all measured data—it also has countless applications.

The wonderful things you learn in schools are the work of many generations, produced by enthusiastic effort and infinite labor in every country.
—Albert Einstein

There is a common misconception that theoretical mathematics is unimportant, yet many of the ideas that eventually had great practical importance were first born in the abstract. For example, in 1854 George Boole published *Laws of Thought,* which outlined the basis for Boolean algebra. This was 85 years before the invention of the first digital computer. However, Boolean algebra became the basis on which modern computer hardware operates.

Much like Boolean algebra, the topic of complex numbers was at first theoretical. However, today complex numbers are used in the design of electrical circuits, ships, and airplanes.

In this chapter we discuss some important topics in algebra that have had an impact on society. We are privileged to read in a few hours what took people centuries to discover. To ignore either the abstract beauty or the profound applicability of mathematics is like seeing a rose but never smelling one.

4.1 More Nonlinear Functions and Their Graphs

- Learn terminology about polynomial functions
- Find extrema of a function
- Identify symmetry in a graph of a function
- Determine if a function is odd, even, or neither

Introduction

Monthly average high temperatures at Daytona Beach are shown in Table 4.1.

Monthly Average High Temperatures at Daytona Beach

Month	1	2	3	4	5	6	7	8	9	10	11	12
Temperature (°F)	69	70	75	80	85	88	90	89	87	81	76	70

Table 4.1 *Source:* J. Williams, *The USA Weather Almanac.*

Figure 4.1 shows a scatterplot of the data. A linear function would not model these data because these data do not lie on a line. One possibility is to model the data with a quadratic function, as shown in Figure 4.2. However, a better fit can be obtained with the nonlinear function f whose graph is shown in Figure 4.3 and is given by

$$f(x) = 0.0145x^4 - 0.426x^3 + 3.53x^2 - 6.23x + 72,$$

A Polynomial Function

where $x = 1$ corresponds to January, $x = 2$ to February, and so on. (Least-squares regression was used to determine $f(x)$.) Function f is a *polynomial function* with degree 4.

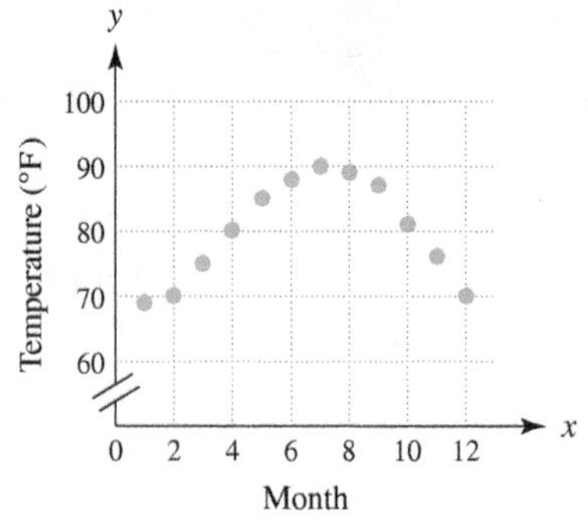

Figure 4.1

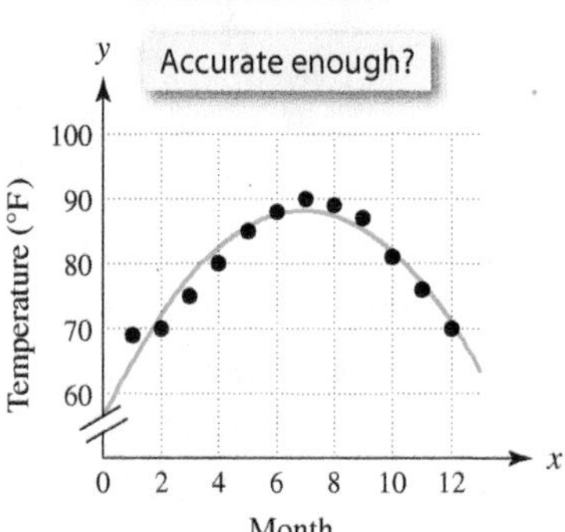

Figure 4.2

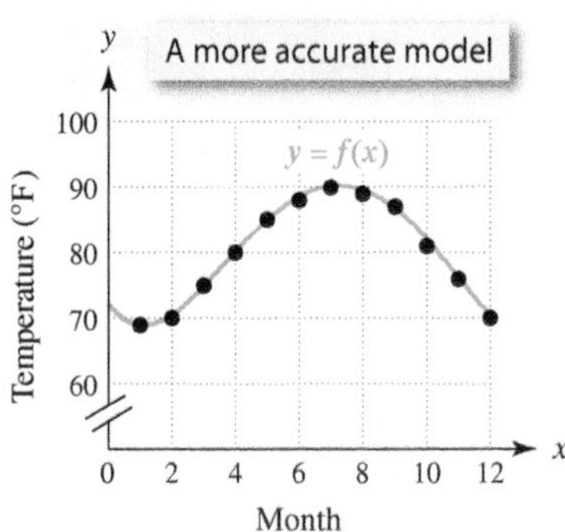

Figure 4.3

Polynomial Functions

The domain of a polynomial function is all real numbers, and its graph is continuous and smooth without breaks or sharp edges.

POLYNOMIAL FUNCTION

A **polynomial function f of degree n in the variable x** can be represented by

$$f(x) = a_n x^n + a_{n-1}x^{n-1} + \cdots + a_2x^2 + a_1x + a_0,$$

where each coefficient a_k is a real number, $a_n \neq 0$, and n is a nonnegative integer. The **leading coefficient** is a_n and the **degree** is n.

Algebra Review
To review polynomials, see Chapter R (page R-12).

Examples of polynomial functions include the following.

Formula	*Degree*	*Leading Coefficient*
$f(x) = 10$	0	$a_0 = 10$
$g(x) = 2x - 3.7$	1	$a_1 = 2$
$h(x) = 1 - 1.4x + 3x^2$	2	$a_2 = 3$
$k(x) = -\frac{1}{2}x^6 + 4x^4 + x$	6	$a_6 = -\frac{1}{2}$

A polynomial function of degree 2 or higher is a *nonlinear* function. Functions f and g are linear, whereas functions h and k are nonlinear.

NOTE Quadratic functions, which were discussed in Chapter 3, are examples of nonlinear functions. This chapter introduces *more* nonlinear functions.

Functions that contain radicals, ratios, or absolute values of variables are not polynomials. For example, $f(x) = 2\sqrt{x}$, $g(x) = \frac{1}{x - 1}$, and $h(x) = |2x + 5|$ are *not* polynomials. However, they *are* nonlinear functions.

Identifying Extrema

In Figure 4.3 the minimum monthly average temperature of 69°F occurs in January ($x = 1$) and the maximum monthly average temperature of 90°F occurs in July ($x = 7$). Minimum and maximum y-values on the graph of a function often represent important data.

Graphs of two polynomial functions with "hills" and "valleys" are shown in Figures 4.4 and 4.5. These hills and valleys are associated with maximum and minimum y-values on the graphs. The following See the Concept shows how these minimum and maximum y-values are classified.

See the Concept: Absolute and Local Maximums and Minimums

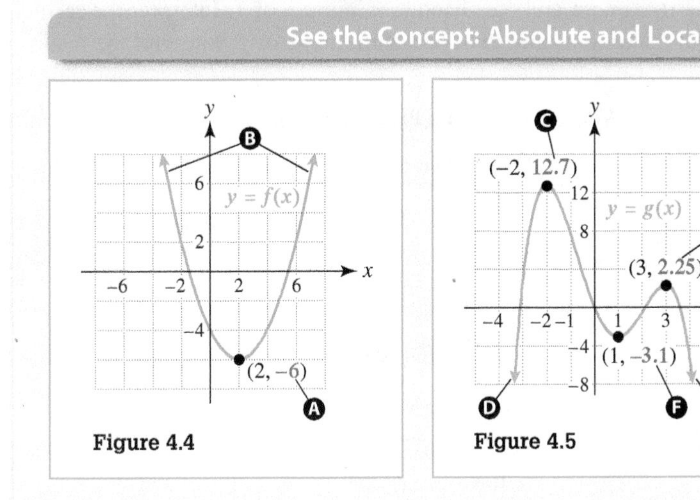

Figure 4.4

Figure 4.5

A Absolute minimum: −6

B Absolute maximum: None

C Absolute maximum: 12.7

D Absolute minimum: None

E Local maximum: 2.25

F Local minimum: −3.1

Note that the absolute minimum of −6 in Figure 4.4 is also a local minimum, and that the absolute maximum of 12.7 in Figure 4.5 is also a local maximum.

In Figure 4.4, the minimum y-value on the graph of f is -6. It is called the *absolute minimum* of f. Function f has no *absolute maximum* because there is no largest y-value on a parabola opening upward.

In Figure 4.5 the peak of the highest "hill" on the graph of g is $(-2, 12.7)$. Therefore the absolute maximum of g is 12.7. There is a smaller peak located at the point $(3, 2.25)$. In a small open interval near $x = 3$, the y-value of 2.25 is locally the largest. We say that g has a *local maximum* of 2.25. Similarly, a "valley" occurs on the graph of g, where the lowest point is $(1, -3.1)$. The value -3.1 is not the smallest y-value on the entire graph of g. Therefore it is not an absolute minimum. Rather, -3.1 is a *local minimum*.

Absolute Maximum: 11
Occurs Twice at $x = \pm 2$

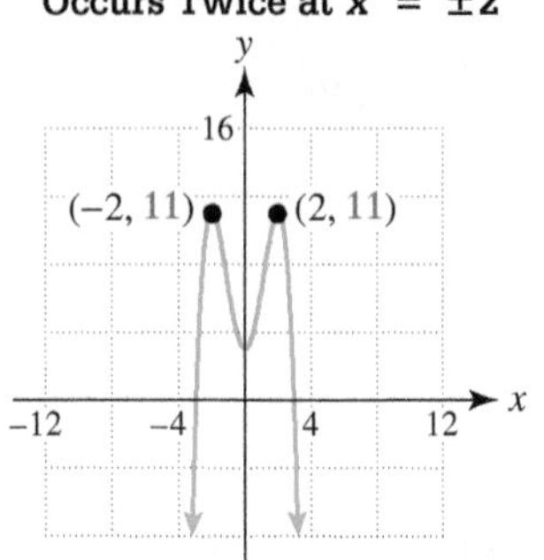

Figure 4.6

Maximum and minimum values that are either absolute or local are called **extrema** (plural of extremum). A function may have several local extrema, but at most one absolute maximum and one absolute minimum. However, it is possible for a function to assume an absolute extremum at two values of x. In Figure 4.6 the absolute maximum is 11. It occurs at $x = \pm 2$.

NOTE In Figure 4.6, the absolute maximum of 11 is *also* a local maximum because it is the largest y-value in a small interval near either $x = -2$ or $x = 2$.

Sometimes an absolute maximum (minimum) is called a *global maximum* (*minimum*). Similarly, sometimes a local maximum (minimum) is called a *relative maximum* (*minimum*).

ABSOLUTE AND LOCAL EXTREMA

Let c be in the domain of f.

$f(c)$ is an **absolute (global) maximum** if $f(c) \geq f(x)$ *for all* x in the domain of f.
$f(c)$ is an **absolute (global) minimum** if $f(c) \leq f(x)$ *for all* x in the domain of f.
$f(c)$ is a **local (relative) maximum** if $f(c) \geq f(x)$ when x is *near* c.
$f(c)$ is a **local (relative) minimum** if $f(c) \leq f(x)$ when x is *near* c.

NOTE The expression "near c" means that there is an open interval in the domain of f containing c where $f(c)$ satisfies the inequality.

EXAMPLE 1 **Identifying and interpreting extrema**

Figure 4.7 shows the graph of a function f that models the volume of air in a person's lungs, measured in liters, after x seconds. (***Source:*** V. Thomas, *Science and Sport.*)

(a) Find the absolute maximum and the absolute minimum of f. Interpret the results.
(b) Identify two local maximums and two local minimums of f. Interpret the results.

Volume of Air in a Person's Lungs

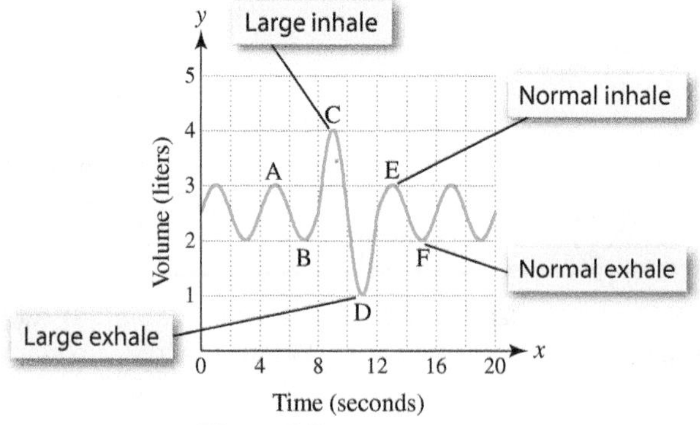

Figure 4.7

SOLUTION

(a) The absolute maximum is 4 liters and occurs at C. The absolute minimum is 1 liter and occurs at D. At C a deep breath has been taken and the lungs are more inflated. After C, the person exhales until the lungs contain only 1 liter of air at D.

(b) One local maximum is 3 liters. It occurs at A and E and represents the amount of air in a person's lungs after inhaling normally. One local minimum is 2 liters. It occurs at B and F and represents the amount of air after exhaling normally. Another local maximum is 4 liters, which is also the absolute maximum. Similarly, 1 liter is a local minimum and also the absolute minimum.

Now Try Exercise 91

EXAMPLE 2 **Identifying extrema**

Use the graph of f in Figure 4.8 to estimate any local and absolute extrema.

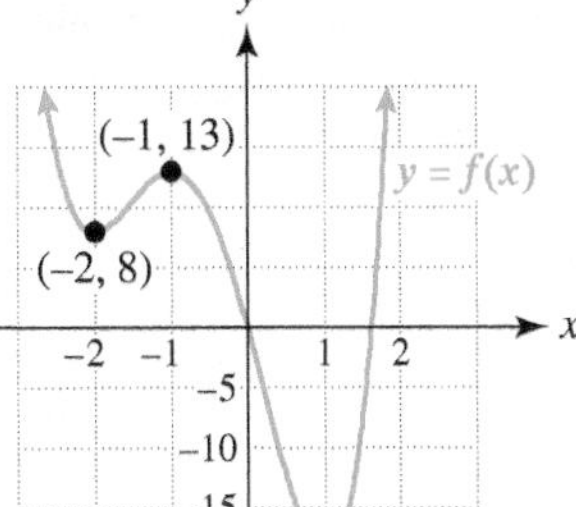

Figure 4.8

SOLUTION

Local Extrema The points $(-2, 8)$ and $(1, -19)$ on the graph of f correspond to the lowest point in a "valley." Thus there are local minimums of 8 and -19. The point $(-1, 13)$ corresponds to the highest point on a "hill." Thus there is a local maximum of 13.

Absolute Extrema Because the arrows point upward, there is no maximum y-value on the graph. Thus there is no absolute maximum. However, the minimum y-value on the graph of f occurs at the point $(1, -19)$. The absolute minimum is -19.

Now Try Exercise 15

NOTE Extrema are y-values on the graph of a function, not x-values.

EXAMPLE 3 **Modeling ocean temperatures**

The monthly average ocean temperature in degrees Fahrenheit at Bermuda can be modeled by $f(x) = 0.0215x^4 - 0.648x^3 + 6.03x^2 - 17.1x + 76.4$, where $x = 1$ corresponds to January and $x = 12$ to December. The domain of f is $D = \{x \mid 1 \leq x \leq 12\}$.

(a) Graph f in [1, 12, 1] by [50, 90, 10].

(b) Estimate the absolute extrema. Interpret the results.

[1, 12, 1] by [50, 90, 10]

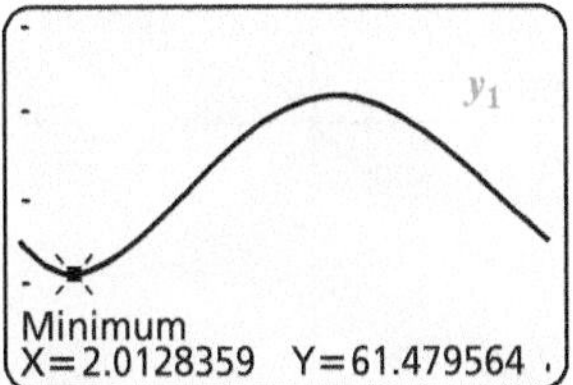

Figure 4.9

[1, 12, 1] by [50, 90, 10]

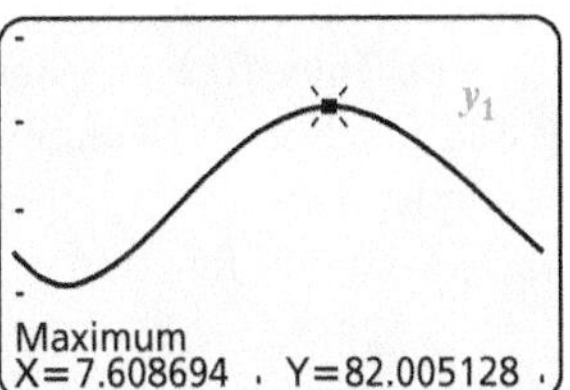

Figure 4.10

SOLUTION

(a) The graph of $y_1 = f(x)$ is shown in Figure 4.9.

(b) Many graphing calculators have the capability to find maximum and minimum y-values. The points associated with absolute extrema are shown in Figures 4.9 and 4.10. An absolute minimum of about 61.5 corresponds to the point (2.01, 61.5). This means that the monthly average ocean temperature is coldest during the month of February ($x \approx 2$) when it reaches a minimum of about 61.5°F.

An absolute maximum of approximately 82 corresponds to (7.61, 82.0). Rounding, we might say that the warmest average temperature occurs during August ($x \approx 8$) when it reaches a maximum of 82°F. (Or we might say that this maximum occurs in late July, since $x \approx 7.61$.)

Now Try Exercise 95

Symmetry

Even Functions Symmetry is used frequently in art, mathematics, science, and computer graphics. Many objects and animals are symmetric along a line so that the left and right sides are mirror images. For example, if a butterfly is viewed from the top, the left wing is typically a mirror image of the right wing. Graphs of functions may also exhibit this type of symmetry, as shown in Figures 4.11–4.13. These graphs are **symmetric with respect to the y-axis.** A function whose graph satisfies this characteristic is called an *even function.*

Even Functions: Symmetry with Respect to the y-Axis

If these graphs are folded on the y-axis, the two halves match.

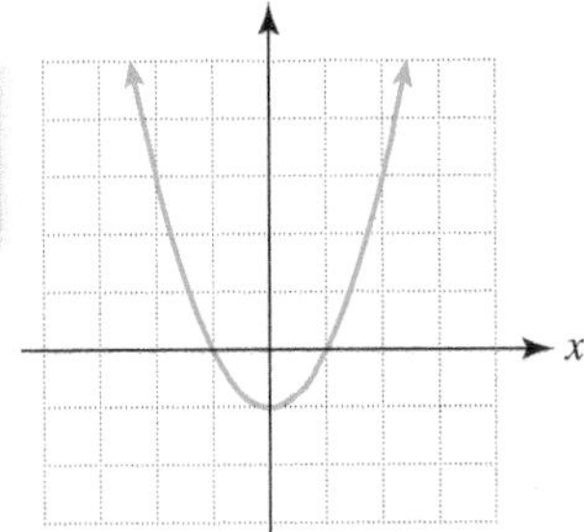

Figure 4.11

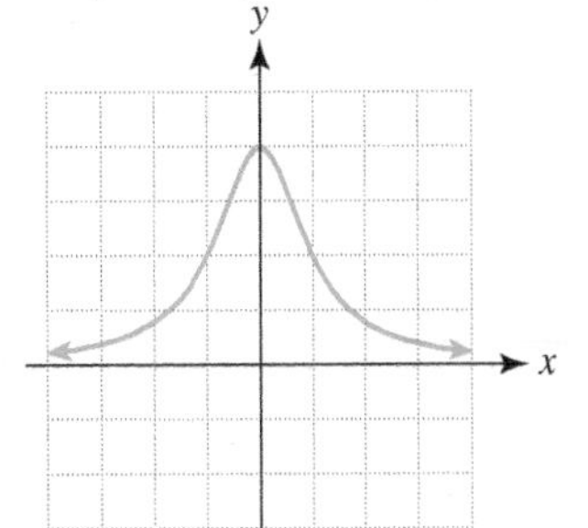

Figure 4.12

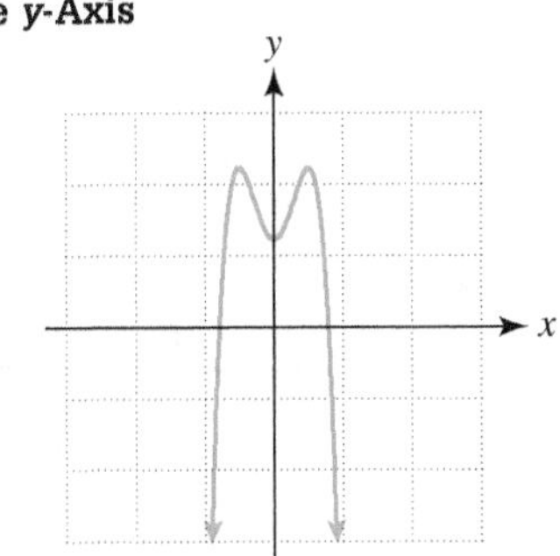

Figure 4.13

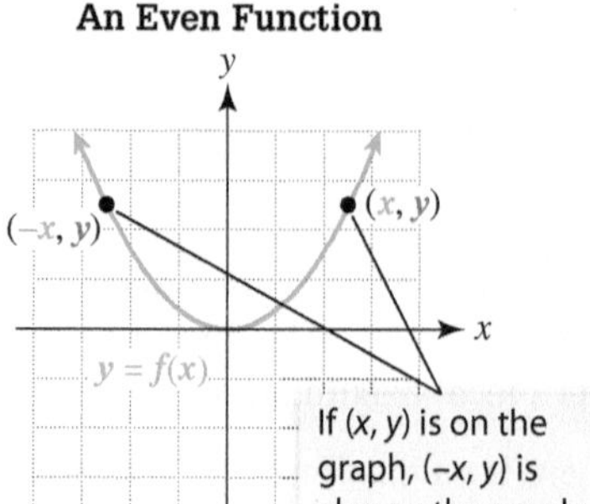

Figure 4.14

Figure 4.14 shows a graph of an even function f. Since the graph is symmetric with respect to the y-axis, the points (x, y) and $(-x, y)$ both lie on the graph of f. Thus $f(x) = y$ and $f(-x) = y$, and so $f(x) = f(-x)$ for an even function. This means that if we change the sign of the input, the output does not change. For example, if $g(x) = x^2$, then $g(2) = g(-2) = 4$. Since this is true for *every input*, g is an even function.

EVEN FUNCTION

A function f is an **even function** if $f(-x) = f(x)$ for every x in its domain. The graph of an even function is symmetric with respect to the y-axis.

Odd Functions A second type of symmetry is shown in Figures 4.15–4.17. If we could spin or rotate the graph about the origin, the original graph would reappear after half a turn. These graphs are **symmetric with respect to the origin** and represent *odd functions*.

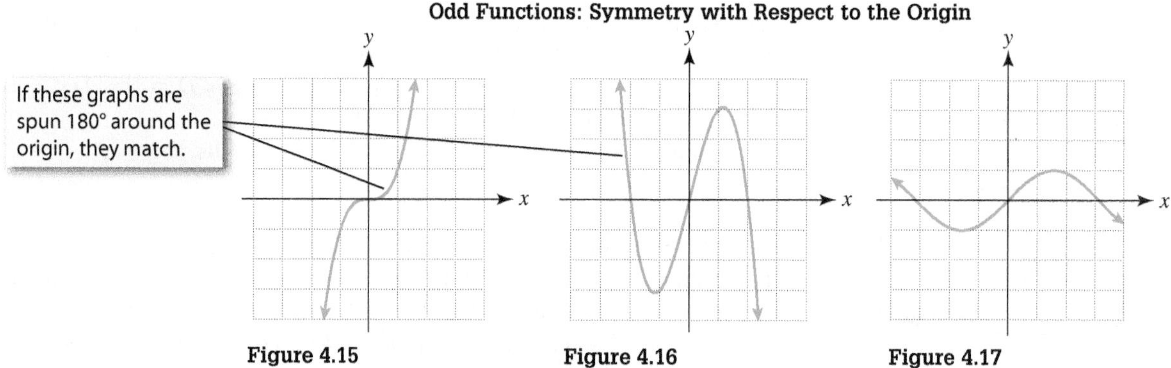

Figure 4.15 Figure 4.16 Figure 4.17

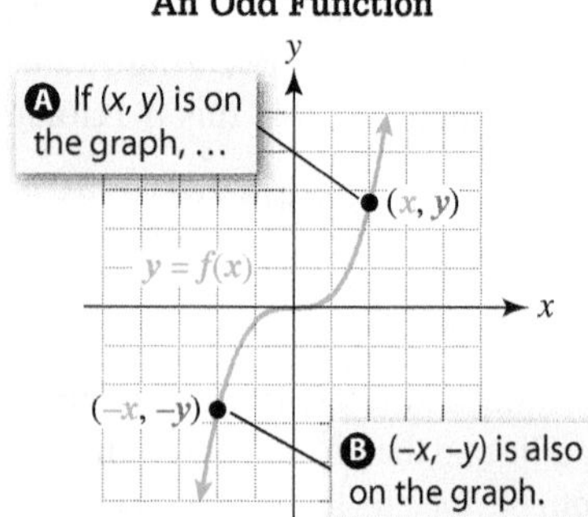

Figure 4.18

In Figure 4.18 the point (x, y) lies on the graph of an odd function f. If this point spins half a turn, or 180°, around the origin, its new location is $(-x, -y)$. Thus $f(x) = y$ and $f(-x) = -y$. It follows that $f(-x) = -y = -f(x)$ for any odd function f. Changing the sign of the input only changes the sign of the output. For example, if $g(x) = x^3$, then $g(3) = 27$ and $g(-3) = -27$. Since this is true for *every input*, g is an odd function.

ODD FUNCTION

A function f is an **odd function** if $f(-x) = -f(x)$ for every x in its domain. The graph of an odd function is symmetric with respect to the origin.

Identifying Odd and Even Functions The terms *odd* and *even* have special meaning when they are applied to a polynomial function f. If $f(x)$ contains terms that have only odd powers of x, then f is an odd function. Similarly, if $f(x)$ contains terms that have only even powers of x (and possibly a constant term), then f is an even function. For example, $f(x) = x^6 - 4x^4 - 2x^2 + 5$ is an even function, whereas $g(x) = x^5 + 4x^3$ is an **odd** function. This fact can be shown *symbolically*.

$$
\begin{aligned}
f(-x) &= (-x)^6 - 4(-x)^4 - 2(-x)^2 + 5 && \text{Substitute } -x \text{ for } x.\\
&= x^6 - 4x^4 - 2x^2 + 5 && \text{Simplify.}\\
&= f(x) && f \text{ is an even function.}
\end{aligned}
$$

$$
\begin{aligned}
g(-x) &= (-x)^5 + 4(-x)^3 && \text{Substitute } -x \text{ for } x.\\
&= -x^5 - 4x^3 && \text{Simplify.}\\
&= -g(x) && g \text{ is an odd function.}
\end{aligned}
$$

CLASS DISCUSSION

If 0 is in the domain of an odd function f, what point must lie on its graph? Explain your reasoning.

NOTE It is important to remember that the graphs of many functions exhibit *no symmetry* with respect to either the y-axis or the origin. These functions are *neither* odd *nor* even.

EXAMPLE 4 **Identifying odd and even functions**

For each representation of a function f, identify whether f is odd, even, or neither.

(a)

x	-3	-2	-1	0	1	2	3
$f(x)$	10.5	2	-0.5	-2	-0.5	2	10.5

(b)

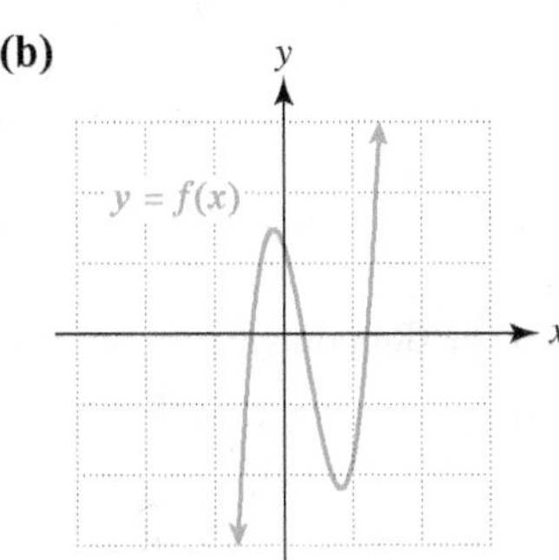

(c) $f(x) = x^3 - 5x$

(d) f is the cube root function.

SOLUTION

Getting Started If either $f(-x) = f(x)$ or its graph is symmetric with respect to the y-axis, then f is even. If either $f(-x) = -f(x)$ or its graph is symmetric with respect to the origin, then f is odd. Otherwise, f is neither even nor odd. ▶

Algebra Review
To review cube roots, see Chapter R (page R-37).

(a) The function defined by the table has domain $D = \{-3, -2, -1, 0, 1, 2, 3\}$. Notice that $f(-3) = 10.5 = f(3)$, $f(-2) = 2 = f(2)$, and $f(-1) = -0.5 = f(1)$. The function f satisfies the statement $f(-x) = f(x)$ for every x in D. Thus f is an even function.

(b) If we fold the graph on the y-axis, the two halves do not match, so f is *not* an even function. Similarly, f is *not* an odd function since spinning its graph half a turn about the origin does not result in the same graph. The function f is neither odd nor even.

(c) Since f is a polynomial containing only odd powers of x, it is an odd function. This fact can also be shown symbolically.

$$\begin{aligned} f(-x) &= (-x)^3 - 5(-x) && \text{Substitute } -x \text{ for } x. \\ &= -x^3 + 5x && \text{Simplify.} \\ &= -(x^3 - 5x) && \text{Distributive property} \\ &= -f(x) && f \text{ is an odd function.} \end{aligned}$$

Cube Root Function

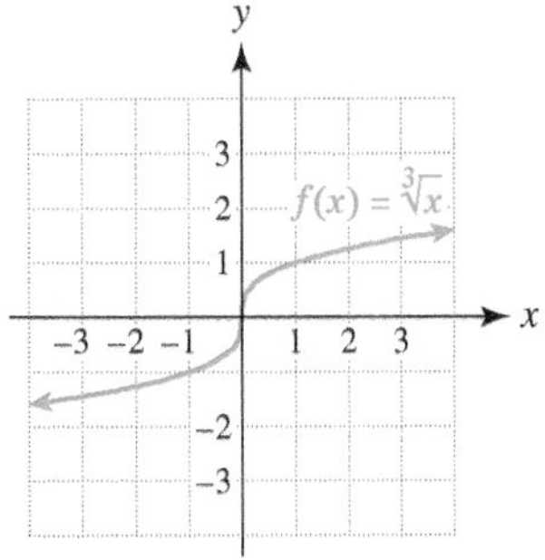

Figure 4.19

(d) Note that $\sqrt[3]{-8} = -2$ and that $\sqrt[3]{8} = 2$. In general, $\sqrt[3]{-x} = -\sqrt[3]{x}$, which indicates that $f(-x) = -f(x)$, where $f(x) = \sqrt[3]{x}$. Thus f is an odd function. This fact can also be seen by graphing $f(x) = \sqrt[3]{x}$, as shown in Figure 4.19. Spinning the graph of $f(x) = \sqrt[3]{x}$ a half a turn about the origin results in the same graph.

Now Try Exercises 47, 59, 63, and 71

CLASS DISCUSSION

Discuss the possibility of the graph of a *function* being symmetric with respect to the x-axis.

4.1 Putting It All Together

The following table summarizes some important concepts related to the graphs of nonlinear functions.

CONCEPT	EXPLANATION	GRAPHICAL EXAMPLE
Absolute, or global, maximum (minimum)	The maximum (minimum) y-value on the graph of $y = f(x)$ A graph of a function may or may not have an absolute maximum (minimum).	
Local, or relative, maximum (minimum)	A maximum (minimum) y-value on the graph of $y = f(x)$ in an open interval of the domain of f A graph of a function may or may not have a local maximum (minimum). Note that it is possible for a y-value on the graph of f to be both an absolute maximum (minimum) *and* a local maximum (minimum).	
Even function	$f(-x) = f(x)$ The graph is symmetric with respect to the y-axis. If the graph is folded on the y-axis, the left and right halves match. Changing the sign of the input does not change the output.	
Odd function	$f(-x) = -f(x)$ The graph is symmetric with respect to the origin. If the graph is spun about the origin, the graph reappears after half a turn, or 180°. Changing the sign of the input only changes the sign of the output.	

4.1 Exercises

Note: Many of the answers in this section involve estimations. Your answers may vary slightly, particularly when you are reading a graph.

Polynomials

Exercises 1–10: Determine if the function is a polynomial function. If it is, state its degree and leading coefficient a.

1. $f(x) = 2x^3 - x + 5$

2. $f(x) = -x^4 + 1$

3. $f(x) = \sqrt{x}$

4. $f(x) = 2x^3 - \sqrt[3]{x}$

5. $f(x) = 1 - 4x - 5x^4$

6. $f(x) = 5 - 4x$

7. $g(t) = \dfrac{1}{t^2 + 3t - 1}$

8. $g(t) = \dfrac{1}{1 - t}$

9. $g(t) = 22$

10. $g(t) = |2t|$

Finding Extrema of Polynomials

Exercises 11–26: Use the graph of f to estimate the

(a) local extrema and

(b) absolute extrema.

11.

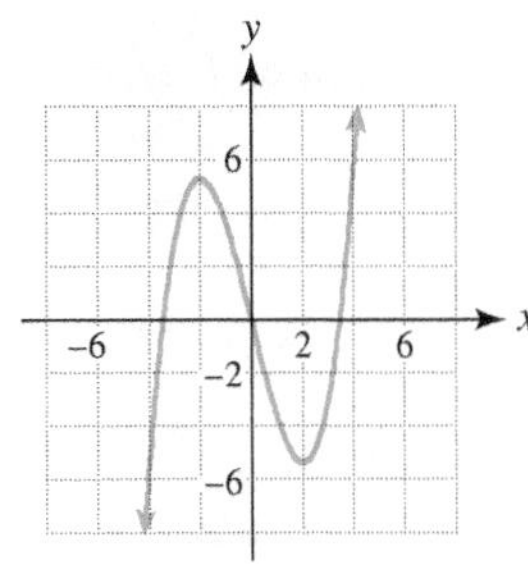

12.

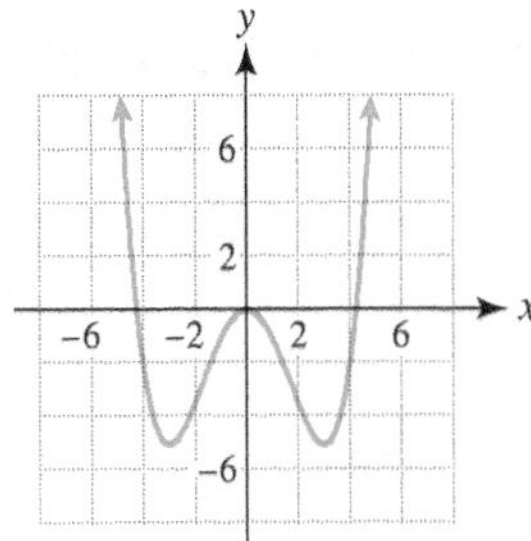

13.

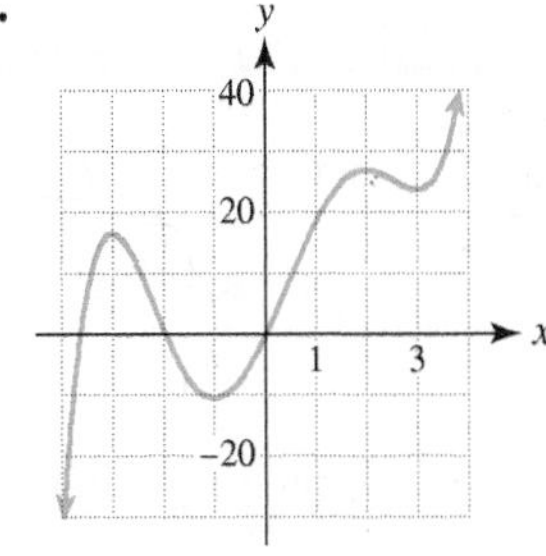

14.

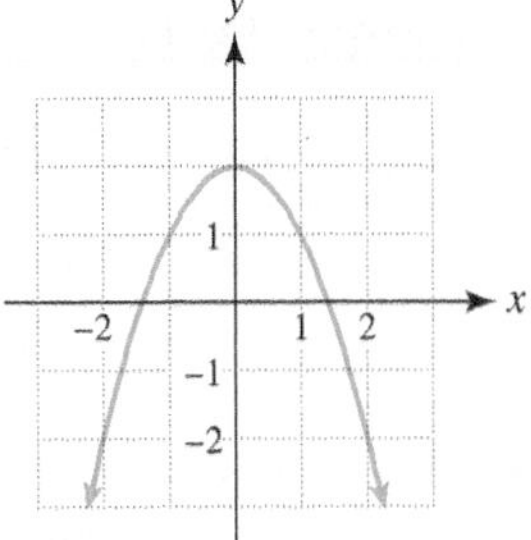

15.

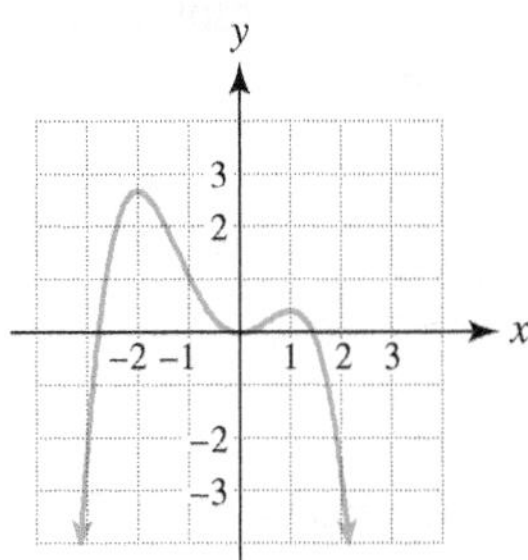

16.

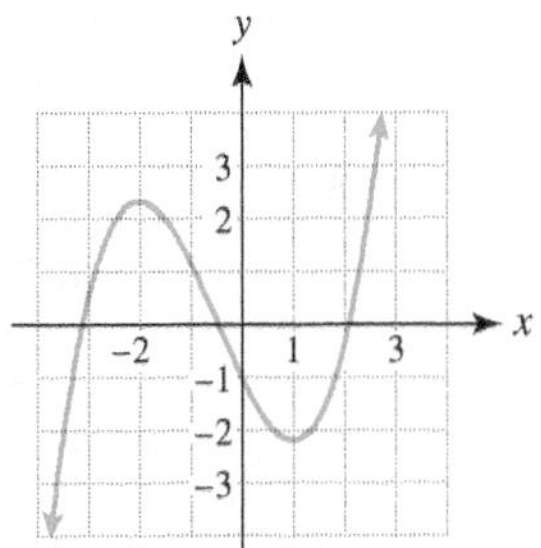

17.

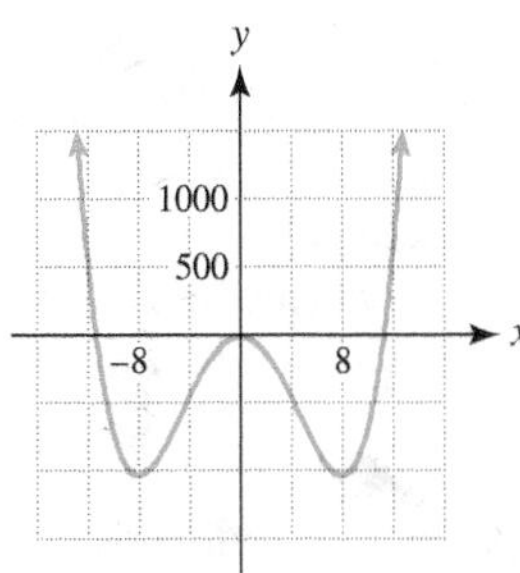

18.

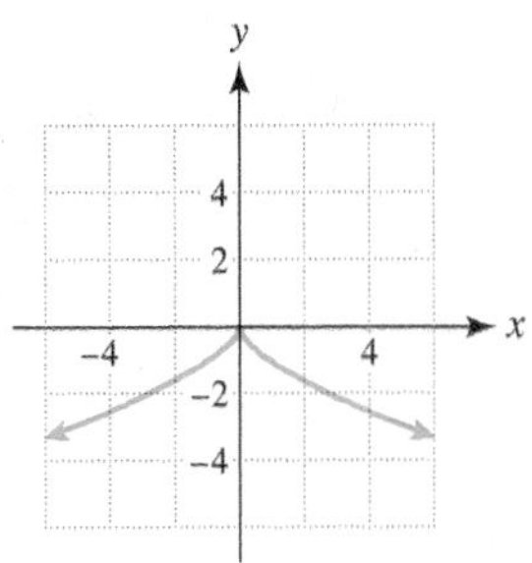

19.

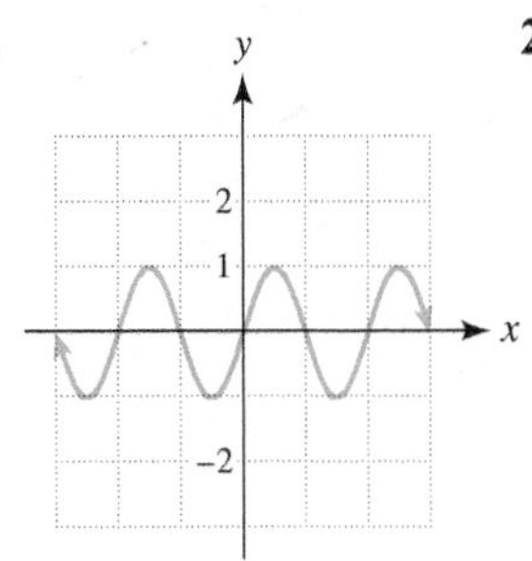

20.

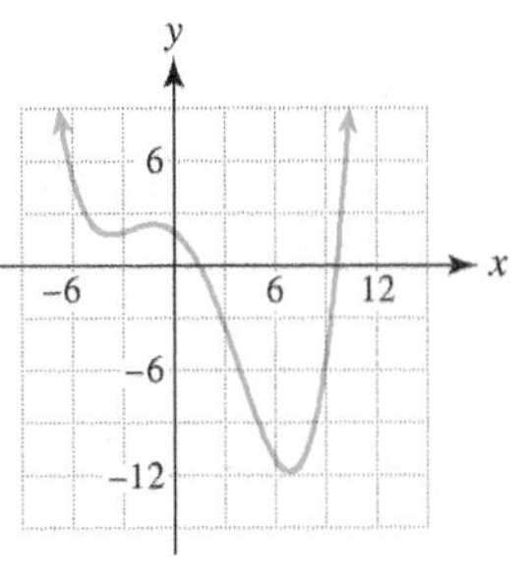

(Hint: *Exercises 21–26: Local extrema cannot occur at endpoints because they only occur on open intervals.*)

21.

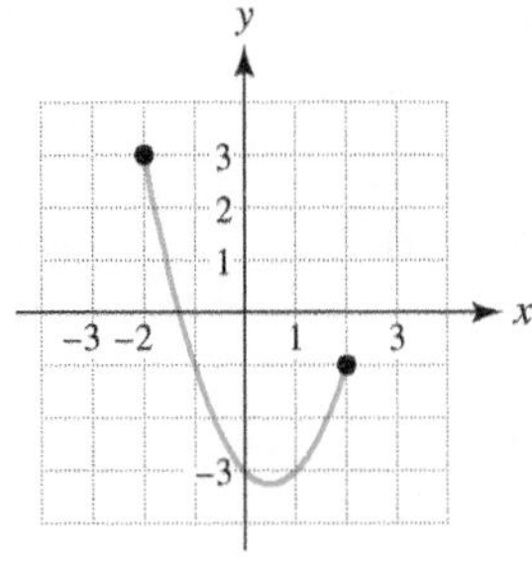

22.

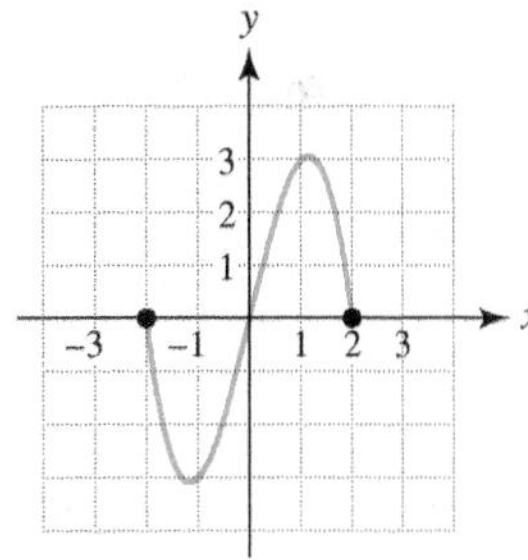

23.

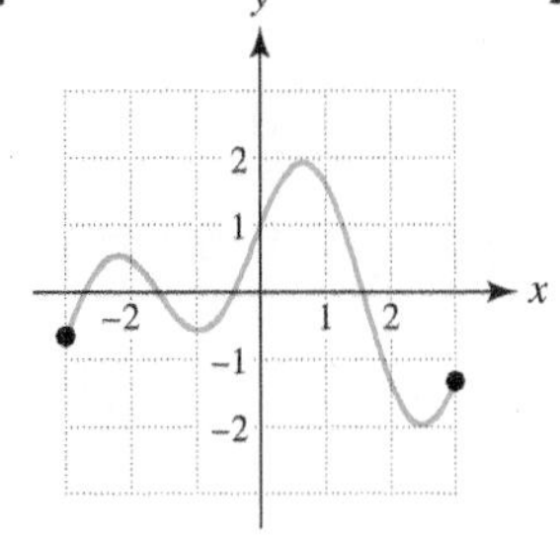

24.

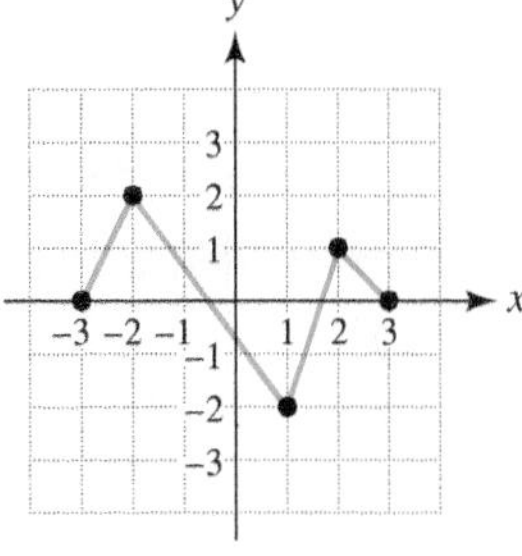

25.

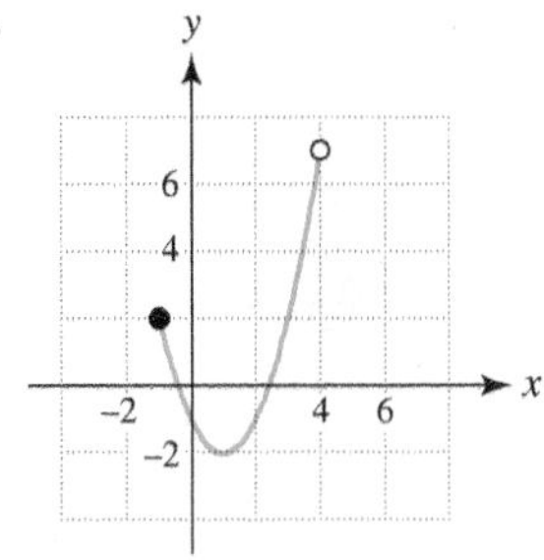

26.

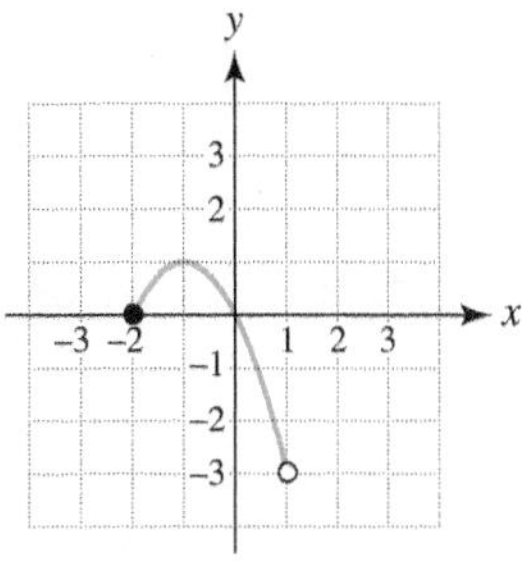

Exercises 27–38: Determine any

(a) local extrema and

(b) absolute extrema.

(Hint: *Consider the graph* $y = g(x)$.)

27. $g(x) = 1 - 3x$

28. $g(x) = \frac{1}{4}x$

29. $g(x) = x^2 + 1$

30. $g(x) = 1 - x^2$

31. $g(x) = -2(x + 3)^2 + 4$

32. $g(x) = \frac{1}{3}(x - 1)^2 - 2$

33. $g(x) = 2x^2 - 3x + 1$

34. $g(x) = -3x^2 + 4x - 1$

35. $g(x) = |x + 3|$

36. $g(x) = -|x| + 2$

37. $g(x) = \sqrt[3]{x}$

38. $g(x) = -x^3$

Exercises 39–46: Determine graphically any

(a) local extrema and

(b) absolute extrema.

39. $g(x) = 3x - x^3$

40. $g(x) = \dfrac{1}{1 + |x|}$

41. $f(x) = -3x^4 + 8x^3 + 6x^2 - 24x$

42. $f(x) = -x^4 + 4x^3 - 4x^2$

43. $f(x) = 0.5x^4 - 5x^2 + 4.5$

44. $f(x) = 0.01x^5 + 0.02x^4 - 0.35x^3 - 0.36x^2 + 1.8x$

45. $f(x) = \dfrac{8}{1 + x^2}$

46. $f(x) = \dfrac{6}{x^2 + 2x + 2}$

Symmetry

Exercises 47–50: Use the graph to determine if f is odd, even, or neither.

47.

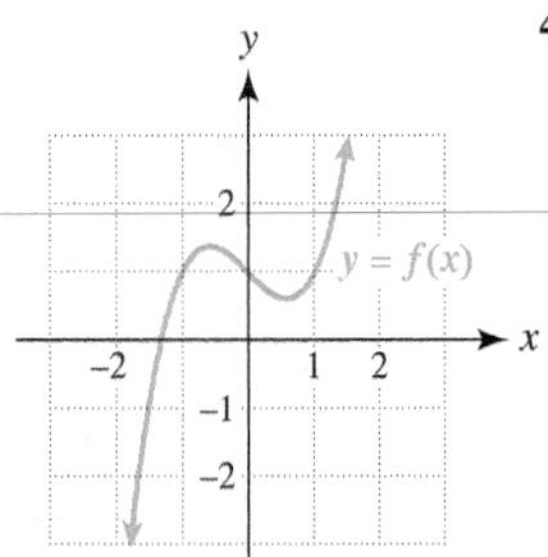

48.

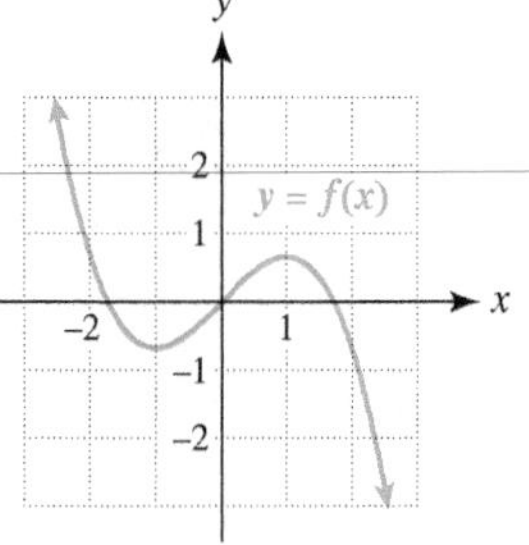

49.

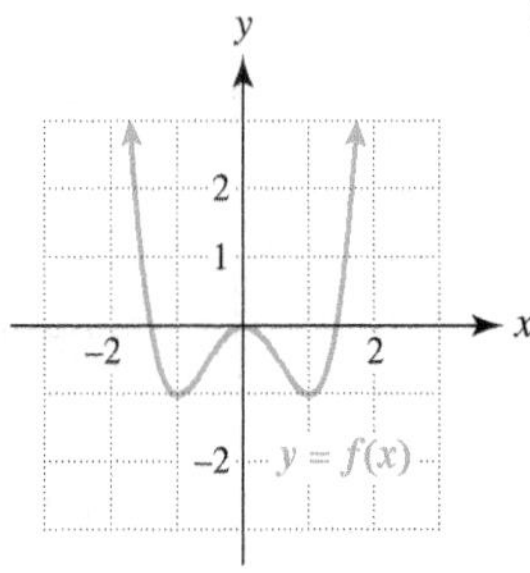

50.

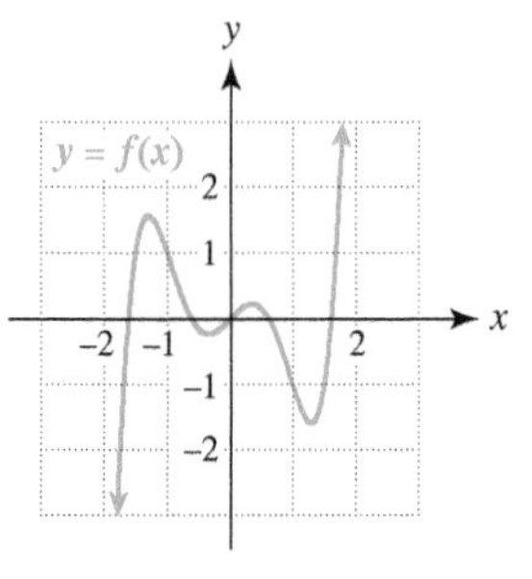

Exercises 51–70: Determine if f is odd, even, or neither.

51. $f(x) = 5x$

52. $f(x) = -3x$

53. $f(x) = x + 3$

54. $f(x) = 2x - 1$

55. $f(x) = x^2 - 10$

56. $f(x) = 8 - 2x^2$

57. $f(x) = x^4 - 6x^2 + 2$

58. $f(x) = -x^6 + 5x^2$

59. $f(x) = x^3 - 2x$

60. $f(x) = -x^5$

61. $f(x) = x^2 - x^3$

62. $f(x) = 3x^3 - 1$

63. $f(x) = \sqrt[3]{x^2}$

64. $f(x) = \sqrt{-x}$

65. $f(x) = \sqrt{1 - x^2}$

66. $f(x) = \sqrt{x^2}$

67. $f(x) = \dfrac{1}{1 + x^2}$

68. $f(x) = \dfrac{1}{x}$

69. $f(x) = |x + 2|$

70. $f(x) = \dfrac{1}{x + 1}$

71. The table is a complete representation of f. Decide if f is even, odd, or neither.

x	-100	-10	-1	0	1	10	100
$f(x)$	56	-23	5	0	-5	23	-56

72. The table is a complete representation of f. Decide if f is even, odd, or neither.

x	-5	-3	-1	1	2	3
$f(x)$	-4	-2	1	1	-2	-4

73. Complete the table if f is an even function.

x	-3	-2	-1	0	1	2	3
$f(x)$	21		-25			-12	

74. Complete the table if f is an odd function.

x	-5	-3	-2	0	2	3	5
$f(x)$	13		-5			-1	

75. If the points $(-5, -6)$ and $(-3, 4)$ lie on the graph of an odd function f, then what do $f(5)$ and $f(3)$ equal?

76. If the point $(1 - a, b + 1)$ lies on the graph of an even function f, then what does $f(a - 1)$ equal?

Concepts

77. Sketch a graph of an odd linear function.

78. Sketch a graph of an even linear function.

79. Does there exist a continuous odd function that is always increasing and whose graph passes through the points $(-3, -4)$ and $(2, 5)$? Explain.

80. Is there an even function whose domain is all real numbers and that is always decreasing? Explain.

81. Sketch a graph of a continuous function with an absolute minimum of -3 at $x = -2$ and a local minimum of -1 at $x = 2$.

82. Sketch a graph of a continuous function with no absolute extrema but with a local minimum of -2 at $x = -1$ and a local maximum of 2 at $x = 1$.

83. Sketch a graph of a continuous function that is increasing on $(-\infty, 2)$ and decreasing on $(2, \infty)$. Could this function be quadratic?

84. Sketch a graph of a continuous function with a local maximum of 2 at $x = -1$ and a local maximum of 0 at $x = 1$.

Translations of Graphs

Exercises 85–88: Use the graph of $f(x) = 4x - \frac{1}{3}x^3$ and translations of graphs to sketch the graph of the equation.

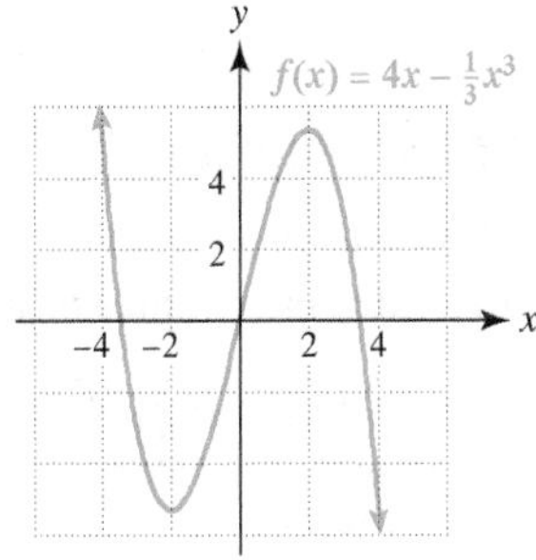

85. $y = f(x + 1)$

86. $y = f(x) - 2$

87. $y = 2f(x)$

88. $y = f\left(\frac{1}{2}x\right)$

89. If the graph of $y = f(x)$ is increasing on $(1, 4)$, then where is the graph of $y = f(x + 1) - 2$ increasing? Where is the graph of $y = -f(x - 2)$ decreasing?

90. If the graph of f is decreasing on $(0, \infty)$, then what can be said about the graph of $y = f(-x) + 1$? The graph of $y = -f(x) - 1$?

Applications

91. Temperature in Sunlight The graph shows the temperature readings of a thermometer (on a partly cloudy day) x hours past noon.

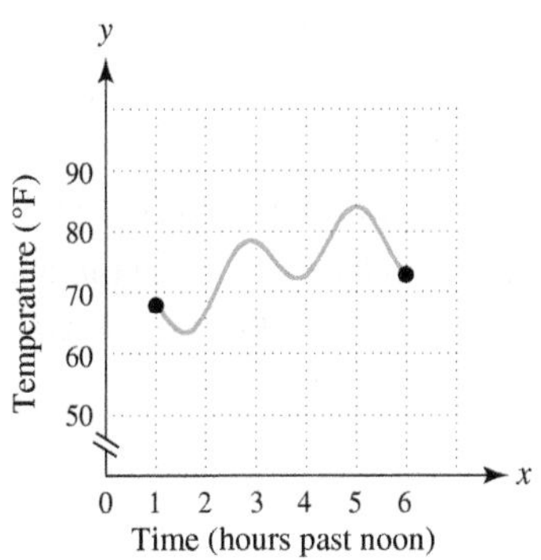

(a) Identify the absolute maximum and minimum. Interpret each.

(b) Identify any local maximums and minimums. (Do not consider the endpoints.)

(c) For what x-values was the temperature increasing?

92. Daytona Beach (Refer to the introduction to this section.) The graph at the top of the next column shows the monthly average high temperatures at Daytona Beach.

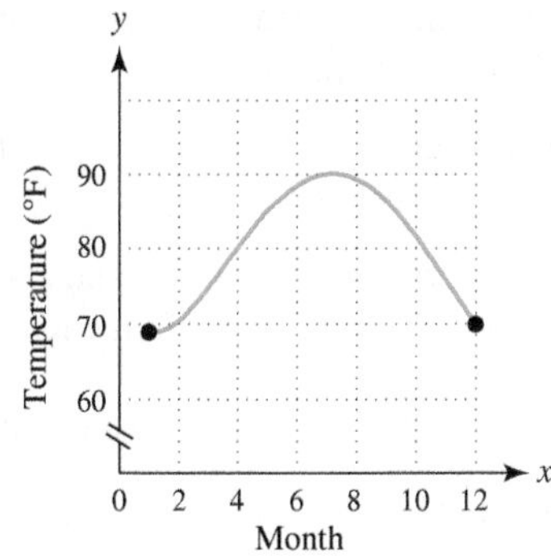

(a) Identify the absolute maximum and minimum.

(b) Identify a local maximum.

(c) For what x-values was the temperature increasing?

93. Facebook Versus Yahoo During 2009, Facebook surpassed Yahoo for the greatest number of unique monthly users. The formula

$$F(x) = 0.0484x^3 - 1.504x^2 + 17.7x + 53$$

models these numbers in millions of unique monthly users x months after December 2008.

(a) Evaluate $F(1)$ and $F(12)$. Interpret the result.

(b) Graph $y = F(x)$ in $[0, 13, 2]$ by $[0, 150, 25]$. Does F have any local extrema for $1 \le x \le 12$?

(c) Where is F increasing if its domain is $1 \le x \le 12$?

94. Google+ Users Google+ experienced an increase in the number of users between July 1, 2011 and February 1, 2012. The total number of users in millions can be modeled by the polynomial function

$$G(x) = 0.000014437x^3 - 0.00406x^2 + 0.603x + 3.7,$$

where x represents days after July 1, 2011.

(a) Evaluate $G(31)$ and interpret the result.

(b) Graph $y = G(x)$ in $[0, 215, 20]$ by $[0, 90, 10]$. Does G have any local extrema for $0 \le x \le 215$?

(c) Where is G increasing if its domain is $0 \le x \le 215$?

95. Heating Costs In colder climates the cost for natural gas to heat homes can vary from one month to the next. The polynomial function given by

$$f(x) = -0.1213x^4 + 3.462x^3 - 29.22x^2 + 64.68x + 97.69$$

models the monthly cost in dollars of heating a typical home. The input x represents the month, where $x = 1$ corresponds to January and $x = 12$ to December.

(a) Where might the absolute extrema occur for $1 \le x \le 12$?

(b) Graph f in $[1, 12, 1]$ by $[0, 150, 10]$. Find the absolute extrema and interpret the results.

96. Natural Gas The U.S. consumption of natural gas from 1965 to 1980 can be modeled by

$$f(x) = 0.0001234x^4 - 0.005689x^3 + 0.08792x^2 - 0.5145x + 1.514,$$

where $x = 6$ corresponds to 1966 and $x = 20$ to 1980. Consumption is measured in trillion cubic feet. (*Source:* Department of Energy.)

(a) Evaluate $f(10)$ and interpret the result.

(b) Graph f in [6, 20, 5] by [0.4, 0.8, 0.1]. Describe the energy usage during this time period.

(c) Determine the local extrema and interpret the results.

97. Average Temperature The graph approximates the monthly *average* temperatures in degrees Fahrenheit in Austin, Texas. In this graph x represents the month, where $x = 0$ corresponds to July.

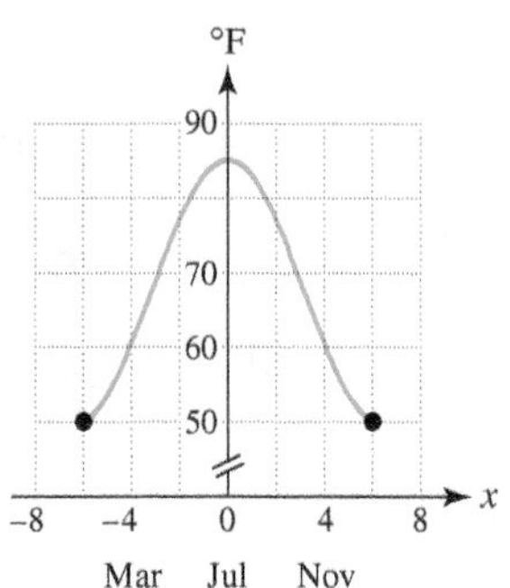

(a) Is this a graph of an odd or even function?

(b) June corresponds to $x = -1$ and August to $x = 1$. The average temperature in June is 83°F. What is the average temperature in August?

(c) March corresponds to $x = -4$ and November to $x = 4$. According to the graph, how do their average temperatures compare?

(d) Interpret what this type of symmetry implies about average temperatures in Austin.

98. Height of a Projectile When a projectile is shot into the air, it attains a maximum height and then falls back to the ground. Suppose that $x = 0$ corresponds to the time when the projectile's height is maximum. If air resistance is ignored, its height h above the ground at any time x may be modeled by $h(x) = -16x^2 + h_{max}$, where h_{max} is the projectile's maximum height above the ground. Height is measured in feet and time in seconds. Let $h_{max} = 400$ feet.

(a) Evaluate $h(-2)$ and $h(2)$. Interpret these results.

(b) Evaluate $h(-5)$ and $h(5)$. Interpret these results.

(c) Graph h for $-5 \le x \le 5$. Is h even or odd?

(d) How do the values of $h(x)$ and $h(-x)$ compare for $-5 \le x \le 5$? What does this result indicate?

Writing About Mathematics

99. Explain the difference between a local and an absolute maximum. Are extrema x-values or y-values?

100. Describe ways to determine if a polynomial function is odd, even, or neither. Give examples.

101. If an odd function f has one local maximum of 5 at $x = 3$, then what else can be said about f? Explain.

102. If an even function f has an absolute minimum of -6 at $x = -2$, then what else can be said about f? Explain.

Extended and Discovery Exercises

1. Maximizing Area Find the dimensions of the rectangle of maximum area that can be inscribed in a semicircle with radius 3. Assume that the rectangle is positioned as shown in the accompanying figure.

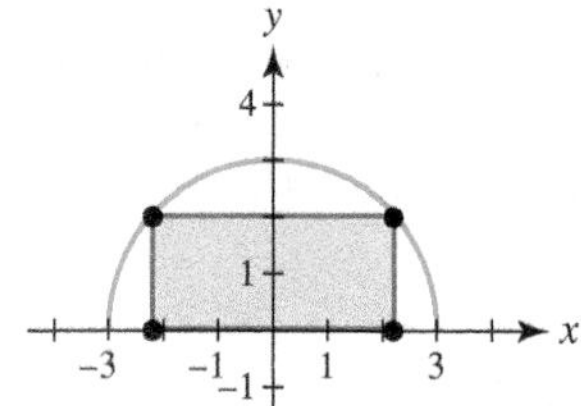

2. Minimizing Area A piece of wire 20 inches long is cut into two pieces. One piece is bent into a square and the other is bent into an equilateral triangle, as illustrated.

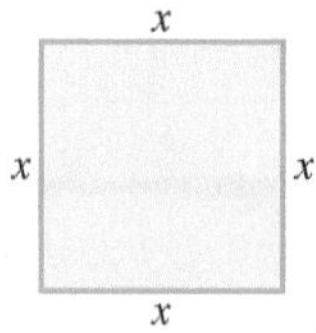

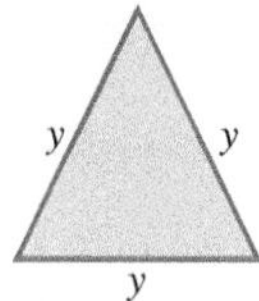

(a) Write a formula that gives the area A of the two shapes in terms of x.

(b) Find the length of wire (to the nearest tenth of an inch) that should be used for the square if the combined area of the two shapes is to be minimized?

3. Minimizing Time A person is in a rowboat 3 miles from the closest point on a straight shoreline, as illustrated in the figure. The person would like to reach a cabin that is 8 miles down the shoreline. The person can row at 4 miles per hour and jog at 7 miles per hour.

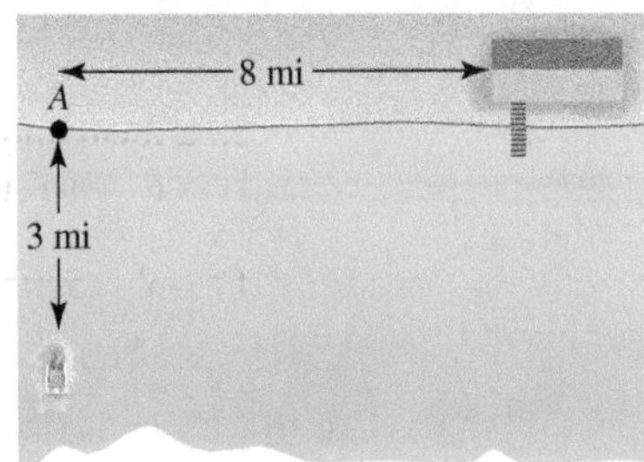

(a) How long will it take to reach the cabin if the person rows straight toward shore at point A and then jogs to the cabin?

(b) How long will it take to reach the cabin if the person rows straight to the cabin and does no jogging?

(c) Find the minimum time to reach the cabin.

4.2 Polynomial Functions and Models

- **Understand the graphs of polynomial functions**
- **Evaluate and graph piecewise-defined functions**
- **Use polynomial regression to model data (optional)**

Introduction

The consumption of natural gas by the United States has varied in the past. As shown in Table 4.2, energy consumption (in quadrillion Btu) increased, decreased, and then increased again. A scatterplot of the data is shown in Figure 4.20, and one possibility for a polynomial modeling function f is shown in Figure 4.21. Notice that f is neither linear nor quadratic. What degree of polynomial might we use to model these data? This question is answered in Example 4.

Natural Gas Consumption

Year	1960	1970	1980	1990	2000
Consumption	12.4	21.8	20.4	19.3	24.0

Table 4.2 ***Source:*** Department of Energy.

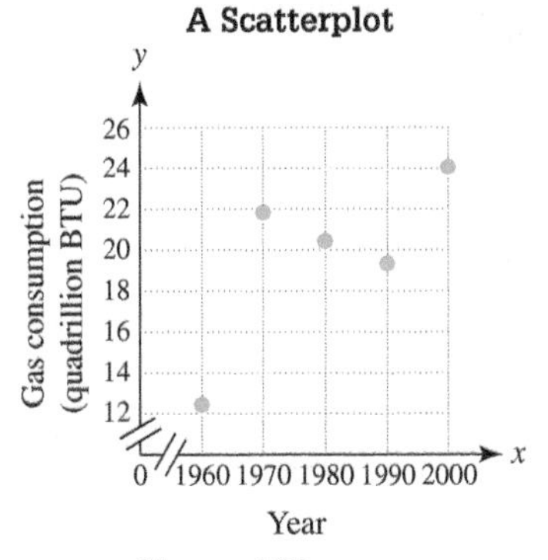

Figure 4.20

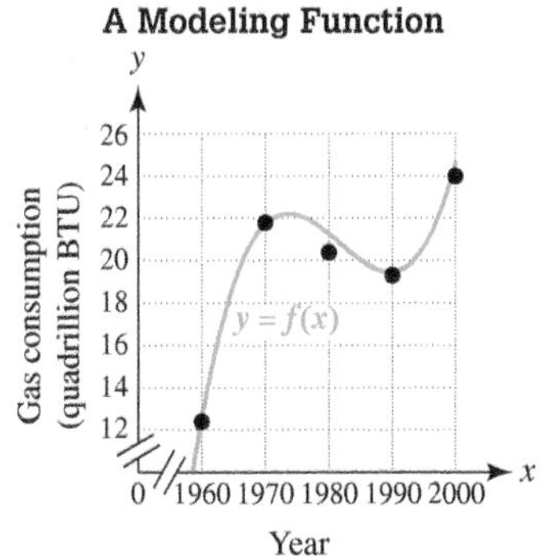

Figure 4.21

Graphs of Polynomial Functions

In Section 4.1 polynomial functions were defined. The following Making Connections helps show the relationship among polynomials, polynomial functions, and polynomial equations with one variable.

MAKING CONNECTIONS

Polynomials, Functions, and Equations

Polynomial of Degree n

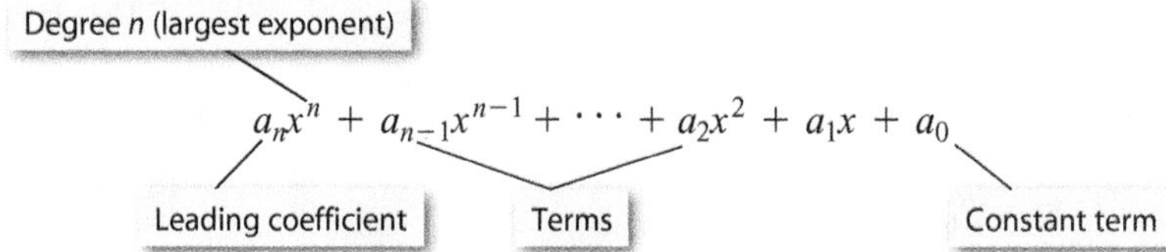

Example: $x^3 - 3x^2 + x - 5$ is a polynomial.

Polynomial Function of Degree n

$$f(x) = a_nx^n + a_{n-1}x^{n-1} + \cdots + a_2x^2 + a_1x + a_0$$

Domain: All real numbers

Graph is continuous and smooth; no breaks or sharp edges.

Example: $f(x) = x^3 - 3x^2 + x - 5$ defines a polynomial function.

Polynomial Equation of Degree n

$$a_nx^n + a_{n-1}x^{n-1} + \cdots + a_2x^2 + a_1x + a_0 = 0$$

At most n real solutions (See Section 4.4)

Example: $x^3 - 3x^2 + x - 5 = 0$ is a polynomial equation.

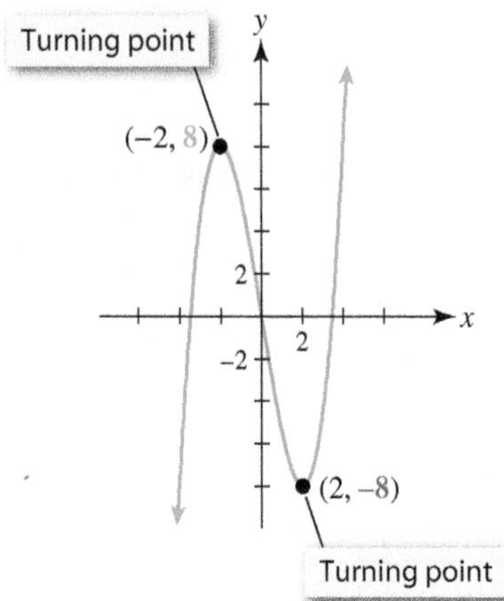

Figure 4.22

A **turning point** occurs whenever the graph of a polynomial function changes from increasing to decreasing or from decreasing to increasing. Turning points are associated with "hills" or "valleys" on a graph. The y-value at a turning point is either a local maximum or a local minimum of the function. In Figure 4.22 the graph has two turning points, $(-2, 8)$ and $(2, -8)$. A local maximum is 8 and a local minimum is -8.

We discuss the graphs of polynomial functions, starting with degree 0 and continuing to degree 5. Look for patterns in the graphs of these polynomial functions.

Constant Polynomial Functions If $f(x) = a$ and $a \neq 0$, then f is both a constant function and a polynomial function of **degree 0.** (If $a = 0$, then f has an **undefined degree.**) Its graph is a horizontal line that does not coincide with the x-axis. Graphs of two constant functions are shown in Figures 4.23 and 4.24. A graph of a polynomial function of degree 0 has no x-intercepts or turning points.

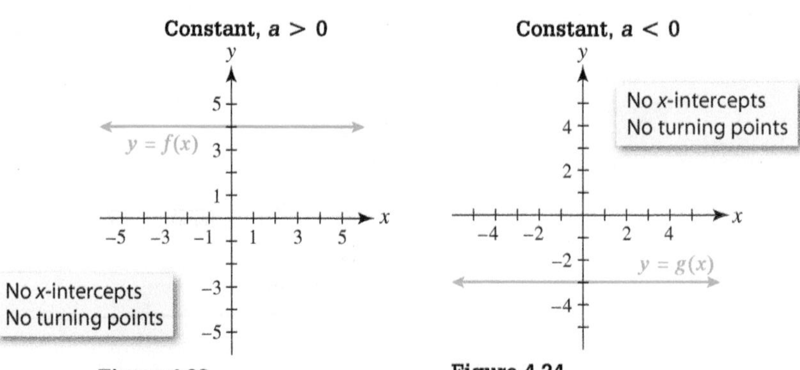

Figure 4.23

Figure 4.24

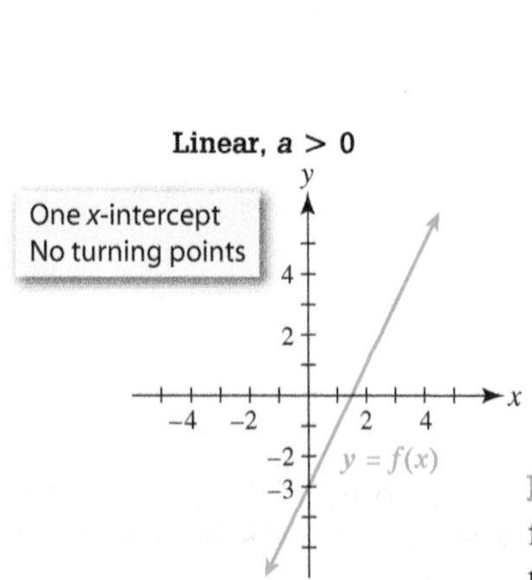

Figure 4.25

Linear Polynomial Functions If $f(x) = ax + b$ and $a \neq 0$, then f is both a linear function and a polynomial function of **degree 1**. Its graph is a line that is neither horizontal nor vertical. The graphs of two linear functions are shown in Figures 4.25 and 4.26. A polynomial function of degree 1 has one x-intercept and no turning points.

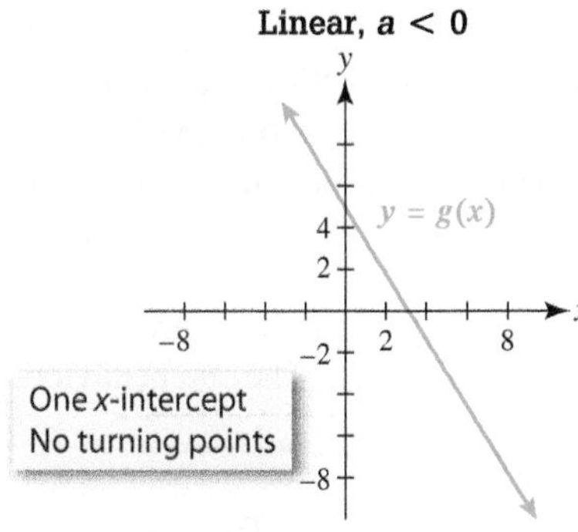

Figure 4.26

The graph of $f(x) = ax + b$ with $a > 0$ is a line sloping upward from left to right. As one traces from left to right, the y-values become larger without a maximum. We say that the **end behavior** of the graph tends to $-\infty$ on the left and ∞ on the right. (Strictly speaking, the graph of a polynomial has infinite length and does not have an end.) More formally, we say that $f(x) \to -\infty$ as $x \to -\infty$ and $f(x) \to \infty$ as $x \to \infty$.

If $a < 0$, then the end behavior is reversed. The line slopes downward from left to right. The y-values on the left side of the graph become large positive values without a maximum and the y-values on the right side become negative without a minimum. The end behavior tends to ∞ on the left and $-\infty$ on the right, or $f(x) \to \infty$ as $x \to -\infty$ and $f(x) \to -\infty$ as $x \to \infty$.

Quadratic Polynomial Functions If $f(x) = ax^2 + bx + c$ and $a \neq 0$, then f is both a quadratic function and a polynomial function of **degree 2.** Its graph is a parabola that opens either upward ($a > 0$) or downward ($a < 0$). The graphs of three quadratic functions are shown in Figures 4.27–4.29, respectively. Quadratic functions can have zero, one, or two x-intercepts. A parabola has *exactly one* turning point, which is also the vertex.

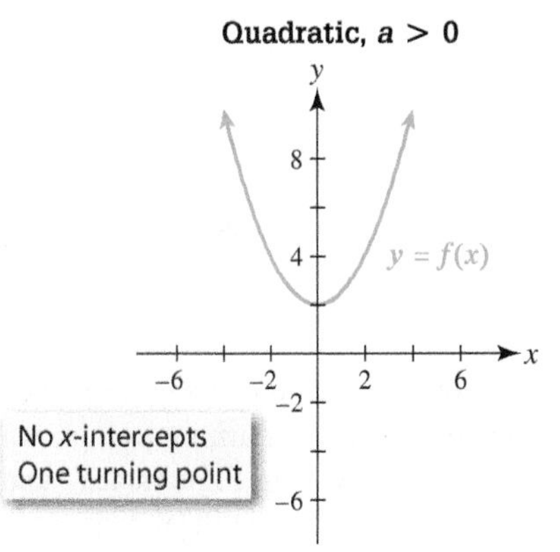

Figure 4.27

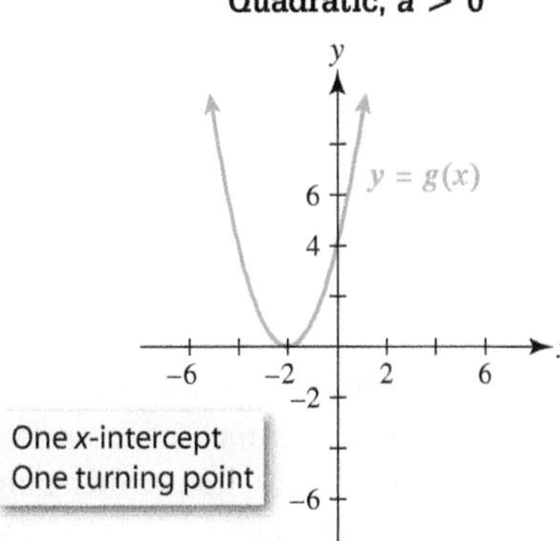

Figure 4.28

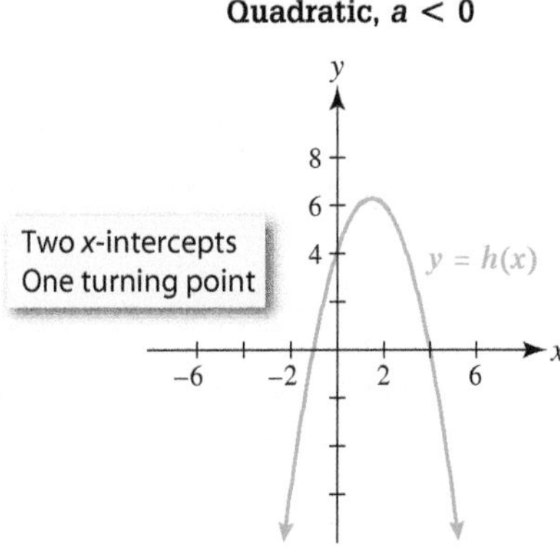

Figure 4.29

If $a > 0$, as in Figure 4.27, then both sides of the graph go up. The end behavior tends to ∞ on both sides, or $f(x) \to \infty$ as $x \to \pm\infty$. If $a < 0$, as in Figure 4.29, then the end behavior is reversed and tends to $-\infty$ on both sides, or $f(x) \to -\infty$ as $x \to \pm\infty$.

Cubic Polynomial Functions If $f(x) = ax^3 + bx^2 + cx + d$ and $a \neq 0$, then f is both a **cubic function** and a polynomial function of **degree 3.** The graph of a cubic function can have zero or two turning points. The graph of $y = f(x)$ in Figure 4.30 has two turning points, whereas the graph of $y = g(x)$ in Figure 4.31 has no turning points.

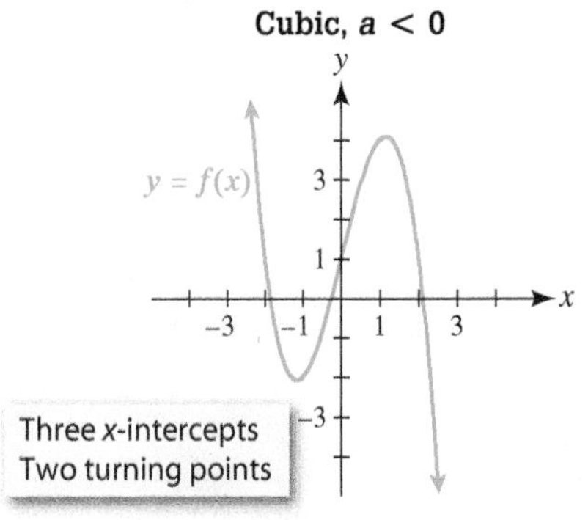

Figure 4.30

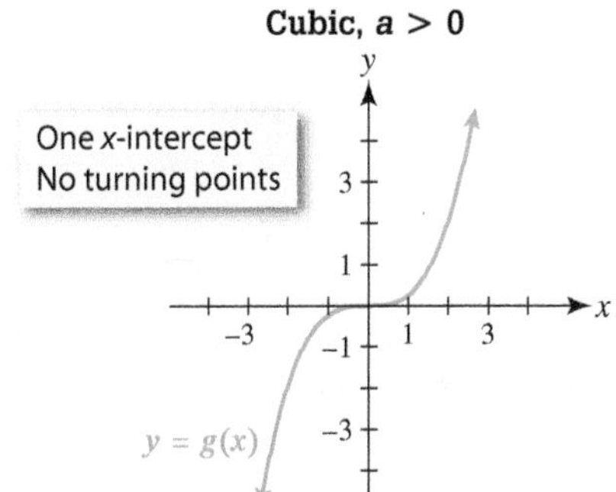

Figure 4.31

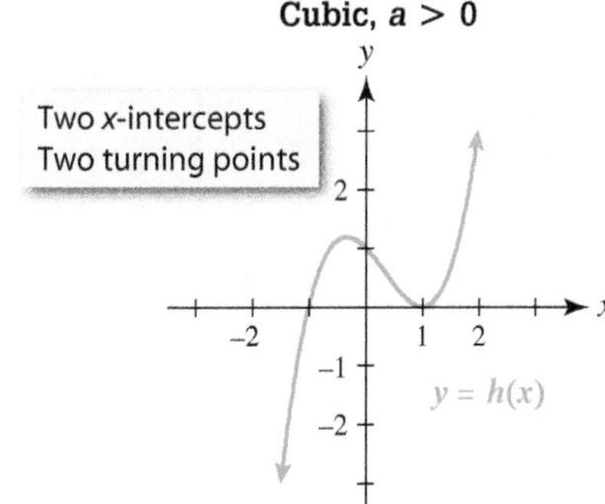

Figure 4.32

If $a > 0$, the graph of a cubic function falls to the left and rises to the right, as in Figure 4.31. If $a < 0$, its graph rises to the left and falls to the right, as in Figure 4.30. The end behavior of a cubic function is similar to that of a linear function, tending to ∞ on one side and $-\infty$ on the other. Therefore its graph must cross the x-axis at least once. A cubic function can have up to three x-intercepts. The graph of $y = h(x)$ in Figure 4.32 has two x-intercepts.

CLASS DISCUSSION

Can a quartic function have both an absolute maximum and an absolute minimum? Explain.

Quartic Polynomial Functions If $f(x) = ax^4 + bx^3 + cx^2 + dx + e$ and $a \neq 0$, then f is both a **quartic function** and a polynomial function of **degree 4**. The graph of a quartic function can have up to four x-intercepts and three turning points; the graph of $y = f(x)$ in Figure 4.33 is an example. The graph in Figure 4.34 of $y = g(x)$ has one turning point and two x-intercepts, and the graph in Figure 4.35 of $y = h(x)$ has three turning points and three x-intercepts.

If $a > 0$, then both ends of the graph of a quartic function go up, as in Figure 4.33. If $a < 0$, then both ends of its graph go down, as in Figures 4.34 and 4.35. The end behaviors of quartic and quadratic functions are similar.

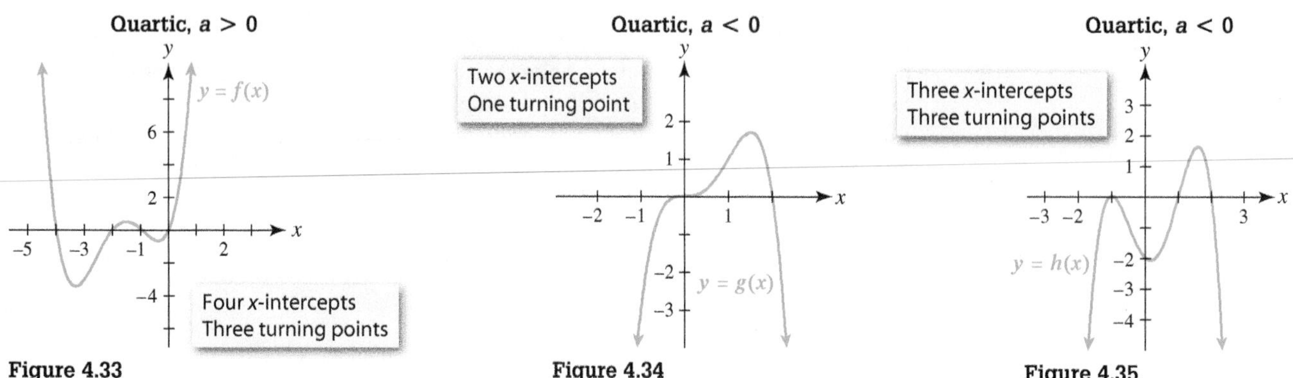

Figure 4.33 Figure 4.34 Figure 4.35

CLASS DISCUSSION

Can you sketch the graph of a quadratic function with no turning points, a cubic function with one turning point, or a quartic function with two turning points? Explain.

Quintic Polynomial Functions If $f(x) = ax^5 + bx^4 + cx^3 + dx^2 + ex + k$ and $a \neq 0$, then f is both a **quintic function** and a polynomial function of **degree 5**. The graph of a quintic function may have up to five x-intercepts and four turning points. An example is shown in Figure 4.36. Other quintic functions are shown in Figures 4.37 and 4.38. The graph of g has one x-intercept and no turning points. The graph of h appears to have two x-intercepts and two turning points. Notice that the end behavior of a quintic function is similar to that of linear and cubic functions.

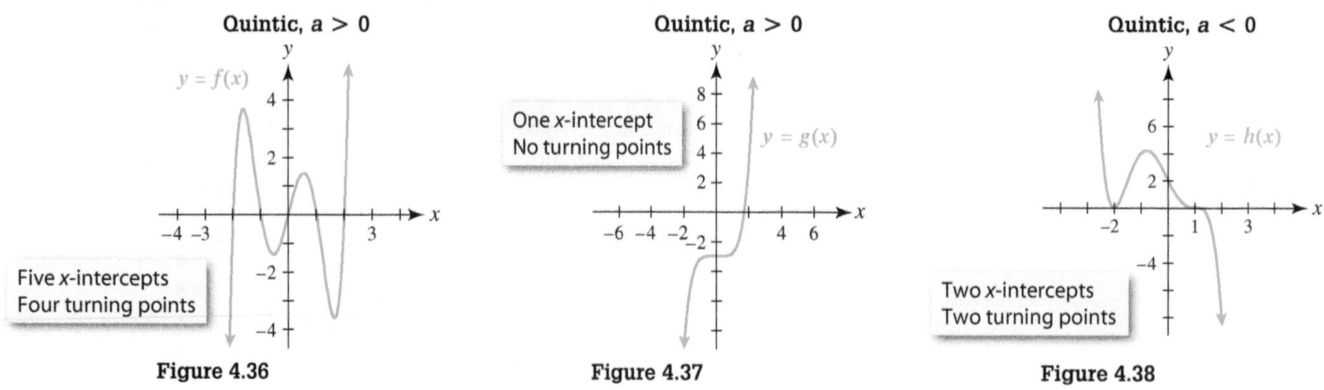

Figure 4.36 Figure 4.37 Figure 4.38

The maximum numbers of x-intercepts and turning points on the graph of a polynomial function of degree n can be summarized as follows.

DEGREE, x-INTERCEPTS, AND TURNING POINTS

The graph of a polynomial function of degree n, with $n \geq 1$, has at most n x-intercepts and at most $n - 1$ turning points.

The end behavior of a polynomial function depends on whether its degree is even or odd and whether its leading coefficient is positive or negative. The following See the Concept summarizes this discussion. The region inside the oval indicates where the graph might have x-intercepts and turning points.

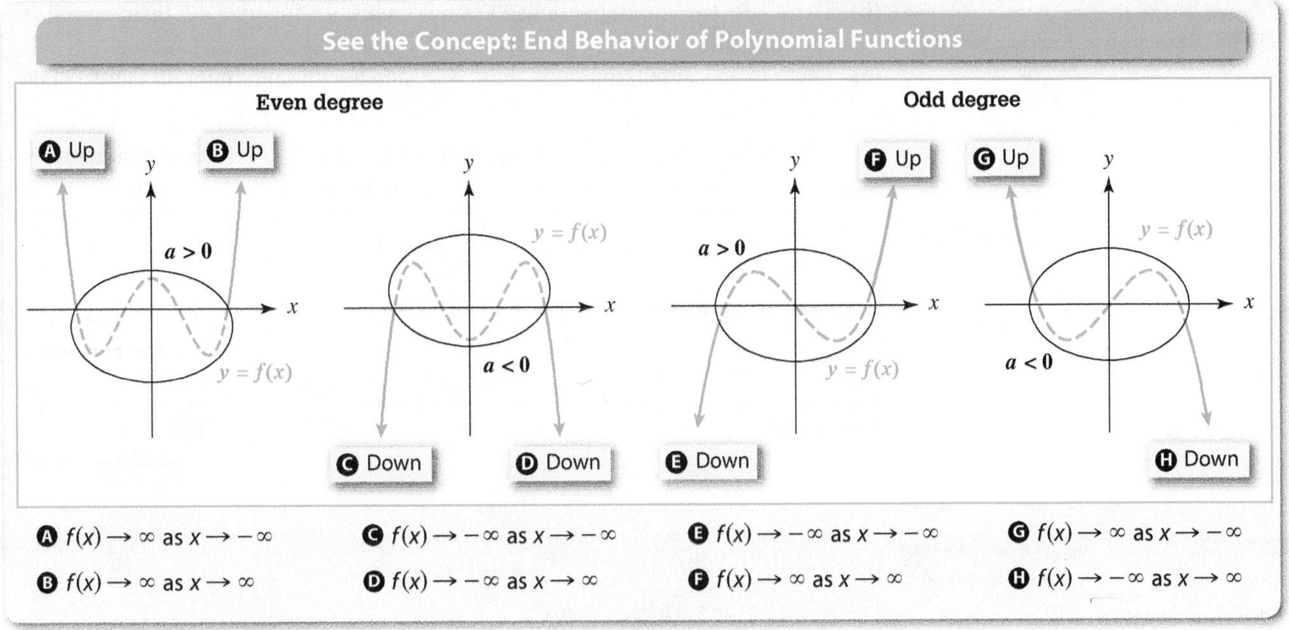

EXAMPLE 1 Analyzing the graph of a polynomial function

Figure 4.39 shows the graph of a polynomial function f.

(a) How many turning points and how many x-intercepts are there?

(b) Is the leading coefficient a positive or negative? Is the degree odd or even?

(c) Determine the minimum possible degree of f.

Figure 4.39

SOLUTION

(a) There are four turning points corresponding to the two "hills" and two "valleys." There appear to be four x-intercepts.

(b) The left side of the graph rises and the right side falls. Therefore $a < 0$ and the polynomial function has odd degree.

(c) The graph has four turning points. A polynomial of degree n can have at most $n - 1$ turning points. Therefore f must be *at least* degree 5.

Now Try Exercise 7

NOTE More examples of graphs of polynomials and their characteristics are found in the "Putting It All Together" for this section.

EXAMPLE 2 Analyzing the graph of a polynomial function

Graph $f(x) = x^3 - 2x^2 - 5x + 6$, and then complete the following.

(a) Identify the x-intercepts.

(b) Approximate the coordinates of any turning points to the nearest hundredth.

(c) Use the turning points to approximate any local extrema.

SOLUTION

(a) A calculator graph of f, shown in Figure 4.40 on the next page, *appears* to intersect the x-axis at the points $(-2, 0)$, $(1, 0)$, and $(3, 0)$. Because $f(-2) = 0$, $f(1) = 0$, and $f(3) = 0$, the x-intercepts are -2, 1, and 3.

Calculator Help
To find a minimum or maximum point on a graph, see Appendix A (page AP-8).

(b) There are two turning points. From Figures 4.41 and 4.42 their coordinates are approximately $(-0.79, 8.21)$ and $(2.12, -4.06)$.

(c) There is a local maximum of about 8.21 and a local minimum of about -4.06.

Given Function

$[-10, 10, 1]$ by $[-10, 10, 1]$

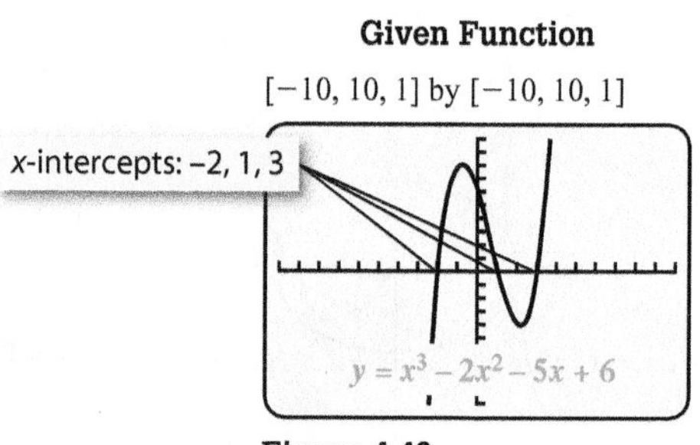

Figure 4.40

Local Maximum ≈ 8.21

$[-10, 10, 1]$ by $[-10, 10, 1]$

Maximum
X=⁻.7862976 Y=8.2088207

Figure 4.41

Local Minimum ≈ −4.06

$[-10, 10, 1]$ by $[-10, 10, 1]$

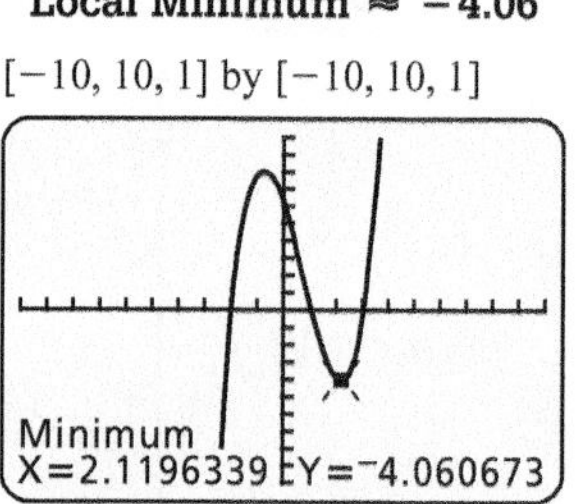

Figure 4.42

Now Try Exercise 25

EXAMPLE 3 Analyzing the end behavior of a graph

Cubic with $a < 0$

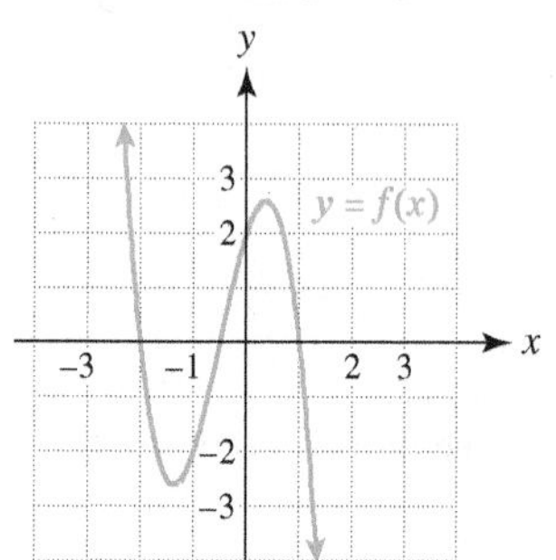

Figure 4.43

Let $f(x) = 2 + 3x - 3x^2 - 2x^3$.

(a) Give the degree and leading coefficient.

(b) State the end behavior of the graph of f.

SOLUTION

(a) Rewriting gives $f(x) = -2x^3 - 3x^2 + 3x + 2$. The term with highest degree is $-2x^3$, so the degree is 3 and the leading coefficient is -2.

(b) The degree of $f(x)$ is odd, and the leading coefficient is negative. Therefore the graph of f rises to the left and falls to the right. More formally,

$$f(x) \to \infty \text{ as } x \to -\infty \qquad \text{and} \qquad f(x) \to -\infty \text{ as } x \to \infty.$$

This conclusion is supported by Figure 4.43.

Now Try Exercise 33

An Application In the next example, we analyze the data presented in the introduction to this section.

EXAMPLE 4 Modeling natural gas consumption

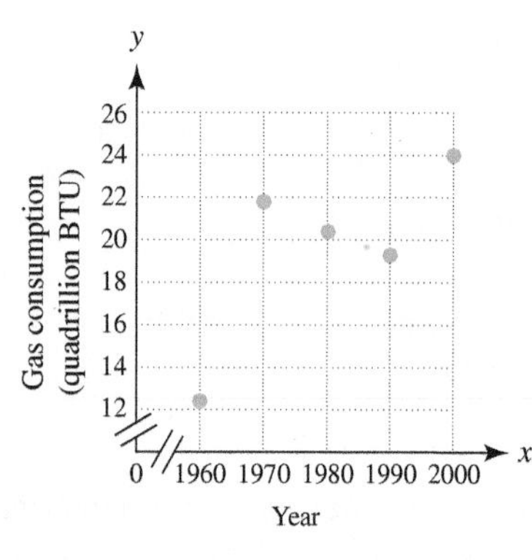

Figure 4.20, which shows natural gas consumption from 1960 to 2000, is repeated in the margin.

(a) Could a linear or quadratic function model the data?

(b) What minimum degree polynomial might be appropriate to model the data?

(c) Should the leading coefficient a be positive or negative?

SOLUTION

(a) The data clearly do not lie on a line, so a linear function is not appropriate. Because natural gas consumption increases, decreases, and then increases, a quadratic function would not be a good choice either. The data are not ⋃-shaped or ⋂-shaped.

(b) Because the data increase, decrease, and then increase, a polynomial with at least two turning points would be appropriate. A cubic, or degree 3, polynomial is a possibility for a modeling function.

(c) The leading coefficient a should be positive because the data fall to the left and rise to the right.

Now Try Exercises 39(a), (b), and (c)

Concavity (Optional) Graphs of polynomial functions with degree 2 or greater are curves. **Concavity** is a mathematical description of how a curve bends. A line exhibits no, or zero, concavity because it is straight. A parabola that opens upward is said to be **concave upward** everywhere on its domain. See Figure 4.44. A parabola that opens downward is said to be **concave downward** everywhere on its domain. See Figure 4.45. A graph of a higher degree polynomial can be concave upward on one interval of its domain and concave downward on a different interval of its domain. See Figure 4.46, where the graph of $f(x) = 4x - x^3$ is concave upward on the interval $(-\infty, 0)$, shown in blue, and concave downward on $(0, \infty)$, shown in red. Concavity is usually defined for *open* intervals. Determining the exact x-value where a graph switches from concave upward to downward or vice versa can be difficult to do visually and often requires techniques learned in calculus. This point is called the **point of inflection.** (See Extended and Discovery Exercises 2–7 for this section.)

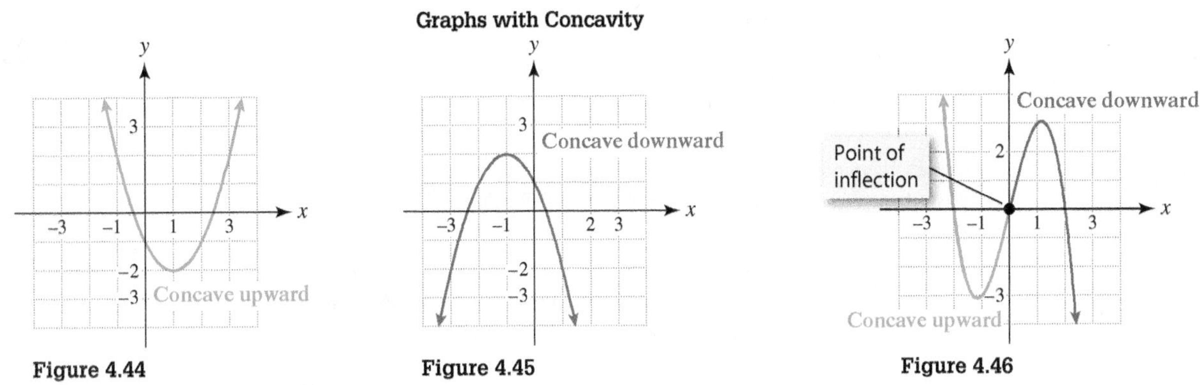

Figure 4.44 Figure 4.45 Figure 4.46

Piecewise-Defined Polynomial Functions

In Section 2.4 piecewise-defined functions were discussed. If each piece is a polynomial, then the function is a **piecewise-defined polynomial function** or **piecewise-polynomial function**. An example is given by $f(x)$.

$$f(x) = \begin{cases} x^3 & \text{if } x < 1 \\ x^2 - 1 & \text{if } x \geq 1 \end{cases}$$

First piece
Second piece

One way to graph f is to first graph $y = x^3$ and $y = x^2 - 1$, as shown in Figures 4.47 and 4.48. Then the graph of f is found by using the blue portion of $y = x^3$ for $x < 1$ and the blue portion of $y = x^2 - 1$ for $x \geq 1$, as illustrated in Figure 4.49. At $x = 1$ there is a break in the graph, where the graph of f is discontinuous.

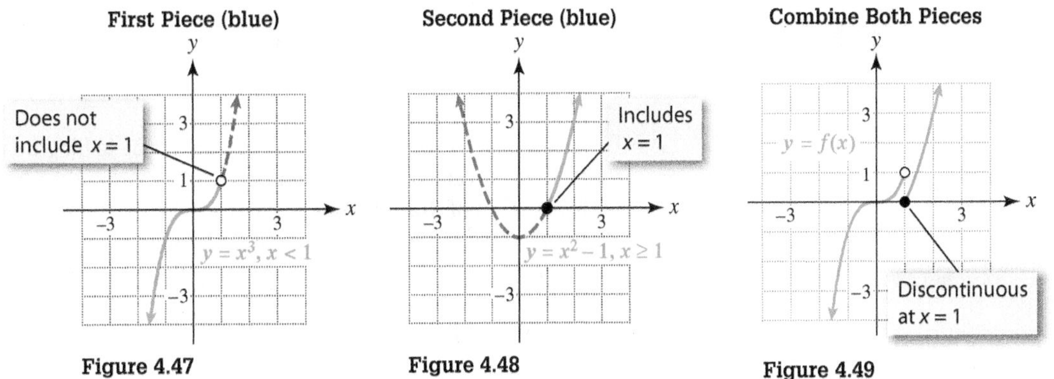

Figure 4.47 Figure 4.48 Figure 4.49

EXAMPLE 5 **Evaluating a piecewise-defined polynomial function**

Evaluate $f(x)$ at $x = -3, -2, 1$, and 2.

$$f(x) = \begin{cases} x^2 - x & \text{if } -5 \le x < -2 \\ -x^3 & \text{if } -2 \le x < 2 \\ 4 - 4x & \text{if } \ 2 \le x \le 5 \end{cases}$$

SOLUTION To evaluate $f(-3)$ we use the formula $f(x) = x^2 - x$, because -3 is in the interval $-5 \le x < -2$.

$$f(-3) = (-3)^2 - (-3) = 12$$

To evaluate $f(-2)$ we use $f(x) = -x^3$, because -2 is in the interval $-2 \le x < 2$.

$$f(-2) = -(-2)^3 = -(-8) = 8$$

Similarly, $f(1) = -1^3 = -1$ and $f(2) = 4 - 4(2) = -4$.

Now Try Exercise 73

EXAMPLE 6 **Graphing a piecewise-defined function**

Complete the following.

(a) Sketch a graph of f.

(b) Determine if f is continuous on its domain.

(c) Solve the equation $f(x) = 1$.

$$f(x) = \begin{cases} \frac{1}{2}x^2 - 2 & \text{if } -4 \le x \le 0 \\ 2x - 2 & \text{if } \ 0 < x < 2 \\ 2 & \text{if } \ 2 \le x \le 4 \end{cases}$$

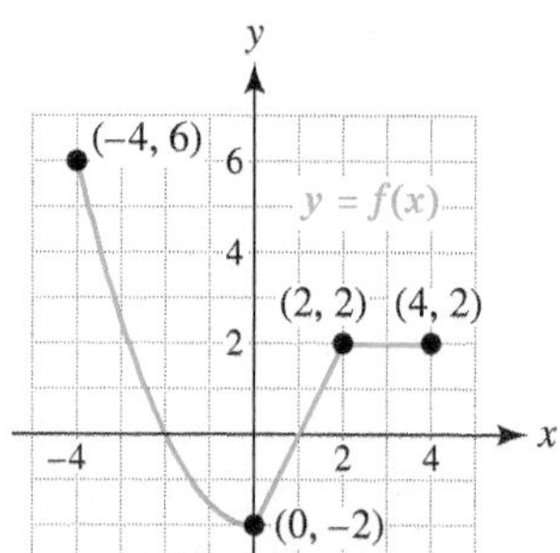

Figure 4.50

SOLUTION

(a) For the first piece, graph the parabola determined by $y = \frac{1}{2}x^2 - 2$ on the interval $-4 \le x \le 0$. Place dots at the endpoints, which are $(-4, 6)$ and $(0, -2)$. See Figure 4.50. For the second piece, graph the line determined by $y = 2x - 2$ *between* the points $(0, -2)$ and $(2, 2)$. Note that the left endpoint of the middle piece coincides with the right endpoint of the first piece. Finally, graph the horizontal line $y = 2$ from the points $(2, 2)$ to $(4, 2)$. Note that the left endpoint of the third piece coincides with the right endpoint of the middle piece.

(b) The domain of f is $-4 \le x \le 4$. Because there are no breaks in the graph of f on its domain, the graph of f is continuous.

(c) The red horizontal line $y = 1$ intersects the blue graph of $y = f(x)$ at two points, as shown in Figure 4.51. The x-coordinates of these two points of intersection coincide with the green segments and can be found by solving the equations

$$\frac{1}{2}x^2 - 2 = 1 \quad \text{and} \quad 2x - 2 = 1.$$

The solutions are $-\sqrt{6} \approx -2.45$ and $\frac{3}{2}$.

Solving $f(x) = 1$

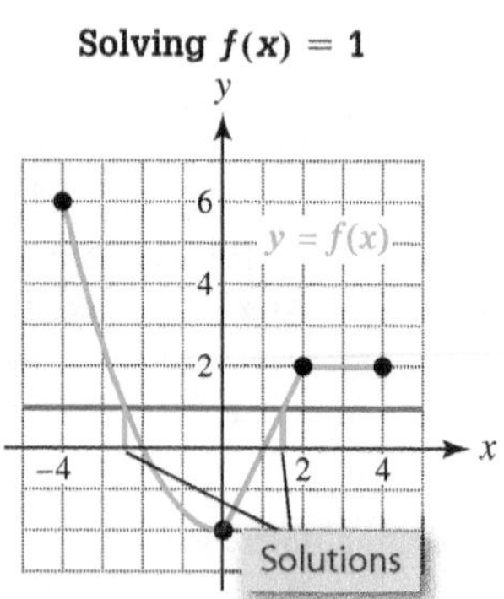

Figure 4.51

Now Try Exercise 79

An Application When there is a small number of fishing boats in a large area of water, each boat tends to catch its limit each trip. As the number of boats increases dramatically, there comes a point of **diminishing returns**, where the yield for each boat begins to decrease even though the total number of fish caught by all fishing boats continues to increase. This phenomenon can be modeled by a piecewise-polynomial function F defined by

$$F(x) = \begin{cases} x & \text{if } 0 \le x \le 5 \\ -0.08x^2 + 1.6x - 1 & \text{if } 5 \le x \le 15 \end{cases}$$

where x is the number of fishing boats in hundreds and $F(x)$ outputs thousands of tons of fish harvested. A graph of F is shown in Figure 4.52.

Diminishing Returns and Overfishing

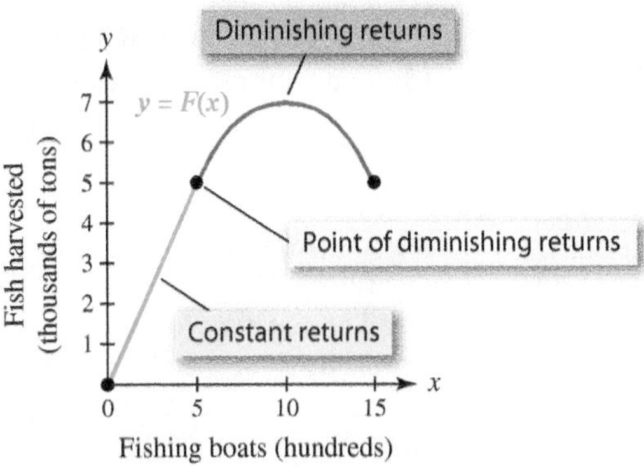

Figure 4.52

EXAMPLE 7 Analyzing diminishing returns

Use the preceding discussion to complete the following.

(a) Evaluate $F(2)$ and interpret the result.

(b) Find the absolute maximum on the graph of F and interpret the result.

SOLUTION

(a) For $0 \le x \le 5$, $F(x) = x$, so $F(2) = 2$. When 200 fishing boats are used, 2 thousand tons of fish are harvested.

(b) The second piece is $F(x) = -0.08x^2 + 1.6x - 1$, so its graph is a parabola opening downward. To find the absolute maximum, we first need to find its vertex.

$$x = -\frac{b}{2a} \qquad \text{Vertex formula}$$

$$= -\frac{1.6}{2(-0.08)} \qquad \text{Substitute.}$$

$$= 10 \qquad x\text{-coordinate of vertex}$$

Because $F(10) = -0.08(10)^2 + 1.6(10) - 1 = 7$, the vertex is $(10, 7)$. This result means that 7 thousand tons of fish is the maximum amount of fish that can be caught in these waters and it occurs when 1000 fishing vessels are used. If more boats are used, there is a decrease in the overall catch.

Now Try Exercise 83

Polynomial Regression (Optional)

Natural Gas Usage

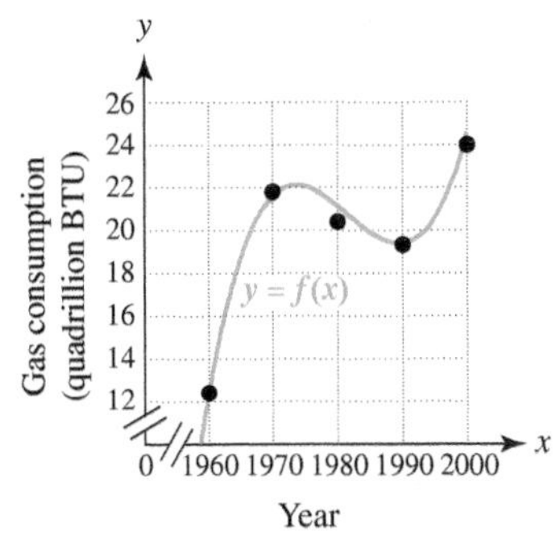

We now have the mathematical understanding to model the data presented in the introduction to this section. The polynomial modeling function f (shown in Figure 4.21 and repeated in the margin) falls to the left and rises to the right, so it has odd degree and the leading coefficient is positive. Since the graph of f has two turning points, it must be at least degree 3. A cubic polynomial $f(x)$ is a possible choice, where

$$f(x) = ax^3 + bx^2 + cx + d.$$

Trial and error would be a difficult way to find values for a, b, c, and d. Instead, we can use least-squares regression, which was also discussed in Sections 2.1 and 3.1, for linear and quadratic functions. The next example illustrates *cubic regression*.

EXAMPLE 8 Determining a cubic modeling function

Year	Consumption
1960	12.4
1970	21.8
1980	20.4
1990	19.3
2000	24.0

The data in Table 4.2 (repeated in the margin) lists natural gas consumption.

(a) Find a polynomial function of degree 3 that models the data.

(b) Graph f and the data together.

(c) Estimate natural gas consumption in 1974 and in 2010. Compare these estimates to the actual values of 21.2 and 24.9 quadrillion Btu, respectively.

(d) Did your estimates in part (c) involve interpolation or extrapolation? Is there a problem with using higher degree polynomials ($n \geq 3$) for extrapolation? Explain.

SOLUTION

(a) Enter the five data points (1960, 12.4), (1970, 21.8), (1980, 20.4), (1990, 19.3), and (2000, 24.0) into your calculator. Then select cubic regression, as shown in Figure 4.53. The equation for $f(x)$ is shown in Figure 4.54.

(b) A graph of f and a scatterplot of the data are shown in Figure 4.55.

(c) $f(1974) \approx 21.9$ and $f(2010) \approx 44.5$; the 1974 estimate is reasonably close to 21.2, whereas the 2010 estimate is not close to 24.9.

(d) The 1974 estimate uses interpolation, and the 2010 estimate uses extrapolation. Because the end behavior of a higher degree polynomial rapidly tends to either ∞ or $-\infty$, extrapolation-based estimates are usually inaccurate with higher degree polynomials.

Calculator Help

To find an equation of least-squares fit, see Appendix A (page AP-9). To copy a regression equation into Y_1, see Appendix A (page AP-11.)

Select Cubic Regression

EDIT CALC TESTS
1:1-Var Stats
2:2-Var Stats
3:Med-Med
4:LinReg(ax+b)
5:QuadReg
6:CubicReg
7↓QuartReg

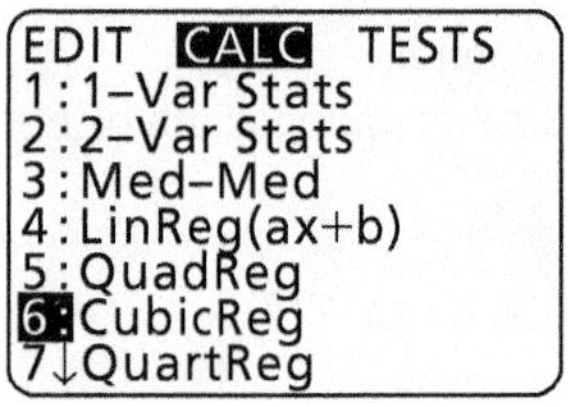

Figure 4.53

Regression Equation

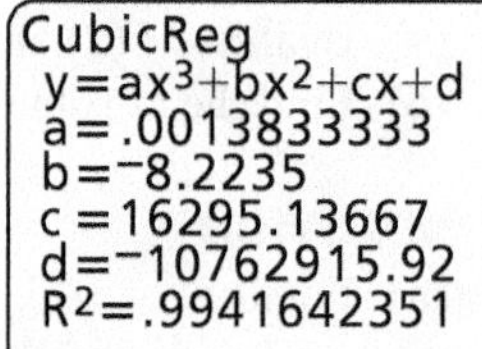

Figure 4.54

Graph of f and Data
[1955, 2005, 5] by [10, 25, 5]

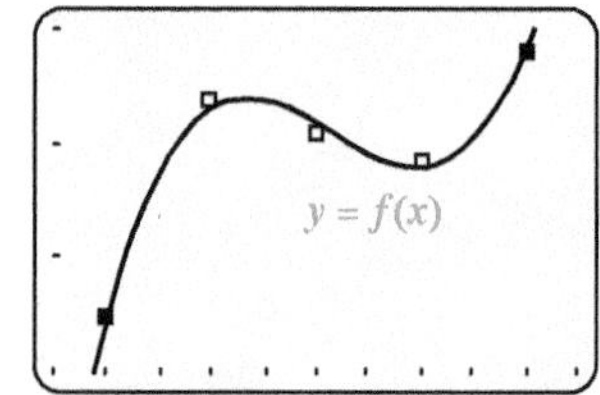

Figure 4.55

Now Try Exercise 91

4.2 Putting It All Together

Higher degree polynomials generally have more complicated graphs. Each additional degree allows the graph to have one more possible turning point and x-intercept. The graph of a polynomial function is continuous and smooth; it has no breaks or sharp edges. Its domain includes all real numbers. The end behavior of a polynomial always tends to either ∞ or $-\infty$. End behavior describes what happens to the y-values as $|x|$ becomes large.

FUNCTION TYPE	CHARACTERISTICS	EXAMPLE GRAPHS
Constant (degree 0)	No x-intercepts and no turning points $f(x) = a, a \neq 0$	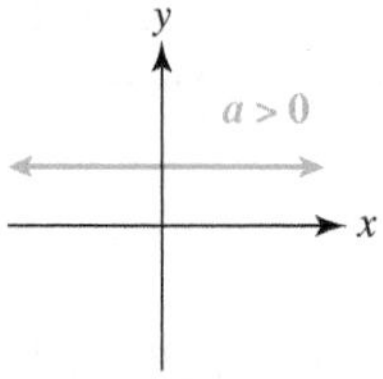 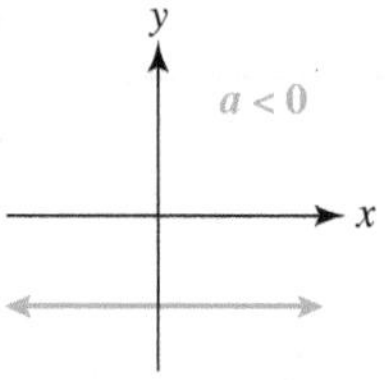 $a > 0$ $a < 0$

FUNCTION TYPE	CHARACTERISTICS	EXAMPLE GRAPHS
Linear (degree 1)	One x-intercept and no turning points $f(x) = ax + b, a \neq 0$	$a > 0$; $a < 0$
Quadratic (degree 2)	At most two x-intercepts and exactly one turning point $f(x) = ax^2 + bx + c, a \neq 0$	$a > 0$; $a < 0$
Cubic (degree 3)	At most three x-intercepts and up to two turning points $f(x) = ax^3 + bx^2 + cx + d, a \neq 0$	$a > 0$; $a < 0$
Quartic (degree 4)	At most four x-intercepts and up to three turning points $f(x) = ax^4 + bx^3 + cx^2 + dx + e, a \neq 0$	$a > 0$; $a < 0$
Quintic (degree 5)	At most five x-intercepts and up to four turning points $f(x) = ax^5 + bx^4 + cx^3 + dx^2 + ex + k,$ $a \neq 0$	$a > 0$; $a < 0$

4.2 Exercises

Note: Many of the answers in this section involve estimations. Your answers may vary slightly, particularly when you are reading a graph.

Graphs of Polynomial Functions

1. A runner is working out on a straight track. The graph on the next page shows the runner's distance y in hundreds of feet from the starting line after t minutes.

   (a) Estimate the turning points.

   (b) Interpret each turning point.

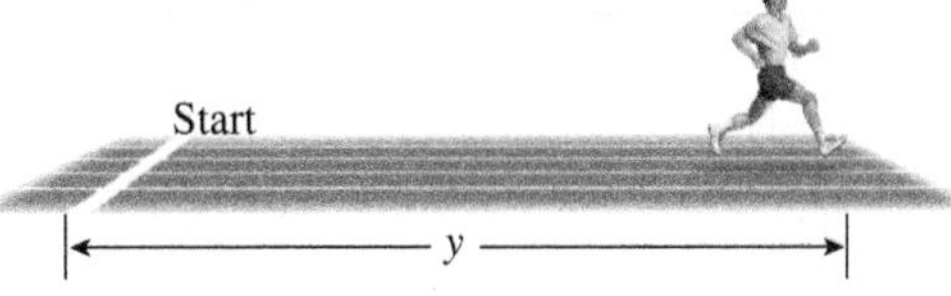

Distance (feet × 100)

Time (minutes)

2. A stone is thrown into the air. Its height y in feet after t seconds is shown in the graph. Use the graph to complete the following.
   (a) Estimate the turning point.
   (b) Interpret this point.

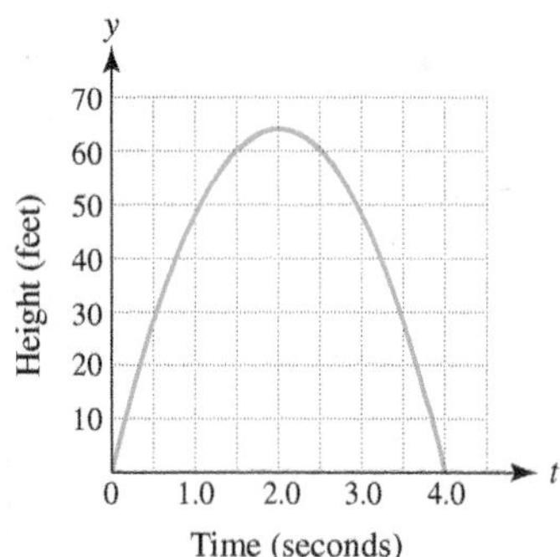

Exercises 3–12: Use the graph of the polynomial function f to complete the following. Let a be the leading coefficient of the polynomial $f(x)$.

(a) Determine the number of turning points and estimate any x-intercepts.
(b) State whether $a > 0$ or $a < 0$.
(c) Determine the minimum degree of f.

3.
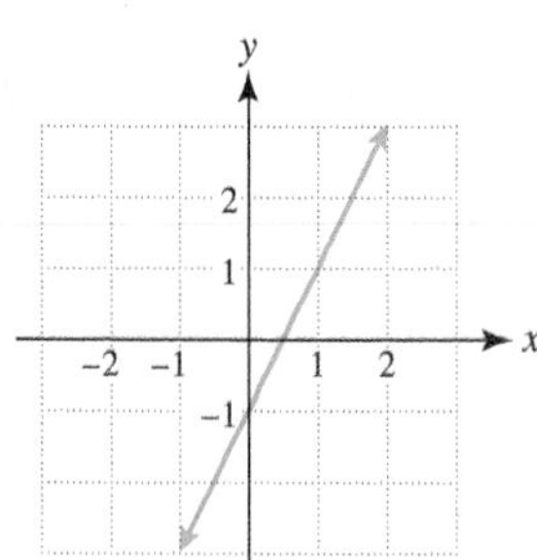

4.
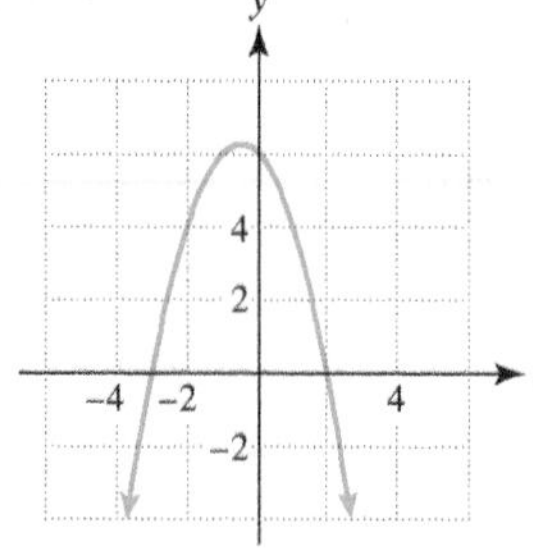

5.
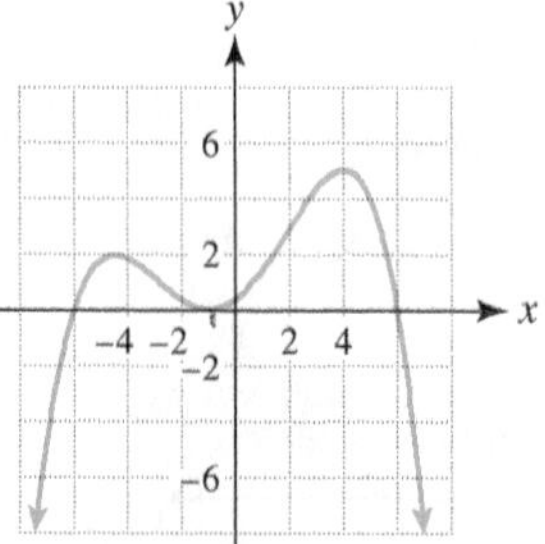

6.
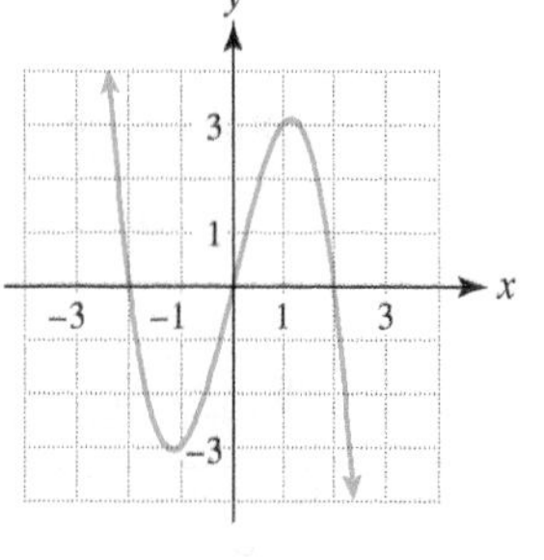

7.
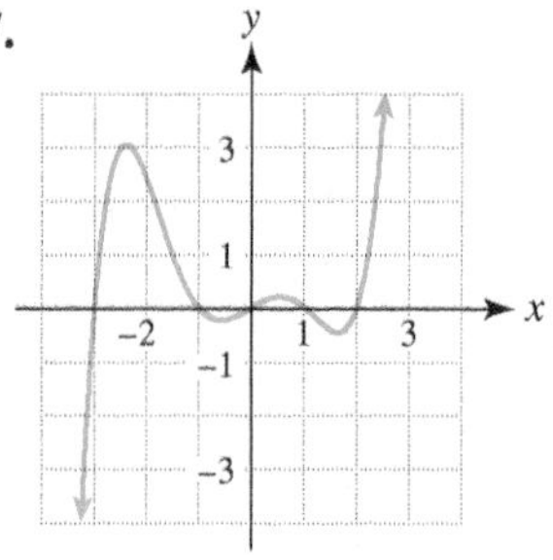

8.
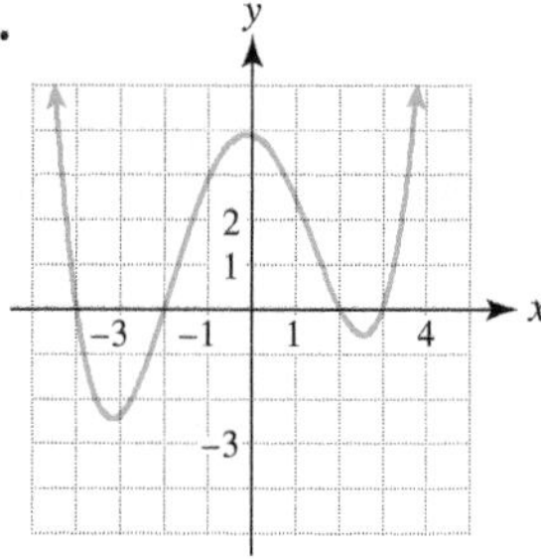

9.
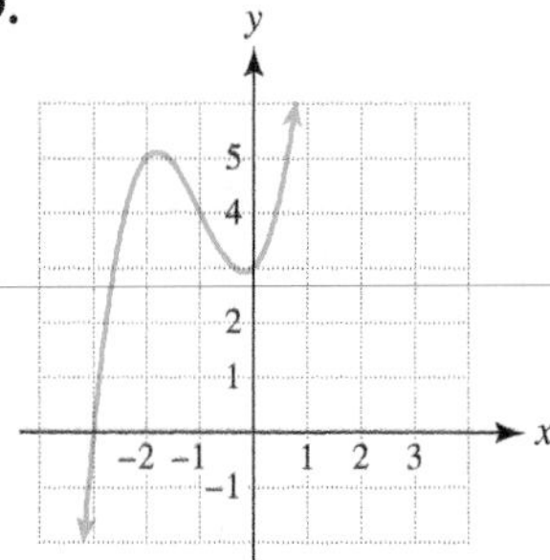

10.
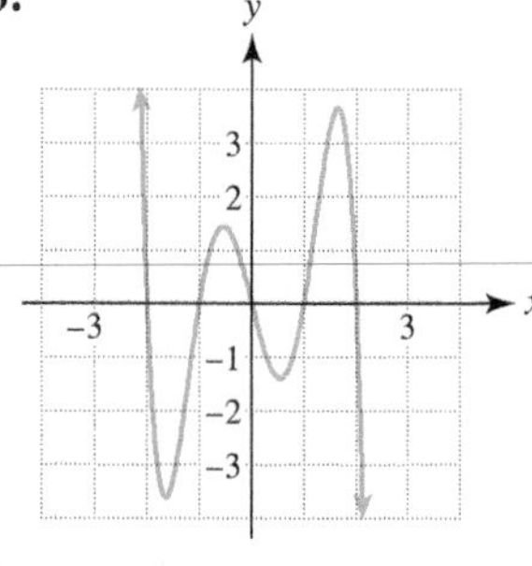

11.
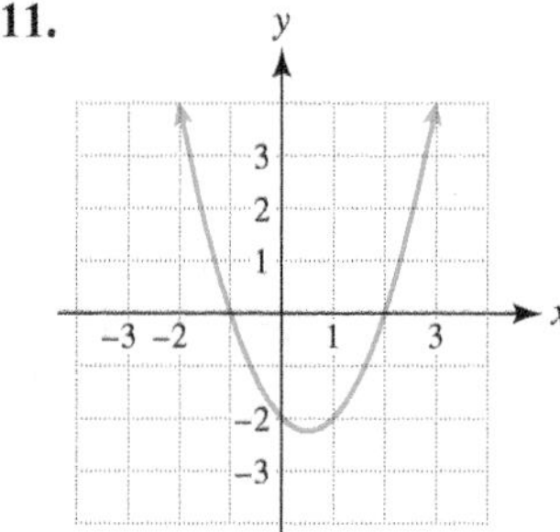

12.
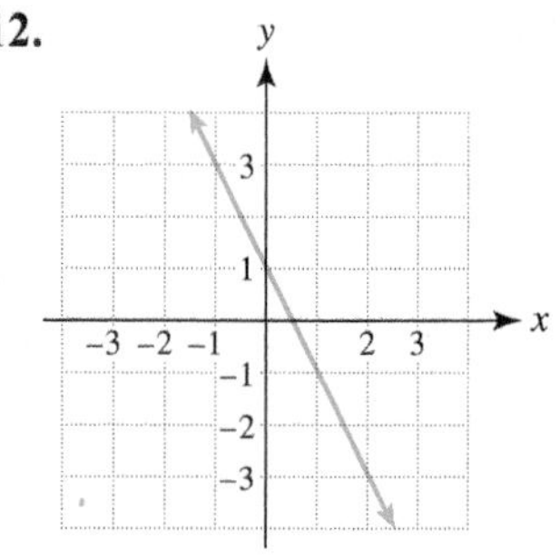

Exercises 13–18: Complete the following without a calculator.

(a) Match the equation with its graph (a–f).
(b) Identify the turning points.
(c) Estimate the x-intercepts.
(d) Estimate any local extrema.
(e) Estimate any absolute extrema.

13. $f(x) = 1 - 2x + x^2$

14. $f(x) = 3x - x^3$

15. $f(x) = x^3 + 3x^2 - 9x$

16. $f(x) = x^4 - 8x^2$

17. $f(x) = 8x^2 - x^4$

18. $f(x) = x^5 + \frac{5}{2}x^4 - \frac{5}{3}x^3 - 5x^2$

a.
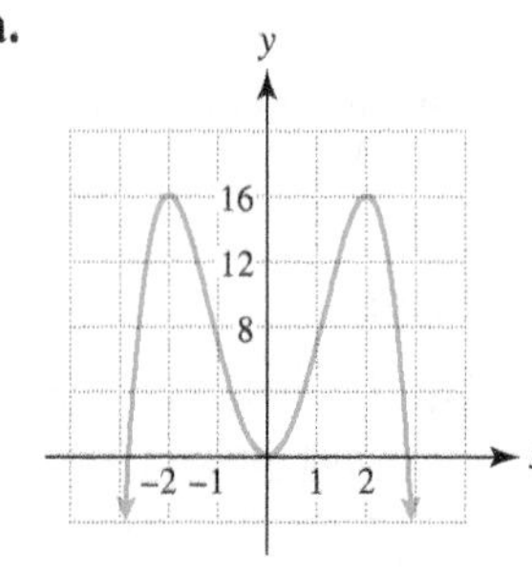

b.
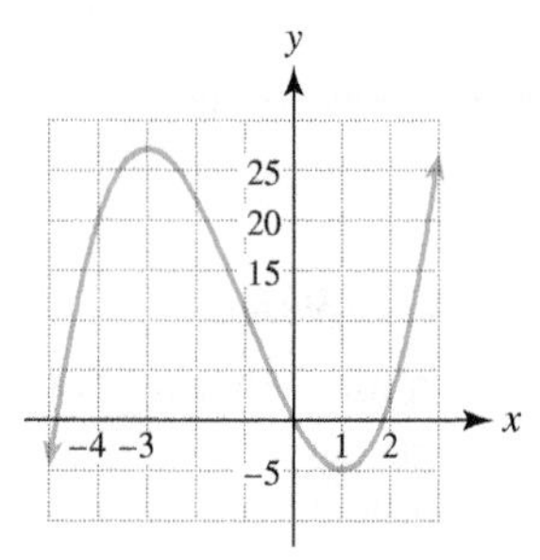

c.

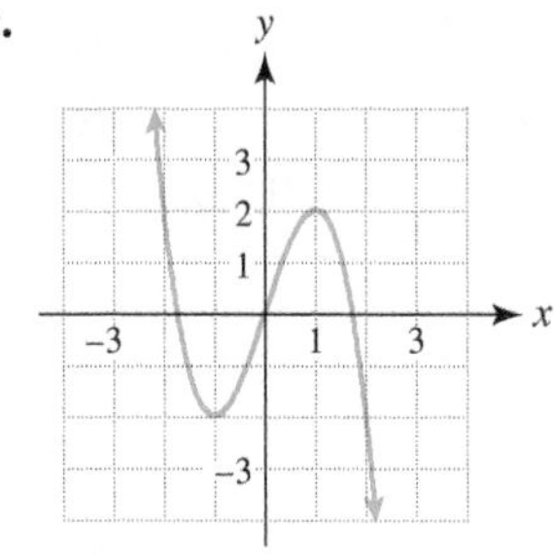

d.

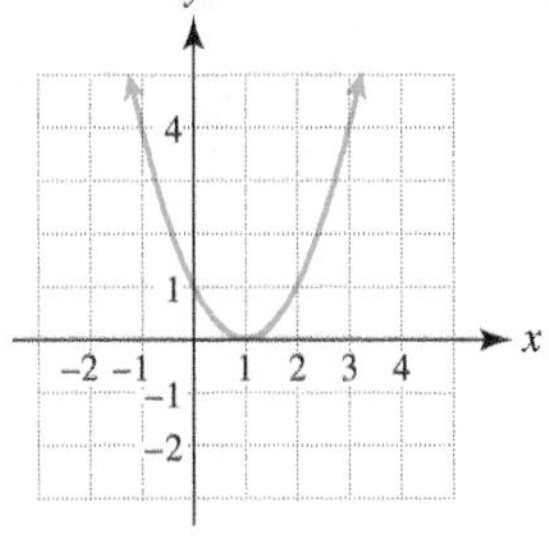

e.

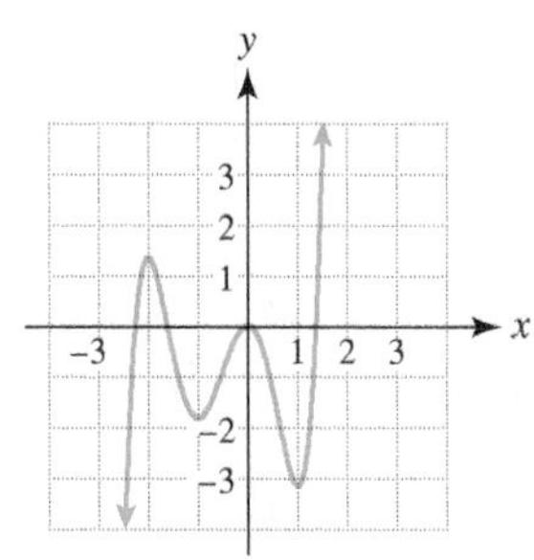

f.

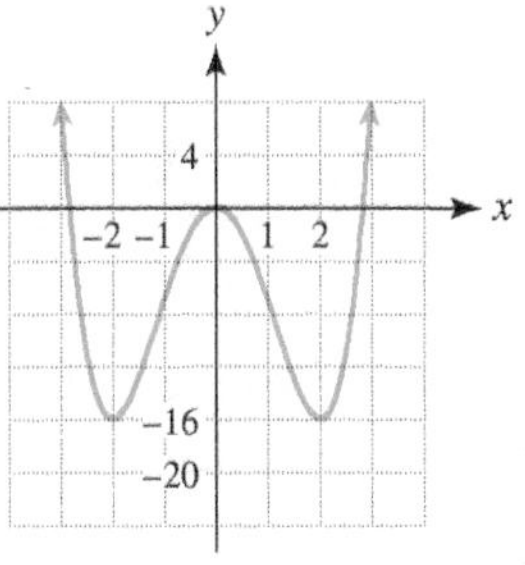

Exercises 19–26: Complete the following.

(a) Graph $y = f(x)$ in the standard viewing rectangle.
(b) Approximate the coordinates of each turning point.
(c) Estimate any local extrema.

19. $f(x) = \frac{1}{9}x^3 - 3x$

20. $f(x) = x^2 - 4x - 3$

21. $f(x) = 0.025x^4 - 0.45x^2 - 5$

22. $f(x) = -\frac{1}{8}x^4 + \frac{1}{3}x^3 + \frac{5}{4}x^2 - 3x + 3$

23. $f(x) = 1 - 2x + 3x^2$

24. $f(x) = 4x - \frac{1}{3}x^3$

25. $f(x) = \frac{1}{3}x^3 + \frac{1}{2}x^2 - 2x$

26. $f(x) = \frac{1}{4}x^4 + \frac{2}{3}x^3 - \frac{1}{2}x^2 - 2x + 1$

Exercises 27–38: Complete the following.

(a) State the degree and leading coefficient of f.
(b) State the end behavior of the graph of f.

27. $f(x) = -2x + 3$

28. $f(x) = \frac{2}{3}x - 2$

29. $f(x) = x^2 + 4x$

30. $f(x) = 5 - \frac{1}{2}x^2$

31. $f(x) = -2x^3$

32. $f(x) = 4x - \frac{1}{3}x^3$

33. $f(x) = x^2 - x^3 - 4$

34. $f(x) = x^4 - 4x^3 + 3x^2 - 3$

35. $f(x) = 0.1x^5 - 2x^2 - 3x + 4$

36. $f(x) = 3x^3 - 2 - x^4$

37. $f(x) = 4 + 2x - \frac{1}{2}x^2$

38. $f(x) = -0.2x^5 + 4x^2 - 3$

Modeling Data with Polynomials

Exercises 39–44: The data are modeled exactly by a linear, quadratic, cubic, or quartic function f with leading coefficient a. All zeros of f are real numbers located in the interval [−3, 3].

(a) Make a line graph of the data.
(b) State the minimum degree of f.
(c) Is $a > 0$ or is $a < 0$?
(d) Find a formula for $f(x)$.

39.

x	−3	−2	−1	0	1	2	3
$f(x)$	3	−8	−7	0	7	8	−3

40.

x	−3	−2	−1	0	1	2	3
$f(x)$	11	9	7	5	3	1	−1

41.

x	−3	−2	−1	0	1	2	3
$f(x)$	14	7	2	−1	−2	−1	2

42.

x	−3	−2	−1	0	1	2	3
$f(x)$	−13	−6	−1	2	3	2	−1

43.

x	−3	−2	−1	0	1	2	3
$f(x)$	−55	−5	1	−1	1	−5	−55

44.

x	−3	−2	−1	0	1	2	3
$f(x)$	−15	0	3	0	−3	0	15

Sketching Graphs of Polynomials

Exercises 45–56: If possible, sketch a graph of a polynomial that satisfies the conditions. Let a be the leading coefficient.

45. Degree 3 with three real zeros and $a > 0$

46. Degree 4 with four real zeros and $a < 0$

47. Linear with $a < 0$

48. Cubic with one real zero and $a > 0$

49. Degree 4 and an even function with four turning points

50. Degree 5 and symmetric with respect to the y-axis

51. Degree 3 and an odd function with no x-intercepts

52. Degree 6 and an odd function with five turning points

53. Degree 3 with turning points $(-1, 2)$ and $\left(1, \frac{2}{3}\right)$

54. Degree 4 with turning points $(-1, -1)$, $(0, 0)$, and $(1, -1)$

55. Degree 2 with turning point $(-1, 2)$, passing through $(-3, 4)$ and $(1, 4)$

56. Degree 5 and an odd function with five x-intercepts and a negative leading coefficient.

Dominant Term of a Polynomial

Exercises 57 and 58: Graph the functions f, g, and h in the same viewing rectangle. What happens to their graphs as the size of the viewing rectangle increases? Explain why the term of highest degree in a polynomial is sometimes called the **dominant term.**

57. $f(x) = 2x^4$, $g(x) = 2x^4 - 5x^2 + 1$, and $h(x) = 2x^4 + 3x^2 - x - 2$

(a) $[-4, 4, 1]$ by $[-4, 4, 1]$

(b) $[-10, 10, 1]$ by $[-100, 100, 10]$

(c) $[-100, 100, 10]$ by $[-10^6, 10^6, 10^5]$

58. $f(x) = -x^3$, $g(x) = -x^3 + x^2 + 2$, and $h(x) = -x^3 - 2x^2 + x - 1$

(a) $[-4, 4, 1]$ by $[-4, 4, 1]$

(b) $[-10, 10, 1]$ by $[-100, 100, 10]$

(c) $[-100, 100, 10]$ by $[-10^5, 10^5, 10^4]$

Average Rates of Change

59. Compare the average rates of change from 0 to $\frac{1}{2}$ for $f(x) = x$, $g(x) = x^2$, and $h(x) = x^3$.

60. Compare the average rates of change from 1 to $\frac{3}{2}$ for $f(x) = x$, $g(x) = x^2$, and $h(x) = x^3$.

Exercises 61–64: Calculate the average rate of change of f on each interval. What happens to this average rate of change as the interval decreases in length?

(a) $[1.9, 2.1]$
(b) $[1.99, 2.01]$
(c) $[1.999, 2.001]$

61. $f(x) = x^3$

62. $f(x) = 4x - \frac{1}{3}x^3$

63. $f(x) = \frac{1}{4}x^4 - \frac{1}{3}x^3$

64. $f(x) = 4x^2 - \frac{1}{2}x^4$

Exercises 65–68: Find the difference quotient of g.

65. $g(x) = 3x^3$

66. $g(x) = -2x^3$

67. $g(x) = 1 + x - x^3$

68. $g(x) = \frac{1}{2}x^3 - 2x$

Piecewise-Defined Functions

Exercises 69–76: Evaluate f(x) at the given values of x.

69. $x = -2$ and 1

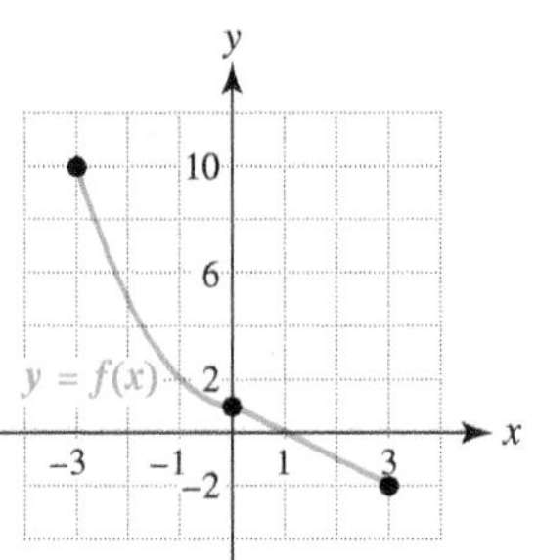

70. $x = -1, 0$, and 3

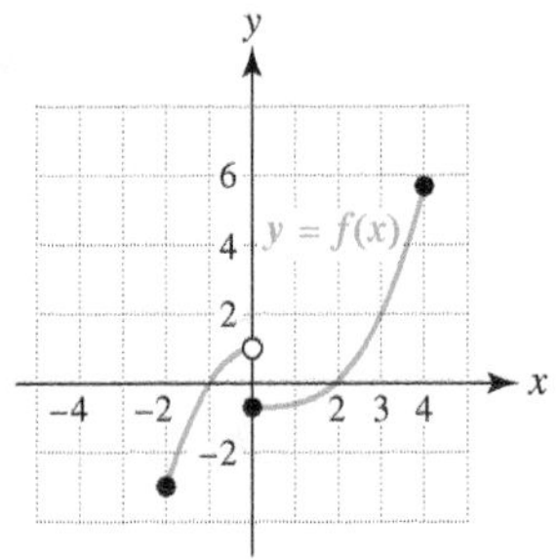

71. $x = -1, 1$, and 2

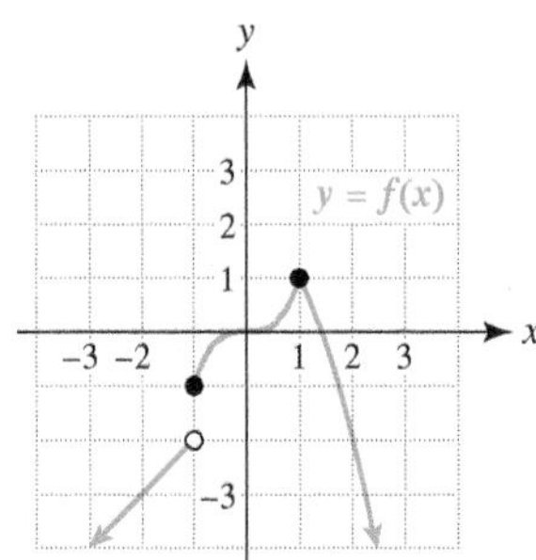

72. $x = -2, 0$, and 2

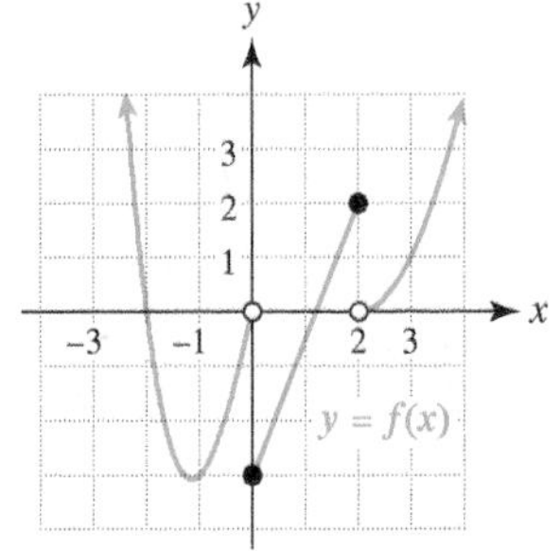

73. $x = -3, 1$, and 4

$$f(x) = \begin{cases} x^3 - 4x^2 & \text{if } x \le -3 \\ 3x^2 & \text{if } -3 < x < 4 \\ x^3 - 54 & \text{if } x \ge 4 \end{cases}$$

74. $x = -4, 0$, and 4

$$f(x) = \begin{cases} -4x & \text{if } x \le -4 \\ x^3 + 2 & \text{if } -4 < x \le 2 \\ 4 - x^2 & \text{if } x > 2 \end{cases}$$

75. $x = -2, 1$, and 2

$$f(x) = \begin{cases} x^2 + 2x + 6 & \text{if } -5 \le x < 0 \\ x + 6 & \text{if } 0 \le x < 2 \\ x^3 + 1 & \text{if } 2 \le x \le 5 \end{cases}$$

76. $x = 1975, 1980$, and 1998

$$f(x) = \begin{cases} 0.2(x - 1970)^3 + 60 & \text{if } 1970 \le x < 1980 \\ 190 - (x - 1980)^2 & \text{if } 1980 \le x < 1990 \\ 2(x - 1990) + 100 & \text{if } 1990 \le x \le 2000 \end{cases}$$

Exercises 77–82: Complete the following.

(a) Sketch a graph of f.
(b) Determine if f is continuous on its domain.
(c) Solve $f(x) = 0$.

77. $f(x) = \begin{cases} 4 - x^2 & \text{if } -3 \le x \le 0 \\ x^2 - 4 & \text{if } 0 < x \le 3 \end{cases}$

78. $f(x) = \begin{cases} x^2 & \text{if } -2 \le x < 0 \\ x + 1 & \text{if } \ \ 0 \le x \le 2 \end{cases}$

79. $f(x) = \begin{cases} 2x & \text{if } -5 \le x < -1 \\ -2 & \text{if } -1 \le x < 0 \\ x^2 - 2 & \text{if } \ \ 0 \le x \le 2 \end{cases}$

80. $f(x) = \begin{cases} 0.5x^2 & \text{if } -4 \le x \le -2 \\ x & \text{if } -2 < x < 2 \\ x^2 - 4 & \text{if } \ \ 2 \le x \le 4 \end{cases}$

81. $f(x) = \begin{cases} x^3 + 3 & \text{if } -2 \le x \le 0 \\ x + 3 & \text{if } \ \ 0 < x < 1 \\ 4 + x - x^2 & \text{if } \ \ 1 \le x \le 3 \end{cases}$

82. $f(x) = \begin{cases} -2x & \text{if } -3 \le x < -1 \\ x^2 + 1 & \text{if } -1 \le x \le 2 \\ \frac{1}{2}x^3 + 1 & \text{if } \ \ 2 < x \le 3 \end{cases}$

Applications

83. **Diminishing Returns** (Refer to Example 7.) Let the function F, defined by

$$F(x) = \begin{cases} 2x & \text{if } 0 \le x \le 4 \\ -\frac{1}{4}x^2 + 4x - 4 & \text{if } 4 \le x \le 12, \end{cases}$$

calculate a fish harvest in thousands of tons when x hundred fishing boats are used in a region.
(a) Evaluate $F(3)$ and interpret the result.

(b) Find the absolute maximum on the graph of F and interpret the result.

84. **Diminishing Returns** The function F, defined by

$$F(x) = \begin{cases} x & \text{if } 0 \le x \le 5 \\ -0.08x^2 + 1.6x - 1 & \text{if } 5 \le x \le 15, \end{cases}$$

was used in Example 7 to describe a fish harvest in a region.
(a) Evaluate $F(6)$ and interpret your answer.

(b) Solve $F(x) = 6$ and interpret the result.

(c) Use Figure 4.52 to find the point of diminishing returns and interpret its meaning.

85. **Electronics** The **Heaviside function** H, used in the study of electrical circuits, is defined by

$$H(t) = \begin{cases} 0 & \text{if } t < 0 \\ 1 & \text{if } t \ge 0. \end{cases}$$

(a) Evaluate $H(-2)$, $H(0)$, and $H(3.5)$.

(b) Graph $y = H(t)$.

86. **A Strange Graph** The following definition is discussed in advanced mathematics courses.

$$f(x) = \begin{cases} 0 & \text{if } x \text{ is a rational number} \\ 1 & \text{if } x \text{ is an irrational number} \end{cases}$$

(a) Evaluate $f\left(-\frac{3}{4}\right)$, $f(-\sqrt{2})$, and $f(\pi)$.

(b) Is f a function? Explain.

(c) Discuss the difficulty with graphing $y = f(x)$.

87. **Modeling Temperature** In the figure the monthly average temperature in degrees Fahrenheit from January to December in Minneapolis is modeled by a polynomial function f, where $x = 1$ corresponds to January and $x = 12$ to December. (***Source:*** A. Miller and J. Thompson, *Elements of Meteorology*.)

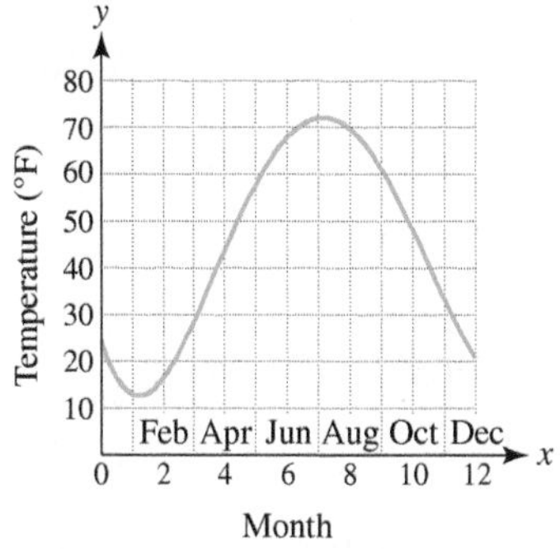

(a) Estimate the turning points.

(b) Interpret each turning point.

88. **Natural Gas Consumption** Refer to Example 8 and the introduction to this section.
(a) Solve the equation $f(x) = 20$ graphically. Interpret the solution set.

(b) Calculate the average rate of change in natural gas consumption from 1970 to 1980. Interpret the result.

89. **Modeling** An object is lifted rapidly into the air at a constant speed and then dropped. Its height h in feet after x seconds is listed in the table.

x (sec)	0	1	2	3	4	5	6	7
h (ft)	0	36	72	108	144	128	80	0

(a) At what time does it appear that the object was dropped?

(b) Identify the time interval when the height could be modeled by a linear function. When could it be modeled by a nonlinear function?

(continued)

(c) Determine values for the constants m, a, and b so that f models the data.

$$f(x) = \begin{cases} mx & \text{if } 0 \le x \le 4 \\ a(x-4)^2 + b & \text{if } 4 < x \le 7 \end{cases}$$

(d) Solve $f(x) = 100$ and interpret your answer.

90. Modeling A water tank is filled with a hose and then drained. The table shows the number of gallons y in the tank after t minutes.

t (min)	0	1	2	3	4	5	6	7
y (gal)	0	9	18	27	36	16	4	0

The following function f models the data in the table.

$$f(t) = \begin{cases} 9t & \text{if } 0 \le t \le 4 \\ 4t^2 - 56t + 196 & \text{if } 4 < t \le 7 \end{cases}$$

Solve the equation $f(t) = 12$ and interpret the results.

91. Aging in America The table lists the number N (in thousands) of Americans over 100 years old for selected years x.

x	1960	1970	1980	1990	2000	2010
N	3	5	15	37	50	70

(a) Use regression to find a polynomial of degree 3 that models the data. Let $x = 0$ correspond to 1960.

(b) Graph f and the data.

(c) Estimate N in 1994 and in 2020.

(d) Did your estimates in part (c) involve interpolation or extrapolation?

92. Modeling Water Flow A cylindrical container has a height of 16 centimeters. Water entered the container at a constant rate until it was completely filled. Then water was allowed to leak out through a small hole in the bottom. The height of the water in the container was recorded every half minute over a 5-minute period.

Time (min)	0	0.5	1.0	1.5	2.0	2.5
Height (cm)	0	4	8	12	16	11.6

Time (min)	3.0	3.5	4.0	4.5	5.0
Height (cm)	8.1	5.3	3.1	1.4	0.5

(a) Plot the data.

(b) Find a piecewise-defined function that models the data. (*Hint:* Use regression.)

(c) Approximate the water level after 1.25 minutes and after 3.2 minutes.

(d) Estimate the time when water was flowing out of the tank and the water level was 5 centimeters.

Writing About Mathematics

Exercises 93–96: Discuss possible local extrema and absolute extrema on the graph of f. Assume that $a > 0$.

93. $f(x) = ax + b$

94. $f(x) = ax^2 + bx + c$

95. $f(x) = ax^3 + bx^2 + cx + d$

96. $f(x) = a|x|$

Extended and Discovery Exercises

1. Torricelli's Law A cylindrical tank contains 500 gallons of water. A plug is pulled from the bottom of the tank, and it takes 10 minutes to drain the tank. The amount A of water in gallons remaining in the tank after t minutes is approximated by

$$A(t) = 500\left(1 - \frac{t}{10}\right)^2.$$

(a) What is a reasonable domain for A?

(b) Evaluate $A(1)$ and interpret the result.

(c) What are the degree and leading coefficient of $A(t)$?

(d) Has half the water drained from the tank after 5 minutes? Does this agree with your intuition? Explain.

Exercises 2–7: **Concavity** *Estimate the intervals where the graph of f is concave upward and where the graph is concave downward. Use interval notation.*

2. **3.**

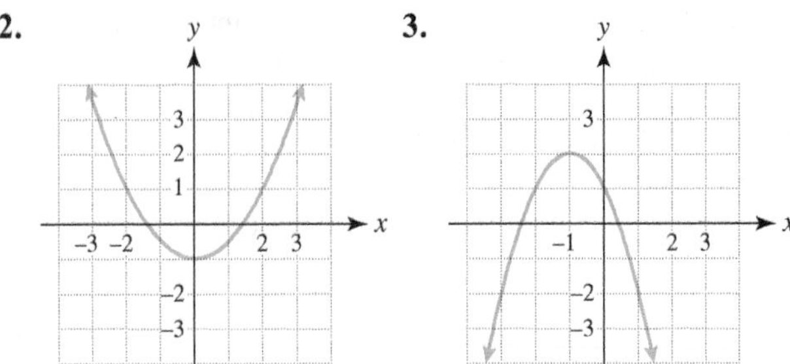

4. 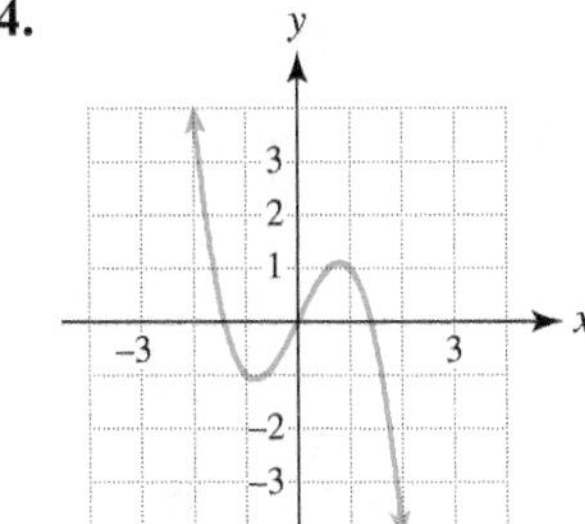

5. 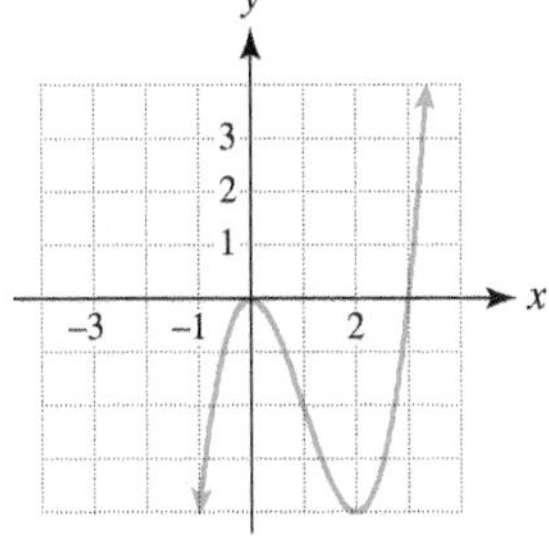

6. 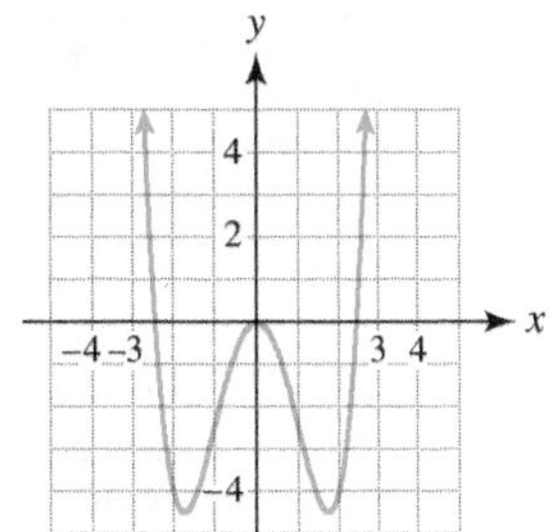

7. 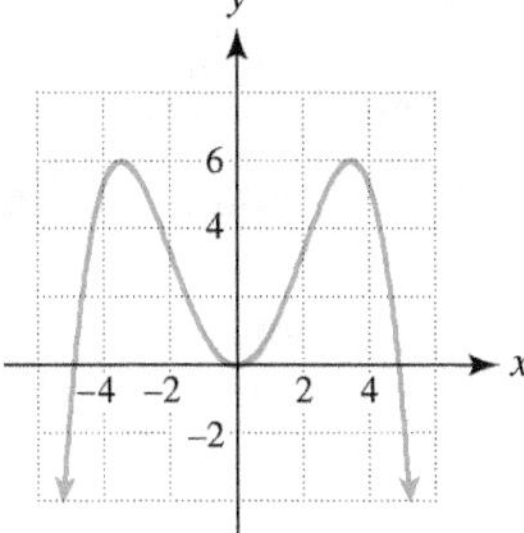

CHECKING BASIC CONCEPTS FOR SECTIONS 4.1 AND 4.2

1. Use the graph of f to complete the following.

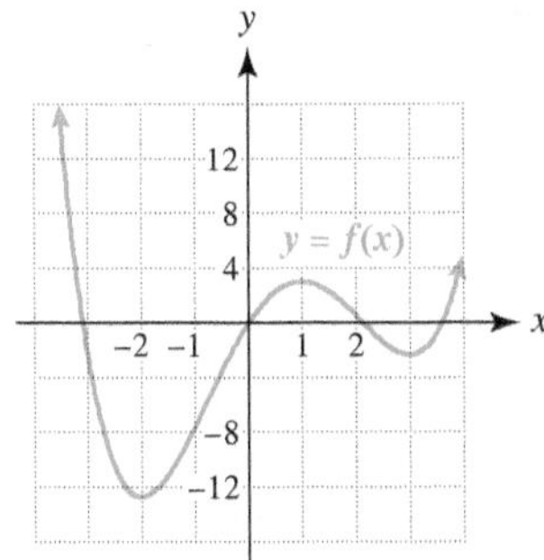

   (a) Determine where f is increasing or decreasing.

   (b) Identify any local extrema.

   (c) Identify any absolute extrema.

   (d) Approximate the x-intercepts and zeros of f. Then solve $f(x) = 0$. How are the x-intercepts, zeros, and solutions to $f(x) = 0$ related?

2. Use the graph to complete the following.

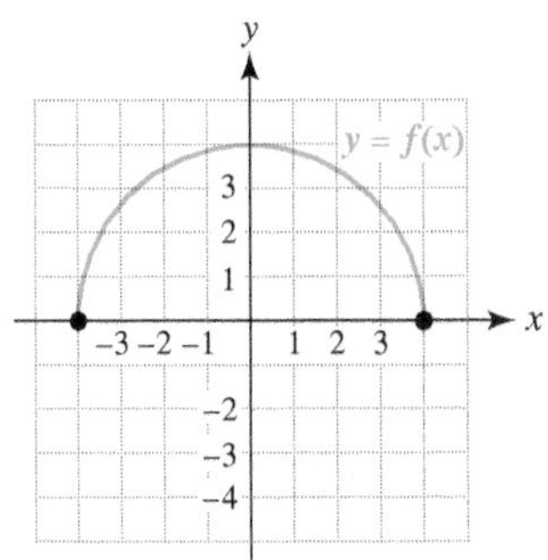

   (a) Evaluate $f(-4)$, $f(0)$, and $f(4)$.

   (b) What type of symmetry does the graph of f exhibit?

   (c) Is f an odd function or an even function? Why?

   (d) Find the domain and range of f.

3. If possible, sketch a graph of a cubic polynomial with a negative leading coefficient that satisfies each of the following conditions.

   (a) Zero x-intercepts

   (b) One x-intercept

   (c) Two x-intercepts

   (d) Four x-intercepts

4. Plot the data in the table.

x	-3.2	-2	0	2	3.2
y	-11	15	-10	15	-11

   (a) What is the minimum degree of the polynomial function f that would be needed to model these data? Explain.

   (b) Should function f be odd, even, or neither? Explain.

   (c) Should the leading coefficient of f be positive or negative? Explain.

5. Use least-squares regression to find a polynomial that models the data in Exercise 4.

4.3 Division of Polynomials

- Divide polynomials by monomials
- Divide polynomials by polynomials
- Apply the division algorithm
- Learn synthetic division
- Understand the remainder theorem

Introduction

The area A of a rectangle with length L and width W is calculated by $A = LW$. If we are given the area and the width of a rectangle, we can find the length L by solving $A = LW$ for L to obtain $L = \frac{A}{W}$. For example, if the area is 48 square feet and the width is 6 feet, then the length of the rectangle equals $L = \frac{48}{6} = 8$ feet. Now consider the more general situation shown in Figure 4.56.

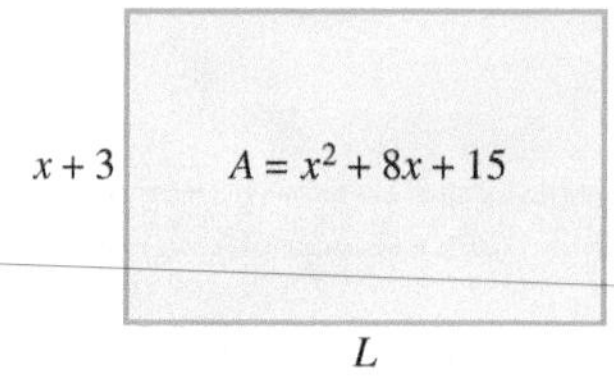

Figure 4.56

The area A is $x^2 + 8x + 15$ and the width W is $x + 3$, so we can find an expression for L in the same way by calculating

$$L = \frac{A}{W} = \frac{x^2 + 8x + 15}{x + 3}.$$

In this case, the calculation of L involves division of polynomials. (See Example 5.) This section discusses basic concepts related to division of polynomials.

Division by Monomials

Adding (or subtracting) fractions having like denominators is straightforward. For example,

$$\frac{3}{17} + \frac{7}{17} = \frac{3 + 7}{17}, \quad \text{and so} \quad \frac{3 + 7}{17} = \frac{3}{17} + \frac{7}{17}.$$

Note that when we reverse the process, the denominator of 17 is divided into each term in the numerator. By reversing the process, we can sometimes simplify expressions.

$$\frac{3x^4 + 5x^3}{5x^3} = \frac{3x^4}{5x^3} + \frac{5x^3}{5x^3} = \frac{3}{5}x + 1$$

Subtract exponents: $\frac{3x^4}{5x^3} = \frac{3}{5}x$.

This process is used in the next example.

EXAMPLE 1 **Dividing by a monomial**

Divide $6x^3 - 3x^2 + 2$ by $2x^2$.

SOLUTION

Getting Started Remember to divide $2x^2$ into *every* term of $6x^3 - 3x^2 + 2$. ▶

Write the problem as $\frac{6x^3 - 3x^2 + 2}{2x^2}$. Then divide $2x^2$ into *every* term in the numerator.

$$\frac{6x^3 - 3x^2 + 2}{2x^2} = \frac{6x^3}{2x^2} - \frac{3x^2}{2x^2} + \frac{2}{2x^2}$$

Write as three terms.

$$= 3x - \frac{3}{2} + \frac{1}{x^2}$$

Now Try Exercise 3

Algebra Review
To review simplification of rational expressions, see Chapter R (page R-28).

Division by Polynomials

Before dividing a polynomial by a binomial, we review division of natural numbers.

$$\begin{array}{r} \text{quotient} \rightarrow 58 \\ \text{divisor} \rightarrow 3\overline{)175} \leftarrow \text{dividend} \\ \underline{15} \\ 25 \\ \underline{24} \\ 1 \leftarrow \text{remainder} \end{array}$$

This result is checked as follows: $3 \cdot 58 + 1 = 175$. That is,

$$\text{(Divisor) (Quotient)} + \text{(Remainder)} = \text{(Dividend)}.$$

The quotient and remainder can also be expressed as $58\frac{1}{3}$. Since 3 does not divide into 175 evenly, 3 is *not* a factor of 175. When the remainder is 0, the divisor is a *factor* of the dividend. Division of polynomials is similar to division of natural numbers.

EXAMPLE 2 **Dividing polynomials**

Divide $2x^3 - 3x^2 - 11x + 7$ by $x - 3$. Check the result.

SOLUTION Begin by dividing x into $2x^3$.

Start by dividing x into $2x^3$ to get $2x^2$.

$$\begin{array}{r} 2x^2 \\ x - 3\overline{)2x^3 - 3x^2 - 11x + 7} \\ \underline{2x^3 - 6x^2} \\ 3x^2 - 11x \end{array}$$

$\frac{2x^3}{x} = 2x^2$

$2x^2(x - 3) = 2x^3 - 6x^2$

Subtract. Bring down $-11x$.

In the next step, divide x into $3x^2$.

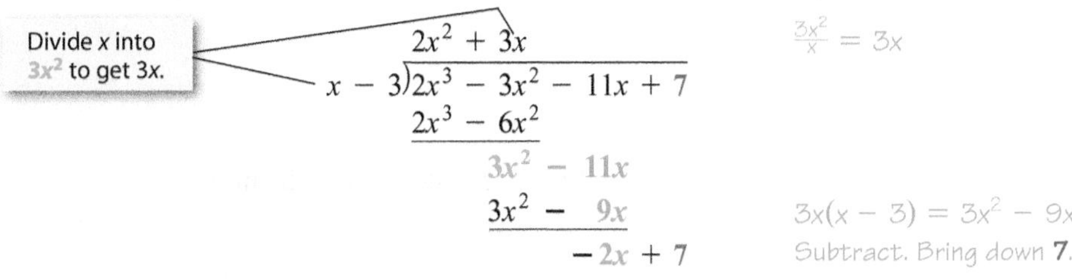

$$\begin{array}{r} 2x^2 + 3x \\ x - 3\overline{)2x^3 - 3x^2 - 11x + 7} \\ \underline{2x^3 - 6x^2} \\ 3x^2 - 11x \\ \underline{3x^2 - 9x} \\ -2x + 7 \end{array}$$

$\frac{3x^2}{x} = 3x$

$3x(x - 3) = 3x^2 - 9x$

Subtract. Bring down 7.

Now divide x into $-2x$.

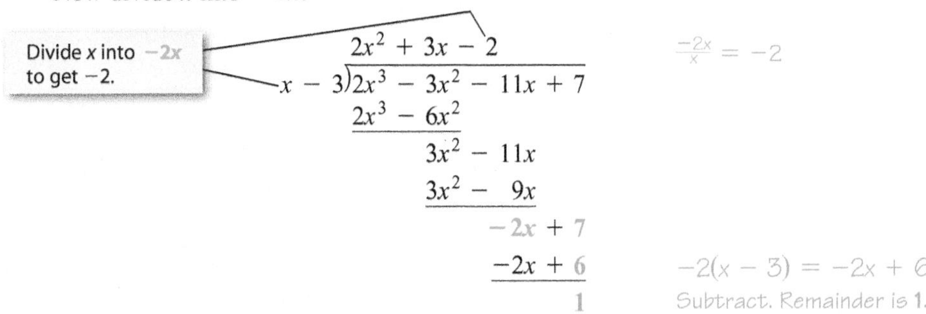

$$\begin{array}{r} 2x^2 + 3x - 2 \\ x - 3\overline{)2x^3 - 3x^2 - 11x + 7} \\ \underline{2x^3 - 6x^2} \\ 3x^2 - 11x \\ \underline{3x^2 - 9x} \\ -2x + 7 \\ \underline{-2x + 6} \\ 1 \end{array}$$

$\frac{-2x}{x} = -2$

$-2(x - 3) = -2x + 6$

Subtract. Remainder is 1.

The quotient is $2x^2 + 3x - 2$ and the remainder is 1. Polynomial division is also checked by multiplying the divisor and quotient and then adding the remainder.

$$\begin{aligned} (x - 3)(2x^2 + 3x - 2) + 1 &= x(2x^2 + 3x - 2) - 3(2x^2 + 3x - 2) + 1 \\ &= 2x^3 + 3x^2 - 2x - 6x^2 - 9x + 6 + 1 \\ &= 2x^3 - 3x^2 - 11x + 7 \checkmark \end{aligned}$$

Divisor Quotient Remainder

Now Try Exercise 9

Algebra Review
To review multiplication of polynomials, see Chapter R (page R-16).

A division problem, such as $\frac{175}{3}$, is typically given in the form $\frac{\text{(Dividend)}}{\text{(Divisor)}}$. If we divide each term in the equation

$$\text{(Dividend)} = \text{(Divisor)}\,\text{(Quotient)} + \text{(Remainder)}$$

by **(Divisor)**, we obtain the equation

$$\frac{\text{(Dividend)}}{\text{(Divisor)}} = \text{(Quotient)} + \frac{\text{(Remainder)}}{\text{(Divisor)}}.$$

For example, because 175 divided by 3 equals 58 remainder 1, we can use this equation to justify writing $\frac{175}{3} = 58 + \frac{1}{3}$, or $58\frac{1}{3}$. We can use the results from Example 2 to write

$$\frac{2x^3 - 3x^2 - 11x + 7}{x - 3} = 2x^2 + 3x - 2 + \frac{1}{x - 3}.$$

This process is applied in the next example.

EXAMPLE 3 **Dividing polynomials**

Divide each expression. Check your answer.

(a) $\dfrac{6x^2 + 5x - 10}{2x + 3}$ **(b)** $(5x^3 - 4x^2 + 7x - 2) \div (x^2 + 1)$

SOLUTION

(a) Begin by dividing $2x$ into $6x^2$.

$$\begin{array}{r} 3x \phantom{{}+5x-10} \\ 2x + 3\overline{)6x^2 + 5x - 10} \\ \underline{6x^2 + 9x} \phantom{{}-10} \\ -4x - 10 \end{array}$$

$\frac{6x^2}{2x} = 3x$

$3x(2x + 3) = 6x^2 + 9x$

Subtract: $5x - 9x = -4x$. Bring down the -10.

In the next step, divide $2x$ into $-4x$.

$$\begin{array}{r} 3x - 2 \phantom{{}-10} \\ 2x + 3\overline{)6x^2 + 5x - 10} \\ \underline{6x^2 + 9x} \phantom{{}-10} \\ -4x - 10 \\ \underline{-4x - 6} \\ -4 \end{array}$$

$\frac{-4x}{2x} = -2$

$-2(2x + 3) = -4x - 6$

Subtract: $-10 - (-6) = -4$.

The quotient is $3x - 2$ with remainder -4. This result can also be written as follows.

$$3x - 2 + \frac{-4}{2x + 3} \qquad \text{(Quotient)} + \frac{\text{(Remainder)}}{\text{(Divisor)}}$$

To check this result use the equation

$$\text{(Divisor)(Quotient)} + \text{(Remainder)} = \text{(Dividend)}.$$

This result can be checked as follows.

$$\begin{aligned} (2x + 3)(3x - 2) + (-4) &= 6x^2 + 5x - 6 - 4 \\ &= 6x^2 + 5x - 10 \checkmark \end{aligned}$$

The result checks.

(b) Begin by writing $x^2 + 1$ as $x^2 + 0x + 1$.

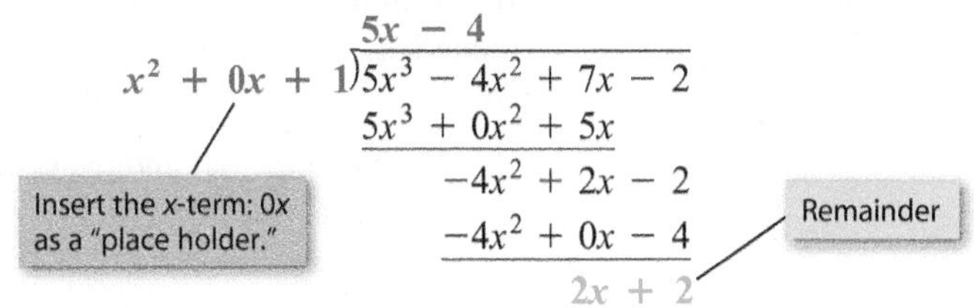

The quotient is $5x - 4$ with remainder of $2x + 2$. This result can also be written as

$$5x - 4 + \frac{2x + 2}{x^2 + 1}. \qquad \text{(Quotient)} + \frac{\text{(Remainder)}}{\text{(Divisor)}}$$

This result can be checked as follows.

$$(x^2 + 1)(5x - 4) + 2x + 2 = 5x^3 - 4x^2 + 5x - 4 + 2x + 2$$
$$= 5x^3 - 4x^2 + 7x - 2 \checkmark \quad \text{The result checks.}$$

Now Try Exercises 21 and 25

This process is summarized by the following *division algorithm for polynomials.*

DIVISION ALGORITHM FOR POLYNOMIALS

Let $f(x)$ and $d(x)$ be two polynomials, with the degree of $d(x)$ greater than zero and less than the degree of $f(x)$. Then there exist unique polynomials $q(x)$ and $r(x)$ such that

$$\begin{array}{ccccccc} f(x) & = & d(x) & \cdot & q(x) & + & r(x), \\ \text{(Dividend)} & = & \text{(Divisor)} & \cdot & \text{(Quotient)} & + & \text{(Remainder)} \end{array}$$

where either $r(x) = 0$ or the degree of $r(x)$ is less than the degree of $d(x)$. The polynomial $r(x)$ is called the remainder.

The Division Algorithm in Real Life Although the division algorithm may seem unrelated to everyday life, it is actually expressing something that is very common. For example, if there are 5 calculators for 16 students to use, then there should be 3 students to a group leaving 1 extra student, who could join a group of 3. That is, $\frac{16}{5} = 3$ with remainder 1.

Synthetic Division

A shortcut called **synthetic division** can be used to divide $x - k$ into a polynomial. For example, to divide $x - 2$ into $3x^4 - 7x^3 - 4x + 5$, we perform the following steps with $k = 2$. The equivalent steps involving long division are shown to the right.

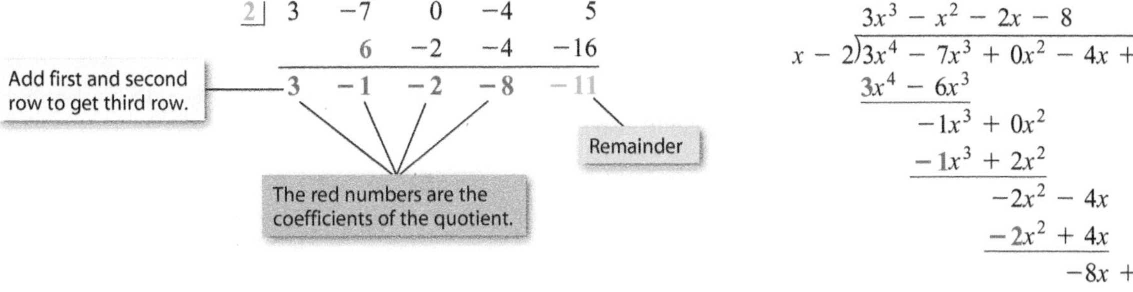

2| 3 −7 0 −4 5
6 −2 −4 −16
3 −1 −2 −8 −11
Add first and second row to get third row.
Remainder
The red numbers are the coefficients of the quotient.

$$\begin{array}{r|rrrrr} 2 & 3 & -7 & 0 & -4 & 5 \\ & & 6 & -2 & -4 & -16 \\ \hline & 3 & -1 & -2 & -8 & -11 \end{array}$$

Notice how the red and green numbers in the expression for long division correspond to the third row in synthetic division. The degree of the quotient, $3x^3 - x^2 - 2x - 8$, is one less than the degree of $f(x)$. The steps to divide a polynomial $f(x)$ by $x - k$ using synthetic division can be summarized as follows.

1. Write k to the left and the coefficients of $f(x)$ to the right in the top row. If any power of x does *not* appear in $f(x)$, include a 0 for that term. In this example, an x^2-term did not appear, so a 0 is included in the first row.
2. Copy the leading coefficient of $f(x)$ into the third row and multiply it by k. Write the result below the next coefficient of $f(x)$ in the second row. Add the numbers in the second column and place the result in the third row. Repeat the process. In this example, the leading coefficient is 3 and $k = 2$. Since $3 \cdot 2 = 6$, 6 is placed below the -7. Then add to obtain $-7 + 6 = -1$. Multiply -1 by 2 and repeat.
3. The last number in the third row is the remainder. If the remainder is 0, then the binomial $x - k$ is a factor of $f(x)$. The other red numbers in the third row are the coefficients of the quotient, with terms written in descending powers.

EXAMPLE 4 Performing synthetic division

Use synthetic division to divide $2x^3 + 4x^2 - x + 5$ by $x + 2$.

SOLUTION

Getting Started To find the value of k, write the divisor as $x - k$. Because $x + 2$ equals $x - (-2)$, the value of k is -2 ▶

Let $k = -2$ and perform synthetic division on the problem $\frac{2x^3 + 4x^2 - x + 5}{x + 2}$.

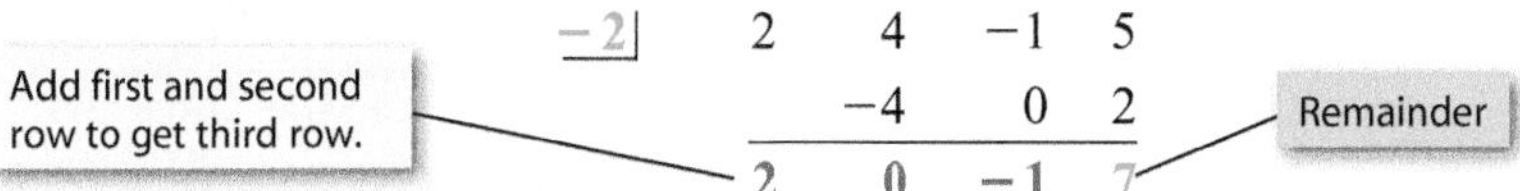

The remainder is 7 and the quotient is $2x^2 + 0x - 1 = 2x^2 - 1$. This result is expressed by the equation

$$\frac{2x^3 + 4x^2 - x + 5}{x + 2} = 2x^2 - 1 + \frac{7}{x + 2}.$$

Now Try Exercise 41

An Application from Geometry In the final example, we use division to solve the problem presented in the introduction to this section.

EXAMPLE 5 Finding the length of a rectangle

If the area of a rectangle is $x^2 + 8x + 15$ and its width is $x + 3$, use division to find its length.

SOLUTION We use synthetic division to divide $x^2 + 8x + 15$ by $x + 3$. However, long division could also be used.

$$\begin{array}{r|rrr} -3 & 1 & 8 & 15 \\ & & -3 & -15 \\ \hline & 1 & 5 & 0 \end{array}$$

The remainder is 0, so $x + 3$ divides evenly into $x^2 + 8x + 15$, and the length is $x + 5$.

Now Try Exercise 51

Remainder Theorem If the divisor $d(x)$ is $x - k$, then the *division algorithm for polynomials* simplifies to

$$f(x) = (x - k)q(x) + r,$$

where r is a constant. If we let $x = k$ in this equation, then

$$f(k) = (k - k)q(k) + r = r.$$

Thus $f(k)$ is equal to the remainder obtained in synthetic division. In Example 4, when $f(x) = 2x^3 + 4x^2 - x + 5$ is divided by $x + 2$, the remainder is 7. It follows that $k = -2$ and $f(-2) = 2(-2)^3 + 4(-2)^2 - (-2) + 5 = 7$. This result is summarized by the *remainder theorem.*

REMAINDER THEOREM

If a polynomial $f(x)$ is divided by $x - k$, the remainder is $f(k)$.

4.3 Putting It All Together

The following table lists some important concepts related to division of polynomials.

CONCEPT	EXPLANATION	EXAMPLE
Division by a monomial	Be sure to divide the denominator into *every term* in the numerator.	$\frac{5a^3 - 10a^2}{5a^2} = \frac{5a^3}{5a^2} - \frac{10a^2}{5a^2} = a - 2$
Division by a polynomial	Division by a polynomial can be done in a manner similar to long division of natural numbers. See Examples 2 and 3.	When $6x^3 + 5x^2 - 8x + 4$ is divided by $2x - 1$, the quotient is $3x^2 + 4x - 2$ with remainder 2 and can be written as $\frac{6x^3 + 5x^2 - 8x + 4}{2x - 1} = 3x^2 + 4x - 2 + \frac{2}{2x - 1}$.
Division algorithm	(Dividend) = (Divisor)(Quotient) + (Remainder) This equation can be written as $\frac{\text{(Dividend)}}{\text{(Divisor)}} = \text{(Quotient)} + \frac{\text{(Remainder)}}{\text{(Divisor)}}$.	$\frac{x^3 - 1}{x + 1} = x^2 - x + 1 + \frac{-2}{x + 1}$ Dividend: $x^3 - 1$ Divisor: $x + 1$ Quotient: $x^2 - x + 1$ Remainder: -2
Synthetic division	An efficient method for dividing $x - k$ into a polynomial	Divide $2x^3 - 3x^2 + x + 2$ by $x + 1$. $k = -1$ $\begin{array}{r\|rrrr} -1 & 2 & -3 & 1 & 2 \\ & & -2 & 5 & -6 \\ \hline & 2 & -5 & 6 & -4 \end{array}$ The quotient is $2x^2 - 5x + 6$, and the remainder is -4.
Remainder theorem	If a polynomial $f(x)$ is divided by $x - k$, the remainder is $f(k)$.	If $f(x) = 3x^2 - 2x + 6$ is divided by $x - 2$, the remainder is $f(2) = 3(2)^2 - 2(2) + 6 = 14$.

4.3 Exercises

Division by Monomials

Exercises 1–8: Divide the expression.

1. $\dfrac{5x^4 - 15}{10x}$

2. $\dfrac{x^2 - 5x}{5x}$

3. $\dfrac{3x^4 - 2x^2 - 1}{3x^3}$

4. $\dfrac{5x^3 - 10x^2 + 5x}{15x^2}$

5. $\dfrac{x^3 - 4}{4x^3}$

6. $\dfrac{2x^4 - 3x^2 + 4x - 7}{-4x}$

7. $\dfrac{5x(3x^2 - 6x + 1)}{3x^2}$

8. $\dfrac{(1 - 5x^2)(x + 1) + x^2}{2x}$

Division by Polynomials

Exercises 9–14: Divide the first polynomial by the second. State the quotient and remainder.

9. $x^3 - 2x^2 - 5x + 6$ $\quad x - 3$

10. $3x^3 - 10x^2 - 27x + 10$ $\quad x + 2$

11. $2x^4 - 7x^3 - 5x^2 - 19x + 17$ $\quad x + 1$

12. $x^4 - x^3 - 4x + 1$ $\quad x - 2$

13. $3x^3 - 7x + 10$ $\quad x - 1$

14. $x^4 - 16x^2 + 1$ $\quad x + 4$

Exercises 15–22: Divide. Check your answer.

15. $\dfrac{x^4 - 3x^3 - x + 3}{x - 3}$

16. $\dfrac{x^3 - 2x^2 - x + 3}{x + 1}$

17. $\dfrac{4x^3 - x^2 - 5x + 6}{x - 1}$

18. $\dfrac{x^4 + 3x^3 - 4x + 1}{x + 2}$

19. $\dfrac{x^3 + 1}{x + 1}$

20. $\dfrac{x^5 + 3x^4 - x - 3}{x + 3}$

21. $\dfrac{6x^3 + 5x^2 - 8x + 4}{2x - 1}$

22. $\dfrac{12x^3 - 14x^2 + 7x - 7}{3x - 2}$

Exercises 23–30: Divide the expression.

23. $\dfrac{3x^4 - 7x^3 + 6x - 16}{3x - 7}$

24. $\dfrac{20x^4 + 6x^3 - 2x^2 + 15x - 2}{5x - 1}$

25. $\dfrac{5x^4 - 2x^2 + 6}{x^2 + 2}$

26. $\dfrac{x^3 - x^2 + 2x - 3}{x^2 + 3}$

27. $\dfrac{8x^3 + 10x^2 - 12x - 15}{2x^2 - 3}$

28. $\dfrac{3x^4 - 2x^2 - 5}{3x^2 - 5}$

29. $\dfrac{2x^4 - x^3 + 4x^2 + 8x + 7}{2x^2 + 3x + 2}$

30. $\dfrac{3x^4 + 2x^3 - x^2 + 4x - 3}{x^2 + x - 1}$

Division Algorithm

Exercises 31 and 32: Use the equation

(Dividend) = (Divisor)(Quotient) + (Remainder)

to complete the following.

31. $\dfrac{x^3 - 8x^2 + 15x - 6}{x - 2} = x^2 - 6x + 3$ implies $(x - 2)(x^2 - 6x + 3) =$ __?__.

32. $\dfrac{x^4 - 15}{x + 2} = x^3 - 2x^2 + 4x - 8 + \dfrac{1}{x + 2}$ implies $x^4 - 15 = (x + 2) \times$ __?__ + __?__.

Exercises 33–38: Use division to express the (Dividend) *as* (Divisor)(Quotient) + (Remainder).

33. $\dfrac{x^2 - 3x + 1}{x - 2}$

34. $\dfrac{2x^2 - x + 2}{x + 4}$

35. $\dfrac{2x^3 + x^2 - 2x}{2x + 1}$

36. $\dfrac{1 - x^2 + x^3}{x - 1}$

37. $\dfrac{x^3 - x^2 + x + 1}{x^2 + 1}$

38. $\dfrac{2x^3 + x^2 - x + 4}{x^2 + x}$

Synthetic Division

Exercises 39–46: Use synthetic division to divide the first polynomial by the second.

39. $x^3 + 2x^2 - 17x - 10$ $\quad x + 5$

40. $x^3 - 2x + 1$ $\quad x + 4$

41. $3x^3 - 11x^2 - 20x + 3$ $\quad x - 5$

42. $x^4 - 3x^3 - 5x^2 + 2x - 16$ $\quad x - 3$

43. $x^4 - 3x^3 - 4x^2 + 12x$ $\quad x - 2$

44. $x^5 + \frac{1}{4}x^4 - x^3 - \frac{1}{4}x^2 + 3x - \frac{5}{4}$ $\quad x + \frac{1}{4}$

45. $2x^5 - x^4 - x^3 + 4x + 3 \qquad x + \frac{1}{2}$

46. $x^4 - \frac{1}{2}x^3 + 3x^2 - \frac{5}{2}x + \frac{9}{2} \qquad x - \frac{1}{2}$

Remainder Theorem

Exercises 47–50: Use the remainder theorem to find the remainder when f(x) is divided by the given x − k.

47. $f(x) = 5x^2 - 3x + 1 \qquad x - 1$

48. $f(x) = -4x^2 + 6x - 7 \qquad x + 4$

49. $f(x) = 4x^3 - x^2 + 4x + 2 \qquad x + 2$

50. $f(x) = -x^4 + 4x^3 - x + 3 \qquad x - 3$

Applications

51. Area of a Rectangle Use the figure to find the length L of the rectangle from its width and area A. Determine the value of L when $x = 10$ feet.

$3x + 1$ | $A = 12x^2 + 13x + 3$

L

52. Area of a Rectangle Use the figure to find the width W of the rectangle from its length and area A. Determine the value of W when $x = 5$ inches.

W | $A = 3x^3 - 5x^2 + 3x - 5$

$x^2 + 1$

Writing About Mathematics

53. Compare division of integers to division of polynomials. Give examples.

54. When can you use synthetic division to divide two polynomials? Give one example where synthetic division can be used and one example where it cannot be used.

4.4 Real Zeros of Polynomial Functions

- **Understand the factor theorem**
- **Factor higher degree polynomials**
- **Analyze polynomials having multiple zeros**
- **Solve higher degree polynomial equations**
- **Understand the rational zeros test, Descartes' rule of signs, and the intermediate value property**

Introduction

Some species of birds, such as robins, have two nesting periods each summer. Because the survival rate for young birds is low, bird populations can fluctuate greatly during the summer months. (***Source:*** S. Kress, *Bird Life*.)

The graph of $f(x) = x^3 - 61x^2 + 839x + 4221$ shown in Figure 4.57 models a population of birds in a small county, x days after May 31.

A Summer Bird Population

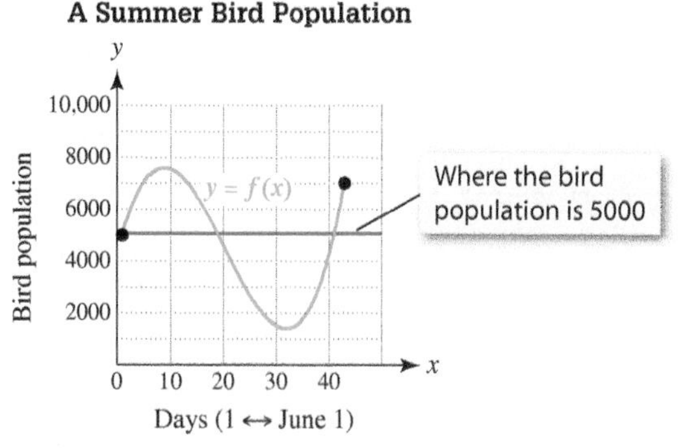

Figure 4.57

If we want to determine the dates when the population was 5000, we can solve

$$x^3 - 61x^2 + 839x + 4221 = 5000.$$

From the graph of f on the preceding page it appears that there were 5000 birds around June 1 ($x = 1$), June 20 ($x = 20$), and July 10 ($x = 40$). See Example 5.

Factoring Polynomials

The polynomial $f(x) = x^2 - 3x + 2$ can be factored as $f(x) = (x - 1)(x - 2)$. Note that $f(1) = 0$ and $(x - 1)$ is a factor of $f(x)$. Similarly, $f(2) = 0$ and $(x - 2)$ is a factor.

This discussion can be generalized. By the remainder theorem we know that

$$f(x) = (x - k)q(x) + r,$$

where r is the remainder. If $r = 0$, then $f(x) = (x - k)q(x)$ and $(x - k)$ is a factor of $f(x)$. Similarly, if $(x - k)$ is a factor of $f(x)$, then $r = 0$. That is,

$$f(x) = (x - k)q(x)$$

and $f(k) = (k - k)q(k) = 0 \cdot q(k) = 0$. This discussion justifies the *factor theorem.*

FACTOR THEOREM

A polynomial $f(x)$ has a factor $x - k$ if and only if $f(k) = 0$.

EXAMPLE 1 **Applying the factor theorem**

Use the graph in Figure 4.58 and the factor theorem to list the factors of $f(x)$.

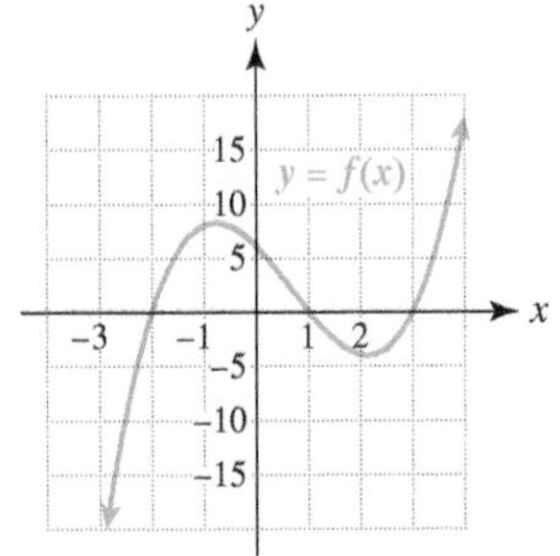

Figure 4.58

SOLUTION

Figure 4.58 shows that the zeros (or x-intercepts) of f are -2, 1, and 3. Since $f(-2) = 0$, the factor theorem states that $(x + 2)$ is a factor of $f(x)$. Similarly, $f(1) = 0$ implies that $(x - 1)$ is a factor, and $f(3) = 0$ implies that $(x - 3)$ is a factor. Thus the factors of $f(x)$ are $(x + 2)$, $(x - 1)$, and $(x - 3)$.

NOTE If $f(-2) = 0$, then $(x - (-2))$, or $(x + 2)$, is a factor.

Now Try Exercise 1

See the Concept: x-Intercepts, Zeros, and Factors

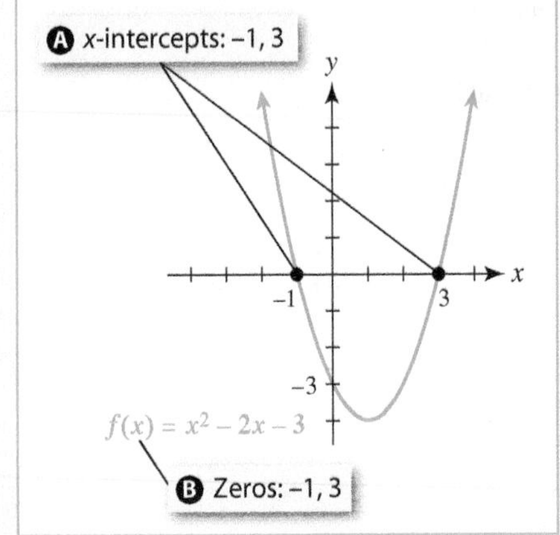

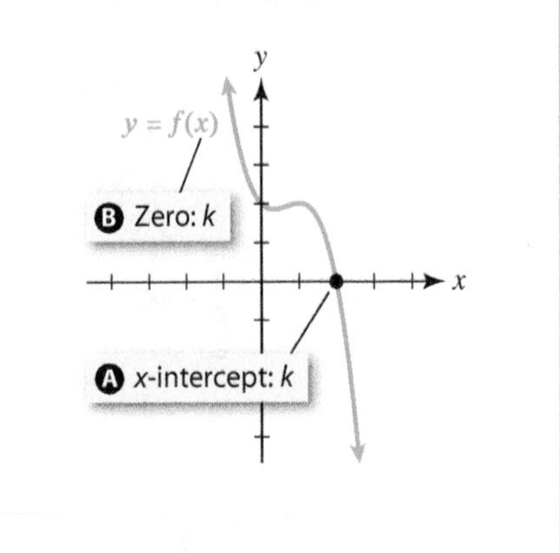

B $f(-1) = 0$ and $f(3) = 0$

C Factors of $x^2 - 2x - 3$ are $(x + 1)$ and $(x - 3)$.

B $f(k) = 0$

C Because k is a zero, $(x - k)$ is a factor of $f(x)$.

Equivalent Concepts:

- The graph of $y = f(x)$ has x-intercept k.
- A real zero of $f(x)$ is k.
- A factor of $f(x)$ is $(x - k)$.

Zeros with Multiplicity If $f(x) = (x + 2)^2$, then the factor $(x + 2)$ occurs twice and the zero -2 is called a **zero of multiplicity** 2. See Figure 4.59. The polynomial $g(x) = (x + 1)^3(x - 2)$ has zeros -1 and 2 with *multiplicities* 3 and 1, respectively. See Figure 4.60. *Counting multiplicities,* a polynomial of degree n has at most n real zeros. For $g(x)$, the sum of the multiplicities is $3 + 1 = 4$, which equals its degree.

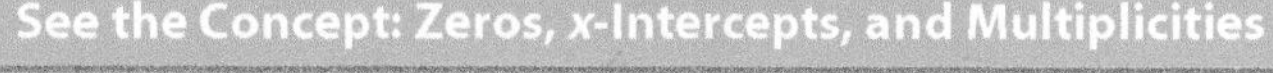

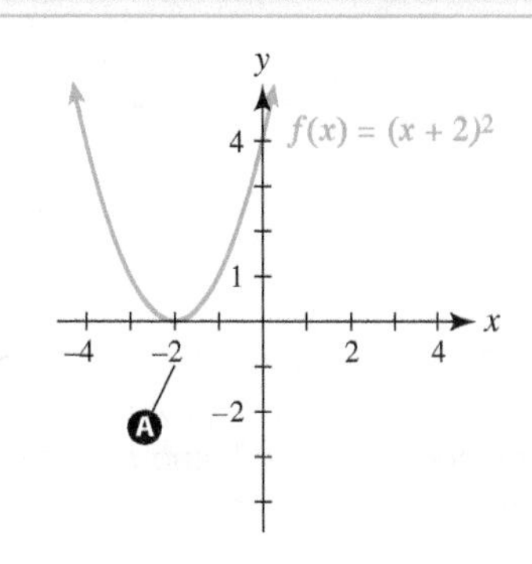

Figure 4.59

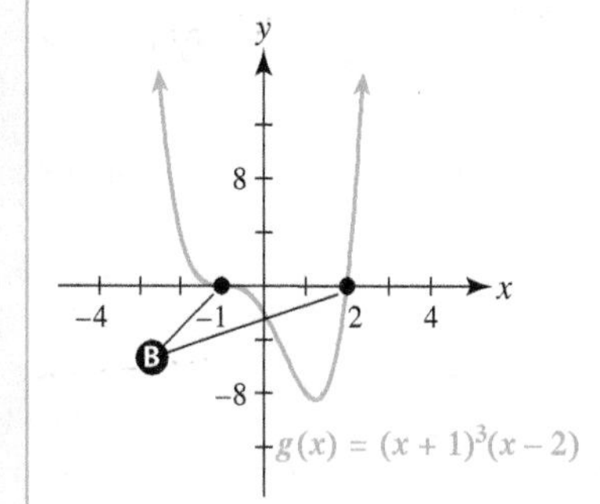

Figure 4.60

A The x-intercept corresponds to the zero -2, which has multiplicity 2.

B The two x-intercepts correspond to zeros -1 and 2, which have multiplicities 3 and 1, respectively.

Complete Factored Form The concepts discussed above, together with the factor theorem, can be used to find the *complete factored form* of a polynomial. The complete factored form of a polynomial is *unique.*

COMPLETE FACTORED FORM

Suppose a polynomial

$$f(x) = a_nx^n + \cdots + a_2x^2 + a_1x + a_0$$

has n real zeros $c_1, c_2, c_3, \ldots, c_n$, where a distinct zero is listed as many times as its multiplicity. Then $f(x)$ can be written in **complete factored form** as

$$f(x) = a_n(x - c_1)(x - c_2)(x - c_3) \cdots (x - c_n).$$

EXAMPLE 2 **Finding a complete factorization**

Write the complete factorization for each polynomial with the given zeros.

(a) $f(x) = 13x^2 - 13x - 26$; zeros: -1 and 2

(b) $f(x) = 7x^3 - 21x^2 - 7x + 21$; zeros: -1, 1, and 3

SOLUTION

(a) The leading coefficient is 13 and the zeros are -1 and 2. By the factor theorem, $(x + 1)$ and $(x - 2)$ are factors. The complete factorization is

$$f(x) = 13(x - (-1))(x - 2) = 13(x + 1)(x - 2).$$

f is degree 2 and has two factors.

(b) The leading coefficient is 7 and the zeros are -1, 1, and 3. The complete factorization is

$$f(x) = 7(x + 1)(x - 1)(x - 3).$$

f is degree 3 and has three factors.

Now Try Exercises 5 and 7

MAKING CONNECTIONS

Types of Factored Forms If the leading coefficient of a polynomial $f(x)$ is 6 and the only zeros are $\frac{1}{3}$ and $\frac{1}{2}$, then the complete factored form is $f(x) = 6\left(x - \frac{1}{3}\right)\left(x - \frac{1}{2}\right)$ and it is *unique.* Sometimes we factor 6 as $3 \cdot 2$ and distribute the 3 over the first factor and the 2 over the second factor to obtain the slightly different factored form of $f(x) = (3x - 1)(2x - 1)$.

EXAMPLE 3 Factoring a polynomial graphically

Use the graph of f in Figure 4.61 to factor $f(x) = 2x^3 - 4x^2 - 10x + 12$.

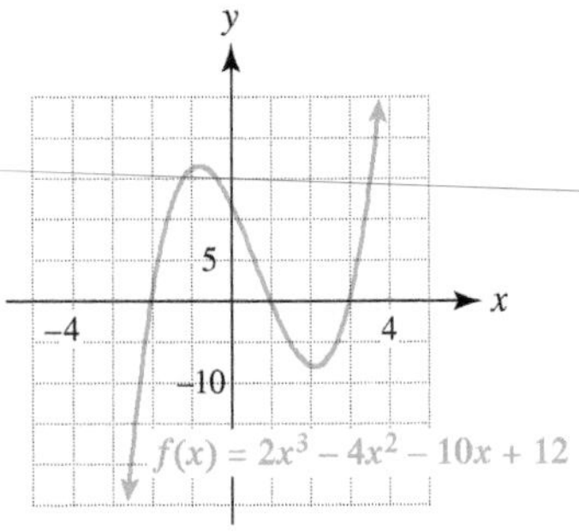

$f(x) = 2x^3 - 4x^2 - 10x + 12$

Figure 4.61

SOLUTION

Getting Started To factor $f(x)$ we need to determine the leading coefficient and the zeros of f. The zeros coincide with the x-intercepts of the graph of f. ▶

The leading coefficient is 2, and from the graph the zeros are -2, 1, and 3. The complete factorization is

$$f(x) = 2(x + 2)(x - 1)(x - 3).$$

f is degree 3 and has three factors.

Now Try Exercise 13

When factoring polynomials by hand, it is sometimes helpful to use the techniques of division discussed in Section 4.3.

EXAMPLE 4 Factoring a polynomial symbolically

One of the zeros of the polynomial $f(x) = 2x^3 - 2x^2 - 34x - 30$ is -1. Express $f(x)$ in complete factored form.

SOLUTION

If -1 is a zero, then by the factor theorem $(x + 1)$ is a factor. To factor $f(x)$, divide $x + 1$ into $2x^3 - 2x^2 - 34x - 30$ by using synthetic division.

$$\begin{array}{r|rrrr} -1 & 2 & -2 & -34 & -30 \\ & & -2 & 4 & 30 \\ \hline & 2 & -4 & -30 & 0 \end{array}$$

Long division could also be used.

Algebra Review
To review factoring trinomials, see Chapter R (pages R22–R23).

The remainder is 0, so $x + 1$ divides evenly into the dividend. By the division algorithm,

$$2x^3 - 2x^2 - 34x - 30 = (x + 1)(2x^2 - 4x - 30).$$

The quotient $2x^2 - 4x - 30$ can be factored further.

$$2x^2 - 4x - 30 = 2(x^2 - 2x - 15) \quad \text{Factor out 2.}$$
$$= 2(x + 3)(x - 5) \quad \text{Factor trinomial.}$$

The complete factored form is $f(x) = 2(x + 1)(x + 3)(x - 5)$.

Now Try Exercise 31

An Application In the introduction to this section we presented the equation

$$x^3 - 61x^2 + 839x + 4221 = 5000, \quad \text{Equation to be solved}$$

which can be rewritten as

$$x^3 - 61x^2 + 839x - 779 = 0. \quad \text{Subtract 5000.}$$

This second equation gives the days when a summer bird population was 5000 and is solved in the next example.

EXAMPLE 5 Factoring a polynomial

Factor $g(x) = x^3 - 61x^2 + 839x - 779$. Use the zeros of $g(x)$ to determine when the bird population was 5000.

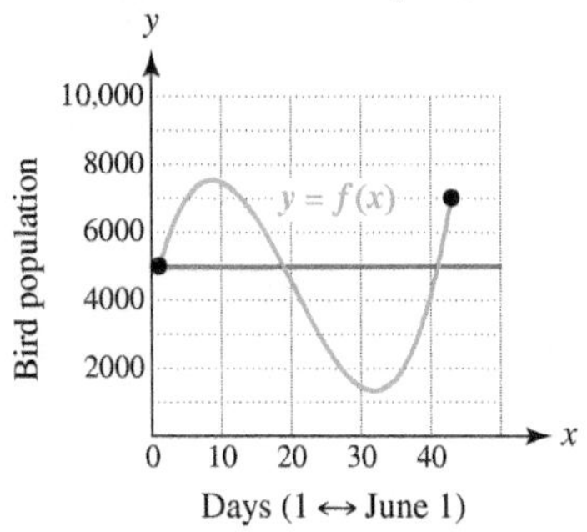

SOLUTION

From Figure 4.57, repeated in the margin, it appears that the bird population was 5000 when $x = 1$. If we substitute $x = 1$ in this polynomial, the result is 0.

$$g(1) = 1^3 - 61(1)^2 + 839(1) - 779 = 0$$

By the factor theorem, $(x - 1)$ is a factor of $g(x)$. We can use synthetic division to divide $x^3 - 61x^2 + 839x - 779$ by $x - 1$.

$$\begin{array}{r|rrrr} 1 & 1 & -61 & 839 & -779 \\ & & 1 & -60 & 779 \\ \hline & 1 & -60 & 779 & 0 \end{array}$$ The remainder is 0.

By the division algorithm,

$$x^3 - 61x^2 + 839x - 779 = (x - 1)(x^2 - 60x + 779).$$

Since it is not obvious how to factor $x^2 - 60x + 779$, we can use the quadratic formula with $a = 1$, $b = -60$, and $c = 779$ to find its zeros.

$$x = \frac{-b \pm \sqrt{b^2 - 4ac}}{2a}$$ Quadratic formula

$$= \frac{-(-60) \pm \sqrt{(-60)^2 - 4(1)(779)}}{2(1)}$$ $a = 1, b = -60, c = 779$

$$= \frac{60 \pm 22}{2}$$ Simplify.

$$= 41 \text{ or } 19$$ Two zeros

The zeros of $g(x) = x^3 - 61x^2 + 839x - 779$ are 1, 19, and 41, and its leading coefficient is 1. The complete factorization is $g(x) = (x - 1)(x - 19)(x - 41)$. The bird population equals 5000 on June 1 ($x = 1$), June 19 ($x = 19$), and July 11 ($x = 41$).

Now Try Exercise 113

Graphs and Multiple Zeros

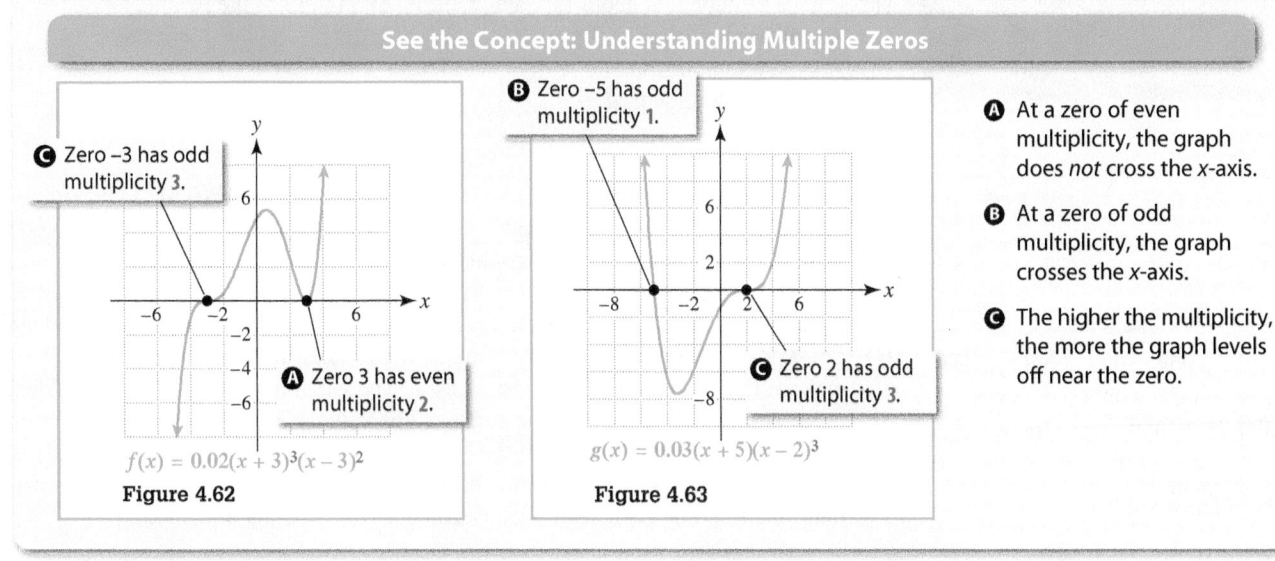

The following See the Concept explains graphs of polynomials with multiple zeros. See Figures 4.62 and 4.63.

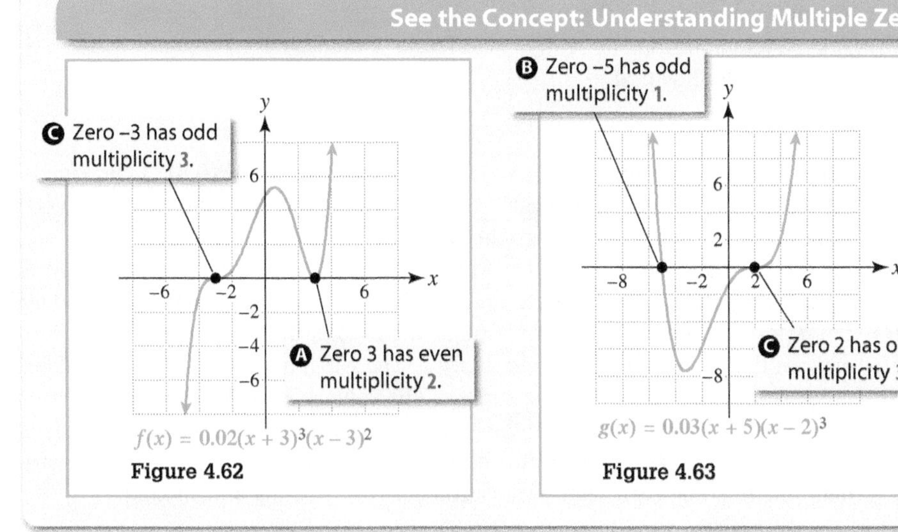

$f(x) = 0.02(x + 3)^3(x - 3)^2$

Figure 4.62

$g(x) = 0.03(x + 5)(x - 2)^3$

Figure 4.63

A At a zero of even multiplicity, the graph does *not* cross the *x*-axis.

B At a zero of odd multiplicity, the graph crosses the *x*-axis.

C The higher the multiplicity, the more the graph levels off near the zero.

EXAMPLE 6 **Finding multiplicities graphically**

Figure 4.64 shows the graph of a sixth-degree polynomial $f(x)$ with leading coefficient 1. All zeros are integers. Write $f(x)$ in complete factored form.

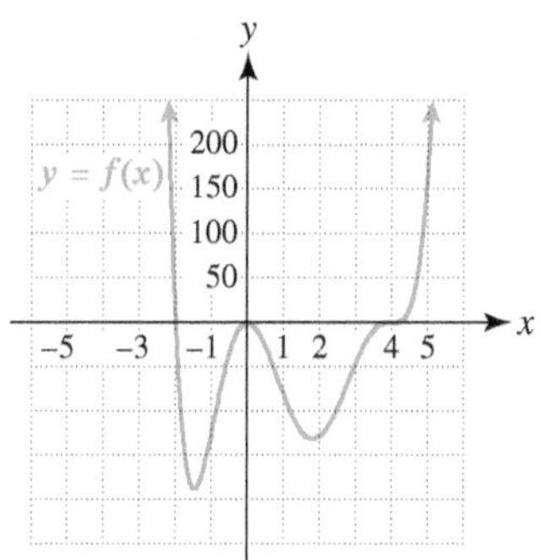

Figure 4.64

SOLUTION

The x-intercepts or zeros of f are -2, 0, and 4. Since the graph crosses the x-axis at -2 and 4, these zeros have odd multiplicity. The graph of f levels off more at $x = 4$ than at $x = -2$, so 4 has a higher multiplicity than -2. At $x = 0$ the graph of f does not cross the x-axis. Thus 0 has even multiplicity. To make $f(x)$ a sixth degree polynomial, -2 has multiplicity 1, 0 has multiplicity 2, and 4 has multiplicity 3. Then the sum of the multiplicities is given by $1 + 2 + 3 = 6$, which equals the degree of $f(x)$. List the zeros as -2, 0, 0, 4, 4, and 4. The leading coefficient is 1, so the complete factorization of $f(x)$ is

$$f(x) = 1(x + 2)(x - 0)(x - 0)(x - 4)(x - 4)(x - 4), \quad \text{or}$$
$$f(x) = x^2(x + 2)(x - 4)^3.$$

Now Try Exercise 47

An Application: "Will It Float?" Multiple zeros can have physical significance. The next example shows how a multiple zero represents the boundary between an object floating and sinking.

EXAMPLE 7 **Interpreting a multiple zero**

The polynomial $f(x) = \frac{\pi}{3}x^3 - 5\pi x^2 + \frac{500\pi d}{3}$ can be used to find the depth that a ball, 10 centimeters in diameter, sinks in water. The constant d is the density of the ball, where the density of water is 1. The smallest *positive* zero of $f(x)$ equals the depth that the sphere sinks. Approximate this depth for each material and interpret the results.

(a) A wood ball with $d = 0.8$
(b) A solid aluminum sphere with $d = 2.7$
(c) A water balloon with $d = 1$

SOLUTION

(a) Let $d = 0.8$ and graph $Y_1 = (\pi/3)X\text{^}3 - 5\pi X\text{^}2 + 500\pi(0.8)/3$. In Figure 4.65 the smallest positive zero is near 7.13. This means that the 10-centimeter wood ball sinks about 7.13 centimeters into the water.

(b) Let $d = 2.7$ and graph $Y_2 = (\pi/3)X\text{^}3 - 5\pi X\text{^}2 + 500\pi(2.7)/3$. In Figure 4.66 there is no positive zero. The aluminum sphere is more dense than water and sinks.

(c) Let $d = 1$ and graph $Y_3 = (\pi/3)X\text{^}3 - 5\pi X\text{^}2 + 500\pi/3$. In Figure 4.67, y_3 has one positive zero of 10 with multiplicity 2. The water balloon has the same density as water and "floats" even with the surface. The value of $d = 1$ represents the boundary between sinking and floating. If the ball floats, $f(x)$ has two positive zeros; if it sinks, $f(x)$ has no positive zeros. With the water balloon there is one positive zero with multiplicity 2 that represents a transition between floating and sinking.

CLASS DISCUSSION

Make a conjecture about the depth that a ball with a 10-centimeter diameter will sink in water if $d = 0.5$. Test your conjecture graphically.

It Floats

$[-20, 20, 5]$ by $[-300, 500, 100]$

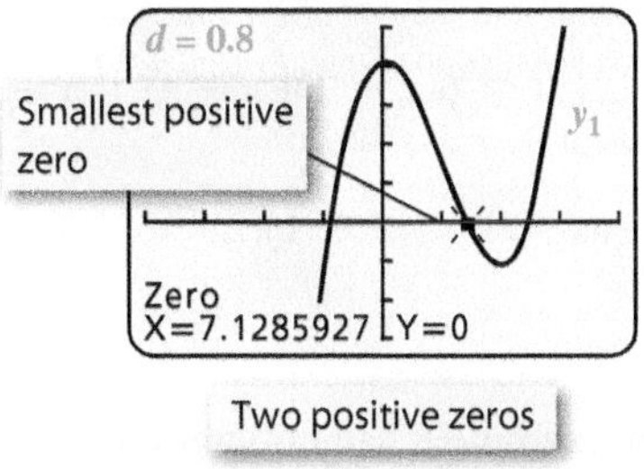

Smallest positive zero

Zero X=7.1285927 Y=0

Two positive zeros

Figure 4.65

It Sinks

$[-20, 20, 5]$ by $[-500, 2000, 500]$

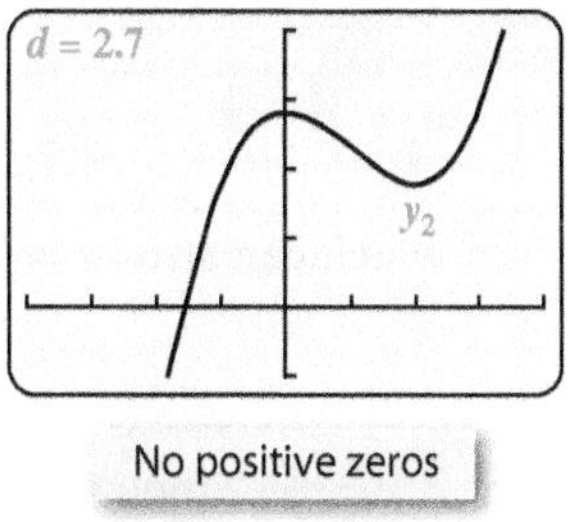

No positive zeros

Figure 4.66

Neither Sinks Nor Floats

$[-20, 20, 5]$ by $[-300, 600, 100]$

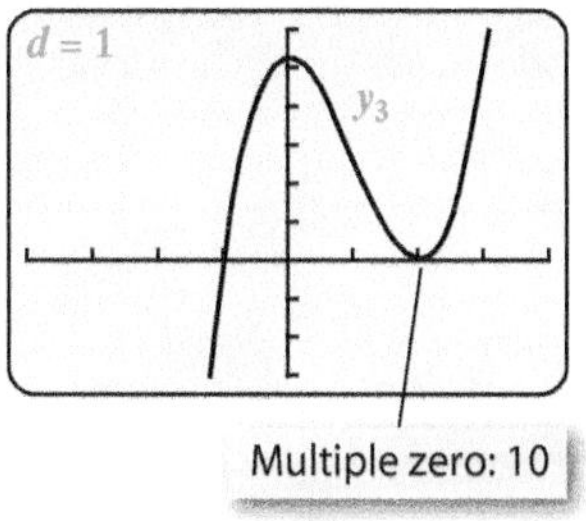

Multiple zero: 10

Figure 4.67

Now Try Exercise 111

Rational Zeros

If a polynomial has a rational zero, it can be found by using the **rational zero test.**

RATIONAL ZERO TEST

Let $f(x) = a_n x^n + \cdots + a_2 x^2 + a_1 x + a_0$, where $a_n \neq 0$, represent a polynomial function f with *integer* coefficients. If $\frac{p}{q}$ is a rational number written in lowest terms and if $\frac{p}{q}$ is a zero of f, then p is a factor of the constant term a_0 and q is a factor of the leading coefficient a_n.

The following example illustrates how to find rational zeros by using this test.

EXAMPLE 8 Finding rational zeros of a polynomial

Find all rational zeros of $f(x) = 6x^3 - 5x^2 - 7x + 4$ and factor $f(x)$.

SOLUTION

If $\frac{p}{q}$ is a rational zero in lowest terms, then p is a factor of the constant term 4 and q is a factor of the leading coefficient 6. The possible values for p and q are as follows.

$$p: \quad \pm 1, \quad \pm 2, \quad \pm 4$$
$$q: \quad \pm 1, \quad \pm 2, \quad \pm 3, \quad \pm 6$$

As a result, any rational zero of $f(x)$ in the form $\frac{p}{q}$ must occur in the list

$$\pm\frac{1}{6}, \quad \pm\frac{1}{3}, \quad \pm\frac{1}{2}, \quad \pm\frac{2}{3}, \quad \pm\frac{1}{1}, \quad \pm\frac{4}{3}, \quad \pm\frac{2}{1}, \quad \text{or} \quad \pm\frac{4}{1}.$$

Evaluate $f(x)$ at each value in the list. See Table 4.3.

x	$f(x)$	x	$f(x)$	x	$f(x)$	x	$f(x)$
$\frac{1}{6}$	$\frac{49}{18}$	$\frac{1}{2}$	0	1	-2	2	18
$-\frac{1}{6}$	5	$-\frac{1}{2}$	$\frac{11}{2}$	-1	0	-2	-50
$\frac{1}{3}$	$\frac{4}{3}$	$\frac{2}{3}$	$-\frac{10}{9}$	$\frac{4}{3}$	0	4	280
$-\frac{1}{3}$	$\frac{50}{9}$	$-\frac{2}{3}$	$\frac{14}{3}$	$-\frac{4}{3}$	$-\frac{88}{9}$	-4	-432

Table 4.3

From Table 4.3 there are three rational zeros: $-1, \frac{1}{2}$, and $\frac{4}{3}$. Since a third-degree polynomial has at most three zeros, the complete factored form of $f(x)$ is

$$f(x) = 6(x + 1)\left(x - \frac{1}{2}\right)\left(x - \frac{4}{3}\right),$$

which can also be written as $f(x) = (x + 1)(2x - 1)(3x - 4)$.

Now Try Exercise 57

NOTE Although $f(x)$ in Example 8 had only rational zeros, it is important to realize that many polynomials have irrational zeros. Irrational zeros cannot be found using the rational zero test.

Descartes' Rule of Signs

Descartes' rule of signs helps to determine the numbers of positive and negative real zeros of a polynomial function.

DESCARTES' RULE OF SIGNS

Let $P(x)$ define a polynomial function with real coefficients and a nonzero constant term, with terms in descending powers of x.

(a) The number of positive real zeros either equals the number of variations in sign occurring in the coefficients of $P(x)$ or is less than the number of variations by a positive even integer.

(b) The number of negative real zeros either equals the number of variations in sign occurring in the coefficients of $P(-x)$ or is less than the number of variations by a positive even integer.

A **variation in sign** is a change from positive to negative or negative to positive in successive terms of the polynomial when written in descending powers of the variable. Missing terms (those with 0 coefficients) can be ignored.

EXAMPLE 9 Applying Descartes' rule of signs

Determine the possible numbers of positive real zeros and negative real zeros of $P(x) = x^4 - 6x^3 + 8x^2 + 2x - 1$.

SOLUTION

We first consider the possible number of positive zeros by observing that $P(x)$ has three variations in sign.

$$+x^4 - 6x^3 + 8x^2 + 2x - 1$$

1 2 3

Three variations in sign.

Thus by Descartes' rule of signs, $P(x)$ has either 3 or $3 - 2 = 1$ positive real zeros.

For negative zeros, consider the variations in sign for $P(-x)$.

$$P(-x) = (-x)^4 - 6(-x)^3 + 8(-x)^2 + 2(-x) - 1$$
$$= x^4 + 6x^3 + 8x^2 - 2x - 1$$

1

One variation in sign.

Since there is only one variation in sign, $P(x)$ has only 1 negative real zero.

Now Try Exercise 65

Polynomial Equations

In Section 3.2, factoring was used to solve quadratic equations. Factoring also can be used to solve polynomial equations with degree greater than 2.

EXAMPLE 10 Solving a cubic equation

Solve $x^3 + 3x^2 - 4x = 0$ symbolically. Support your answer graphically and numerically.

SOLUTION

Symbolic Solution

$$x^3 + 3x^2 - 4x = 0 \quad \text{Given equation}$$
$$x(x^2 + 3x - 4) = 0 \quad \text{Factor out } x.$$
$$x(x + 4)(x - 1) = 0 \quad \text{Factor the quadratic expression}$$
$$x = 0, \quad x + 4 = 0, \quad \text{or} \quad x - 1 = 0 \quad \text{Zero-product property}$$
$$x = 0, -4, \text{ or } 1 \quad \text{Solve.}$$

Graphical Solution Graph $y = x^3 + 3x^2 - 4x$ as in Figure 4.68. The x-intercepts are -4, 0, and 1, which correspond to the solutions.

Numerical Solution Table $y = x^3 + 3x^2 - 4x$ as in Figure 4.69. The zeros of y occur at $x = -4$, 0, and 1.

Solving $x^3 + 3x^2 - 4x = 0$

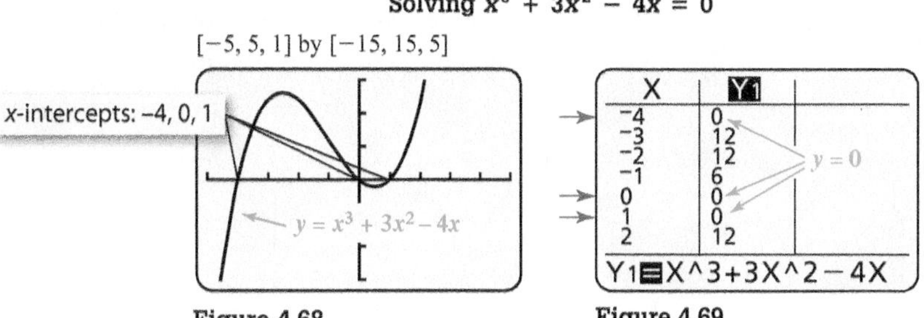

Figure 4.68 **Figure 4.69**

Now Try Exercise 71

EXAMPLE 11 Solving a polynomial equation

Find all real solutions to each equation symbolically.

(a) $4x^4 - 5x^2 - 9 = 0$ **(b)** $2x^3 + 12 = 3x^2 + 8x$

SOLUTION

(a) The expression $4x^4 - 5x^2 - 9$ can be factored in a manner similar to the way quadratic expressions are factored.

$$4x^4 - 5x^2 - 9 = 0 \quad \text{Given equation}$$
$$(4x^2 - 9)(x^2 + 1) = 0 \quad \text{Factor.}$$
$$4x^2 - 9 = 0 \quad \text{or} \quad x^2 + 1 = 0 \quad \text{Zero-product property}$$
$$4x^2 = 9 \quad \text{or} \quad x^2 = -1 \quad \text{Add 9 or subtract 1.}$$
$$x^2 = \frac{9}{4} \quad \text{or} \quad x^2 = -1 \quad \text{Divide left equation by 4.}$$
$$x = \pm\frac{3}{2} \quad \text{or} \quad x^2 = -1 \quad \text{Square root property}$$

The equation $x^2 = -1$ has no *real* solutions. The solutions are $-\frac{3}{2}$ and $\frac{3}{2}$.

Algebra Review
To review factoring a cubic polynomial by grouping, see Chapter R (page R-20).

(b) First transpose each term on the right side of the equation to the left side of the equation. Then use *grouping* to factor the polynomial.

$2x^3 + 12 = 3x^2 + 8x$	Given equation
$2x^3 - 3x^2 - 8x + 12 = 0$	Rewrite the equation.
$(2x^3 - 3x^2) + (-8x + 12) = 0$	Associative property
$x^2(2x - 3) - 4(2x - 3) = 0$	Factor.
$(x^2 - 4)(2x - 3) = 0$	Factor out $2x - 3$.
$x^2 - 4 = 0$ or $2x - 3 = 0$	Zero-product property
$x = \pm 2$ or $x = \frac{3}{2}$	Solve each equation.

The solutions are -2, $\frac{3}{2}$, and 2.

Now Try Exercises 79 and 89

Some types of polynomial equations cannot be solved easily by factoring. The next example illustrates how we can obtain an approximate solution graphically.

EXAMPLE 12 **Finding a solution graphically**

Solve the equation $\frac{1}{2}x^3 - 2x - 4 = 0$ graphically. Round to the nearest hundredth.

SOLUTION
A graph of $y = \frac{1}{2}x^3 - 2x - 4$ is shown in Figure 4.70. Since there is only one x-intercept, the equation has one *real* solution: $x \approx 2.65$.

Calculator Help
To find a zero of a function, see Appendix A (page AP-7).

Graphical Solution

$[-9, 9, 1]$ by $[-6, 6, 1]$

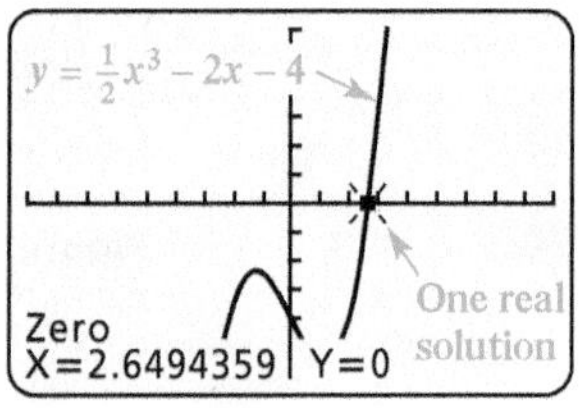

$y = \frac{1}{2}x^3 - 2x - 4$

Zero
X=2.6494359 Y=0

One real solution

Figure 4.70

Now Try Exercise 97

Intermediate Value Property

In Example 12, we approximated a solution to $\frac{1}{2}x^3 - 2x - 4 = 0$ to be 2.65. How do we know for sure that there is indeed such a solution? The *intermediate value property* helps answer this question.

INTERMEDIATE VALUE PROPERTY

Let (x_1, y_1) and (x_2, y_2), with $y_1 \neq y_2$ and $x_1 < x_2$, be two points on the graph of a continuous function f. Then, on the interval $x_1 \leq x \leq x_2$, f assumes every value between y_1 and y_2 at least once.

From Example 12, let $f(x) = \frac{1}{2}x^3 - 2x - 4$. Because $f(0) = -4$ and $f(3) = 3.5$, the points $(0, -4)$ and $(3, 3.5)$ lie on the graph of f in Figure 4.70. By the intermediate value property, $f(x) = 0$ for at least one x-value, because 0 is between -4 and 3.5. Although we have not found the exact x-value, we know that a real zero of f does exist. Loosely speaking, the intermediate value property says that if $y_1 < 0$ and $y_2 > 0$, then we cannot draw a continuous graph of f without crossing the x-axis. The only way not to cross the x-axis would be to pick up the pencil, but this would create a discontinuous graph.

Applications There are many examples of the intermediate value property. Physical motion is usually considered to be continuous. Suppose at one time a car is traveling at 20 miles per hour and at another time it is traveling at 40 miles per hour. It is logical to assume that the car traveled 30 miles per hour at least once between these times. In fact, by the intermediate value property, the car must have assumed all speeds between 20 and 40 miles per hour at least once. Similarly, if a jet airliner takes off and flies at an altitude of 30,000 feet, then by the intermediate value property we may conclude that the airliner assumed all altitudes between ground level and 30,000 feet at least once.

4.4 Putting It All Together

The following table summarizes important topics about real zeros of polynomial functions.

CONCEPT	EXPLANATION	EXAMPLES
Factor theorem	$(x - k)$ is a factor of $f(x)$ if and only if $f(k) = 0$.	$f(x) = x^2 + 3x - 4$, $f(-4) = 0$, and $f(1) = 0$ imply that $(x + 4)$ and $(x - 1)$ are factors of $f(x)$. That is, $f(x) = (x + 4)(x - 1)$.
x-intercepts, zeros, and factors	The following are *equivalent:* **1.** The graph of f has x-intercept k. **2.** A real zero of f is k. That is, $f(k) = 0$. **3.** A factor of f is $(x - k)$.	Let $f(x) = x^2 - 2x - 3$. See the graph below. **1.** The graph of f has x-intercepts -1 and 3. **2.** $f(-1) = 0$ and $f(3) = 0$ **3.** $f(x) = (x + 1)(x - 3)$ y, x, 4, −1, 3, −4, 1, 2, 4, −4 $f(x) = x^2 - 2x - 3$
Complete factored form	$f(x) = a_n(x - c_1) \cdots (x - c_n)$, where the c_k are zeros of f, with a distinct zero listed as many times as its multiplicity. This form is unique.	$f(x) = 3(x - 5)(x + 3)(x + 3)$ $= 3(x - 5)(x + 3)^2$ $a_n = 3$, $c_1 = 5$, $c_2 = -3$, $c_3 = -3$
Factoring a polynomial graphically (only real zeros)	Graph $y = f(x)$ and locate all the zeros or x-intercepts. If the leading coefficient is a and the zeros are c_1, c_2, and c_3, then $f(x) = a(x - c_1)(x - c_2)(x - c_3)$.	$f(x) = 2x^3 + 4x^2 - 2x - 4$ has zeros $-2, -1$, and 1 and leading coefficient 2. Thus $f(x) = 2(x + 2)(x + 1)(x - 1)$. y, x, 2, 1, 2, −4 $y = f(x)$
Solving polynomial equations	Polynomial equations can be solved symbolically, graphically, and numerically. Factoring is a useful symbolic technique.	Solve $x^3 - 4x^2 - 5x = 0$. $x(x^2 - 4x - 5) = 0$ $x(x - 5)(x + 1) = 0$ $x = 0, 5, \text{ or } -1$ See also Examples 10 and 11.

continued on next page

The following explains the concepts of multiple zeros and graphs of polynomials.

CONCEPT	DESCRIPTION
Zeros and multiplicity	If a zero of a polynomial has odd multiplicity, then the graph crosses the x-axis at the zero. If a polynomial has a zero of even multiplicity, then the graph intersects, but does not cross, the x-axis at the zero. The higher the multiplicity of a zero, the more the graph levels off near the zero. **Multiplicity 1 (odd)** **Multiplicity 2 (even)** **Multiplicity 3 (odd)** **Multiplicity 4 (even)**

4.4 Exercises

Factoring Polynomials

Exercises 1–4: Use the graph and the factor theorem to list the factors of $f(x)$.

1.

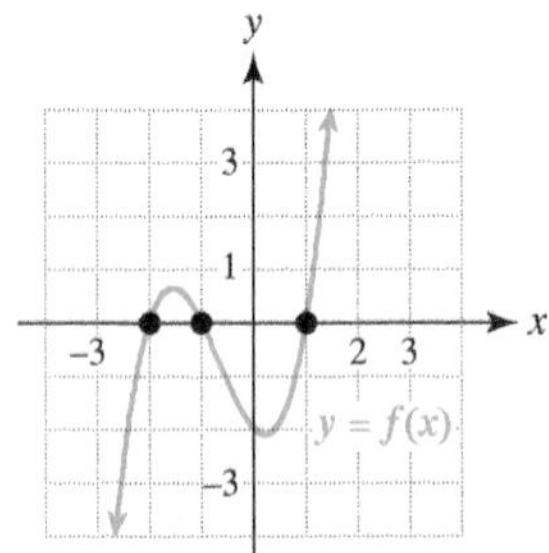

2.

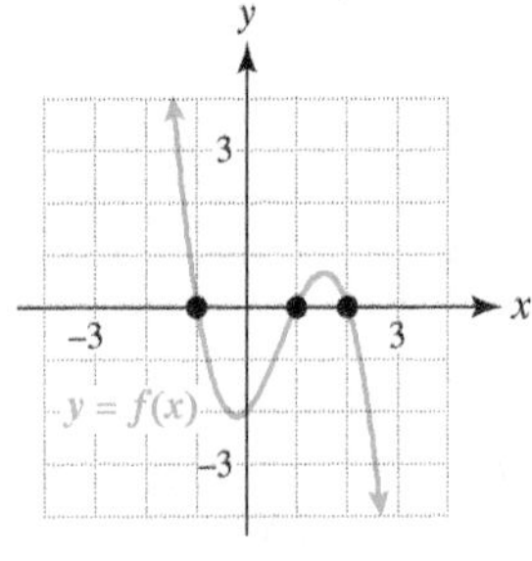

3.

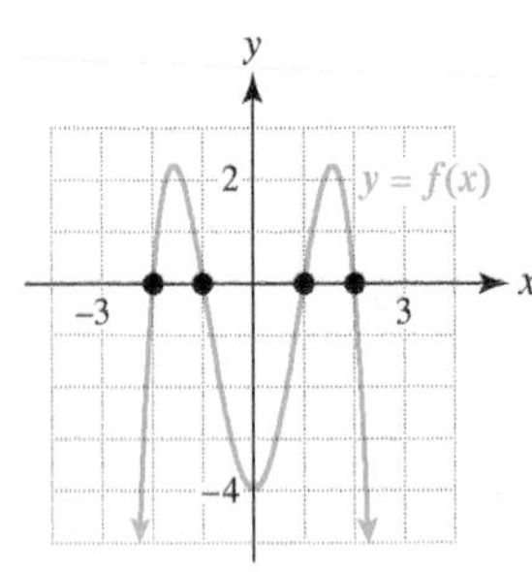

4.

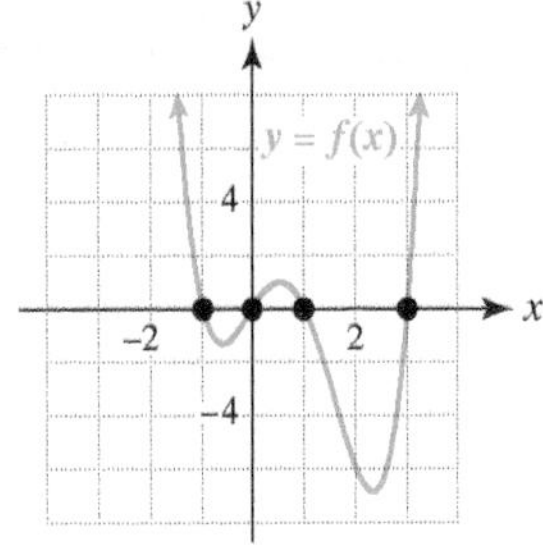

Exercises 5–12: Use the given zeros to write the complete factored form of $f(x)$.

5. $f(x) = 2x^2 - 25x + 77$; zeros: $\frac{11}{2}$ and 7

6. $f(x) = 6x^2 + 21x - 90$; zeros: -6 and $\frac{5}{2}$

7. $f(x) = x^3 - 2x^2 - 5x + 6$; zeros: -2, 1, and 3

8. $f(x) = x^3 + 6x^2 + 11x + 6$; zeros: -3, -2, and -1

9. $f(x) = -2x^3 + 3x^2 + 59x - 30$; zeros: -5, $\frac{1}{2}$, and 6

10. $f(x) = 3x^4 - 8x^3 - 67x^2 + 112x + 240$; zeros: -4, $-\frac{4}{3}$, 3, and 5

11. Let $f(x)$ be a quadratic polynomial with leading coefficient 7. Suppose that $f(-3) = 0$ and $f(2) = 0$. Write the complete factored form of $f(x)$.

12. Let $g(x)$ be a cubic polynomial with leading coefficient -4. Suppose that $g(-2) = 0$, $g(1) = 0$, and $g(4) = 0$. Write the complete factored form of $g(x)$.

Exercises 13 and 14: Use the graph to factor $f(x)$.

13. $f(x) = -2x^3 + 2x$

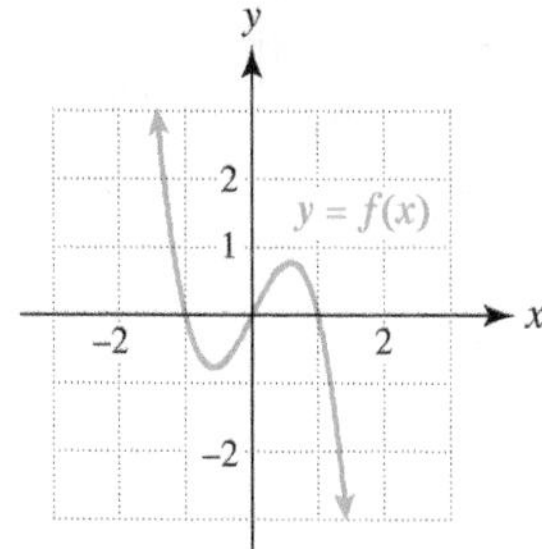

14. $f(x) = \frac{1}{4}x^4 - \frac{3}{2}x^3 + \frac{3}{4}x^2 + \frac{13}{2}x - 6$

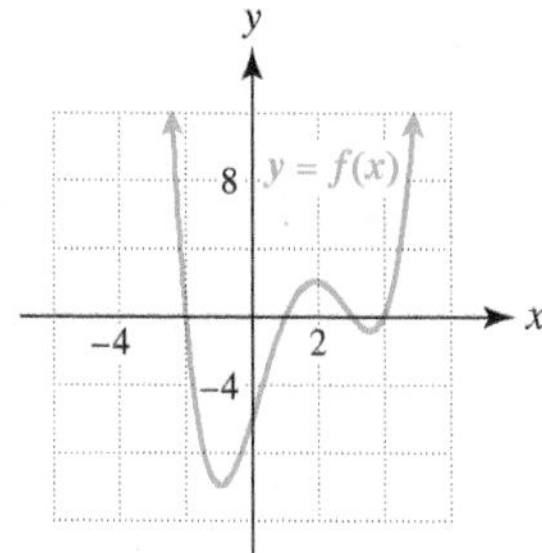

Exercises 15–18: The graph of a polynomial $f(x)$ with leading coefficient ± 1 and integer zeros is shown in the figure. Write its complete factored form.

15.

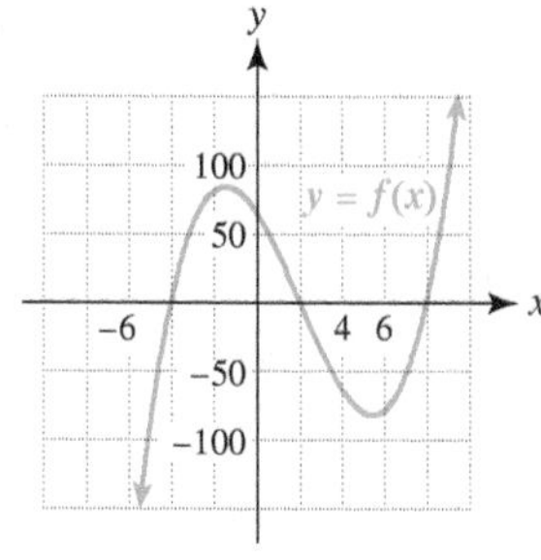

16.

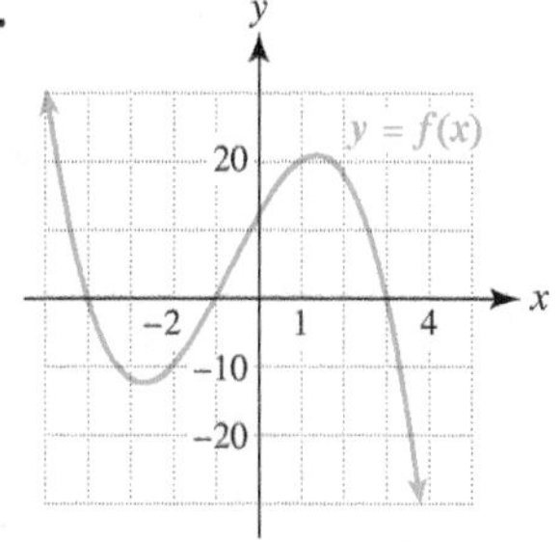

17.

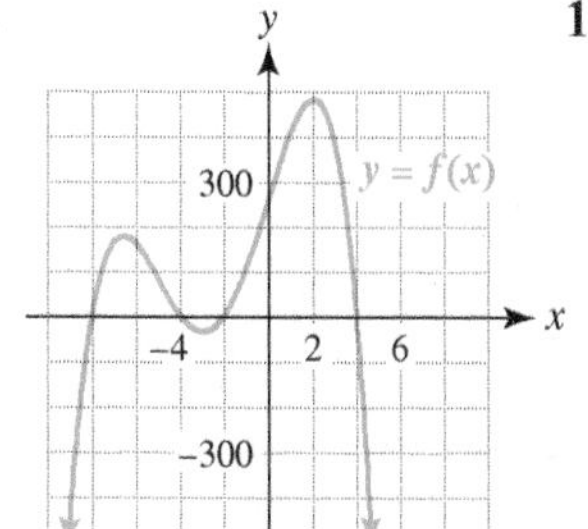

18.

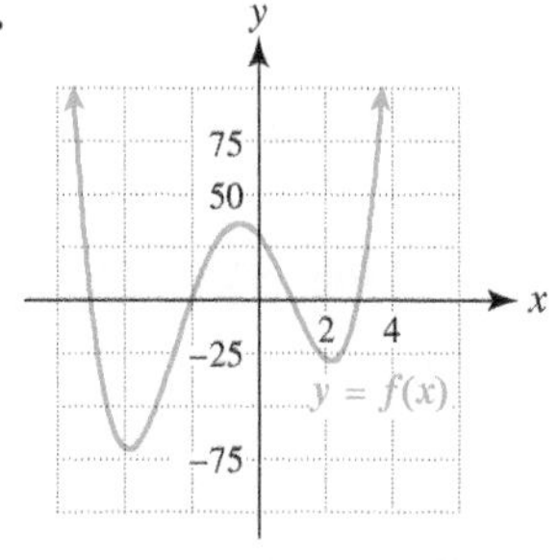

19. Let $f(x)$ be a cubic polynomial with zeros -1, 2, and 3. If the graph of f passes through the point (0, 3), write the complete factored form of $f(x)$.

20. Let $g(x)$ be a quartic polynomial with zeros $-2, -1, 1$, and 2. If the graph of g passes through the point (0, 8), write the complete factored form of $g(x)$.

Exercises 21–24: The graph of a polynomial $f(x)$ with integer zeros is shown in the figure. Write its complete factored form. Note that the leading coefficient of $f(x)$ is not ± 1.

21.

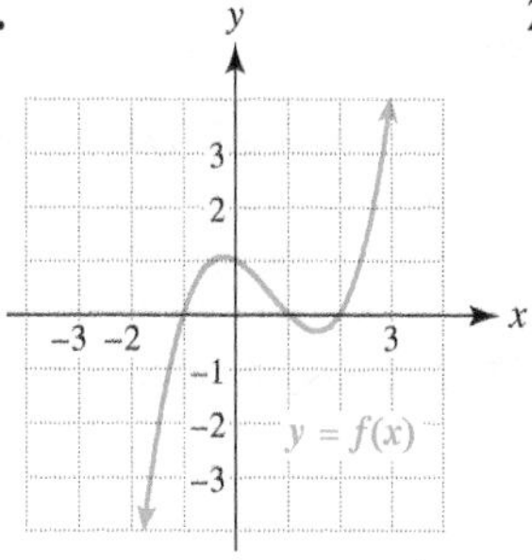

22.

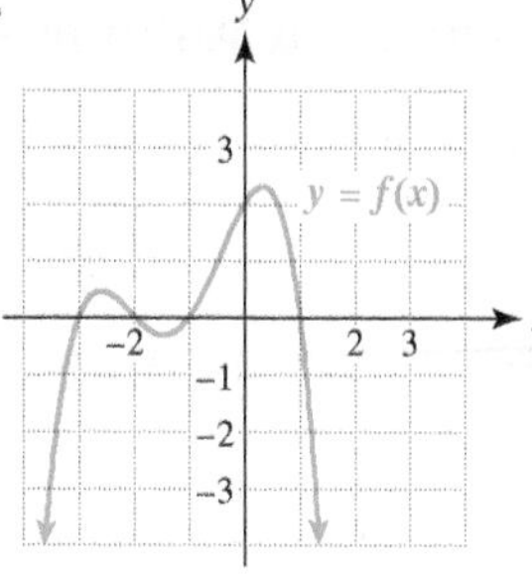

23.

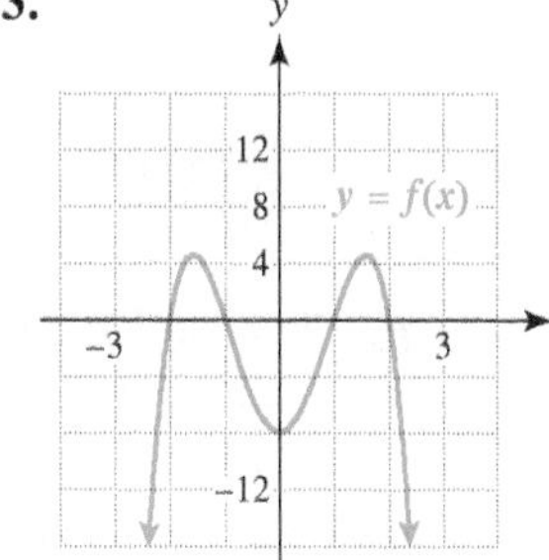

24.

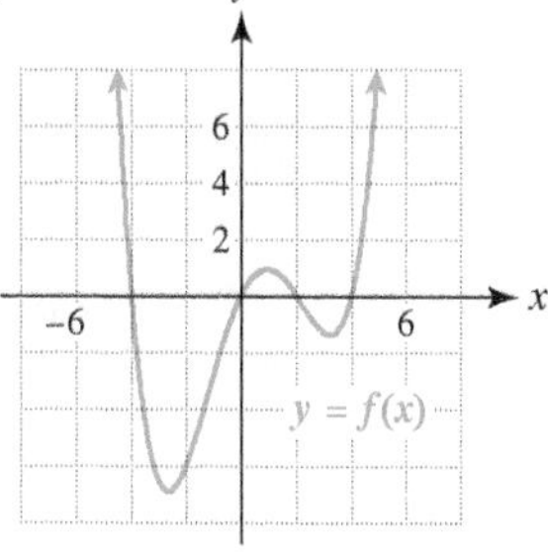

Exercises 25–30: Use graphing to factor $f(x)$.

25. $f(x) = 10x^2 + 17x - 6$

26. $f(x) = 2x^3 + 7x^2 + 2x - 3$

27. $f(x) = -3x^3 - 3x^2 + 18x$

28. $f(x) = \frac{1}{2}x^3 + \frac{5}{2}x^2 + x - 4$

29. $f(x) = x^4 + \frac{5}{2}x^3 - 3x^2 - \frac{9}{2}x$

30. $f(x) = 10x^4 + 7x^3 - 27x^2 + 2x + 8$

Exercises 31–36: (Refer to Example 4.) Write the complete factored form of the polynomial $f(x)$, given that k is a zero.

31. $f(x) = x^3 - 9x^2 + 23x - 15$ $\quad k = 1$

32. $f(x) = 2x^3 + x^2 - 11x - 10$ $\quad k = -2$

33. $f(x) = -4x^3 - x^2 + 51x - 36$ $\quad k = -4$

34. $f(x) = 3x^3 - 11x^2 - 35x + 75$ $\quad k = 5$

35. $f(x) = 2x^4 - x^3 - 13x^2 - 6x$ $\quad k = -2$

36. $f(x) = 35x^4 + 48x^3 - 41x^2 + 6x$ $\quad k = \frac{3}{7}$

Factor Theorem

Exercises 37–40: Use the factor theorem to decide if $x - k$ is a factor of $f(x)$ for the given k.

37. $f(x) = x^3 - 6x^2 + 11x - 6$ $\quad k = 2$

38. $f(x) = x^3 + x^2 - 14x - 24$ $\quad k = -3$

39. $f(x) = x^4 - 2x^3 - 13x^2 - 10x \qquad k = 3$

40. $f(x) = 2x^4 - 11x^3 + 9x^2 + 14x \qquad k = \frac{1}{2}$

Graphs and Multiple Zeros

Exercises 41 and 42: The graph of a polynomial $f(x)$ is shown in the figure. Estimate the zeros and state whether their multiplicities are odd or even. State the minimum degree of $f(x)$.

41. **42.**

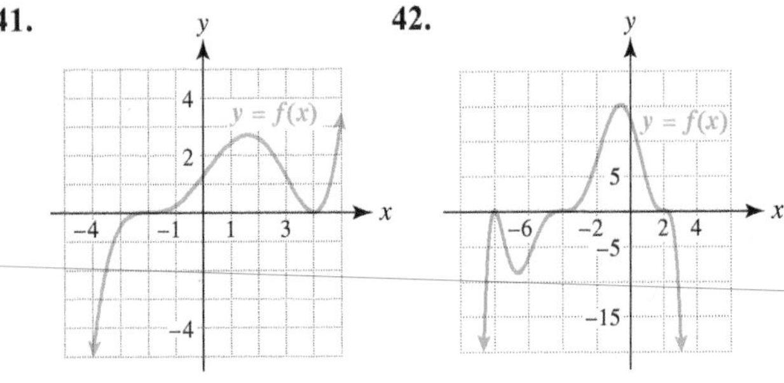

Exercises 43–46: Write a polynomial $f(x)$ in complete factored form that satisfies the conditions. Let the leading coefficient be 1.

43. Degree 3; zeros: -1 with multiplicity 2, and 6 with multiplicity 1

44. Degree 4; zeros: 5 and 7, both with multiplicity 2

45. Degree 4; zeros: 2 with multiplicity 3, and 6 with multiplicity 1

46. Degree 5; zeros: -2 with multiplicity 2, and 4 with multiplicity 3

Exercises 47–52: The graph of either a cubic, quartic, or quintic polynomial $f(x)$ with integer zeros is shown. Write the complete factored form of $f(x)$. (Hint: In Exercises 51 and 52 the leading coefficient is not ± 1.)

47.

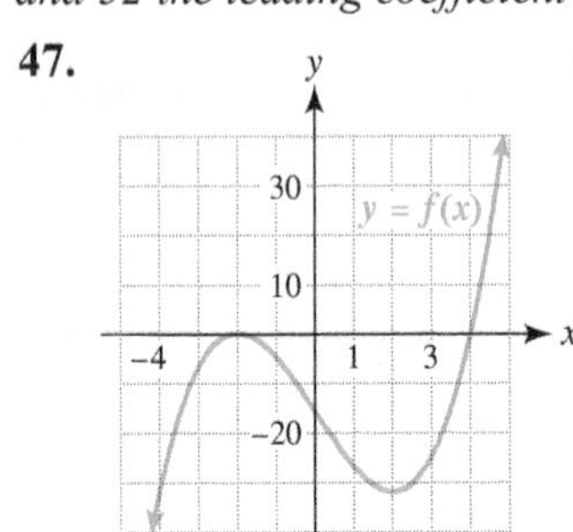

48.

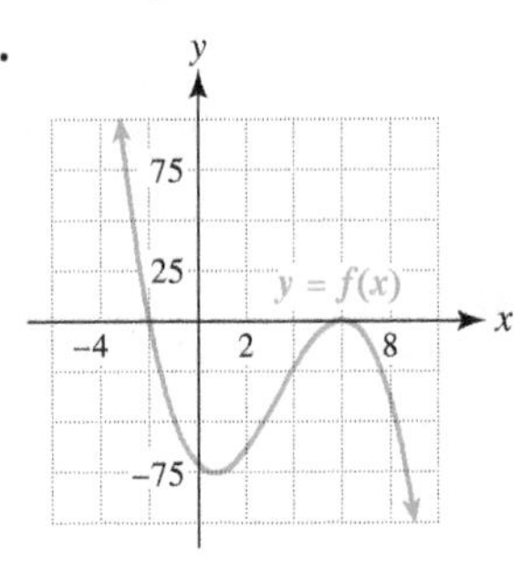

49.

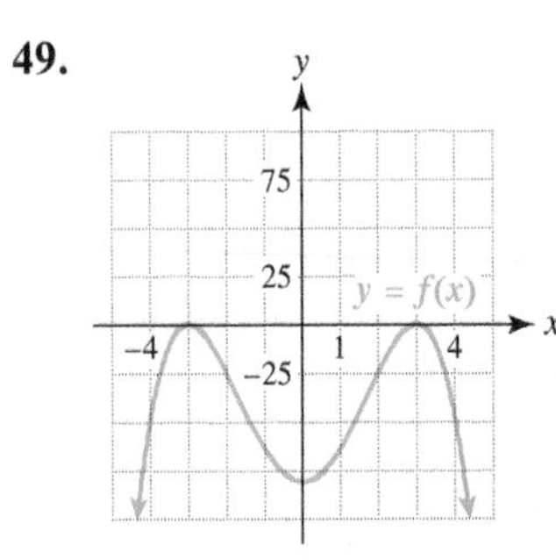

50.

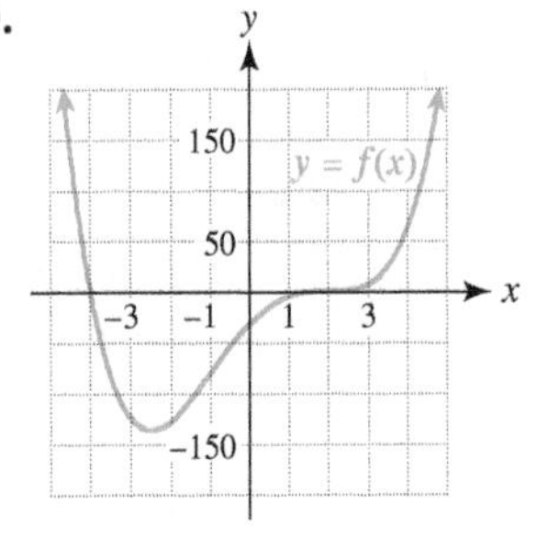

51. **52.**

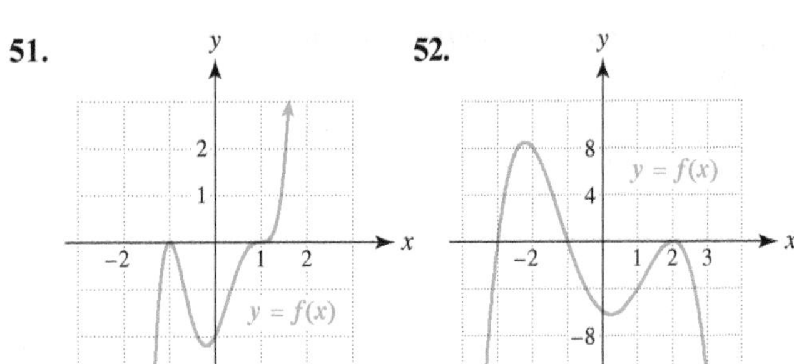

Exercises 53–56: Complete the following.

(a) Find the x- and y-intercepts.
(b) Determine the multiplicity of each zero of f.
(c) Sketch a graph of $y = f(x)$ by hand.

53. $f(x) = 2(x + 2)(x + 1)^2$

54. $f(x) = -(x + 1)(x - 1)(x - 2)$

55. $f(x) = x^2(x + 2)(x - 2)$

56. $f(x) = -\frac{1}{2}(x + 2)^2(x - 1)^3$

Rational Zeros

Exercises 57–64: (Refer to Example 8.)

(a) Use the rational zero test to find any rational zeros of the polynomial $f(x)$.
(b) Write the complete factored form of $f(x)$.

57. $f(x) = 2x^3 + 3x^2 - 8x + 3$

58. $f(x) = x^3 - 7x + 6$

59. $f(x) = 2x^4 + x^3 - 8x^2 - x + 6$

60. $f(x) = 2x^4 + x^3 - 19x^2 - 9x + 9$

61. $f(x) = 3x^3 - 16x^2 + 17x - 4$

62. $f(x) = x^3 + 2x^2 - 3x - 6$

63. $f(x) = x^3 - x^2 - 7x + 7$

64. $f(x) = 2x^3 - 5x^2 - 4x + 10$

Descartes' Rule of Signs

Exercises 65–70: Use Descartes' rule of signs to determine the possible number of positive and negative real zeros for each function. Then, use a graph to determine the actual numbers of positive and negative real zeros.

65. $P(x) = 2x^3 - 4x^2 + 2x + 7$

66. $P(x) = x^3 + 2x^2 + x - 10$

67. $P(x) = 5x^4 + 3x^2 + 2x - 9$

68. $P(x) = 3x^4 + 2x^3 - 8x^2 - 10x - 1$

69. $P(x) = x^5 + 3x^4 - x^3 + 2x + 3$

70. $P(x) = 2x^5 - x^4 + x^3 - x^2 + x + 5$

Polynomial Equations

Exercises 71–76: Solve the equation

(a) symbolically,

(b) graphically, and

(c) numerically.

71. $x^3 + x^2 - 6x = 0$
72. $2x^2 - 8x + 6 = 0$
73. $x^4 - 1 = 0$
74. $x^4 - 5x^2 + 4 = 0$
75. $-x^3 + 4x = 0$
76. $6 - 4x - 2x^2 = 0$

Exercises 77–96: Solve the equation.

77. $x^3 - 25x = 0$
78. $x^4 - x^3 - 6x^2 = 0$
79. $x^4 - x^2 = 2x^2 + 4$
80. $x^4 + 5 = 6x^2$
81. $x^3 - 3x^2 - 18x = 0$
82. $x^4 - x^2 = 0$
83. $2x^3 = 4x^2 - 2x$
84. $x^3 = x$
85. $12x^3 = 17x^2 + 5x$
86. $3x^3 + 3x = 10x^2$
87. $9x^4 + 4 = 13x^2$
88. $4x^4 + 7x^2 - 2 = 0$
89. $4x^3 + 4x^2 - 3x - 3 = 0$
90. $9x^3 + 27x^2 - 2x - 6 = 0$
91. $2x^3 + 4 = x(x + 8)$
92. $3x^3 + 18 = x(2x + 27)$
93. $8x^4 = 30x^2 - 27$
94. $4x^4 - 21x^2 + 20 = 0$
95. $x^6 - 19x^3 = 216$
96. $x^6 = 7x^3 + 8$

Exercises 97–102: (Refer to Example 12.) Solve the equation graphically. Round your answers to the nearest hundredth.

97. $x^3 - 1.1x^2 - 5.9x + 0.7 = 0$
98. $x^3 + x^2 - 18x + 13 = 0$
99. $-0.7x^3 - 2x^2 + 4x + 2.5 = 0$
100. $3x^3 - 46x^2 + 180x - 99 = 0$
101. $2x^4 - 1.5x^3 + 13 = 24x^2 + 10x$
102. $-x^4 + 2x^3 + 20x^2 = 22x + 41$

Intermediate Value Property

Exercises 103–106: Use the intermediate value property to show that $f(x) = 0$ for some x on the given interval.

103. $f(x) = x^2 - 5, 2 \le x \le 3$ (*Hint:* Evaluate $f(2)$ and $f(3)$ and then apply the intermediate value property.)
104. $f(x) = x^3 - x - 1, 1 \le x \le 2$
105. $f(x) = 2x^3 - 1, 0 \le x \le 1$
106. $f(x) = 4x^2 - x - 1, -1 \le x \le 0$
107. Let $f(x) = x^5 - x^2 + 4$. Evaluate $f(1)$ and $f(2)$. Is there a real number k such that $f(k) = 20$? Explain your answer.
108. Sketch a graph of a function f that passes through the points $(-2, 3)$ and $(1, -2)$ but never assumes a value of 0. What must be true about the graph of f?

Applications

109. **Winter Temperature** The temperature T in degrees Fahrenheit on a cold night x hours past midnight can be approximated by $T(x) = x^3 - 6x^2 + 8x$, where $0 \le x \le 4$. Determine when the temperature was 0°F.
110. **Geometry** A rectangular box has sides with lengths $x, x + 1$, and $x + 2$. If the volume of the box is 504 cubic inches, find the dimensions of the box.

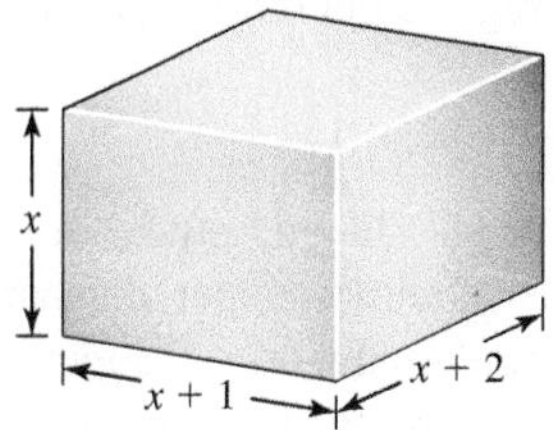

111. **Floating Ball** (Refer to Example 7.) If a ball has a 20-centimeter diameter, then

$$f(x) = \frac{\pi}{3}x^3 - 10\pi x^2 + \frac{4000\pi d}{3}$$

determines the depth that it sinks in water. Find the depth that this size ball sinks when $d = 0.6$.

112. **Floating Ball** (Refer to Example 7.) Determine the depth that a pine ball with a 10-centimeter diameter sinks in water if $d = 0.55$.
113. **Bird Populations** (Refer to Example 5.) A bird population can be modeled by

$$f(x) = x^3 - 66x^2 + 1052x + 1652,$$

where $x = 1$ corresponds to June 1, $x = 2$ to June 2, and so on. Find the days when f estimates that there were 3500 birds.

114. **Insect Population** An insect population P in thousands per acre x days past May 31 is approximated by $P(x) = 2x^3 - 18x^2 + 46x$, where $0 \le x \le 6$. Determine the dates when the insect population equaled 30 thousand per acre.
115. **Modeling Temperature** Complete the following.
    (a) Approximate the complete factored form of $f(x) = -0.184x^3 + 1.45x^2 + 10.7x - 27.9$.
    (b) The cubic polynomial $f(x)$ models monthly average temperature at Trout Lake, Canada, in degrees Fahrenheit, where $x = 1$ corresponds to January and $x = 12$ represents December. Interpret the zeros of f.

116. Average High Temperatures The monthly average high temperatures in degrees Fahrenheit at Daytona Beach can be modeled by

$$f(x) = 0.0151x^4 - 0.438x^3 + 3.60x^2 - 6.49x + 72.5,$$

where $x = 1$ corresponds to January and $x = 12$ represents December.

(a) Find the average high temperature during March and July.

(b) Graph f in $[0.5, 12.5, 1]$ by $[60, 100, 10]$. Interpret the graph.

(c) Estimate graphically and numerically when the average high temperature is 80°F.

Polynomial Regression

117. Water Pollution In one study, freshwater mussels were used to monitor copper discharge into a river from an electroplating works. Copper in high doses can be lethal to aquatic life. The table lists copper concentrations in mussels after 45 days at various distances downstream from the plant. The concentration C is measured in micrograms of copper per gram of mussel x kilometers downstream.

x	5	21	37	53	59
C	20	13	9	6	5

Source: R. Foster and J. Bates, "Use of mussels to monitor point source industrial discharges."

(a) Describe the relationship between x and C.

(b) Use regression to find a cubic polynomial function $f(x)$ that models the data.

(c) Graph C and the data.

(d) Concentrations above 10 are lethal to mussels. Locate this region in the river.

118. Dog Years There is a saying that every year of a dog's life is equal to 7 years for a human. A more accurate approximation is given by the graph of f. Given a dog's age x, where $x \geq 1$, $f(x)$ models the equivalent age in human years. According to the Bureau of the Census, middle age for people begins at age 45. (***Source:*** J. Brearley and A. Nicholas, *This Is the Bichon Frise.*)

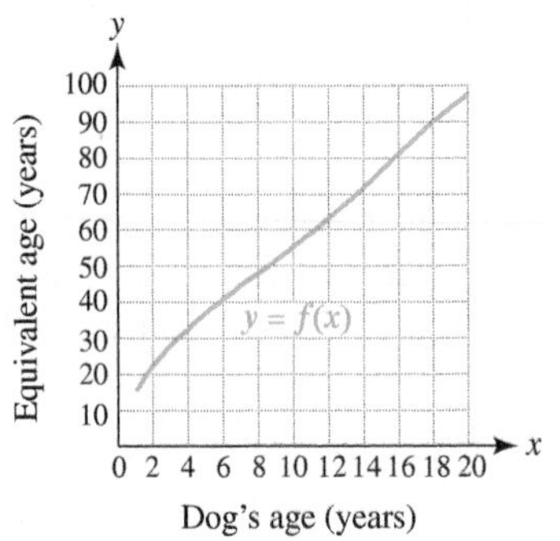

(a) Use the graph of f to estimate the equivalent age for dogs.

(b) Estimate $f(x)$ at $x = 2, 6, 10, 14,$ and 18.

(c) Use regression and the points you estimated to find a quartic polynomial function f that models the data points.

(d) Use $f(x)$ to solve part (a) either graphically or numerically.

Writing About Mathematics

119. Suppose that $f(x)$ is a quintic polynomial with distinct real zeros. Assuming you have access to technology, explain how to factor $f(x)$ approximately. Have you used the factor theorem? Explain.

120. Explain how to determine graphically whether a zero of a polynomial is a multiple zero. Sketch examples.

Extended and Discovery Exercises

Exercises 1–6: **Boundedness Theorem** *The boundedness theorem shows how the bottom row of a synthetic division is used to place upper and lower bounds on possible real zeros of a polynomial function.*

Let $P(x)$ define a polynomial function of degree $n \geq 1$ with real coefficients and with a positive leading coefficient. If $P(x)$ is divided synthetically by $x - c$ and

(a) if $c > 0$ and all numbers in the bottom row of the synthetic division are nonnegative, then $P(x)$ has no zero greater than c;

(b) if $c < 0$ and the numbers in the bottom row of the synthetic division alternate in sign (with 0 considered positive or negative, as needed), then $P(x)$ has no zero less than c.

Use the boundedness theorem to show that the real zeros of each polynomial function satisfy the given conditions.

1. $P(x) = x^4 - x^3 + 3x^2 - 8x + 8$; no real zero greater than 2

2. $P(x) = 2x^5 - x^4 + 2x^3 - 2x^2 + 4x - 4$; no real zero greater than 1

3. $P(x) = x^4 + x^3 - x^2 + 3$; no real zero less than -2

4. $P(x) = x^5 + 2x^3 - 2x^2 + 5x + 5$; no real zero less than -1

5. $P(x) = 3x^4 + 2x^3 - 4x^2 + x - 1$; no real zero greater than 1

6. $P(x) = 3x^4 + 2x^3 - 4x^2 + x - 1$; no real zero less than -2

CHECKING BASIC CONCEPTS FOR SECTIONS 4.3 AND 4.4

1. Simplify the expression $\dfrac{5x^4 - 10x^3 + 5x^2}{5x^2}$.

2. Divide the expression.

(a) $\dfrac{x^3 - x^2 + 4x - 4}{x - 1}$

(b) $\dfrac{2x^3 - 3x^2 + 4x + 4}{2x + 1}$

(c) $\dfrac{x^4 - 3x^3 + 6x^2 - 13x + 9}{x^2 + 4}$

3. Use the graph of the cubic polynomial $f(x)$ in the next column to determine its complete factored form. State the multiplicity of each zero. Assume that all zeros are integers and that the leading coefficient is *not* ± 1.

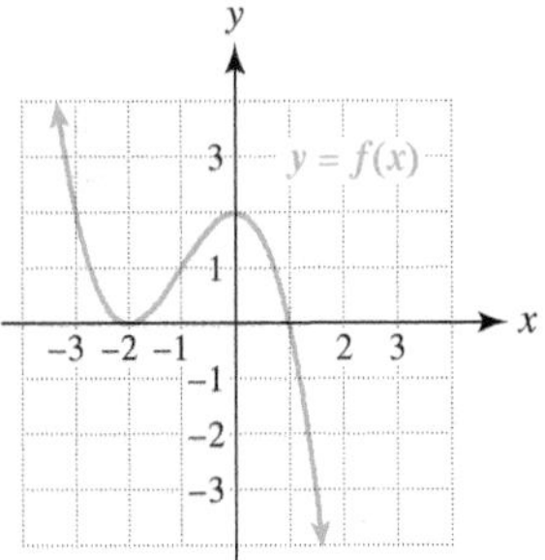

4. Solve $x^3 - 2x^2 - 15x = 0$.

5. Determine graphically the zeros of

$$f(x) = x^4 - x^3 - 18x^2 + 16x + 32.$$

Write $f(x)$ in complete factored form.

4.5 The Fundamental Theorem of Algebra

- **Apply the fundamental theorem of algebra**
- **Factor polynomials having complex zeros**
- **Solve polynomial equations having complex solutions**

Introduction

In Section 3.2 the quadratic formula was used to solve $ax^2 + bx + c = 0$. Are there similar formulas for higher degree polynomial equations? One of the most spectacular mathematical achievements during the sixteenth century was the discovery of formulas for solving cubic and quartic equations. This was accomplished by the Italian mathematicians Tartaglia, Cardano, Fior, del Ferro, and Ferrari between 1515 and 1545. These formulas are quite complicated and typically used only in computer software. In about 1805, the Italian physician Ruffini proved that finding formulas for quintic or higher degree equations was impossible. Another spectacular result came from Carl Friedrich Gauss. He proved that all polynomials can be completely factored by using complex numbers. This result is called the **fundamental theorem of algebra**. (***Source:*** H. Eves, *An Introduction to the History of Mathematics*.)

Fundamental Theorem of Algebra

One of the most brilliant mathematicians of all time, Carl Friedrich Gauss proved the fundamental theorem of algebra as part of his doctoral thesis at age 20. Although his theorem and proof were completed in 1797, they are still valid today.

FUNDAMENTAL THEOREM OF ALGEBRA

A polynomial $f(x)$ of degree n, with $n \geq 1$, has at least one complex zero.

NOTE The fundamental theorem of algebra guarantees that *every polynomial has a complete factorization*, provided we are allowed to use complex numbers.

Justification for Complete Factorization of Polynomials If $f(x)$ is a polynomial of degree 1 or higher, then by the fundamental theorem of algebra there is a zero c_1 such that $f(c_1) = 0$. By the factor theorem, $(x - c_1)$ is a factor of $f(x)$ and $f(x) = (x - c_1)\,q_1(x)$ for some polynomial $q_1(x)$. If $q_1(x)$ has positive degree, then by the fundamental theorem of algebra there exists a zero c_2 of $q_1(x)$. By the factor theorem, $q_1(x)$ can be written as $q_1(x) = (x - c_2)\,q_2(x)$. Then

$$f(x) = (x - c_1)q_1(x) = (x - c_1)(x - c_2)q_2(x).$$

If $f(x)$ has degree n, this process can be continued until $f(x)$ is written in the complete factored form

$$f(x) = a_n(x - c_1)(x - c_2)\cdots(x - c_n),$$

where a_n is the leading coefficient and the c_k are complex zeros of $f(x)$. If each c_k is distinct, then $f(x)$ has n zeros. However, in general the c_k may not be distinct since multiple zeros are possible.

NUMBER OF ZEROS THEOREM

A polynomial of degree n has at most n distinct zeros.

EXAMPLE 1 **Classifying zeros**

All zeros for the given polynomials are distinct. Use Figures 4.71–4.73 to determine graphically the number of real zeros and the number of imaginary zeros.

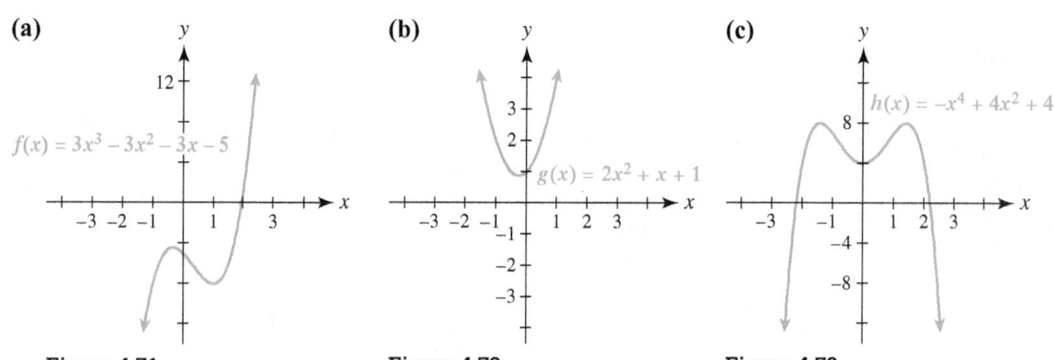

Figure 4.71 Figure 4.72 Figure 4.73

SOLUTION

Getting Started Each (distinct) real zero corresponds to an x-intercept. Imaginary zeros do *not* correspond to x-intercepts, but their number can be determined after the number of real zeros is known. ▶

(a) The graph of $f(x)$ in Figure 4.71 crosses the x-axis once, so there is one real zero. Since f is degree 3 and all zeros are distinct, there are two imaginary zeros.

(b) The graph of $g(x)$ in Figure 4.72 never crosses the x-axis. Since g is degree 2, there are no real zeros and two imaginary zeros.

(c) The graph of $h(x)$ is shown in Figure 4.73. Since h is degree 4, there are two real zeros and the remaining two zeros are imaginary.

Now Try Exercises 1, 3, and 5

NOTE The sum of the imaginary zeros and the real zeros (counting multiplicities) equals the degree n of the polynomial. A polynomial with real coefficients always has an even number of imaginary zeros.

EXAMPLE 2 **Constructing a polynomial with prescribed zeros**

Determine a polynomial $f(x)$ of degree 4 with leading coefficient 2 and zeros -3, 5, i, and $-i$ in **(a)** complete factored form and **(b)** expanded form.

SOLUTION

(a) Let $a_n = 2$, $c_1 = -3$, $c_2 = 5$, $c_3 = i$, and $c_4 = -i$. Then

$$f(x) = 2(x + 3)(x - 5)(x - i)(x + i).$$

(b) To expand this expression for $f(x)$, perform the following steps.

$$\begin{aligned} 2(x + 3)(x - 5)(x - i)(x + i) &= 2(x + 3)(x - 5)(x^2 + 1) \\ &= 2(x + 3)(x^3 - 5x^2 + x - 5) \\ &= 2(x^4 - 2x^3 - 14x^2 - 2x - 15) \\ &= 2x^4 - 4x^3 - 28x^2 - 4x - 30 \end{aligned}$$

Thus $f(x) = 2x^4 - 4x^3 - 28x^2 - 4x - 30$.

Now Try Exercise 13

EXAMPLE 3 **Factoring a cubic polynomial with imaginary zeros**

Determine the complete factored form for $f(x) = x^3 + 2x^2 + 4x + 8$.

SOLUTION

We can use factoring by grouping to determine the complete factored form.

$$\begin{aligned} x^3 + 2x^2 + 4x + 8 &= (x^3 + 2x^2) + (4x + 8) && \text{Associative property} \\ &= x^2(x + 2) + 4(x + 2) && \text{Distributive property} \\ &= (x^2 + 4)(x + 2) && \text{Factor out } x + 2. \end{aligned}$$

Algebra Review
To review factoring a cubic polynomial by grouping, see Chapter R (page R-20).

To factor $x^2 + 4$, first find its zeros.

$$\begin{aligned} x^2 + 4 &= 0 \\ x^2 &= -4 \\ x &= \pm\sqrt{-4} \\ x &= \pm 2i \end{aligned}$$

The zeros of $f(x)$ are -2, $2i$, and $-2i$. Its complete factored form is

$$f(x) = (x + 2)(x - 2i)(x + 2i).$$

Now Try Exercise 29

Conjugate Zeros Notice that in Example 3 both $2i$ and $-2i$ were zeros of $f(x)$. The numbers $2i$ and $-2i$ are *conjugates*. See Section 3.3. This result can be generalized.

CONJUGATE ZEROS THEOREM

If a polynomial $f(x)$ has only real coefficients and if $a + bi$ is a zero of $f(x)$, then the conjugate $a - bi$ is also a zero of $f(x)$.

EXAMPLE 4 **Constructing a polynomial with prescribed zeros**

Determine a cubic polynomial $f(x)$ with real coefficients, leading coefficient 2, and zeros 3 and $5i$. Express $f(x)$ in **(a)** complete factored form and **(b)** expanded form.

SOLUTION

(a) Since $f(x)$ has real coefficients, it must also have a third zero of $-5i$, the conjugate of $5i$. Let $c_1 = 3$, $c_2 = 5i$, $c_3 = -5i$, and $a_n = 2$. The complete factored form is

$$f(x) = 2(x - 3)(x - 5i)(x + 5i).$$

(b) To expand $f(x)$, perform the following steps.

$$\begin{aligned} 2(x - 3)(x - 5i)(x + 5i) &= 2(x - 3)(x^2 + 25) \\ &= 2(x^3 - 3x^2 + 25x - 75) \\ &= 2x^3 - 6x^2 + 50x - 150 \end{aligned}$$

Now Try Exercise 15

EXAMPLE 5 **Finding imaginary zeros of a polynomial**

Find the zeros of $f(x) = x^4 + x^3 + 2x^2 + x + 1$, given that one zero is $-i$.

SOLUTION

By the conjugate zeros theorem, it follows that i must also be a zero of $f(x)$. Therefore $(x - i)$ and $(x + i)$ are factors of $f(x)$. Because $(x - i)(x + i) = x^2 + 1$, we can use long division to find another quadratic factor of $f(x)$.

$$\begin{array}{r} x^2 + x + 1 \\ x^2 + 0x + 1 \overline{)\, x^4 + x^3 + 2x^2 + x + 1} \\ \underline{x^4 + 0x^3 + x^2 \qquad\quad} \\ x^3 + x^2 + x \qquad \\ \underline{x^3 + 0x^2 + x \qquad} \\ x^2 + 0x + 1 \\ \underline{x^2 + 0x + 1} \\ 0 \end{array}$$

The quotient is $x^2 + x + 1$ with remainder 0. By the division algorithm,

$$x^4 + x^3 + 2x^2 + x + 1 = (x^2 + 1)(x^2 + x + 1).$$

We can use the quadratic formula to find the zeros of $x^2 + x + 1$.

$$\begin{aligned} x &= \frac{-b \pm \sqrt{b^2 - 4ac}}{2a} \\ &= \frac{-1 \pm \sqrt{1^2 - 4(1)(1)}}{2(1)} \\ &= -\frac{1}{2} \pm i\frac{\sqrt{3}}{2} \end{aligned}$$

The four zeros of $f(x)$ are $\pm i$ and $-\frac{1}{2} \pm i\frac{\sqrt{3}}{2}$.

Now Try Exercise 21

Polynomial Equations with Complex Solutions

Every polynomial equation of degree n can be written in the form

$$a_n x^n + \cdots + a_2 x^2 + a_1 x + a_0 = 0.$$

If we let $f(x) = a_n x^n + \cdots + a_2 x^2 + a_1 x + a_0$ and write $f(x)$ in complete factored form as

$$f(x) = a_n(x - c_1)(x - c_2) \cdots (x - c_n),$$

then the solutions to the polynomial equation are the zeros $c_1, c_2, \ldots, c_n$ of $f(x)$. Solving cubic and quartic polynomial equations with this technique is illustrated in the next two examples.

EXAMPLE 6 **Solving a polynomial equation**

Solve $x^3 = 3x^2 - 7x + 21$.

SOLUTION

Write the equation as $f(x) = 0$, where $f(x) = x^3 - 3x^2 + 7x - 21$. Although we could use factoring by grouping, as is done in Example 3, we use graphing instead to find one real zero of $f(x)$. Figure 4.74 shows that 3 is a zero of $f(x)$. By the factor theorem, $x - 3$ is a factor of $f(x)$. Using synthetic division, we divide $x - 3$ into $f(x)$.

[−5, 5, 1] by [−30, 30, 10]

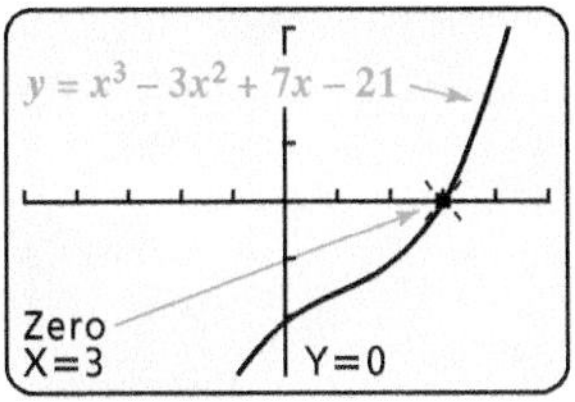

Figure 4.74

$$\begin{array}{r|rrrr} 3 & 1 & -3 & 7 & -21 \\ & & 3 & 0 & 21 \\ \hline & 1 & 0 & 7 & 0 \end{array}$$

Thus $x^3 - 3x^2 + 7x - 21 = (x - 3)(x^2 + 7)$, and we can solve as follows.

$$\begin{aligned} x^3 - 3x^2 + 7x - 21 &= 0 && \text{Solve } f(x) = 0. \\ (x - 3)(x^2 + 7) &= 0 && \text{Factor.} \\ x - 3 = 0 \quad \text{or} \quad x^2 + 7 &= 0 && \text{Zero-product property} \\ x = 3 \quad \text{or} \quad x^2 &= -7 && \text{Solve.} \\ x = 3 \quad \text{or} \quad x &= \pm i\sqrt{7} && \text{Property of } i \end{aligned}$$

The solutions are 3 and $\pm i\sqrt{7}$.

Now Try Exercise 33

EXAMPLE 7 **Solving a polynomial equation**

Solve $x^4 + x^2 = x^3$.

SOLUTION

Write the equation as $f(x) = 0$, where $f(x) = x^4 - x^3 + x^2$.

[−3, 3, 1] by [−2, 2, 1]

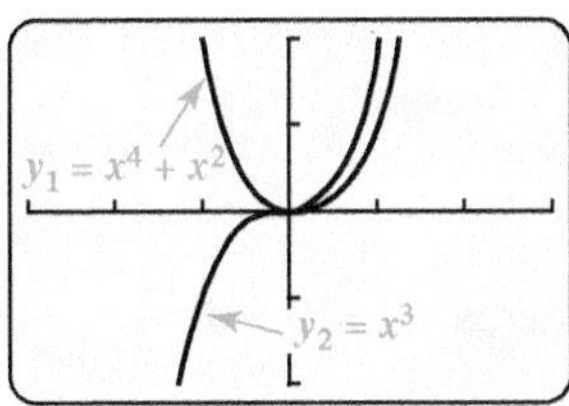

Figure 4.75

$$\begin{aligned} x^4 - x^3 + x^2 &= 0 && f(x) = 0 \\ x^2(x^2 - x + 1) &= 0 && \text{Factor out } x^2. \\ x^2 = 0 \quad \text{or} \quad x^2 - x + 1 &= 0 && \text{Zero-product property} \end{aligned}$$

The only solution to $x^2 = 0$ is 0. To solve $x^2 - x + 1 = 0$, use the quadratic formula, as in Example 5. The solutions are 0 and $\frac{1}{2} \pm i\frac{\sqrt{3}}{2}$.

The graphs of $y_1 = x^4 + x^2$ and $y_2 = x^3$ are shown in Figure 4.75. Notice that they appear to intersect only at the origin. This indicates that the only *real* solution is 0.

Now Try Exercise 37

4.5 Putting It All Together

Some of the important topics in this section are summarized in the following table.

CONCEPT	EXPLANATION	COMMENTS AND EXAMPLES
Number of zeros theorem	A polynomial of degree n has at most n distinct zeros. These zeros can be real or imaginary numbers.	The cubic polynomial, $ax^3 + bx^2 + cx + d$, has *at most* three distinct zeros.
Fundamental theorem of algebra	A polynomial of degree n, with $n \geq 1$, has at least one complex zero.	This theorem guarantees that we can always factor a polynomial $f(x)$ into complete factored form: $f(x) = a_n(x - c_1) \cdots (x - c_n)$, where the c_k are complex numbers.

continued on next page

CONCEPT	EXPLANATION	COMMENTS AND EXAMPLES
Conjugate zeros theorem	If a polynomial has *real* coefficients and $a + bi$ is a zero, then $a - bi$ is also a zero.	Since $\frac{1}{2} + \frac{1}{2}i$ is a zero of $2x^2 - 2x + 1$, it follows that $\frac{1}{2} - \frac{1}{2}i$ is also a zero.

4.5 Exercises

Zeros of Polynomials

Exercises 1–8: The graph and degree of a polynomial with real coefficients $f(x)$ are given. Determine the number of real zeros and the number of imaginary zeros. Assume that all zeros of $f(x)$ are distinct.

1. Degree 2

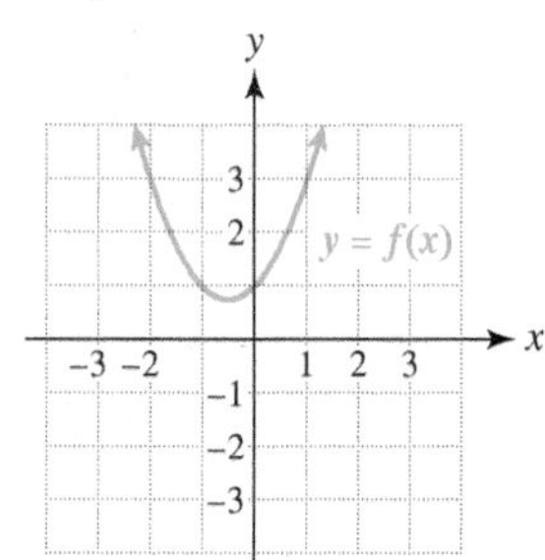

2. Degree 2

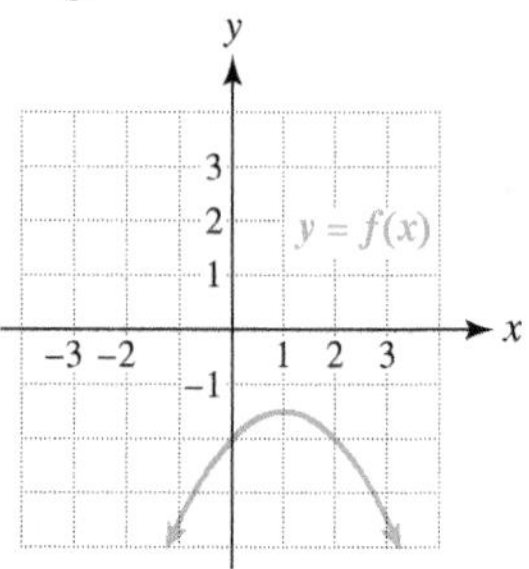

3. Degree 3

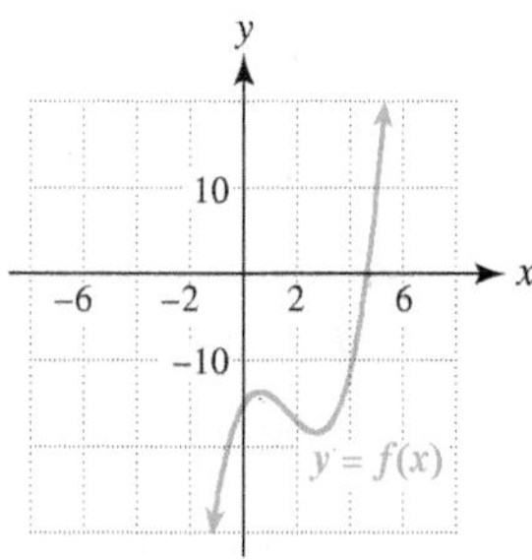

4. Degree 3

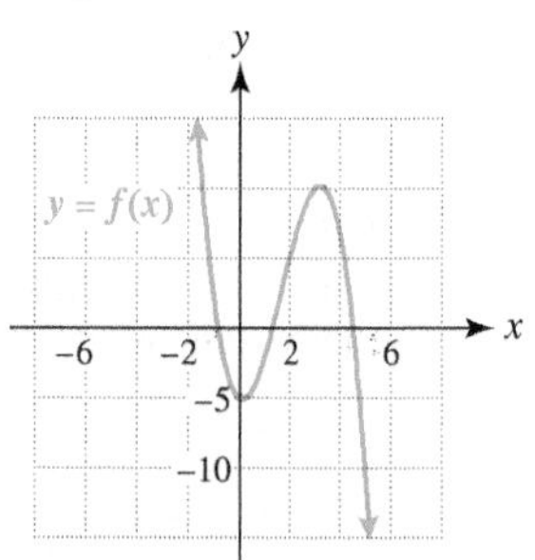

5. Degree 4

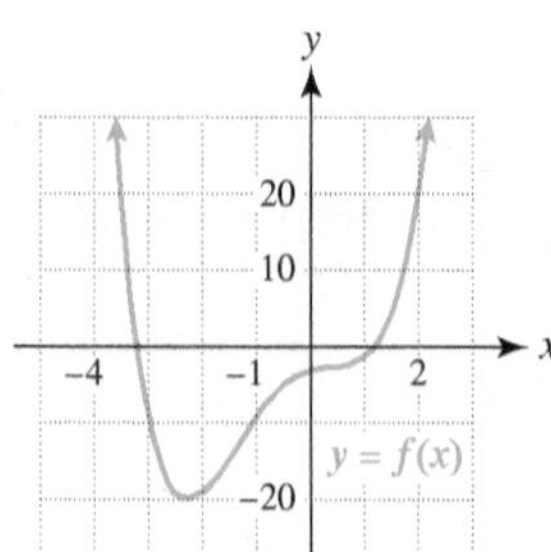

6. Degree 4

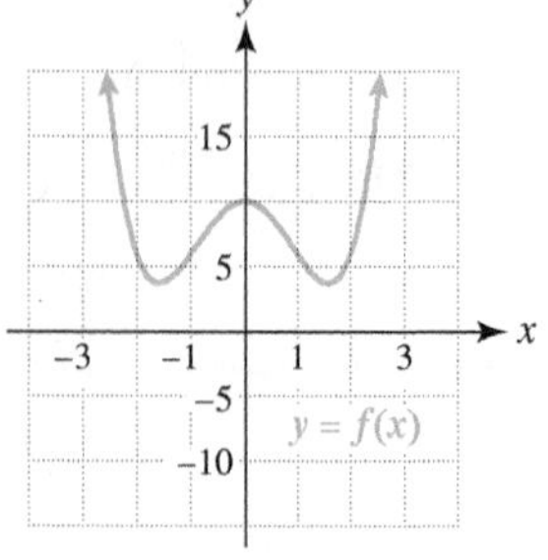

7. Degree 5

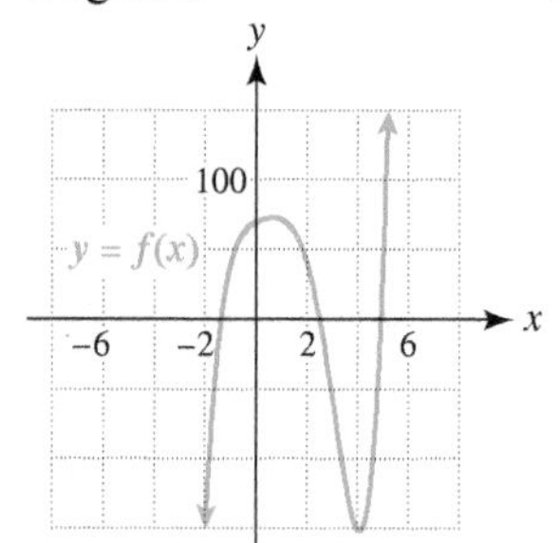

8. Degree 5

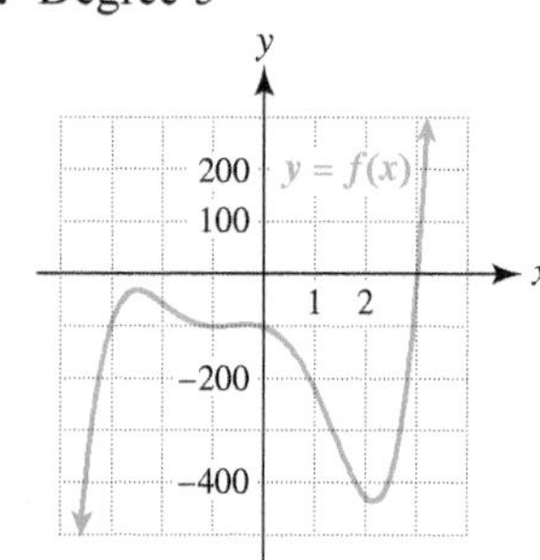

Exercises 9–18: Let a_n be the leading coefficient.

(a) Find the complete factored form of a polynomial with real coefficients $f(x)$ that satisfy the conditions.

(b) Express $f(x)$ in expanded form.

9. Degree 2; $a_n = 1$; zeros $6i$ and $-6i$

10. Degree 3; $a_n = 5$; zeros 2, i, and $-i$

11. Degree 3; $a_n = -1$; zeros -1, $2i$, and $-2i$

12. Degree 4; $a_n = 3$; zeros -2, 4, i, and $-i$

13. Degree 4; $a_n = 10$; zeros 1, -1, $3i$, and $-3i$

14. Degree 2; $a_n = -5$; zeros $1 + i$ and $1 - i$

15. Degree 4; $a_n = \frac{1}{2}$; zeros $-i$ and $2i$

16. Degree 3; $a_n = -\frac{3}{4}$; zeros $-3i$ and $\frac{2}{5}$

17. Degree 3; $a_n = -2$; zeros $1 - i$ and 3

18. Degree 4; $a_n = 7$; zeros $2i$ and $3i$

Exercises 19–22: (Refer to Example 5.) Find the zeros of $f(x)$, given that one zero is k.

19. $f(x) = 3x^3 - 5x^2 + 75x - 125$ $\quad k = \frac{5}{3}$

20. $f(x) = x^4 + 2x^3 + 8x^2 + 8x + 16$ $\quad k = 2i$

21. $f(x) = 2x^4 - x^3 + 19x^2 - 9x + 9$ $\quad k = -3i$

22. $f(x) = 7x^3 + 5x^2 + 12x - 4$ $\quad k = \frac{2}{7}$

Exercises 23–30: Complete the following.

(a) Find all zeros of $f(x)$.

(b) Write the complete factored form of $f(x)$.

23. $f(x) = x^2 + 25$

24. $f(x) = x^2 + 11$

25. $f(x) = 3x^3 + 3x$

26. $f(x) = 2x^3 + 10x$

27. $f(x) = x^4 + 5x^2 + 4$

28. $f(x) = x^4 + 4x^2$

29. $f(x) = x^3 + 2x^2 + 16x + 32$

30. $f(x) = x^4 + 2x^3 + x^2 + 8x - 12$

Exercises 31–42: Solve the polynomial equation.

31. $x^3 + x = 0$

32. $2x^3 - x + 1 = 0$

33. $x^3 = 2x^2 - 7x + 14$

34. $x^2 + x + 2 = x^3$

35. $x^4 + 5x^2 = 0$

36. $x^4 - 2x^3 + x^2 - 2x = 0$

37. $x^4 = x^3 - 4x^2$

38. $x^5 + 9x^3 = x^4 + 9x^2$

39. $x^4 + x^3 = 16 - 8x - 6x^2$

40. $x^4 + 2x^2 = x^3$

41. $3x^3 + 4x^2 + 6 = x$

42. $2x^3 + 5x^2 + x + 12 = 0$

Writing About Mathematics

43. Could a cubic function with real coefficients have only imaginary zeros? Explain.

44. Give an example of a polynomial function that has only imaginary zeros and a polynomial function that has only real zeros. Explain how to determine graphically if a function has only imaginary zeros.

4.6 Rational Functions and Models

- **Identify a rational function and state its domain**
- **Identify asymptotes**
- **Interpret asymptotes**
- **Graph a rational function by using transformations**
- **Graph a rational function by hand (optional)**

Introduction

Rational functions are (typically) nonlinear functions that frequently occur in applications. For example, rational functions are used to model postings on social networks, design curves for railroad tracks, determine stopping distances on hills, and calculate the average number of people waiting in a line.

Rational Functions

A *ratio*nal number can be expressed as a *ratio* $\frac{p}{q}$, where p and q are integers with $q \neq 0$. A rational function is defined similarly by using the concept of a polynomial.

RATIONAL FUNCTION

A function f represented by $f(x) = \frac{p(x)}{q(x)}$, where $p(x)$ and $q(x)$ are polynomials and $q(x) \neq 0$, is a **rational function**.

The domain of a rational function includes all real numbers *except* the zeros of the denominator $q(x)$. The graph of a rational function is continuous except at x-values where $q(x) = 0$.

EXAMPLE 1 Identifying rational functions

Algebra Review
To review rational expressions, see Chapter R (page R-28).

Determine if the function is rational and state its domain.

(a) $f(x) = \dfrac{2x - 1}{x^2 + 1}$ **(b)** $g(x) = \dfrac{1}{\sqrt{x}}$ **(c)** $h(x) = \dfrac{x^3 - 2x^2 + 1}{x^2 - 3x + 2}$

SOLUTION

(a) Both the numerator, $2x - 1$, and the denominator, $x^2 + 1$, are polynomials, so f is a rational function. The domain of f includes all real numbers because its denominator $x^2 + 1 \neq 0$ for any real number x.

(b) The expression $\sqrt{x}$ is not a polynomial, so $g(x) = \frac{1}{\sqrt{x}}$ is not a rational function. The domain is $\{x \mid x > 0\}$.

(c) Both the numerator and the denominator are polynomials, so $h(x) = \frac{x^3 - 2x^2 + 1}{x^2 - 3x + 2}$ is a rational function. Because

$$x^2 - 3x + 2 = (x - 1)(x - 2) = 0$$

when $x = 1$ or $x = 2$, the domain of h is $\{x \mid x \neq 1, x \neq 2\}$.

Now Try Exercises 1, 7, and 9

CLASS DISCUSSION

Is an integer a rational number? Is a polynomial function a rational function?

Vertical Asymptotes

A rational function given by $f(x) = \frac{p(x)}{q(x)}$ is undefined whenever $q(x) = 0$. If $q(k) = 0$ for some k, then a *vertical asymptote* of the graph of f *may* occur at $x = k$. Near a vertical asymptote, the y-values on the graph of f become very large (unbounded) in absolute value.

For example, Figure 4.76 shows the graph of a rational function defined by $f(x) = \frac{1}{x - 2}$. It has a vertical asymptote, which is shown as a dashed red line at $x = 2$. Note that $x = 2$ is *not* in the domain of f.

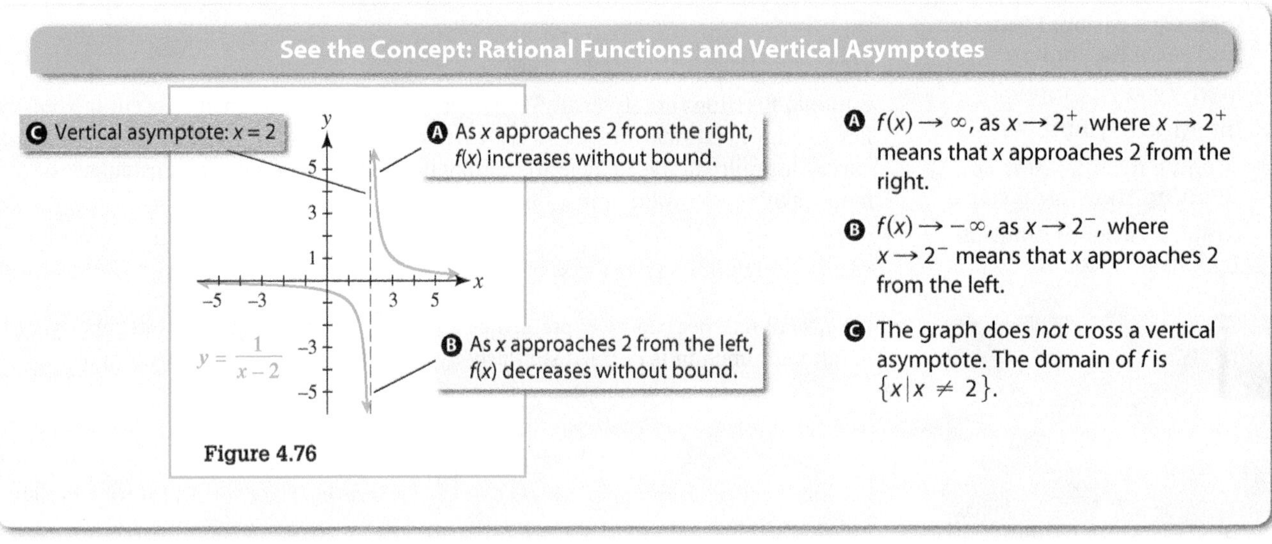

See the Concept: Rational Functions and Vertical Asymptotes
C Vertical asymptote: x = 2
A As x approaches 2 from the right, f(x) increases without bound.
B As x approaches 2 from the left, f(x) decreases without bound.
y = 1/(x − 2)
A f(x) → ∞, as x → 2⁺, where x → 2⁺ means that x approaches 2 from the right.
B f(x) → −∞, as x → 2⁻, where x → 2⁻ means that x approaches 2 from the left.
C The graph does not cross a vertical asymptote. The domain of f is {x | x ≠ 2}.

Figure 4.76

NOTE A vertical asymptote is not part of the graph of a rational function; rather, it is an aid that is used to sketch and to better understand the graph of a rational function.

VERTICAL ASYMPTOTE

The line $x = k$ is a **vertical asymptote** of the graph of f if $f(x) \to \infty$ or $f(x) \to -\infty$ as x approaches k from either the left or the right.

An Application If cars leave a parking garage randomly and stop to pay the parking attendant on the way out, then the average length of the line depends on two factors: the average traffic rate at which cars are exiting the ramp and the average rate at which the parking attendant can wait on cars. For instance, if the average traffic rate is three cars per minute and the parking attendant can serve four cars per minute, then at times a line may form *if* cars arrive in a *random* manner. The **traffic intensity** x is the ratio of the average traffic rate to the average working rate of the attendant. In this example, $x = \frac{3}{4}$. (***Source:*** F. Mannering and W. Kilareski, *Principles of Highway Engineering and Traffic Control.*)

EXAMPLE 2 **Estimating the length of parking garage lines**

If the traffic intensity is x, then the average number of cars waiting in line to exit a parking garage can be estimated by $N(x) = \frac{x^2}{2 - 2x}$, where $0 \le x < 1$.

(a) Evaluate $N(0.5)$ and $N(0.9)$. Interpret the results.

(b) Use the graph of $y = N(x)$ in Figure 4.77 to explain what happens to the length of the line as the traffic intensity x increases to 1 from the left (denoted $x \to 1^-$.)

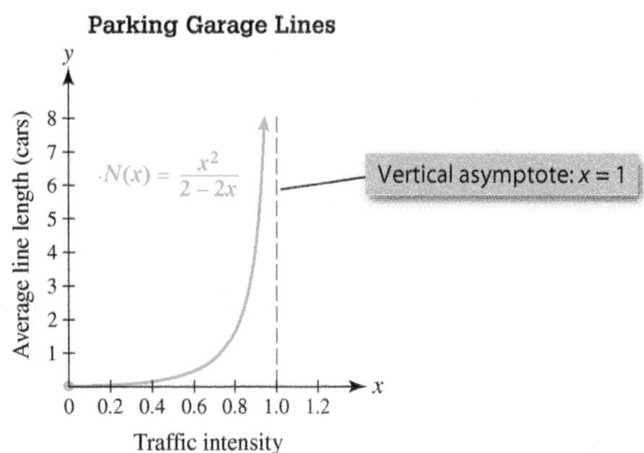

Figure 4.77

SOLUTION

(a) $N(0.5) = \frac{0.5^2}{2 - 2(0.5)} = 0.25$ and $N(0.9) = \frac{0.9^2}{2 - 2(0.9)} = 4.05$. This means that if the traffic intensity is 0.5, there is little waiting in line. As the traffic intensity increases to 0.9, the average line has more than four cars.

(b) As the traffic intensity x approaches 1 from the left in Figure 4.77 the graph of f increases rapidly without bound. Numerical support is given in Table 4.4. With a traffic intensity slightly less than 1, the attendant has difficulty keeping up. If cars occasionally arrive in groups, long lines will form. At $x = 1$ the denominator, $2 - 2x$, equals 0 and $N(x)$ is undefined.

Traffic Intensity Approaching 1

x	0.94	0.95	0.96	0.97	0.98	0.99	1
$\frac{x^2}{2 - 2x}$	7.36	9.03	11.52	15.68	24.01	49.01	—

Table 4.4

Long lines form

Now Try Exercise 97

Horizontal Asymptotes

If the absolute value of x becomes large in the formula $f(x)$ for a rational function, then the graph of f *may* level off and begin to approximate a horizontal line. This horizontal line is called a *horizontal asymptote.*

In See the Concept on the next page, Figure 4.78 shows the graph of the rational function $f(x) = \frac{x^2}{x^2 + 1}$. This rational function does not have a vertical asymptote because the denominator, $x^2 + 1$, has no real zeros. However, the graph does have a horizontal asymptote, which is shown as a dashed red line at $y = 1$.

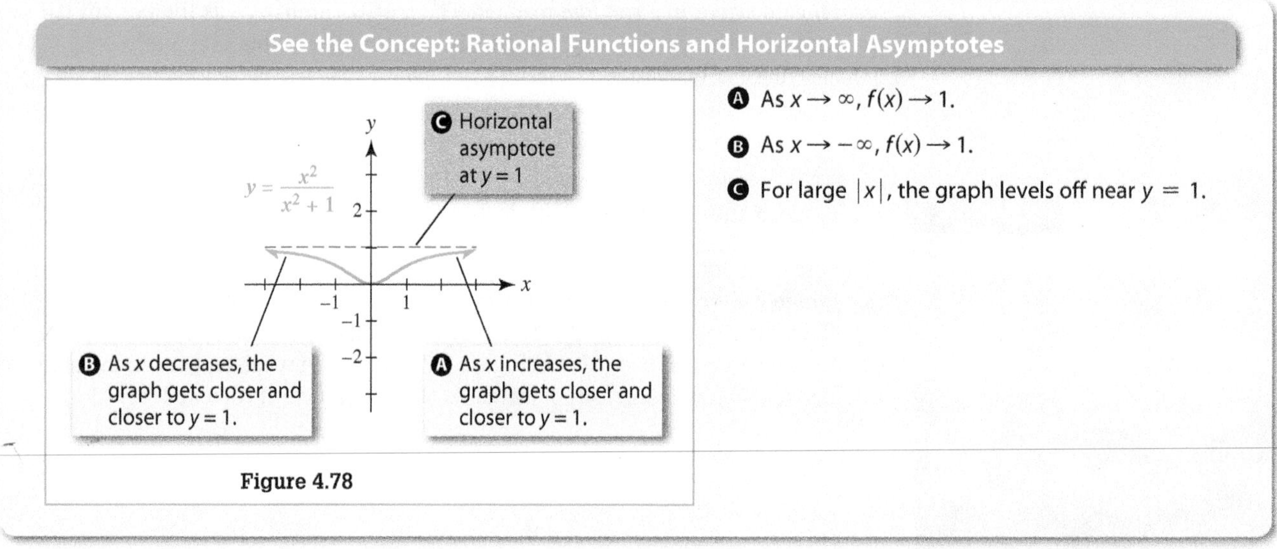

Figure 4.78

Asymptotes and Tables of Values A table of values can be used to illustrate the concept of a horizontal asymptote for $y = \frac{x^2}{x^2 + 1}$. See Figures 4.79 and 4.80. Notice that the y-values level off slightly below 1, which agrees with the graph in Figure 4.78.

Tables and Horizontal Asymptotes

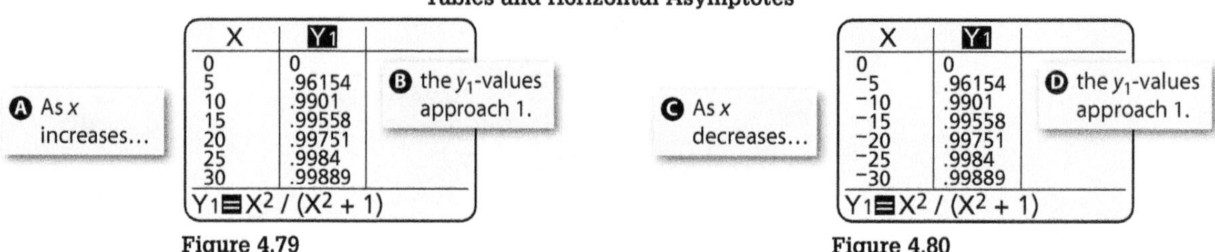

X	Y1
0	0
5	.96154
10	.9901
15	.99558
20	.99751
25	.9984
30	.99889

Y1 = X2 / (X2 + 1)

X	Y1
0	0
−5	.96154
−10	.9901
−15	.99558
−20	.99751
−25	.9984
−30	.99889

Y1 = X2 / (X2 + 1)

Figure 4.79 Figure 4.80

HORIZONTAL ASYMPTOTE

The line $y = b$ is a **horizontal asymptote** of the graph of f if $f(x) \to b$ as x approaches either ∞ or $-\infty$.

NOTE Like a vertical asymptote, a horizontal asymptote is *not* part of the graph of a rational function; rather, it is an aid that is used to sketch and to better understand the graph of a rational function. However, unlike in the case of vertical asymptotes, it *is possible* for the graph of a rational function to *cross* a horizontal asymptote. See Examples 4(b) and 11.

An Application The graph of f in Figure 4.81 is an example of a growth curve. It models the length in millimeters of a small fish after x weeks.

Length of a Small Fish

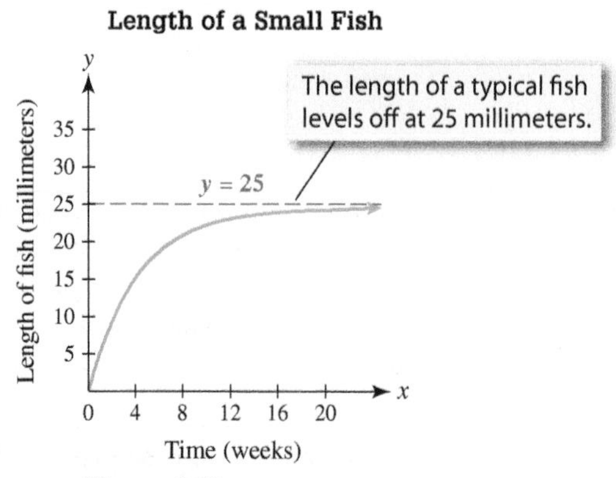

Figure 4.81

After several weeks the length of the fish begins to level off near 25 millimeters. Thus $y = 25$ is a horizontal asymptote of the graph of f. This is denoted by $f(x) \rightarrow 25$ as $x \rightarrow \infty$. (***Source:*** D. Brown and P. Rothery, *Models in Biology*.)

In real-life applications, time does not actually approach infinity. For example, a fish does not live forever. However, the asymptote $y = 25$ does tend to model the length of the fish as it becomes older.

Identifying Asymptotes

Asymptotes can be found visually from a graph and symbolically from a formula. The next two examples discuss these techniques.

EXAMPLE 3 **Determining horizontal and vertical asymptotes visually**

Use the graph of each rational function to determine any vertical or horizontal asymptotes.

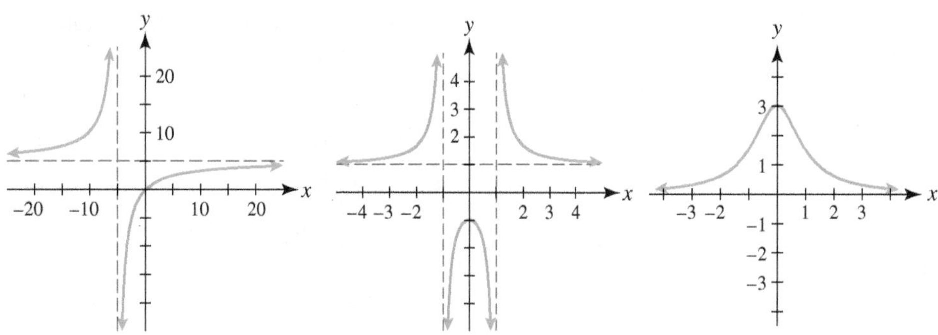

Figure 4.82 **Figure 4.83** **Figure 4.84**

SOLUTION

In Figure 4.82, $x = -5$ is a vertical asymptote and $y = 5$ is a horizontal asymptote. In Figure 4.83, $x = \pm 1$ are vertical asymptotes and $y = 1$ is a horizontal asymptote. In Figure 4.84, there are no vertical asymptotes. The x-axis ($y = 0$) is a horizontal asymptote.

Now Try Exercises 13, 15, and 17

The following technique can be used for rational functions to find vertical and horizontal asymptotes symbolically.

FINDING VERTICAL AND HORIZONTAL ASYMPTOTES

Let f be a rational function given by $f(x) = \frac{p(x)}{q(x)}$ written in *lowest* terms.

Vertical Asymptote

To find a vertical asymptote, set the denominator, $q(x)$, equal to 0 and solve. If k is a zero of $q(x)$, then $x = k$ is a vertical asymptote. *Caution:* If k is a zero of both $q(x)$ *and* $p(x)$, then $f(x)$ is not written in lowest terms, and $x - k$ is a common factor.

Horizontal Asymptote

(a) If the degree of the numerator is less than the degree of the denominator, then $y = 0$ (the x-axis) is a horizontal asymptote.

(b) If the degree of the numerator equals the degree of the denominator, then $y = \frac{a}{b}$ is a horizontal asymptote, where a is the leading coefficient of the numerator and b is the leading coefficient of the denominator.

(c) If the degree of the numerator is greater than the degree of the denominator, then there are no horizontal asymptotes.

EXAMPLE 4 Finding asymptotes

For each rational function, determine any horizontal or vertical asymptotes.

(a) $f(x) = \dfrac{6x - 1}{3x + 3}$ **(b)** $g(x) = \dfrac{x + 1}{x^2 - 4}$ **(c)** $h(x) = \dfrac{x^2 - 1}{x + 1}$

SOLUTION

(a) The numerator and denominator have no common factors, so the expression is in lowest terms.

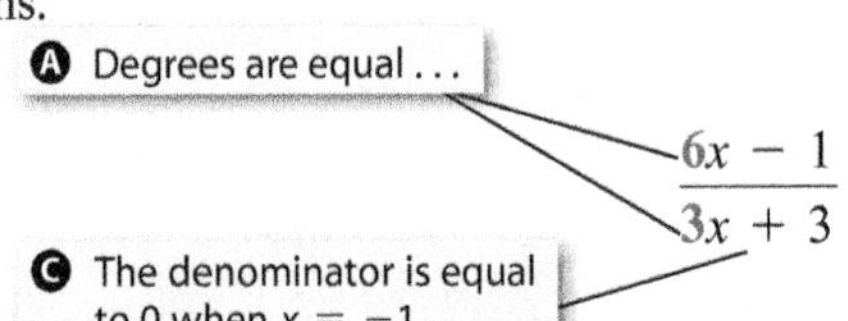

A graph of $f(x) = \frac{6x - 1}{3x + 3}$ is shown in Figure 4.85. In Figures 4.86 and 4.87, the tables support that $y = 2$ is a horizontal asymptote.

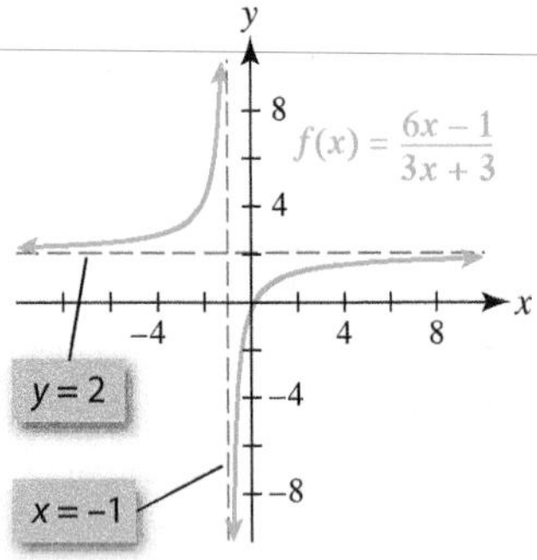

Figure 4.85

Horizontal Asymptote: y = 2

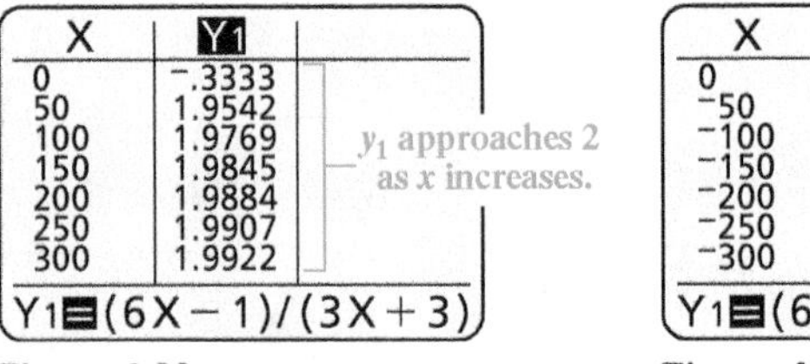

X	Y1
0	−.3333
50	1.9542
100	1.9769
150	1.9845
200	1.9884
250	1.9907
300	1.9922

Y1=(6X−1)/(3X+3)

Figure 4.86

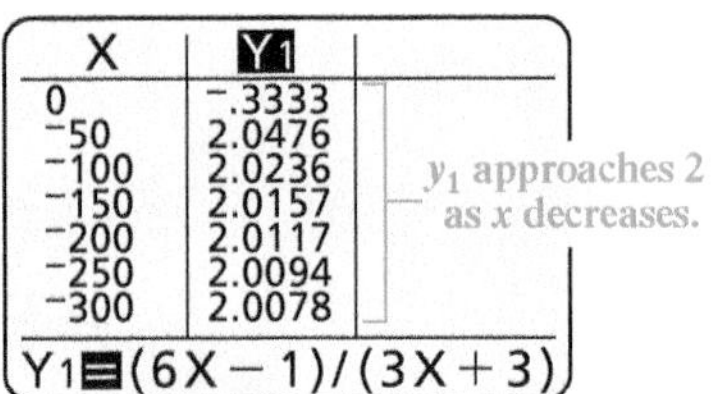

X	Y1
0	−.3333
−50	2.0476
−100	2.0236
−150	2.0157
−200	2.0117
−250	2.0094
−300	2.0078

Y1=(6X−1)/(3X+3)

Figure 4.87

(b) In the expression $\frac{x + 1}{x^2 - 4}$, the degree of the numerator is one less than the degree of the denominator, so the x-axis, or $y = 0$, is a horizontal asymptote. When $x = \pm 2$, the denominator, $x^2 - 4$, equals 0 and the numerator, $x + 1$, does not equal 0. Thus $x = \pm 2$ are vertical asymptotes. See Figure 4.88. Note that the graph crosses the horizontal asymptote $y = 0$ but does not cross either vertical asymptote.

Algebra Review
To review simplifying rational expressions, see Chapter R (page R-28).

(c) The degree of the numerator, $x^2 - 1$, is greater than the degree of the denominator, $x + 1$, so there are no horizontal asymptotes. When $x = -1$, both numerator and denominator equal 0, so the expression is *not* in lowest terms. We can simplify $h(x)$ as follows.

$$h(x) = \frac{x^2 - 1}{x + 1} = \frac{(x + 1)(x - 1)}{x + 1} = x - 1, \qquad x \neq -1$$

The graph of $h(x)$ is the line $y = x - 1$ with the point $(-1, -2)$ missing. There are no vertical asymptotes. See Figure 4.89.

Graph with Asymptotes

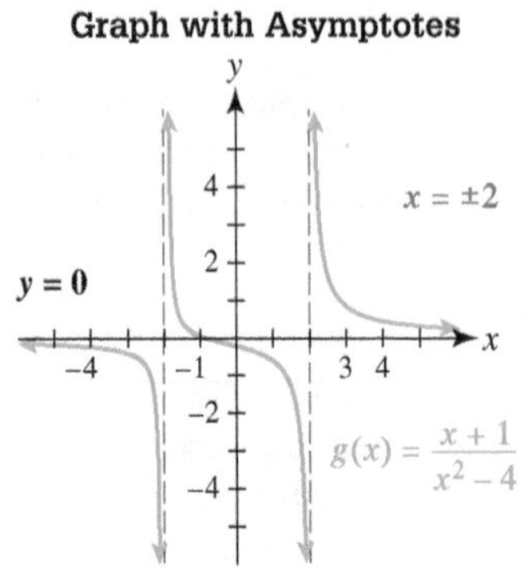

Figure 4.88

Graph with a "Hole"

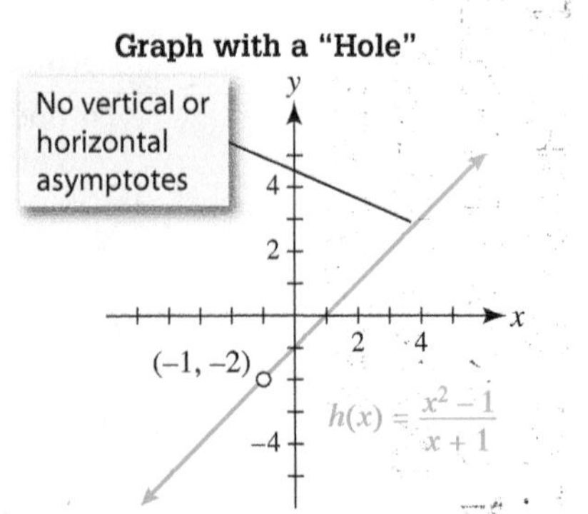

Figure 4.89

Now Try Exercises 21, 23, and 31

Slant Asymptote

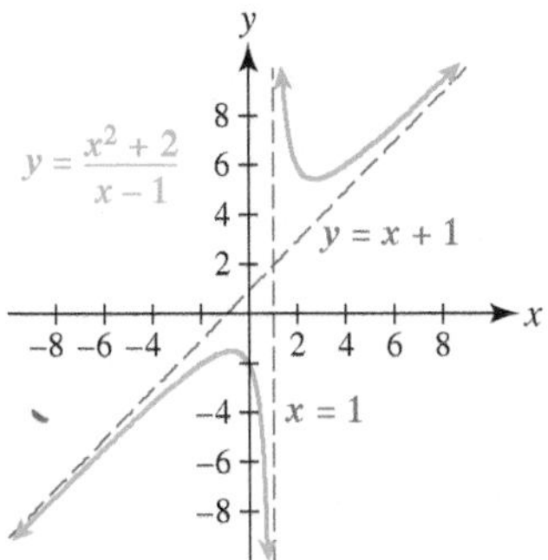

Figure 4.90

Slant, or Oblique, Asymptotes A third type of asymptote, which is neither vertical nor horizontal, occurs when the numerator of a rational function has degree *one more* than the degree of the denominator. For example, let $f(x) = \frac{x^2 + 2}{x - 1}$. If $x - 1$ is divided into $x^2 + 2$, the quotient is $x + 1$ with remainder 3. Thus

$$f(x) = x + 1 + \frac{3}{x - 1}$$

is an equivalent representation of $f(x)$. For large values of $|x|$, the ratio $\frac{3}{x - 1}$ approaches 0 and the graph of f approaches $y = x + 1$. The line $y = x + 1$ is called a **slant asymptote,** or **oblique asymptote,** of the graph of f. A graph of $f(x) = \frac{x^2 + 2}{x - 1}$ with vertical asymptote $x = 1$ and slant asymptote $y = x + 1$ is shown in Figure 4.90.

MAKING CONNECTIONS

Division Algorithm and Asymptotes Suppose that the division algorithm is used to write a rational function f in the form

$$f(x) = (\text{Quotient}) + \frac{(\text{Remainder})}{(\text{Divisor})}.$$

1. If the quotient equals a constant k, then $y = k$ is a horizontal asymptote.

   Example: $f(x) = \frac{2x - 1}{x - 1} = 2 + \frac{1}{x - 1}$, so $y = 2$ is a horizontal asymptote.

2. If the quotient equals $ax + b$ with $a \neq 0$ (linear), then $y = ax + b$ is a slant asymptote.

   Example: $f(x) = \frac{x^2 + 2}{x - 1} = x + 1 + \frac{3}{x - 1}$, so $y = x + 1$ is a slant asymptote.

Graphs and Transformations of Rational Functions

Graphs of rational functions can vary greatly in complexity. We begin by graphing $y = \frac{1}{x}$ and then use transformations to graph other rational functions.

EXAMPLE 5 **Analyzing the graph of $y = \frac{1}{x}$**

Sketch a graph of $y = \frac{1}{x}$ and identify any asymptotes.

SOLUTION

Note that when $x = 0$, the denominator is 0 but the numerator is not. Thus $x = 0$ (the y-axis) is a vertical asymptote. Also, the degree of the numerator is less than the degree of the denominator, so $y = 0$ (the x-axis) is a horizontal asymptote. Table 4.5 lists points that lie on the graph of $y = \frac{1}{x}$. These points and the graph are shown in Figure 4.91.

x	$y = \frac{1}{x}$
-2	$-\frac{1}{2}$
-1	-1
$-\frac{1}{2}$	-2
0	—
$\frac{1}{2}$	2
1	1
2	$\frac{1}{2}$

Table 4.5

Graph of $y = \frac{1}{x}$

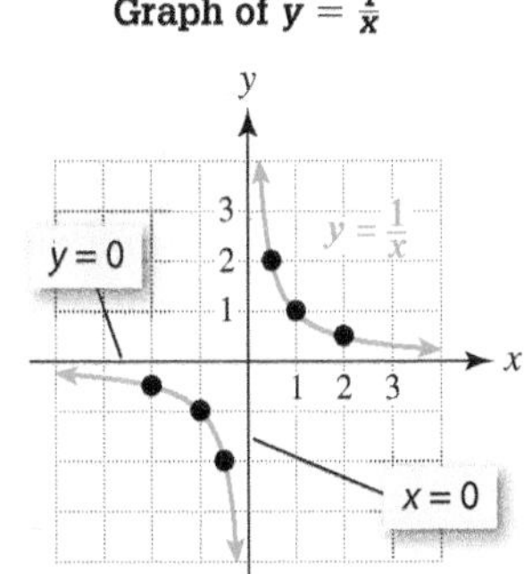

Figure 4.91

Now Try Exercise 41

Transformations Transformations of graphs can be used to graph some types of rational functions by hand, as illustrated in Figures 4.92 and 4.93.

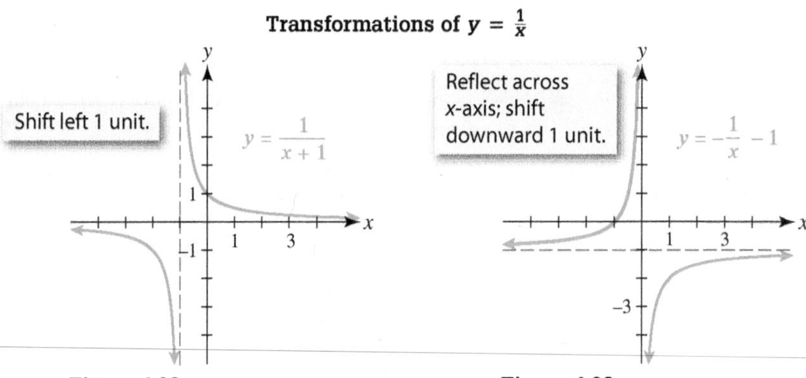

Figure 4.92

Figure 4.93

EXAMPLE 6 **Graphing with transformations**

Graph $y = \dfrac{1}{x - 1} + 2$.

SOLUTION

We can graph $g(x) = \frac{1}{x - 1} + 2$ by translating the graph of $f(x) = \frac{1}{x}$ right 1 unit and upward 2 units. That is, $g(x)$ can be written in terms of $f(x)$ using $g(x) = f(x - 1) + 2$. Because the graph of $y = \frac{1}{x}$ in Figure 4.91 has vertical asymptote $x = 0$ and horizontal asymptote $y = 0$, the graph of g in Figure 4.94 has vertical asymptote $x = 1$ and horizontal asymptote $y = 2$.

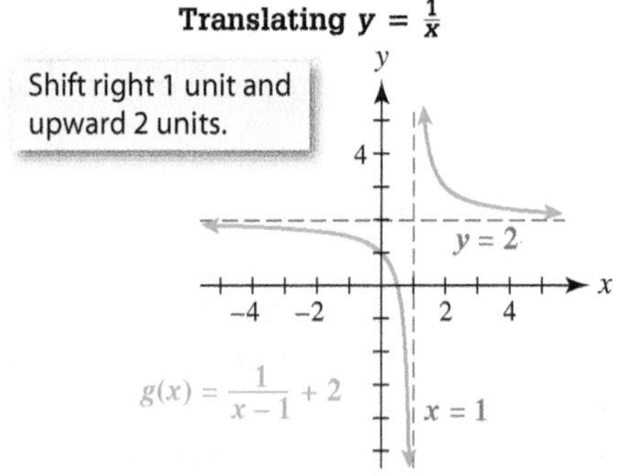

Figure 4.94

Now Try Exercise 49

NOTE If we are given function g from Example 6 in the form $g(x) = \frac{2x - 1}{x - 1}$, then we can use the division algorithm to divide $x - 1$ into $2x - 1$ and obtain quotient 2 with remainder 1.

$$\begin{array}{r|l} 2 & \\ x - 1\overline{)2x - 1} & \frac{2x}{x} = 2 \\ \underline{2x - 2} & 2(x - 1) = 2x - 2 \\ 1 & \text{Subtract: } -1 - (-2) = 1. \end{array}$$

Thus $g(x) = 2 + \frac{1}{x - 1}$, and we can graph g as in Figure 4.94.

EXAMPLE 7 **Using transformations to graph a rational function**

Use the graph of $f(x) = \frac{1}{x^2}$ in Figure 4.95 to sketch a graph of $g(x) = -\frac{1}{(x + 2)^2}$. Include all asymptotes in your graph. Write $g(x)$ in terms of $f(x)$.

Graph of $y = \frac{1}{x^2}$

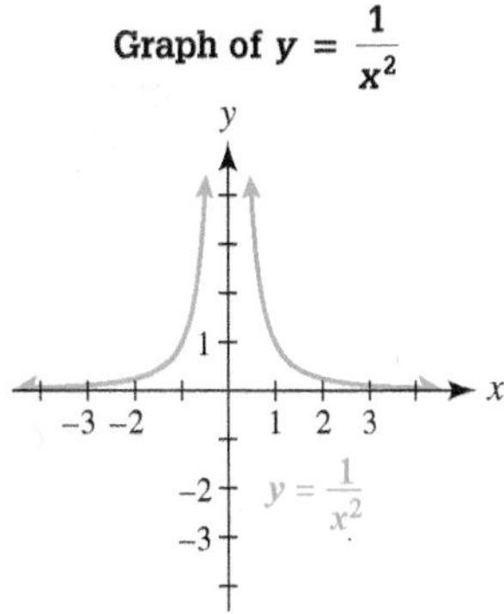

Figure 4.95

SOLUTION

The graph of $y = \frac{1}{x^2}$ has vertical asymptote $x = 0$ and horizontal asymptote $y = 0$. The graph of $g(x) = -\frac{1}{(x + 2)^2}$ is a translation of the graph of $f(x) = \frac{1}{x^2}$ left 2 units and then a reflection across the x-axis. The vertical asymptote for $y = g(x)$ is $x = -2$ and the horizontal asymptote is $y = 0$, as shown in Figure 4.96. We can write $g(x)$ in terms of $f(x)$ as $g(x) = -f(x + 2)$.

Translating $y = \frac{1}{x^2}$

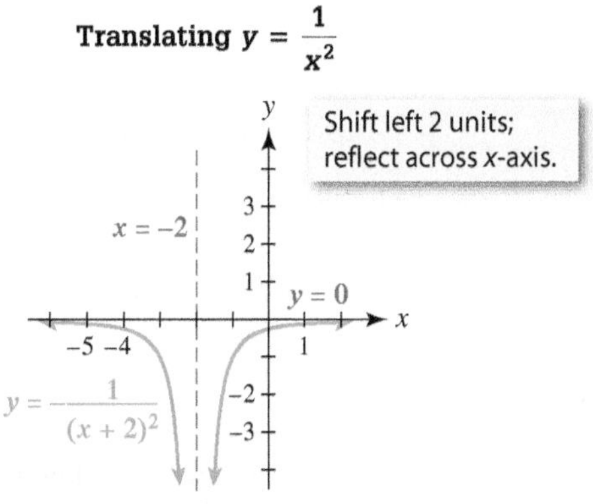

Figure 4.96

Now Try Exercise 51

Graphing with Technology Although many graphing calculators have difficulty accurately showing some features of the graph of a rational function, they can be helpful when they are used in conjunction with symbolic techniques.

Calculator Help
To set dot mode, see Appendix A (page AP-8). To set a decimal window, see Appendix A (page AP-11).

NOTE Calculators often graph in connected or dot mode. (See Figure 4.97 on the next page.) If connected mode is used to graph a rational function, it may appear as though the calculator is graphing vertical asymptotes automatically. However, in most instances the calculator is connecting points inappropriately. Sometimes rational functions can be graphed in connected mode using a *decimal* or *friendly* viewing rectangle.

EXAMPLE 8 **Analyzing a rational function with technology**

Let $f(x) = \frac{2x^2 + 1}{x^2 - 4}$.

(a) Use a calculator to graph f. Find the domain of f.
(b) Identify any vertical or horizontal asymptotes.
(c) Sketch a graph of f that includes the asymptotes.

Graphing in Dot Mode

$[-6, 6, 1]$ by $[-6, 6, 1]$

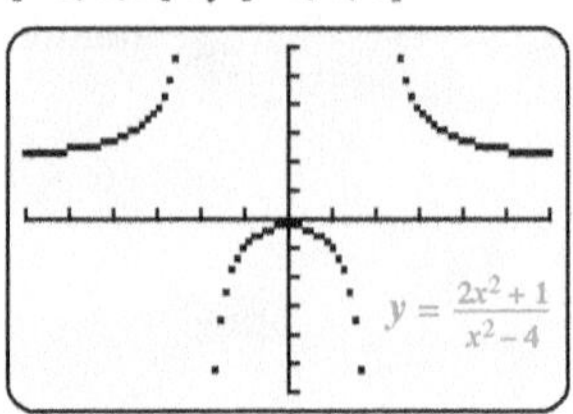

Figure 4.97

SOLUTION

(a) A calculator graph of $f(x) = \frac{2x^2 + 1}{x^2 - 4}$ using dot mode is shown in Figure 4.97. The function is undefined when $x^2 - 4 = 0$, or when $x = \pm 2$. The domain of function f is given by $D = \{x \mid x \neq 2, x \neq -2\}$.

(b) When $x = \pm 2$, the denominator, $x^2 - 4$, equals 0 and the numerator, $2x^2 + 1$, does not equal 0. Therefore $x = \pm 2$ are vertical asymptotes. The degree of the numerator equals the degree of the denominator, and the ratio of the leading coefficients is $\frac{2}{1} = 2$. A horizontal asymptote of the graph of f is $y = 2$.

(c) A second graph of f and its asymptotes is shown in Figure 4.98.

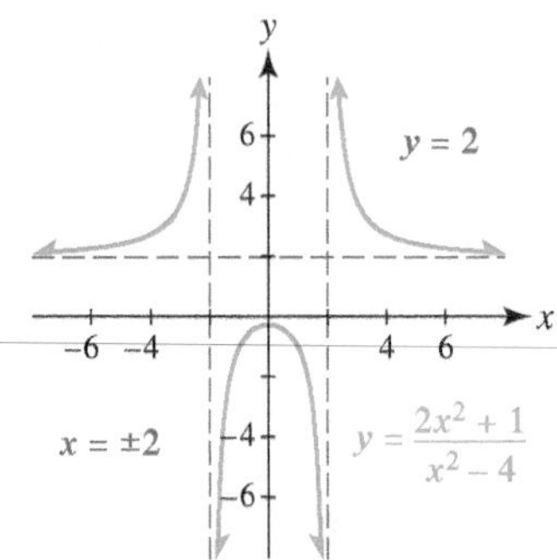

Figure 4.98

Now Try Exercise 57

Graphs with "Holes" If $f(x) = \frac{p(x)}{q(x)}$ is *not* in lowest terms, then it is possible that for some number k both $p(k) = 0$ and $q(k) = 0$. In this case, the graph of f may *not* have a vertical asymptote at $x = k$; rather, it may have a "hole" at $x = k$. See the next example and Figure 4.89.

EXAMPLE 9 **Graphing a rational function having a "hole"**

Graph $f(x) = \frac{2x^2 - 5x + 2}{x^2 - 3x + 2}$ by hand.

SOLUTION First factor the numerator and the denominator.

$$\frac{2x^2 - 5x + 2}{x^2 - 3x + 2} = \frac{(2x - 1)(x - 2)}{(x - 1)(x - 2)} = \frac{2x - 1}{x - 1}, \qquad x \neq 2$$

After factoring, it is apparent that both the numerator and the denominator equal 0 when $x = 2$. Therefore we simplify the rational expression to lowest terms and restrict the domain to $x \neq 2$.

From our previous work, long division can be used to show that $f(x) = \frac{2x - 1}{x - 1}$ is equivalent to $f(x) = 2 + \frac{1}{x - 1}$. Thus the graph of f is similar to Figure 4.94 except that the point (2, 3) is missing and an open circle appears in its place. See Figure 4.99.

Figure 4.99

Now Try Exercise 69

Graphing Rational Functions by Hand (Optional)

To graph a rational function by hand, we sometimes need to solve a rational equation of the form $\frac{a}{b} = \frac{c}{d}$. One way to solve this equation is to **cross multiply** and obtain $ad = bc$, provided b and d are nonzero. Consider the following example.

$\frac{2x - 1}{3x + 2} = \frac{5}{4}$	Given equation
$4(2x - 1) = 5(3x + 2)$	Cross multiply.
$8x - 4 = 15x + 10$	Simplify.
$-7x = 14$	Subtract 15x; add 4.
$x = -2$	Divide by −7. The answer checks.

The following guidelines can be used to graph a rational function by hand.

GRAPHING A RATIONAL FUNCTION

Let $f(x) = \frac{p(x)}{q(x)}$ define a rational function in *lowest* terms. To sketch its graph, follow these steps:

STEP 1: Find all vertical asymptotes.

STEP 2: Find all horizontal or oblique asymptotes.

STEP 3: Find the y-intercept, if possible, by evaluating $f(0)$.

STEP 4: Find the x-intercepts, if any, by solving $f(x) = 0$. (These will be the zeros of the numerator $p(x)$.)

STEP 5: Determine whether the graph will intersect its nonvertical asymptote $y = b$ by solving $f(x) = b$, where b is the y-value of the horizontal asymptote, or by solving $f(x) = mx + b$, where $y = mx + b$ is the equation of the oblique asymptote.

STEP 6: Plot selected points as necessary. Choose an x-value in each interval of the domain determined by the vertical asymptotes and x-intercepts.

STEP 7: Complete the sketch.

EXAMPLE 10 Graphing a rational function by hand

Graph $f(x) = \frac{2x + 1}{x - 3}$.

SOLUTION

Getting Started As you go through Steps 1 through 7, be sure to sketch all asymptotes first and then plot some key points. Finally, sketch the entire graph. ▶

STEP 1: The vertical asymptote has equation $x = 3$.

STEP 2: The horizontal asymptote has equation $y = 2$.

STEP 3: $f(0) = -\frac{1}{3}$, so the y-intercept is $-\frac{1}{3}$.

STEP 4: Solve $f(x) = 0$ to find any x-intercepts.

$$\frac{2x + 1}{x - 3} = 0$$

$$2x + 1 = 0 \quad \text{If a fraction equals 0, its numerator must be 0.}$$

$$x = -\frac{1}{2}$$

The x-intercept is $-\frac{1}{2}$.

STEP 5: The graph does not intersect its horizontal asymptote, since $f(x) = 2$ has no solutions. (Verify this.)

STEP 6 AND 7: The points $(-4, 1)$, $\left(1, -\frac{3}{2}\right)$, and $\left(6, \frac{13}{3}\right)$ are on the graph and can be used to complete the sketch, shown in Figure 4.100.

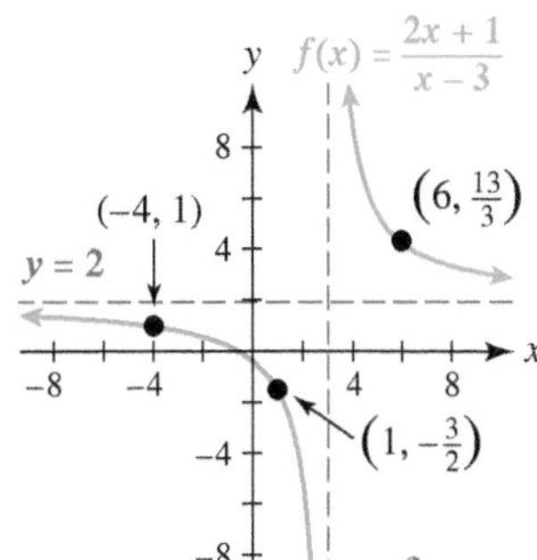

Figure 4.100

Now Try Exercise 87

EXAMPLE 11 Graphing a function that intersects its horizontal asymptote

Graph $f(x) = \frac{3x^2 - 3x - 6}{x^2 + 8x + 16}$.

SOLUTION

Let $f(x) = \dfrac{3x^2 - 3x - 6}{x^2 + 8x + 16}$.

STEP 1: To find the vertical asymptote(s), solve $x^2 + 8x + 16 = 0$.

$$x^2 + 8x + 16 = 0$$
$$(x + 4)^2 = 0$$
$$x = -4$$

Since the numerator is not 0 when $x = -4$, the only vertical asymptote has equation $x = -4$.

STEP 2: Because the degrees of the numerator and denominator both equal 2, the ratio of the leading coefficients gives the horizontal asymptote, which is,

$$y = \frac{3}{1}, \quad \begin{array}{l} \leftarrow \text{Leading coefficient of numerator} \\ \leftarrow \text{Leading coefficient of denominator} \end{array}$$

or $y = 3$.

STEP 3: The y-intercept is $f(0) = -\frac{3}{8}$.

STEP 4: To find the x-intercept(s), if any, solve $f(x) = 0$.

$$\frac{3x^2 - 3x - 6}{x^2 + 8x + 16} = 0 \quad \text{Set } f(x) \text{ equal to 0.}$$
$$3x^2 - 3x - 6 = 0 \quad \text{Set the numerator equal to 0.}$$
$$x^2 - x - 2 = 0 \quad \text{Divide by 3.}$$
$$(x - 2)(x + 1) = 0 \quad \text{Factor.}$$
$$x = 2 \quad \text{or} \quad x = -1 \quad \text{Zero-product property}$$

The x-intercepts are -1 and 2.

STEP 5: Because the horizontal asymptote is $y = 3$, set $f(x) = 3$ and solve to locate the point where the graph intersects the horizontal asymptote.

$$\frac{3x^2 - 3x - 6}{x^2 + 8x + 16} = 3$$
$$3x^2 - 3x - 6 = 3x^2 + 24x + 48 \quad \text{Let } 3 = \tfrac{3}{1}\text{; cross multiply.}$$
$$-3x - 6 = 24x + 48 \quad \text{Subtract } 3x^2.$$
$$-27x = 54 \quad \text{Subtract } 24x\text{, add 6.}$$
$$x = -2 \quad \text{Divide by } -27.$$

The graph intersects its horizontal asymptote at $(-2, 3)$.

STEP 6 AND 7: Some other points that lie on the graph are $(-10, 9)$, $\left(-8, 13\frac{1}{8}\right)$, and $\left(5, \frac{2}{3}\right)$. These can be used to complete the graph, shown in Figure 4.101.

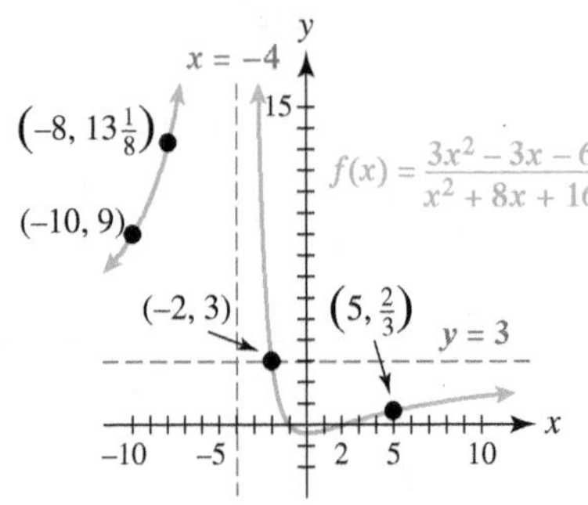

Figure 4.101

Now Try Exercise 91

4.6 Putting It All Together

The following table summarizes some concepts about rational functions (in lowest terms) and rational equations. To determine vertical and horizontal asymptotes see the box on page 301.

CONCEPT	EXPLANATION	EXAMPLES
Rational function	$f(x) = \frac{p(x)}{q(x)}$, where $p(x)$ and $q(x)$ are polynomials with $q(x) \neq 0$.	$f(x) = \dfrac{x - 1}{x^2 + 2x + 1}$ $g(x) = 1 + \dfrac{1}{x}$ $\left(\textit{Note}: 1 + \dfrac{1}{x} = \dfrac{x + 1}{x}.\right)$
Vertical asymptote	If k is a zero of the denominator, but not of the numerator, then $x = k$ is a vertical asymptote.	The graph of $f(x) = \frac{2x + 1}{x - 2}$ has a vertical asymptote at $x = 2$ because 2 is a zero of $x - 2$, but not a zero of $2x + 1$.
Horizontal asymptote	A horizontal asymptote occurs when the degree of the numerator is less than or equal to the degree of the denominator.	$f(x) = \dfrac{1 - 4x^2}{3x^2 - x}$ Horizontal asymptote: $y = -\frac{4}{3}$ $g(x) = \dfrac{x}{4x^2 + 2x}$ Horizontal asymptote: $y = 0$
Graph of a rational function	The graph of a rational function is continuous, except at x-values where the denominator equals zero.	The graph of $f(x) = \frac{3x^2 + 1}{x^2 - 4}$ is discontinuous at $x = \pm 2$. It has vertical asymptotes of $x = \pm 2$ and a horizontal asymptote of $y = 3$.
Basic rational equation	$\frac{a}{b} = \frac{c}{d}$ is equivalent to $ad = bc$, provided b and d are nonzero. Check your answer. Can be used to graph a rational function by hand	To solve the rational equation $\dfrac{4}{2x - 1} = 8,$ write 8 as $\frac{8}{1}$ and cross multiply. $4 = 8(2x - 1)$ $12 = 16x$ $x = \dfrac{3}{4}$

4.6 Exercises

Rational Functions

Exercises 1–12: Determine whether f is a rational function and state its domain.

1. $f(x) = \dfrac{x^3 - 5x + 1}{4x - 5}$

2. $f(x) = \dfrac{6}{x^2}$

3. $f(x) = x^2 - x - 2$

4. $f(x) = \dfrac{x^2 + 1}{\sqrt{x - 8}}$

5. $f(x) = \dfrac{|x - 1|}{x + 1}$

6. $f(x) = \dfrac{4}{x} + 1$

7. $f(x) = \dfrac{3x}{x^2 + 1}$

8. $f(x) = \dfrac{|x + 1|}{x + 1}$

9. $f(x) = \dfrac{3 - \sqrt{x}}{x^2 + x}$

10. $f(x) = \dfrac{x^3 - 3x + 1}{x^2 - 5}$

11. $f(x) = 4 - \dfrac{3}{x + 1}$

12. $f(x) = 5x^3 - 4x$

Asymptotes and Graphs

Exercises 13–18: Identify any horizontal or vertical asymptotes in the graph. State the domain of f.

13.

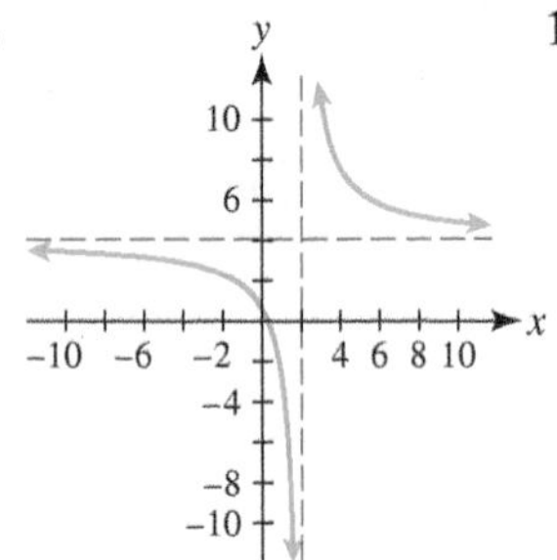

14.

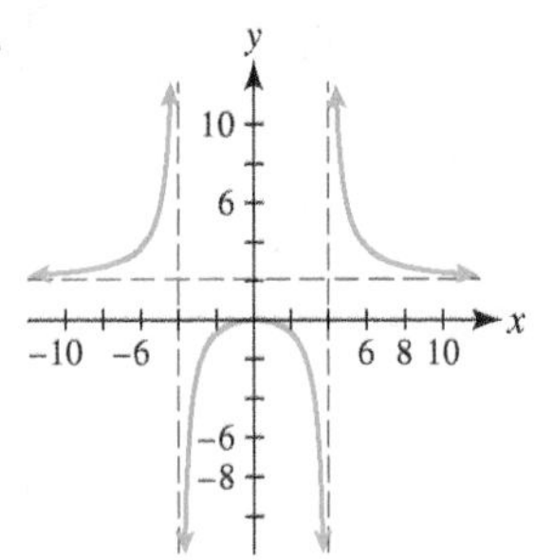

15.

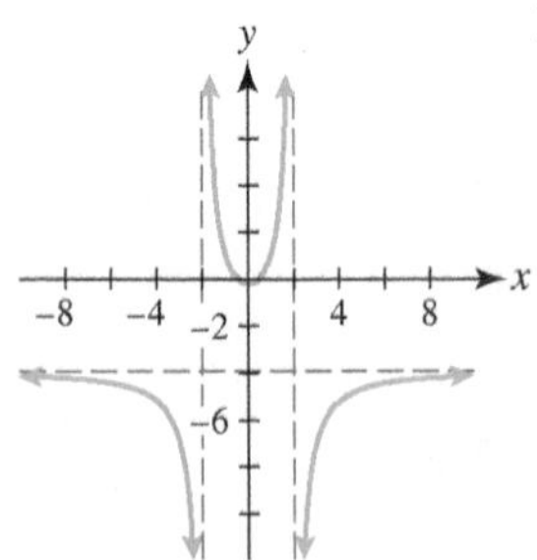

16.

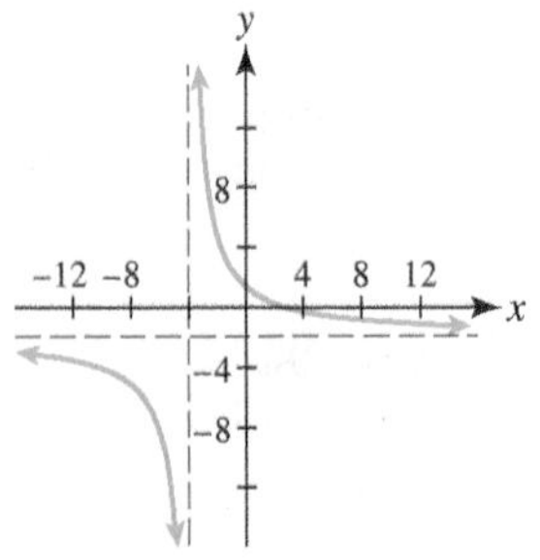

17.

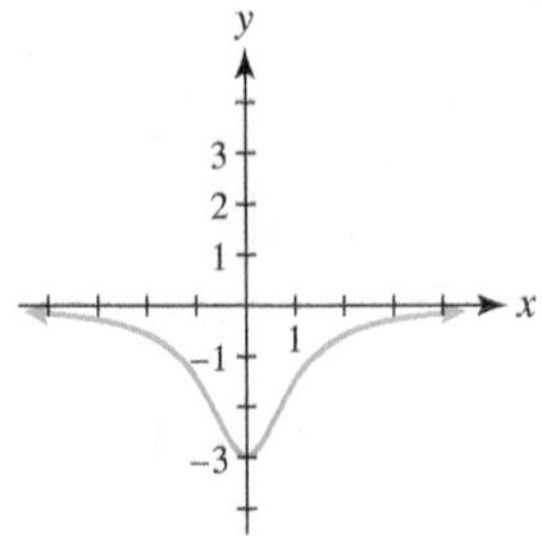

18.

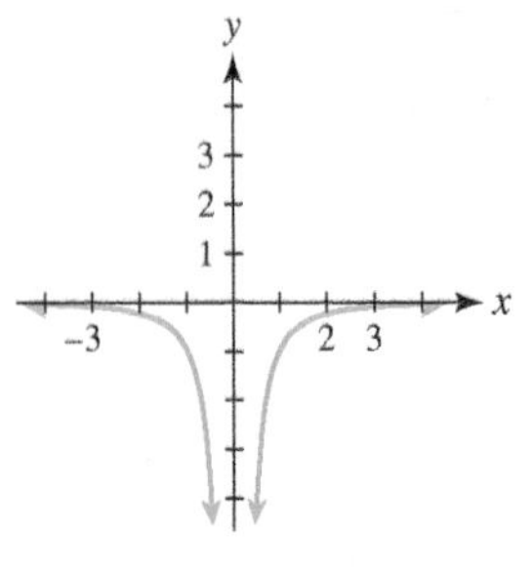

Exercises 19 and 20: In the table, Y_1 is a rational function. Give a possible equation for a horizontal asymptote.

19.

X	Y1
50	2.8654
100	2.9314
150	2.9539
200	2.9653
250	2.9722
300	2.9768
350	2.9801

X=50

20.

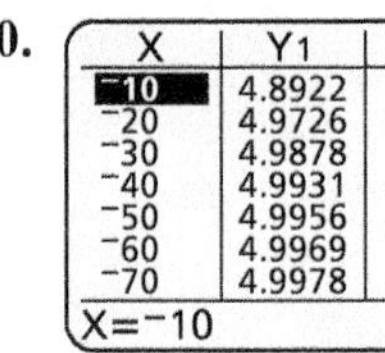

X	Y1
−10	4.8922
−20	4.9726
−30	4.9878
−40	4.9931
−50	4.9956
−60	4.9969
−70	4.9978

X=−10

Exercises 21–32: Find any horizontal or vertical asymptotes.

21. $f(x) = \dfrac{4x + 1}{2x - 6}$

22. $f(x) = \dfrac{x + 6}{5 - 2x}$

23. $f(x) = \dfrac{3}{x^2 - 5}$

24. $f(x) = \dfrac{3x^2}{x^2 - 9}$

25. $f(x) = \dfrac{x^4 + 1}{x^2 + 3x - 10}$

26. $f(x) = \dfrac{4x^3 - 2}{x + 2}$

27. $f(x) = \dfrac{x^2 + 2x + 1}{2x^2 - 3x - 5}$

28. $f(x) = \dfrac{6x^2 - x - 2}{2x^2 + x - 6}$

29. $f(x) = \dfrac{3x(x + 2)}{(x + 2)(x - 1)}$

30. $f(x) = \dfrac{x}{x^3 - x}$

31. $f(x) = \dfrac{x^2 - 9}{x + 3}$

32. $f(x) = \dfrac{2x^2 - 3x + 1}{2x - 1}$

Exercises 33–36: Let a be a positive constant. Match f(x) with its graph (a–d) without using a calculator.

33. $f(x) = \dfrac{a}{x - 1}$

34. $f(x) = \dfrac{2x + a}{x - 1}$

35. $f(x) = \dfrac{x - a}{x + 2}$

36. $f(x) = \dfrac{-2x}{x^2 - a}$

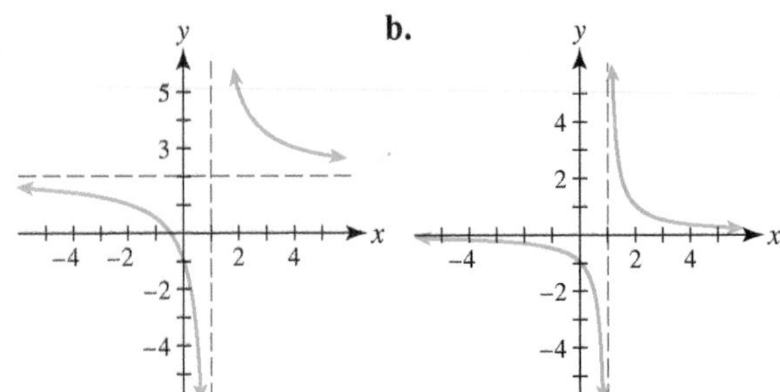

c.

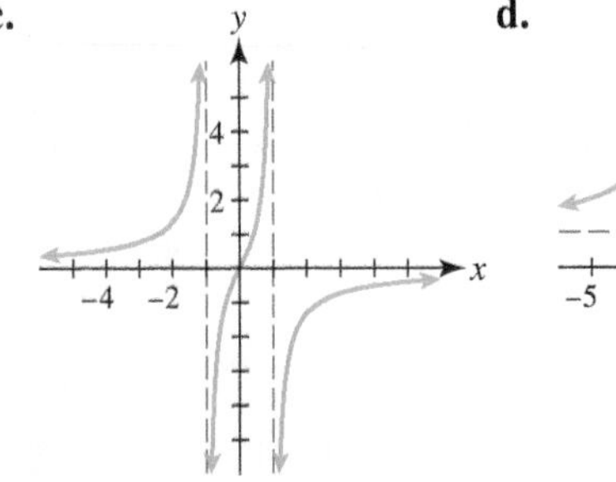

d.

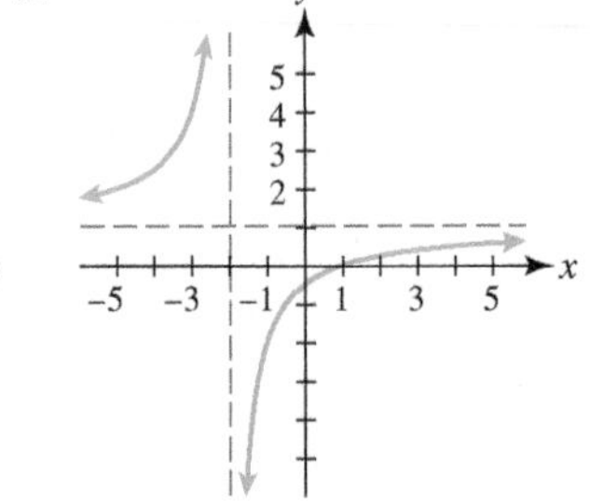

Exercises 37–40: Write a formula f(x) for a rational function so that its graph has the specified asymptotes.

37. Vertical: $x = -3$; horizontal: $y = 1$

38. Vertical: $x = 4$; horizontal: $y = -3$

39. Vertical: $x = \pm 3$; horizontal: $y = 0$

40. Vertical: $x = -2$ and $x = 4$; horizontal: $y = 5$

Graphing Rational Functions

Exercises 41–44: Graph f and identify any asymptotes.

41. $f(x) = \frac{1}{x^2}$

42. $f(x) = -\frac{1}{x}$

43. $f(x) = -\frac{1}{2x}$

44. $f(x) = \frac{2}{x^2}$

Exercises 45–54: **Transformations** *Use transformations of the graph of either $f(x) = \frac{1}{x}$ or $h(x) = \frac{1}{x^2}$ to sketch a graph of $y = g(x)$ by hand. Show all asymptotes. Write $g(x)$ in terms of either $f(x)$ or $h(x)$.*

45. $g(x) = \frac{1}{x - 3}$

46. $g(x) = \frac{1}{x + 2}$

47. $g(x) = \frac{1}{x} + 2$

48. $g(x) = 1 - \frac{2}{x}$

49. $g(x) = \frac{1}{x + 1} - 2$

50. $g(x) = \frac{1}{x - 2} + 1$

51. $g(x) = -\frac{2}{(x - 1)^2}$

52. $g(x) = \frac{1}{x^2} - 1$

53. $g(x) = \frac{1}{(x + 1)^2} - 2$

54. $g(x) = 1 - \frac{1}{(x - 2)^2}$

Exercises 55–62: Complete the following.

(a) Find the domain of f.
(b) Graph f in an appropriate viewing rectangle.
(c) Find any horizontal or vertical asymptotes.
(d) Sketch a graph of f that includes any asymptotes.

55. $f(x) = \frac{x + 3}{x - 2}$

56. $f(x) = \frac{6 - 2x}{x + 3}$

57. $f(x) = \frac{4x + 1}{x^2 - 4}$

58. $f(x) = \frac{0.5x^2 + 1}{x^2 - 9}$

59. $f(x) = \frac{4}{1 - 0.25x^2}$

60. $f(x) = \frac{x^2}{1 + 0.25x^2}$

61. $f(x) = \frac{x^2 - 4}{x - 2}$

62. $f(x) = \frac{4(x - 1)}{x^2 - x - 6}$

Exercises 63–72: Graph $y = f(x)$. You may want to use division, factoring, or transformations as an aid. Show all asymptotes and "holes."

63. $f(x) = \frac{x^2 - 2x + 1}{x - 1}$

64. $f(x) = \frac{4x^2 + 4x + 1}{2x + 1}$

65. $f(x) = \frac{x + 2}{x + 1}$

66. $f(x) = \frac{2x + 3}{x + 1}$

67. $f(x) = \frac{2x^2 - 3x - 2}{x^2 - 4x + 4}$

68. $f(x) = \frac{x^2 - x - 2}{x^2 - 2x - 3}$

69. $f(x) = \frac{2x^2 + 9x + 9}{2x^2 + 7x + 6}$

70. $f(x) = \frac{x^2 - 4}{x^2 - x - 6}$

71. $f(x) = \frac{-2x^2 + 11x - 14}{x^2 - 5x + 6}$

72. $f(x) = \frac{2x^2 - 3x - 14}{x^2 - 2x - 8}$

Slant Asymptotes

Exercises 73–80: Complete the following.

(a) Find any slant or vertical asymptotes.
(b) Graph $y = f(x)$. Show all asymptotes.

73. $f(x) = \frac{x^2 + 1}{x + 1}$

74. $f(x) = \frac{2x^2 - 5x - 2}{x - 2}$

75. $f(x) = \frac{0.5x^2 - 2x + 2}{x + 2}$

76. $f(x) = \frac{0.5x^2 - 5}{x - 3}$

77. $f(x) = \frac{x^2 + 2x + 1}{x - 1}$

78. $f(x) = \frac{2x^2 + 3x + 1}{x - 2}$

79. $f(x) = \frac{4x^2}{2x - 1}$

80. $f(x) = \frac{4x^2 + x - 2}{4x - 3}$

Basic Rational Equations

Exercises 81–86: Solve the equation.

81. $\frac{4}{x + 2} = -4$

82. $\frac{3}{2x + 1} = -1$

83. $\frac{x + 1}{x} = 2$

84. $\frac{2x}{x - 3} = -4$

85. $\frac{1 - x}{3x - 1} = -\frac{3}{5}$

86. $\frac{3 - 2x}{x + 2} = 12$

Graphing Rational Functions by Hand

Exercises 87–92: (Refer to Examples 10 and 11.) Graph f. Use the steps for graphing a rational function described in this section.

87. $f(x) = \frac{2x - 4}{x - 1}$

88. $f(x) = \frac{x + 3}{2x - 4}$

89. $f(x) = \dfrac{x^2 - 2x}{x^2 + 6x + 9}$ **90.** $f(x) = \dfrac{2x + 1}{x^2 + 6x + 8}$

91. $f(x) = \dfrac{x^2 + 2x + 1}{x^2 - x - 6}$ **92.** $f(x) = \dfrac{3x^2 + 3x - 6}{x^2 - x - 12}$

Applications

93. Social Network Participation You may have noticed that a relatively small percentage of people do the vast majority of postings on social networks. The rational function defined by

$$f(x) = \frac{100}{101 - x}, \qquad 5 \le x \le 100,$$

models this participation inequality. In this formula, $f(x)$ outputs the percentage of the postings done by the least active (bottom) x percent of the population.

(a) Evaluate $f(98)$. Interpret your answer.

(b) Evaluate $f(100) - f(98)$. Interpret your answer.

94. Probability A container holds x balls numbered 1 through x. Only one ball has the winning number.

(a) Find a function f that computes the probability, or likelihood, of *not* drawing the winning ball.

(b) What is the domain of f?

(c) What happens to the probability of *not* drawing the winning ball as the number of balls increases?

(d) Interpret the horizontal asymptote of the graph of f.

95. Abandoning Websites The first minute is critical to a visitor's decision whether to stay or leave a website. The longer a person visits a website, the less likely it is that he or she will leave the page. If x represents the number of seconds that a visitor has been visiting a website, then the likelihood as a percentage that this visitor is abandoning the website at x seconds is modeled by

$$P(x) = \frac{5}{0.03x + 0.97}, \qquad 1 \le x \le 60.$$

(a) Approximate $P(1)$ and interpret your answer.

(b) Approximate $P(60)$ and interpret your answer.

96. Concentration of a Drug The concentration of a drug in a medical patient's bloodstream is given by the formula $f(t) = \frac{5}{t^2 + 1}$, where the input t is in hours, $t \ge 0$, and the output is in milligrams per liter.

(a) Does the concentration of the drug increase or decrease? Explain.

(b) The patient should not take a second dose until the concentration is below 1.5 milligrams per liter. How long should the patient wait before taking a second dose?

97. Time Spent in Line If two parking attendants can wait on 8 vehicles per minute and vehicles are leaving the parking garage randomly at an average rate of x vehicles per minute, then the average time T in minutes spent waiting in line *and* paying the attendant is given by the formula $T(x) = -\frac{1}{x - 8}$, where $0 \le x < 8$. A graph of T is shown in the figure.

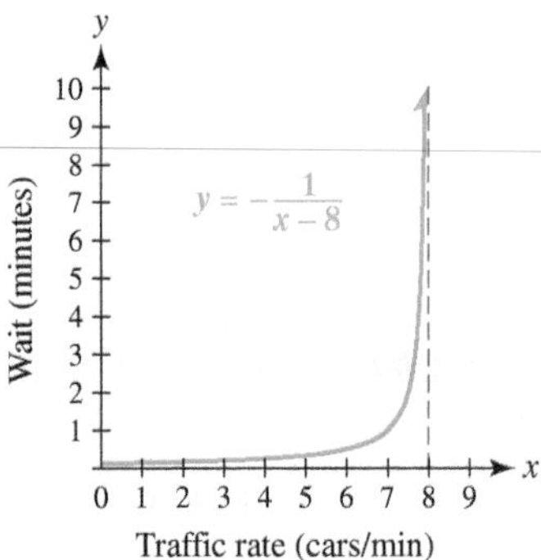

(a) Evaluate $T(4)$ and $T(7.5)$. Interpret the results.

(b) What happens to the wait as vehicles arrive at an average rate that approaches 8 cars per minute?

98. Time Spent in Line (Refer to Exercise 97.) If the parking attendants can wait on 5 vehicles per minute, the average time T in minutes spent waiting in line *and* paying the attendant becomes $T(x) = -\frac{1}{x - 5}$.

(a) What is a reasonable domain for T?

(b) Graph $y = T(x)$. Be sure to include any vertical asymptotes.

(c) Explain what happens to $T(x)$ as $x \to 5^-$.

99. Length of Lines (Refer to Example 2.) Suppose that a parking attendant can wait on 40 cars per hour and that cars arrive randomly at a rate of x cars per hour. Then the average number of cars waiting in line can be estimated by

$$N(x) = \frac{x^2}{1600 - 40x}.$$

(a) Evaluate $N(20)$ and $N(39)$.

(b) Explain what happens to the length of the line as x approaches 40.

(c) Find any vertical asymptotes of the graph of N.

100. **Construction Zone** Suppose that a construction zone can allow 50 cars per hour to pass through and that cars arrive randomly at a rate of x cars per hour. Then the average number of cars waiting in line to get through the construction zone can be estimated by

$$N(x) = \frac{x^2}{2500 - 50x}.$$

(a) Evaluate $N(20)$, $N(40)$, and $N(49)$.

(b) Explain what happens to the length of the line as x approaches 50.

(c) Find any vertical asymptotes of the graph of N.

101. **Interpreting an Asymptote** Suppose that an insect population in millions is modeled by $f(x) = \frac{10x + 1}{x + 1}$, where $x \geq 0$ is in months.

(a) Graph f in [0, 14, 1] by [0, 14, 1]. Find the equation of the horizontal asymptote.

(b) Determine the initial insect population.

(c) What happens to the population over time?

(d) Interpret the horizontal asymptote.

102. **Interpreting an Asymptote** Suppose that the population of a species of fish (in thousands) is modeled by $f(x) = \frac{x + 10}{0.5x^2 + 1}$, where $x \geq 0$ is in years.

(a) Graph f in [0, 12, 1] by [0, 12, 1]. What is the horizontal asymptote?

(b) Determine the initial population.

(c) What happens to the population of this fish?

(d) Interpret the horizontal asymptote.

103. **Train Curves** When curves are designed for trains, sometimes the outer rail is elevated or banked, so that a locomotive can safely negotiate the curve at a higher speed. See the figure at the top of the next column. Suppose a circular curve is designed for 60 miles per hour. The formula $f(x) = \frac{2540}{x}$ computes the elevation y in inches of the outer track for a curve having a radius of x feet, where $y = f(x)$. (*Source:* L. Haefner, *Introduction to Transportation Systems.*)

(a) Evaluate $f(400)$ and interpret the result.

(b) Graph f in [0, 600, 100] by [0, 50, 5]. How does the elevation change as the radius increases?

(c) Interpret the horizontal asymptote.

(d) Find the radius if the elevation is 12.7 inches.

104. **Slippery Roads** If a car is moving at 50 miles per hour on a level highway, then its braking distance depends on the road conditions. This distance in feet can be computed by $D(x) = \frac{250}{30x}$, where x is the coefficient of friction between the tires and the road and $0 < x \leq 1$. A smaller value of x indicates that the road is more slippery.

(a) Identify and interpret the vertical asymptote.

(b) Estimate the coefficient of friction associated with a braking distance of 340 feet.

Writing About Mathematics

105. Let $f(x)$ be the formula for a rational function.

(a) Explain how to find any vertical or horizontal asymptotes of the graph of f.

(b) Discuss what a horizontal asymptote represents.

106. Discuss how to find the domain of a rational function symbolically and graphically.

Extended and Discovery Exercises

Exercises 1–4: **Rate of Change/Difference Quotient** *Find the average rate of change of f from* $x_1 = 1$ *to* $x_2 = 3$. *Then find the difference quotient of f.*

1. $f(x) = \dfrac{1}{x}$

2. $f(x) = \dfrac{1}{x^2}$

3. $f(x) = \dfrac{3}{2x}$

4. $f(x) = \dfrac{1}{5 - x}$

CHECKING BASIC CONCEPTS FOR SECTIONS 4.5 AND 4.6

1. Find a quadratic polynomial $f(x)$ with zeros $\pm 4i$ and leading coefficient 3. Write $f(x)$ in complete factored form and expanded form.

2. Sketch a graph of a quartic function (degree 4) with a negative leading coefficient, two real zeros, and two imaginary zeros.

3. Write $x^3 - x^2 + 4x - 4$ in complete factored form.

4. Solve each equation.
   (a) $2x^3 + 45 = 5x^2 - 18x$

   (b) $x^4 + 5x^2 = 36$

5. Let $f(x) = \frac{1}{x-1} + 2$.
   (a) Find the domain of f.

   (b) Identify any vertical or horizontal asymptotes.

   (c) Sketch a graph of f that includes all asymptotes.

6. Find any vertical or horizontal asymptotes for the graph of $f(x) = \frac{4x^2}{x^2 - 4}$. State the domain of f.

7. Sketch a graph of each rational function f. Include all asymptotes and any "holes" in your graph.
   (a) $f(x) = \dfrac{3x - 1}{2x - 2}$ (b) $f(x) = \dfrac{1}{(x + 1)^2}$
   (c) $f(x) = \dfrac{x + 2}{x^2 - 4}$ (d) $f(x) = \dfrac{x^2 + 1}{x^2 - 1}$

4.7 More Equations and Inequalities

- Solve rational equations
- Solve variation problems
- Solve polynomial inequalities
- Solve rational inequalities

Introduction

Waiting in line is a part of almost everyone's life. When people arrive randomly at a line, rational functions can be used to estimate the average number of people standing in line. For example, if an attendant at a ticket booth can wait on 30 customers per hour and if customers arrive at an average rate of x per hour, then the average number of customers waiting in line is computed by

$$f(x) = \frac{x^2}{900 - 30x}, \qquad \text{Rational function}$$

where $0 \le x < 30$. Thus $f(28) \approx 13$ indicates that if customers arrive, on average, at 28 per hour, then the average number of people in line is 13. If a line length of 8 customers or fewer is acceptable, then we can use $f(x)$ to estimate customer arrival rates x that one attendant can accommodate by solving the *rational inequality*

$$\frac{x^2}{900 - 30x} \le 8. \qquad \text{Rational inequality}$$

(See Example 8.) Rational inequalities are discussed in this section along with other types of inequalities and equations. (***Source:*** N. Garber and L. Hoel, *Traffic and Highway Engineering.*)

Rational Equations

If $f(x)$ represents a rational function, then an equation that can be written in the form $f(x) = k$ for some constant k is a **rational equation.**

$$\frac{x^2 - 1}{x^2 + x + 3} = 0, \quad \frac{3x}{x^3 + x} = \frac{3}{2}, \quad \text{and} \quad \frac{2}{x - 1} + \frac{1}{x} = -2$$

Rational Equations

Rational equations can be solved symbolically, graphically, and numerically.

EXAMPLE 1 Solving a rational equation

Solve $\frac{4x}{x - 1} = 6$ symbolically, graphically, and numerically.

SOLUTION

Getting Started The equation $\frac{a}{b} = \frac{c}{d}$ with $b \neq 0$ and $d \neq 0$ is equivalent to $ad = bc$. In this example, you can think of 6 as the ratio $\frac{6}{1}$. This technique is sometimes called *cross multiplying.* ▶

Symbolic Solution

$$\frac{4x}{x-1} = 6 \quad \text{Given equation}$$
$$4x = 6(x-1) \quad \text{Cross multiply: } \tfrac{a}{b} = \tfrac{c}{d} \text{ implies } ad = bc.$$
$$4x = 6x - 6 \quad \text{Distributive property}$$
$$-2x = -6 \quad \text{Subtract } 6x.$$
$$x = 3 \quad \text{Divide by } -2. \text{ (Check this answer.)}$$

The only solution is 3.

Graphical Solution Graph $Y_1 = 4X/(X - 1)$ and $Y_2 = 6$. Their graphs intersect at (3, 6), so the solution is 3. See Figure 4.102.

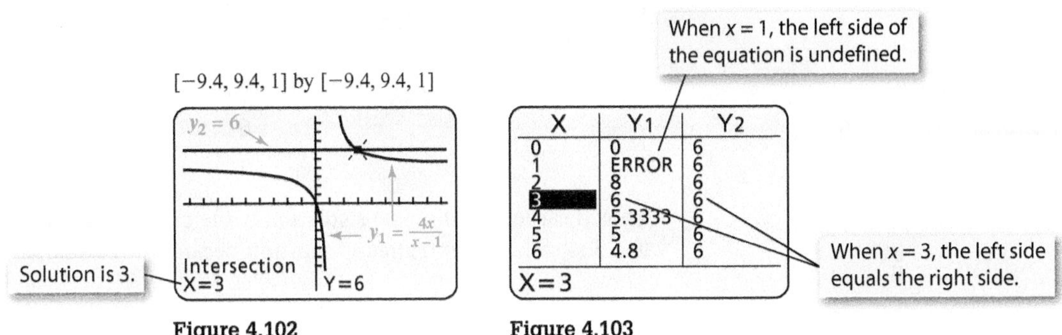

Figure 4.102 **Figure 4.103**

Numerical Solution In Figure 4.103, $y_1 = y_2$ when $x = 3$.

Now Try Exercise 1

Algebra Review
To review clearing fractions, see Chapter R (page R-33).

A common approach to solving rational equations symbolically is to multiply each side of the equation by a common denominator. This technique, which clears fractions from an equation, is used in Examples 2 and 3.

EXAMPLE 2 **Solving a rational equation**

Solve $\frac{6}{x^2} - \frac{5}{x} = 1$ symbolically.

SOLUTION

The least common denominator for x^2 and x is x^2. Multiply each side of the equation by x^2.

Algebra Review
To review finding a least common denominator, see Chapter R (page R-30).

$$\frac{6}{x^2} - \frac{5}{x} = 1 \quad \text{Given equation}$$
$$\frac{6}{x^2} \cdot x^2 - \frac{5}{x} \cdot x^2 = 1 \cdot x^2 \quad \text{Multiply each term by } x^2.$$
$$6 - 5x = x^2 \quad \text{Simplify.}$$
$$0 = x^2 + 5x - 6 \quad \text{Add } 5x \text{ and subtract 6.}$$
$$0 = (x+6)(x-1) \quad \text{Factor.}$$
$$x + 6 = 0 \quad \text{or} \quad x - 1 = 0 \quad \text{Zero-product property}$$
$$x = -6 \quad \text{or} \quad x = 1 \quad \text{Solve.}$$

Check to verify that each answer is correct.

Now Try Exercise 17

The next example illustrates the importance of checking possible solutions.

EXAMPLE 3 Solving a rational equation

Solve $\frac{1}{x+3} + \frac{1}{x-3} = \frac{6}{x^2-9}$ symbolically. Check the result.

SOLUTION

The least common denominator is $(x + 3)(x - 3)$, or $x^2 - 9$.

NOTE If either -3 or 3 is substituted into the given equation, two of the expressions are undefined. (Their denominators equal 0.) Thus neither of these values can be a solution to the *given* equation.

$$\frac{1}{x+3} + \frac{1}{x-3} = \frac{6}{x^2-9} \quad \text{Given equation}$$

$$\frac{(x+3)(x-3)}{x+3} + \frac{(x+3)(x-3)}{x-3} = \frac{6(x+3)(x-3)}{x^2-9} \quad \text{Multiply by } (x+3)(x-3).$$

$$(x-3) + (x+3) = 6 \quad \text{Simplify.}$$

$$2x = 6 \quad \text{Combine terms.}$$

$$x = 3 \quad \text{Divide by 2.}$$

As noted earlier, 3 cannot be a solution to the *given* equation. There are no solutions. (The value 3 is called an **extraneous solution** because it does not satisfy the given equation.)

Now Try Exercise 21

An Application Rational equations are used in real-world applications such as the construction problem in the next example. Steps for solving application problems (see page 103) have been used to structure the solution.

EXAMPLE 4 Designing a box

A box with rectangular sides and a top is being designed to hold 324 cubic inches and to have a surface area of 342 square inches. If the length of the box is four times the height, find possible dimensions of the box.

SOLUTION

STEP 1: We are asked to find the dimensions of a box. If x is the height of the box and y is the width, then the length of the box is $4x$, or four times the height.

x: Height of the box y: Width of the box $4x$: Length of the box

STEP 2: To relate these variables to an equation, sketch a box as shown in Figure 4.104. The volume V of the box is height times **width** times length.

$$V = xy(4x) = 4x^2y$$

Designing a Box

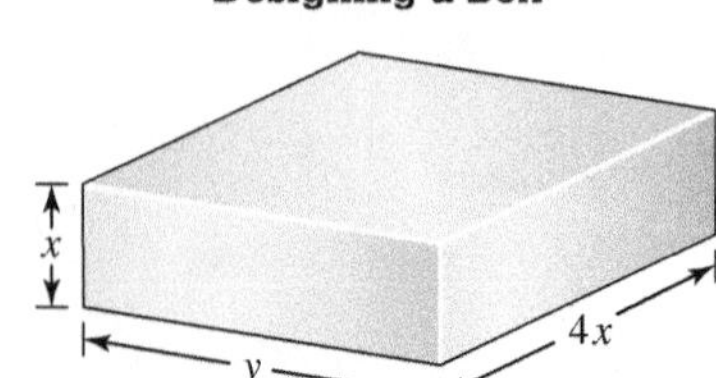

Figure 4.104

The surface area A of this box is determined by finding the area of the 6 rectangular sides: left and right sides, front and back, and top and bottom.

$$A = 2(4x \cdot x) + 2(x \cdot y) + 2(4x \cdot y)$$
$$= 8x^2 + 10xy$$

If we solve $V = 4x^2y$ for y and let $V = 324$, we obtain

$$y = \frac{V}{4x^2} = \frac{324}{4x^2} = \frac{81}{x^2}.$$

Substituting $y = \frac{81}{x^2}$ in the formula for A eliminates the y variable.

$$A = 8x^2 + 10xy \quad \text{Area formula}$$

$$= 8x^2 + 10x \cdot \frac{81}{x^2} \quad \text{Let } y = \frac{81}{x^2}.$$

$$= 8x^2 + \frac{810}{x} \quad \text{Simplify.}$$

Geometry Review
To review formulas related to box shapes, see Chapter R (page R-3).

Since the surface area is $A = 342$ square inches, the height x can be determined by solving the rational equation

$$8x^2 + \frac{810}{x} = 342. \qquad \text{Area} = 342$$

STEP 3: Figures 4.105 and 4.106 show the graphs of $Y_1 = 8X\wedge2 + 810/X$ and $Y_2 = 342$. There are two *positive* solutions: $x = 3$ and $x = 4.5$.

Calculator Help
To find a point of intersection, see Appendix A (page AP-7).

Locating Solutions Graphically

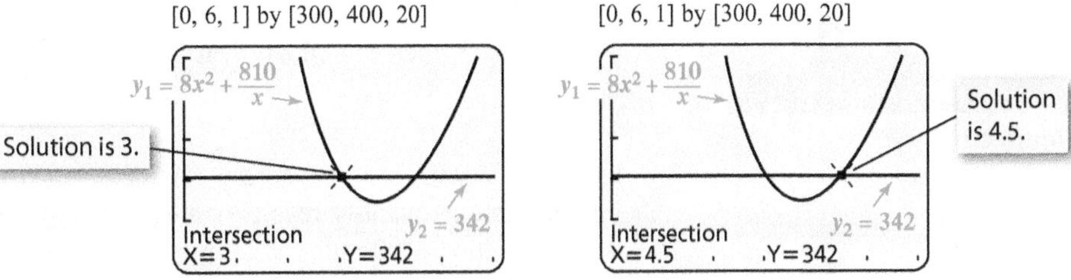

Figure 4.105 **Figure 4.106**

NOTE This equation can be written as $8x^3 - 342x + 810 = 0$, and the rational zeros test or factoring could be used to find the solutions, 3 and $\frac{9}{2}$.

For the first solution, the height is $x = 3$ inches, so the length is $4 \cdot 3 = 12$ inches and the width is $y = \frac{81}{3^2} = 9$ inches. (Note that $y = \frac{81}{x^2}$.) For the second solution, the height is 4.5 inches, so the length is $4 \cdot 4.5 = 18$ inches and the width is $y = \frac{81}{4.5^2} = 4$ inches. Thus the dimensions of the box in inches can be either $3 \times 9 \times 12$ or $4.5 \times 4 \times 18$.

STEP 4: We can check our results directly. If the dimensions are $3 \times 9 \times 12$, then

$$V = 3 \cdot 9 \cdot 12 = 324 \checkmark \text{ and}$$

$$S = 2(3 \cdot 9) + 2(3 \cdot 12) + 2(9 \cdot 12) = 342. \checkmark$$

If the dimensions are $4.5 \times 4 \times 18$, then

$$V = 4.5 \cdot 4 \cdot 18 = 324 \checkmark \text{ and}$$

$$S = 2(4.5 \cdot 4) + 2(4.5 \cdot 18) + 2(4 \cdot 18) = 342. \checkmark$$

In both cases our results check.

Now Try Exercise 79

Variation

Direct Variation with the nth Power In Section 2.4 direct variation was discussed. Sometimes a quantity y varies directly with a *power* of a variable. For example, the area A of a circle varies directly with the second power (square) of the radius r. That is, $A = \pi r^2$.

DIRECT VARIATION WITH THE nTH POWER

Let x and y denote two quantities and n be a positive real number. Then y is **directly proportional to the nth power** of x, or y **varies directly with the nth power** of x, if there exists a nonzero number k such that

$$y = kx^n.$$

The number k is called the *constant of variation* or the *constant of proportionality.* In the formula $A = \pi r^2$, the constant of variation is π.

EXAMPLE 5 **Modeling a pendulum**

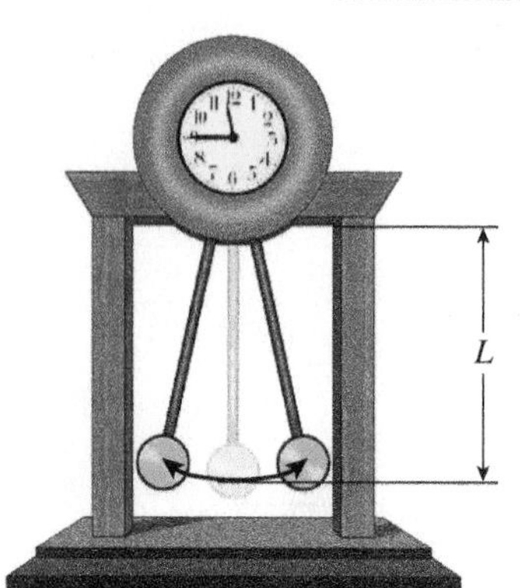

Figure 4.107

The time T required for a pendulum to swing back and forth once is called its *period*. The length L of a pendulum is directly proportional to the square of T. See Figure 4.107. A 2-foot pendulum has a 1.57-second period.

(a) Find the constant of proportionality k.

(b) Predict T for a pendulum having a length of 5 feet.

SOLUTION

(a) Because L is directly proportional to the square of T, we can write $L = kT^2$. If $L = 2$, then $T = 1.57$. Thus $k = \frac{L}{T^2} = \frac{2}{1.57^2} \approx 0.81$ and $L = 0.81T^2$.

(b) If $L = 5$, then $5 = 0.81T^2$. It follows that $T = \sqrt{5/0.81} \approx 2.48$ seconds.

Now Try Exercise 107

Inverse Variation with the nth Power When two quantities vary inversely, an increase in one quantity results in a decrease in the second quantity. For example, it takes 4 hours to travel 100 miles at 25 miles per hour and 2 hours to travel 100 miles at 50 miles per hour. Greater speed results in less travel time. If s represents the average speed of a car and t is the time to travel 100 miles, then $s \cdot t = 100$, or $t = \frac{100}{s}$. Doubling the speed cuts the time in half; tripling the speed reduces the time by one-third. The quantities t and s are said to *vary inversely*. The constant of variation is 100.

INVERSE VARIATION WITH THE nTH POWER

Let x and y denote two quantities and n be a positive real number. Then y is **inversely proportional to the nth power** of x, or y **varies inversely with the nth power** of x, if there exists a nonzero number k such that

$$y = \frac{k}{x^n}.$$

If $y = \frac{k}{x}$, then y is **inversely proportional** to x or y **varies inversely** with x.

NOTE To review steps for solving variation problems see the box on page 133.

Inverse variation occurs in measuring the intensity of light. If we increase our distance from a lightbulb, the intensity of the light decreases. Intensity I is inversely proportional to the second power of the distance d. The equation $I = \frac{k}{d^2}$ models this phenomenon.

EXAMPLE 6 **Modeling the intensity of light**

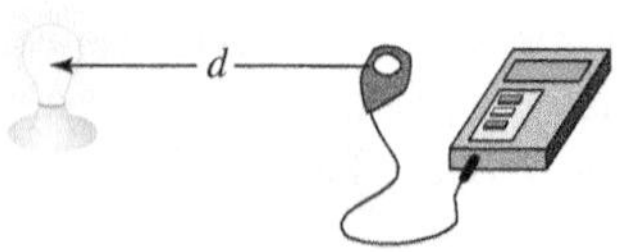

At a distance of 3 meters, a 100-watt bulb produces an intensity of 0.88 watt per square meter. (***Source:*** R. Weidner and R. Sells, *Elementary Classical Physics*, Volume 2.)

(a) Find the constant of proportionality k.

(b) Determine the intensity at a distance of 2 meters.

SOLUTION

(a) Substitute $d = 3$ and $I = 0.88$ in the equation $I = \frac{k}{d^2}$. Solve for k.

$$0.88 = \frac{k}{3^2}, \quad \text{or} \quad k = 7.92$$

(b) Let $I = \frac{7.92}{d^2}$ and $d = 2$. Then $I = \frac{7.92}{2^2} = 1.98$. The intensity at 2 meters is 1.98 watts per square meter.

Now Try Exercise 111

Polynomial Inequalities

Algebra Review
To review interval notation, see Section 1.4.

Graphical Solutions In Section 3.4 a strategy for solving quadratic inequalities was presented. This strategy involves first finding boundary numbers (x-values) where equality holds. Once the boundary numbers are known, a graph or a table of test values can be used to determine the intervals where inequality holds. This strategy can be applied to other types of inequalities.

The following See the Concept illustrates how to solve polynomial inequalities, where $p(x) = -x^4 + 5x^2 - 4$. Note that the solution sets are also shown on the number line above each graph.

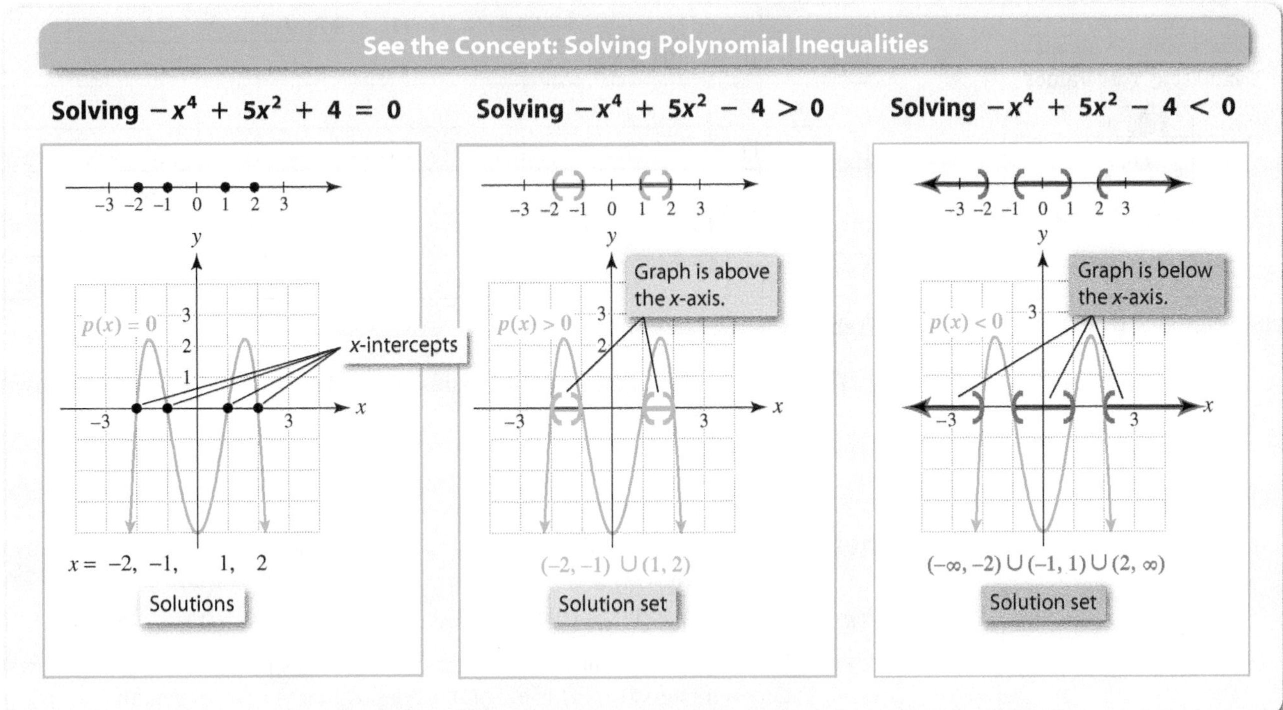

MAKING CONNECTIONS

Visualization and Inequalities A *precise* graph of p is *not* necessary to solve the polynomial inequality $p(x) > 0$ or $p(x) < 0$. Once the x-intercepts have been determined, we can use our knowledge about graphs of quartic polynomials (see Section 4.2) to visualize the graph of p. Then we can determine where the graph of p is above the x-axis and where it is below the x-axis.

Symbolic Solutions Polynomial inequalities can also be solved symbolically. For example, to solve the inequality $-x^4 + 5x^2 - 4 > 0$, begin by finding the boundary numbers.

$$-x^4 + 5x^2 - 4 = 0 \quad \text{Replace > with =.}$$
$$x^4 - 5x^2 + 4 = 0 \quad \text{Multiply by } -1.$$
$$(x^2 - 4)(x^2 - 1) = 0 \quad \text{Factor.}$$
$$x^2 - 4 = 0 \quad \text{or} \quad x^2 - 1 = 0 \quad \text{Zero-product property}$$
$$x = \pm 2 \quad \text{or} \quad x = \pm 1 \quad \text{Square root property}$$

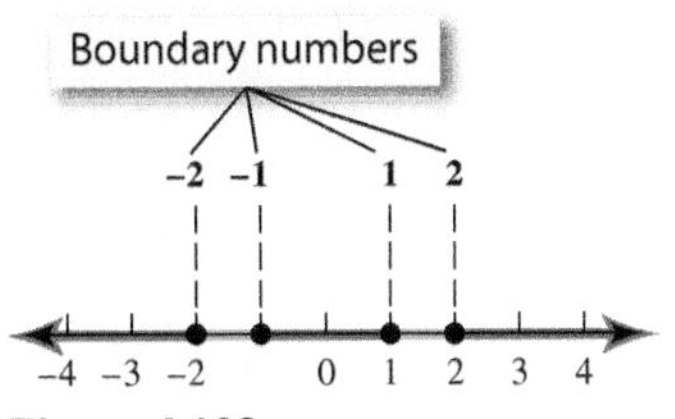

Figure 4.108

The boundary numbers $-2, -1, 1$, and 2 separate the number line into five intervals:

$$(-\infty, -2), (-2, -1), (-1, 1), (1, 2), \text{ and } (2, \infty),$$

as illustrated in Figure 4.108.

The polynomial $p(x) = -x^4 + 5x^2 - 4$ is either always positive or always negative on each of these intervals. To determine which is the case, we can choose one test value (x-value) from each interval and substitute this test value in $p(x)$. From Table 4.6 we see that the test value $x = -1.5$ results in

$$p(-1.5) = -(-1.5)^4 + 5(-1.5)^2 - 4 = 2.1875 > 0.$$

Figure 4.109, which was created by a graphing calculator, is similar to Table 4.6. Since $x = -1.5$ is in the interval $(-2, -1)$, it follows that $p(x)$ is positive on this interval. The sign of $p(x)$ on the other intervals is determined similarly. Thus the solution set to $p(x) = -x^4 + 5x^2 - 4 > 0$ is $(-2, -1) \cup (1, 2)$.

Evaluating Test Values

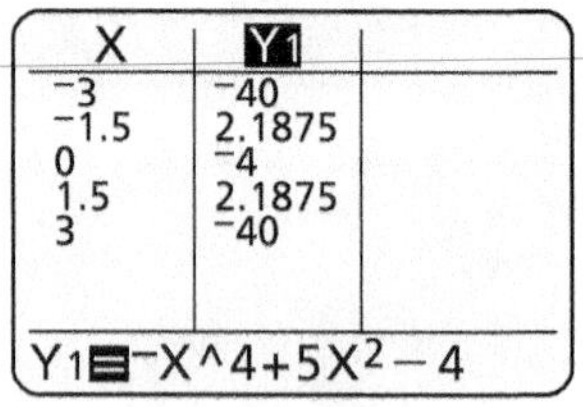

X	Y1
−3	−40
−1.5	2.1875
0	−4
1.5	2.1875
3	−40

Y1 = −X^4+5X²−4

Figure 4.109

Solving $-x^4 + 5x^2 - 4 > 0$

Interval	Test Value x	$-x^4 + 5x^2 - 4$	Positive or Negative?
$(-\infty, -2)$	-3	-40	Negative
$(-2, -1)$	-1.5	2.1875	Positive
$(-1, 1)$	0	-4	Negative
$(1, 2)$	1.5	2.1875	Positive
$(2, \infty)$	3	-40	Negative

Table 4.6

These symbolic and graphical procedures can be summarized verbally as follows.

SOLVING POLYNOMIAL INEQUALITIES

STEP 1: If necessary, write the inequality as $p(x) < 0$, where $p(x)$ is a polynomial and the inequality symbol $<$ may be replaced by $>$, $\le$, or $\ge$.

STEP 2: Solve $p(x) = 0$. The solutions are called boundary numbers.

STEP 3: Use the boundary numbers to separate the number line into disjoint intervals. On each interval, $p(x)$ is either always positive or always negative.

STEP 4: To solve the inequality, either make a table of test values for $p(x)$ or use a graph of $y = p(x)$. For example, the solution set for $p(x) < 0$ corresponds to intervals where test values result in negative outputs or to intervals where the graph of $y = p(x)$ is below the x-axis.

EXAMPLE 7 Solving a polynomial inequality

Solve $x^3 \ge 2x^2 + 3x$ symbolically and graphically.

SOLUTION

Symbolic Solution

STEP 1: Begin by writing the inequality as $x^3 - 2x^2 - 3x \ge 0$.

STEP 2: Replace the $\ge$ symbol with an equals sign and solve the resulting equation.

$$x^3 - 2x^2 - 3x = 0 \quad \text{Replace} \ge \text{with} =.$$
$$x(x^2 - 2x - 3) = 0 \quad \text{Factor out } x.$$
$$x(x + 1)(x - 3) = 0 \quad \text{Factor the trinomial.}$$
$$x = 0 \quad \text{or} \quad x = -1 \quad \text{or} \quad x = 3 \quad \text{Zero-product property}$$

The boundary numbers are -1, 0, and 3.

Algebra Review
To review factoring, see Chapter R, (page R-23).

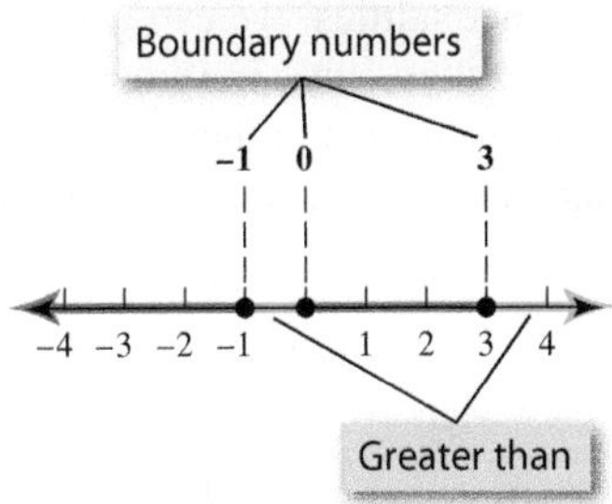

Figure 4.110

STEP 3: The boundary numbers separate the number line into four disjoint intervals:

$$(-\infty, -1), (-1, 0), (0, 3), \text{ and } (3, \infty),$$

as illustrated in Figure 4.110.

STEP 4: In Table 4.7 the expression $x^3 - 2x^2 - 3x$ is evaluated at a test value from each interval. The solution set is $[-1, 0] \cup [3, \infty)$. In Figure 4.111 a graphing calculator has been used to evaluate the same test values. (*Note*: The boundary numbers are included in the solution set because the inequality involves $\geq$ rather than $>$.)

Evaluating Test Values

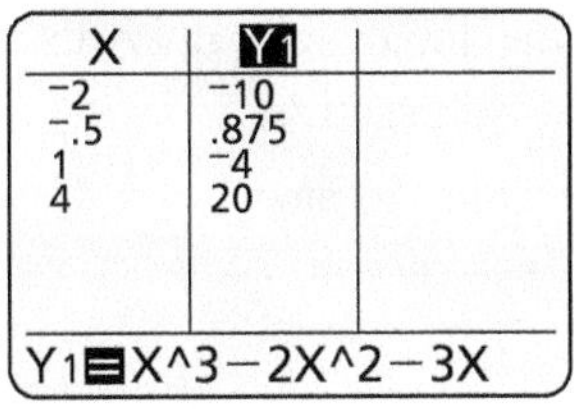

X	Y1
-2	-10
-.5	.875
1	-4
4	20

Y1=X^3−2X^2−3X

Figure 4.111

Interval	Test Value x	$x^3 - 2x^2 - 3x$	Positive or Negative?
$(-\infty, -1)$	-2	-10	Negative
$(-1, 0)$	-0.5	0.875	Positive
$(0, 3)$	1	-4	Negative
$(3, \infty)$	4	20	Positive

Table 4.7

[−5, 5, 1 by [−7, 7, 1]

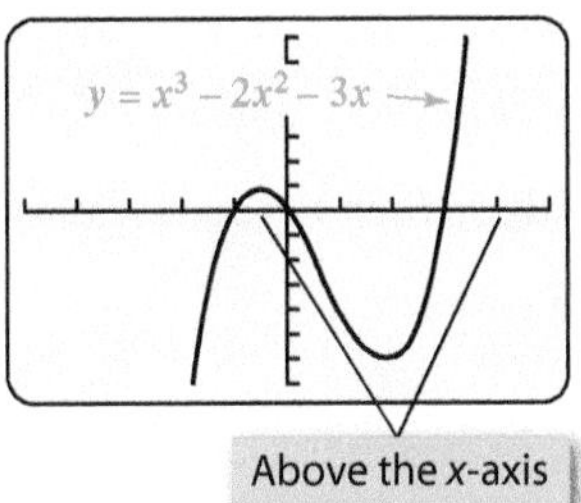

Figure 4.112

Graphical Solution Graph $y = x^3 - 2x^2 - 3x$, as shown in Figure 4.112. The zeros or x-intercepts are located at -1, 0, and 3. The graph of y is positive (or above the x-axis) for $-1 < x < 0$ or $3 < x < \infty$. If we include the boundary numbers, this result agrees with the symbolic solution.

Now Try Exercise 43

MAKING CONNECTIONS

Functions, Equations, and Inequalities The three concepts are related. For example,

$$f(x) = ax^3 + bx^2 + cx + d \qquad \text{Cubic function}$$
$$ax^3 + bx^2 + cx + d = 0 \qquad \text{Cubic equation}$$
$$ax^3 + bx^2 + cx + d < 0 \qquad \text{Cubic inequality}$$

where $a \neq 0$. These concepts also apply to higher degree polynomials and to rational expressions.

Rational Inequalities

An Application In the introduction we looked at how a rational inequality can be used to estimate the number of people standing in line at a ticket booth. In the next example, this inequality is solved graphically.

EXAMPLE 8 **Modeling customers in a line**

A ticket booth attendant can wait on 30 customers per hour. To keep the time waiting in line reasonable, the line length should not exceed 8 customers on average. Solve the inequality $\frac{x^2}{900 - 30x} \leq 8$ to determine the rates x at which customers can arrive before a second attendant is needed. Note that the x-values are limited to $0 \leq x < 30$.

[0, 30, 5] by [0, 10, 2]

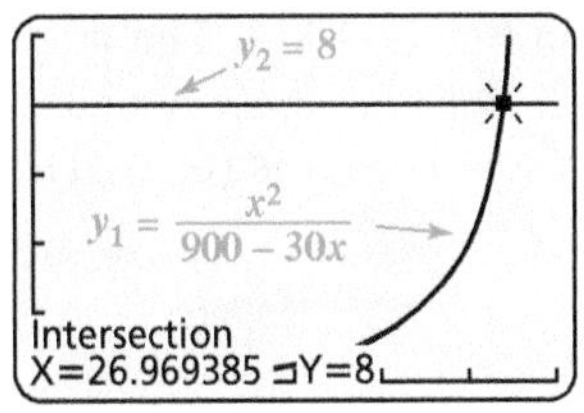

$y_2 = 8$

$y_1 = \frac{x^2}{900 - 30x}$

Intersection
X=26.969385 Y=8

Figure 4.113

SOLUTION Graph $Y_1 = X^\wedge 2/(900 - 30X)$ and $Y_2 = 8$ for $0 \leq x \leq 30$, as shown in Figure 4.113. The only point of intersection on this interval is near (26.97, 8). The graph of y_1 is below the graph of y_2 for x-values to the left of this point. We conclude that if the arrival rate is about 27 customers per hour *or less*, then the line length does not exceed 8 customers on average. If the arrival rate is more than 27 customers per hour, a second ticket booth attendant is needed.

Now Try Exercise 85

Graphical and Symbolic Solutions To solve rational inequalities, we can use the same basic techniques that we used to solve polynomial inequalities, with one important modification: boundary numbers also occur at x-values where the denominator of any rational expression in the inequality equals 0. The following steps can be used to solve a rational inequality.

SOLVING RATIONAL INEQUALITIES

STEP 1: If necessary, write the inequality in the form $\frac{p(x)}{q(x)} > 0$, where $p(x)$ and $q(x)$ are polynomials. Note that $>$ may be replaced by $<$, $\le$, or $\ge$.

STEP 2: Solve $p(x) = 0$ and $q(x) = 0$. The solutions are boundary numbers.

STEP 3: Use the boundary numbers to separate the number line into disjoint intervals. On each interval, $\frac{p(x)}{q(x)}$ is either always positive or always negative.

STEP 4: Use a table of test values or a graph to solve the inequality in Step 1.

EXAMPLE 9 **Solving a rational inequality**

Solve $\frac{2 - x}{2x} > 0$ symbolically. Support your answer graphically.

SOLUTION

Symbolic Solution The inequality is written in the form $\frac{p(x)}{q(x)} > 0$, so Step 1 is unnecessary.

STEP 2: Set the numerator and the denominator equal to 0 and solve.

Numerator	***Denominator***
$2 - x = 0$	$2x = 0$
$x = 2$	$x = 0$

STEP 3: The boundary numbers are 0 and 2, which separate the number line into three disjoint intervals: $(-\infty, 0)$, $(0, 2)$, and $(2, \infty)$.

STEP 4: Table 4.8 shows that the expression is positive between the two boundary numbers or when $0 < x < 2$. In interval notation the solution set is $(0, 2)$.

[−4.7, 4.7, 1] by [−3.1, 3.1, 1]

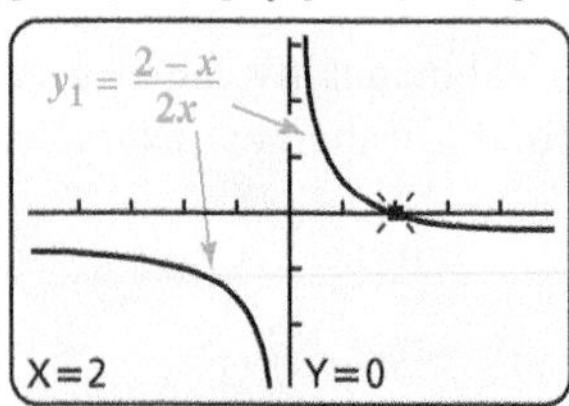

Figure 4.114

Solving $\frac{2 - x}{2x} > 0$

Interval	Test Value x	$(2 - x)/(2x)$	Positive or Negative?
$(-\infty, 0)$	-1	-1.5	Negative
$(0, 2)$	1	0.5	Positive
$(2, \infty)$	4	-0.25	Negative

Table 4.8

Graphical Solution Graph $Y_1 = (2 - X)/(2X)$, as shown in Figure 4.114. The graph has a vertical asymptote at $x = 0$ and an x-intercept at $x = 2$. Between these boundary numbers the graph of y_1 is positive (or above the x-axis). The solution set is $(0, 2)$. This agrees with our symbolic solution.

Now Try Exercise 59

EXAMPLE 10 **Solving a rational inequality symbolically**

Solve $\frac{1}{x} \le \frac{2}{x + 1}$.

SOLUTION

STEP 1: Begin by writing the inequality in the form $\frac{p(x)}{q(x)} \le 0$.

$$\frac{1}{x} - \frac{2}{x+1} \le 0 \quad \text{Subtract } \frac{2}{x+1}.$$

$$\frac{1}{x} \cdot \frac{(x+1)}{(x+1)} - \frac{2}{x+1} \cdot \frac{x}{x} \le 0 \quad \text{Common denominator is } x(x+1).$$

$$\frac{x+1}{x(x+1)} - \frac{2x}{x(x+1)} \le 0 \quad \text{Multiply.}$$

$$\frac{1-x}{x(x+1)} \le 0 \quad \text{Subtract numerators: } x+1-2x = 1-x.$$

Algebra Review
To review subtraction of rational expressions, see Chapter R (page R-32).

STEP 2: Find the zeros of the numerator and the denominator.

Numerator	***Denominator***
$1 - x = 0$	$x(x+1) = 0$
$x = 1$	$x = 0$ or $x = -1$

STEP 3: The boundary numbers are -1, 0, and 1, which separate the number line into four disjoint intervals: $(-\infty, -1)$, $(-1, 0)$, $(0, 1)$, and $(1, \infty)$.

STEP 4: Table 4.9 can be used to solve the inequality $\frac{1-x}{x(x+1)} \le 0$. The solution set is $(-1, 0) \cup [1, \infty)$.

NOTE The boundary numbers -1 and 0 are not included in the solution set because the given inequality is undefined when $x = -1$ or $x = 0$.

Solving $\frac{1-x}{x(x+1)} \le 0$

Interval	Test Value x	$(1-x)/(x(x+1))$	Positive or Negative?
$(-\infty, -1)$	-2	1.5	Positive
$(-1, 0)$	-0.5	-6	Negative
$(0, 1)$	0.5	$0.\overline{6}$	Positive
$(1, \infty)$	2	$-0.1\overline{6}$	Negative

Table 4.9

Now Try Exercise 75

Multiplying an Inequality by a Variable When solving a rational inequality, it is essential *not* to multiply or divide each side of the inequality by the LCD (least common denominator) if the LCD contains a *variable*. This technique often leads to an incorrect solution set.

For example, if each side of the rational inequality

$$\frac{1}{x} < 2$$

is multiplied by x to clear fractions, the inequality becomes

$$1 < 2x \quad \text{or} \quad x > \frac{1}{2}.$$

However, this solution set is clearly incomplete because $x = -1$ is also a solution to the given inequality. In general, the variable x can be either negative or positive. If $x < 0$, the inequality symbol should be reversed, whereas if $x > 0$, the inequality symbol should not be reversed. Because we have no way of knowing ahead of time which is the case, this technique of multiplying by a variable should be *avoided*.

4.7 Putting It All Together

The following table outlines basic concepts for this section.

CONCEPT	DESCRIPTION
Rational equation	Can be written as $f(x) = k$, where f is a rational function. To solve a rational equation, first clear fractions by multiplying each side by the LCD. *Check your answers.* **Example:** Solve $\frac{1}{x} + \frac{1}{x+2} = \frac{1}{x(x+2)}$. Multiply each side of the equation by the LCD: $x(x + 2)$. $$\frac{x(x+2)}{x} + \frac{x(x+2)}{x+2} = \frac{x(x+2)}{x(x+2)}$$ $$(x + 2) + x = 1$$ $$x = -\frac{1}{2}$$ It checks.
Variation	*y varies directly with the nth power of x:* $y = kx^n$. **Example:** Let y vary directly with the cube (third power) of x. If the constant of variation is 5, then the variation equation is $y = 5x^3$. *y varies inversely with the nth power of x:* $y = \frac{k}{x^n}$. **Example:** Let y vary inversely with the square (second power) of x. If the constant of variation is 3, then the variation equation is $y = \frac{3}{x^2}$.
Polynomial inequality	Can be written as $p(x) < 0$, where $p(x)$ is a polynomial and $<$ may be replaced by $>$, $\leq$, or $\geq$ **Examples:** $x^3 - x \leq 0$, $2x^4 - 3x^2 \geq 5x + 1$
Solving a polynomial inequality	Follow the steps for solving a polynomial inequality presented on page 320. Either graphical or symbolic methods can be used. **Example:** A graph of $y = x^3 - 2x^2 - 5x + 6$ is shown. The boundary numbers are -2, 1, and 3. The solution set to $x^3 - 2x^2 - 5x + 6 > 0$ is $(-2, 1) \cup (3, \infty)$, because the graph is above the x-axis on these intervals.
Rational inequality	Can be written as $\frac{p(x)}{q(x)} < 0$, where $p(x)$ and $q(x) \neq 0$ are polynomials and $<$ may be replaced by $>$, $\leq$, or $\geq$ **Examples:** $\frac{x-3}{x+2} \geq 0$, $2x - \frac{2}{x^2 - 1} > 5$

CONCEPT	DESCRIPTION
Solving a rational inequality	Follow the steps for solving a rational inequality presented on page 322. Either graphical or symbolic methods can be used. **Example:** A graph of $y = \frac{x-1}{2x+1}$ is shown. Boundary numbers occur where either the numerator or denominator equals zero: $x = 1$ or $x = -\frac{1}{2}$. The solution set to $\frac{x-1}{2x+1} < 0$ is $\left(-\frac{1}{2}, 1\right)$, because the graph is below the x-axis on this interval. 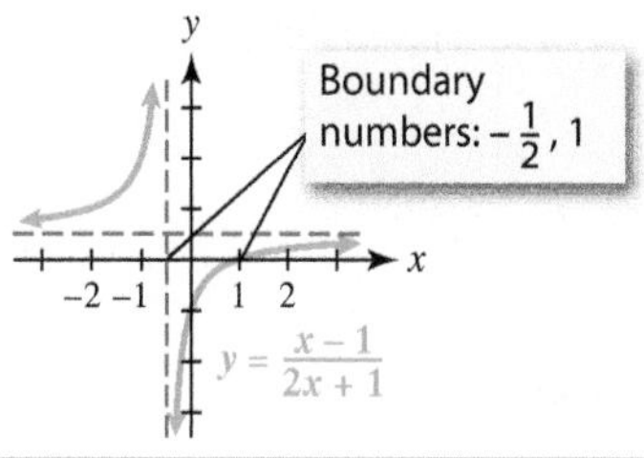

4.7 Exercises

Rational Equations

Exercises 1–6: Solve the rational equation

(a) symbolically,

(b) graphically, and

(c) numerically.

1. $\frac{2x}{x+2} = 6$

2. $\frac{3x}{2x-1} = 3$

3. $2 - \frac{5}{x} + \frac{2}{x^2} = 0$

4. $\frac{1}{x^2} + \frac{1}{x} = 2$

5. $\frac{1}{x+1} + \frac{1}{x-1} = \frac{1}{x^2-1}$

6. $\frac{4}{x-2} = \frac{3}{x-1}$

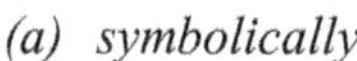

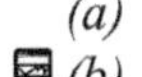

Exercises 7–28: Find all real solutions. Check your results.

7. $\frac{x+1}{x-5} = 0$

8. $\frac{x-2}{x+3} = 1$

9. $\frac{6(1-2x)}{x-5} = 4$

10. $\frac{2}{5(2x+5)} + 3 = -1$

11. $\frac{1}{x+2} + \frac{1}{x} = 1$

12. $\frac{2x}{x-1} = 5 + \frac{2}{x-1}$

13. $\frac{1}{x} - \frac{2}{x^2} = 5$

14. $\frac{1}{x^2-2} = \frac{1}{x}$

15. $\frac{x^3-4x}{x^2+1} = 0$

16. $\frac{1}{x+2} + \frac{1}{x+3} = \frac{2}{x^2+5x+6}$

17. $\frac{35}{x^2} = \frac{4}{x} + 15$

18. $6 - \frac{35}{x} + \frac{36}{x^2} = 0$

19. $\frac{x+5}{x+2} = \frac{x-4}{x-10}$

20. $\frac{x-1}{x+1} = \frac{x+3}{x-4}$

21. $\frac{1}{x-2} - \frac{2}{x-3} = \frac{-1}{x^2-5x+6}$

22. $\frac{1}{x-1} + \frac{3}{x+1} = \frac{4}{x^2-1}$

23. $\frac{2}{x-1} + 1 = \frac{4}{x^2-1}$

24. $\frac{1}{x} + 2 = \frac{1}{x^2 + x}$

25. $\frac{1}{x + 2} = \frac{4}{4 - x^2} - 1$

26. $\frac{1}{x - 3} + 1 = \frac{6}{x^2 - 9}$

27. $\frac{1}{x - 1} + \frac{1}{x + 1} = \frac{2}{x^2 - 1}$

28. $\frac{1}{2x + 1} + \frac{1}{2x - 1} = \frac{2}{4x^2 - 1}$

Graphical Solutions to Inequalities

Exercises 29–34: Solve the equation and inequalities.

(a) $f(x) = 0$ *(b)* $f(x) > 0$ *(c)* $f(x) < 0$

29.

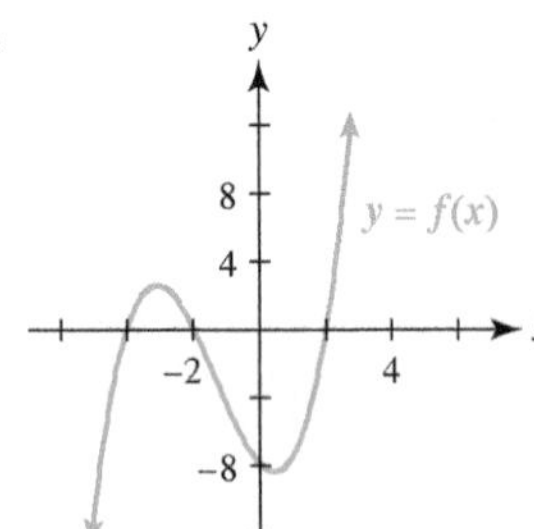

30.

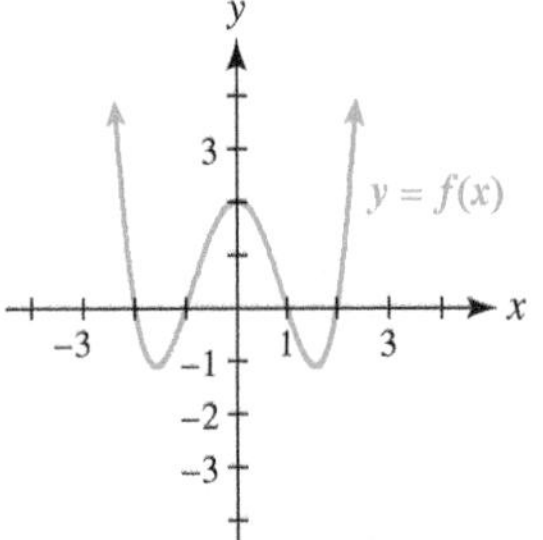

31.

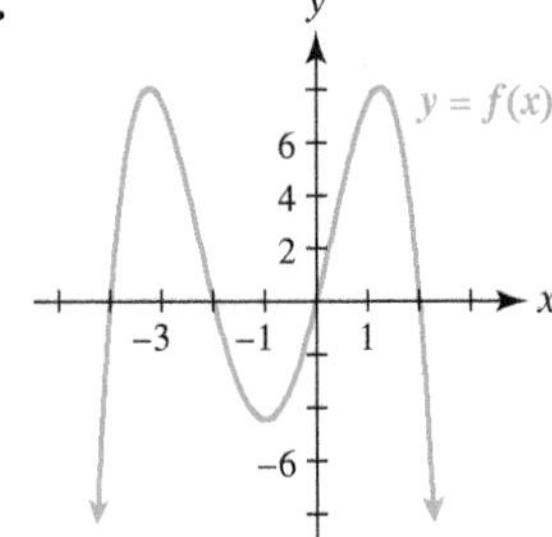

32.

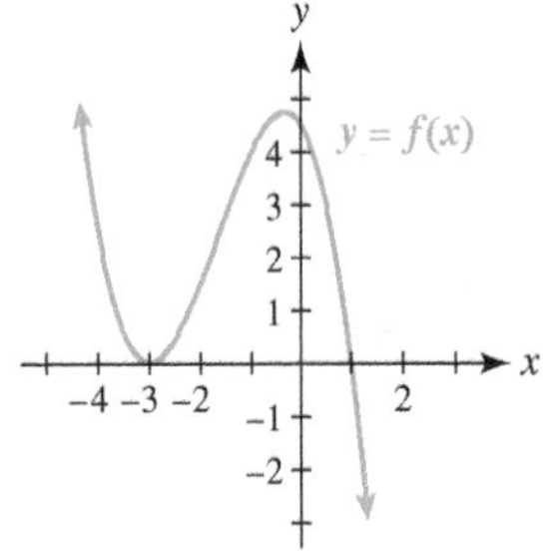

33.

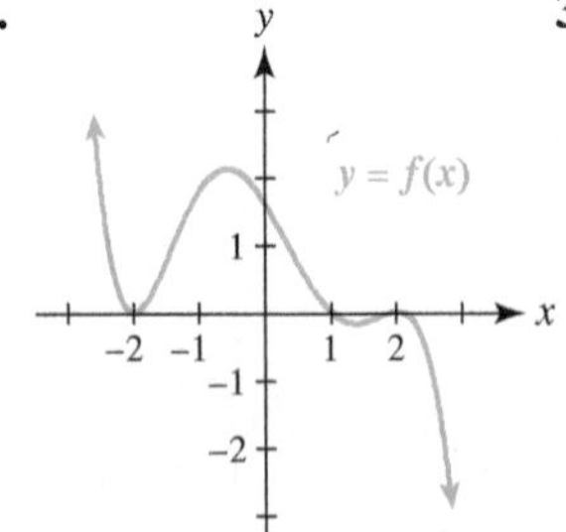

34.

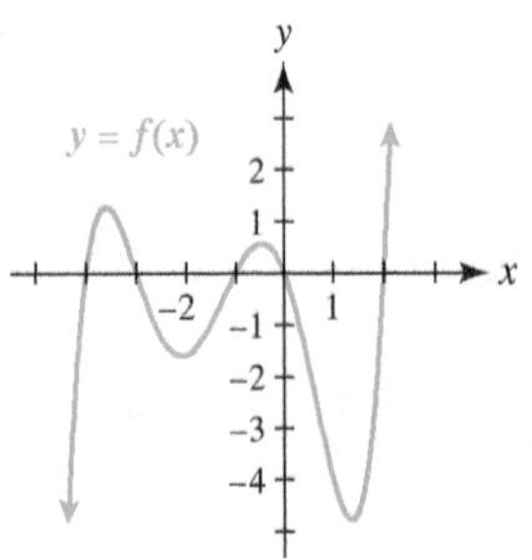

Exercises 35–40: Complete the following.

(a) Identify where $f(x)$ *is undefined or* $f(x) = 0$.

(b) Solve $f(x) > 0$.

(c) Solve $f(x) < 0$.

35.

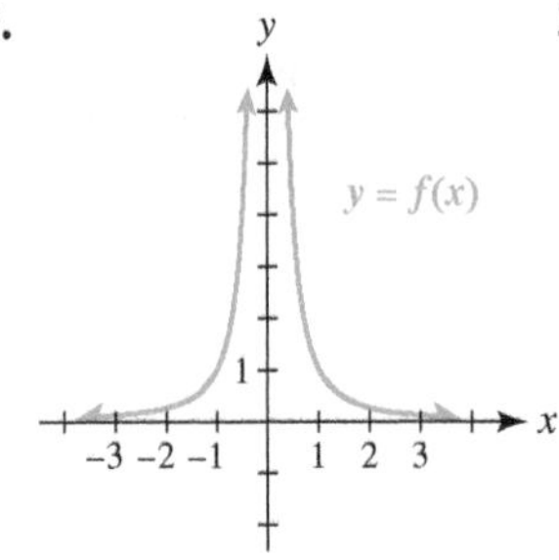

36.

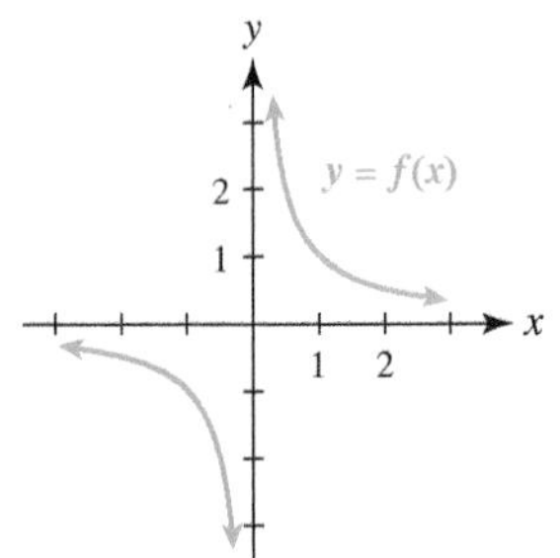

37.

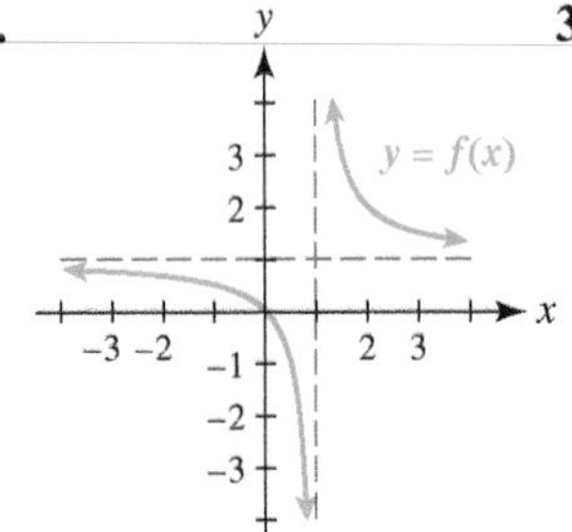

38.

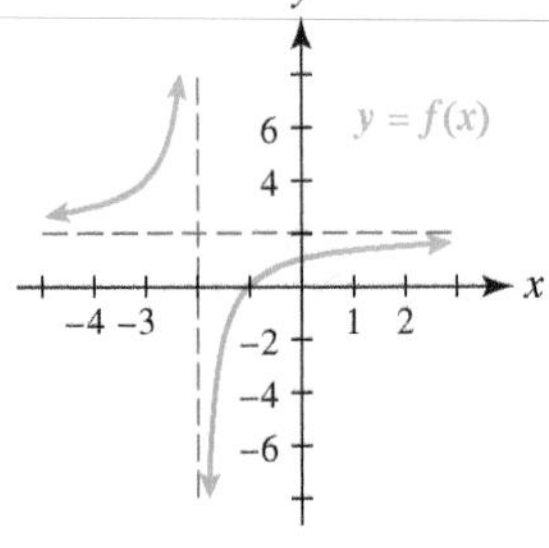

39.

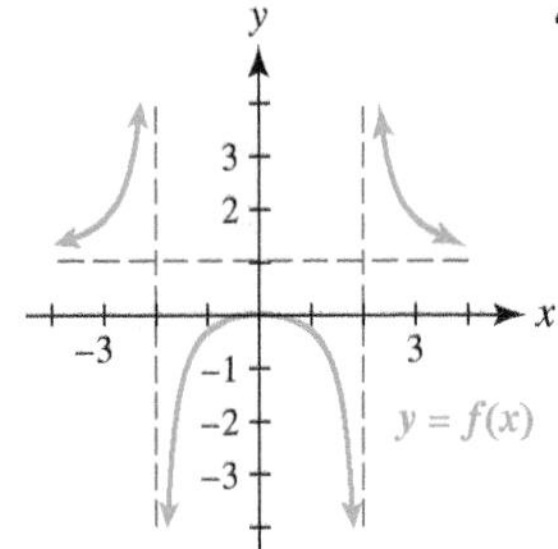

40.

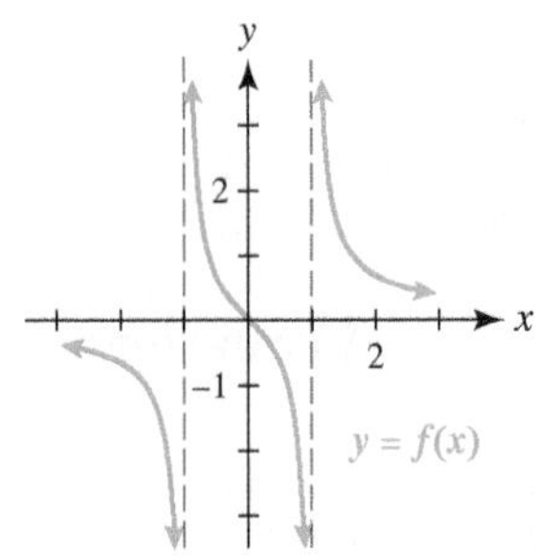

Polynomial Inequalities

Exercises 41–46: Solve the polynomial inequality

(a) symbolically and (b) graphically.

41. $x^3 - x > 0$

42. $8x^3 < 27$

43. $x^3 + x^2 \geq 2x$

44. $2x^3 \leq 3x^2 + 5x$

45. $x^4 - 13x^2 + 36 < 0$

46. $4x^4 - 5x^2 - 9 \geq 0$

Exercises 47–52: Solve the polynomial inequality.

47. $7x^4 > 14x^2$

48. $3x^4 - 4x^2 < 7$

49. $(x - 1)(x - 2)(x + 2) \geq 0$

50. $-(x + 1)^2(x - 2) \geq 0$

51. $2x^4 + 2x^3 \leq 12x^2$

52. $x^3 + 6x^2 + 9x > 0$

Exercises 53–56: Solve the polynomial inequality graphically.

53. $x^3 - 7x^2 + 14x \leq 8$

54. $2x^3 + 3x^2 - 3x < 2$

55. $3x^4 - 7x^3 - 2x^2 + 8x > 0$

56. $x^4 - 5x^3 \leq 5x^2 + 45x + 36$

Rational Inequalities

Exercises 57–62: Solve the rational inequality (a) symbolically and (b) graphically.

57. $\frac{1}{x} < 0$

58. $\frac{1}{x^2} > 0$

59. $\frac{4}{x + 3} \geq 0$

60. $\frac{x - 1}{x + 1} < 0$

61. $\frac{5}{x^2 - 4} < 0$

62. $\frac{x}{x^2 - 1} \geq 0$

Exercises 63–76: Solve the rational inequality.

63. $\frac{(x + 1)^2}{x - 2} \leq 0$

64. $\frac{2x}{(x - 2)^2} > 0$

65. $\frac{3 - 2x}{1 + x} < 0$

66. $\frac{x + 1}{4 - 2x} \geq 1$

67. $\frac{(x + 1)(x - 2)}{(x + 3)} < 0$

68. $\frac{x(x - 3)}{x + 2} \geq 0$

69. $\frac{2x - 5}{x^2 - 1} \geq 0$

70. $\frac{5 - x}{x^2 - x - 2} < 0$

71. $\frac{1}{x - 3} \leq \frac{5}{x - 3}$

72. $\frac{3}{2 - x} > \frac{x}{2 + x}$

73. $2 - \frac{5}{x} + \frac{2}{x^2} \geq 0$

74. $\frac{1}{x - 1} + \frac{1}{x + 1} > \frac{3}{4}$

75. $\frac{1}{x} \leq \frac{2}{x + 2}$

76. $\frac{1}{x + 1} < \frac{1}{x} + 1$

Applications

77. **Time Spent in Line** Suppose the average number of vehicles arriving at the main gate of an amusement park is equal to 10 per minute, while the average number of vehicles being admitted through the gate per minute is equal to x. Then the average waiting time in minutes for each vehicle at the gate can be computed by $f(x) = \frac{x - 5}{x^2 - 10x}$, where $x > 10$. (***Source:*** F. Mannering.)
   (a) Estimate the admittance rate x that results in an average wait of 15 seconds.
   (b) If one attendant can serve 5 vehicles per minute, how many attendants are needed to keep the average wait to 15 seconds or less?

78. **Length of Lines** (Refer to Example 2 in Section 4.6.) Solve $\frac{x^2}{2 - 2x} = 3$ to determine the traffic intensity x when the average number of vehicles in line equals 3.

79. **Construction** (Refer to Example 4.) Find possible dimensions for a box with a volume of 196 cubic inches, a surface area of 280 square inches, and a length that is twice the width.

80. **Minimizing Surface Area** An aluminum can is being designed to hold a volume of 100π cubic centimeters.

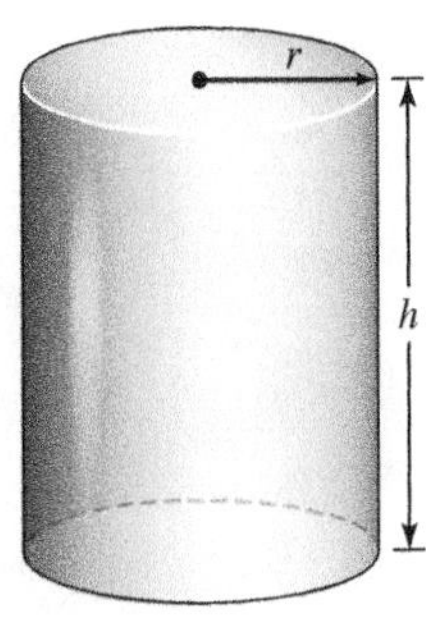

Geometry Review
To review formulas for cylinders, see Chapter R (page R-4).

   (a) Find a formula for the volume V in terms of r and h.
   (b) Write a formula for a function S that calculates the outside surface area of the can in terms of only r. Evaluate $S(2)$ and interpret the result.
   (c) Find the dimensions that result in the least amount of aluminum being used in its construction.

81. **Minimizing Cost** A cardboard box with no top and a square base is being constructed and must have a volume of 108 cubic inches. Let x be the length of a side of its base in inches.
   (a) Write a formula $A(x)$ that calculates the outside surface area in square feet of the box.
   (b) If cardboard costs \$0.10 per square foot, write a formula $C(x)$ that gives the cost in dollars of the cardboard in the box.
   (c) Find the dimensions of the box that would minimize the cost of the cardboard.

82. Cost-Benefit A cost-benefit function C computes the cost in millions of dollars of implementing a city recycling project when x percent of the citizens participate, where $C(x) = \frac{1.2x}{100 - x}$.

(a) Graph C in [0, 100, 10] by [0, 10, 1]. Interpret the graph as x approaches 100.

(b) If 75% participation is expected, determine the cost for the city.

(c) The city plans to spend \$5 million on this recycling project. Estimate the percentage of participation that can be expected.

83. Braking Distance The *grade* x of a hill is a measure of its steepness. For example, if a road rises 10 feet for every 100 feet of horizontal distance, then it has an uphill grade of $x = \frac{10}{100}$, or 10%. See the figure. The braking distance D for a car traveling at 50 miles per hour on a wet uphill grade is given by the formula $D(x) = \frac{2500}{30(0.3 + x)}$. (*Source:* L. Haefner.)

(a) Evaluate $D(0.05)$ and interpret the result.

(b) Describe what happens to the braking distance as the hill becomes steeper. Does this agree with your driving experience?

(c) Estimate the grade associated with a braking distance of 220 feet.

84. Braking Distance (Refer to Exercise 83.) If a car is traveling 50 miles per hour downhill, then the car's braking distance on a wet pavement is given by

$$D(x) = \frac{2500}{30(0.3 + x)},$$

where $x < 0$ for a downhill grade.

(a) Evaluate $D(-0.1)$ and interpret the result.

(b) What happens to the braking distance as the downhill grade becomes steeper? Does this agree with your driving experience?

(c) The graph of D has a vertical asymptote at $x = -0.3$. Give the physical significance of this asymptote.

(d) Estimate the grade associated with a braking distance of 350 feet.

85. Waiting in Line (Refer to Example 8.) A parking garage attendant can wait on 40 cars per hour. If cars arrive randomly at a rate of x cars per hour, then the average line length is given by

$$f(x) = \frac{x^2}{1600 - 40x},$$

where the x-values are limited to $0 \leq x < 40$.

(a) Solve the inequality $f(x) \leq 8$.

(b) Interpret your answer from part (a).

86. Time Spent in Line If a parking garage attendant can wait on 3 vehicles per minute and vehicles are leaving the ramp at x vehicles per minute, then the average wait in minutes for a car trying to exit is given by the formula $f(x) = \frac{1}{3 - x}$.

(a) Solve the three-part inequality $5 \leq \frac{1}{3 - x} \leq 10$.

(b) Interpret your result from part (a).

87. Slippery Roads The coefficient of friction x measures the friction between the tires of a car and the road, where $0 < x \leq 1$. A smaller value of x indicates that the road is more slippery. If a car is traveling at 60 miles per hour, then the braking distance D in feet is given by the formula $D(x) = \frac{120}{x}$.

(a) What happens to the braking distance as the coefficient of friction becomes smaller?

(b) Find values for the coefficient of friction x that correspond to a braking distance of 400 feet or more.

88. Average Temperature The monthly average high temperature in degrees Fahrenheit at Daytona Beach, Florida, can be approximated by

$$f(x) = 0.0145x^4 - 0.426x^3 + 3.53x^2 - 6.22x + 72,$$

where $x = 1$ corresponds to January, $x = 2$ to February, and so on. Estimate graphically when the monthly average high temperature is 75°F or more.

89. Geometry A cubical box is being manufactured to hold 213 cubic inches. If this measurement can vary between 212.8 cubic inches and 213.2 cubic inches inclusive, by how much can the length x of a side of the cube vary?

90. Construction A cylindrical aluminum can is being manufactured so that its height h is 8 centimeters more than its radius r. Estimate values for the radius (to the nearest hundredth) that result in the can having a volume between 1000 and 1500 cubic centimeters inclusive.

Variation

Exercises 91–94: Find the constant of proportionality k.

91. $y = \frac{k}{x}$, and $y = 2$ when $x = 3$

92. $y = \frac{k}{x^2}$, and $y = \frac{1}{4}$ when $x = 8$

93. $y = kx^3$, and $y = 64$ when $x = 2$

94. $y = kx^{3/2}$, and $y = 96$ when $x = 16$

Exercises 95–98: Solve the variation problem.

95. Suppose T varies directly with the $\frac{3}{2}$ power of x. When $x = 4$, $T = 20$. Find T when $x = 16$.

96. Suppose y varies directly with the second power of x. When $x = 3$, $y = 10.8$. Find y when $x = 1.5$.

97. Let y be inversely proportional to x. When $x = 6$, $y = 5$. Find y when $x = 15$.

98. Let z be inversely proportional to the third power of t. When $t = 5$, $z = 0.08$. Find z when $t = 2$.

Exercises 99–102: Assume that the constant of proportionality is positive.

99. Let y be inversely proportional to x. If x doubles, what happens to y?

100. Let y vary inversely with the second power of x. If x doubles, what happens to y?

101. Suppose y varies directly with the third power of x. If x triples, what happens to y?

102. Suppose y is directly proportional to the second power of x. If x is halved, what happens to y?

Exercises 103 and 104: The data satisfy the equation $y = kx^n$, where n is a positive integer. Determine k and n.

103.

x	2	3	4	5
y	2	4.5	8	12.5

104.

x	3	5	7	9
y	32.4	150	411.6	874.8

Exercises 105 and 106: The data in the table satisfy the equation $y = \frac{k}{x^n}$, where n is a positive integer. Determine k and n.

105.

x	2	3	4	5
y	1.5	1	0.75	0.6

106.

x	2	4	6	8
y	9	2.25	1	0.5625

107. Fiddler Crab Growth The weight y of a fiddler crab is directly proportional to the 1.25 power of the weight x of its claws. A crab with a body weight of 1.9 grams has claws weighing 1.1 grams. Estimate the weight of a fiddler crab with claws weighing 0.75 gram. (***Source:*** D. Brown.)

108. Gravity The weight of an object varies inversely with the second power of the distance from the *center* of Earth. The radius of Earth is approximately 4000 miles. If a person weighs 160 pounds on Earth's surface, what would this individual weigh 8000 miles above the surface of Earth?

109. Hubble Telescope The brightness, or intensity, of starlight varies inversely with the square of its distance from Earth. The Hubble Telescope can see stars whose intensities are $\frac{1}{50}$ that of the faintest star now seen by ground-based telescopes. Determine how much farther the Hubble Telescope can see into space than ground-based telescopes. (***Source:*** National Aeronautics and Space Administration.)

110. Volume The volume V of a cylinder with a fixed height is directly proportional to the square of its radius r. If a cylinder with a radius of 10 inches has a volume of 200 cubic inches, what is the volume of a cylinder with the same height and a radius of 5 inches?

111. Electrical Resistance The electrical resistance R of a wire varies inversely with the square of its diameter d. If a 25-foot wire with a diameter of 2 millimeters has a resistance of 0.5 ohm, find the resistance of a wire having the same length and a diameter of 3 millimeters.

112. Strength of a Beam The strength of a rectangular wood beam varies directly with the square of the depth of its cross section. If a beam with a depth of 3.5 inches can support 1000 pounds, how much weight can the same type of beam hold if its depth is 12 inches?

Exercises 113 and 114: **Violin String** *The frequency F of a vibrating string is directly proportional to the square root of the tension T on the string and inversely proportional to the length L of the string.*

113. If both the tension and the length are doubled, what happens to F?

114. Give two ways to double the frequency F.

Writing About Mathematics

115. Describe the steps to graphically solve a polynomial inequality in the form $p(x) > 0$.

116. Describe the steps to symbolically solve a rational inequality in the form $f(x) > 0$.

4.8 Radical Equations and Power Functions

- **Learn properties of rational exponents**
- **Learn radical notation**
- **Use radical functions and solve radical equations**
- **Understand properties and graphs of power functions**
- **Use power functions to model data**
- **Solve equations involving rational exponents**
- **Use power regression to model data (optional)**

Introduction

Johannes Kepler (1571–1630) was the first to recognize that a power function models the relationship between a planet's distance from the sun and its period of revolution. Table 4.10 lists the average distance x from the sun and the time y in years for several planets to orbit the sun. The distance x has been normalized so that Earth is one unit away from the sun. For example, Jupiter is 5.2 times farther from the sun than Earth and requires 11.9 years to orbit the sun.

Planets and Their Orbits

Planet	Mercury	Venus	Earth	Mars	Jupiter	Saturn
x (distance)	0.387	0.723	1.00	1.52	5.20	9.54
y (period)	0.241	0.615	1.00	1.88	11.9	29.5

Table 4.10 ***Source:*** C. Ronan, *The Natural History of the Universe.*

A scatterplot of the data in Table 4.10 is shown in Figure 4.115. To model these data, we might try a polynomial, such as $f(x) = x$ or $g(x) = x^2$. Figure 4.116 shows that $f(x) = x$ increases too slowly and $g(x) = x^2$ increases too fast. To model these data, a new type of function is required. That is, we need a function in the form $h(x) = x^b$, where $1 < b < 2$. Polynomials allow the exponent b to be only a nonnegative integer, whereas *power functions* allow b to be any real number. See Figure 4.117 and Example 11.

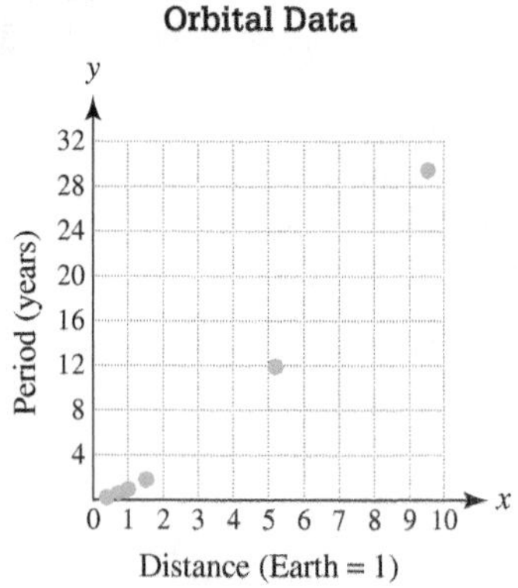

Figure 4.115

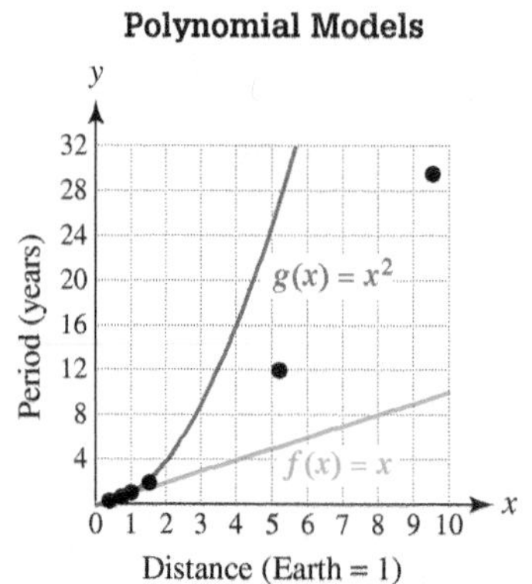

Figure 4.116

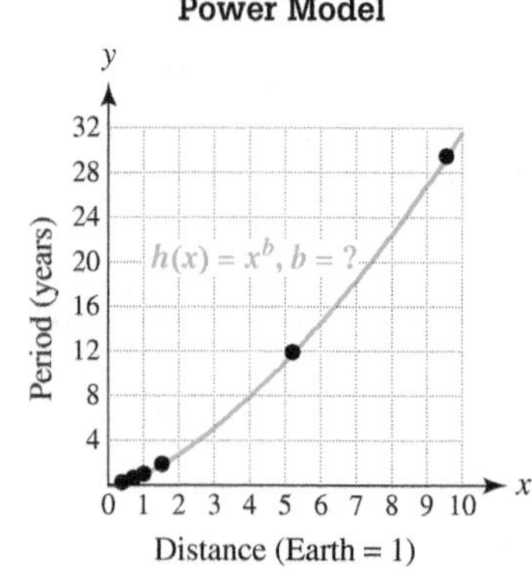

Figure 4.117

Rational Exponents and Radical Notation

The following properties can be used to simplify expressions with rational exponents.

Algebra Review
To review integer exponents, see Chapter R (page R-7). To review radical notation and rational exponents, see Chapter R (page R-38).

PROPERTIES OF RATIONAL EXPONENTS

Let m and n be positive integers with $\frac{m}{n}$ in *lowest* terms and $n \geq 2$. Let r and p be rational numbers. Assume that b is a nonzero real number and that each expression is a real number.

Property	***Example***
1. $b^{m/n} = (b^m)^{1/n} = (b^{1/n})^m$	$4^{3/2} = (4^3)^{1/2} = (4^{1/2})^3 = 2^3 = 8$
2. $b^{m/n} = \sqrt[n]{b^m} = (\sqrt[n]{b})^m$	$8^{2/3} = \sqrt[3]{8^2} = (\sqrt[3]{8})^2 = 2^2 = 4$
3. $(b^r)^p = b^{rp}$	$(2^{3/2})^4 = 2^{(3/2)4} = 2^6 = 64$
4. $b^{-r} = \dfrac{1}{b^r}$	$4^{-1/2} = \dfrac{1}{4^{1/2}} = \dfrac{1}{2}$
5. $b^r b^p = b^{r+p}$	$3^{5/2} \cdot 3^{3/2} = 3^{(5/2)+(3/2)} = 3^4 = 81$
6. $\dfrac{b^r}{b^p} = b^{r-p}$	$\dfrac{5^{5/4}}{5^{3/4}} = 5^{(5/4)-(3/4)} = 5^{1/2}$

EXAMPLE 1 Applying properties of exponents

Simplify each expression by hand.

(a) $16^{3/4}$ **(b)** $\dfrac{4^{1/3}}{4^{5/6}}$ **(c)** $27^{-2/3} \cdot 27^{1/3}$ **(d)** $(5^{3/4})^{2/3}$ **(e)** $(-125)^{-4/3}$

SOLUTION

(a) $16^{3/4} = (\sqrt[4]{16})^3 = (2)^3 = 8$ — $b^{m/n} = \sqrt[n]{b^m} = (\sqrt[n]{b})^m$

(b) $\dfrac{4^{1/3}}{4^{5/6}} = 4^{(1/3)-(5/6)} = 4^{-1/2} = \dfrac{1}{\sqrt{4}} = \dfrac{1}{2}$ — $\frac{b^r}{b^p} = b^{r-p}$

(c) $27^{-2/3} \cdot 27^{1/3} = 27^{(-2/3)+(1/3)} = 27^{-1/3} = \dfrac{1}{\sqrt[3]{27}} = \dfrac{1}{3}$ — $b^r b^p = b^{r+p}$

(d) $(5^{3/4})^{2/3} = 5^{(3/4)(2/3)} = 5^{1/2}$ or $\sqrt{5}$ — $(b^r)^p = b^{rp}$

(e) $(-125)^{-4/3} = \dfrac{1}{(\sqrt[3]{-125})^4} = \dfrac{1}{(-5)^4} = \dfrac{1}{625}$ — $b^{-r} = \frac{1}{b^r}$

Now Try Exercises 1, 7, 9, 11, and 13

EXAMPLE 2 Writing radicals with rational exponents

Use positive rational exponents to write each expression.

(a) $\sqrt{x}$ **(b)** $\sqrt[3]{x^2}$ **(c)** $(\sqrt[4]{z})^{-5}$ **(d)** $\sqrt{\sqrt[3]{y} \cdot \sqrt[4]{y}}$

SOLUTION

(a) $\sqrt{x} = x^{1/2}$ **(b)** $\sqrt[3]{x^2} = (x^2)^{1/3} = x^{2/3}$

(c) $(\sqrt[4]{z})^{-5} = (z^{1/4})^{-5} = z^{-5/4} = \dfrac{1}{z^{5/4}}$

(d) $\sqrt{\sqrt[3]{y} \cdot \sqrt[4]{y}} = \left(y^{1/3} \cdot y^{1/4}\right)^{1/2} = \left(y^{(1/3)+(1/4)}\right)^{1/2} = \left(y^{7/12}\right)^{1/2} = y^{7/24}$

Now Try Exercises 19, 21, 23, and 27

Functions Involving Radicals

Expressions involving radicals are sometimes used to define **radical functions**. Two common radical functions are the **square root function** and the **cube root function**. Their graphs and domains are shown in Figure 4.118 and 4.119. The fourth root function is also shown in Figure 4.120.

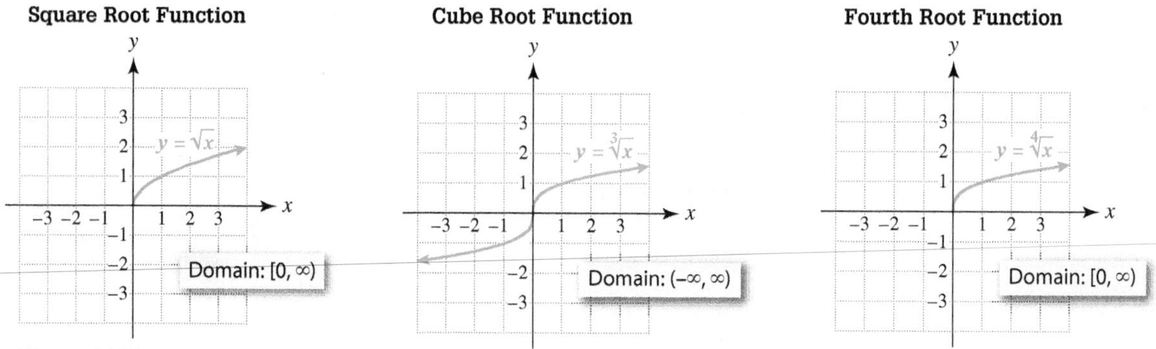

Figure 4.118 Figure 4.119 Figure 4.120

EXAMPLE 3 Evaluating radical functions

Evaluate each function for the given value of x.

(a) $f(x) = 2\sqrt[3]{x}$ for $x = 27$
(b) $g(x) = \sqrt{x^3}$ for $x = 4$
(c) $h(x) = \sqrt[4]{2x}$ for $x = 8$

SOLUTION

(a) $f(27) = 2\sqrt[3]{27} = 2(3) = 6$
(b) $g(4) = \sqrt{4^3} = \sqrt{64} = 8$
(c) $h(8) = \sqrt[4]{2(8)} = \sqrt[4]{16} = 2$

Now Try Exercises 33, 35, and 37

In the next example, we use transformations to graph a function.

EXAMPLE 4 Using transformations to graph a function

Graph $g(x) = -\sqrt[3]{x + 1}$.

SOLUTION

To obtain the graph of g we can reflect the graph of $f(x) = \sqrt[3]{x}$ (see Figure 4.119) across the x-axis to obtain $y = -\sqrt[3]{x}$, and then shift this new graph left 1 unit to obtain $y = -\sqrt[3]{(x + 1)}$, as shown in Figures 4.121 and 4.122. (In this example, we could also shift left 1 unit and then reflect across the x-axis.)

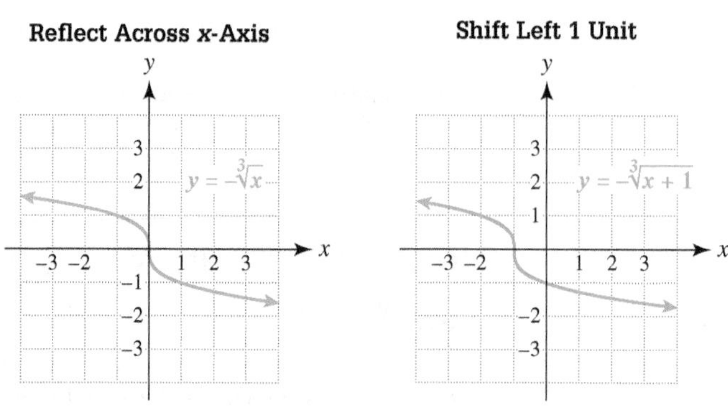

Figure 4.121 Figure 4.122

Now Try Exercise 43

Functions involving radicals have many applications. In the next example we use the cube root function to model numbers of plant species on different Galápagos islands.

EXAMPLE 5 Estimating numbers of plant species

The number N of different plant species that live on a Galápagos island is sometimes related to the island's area A in square miles by the function

$$N(A) = 28.6\sqrt[3]{A}.$$

(a) Approximate N to the nearest whole number for islands of 100 square miles and 200 square miles. Interpret your answers.
(b) Does N double if A doubles?

SOLUTION

(a) $N(100) = 28.6\sqrt[3]{100} \approx 133$ and $N(200) = 28.6\sqrt[3]{200} \approx 167$. If the island is 100 square miles, there are about 133 different species of plants. This number increases to 167 on an island of 200 square miles.
(b) From part (a), we see that N does not double if A doubles. It increases by a factor of $\sqrt[3]{2} \approx 1.26$, not 2.

Now Try Exercise 111

Equations Involving Radicals

In solving equations that contain square roots, it is common to square each side of an equation and then check the results. This is done in the next example.

EXAMPLE 6 Solving an equation containing a square root

Solve $x = \sqrt{15 - 2x}$. Check your answers.

SOLUTION

Begin by squaring each side of the equation.

$$x = \sqrt{15 - 2x} \quad \text{Given equation}$$
$$x^2 = \left(\sqrt{15 - 2x}\right)^2 \quad \text{Square each side.}$$
$$x^2 = 15 - 2x \quad \text{Simplify.}$$
$$x^2 + 2x - 15 = 0 \quad \text{Add 2x and subtract 15.}$$
$$(x + 5)(x - 3) = 0 \quad \text{Factor.}$$
$$x = -5 \quad \text{or} \quad x = 3 \quad \text{Solve.}$$

Check: Now substitute these values in the *given* equation $x = \sqrt{15 - 2x}$.

$$-5 \neq \sqrt{15 - 2(-5)} = 5, \qquad 3 = \sqrt{15 - 2(3)} \ \checkmark$$

[−9, 9, 1] by [−6, 6, 1]

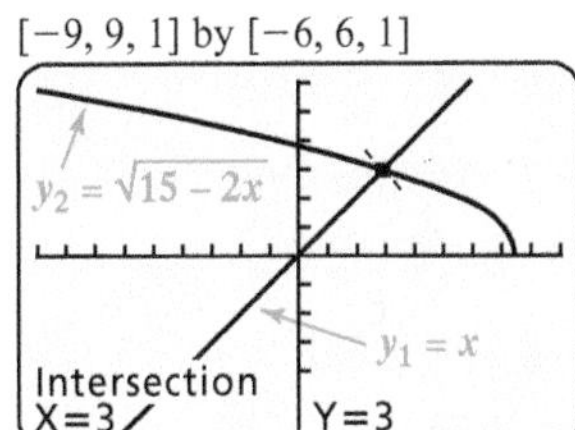

Figure 4.123

Thus 3 is the only solution. This result is supported graphically in Figure 4.123. Notice that *no* point of intersection occurs when $x = -5$.

Now Try Exercise 57

The value -5 in Example 6 is called an **extraneous solution** because it does not satisfy the given equation. It is important to check results whenever *squaring* has been used to solve an equation. (Graphical solutions do not have extraneous solutions.)

NOTE If each side of an equation is raised to the same positive integer power, then any solutions to the given equation are *among* the solutions to the new equation. That is, the solutions to the equation $a = b$ are *among* the solutions to $a^n = b^n$. For this reason, we *must* check our answers.

In the next example, we cube each side of an equation that contains a cube root.

EXAMPLE 7 **Solving an equation containing a cube root**

Solve $\sqrt[3]{2x + 5} - 2 = 1$.

SOLUTION Start by adding 2 to each side. Then cube each side.

$$\begin{aligned} \sqrt[3]{2x + 5} &= 3 && \text{Add 2 to each side.} \\ \left(\sqrt[3]{2x + 5}\right)^3 &= 3^3 && \text{Cube each side.} \\ 2x + 5 &= 27 && \text{Simplify.} \\ 2x &= 22 && \text{Subtract 5 from each side.} \\ x &= 11 && \text{Divide each side by 2.} \end{aligned}$$

The only solution is 11. The answer checks.

Now Try Exercise 65

Squaring Twice In the next example, we need to square twice to solve a radical equation.

EXAMPLE 8 **Squaring twice**

Solve $\sqrt{2x + 3} - \sqrt{x + 1} = 1$.

SOLUTION

Getting Started When an equation contains two square root expressions, we frequently need to square twice. Start by isolating the more complicated radical expression and then square each side. ▶

$$\begin{aligned} \sqrt{2x + 3} - \sqrt{x + 1} &= 1 && \text{Given equation} \\ \sqrt{2x + 3} &= 1 + \sqrt{x + 1} && \text{Isolate } \sqrt{2x + 3}. \\ \left(\sqrt{2x + 3}\right)^2 &= \left(1 + \sqrt{x + 1}\right)^2 && \text{Square each side.} \\ 2x + 3 &= 1 + 2\sqrt{x + 1} + x + 1 && \text{Simplify.} \\ x + 1 &= 2\sqrt{x + 1} && \text{Isolate the remaining radical.} \\ (x + 1)^2 &= \left(2\sqrt{x + 1}\right)^2 && \text{Square each side again.} \\ x^2 + 2x + 1 &= 4(x + 1) && \text{Simplify.} \\ x^2 + 2x + 1 &= 4x + 4 && \text{Distributive property} \\ x^2 - 2x - 3 &= 0 && \text{Subtract } 4x + 4. \\ (x - 3)(x + 1) &= 0 && \text{Factor.} \\ x - 3 = 0 \quad \text{or} \quad x + 1 &= 0 && \text{Zero-product property} \\ x = 3 \quad \text{or} \quad x &= -1 && \text{Solve each equation.} \end{aligned}$$

Checking reveals that both -1 and 3 are solutions to the *given* equation.

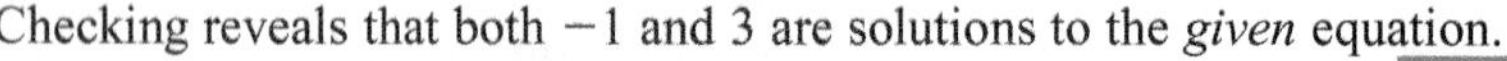

Now Try Exercise 63

Power Functions and Models

Functions with rational exponents are often used to model physical characteristics of living organisms. For example, larger animals tend to have slower heart rates and larger birds tend to have bigger wings. There is a relationship between a bird's weight and its wing size. (See Example 10.)

Power functions often have rational exponents, and can be written in radical notation. A special type of power function is a root function.

POWER FUNCTION

A function f given by $f(x) = x^b$, where b is a constant, is a **power function**. If $b = \frac{1}{n}$ for some integer $n \geq 2$, then f is a **root function** given by $f(x) = x^{1/n}$, or equivalently, $f(x) = \sqrt[n]{x}$.

Cube Root Square

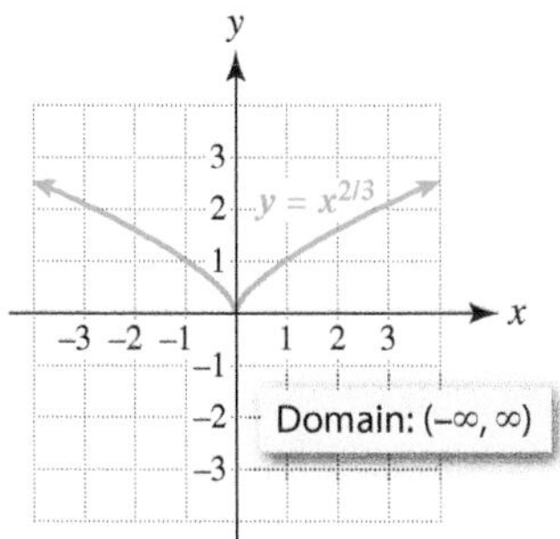

Figure 4.124

Examples of power functions include

$$f_1(x) = x^2, \quad f_2(x) = x^{3/4}, \quad f_3(x) = x^{0.4}, \quad \text{and} \quad f_4(x) = \sqrt[3]{x^2}.$$

Power Functions

Domains of Power Functions Suppose a positive rational number $\frac{p}{q}$ is written in lowest terms. Then the domain of $f(x) = x^{p/q}$ is all real numbers whenever q is odd and all *nonnegative* real numbers whenever q is even. A graph of a common power function is shown in Figure 4.124.

EXAMPLE 9 **Graphing power functions**

Graph $f(x) = x^b$, where $b = 0.3$, 1, and 1.7, for $x \geq 0$. Discuss the effect that b has on the graph of f for $x \geq 1$.

SOLUTION

The graphs of $y = x^{0.3}$, $y = x^1$, and $y = x^{1.7}$ are shown in Figure 4.125. For $x \geq 1$, larger values of b cause the graph of f to increase faster. Note that each graph passes through the point (1, 1). Why?

$f(x) = x^b, x \geq 0$

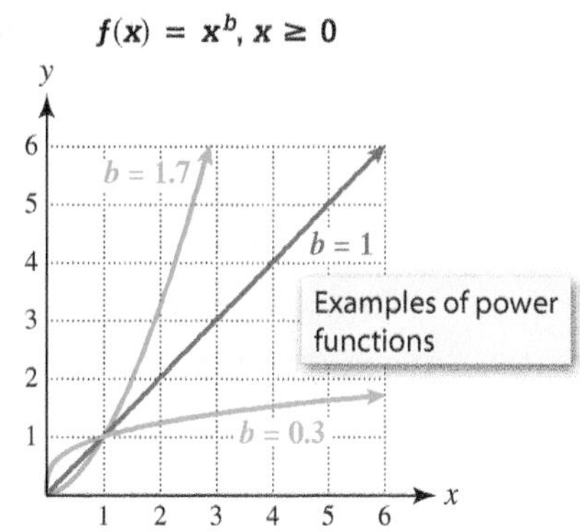

Figure 4.125

Now Try Exercises 73 and 74

Modeling In the next two examples, we use power functions to determine weights of birds based on wing size and to describe planetary motion.

EXAMPLE 10 **Modeling wing size of a bird**

Heavier birds have larger wings with more surface area than do lighter birds. For some species of birds, this relationship can be modeled by $S(w) = 0.2w^{2/3}$, where w is the weight of the bird in kilograms, with $0.1 \leq w \leq 5$, and S is the surface area of the wings in square meters. (***Source:*** C. Pennycuick, *Newton Rules Biology*.)

(a) Approximate $S(0.5)$ and interpret the result.

(b) What weight corresponds to a surface area of 0.25 square meter?

SOLUTION

(a) $S(0.5) = 0.2(0.5)^{2/3} \approx 0.126$. The wings of a bird that weighs 0.5 kilogram have a surface area of about 0.126 square meter.

(b) To determine the weight that corresponds to a surface area of 0.25 square meter, we must solve the equation $0.2w^{2/3} = 0.25$.

$$0.2w^{2/3} = 0.25 \qquad \text{Equation to solve}$$

$$w^{2/3} = \frac{0.25}{0.2} \qquad \text{Divide by 0.2.}$$

$$(w^{2/3})^3 = \left(\frac{0.25}{0.2}\right)^3 \qquad \text{Cube each side.}$$

$$w^2 = \left(\frac{0.25}{0.2}\right)^3 \qquad \text{Simplify.}$$

$$w = \pm\sqrt{\left(\frac{0.25}{0.2}\right)^3} \qquad \text{Square root property}$$

$$w \approx \pm 1.4 \qquad \text{Approximate.}$$

Since w must be positive, the wings of a 1.4-kilogram bird have a surface area of about 0.25 square meter.

Now Try Exercise 105

EXAMPLE 11 Modeling the period of planetary orbits

Use the data in Table 4.10 on page 330 to complete the following.

(a) Make a scatterplot of the data. Graphically estimate a value for b so that $f(x) = x^b$ models the data.

(b) Check the accuracy of $f(x)$.

(c) The average distances of Uranus, Neptune, and Pluto (no longer a major planet) from the sun are 19.2, 30.1, and 39.5, respectively. Use f to estimate their periods of revolution. Compare these estimates to the actual values of 84.0, 164.8, and 248.5 years.

SOLUTION

(a) Graph the data and $y = x^b$ for different values of b. From the graphs of $y = x^{1.4}$, $y = x^{1.5}$, and $y = x^{1.6}$ in Figures 4.126–4.128, it can be seen that $b \approx 1.5$.

Calculator Help

To make a scatterplot, see Appendix A (page AP-3). To make a table like Figure 4.129, see Appendix A (page AP-9).

Exponent Too Small

[0, 10, 1] by [0, 30, 10]

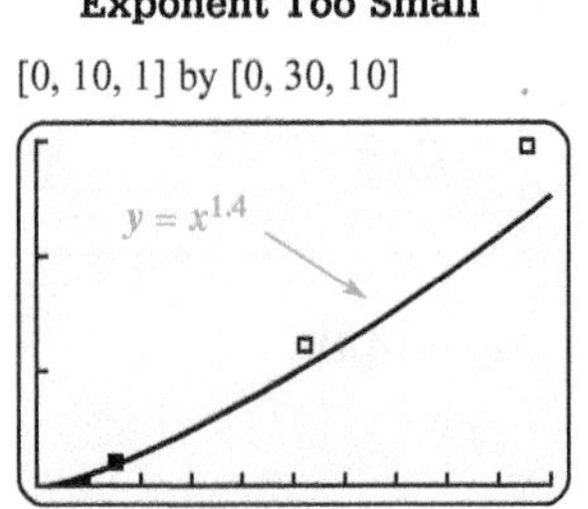

Figure 4.126

Exponent About Right?

[0, 10, 1] by [0, 30, 10]

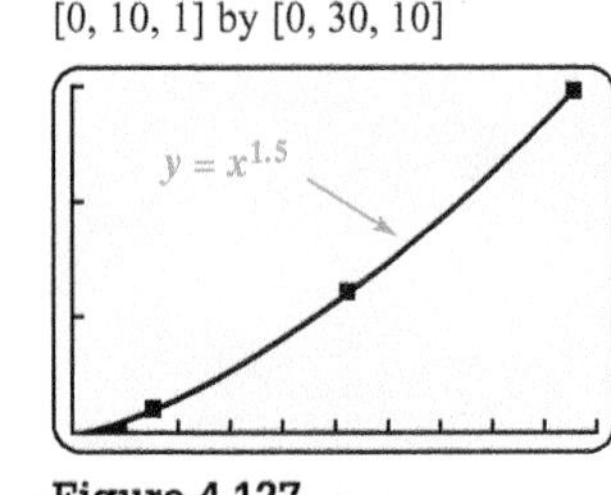

Figure 4.127

Exponent Too Large

[0, 10, 1] by [0, 30, 10]

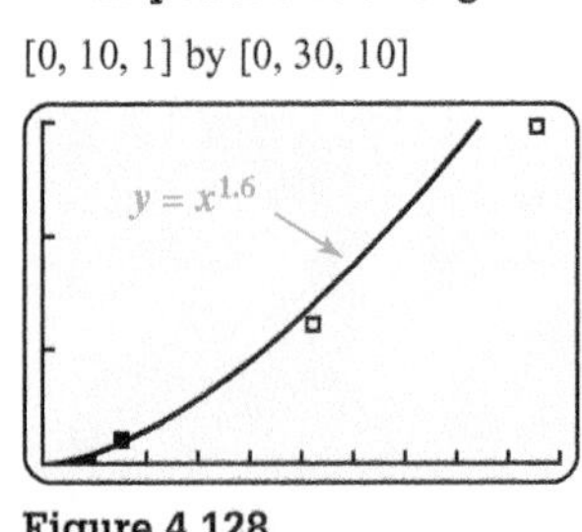

Figure 4.128

(b) Let $y_1 = x^{1.5}$. The values shown in Figure 4.129 model the data in Table 4.10 remarkably well.

Comparing Model with True Values

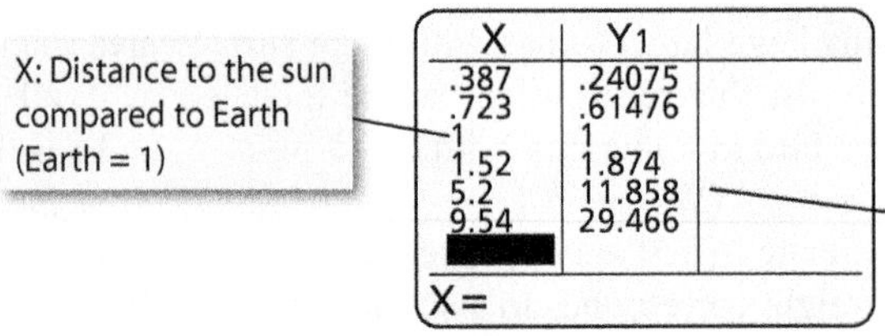

X: Distance to the sun compared to Earth (Earth = 1)

X	Y1
.387	.24075
.723	.61476
1	1
1.52	1.874
5.2	11.858
9.54	29.466

X=

Figure 4.129

X	Y1	
19.2	84.13	Uranus
30.1	165.14	Neptune
39.5	248.25	Pluto

X=

Y_1: Years to orbit the sun

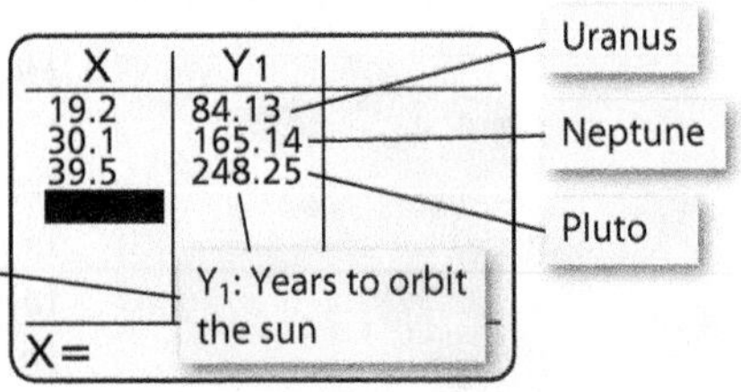

Figure 4.130

(c) To approximate the number of years required for Uranus, Neptune, and Pluto to orbit the sun, evaluate $y_1 = x^{1.5}$ at $x = 19.2$, 30.1, and 39.5, as shown in Figure 4.130. These values are close to the actual values.

Now Try Exercise 109

Equations Involving Rational Exponents

The next example demonstrates a basic technique that can be used to solve equations with rational exponents.

EXAMPLE 12 Solving an equation with rational exponents

Solve $2x^{5/2} - 7 = 23$. Round to the nearest hundredth and give graphical support.

SOLUTION

Symbolic Solution Start by adding 7 to each side of the given equation.

$$\begin{aligned} 2x^{5/2} &= 30 && \text{Add 7 to each side.} \\ x^{5/2} &= 15 && \text{Divide each side by 2.} \\ (x^{5/2})^2 &= 15^2 && \text{Square each side.} \\ x^5 &= 225 && \text{Properties of exponents} \\ x &= 225^{1/5} && \text{Take the fifth root of each side.} \\ x &\approx 2.95 && \text{Approximate.} \end{aligned}$$

Calculator Help
When entering X^(5/2), be sure to put parentheses around the fraction 5/2.

[−5, 5, 1] by [−40, 40, 10]

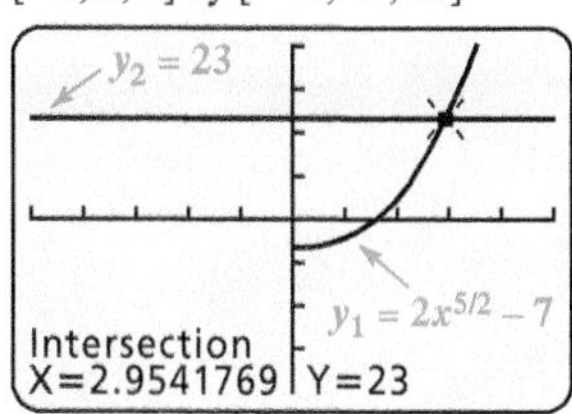

Figure 4.131

Graphic Solution Graphical support is shown in Figure 4.131, where the graphs of $Y_1 = 2X^{\wedge}(5/2) - 7$ and $Y_2 = 23$ intersect near (2.95, 23).

Now Try Exercise 89

MAKING CONNECTIONS

Solutions to $x^n = k$ (k a constant and $n \geq 2$ an integer)

***n* odd:** The real solution to $x^n = k$ is $x = \sqrt[n]{k}$, or $x = k^{1/n}$, for all k. See Example 12.

***n* even:** The real solutions to $x^n = k$ are $x = \pm\sqrt[n]{k}$, or $x = \pm k^{1/n}$, for $k \geq 0$. See Example 10.

Equations that have rational exponents are sometimes reducible to quadratic form.

EXAMPLE 13 Solving an equation having negative exponents

Solve $15n^{-2} - 19n^{-1} + 6 = 0$.

SOLUTION Two methods for solving this equation are presented.

Method 1: Use the substitution $u = n^{-1} = \frac{1}{n}$ and $u^2 = n^{-2} = \frac{1}{n^2}$.

$$\begin{aligned} 15n^{-2} - 19n^{-1} + 6 &= 0 && \text{Given equation} \\ 15u^2 - 19u + 6 &= 0 && \text{Let } u = n^{-1} \text{ and } u^2 = n^{-2}. \\ (3u - 2)(5u - 3) &= 0 && \text{Factor.} \\ u = \frac{2}{3} \quad \text{or} \quad u &= \frac{3}{5} && \text{Zero-product property} \end{aligned}$$

Because $u = \frac{1}{n}$, it follows that $n = \frac{1}{u}$. Thus $n = \frac{3}{2}$ or $n = \frac{5}{3}$.

Method 2: Another way to solve this equation is to multiply each side by n^2 to eliminate negative exponents.

$$\begin{aligned} 15n^{-2} - 19n^{-1} + 6 &= 0 && \text{Given equation} \\ n^2(15n^{-2} - 19n^{-1} + 6) &= n^2(0) && \text{Multiply each side by } n^2. \\ 15n^2n^{-2} - 19n^2n^{-1} + 6n^2 &= 0 && \text{Distributive property} \\ 15 - 19n + 6n^2 &= 0 && \text{Properties of exponents} \end{aligned}$$

$$6n^2 - 19n + 15 = 0 \quad \text{Rewrite the equation.}$$
$$(2n - 3)(3n - 5) = 0 \quad \text{Factor.}$$
$$n = \frac{3}{2} \quad \text{or} \quad n = \frac{5}{3} \quad \text{Zero-product property}$$

Now Try Exercise 93

In the next example, we solve an equation with fractional exponents that can be written in quadratic form by using substitution.

EXAMPLE 14 **Solving an equation having fractions for exponents**

Solve $2x^{2/3} + 5x^{1/3} - 3 = 0$.

SOLUTION

To solve this equation, use the substitution $u = x^{1/3}$.

$$2x^{2/3} + 5x^{1/3} - 3 = 0 \quad \text{Given equation}$$
$$2(x^{1/3})^2 + 5(x^{1/3}) - 3 = 0 \quad \text{Properties of exponents}$$
$$2u^2 + 5u - 3 = 0 \quad \text{Let } u = x^{1/3}.$$
$$(2u - 1)(u + 3) = 0 \quad \text{Factor.}$$
$$u = \frac{1}{2} \quad \text{or} \quad u = -3 \quad \text{Zero-product property}$$

Because $u = x^{1/3}$, it follows that $x = u^3$. Thus $x = \left(\frac{1}{2}\right)^3 = \frac{1}{8}$ or $x = (-3)^3 = -27$.

Now Try Exercise 97

Power Regression (Optional)

Rather than visually fit a curve to data, as was done in Example 11, we can use least-squares regression to fit the data. Least-squares regression was introduced in Section 2.1. In the next example, we apply this technique to data from biology.

EXAMPLE 15 **Modeling the length of a bird's wing**

Table 4.11 lists the weight W and the wingspan L for birds of a particular species.

Weights and Wingspans

W (kilograms)	0.5	1.5	2.0	2.5	3.0
L (meters)	0.77	1.10	1.22	1.31	1.40

Table 4.11 *Source:* C. Pennycuick.

(a) Use power regression to model the data with $L = aW^b$. Graph the data and the equation.
(b) Approximate the wingspan for a bird weighing 3.2 kilograms.

SOLUTION

(a) Let x be the weight W and y be the length L. Enter the data, and then select power regression (PwrReg), as shown in Figures 4.132 and 4.133. The results are shown in Figure 4.134. Let

$$y = 0.9674x^{0.3326} \quad \text{or} \quad L = 0.9674W^{0.3326}.$$

The data and equation are graphed in Figure 4.135.

(b) If a bird weighs 3.2 kilograms, this model predicts the wingspan to be

$$L = 0.9674(3.2)^{0.3326} \approx 1.42 \text{ meters.}$$

Calculator Help
To find an equation of least-squares fit, see Appendix A (page AP-9).

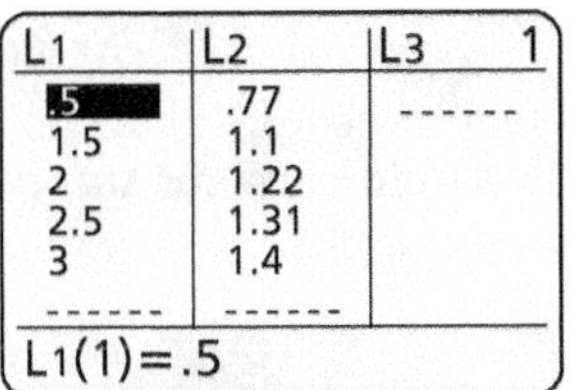

Figure 4.132

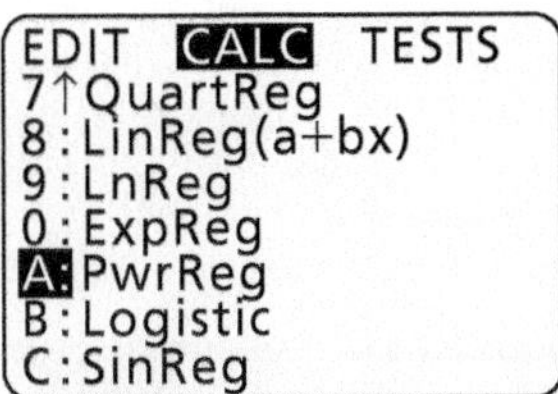

Figure 4.133

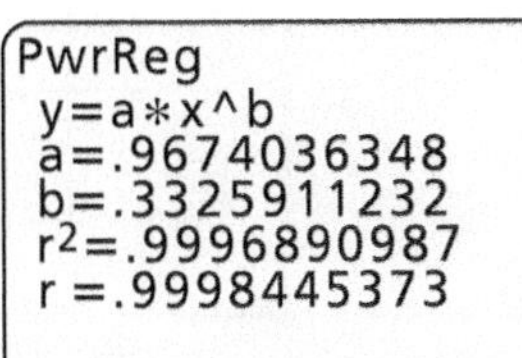

Figure 4.134

[0, 4, 1] by [0.5, 1.5, 0.5]

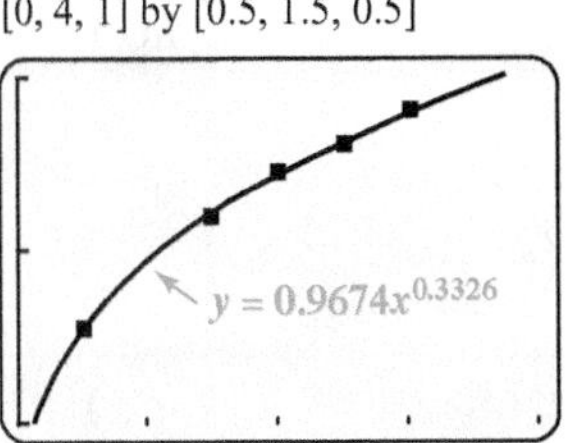

Figure 4.135

Now Try Exercise 115

4.8 Putting It All Together

The following table outlines important concepts in this section.

CONCEPT	EXPLANATION	EXAMPLES
Rational exponents	$x^{m/n} = (x^m)^{1/n}$ $= (x^{1/n})^m$	$9^{3/2} = (9^3)^{1/2} = (729)^{1/2} = 27$ $9^{3/2} = (9^{1/2})^3 = (3)^3 = 27$
Radical notation	$x^{1/2} = \sqrt{x}$ $x^{1/3} = \sqrt[3]{x}$ $x^{m/n} = \sqrt[n]{x^m}$ $= (\sqrt[n]{x})^m$	$25^{1/2} = \sqrt{25} = 5$ $27^{1/3} = \sqrt[3]{27} = 3$ $8^{2/3} = \sqrt[3]{8^2} = \sqrt[3]{64} = 4$ $4^{3/2} = \sqrt{4^3} = (\sqrt{4})^3 = (2)^3 = 8$
Solving radical equations	The solutions to $a = b$ are among the solutions to $a^n = b^n$ when n is a positive integer. *Check your results.*	Solve $\sqrt{2x + 3} = x$. $2x + 3 = x^2$ Square each side. $x^2 - 2x - 3 = 0$ Rewrite equation. $(x + 1)(x - 3) = 0$ Factor. $x = -1$ or $x = 3$ Solve. Checking reveals that 3 is the only solution.
Power function	$f(x) = x^b$, where b is a constant	$f(x) = x^{5/4}$ $g(x) = x^{-3.14}$ $h(x) = x^{1/3}$
Root function	$f(x) = x^{1/n}$, where $n \geq 2$ is an integer	$f(x) = x^{1/2}$ or $f(x) = \sqrt{x}$ $g(x) = x^{1/5}$ or $g(x) = \sqrt[5]{x}$

continued on next page

Several types of functions are listed in the following summary, which may be used as a reference for future work. Unless specified otherwise, each tick mark represents 1 unit.

TYPE OF FUNCTION	EXAMPLES	GRAPHS
Linear function $f(x) = ax + b$	$f(x) = 0.5x - 1$ $g(x) = -3x + 2$ $h(x) = 2$	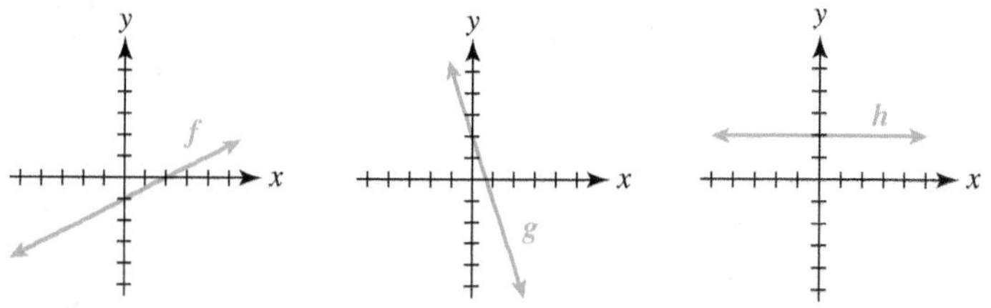
Polynomial function $f(x) = a_n x^n + \cdots + a_2 x^2 + a_1 x + a_0$	$f(x) = x^2 - 1$ $g(x) = x^3 - 4x - 1$ $h(x) = -x^4 + 4x^2 - 2$	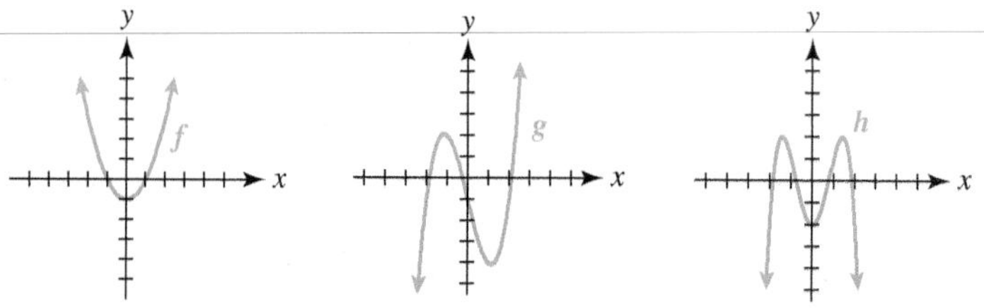
Rational function $f(x) = \frac{p(x)}{q(x)}$, where $p(x)$ and $q(x)$ are polynomials with $q(x) \neq 0$	$f(x) = \dfrac{1}{x}$ $g(x) = \dfrac{2x - 1}{x + 2}$ $h(x) = \dfrac{1}{x^2 - 1}$	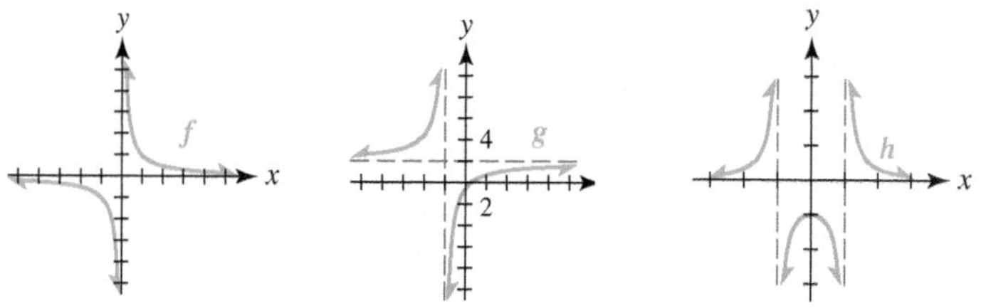
Root function $f(x) = x^{1/n}$, where $n \geq 2$ is an integer	$f(x) = x^{1/2} = \sqrt{x}$ $g(x) = x^{1/3} = \sqrt[3]{x}$ $h(x) = x^{1/4} = \sqrt[4]{x}$	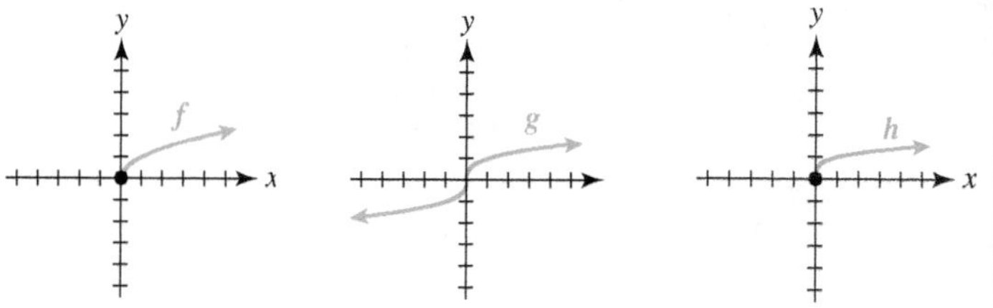
Power function $f(x) = x^b$, where b is a constant	$f(x) = x^{2/3}$ $g(x) = x^{1.41}$ $h(x) = x^3$	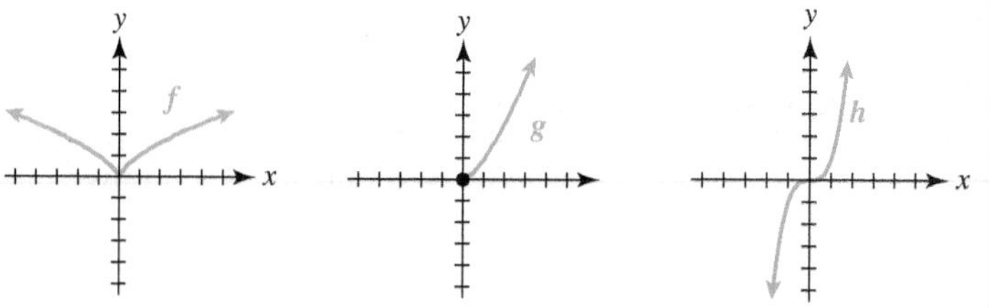

4.8 Exercises

Properties of Exponents

Exercises 1–18: Evaluate the expression by hand.

1. $8^{2/3}$
2. $-16^{3/2}$
3. $16^{-3/4}$
4. $25^{-3/2}$
5. $-81^{0.5}$
6. $32^{1/5}$
7. $(9^{3/4})^2$
8. $(4^{-1/2})^{-4}$
9. $\dfrac{8^{5/6}}{8^{1/2}}$
10. $\dfrac{4^{-1/2}}{4^{3/2}}$
11. $27^{5/6} \cdot 27^{-1/6}$
12. $16^{2/3} \cdot 16^{-1/6}$
13. $(-27)^{-5/3}$
14. $(-32)^{-3/5}$
15. $(0.5^{-2})^2$
16. $(2^{-2})^{-3/2}$
17. $(\frac{2}{3})^{-2}$
18. $(8^{-1/3} + 27^{-1/3})^2$

Exercises 19–28: Use positive exponents to rewrite.

19. $\sqrt{2x}$
20. $\sqrt{x + 1}$
21. $\sqrt[3]{z^5}$
22. $\sqrt[5]{x^2}$
23. $(\sqrt[4]{y})^{-3}$
24. $(\sqrt[3]{y^2})^{-5}$
25. $\sqrt{x} \cdot \sqrt[3]{x}$
26. $(\sqrt[5]{z})^{-3}$
27. $\sqrt{y \cdot \sqrt{y}}$
28. $\dfrac{\sqrt[3]{x}}{\sqrt{x}}$

Exercises 29–32: Use radical notation to rewrite.

29. $a^{-3/4}b^{1/2}$
30. $a^{-2/3}b^{3/5}$
31. $(a^{1/2} + b^{1/2})^{1/2}$
32. $(a^{3/4} - b^{3/2})^{1/3}$

Functions Involving Radicals

Exercises 33–40: Evaluate the function for the given value of x.

33. $f(x) = \sqrt[3]{2x}$ for $x = 32$
34. $f(x) = 5\sqrt[3]{-x}$ for $x = 8$
35. $f(x) = 2\sqrt{x^5}$ for $x = 4$
36. $f(x) = \sqrt{2x^3}$ for $x = 2$
37. $f(x) = \sqrt[4]{5x}$ for $x = 125$
38. $f(x) = 2\sqrt[4]{-x}$ for $x = -81$
39. $f(x) = \sqrt[5]{32x}$ for $x = -1$
40. $f(x) = 3\sqrt[5]{-x}$ for $x = 32$

Exercises 41–52: Use transformations of $y = \sqrt{x}$, $y = \sqrt[3]{x}$, or $y = \sqrt[4]{x}$ to graph $y = f(x)$.

41. $f(x) = \sqrt[3]{-x}$
42. $f(x) = \sqrt[3]{x + 1} - 2$
43. $f(x) = \sqrt[3]{x - 1} + 1$
44. $f(x) = -2\sqrt[3]{x}$
45. $f(x) = \sqrt[4]{x + 2} - 1$
46. $f(x) = \sqrt[4]{-x - 1}$
47. $f(x) = 2\sqrt[4]{x - 1}$
48. $f(x) = \sqrt[4]{2x}$
49. $f(x) = \sqrt{x + 3} + 2$
50. $f(x) = -\sqrt{-x}$
51. $f(x) = 2\sqrt{x}$
52. $f(x) = \sqrt{-x} + 1$

Equations Involving Radicals

Exercises 53–70: Solve the equation. Check your answers.

53. $\sqrt{x + 2} = x - 4$
54. $\sqrt{2x + 1} = 13$
55. $\sqrt{3x + 7} = 3x + 5$
56. $\sqrt{1 - x} = x + 5$
57. $\sqrt{5x - 6} = x$
58. $x - 5 = \sqrt{5x - 1}$
59. $\sqrt{x + 5} + 1 = x$
60. $\sqrt{4 - 3x} = x + 8$
61. $\sqrt{x + 1} + 3 = \sqrt{3x + 4}$
62. $\sqrt{x} = \sqrt{x - 5} + 1$
63. $\sqrt{2x} - \sqrt{x + 1} = 1$
64. $\sqrt{2x - 4} + 2 = \sqrt{3x + 4}$
65. $\sqrt[3]{z + 1} = -3$
66. $\sqrt[3]{z} + 5 = 4$
67. $\sqrt[3]{x + 1} = \sqrt[3]{2x - 1}$
68. $\sqrt[3]{2x^2 + 1} = \sqrt[3]{1 - x}$
69. $\sqrt[4]{x - 2} + 4 = 20$
70. $\sqrt[4]{2x + 3} = \sqrt{x + 1}$

Power Functions

Exercises 71 and 72: Evaluate each f(x) at the given x. Approximate each result to the nearest hundredth.

71. $f(x) = x^{3/2} - x^{1/2}$, $x = 50$
72. $f(x) = x^{5/4} - x^{-3/4}$, $x = 7$

Exercises 73 and 74: Match $f(x)$ with its graph. Assume that a and b are constants with $0 < a < 1 < b$.

73. $f(x) = x^a$

74. $f(x) = x^b$

(a)

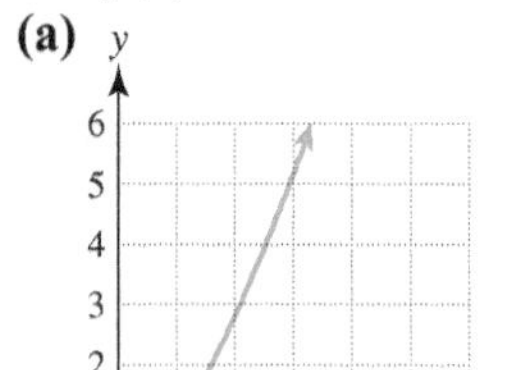

(b)

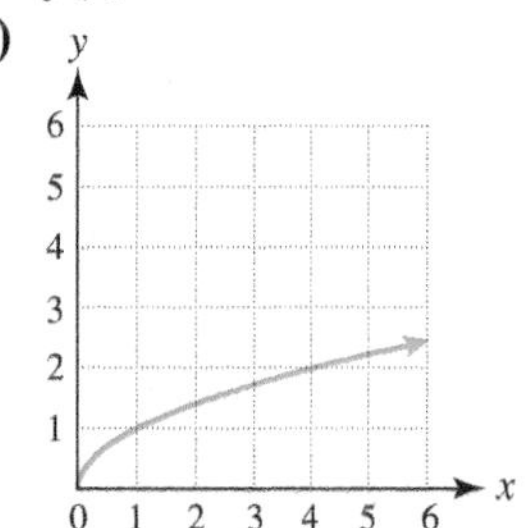

Exercises 75–80: Use translations to graph f.

75. $f(x) = x^{1/2} + 1$

76. $f(x) = (x - 1)^{1/3}$

77. $f(x) = x^{2/3} - 1$

78. $f(x) = (x - 1)^{1/4}$

79. $f(x) = (x + 1)^{2/3} - 2$

80. $f(x) = (x - 1)^{2/3}$

Equations Involving Rational Exponents

Exercises 81–102: Solve the equation. Check your answers.

81. $x^3 = 8$

82. $x^4 = \frac{1}{81}$

83. $x^{1/4} = 3$

84. $x^{1/3} = \frac{1}{5}$

85. $x^{2/5} = 4$

86. $x^{2/3} = 16$

87. $x^{4/3} = 16$

88. $x^{4/5} = 16$

89. $4x^{3/2} + 5 = 21$

90. $2x^{1/3} - 5 = 1$

91. $n^{-2} + 3n^{-1} + 2 = 0$

92. $2n^{-2} - n^{-1} = 3$

93. $5n^{-2} + 13n^{-1} = 28$

94. $3n^{-2} - 19n^{-1} + 20 = 0$

95. $x^{2/3} - x^{1/3} - 6 = 0$

96. $x^{2/3} + 9x^{1/3} + 14 = 0$

97. $6x^{2/3} - 11x^{1/3} + 4 = 0$

98. $10x^{2/3} + 29x^{1/3} + 10 = 0$

99. $x^{3/4} - x^{1/2} - x^{1/4} + 1 = 0$

100. $x^{3/4} - 2x^{1/2} - 4x^{1/4} + 8 = 0$

101. $x^{-2/3} - 2x^{-1/3} - 3 = 0$

102. $6x^{-2/3} - 13x^{-1/3} - 5 = 0$

Exercises 103 and 104: **Average Rate of Change** *Let the distance from home in miles of a person after t hours on a straight path be given by $s(t)$. Approximate the average rate of change of s from $t_1 = \frac{1}{2}$ to $t_2 = \frac{9}{2}$ to the nearest tenth and interpret the result.*

103. $s(t) = \sqrt{96t}$

104. $s(t) = 3t^{3/4}$

Applications and Models

105. Modeling Wing Size Suppose that the surface area S of a bird's wings in square feet can be modeled by $S(w) = 1.27w^{2/3}$, where w is the weight of the bird in pounds, with $1 \leq w \leq 10$. Estimate the weight of a bird with wings having a surface area of 3 square feet.

106. Modeling Wingspan The wingspan L in feet of a bird weighing W pounds is given by $L = 2.43W^{0.3326}$. Estimate the wingspan of a bird that weighs 5.2 pounds.

107. Modeling Planetary Orbits The formula $f(x) = x^{1.5}$ calculates the number of years it takes for a planet to orbit the sun if its average distance from the sun is x times that of Earth. If there were a planet located 15 times as far from the sun as Earth, how many years would it take for the planet to orbit the sun?

108. Modeling Planetary Orbits (Refer to Exercise 107.) If there were a planet that took 200 years to orbit the sun, what would be its average distance x from the sun compared to that of Earth?

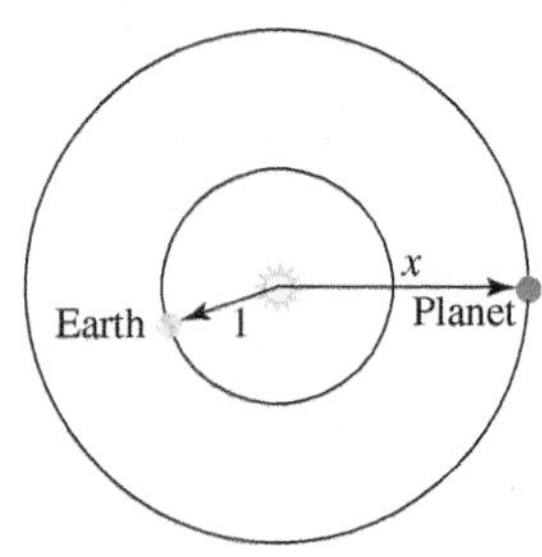

(Not to scale)

109. Trout and Pollution Rainbow trout are sensitive to zinc ions in the water. High concentrations are lethal. The average survival times x in minutes for trout in various concentrations of zinc ions y in milligrams per liter (mg/L) are listed in the table.

x (min)	0.5	1	2	3
y (mg/L)	4500	1960	850	525

Source: C. Mason, *Biology of Freshwater Pollution.*

(a) These data can be modeled by $f(x) = ax^b$, where a and b are constants. Determine an appropriate value for a. (*Hint:* Let $f(1) = 1960$.)

(b) Estimate b.

(c) Evaluate $f(4)$ and interpret the result.

110. Lunar Orbits for Jupiter Use the data in the table to complete the following.

Moons of Jupiter	Distance (10^3 km)	Period (days)
Metis	128	0.29
Almathea	181	0.50
Thebe	222	0.67
Europa	671	3.55
Ganymede	1070	7.16
Callisto	1883	16.69

(a) Make a scatterplot of the data. Estimate a value for b so that $f(x) = 0.0002x^b$ models the data.

(b) Check the accuracy of $f(x)$.

(c) The moon Io is 422 thousand kilometers from Jupiter. Estimate its period and compare the estimate to the actual value of 1.77 days. Did your estimate involve interpolation or extrapolation?

111. Fiddler Crab Size One study showed that for a male fiddler crab weighing over 0.75 gram, the weight of its claws can be estimated by $f(x) = 0.445x^{5/4}$. The input x is the weight of the crab in grams, and the output $f(x)$ is the weight of the claws in grams. (***Source:*** J. Huxley, *Problems of Relative Growth.*)

(a) Predict the weight of the claws of a 2-gram crab.

(b) Approximate graphically the weight of a crab that has 0.5-gram claws.

(c) Solve part (b) symbolically.

112. Weight and Height The average weight in pounds for men and women can sometimes be estimated by $f(x) = ax^{1.7}$, where x is a person's height in inches and a is a constant determined by the sex of the individual.

(a) If the average weight of a 68-inch-tall man is 152 pounds, approximate a. Use f to estimate the average weight of a 66-inch-tall man.

(b) If the average weight of a 68-inch-tall woman is 137 pounds, approximate a. Use f to estimate the average weight of a 70-inch-tall woman.

Power Regression

Exercises 113 and 114: The table contains data that can be modeled by a function of the form $f(x) = ax^b$. Use regression to find the constants a and b to the nearest hundredth. Graph f and the data.

113.

x	2	4	6	8
$f(x)$	3.7	4.2	4.6	4.9

114.

x	3	6	9	12
$f(x)$	23.8	58.5	99.2	144

115. Walmart Employees The table lists numbers N of Walmart employees (in millions) x years after 1980.

x	7	12	17	22	27
N	0.20	0.37	0.68	1.4	2.2

Source: Walmart.

(a) Find a power function f that models the data in the table.

(b) Use f to predict the number of employees in the year 2012. Compare to the true value of 2.1 million employees. Did your answer involve interpolation or extrapolation?

(c) When did the number of employees first reach 1 million?

116. DVD Rentals The table lists numbers of titles T released for DVD rentals x years after 1995.

x	3	4	5	6	7
T	2049	4787	8723	14,321	21,260

Source: DVD Release Report.

(a) Find a power function f that models the data in the table.

(b) Use f to estimate the number of titles released in 2006. Did your answer involve interpolation or extrapolation?

(c) When did the number of releases first surpass 45,000?

117. Pulse Rate and Weight According to one model, the rate at which an animal's heart beats varies with its weight. Smaller animals tend to have faster pulses, whereas larger animals tend to have slower pulses. The table lists average pulse rates in beats per minute (bpm) for animals with various weights in pounds (lb). Use regression (or some other method) to find values for a and b so that $f(x) = ax^b$ models these data.

Weight (lb)	40	150	400	1000	2000
Pulse (bpm)	140	72	44	28	20

Source: C. Pennycuick.

118. Pulse Rate and Weight (Continuation of Exercise 117) Use the results in the previous exercise to calculate the pulse rates for a 60-pound dog and a 2-ton whale.

Writing About Mathematics

119. Can a function be both a polynomial function and a power function? Explain.

120. Explain the basic steps needed to solve equations that contain square roots of variables.

Extended and Discovery Exercises

1. Odd Root Functions Graph $y = \sqrt[n]{x}$ for $n = 3, 5,$ and 7. State some generalizations about a graph of an odd root function.

2. Even Root Functions Graph $y = \sqrt[n]{x}$ for $n = 2, 4,$ and 6. State some generalizations about a graph of an even root function.

Exercises 3 and 4: **Difference Quotient** *Find the difference quotient of f.*

3. $f(x) = \sqrt{x}$ **4.** $f(x) = \frac{1}{x}$

Exercises 5–8: **Negative Rational Exponents** *Write the expression as one ratio without any negative exponents.*

5. $\dfrac{x^{-2/3} + x^{1/3}}{x}$

6. $\dfrac{x^{1/4} - x^{-3/4}}{x}$

7. $\dfrac{\frac{2}{3}(x + 1)x^{-1/3} - x^{2/3}}{(x + 1)^2}$

8. $\dfrac{(x^2 + 1)^{1/2} - \frac{1}{2}x(x^2 + 1)^{-1/2}(2x)}{x^2 + 1}$

9. Wire Between Two Poles Two vertical poles of lengths 12 feet and 16 feet are situated on level ground, 20 feet apart, as shown in the figure. A piece of wire is to be strung from the top of the 12-foot pole to the top of the 16-foot pole, attached to a stake in the ground at a point P on a line connecting the bottoms of the vertical poles. Let x represent the distance from P to D.

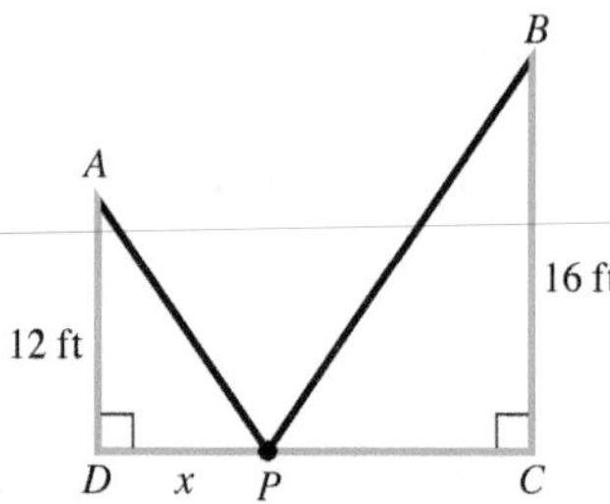

(a) Express the distance from P to C in terms of x.

(b) Express the lengths AP and BP in terms of x.

(c) Give a function f that expresses the total length of the wire used.

(d) Graph f in the window [0, 20, 5] by [0, 50, 10].

(e) Approximate the value of x that will minimize the amount of wire used. What is this minimum?

CHECKING BASIC CONCEPTS FOR SECTIONS 4.7 AND 4.8

1. Solve.

(a) $\dfrac{3x - 1}{1 - x} = 1$

(b) $3 + \dfrac{8}{x} = \dfrac{35}{x^2}$

(c) $\dfrac{1}{x - 1} - \dfrac{1}{3(x + 2)} = \dfrac{1}{x^2 + x - 2}$

2. Solve $2x^3 + x^2 - 6x < 0$.

3. Solve $\frac{x^2 - 1}{x + 2} \geq 0$.

4. Let y vary inversely with the cube of x. If $x = \frac{1}{5}$, then $y = 150$. Find y if $x = \frac{1}{2}$.

5. Simplify each expression without a calculator.
(a) $-4^{3/2}$ **(b)** $(8^{-2})^{1/3}$ **(c)** $\sqrt[3]{27^2}$

6. Solve the equation $4x^{3/2} - 3 = 29$.

7. Solve the equation $\sqrt{5x - 4} = x - 2$.

8. Solve each equation.
(a) $n^{-2} + 6n^{-1} = 16$

(b) $2x^{2/3} + 5x^{1/3} - 12 = 0$

9. Find a and b so that $f(x) = ax^b$ models the data.

x	1	2	3	4
$f(x)$	2	2.83	3.46	4

Power Functions with Integer Exponents

The graphs of power functions in the form $y = x^p$ where p is a **positive integer** can be generalized to two basic shapes depending on whether p is even or odd.

$y = x^p$, p is a positive, even integer

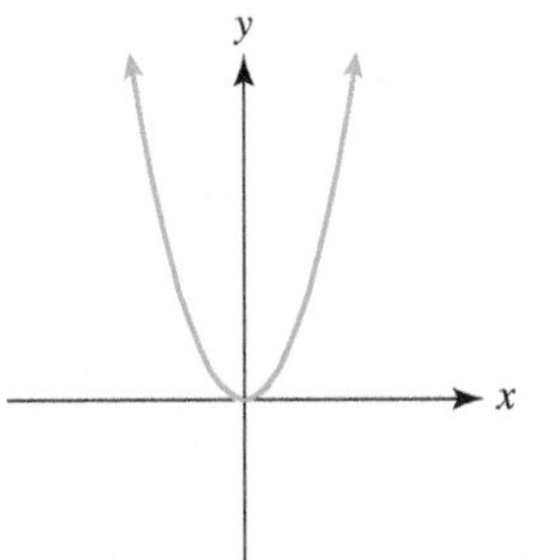

$y = x^p$, p is a positive, odd integer

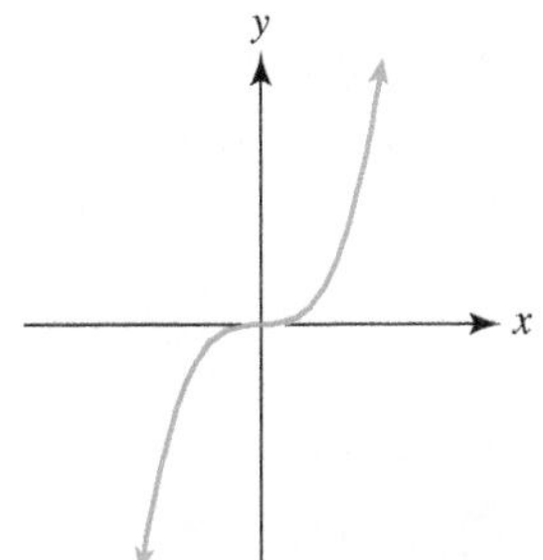

Power Functions with Positive Integer Exponents Share the Following Properties:

- Their graphs have intercepts at the origin.
- Their domains are all real numbers, $(-\infty, \infty)$.
- For functions of the form $y = kx^p$, the coefficient k **vertically compresses or stretches** the graph of $y = x^p$. If $|k| > 1$, the graph will be vertically stretched (appear "thinner"). If $|k|$ is between 0 and 1, $0 < |k| < 1$, the graph will be vertically compressed (appear "wider").
- If **k is negative**, the graph will be **reflected over the horizontal axis.**
- y is **directly proportional** to x^p and k is the **constant of proportionality.**

The graphs of power functions in the form $y = x^p$ where p is a **negative integer** can be generalized to two basic shapes depending on whether p is even or odd.

$y = x^p$, p is a negative, even integer

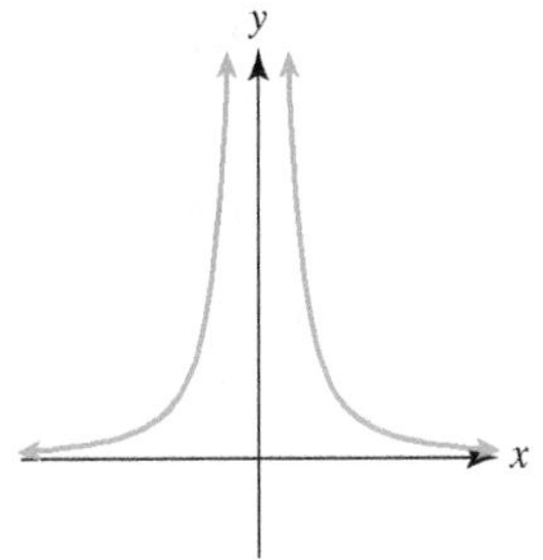

$y = x^p$, p is a negative, odd integer

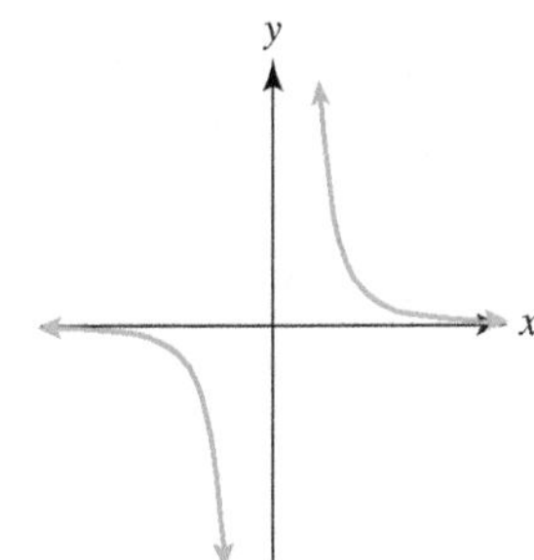

Power Functions, $y = kx^p$, with Negative Integer Exponents ($p < 0$) Share the Following Properties:

- There are **no intercepts,** but there is a **vertical asymptote** at $x = 0$ (along the y-axis), and a **horizontal asymptote** at $y = 0$ (along the x-axis).
- Their domains are all real numbers except 0, $(-\infty, 0) \cup (0, \infty)$.
- y is **inversely proportional** to $x^{|p|}$ and k is the **constant of proportionality.**

EXERCISES

1. Consider the accompanying graph of $f(x) = kx^p$, where p is an integer.

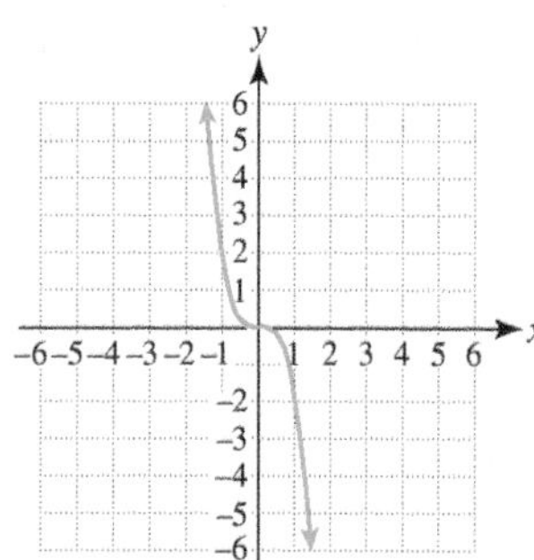

(a) Is p positive or negative?

(b) Is p even or odd?

(c) Is $k > 0$ or $k < 0$?

(d) Does $f(-x) = f(x)$?

(e) As $x \to +\infty$, $f(x) \to$ ______.

(f) As $x \to -\infty$, $f(x) \to$ ______.

(g) Give the interval(s) over which is $f(x) > 0$.

(h) Determine whether $f(x)$ is symmetrical with respect to the origin or the y-axis.

2. Consider the accompanying graph of $f(x) = kx^p$, where p is an integer.

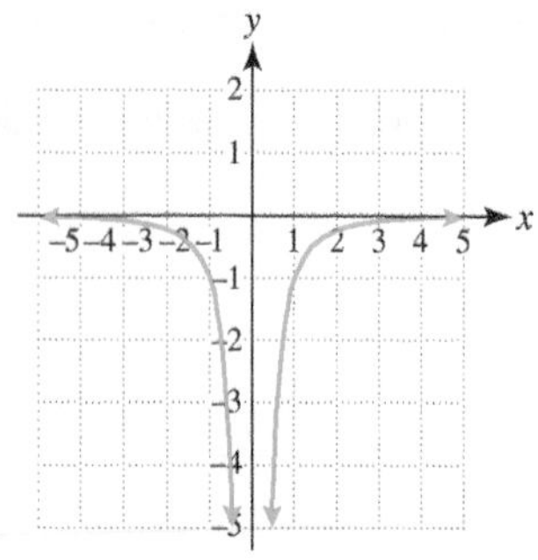

(a) Is $p > 0$ or $p < 0$? **(b)** Is p even or odd?

(c) Is $k > 0$ or $k < 0$? **(d)** Does $f(-x) = f(x)$?

(e) As $x \to +\infty$, $f(x) \to$ ______.

(f) As $x \to 0$, $f(x) \to$ ______.

(g) Where does $f(x) = 0$?

(h) Determine whether $f(x)$ is symmetrical with respect to the origin or the y-axis.

3. Let $f(x) = 1/x^4$ and $g(x) = 1/x^5$.

(a) As $x \to \infty$, $f(x) \to$ ______.

(b) As $x \to \infty$, $g(x) \to$ ______.

(c) As $x \to 0$, $f(x) \to$ ______.

(d) As $x \to 0$, $g(x) \to$ ______ from the left and ______ from the right.

4. Use $y = 3x^{-5}$ to answer the questions.

(a) Give the domain in interval notation.

(b) Give the range in interval notation.

(c) Give the interval(s) over which the function is concave up.

(d) Give the interval(s) over which the function is concave down.

(e) Give the interval(s) over which the function is increasing.

(f) Give the interval(s) over which the function is decreasing.

(g) Determine whether $f(x)$ is symmetrical with respect to the origin or the y-axis.

5. Without graphing the functions, describe the differences in the graphs of each pair of functions.

(a) $y_1 = 5x^{-4}$ and $y_2 = 2x^{-4}$

(b) $y_1 = 6x^{-4}$ and $y_2 = 6x^{-3}$

(c) $y_1 = -6x^{-4}$ and $y_2 = 6x^{-4}$

6. Let $f(x) = kx^p$, where k is negative and p is a negative, even integer.

(a) As $x \to +\infty, f(x) \to$ ______.

(b) As $x \to 0, f(x) \to$ ______.

(c) Give the interval(s) over which $f(x)$ is increasing.

(d) Determine the interval(s) over which $f(x)$ has a positive rate of change.

7. Use $g(x) = 10x^5$, to answer the questions.

(a) What happens to the value of $g(x)$ if x doubles in value?

(b) What happens to $g(x)$ if x is divided by two?

(c) What happens to $g(x)$ if x is tripled?

8. Use $h(x) = 4x^{-3}$ to answer the questions.

(a) What happens to the value of $h(x)$ if x doubles in value?

(b) What happens to $h(x)$ if x is tripled?

9. Identify which type of proportionality relationship, direct or inverse, exists between y and x^3 in each of the power functions represented below.

(a) $y = 1.6x^{-3}$

(b) $y = 50x^3$

10. Find a power function for each of the relationships described below.

(a) The time traveled, t, is inversely proportional to the rate r traveled, and the constant of proportionality is 3.5.

(b) q is inversely proportional to the square of p.

Solutions to Exercises

1. (a) positive

(b) odd

(c) $k < 0$

(d) no

(e) $-\infty$

(f) ∞

(g) $(-\infty, 0)$

(h) origin

2. (a) negative

(b) even

(c) $k < 0$

(d) yes

(e) 0

(f) $-\infty$

(g) nowhere

(h) y-axis

3. (a) 0

(b) 0

(c) ∞

(d) $-\infty; \infty$

4. (a) $(-\infty, 0) \cup (0, \infty)$;

(b) $(-\infty, 0) \cup (0, \infty)$;

(c) $(0, \infty)$;

(d) $(-\infty, 0)$;

(e) nowhere

(f) $(-\infty, 0) \cup (0, \infty)$;

(g) origin

5. (answers may vary) **(a)** y_1 is stretched more than y_2; **(b)** y_1 is always above the x-axis, while y_2 is not; **(c)** y_1 is always below the x-axis and y_2 is above

6. (a) 0

(b) $-\infty$

(c) $(0, \infty)$

(d) $(0, \infty)$

7. (a) $g(2x) = 10(2x)^5\ 10(32x^5) = 320x^5$ It multiplies by a factor of 32.

(b) $g(x/2) = 10(x/2)^5\ 10(x^5/32) = 10x^5/32$ It multiplies by a factor of 1/32.

(c) $g(3x) = 10(3x)^5\ 10(243x^5) = 2430x^5$ $g(x)$ is multiplied by a factor of 243.

8. (a) $h(2x) = 4(2x)^{-3} = 4(2^{-3}x^{-3}) = 4\frac{x^{-3}}{2^3} = \frac{4x^{-3}}{8}$; $h(x)$ is divided by 8 (or multiplied by a factor of 1/8).

(b) $h(3x) = 4(3x)^{-3} = 4(3^{-3}x^{-3}) = 4\frac{x^{-3}}{3^3} = \frac{4x^{-3}}{27}$; $h(x)$ is divided by 27 (or multiplied by a factor of 1/27).

9. (a) inverse proportionality

(b) direct proportionality

10. (a) $t = 3.5/r$ or $t = 3.5r^{-1}$;

(b) $q = k/p^2$ or $q = kp^{-2}$

4 Summary

CONCEPT	EXPLANATION AND EXAMPLES
Section 4.1 More Nonlinear Functions and Their Graphs	
Polynomial Function	Can be represented by $f(x) = a_n x^n + a_{n-1}x^{n-1} + \cdots + a_2 x^2 + a_1 x + a_0$ The leading coefficient is $a_n \neq 0$ and the degree is n. **Example:** $f(x) = -4x^3 - 2x^2 + 6x + \frac{1}{2}$; $a_n = -4$; $n = 3$
Absolute and Local Extrema	The accompanying graph has the following extrema. Absolute maximum: none. Absolute minimum: -14.8. Local maximum: 1. Local minimums: -4.3, -14.8
Symmetry	*Even function:* $f(-x) = f(x)$; the graph is symmetric with respect to the y-axis. *Odd function:* $f(-x) = -f(x)$; the graph is symmetric with respect to the origin. **Examples:** $f(x) = x^4 - 3x^2$ $f(x) = x - x^3$
Section 4.2 Polynomial Functions and Models	
Graphs of Polynomial Functions	Their graphs are continuous with no breaks, and their domains include all real numbers. The graph of a polynomial function of degree $n \geq 1$ has at most n x-intercepts and at most $n - 1$ turning points. For a discussion of the end behavior for graphs of polynomial functions, see page 255. **Examples:** See "Putting It All Together" for Section 4.2.
Piecewise-Polynomial Functions	**Example:** $f(x) = \begin{cases} x^2 - 2 & \text{if } x < 0 \\ 1 - 2x & \text{if } x \geq 0 \end{cases}$ $f(-2) = (-2)^2 - 2 = 2$ $f(0) = 1 - 2(0) = 1$ $f(2) = 1 - 2(2) = -3$ f is discontinuous at $x = 0$.

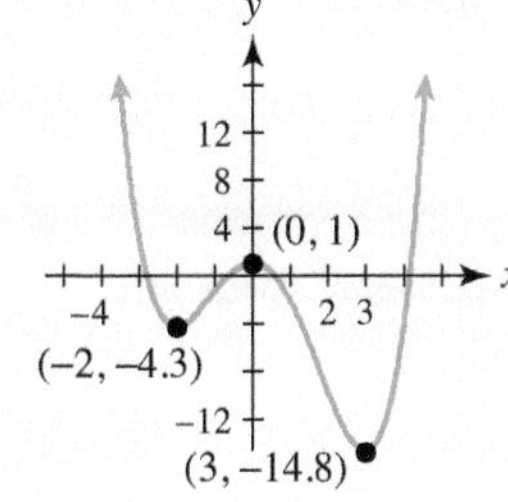

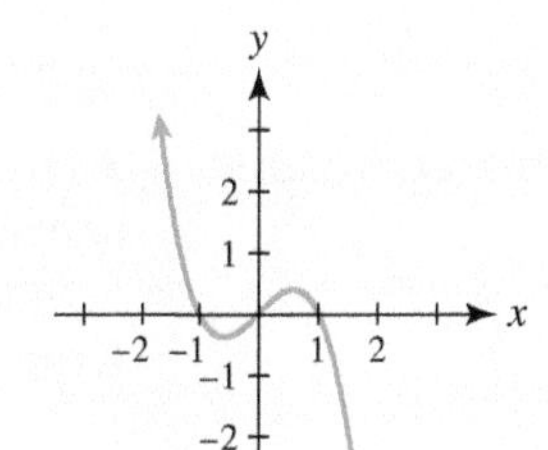

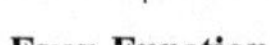

Even Function

Odd Function

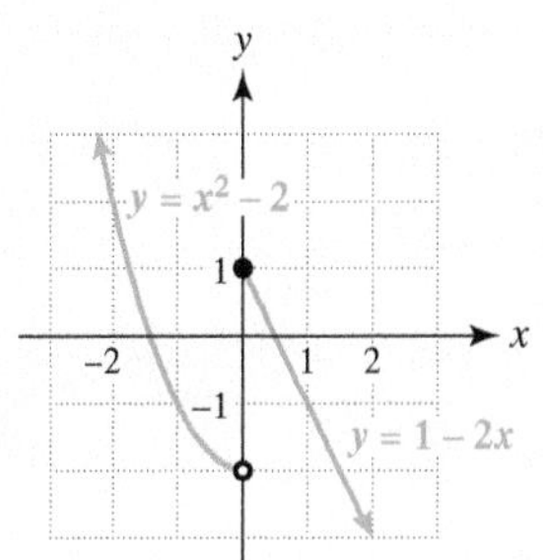

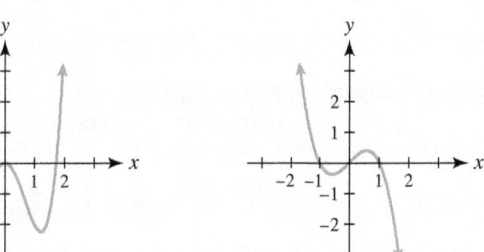

CONCEPT	EXPLANATION AND EXAMPLES
Section 4.3 Division of Polynomials	
Division Algorithm	Let $f(x)$ and $d(x)$ be two polynomials with the degree of $d(x)$ greater than zero and less than the degree of $f(x)$. Then there exist unique polynomials $q(x)$ and $r(x)$ such that $$f(x) = d(x) \cdot q(x) + r(x),$$ where either $r(x) = 0$ or the degree of $r(x)$ is less than the degree of $d(x)$. That is, (Dividend) = (Divisor) · (Quotient) + (Remainder). **Example:** $\frac{x^2 - 4x + 5}{x - 1} = x - 3 + \frac{2}{x - 1}$. That is, $x^2 - 4x + 5 = (x - 1)(x - 3) + 2$.
Remainder Theorem	If a polynomial $f(x)$ is divided by $x - k$, the remainder is $f(k)$. **Example:** If $x^2 - 4x + 5$ is divided by $x - 1$, the remainder is $f(1) = 1^2 - 4(1) + 5 = 2$.
Section 4.4 Real Zeros of Polynomial Functions	
Factor Theorem	A polynomial $f(x)$ has a factor $x - k$ if and only if $f(k) = 0$. **Example:** $f(x) = x^2 - 3x + 2$; $f(1) = 0$ implies that $(x - 1)$ is a factor of $x^2 - 3x + 2$.
Complete Factored Form	$f(x) = a_n(x - c_1)(x - c_2) \cdots (x - c_n)$, where a_n is the leading coefficient of the polynomial $f(x)$ and the c_k are its zeros. This form is unique. **Example:** $f(x) = -2x^3 + 8x$ has zeros of -2, 0, and 2; therefore $f(x) = -2(x + 2)(x - 0)(x - 2)$.
Multiple Real Zeros	*Odd multiplicity:* Graph crosses the x-axis. *Even multiplicity:* Graph touches but does not cross the x-axis. *Higher multiplicities:* Graph levels off more at a zero of higher multiplicity. **Example:** Let $f(x) = -2(x + 1)^3(x - 4)^2$; $f(x)$ has a zero of -1 with odd multiplicity 3 and a zero of 4 with even multiplicity 2. 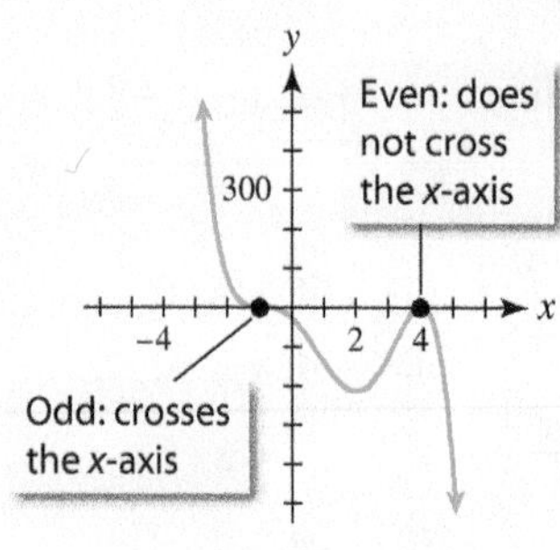

CONCEPT	EXPLANATION AND EXAMPLES

Section 4.4 Real Zeros of Polynomial Functions (CONTINUED)

Polynomial Equations

Polynomial equations can be solved symbolically, graphically, and numerically. A common symbolic technique is factoring.

Example: Solve $x^3 - 4x = 0$ symbolically and graphically.

Symbolic Solution

$$x(x^2 - 4) = 0$$
$$x(x - 2)(x + 2) = 0$$
$$x = 0,\ x = 2, \quad \text{or} \quad x = -2$$

Graphical Solution

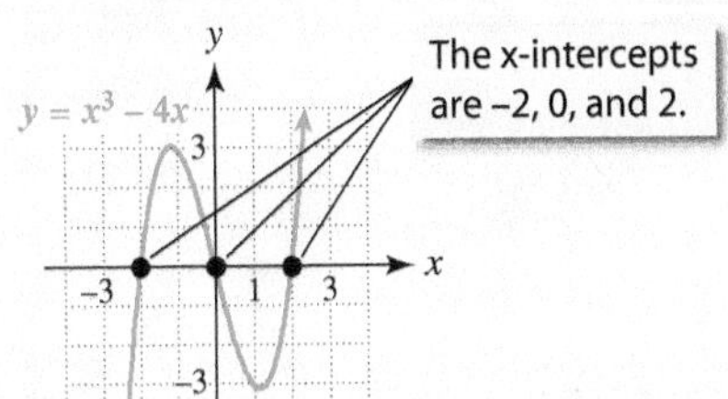

Section 4.5 The Fundamental Theorem of Algebra

Fundamental Theorem of Algebra

A polynomial $f(x)$ of degree $n \geq 1$ has at least one complex zero.

Explanation: With complex numbers, any polynomial can be written in complete factored form.

Examples: $x^2 + 1 = (x + i)(x - i)$

$3x^2 - 3x - 6 = 3(x + 1)(x - 2)$

Number of Zeros Theorem

A polynomial of degree n has at most n distinct zeros.

Example: A cubic polynomial has at most three distinct zeros.

Polynomial Equations with Complex Solutions

Polynomial equations can have both real and imaginary solutions.

Example: Solve $x^4 - 1 = 0$.

$$(x^2 - 1)(x^2 + 1) = 0$$
$$(x - 1)(x + 1)(x^2 + 1) = 0$$
$$x = 1, \quad x = -1, \quad \text{or} \quad x^2 = -1$$
$$x = \pm 1, \pm i$$

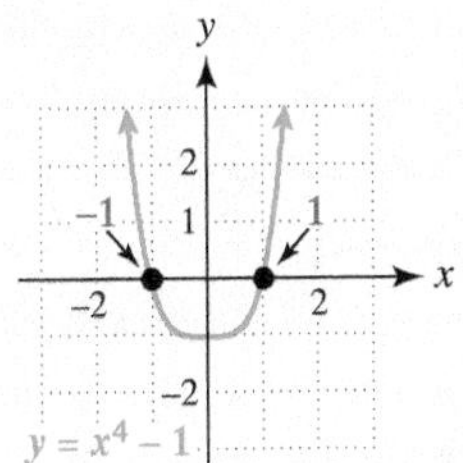

The x-intercepts are -1 and 1. The imaginary solutions $\pm i$ cannot be found from a graph.

Section 4.6 Rational Functions and Models

Rational Functions

$f(x) = \dfrac{p(x)}{q(x)}$, where $p(x)$ and $q(x) \neq 0$ are polynomials

Example: $f(x) = \dfrac{2x - 3}{x - 1}$

Horizontal asymptote: $y = 2$

Vertical asymptote: $x = 1$

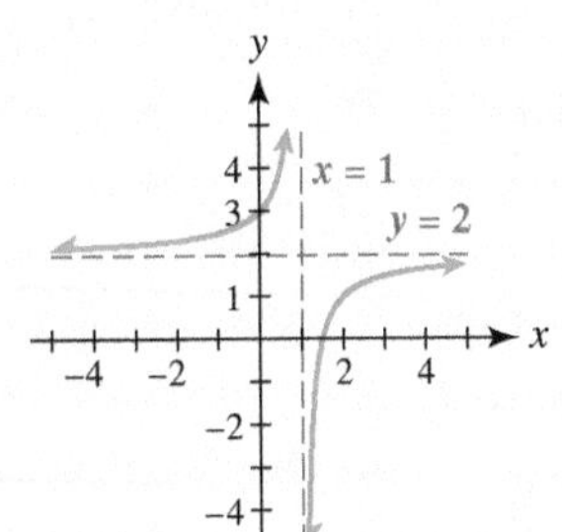

To find vertical and horizontal asymptotes, see page 301.
To graph rational functions by hand, see page 307.

CONCEPT	EXPLANATION AND EXAMPLES

Section 4.7 More Equations and Inequalities

Solving Rational Equations

Multiply each side by the LCD. Check your results.

Example: $\frac{-24}{x-3} - 4 = x + 3$ — LCD is $x - 3$.

$-24 - 4(x - 3) = (x + 3)(x - 3)$ — Multiply each term by $x - 3$.

$-24 - 4x + 12 = x^2 - 9$ — Multiply.

$0 = x^2 + 4x + 3$ — Combine terms.

$0 = (x + 3)(x + 1)$ — Factor.

$x = -3$ or $x = -1$ — Both solutions check.

Direct Variation

Let x and y denote two quantities and n be a positive number. Then y is *directly proportional to the nth power of x*, or *y varies directly with the nth power of x*, if there exists a nonzero number k such that $y = kx^n$.

Example: Because $V = \frac{4}{3}\pi r^3$, the volume of a sphere varies directly with the third power of the radius. The constant of variation is $\frac{4}{3}\pi$.

Inverse Variation

Let x and y denote two quantities and n be a positive number. Then y is *inversely proportional to the nth power of x*, or *y varies inversely with the nth power of x*, if there exists a nonzero number k such that $y = \frac{k}{x^n}$.

Example: Because $I = \frac{k}{d^2}$, the intensity of a light source varies inversely with the square of the distance from the light source.

Polynomial Inequality

Write the inequality as $p(x) > 0$, where $>$ may be replaced by $\geq$, $<$, or $\leq$. Replace the inequality sign with an equals sign, and solve this equation. The solutions are called boundary numbers. Then use a graph or table to find the solution set to the given inequality.

Example: $4x - x^3 > 0$; Boundary numbers: $-2, 0, 2$
The solution set is $(-\infty, -2) \cup (0, 2)$ because the graph is above the x-axis for these intervals of x-values.

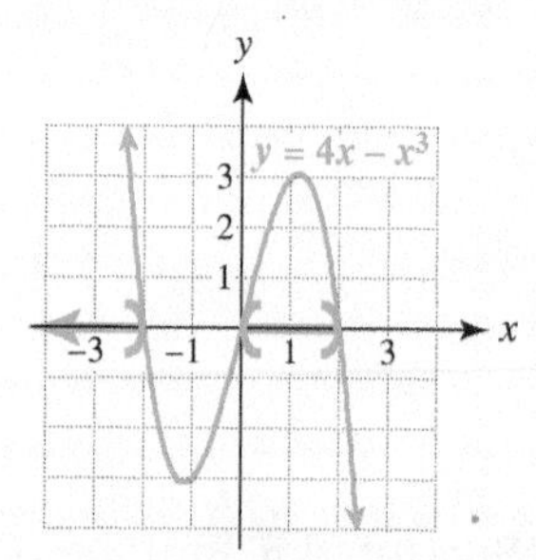

Rational Inequality

As with polynomial inequalities, find the boundary numbers, including x-values where any expressions are undefined.

Example: $\frac{(x + 2)(x - 3)}{x} \geq 0$

Boundary numbers: $-2, 0, 3$
Solution set: $[-2, 0) \cup [3, \infty)$

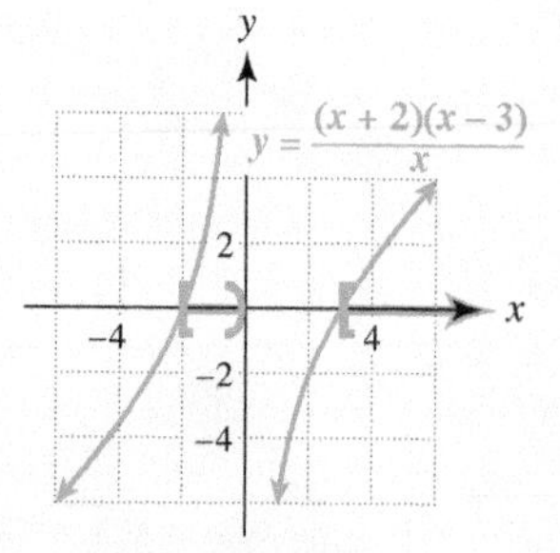

CONCEPT	EXPLANATION AND EXAMPLES
Section 4.8 Radical Equations and Power Functions	
Rational Exponents	$x^{m/n} = \sqrt[n]{x^m} = (\sqrt[n]{x})^m$ **Example:** $25^{3/2} = \sqrt{25^3} = (\sqrt{25})^3 = 5^3 = 125$
Functions Involving Radicals	Functions defined by radical expressions **Examples:** $f(x) = \sqrt[3]{x}$; $f(-8) = \sqrt[3]{-8} = -2$ $f(x) = \sqrt[4]{x^3} + 1$; $f(81) = \sqrt[4]{81^3} + 1 = 28$
Solving Radical Equations	When an equation contains a square root, isolate the square root and then square each side. *Be sure to check your results.* **Example:** $x + \sqrt{3x - 3} = 1$ Given equation $\sqrt{3x - 3} = 1 - x$ Subtract x. $3x - 3 = (1 - x)^2$ Square each side. $3x - 3 = 1 - 2x + x^2$ Square binomial. $0 = x^2 - 5x + 4$ Combine terms. $0 = (x - 1)(x - 4)$ Factor. $x = 1$ or $x = 4$ Solve. *Check:* 1 is a solution, but 4 is not. $1 + \sqrt{3(1) - 3} = 1$ ✓ $4 + \sqrt{3(4) - 3} \neq 1$
Power Function	$f(x) = x^b$, where b is a constant **Example:** $f(x) = x^{4/3}$, $g(x) = x^{1.72}$

4 Review Exercises

1. State the degree and leading coefficient of the polynomial $f(x) = 4 + x - 2x^2 - 7x^3$.

Exercises 2 and 3: Use the graph of f to estimate any (a) local extrema and (b) absolute extrema.

2.

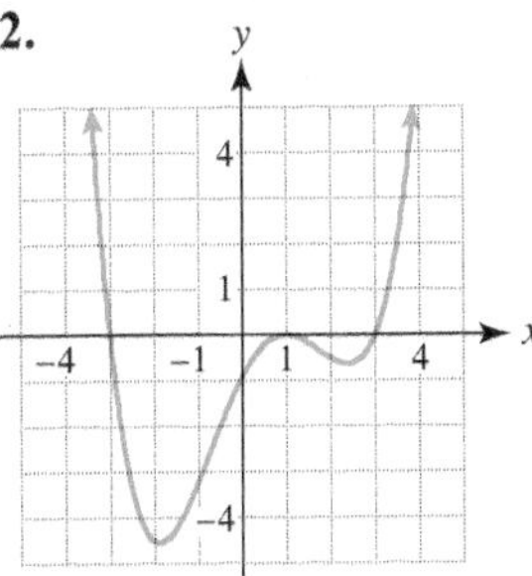

3.

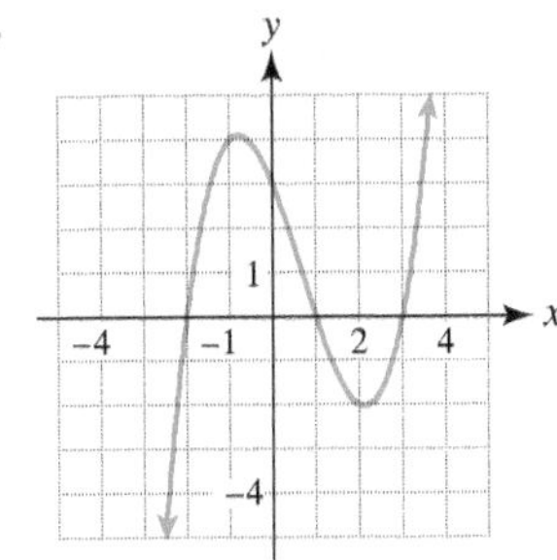

4. Graph $f(x) = -0.25x^4 + 0.67x^3 + 9.5x^2 - 20x - 50$.
   (a) Approximate any local extrema.
   (b) Approximate any absolute extrema.
   (c) Determine where f is increasing or decreasing.

Exercises 5–8: Determine if f is even, odd, or neither.

5. $f(x) = 2x^6 - 5x^4 - x^2$
6. $f(x) = -5x^3 - 18$
7. $f(x) = 7x^5 + 3x^3 - x$
8. $f(x) = \dfrac{1}{1 + x^2}$

Exercises 9 and 10: The table is a complete representation of f. Decide if f is even, odd, or neither.

9.

x	-4	-2	0	2	-4
$f(x)$	13	7	0	-7	-13

10.

x	-5	-3	-1	1	3	5
$f(x)$	-6	2	7	7	2	-6

Exercises 11 and 12: Sketch a graph of a polynomial function that satisfies the given conditions.

11. Cubic polynomial, two x-intercepts, and a positive leading coefficient

12. Degree 4 with a positive leading coefficient, three turning points, and one x-intercept

Exercises 13 and 14: Use the graph of the polynomial function f to complete the following.

(a) Determine the number of turning points and estimate any x-intercepts.

(b) State whether $a > 0$ or $a < 0$.

(c) Determine the minimum degree of f.

13.

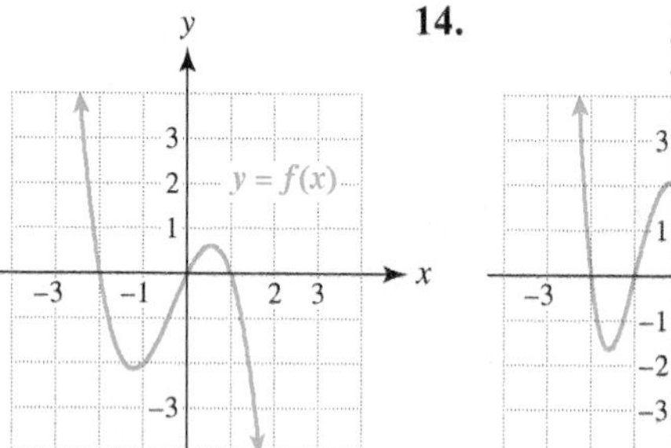

14.

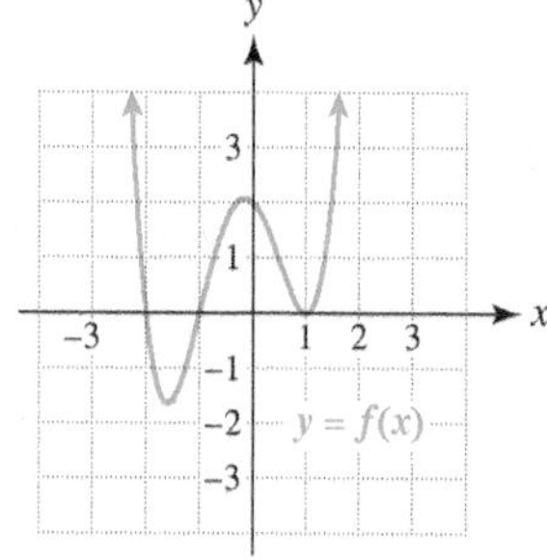

Exercises 15 and 16: State the end behavior of f.

15. $f(x) = -2x^3 + 4x - 2$

16. $f(x) = 1 - 2x - x^4$

17. Find the average rate of change of $f(x) = x^3 + 1$ from $x = -2$ to $x = -1$.

18. Find the difference quotient for $g(x) = 4x^3$.

19. Let $f(x)$ be given by

$$f(x) = \begin{cases} 2x & \text{if } 0 \leq x < 2 \\ 8 - x^2 & \text{if } 2 \leq x \leq 4. \end{cases}$$

(a) Sketch a graph of f. Is f continuous on its domain?

(b) Evaluate $f(1)$ and $f(3)$.

(c) Solve the equation $f(x) = 2$.

20. Determine the type of symmetry that the graph of $g(x) = x^5 - 4x^3$ exhibits.

Exercises 21–24: Divide the expression.

21. $\dfrac{14x^3 - 21x^2 - 7x}{7x}$

22. $\dfrac{2x^3 - x^2 - 4x + 1}{x + 2}$

23. $\dfrac{4x^3 - 7x + 4}{2x + 3}$

24. $\dfrac{3x^3 - 5x^2 + 13x - 18}{x^2 + 4}$

25. The polynomial given by $f(x) = \frac{1}{2}x^3 - 3x^2 + \frac{11}{2}x - 3$ has zeros 1, 2, and 3. Write its complete factored form.

26. Write a complete factored form of a quintic (degree 5) polynomial $f(x)$ that has zeros -2 and 2 with multiplicities 2 and 3, respectively.

27. Use the graph of $y = f(x)$ to write its complete factored form. (Do not assume that the leading coefficient is ± 1.)

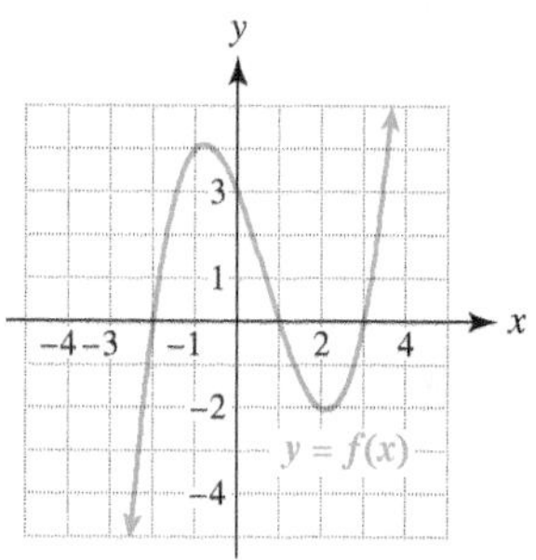

28. What is the maximum number of times that a horizontal line can intersect the graph of each type of polynomial?
(a) linear (degree 1) **(b)** quadratic **(c)** cubic

Exercises 29 and 30: Use the rational zero test to determine any rational zeros of $f(x)$.

29. $f(x) = 2x^3 + x^2 - 13x + 6$

30. $f(x) = x^3 + x^2 - 11x - 11$

Exercises 31–32: Solve the equation.

31. $9x = 3x^3$

32. $x^4 - 3x^2 + 2 = 0$

Exercises 33 and 34: Solve the equation graphically. Round your answers to the nearest hundredth.

33. $x^3 - 3x + 1 = 0$

34. $x^4 - 2x = 2$

Exercises 35 and 36: Find all real and imaginary solutions.

35. $x^3 + x = 0$

36. $x^4 + 3x^2 + 2 = 0$

37. Write a polynomial $f(x)$ in complete factored form that has degree 3, leading coefficient 4, and zeros 1, $3i$, and $-3i$. Then write $f(x)$ in expanded form.

38. Use the graph of $f(x) = 2x^4 - x^2 - 1$ to predict the number of real zeros and the number of imaginary zeros of f. Find these zeros symbolically.

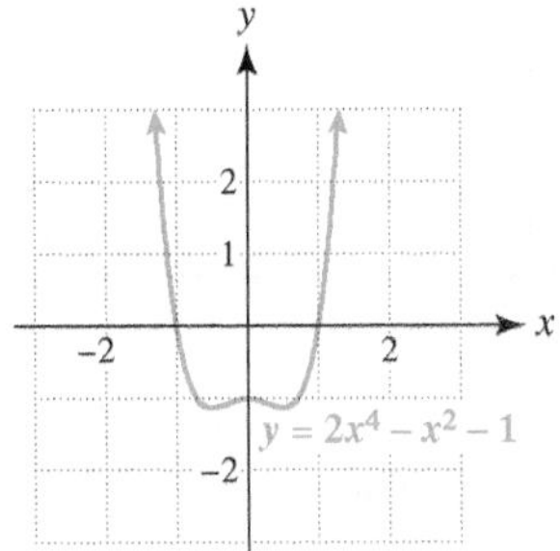

39. If a zero of f is i, find the complete factored form of $f(x) = x^4 + x^3 + 2x^2 + x + 1$.

40. State the domain of $f(x) = \frac{3x - 2}{5x + 4}$. Identify any horizontal or vertical asymptotes in the graph of f.

41. Find any horizontal or vertical asymptotes in the graph of

$$f(x) = \frac{2x^2 + x - 15}{3x^2 + 8x - 3}.$$

42. Let $f(x) = \frac{2x^2}{x^2 - 4}$.
   (a) Find the domain of f.
   (b) Identify any horizontal or vertical asymptotes.
   (c) Graph f with a graphing calculator.
   (d) Sketch a graph of f that includes all asymptotes.

Exercises 43–46: Graph $y = g(x)$ by hand.

43. $g(x) = \dfrac{1}{x + 1} - 2$
44. $g(x) = \dfrac{x}{x - 1}$

45. $g(x) = \dfrac{x^2 - 1}{x^2 + 2x + 1}$
46. $g(x) = \dfrac{2x - 3}{2x^2 + x - 6}$

47. Sketch a graph of a function f with vertical asymptote $x = -2$ and horizontal asymptote $y = 2$.

48. Solve the equation $\frac{3x}{x - 2} = 2$ symbolically, graphically, and numerically.

Exercises 49–52: Solve the equation. Check your results.

49. $\dfrac{5x + 1}{x + 3} = 3$
50. $\dfrac{1}{x} - \dfrac{1}{x^2} + 2 = 0$

51. $\dfrac{1}{x + 2} + \dfrac{1}{x - 2} = \dfrac{4}{x^2 - 4}$

52. $\dfrac{x + 5}{x - 2} = \dfrac{x - 1}{x + 1}$

Exercises 53 and 54: Use the graph of f to solve each inequality.

(a) $f(x) > 0$ *(b)* $f(x) < 0$

53. **54.**

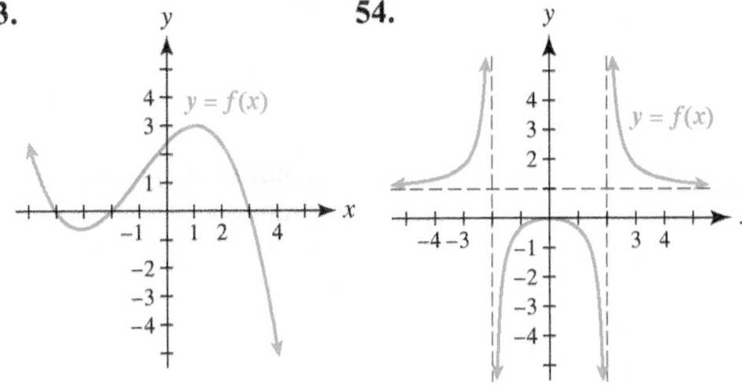

Exercises 55–58: Solve the inequality.

55. $x^3 + x^2 - 6x > 0$
56. $x^4 + 4 < 5x^2$

57. $\dfrac{2x - 1}{x + 2} > 0$
58. $\dfrac{1}{x} + \dfrac{1}{x + 2} \le \dfrac{4}{3}$

Exercises 59–62: Evaluate the radical expression by hand.

59. $(36^{3/4})^2$
60. $(9^{-3/2})^{-2}$

61. $(2^{-3/2} \cdot 2^{1/2})^{-3}$
62. $\left(\dfrac{4}{9}\right)^{-3/2}$

Exercises 63–66: Write the radical expression using positive exponents.

63. $\sqrt[3]{x^4}$
64. $\left(\sqrt[4]{z}\right)^{-1/2}$

65. $\sqrt[3]{y} \cdot \sqrt{y}$
66. $\sqrt{x} \cdot \sqrt[3]{x^2} \cdot \sqrt[4]{x^3}$

Exercises 67 and 68: Give the domain of the power function. Approximate $f(3)$ to the nearest hundredth.

67. $f(x) = x^{5/2}$
68. $f(x) = x^{-2/3}$

Exercises 69–80: Solve the equation. Check your results.

69. $x^5 = 1024$
70. $x^{1/3} = 4$

71. $\sqrt{x - 2} = x - 4$
72. $x^{3/2} = 27$

73. $2x^{1/4} + 3 = 6$
74. $x^{1/3} + 3x^{1/3} = -2$

75. $\sqrt[3]{2x - 3} + 1 = 4$

76. $m^{-3} + 2m^{-2} + m^{-1} = 0$

77. $2n^{-2} - 5n^{-1} = 3$

78. $x^{3/4} - 16x^{1/4} = 0$

79. $k^{2/3} - 4k^{1/3} - 5 = 0$

80. $\sqrt{x - 2} = 5 - \sqrt{x + 3}$

Applications

81. Pulse Rate and Length During the eighteenth century Bryan Robinson found that the pulse rate of an animal could be approximated by

$$f(x) = \frac{1607}{\sqrt[4]{x^3}}.$$

The input x is the length of the animal in inches, and the output $f(x)$ is the approximate number of heartbeats per minute. (***Source:*** H. Lancaster, *Quantitative Methods in Biology and Medical Sciences.*)

(a) Use f to estimate the pulse rates of a 2-foot dog and a 5.5-foot person.

(b) What length corresponds to a pulse rate of 400 beats per minute?

82. Time Spent in Line Suppose a parking garage attendant can wait on 4 vehicles per minute and vehicles are leaving the ramp randomly at an average rate of x vehicles per minute. Then the average time T in minutes spent waiting in line and paying the attendant is given by

$$T(x) = \frac{1}{4 - x},$$

where $0 \le x < 4$. (***Source:*** N. Garber and L. Hoel, *Traffic and Highway Engineering.*)

(a) Evaluate $T(2)$ and interpret the result.

(b) Graph T for $0 \le x < 4$.

(c) What happens to the waiting time as x increases from 0 to (nearly) 4?

(d) Find x if the waiting time is 5 minutes.

83. Modeling Ocean Temperatures The formula

$$T(m) = -0.064m^3 + 0.56m^2 + 2.9m + 61$$

approximates the ocean temperature in degrees Fahrenheit at Naples, Florida. In this formula m is the month, with $m = 1$ corresponding to January.

(a) What is the average ocean temperature in May?

(b) Estimate the absolute maximum of T on the closed interval [1, 12] and interpret the result.

84. Minimizing Surface Area Find possible dimensions that minimize the surface area of a box with no top that has a volume of 96 cubic inches and a length that is three times the width.

85. Falling Object If an object is dropped from a height h, then the time t required for the object to strike the ground is directly proportional to the square root of h. If it requires 1 second for an object to fall 16 feet, how long does it take for an object to fall 256 feet?

86. Animals and Trotting Speeds Taller animals tend to take longer, but fewer, steps per second than shorter animals. The relationship between the shoulder height h in meters of an animal and an animal's stepping frequency F in steps per second, while *trotting*, is shown in the table.

h	0.5	1.0	1.5	2.0	2.5
F	2.6	1.8	1.5	1.3	1.2

Source: C. Pennycuick, *Newton Rules Biology.*

(a) Find values for constants a and b so that the formula $f(x) = ax^b$ models the data.

(b) Estimate the stepping frequency for an elephant with a 3-meter shoulder height.

Extended and Discovery Exercises

Exercises 1 and 2: **Velocity** *Suppose that a person is riding a bicycle on a straight road and that $f(t)$ computes the total distance in feet that the rider has traveled after t seconds. To calculate the person's average velocity between time t_1 and time t_2, we can evaluate the difference quotient*

$$\frac{f(t_2) - f(t_1)}{t_2 - t_1}.$$

(a) For the given $f(t)$ and the indicated values of t_1 and t_2, calculate the average velocity of the bike rider. Make a table to organize your work.

(b) Make a conjecture about the velocity of the bike rider precisely at time t_1.

1. $f(t) = t^2, t_1 = 10$
(i) $t_2 = 11$
(ii) $t_2 = 10.1$
(iii) $t_2 = 10.01$
(iv) $t_2 = 10.001$

2. $f(t) = \sqrt{t}, t_1 = 4$
(i) $t_2 = 5$
(ii) $t_2 = 4.1$
(iii) $t_2 = 4.01$
(iv) $t_2 = 4.001$

Exercises 3–6: **Average Rates of Change** *These exercises investigate the relationship between polynomial functions and their average rates of change. For example, the average rate of change of $f(x) = x^2$ from x to $x + 0.001$ for any x can be calculated and graphed as shown in the figures. The graph of f is a parabola, and the graph of its average rate of change is a line. Try to discover what this relationship is by completing the following.*

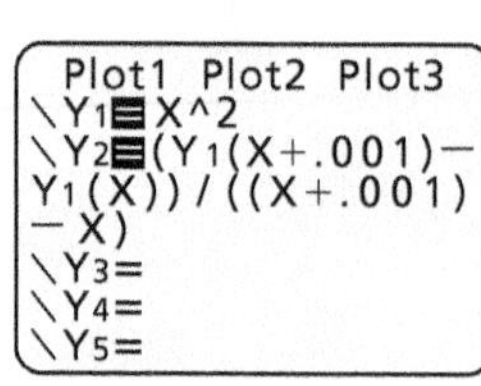

[−10, 10, 1] by [−10, 10, 1]

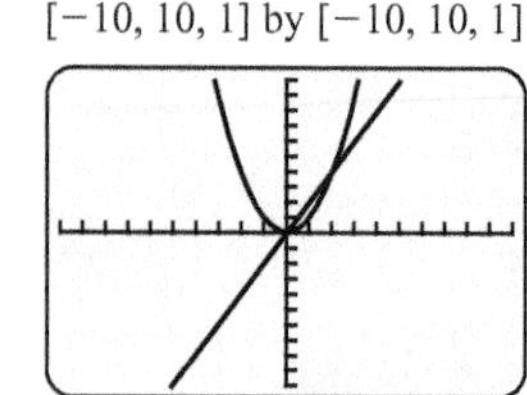

(a) Graph each function and its average rate of change from x to $x + 0.001$.
(b) Compare the graphs. How are turning points on the graph of a function related to its average rate of change?
(c) Generalize your results. Test your generalization.

3. Linear Functions
$f_1(x) = 3x + 1$ $\quad f_2(x) = -2x + 6$
$f_3(x) = 1.5x - 5$ $\quad f_4(x) = -4x - 2.5$

4. Quadratic Functions
$f_1(x) = 2x^2 - 3x + 1$ $\quad f_2(x) = -0.5x^2 + 2x + 2$
$f_3(x) = x^2 + x - 2$ $\quad f_4(x) = -1.5x^2 - 4x + 6$

5. Cubic Functions
$f_1(x) = 0.5x^3 - x^2 - 2x + 1$
$f_2(x) = -x^3 + x^2 + 3x - 5$
$f_3(x) = 2x^3 - 5x^2 + x - 3$
$f_4(x) = -x^3 + 3x - 4$

6. Quartic Functions
$f_1(x) = 0.05x^4 + 0.2x^3 - x^2 - 2.4x$
$f_2(x) = -0.1x^4 + 0.1x^3 + 1.3x^2 - 0.1x - 1.2$
$f_3(x) = 0.1x^4 + 0.4x^3 - 0.2x^2 - 2.4x - 2.4$

1–4 Cumulative Review Exercises

1. Let $S = \{(-3, 4), (-1, -2), (0, 4), (1, -2), (-1, 5)\}$.
   (a) Find the domain and range of S.
   (b) Is S a function?

2. Find the exact distance between $(-1, 4)$ and $(3, -9)$.

3. Use the graph to express the domain and range of f. Then evaluate $f(0)$.

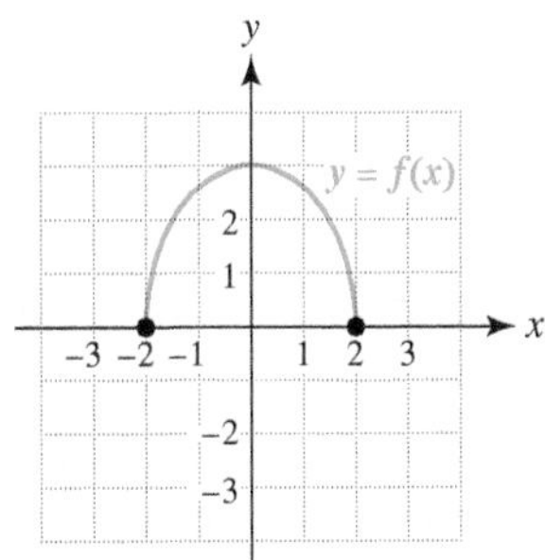

4. Graph $y = g(x)$ by hand.
   (a) $g(x) = 2 - 3x$ **(b)** $g(x) = |2x - 1|$
   (c) $g(x) = \frac{1}{2}(x - 2)^2 + 2$ **(d)** $g(x) = x^3 - 1$
   (e) $g(x) = \sqrt{-x}$ **(f)** $g(x) = \sqrt[3]{x}$
   (g) $g(x) = \dfrac{1}{x - 4} + 2$ **(h)** $g(x) = x^2 - x$

5. The monthly cost of driving a car is \$200 for maintenance plus \$0.25 a mile. Write a formula for a function C that calculates the monthly cost of driving a car x miles. Evaluate $C(2000)$ and interpret the result.

6. The graph of a linear function f is shown.

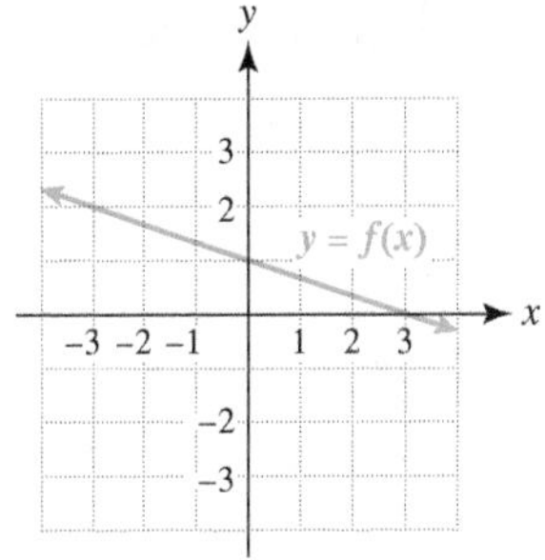

   (a) Identify the slope, y-intercept, and x-intercept.
   (b) Write a formula for $f(x)$.
   (c) Evaluate $f(-3)$ symbolically and graphically.
   (d) Find any zeros of f.

7. Find the average rate of change of $f(x) = x^3 - x$ from $x = -3$ to $x = -2$.

8. Find the difference quotient for $f(x) = x^2 + 6x$.

9. Write the slope-intercept form for a line that passes through $(-2, 5)$ and $(3, -4)$.

10. Write the slope-intercept form for a line that passes through $(-1, 4)$ and is perpendicular to the line $3x - 4y = 12$.

11. Write an equation of a line that is parallel to the x-axis and passes through $(4, -5)$.

12. Determine the x- and y-intercepts on the graph of $5x - 4y = 10$. Graph the equation.

13. If $C(x) = 15x + 2000$ calculates the cost in dollars of producing x radios, interpret the numbers 15 and 2000 in the formula for $C(x)$.

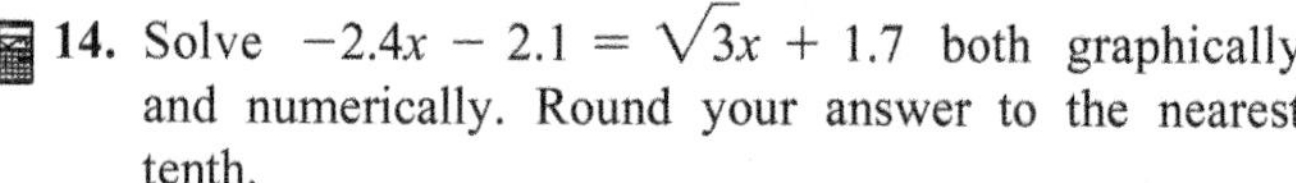

14. Solve $-2.4x - 2.1 = \sqrt{3}x + 1.7$ both graphically and numerically. Round your answer to the nearest tenth.

Exercises 15–24: Solve the equation.

15. $-3(2 - 3x) - (-x - 1) = 1$

16. $x^3 + 5 = 5x^2 + x$

17. $|3x - 4| + 1 = 5$

18. $2x^2 + x + 2 = 0$

19. $7x^2 + 9x = 10$

20. $x^4 + 9 = 10x^2$

21. $3x^{2/3} + 5x^{1/3} - 2 = 0$

22. $\sqrt{5 + 2x} + 4 = x + 5$

23. $\dfrac{2x - 3}{5 - x} = \dfrac{4x - 3}{1 - 2x}$

24. $\sqrt[3]{x - 4} - 1 = 3$

25. Solve $\frac{1}{2}x - (4 - x) + 1 = \frac{3}{2}x - 5$. Is this equation either an identity or a contradiction?

26. Graph f. Is f continuous on its domain? Evaluate $f(1)$.

$$f(x) = \begin{cases} x^2 - 1 & \text{if } -3 \le x \le -1 \\ x + 1 & \text{if } -1 < x < 1 \\ 1 - x^2 & \text{if } \ 1 \le x \le 3 \end{cases}$$

Exercises 27–32: Solve the inequality.

27. $-\frac{1}{3}x - (1 + x) > \frac{2}{3}x$

28. $-4 \le 4x - 6 < \frac{5}{2}$

29. $|5x - 7| \ge 3$

30. $5x^2 + 13x - 6 < 0$

31. $x^3 - 9x \le 0$

32. $\dfrac{4x - 3}{x + 2} > 0$

33. The graph of a nonlinear function f is shown. Solve each equation or inequality.
(a) $f(x) = 0$ **(b)** $f(x) > 0$ **(c)** $f(x) \le 0$

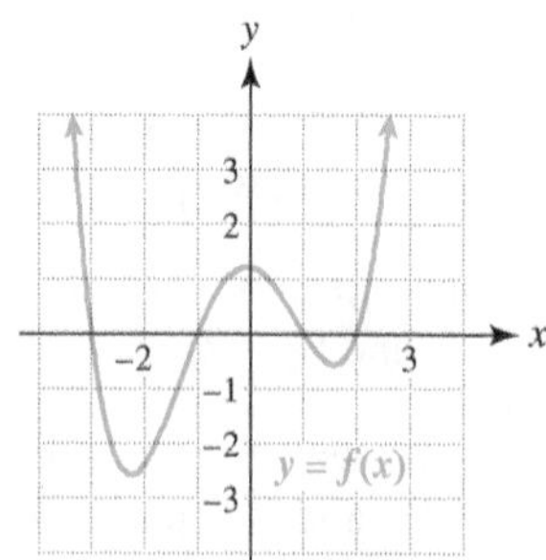

34. Write the quadratic polynomial $f(x) = 2x^2 - 4x + 1$ in the form $f(x) = a(x - h)^2 + k$.

35. Use the given graph of $y = f(x)$ at the top of the next column to sketch a graph of each equation.

(a) $y = f(x + 2) - 1$ **(b)** $y = -2f(x)$

(c) $y = f(-x) + 1$ **(d)** $y = f\left(\frac{1}{2}x\right)$

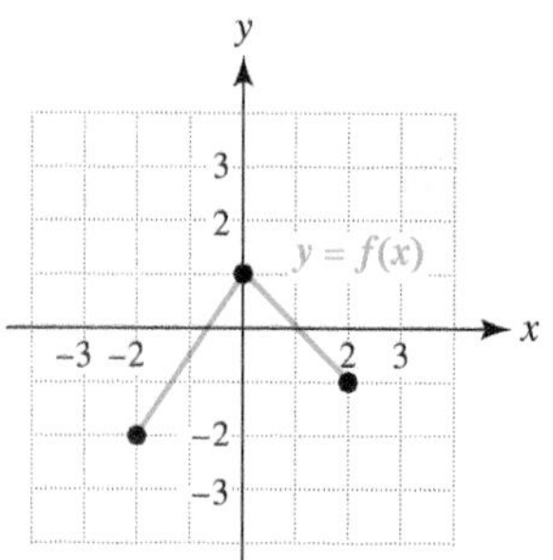

36. Use transformations of graphs to sketch a graph of $y = 2\sqrt{x + 1}$.

37. Use the graph of f to estimate each of the following.
(a) Where f is increasing or decreasing

(b) The zeros of f

(c) The coordinates of any turning points

(d) Any local extrema

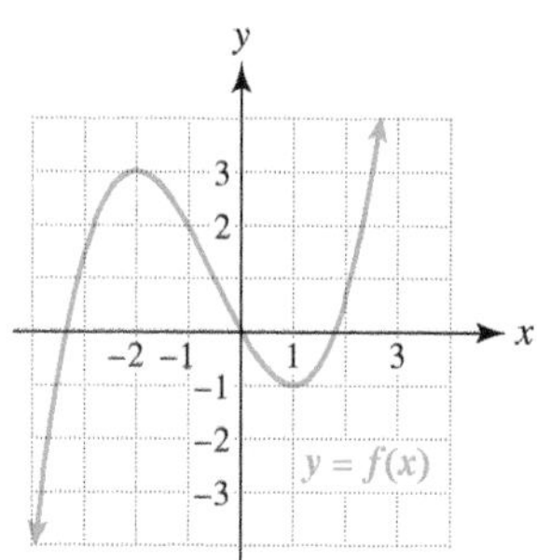

38. Are $f(x) = x^4 - 5x^3 - 7$ and $g(x) = \sqrt{9 - x^2}$ even, odd, or neither?

39. Sketch a graph of a quartic (degree 4) function with a negative leading coefficient, three x-intercepts, and three turning points.

40. State the end behavior of $f(x) = 4 + 3x - x^3$.

41. Divide each expression.

(a) $\dfrac{4a^3 - 8a^2 + 12}{4a^2}$ **(b)** $\dfrac{2x^3 - 4x + 1}{x - 1}$

42. A quintic (degree 5) function f with real coefficients has leading coefficient $\frac{1}{2}$ and zeros -2, i, and $-2i$. Write $f(x)$ in complete factored form and expanded form.

43. A degree 6 function f has zeros -3, 1, and 4 with multiplicities 1, 2, and 3, respectively. If the leading coefficient is 4, write the complete factored form of $f(x)$.

44. Use the graph to write the complete factored form of the cubic polynomial $f(x)$.

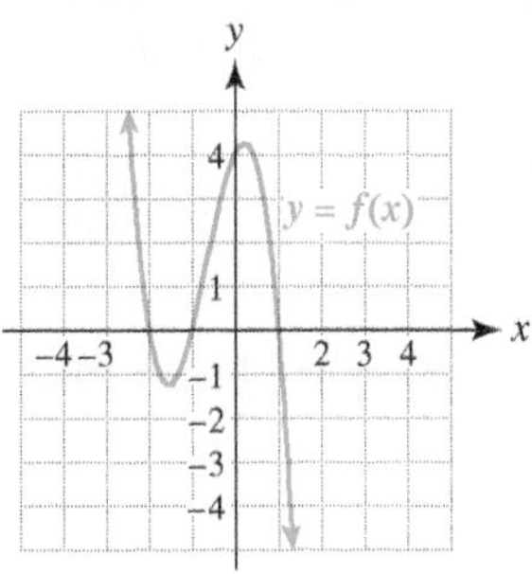

45. Write $\frac{3 + 4i}{1 - i}$ in standard form.

46. Find all solutions, real or imaginary, to $x^4 - 25 = 0$.

47. State the domain of $f(x) = \frac{2x - 5}{x^2 - 3x - 4}$. Find any vertical or horizontal asymptotes.

48. Write $\sqrt[3]{x^5}$ using rational exponents. Evaluate the expression for $x = 8$.

Applications

49. Water in a Pool The graph shows the amount of water in a swimming pool x hours past noon. Find the slope of each line segment and interpret each slope.

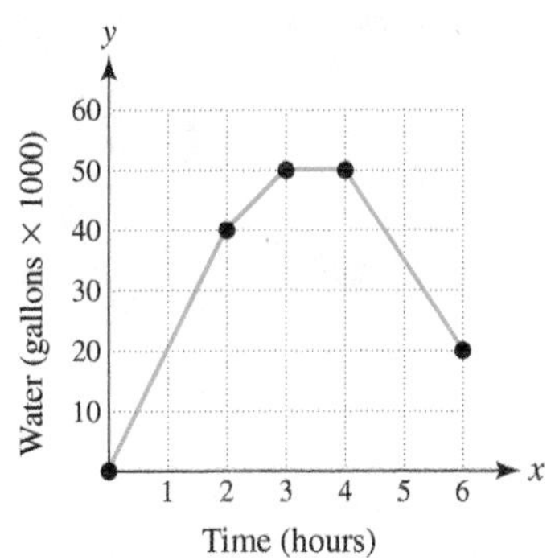

50. Distance At noon, one runner is heading south at 8 miles per hour and is located 2 miles north of a second runner, who is heading west at 7 miles per hour. Approximate the distance between the runners to the nearest tenth of a mile at 12:30 P.M.

51. Mixing Acid Two liters of a 35% sulfuric acid solution need to be diluted to a 20% solution. How many liters of a 12% sulfuric acid solution should be mixed with the 2-liter solution?

52. Working Together Suppose one person can paint a room in 10 hours and another person can paint the same room in 8 hours. How long will it take to paint the room if they work together?

53. Maximizing Revenue The revenue R in dollars from selling x thousand toy figures is given by the formula $R(x) = x(800 - x)$. How many toy figures should be sold to maximize revenue?

54. Construction A box is being constructed by cutting 2-inch squares from the corners of a rectangular sheet of metal that is 6 inches longer than it is wide. If the box is to have a volume of 270 cubic inches, find the dimensions of the metal sheet.

55. Group Rates Round-trip airline tickets to Hawaii are regularly \$800, but for each additional ticket purchased the price is reduced by \$5. For example, 1 ticket costs \$800, 2 tickets cost 2(795) = \$1590, and 3 tickets cost 3(790) = \$2370.

(a) Write a quadratic function C that gives the total cost of purchasing t tickets.

(b) Solve $C(t) = 17{,}000$ and interpret the result.

(c) Find the absolute maximum for C and interpret your result. Assume that t must be an integer.

56. Modeling Data Find a quadratic function in the form $f(x) = a(x - h)^2 + k$ that models the data in the table. Graph $y = f(x)$ and the data if a graphing calculator is available.

x	4	6	8	10
y	6	15	37	80

57. Minimizing Surface Area A cylindrical can is being constructed to have a volume of 10π cubic inches. Find the dimensions of the can that result in the least amount of aluminum being used in its construction.

5 Exponential and Logarithmic Functions

When a link is posted on a social network, the majority of the engagements with this link occur within the first few hours. For example, within the first 3 hours a link on Facebook will have received half of its "hits." This *half life for* Twitter is even shorter, 2.8 hours, but much longer, 400 hours, for StumbleUpon.

PGA golfers make about 99.2% of their putts that are 3 feet or less. However, every time a putt's distance increases by 6.6 feet, the chances of a pro making it decrease by about half.

One reason for the explosive growth in mobile communication is the ability of researchers to increase the electrical efficiency of electronic devices. Since the era of the vacuum tube, the number of calculations that can be made using 1 kilowatt-hour of electricity has doubled every 1.6 years. (See Section 5.6, Example 4.)

Each of the examples above makes use of the mathematical concept of an exponential function. This chapter discusses this important topic.

> The important thing is not to stop questioning.
> —Albert Einstein

Sources: "The Half-Life of a Link", Column Five; "A Deeper Law than Moore's," *The Economist.*

5.1 Combining Functions

- Perform arithmetic operations on functions
- Review function notation
- Perform composition of functions

Introduction

Addition, subtraction, multiplication, and division can be performed on numbers and variables. These arithmetic operations can also be used to combine functions. For example, to model the stopping distance of a car traveling at x miles per hour, we compute two functions. The first function is the *reaction distance,* $r(x)$, which is the distance that a car travels between the time when a driver first recognizes a hazard and the time when the brakes are applied. The second function is *braking distance,* $b(x)$, which is the distance that a car travels after the brakes have been applied. *Stopping distance,* $s(x)$, is equal to the sum of $r(x)$ and $b(x)$. Figure 5.1 illustrates this example of addition of functions.

Stopping Distance Is a Sum of Functions:

$$s(x) = r(x) + b(x)$$

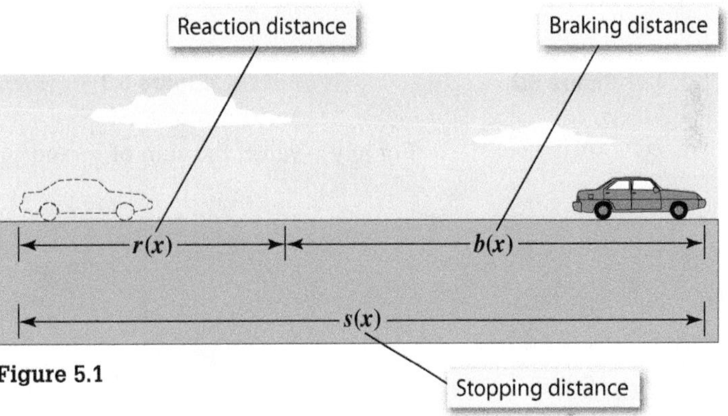

Figure 5.1

Arithmetic Operations on Functions

The concept of finding the sum of two functions can be represented symbolically, graphically, and numerically, as illustrated in the next example.

EXAMPLE 1 Representing stopping distance

For wet, level pavement, highway engineers sometimes let $r(x) = \frac{11}{3}x$ and $b(x) = \frac{1}{9}x^2$. (***Source:*** L. Haefner, *Introduction to Transportation Systems.*)

(a) Evaluate $r(60)$ and $b(60)$ and interpret each result.
(b) Write a formula for $s(x)$ and evaluate $s(60)$. Interpret the result.
(c) Graph r, b, and s. Interpret the graphs.
(d) Illustrate the relationship among r, b, and s numerically.

SOLUTION

(a) Substitute 60 into each formula.

$$r(60) = \frac{11}{3}(60) = 220 \quad \text{and} \quad b(60) = \frac{1}{9}(60)^2 = 400.$$

At 60 miles per hour the reaction distance is 220 feet and the braking distance is 400 feet.

(b) ***Symbolic Representation*** Let $s(x)$ be the sum of $r(x)$ and $b(x)$.

$$s(x) = r(x) + b(x) = \frac{11}{3}x + \frac{1}{9}x^2$$

Stopping Distance = Reaction Distance + Braking Distance

The stopping distance for a car traveling at 60 miles per hour is

$$s(60) = \frac{11}{3}(60) + \frac{1}{9}(60)^2 = 620 \text{ feet.}$$

(c) ***Graphical Representation*** Graph $y_1 = \frac{11}{3}x$, $y_2 = \frac{1}{9}x^2$, and $y_3 = \frac{11}{3}x + \frac{1}{9}x^2$, as shown in Figures 5.2–5.4.

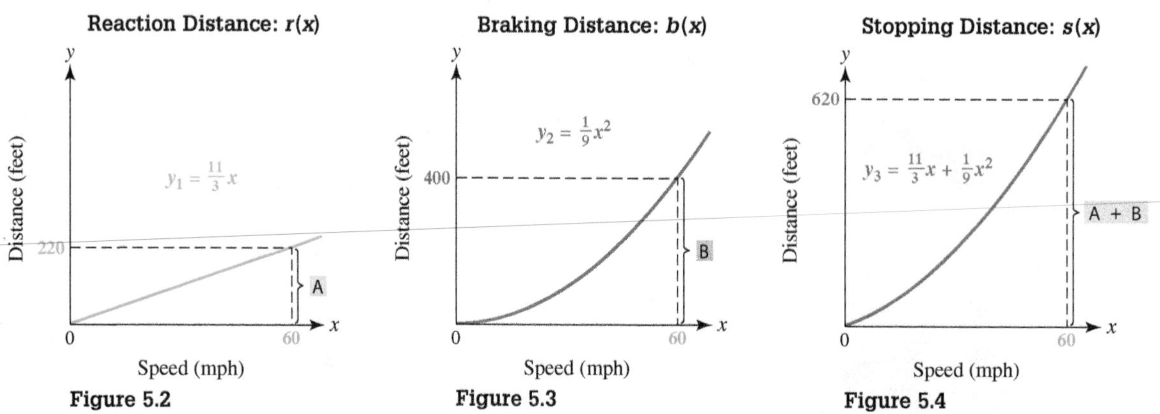

Figure 5.2 **Figure 5.3** **Figure 5.4**

For any x-value, the sum of y_1 and y_2 equals y_3. For example, if $x = 60$, then

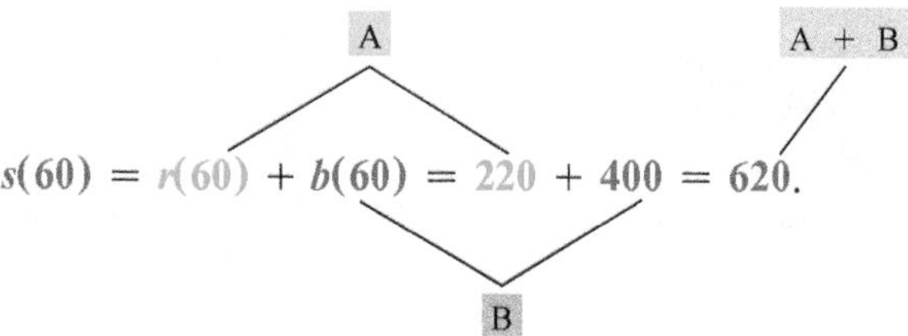

$$s(60) = r(60) + b(60) = 220 + 400 = 620.$$

(d) ***Numerical Representation*** Table 5.1 shows $r(x)$, $b(x)$, and $s(x) = r(x) + b(x)$. Values for $s(x)$ can be found by adding $r(x)$ and $b(x)$. For example, $s(60) = 220 + 400 = 620$.

Adding Functions

x	0	12	24	36	48	60	— Speed
$r(x)$	0	44	88	132	176	220	— Reaction distance
$b(x)$	0	16	64	144	256	400	— Braking distance
$s(x)$	0	60	152	276	432	620	— Stopping distance: $s(x) = r(x) + b(x)$

Table 5.1

Now Try Exercise 99

We now formally define arithmetic operations on functions.

OPERATIONS ON FUNCTIONS

If $f(x)$ and $g(x)$ both exist, the sum, difference, product, and quotient of two functions f and g are defined by

$$(f + g)(x) = f(x) + g(x),$$
$$(f - g)(x) = f(x) - g(x),$$
$$(fg)(x) = f(x) \cdot g(x), \quad \text{and}$$
$$\left(\frac{f}{g}\right)(x) = \frac{f(x)}{g(x)}, \quad \text{where } g(x) \neq 0.$$

Operations on Functions and Domains The domains of the sum, difference, and product of f and g include x-values that are in *both* the domain of f and the domain of g. The domain of the quotient f/g includes all x-values in both the domain of f and the domain of g, where $g(x) \neq 0$.

Graphical, Numerical, and Symbolic Evaluation In the next example, we evaluate the sum, difference, product, and quotient of two functions in three ways: graphically, numerically, and symbolically.

EXAMPLE 2 **Evaluating combinations of functions**

If possible, use each representation of f and g to evaluate $(f + g)(4)$, $(f - g)(-2)$, $(fg)(1)$, and $(f/g)(0)$.

(a)

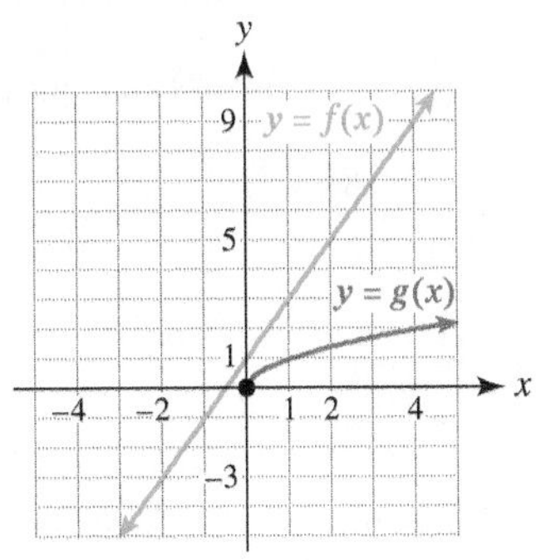

(b)

x	-2	0	1	4
$f(x)$	-3	1	3	9

x	-2	0	1	4
$g(x)$	—	0	1	2

(c) $f(x) = 2x + 1$, $g(x) = \sqrt{x}$

SOLUTION

(a) ***Graphical Evaluation*** From Figure 5.5, $f(4) = 9$ and $g(4) = 2$. Thus

$$(f + g)(4) = f(4) + g(4) = 9 + 2 = 11.$$

Although $f(-2) = -3$, $g(-2)$ is undefined because -2 is not in the domain of g. Thus $(f - g)(-2)$ is undefined. The domains of f and g include 1, and it follows that

$$(fg)(1) = f(1)g(1) = 3(1) = 3.$$

The graph of g intersects the origin, so $g(0) = 0$. Thus $(f/g)(0) = \frac{f(0)}{g(0)}$ is undefined.

$f(4) = 9$ and $g(4) = 2$

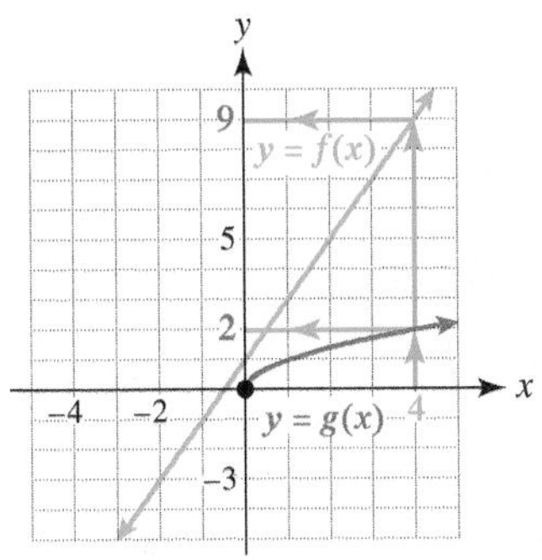

Figure 5.5

(b) ***Numerical Evaluation*** From the tables, $f(4) = 9$ and $g(4) = 2$. As in part (a),

$$(f + g)(4) = f(4) + g(4) = 9 + 2 = 11.$$

A dash in the table indicates that $g(-2)$ is undefined, so $(f - g)(-2)$ is also undefined. The calculations of $(fg)(1)$ and $(f/g)(0)$ are done in a similar manner.

(c) ***Symbolic Evaluation*** Use the formulas $f(x) = 2x + 1$ and $g(x) = \sqrt{x}$.

$(f + g)(4) = f(4) + g(4) = (2 \cdot 4 + 1) + \sqrt{4} = 9 + 2 = 11$

$(f - g)(-2) = f(-2) - g(-2) = (2 \cdot (-2) + 1) - \sqrt{-2}$ is undefined.

$(fg)(1) = f(1)g(1) = (2 \cdot 1 + 1)\sqrt{1} = 3(1) = 3$

$\left(\frac{f}{g}\right)(0) = \frac{f(0)}{g(0)}$ is undefined, since $g(0) = 0$.

Now Try Exercises 7, 31, and 35

EXAMPLE 3 Performing arithmetic operations on functions symbolically

Let $f(x) = 2 + \sqrt{x - 1}$ and $g(x) = x^2 - 4$.

(a) Find the domains of $f(x)$ and $g(x)$. Then find the domains of $(f + g)(x)$, $(f - g)(x)$, $(fg)(x)$, and $(f/g)(x)$.

(b) If possible, evaluate $(f + g)(5)$, $(f - g)(1)$, $(fg)(0)$, and $(f/g)(3)$.

(c) Write expressions for $(f + g)(x)$, $(f - g)(x)$, $(fg)(x)$, and $(f/g)(x)$.

SOLUTION

(a) Whenever $x \geq 1$, $f(x) = 2 + \sqrt{x - 1}$ is defined. Therefore the domain of $f(x)$ is $\{x | x \geq 1\}$. The domain of $g(x) = x^2 - 4$ is all real numbers. The domains of $(f + g)(x)$, $(f - g)(x)$, and $(fg)(x)$ include all x-values in *both* the domain of $f(x)$ and the domain of $g(x)$. Thus their domains are $\{x | x \geq 1\}$.

To determine the domain of $(f/g)(x)$, we must also exclude x-values for which $g(x) = x^2 - 4 = 0$. This occurs when $x = \pm 2$. Thus the domain of $(f/g)(x)$ is $\{x | x \geq 1, x \neq 2\}$. (Note that $x \neq -2$ is satisfied if $x \geq 1$.)

(b) The expressions can be evaluated as follows.

$$(f + g)(5) = f(5) + g(5) = \left(2 + \sqrt{5 - 1}\right) + (5^2 - 4) = 4 + 21 = 25$$

$$(f - g)(1) = f(1) - g(1) = \left(2 + \sqrt{1 - 1}\right) - (1^2 - 4) = 2 - (-3) = 5$$

$(fg)(0)$ is undefined, since 0 is not in the domain of $f(x)$.

$$(f/g)(3) = \frac{f(3)}{g(3)} = \frac{2 + \sqrt{3 - 1}}{3^2 - 4} = \frac{2 + \sqrt{2}}{5}$$

(c) The sum, difference, product, and quotient of f and g are calculated as follows.

$$(f + g)(x) = f(x) + g(x) = \left(2 + \sqrt{x - 1}\right) + (x^2 - 4) = \sqrt{x - 1} + x^2 - 2$$

$$(f - g)(x) = f(x) - g(x) = \left(2 + \sqrt{x - 1}\right) - (x^2 - 4) = \sqrt{x - 1} - x^2 + 6$$

$$(fg)(x) = f(x) \cdot g(x) = \left(2 + \sqrt{x - 1}\right)(x^2 - 4)$$

$$\left(\frac{f}{g}\right)(x) = \frac{f(x)}{g(x)} = \frac{2 + \sqrt{x - 1}}{x^2 - 4}$$

Now Try Exercises 9 and 15

An Application The next example is an application from business involving the difference between two functions.

EXAMPLE 4 Finding the difference of two functions

The expenses for a band to produce the master sound track for an album include renting a music studio and hiring a music engineer. These *fixed costs* are \$12,000, and the cost to produce each album with packaging is \$5.

(a) Assuming no other expenses, find a function C that outputs the cost of producing the master sound track plus x albums. Find the cost of making the master track and 3000 albums.

(b) Suppose that each album is sold for \$12. Find a function R that computes the revenue from selling x albums. Find the revenue from selling 3000 albums.

(c) Determine a function P that outputs the profit from selling x albums. How much profit is there from selling 3000 albums?

SOLUTION

(a) The cost of producing the master sound track for \$12,000 plus x albums at \$5 each is given by $C(x) = 5x + 12{,}000$. The cost of manufacturing the master sound track and 3000 albums is

$$C(3000) = 5(3000) + 12{,}000 = \$27{,}000.$$

(b) The revenue from x albums at \$12 each is computed by $R(x) = 12x$. The revenue from selling 3000 albums is $R(3000) = 12(3000) = \$36{,}000$.

(c) Profit P is equal to revenue minus cost. This can be written using function notation.

$$\begin{aligned} P(x) &= R(x) - C(x) \\ &= 12x - (5x + 12{,}000) \\ &= 12x - 5x - 12{,}000 \\ &= 7x - 12{,}000 \end{aligned}$$

If $x = 3000$, $P(3000) = 7(3000) - 12{,}000 = \$9000$.

Now Try Exercise 95

Review of Function Notation

In the next example, we review how to evaluate function notation before we discuss composition of functions.

EXAMPLE 5 **Evaluating function notation**

Let $g(x) = 3x^2 - 6x + 2$. Evaluate each expression.

(a) $g(2)$ **(b)** $g(k)$ **(c)** $g(x^2)$ **(d)** $g(x + 2)$

SOLUTION

(a) $g(2) = 3(2)^2 - 6(2) + 2 = 12 - 12 + 2 = 2$

(b) $g(k) = 3k^2 - 6k + 2$

(c) $g(x^2) = 3(x^2)^2 - 6(x^2) + 2 = 3x^4 - 6x^2 + 2$

(d)
$$\begin{aligned} g(x + 2) &= 3(x + 2)^2 - 6(x + 2) + 2 \\ &= 3(x^2 + 4x + 4) - 6(x + 2) + 2 \\ &= 3x^2 + 12x + 12 - 6x - 12 + 2 \\ &= 3x^2 + 6x + 2 \end{aligned}$$

Algebra Review
To review squaring a binomial, see Chapter R (page R-17).

Now Try Exercise 45

Composition of Functions

Many tasks in life are performed in sequence. For example, to go to a movie we might get into a car, drive to the movie theater, and get out of the car. A similar situation occurs with functions. For example, to convert miles to inches we might first convert miles to feet and then convert feet to inches in sequence. Since there are 5280 feet in a mile, $f(x) = 5280x$ converts x miles to an equivalent number of feet. Then $g(x) = 12x$ changes feet to inches. To convert x miles to inches, we combine the functions f and g in sequence. Figure 5.6 illustrates how to convert 5 miles to inches. First, $f(5) = 5280(5) = 26{,}400$. Then the output of 26,400 feet from f is used as input for g. The number of inches in 26,400 feet is $g(26{,}400) = 12(26{,}400) = 316{,}800$. This computation is called the *composition* of g and f.

The composition of g and f shown in Figure 5.6 can be expressed symbolically. The symbol $\circ$ is used to denote composition of two functions.

Composition of Functions (converting 5 miles to inches)

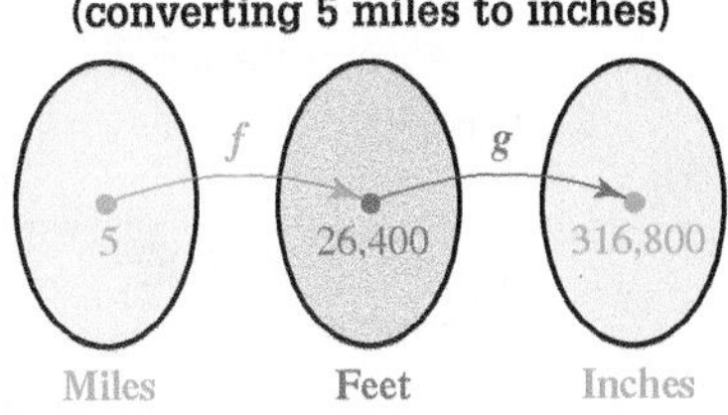

Figure 5.6

Composition of g and f

$(g \circ f)(5)$	$= g(f(5))$	First compute $f(5)$.
	$= g(5280 \cdot 5)$	$f(x) = 5280x$
	$= g(26{,}400)$	Simplify.
	$= 12(26{,}400)$	$g(x) = 12x$
	$= 316{,}800$	Simplify.

A distance of 5 miles is equivalent to 316,800 inches. The concept of composition of two functions relates to applying functions in sequence and is now defined formally.

COMPOSITION OF FUNCTIONS

If f and g are functions, then the **composite function** $g \circ f$, or **composition** of g and f is defined by

$$(g \circ f)(x) = g(f(x)).$$

We read $g(f(x))$ as "g of f of x."

The domain of $g \circ f$ is all x in the domain of f such that $f(x)$ is in the domain of g.

Symbolic Evaluation of Composite Functions The next three examples discuss how to evaluate composite functions and find their domains symbolically.

EXAMPLE 6 Finding a symbolic representation of a composite function

Find a formula for the composite function $g \circ f$ that converts x miles into inches.

SOLUTION Let $f(x) = 5280x$ and $g(x) = 12x$.

$$\begin{aligned}(g \circ f)(x) &= g(f(x)) && \text{Definition of composition}\\ &= g(5280x) && f(x) = 5280x \text{ is the input for } g.\\ &= 12(5280x) && g \text{ multiplies the input by 12.}\\ &= 63{,}360x && \text{Simplify.}\end{aligned}$$

Thus $(g \circ f)(x) = 63{,}360x$ converts x miles into inches.

Now try Exercises 97

NOTE Converting units is only one application of composition of functions. Another application involves examining how a decrease in the ozone layer causes an increase in ultraviolet sunlight, which in turn causes increases in the number of skin cancer cases. See Example 10.

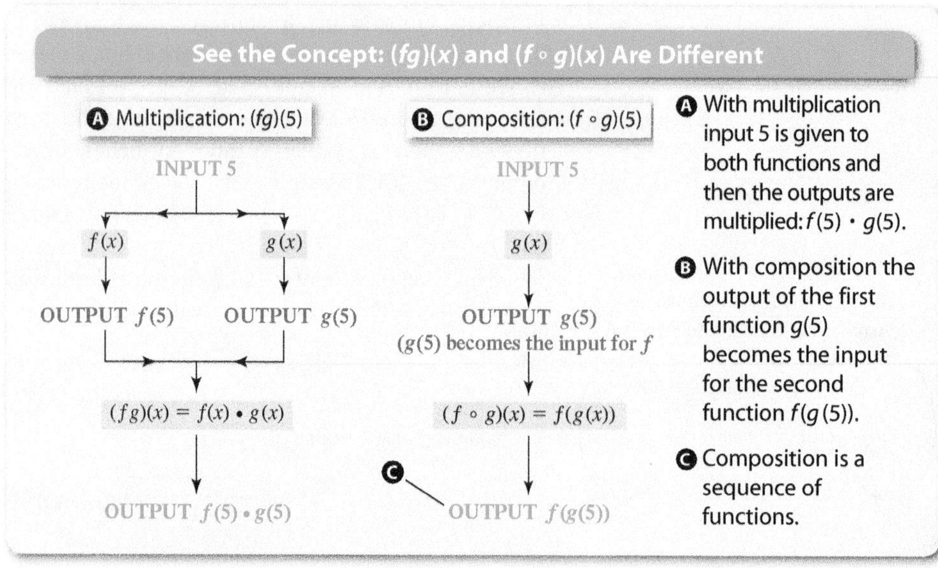
See the Concept: (fg)(x) and (f ∘ g)(x) Are Different
A Multiplication: (fg)(5)
INPUT 5
f(x)
g(x)
OUTPUT f(5)
OUTPUT g(5)
(fg)(x) = f(x) • g(x)
OUTPUT f(5) • g(5)
B Composition: (f ∘ g)(5)
INPUT 5
g(x)
OUTPUT g(5)
(g(5) becomes the input for f
(f ∘ g)(x) = f(g(x))
C
OUTPUT f(g(5))
A With multiplication input 5 is given to both functions and then the outputs are multiplied: f(5) · g(5).
B With composition the output of the first function g(5) becomes the input for the second function f(g(5)).
C Composition is a sequence of functions.

EXAMPLE 7 **Evaluating a composite function symbolically**

Let $f(x) = x^2 + 3x + 2$ and $g(x) = \frac{1}{x}$.

(a) Evaluate $(f \circ g)(2)$ and $(g \circ f)(2)$. How do they compare?

(b) Find the composite functions defined by $(f \circ g)(x)$ and $(g \circ f)(x)$. Are they equivalent expressions?

(c) Find the domains of $(f \circ g)(x)$ and $(g \circ f)(x)$.

SOLUTION

(a) $(f \circ g)(2) = f(g(2)) = f\left(\frac{1}{2}\right) = \left(\frac{1}{2}\right)^2 + 3\left(\frac{1}{2}\right) + 2 = \frac{15}{4} = 3.75$

$(g \circ f)(2) = g(f(2)) = g(2^2 + 3 \cdot 2 + 2) = g(12) = \frac{1}{12} \approx 0.0833$

The results are *not* equal.

(b) $$(f \circ g)(x) = f(g(x)) = f\left(\frac{1}{x}\right) = \left(\frac{1}{x}\right)^2 + 3\left(\frac{1}{x}\right) + 2 = \frac{1}{x^2} + \frac{3}{x} + 2$$

$$(g \circ f)(x) = g(f(x)) = g(x^2 + 3x + 2) = \frac{1}{x^2 + 3x + 2}$$

The expressions for $(f \circ g)(x)$ and $(g \circ f)(x)$ are *not* equivalent.

(c) The domain of f is all real numbers, and the domain of g is $\{x \mid x \neq 0\}$. The domain of $(f \circ g)(x) = f(g(x))$ consists of all x in the domain of g such that $g(x)$ is in the domain of f. Thus the domain of $(f \circ g)(x) = \frac{1}{x^2} + \frac{3}{x} + 2$ is $\{x \mid x \neq 0\}$.

The domain of $(g \circ f)(x) = g(f(x))$ consists of all x in the domain of f such that $f(x)$ is in the domain of g. Since $x^2 + 3x + 2 = 0$ when $x = -1$ or $x = -2$, the domain of $(g \circ f)(x) = \frac{1}{x^2 + 3x + 2}$ is $\{x \mid x \neq -1, x \neq -2\}$.

Now try Exercises 53 and 57

MAKING CONNECTIONS

Composition and Domains To find the domain of a composition of two functions, it is sometimes helpful not to immediately simplify the resulting expression. For example, if $f(x) = x^2$ and $g(x) = \sqrt{x - 1}$, then

$$(f \circ g)(x) = \left(\sqrt{x - 1}\right)^2.$$

From this unsimplified expression, we can see that the domain (input) of $f \circ g$ must be restricted to $x \geq 1$ for the output to be a real number. As a result,

$$(f \circ g)(x) = x - 1, \quad x \geq 1.$$

EXAMPLE 8 **Finding symbolic representations for composite functions**

Find $(f \circ g)(x)$ and $(g \circ f)(x)$.

(a) $f(x) = x + 2$, $\quad g(x) = x^3 - 2x^2 - 1$

(b) $f(x) = \sqrt{2x}$, $\quad g(x) = \frac{1}{x + 1}$

(c) $f(x) = 2x - 3$, $\quad g(x) = x^2 + 5$

SOLUTION

Getting Started When finding a composition of functions, the first step is often to write $(f \circ g)(x) = f(g(x))$ or $(g \circ f)(x) = g(f(x))$. ▶

(a) Begin by writing $(f \circ g)(x) = f(g(x)) = f(x^3 - 2x^2 - 1)$. Function f adds 2 to the input. That is, $f(\text{input}) = (\text{input}) + 2$ because $f(x) = x + 2$. Thus

$$f(x^3 - 2x^2 - 1) = (x^3 - 2x^2 - 1) + 2 = x^3 - 2x^2 + 1.$$

To find the composition $(g \circ f)(x)$, write $(g \circ f)(x) = g(f(x)) = g(x + 2)$. Because $g(x) = x^3 - 2x^2 - 1$, it follows that $g(\text{input}) = (\text{input})^3 - 2(\text{input})^2 - 1$. Thus

$$g(x + 2) = (x + 2)^3 - 2(x + 2)^2 - 1.$$

(b) $(f \circ g)(x) = f(g(x)) = f\left(\frac{1}{x + 1}\right) = \sqrt{2 \cdot \frac{1}{x + 1}} = \sqrt{\frac{2}{x + 1}}$ $\quad f(x) = \sqrt{2x}$

$(g \circ f)(x) = g(f(x)) = g\left(\sqrt{2x}\right) = \frac{1}{\sqrt{2x} + 1}$ $\quad g(x) = \frac{1}{x + 1}$

(c) $(f \circ g)(x) = f(g(x)) = f(x^2 + 5) = 2(x^2 + 5) - 3 = 2x^2 + 7$

$(g \circ f)(x) = g(f(x)) = g(2x - 3) = (2x - 3)^2 + 5 = 4x^2 - 12x + 14$

Now Try Exercises 59, 63, and 65

NOTE A composition of f with itself is denoted $(f \circ f)(x)$. For example, if $f(x) = 3x$, then

$$(f \circ f)(x) = f(3x) = 3(3x) = 9x.$$

That is, f multiplies the input by 3, so $(f \circ f)(x)$ multiplies the input by 3 twice, which is equivalent to multiplying the input by 9.

Graphical Evaluation of Composite Functions The next example shows how to evaluate a composition of functions graphically.

EXAMPLE 9 **Evaluating a composite function graphically**

Use the graphs of f and g shown in Figure 5.7 to evaluate each expression.

(a) $(f \circ g)(2)$ **(b)** $(g \circ f)(-3)$ **(c)** $(f \circ f)(-3)$

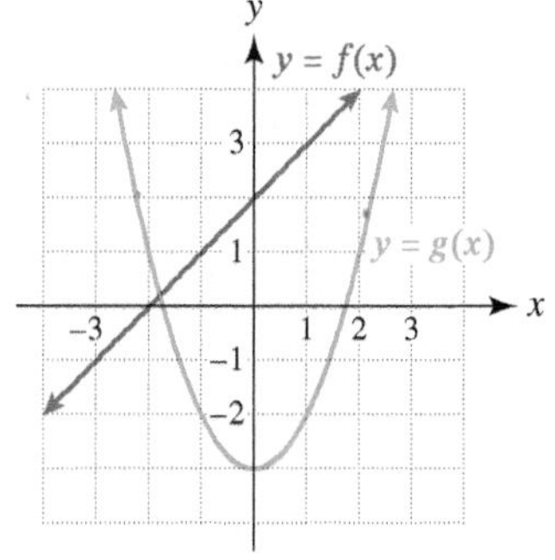

Figure 5.7

SOLUTION

(a) Because $(f \circ g)(2) = f(g(2))$, first evaluate $g(2)$. From Figure 5.8, $g(2) = 1$ and

$$(f \circ g)(2) = f(g(2)) = f(1).$$

To complete the evaluation of $(f \circ g)(2)$, use Figure 5.9 to determine that $f(1) = 3$. Thus $(f \circ g)(2) = 3$.

(b) Because $(g \circ f)(-3) = g(f(-3))$, first evaluate the expression $f(-3)$. Figure 5.10 shows that $f(-3) = -1$, so

$$(g \circ f)(-3) = g(f(-3)) = g(-1).$$

From Figure 5.11, $g(-1) = -2$. Thus $(g \circ f)(-3) = -2$.

(c) Similarly, $(f \circ f)(-3) = f(f(-3)) = f(-1) = 1$.

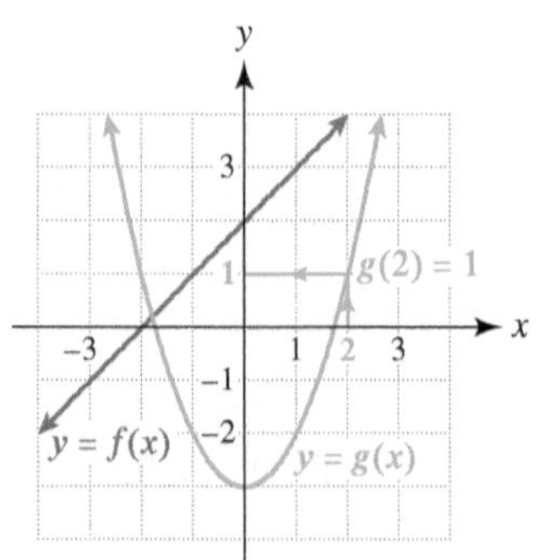

Figure 5.8

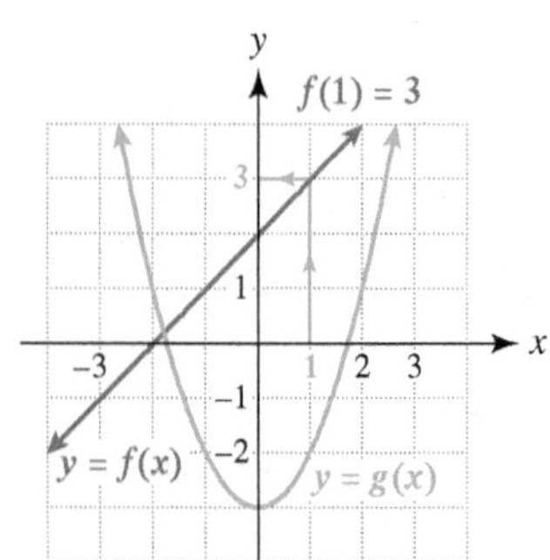

Figure 5.9

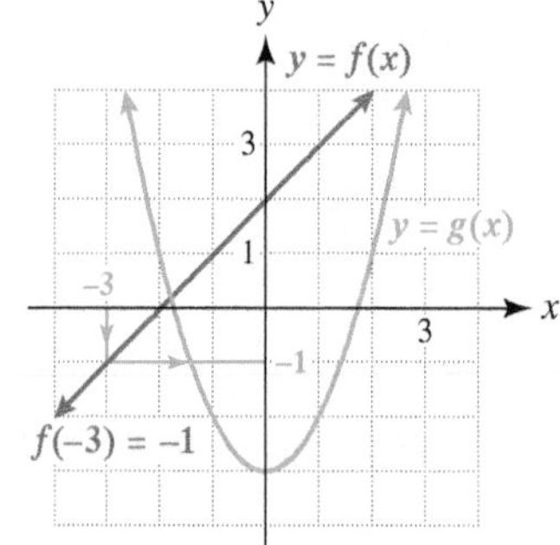

Figure 5.10

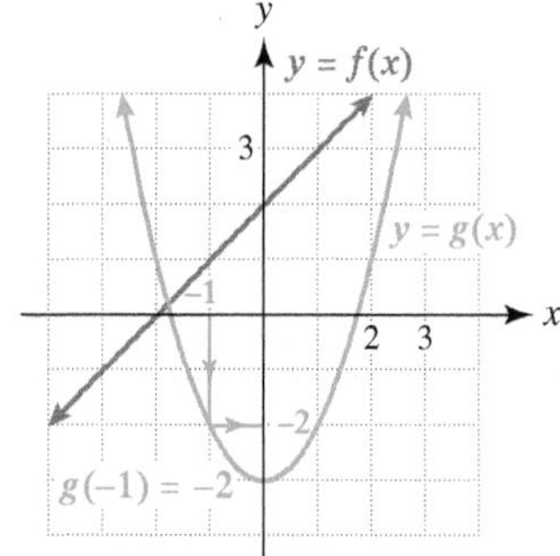

Figure 5.11

Now Try Exercise 75

Numerical Evaluation of Composite Functions Tables 5.2 and 5.3 represent two functions f and g.

x	1	2	3	4
$f(x)$	2	3	4	1

Table 5.2

x	1	2	3	4
$g(x)$	4	3	2	1

Table 5.3

We can use these tables to evaluate expressions, such as $(g \circ f)(3)$ and $(f \circ g)(3)$.

$$\begin{aligned}(g \circ f)(3) &= g(f(3)) && \text{Definition of composition}\\ &= g(4) && f(3) = 4 \text{ in Table 5.2.}\\ &= 1 && g(4) = 1 \text{ in Table 5.3.}\end{aligned}$$

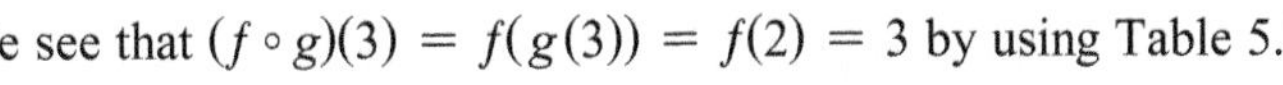

We see that $(f \circ g)(3) = f(g(3)) = f(2) = 3$ by using Table 5.3 and then Table 5.2.

NOTE Composition of functions is *not* commutative. That is, $(g \circ f)(x) \neq (f \circ g)(x)$ in general. For example, from above, $(g \circ f)(3) \neq (f \circ g)(3)$.

An Application The next example illustrates how composition of functions occurs in the analysis of the ozone layer, ultraviolet (UV) radiation, and cases of skin cancer.

EXAMPLE 10 Evaluating a composite function numerically

Depletion of the ozone layer can cause an increase in the amount of UV radiation reaching the surface of the earth. An increase in UV radiation is associated with skin cancer. In Table 5.4 the function f computes the approximate percent *increase* in UV radiation resulting from an x percent *decrease* in the thickness of the ozone layer. The function g shown in Table 5.5 computes the expected percent increase in cases of skin cancer resulting from an x percent increase in UV radiation. (***Source:*** R. Turner, D. Pearce, and I. Bateman, *Environmental Economics*.)

Percent Increase in UV Radiation

x	0	1	2	3	4	5	6	Percent decrease in the ozone layer
$f(x)$	0	1.5	3.0	4.5	6.0	7.5	9.0	Percent increase in UV radiation

Table 5.4

Percent Increase in Skin Cancer

x	0	1.5	3.0	4.5	6.0	7.5	9.0	Percent increase in UV radiation
$g(x)$	0	5.25	10.5	15.75	21.0	26.25	31.5	Percent increase in cases of skin cancer

Table 5.5

(a) Find $(g \circ f)(2)$ and interpret this calculation.
(b) Create a table for $g \circ f$. Describe what $(g \circ f)(x)$ computes.

SOLUTION

(a) $(g \circ f)(2) = g(f(2)) = g(3.0) = 10.5$. This means that a 2% decrease in the thickness of the ozone layer results in a 3% increase in UV radiation, which could cause a 10.5% increase in skin cancer.

(b) The values for $(g \circ f)(x)$ can be found in a similar manner. See Table 5.6.

x	0	1	2	3	4	5	6	Percent decrease in the ozone layer
$(g \circ f)(x)$	0	5.25	10.5	15.75	21.0	26.25	31.5	Percent increase in cases of skin cancer

Table 5.6

The composition $(g \circ f)(x)$ computes the percent increase in cases of skin cancer resulting from an x percent decrease in the ozone layer.

Now Try Exercise 101

Writing Compositions When you are solving problems, it is sometimes helpful to recognize a function as the composition of two simpler functions. For example, $h(x) = \sqrt[3]{x^2}$ can be thought of as the composition of the cube root function, $g(x) = \sqrt[3]{x}$, and the squaring function, $f(x) = x^2$. Then h can be written as $h(x) = g(f(x)) = \sqrt[3]{x^2}$. This concept is demonstrated in the next example. Note that answers may vary.

EXAMPLE 11 **Writing a function as a composition of two functions**

Find $f(x)$ and $g(x)$ so that $h(x) = (g \circ f)(x)$.

(a) $h(x) = (x + 3)^2$ **(b)** $h(x) = \sqrt{2x - 7}$ **(c)** $h(x) = \dfrac{1}{x^2 + 2x}$

SOLUTION

(a) Let $f(x) = x + 3$ and $g(x) = x^2$. Then

$$(g \circ f)(x) = g(f(x)) = g(x + 3) = (x + 3)^2.$$

(b) Let $f(x) = 2x - 7$ and $g(x) = \sqrt{x}$. Then

$$(g \circ f)(x) = g(f(x)) = g(2x - 7) = \sqrt{2x - 7}.$$

(c) Let $f(x) = x^2 + 2x$ and $g(x) = \frac{1}{x}$. Then

$$(g \circ f)(x) = g(f(x)) = g(x^2 + 2x) = \frac{1}{x^2 + 2x}.$$

Now try Exercises 81, 85, and 91

5.1 Putting It All Together

The following table summarizes some concepts involved with combining functions.

CONCEPT	NOTATION	EXAMPLES
Sum of two functions	$(f + g)(x) = f(x) + g(x)$	$f(x) = x^2, g(x) = 2x + 1$ $(f + g)(3) = f(3) + g(3) = 9 + 7 = 16$ $(f + g)(x) = f(x) + g(x) = x^2 + 2x + 1$
Difference of two functions	$(f - g)(x) = f(x) - g(x)$	$f(x) = 3x, g(x) = 2x + 1$ $(f - g)(1) = f(1) - g(1) = 3 - 3 = 0$ $(f - g)(x) = f(x) - g(x) = 3x - (2x + 1)$ $= x - 1$
Product of two functions	$(fg)(x) = f(x) \cdot g(x)$	$f(x) = x^3, g(x) = 1 - 3x$ $(fg)(-2) = f(-2) \cdot g(-2) = (-8)(7) = -56$ $(fg)(x) = f(x) \cdot g(x) = x^3(1 - 3x) = x^3 - 3x^4$
Quotient of two functions	$\left(\frac{f}{g}\right)(x) = \frac{f(x)}{g(x)}, g(x) \neq 0$	$f(x) = x^2 - 1, g(x) = x + 2$ $\left(\frac{f}{g}\right)(2) = \frac{f(2)}{g(2)} = \frac{3}{4}$ $\left(\frac{f}{g}\right)(x) = \frac{f(x)}{g(x)} = \frac{x^2 - 1}{x + 2}, x \neq -2$
Composition of two functions	$(g \circ f)(x) = g(f(x))$	$f(x) = x^3, g(x) = x^2 - 2x + 1$ $(g \circ f)(2) = g(f(2)) = g(8)$ $= 64 - 16 + 1 = 49$ $(g \circ f)(x) = g(f(x)) = g(x^3)$ $= (x^3)^2 - 2(x^3) + 1$ $= x^6 - 2x^3 + 1$

5.1 Exercises

Concepts

1. If $f(3) = 2$ and $g(3) = 5$, $(f + g)(3) =$ ____.

2. If $f(3) = 2$ and $g(2) = 5$, $(g \circ f)(3) =$ ____.

3. If $f(x) = x^2$ and $g(x) = 4x$, $(fg)(x) =$ ____.

4. If $f(x) = x^2$ and $g(x) = 4x$, $(f \circ g)(x) =$ ____.

5. **Cost of Carpet** If $f(x)$ calculates the number of square feet in x square yards and $g(x)$ calculates the cost in dollars of x square feet of carpet, what does $(g \circ f)(x)$ calculate?

6. **Time Conversion** If $f(x)$ calculates the number of days in x hours and $g(x)$ calculates the number of years in x days, what does $(g \circ f)(x)$ calculate?

Arithmetic Operations on Functions

Exercises 7–10: Use $f(x)$ and $g(x)$ to evaluate each expression symbolically.

7. $f(x) = 2x - 3$, $g(x) = 1 - x^2$
   (a) $(f + g)(3)$ (b) $(f - g)(-1)$
   (c) $(fg)(0)$ (d) $(f/g)(2)$

8. $f(x) = 4x - x^3$, $g(x) = x + 3$
   (a) $(g + g)(-2)$ (b) $(f - g)(0)$
   (c) $(gf)(1)$ (d) $(g/f)(-3)$

9. $f(x) = 2x + 1$, $g(x) = \dfrac{1}{x}$
   (a) $(f + g)(2)$ (b) $(f - g)\left(\frac{1}{2}\right)$
   (c) $(fg)(4)$ (d) $(f/g)(0)$

10. $f(x) = \sqrt[3]{x^2}$, $g(x) = |x - 3|$
   (a) $(f + g)(-8)$ (b) $(f - g)(-1)$
   (c) $(fg)(0)$ (d) $(f/g)(27)$

Exercises 11–30: Use $f(x)$ and $g(x)$ to find a formula for each expression. Identify its domain.

(a) $(f + g)(x)$ *(b)* $(f - g)(x)$
(c) $(fg)(x)$ *(d)* $(f/g)(x)$

11. $f(x) = 2x$, $g(x) = x^2$

12. $f(x) = 1 - 4x$, $g(x) = 3x + 1$

13. $f(x) = x^2 - 1$, $g(x) = x^2 + 1$

14. $f(x) = 4x^3 - 8x^2$, $g(x) = 4x^2$

15. $f(x) = x - \sqrt{x - 1}$, $g(x) = x + \sqrt{x - 1}$

16. $f(x) = 3 + \sqrt{2x + 9}$, $g(x) = 3 - \sqrt{2x + 9}$

17. $f(x) = \sqrt{x} - 1$, $g(x) = \sqrt{x} + 1$

18. $f(x) = \sqrt{1 - x}$, $g(x) = x^3$

19. $f(x) = \dfrac{1}{x + 1}$, $g(x) = \dfrac{3}{x + 1}$

20. $f(x) = x^{1/2}$, $g(x) = 3$

21. $f(x) = \dfrac{1}{2x - 4}$, $g(x) = \dfrac{x}{2x - 4}$

22. $f(x) = \dfrac{1}{x}$, $g(x) = x^3$

23. $f(x) = x^2 - 1$, $g(x) = |x + 1|$

24. $f(x) = |2x - 1|$, $g(x) = |2x + 1|$

25. $f(x) = \dfrac{x^2 - 3x + 2}{x + 1}$, $g(x) = \dfrac{x^2 - 1}{x - 2}$

26. $f(x) = \dfrac{4x - 2}{x + 2}$, $g(x) = \dfrac{2x - 1}{3x + 6}$

27. $f(x) = \dfrac{2}{x^2 - 1}$, $g(x) = \dfrac{x + 1}{x^2 - 2x + 1}$

28. $f(x) = \dfrac{1}{x + 2}$, $g(x) = x^2 + x - 2$

29. $f(x) = x^{5/2} - x^{3/2}$, $g(x) = x^{1/2}$

30. $f(x) = x^{2/3} - 2x^{1/3} + 1$, $g(x) = x^{1/3} - 1$

Exercises 31–34: Use the graph to evaluate each expression.

31.

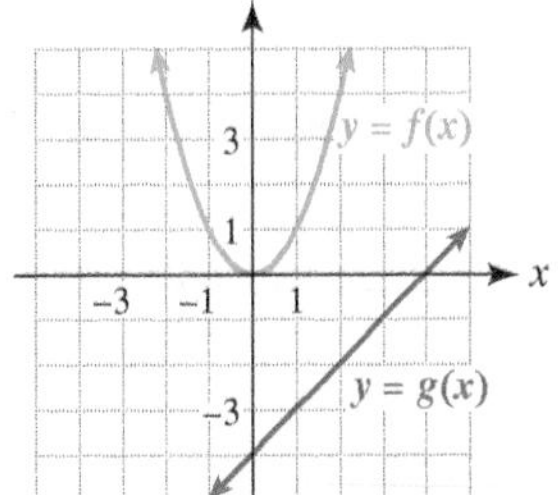

(a) $(f + g)(2)$
(b) $(f - g)(1)$
(c) $(fg)(0)$
(d) $(f/g)(1)$

32.

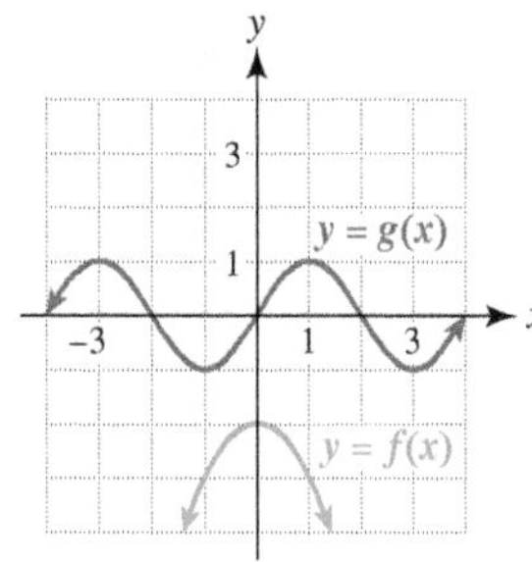

(a) $(f + g)(1)$

(b) $(f - g)(0)$

(c) $(fg)(-1)$

(d) $(f/g)(1)$

33.

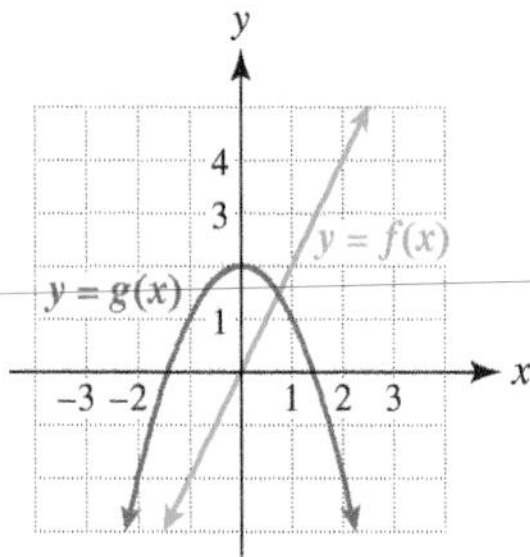

(a) $(f + g)(0)$

(b) $(f - g)(-1)$

(c) $(fg)(1)$

(d) $(f/g)(2)$

34.

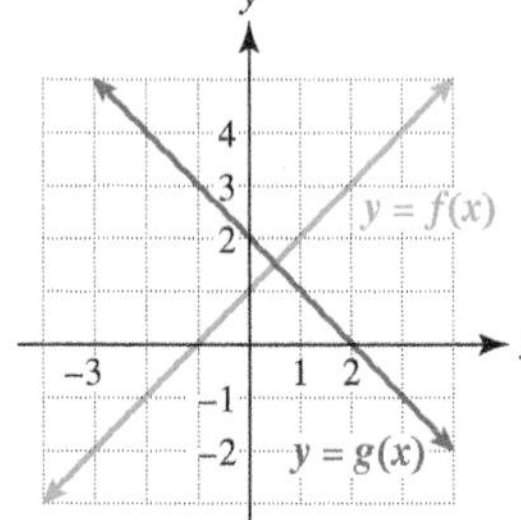

(a) $(f + g)(-1)$

(b) $(f - g)(-2)$

(c) $(fg)(0)$

(d) $(f/g)(2)$

Exercises 35 and 36: Use the tables to evaluate each expression, if possible.

(a) $(f + g)(-1)$ *(b)* $(g - f)(0)$

(c) $(gf)(2)$ *(d)* $(f/g)(2)$

35.

x	-1	0	2
$f(x)$	-3	5	1

x	-1	0	2
$g(x)$	-2	3	0

36.

x	-1	0	2
$f(x)$	4	1	3

x	-1	0	2
$g(x)$	2	0	1

Exercises 37 and 38: Use the table to evaluate each expression, if possible.

(a) $(f + g)(2)$ *(b)* $(f - g)(4)$

(c) $(fg)(-2)$ *(d)* $(f/g)(0)$

37.

x	-2	0	2	4
$f(x)$	0	5	7	10
$g(x)$	6	0	-2	5

38.

x	-2	0	2	4
$f(x)$	-4	8	5	0
$g(x)$	2	-1	4	0

39. Use the table in Exercise 37 to complete the following table.

x	-2	0	2	4
$(f + g)(x)$				
$(f - g)(x)$				
$(fg)(x)$				
$(f/g)(x)$				

40. Use the table in Exercise 38 to complete the table in Exercise 39.

Review of Function Notation

Exercises 41–52: For the given $g(x)$, evaluate each of the following.

(a) $g(-3)$ *(b)* $g(b)$ *(c)* $g(x^3)$ *(d)* $g(2x - 3)$

41. $g(x) = 2x + 1$

42. $g(x) = 5 - \frac{1}{2}x$

43. $g(x) = 2(x + 3)^2 - 4$

44. $g(x) = -(x - 1)^2$

45. $g(x) = \frac{1}{2}x^2 + 3x - 1$

46. $g(x) = 2x^2 - x - 9$

47. $g(x) = \sqrt{x + 4}$

48. $g(x) = \sqrt{2 - x}$

49. $g(x) = |3x - 1| + 4$

50. $g(x) = 2|1 - x| - 7$

51. $g(x) = \dfrac{4x}{x + 3}$

52. $g(x) = \dfrac{x + 3}{2}$

Composition of Functions

Exercises 53–56: Use the given $f(x)$ and $g(x)$ to evaluate each expression.

53. $f(x) = \sqrt{x + 5}$, $g(x) = x^2$

(a) $(f \circ g)(2)$ **(b)** $(g \circ f)(-1)$

54. $f(x) = |x^2 - 4|$, $g(x) = 2x^2 + x + 1$

(a) $(f \circ g)(1)$ **(b)** $(g \circ f)(-3)$

55. $f(x) = 5x - 2$, $g(x) = |x|$

(a) $(f \circ g)(-4)$ **(b)** $(g \circ f)(5)$

56. $f(x) = \dfrac{1}{x - 4}$, $g(x) = 5$

(a) $(f \circ g)(3)$ **(b)** $(g \circ f)(8)$

Exercises 57–72: Use the given $f(x)$ and $g(x)$ to find each of the following. Identify its domain.

(a) $(f \circ g)(x)$ *(b)* $(g \circ f)(x)$ *(c)* $(f \circ f)(x)$

57. $f(x) = x^3$, $g(x) = x^2 + 3x - 1$

58. $f(x) = 2 - x$, $g(x) = \frac{1}{x^2}$

59. $f(x) = x + 2$, $g(x) = x^4 + x^2 - 3x - 4$

60. $f(x) = x^2$, $g(x) = \sqrt{1 - x}$

61. $f(x) = 2 - 3x$, $g(x) = x^3$

62. $f(x) = \sqrt{x}$, $g(x) = 1 - x^2$

63. $f(x) = \frac{1}{x + 1}$, $g(x) = 5x$

64. $f(x) = \frac{1}{3x}$, $g(x) = \frac{2}{x - 1}$

65. $f(x) = x + 4$, $g(x) = \sqrt{4 - x^2}$

66. $f(x) = 2x + 1$, $g(x) = 4x^3 - 5x^2$

67. $f(x) = \sqrt{x - 1}$, $g(x) = 3x$

68. $f(x) = \frac{x - 3}{2}$, $g(x) = 2x + 3$

69. $f(x) = 1 - 5x$, $g(x) = \frac{1 - x}{5}$

70. $f(x) = \sqrt[3]{x - 1}$, $g(x) = x^3 + 1$

71. $f(x) = \frac{1}{kx}, k > 0$, $g(x) = \frac{1}{kx}, k > 0$

72. $f(x) = ax^2, a > 0$, $g(x) = \sqrt{ax}, a > 0$

Exercises 73–76: Use the graph to evaluate each expression.

73.

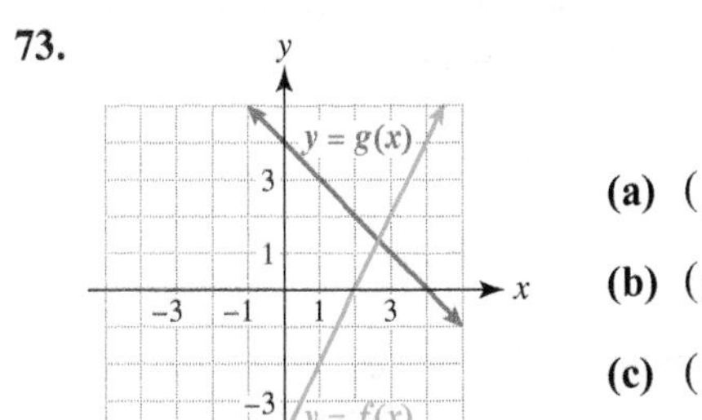

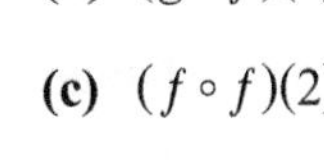

(a) $(f \circ g)(4)$

(b) $(g \circ f)(3)$

(c) $(f \circ f)(2)$

74.

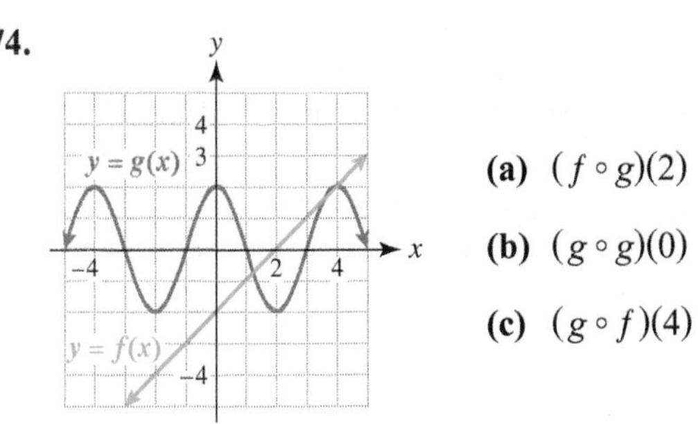

(a) $(f \circ g)(2)$

(b) $(g \circ g)(0)$

(c) $(g \circ f)(4)$

75.

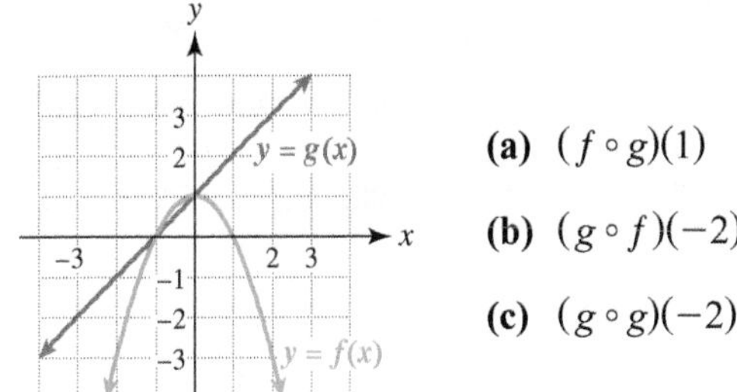

(a) $(f \circ g)(1)$

(b) $(g \circ f)(-2)$

(c) $(g \circ g)(-2)$

76.

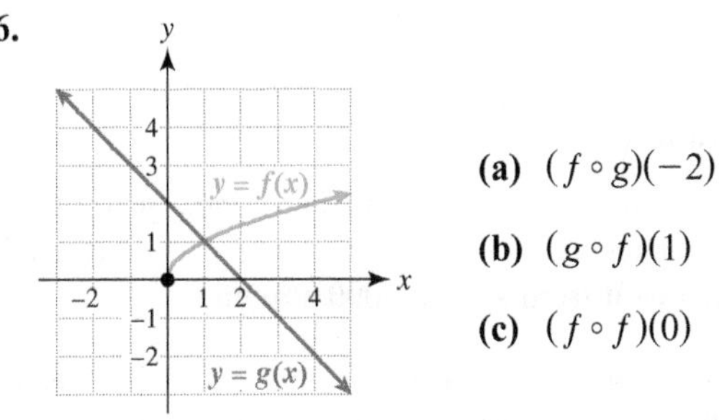

(a) $(f \circ g)(-2)$

(b) $(g \circ f)(1)$

(c) $(f \circ f)(0)$

Exercises 77 and 78: Tables for the functions f and g are given. Evaluate the expression, if possible.

(a) $(g \circ f)(1)$ *(b)* $(f \circ g)(4)$ *(c)* $(f \circ f)(3)$

77.

x	1	2	3	4
$f(x)$	4	3	1	2

x	1	2	3	4
$g(x)$	2	3	4	5

78.

x	1	3	4	6
$f(x)$	2	6	5	7

x	2	3	5	7
$g(x)$	4	2	6	0

79. Use the tables for $f(x)$ and $g(x)$ in Exercise 77 to complete the composition shown in the diagram.

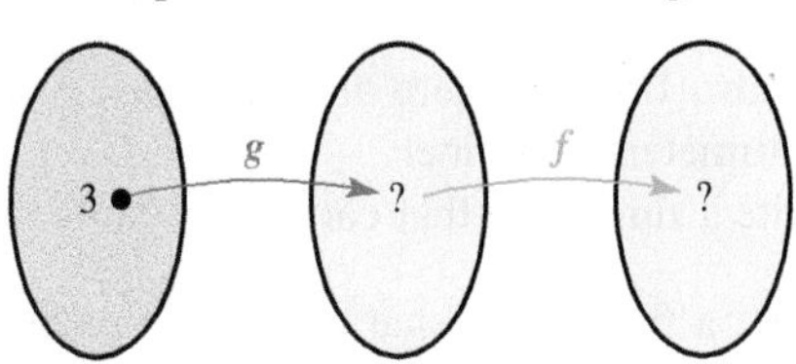

80. Use the tables for $f(x)$ and $g(x)$ in Exercise 78 to complete the composition shown in the diagram.

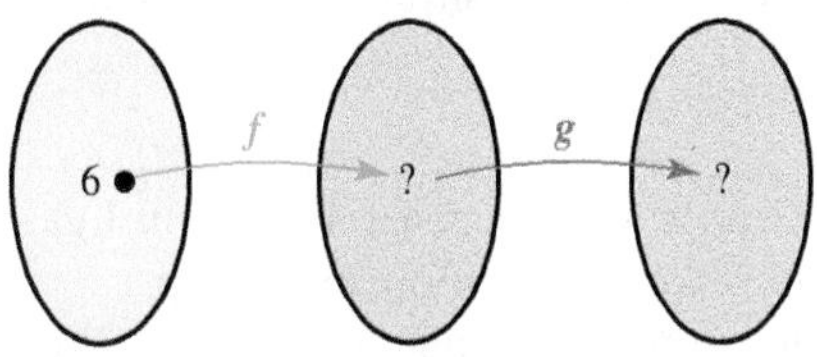

Exercises 81–94: (Refer to Example 11.) Find $f(x)$ and $g(x)$ so that $h(x) = (g \circ f)(x)$. Answers may vary.

81. $h(x) = \sqrt{x - 2}$

82. $h(x) = (x + 2)^4$

83. $h(x) = \frac{1}{x + 2}$

84. $h(x) = 5(x + 2)^2 - 4$

85. $h(x) = 4(2x + 1)^3$

86. $h(x) = \sqrt[3]{x^2 + 1}$

87. $h(x) = (x^3 - 1)^2$

88. $h(x) = 4(x - 5)^{-2}$

89. $h(x) = -4|x + 2| - 3$

90. $h(x) = 5\sqrt{x - 1}$

91. $h(x) = \dfrac{1}{(x - 1)^2}$

92. $h(x) = \dfrac{2}{x^2 - x + 1}$

93. $h(x) = x^{3/4} - x^{1/4}$

94. $h(x) = x^{2/3} - 5x^{1/3} + 4$

Applications

95. Profit (Refer to Example 4.) Determine a profit function P that results if the albums are sold for \$15 each. Find the profit from selling 3000 albums.

96. Revenue, Cost, and Profit Suppose that for a major production company it costs \$150,000 to produce a master track for a music video and \$1.50 to produce each copy.

(a) Write a cost function C that outputs the cost of producing the master track and x copies.

(b) If the music videos are sold for \$6.50 each, find a function R that outputs the revenue received from selling x music videos. What is the revenue from selling 8000 videos?

(c) Find a function P that outputs the profit from selling x music videos. What is the profit from selling 40,000 videos?

(d) How many videos must be sold to break even? That is, how many videos must be sold for the revenue to equal the cost?

97. Converting Units There are 36 inches in a yard and 2.54 centimeters in an inch.

(a) Write a function I that converts x yards to inches.

(b) Write a function C that converts x inches to centimeters.

(c) Express a function F that converts x yards to centimeters as a composition of two functions.

(d) Write a formula for F.

98. Converting Units There are 4 quarts in 1 gallon, 4 cups in 1 quart, and 16 tablespoons in 1 cup.

(a) Write a function Q that converts x gallons to quarts.

(b) Write a function C that converts x quarts to cups.

(c) Write a function T that converts x cups to tablespoons.

(d) Express a function F that converts x gallons to tablespoons as a composition of *three* functions.

(e) Write a formula for F.

99. Stopping Distance (Refer to Example 1.) A driver's reaction distance is $r(x) = \frac{11}{6}x$ and braking distance is $b(x) = \frac{1}{9}x^2$.

(a) Find a formula $s(x)$ that computes the stopping distance for this driver traveling at x miles per hour.

(b) Evaluate $s(60)$ and interpret the result.

100. Stopping Distance (Refer to Example 1.) If a driver attempts to stop while traveling at x miles per hour on dry, level pavement, the reaction distance is $r(x) = \frac{11}{5}x$ and the braking distance is $b(x) = \frac{1}{11}x^2$, where both distances are in feet.

(a) Write a formula for a function s in terms of $r(x)$ and $b(x)$ that gives the stopping distance when driving at x miles per hour. Evaluate $s(55)$.

(b) Graph r, b, and s on the same axes. Explain how the graph of s can be found using the graphs of r and b.

(c) Make tables for $r(x)$ and $b(x)$ at $x = 11, 22, 33, 44,$ and 55. Then use these tables to construct a table for $s(x)$.

101. Skin Cancer (Refer to Example 10 and Tables 5.4 and 5.5.) If possible, calculate the composition and interpret the result.

(a) $(g \circ f)(1)$ **(b)** $(f \circ g)(21)$

102. Skin Cancer In Example 10, f and g are both linear.

(a) Find symbolic representations for f and g.

(b) Determine $(g \circ f)(x)$.

(c) Evaluate $(g \circ f)(3.5)$ and interpret the result.

103. Urban Heat Island Urban areas tend to be warmer than the surrounding rural areas. This effect is called the *urban heat island.* In the first figure at the top of the next page, f computes the average increase in nighttime summer temperatures in degrees Celsius at Sky Harbor Airport in Phoenix from 1948 to 1990. In this graph, 1948 is the base year with a zero temperature increase. The rise in urban temperature increased peak demand for electricity. In the second figure at the top of the next page, g computes the percent increase in electrical demand for an average nighttime temperature increase of x degrees Celsius. (***Source:*** W. Cotton and R. Pielke, *Human Impacts on Weather and Climate*.)

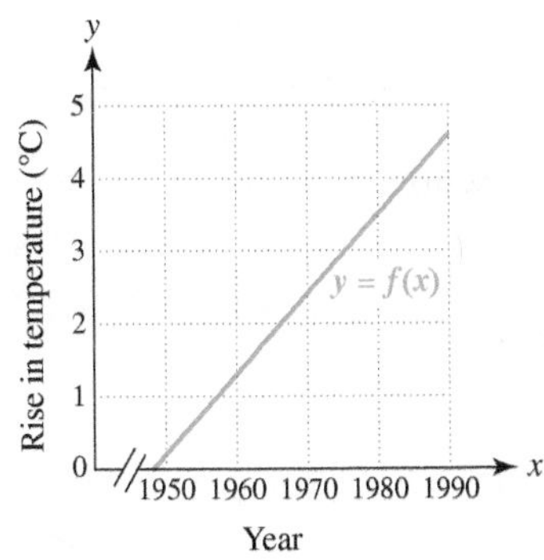

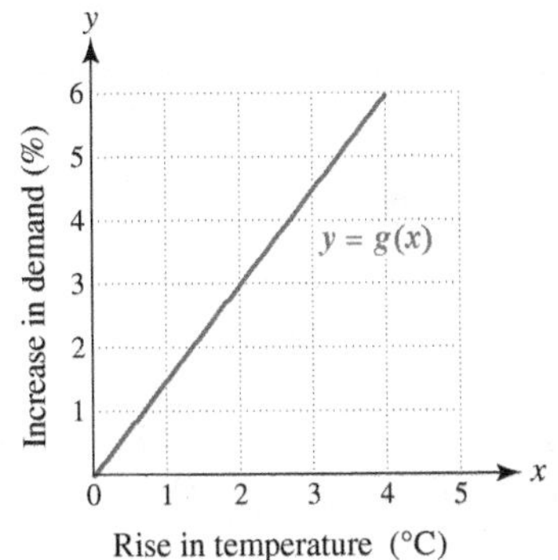

(a) Evaluate $(g \circ f)(1975)$ graphically.

(b) Interpret $(g \circ f)(x)$.

104. Urban Heat Island (Refer to Exercise 103.) If possible, calculate the composition and interpret the result.
(a) $(g \circ f)(1980)$ **(b)** $(f \circ g)(3)$

105. Urban Heat Island (Refer to Exercise 103.) The functions f and g are given by $f(x) = 0.11(x - 1948)$ and $g(x) = 1.5x$.
(a) Evaluate $(g \circ f)(1960)$.

(b) Find $(g \circ f)(x)$.

(c) What type of functions are, f, g, and $g \circ f$?

106. Swimming Pools In the figures, f computes the cubic feet of water in a pool after x days, and g converts cubic feet to gallons.

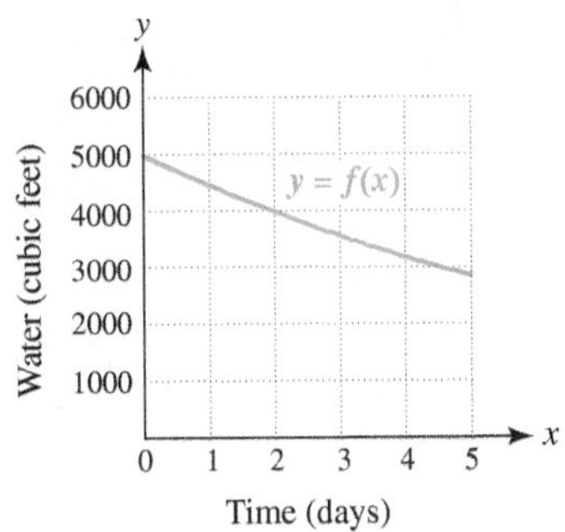

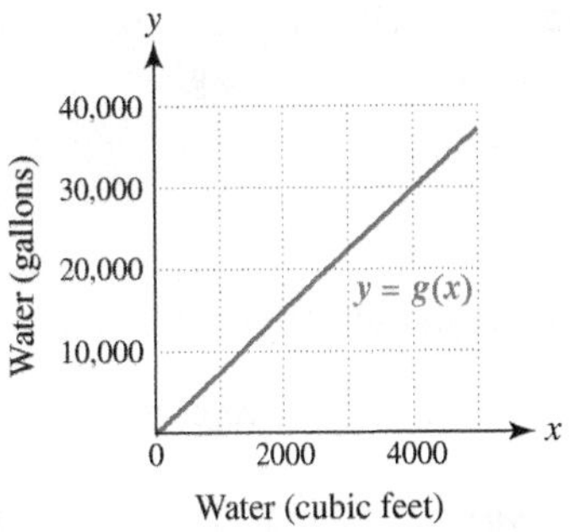

(a) Find the gallons of water in the pool after 2 days.

(b) Interpret $(g \circ f)(x)$.

107. Temperature The function f computes the temperature on a summer day after x hours, and g converts Fahrenheit temperature to Celsius temperature. See the figures.

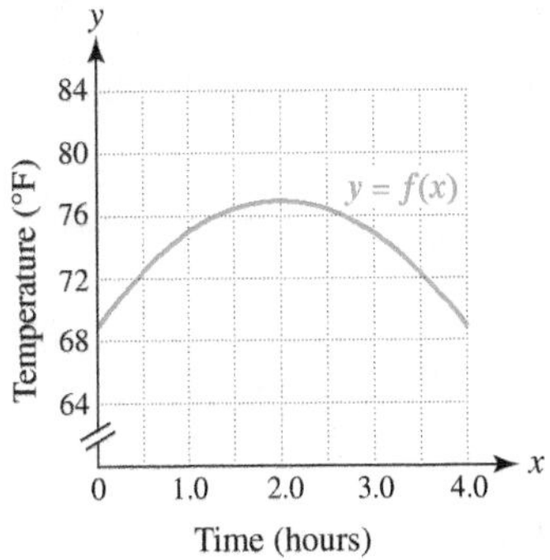

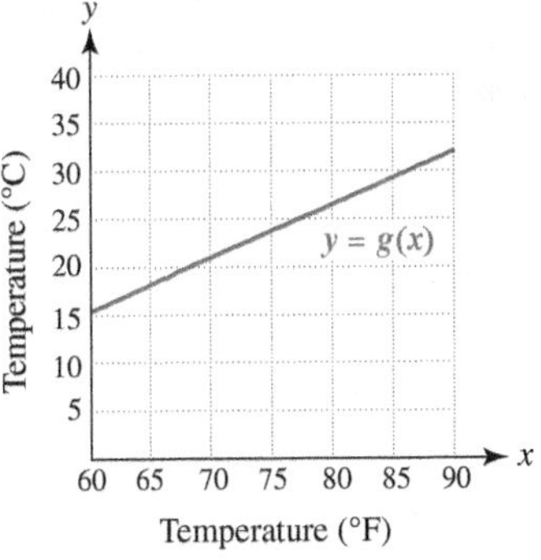

(a) Evaluate $(g \circ f)(2)$.
(b) Interpret $(g \circ f)(x)$.

108. Surface Area of a Balloon The surface area A of a balloon with radius r is given by $A(r) = 4\pi r^2$. Suppose that the radius of the balloon increases from r to $r + h$, where h is a small positive number.
(a) Find $A(r + h) - A(r)$. Interpret your answer.

(b) Evaluate your expression in part (a) for $r = 3$ and $h = 0.1$, and then for $r = 6$ and $h = 0.1$.

(c) If the radius of the balloon increases by 0.1, does the surface area always increase by a fixed amount or does the amount depend on the value of r?

109. Equilateral Triangle The area of an equilateral triangle with sides of length s is given by

$$A(s) = \frac{\sqrt{3}}{4}s^2.$$

(a) Find $A(4s)$ and interpret the result.

(b) Find $A(s + 2)$ and interpret the result.

110. Circular Wave A marble is dropped into a lake, resulting in a circular wave whose radius increases at a rate of 6 inches per second. Write a formula for C that gives the circumference of the circular wave in inches after t seconds.

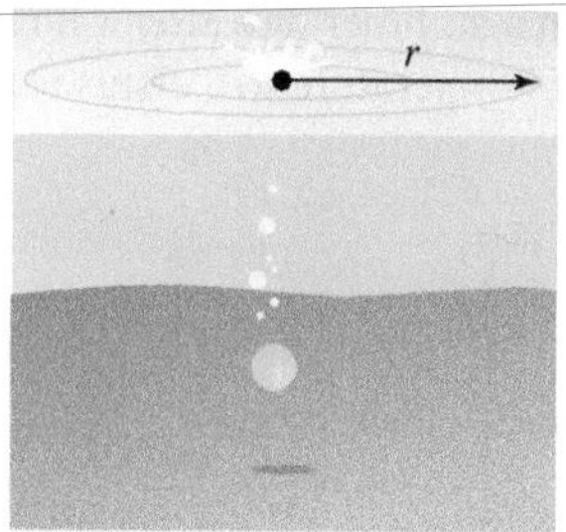

111. Circular Wave (Refer to Exercise 110.) Write a function A that gives the area contained inside the circular wave in square inches after t seconds.

112. Geometry The surface area of a cone (excluding the bottom) is given by $S = \pi r\sqrt{r^2 + h^2}$, where r is its radius and h is its height, as shown in the figure. If the height is twice the radius, write a formula for S in terms of r.

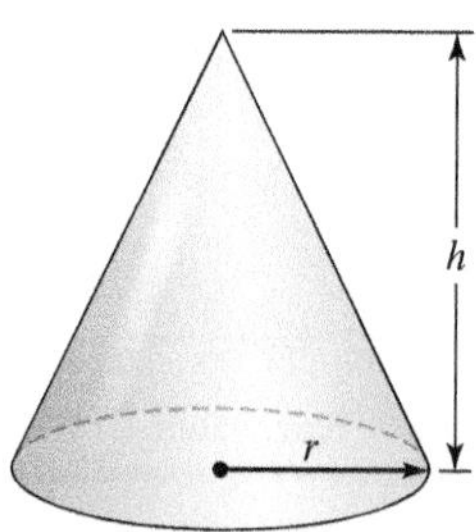

113. Methane Emissions Methane is a greenhouse gas that lets sunlight into the atmosphere but blocks heat from escaping Earth's atmosphere. In the table, $f(x)$ models the predicted methane emissions in millions of tons produced by *developed* countries. The function $g(x)$ models the same emissions for *developing* countries.

x	1990	2000	2010	2020	2030
$f(x)$	27	28	29	30	31
$g(x)$	5	7.5	10	12.5	15

Source: A. Nilsson, *Greenhouse Earth.*

(a) Make a table for a function h that models the total predicted methane emissions for developed *and* developing countries.

(b) Write an equation that relates $f(x)$, $g(x)$, and $h(x)$.

114. Methane Emissions (Refer to Exercise 113.) The figure shows graphs of the functions f and g that model methane emissions. Use these graphs to sketch a graph of the function h.

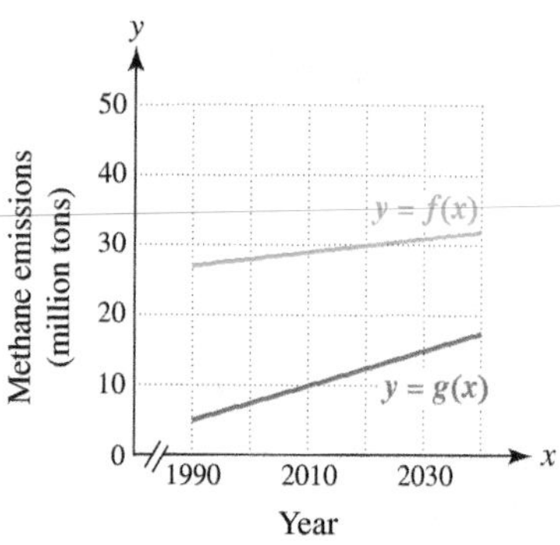

115. Methane Emissions (Refer to Exercises 113 and 114.) Formulas for f and g are $f(x) = 0.1x - 172$ and $g(x) = 0.25x - 492.5$, where x is the year. Find a symbolic representation for h.

116. Energy of a Falling Object A ball with mass m is dropped from an initial height of h_0 and lands with a final velocity of v_f. The kinetic energy of the ball is $K(v) = \frac{1}{2}mv^2$, where v is its velocity, and the potential energy of the ball is $P(h) = mgh$, where h is its height and g is a constant.

(a) Show that $P(h_0) = K(v_f)$. (*Hint:* $v_f = \sqrt{2gh_0}$.)

(b) Interpret your result from part (a).

117. Income Differences From 1990 to 2012, the 50th percentile (median) of U.S. household income in thousands of dollars could be approximated by $M(x) = 0.1x + 48$, where $M(x)$ is in 2012 dollars and x is years after 1990. The 90th percentile could be modeled by $N(x) = -0.15x^2 + 4x + 120$.

(a) Evaluate $M(20)$ and $N(20)$. Interpret the results.

(b) Determine a formula for $D(x) = N(x) - M(x)$. Interpret this formula.

(c) Evaluate $D(20)$. Interpret the results.

118. Sphere The volume V of a sphere with radius r is given by $V = \frac{4}{3}\pi r^3$, and the surface area S is given by $S = 4\pi r^2$. Show that $V = \frac{4}{3}\pi\left(\frac{S}{4\pi}\right)^{3/2}$.

Applying Concepts

119. Show that the sum of two linear functions is a linear function.

120. Show that if f and g are odd functions, then the composition $g \circ f$ is also an odd function.

121. Let $f(x) = k$ and $g(x) = ax + b$, where k, a, and b are constants.

(a) Find $(f \circ g)(x)$. What type of function is $f \circ g$?

(b) Find $(g \circ f)(x)$. What type of function is $g \circ f$?

122. Show that if $f(x) = ax + b$ and $g(x) = cx + d$, then $(g \circ f)(x)$ also represents a linear function. Find the slope of the graph of $(g \circ f)(x)$.

Writing about Mathematics

123. Describe differences between $(fg)(x)$ and $(f \circ g)(x)$. Give examples.

124. Describe differences between $(f \circ g)(x)$ and $(g \circ f)(x)$. Give examples.

5.2 Inverse Functions and Their Representations

- **Calculate inverse operations**
- **Identify one-to-one functions**
- **Find inverse functions symbolically**
- **Use other representations to find inverse functions**

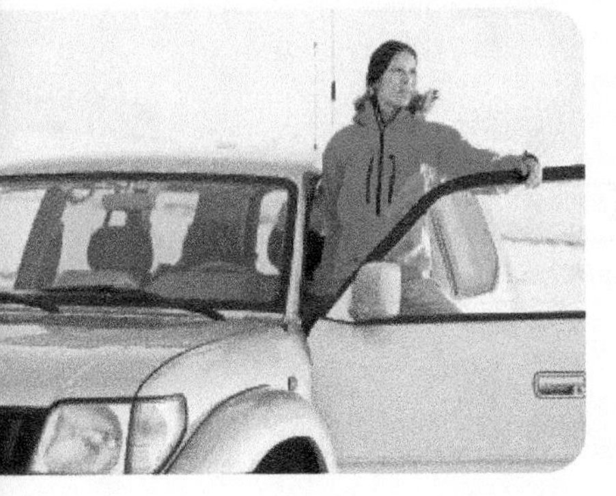

Introduction

Many actions are reversible. A closed door can be opened—an open door can be closed. One hundred dollars can be withdrawn from and deposited into a savings account. These actions undo or cancel each other. But not all actions are reversible. Explosions and weather are two examples. In mathematics the concept of reversing a calculation and arriving at the original value is associated with an *inverse*.

Actions and their inverses occur in everyday life. Suppose a person opens a car door, gets in, and starts the engine. What are the inverse actions? The person turns off the engine, gets out, and closes the car door. Notice that we must reverse the order as well as apply the inverse operation at each step.

Inverse Operations and Inverse Functions

Inverse Operations In mathematics there are basic operations that can be considered inverse operations.

Inverse Operations: Addition and Subtraction

Start with 10. — $10 + 5 = 15$ (Add 5.)

$15 - 5 = 10$ (Subtract 5.) — End with 10.

Addition and subtraction are inverse operations. The same is true for multiplication and division, as illustrated by the following.

Inverse Operations: Multiplication and Division

Start with 10. — $10 \times 2 = 20$ (Multiply by 2.)

$20 \div 2 = 10$ (Divide by 2.) — End with 10.

In the next example, we discuss inverse operations further.

EXAMPLE 1 **Finding inverse actions and operations**

For each of the following, state the inverse actions or operations.

(a) Put on a coat and go outside.

(b) Subtract 5 from x and divide the result by 2.

SOLUTION

(a) To find the inverse actions, reverse the order and apply the inverse action at each step. The inverse actions would be to come inside and take off the coat.

(b) We must reverse the order and apply the inverse operation at each step. The inverse operations would be to multiply x by 2 and add 5. The original operations could be expressed as $\frac{x-5}{2}$, and the inverse operations could be written as $2x + 5$.

Now try Exercises 3 and 7

Inverse Functions Table 5.7 can be used to convert *gallons* to *pints*. There are 8 pints in a gallon, so $f(x) = 8x$ converts x gallons to an equivalent number of pints. If we want to convert *pints* to *gallons*, we need to divide by 8. This conversion is calculated by $g(x) = \frac{x}{8}$, where x is the number of pints. We say that f and g are *inverse functions* and write this as $g(x) = f^{-1}(x)$. See Table 5.8. We read f^{-1} as "f inverse."

Inverse Functions

Gallons to Pints

x	1	2	3	4
$f(x)$	8	16	24	32

Table 5.7 $f(1) = 8$

Pints to Gallons

x	8	16	24	32
$f^{-1}(x)$	1	2	3	4

Table 5.8 $f^{-1}(8) = 1$

Multiplying by 8 and dividing by 8 are inverse operations. As discussed earlier, adding 5 and subtracting 5 are also inverse operations. If $f(x) = x + 5$, then the *inverse function* of f is given by $f^{-1}(x) = x - 5$. For example, $f(5) = 10$, and $f^{-1}(10) = 5$. If input x produces output y with function f, input y produces output x with function f^{-1}. This can be seen in Tables 5.9 and 5.10.

Inverse Functions

Add 5

x	0	5	10	15
$f(x)$	5	10	15	20

Table 5.9 $f(0) = 5$

Subtract 5

x	5	10	15	20
$f^{-1}(x)$	0	5	10	15

Table 5.10 $f^{-1}(5) = 0$

From Tables 5.9 and 5.10, if $f(a) = b$, then $f^{-1}(b) = a$. That is, if f outputs b with input a, then f^{-1} must output a with input b. *Inputs and outputs* (domains and ranges) *are interchanged for inverse functions.* This statement is illustrated in Figure 5.12.

Inverse Functions

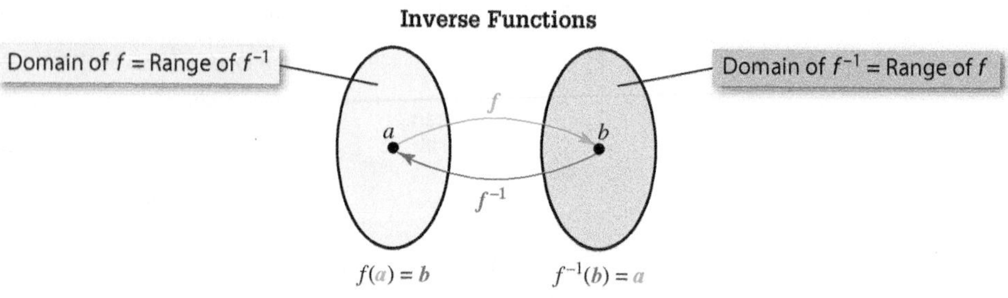

Figure 5.12

When $f(x) = x + 5$ and $f^{-1}(x) = x - 5$ are applied in sequence, the output of f is used as input for f^{-1}. This is *composition* of functions.

$$\begin{aligned}(f^{-1} \circ f)(x) &= f^{-1}(f(x)) && \text{Definition of composition}\\ &= f^{-1}(x + 5) && f(x) = x + 5\\ &= (x + 5) - 5 && f^{-1} \text{ subtracts 5 from its input.}\\ &= x && \text{Simplify.}\end{aligned}$$

The composition $f^{-1} \circ f$ with input x produces output x. The same action occurs when computing the composition $f \circ f^{-1}$.

$$\begin{aligned}(f \circ f^{-1})(x) &= f(f^{-1}(x)) && \text{Definition of composition}\\ &= f(x - 5) && f^{-1}(x) = x - 5\\ &= (x - 5) + 5 && f \text{ adds 5 to its input.}\\ &= x && \text{Simplify.}\end{aligned}$$

Another pair of inverse functions is given by $f(x) = x^3$ and $f^{-1}(x) = \sqrt[3]{x}$. Before a formal definition of inverse functions is given, we must discuss one-to-one functions.

MAKING CONNECTIONS

The Notation f^{-1} and Negative Exponents If a represents a real number, then $a^{-1} = \frac{1}{a}$. For example, $4^{-1} = \frac{1}{4}$. On the other hand, if f represents a function, note that $f^{-1}(x) \neq \frac{1}{f(x)}$. Instead, $f^{-1}(x)$ represents the inverse function of f. For instance, if $f(x) = 5x$, then $f^{-1}(x) = \frac{x}{5} \neq \frac{1}{5x}$.

One-to-One Functions

Does every function have an inverse function? The next example answers this question.

EXAMPLE 2 **Determining if a function has an inverse function**

Table 5.11 represents a function C that computes the percentage of the time that the sky is cloudy in Augusta, Georgia, where x corresponds to the standard numbers for the months. Determine if C has an inverse function.

Cloudy Skies in Augusta

x (month)	1	2	3	4	5	6	7	8	9	10	11	12
$C(x)$(%)	43	40	39	29	28	26	27	25	30	26	31	39

Source: J. Williams, *The Weather Almanac*.

Table 5.11

SOLUTION

For each input (month), C computes exactly one output. For example, $C(3) = 39$ means that during March the sky is cloudy 39% of the time. If C has an inverse function, the inverse must receive 39 as input and produce exactly one output. Both March and December have cloudy skies 39% of the time. Given an input of 39, it is impossible for an inverse *function* to output both 3 and 12. Therefore C does *not* have an inverse function.

Now Try Exercise 19

If *different inputs* of a function f produce the *same output*, then an inverse function of f does *not* exist. However, if different inputs always produce different outputs, f is a *one-to-one function. Every one-to-one function has an inverse function.* For example, $f(x) = x^2$ is *not* one-to-one because

Different Inputs

$f(-2) = 4$ and $f(2) = 4$. *Not one-to-one*

Same Output

Therefore $f(x) = x^2$ does not have an inverse function because an inverse *function* cannot receive input 4 and produce both -2 and 2 as outputs. However, $g(x) = 5x$ is one-to-one because different inputs always result in different outputs. Therefore g has an inverse function: $g^{-1}(x) = \frac{x}{5}$.

ONE-TO-ONE FUNCTION

A function f is a **one-to-one function** if, for elements c and d in the domain of f,

$$c \neq d \quad \text{implies} \quad f(c) \neq f(d).$$

That is, different inputs always result in different outputs.

NOTE A function f is one-to-one if equal outputs always have the same input. This statement can be written as $f(c) = f(d)$ implies $c = d$, which is an equivalent definition.

EXAMPLE 3 **Determining if a function is one-to-one graphically**

Use each graph to determine if f is one-to-one and if f has an inverse function.

(a)

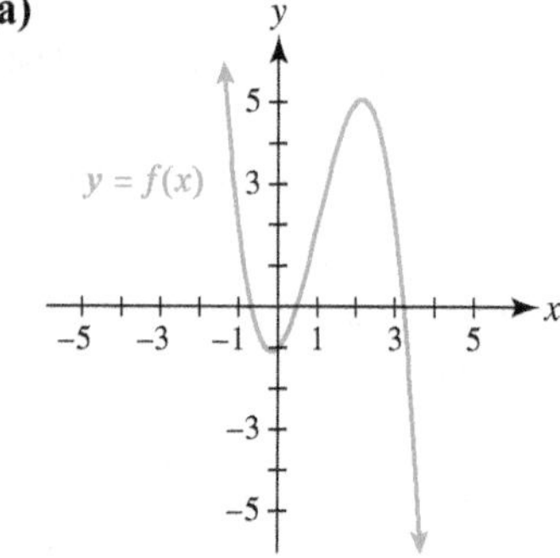

(b)

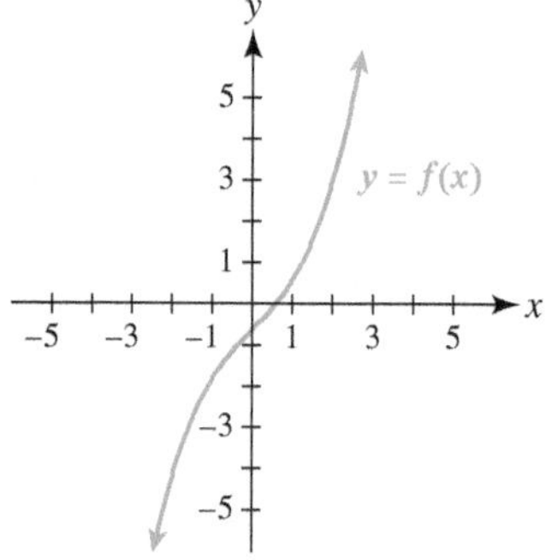

SOLUTION

(a) In Figure 5.13 the horizontal line $y = 2$ intersects the graph of f at $(-1, 2)$, $(1, 2)$, and $(3, 2)$. This means that $f(-1) = f(1) = f(3) = 2$. Three distinct inputs, -1, 1, and 3, produce the same output, 2. Therefore f is *not* one-to-one and does *not* have an inverse function.

(b) See Figure 5.14. Because every horizontal line intersects the graph at most once, different inputs (x-values) always result in different outputs (y-values). Therefore f *is* one-to-one and *has* an inverse function.

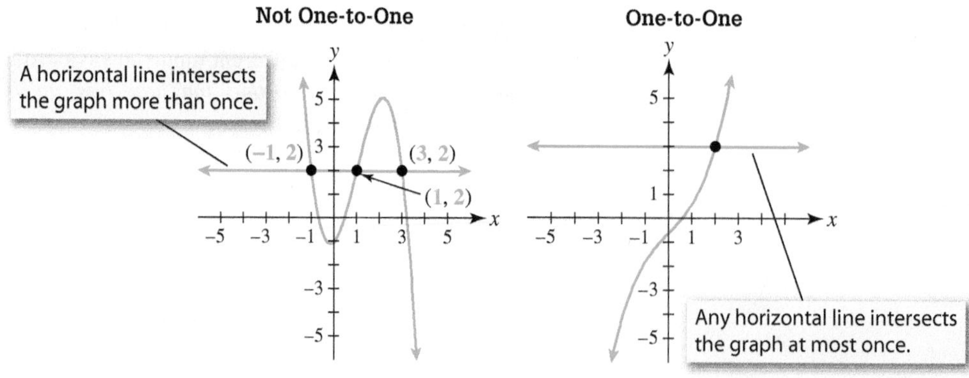

Figure 5.13 **Figure 5.14**

Now Try Exercises 13 and 15

NOTE To show that f is not one-to-one, it is not necessary to find the actual points of intersection—we have to show only that a horizontal line can intersect the graph of f more than once.

The technique of visualizing horizontal lines to determine if a graph represents a one-to-one function is called the *horizontal line test.*

CLASS DISCUSSION

Use the horizontal line test to explain why a nonconstant linear function has an inverse function, whereas a quadratic function does not.

HORIZONTAL LINE TEST

If every horizontal line intersects the graph of a function f at most once, then f is a one-to-one function.

Increasing, Decreasing, and One-to-One Functions If a continuous function f is always increasing on its domain, then every horizontal line will intersect the graph of f at most once. By the horizontal line test, f is a one-to-one function. For example, the function f shown in Example 3(b) is always increasing on its domain and so it is one-to-one. Similarly, if a continuous function g is only decreasing on its domain, then g is a one-to-one function.

Symbolic Representations of Inverse Functions

If a function f is one-to-one, then an inverse function f^{-1} exists. Therefore $f(a) = b$ implies $f^{-1}(b) = a$ for every a in the domain of f. That is,

$$(f^{-1} \circ f)(a) = f^{-1}(f(a)) = f^{-1}(b) = a.$$

Similarly, $f^{-1}(b) = a$ implies $f(a) = b$ for every b in the domain of f^{-1} and so

$$(f \circ f^{-1})(b) = f(f^{-1}(b)) = f(a) = b.$$

These two properties can be used to define an inverse function.

INVERSE FUNCTION

Let f be a one-to-one function. Then f^{-1} is the **inverse function** of f if

$$(f^{-1} \circ f)(x) = f^{-1}(f(x)) = x \quad \text{for every } x \text{ in the domain of } f \text{ and}$$

$$(f \circ f^{-1})(x) = f(f^{-1}(x)) = x \quad \text{for every } x \text{ in the domain of } f^{-1}.$$

In the next two examples, we find an inverse function and verify that it is correct.

EXAMPLE 4 **Finding and verifying an inverse function**

Let f be the one-to-one function given by $f(x) = x^3 - 2$.
(a) Find a formula for $f^{-1}(x)$. **(b)** Identify the domain and range of f^{-1}.
(c) Verify that your result from part (a) is correct.

SOLUTION

(a) Since $f(x) = x^3 - 2$, function f cubes the input x and then **subtracts 2**. To reverse this calculation, the inverse function must **add 2** to the input x and then take the cube root. That is, $f^{-1}(x) = \sqrt[3]{x + 2}$. An important symbolic technique for finding $f^{-1}(x)$ is to solve the equation $y = f(x)$ for x.

$$y = x^3 - 2 \qquad y = f(x)\text{; now solve for } x.$$

$$y + 2 = x^3 \qquad \text{Add 2.}$$

$$\sqrt[3]{y + 2} = x \qquad \text{Take the cube root.}$$

Interchange x and y to obtain $y = \sqrt[3]{x + 2}$. This gives us the formula for $f^{-1}(x)$.

(b) Both the domain and the range of the cube root function include all real numbers. The graph of $f^{-1}(x) = \sqrt[3]{x+2}$ is the graph of the cube root function shifted left 2 units. Therefore the domain and range of f^{-1} also include all real numbers.

(c) To verify that $f^{-1}(x) = \sqrt[3]{x+2}$ is indeed the inverse of $f(x) = x^3 - 2$, we must show that $f^{-1}(f(x)) = x$ and that $f(f^{-1}(x)) = x$.

$$\begin{aligned} f^{-1}(f(x)) &= f^{-1}(x^3 - 2) && f(x) = x^3 - 2 \\ &= \sqrt[3]{(x^3 - 2) + 2} && f^{-1}(x) = \sqrt[3]{x+2} \\ &= \sqrt[3]{x^3} && \text{Combine terms.} \\ &= x \;\checkmark && \text{Simplify.} \\ f(f^{-1}(x)) &= f(\sqrt[3]{x+2}) && f^{-1}(x) = \sqrt[3]{x+2} \\ &= (\sqrt[3]{x+2})^3 - 2 && f(x) = x^3 - 2 \\ &= (x+2) - 2 && \text{Cube the expression.} \\ &= x \;\checkmark && \text{Combine terms.} \end{aligned}$$

These calculations verify that our result is correct.

Now Try Exercise 73

The symbolic technique used in Example 4(a) is now summarized.

FINDING A SYMBOLIC REPRESENTATION FOR f^{-1}

To find a formula for f^{-1}, perform the following steps.

STEP 1: Verify that f is a one-to-one function.

STEP 2: Solve the equation $y = f(x)$ for x, obtaining the equation $x = f^{-1}(y)$.

STEP 3: Interchange x and y to obtain $y = f^{-1}(x)$.

To verify $f^{-1}(x)$, show that $(f^{-1} \circ f)(x) = x$ and $(f \circ f^{-1})(x) = x$.

NOTE One reason for interchanging the variables in Step 3 is to make it easier to graph $y = f^{-1}(x)$ in the xy-plane.

EXAMPLE 5 Finding an inverse function

The function $f(x) = \frac{3}{4}x + 39$ gives the percentage of China's population that may live in urban areas x years after 2000, where $0 \le x \le 40$.

(a) Explain why f is a one-to-one function.

(b) Find a formula for $f^{-1}(x)$.

(c) Evaluate and interpret the meaning of $f^{-1}(60)$.

SOLUTION

(a) Since f is a linear function, its graph is a line with a nonzero slope of $\frac{3}{4}$. Every horizontal line intersects it at most once. By the horizontal line test, f is one-to-one.

(b) To find $f^{-1}(x)$, solve the equation $y = f(x)$ for x.

$$\begin{aligned} y &= \frac{3}{4}x + 39 && y = f(x) \\ y - 39 &= \frac{3}{4}x && \text{Subtract 39.} \\ \frac{4}{3}(y - 39) &= x && \text{Multiply by } \tfrac{4}{3}\text{, the reciprocal of } \tfrac{3}{4}. \\ \frac{4}{3}y - 52 &= x && \text{Distributive property} \end{aligned}$$

Now interchange x and y to obtain $y = \frac{4}{3}x - 52$. The formula for the inverse is, therefore,

$$f^{-1}(x) = \frac{4}{3}x - 52.$$

(c) Substitute 60 for x in $f^{-1}(x) = \frac{4}{3}x - 52$.

$$f^{-1}(60) = \tfrac{4}{3}(60) - 52 = 28$$

The expression $f^{-1}(x)$ predicts the number of years after 2000 when x percent of China's population will live in urban areas. In 2028, it is estimated that 60 percent of China's population will live in urban areas.

Now Try Exercise 123

EXAMPLE 6 Restricting the domain of a function

Let $f(x) = (x - 1)^2$.

(a) Does f have an inverse function? Explain.
(b) Restrict the domain of f so that f^{-1} exists.
(c) Find $f^{-1}(x)$ for the restricted domain.

SOLUTION

(a) The graph of $f(x) = (x - 1)^2$, shown in Figure 5.15, does not pass the horizontal line test. Therefore f is not one-to-one and does not have an inverse function.

Not One-to-One

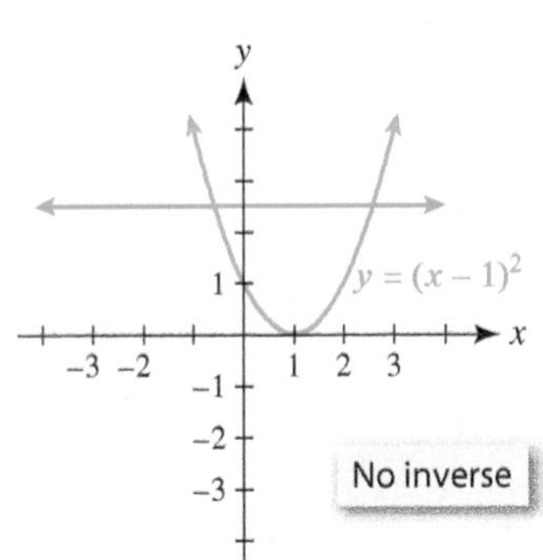

Figure 5.15

Restricting the Domain

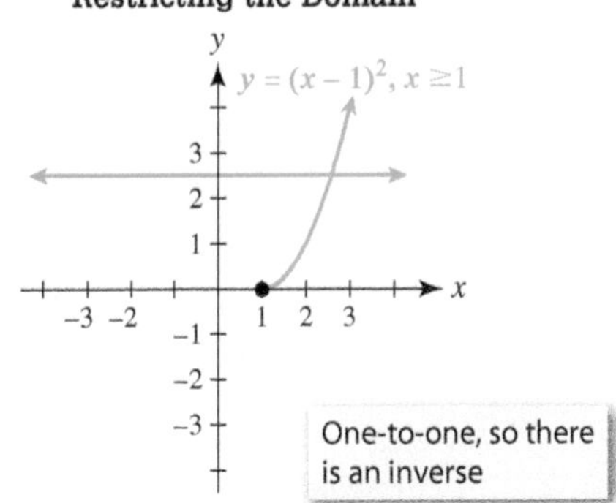

Figure 5.16

(b) If we restrict the domain of f to $D = \{x | x \geq 1\}$, then f becomes a one-to-one function. To illustrate this, the graph of $y = (x - 1)^2$ for $x \geq 1$ is shown in Figure 5.16. This graph passes the horizontal line test and f^{-1} exists on the restricted domain.

(c) Assume that $x \geq 1$ and solve the equation $y = f(x)$ for x.

$y = (x - 1)^2$	$y = f(x)$
$\sqrt{y} = x - 1$	Take the positive square root. Note: $x \geq 1$ implies that $x - 1 \geq 0$.
$\sqrt{y} + 1 = x$	Add 1.
Thus $f^{-1}(x) = \sqrt{x} + 1$.	Write the formula for $f^{-1}(x)$.

Now Try Exercise 63

NOTE In Example 6 we could have restricted the domain to $x \leq 1$, rather than $x \geq 1$. In this case, we would obtain the left half of the parabola, which would also represent a one-to-one function that has an inverse.

College Graduates (%)

x	1940	1970	2010
$f(x)$	5	11	30

Table 5.12

x	5	11	30
$f^{-1}(x)$	1940	1970	2010

Table 5.13

Other Representations of Inverse Functions

Tables and graphs of a one-to-one function can also be used to find its inverse.

Numerical Representations In Table 5.12, f has domain $D = \{1940, 1970, 2010\}$ and it computes the percentage of the U.S. population with 4 or more years of college in year x.

Function f is one-to-one because different inputs always produce different outputs. Therefore f^{-1} exists. Since $f(1940) = 5$, it follows that $f^{-1}(5) = 1940$. Similarly, $f^{-1}(11) = 1970$ and $f^{-1}(30) = 2010$. Table 5.13 shows a table for f^{-1}.

The domain of f is $\{1940, 1970, 2010\}$ and the range of f is $\{5, 11, 30\}$. The domain of f^{-1} is $\{5, 11, 30\}$ and the range of f^{-1} is $\{1940, 1970, 2010\}$. The functions f and f^{-1} interchange domains and ranges. Figures 5.17 and 5.18 demonstrate this property.

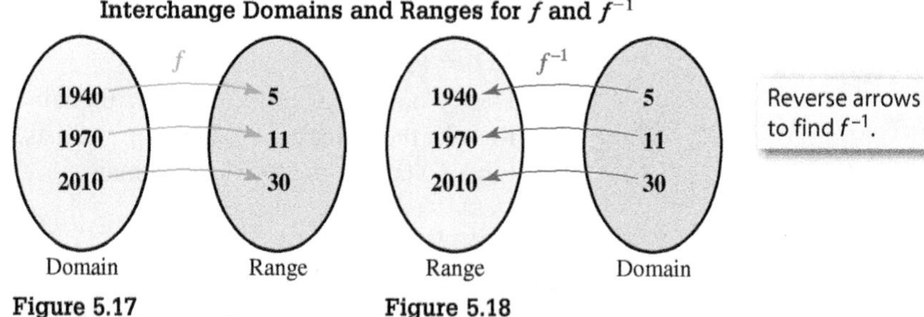

Figure 5.17 Figure 5.18

Figure 5.19 shows a function f that is *not* one-to-one. In Figure 5.20 the arrows have been reversed. This relation does *not* represent the inverse *function* because input 4 produces two outputs, 1 and 2.

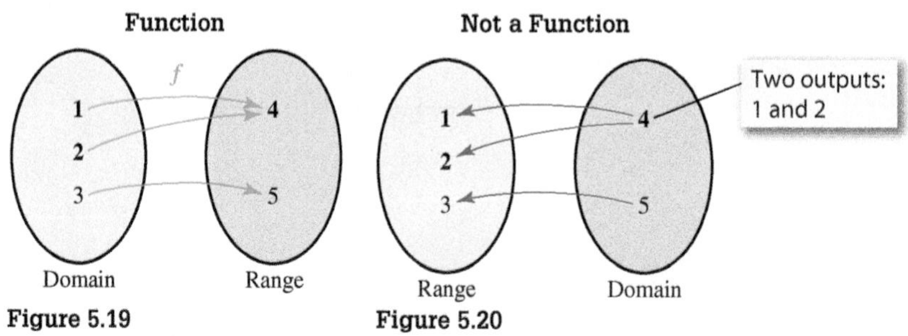

Figure 5.19 Figure 5.20

The relationship between domains and ranges is summarized in the following box.

DOMAINS AND RANGES OF INVERSE FUNCTIONS

The domain of f equals the range of f^{-1}.
The range of f equals the domain of f^{-1}.

Graphical Representations If the point $(2, 5)$ lies on the graph of f, then $f(2) = 5$ and $f^{-1}(5) = 2$. Therefore the point $(5, 2)$ must lie on the graph of f^{-1}. In general, if the point (a, b) lies on the graph of f, then the point (b, a) lies on the graph of f^{-1}. Refer to Figure 5.21. If a line segment is drawn between the points (a, b) and (b, a), the line $y = x$ is a perpendicular bisector of this line segment. Figure 5.22 shows pairs of points in the form (a, b) and (b, a). Figure 5.23 shows continuous graphs of f and f^{-1} passing through these points. The graph of f^{-1} is a *reflection* of the graph of f across the line $y = x$.

Reflecting to Find f^{-1}

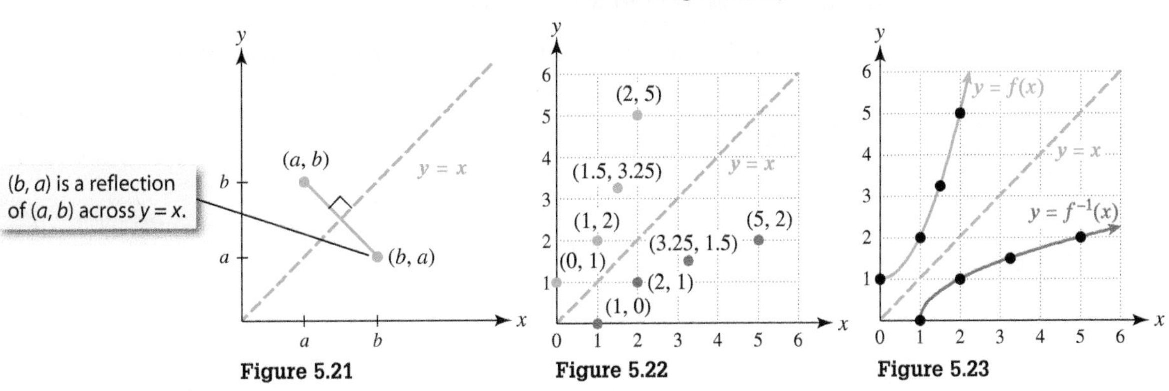

Figure 5.21 Figure 5.22 Figure 5.23

GRAPHS OF FUNCTIONS AND THEIR INVERSES

The graph of f^{-1} is a reflection of the graph of f across the line $y = x$.

EXAMPLE 7 **Representing an inverse function graphically**

Let $f(x) = x^3 + 2$. Graph f. Then sketch a graph of f^{-1}.

SOLUTION Figure 5.24 shows a graph of f. To sketch a graph of f^{-1}, reflect the graph of f across the line $y = x$. The graph of f^{-1} appears as though it were the "reflection" of the graph of f in a mirror located along $y = x$. See Figure 5.25.

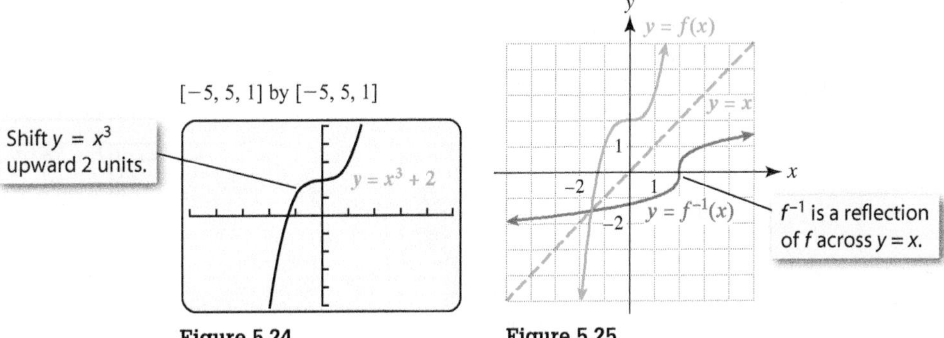

Figure 5.24 Figure 5.25

Calculator Help
To graph an inverse function, see Appendix A (page AP-11).

Now Try Exercise 113

The following See the Concept shows how to represent and find inverse functions.

See the Concept: Representing Inverse Functions

Verbal

f: Multiply x by 2 and add 1.

f^{-1}: Subtract 1 from x and divide by 2.

Use the inverse operations in the reverse order.

Symbolic

$f(x) = 2x + 1$

To find $f^{-1}(x)$:

$$y = 2x + 1$$
$$y - 1 = 2x$$
$$\frac{y-1}{2} = x$$
$$f^{-1}(x) = \frac{x-1}{2}$$

Solve for x.

Numerical

x	$f(x)$
−2	−3
−1	−1
0	1
1	3
2	5

x	$f^{-1}(x)$
−3	−2
−1	−1
1	0
3	1
5	2

Interchange the x-and y-values.

Graphical

$f(x) = 2x + 1$ $y = x$ $f^{-1}(x) = \frac{x-1}{2}$

Reflect the graph of f across $y = x$.

EXAMPLE 8 **Evaluating f and f^{-1} graphically**

Use the graph of f in Figure 5.26 to evaluate each expression.

(a) $f(2)$ **(b)** $f^{-1}(3)$ **(c)** $f^{-1}(-3)$

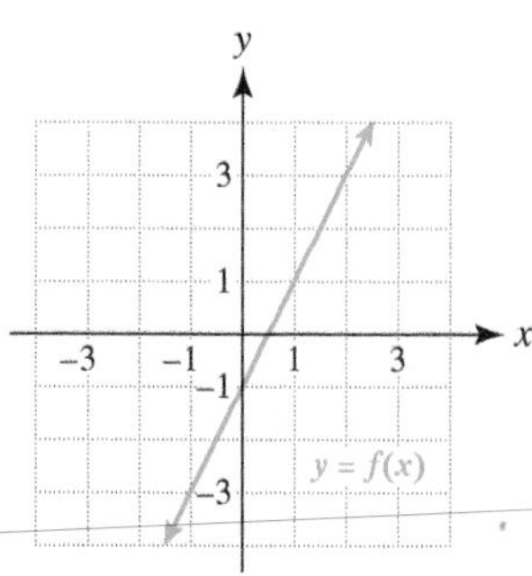

Figure 5.26

SOLUTION

Getting Started To evaluate $f(a)$ graphically, find a on the x-axis. Move upward or downward to the graph of f and determine the corresponding y-value. To evaluate $f^{-1}(b)$ graphically, find b on the y-axis. Move left or right to the graph of f and determine the corresponding x-value. ▶

(a) To evaluate $f(2)$, find 2 on the x-axis, move upward to the graph of f and then move left to the y-axis to obtain $f(2) = 3$, as shown in Figure 5.27.

CLASS DISCUSSION

Does an inverse function for $f(x) = |2x - 1|$ exist? Explain. What difficulties would you encounter if you tried to evaluate $f^{-1}(3)$ graphically?

$f(2) = 3$

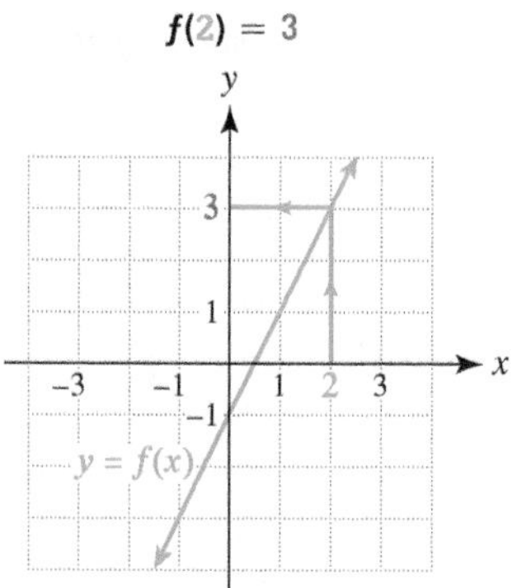

Figure 5.27

(b) Start by finding 3 on the y-axis, move right to the graph of f, and then move downward to the x-axis to obtain $f^{-1}(3) = 2$, as shown in Figure 5.28. Notice that $f(2) = 3$ from part (a) and $f^{-1}(3) = 2$ here.

(c) Find -3 on the y-axis, move left to the graph of f, and then move upward to the x-axis. We can see from Figure 5.29 that $f^{-1}(-3) = -1$.

$f^{-1}(3) = 2$

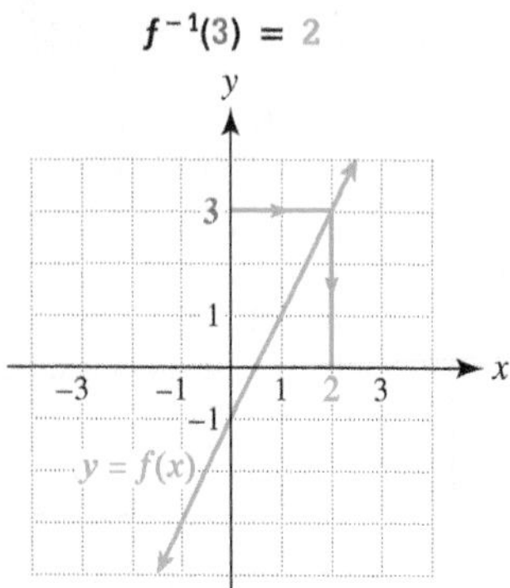

Figure 5.28

$f^{-1}(-3) = -1$

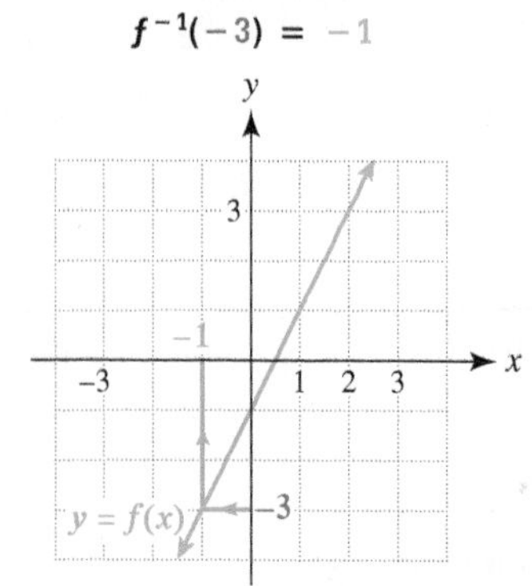

Figure 5.29

Now Try Exercise 101

5.2 Putting It All Together

The following table summarizes some important concepts about inverse functions.

CONCEPT	COMMENTS	EXAMPLES
One-to-one function	f is one-to-one if different inputs always result in different outputs. That is, $a \neq b$ implies $f(a) \neq f(b)$.	$f(x) = x^2 - 4x$ is not one-to-one because $f(0) = 0$ and $f(4) = 0$. With this function, *different* inputs can result in the *same* output.
Horizontal line test	If every horizontal line intersects the graph of f at most once, then f is one-to-one.	y $y = f(x)$ x Not one-to-one
Inverse function	If a function f is one-to-one, it has an inverse function f^{-1} that satisfies both $(f^{-1} \circ f)(x) = f^{-1}(f(x)) = x$ and $(f \circ f^{-1})(x) = f(f^{-1}(x)) = x.$	$f(x) = 3x - 1$ is one-to-one and has inverse function $f^{-1}(x) = \frac{x+1}{3}$. $f^{-1}(f(x)) = f^{-1}(3x - 1) = \frac{(3x-1)+1}{3} = x$ Similarly, $f(f^{-1}(x)) = x.$
Domains and ranges of inverse functions	The domain of f equals the range of f^{-1}. The range of f equals the domain of f^{-1}.	Let $f(x) = (x + 2)^2$ with restricted domain $x \geq -2$ and range $y \geq 0$. It follows that $f^{-1}(x) = \sqrt{x} - 2$ with domain $x \geq 0$ and range $y \geq -2$.

5.2 Exercises

Inverse Operations

Exercises 1–4: State the inverse action or actions.

1. Opening a window
2. Climbing up a ladder
3. Walking into a classroom, sitting down, and opening a book
4. Opening the door and turning on the lights

Exercises 5–12: Describe verbally the inverse of the statement. Then express both the given statement and its inverse symbolically.

5. Add 2 to x.
6. Multiply x by 5.
7. Subtract 2 from x and multiply the result by 3.
8. Divide x by 20 and then add 10.
9. Take the cube root of x and add 1.
10. Multiply x by -2 and add 3.
11. Take the reciprocal of a nonzero number x.
12. Take the square root of a positive number x.

One-to-One Functions

Exercises 13–18: Use the graph of $y = f(x)$ to determine if f is one-to-one.

13.

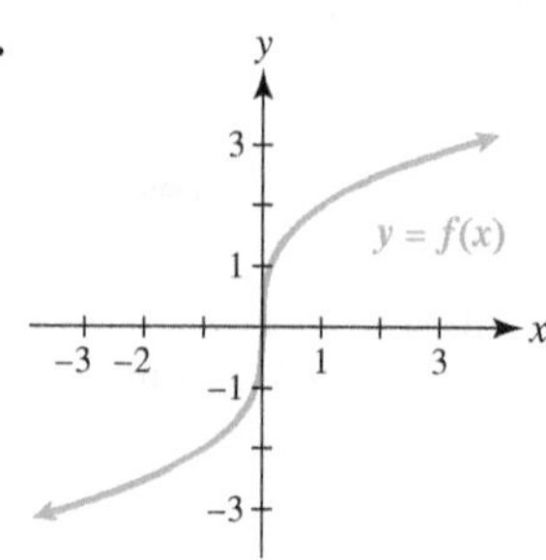

14.

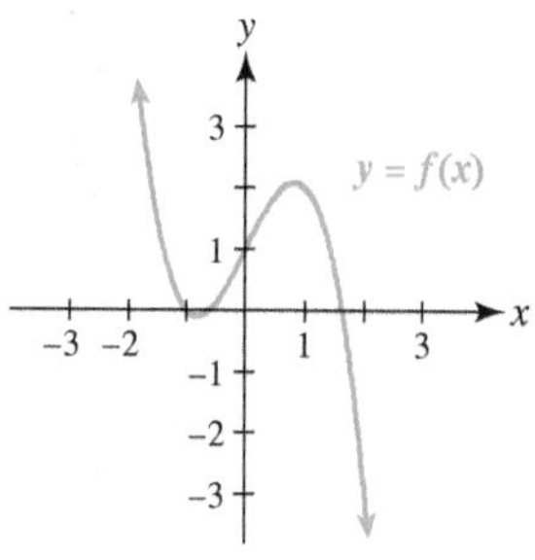

15.

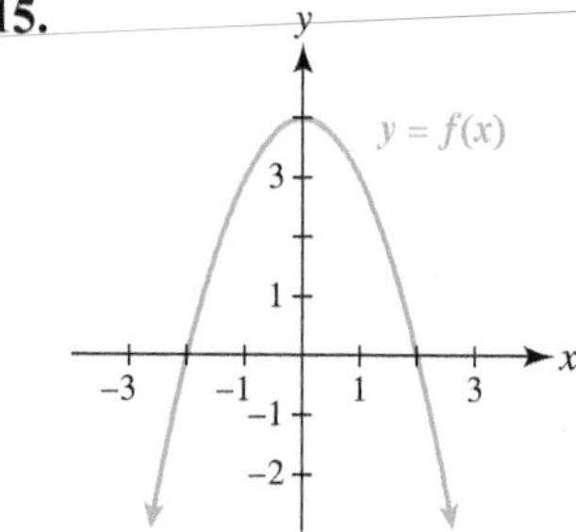

16.

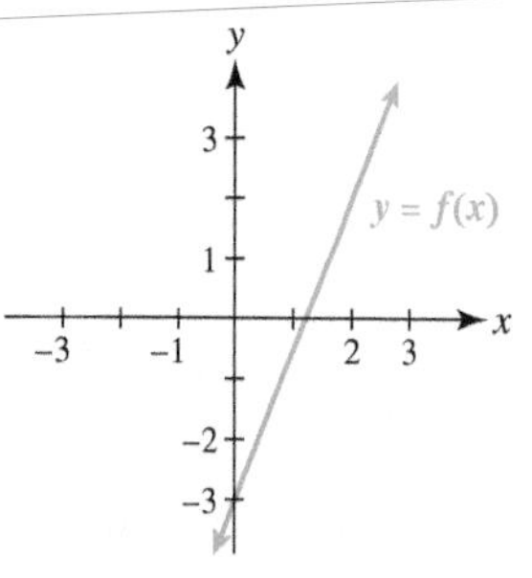

17.

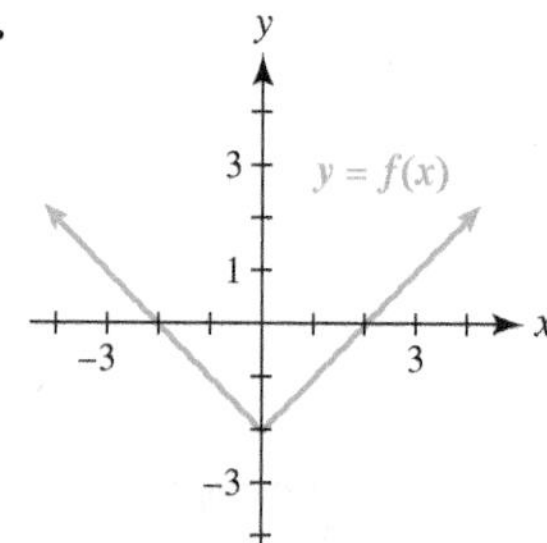

18.

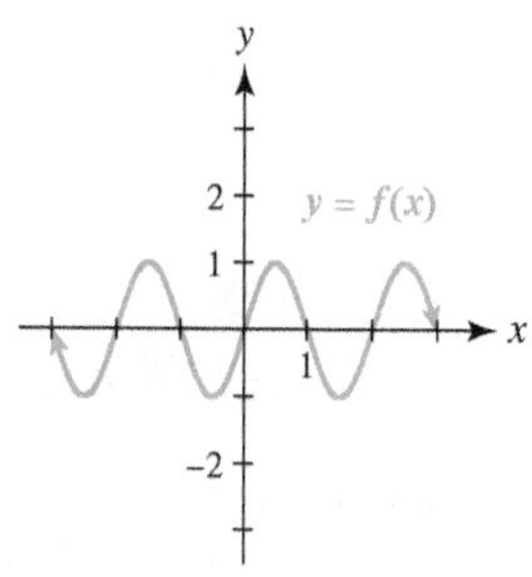

Exercises 19–22: The table is a complete representation of f. Use the table to determine if f is one-to-one and has an inverse.

19.

x	1	2	3	4
$f(x)$	4	3	3	5

20.

x	−2	0	2	4
$f(x)$	4	2	0	−2

21.

x	0	2	4	6	8
$f(x)$	−1	0	4	1	−3

22.

x	−2	−1	0	1	2
$f(x)$	4	1	0	1	4

Exercises 23–36: Determine if f is one-to-one. You may want to graph $y = f(x)$ and apply the horizontal line test.

23. $f(x) = 2x - 7$

24. $f(x) = x^2 - 1$

25. $f(x) = -2x^2 + x$

26. $f(x) = 4 - \frac{3}{4}x$

27. $f(x) = x^4$

28. $f(x) = |2x - 5|$

29. $f(x) = |x - 1|$

30. $f(x) = x^3$

31. $f(x) = \dfrac{1}{1 + x^2}$

32. $f(x) = \dfrac{1}{x}$

33. $f(x) = 3x - x^3$

34. $f(x) = x^{2/3}$

35. $f(x) = x^{1/2}$

36. $f(x) = x^3 - 4x$

Exercises 37–40: **Modeling** *Decide if the situation could be modeled by a one-to-one function.*

37. The distance between the ground and a person who is riding a Ferris wheel after x seconds

38. The cumulative numbers of AIDS cases from 1980 to 2010

39. The population of the United States from 1980 to 2010

40. The height y of a stone thrown upward after x seconds

Symbolic Representations of Inverse Functions

Exercises 41–62: Find a symbolic representation for $f^{-1}(x)$.

41. $f(x) = \sqrt[3]{x}$

42. $f(x) = 2x$

43. $f(x) = -2x + 10$

44. $f(x) = x^3 + 2$

45. $f(x) = 3x - 1$

46. $f(x) = \dfrac{x - 1}{2}$

47. $f(x) = 2x^3 - 5$

48. $f(x) = 1 - \frac{1}{2}x^3$

49. $f(x) = x^2 - 1, x \geq 0$

50. $f(x) = (x + 2)^2, x \leq -2$

51. $f(x) = \dfrac{1}{2x}$

52. $f(x) = \dfrac{2}{\sqrt{x}}$

53. $f(x) = \frac{1}{2}(4 - 5x) + 1$

54. $f(x) = 6 - \frac{3}{4}(2x - 4)$

55. $f(x) = \dfrac{x}{x + 2}$

56. $f(x) = \dfrac{3x}{x - 1}$

57. $f(x) = \dfrac{2x + 1}{x - 1}$

58. $f(x) = \dfrac{1 - x}{3x + 1}$

59. $f(x) = \dfrac{1}{x} - 3$

60. $f(x) = \dfrac{1}{x + 5} + 2$

61. $f(x) = \dfrac{1}{x^3 - 1}$

62. $f(x) = \dfrac{2}{2 - x^3}$

Exercises 63–70: Restrict the domain of $f(x)$ so that f is one-to-one. Then find $f^{-1}(x)$. Answers may vary.

63. $f(x) = 4 - x^2$

64. $f(x) = 2(x + 3)^2$

65. $f(x) = (x - 2)^2 + 4$

66. $f(x) = x^4 - 1$

67. $f(x) = x^{2/3} + 1$

68. $f(x) = 2(x + 3)^{2/3}$

69. $f(x) = \sqrt{9 - 2x^2}$

70. $f(x) = \sqrt{25 - x^2}$

Exercises 71–84: Find a formula for $f^{-1}(x)$. Identify the domain and range of f^{-1}. Verify that f and f^{-1} are inverses.

71. $f(x) = 5x - 15$

72. $f(x) = (x + 3)^2, x \geq -3$

73. $f(x) = \sqrt[3]{x - 5}$

74. $f(x) = 6 - 7x$

75. $f(x) = \dfrac{x - 5}{4}$

76. $f(x) = \dfrac{x + 2}{9}$

77. $f(x) = \sqrt{x - 5}, x \geq 5$

78. $f(x) = \sqrt{5 - 2x}, x \leq \frac{5}{2}$

79. $f(x) = \dfrac{1}{x + 3}$

80. $f(x) = \dfrac{2}{x - 1}$

81. $f(x) = 2x^3$

82. $f(x) = 1 - 4x^3$

83. $f(x) = x^2, x \geq 0$

84. $f(x) = \sqrt[3]{1 - x}$

Numerical Representations of Inverse Functions

Exercises 85–88: Use the table for $f(x)$ to find a table for $f^{-1}(x)$. Identify the domains and ranges of f and f^{-1}.

85.

x	1	2	3
$f(x)$	5	7	9

86.

x	1	10	100
$f(x)$	0	1	2

87.

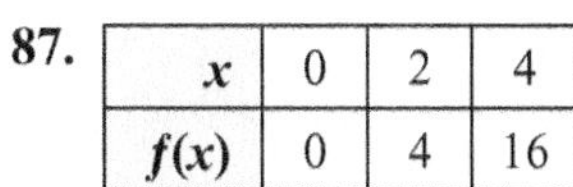

x	0	2	4
$f(x)$	0	4	16

88.

x	0	1	2
$f(x)$	1	2	4

Exercises 89 and 90: Use $f(x)$ to complete the table.

89. $f(x) = 4x$

x	0	2	4	6
$f^{-1}(x)$				

90. $f(x) = x^3$

x	−8	−1	8	27
$f^{-1}(x)$				

Exercises 91–98: Use the tables to evaluate the following.

x	0	1	2	3	4
$f(x)$	1	3	5	4	2

x	−1	1	2	3	4
$g(x)$	0	2	1	4	5

91. $f^{-1}(3)$

92. $f^{-1}(5)$

93. $g^{-1}(4)$

94. $g^{-1}(0)$

95. $(f \circ g^{-1})(1)$

96. $(g^{-1} \circ g^{-1})(2)$

97. $(g \circ f^{-1})(5)$

98. $(f^{-1} \circ g)(4)$

Graphs and Inverse Functions

99. Interpreting an Inverse The graph of f computes the balance in a savings account after x years. Estimate each expression. Interpret what $f^{-1}(x)$ computes.

(a) $f(1)$ **(b)** $f^{-1}(110)$ **(c)** $f^{-1}(160)$

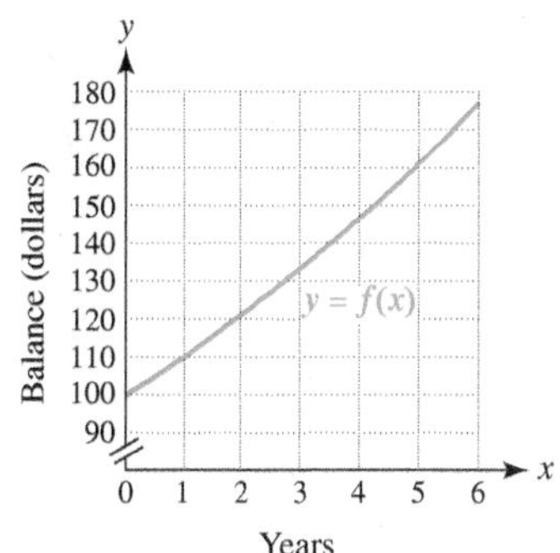

100. Interpreting an Inverse The graph of f computes the Celsius temperature of a pan of water after x minutes. Estimate each expression. Interpret what the expression $f^{-1}(x)$ computes.

(a) $f(4)$ **(b)** $f^{-1}(90)$ **(c)** $f^{-1}(80)$

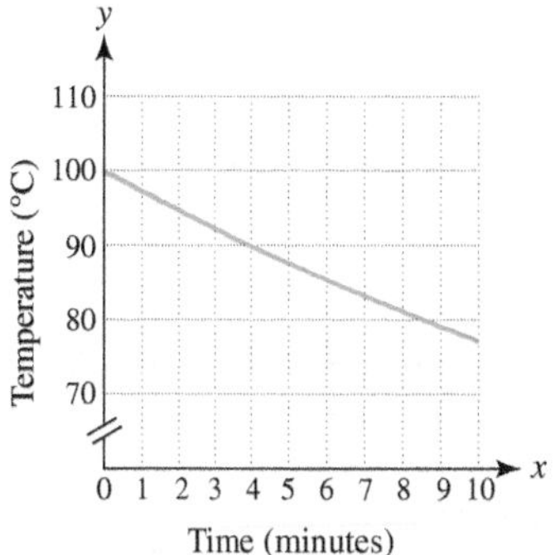

Exercises 101–104: Use the graph to evaluate the expression.

101.

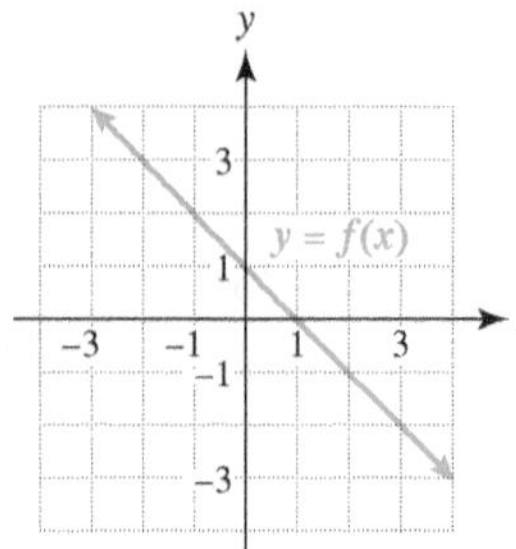

(a) $f(-1)$

(b) $f^{-1}(-2)$

(c) $f^{-1}(0)$

(d) $(f^{-1} \circ f)(3)$

102.

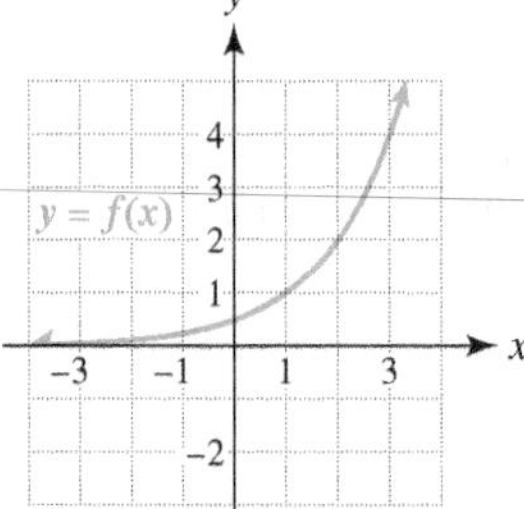

(a) $f(1)$

(b) $f^{-1}(1)$

(c) $f^{-1}(4)$

(d) $(f \circ f^{-1})(2.5)$

103.

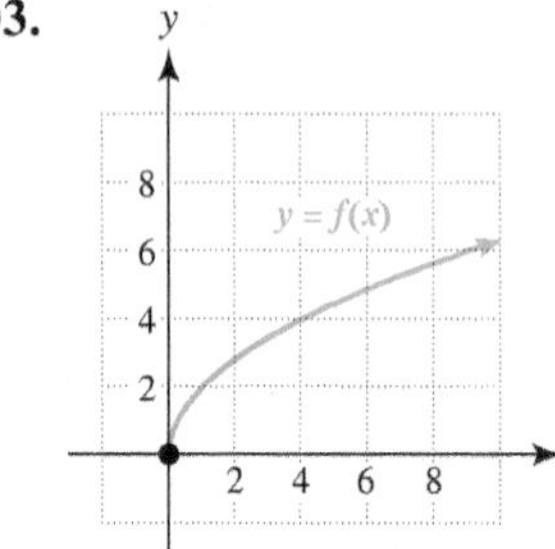

(a) $f(4)$

(b) $f^{-1}(0)$

(c) $f^{-1}(6)$

(d) $(f \circ f^{-1})(4)$

104.

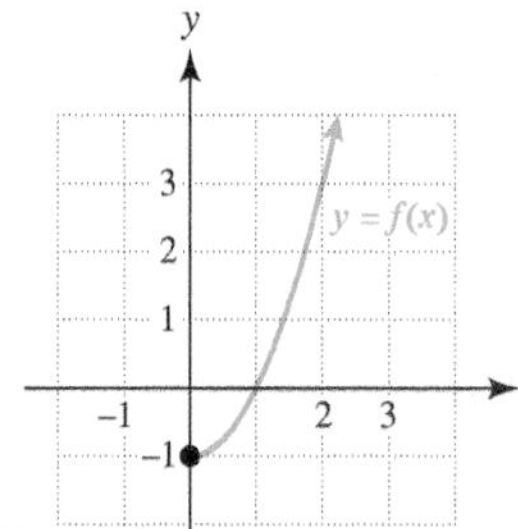

(a) $f(1)$

(b) $f^{-1}(-1)$

(c) $f^{-1}(3)$

(d) $(f \circ f^{-1})(1)$

Exercises 105–110: Use the graph of $y = f(x)$ to sketch a graph of $y = f^{-1}(x)$.

105.

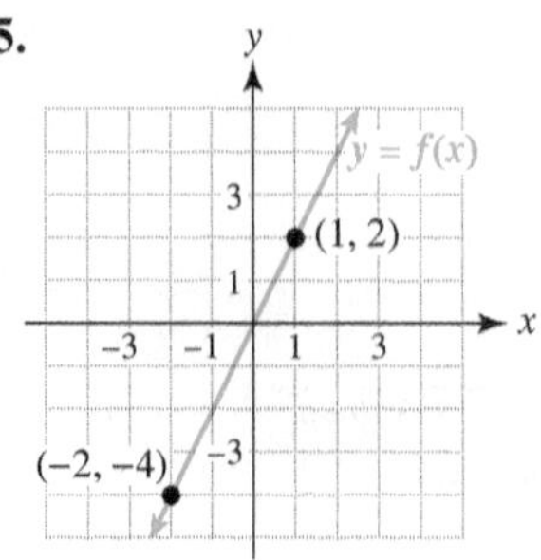

106.

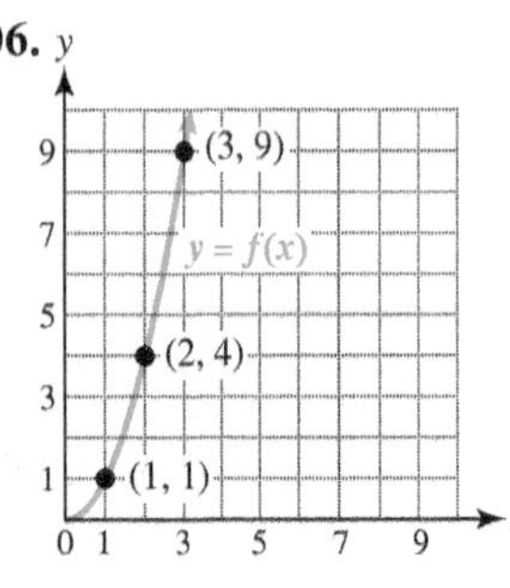

107.

(2, 4)

$\left(-2, \frac{1}{4}\right)$

(1, 2)

(0, 1)

y = f(x)

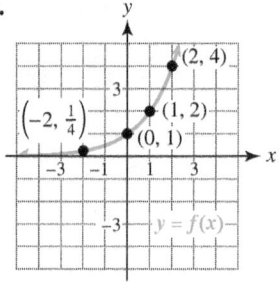

108.

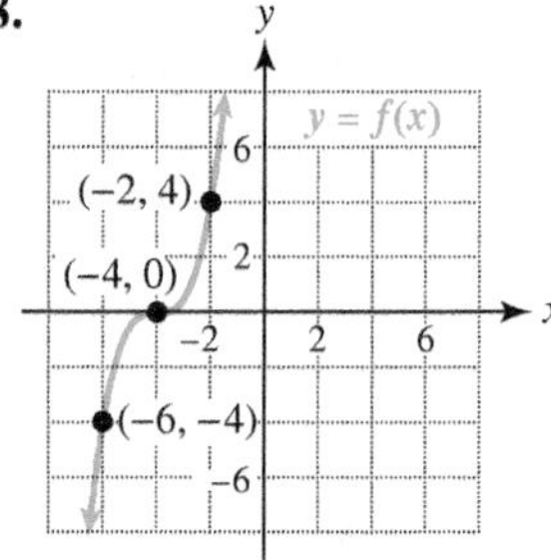

109.

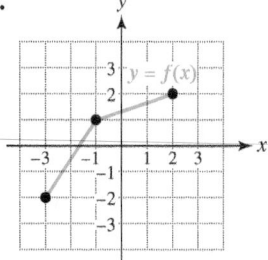

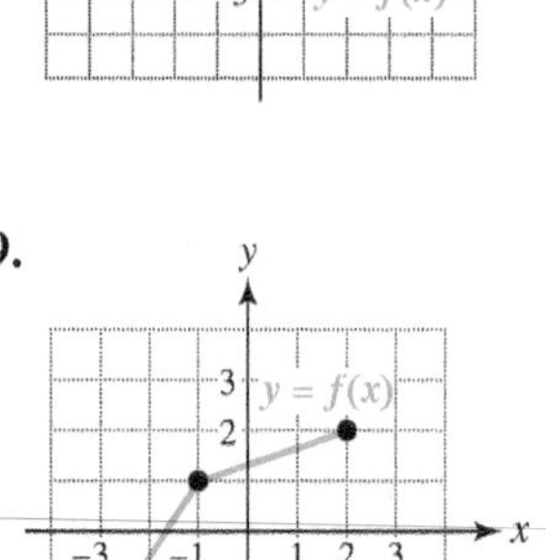

110.

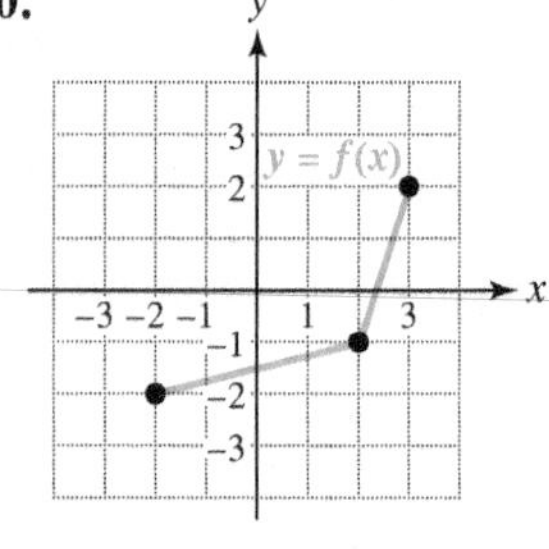

Exercises 111–116: Graph $y = f(x)$ and $y = x$. Then graph $y = f^{-1}(x)$

111. $f(x) = 2x - 1$

112. $f(x) = -\frac{1}{2}x + 1$

113. $f(x) = x^3 - 1$

114. $f(x) = \sqrt[3]{x - 1}$

115. $f(x) = (x + 1)^2, x \geq -1$

116. $f(x) = \sqrt{x + 1}$

Exercises 117–120: Graph $y = f(x)$, $y = f^{-1}(x)$, and $y = x$ in a square viewing rectangle such as $[-4.7, 4.7, 1]$ by $[-3.1, 3.1, 1]$.

117. $f(x) = 3x - 1$

118. $f(x) = \dfrac{3 - x}{2}$

119. $f(x) = \frac{1}{3}x^3 - 1$

120. $f(x) = \sqrt[3]{x - 1}$

Applications

121. Volume The volume V of a sphere with radius r is given by $V = \frac{4}{3}\pi r^3$.

(a) Does V represent a one-to-one function?

(b) What does the inverse of V compute?

(c) Find a formula for the inverse.

(d) Normally we interchange x and y to find the inverse function. Does it make sense to interchange V and r in part (c) of this exercise? Explain.

122. Temperature The formula $F = \frac{9}{5}C + 32$ converts a Celsius temperature to Fahrenheit temperature.

(a) Find a formula for the inverse.

(b) Normally we interchange x and y to find the inverse function. Does it makes sense to interchange F and C in part (a) of this exercise? Explain.

(c) What Celsius temperature is equivalent to 68°F?

123. Height and Weight The formula $W = \frac{25}{7}h - \frac{800}{7}$ approximates the recommended minimum weight for a person h inches tall, where $62 \leq h \leq 76$.

(a) What is the recommended minimum weight for someone 70 inches tall?

(b) Does W represent a one-to-one function?

(c) Find a formula for the inverse.

(d) Evaluate the inverse for 150 pounds and interpret the result.

(e) What does the inverse compute?

124. Planetary Orbits The formula $T(x) = x^{3/2}$ calculates the time in years that it takes a planet to orbit the sun if the planet is x times farther from the sun than Earth is.

(a) Find the inverse of T.

(b) What does the inverse of T calculate?

125. Converting Units The tables represent a function F that converts yards to feet and a function Y that converts miles to yards. Evaluate each expression and interpret the results.

x (yd)	1760	3520	5280	7040	8800
$F(x)$ (ft)	5280	10,560	15,840	21,120	26,400

x (mi)	1	2	3	4	5
$Y(x)$ (yd)	1760	3520	5280	7040	8800

(a) $(F \circ Y)(2)$

(b) $F^{-1}(26,400)$

(c) $(Y^{-1} \circ F^{-1})(21,120)$

126. Converting Units (Refer to Exercise 125.)

(a) Find formulas for $F(x)$, $Y(x)$, and $(F \circ Y)(x)$.

(b) Find a formula for $(Y^{-1} \circ F^{-1})(x)$. What does this function compute?

127. Converting Units The tables at the top of the next column represent a function C that converts tablespoons to cups and a function Q that converts cups to quarts. Evaluate each expression and interpret the results.

x (tbsp)	32	64	96	128
$C(x)$ (c)	2	4	6	8

x (c)	2	4	6	8
$Q(x)$ (qt)	0.5	1	1.5	2

(a) $(Q \circ C)(96)$

(b) $Q^{-1}(2)$

(c) $(C^{-1} \circ Q^{-1})(1.5)$

128. Rise in Sea Level The global sea level could rise due to partial melting of the polar ice caps. The table represents a function R that models this expected rise in sea level in centimeters for the year t. (This model assumes no changes in current trends.)

t (yr)	1990	2000	2030	2070	2100
$R(t)$ (cm)	0	1	18	44	66

Source: A. Nilsson, *Greenhouse Earth.*

(a) Is R a one-to-one function? Explain.

(b) Use $R(t)$ to find a table for $R^{-1}(t)$. Interpret R^{-1}.

Writing about Mathematics

129. Explain how to find verbal, numerical, graphical, and symbolic representations of an inverse function. Give examples.

130. Can a one-to-one function have more than one x-intercept or more than one y-intercept? Explain.

131. If the graphs of $y = f(x)$ and $y = f^{-1}(x)$ intersect at a point (a, b), what can be said about these graphs? Explain.

132. If $f(x) = ax^2 + bx + c$ with $a \neq 0$, does $f^{-1}(x)$ exist? Explain.

Extended and Discovery Exercises

1. Interpreting an Inverse Let $f(x)$ compute the height in feet of a rocket after x seconds of upward flight.

(a) Explain what $f^{-1}(x)$ computes.

(b) Interpret the solution to the equation $f(x) = 5000$.

(c) Explain how to solve the equation in part (b) using $f^{-1}(x)$.

2. If the graph of f lies entirely in quadrants I and II, in which quadrant(s) does the graph of f^{-1} lie?

CHECKING BASIC CONCEPTS FOR SECTIONS 5.1 AND 5.2

1. Use the table to evaluate each expression, if possible.

x	-2	-1	0	1	2
$f(x)$	0	1	-2	-1	2
$g(x)$	1	-2	-1	2	0

(a) $(f + g)(1)$ **(b)** $(f - g)(-1)$

(c) $(fg)(0)$ **(d)** $(f/g)(2)$

(e) $(f \circ g)(2)$ **(f)** $(g \circ f)(-2)$

2. Use the graph to evaluate each expression, if possible.

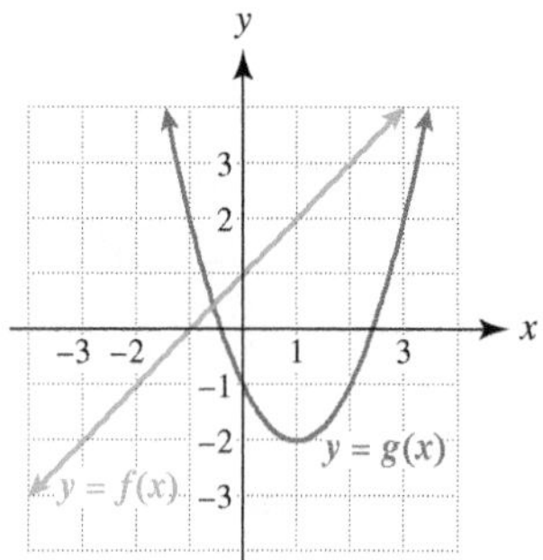

(a) $(f + g)(1)$ **(b)** $(g - f)(0)$

(c) $(fg)(2)$ **(d)** $(g/f)(-1)$

(e) $(f \circ g)(2)$ **(f)** $(g \circ f)(1)$

3. Let $f(x) = x^2 + 3x - 2$ and $g(x) = 3x - 1$. Find each expression.
(a) $(f + g)(x)$ **(b)** $(f/g)(x)$ **(c)** $(f \circ g)(x)$

4. If $f(x) = 5 - 2x$, find $f^{-1}(x)$.

5. Use the graph in Exercise 2 to answer the following.
(a) Is f one-to-one? Does f^{-1} exist? If so, find it.

(b) Is g one-to-one? Does g^{-1} exist? If so, find it.

6. Graph $f(x) = \sqrt[3]{x}$ and $y = x$. Then graph $y = f^{-1}(x)$.

7. Use the table in Exercise 1 to evaluate the following. (Assume that f^{-1} exists.)
(a) $f^{-1}(-2)$ **(b)** $(f^{-1} \circ g)(1)$

8. Use the graph in Exercise 2 to evaluate the following.
(a) $f^{-1}(2)$ **(b)** $(f^{-1} \circ g)(0)$

5.3 Exponential Functions and Models (Part I)

- **Distinguish between linear and exponential growth**
- **Recognize exponential growth and decay**
- **Find exponential models**
- **Model data with exponential functions**

Introduction

Though modern exponential notation was not developed until 1637 by the great French mathematician René Descartes, some of the earliest applications involving exponential functions occurred in the calculation of interest. The custom of charging interest dates back to at least 2000 B.C. in ancient Babylon, where interest rates ran as high as 33%. Today, exponential functions are used not only to calculate interest, but also to model a wide variety of phenomena in business, biology, medicine, engineering, and education. This section discusses exponential functions and their representations. (Source: *Historical Topics for the Mathematics Classroom, Thirty-first Yearbook,* NCTM.)

Linear and Exponential Growth

A linear function g can be written as $g(x) = mx + b$, where m represents the rate of change in $g(x)$ for each unit increase in x. For example, Table 5.14 shows a numerical representation of a linear function g. Each time x increases by 1 unit, $g(x)$ increases by 2 units. We can write a formula $g(x) = 2x + 3$ because the rate of change is 2 and $g(0) = 3$.

A Linear Function

x	0	1	2	3	4	5
$y = g(x)$	3	5	7	9	11	13

Table 5.14

An exponential function is fundamentally different from a linear function. Rather than *adding* a fixed amount to the previous y-value for each unit increase in x, an exponential function *multiplies* the previous y-value by a fixed amount for each unit increase in x. Table 5.15 shows an exponential function f. Note that in Table 5.15 consecutive y-values are found by multiplying the previous y-value by 2.

An Exponential Function

x	0	1	2	3	4	5
$y = f(x)$	3	6	12	24	48	96

Table 5.15

Compare the following patterns for calculating $g(x)$ and $f(x)$.

Linear Growth

$$g(0) = 3$$
$$g(1) = \underbrace{3}_{g(0)} + 2 = 3 + 2 \cdot 1 = 5$$
$$g(2) = \underbrace{3 + 2}_{g(1)} + 2 = 3 + 2 \cdot 2 = 7$$
$$g(3) = \underbrace{3 + 2 + 2}_{g(2)} + 2 = 3 + 2 \cdot 3 = 9$$
$$g(4) = \underbrace{3 + 2 + 2 + 2}_{g(3)} + 2 = 3 + 2 \cdot 4 = 11$$
$$g(5) = \underbrace{3 + 2 + 2 + 2 + 2}_{g(4)} + 2 = 3 + 2 \cdot 5 = 13$$

Exponential Growth

$$f(0) = 3$$
$$f(1) = \underbrace{3}_{f(0)} \cdot 2 = 3 \cdot 2^1 = 6$$
$$f(2) = \underbrace{3 \cdot 2}_{f(1)} \cdot 2 = 3 \cdot 2^2 = 12$$
$$f(3) = \underbrace{3 \cdot 2 \cdot 2}_{f(2)} \cdot 2 = 3 \cdot 2^3 = 24$$
$$f(4) = \underbrace{3 \cdot 2 \cdot 2 \cdot 2}_{f(3)} \cdot 2 = 3 \cdot 2^4 = 48$$
$$f(5) = \underbrace{3 \cdot 2 \cdot 2 \cdot 2 \cdot 2}_{f(4)} \cdot 2 = 3 \cdot 2^5 = 96$$

Notice that if x is a positive integer then

$$g(x) = 3 + \underbrace{(2 + 2 + \cdots + 2)}_{x \text{ terms}} \quad \text{and} \quad f(x) = 3 \cdot \underbrace{(2 \cdot 2 \cdot \cdots \cdot 2)}_{x \text{ factors}}.$$

Using these patterns, we can write formulas for $g(x)$ and $f(x)$ as follows.

$$g(x) = 3 + 2x \quad \text{and} \quad f(x) = 3 \cdot 2^x$$

This discussion gives motivation for the following definition.

EXPONENTIAL FUNCTION

A function f represented by

$$f(x) = Ca^x, \qquad a > 0, \quad a \neq 1, \quad \text{and} \quad C > 0,$$

is an **exponential function with base a and coefficient C.** The base a is called the **growth factor** when $a > 1$ and the **decay factor** when $0 < a < 1$. If x represents time, then C is called the **initial value.**

NOTE Some definitions for an exponential function require that $C = 1$. In this case, an exponential function is defined as $f(x) = a^x$.

Examples of exponential functions include

$$f(x) = 3^x, \qquad g(x) = 5(1.7)^x, \quad \text{and} \quad h(x) = 4\left(\frac{1}{2}\right)^x.$$

Their bases are 3, 1.7, and $\frac{1}{2}$, respectively. When evaluating exponential functions, remember that any *nonzero* number raised to the 0 power equals 1. Thus $f(0) = 3^0 = 1$, $g(0) = 5(1.7)^0 = 5$, and $h(0) = 4\left(\frac{1}{2}\right)^0 = 4$.

NOTE If $f(x) = Ca^x$, then $f(0) = Ca^0 = C(1) = C$. That is, C equals the value of the function at $x = 0$. If x represents time, then C often equals the *initial value* of the quantity being modeled by f.

For large values of x, an exponential function with $a > 1$ grows faster than any linear function. Figures 5.30 and 5.31 show graphs of $f(x) = 2^x$ and $g(x) = 2x$, respectively. The points shown in the corresponding tables have also been plotted. Notice that the graph of the exponential function f increases more rapidly than the graph of the linear function g for large values of x.

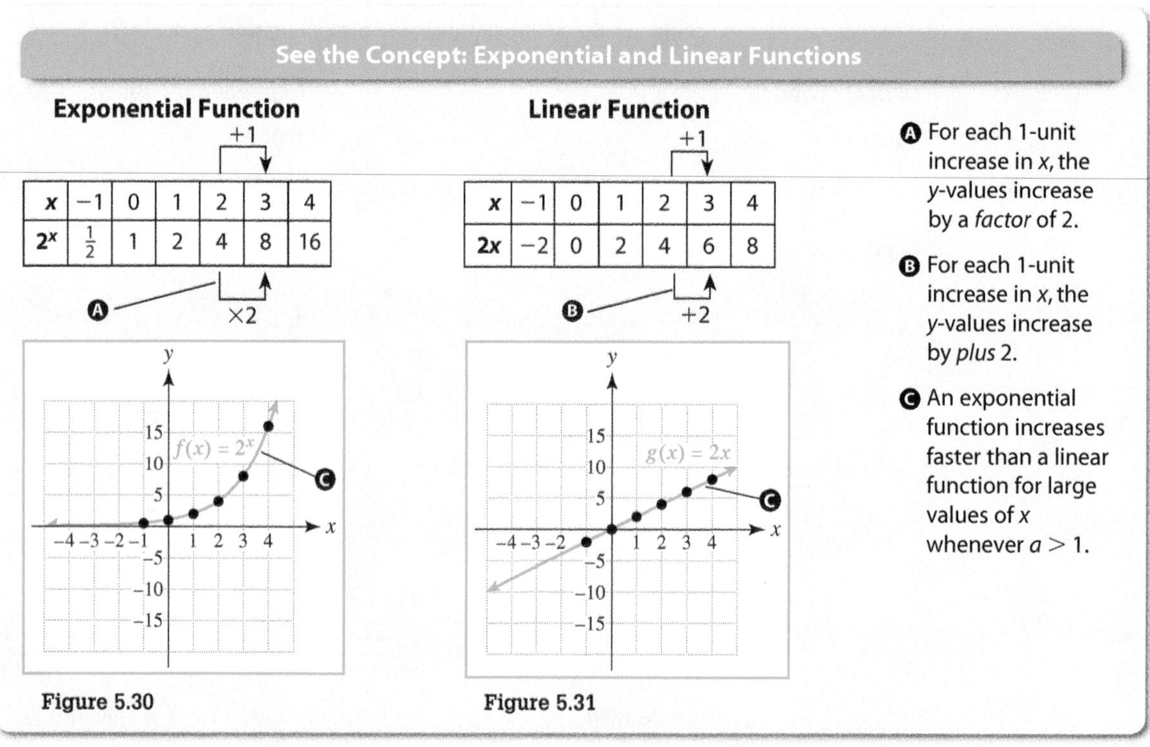

See the Concept: Exponential and Linear Functions
Exponential Function
+1
x | −1 | 0 | 1 | 2 | 3 | 4
2^x | 1/2 | 1 | 2 | 4 | 8 | 16
×2
f(x) = 2^x
Linear Function
+1
x | −1 | 0 | 1 | 2 | 3 | 4
2x | −2 | 0 | 2 | 4 | 6 | 8
+2
g(x) = 2x
A For each 1-unit increase in x, the y-values increase by a factor of 2.
B For each 1-unit increase in x, the y-values increase by plus 2.
C An exponential function increases faster than a linear function for large values of x whenever a > 1.

Figure 5.30

Figure 5.31

EXAMPLE 1 **Recognizing linear and exponential data**

For each table, find either a linear or an exponential function that models the data.

(a)

x	0	1	2	3
y	−3	−1.5	0	1.5

(b)

x	0	1	2	3	4
y	16	4	1	$\frac{1}{4}$	$\frac{1}{16}$

(c)

x	0	1	2	3
y	3	4.5	6.75	10.125

(d)

x	0	1	2	3	4
y	16	12	8	4	0

(e)

x	−5	−1	3	7
y	11	3	−5	−13

(f)

x	−5	−1	3	7
y	$\frac{3}{32}$	$\frac{3}{2}$	24	384

SOLUTION

(a) For each unit increase in x, the y-values increase by 1.5, so the data are linear. Because $y = -3$ when $x = 0$, it follows that the data can be modeled by $f(x) = 1.5x - 3$.

(b) For each unit increase in x, the y-values are multiplied by $\frac{1}{4}$. This is an exponential function given by $f(x) = Ca^x$ with $C = f(0) = 16$ and $a = \frac{1}{4}$, so $f(x) = 16\left(\frac{1}{4}\right)^x$.

(c) Since the data do not change by a fixed amount *for each unit increase in x*, the data are not linear. To determine if the data are exponential, calculate ratios of consecutive y-values.

$$\frac{4.5}{3} = 1.5, \quad \frac{6.75}{4.5} = 1.5, \quad \frac{10.125}{6.75} = 1.5$$

For each unit increase in x, the next y-value in the table can be found by multiplying the previous y-value by 1.5, so let $a = 1.5$. Since $y = 3$ when $x = 0$, let $C = 3$. Thus $f(x) = 3(1.5)^x$.

(d) For each unit increase in x, the next y-value is found by adding -4 to the previous y-value, so $f(x) = -4x + 16$.

(e) For each 4-unit increase in x, there is a constant decrease in y of 8 units, so the equation is linear and the slope between these points is $\frac{-8}{4} = -2$. Thus $f(x) = -2x + b$ models the data. The value of y at $x = 0$ is not given in the table, so the y-intercept b is not apparent. However, we can determine b by substituting any point from the table, such as $(3, -5)$, into $f(x)$ to obtain

$$f(3) = -2(3) + b = -5, \quad \text{or} \quad b = 1.$$

Thus, $f(x) = -2x + 1$.

(f) For each 4-unit increase in x, there is not a constant change in y, so the data is not linear. If $f(x) = Ca^x$ models the data, then $f(3) = 24$ and $f(7) = 384$. We can find a by simplifying the following ratios:

$$\frac{f(7)}{f(3)} = \frac{Ca^7}{Ca^3} = a^4 \quad \text{and} \quad \frac{f(7)}{f(3)} = \frac{384}{24} = 16.$$

Thus $a^4 = 16$, or $a = \sqrt[4]{16} = 2$, and $f(x) = C(2)^x$. To determine C, substitute a point, such as $(3, 24)$, into the formula $f(x)$ to obtain

$$f(3) = C(2)^3 = 24, \quad \text{or} \quad C = \frac{24}{8} = 3.$$

Thus $f(x) = 3(2)^x$.

Now Try Exercises 13, 15, and 17

EXAMPLE 2 **Finding exponential functions**

Find values for C and a so that $f(x) = Ca^x$ satisfies the conditions.

(a) $f(0) = 4$ and $f(1) = 8$ **(b)** $f(-1) = 8$ and $f(2) = 1$

SOLUTION

(a) $f(0) = 4$, so $C = 4$. Because $\frac{f(1)}{f(0)} = \frac{8}{4} = 2$, it follows that for each unit increase in x, the output is multiplied by 2. Thus $a = 2$ and $f(x) = 4(2)^x$.

(b) **Getting Started** Because we are not given $f(0)$, we cannot immediately determine C. Instead, first find a by evaluating the following ratios. ▶

$$\frac{f(2)}{f(-1)} = \frac{1}{8} \quad \text{and} \quad \frac{f(2)}{f(-1)} = \frac{Ca^2}{Ca^{-1}} = a^3$$

$f(x) = Ca^x$; subtract exponents.

It follows that $a^3 = \frac{1}{8}$, so $a = \frac{1}{2}$. Thus $f(x) = C\left(\frac{1}{2}\right)^x$. Next determine C by using the fact that $f(2) = 1$.

$$f(2) = C\left(\frac{1}{2}\right)^2 = \frac{1}{4}C = 1, \quad \text{or} \quad C = 4$$

Thus $f(x) = 4\left(\frac{1}{2}\right)^x$.

Now Try Exercises 35 and 39

Finding Slope and Growth Factors (Optional) The tables for parts (a)–(d) in Example 1 all have consecutive x-values that increase by 1 unit. For these tables we say that the *change in* x equals 1 and write $\Delta x = 1$ (read "delta x equals one"). When the data is *linear* and $\Delta x = 1$, the slope m simplifies to the *difference* of consecutive y-values. That is, if (x_1, y_1) and (x_2, y_2) are two data points with $\Delta x = x_2 - x_1 = 1$, then $m = y_2 - y_1$ in the *linear* formula $f(x) = mx + b$. Similarly, when the data is *exponential* and $\Delta x = 1$, the growth factor a simplifies to the *ratio* of consecutive y-values. That is, $a = \frac{y_2}{y_1}$ in the exponential formula $g(x) = Ca^x$. See Example 2(a).

On the other hand, the tables for parts (e) and (f) in Example 1 have consecutive x-values that increase by 4 units, so the change in x equals 4 and $\Delta x = 4$. Suppose that we are given two data points, (2, 10) and (6, 50), that lie on the graph of a *linear* function f given by $f(x) = mx + b$. Because f is linear, $f(x)$ changes by m units for each unit increase in x. In this case, $\Delta x = 6 - 2 = 4$ and $y_2 - y_1 = 50 - 10 = 40$, so a 4-unit increase in x corresponds to a 40-unit increase in $f(x)$. Thus

$$m = \frac{y_2 - y_1}{\Delta x} = \frac{40}{4} = 10.$$

Now suppose that the same two data points, (2, 10) and (6, 50), lie on the graph of an *exponential* function given by $g(x) = Ca^x$. Because g is exponential, $g(x)$ is multiplied by a for each unit increase in x. It follows that points (x, y) on the graph of $g(x)$ must satisfy the following table.

x	2	3	4	5	6
y	10	$10a$	$10a^2$	$10a^3$	$10a^4 = 50$

Notice that each consecutive y-value in the table is multiplied by a. We use the table to find a.

$$10a^4 = 50$$

$$a^4 = 5 \qquad \text{Divide by 10.}$$

$$a = \sqrt[4]{5} \qquad \text{Take the fourth root.}$$

In our example, $\Delta x = 4$, $y_1 = 10$, $y_2 = 50$, and $a = \sqrt[4]{\frac{50}{10}}$, or $a = \sqrt[4]{5}$.

In summary, suppose that two points, (x_1, y_1) and (x_2, y_2), lie on the graph of a function with $\Delta x = x_2 - x_1$. If the function is linear, then the slope m is given by

$$m = \frac{y_2 - y_1}{\Delta x}. \qquad \text{Slope formula}$$

If the function is exponential, then the growth factor a is given by the **root of the ratio formula**

$$a = \sqrt[\Delta x]{\frac{y_2}{y_1}}. \qquad \text{Root of the ratio formula}$$

See Example 2(b).

NOTE When $\Delta x = 1$, then $m = y_2 - y_1$ in the slope formula and $a = \sqrt[1]{\frac{y_2}{y_1}} = \frac{y_2}{y_1}$ in the root of the ratio formula, as discussed previously. The *first root* is simply the *ratio* of the y-values.

EXAMPLE 3 Finding linear and exponential functions

Find a linear function f and an exponential function g whose graph passes through the two given points.

(a) (0, 4), (1, 6) **(b)** (−1, 8), (2, 1)

SOLUTION

(a) ***Linear*** The graph of f passes through the points $(0, 4)$ and $(1, 6)$, so $\Delta x = 1 - 0 = 1$ and

$$m = y_2 - y_1 = 6 - 4 = 2.$$

Because $f(0) = 4$, the y-intercept is 4 and so $f(x) = 2x + 4$.
Exponential With $\Delta x = 1$, $y_1 = 4$, and $y_2 = 6$, the growth factor is the ratio of consecutive y-values, or

$$a = \frac{y_2}{y_1} = \frac{6}{4} = 1.5$$

Because $g(0) = 4$, the initial value is $C = 4$ and so $g(x) = 4(1.5)^x$.

(b) ***Linear*** The graph of f passes through $(-1, 8)$ and $(2, 1)$, so $\Delta x = 2 - (-1) = 3$ and $m = \frac{1-8}{3} = -\frac{7}{3}$. Thus $f(x) = -\frac{7}{3}x + b$. Because $f(2) = -\frac{7}{3}(2) + b = 1$, it follows that $b = 1 + \frac{14}{3} = \frac{17}{3}$ and $f(x) = -\frac{7}{3}x + \frac{17}{3}$.
Exponential With $\Delta x = 3$, $y_1 = 8$, and $y_2 = 1$, the *root of the ratio formula* becomes

$$a = \sqrt[3]{\frac{1}{8}} = \frac{1}{2}.$$

Thus $g(x) = C\left(\frac{1}{2}\right)^x$. Because $g(2) = 1$ it follows that $C\left(\frac{1}{2}\right)^2 = 1$, or $C = 4$. Thus $g(x) = 4\left(\frac{1}{2}\right)^x$.

Now Try Exercises 23 and 25

Exponential Models If we use an exponential function to model data, then we call this model an **exponential model**. In the next example we find an exponential model.

EXAMPLE 4 Finding an exponential model

A sample of bacteria from a culture doubles its concentration each day. The initial concentration is 1.5 million bacteria per milliliter.

(a) Find an exponential model that calculates the concentration in millions of bacteria per milliliter after x days.

(b) Estimate the concentration after 5 days.

SOLUTION

(a) An exponential model is given by $f(x) = Ca^x$, where the input x is elapsed days and the output $f(x)$ is millions of bacteria per milliliter. We need to determine the *initial value* C and the *growth factor* a. We can determine C because initially $(x = 0)$ the concentration is 1.5 million per milliliter, or $f(0) = 1.5$.

$$f(0) = Ca^0 = C = 1.5. \qquad a^0 = 1$$

Thus the initial value is $C = 1.5$ and the exponential model becomes $f(x) = 1.5a^x$.

Next we determine the growth factor a. After 1 day the concentration doubles and is 3 million per milliliter, so $f(1) = 3$.

$$f(1) = 1.5a^1 = 1.5a = 3$$

Solving $1.5a = 3$ gives a growth factor of $a = 2$ and the exponential model $f(x) = 1.5(2)^x$.

(b) The concentration after 5 days is

$$f(5) = 1.5(2)^5 = 1.5(32) = 48 \text{ million bacteria per milliliter.}$$

Now Try Exercise 63

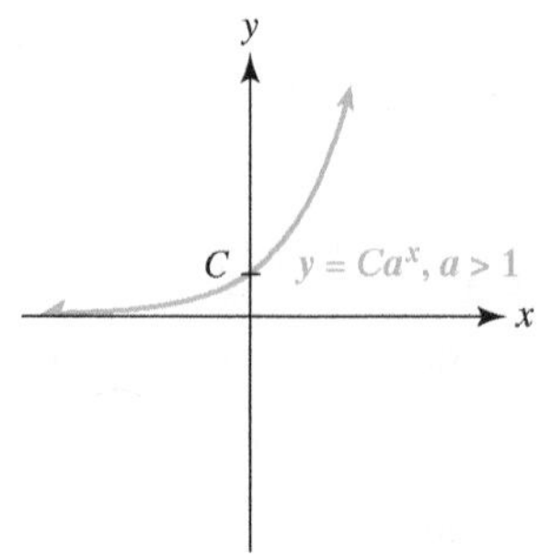

Figure 5.32 Exponential Growth

Exponential Growth and Decay

If an exponential function is written as $f(x) = Ca^x$ with $a > 1$, then $f(x)$ experiences **exponential growth**, as illustrated in Figure 5.32. If $a > 1$, then the y-values increase by a factor of a for each unit increase in x. The *growth factor* is a. For example, if $f(x) = 5(4)^x$, then the growth factor is 4. If $0 < a < 1$, then the y-values decrease by a factor of a for each unit increase in x. In this case, $f(x) = Ca^x$ experiences **exponential decay** with *decay factor* a. See Figure 5.33. Exponential decay was modeled in Example 1(b), where the decay factor was $a = \frac{1}{4}$.

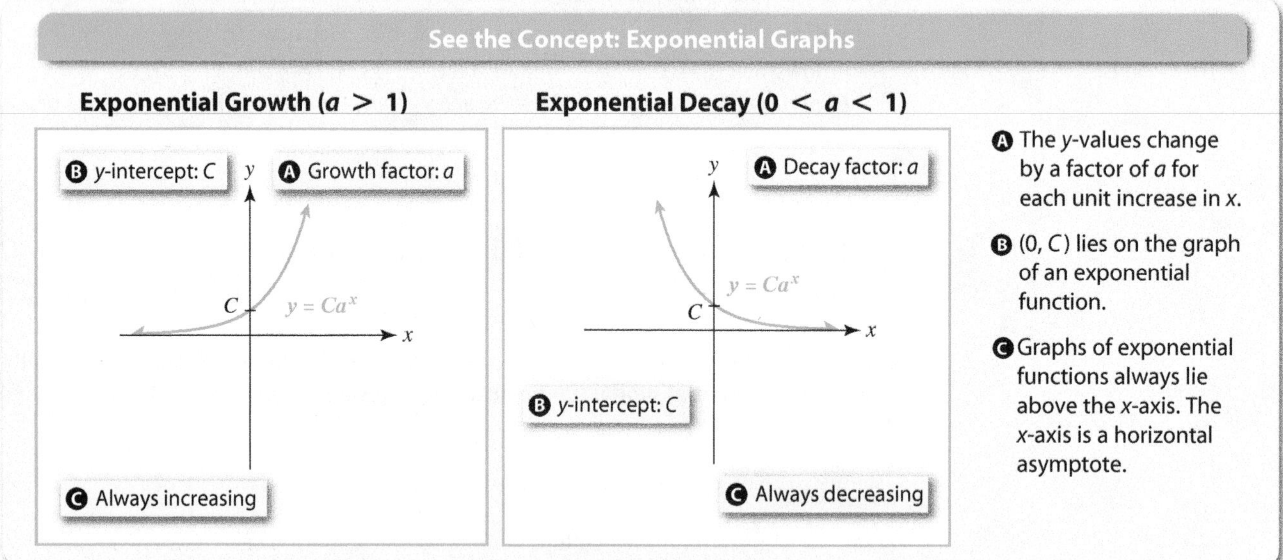

See the Concept: Exponential Graphs
Exponential Growth ($a > 1$)
B y-intercept: C
A Growth factor: a
C
$y = Ca^x$
y
x
C Always increasing
Exponential Decay ($0 < a < 1$)
A Decay factor: a
$y = Ca^x$
C
y
x
B y-intercept: C
C Always decreasing
A The y-values change by a factor of a for each unit increase in x.
B (0, C) lies on the graph of an exponential function.
C Graphs of exponential functions always lie above the x-axis. The x-axis is a horizontal asymptote.

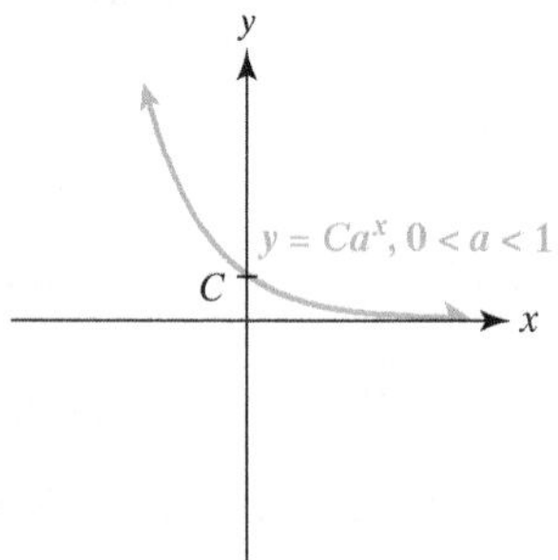

Figure 5.33 Exponential Decay

PROPERTIES OF EXPONENTIAL FUNCTIONS

An *exponential function* f, defined by $f(x) = Ca^x$ with $a > 0$, $a \neq 1$, and $C > 0$, has the following properties.

1. The domain of f is $(-\infty, \infty)$ and the range of f is $(0, \infty)$.
2. The graph of f is continuous with no breaks. The x-axis is a horizontal asymptote. There are no x-intercepts and the y-intercept is C.
3. If $a > 1$, f is increasing on its domain; if $0 < a < 1$, f is decreasing on its domain.
4. f is one-to-one and therefore has an inverse. (See Section 5.4.)

When sunlight enters lake water, its intensity decreases exponentially. In the next example we model this phenomenon.

EXAMPLE 5 Modeling the intensity of sunlight

The intensity I of sunlight at the surface of a polluted pond is 200 watts per square meter. For each 1-foot increase in depth, the intensity of sunlight decreases by a factor of $\frac{4}{5}$.

(a) Estimate the intensity I of sunlight at a depth of 10 feet.

(b) Graph the intensity of sunlight to a depth of 10 feet. Interpret the y-intercept.

SOLUTION

(a) Because the intensity I is decreasing by a constant factor for each 1-foot increase in depth, an exponential model can be use to solve this problem. Let $I(x) = Ca^x$. The initial value is given as $C = 200$. The decay factor is $\frac{4}{5}$ for each 1-foot increase in depth.

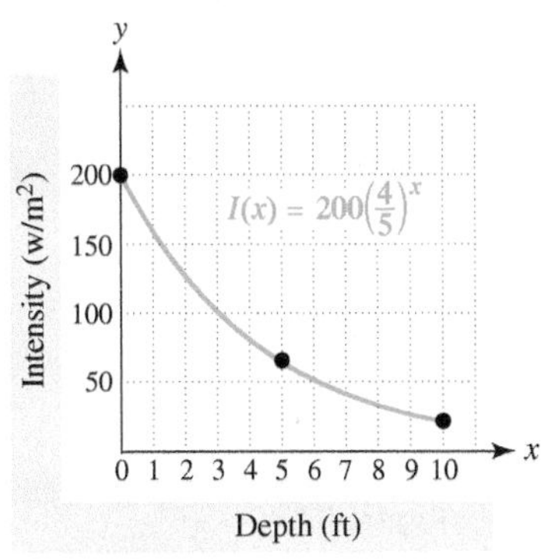

Figure 5.34

If we let x be in feet, then $I(x) = 200\left(\frac{4}{5}\right)^x$. At 10 feet the intensity is

$$I(10) = 200\left(\tfrac{4}{5}\right)^{10} \approx 21.5 \text{ watts per square meter.}$$

(b) The graph of I exhibits exponential decay as in Figure 5.33 when $x \geq 0$. Note that $I(0) = 200$, $I(5) \approx 65.5$, and $I(10) \approx 21.5$. We plot these points and sketch a curve for $0 \leq x \leq 10$, as shown in Figure 5.34.

The y-intercept is 200, which corresponds to both the initial value C and the initial intensity of the sunlight at the surface.

Now Try Exercise 65

In the next example, we model the life spans of a sample of robins.

EXAMPLE 6 Modeling exponential decay

In a study of the life spans of 133 robins, it was found that after 2 years only 19 robins survived.

(a) Find an exponential model f that approximates the number of surviving robins after x years.

(b) Estimate the number of robins after 1.5 years.

(c) Evaluate $f(10)$ and interpret the answer.

SOLUTION

(a) We must determine the initial value C and the decay factor a for $f(x) = Ca^x$. The initial number of robins is 133, so let $C = 133$ and $f(x) = 133a^x$. To determine a, use the fact that $f(2) = 19$.

$$133a^2 = 19 \qquad \text{Let } x = 2.$$

$$a^2 = \frac{19}{133} \qquad \text{Divide each side by 133.}$$

$$a^2 = \frac{1}{7} \qquad \text{Simplify.}$$

$$a = \sqrt{\frac{1}{7}} \qquad \text{Square root property}$$

Thus $f(x) = 133\left(\sqrt{\frac{1}{7}}\right)^x$.

NOTE By the root of the ratio formula, $a = \sqrt[\Delta x]{\frac{y_2}{y_1}} = \sqrt{\frac{19}{133}} = \sqrt{\frac{1}{7}}$

(b) If $x = 1.5$, then $f(1.5) = 133\left(\sqrt{\frac{1}{7}}\right)^{1.5} \approx 31$. This model estimates that 31 robins survived 1.5 years.

(c) Because $f(10) = 133\left(\sqrt{\frac{1}{7}}\right)^{10} \approx 0.0079$, this model is predicting that none of the robins survived 10 years.

NOTE Regardless of how large the value of x, an exponential model continues to give a positive output. We need to interpret that beyond a certain time, none of the robins survive.

Now Try Exercise 66

Graphs of Exponential Functions To investigate further the effect that a has on the graph of an exponential function, we can let $C = 1$ in $f(x) = Ca^x$ and graph $y = 1^x$, $y = 1.3^x$, $y = 1.7^x$, and $y = 2.5^x$, as shown in Figure 5.35. (Note that $f(x) = 1^x$ does *not* represent an exponential function. However, the graph of $y = 1^x$ represents the boundary between exponential growth and decay.) As a increases, the graph of $y = a^x$ increases at a faster rate. On the other hand, the graphs of the equations $y = 0.7^x$, $y = 0.5^x$, and $y = 0.15^x$ decrease faster as a decreases. See Figure 5.36. The graph of $y = a^x$ is **increasing** when $a > 1$ and **decreasing** when $0 < a < 1$. Note that the graph of $y = a^x$, $a > 0$, always passes through the point $(0, 1)$.

Algebra Review
To review properties of exponents, see Chapter R (page R-7) and Section 4.8.

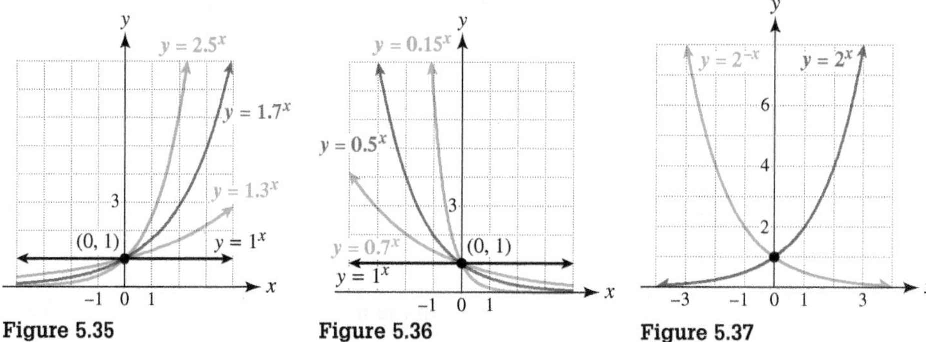

Figure 5.35 Figure 5.36 Figure 5.37

In Section 3.5 we saw that the graph of $y = f(-x)$ is a reflection of the graph of $y = f(x)$ across the y-axis. As a result, the graph of $y = a^{-x}$ is a reflection of $y = a^x$ across the y-axis. For example, the graphs of $y = 2^x$ and $y = 2^{-x}$ are reflections across the y-axis. See Figure 5.37. Note that, by properties of exponents, $2^{-x} = \left(\frac{1}{2}\right)^x$.

MAKING CONNECTIONS

Exponential Functions and Polynomial Functions An exponential function has a *variable* for an exponent, whereas a polynomial function has *constants* for exponents. For example, $f(x) = 3^x$ represents an exponential function, and $g(x) = x^3$ represents a polynomial function.

EXAMPLE 7 Comparing exponential and polynomial functions

Compare $f(x) = 3^x$ and $g(x) = x^3$ graphically and numerically for $x \geq 0$.

SOLUTION

Graphical Comparison The graphs $Y_1 = 3$^X and $Y_2 =$ X^3 are shown in Figure 5.38. For $x \geq 6$, the graph of the exponential function y_1 increases significantly faster than the graph of the polynomial function y_2.

Numerical Comparison Tables for y_1 and y_2 are shown in Figure 5.39. The values for y_1 increase faster than the values for y_2.

[0, 12, 1] by [0, 10000, 1000]

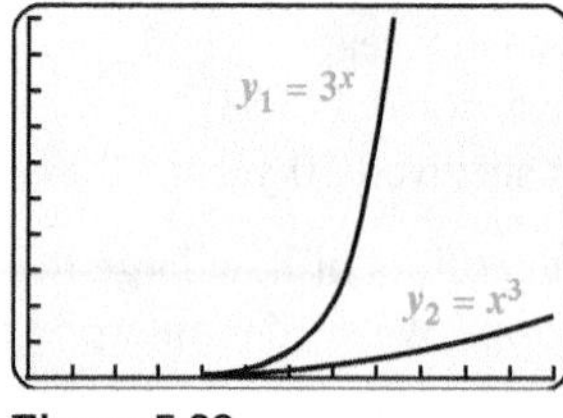

Figure 5.38

X	Y1	Y2
0	1	0
2	9	8
4	81	64
6	729	216
8	6561	512
10	59049	1000
12	531441	1728

X=0

Figure 5.39

Now Try Exercise 29

The results of Example 7 are true in general; that is, for large enough inputs, exponential functions with $a > 1$ eventually become greater than *any* polynomial function.

Exponential Models

Exponential functions have many applications. The next example analyzes the increase in atmospheric carbon dioxide (CO_2). Carbon dioxide is a greenhouse gas.

EXAMPLE 8 Modeling atmospheric CO_2 concentrations

Predicted concentrations of atmospheric carbon dioxide (CO_2) in parts per million (ppm) are shown in Table 5.16. (These concentrations assume that current trends continue.) The CO_2 levels in the year 2000 were greater than they had been at any time in the previous 160,000 years.

Concentrations of Atmospheric CO_2

Year	2000	2050	2100	2150	2200
CO_2 (ppm)	364	467	600	769	987

Table 5.16
Source: R. Turner, *Environmental Economics.*

(a) Let $x = 0$ correspond to 2000 and $x = 200$ to 2200. Use an exponential model f to model these data.
(b) Estimate CO_2 concentrations for the year 2025.
(c) How are the initial value of f and the y-intercept on the graph of f related?

SOLUTION

(a) Getting Started When modeling data by hand with the exponential model $f(x) = Ca^x$, one strategy is to let C equal $f(0)$. Then substitute a data point into this formula and find a. ▶

The concentration is 364 when $x = 0$, so $C = 364$. This gives $f(x) = 364a^x$. One possibility for determining a is to use the last data point and require that the graph of f pass through the point (200, 987). It then follows that $f(200) = 987$.

$$364a^{200} = 987 \qquad f(200) = 987$$

$$a^{200} = \frac{987}{364} \qquad \text{Divide by 364.}$$

$$(a^{200})^{1/200} = \left(\frac{987}{364}\right)^{1/200} \qquad \text{Take the } \tfrac{1}{200}\text{th power.}$$

$$a = \left(\frac{987}{364}\right)^{1/200} \qquad \text{Properties of exponents}$$

$$a \approx 1.005 \qquad \text{Approximate.}$$

Thus $f(x) = 364(1.005)^x$. Answers for $f(x)$ may vary slightly.

(b) Since 2025 corresponds to $x = 25$, evaluate $f(25)$.

$$f(25) = 364(1.005)^{25} \approx 412$$

Concentration of CO_2 could reach 412 ppm by 2025.

(c) The y-intercept is $f(0) = 364$ and is equal to the initial value $C = 364$ because $f(0) = C$ for an exponential function.

Now Try Exercise 67

EXAMPLE 9 **Modeling the half-life of a Facebook link**

Initially a link on Facebook has had no hits, so 100% of its hits are yet to occur. Write an exponential function F that gives the percentage of engagements yet to occur on a typical Facebook link if its half-life is 3 hours. Estimate this percentage after 4 hours.

SOLUTION

Let $F(t) = Ca^t$, where t is time in hours. Initially $F(0) = 100$, so $C = 100$ and $F(t) = 100a^t$. Next we must find the value of a. Because the half-life is 3 hours, 50% of the hits remain to occur after 3 hours, so $F(3) = 50$.

$$\begin{aligned} 100a^3 &= 50 && F(3) = 50 \\ a^3 &= \tfrac{1}{2} && \text{Divide each side by 100.} \\ (a^3)^{1/3} &= \left(\tfrac{1}{2}\right)^{1/3} && \text{Take the cube root of each side.} \\ a &= \left(\tfrac{1}{2}\right)^{1/3} && \text{Simplify.} \end{aligned}$$

Thus we can write $F(t)$ as

$$F(t) = 100\left(\left(\tfrac{1}{2}\right)^{1/3}\right)^t = 100\left(\tfrac{1}{2}\right)^{t/3}.$$

After 4 hours,

$$F(4) = 100\left(\tfrac{1}{2}\right)^{4/3} \approx 40\%.$$

The link has about 40% of its total hits remaining while 60% have already occurred. Note that 4 hours is more than the half-life of 3 hours, so $F(4)$ is less than 50%.

Now Try Exercise 77

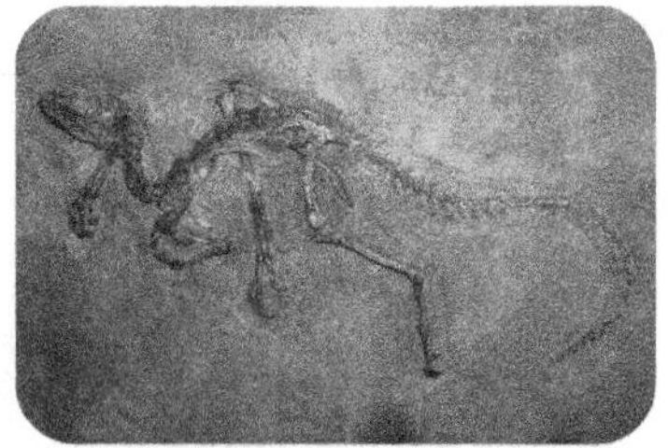

Radioactive Decay Radioactivity is an application of exponential decay. When an element such as uranium undergoes radioactive decay, atoms change from one element to another. The time it takes for half of the atoms to decay into a different element is called the **half-life**, and this time varies for different elements. Radioactive carbon-14, which is found in all living things, has a half-life of about 5700 years and can be used to date fossils.

If the initial amount of carbon-14 equals C grams, then $f(x) = Ca^x$ models the amount of carbon-14 present after x years, where a needs to be determined for carbon-14. After 5700 years, there will be $\frac{1}{2}C$ grams, so $f(5700) = \frac{1}{2}C$ implies that

$$Ca^{5700} = \frac{1}{2}C.$$

To solve this equation for a, begin by dividing each side by C.

$$\begin{aligned} a^{5700} &= \frac{1}{2} && \text{Divide each side by } C. \\ (a^{5700})^{1/5700} &= \left(\frac{1}{2}\right)^{1/5700} && \text{Raise to the } \tfrac{1}{5700}\text{th power.} \\ a &= \left(\frac{1}{2}\right)^{1/5700} && \text{Properties of exponents} \end{aligned}$$

Using properties of exponents, we write $f(x) = Ca^x$ as

$$f(x) = C\left(\left(\frac{1}{2}\right)^{1/5700}\right)^x = C\left(\frac{1}{2}\right)^{x/5700}.$$

This discussion is summarized in the following box.

MODELING HALF-LIFE

If a quantity initially equals C and has a half-life of k years, then the amount A remaining after time t is given by

$$A(t) = C\left(\frac{1}{2}\right)^{t/k}.$$

The half-life of radium-226 is about 1600 years. After 9600 years, a 2-gram sample decays to

$$A(9600) = 2\left(\frac{1}{2}\right)^{9600/1600} = 0.03125 \text{ gram.}$$

EXAMPLE 10 Finding the age of a fossil

A fossil contains 5% of the amount of carbon-14 that the organism contained when it was alive. Graphically estimate its age. The situation is illustrated in Figure 5.40.

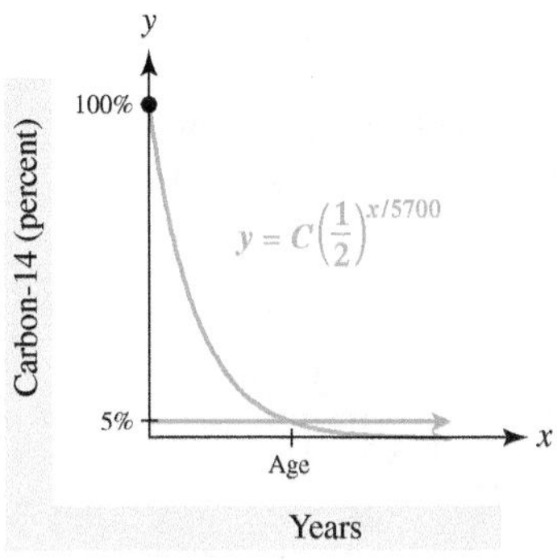

Figure 5.40

SOLUTION The initial amount of carbon-14 is 100% (or 1), the final amount is 5% (or 0.05), and the half-life is 5700 years, so $A = 0.05$, $C = 1$, and $k = 5700$ in $A(x) = C\left(\frac{1}{2}\right)^{x/k}$. To determine the age of the fossil, solve

$$0.05 = 1\left(\frac{1}{2}\right)^{x/5700}$$

for x. Graph $Y_1 = 0.05$ and $Y_2 = 0.5$^(X/5700), as shown in Figure 5.41. Their graphs intersect near (24635, 0.05), so the fossil is about 24,635 years old.

[0, 50000, 10000] by [0, 0.1, 0.01]

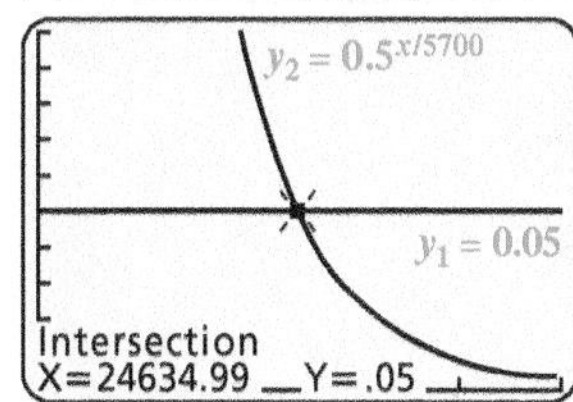

Figure 5.41

NOTE In Figure 5.40 the y-intercept is equal to 100%, or 1 in decimal form, and so $C = 1$. That is, the initial value for $f(x)$ corresponds to the y-intercept on the graph of $y = f(x)$.

Now Try Exercise 69

5.3 Putting It All Together (Part I)

The following table summarizes some important concepts about exponential functions and types of growth and decay.

<table>
<tr><th>CONCEPT</th><th>COMMENTS</th><th>EXAMPLES</th></tr>
<tr><td>Exponential function (model)

$f(x) = Ca^x$,

where $a > 0$, $a \neq 1$, and $C > 0$</td><td>Exponential growth occurs when $a > 1$, and exponential decay occurs when $0 < a < 1$. C often represents the initial amount present because $f(0) = C$.

The y-intercept on the graph of f equals the initial amount C because $f(0) = C$.</td><td>$f(x) = 5(0.8)^x$ Decay
$g(x) = 3^x$ Growth

Decay: $0 < a < 1$
Growth: $a > 1$</td></tr>
<tr><td>Linear growth

$y = mx + b$</td><td>If data increase by a fixed amount m for each unit increase in x, they can be modeled by a linear function.</td><td>The following data can be modeled by $f(x) = 3x + 2$ because the data increase 3 units for each unit increase in x and because $y = 2$ when $x = 0$.

<table><tr><td>x</td><td>0</td><td>1</td><td>2</td><td>3</td></tr><tr><td>y</td><td>2</td><td>5</td><td>8</td><td>11</td></tr></table>+3 +3 +3</td></tr>
<tr><td>Exponential growth

$y = Ca^x$</td><td>If data increase by a constant factor a for each unit increase in x, they can be modeled by an exponential function.</td><td>The following data can be modeled by $f(x) = 2(3)^x$ because the data increase by a factor of 3 for each unit increase in x and because $y = 2$ when $x = 0$.

<table><tr><td>x</td><td>0</td><td>1</td><td>2</td><td>3</td></tr><tr><td>y</td><td>2</td><td>6</td><td>18</td><td>54</td></tr></table>×3 ×3 ×3</td></tr>
<tr><td>Radioactive decay</td><td>If a radioactive sample has a half-life of k years and contains C units, then the amount A remaining after x years is given by

$$A(x) = C\left(\frac{1}{2}\right)^{x/k}.$$</td><td>A 5-gram sample of radioactive material with a half-life of 300 years is modeled by

$$A(x) = 5\left(\frac{1}{2}\right)^{x/300}.$$</td></tr>
</table>

5.3 Exercises (Part I)

Exponents

Exercises 1–12: Simplify the expression without a calculator.

1. 2^{-3}
2. $(-3)^{-2}$
3. $3(4)^{1/2}$
4. $5\left(\frac{1}{2}\right)^{-3}$
5. $-2(27)^{2/3}$
6. $-4(8)^{-2/3}$
7. $4^{1/6}4^{1/3}$
8. $\frac{9^{5/6}}{9^{1/3}}$
9. 3^0
10. $5\left(\frac{3}{4}\right)^0$
11. $(5^{101})^{1/101}$
12. $(8^{27})^{1/27}$

Linear and Exponential Growth

Exercises 13–22: Linear and Exponential Models (Refer to Example 1.) Find either a linear or an exponential function that models the data in the table.

13.

x	0	1	2	3	4
y	2	0.8	−0.4	−1.6	−2.8

14.

x	0	1	2	3	4
y	2	8	32	128	512

15.

x	−3	−2	−1	0	1
y	64	32	16	8	4

16.

x	−2	−1	0	1	2
y	3	5.5	8	10.5	13

17.

x	−4	−2	0	2	4
y	0.3125	1.25	5	20	80

18.

x	−15	−5	5	15	25
y	22	24	26	28	30

19.

x	−6	−2	2	6
y	−23	−9	5	19

20.

x	−2	3	5	8
y	$\frac{3}{4}$	24	96	768

21.

x	−4	−1	2	5
y	6561	243	9	$\frac{1}{3}$

22.

x	−20	−4	16	36
y	246	234	219	204

Exercises 23–28: (Refer to Example 2) Find a linear function f and an exponential function g whose graphs pass through the two given points.

23. $(0, 4), (1, 8)$
24. $\left(0, \frac{3}{2}\right), (1, 2)$
25. $(-2, 12), (1, 1.5)$
26. $(1, 3), (5, 48)$
27. $(-2, 9), (2, 1)$
28. $(-2, 1), (4, 8)$

29. *Comparing Growth* Which function becomes larger for $0 \le x \le 10$: $f(x) = 2^x$ or $g(x) = x^2$?

30. *Comparing Growth* Which function becomes larger for $0 \le x \le 10$: $f(x) = 4 + 3x$ or $g(x) = 4(3)^x$?

31. *Comparing Growth* Which function becomes larger for $0 \le x \le 10$: $f(x) = 2x + 1$ or $g(x) = 2^{-x}$?

32. *Salaries* If you were offered 1¢ for the first week of work, 3¢ for the second week, 5¢ for the third week, 7¢ for the fourth week, and so on for a year, would you accept the offer? Would you accept an offer that pays 1¢ for the first week of work, 2¢ for the second week, 4¢ for the third week, 8¢ for the fourth week, and so on for a year? Explain your answers.

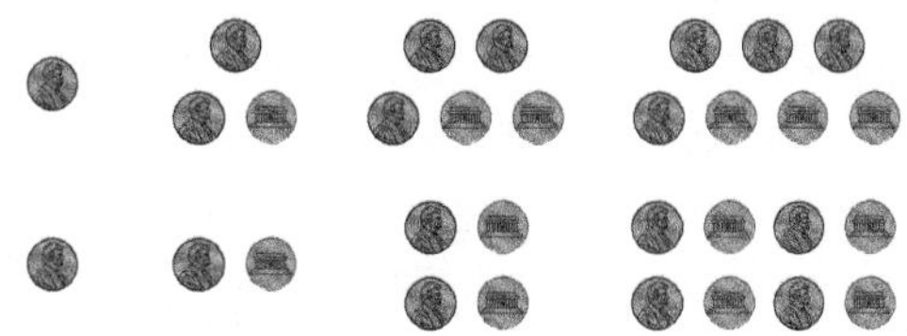

Exponential Functions

Exercises 33–40: Find C and a so that $f(x) = Ca^x$ satisfies the given conditions.

33. $f(0) = 5$ and for each unit increase in x, the output is multiplied by the constant factor 1.5.

34. $f(1) = 3$ and for each unit increase in x, the output is multiplied by the constant factor $\frac{3}{4}$.

35. $f(0) = 10$ and $f(1) = 20$

36. $f(0) = 7$ and $f(-1) = 1$

37. $f(1) = 9$ and $f(2) = 27$

38. $f(-1) = \frac{1}{4}$ and $f(1) = 4$

39. $f(-2) = \frac{9}{2}$ and $f(2) = \frac{1}{18}$

40. $f(-2) = \frac{3}{4}$ and $f(2) = 12$

Exercises 41–44: Find an exponential model that models the situation described. State what the variable x represents in your model. (Answers may vary.)

41. There are initially 5000 bacteria, and this sample doubles in size every hour.

42. Fifteen hundred dollars is deposited in an account that triples in value every decade.

43. In 2000 a house was worth \$200,000, and its value *decreases* by a constant factor of 0.95 each year thereafter.

44. A fish population is initially 6000 and decreases by half each year.

45. *Tire Pressure* The pressure in a tire with a leak is 30 pounds per square inch initially and can be modeled by $f(x) = 30(0.9)^x$ after x minutes. What is the tire's pressure after 9.5 minutes?

46. *Population* The population of California was about 38 million in 2007 and is increasing by a constant factor of 1.016 each year. Estimate the population of California in 2012.

Graphs of Exponential Functions

Exercises 47–54: Sketch a graph of $y = f(x)$.

47. $f(x) = 2^x$

48. $f(x) = 4^x$

49. $f(x) = 3^{-x}$

50. $f(x) = 3(2^{-x})$

51. $f(x) = 2\left(\frac{1}{3}\right)^x$

52. $f(x) = 2(3^x)$

53. $f(x) = \left(\frac{1}{2}\right)^x$

54. $f(x) = \left(\frac{1}{4}\right)^x$

Exercises 55–58: Use the graph of the exponential model to determine values for C and a.

55.

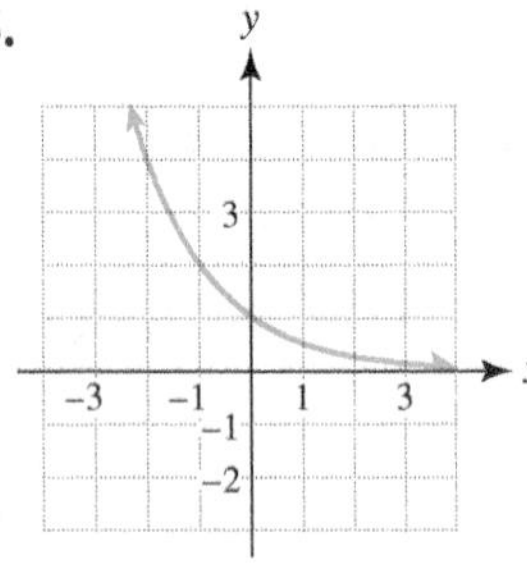

56.

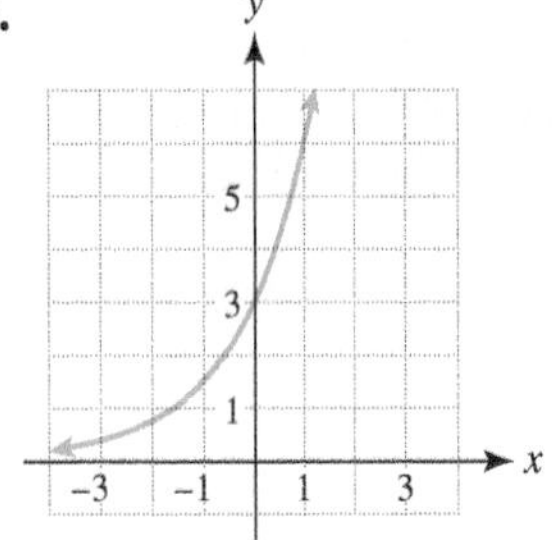

57.

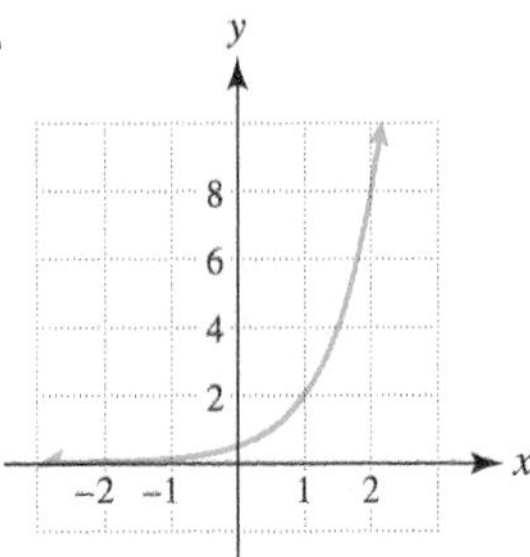

58.

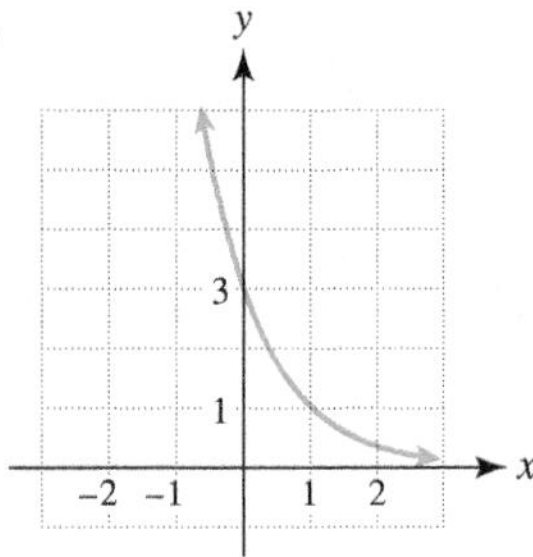

59. Let $f(x) = 7\left(\frac{1}{8}\right)^x$.

(a) What are the domain and range of f?

(b) Is f either increasing or decreasing on its domain?

(c) Find any asymptotes on the graph of f.

(d) Find any x- or y-intercepts on the graph of f.

(e) Is f a one-to-one function? Does f have an inverse?

60. Repeat Exercise 59 with $f(x) = 2^x$.

61. Match the symbolic representation of f with its graphical representation (a–d). Do *not* use a calculator.

(i) $f(x) = 2.7^x$ **(ii)** $f(x) = 3^{-x}$

(iii) $f(x) = 1.5^x$ **(iv)** $f(x) = 0.99^x$

a.

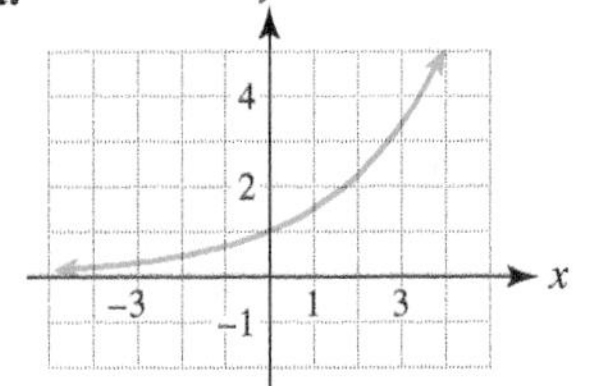

b.

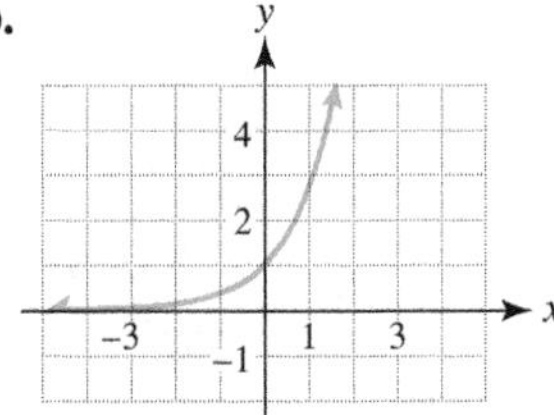

c.

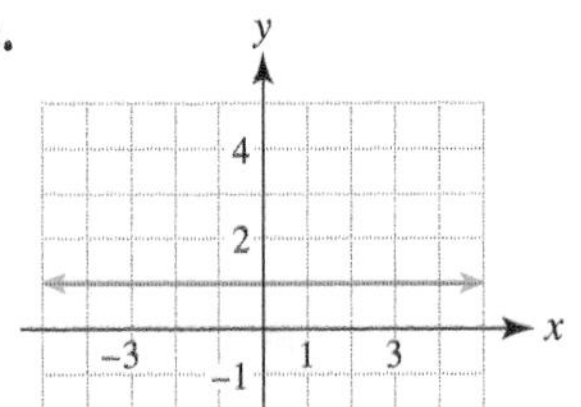

d.

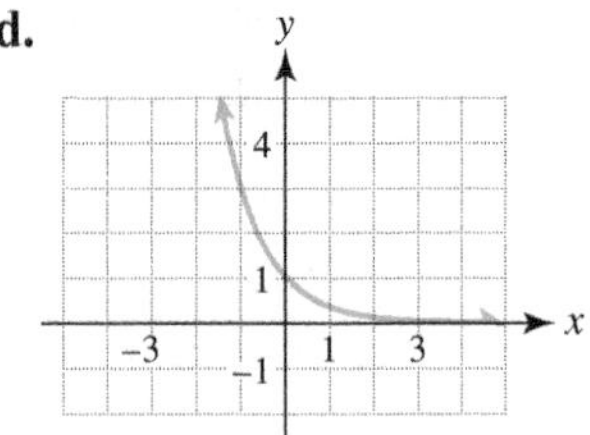

62. Complete the following for an exponential model f.

(a) Give a general formula for f.

(b) Give the initial value and the growth (or decay) factor for your formula in part (a).

(c) How are the y-intercept for the graph of f and the initial value related?

Applications

63. Bacteria Growth A sample of bacteria taken from a river has an initial concentration of 2.5 million bacteria per milliliter and its concentration triples each week.

(a) Find an exponential model that calculates the concentration in millions of bacteria per milliliter after x weeks.

(b) Estimate the concentration after 1.5 weeks.

64. Fish Population A fish population in a small lake is estimated to be 6000. Due to a change in water quality, this population is decreasing by half each year.

(a) Find an exponential model that approximates the number of fish in the lake after x years.

(b) Estimate the fish population to nearest hundred after 3.5 years.

65. Intensity of Sunlight (Refer to Example 5) The intensity I of sunlight at the surface of a lake is 300 watts per square meter. For each 1-foot increase in depth of a lake, the intensity of sunlight decreases by a factor of $\frac{9}{10}$.

(a) Estimate the intensity I of sunlight at a depth of 50 feet.

(b) Graph the intensity of sunlight to a depth of 50 feet. Interpret the y-intercept.

66. Life Spans of Rabbits (Refer to Example 6) From a sample of 198 rabbits, it was found that after 2 years only 88 rabbits survived.

(a) Find an exponential model f that approximates the number of surviving rabbits after x years.

(b) Estimate the number of rabbits after 3.5 years.

67. Greenhouse Gases (Refer to Example 8). Chlorofluorocarbons (CFCs) are gases created by people that increase the greenhouse effect and damage the ozone layer. The following table lists future concentrations of CFC-12 in parts per billion (ppb) if current trends continue.

Year	2000	2005	2010	2015	2020
CFC-12 (ppb)	0.72	0.88	1.07	1.31	1.60

Source: R. Turner, Environmental Economics.

(a) Find values for C and a so that an exponential function models these data, where x is years after 2000.

(b) Estimate the CFC-12 concentration in 2013.

68. Bacteria Growth The table lists the concentration in a sample of *E. coli* bacteria B (in billions per liter) after x hours.

x	0	3	5	8
B	0.5	6.2	33.3	414

Source: G. S. Stent, *Molecular Biology of Bacterial Viruses.*

(a) Find values for C and a so that an exponential function models these data.

(b) Estimate the bacteria concentration after 6.2 hours.

69. Radioactive Carbon-14 (Refer to Example 10.) A fossil contains 10% of the carbon-14 that the organism contained when it was alive. Graphically estimate its age.

70. Radioactive Carbon-14 A fossil contains 20% of the carbon-14 that the organism contained when it was alive. Estimate its age.

71. Radioactive Radium-226 The half-life of radium-226 is about 1600 years. After 3000 years, what percentage P of a sample of radium remains?

72. Radioactive Strontium-90 Radioactive strontium-90 has a half-life of about 28 years and sometimes contaminates the soil. After 50 years, what percentage of a sample of radioactive strontium would remain?

73. Swimming Pool Maintenance Chlorine is frequently used to disinfect swimming pools. The chlorine concentration should remain between 1.5 and 2.5 parts per million. On warm sunny days with many swimmers agitating the water, $\frac{3}{10}$ of the chlorine can dissipate into the air or combine with other chemicals. (**Source:** D. Thomas, *Swimming Pool Operators Handbook.*)

(a) Find C and a so that an exponential function models the amount of chlorine in the pool after x days. Assume that the initial amount is 2.5 parts per million.

(b) What is the chlorine concentration after 2 days if no chlorine is added?

(c) Estimate graphically or numerically the number of days before chlorine should be added.

74. Thickness of Runways Heavier aircraft require runways with thicker pavement for landings and takeoffs. A pavement 6 inches thick can accommodate an aircraft weighing 80,000 pounds, whereas a 12-inch-thick pavement is necessary for a 350,000-pound plane. The relation between pavement thickness t in inches and gross weight W in thousands of pounds can be described by an exponential model. (**Source:** FAA.)

(a) Find values for C and a.

(b) How heavy an airplane can a 9-inch-thick runway accommodate?

(c) What is the minimum thickness for a 242,000-pound plane?

75. Trains The faster a locomotive travels, the more horsepower is needed. The formula $H(x) = 0.157(1.033)^x$ calculates this horsepower for a level track. The input x is in miles per hour and the output $H(x)$ is the horsepower required per ton of cargo. (**Source:** L. Haefner, *Introduction to Transportation Systems.*)
   (a) Evaluate $H(30)$ and interpret the result.

   (b) Determine the horsepower needed to move a 5000-ton train 30 miles per hour.

   (c) Some types of locomotives are rated for 1350 horsepower. How many locomotives of this type would be needed in part (b)?

76. Survival of Reindeer For all types of animals, the percentage that survive into the next year decreases. In one study, the survival rate of a sample of reindeer was modeled by $S(t) = 100(0.999993)^{t^5}$. The function S outputs the percentage of reindeer that survive t years. (**Source:** D. Brown.)
   (a) Evaluate $S(4)$ and $S(15)$. Interpret the results.

   (b) Graph S in [0, 15, 5] by [0, 110, 10]. Interpret the graph. Does the graph have a horizontal asymptote?

77. **Half-Life for Twitter** (Refer to Example 9.) The half-life for a link on Twitter is 2.8 hours. Write an exponential function T that gives the percentage of engagements remaining on a typical Twitter link after t hours. Estimate this percentage after 5.5 hours.

78. **Half-Life for StumbleUpon** (Refer to Example 9.) The half-life for a link on StumbleUpon is 400 hours. Write an exponential function S that gives the percentage of engagements remaining on a typical StumbleUpon link after t hours. Estimate this percentage after 250 hours.

79. **Putts and Pros** At a distance of 3 feet, professional golfers make about 95% of their putts. For each additional foot of distance, this percentage decreases by a factor of 0.9.
   (a) Write an exponential function P that gives the percentage of putts pros make at a distance of x feet beyond a 3-foot distance.

   (b) Estimate this percentage for 23 feet ($x = 20$).

   (c) What additional distance decreases this percentage by half?

80. **Putts and Amateurs** Suppose that at a distance of 3 feet, a group of amateur golfers make about 85% of their putts, and for each additional foot of distance, this percentage decreases by a factor of 0.7.
   (a) Write an exponential function A that gives the percentage of putts these amateurs make at a distance of x feet beyond a 3-foot distance.

   (b) Estimate this percentage at 10 feet ($x = 7$).

   (c) What additional distance decreases this percentage by half?

Exercises 81–86: Growth and Decay Models If an initial quantity A_0 either grows or decays by a factor of b each k units of time, then the amount A after t units of time is given by the exponential model

$$A(t) = A_0 b^{t/k}.$$

For example, if 700 bacteria triple every 5 days, the formula

$$A(t) = 700(3)^{t/5}$$

models their growth after t days. Write a formula that models the situation and then answer the question.

81. A sample of 1000 bacteria triples in number every 7 hours. How many bacteria are there after 11 hours?

82. A sample of 5 million insects decreases by a factor of $\frac{2}{3}$ every 10 days. In millions, how many insects are there after 65 days?

83. The intensity I_0 of a light passing through colored glass decreases by a factor of $\frac{1}{3}$ for each 2 millimeters in thickness of the glass. What is the intensity of the light in terms of I_0 after passing through 4.3 millimeters of colored glass.

84. The intensity I_0 of a sound passing through the atmosphere decreases by 80% for each 100 feet of distance. What is the intensity of the sound in terms of I_0 after traveling a distance of 450 feet.

85. An investment of $5000 will quadruple every 35 years. How much is the investment worth after 8 years?

86. An investment of $2500 increases by a factor of 1.2 every 4 years. How much is the investment worth after 9 years?

Writing about Mathematics

87. Explain how linear and exponential functions differ. Give examples.

88. Discuss the domain and range of an exponential function f. Is f one-to-one? Explain.

5.3 Exponential Functions and Models (Part II)

- **Relate exponential functions to constant percent change**
- **Calculate compound interest**
- **Model with natural exponential functions**
- **Solve applications**

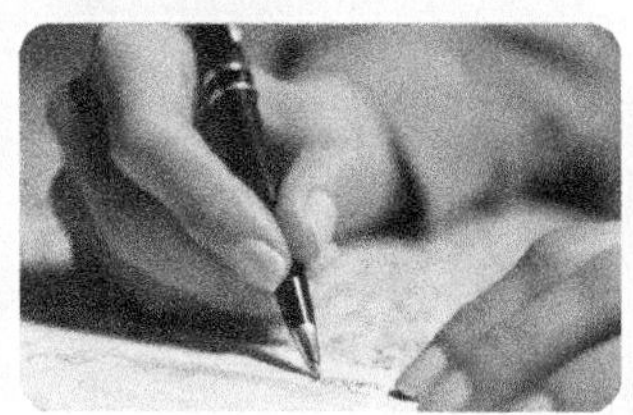

Introduction

Suppose that we deposit \$500 into a savings account that pays 2% annual interest. If none of the money or interest is withdrawn, then the account increases in value by 2% each year. In general, when an amount A changes by a constant percent over each fixed time period, such as a year or a month, then the growth (or possibly decay) in A can be described by an exponential model. In this section we relate the concept of constant percent change to exponential models.

Exponential Functions and Constant Percent Change

Section 5.3 (Part I) discussed how an exponential function results when the *initial value C* is multiplied by a *constant factor a* for each unit increase in x. For example, if an initial value of $C = 3$ is multiplied by a *constant growth factor* of $a = 2$ for each unit increase in x, then the exponential function

$$f(x) = 3(2)^x \qquad \text{Initial value} = 3,\ \text{growth factor} = 2$$

models this growth. This concept can be used to describe exponential functions and models in terms of *constant percent change, r.*

Suppose that an initial population of a country is $P_0 = 10$ million and the population increases by 1.2% in 1 year. Then the increase is

$$rP_0 = 0.012(10) = 0.12 \text{ million.} \qquad 1.2\% \text{ equals } 0.012 \text{ in decimal form.}$$

and after 1 year the new population is

$$P_0(1 + r)^1 = 10(1.012)^1 = 10.12 \text{ million.}$$

After 1 year the population has increased by a *growth factor* of $1 + r$, or 1.012. If the rate of growth were to remain constant in future years, then after x years the population in millions would be

$$P_0(1 + r)^x = 10(1.012)^x.$$

In summary, if a population of 10 million experiences a 1.2% increase each year, then the population P in millions after x years is given by the exponential model

$$P(x) = 10(1.012)^x$$

with initial value $C = 10$ and growth factor $a = 1.012$.

EXAMPLE 1 **Finding exponential models**

A sample of 10,000 insects is decreasing in number by 8% per week. Find an exponential model f that describes this population after x weeks.

SOLUTION The initial value is $C = 10{,}000$, the rate of decrease is $r = -0.08$, and the decay factor is

$$a = 1 + r = 1 + (-0.08) = 0.92.$$

Thus the sample of insects contains

$$f(x) = 10{,}000(0.92)^x$$

insects after x weeks.

Now Try Exercise 1

These concepts are summarized in the following box.

PERCENT CHANGE AND EXPONENTIAL FUNCTIONS

Suppose that an amount A changes by a given rate r (or percent expressed in decimal form) for each unit increase in x. Then the following hold.

1. If $r > 0$, the **constant growth factor** is $a = 1 + r$ and $a > 1$.
2. If $r < 0$, the **constant decay factor** is $a = 1 + r$ and $0 < a < 1$.
3. If the initial amount is C, then the amount A after an x-unit increase in time is given by the exponential model

$$A(x) = C(1 + r)^x, \quad \text{or} \quad A(x) = Ca^x.$$

EXAMPLE 2 Analyzing constant percent change

For each $f(x)$, give the initial value, the growth or decay factor, and percent change for each unit increase in x.

(a) $f(x) = 5(1.034)^x$ **(b)** $f(x) = 10(0.45)^x$ **(c)** $f(x) = 3^x$

SOLUTION

(a) For $f(x) = 5(1.034)^x$ the initial value is $C = 5$ and the growth factor is $a = 1.034$. Because $a = 1 + r$, it follows that

$$r = a - 1 = 1.034 - 1 = 0.034.$$

The percent change for each unit increase in x is 3.4%

(b) For $f(x) = 10(0.45)^x$ the initial value is $C = 10$ and the decay factor is $a = 0.45$. The percent change for each unit increase in x is

$$r = a - 1 = 0.45 - 1 = -0.55, \text{ or } -55\%.$$

(c) For $f(x) = 3^x$ the initial value is $C = 1$ and the growth factor is $a = 3$. The percent change for each unit increase in x is $r = a - 1 = 3 - 1 = 2$, or 200%.

Now Try Exercises 7, 9 and 11

Compound Interest

We can use our knowledge about exponential functions and constant percent change to calculate interest earned on deposits. For example, suppose \$1000 is deposited in an account paying 10% annual interest. The growth factor is

$$a = 1 + r = 1 + 0.10 = 1.10,$$

and the amount in the account after 1 year is $1000(1.10) = \$1100$. If the interest rate remains constant in the future, then the amount A in the account after t years will be $A = 1000(1.10)^t$ dollars. For example, after 3 years there would be

$$A = 1000(1.10)^3 = \$1331.$$

This type of interest is said to be *compounded annually*, because it is paid once a year. If the interest rate is r, *expressed in decimal form*, then the amount A after t years is

$$A = P(1 + r)^t.$$

Notice that the formula $A = P(1 + r)^t$ represents an exponential model with initial value P, growth factor $1 + r$, and annual percent change r in decimal form.

EXAMPLE 3 Calculating an account balance

If the principal is \$2000 and the interest rate is 8% compounded annually, calculate the account balance after 4 years.

SOLUTION The principal is $P = 2000$, the interest rate is $r = 0.08$, and the number of years is $t = 4$.

$$A = P(1 + r)^t = 2000(1 + 0.08)^4 \approx 2720.98$$

After 4 years, the account contains \$2720.98.

Now Try Exercise 25

In most savings accounts, interest is paid more often than once a year. In this case a smaller amount of interest is paid more frequently. For example, suppose \$1000 is deposited in an account paying 10% annual interest, compounded quarterly. After 3 months, the interest would amount to one-fourth of 10%, or 2.5%, of \$1000. The account balance would be $1000(1 + 0.025) = \$1025$. After the next 3-month period, interest would be paid on the \$1025. In a manner similar to that used for annual compounding, the balance would be $\$1000(1 + 0.025)^2 \approx \$1050.63$ after 6 months, $\$1000(1 + 0.025)^3 \approx \$1076.89$ after 9 months, and $\$1000(1 + 0.025)^4 \approx \$1103.81$ after a year. With annual compounding the amount is \$1100. The difference of \$3.81 is due to compounding quarterly. Although this amount is small after 1 year, compounding more frequently can have a dramatic effect over a long time.

COMPOUND INTEREST

If a principal of P dollars is deposited in an account paying an annual rate of interest r (expressed in decimal form) compounded (paid) n times per year, then after t years the account will contain A dollars, where

$$A = P\left(1 + \frac{r}{n}\right)^{nt}.$$

EXAMPLE 4 **Comparing compound interest**

Suppose \$1000 is deposited by a 20-year-old worker in an Individual Retirement Account (IRA) that pays an annual interest rate of 12%. Describe the effect on the balance after 45 years at age 65 if interest were compounded quarterly rather than annually.

SOLUTION

Compounded Annually Let $P = 1000$, $r = 0.12$, $n = 1$, and $t = 65 - 20 = 45$.

$$A = P\left(1 + \frac{r}{n}\right)^{nt} = 1000(1 + 0.12)^{45} \approx \$163{,}987.60$$

Compounded Quarterly Let $P = 1000$, $r = 0.12$, $n = 4$, and $t = 45$.

$$A = 1000\left(1 + \frac{0.12}{4}\right)^{4(45)} = 1000(1 + 0.03)^{180} \approx \$204{,}503.36$$

Quarterly compounding results in an increase of \$40,515.76!

Now Try Exercise 33

CLASS DISCUSSION

Make a conjecture about the effect on the IRA balance after 45 years if the interest rate in Example 4 were 6% instead of 12%. Test your conjecture.

The Natural Exponential Function

In Example 4, compounding interest quarterly rather than annually made a significant difference in the balance after 45 years. What would happen if interest were compounded daily or even hourly? Would there be a limit to the amount of interest that could be earned? To answer these questions, suppose \$1 was deposited in an account at the very high interest rate of 100%. Table 5.17 shows the amount of money after 1 year, compounding n times during the year. The first column represents the time interval between compound interest payments. In Table 5.17, the formula $A = P\left(1 + \frac{r}{n}\right)^{nt}$ simplifies to $A = \left(1 + \frac{1}{n}\right)^n$, since

$P = t = r = 1$. Notice that A levels off near \$2.72. The graph $y = \left(1 + \frac{1}{x}\right)^x$ is shown in Figure 5.42. The graph approaches the horizontal asymptote $y \approx 2.7183$. This means that the y-values never exceed the value of about 2.7183.

Table 5.17

Time	n	A
Year	1	2.000000
Month	12	2.613035
Day	365	2.714567
Hour	8760	2.718127
Minute	525,600	2.718279
Second	31,536,000	2.718282

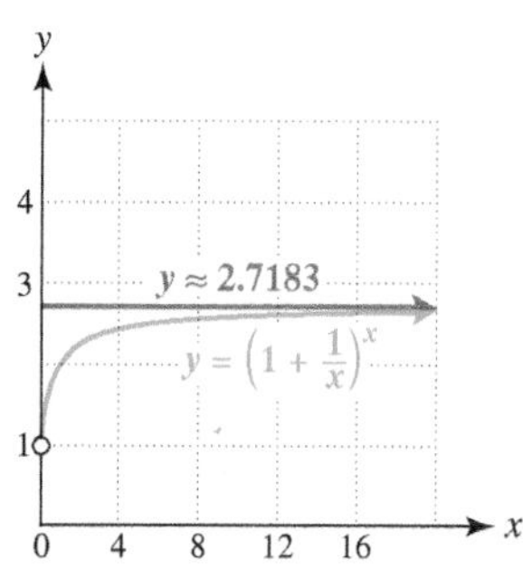

Figure 5.42

Compounding that is done more frequently, by letting n become large without bound, is called **continuous compounding**. The exponential expression $\left(1 + \frac{1}{n}\right)^n$ reaches a limit of approximately 2.718281828 as $n \rightarrow \infty$. This value is so important in mathematics that it has been given its own symbol, e, sometimes called **Euler's number**. Furthermore it follows that

$$\left(1 + \frac{1}{x}\right)^x \rightarrow e \quad \text{as} \quad x \rightarrow \infty.$$

The number e has many of the same characteristics as π. Its decimal expansion never terminates or repeats in a pattern. It is an irrational number.

VALUE OF *E*

To eleven decimal places, $e \approx 2.71828182846$.

Continuous compounding can be applied to population growth. Compounding annually would mean that all births and deaths occurred on December 31. Similarly, compounding quarterly would mean that births and deaths occurred at the end of March, June, September, and December. In large populations, births and deaths occur *continuously* throughout the year. Compounding continuously is a *natural* way to model large populations.

Calculator Help

When evaluating e^x, be sure to use the built-in key for e^x, rather than using an approximation for e, such as 2.72.

THE NATURAL EXPONENTIAL FUNCTION

The function f, represented by $f(x) = e^x$, is the **natural exponential function.**

```
e^(1)
         2.718281828
e^(.5)
         1.648721271
e^(-2.56)
         .0773047404
```

Figure 5.43

EXAMPLE 5 **Evaluating the natural exponential function**

Approximate to four decimal places $f(x) = e^x$ when $x = 1, 0.5$, and -2.56.

SOLUTION In Figure 5.43 these values are approximated as follows: $f(1) = e^1 \approx 2.7183$, $f(0.5) = e^{0.5} \approx 1.6487$, and $f(-2.56) = e^{-2.56} \approx 0.0773$.

Now Try Exercise 17

To derive the formula for continuous compounding, we begin with the compound interest formula,

$$A = P\left(1 + \frac{r}{n}\right)^{nt}.$$

Let $k = \frac{n}{r}$. Then $n = rk$, and with these substitutions, the formula becomes

$$A = P\left(1 + \frac{1}{k}\right)^{rkt} = P\left[\left(1 + \frac{1}{k}\right)^{k}\right]^{rt}.$$

If $n \rightarrow \infty$, $k \rightarrow \infty$ as well, and the expression $\left(1 + \frac{1}{k}\right)^k \rightarrow e$, as discussed earlier. This leads to the formula $A = Pe^{rt}$.

CONTINUOUSLY COMPOUNDED INTEREST

If a principal of P dollars is deposited in an account paying an annual rate of interest r (expressed in decimal form), compounded continuously, then after t years the account will contain A dollars, where

$$A = Pe^{rt}.$$

The formula $A = Pe^{rt}$ calculates an exponential model having a *continuous* growth (or decay) rate r, whereas the formula $A = P(1 + r)^t$ calculates an exponential model with a *constant* growth (or decay) rate r. In both cases r is expressed in decimal form. Note that the value of r can be either positive or negative, depending on whether A is increasing or decreasing. With money and interest we often think of r as being positive, but with populations r could be positive or negative.

EXAMPLE 6 **Calculating continuously compounded interest**

The principal in an IRA is \$1000 and the interest rate is 12%, compounded continuously.

(a) How much money will there be after 45 years?

(b) Determine graphically and numerically the 10-year period when the account balance increases the most.

SOLUTION

(a) Let $P = 1000$, $r = 0.12$, and $t = 45$. Then $A = 1000e^{(0.12)45} \approx \$221{,}406.42$. This is more than the \$204,503.36 that resulted from compounding quarterly in Example 4.

(b) Graph $Y_1 = 1000e^{\wedge}(.12X)$, as shown in Figure 5.44. From the graph we can see that the account balance increases the most during the last 10 years. Numerical support for this conclusion is shown in Figure 5.45.

Calculator Help

To make a table like Figure 5.45, see Appendix A (page AP-5).

[0, 45, 5] by [0, 250000, 100000]

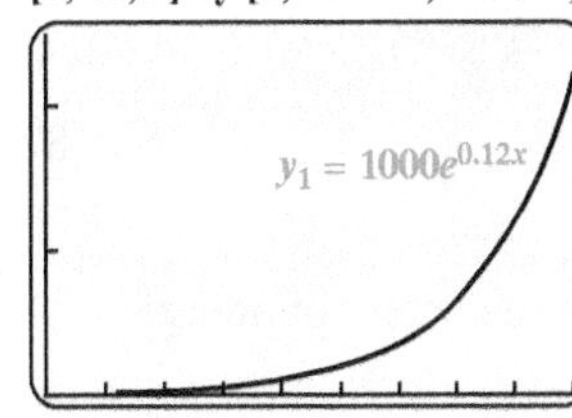

Figure 5.44

X	Y1
5	1822.1
15	6049.6
25	20086
35	66686
45	221406

Y1=1000e^(.12X)

Figure 5.45

Now Try Exercise 29

Nominal and Effective Interest Rates When investing money, it is important to understand that there are different ways to calculate interest. The **nominal interest rate** is the periodic interest rate times the number of periods per year. In Example 6, the nominal interest rate is 12%. Sometimes a business charges 1% interest per month on an unpaid balance. In this case the nominal interest rate is again $12 \times 1\% = 12\%$ per year. However, if the interest is compounded monthly or continuously, then the *effective interest rate* will be higher than the nominal interest. For example, the amount A owed after 1 year for a \$1000 balance at a nominal rate of 12% compound monthly equals

$$A = P\left(1 + \frac{r}{n}\right)^{nt} = 1000\left(1 + \frac{0.12}{12}\right)^{12(1)} \approx \$1126.83.$$

Thus the interest on \$1000 is \$126.83, and so the effective interest rate is about

$$\frac{126.83}{1000} \times 100 = 12.683\%.$$

Because of monthly compounding, the effective rate is slightly higher than the nominal interest rate of 12%. Without compounding, the interest would be \$120, or 12% of \$1000. Generally a consumer is more concerned about the effective (annual) interest rate than the nominal interest rate, because the effective interest rate reflects the actual amount of interest the consumer pays (or receives) after 1 year.

Different ways of compounding interest lead to different effective interest rates. If a nominal interest rate of 12% is compounded continuously, rather than monthly, then the amount A after 1 year for a \$1000 balance is

$$A = Pe^{rt} = 1000e^{0.12(1)} \approx \$1127.50.$$

In this case the interest on \$1000 is \$127.50, and so the effective interest rate equals

$$\frac{127.50}{1000} = 0.1275 = 12.75\%,$$

which is slightly higher than the effective interest rate for monthly compounding.

EXAMPLE 7 Finding effective rates of interest

Suppose that \$5000 is deposited in an account with a nominal interest rate of 6%. Find the effective interest rate with quarterly compounding and with continuous compounding. Does the principal amount P influence the effective rate of interest?

SOLUTION First, let $P = 5000$, $r = 0.06$, $n = 4$, and $t = 1$ in the compound interest formula. Then

$$A = 5000\left(1 + \frac{0.06}{4}\right)^{4(1)} \approx \$5306.82.$$

The interest is \$306.82 with an effective interest rate of

$$\frac{306.82}{5000} \approx 0.0614 = 6.14\%.$$

With continuous compounding,

$$A = 5000e^{0.06(1)} \approx \$5309.18$$

and the effective interest rate is

$$\frac{309.18}{5000} \approx 0.0618 = 6.18\%.$$

The principal P does *not* affect the effective rate. It only affects the *total amount* of interest earned. To see this, rework the example with $P = 1$.

Now Try Exercises 39 and 41

Natural Exponential Models

Exponential models for growth or decay with initial value A_0 can also be written in terms of the natural exponential function and time t in the form

$$A(t) = A_0 e^{kt}$$

where $k > 0$ models exponential growth and $k < 0$ models exponential decay.

To justify that $A(t) = A_0 e^{kt}$ with $k > 0$ models exponential growth, we equate the exponential expressions a^t and e^{kt} to obtain the following.

$$a^t = e^{kt}$$

$$(a)^t = (e^k)^t \quad \text{Properties of exponents}$$

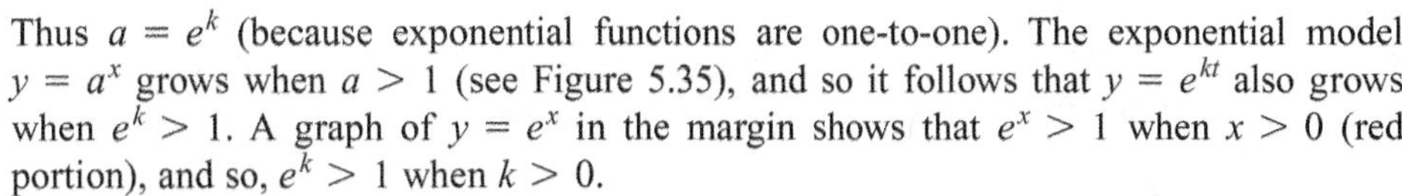

Thus $a = e^k$ (because exponential functions are one-to-one). The exponential model $y = a^x$ grows when $a > 1$ (see Figure 5.35), and so it follows that $y = e^{kt}$ also grows when $e^k > 1$. A graph of $y = e^x$ in the margin shows that $e^x > 1$ when $x > 0$ (red portion), and so, $e^k > 1$ when $k > 0$.

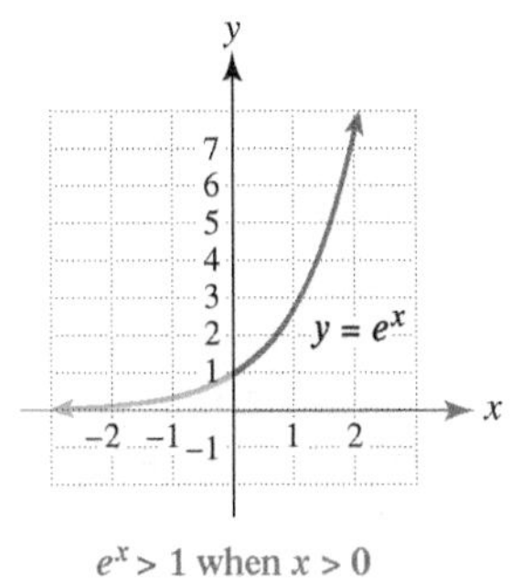

$e^x > 1$ when $x > 0$
$0 < e^x < 1$ when $x < c$

Thus any exponential function written as $y = Ca^t\ (a > 1)$ can also be written as $y = A_0 e^{kt}$, where $C = A_0$ and $a = e^k$ with $k > 0$. In a similar way, it can justified that $y = A_0 e^{kt}$ models exponential decay when $k < 0$. See the blue portion of the graph of $y = e^x$ in the margin.

In summary, if A_0 is the initial amount of a quantity A at time $t = 0$ and if k is a nonzero constant, then exponential growth of A can be modeled by

$$A(t) = A_0 e^{kt}. \quad \text{Growth } (k > 0)$$

Figure 5.46 illustrates this type of growth graphically. Similarly,

$$A(t) = A_0 e^{kt} \quad \text{Decay } (k < 0)$$

can be used to model exponential decay. Figure 5.47 illustrates this type of decay graphically. A larger absolute value of k causes the graph of A to increase or decrease more rapidly. That is, a larger absolute value of k causes the rate of change in A to be greater in absolute value. The value of k also represents the continuous percent growth (or decay), written in decimal form.

CLASS DISCUSSION

Graph $y = 2^x$ and $y = 3^x$ on the same coordinate axes, using the viewing rectangle $[-3, 3, 1]$ by $[0, 4, 1]$. Make a conjecture about how the graph of $y = e^x$ will appear. Test your conjecture.

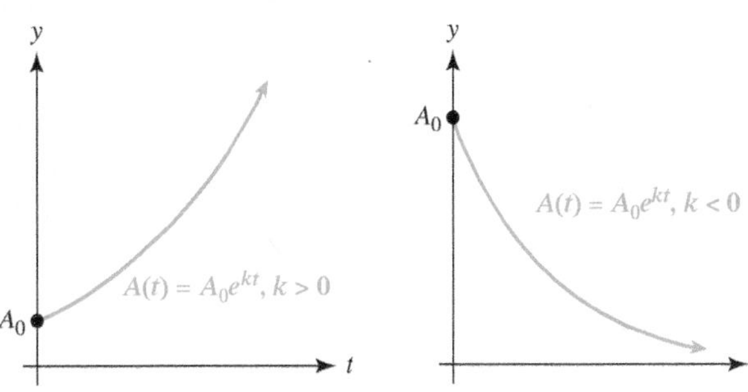

Figure 5.46 Exponential Growth

Figure 5.47 Exponential Decay

NOTE In the compound interest formula $A = Pe^{rt}$, the value of r corresponds to the value of k in the formula $A = A_0 e^{kt}$. If $r > 0$, the principal P grows and if $r < 0$, the principal P decays.

Sometimes variables such as N or Q are used instead of the variable A. In the next example, we model the number of bacteria N in a sample that undergoes exponential growth.

EXAMPLE 8 Modeling the growth of *E. coli* bacteria

E. coli (*Escherichia coli*) is a type of bacteria that inhabits the intestines of animals. These bacteria are capable of rapid growth and can be dangerous to humans—especially children. In one study, *E. coli* bacteria were found to be capable of doubling in number about every 49.5 minutes. Their number N after t minutes could be modeled by $N(t) = N_0e^{0.014t}$. Suppose that $N_0 = 500{,}000$ is the initial number of bacteria per milliliter. (**Source:** G. S. Stent, *Molecular Biology of Bacterial Viruses.*)

(a) Make a conjecture about the number of bacteria per milliliter after 99 minutes. Verify your conjecture.

(b) Determine graphically when there were 25 million bacteria per milliliter.

(c) The y-intercept is not apparent in Figure 5.48. Without graphing, determine the y-intercept on the graph of $y = N(t)$. Explain how the y-intercept relates to the formula $N(t)$.

[0, 400, 100] by [0, 3×10^7, 1×10^7]

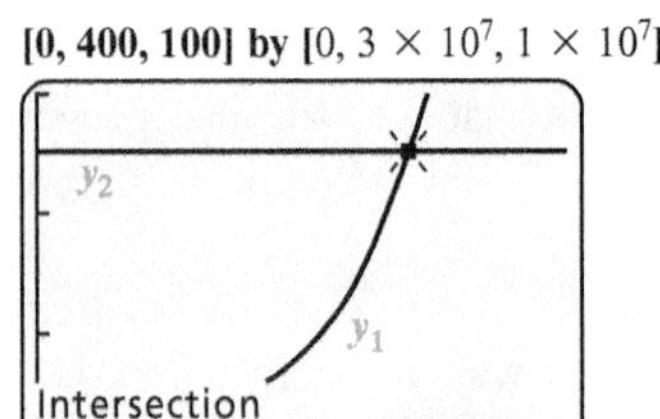

Figure 5.48

SOLUTION

(a) Since the bacteria double every 49.5 minutes, there would be 1,000,000 per milliliter after 49.5 minutes and 2,000,000 after 99 minutes. This is verified by evaluating

$$N(99) = 500{,}000e^{0.014(99)} \approx 2{,}000{,}000.$$

(b) ***Graphical Solution*** Solve $N(t) = 25{,}000{,}000$ by graphing $Y_1 = 500000e\text{^}(0.014X)$ and $Y_2 = 25000000$. Their graphs intersect near (279.4, 25,000,000), as shown in Figure 5.48. Thus in a 1-milliliter sample, half a million *E. coli* bacteria could increase to 25 million in approximately 279 minutes, or 4 hours and 39 minutes.

(c) Because $N(0) = 500{,}000e^0 = 500{,}000$ the point (0, 500000) lies on the graph of $y = N(t)$, and so the y-intercept is 500,000. This value is equal to the initial value $N_0 = 500{,}000$ bacteria per milliliter.

Now Try Exercise 65

NOTE You will learn how to solve this equation symbolically in Section 5.6. See Exercise 94 in that section.

EXAMPLE 9 Modeling traffic flow

Cars arrive randomly at an intersection with an average rate of 30 cars per hour. Highway engineers estimate the likelihood, or probability, that at least one car will enter the intersection within a period of x minutes with $f(x) = 1 - e^{-0.5x}$. (**Source:** F. Mannering and W. Kilareski, *Principles of Highway Engineering and Traffic Analysis.*)

(a) Evaluate $f(2)$ and interpret the answer.

(b) Graph f for $0 \le x \le 60$. What is the likelihood that at least one car will enter the intersection during a 60-minute period?

[0, 60, 10] by [0, 1.2, 0.2]

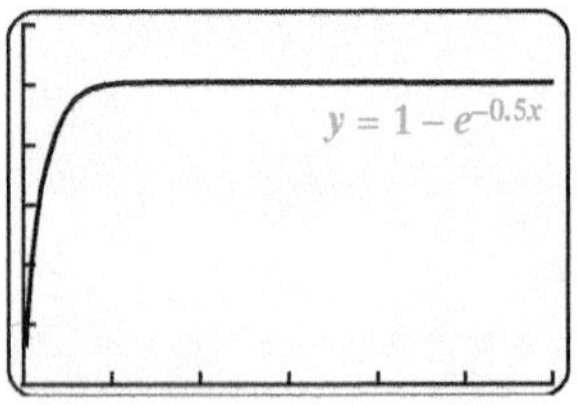

$y = 1 - e^{-0.5x}$

Figure 5.49

SOLUTION

(a) $f(2) = 1 - e^{-0.5(2)} = 1 - e^{-1} \approx 0.63$. There is a 63% chance that at least one car will enter the intersection during a 2-minute period.

(b) Graph $Y_1 = 1 - e\text{^}(-0.5X)$, as shown in Figure 5.49. As time progresses, the probability increases and begins to approach 1. It is almost certain that at least one car will enter the intersection during a 60-minute period. (Note that a horizontal asymptote is $y = 1$.)

Now Try Exercise 67

5.3 Putting It All Together (Part II)

The following table summarizes some important concepts about exponential functions and types of growth and decay.

CONCEPT	COMMENTS	EXAMPLES
Exponential model	If an initial amount A_0 experiences a constant *percent* change r for each unit increase in x, then the exponential model $$A(x) = A_0(1 + r)^x$$ describes this change.	A bacteria population N grows 25% each day x. The exponential model $$N(x) = N_0(1 + 0.25)^x$$ describes this population after x days, where N_0 is the initial population and $1 + r$ is the growth factor.
Interest compounded n times per year $$A = P\left(1 + \frac{r}{n}\right)^{nt}$$	P is the principal, r is the interest rate (expressed in decimal form), n is the number of times interest is paid each year, t is the number of years, and A is the amount after t years.	\$500 at 8%, compounded monthly, for 3 years yields $$500\left(1 + \frac{0.08}{12}\right)^{12(3)} \approx \$635.12.$$
The number e	The number e is an irrational number important in mathematics, much like π.	$e \approx 2.718282$
Natural exponential function	This function is an exponential function with base e and $C = 1$.	$f(x) = e^x$
Interest compounded continuously $$A = Pe^{rt}$$	P is the principal, r is the interest rate (expressed in decimal form), t is the number of years, and A is the amount after t years.	\$500 at 8% compounded continuously for 3 years yields $$500e^{0.08(3)} \approx \$635.62.$$
Natural exponential model	Exponential growth ($k > 0$) and decay ($k < 0$) can be modeled by $A(t) = A_0e^{kt}$. Any natural exponential model can be written in the form $f(x) = Ca^t$ by letting $C = A_0$ and $a = e^k$. The exponential models $A = Pe^{rt}$ and $A = A_0e^{kt}$ are equivalent with $P = A_0$ and $r = k$.	$A(t) = 100e^{2t}$ models exponential *growth* because $k = 2$ is *positive.* $A(t) = 100e^{-0.25t}$ models exponential *decay* because $k = -0.25$ is *negative.* $A(t) = 100e^{2t}$ can be written approximately as $A(t) = 100(7.389)^t$ because $a = e^2 \approx 7.389$. The exponential model $A = 100e^{0.25t}$ describes the growth of \$100 at an interest rate of 25%, compounded continuously.

5.3 Exercises (Part II)

Exponential Models and Graphs

Exercises 1–6: Find an exponential model that describes each situation.

1. A sample of 9500 insects decreases in number by 35% per week
2. A sample of 5000 insects increases in number by 120% per day
3. A sample of 2500 fish increases in number by 5% per month
4. A sample of 152 birds decreases in number by 3.4% per week
5. A mutual fund account contains \$1000 and decreases by 6.5% per year
6. A mutual fund account contains \$2500 and increases by 2.1% per year

Exercises 7–16: For the given f(x), state the initial value, the growth or decay factor, and percent change for each unit increase in x.

7. $f(x) = 8(1.12)^x$
8. $f(x) = 9(1.005)^x$
9. $f(x) = 1.5(0.35)^x$
10. $f(x) = 100(1.23)^x$
11. $f(x) = 0.55^x$
12. $f(x) = 0.4^x$
13. $f(x) = 7e^x$
14. $f(x) = 91e^{x/2}$
15. $f(x) = 6(3^{-x})$
16. $f(x) = 9(4^{-x})$

Exercises 17–20: Approximate f(x) to four decimal places.

17. $f(x) = 4e^{-1.2x}$, $x = -2.4$
18. $f(x) = -2.1e^{-0.71x}$, $x = 1.9$
19. $f(x) = \frac{1}{2}(e^x - e^{-x})$, $x = -0.7$
20. $f(x) = 4(e^{-0.3x} - e^{-0.6x})$, $x = 1.6$

21. **Modeling Phenomena** Match the situation with the graph (a–d) that models it best.
    (i) Balance in an account after x years earning 10% interest compounded continuously
    (ii) Balance in an account after x years earning 5% interest compounded annually
    (iii) Air pressure in a car tire with a large hole in it after x minutes
    (iv) Air pressure in a car tire with a pinhole in it after x minutes

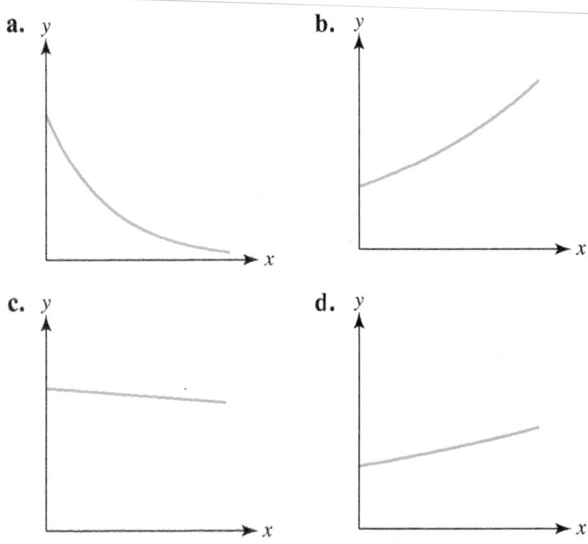

22. **Population** A city's population decreases at a continuous exponential rate of 2% per year over 35 years.
    (a) What happens to the city's population over the 35-years period?
    (b) If after 35 years the city's population was 250,000, what was the city's initial population?
    (c) Sketch a graph of this decrease in population. What is the y-intercept?

Exercises 23 and 24: The graph of $y = f(x)$ is shown in the figure. Sketch a graph of each equation using translations of graphs and reflections. Do not use a graphing calculator.

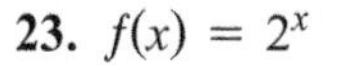

23. $f(x) = 2^x$

(a) $y = 2^x - 2$

(b) $y = 2^{x-1}$

(c) $y = 2^{-x}$

(d) $y = -2^x$

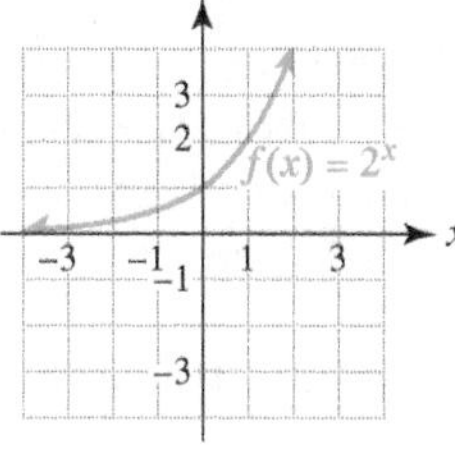

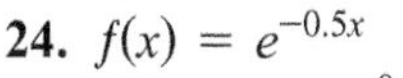

24. $f(x) = e^{-0.5x}$

(a) $y = -e^{-0.5x}$

(b) $y = e^{-0.5x} - 3$

(c) $y = e^{-0.5(x-2)}$

(d) $y = e^{0.5x}$

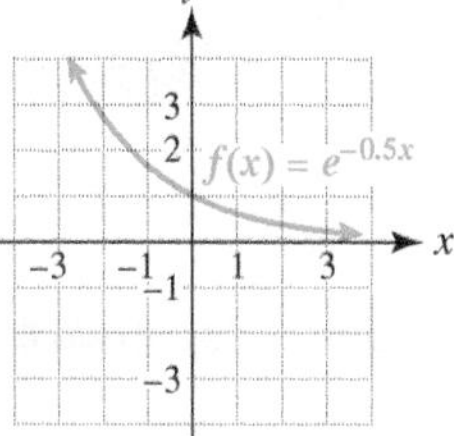

Compound Interest

Exercises 25–32: Use the compound interest formula to determine the final value of each amount.

25. \$600 at 7% compounded annually for 5 years

26. \$2300 at 11% compounded semiannually for 10 years

27. \$950 at 3% compounded daily for 20 years

28. \$3300 at 8% compounded quarterly for 2 years

29. \$2000 at 10% compounded continuously for 8 years

30. \$100 at 19% compounded continuously for 50 years

31. \$1600 at 10.4% compounded monthly for 2.5 years

32. \$2000 at 8.7% compounded annually for 5 years

33. Investments Compare investing \$2000 at 10% compounded monthly for 20 years with investing \$2000 at 13% compounded monthly for 20 years.

34. Lake Property In some states, lake shore property is increasing in value by 15% per year. Determine the value of a \$90,000 lake lot after 5 years.

35. College Tuition If college tuition is currently \$8000 per year, inflating at 6% per year, what will be the cost of tuition in 10 years?

36. Doubling Time How long does it take for an investment to double its value if the interest is 12% compounded annually? 6% compounded annually?

37. Investment Choice Determine the best investment: compounding continuously at 6.0% or compounding annually at 6.3%.

38. Investment Choice Determine the best investment: compounding quarterly at 3.1% or compounding daily at 2.9%.

Nominal and Effective Interest

Exercises 39–42: A deposit of \$4000 is made at a nominal interest rate of 5.5%. To the nearest thousandth of a percent, find the effective (annual) interest rate for each type of compounding.

39. Monthly

40. Quarterly

41. Continuously

42. Weekly

43. Effective Interest Rate An account pays 4.25% interest compounded continuously. To the nearest hundredth of a percent, what is the effective interest rate?

44. Effective Interest Rate An account pays 5.5% interest compounded monthly. To the nearest hundredth of a percent, what is the effective interest rate?

Exercises 45–48: Effective Interest Formula *If the nominal interest rate is r (in decimal form) and is compounded n times per year, then the effective interest rate E (in decimal form) is given by $E = (1 + \frac{r}{n})^n - 1$. For continuous compounding the formula $E = e^r - 1$ can be used. Use these formulas to find the effective interest rate (in percent form rounded to the nearest hundredth) for the given r and type of compounding.*

45. $r = 0.04$, monthly compounding

46. $r = 0.065$, quarterly compounding

47. $r = 0.09$, continuous compounding

48. $r = 0.071$, continuous compounding

Applications

49. Bacteria Growth A population of bacteria increases by 6% every 8 hours. By what percentage does the sample increase in 3 hours?

50. Bacteria Growth A population of bacteria decreases by 40% every 4 hours. By what percentage does the sample decrease in 7 hours?

51. Percent Change The number of cell phone subscribers to a company increases by 25% during the first year and then decreases by 20% the second year. Compare the number of subscribers at the beginning of the first year with the number of subscribers at the end of the second year.

52. Wage Increase If your wages are \$8 per hour and you receive a 300% raise for excellent work, determine your new wages.

53. Wages If a wage of \$8.81 increases by 9% each year, what is the new wage after 3 years?

54. Pollution A pollutant in a river has an initial concentration of 3 parts per million and degrades at a rate of 1.5% per year. Approximate its concentration after 20 years.

55. Radioactive Half-Life A radioactive element decays to 50% of its original amount every 2 years. Approximate the percentage that remains after 8 years.

56. Radioactive Half-Life A radioactive element decays to 50% of its original amount every 3 years. Approximate the percentage that remains after 8 years.

57. Saving for Retirement Suppose \$1500 is deposited into an IRA with an interest rate of 6%, compounded continuously.

(a) How much money will there be after 30 years?

(b) Determine graphically or numerically the 10-year period when the account balance increases the most.

58. Population Growth The population of Phoenix, Arizona, was 1.3 million in 2000 and growing continuously at a 3% rate.

(a) Assuming this trend continues, estimate the population of Phoenix in 2010.

(b) Determine graphically or numerically when this population might reach 2 million.

59. Federal Debt In fiscal year 2008 the federal budget deficit was about \$340 billion. At the same time, 30-year treasury bonds were paying 4.54% interest. Suppose the American taxpayer loaned \$340 billion to the federal government at 4.54% compounded annually. If the federal government waited 30 years to pay the entire amount back, including the interest, how much would this be? (**Source:** Department of the Treasury.)

60. Federal Debt Suppose that interest rates in Exercise 59 were 2% higher. How much would the federal government owe after 30 years? Is the national debt sensitive to interest rates?

61. Annuity If x dollars is deposited every 2 weeks (26 times per year) into an account paying an annual interest rate r, expressed in decimal form, then the amount A in the account after t years can be approximated by the formula

$$A = x\left(\frac{(1 + r/26)^{26t} - 1}{(r/26)}\right).$$

If \$50 is deposited every 2 weeks into an account paying 8% interest, approximate the amount after 10 years.

62. Annuity (Refer to Exercise 61.) Suppose a retirement account pays 10% annual interest. Determine how much a 20-year-old worker should deposit in this account every 2 weeks in order to have \$1 million at age 65.

63. Continuous Compounding Over 5 years, the total value of a mutual fund account decreases continuously by 15%. Find a formula $A(x)$ that calculates the amount of money in the account after x years.

64. Continuous Compounding A sum of money P in an account receives continuous interest and triples in 15 years. Find a formula $A(x)$ that calculates the amount of money in the account after x years.

65. E. Coli Growth (Refer to Example 8.)

(a) Approximate the number of *E. coli* after 3 hours.

(b) Estimate graphically the elapsed time when there are 10 million bacteria per milliliter.

66. Drug Concentrations Sometimes after a patient takes a drug, the amount of medication A in the bloodstream can be modeled by $A = A_0e^{rt}$, where A_0 is the initial concentration in milligrams per liter, r is the hourly percentage decrease (in decimal form) of the drug in the bloodstream, and t is the elapsed time in hours. Suppose that a drug's concentration is initially 2 milligrams per liter and that $r = -0.02$.

(a) Find the drug concentration after 3.5 hours.

(b) When did the drug concentration reach 1.5 milligrams per liter?

67. Modeling Traffic Flow Cars arrive randomly at an intersection with an average rate of 50 cars per hour. The likelihood, or probability, that at least one car will enter the intersection within a period of x minutes can be estimated by $P(x) = 1 - e^{-5x/6}$.

(a) Find the likelihood that at least one car enters the intersection during a 3-minute period.

(b) Graphically determine the value of x that gives a 50–50 chance of at least one car entering the intersection during an interval of x minutes.

68. Tree Density Ecologists studied the spacing between individual trees in a forest in British Columbia. The probability, or likelihood, that there is at least one tree located in a circle with a radius of x feet can be estimated by $P(x) = 1 - e^{-0.1144x}$. For example, $P(7) \approx 0.55$ means that if a person picks a point at random in the forest, there is a 55% chance that at least one tree will be located within 7 feet. See the figure. **(Source:** E. Pielou, *Populations and Community Ecology.*)

(a) Evaluate $P(2)$ and $P(20)$, and interpret the results.

(b) Graph P. Explain verbally why it is logical for P to be an increasing function. Does the graph have a horizontal asymptote?

(c) Solve $P(x) = 0.5$ and interpret the result.

69. Radioactive Cesium-137 Radioactive cesium-137 was emitted in large amounts in the Chernobyl nuclear power station accident in Russia. The amount of a 100-milligram sample of cesium remaining after x years can be described by $A(x) = 100e^{-0.02295x}$. **(Source:** C. Mason, *Biology of Freshwater Pollution.*)

(a) How much remains after 50 years? Is the half-life of cesium more or less than 50 years?

(b) Estimate graphically the half-life of cesium-137.

70. Filters Impurities in water are frequently removed using filters. Suppose that a 1-inch filter allows 10% of the impurities to pass through it. The other 90% is trapped in the filter.

(a) Find a formula in the form $f(x) = 100a^x$ that calculates the percentage of impurities passing through x inches of this type of filter.

(b) Use $f(x)$ to estimate the percentage of impurities passing through 2.3 inches of the filter.

Writing about Mathematics

71. If a quantity Q increases by R% and then decreases by R%, is the final result equal to Q? Explain your answer.

72. If a quantity Q increases by R%, by what factor does Q increase? Explain your answer.

EXTENDED AND DISCOVERY EXERCISES

Exercises 1–4: Present Value In the compound interest formula $A = P(1 + r/n)^{nt}$, we can think of P as the present value of an investment and A as the future value of an investment after t years. For example, if you were saving for college and needed a future value of A dollars, then P would represent the amount needed in an account today to reach your goal in t years at an interest rate of r, compounded n times per year. If we solve the equation for P, it results in

$$P = A(1 + r/n)^{-nt}.$$

1. Verify that the two formulas are equivalent by transforming the first equation into the second.

2. What should the present value of a savings account be to cover $30,000 of college expenses in 12.5 years, if the account pays 7.5% interest compounded quarterly?

3. Suppose you want to have $15,000 to buy a car in 3 years. What should the present value of a savings account be to reach this goal, if the account pays 5% compounded monthly?

4. A parent expects college costs to reach $40,000 in 6 years. To cover the $40,000 in future expenses, how much should the parent deposit in an account that pays 6% interest compounded *continuously*?

Exercises 5–8: Average Rate of Change of e^x *Complete the following. Round your answers to two decimal places.*

(a) *Find the average rate of change of* $f(x) = e^x$ *from* x *to* $x + 0.001$ *for the given* x.

(b) *Approximate* $f(x) = e^x$ *for the given* x.

(c) *Compare your answers in parts (a) and (b).*

5. $x = 0$ **6.** $x = -2$ **7.** $x = -0.5$ **8.** $x = 1.5$

9. Average Rate of Change What is the pattern in the results from Exercises 5–8? You may want to test your conjecture by trying different values of x.

10. Average Rate of Change For any real number k, what is a good approximation for the average rate of change of $f(x) = e^x$ on a small interval near $x = k$? Explain how your answer relates to the graph of $f(x) = e^x$.

5.4 Logarithmic Functions and Models

- Evaluate the common logarithmic function
- Evaluate logarithms with other bases
- Solve basic exponential and logarithmic equations
- Solve general exponential and logarithmic equations
- Convert between exponential and logarithmic forms

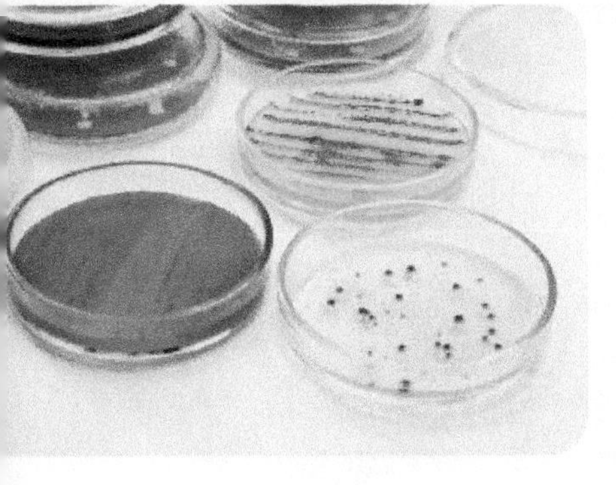

Introduction

Bacteria growth is often exponential. For example, Table 5.18 and Figure 5.50 show the concentration B (in thousands per milliliter) in a bacteria sample after x days, where $B(x) = 10^x$. To determine how long it takes for the concentration to reach 500 thousand per milliliter, we can solve the equation $10^x = 500$. The graphical solution in Figure 5.51 is about 2.7, but finding this value symbolically requires *logarithms*.

Growth of Bacteria (1000/mL)

x	0	1	2	3
$B(x)$	1	10	100	1000

Elapsed days

Table 5.18

Exponential Growth

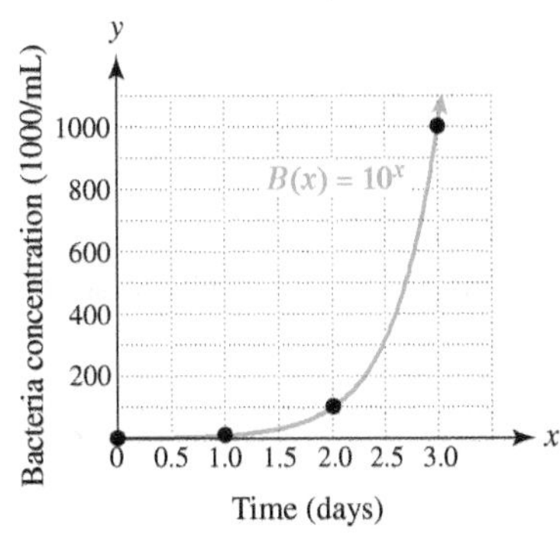

Figure 5.50

Solving $10^x = 500$

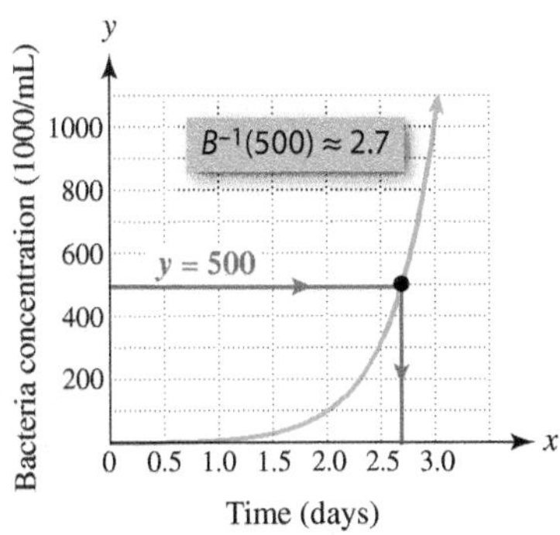

Figure 5.51

The Common Logarithmic Function

Notice that the graph of $B(x) = 10^x$ in Figure 5.50 is increasing and one-to-one. Its graph passes the horizontal line test. Therefore B has an inverse function. Because $B(1) = 10$, it follows that $B^{-1}(10) = 1$. Similarly, $B(2) = 100$ implies that $B^{-1}(100) = 2$, and in general, $B(k) = 10^k$ implies that $B^{-1}(10^k) = k$. Table 5.19 lists values for $B^{-1}(x)$. Notice that, unlike B, B^{-1} increases *very slowly* for large values of x.

Inverse Function of B

x	1	10	100	1000
$B^{-1}(x)$	0	1	2	3

Table 5.19

The solution to $10^x = 500$ represents the number of days needed for the bacteria concentration to reach 500 thousand per milliliter. To solve this equation, we must find an exponent k such that $10^k = 500$. Because $B^{-1}(10^k) = k$, this is equivalent to evaluating $B^{-1}(500)$, as shown graphically in Figure 5.51. From Table 5.19, k is between 2 and 3 because $100 \leq 500 \leq 1000$.

The inverse of $y = 10^x$ is defined to be the *common (base-10) logarithm*, denoted $\log x$ or $\log_{10} x$. Thus $10^2 = 100$ implies $\log 100 = 2$, $10^3 = 1000$ implies $\log 1000 = 3$, and in general, $10^a = b$ implies $\log b = a$. Thus $B^{-1}(500) = \log 500$ and $B^{-1}(x) = \log x$.

The common exponential function and the common logarithmic function, represented in Tables 5.20 and 5.21, are inverse functions.

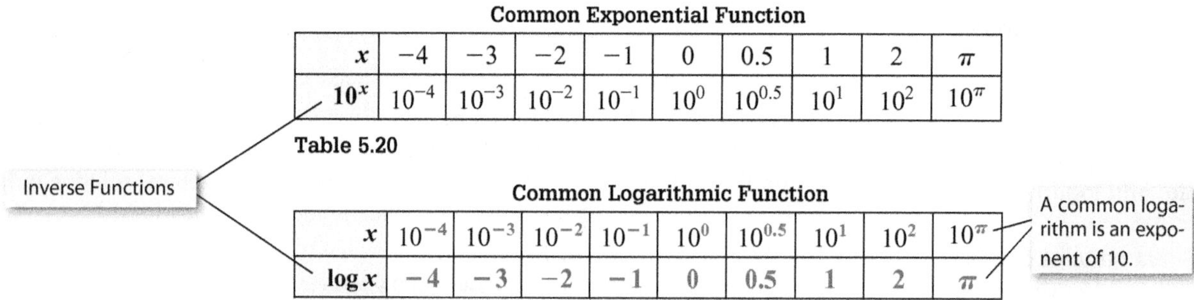

Common Exponential Function

x	-4	-3	-2	-1	0	0.5	1	2	π
10^x	10^{-4}	10^{-3}	10^{-2}	10^{-1}	10^0	$10^{0.5}$	10^1	10^2	10^π

Table 5.20

Common Logarithmic Function

x	10^{-4}	10^{-3}	10^{-2}	10^{-1}	10^0	$10^{0.5}$	10^1	10^2	10^π
$\log x$	-4	-3	-2	-1	0	0.5	1	2	π

Table 5.21

The common logarithm of a positive number x is the exponent k, such that $10^k = x$. This concept can be illustrated visually.

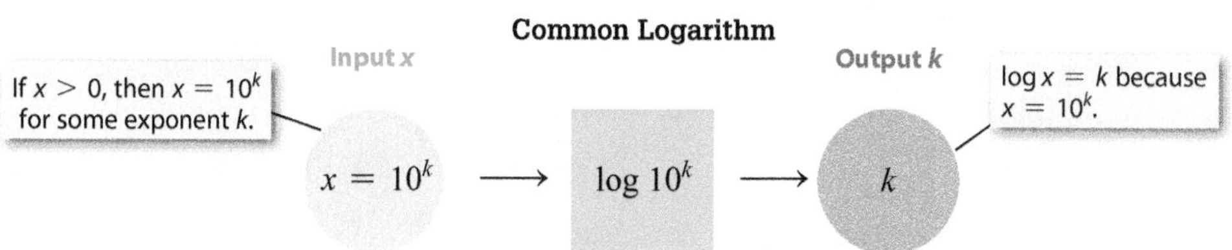

$\log x = k$ because $x = 10^k$.

The following See the Concept discusses the graph of $y = \log x$.

See the Concept: The Graph of $y = \log x$

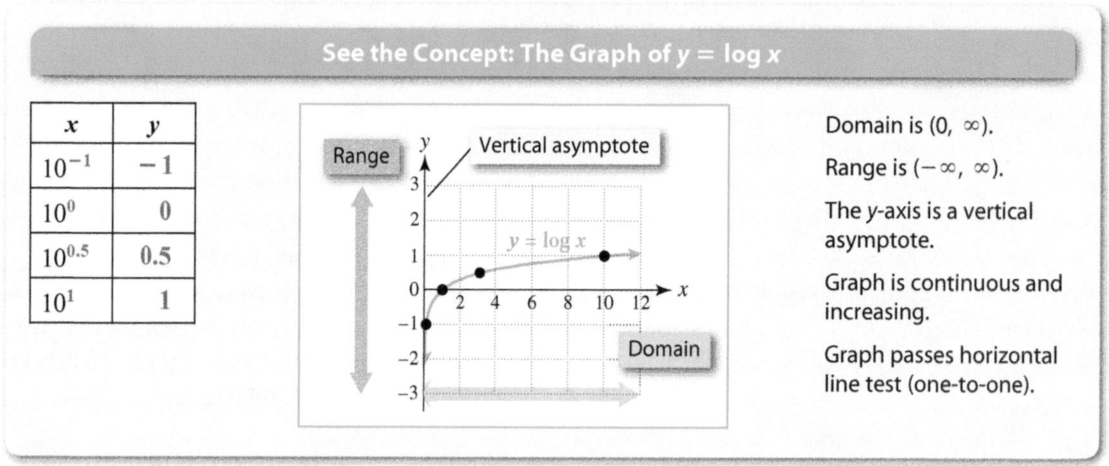

x	y
10^{-1}	-1
10^0	0
$10^{0.5}$	0.5
10^1	1

Range
Vertical asymptote
$y = \log x$
Domain
Domain is $(0, \infty)$.
Range is $(-\infty, \infty)$.
The y-axis is a vertical asymptote.
Graph is continuous and increasing.
Graph passes horizontal line test (one-to-one).

We have shown *verbal*, *numerical*, *graphical*, and *symbolic* descriptions of the common logarithmic function. A formal definition of the common logarithm is now given.

COMMON LOGARITHM
If $x > 0$, then $x = 10^k$ for some exponent k.

The **common logarithm of a positive number x,** denoted $\log x$, is defined by

$$\log x = k \quad \text{if and only if} \quad x = 10^k,$$

where k is a real number. The function given by

$$f(x) = \log x$$

is called the **common logarithmic function.**

NOTE The common logarithmic function outputs an *exponent k,* which may be positive, negative, or zero. However, a valid input must be positive. Thus its range is $(-\infty, \infty)$ and its domain is $(0, \infty)$.

The equation $\log x = k$ is called **logarithmic form** and the equation $x = 10^k$ is called **exponential form.** These forms are *equivalent*. That is, if one equation is true, the other equation must also be true.

Logarithmic Form	Exponential Form
$\log 100 = 2$	$10^2 = 100$
$\log 1000 = 3$	$10^3 = 1000$
$\log \frac{1}{10} = -1$	$10^{-1} = \frac{1}{10}$
$\log x = k$	$10^k = x$

Pairs of equivalent equations

General forms

MAKING CONNECTIONS

Logarithms and Exponents *A logarithm is an exponent.* For example, to evaluate the logorithm log 1000 ask, "10 to what power equals 1000?" The necessary *exponent* equals log 1000. That is, $\log 1000 = 3$ because $10^3 = 1000$.

EXAMPLE 1 Evaluating common logarithms

Simplify each logarithm by hand.

(a) $\log 100{,}000$ **(b)** $\log 1$ **(c)** $\log \frac{1}{1000}$ **(d)** $\log \sqrt{10}$ **(e)** $\log(-2)$

SOLUTION

(a) Ask, "10 to what power equals 100,000?" Because $10^5 = 100{,}000$, it follows that $\log 100{,}000 = 5$. That is,

$$\log 100{,}000 = \log 10^5 = 5.$$

(b) Ask, "10 to what power equals 1?" Because $10^0 = 1$, it follows that $\log 1 = 0$. That is,

$$\log 1 = \log 10^0 = 0.$$

(c) $\log \frac{1}{1000} = \log 10^{-3} = -3$

(d) $\log \sqrt{10} = \log(10^{1/2}) = \frac{1}{2}$

(e) The domain of $f(x) = \log x$ is $(0, \infty)$, so $\log(-2)$ is undefined because the input is negative.

Now Try Exercise 3

```
log(12)
         1.079181246
10^1.079181246
                  12
```

Figure 5.52

MAKING CONNECTIONS

Square Roots and Logarithms Much like the square root function, the common logarithmic function does not have an easy-to-evaluate formula. For example, $\sqrt{4} = 2$ and $\sqrt{100} = 10$ can be calculated mentally, but for $\sqrt{2}$ we usually rely on a calculator. Similarly, $\log 100 = 2$ can be found mentally since $100 = 10^2$, whereas log 12 can be approximated using a calculator. See Figure 5.52. To check that $\log 12 \approx 1.079181246$, evaluate $10^{1.079181246} \approx 12$. Another similarity between the square root function and the common logarithmic function is that their domains do not include negative numbers. If outputs are restricted to real numbers, both $\sqrt{-3}$ and $\log(-3)$ are undefined expressions.

Reflection Across $y = x$

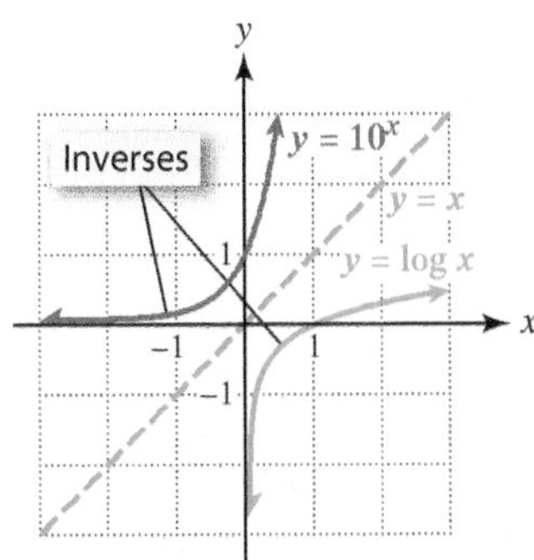

Figure 5.53

Graphs and Inverse Properties Because $\log x$ and 10^x are inverses, we can write $f(x) = \log x$ and $f^{-1}(x) = 10^x$. Their graphs are reflections across the line $y = x$, as shown in Figure 5.53. For inverse functions, $f(f^{-1}(x)) = x$ and $f^{-1}(f(x)) = x$, so the following inverse properties hold for all valid inputs x.

INVERSE PROPERTIES OF THE COMMON LOGARITHM

The following inverse properties hold for the common logarithm.

$$\log 10^x = x \quad \text{for any real number } x \text{ and}$$

$$10^{\log x} = x \quad \text{for any positive number } x$$

In Figures 5.54 and 5.55 a graphing calculator has been used to illustrate these properties. (If you have a calculator available, try some other examples.)

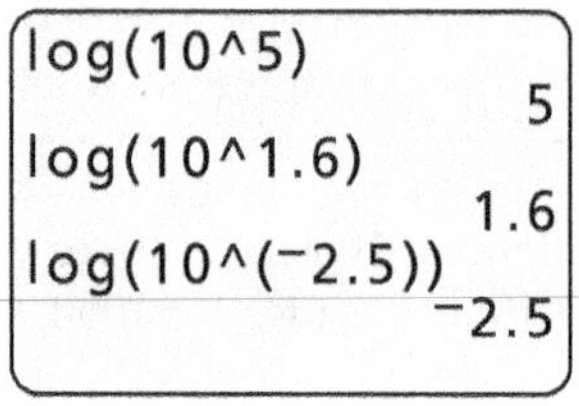

```
log(10^5)
                5
log(10^1.6)
              1.6
log(10^(-2.5))
             -2.5
```

Figure 5.54

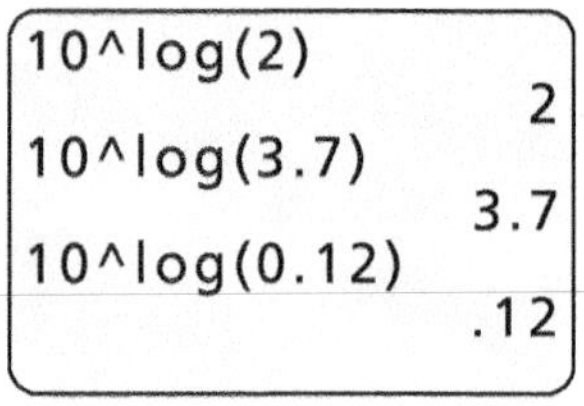

```
10^log(2)
                2
10^log(3.7)
              3.7
10^log(0.12)
              .12
```

Figure 5.55

An Application Malaria deaths on the continent of Africa have gradually decreased during the past decade largely due to vaccines. These deaths can be modeled by a function that involves the common logarithm. (***Sources:*** WHO; Malaria Vaccine Initiative.)

EXAMPLE 2 **Modeling malaria deaths in Africa**

The number of malaria deaths in millions x years after the year 2000 can be modeled by $D(x) = 0.9 \log\left(10 - \frac{2}{5}x\right)$.

(a) Evaluate $D(0)$ by hand and interpret the result.

(b) Approximate $D(10)$ and interpret the result.

SOLUTION

(a) $D(0) = 0.9\log\left(10 - \frac{2}{5}(0)\right) = 0.9 \log 10 = 0.9(1) = 0.9$. In 2000 there were about 0.9 million deaths from malaria in Africa.

(b) $D(10) = 0.9\log\left(10 - \frac{2}{5}(10)\right) = 0.9\log 6 \approx 0.7$. (Use a calculator.) In 2010 there were about 0.7 million deaths from malaria in Africa.

Now Try Exercise 133(a)

Logarithms with Other Bases

Base-2 Logarithm It is possible to develop base-a logarithms with any positive base $a \neq 1$. For example, in computer science base-2 logarithms are frequently used. The base-2 logarithmic function, denoted $f(x) = \log_2 x$, is shown in Table 5.22. If x can be expressed in the form $x = 2^k$ for some k, then $\log_2 x = k$. Thus $\log_2 x$ is an *exponent*. A graph of $y = \log_2 x$ is shown in Figure 5.56.

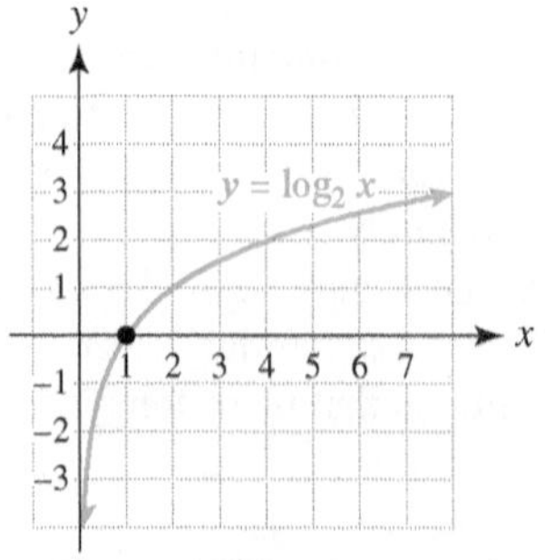

Base-2 Logarithm

Figure 5.56

Base-2 Logarithm

x	$2^{-3.1}$	2^{-2}	$2^{-0.5}$	2^0	$2^{0.5}$	2^2	$2^{3.1}$
$\log_2 x$	-3.1	-2	-0.5	0	0.5	2	3.1

A logarithm is an exponent.

Table 5.22

Natural Logarithm In a similar manner, a table of values for the base-e logarithm is shown in Table 5.23. The base-e logarithm is referred to as the **natural logarithm** and denoted either $\log_e x$ or $\ln x$. Natural logarithms are used in mathematics, science, economics, and technology. A graph of $y = \ln x$ is shown in Figure 5.57.

Natural Logarithm

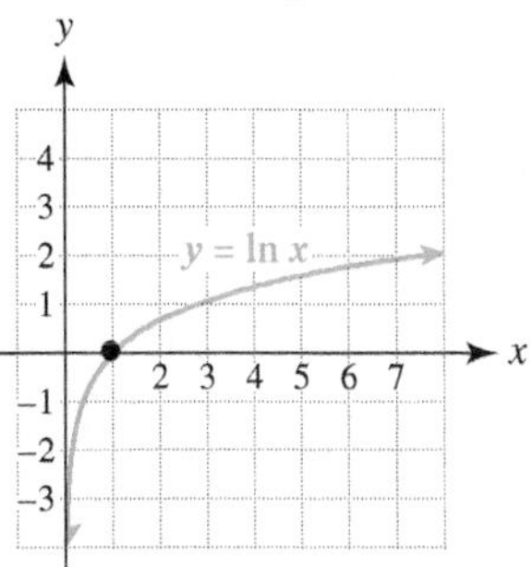

Figure 5.57

Natural Logarithm

x	$e^{-3.1}$	e^{-2}	$e^{-0.5}$	e^{0}	$e^{0.5}$	e^{2}	$e^{3.1}$
$\ln x$	-3.1	-2	-0.5	0	0.5	2	3.1

A logarithm is an exponent.

Table 5.23

Base-a Logarithm We can define a logarithm for any positive base a, where $a \neq 1$. As with other logarithms we have discussed, any base-a logarithm has domain $(0, \infty)$ and range $(-\infty, \infty)$.

LOGARITHM

The **logarithm with base a of a positive number x,** denoted by $\log_a x$, is defined by

$$\log_a x = k \quad \text{if and only if} \quad x = a^k,$$

where $a > 0$, $a \neq 1$, and k is a real number. The function, given by

$$f(x) = \log_a x,$$

is called the **logarithmic function with base a.**

Evaluating Base-a Logarithms *A base-a logarithm is an exponent.* For example, to evaluate $\log_2 16$ ask, "2 to what power equals 16?" The required *exponent* equals $\log_2 16$. That is, $\log_2 16 = 4$ because $2^4 = 16$.

EXAMPLE 3 **Evaluating logarithms**

Evaluate each logarithm.

(a) $\log_2 8$ **(b)** $\log_5 \frac{1}{25}$ **(c)** $\log_7 49$ **(d)** $\ln e^{-7}$

SOLUTION

(a) Ask, "2 to what power equals 8?" Because $2^3 = 8$, it follows that $\log_2 8 = 3$. That is, $\log_2 8 = \log_2 2^3 = 3$.

(b) Ask, "5 to what power equals $\frac{1}{25}$?" Because $5^{-2} = \frac{1}{25}$, it follows that $\log_5 \frac{1}{25} = -2$. That is, $\log_5 \frac{1}{25} = \log_5 5^{-2} = -2$.

(c) $\log_7 49 = \log_7 7^2 = 2$

(d) $\ln e^{-7} = \log_e e^{-7} = -7$

Now Try Exercises 33, 37, 39, and 49

Although the output from a base-a logarithm can be positive *or* negative, the input for a base-a logarithm must be positive. This fact can be used to determine the domain of logarithmic functions, as demonstrated in the next example.

EXAMPLE 4 **Finding the domain of a logarithmic function**

State the domain of f.

(a) $f(x) = \log_2(x - 4)$ **(b)** $f(x) = \ln(10^x)$

SOLUTION

(a) *The input for a logarithmic function must be positive.* Any x in the domain of f must satisfy $x - 4 > 0$, or equivalently, $x > 4$. Thus $D = (4, \infty)$.

(b) The expression 10^x is positive for all real numbers x. (See Figure 5.53, where the red graph of $y = 10^x$ is above the x-axis for all values of x.) Thus $D = (-\infty, \infty)$, or all real numbers.

Now Try Exercises 13 and 17

CLASS DISCUSSION

Make a table of values for a base-4 logarithm. Evaluate $\log_4 16$.

Remember that *a logarithm is an exponent.* The expression $\log_a x$ is the exponent k such that $a^k = x$. Logarithms with base a also satisfy inverse properties.

INVERSE PROPERTIES

The following inverse properties hold for logarithms with base a.

$$\log_a a^x = x \quad \text{for any real number } x \text{ and}$$

$$a^{\log_a x} = x \quad \text{for any positive number } x$$

EXAMPLE 5 **Applying inverse properties**

Use inverse properties to evaluate each expression.

(a) $\log_6 6^{-1.3}$ **(b)** $5^{\log_5(x+8)}$ **(c)** $\log_{1/2}\left(\frac{1}{2}\right)^{45}$

SOLUTION

(a) $\log_a a^x = x$, so $\log_6 6^{-1.3} = -1.3$.

(b) $a^{\log_a x} = x$, so $5^{\log_5(x+8)} = x + 8$, provided $x > -8$.

(c) $\log_a a^x = x$, so $\log_{1/2}\left(\frac{1}{2}\right)^{45} = 45$. Note that the base of a logarithmic function can be a positive fraction less than 1.

Now Try Exercises 21, 23, and 25

Graphs and Inverse Functions If $f(x) = a^x$, then its inverse function is given by $f^{-1}(x) = \log_a x$ and their graphs are reflections across the line $y = x$. These and other properties are illustrated for $f(x) = 2^x$ and $g(x) = e^x$ in the following See the Concept.

See the Concept: Inverses and Logarithms

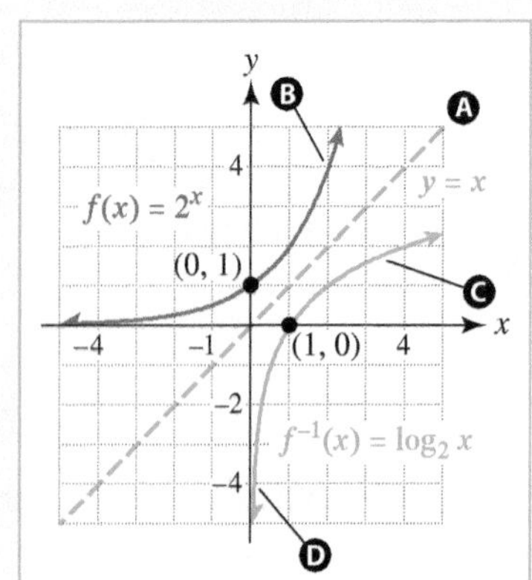

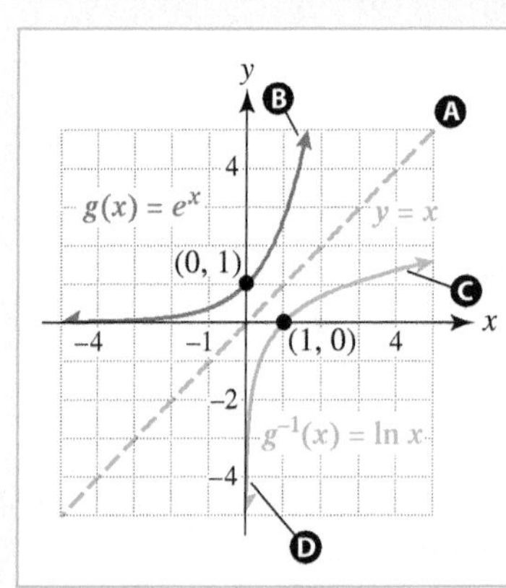

A The graph of the inverse is a reflection across the line $y = x$.

B Rapid exponential growth

C Slow logarithmic growth

D $\log_a x$ is negative (below the x-axis) for x between 0 and 1.

MAKING CONNECTIONS

Exponential and Logarithmic Functions The inverse of an exponential function is a logarithmic function, and the inverse of a logarithmic function is an exponential function. For example,

if $f(x) = 10^x$	then	$f^{-1}(x) = \log x$,
if $g(x) = \ln x$	then	$g^{-1}(x) = e^x$, and
if $h(x) = 2^x$	then	$h^{-1}(x) = \log_2 x$.

Domains and Ranges of Inverses The domain of $f(x) = \log_a x$ is $(0, \infty)$ and its range is $(-\infty, \infty)$. The domain of its inverse $f^{-1}(x) = a^x$ is $(-\infty, \infty)$ and its range is $(0, \infty)$. Notice how domains and ranges are *interchanged* because they are inverse functions.

Transformations of Logarithmic Graphs

We discussed how to shift, reflect, stretch, and shrink graphs of functions. For example, to graph $y = (x - 2)^2$ we can shift the graph of $y = x^2$ right 2 units. In a similar manner, we can graph $y = \log_2(x - 2)$ by shifting the graph of $y = \log_2 x$ right 2 units. The graph of $y = \log_2 x$ has a vertical asymptote at $x = 0$, so the graph of $y = \log_2(x - 2)$ has a vertical asymptote at $x = 2$. See Figure 5.58.

Shifting a Logarithmic Graph

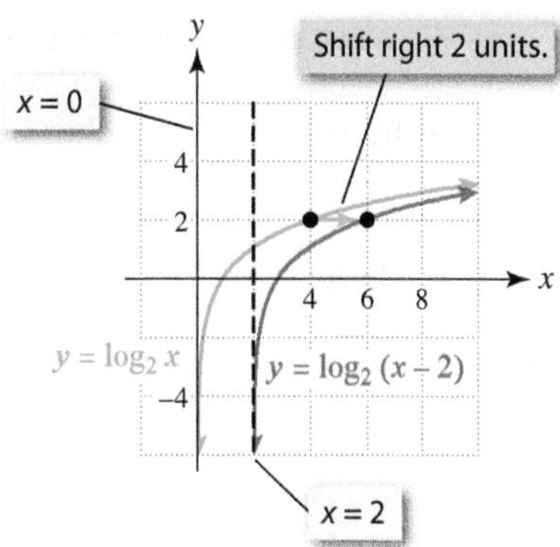

Figure 5.58

EXAMPLE 6 **Transformations of a logarithmic graph**

Explain how to obtain the graph of $g(x) = \log(-x) + 1$ from the graph of $f(x) = \log x$. Graph both functions in the same xy-plane.

SOLUTION

The graph of $y = \log(-x) + 1$ is similar to the graph of $f(x) = \log x$, except it is reflected about the y-axis and shifted upward 1 unit. Both graphs have a vertical asymptote at $x = 0$. See Figure 5.59.

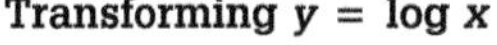

Transforming y = log x

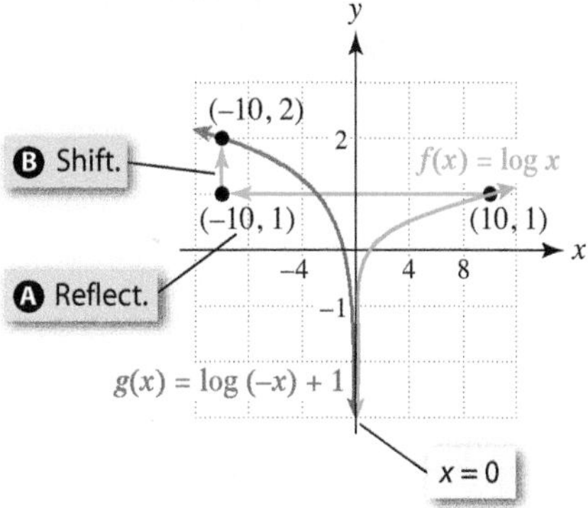

Figure 5.59

Now Try Exercise 113

Basic Equations

Base-10 Exponential Equations To solve the equation $10 + x = 100$, we **subtract 10 from each side** because addition and subtraction are inverse operations.

$$10 + x - \mathbf{10} = 100 - \mathbf{10} \quad \text{Subtract 10.}$$

$$x = 90$$

To solve the equation $10x = 100$, we **divide each side by 10** because multiplication and division are inverse operations.

$$\frac{10x}{10} = \frac{100}{10} \qquad \text{Divide by 10.}$$

$$x = 10$$

Now suppose that we want to solve the exponential equation

$$10^x = 100.$$

What is new about this type of equation is that the variable x is an *exponent*. The inverse operation of 10^x is $\log x$. Rather than subtracting 10 from each side or dividing each side by 10, we **take the base-10 logarithm of each side**. Doing so results in

$$\log 10^x = \log 100. \qquad \text{Take base-10 logarithm.}$$

Because $\log 10^x = x$ for all real numbers x, the equation becomes

$$x = \log 100, \quad \text{or equivalently,} \quad x = 2.$$

These concepts are applied in the next example. Note that if $m = n$ (m and n positive), then $\log m = \log n$.

EXAMPLE 7 Solving equations of the form $10^x = k$

Solve each equation, if possible.

(a) $10^x = 0.001$ **(b)** $10^x = 55$ **(c)** $10^x = -1$

SOLUTION

(a) Take the common logarithm of each side of the equation $10^x = 0.001$. Then

$$\log 10^x = \log 0.001, \quad \text{or} \quad x = \log 10^{-3} = -3.$$

(b) In a similar manner, $10^x = 55$ is equivalent to $x = \log 55 \approx 1.7404$.

(c) Taking the common logarithm of each side gives

$$\log 10^x = \log(-1).$$

Because $\log(-1)$ is undefined, there are no solutions. Graphical support is given in Figure 5.60, where the graphs of $y_1 = 10^x$ and $y_2 = -1$ do not intersect. The exponential expression 10^x is never negative.

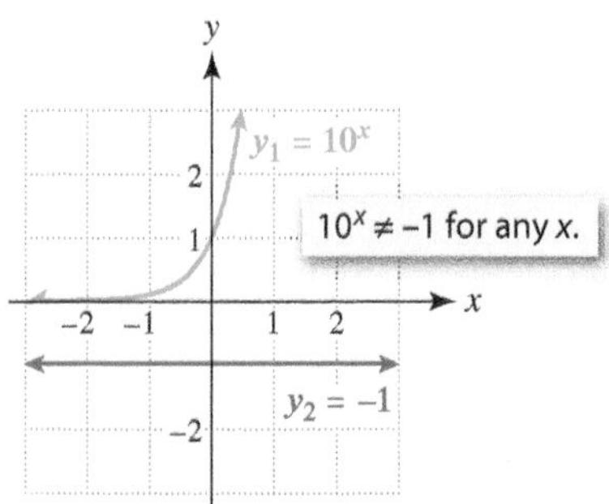

Figure 5.60

Now Try Exercise 57

EXAMPLE 8 Solving a base-10 exponential equation

Solve $4(10^{3x}) = 244$.

SOLUTION Begin by dividing each side by 4.

Changing exponential form to logarithmic form

$$
\begin{aligned}
4(10^{3x}) &= 244 && \text{Given equation}\\
10^{3x} &= 61 && \text{Divide by 4.}\\
\log 10^{3x} &= \log 61 && \text{Take the common logarithm.}\\
3x &= \log 61 && \text{Inverse property: } \log 10^k = k\\
x &= \frac{\log 61}{3} && \text{Divide by 3.}\\
x &\approx 0.595 && \text{Approximate.}
\end{aligned}
$$

Now Try Exercise 69

Converting $10^{3x} = 61$ to $3x = \log 61$ is referred to as changing *exponential form* to *logarithmic form.* We usually include the step of taking the common logarithm of each side to emphasize the fact that *inverse properties* are being used to solve these equations.

Common Logarithmic Equations A **logarithmic equation** contains logarithms. To solve logarithmic equations we *exponentiate* each side of the equation and then apply the inverse property $10^{\log x} = x$. Note that if $m = n$, then $10^m = 10^n$.

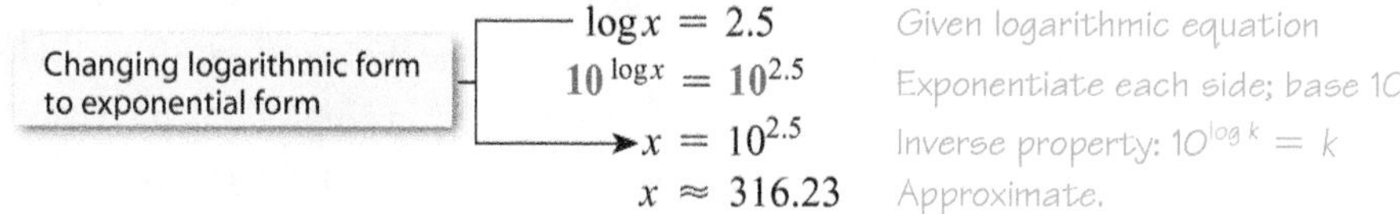

$$
\begin{aligned}
\log x &= 2.5 && \text{Given logarithmic equation}\\
10^{\log x} &= 10^{2.5} && \text{Exponentiate each side; base 10.}\\
x &= 10^{2.5} && \text{Inverse property: } 10^{\log k} = k\\
x &\approx 316.23 && \text{Approximate.}
\end{aligned}
$$

Converting the equation $\log x = 2.5$ to the equivalent equation $x = 10^{2.5}$ is called changing *logarithmic form* to *exponential form.*

EXAMPLE 9 **Solving equations of the form $\log x = k$**

Solve each equation.

(a) $\log x = 3$ **(b)** $\log x = -2$ **(c)** $\log x = 2.7$

SOLUTION

(a)

$$
\begin{aligned}
\log x &= 3 && \text{Given equation}\\
10^{\log x} &= 10^3 && \text{Exponentiate each side; base 10.}\\
x &= 10^3 && \text{Inverse property: } 10^{\log k} = k\\
x &= 1000 && \text{Simplify.}
\end{aligned}
$$

(b) Similarly, $\log x = -2$ is equivalent to $x = 10^{-2} = 0.01$.

(c) $\log x = 2.7$ is equivalent to $x = 10^{2.7} \approx 501.19$.

Now Try Exercise 81

EXAMPLE 10 **Solving a common logarithmic equation**

Solve $5 \log 2x = 16$.

SOLUTION Begin by dividing each side by 5.

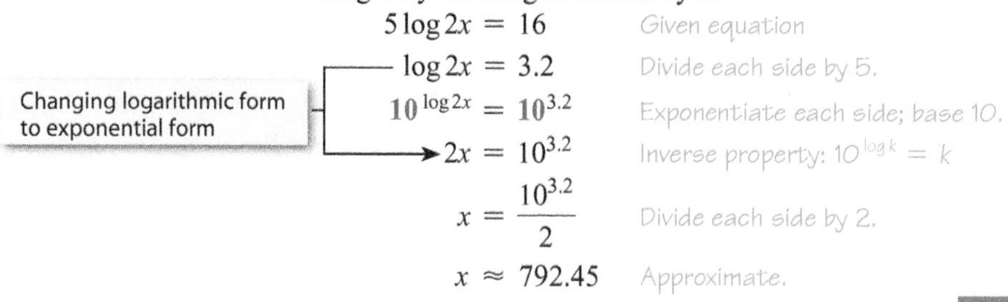

$$
\begin{aligned}
5 \log 2x &= 16 && \text{Given equation}\\
\log 2x &= 3.2 && \text{Divide each side by 5.}\\
10^{\log 2x} &= 10^{3.2} && \text{Exponentiate each side; base 10.}\\
2x &= 10^{3.2} && \text{Inverse property: } 10^{\log k} = k\\
x &= \frac{10^{3.2}}{2} && \text{Divide each side by 2.}\\
x &\approx 792.45 && \text{Approximate.}
\end{aligned}
$$

Now Try Exercise 91

An Application of Logarithms Some types of data grow slowly and can be modeled by the function given by $f(x) = a + b\log x$. For example, a larger area of land tends to have a wider variety of birds. However, if the land area doubles, the number of species of birds does not double; the land area has to more than double before the number of species doubles.

EXAMPLE 11 **Modeling data with logarithms**

The number of species of tropical birds on islands of different sizes x near New Guinea can be modeled by $f(x) = 39 + 13\log x$, where x is in square miles. (***Source:*** B. Freedman, *Environmental Ecology*.)

(a) If the number of square miles x of an island increases tenfold, how many additional species of birds are there?

(b) Determine both symbolically and graphically the size of an island that might have 50 different species of birds.

SOLUTION

(a) Start by evaluating $f(1)$, $f(10)$, and $f(100)$.

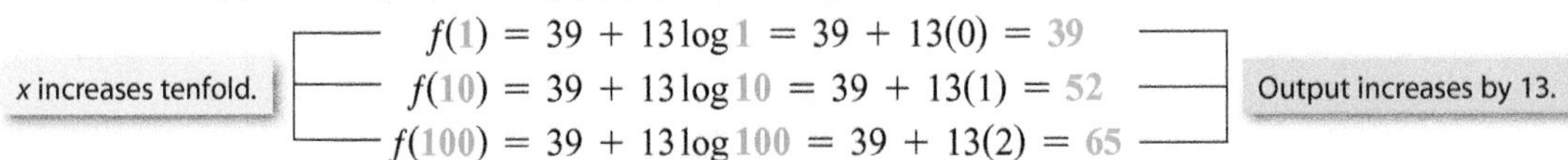

$$f(1) = 39 + 13\log 1 = 39 + 13(0) = 39$$
$$f(10) = 39 + 13\log 10 = 39 + 13(1) = 52$$
$$f(100) = 39 + 13\log 100 = 39 + 13(2) = 65$$

Each time x increases tenfold, the number of bird species does not increase by a factor of 10; rather, it only increases by 13 species of birds. This slow growth is an example of *logarithmic growth*.

(b) ***Symbolic Solution*** We must solve the equation $39 + 13\log x = 50$.

$$\begin{aligned} 39 + 13\log x &= 50 && \text{Equation to solve} \\ 13\log x &= 11 && \text{Subtract 39.} \\ \log x &= \frac{11}{13} && \text{Divide by 13.} \\ 10^{\log x} &= 10^{11/13} && \text{Exponentiate each side; base 10.} \\ x &= 10^{11/13} && \text{Inverse property: } 10^{\log k} = k \\ x &\approx 7 && \text{Approximate.} \end{aligned}$$

To have 50 species of birds, an island should be about 7 square miles.

[0, 15, 5] by [0, 70, 10]

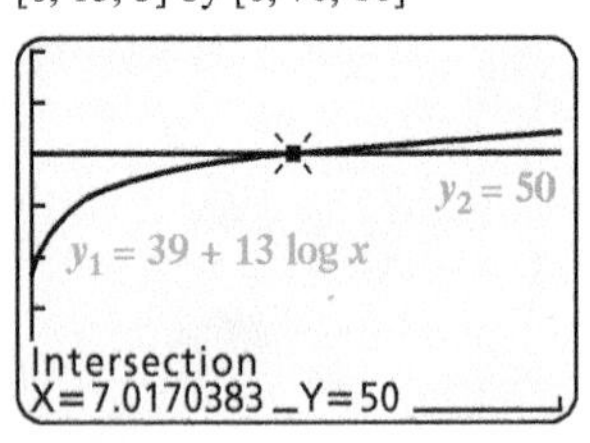

Figure 5.61

Graphical Solution The graphs of $y_1 = 39 + 13\log x$ and $y_2 = 50$ in Figure 5.61 intersect near the point (7.02, 50). This result agrees with our symbolic solution.

Now Try Exercise 139

General Equations

Base-a Exponential Equations The exponential function $f(x) = a^x$ is one-to-one and therefore has an inverse function $f^{-1}(x) = \log_a x$. Because $f^{-1}(f(x)) = x$ for all real numbers x, or equivalently $\log_a a^x = x$, it follows that to solve an exponential equation we can take the base-a logarithm of each side. Note that if $m = n$ (m and n positive), then $\log_a m = \log_a n$.

EXAMPLE 12 **Solving exponential equations**

Solve each equation.

(a) $3^x = \dfrac{1}{27}$ **(b)** $e^x = 5$ **(c)** $3(2^x) - 7 = 20$

SOLUTION

(a)
$$\log_3 3^x = \log_3 \frac{1}{27} \quad \text{Take the base-3 logarithm of each side.}$$
$$\log_3 3^x = \log_3 3^{-3} \quad \text{Properties of exponents}$$
$$x = -3 \quad \text{Inverse property: } \log_a a^k = k$$

ln(5)
1.609437912
e^(1.609437912)
4.999999998

Figure 5.62

(b) Take the natural logarithm of each side. Then

$$\ln e^x = \ln 5 \quad \text{is equivalent to} \quad x = \ln 5 \approx 1.609.$$

Many calculators are able to compute natural logarithms. The evaluation of $\ln 5$ is shown in Figure 5.62. Notice that $e^{1.609437912} \approx 5$.

(c)
$$3(2^x) - 7 = 20 \quad \text{Given equation}$$
$$3(2^x) = 27 \quad \text{Add 7 to each side.}$$
$$2^x = 9 \quad \text{Divide each side by 3.}$$
$$\log_2 2^x = \log_2 9 \quad \text{Take the base-2 logarithm of each side.}$$
$$x = \log_2 9 \quad \text{Inverse property: } \log_a a^k = k$$

Changing exponential form to logarithmic form

Now Try Exercises 59 and 71

[−5, 5, 1] by [−10, 30, 10]

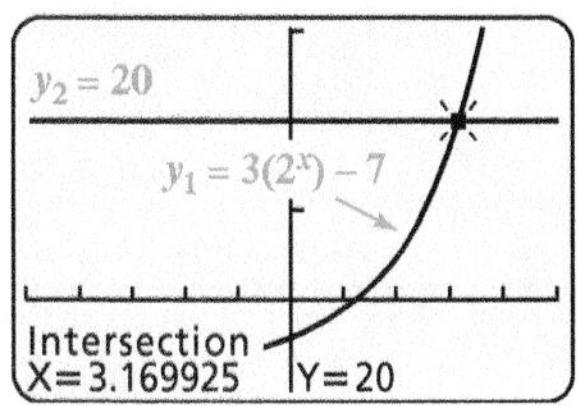

Figure 5.63

Introduction to the Change of Base Formula Figure 5.63 gives a graphical solution of about 3.17 for the equation in Example 12(c). The exact solution of $\log_2 9$ can be approximated as 3.17 by using the following **change of base formula.** (Its derivation is given in Section 5.5.)

$$\log_a x = \frac{\log_b x}{\log_b a} \quad \text{Change of base formula}$$

Because calculators typically have only $\log x$ and $\ln x$ keys, this formula is often written as

Example of change of base formulas

$$\log_a x = \frac{\log x}{\log a} \quad \text{or} \quad \log_a x = \frac{\ln x}{\ln a}$$

For example, $\log_2 9 = \frac{\log 9}{\log 2} \approx 3.17$, which agrees with the graphical solution.

Base-a Logarithmic Equations To solve the equation $\log_a x = k$, we exponentiate each side of the equation by using base a. That is, we use the inverse property: $a^{\log_a x} = x$ for all positive x. This is illustrated in the next example. Note that if $m = n$, then $a^m = a^n$.

EXAMPLE 13 **Solving logarithmic equations**

Solve each equation.

(a) $\log_2 x = 5$ **(b)** $\log_5 x = -2$ **(c)** $\ln x = 4.3$ **(d)** $3\log_2 5x = 9$

SOLUTION

(a)
$$\log_2 x = 5 \quad \text{Given equation}$$
$$2^{\log_2 x} = 2^5 \quad \text{Exponentiate each side; base 2.}$$
$$x = 2^5 \quad \text{Inverse property: } a^{\log_a k} = k$$
$$x = 32 \quad \text{Simplify.}$$

(b) Similarly, $\log_5 x = -2$ is equivalent to $x = 5^{-2} = \frac{1}{25}$.

(c) $\ln x = 4.3$ is equivalent to $x = e^{4.3} \approx 73.7$.

(d)

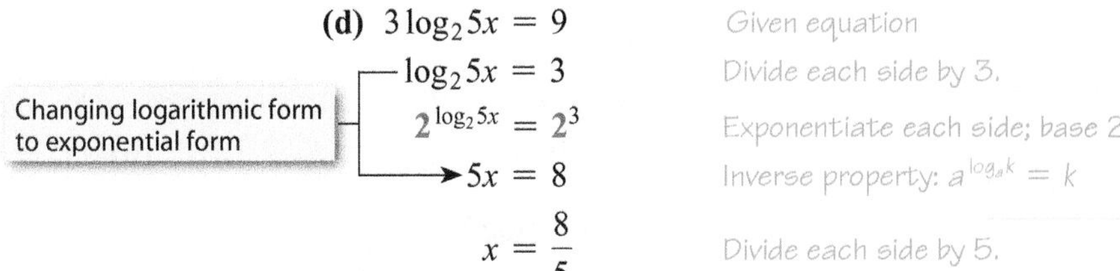

$$3\log_2 5x = 9 \quad \text{Given equation}$$
$$\log_2 5x = 3 \quad \text{Divide each side by 3.}$$
$$2^{\log_2 5x} = 2^3 \quad \text{Exponentiate each side; base 2.}$$
$$5x = 8 \quad \text{Inverse property: } a^{\log_a k} = k$$
$$x = \frac{8}{5} \quad \text{Divide each side by 5.}$$

Changing logarithmic form to exponential form

Now Try Exercises 83 and 87

5.4 Putting It All Together

The following table summarizes some important concepts about base-*a* logarithms. Common and natural logarithms satisfy the same properties.

CONCEPT	EXPLANATION	EXAMPLES
Base-*a* logarithm $a > 0, a \neq 1$	The base-*a* logarithm of a positive number *x* is $\log_a x = k$ if and only if $x = a^k$. That is, a logarithm is an exponent *k*.	$\log 100 = \log 10^2 = 2$ $\log_2 8 = \log_2 2^3 = 3$ $\log_3 \sqrt[3]{3} = \log_3 3^{1/3} = \frac{1}{3}$ $\ln 5 \approx 1.609$ (using a calculator)
Graph of $y = \log_a x$	The graph of the base-*a* logarithmic function *always* passes through the point (1, 0) because $\log_a 1 = \log_a a^0 = 0$. The *y*-axis is a vertical asymptote. The graph passes the horizontal line test, so $f(x) = \log_a x$ is one-to-one and has an inverse given by $f^{-1}(x) = a^x$.	y; $y = \log_a x$, $a > 1$; x; (1, 0)
Inverse properties	a^x and $\log_a x$ represent inverse operations. That is, $\log_a a^x = x$ and $a^{\log_a x} = x$ for $x > 0$.	$\log 10^{-3} = -3$ $\log_4 4^6 = 6$ $10^{\log x} = x, x > 0$ $4^{\log_4 2x} = 2x, x > 0$ $e^{\ln 5} = 5$
Inverse functions	The inverse function of $f(x) = a^x$ is $f^{-1}(x) = \log_a x$.	$f(x) = 10^x \leftrightarrow f^{-1}(x) = \log x$ $g(x) = e^x \leftrightarrow g^{-1}(x) = \ln x$ $h(x) = \log_2 x \leftrightarrow h^{-1}(x) = 2^x$
Exponential and logarithmic forms	$\log_a x = k$ is equivalent to $x = a^k$.	$\log_5 25 = 2$ is equivalent to $25 = 5^2$. $4^3 = 64$ is equivalent to $\log_4 64 = 3$.
Exponential equations	To solve $a^x = k$, take the base-*a* logarithm of each side.	$10^x = 15$; $\log 10^x = \log 15$; $x = \log 15$ | $e^x = 20$; $\ln e^x = \ln 20$; $x = \ln 20$
Logarithmic equations	To solve $\log_a x = k$, exponentiate each side; use base *a*.	$\log x = 3$; $10^{\log x} = 10^3$; $x = 1000$ | $\ln x = 5$; $e^{\ln x} = e^5$; $x = e^5$

5.4 Exercises

Common Logarithms

Exercises 1 and 2: Complete the table.

1.

x	10^0	10^4	10^{-8}	$10^{1.26}$
$\log x$		4		

2.

x	10^{-2}	$10^{-\pi}$	10^5	$10^{7.89}$
$\log x$			5	

Exercises 3–8: Evaluate each expression by hand, if possible.

3. **(a)** $\log(-3)$ **(b)** $\log \frac{1}{100}$
 (c) $\log \sqrt{0.1}$ **(d)** $\log 5^0$

4. **(a)** $\log 10{,}000$ **(b)** $\log(-\pi)$
 (c) $\log \sqrt{0.001}$ **(d)** $\log 8^0$

5. (a) $\log 10$ (b) $\log 10{,}000$
(c) $20 \log 0.1$ (d) $\log 10 + \log 0.001$

6. (a) $\log 100$ (b) $\log 1{,}000{,}000$
(c) $5 \log 0.01$ (d) $\log 0.1 - \log 1000$

7. (a) $2 \log 0.1 + 4$ (b) $\log 10^{1/2}$
(c) $3 \log 100 - \log 1000$ (d) $\log(-10)$

8. (a) $\log(-4)$ (b) $\log 1$
(c) $\log 0$ (d) $-6 \log 100$

Exercises 9 and 10: Determine mentally an integer n so that the logarithm is between n and n + 1. Check your result with a calculator.

9. (a) $\log 79$ (b) $\log 500$
(c) $\log 5$ (d) $\log 0.5$

10. (a) $\log 63$ (b) $\log 5000$
(c) $\log 9$ (d) $\log 0.04$

Exercises 11 and 12: Find the exact value of each expression.

11. (a) $\log \sqrt{1000}$ (b) $\log \sqrt[3]{10}$
(c) $\log \sqrt[5]{0.1}$ (d) $\log \sqrt{0.01}$

12. (a) $\log \sqrt{100{,}000}$ (b) $\log \sqrt[3]{100}$
(c) $2 \log \sqrt{0.1}$ (d) $10 \log \sqrt[3]{10}$

Domains of Logarithmic Functions

Exercises 13–20: Find the domain of f and write it in set-builder or interval notation.

13. $f(x) = \log(x + 3)$
14. $f(x) = \ln(2x - 4)$
15. $f(x) = \log(x^2 - 1)$
16. $f(x) = \log(4 - x^2)$
17. $f(x) = \log(4^x)$
18. $f(x) = \log(5^x - 25)$
19. $f(x) = \ln(\sqrt{3 - x} - 1)$
20. $f(x) = \log(4 - \sqrt{2 - x})$

General Logarithms

Exercises 21–50: Simplify the expression.

21. $\log 10^{-5.7}$
22. $\log 10^{-1.23}$
23. $10^{\log 2x}$
24. $10^{\log(x + 1)}$
25. $\ln e^{64}$
26. $\ln e^{-3}$
27. $\ln e^{-4}$
28. $e^{\ln k}$
29. $\ln e^{\pi}$
30. $\ln e^{9}$
31. $e^{\ln(x - 1)}$
32. $e^{\ln(\pi + 1)}$
33. $\log_2 64$
34. $\log_2 \frac{1}{4}$
35. $\log_4 2$
36. $\log_3 9$
37. $\ln e^{-3}$
38. $\ln e$
39. $\log_8 64$
40. $\ln \sqrt[3]{e}$
41. $\log 10^{-2}$
42. $\log \frac{1}{1000}$
43. $\log \frac{1}{1000}$
44. $\ln \frac{1}{e^3}$
45. $\log_a \frac{1}{a}$
46. $\log_a(a^2 \cdot a^3)$
47. $\log_5 5^0$
48. $\ln \sqrt{e}$
49. $\log_2 \frac{1}{16}$
50. $\log_8 8^k$

Exercises 51 and 52: Complete the table by hand.

51. $f(x) = 2 \log(x - 5)$

x	6	15	105
$f(x)$			

52. $f(x) = 2 \log_3(2x)$

x	$\frac{1}{18}$	$\frac{3}{2}$	$\frac{9}{2}$
$f(x)$			

Exponential and Logarithmic Forms

Exercises 53 and 54: Change each equation to its equivalent logarithmic form.

53. (a) $10^{4x} = 4$ (b) $e^x = 7$ (c) $c^x = b$

54. (a) $10^{2x} = 9$ (b) $e^x = a$ (c) $d^{2x} = b$

Exercises 55 and 56: Change each equation to its equivalent exponential form.

55. (a) $\log x = 3$ (b) $\ln(2 + x) = 5$ (c) $\log_k b = c$

56. (a) $\log x = 4$ (b) $\ln 8x = 7$ (c) $\log_a x = b$

Solving Exponential Equations

Exercises 57–80: Solve each equation. Use the change of base formula to approximate exact answers to the nearest hundredth when appropriate.

57. (a) $10^x = 0.01$ (b) $10^x = 7$ (c) $10^x = -4$

58. (a) $10^x = 1000$ (b) $10^x = 5$ (c) $10^x = -2$

59. (a) $4^x = \frac{1}{16}$ (b) $e^x = 2$ (c) $5^x = 125$

60. (a) $10^x = 9$ (b) $10^x = \frac{1}{1000}$ (c) $e^x = 8$

61. (a) $9^x = 1$ (b) $10^x = \sqrt{10}$ (c) $4^x = \sqrt[3]{4}$

62. (a) $2^x = \sqrt{8}$ (b) $7^x = 1$ (c) $e^x = \sqrt[3]{e}$

63. $e^{-x} = 3$
64. $e^{-x} = \frac{1}{2}$
65. $10^x - 5 = 95$
66. $2 \cdot 10^x = 66$
67. $10^{3x} = 100$
68. $4 \cdot 10^{2x} + 1 = 21$
69. $5(10^{4x}) = 65$
70. $3(10^{x-2}) = 72$

71. $4(e^x) - 3 = 13$ **72.** $5(e^x) + 3 = 83$

73. $e^x + 1 = 24$ **74.** $1 - 2e^x = -5$

75. $e^x + 1 = 15$ **76.** $3 \cdot e^x = 125$

77. $5e^x + 2 = 20$ **78.** $6 - 2e^{3x} = -10$

79. $8 - 3(2)^{0.5x} = -40$ **80.** $2(3)^{-2x} + 5 = 167$

Solving Logarithmic Equations

Exercises 81–102: Solve each equation. Approximate answers to four decimal places when appropriate.

81. **(a)** $\log x = 2$ **(b)** $\log x = -3$ **(c)** $\log x = 1.2$

82. **(a)** $\log x = 1$ **(b)** $\log x = -4$ **(c)** $\log x = 0.3$

83. **(a)** $\ln x = 6$ **(b)** $\ln x = -2$ **(c)** $\ln x = 2$

84. **(a)** $\log x = 2$ **(b)** $\log x = -1$ **(c)** $\ln x = -2$

85. $\log x = 1.2$ **86.** $\log x = 3.7$

87. $5 \log_7 2x = 10$ **88.** $2 \log_4 x = 3.4$

89. $2 \log x = 6$ **90.** $\log 4x = 2$

91. $2 \log 5x = 4$ **92.** $6 - \log x = 3$

93. $4 \ln x = 3$ **94.** $\ln 5x = 8$

95. $5 \ln x - 1 = 6$ **96.** $2 \ln 3x = 8$

97. $4 \log_2 x = 16$ **98.** $\log_3 5x = 10$

99. $5 \ln(2x) + 6 = 12$ **100.** $16 - 4 \ln 3x = 2$

101. $9 - 3 \log 2x = 3$ **102.** $7 \log(4x) + 5 = -2$

Exercises 103 and 104: Find values for a and b so that f(x) models the data exactly.

103. $f(x) = a + b \log x$

x	1	10	100
$f(x)$	5	7	9

104. $f(x) = a + b \log_2 x$

x	1	2	4
$f(x)$	3.1	6	8.9

Graphs of Logarithmic Functions

Exercises 105–108: Use the graph of f to sketch a graph of f^{-1}. Give a symbolic representation of f^{-1}.

105.

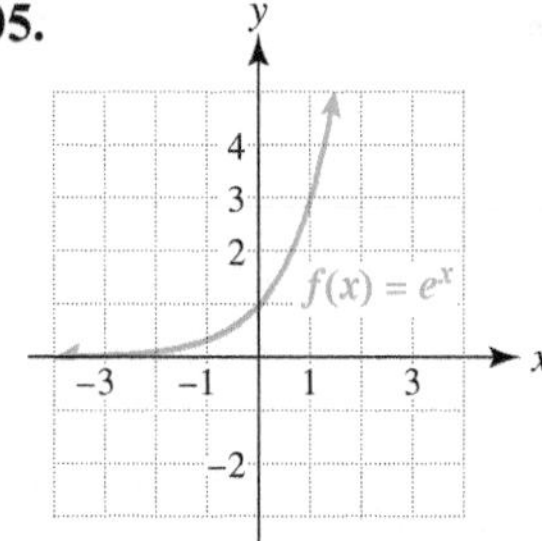

106.

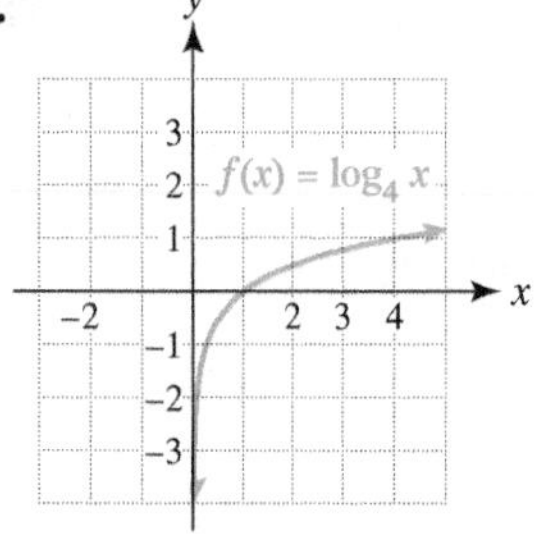

107. **108.**

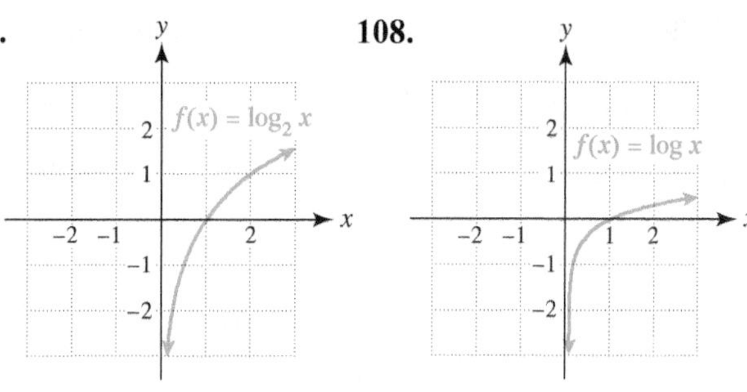

Exercises 109 and 110: Graph $y = f(x)$. Is f increasing or decreasing on its domain?

109. $f(x) = \log_{1/2} x$ **110.** $f(x) = \log_{1/3} x$

Exercises 111 and 112: Complete the following.

(a) Graph $y = f(x)$, $y = f^{-1}(x)$, and $y = x$.

(b) Determine the intervals where f and f^{-1} are increasing or decreasing.

111. $f(x) = \log_3 x$ **112.** $f(x) = \log_{1/2} x$

Transformations of Graphs

Exercises 113–120: Use transformations to graph $y = g(x)$. Give the equation of any asymptotes.

113. $g(x) = \log(x - 2)$ **114.** $g(x) = \log(x + 2)$

115. $g(x) = 3 \log x$ **116.** $g(x) = 2 \log_2 x$

117. $g(x) = \log_2(-x)$ **118.** $g(x) = -\log_2 x$

119. $g(x) = 2 + \ln(x - 1)$ **120.** $g(x) = \ln(x + 1) - 1$

Exercises 121–124: Graph f and state its domain.

121. $f(x) = \log(x + 1)$ **122.** $f(x) = \log(x - 3)$

123. $f(x) = \ln(-x)$ **124.** $f(x) = \ln(x^2 + 1)$

Applications

125. Decibels Sound levels in decibels (dB) can be calculated by

$$D(x) = 10 \log(10^{16} x),$$

where x is the intensity of the sound in watts per square meter. The human ear begins to hurt when the intensity reaches $x = 10^{-4}$. Find how many decibels this represents.

126. Decibels (Refer to Exercise 125.) If the intensity increases by a *factor* of 10, find the increase in decibels.

127. Runway Length There is a relation between an airplane's weight x and the runway length L required for takeoff. For some airplanes the minimum runway length L in thousands of feet is given by $L(x) = 3 \log x$, where x is measured in thousands of pounds. (***Source:*** L. Haefner, *Introduction to Transportation Systems.*)

(a) Evaluate $L(100)$ and interpret the result.

(b) If the weight of an airplane increases tenfold from 10,000 to 100,000 pounds, does the length of the required runway also increase by a factor of 10? Explain.

(c) Generalize your answer from part (b).

128. Runway Length (Refer to Exercise 127.) Estimate the maximum weight of a plane that can take off from a runway that is 5 thousand feet long.

129. Acid Rain Air pollutants frequently cause acid rain. A measure of the acidity is pH, which ranges between 1 and 14. Pure water is neutral and has a pH of 7. Acidic solutions have a pH less than 7, whereas alkaline solutions have a pH greater than 7. A pH value can be computed by $\text{pH} = -\log x$, where x represents the hydrogen ion concentration in moles per liter. In rural areas of Europe, rainwater typically has $x = 10^{-4.7}$. (*Source*: G. Howells, *Acid Rain and Acid Water*.)

(a) Find its pH.

(b) Seawater has a pH of 8.2. How many times greater is the hydrogen ion concentration in rainwater from rural Europe than in seawater?

130. Acid Rain (Refer to Exercise 129.) Find the hydrogen ion concentration for the following pH levels of acid rain. (*Source:* G. Howells.)

(a) 4.92 (pH of rain at Amsterdam Islands)

(b) 3.9 (pH of some rain in the eastern United States)

131. Earthquakes The Richter scale is used to measure the intensity of earthquakes, where intensity corresponds to the amount of energy released by an earthquake. If an earthquake has an intensity of x, then its *magnitude*, as computed by the Richter scale, is given by the formula $R(x) = \log \frac{x}{I_0}$, where I_0 is the intensity of a small measurable earthquake.

(a) On July 26, 1963, an earthquake in Yugoslavia had a magnitude of 6.0 on the Richter scale, and on August 19, 1977, an earthquake in Indonesia measured 8.0. Find the intensity x for each of these earthquakes if $I_0 = 1$.

(b) How many times more intense was the Indonesian earthquake than the Yugoslavian earthquake?

132. Earthquakes (Refer to Exercise 131.) If the intensity x of an earthquake increases by a *factor* of 10^3, by how much does the Richter number R increase? Generalize your results.

133. Hurricanes Hurricanes are some of the largest storms on Earth. They are very low pressure areas with diameters of over 500 miles. The barometric air pressure in inches of mercury at a distance of x miles from the eye of a severe hurricane is modeled by the formula $f(x) = 0.48 \ln(x + 1) + 27$ (*Source:* A. Miller and R. Anthes, *Meteorology*.)

(a) Evaluate $f(0)$ and $f(100)$. Interpret the results.

(b) Graph f in [0, 250, 50] by [25, 30, 1]. Describe how air pressure changes as one moves away from the eye of the hurricane.

(c) At what distance from the eye of the hurricane is the air pressure 28 inches of mercury?

134. Predicting Wind Speed Wind speed typically varies in the first 20 meters above the ground. For a particular day, let the formula $f(x) = 1.2 \ln x + 2.3$ compute the wind speed in meters per second at a height x meters above the ground for $x \geq 1$. (*Source*: A. Miller.)

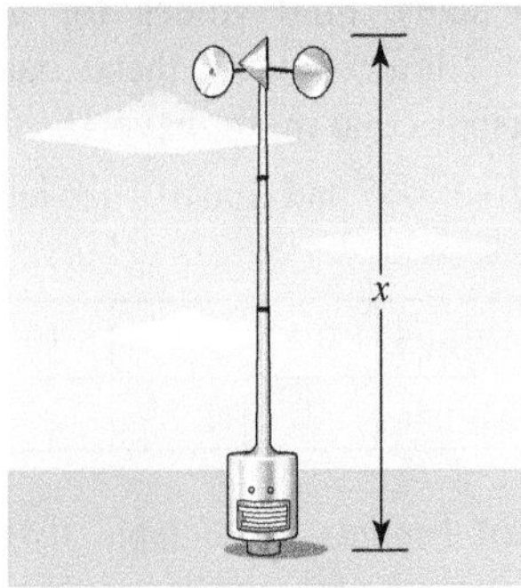

(a) Find the wind speed at a height of 5 meters.

(b) Graph f in the window [0, 20, 5] by [0, 7, 1]. Interpret the graph.

(c) Estimate the height where the wind speed is 5 meters per second.

135. Cooling an Object A pot of boiling water with a temperature of 100°C is set in a room with a temperature of 20°C. The temperature T of the water after x hours is given by $T(x) = 20 + 80e^{-x}$.

(a) Estimate the temperature of the water after 1 hour.

(b) How long did it take the water to cool to 60°C?

136. Warming an Object A can of soda with a temperature of 5°C is set in a room with a temperature of 20°C. The temperature T of the soda after x minutes is given by $T(x) = 20 - 15(10)^{-0.05x}$.

(a) Estimate the temperature of the soda after 5 minutes.

(b) After how many minutes was the temperature of the soda 15°C?

137. Traffic Flow (Refer to Example 11 (Part II), Section 5.3.) Cars arrive randomly at an intersection with an average rate of 20 cars per hour. The likelihood, or

(continued)

probability, that no car enters the intersection within a period of x minutes can be estimated by $f(x) = e^{-x/3}$.

(a) What is the probability that no car enters the intersection during a 5-minute period?

(b) Determine the value of x that gives a 30% chance that no car enters the intersection during an interval of x minutes.

138. Population Growth The population of Nevada in millions is given by $P(x) = 2.7e^{0.014x}$, where $x = 0$ corresponds to 2010. (***Source:*** Bureau of the Census.)

(a) Determine symbolically the year when the population of Nevada might be 3 million.

(b) Solve part (a) graphically.

139. Diversity of Birds (Refer to Example 11.) The table lists the number of species of birds on islands of various sizes. Find values for a and b so that $f(x) = a + b\log x$ models these data. Estimate the size of an island that might have 16 species of birds.

(*Hint:* Let $f(1) = 7$ and find a. Then let $f(10) = 11$ and find b.)

Area (km^2)	0.1	1	10	100	1000
Species of birds	3	7	11	15	19

140. Diversity of Insects The table lists the number of types of insects found in wooded regions with various acreages. Find values for a and b so that $f(x) = a + b\log x$ models these data. Then use f to estimate an acreage that might have 1200 types of insects.

Area (acres)	10	100	1000	10,000
Insect Types	500	800	1100	1400

141. Growth of Bacteria The table lists the number of bacteria y in millions after an elapsed time of x days.

x	0	1	2	3	4
y	3	6	12	24	48

(a) Find values for C and a so that $f(x) = Ca^x$ models the data.

(b) Estimate when there were 16 million bacteria.

142. Growth of an Investment The growth of an investment is shown in the table in the next column.

x (years)	0	5	10	15	20
y (dollars)	100	300	900	2700	8100

(a) Find values for C and a so that $f(x) = Ca^x$ models the data.

(b) Estimate when the account contained $2000.

Writing about Mathematics

143. Describe the relationship among exponential functions and logarithmic functions. Explain why logarithms are needed to solve exponential equations.

144. Give verbal, numerical, graphical, and symbolic representations of a base-5 logarithmic function.

Extended And Discovery Exercises

1. Average Rate of Change of ln x Find the average rate of change of $f(x) = \ln x$ from x to $x + 0.001$ for each value of x. Round your answers to two decimal places.

(a) $x = 1$ **(b)** $x = 2$

(c) $x = 3$ **(d)** $x = 4$

2. Average Rate of Change of ln x (See Exercise 1.) Compare each average rate of change of $\ln x$ to x. What is the pattern? Make a generalization.

3. Climate Change According to one model, the future increases in average global temperatures (due to carbon dioxide levels exceeding 280 parts per million) can be estimated using $T = 6.5\ln(C/280)$, where C is the concentration of atmospheric carbon dioxide in parts per million (ppm) and T is in degrees Fahrenheit. Let future amounts of carbon dioxide x years after 2000 be modeled by the formula $C(x) = 364(1.005)^x$. (***Source:*** W. Clime, *The Economics of Global Warming*.)

(a) Use composition of functions to write T as a function of x. Evaluate T when $x = 100$ and interpret the result.

(b) Graph $C(x)$ in [0, 200, 50] by [0, 1000, 100] and $T(x)$ in [0, 200, 50] by [0, 10, 1]. Describe each graph.

(c) How does an exponential growth in carbon dioxide concentrations affect the increase in temperature?

CHECKING BASIC CONCEPTS FOR SECTIONS 5.3 AND 5.4

1. If the principal is $1200 and the interest rate is 9.5% compounded monthly, calculate the account balance after 4 years. Determine the balance if the interest is compounded continuously.

2. Find values for C and a so that $f(x) = Ca^x$ models the data in the table.

x	0	1	2	3
y	4	2	1	0.5

3. Explain verbally what $\log_2 15$ represents. Is it equal to an integer? (Do not use a calculator.)

4. Evaluate each of the following logarithms by hand.

(a) $\log_6 36$ **(b)** $\log\sqrt{10} + \log 0.01$ **(c)** $\ln\frac{1}{e^2}$

5. Solve each equation.

(a) $e^x = 5$ **(b)** $10^x = 25$ **(c)** $\log x = 1.5$

6. Solve each equation.

(a) $2e^x + 1 = 25$ **(b)** $\log 2x = 2.3$

(c) $\log x^2 = 1$

7. **Population** The population of California in millions x years after 2010 can be modeled by $P(x) = 37.3e^{0.01x}$. (***Source:*** Bureau of the Census.)

(a) Evaluate $P(2)$. Interpret this result.

(b) Find the y-intercept on the graph of $y = f(x)$. Interpret this result.

(c) Estimate the annual percent increase in the population of California.

(d) Predict when the population might reach 40 million.

8. **Growth in Salary** Suppose that a person's salary is initially \$30,000 and is modeled by $f(x)$, where x represents the number of years of experience. Use $f(x)$ to approximate the years of experience when the salary first *exceeds* \$60,000.

(a) $f(x) = 30{,}000(1.1)^x$

(b) $f(x) = 30{,}000 \log(10 + x)$

Would most people prefer that their salaries increase exponentially or logarithmically?

5.5 Properties of Logarithms

- **Apply basic properties of logarithms**
- **Expand and combine logarithmic expressions**
- **Use the change of base formula**

Introduction

The discovery of logarithms by John Napier (1550–1617) played an important role in the history of science. Logarithms were instrumental in allowing Johannes Kepler (1571–1630) to calculate the positions of the planet Mars, which led to his discovery of the laws of planetary motion. Kepler's laws were used by Isaac Newton (1643–1727) to discover the universal laws of gravitation. Although calculators and computers have made tables of logarithms obsolete, applications involving logarithms still play an important role in modern-day computation. One reason is that logarithms possess important properties. For example, the loudness of a sound can be measured in decibels by the formula $f(x) = 10\log(10^{16}x)$, where x is the intensity of the sound. In Example 4, we use properties of logarithms to simplify this formula.

Basic Properties of Logarithms

Logarithms possess several important properties. One property of logarithms states that

the sum of the logarithms of two numbers equals the logarithm of their product.

For example, we see in Figure 5.64 that

$$\log 5 + \log 2 = \log 10 \qquad 5 \cdot 2 = 10$$

and in Figure 5.65 that

$$\log 4 + \log 25 = \log 100. \qquad 4 \cdot 25 = 100$$

These calculations show the product rule of logarithms: $\log_a m + \log_a n = \log_a(mn)$.

Product Rule: $\log m + \log n = \log(m \cdot n)$

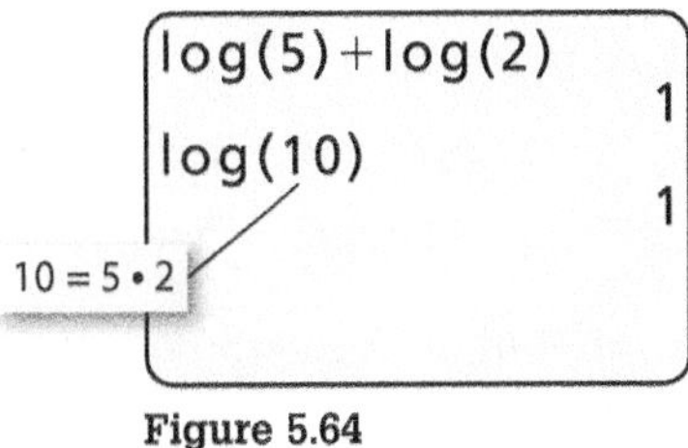

Figure 5.64

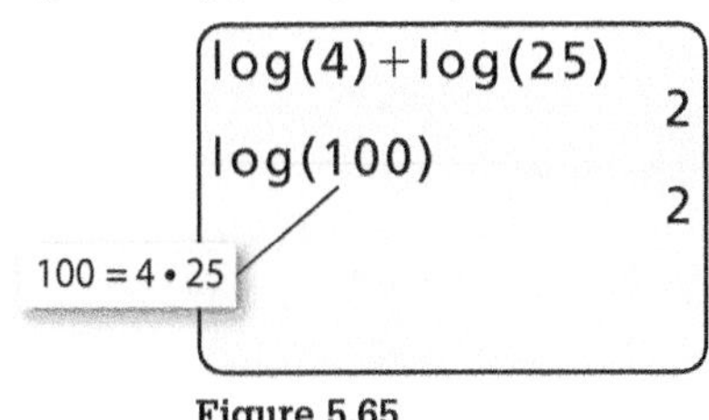

Figure 5.65

Four properties, or rules, of logarithms are as follows.

PROPERTIES OF LOGARITHMS

For positive numbers m, n, and $a \neq 1$ and any real number r:

1. $\log_a 1 = 0$ and $\log_a a = 1$ — Logarithms of 1 and a
2. $\log_a m + \log_a n = \log_a (mn)$ — Product rule
3. $\log_a m - \log_a n = \log_a \left(\frac{m}{n}\right)$ — Quotient rule
4. $\log_a (m^r) = r \log_a m$ — Power rule

Algebra Review
To review properties of exponents, see Section 4.8 and Chapter R (page R-7).

The properties of logarithms are a direct result of the properties of exponents and the inverse property $\log_a a^k = k$, as shown below.

Logarithms of 1 and a: This property is a direct result of the inverse property: $\log_a a^x = x$.

$$\log_a 1 = \log_a a^0 = 0 \quad \text{and} \quad \log_a a = \log_a a^1 = 1$$

Examples: $\log 1 = 0$ and $\ln e = 1$

Product Rule: If m and n are positive numbers, then we can write $m = a^c$ and $n = a^d$ for some real numbers c and d.

$$\log_a m + \log_a n = \log_a a^c + \log_a a^d = c + d$$
$$\log_a (mn) = \log_a (a^c a^d) = \log_a (a^{c+d}) = c + d$$

Both expressions equal $c + d$.

Thus $\log_a m + \log_a n = \log_a (mn)$.

Example: Let $m = 100$ and $n = 1000$.

$$\log 100 + \log 1000 = \log 10^2 + \log 10^3 = 2 + 3 = 5$$
$$\log (100 \cdot 1000) = \log 100{,}000 = \log 10^5 = 5$$

Quotient Rule: Let $m = a^c$ and $n = a^d$ for some real numbers c and d.

$$\log_a m - \log_a n = \log_a a^c - \log_a a^d = c - d$$
$$\log_a \left(\frac{m}{n}\right) = \log_a \left(\frac{a^c}{a^d}\right) = \log_a (a^{c-d}) = c - d$$

Both expressions equal $c - d$.

Thus $\log_a m - \log_a n = \log_a \left(\frac{m}{n}\right)$.

Example: Let $m = 100$ and $n = 1000$.

$$\log 100 - \log 1000 = \log 10^2 - \log 10^3 = 2 - 3 = -1$$
$$\log \left(\frac{100}{1000}\right) = \log \left(\frac{1}{10}\right) = \log (10^{-1}) = -1$$

Power Rule: Let $m = a^c$ and r be any real number.

$$\log_a m^r = \log_a (a^c)^r = \log_a (a^{cr}) = cr$$
$$r \log_a m = r \log_a a^c = rc = cr$$

Both expressions equal cr.

Thus $\log_a (m^r) = r \log_a m$.

Example: Let $m = 100$ and $r = 3$.

$$\log 100^3 = \log 1{,}000{,}000 = \log 10^6 = 6$$
$$3 \log 100 = 3 \log 10^2 = 3 \cdot 2 = 6$$

Caution: $\log_a (m + n) \neq \log_a m + \log_a n$; $\log_a (m - n) \neq \log_a m - \log_a n$

EXAMPLE 1 **Recognizing properties of logarithms**

Use a calculator to evaluate each pair of expressions. Then state which rule of logarithms this calculation illustrates.

(a) $\ln 5 + \ln 4$, $\ln 20$ **(b)** $\log 10 - \log 5$, $\log 2$ **(c)** $\log 5^2$, $2 \log 5$

SOLUTION

(a) From Figure 5.66, we see that the two expressions are equal. These calculations illustrate the product rule because $\ln 5 + \ln 4 = \ln(5 \cdot 4) = \ln 20$.

(b) The two expressions are equal in Figure 5.67, and these calculations illustrate the quotient rule because $\log 10 - \log 5 = \log \frac{10}{5} = \log 2$.

(c) The two expressions are equal in Figure 5.68, and these calculations illustrate the power rule because $\log 5^2 = 2 \log 5$.

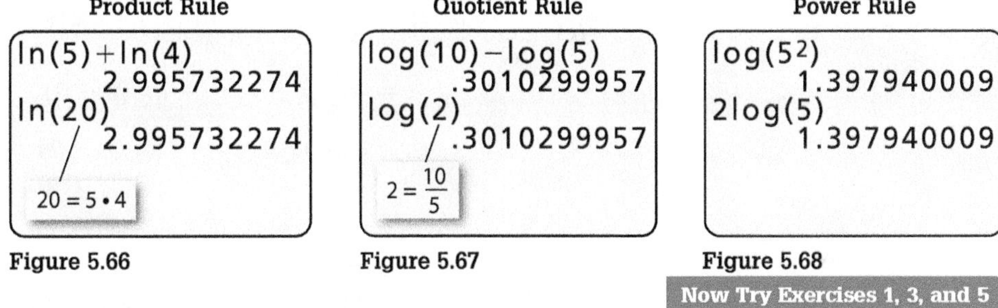

Product Rule
ln(5)+ln(4)
2.995732274
ln(20)
2.995732274
20 = 5 • 4
Quotient Rule
log(10)−log(5)
.3010299957
log(2)
.3010299957
2 = 10/5
Power Rule
log(5²)
1.397940009
2log(5)
1.397940009

Figure 5.66 **Figure 5.67** **Figure 5.68**

Now Try Exercises 1, 3, and 5

Expanding and Combining Logarithmic Expressions

We can use the properties of logarithms to expand and combine logarithmic expressions, as illustrated by the following.

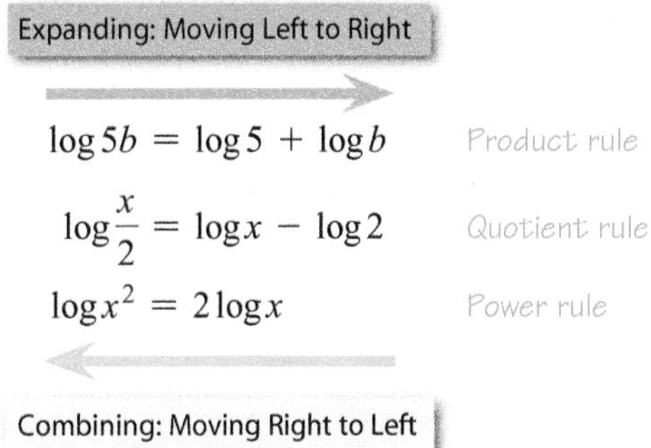

The next two examples demonstrate how to expand logarithmic expressions.

EXAMPLE 2 **Expanding logarithmic expressions**

Use properties of logarithms to expand each expression. Write your answers without exponents.

(a) $\log xy$ **(b)** $\ln \frac{5}{z}$ **(c)** $\log_4 \frac{\sqrt[3]{x}}{\sqrt{k}}$

SOLUTION

(a) By the product rule, $\log xy = \log x + \log y$.

(b) By the quotient rule, $\ln \frac{5}{z} = \ln 5 - \ln z$.

(c) Begin by using the quotient rule.

$$\begin{aligned} \log_4 \frac{\sqrt[3]{x}}{\sqrt{k}} &= \log_4 \sqrt[3]{x} - \log_4 \sqrt{k} && \text{Quotient rule} \\ &= \log_4 x^{1/3} - \log_4 k^{1/2} && \text{Properties of exponents} \\ &= \tfrac{1}{3}\log_4 x - \tfrac{1}{2}\log_4 k && \text{Power rule} \end{aligned}$$

Now Try Exercises 7, 11, and 21

EXAMPLE 3 Expanding logarithmic expressions

Expand each expression. Write your answers without exponents.

(a) $\log_2 2x^4$ **(b)** $\ln\frac{7x^3}{k^2}$ **(c)** $\log\frac{\sqrt{x+1}}{(x-2)^3}$

SOLUTION

(a) $\log_2 2x^4 = \log_2 2 + \log_2 x^4$ — Product rule

$= 1 + 4\log_2 x$ — Power rule; logarithm of *a*

(b) $\ln\frac{7x^3}{k^2} = \ln 7x^3 - \ln k^2$ — Quotient rule

$= \ln 7 + \ln x^3 - \ln k^2$ — Product rule

$= \ln 7 + 3\ln x - 2\ln k$ — Power rule

(c) $\log\frac{\sqrt{x+1}}{(x-2)^3} = \log\sqrt{x+1} - \log(x-2)^3$ — Quotient rule

$= \log(x+1)^{1/2} - \log(x-2)^3$ — Property of exponents

$= \frac{1}{2}\log(x+1) - 3\log(x-2)$ — Power rule

Now Try Exercises 9, 15, and 27

An Application Sometimes properties of logarithms are used in applications to simplify a formula. This is illustrated in the next example.

EXAMPLE 4 Analyzing sound with decibels

Sound levels in decibels (dB) can be computed by $D(x) = 10\log(10^{16}x)$.

(a) Use properties of logarithms to simplify the formula for D.

(b) Ordinary conversation has an intensity of $x = 10^{-10}$ w/cm^2. Find the decibel level.

SOLUTION

(a) To simplify the formula, use the product rule.

$D(x) = 10\log(10^{16}x)$ — Given formula

$= 10(\log 10^{16} + \log x)$ — Product rule

$= 10(16 + \log x)$ — Inverse property

$= 160 + 10\log x$ — Distributive property

(b) $D(10^{-10}) = 160 + 10\log(10^{-10}) = 160 + 10(-10) = 160 - 100 = 60$

Ordinary conversation occurs at about 60 decibels.

Now Try Exercise 83

The next two examples demonstrate how properties of logarithms can be used to combine logarithmic expressions.

EXAMPLE 5 Combining terms in logarithmic expressions

Write each expression as the logarithm of a single expression.

(a) $\ln 2e + \ln\frac{1}{e}$ **(b)** $\log_2 27 + \log_2 x^3$ **(c)** $\log x^3 - \log x^2$

SOLUTION

(a) By the product rule, $\ln 2e + \ln\frac{1}{e} = \ln\left(2e \cdot \frac{1}{e}\right) = \ln 2$.

(b) By the product rule, $\log_2 27 + \log_2 x^3 = \log_2(27x^3)$.

(c) By the quotient rule, $\log x^3 - \log x^2 = \log\frac{x^3}{x^2} = \log x$.

Now Try Exercises 41, 43, and 49

EXAMPLE 6 Combining terms in logarithmic expressions

Write each expression as the logarithm of a single expression.

(a) $\log 5 + \log 15 - \log 3$ **(b)** $2\ln x - \frac{1}{2}\ln y - 3\ln z$

(c) $5\log_3 x + \log_3 2x - \log_3 y$

SOLUTION

(a)

$$\begin{aligned} \log 5 + \log 15 - \log 3 &= \log(5 \cdot 15) - \log 3 && \text{Product rule} \\ &= \log\left(\frac{5 \cdot 15}{3}\right) && \text{Quotient rule} \\ &= \log 25 && \text{Simplify.} \end{aligned}$$

Algebra Review
To review rational exponents and radical notation, see Chapter R (page R-38).

(b)

$$\begin{aligned} 2\ln x - \frac{1}{2}\ln y - 3\ln z &= \ln x^2 - \ln y^{1/2} - \ln z^3 && \text{Power rule} \\ &= \ln\left(\frac{x^2}{y^{1/2}}\right) - \ln z^3 && \text{Quotient rule} \\ &= \ln\frac{x^2}{y^{1/2}z^3} && \text{Quotient rule} \\ &= \ln\frac{x^2}{z^3\sqrt{y}} && \text{Properties of exponents} \end{aligned}$$

(c)

$$\begin{aligned} 5\log_3 x + \log_3 2x - \log_3 y &= \log_3 x^5 + \log_3 2x - \log_3 y && \text{Power rule} \\ &= \log_3(x^5 \cdot 2x) - \log_3 y && \text{Product rule} \\ &= \log_3\frac{2x^6}{y} && \text{Quotient rule} \end{aligned}$$

Now Try Exercises 39, 47, and 51

Change of Base Formula

Calculators usually have keys to approximate common and natural logarithms. Occasionally it is necessary to evaluate a logarithm with a base other than 10 or e. This computation can be accomplished by using a change of base formula.

CHANGE OF BASE FORMULA

Let x, $a \neq 1$, and $b \neq 1$ be positive real numbers. Then

$$\log_a x = \frac{\log_b x}{\log_b a}.$$

The change of base formula can be derived as follows.

$$\begin{aligned} y &= \log_a x \\ a^y &= a^{\log_a x} && \text{Exponentiate each side; base } a. \\ a^y &= x && \text{Inverse property} \\ \log_b a^y &= \log_b x && \text{Take base-}b\text{ logarithm of each side.} \\ y\log_b a &= \log_b x && \text{Power rule} \\ y &= \frac{\log_b x}{\log_b a} && \text{Divide by } \log_b a. \\ \log_a x &= \frac{\log_b x}{\log_b a} && \text{Substitute } \log_a x \text{ for } y. \text{ (First equation)} \end{aligned}$$

To calculate $\log_2 5$, evaluate $\frac{\log 5}{\log 2} \approx 2.322$. The change of base formula was used with $x = 5$, $a = 2$, and $b = 10$. We could also have evaluated $\frac{\ln 5}{\ln 2} \approx 2.322$.

EXAMPLE 7 **Applying the change of base formula**

Use a calculator to approximate each expression to the nearest thousandth.
(a) $\log_4 20$ **(b)** $\log_2 125 + \log_7 39$

SOLUTION

(a) Using the change of base formula, we have $\log_4 20 = \frac{\log 20}{\log 4} \approx 2.161$. We could also evaluate $\frac{\ln 20}{\ln 4}$, as shown in Figure 5.69.

(b) $\log_2 125 + \log_7 39 = \frac{\log 125}{\log 2} + \frac{\log 39}{\log 7} \approx 8.848$. See Figure 5.70.

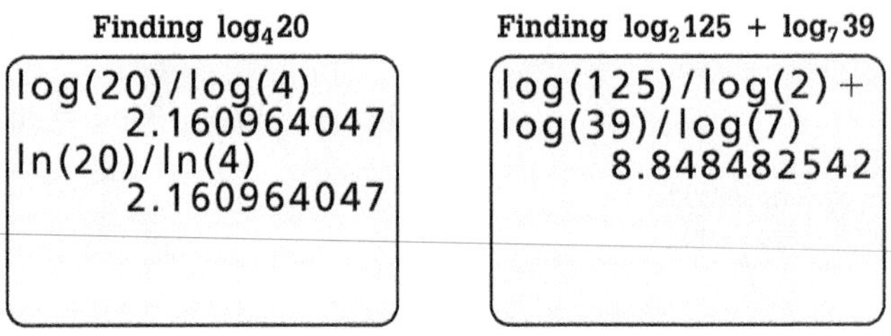

Figure 5.69 Figure 5.70

Now Try Exercises 67 and 71

The change of base formula can be used to graph base-a logarithmic functions.

EXAMPLE 8 **Using the change of base formula for graphing**

Solve the equation $\log_2(x^3 + x - 1) = 5$ graphically.

SOLUTION

Graph $y_1 = \log(x^3 + x - 1)/\log 2$ and $y_2 = 5$. See Figure 5.71. Their graphs intersect near the point (3.104, 5). The solution is given by $x \approx 3.104$.

Now Try Exercise 77

[−10, 10, 1] by [−10, 10, 1]

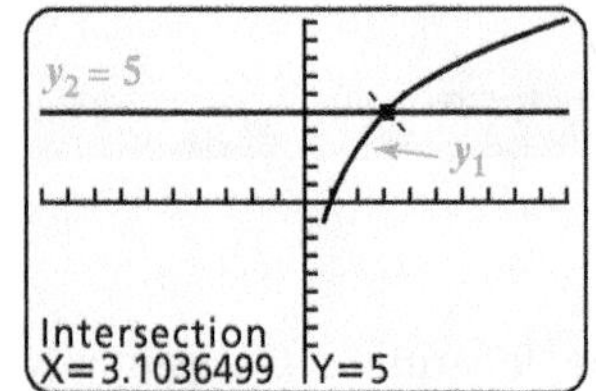

Figure 5.71

5.5 Putting It All Together

The following table summarizes some properties of logarithms.

CONCEPT	EXPLANATION	EXAMPLES
Properties of logarithms	**1.** $\log_a 1 = 0$ and $\log_a a = 1$ **2.** $\log_a m + \log_a n = \log_a(mn)$ **3.** $\log_a m - \log_a n = \log_a\left(\frac{m}{n}\right)$ **4.** $\log_a(m^r) = r\log_a m$	**1.** $\ln 1 = 0$ and $\log_2 2 = 1$ **2.** $\log 3 + \log 6 = \log(3 \cdot 6) = \log 18$ **3.** $\log_3 8 - \log_3 2 = \log_3 \frac{8}{2} = \log_3 4$ **4.** $\log 6^7 = 7\log 6$
Change of base formula	Let x, $a \neq 1$, and $b \neq 1$ be positive real numbers. Then $\log_a x = \frac{\log_b x}{\log_b a}$.	$\log_3 6 = \frac{\log 6}{\log 3} = \frac{\ln 6}{\ln 3} \approx 1.631$
Graphing logarithmic functions	Use the change of base formula to graph $y = \log_a x$ whenever $a \neq 10$ and $a \neq e$.	To graph $y = \log_2 x$, let $Y_1 = \log(X)/\log(2)$ or $Y_1 = \ln(X)/\ln(2)$.

5.5 Exercises

Note: *When applying properties of logarithms, assume that all variables are positive.*

Properties of Logarithms

Exercises 1–6: (Refer to Example 1.) Use a calculator to approximate each pair of expressions. Then state which property of logarithms this calculation illustrates.

1. $\log 4 + \log 7,\quad \log 28$

2. $\ln 12 + \ln 5,\quad \ln 60$

3. $\ln 72 - \ln 8,\quad \ln 9$

4. $3\log 4,\quad \log 4^3$

5. $10\log 2,\quad \log 1024$

6. $\log 100 - \log 20,\quad \log 5$

Exercises 7–32: (Refer to Examples 2 and 3.) Expand the expression. If possible, write your answer without exponents.

7. $\log ab$

8. $\ln 3x$

9. $\ln 7a^4$

10. $\log \dfrac{a^3}{3}$

11. $\log \dfrac{6}{z}$

12. $\ln \dfrac{xy}{z}$

13. $\log \dfrac{x^2}{3}$

14. $\log 3x^6$

15. $\ln \dfrac{2x^7}{3k}$

16. $\ln \dfrac{kx^3}{5}$

17. $\log 4k^2x^3$

18. $\log \dfrac{5kx^2}{11}$

19. $\log \dfrac{25x^3}{y^4}$

20. $\log \dfrac{32}{xy^2}$

21. $\ln \dfrac{x^4}{y^2\sqrt{z^3}}$

22. $\ln \dfrac{x\sqrt[3]{y^2}}{z^6}$

23. $\log(0.25(x+2)^3)$

24. $\log(0.001(a-b)^{-3})$

25. $\ln \dfrac{x^3}{(x-4)^4}$

26. $\ln \dfrac{(3x-2)^2}{x^2+1}$

27. $\log \dfrac{\sqrt{x}}{z^2}$

28. $\log \sqrt{\dfrac{xy^2}{z}}$

29. $\ln \sqrt[3]{\dfrac{2x+6}{(x+1)^5}}$

30. $\log \dfrac{\sqrt{x^2+4}}{\sqrt[3]{x-1}}$

31. $\log \dfrac{\sqrt[3]{x^2-1}}{\sqrt{1+x^2}}$

32. $\log \sqrt[3]{\dfrac{x+y^2}{2z+1}}$

Exercises 33–56: (Refer to Examples 5 and 6.) Combine the expressions by writing them as a logarithm of a single expression.

33. $\log 2 + \log 3$

34. $\log \sqrt{2} + \log \sqrt[3]{2}$

35. $\ln \sqrt{5} - \ln 25$

36. $\ln 33 - \ln 11$

37. $\log 20 + \log \frac{1}{10}$

38. $\log 24 + \log \frac{1}{48}$

39. $\log 4 + \log 3 - \log 2$

40. $\log 5 - \log 10 - \log \frac{1}{2}$

41. $\ln 5 + \ln k^2$

42. $\ln 45 + \ln b^3$

43. $\ln x^6 - \ln x^3$

44. $\log 10x^5 - \log 5x$

45. $\log \sqrt{x} + \log x^2 - \log x$

46. $\log \sqrt[4]{x} + \log x^4 - \log x^2$

47. $3\ln x - \frac{3}{2}\ln y + 4\ln z$

48. $\frac{2}{3}\ln y - 4\ln x - \frac{1}{2}\ln z$

49. $\ln \dfrac{1}{e^2} + \ln 2e$

50. $\ln 4e^3 - \ln 2e^2$

51. $2\ln x - 4\ln y + \frac{1}{2}\ln z$

52. $\frac{1}{3}\ln(x+1) + \frac{1}{3}\ln(x-1)$

53. $\log 4 - \log x + 7\log \sqrt{x}$

54. $\ln 3e - \ln \dfrac{1}{4e}$

55. $2\log(x^2-1) + 4\log(x-2) - \frac{1}{2}\log y$

56. $\log x + \log\sqrt{x+3} - \frac{1}{3}\log(x-4)$

Exercises 57–62: Complete the following.

(a) Make a table of $f(x)$ and $g(x)$ to determine whether $f(x) = g(x)$.

(b) If possible, use properties of logarithms to show that $f(x) = g(x)$.

57. $f(x) = \log 3x + \log 2x,\quad g(x) = \log 6x^2$

58. $f(x) = \ln 3x - \ln 2x,\quad g(x) = \ln x$

59. $f(x) = \ln 2x^2 - \ln x,\quad g(x) = \ln 2x$

60. $f(x) = \log x^2 + \log x^3,\quad g(x) = 5\log x$

61. $f(x) = \ln x^4 - \ln x^2$, $g(x) = 2 \ln x$

62. $f(x) = (\ln x)^2$, $g(x) = 2 \ln x$

Exercises 63–66: Sketch a graph of f.

63. $f(x) = \log_2 x$

64. $f(x) = \log_2 x^2$

65. $f(x) = \log_3 |x|$

66. $f(x) = \log_4 2x$

Change of Base Formula

Exercises 67–76: Use the change of base formula to approximate the logarithm to the nearest thousandth.

67. $\log_2 25$

68. $\log_3 67$

69. $\log_5 130$

70. $\log_6 0.77$

71. $\log_2 5 + \log_2 7$

72. $\log_9 85 + \log_7 17$

73. $\sqrt{\log_4 46}$

74. $2 \log_5 15 + \sqrt[3]{\log_3 67}$

75. $\dfrac{\log_2 12}{\log_2 3}$

76. $\dfrac{\log_7 125}{\log_7 25}$

Exercises 77–80: Solve the equation graphically. Express any solutions to the nearest thousandth.

77. $\log(x^3 + x^2 + 1) = 7$

78. $\ln(1 + x^2 + 2x^4) = 4$

79. $\log_2(x^2 + 1) = 5 - \log_3(x^4 + 1)$

80. $\ln(x^2 + 2) = \log_2(10 - x^2)$

Applications

81. **Runway Length** (Refer to Exercise 127, Section 5.4.) Use a natural logarithm (instead of a common logarithm) to write the formula $L(x) = 3 \log x$. Evaluate $L(50)$ for each formula. Do your answers agree?

82. **Biology** The equation $y = bx^a$ is used in applications involving biology. Another form of this equation is $\log y = \log b + a \log x$. Use properties of logarithms to obtain this second equation from the first. (***Source:*** H. Lancaster, *Quantitative Methods in Biological and Medical Sciences*.)

83. **Decibels** (Refer to Example 4.) If the intensity x of a sound increases by a factor of 10, by how much does the decibel level increase?

84. **Decibels** (Refer to Example 4.) Use a natural logarithm to write the formula $f(x) = 160 + 10 \log x$. Evaluate $f(5 \times 10^{-8})$ for each formula. Do your answers agree?

85. **Light Absorption** When sunlight passes through lake water, its initial intensity I_0 decreases to a weaker intensity I at a depth of x feet according to the formula

$$\ln I - \ln I_0 = -kx,$$

where k is a positive constant and I_0 is the sun's intensity at the surface. Solve this equation for I.

86. **Dissolving Salt** If C grams of salt are added to a sample of water, the amount A of undissolved salt is modeled by $A = Ca^x$, where x is time. Solve the equation for x.

87. **Population Growth** The population P (in millions) of California x years after 2010 can be modeled by $P = 37.3e^{0.01x}$.
   (a) Use properties of logarithms to solve this equation for x.
   (b) Use your equation to find x when $P = 40$. Interpret your answer.

88. **Population Growth** The population P (in millions) of Georgia x years after 2010 can be modeled by the equation $P = 9.7e^{0.017x}$.
   (a) Use properties of logarithms to solve this equation for x.
   (b) Use your equation to find x when $P = 12$. Interpret your answer.

89. Solve $A = Pe^{rt}$ for t.

90. Solve $P = P_0 e^{r(t - t_0)} + 5$ for t.

91. Write the sum

$$\log 1 + 2 \log 2 + 3 \log 3 + 4 \log 4 + 5 \log 5$$

as a logarithm of a single expression.

92. Show that

$$\log_2\left(x + \sqrt{x^2 - 4}\right) + \log_2\left(x - \sqrt{x^2 - 4}\right)$$

equals 2. What is the domain of the given expression?

Writing about Mathematics

93. A student insists that $\log(x + y)$ and $\log x + \log y$ are equal. How could you convince the student otherwise?

94. A student insists that $\log\left(\frac{x}{y}\right)$ and $\frac{\log x}{\log y}$ are equal. How could you convince the student otherwise?

5.6 Exponential and Logarithmic Equations

- **Solve exponential equations**
- **Solve logarithmic equations**

Introduction

The population of the world has grown rapidly during the past century. Near the end of 2011, world population was estimated to be 7 billion. Exponential functions and equations are often used to model this type of rapid growth, whereas logarithms are used to model slower growth.

Exponential Equations

The population P of the world was 7 billion in 2011 and can be modeled by the function $P(x) = 7(1.01)^{x-2011}$, where x is the year. We can use P to predict the year when world population might reach 8 billion by solving the *exponential equation*

$$7(1.01)^{x-2011} = 8. \qquad \text{Exponential equation}$$

An equation in which the variable occurs in the *exponent* of an expression is called an **exponential equation**. In the next example, we use the power rule of logarithms, $\log_a(m^r) = r\log_a m$, to solve this equation.

EXAMPLE 1 Modeling world population

World population in billions during year x can be modeled by $P(x) = 7(1.01)^{x-2011}$, shown in Figure 5.72. Solve the equation $7(1.01)^{x-2011} = 8$ symbolically to predict the year when world population might reach 8 billion.

World Population

Figure 5.72

SOLUTION First divide each side by 7, and then take the common logarithm of each side. (The natural logarithm could also be used.)

$$7(1.01)^{x-2011} = 8 \qquad \text{Given equation}$$

$$(1.01)^{x-2011} = \frac{8}{7} \qquad \text{Divide by 7.}$$

$$\log(1.01)^{x-2011} = \log\frac{8}{7} \qquad \text{Take the common logarithm.}$$

$$(x - 2011)\log(1.01) = \log\frac{8}{7} \qquad \log(m^r) = r\log m$$

$$x - 2011 = \frac{\log(8/7)}{\log(1.01)} \qquad \text{Divide by } \log(1.01).$$

$$x = 2011 + \frac{\log(8/7)}{\log(1.01)} \qquad \text{Add 2011.}$$

$$x \approx 2024 \qquad \text{Approximate.}$$

This model predicts that world population might reach 8 billion during 2024.

Now Try Exercise 85

CLASS DISCUSSION

What is the growth factor for $P(x) = 7(1.01)^{x-2011}$? By what percentage is it predicted that world population will grow, on average, each year after 2011?

SOLVING EXPONENTIAL EQUATIONS SYMBOLICALLY

The following steps can be used to solve several types of exponential equations.

STEP 1: Isolate the exponential expression on one side of the equation.

STEP 2: Take a logarithm of each side of the equation.

STEP 3: Apply either the inverse property or the power rule.

STEP 4: Solve for the variable.

The steps above are applied in Example 2 to solve the equation symbolically.

EXAMPLE 2 Calculating the thickness of a runway

Heavier aircraft require runways with thicker pavement for landings and takeoffs. The relation between the thickness of the pavement t in inches and gross weight W in thousands of pounds can be approximated by

$$W(t) = 18.29e^{0.246t}.$$

(a) Determine the required thickness of the runway for a 130,000-pound plane.
(b) Solve part (a) graphically and numerically.

SOLUTION

(a) ***Symbolic Solution*** Because the unit for W is thousands of pounds, we can solve the equation $W(t) = 130$ for t.

$$18.29e^{0.246t} = 130 \qquad W(t) = 130$$

$$e^{0.246t} = \frac{130}{18.29} \qquad \text{STEP 1: Divide by 18.29.}$$

$$\ln e^{0.246t} = \ln\frac{130}{18.29} \qquad \text{STEP 2: Take the natural logarithm of each side.}$$

$$0.246t = \ln\frac{130}{18.29} \qquad \text{STEP 3: Inverse property: } \ln e^k = k$$

$$t = \frac{\ln(130/18.29)}{0.246} \qquad \text{STEP 4: Divide by 0.246.}$$

$$t \approx 7.97 \qquad \text{Approximate.}$$

The runway should be about 8 inches thick.

Graphical Solution

[0, 10, 1] by [0, 200, 50]

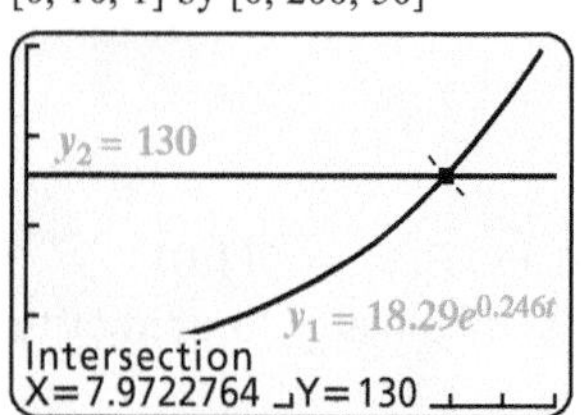

Figure 5.73

Numerical Solution

X	Y1	Y2
5	62.574	130
6	80.026	130
7	102.35	130
8	130.89	130 ← $y_1 \approx y_2$
9	167.39	130
10	214.08	130
11	273.79	130

X=8

Figure 5.74

(b) ***Graphical Solution*** Let $Y_1 = 18.29e\hat{}(.246X)$ and $Y_2 = 130$. In Figure 5.73, their graphs intersect near (7.97, 130).

Numerical Solution Numerical support of this result is shown in Figure 5.74, where $y_1 \approx y_2$ when $x = 8$.

Now Try Exercise 87

To solve an exponential equation with a base other than 10 or e, the power rule of logarithms can be used. This technique is used in Examples 1 and 3.

EXAMPLE 3 Modeling the decline of bluefin tuna

Bluefin tuna are large fish that can weigh 1500 pounds and swim at speeds of 55 miles per hour. Because they are used for sushi, a prime fish can be worth over $50,000. As a result, the western Atlantic bluefin tuna have had their numbers decline exponentially. Their numbers in thousands from 1974 to 1991 can be modeled by the formula $f(x) = 230(0.881)^x$, where x is years after 1974. (In more recent years, controls have helped slow this decline.) (***Source:*** B. Freedman, *Environmental Ecology*.)

(a) Estimate the number of bluefin tuna in 1974 and 1991.
(b) Determine symbolically the year when they numbered 50 thousand.

SOLUTION

(a) To determine their numbers in 1974 and 1991, evaluate $f(0)$ and $f(17)$.

$$f(0) = 230(0.881)^0 = 230(1) = 230$$
$$f(17) = 230(0.881)^{17} \approx 26.7$$

Bluefin tuna decreased from 230 thousand in 1974 to fewer than 27 thousand in 1991.

(b) Solve the equation $f(x) = 50$ for x.

$$230(0.881)^x = 50 \qquad f(x) = 50$$
$$0.881^x = \frac{5}{23} \qquad \text{STEP 1: Divide by 230; simplify.}$$
$$\ln 0.881^x = \ln\frac{5}{23} \qquad \text{STEP 2: Take the natural logarithm of each side.}$$
$$x \ln 0.881 = \ln\frac{5}{23} \qquad \text{STEP 3: } \ln m^r = r \ln m$$
$$x = \frac{\ln(5/23)}{\ln 0.881} \qquad \text{STEP 4: Divide by } \ln 0.881.$$
$$x \approx 12.04 \qquad \text{Approximate.}$$

The common logarithm could also be used.

They numbered about 50 thousand in $1974 + 12.04 \approx 1986$.

Now Try Exercise 93

Moore's law states that the processing speed and memory capacity of computers doubles every 2 years. Researchers have recently found an even more profound law relating energy efficiency and computing power. This law says that the number of computations that a computer can perform on a fixed amount of electricity (such as a kilowatt-hour) has doubled every 1.6 years since the mid-1940s, when vacuum tubes were used in computers. In the next example we use an exponential function to model this new law and make a prediction. (***Source:*** *The Economist.*)

EXAMPLE 4 Modeling the electrical efficiency of computers

In 1945 computers could perform about 1000 computations with 1 kilowatt-hour of electricity. This number has doubled every 1.6 years.

(a) Find an exponential function $E(x) = Ca^x$ that gives the number of computations a computer can perform on 1 kilowatt-hour, where x is years after 1945.

(b) Evaluate $E(65)$ and interpret your result.

(c) In what year did computers first perform 1,000,000 calculations per kilowatt-hour?

SOLUTION

(a) The initial value is 1000 when $x = 0$, so $C = 1000$ and $E(x) = 1000a^x$. When $x = 1.6$ the number of computations doubles to 2000 per kilowatt-hour, so let $E(1.6) = 2000$ and solve for a.

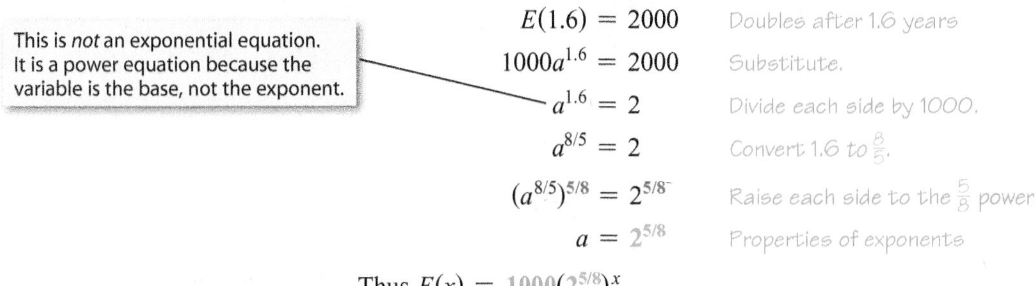

$$E(1.6) = 2000 \qquad \text{Doubles after 1.6 years}$$
$$1000a^{1.6} = 2000 \qquad \text{Substitute.}$$
$$a^{1.6} = 2 \qquad \text{Divide each side by 1000.}$$
$$a^{8/5} = 2 \qquad \text{Convert 1.6 to } \tfrac{8}{5}.$$
$$(a^{8/5})^{5/8} = 2^{5/8} \qquad \text{Raise each side to the } \tfrac{5}{8} \text{ power.}$$
$$a = 2^{5/8} \qquad \text{Properties of exponents}$$

This is *not* an exponential equation. It is a power equation because the variable is the base, not the exponent.

Thus $E(x) = 1000(2^{5/8})^x$.

(b) $E(65) = 1000(2^{5/8})^{65} \approx 1.7 \times 10^{15}$. In $1945 + 65 = 2010$, computers could perform about 1.7 *quadrillion* computations on 1 kilowatt-hour.

(c) We must determine a value for x, so that $E(x) = 1{,}000{,}000$.

$$\begin{aligned} 1000(2^{5/8})^x &= 1{,}000{,}000 && E(x) = 1{,}000{,}000. \\ (2^{5/8})^x &= 1000 && \text{STEP 1: Divide by 1000.} \\ \log(2^{5/8})^x &= \log 1000 && \text{STEP 2: Take common logarithm.} \\ x \log 2^{5/8} &= 3 && \text{STEP 3: Power rule} \\ x &= \frac{3}{\log 2^{5/8}} && \text{STEP 4: Divide by } \log 2^{5/8}. \\ x &\approx 16 && \text{Approximate.} \end{aligned}$$

Thus in $1945 + 16 = 1961$ computers first performed 1 million computations on 1 kilowatt-hour.

Now Try Exercise 89

Exponential equations can occur in many forms. Although some types of exponential equations cannot be solved symbolically, Example 5 shows four equations that can.

EXAMPLE 5 **Solving exponential equations symbolically**

Solve each equation.

(a) $10^{x+2} = 10^{3x}$ **(b)** $5(1.2)^x + 1 = 26$ **(c)** $\left(\frac{1}{4}\right)^{x-1} = \frac{1}{9}$ **(d)** $5^{x-3} = e^{2x}$

SOLUTION

(a) Start by taking the common logarithm of each side.

$$\begin{aligned} 10^{x+2} &= 10^{3x} && \text{Given equation} \\ \log 10^{x+2} &= \log 10^{3x} && \text{Take the common logarithm.} \\ x + 2 &= 3x && \text{Inverse property: } \log 10^k = k \\ 2 &= 2x && \text{Subtract } x. \\ x &= 1 && \text{Divide by 2; rewrite.} \end{aligned}$$

(b) Start by isolating the exponential term on one side of the equation.

$$\begin{aligned} 5(1.2)^x &= 25 && \text{Subtract 1.} \\ (1.2)^x &= 5 && \text{Divide by 5.} \\ \log(1.2)^x &= \log 5 && \text{Take the common logarithm.} \\ x \log 1.2 &= \log 5 && \log m^r = r \log m \\ x &= \frac{\log 5}{\log 1.2} && \text{Divide by } \log 1.2. \\ x &\approx 8.827 && \text{Approximate.} \end{aligned}$$

(c) Begin by taking the common logarithm of each side.

$$\begin{aligned} \left(\frac{1}{4}\right)^{x-1} &= \frac{1}{9} && \text{Given equation} \\ \log\left(\frac{1}{4}\right)^{x-1} &= \log\frac{1}{9} && \text{Take the common logarithm.} \\ (x-1)\log\left(\frac{1}{4}\right) &= \log\frac{1}{9} && \log m^r = r \log m \\ x - 1 &= \frac{\log(1/9)}{\log(1/4)} && \text{Divide by } \log\tfrac{1}{4}. \\ x &= 1 + \frac{\log(1/9)}{\log(1/4)} \approx 2.585 && \text{Add 1 and approximate.} \end{aligned}$$

This equation could also be solved by taking the natural logarithm of each side.

(d) Begin by taking the natural (or common) logarithm of each side.

$$
\begin{aligned}
5^{x-3} &= e^{2x} && \text{Given equation} \\
\ln 5^{x-3} &= \ln e^{2x} && \text{Take the natural logarithm.} \\
(x-3)\ln 5 &= 2x && \ln m^r = r\ln m \\
x\ln 5 - 3\ln 5 &= 2x && \text{Distributive property} \\
x\ln 5 - 2x &= 3\ln 5 && \text{Subtract } 2x\text{; add } 3\ln 5. \\
x(\ln 5 - 2) &= 3\ln 5 && \text{Factor out } x. \\
x &= \frac{3\ln 5}{\ln 5 - 2} && \text{Divide by } \ln 5 - 2. \\
x &\approx -12.36 && \text{Approximate.}
\end{aligned}
$$

Now Try Exercises 13, 17, 23, and 25

Solving Equations Involving Like Bases If a function is one-to-one, then $f(a) = f(b)$ implies that $a = b$. In Example 5(a) we were given the equation $10^{x+2} = 10^{3x}$. Because $f(x) = 10^x$ is one-to-one, it follows that $x + 2 = 3x$, or $x = 1$. We can use this technique to solve some exponential equations if we can write the expressions on each side of the equation in terms of the same base a. Then $a^x = a^y$ implies that $x = y$.

EXAMPLE 6 **Solving an exponential equation using like bases**

Solve the equation $4^{x+1} = 8^{2-x}$.

SOLUTION

Because $4 = 2^2$ and $8 = 2^3$, we can write this equation using only base 2.

$$
\begin{aligned}
4^{x+1} &= 8^{2-x} && \text{Given equation} \\
(2^2)^{x+1} &= (2^3)^{2-x} && \text{Substitute.} \\
2^{2x+2} &= 2^{6-3x} && \text{Properties of exponents} \\
2x + 2 &= 6 - 3x && 2^x \text{ is one-to-one.} \\
5x &= 4 && \text{Add } 3x \text{ and subtract 2.} \\
x &= \frac{4}{5} && \text{Divide by 5.}
\end{aligned}
$$

Now Try Exercise 37

NOTE The technique used in Example 6 does not work for some exponential equations. For example, $5^{x-3} = e^{2x}$ cannot easily be written in terms of equal bases. However, this equation can be solved by taking a logarithm of each side as in Example 5(d).

An Application If a hot object is put in a room with temperature T_0, then according to **Newton's law of cooling**, the temperature T of the object after time t is modeled by

$$T(t) = T_0 + Da^t, \qquad 0 < a < 1,$$

where D is the initial temperature *difference* between the object and the room.

EXAMPLE 7 **Modeling coffee cooling**

A pot of coffee with a temperature of 100°C is set down in a room with a temperature of 20°C. The coffee cools to 60°C after 1 hour.

(a) Find values for T_0, D, and a so that $T(t) = T_0 + Da^t$ models the data.

(b) Find the temperature of the coffee after half an hour.

(c) How long did it take for the coffee to reach 50°C? Support your result graphically.

SOLUTION

(a) The room has temperature $T_0 = 20$°C, and the initial temperature difference between the coffee and the room is $D = 100 - 20 = 80$°C. Thus $T(t) = 20 + 80a^t$. To find a, use the fact that the temperature of the coffee after 1 hour was 60°C.

Let $t = 1$ and $T = 60$ in $T(t) = 20 + 80a^t$ and solve for a.

$$T(1) = 60 \qquad \text{Temperature is } 60° \text{ after 1 hour.}$$
$$20 + 80a^1 = 60 \qquad \text{Let } t = 1 \text{ in } T(t) = 20 + 80a^t.$$
$$80a = 40 \qquad \text{Subtract 20.}$$
$$a = \frac{1}{2} \qquad \text{Divide by 80.}$$

Thus $T(t) = 20 + 80\left(\frac{1}{2}\right)^t$.

(b) After half an hour, the temperature is

$$T\left(\frac{1}{2}\right) = 20 + 80\left(\frac{1}{2}\right)^{1/2} \approx 76.6°\text{C}.$$

(c) ***Symbolic Solution*** To determine when the coffee reached 50°C, solve $T(t) = 50$.

$$20 + 80\left(\frac{1}{2}\right)^t = 50 \qquad T(t) = 50$$
$$80\left(\frac{1}{2}\right)^t = 30 \qquad \text{Subtract 20.}$$
$$\left(\frac{1}{2}\right)^t = \frac{3}{8} \qquad \text{Divide by 80; simplify.}$$
$$\log\left(\frac{1}{2}\right)^t = \log\frac{3}{8} \qquad \text{Take the common logarithm.}$$
$$t\log\left(\frac{1}{2}\right) = \log\frac{3}{8} \qquad \text{Power rule}$$
$$t = \frac{\log(3/8)}{\log(1/2)} \qquad \text{Divide by } \log\tfrac{1}{2}.$$
$$t \approx 1.415 \qquad \text{Approximate.}$$

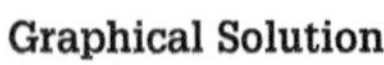

Graphical Solution

[0, 3, 1] by [0, 100, 10]

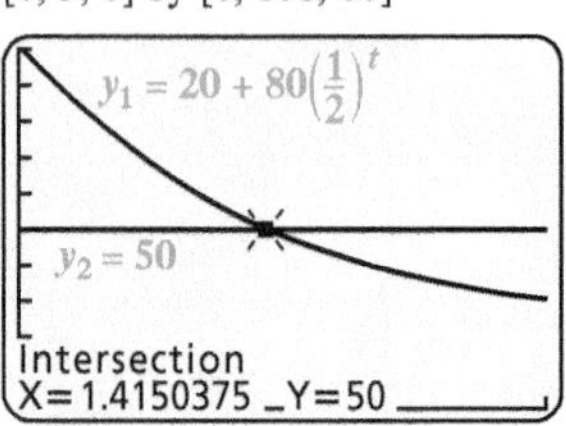

Figure 5.75

The temperature reaches 50°C after about 1.415 hours, or 1 hour and 25 minutes.

Graphical Solution The graphs of $Y_1 = 20 + 80(1/2)$^X and $Y_2 = 50$ intersect near (1.415, 50), as shown in Figure 5.75. This result agrees with the symbolic solution.

Now Try Exercise 97

NOTE Newton's law of cooling can also model the temperature of a cold object that is brought into a warm room. In this case, the temperature difference D is *negative*.

Some exponential equations *cannot* be solved symbolically but can be solved graphically. This is demonstrated in the next example.

EXAMPLE 8 Solving an exponential equation graphically

Solve $e^{-x} + 2x = 3$ graphically. Approximate all solutions to the nearest hundredth.

SOLUTION The graphs of $Y_1 = $ e^(−X) + 2X and $Y_2 = 3$ intersect near the points (−1.92, 3) and (1.37, 3), as shown in Figures 5.76 and 5.77. Thus the solutions are approximately −1.92 and 1.37.

Graphical Solutions

[−6, 6, 1] by [−4, 4, 1]

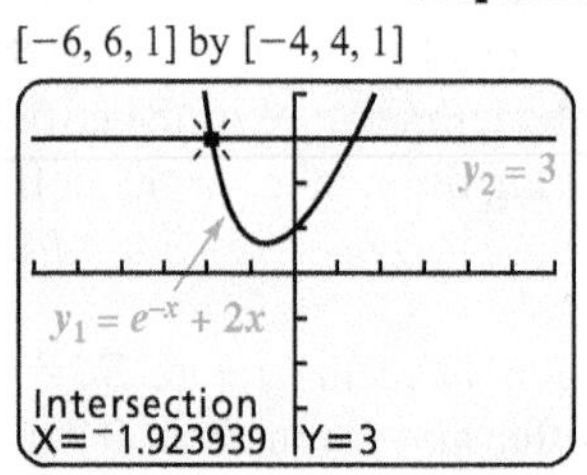

Figure 5.76

[−6, 6, 1] by [−4, 4, 1]

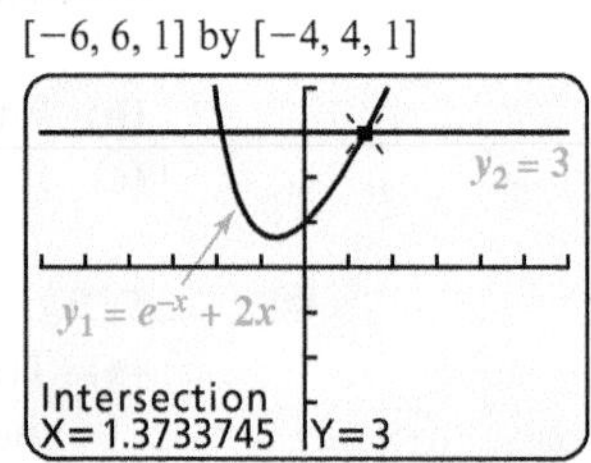

Figure 5.77

Now Try Exercise 79

Logarithmic Equations

Logarithmic equations contain logarithms. To solve a logarithmic equation, we use the inverse property $a^{\log_a x} = x$. This technique is illustrated in the next example.

EXAMPLE 9 **Solving a logarithmic equation**

Solve $3\log_3 x = 12$.

SOLUTION Begin by dividing each side by 3.

$$\log_3 x = 4 \quad \text{Divide by 3.}$$
$$3^{\log_3 x} = 3^4 \quad \text{Exponentiate each side; base 3.}$$
$$x = 81 \quad \text{Inverse property: } a^{\log_a k} = k$$

Now Try Exercise 57

We can solve logarithmic equations by using the following steps.

SOLVING LOGARITHMIC EQUATIONS SYMBOLICALLY

The following steps can be used to solve several types of logarithmic equations.

STEP 1: Isolate the logarithmic expression on one side of the equation. (You may need to apply properties of logarithms.)

STEP 2: Exponentiate each side of the equation with the same base as the logarithm.

STEP 3: Apply the inverse property $a^{\log_a k} = k$.

STEP 4: Solve for the variable. *Check your answer.*

EXAMPLE 10 **Solving a logarithmic equation symbolically**

In developing countries, there is a relationship between the amount of land a person owns and the average daily calories consumed. This relationship is modeled by the formula $C(x) = 280 \ln(x + 1) + 1925$, where x is the amount of land owned in acres and $0 \le x \le 4$. (***Source:*** D. Grigg, *The World Food Problem.*)

(a) Find the average caloric intake for a person who owns no land.

(b) A graph of C is shown in Figure 5.78. Interpret the graph.

(c) Determine symbolically the number of acres owned by someone whose average intake is 2000 calories per day.

Land and Calories

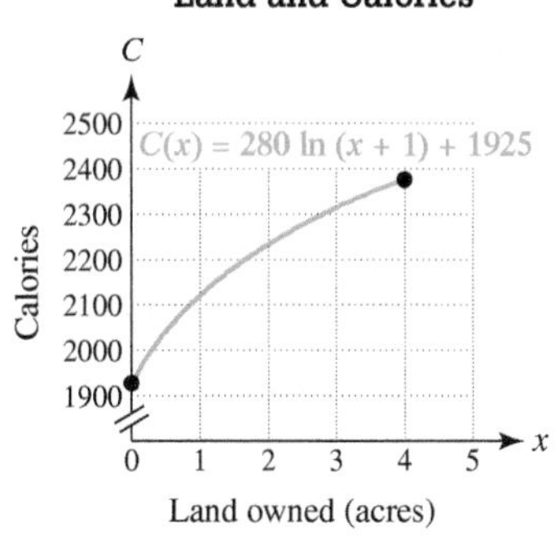

Figure 5.78

SOLUTION

(a) Since $C(0) = 280\ln(0 + 1) + 1925 = 1925$, a person without land consumes an average of 1925 calories per day.

(b) The y-intercept of 1925 represents the caloric intake for a person who owns no land. As the amount of land x increases, the caloric intake y also increases. However, the rate of increase slows. This would be expected because there is a limit to the number of calories an average person would eat, regardless of his or her economic status.

(c) Solve the equation $C(x) = 2000$ for x.

$$280\ln(x + 1) + 1925 = 2000 \quad C(x) = 2000$$
$$280\ln(x + 1) = 75 \quad \text{STEP 1: Subtract 1925.}$$
$$\ln(x + 1) = \frac{75}{280} \quad \text{STEP 1: Divide by 280.}$$
$$e^{\ln(x+1)} = e^{75/280} \quad \text{STEP 2: Exponentiate each side; base } e.$$
$$x + 1 = e^{75/280} \quad \text{STEP 3: Inverse property: } e^{\ln k} = k$$
$$x = e^{75/280} - 1 \quad \text{STEP 4: Subtract 1.}$$
$$x \approx 0.307 \quad \text{Approximate.}$$

A person who owns about 0.3 acre has an average intake of 2000 calories per day.

Now Try Exercise 101

Like exponential equations, logarithmic equations can occur in many forms. The next example illustrates three equations that can be solved symbolically.

EXAMPLE 11 **Solving logarithmic equations symbolically**

Solve each equation.

(a) $\log(2x + 1) = 2$ **(b)** $\log_2 4x = 2 - \log_2 x$

(c) $2\ln(x + 1) = \ln(1 - 2x)$

SOLUTION

(a) To solve the equation, exponentiate each side of the equation using base 10.

$$\log(2x + 1) = 2 \quad \text{Given equation (Step 1 not needed)}$$
$$10^{\log(2x+1)} = 10^2 \quad \text{STEP 2: Exponentiate each side; base 10.}$$
$$2x + 1 = 100 \quad \text{STEP 3: Inverse property: } 10^{\log k} = k$$
$$x = 49.5 \quad \text{STEP 4: Solve for } x.$$

(b) To solve this equation, apply properties of logarithms.

$$\log_2 4x = 2 - \log_2 x \quad \text{Given equation}$$
$$\log_2 4x + \log_2 x = 2 \quad \text{STEP 1: Add } \log_2 x.$$
$$\log_2 4x^2 = 2 \quad \text{STEP 1: } \log_a m + \log_a n = \log_a(mn)$$
$$2^{\log_2 4x^2} = 2^2 \quad \text{STEP 2: Exponentiate each side; base 2.}$$
$$4x^2 = 4 \quad \text{STEP 3: Inverse property: } a^{\log_a k} = k$$
$$x = \pm 1 \quad \text{STEP 4: Solve for } x.$$

However, -1 is not a solution since $\log_2 x$ in the given equation is undefined for negative values of x. Thus the only solution is 1.

(c) For this equation we isolate a logarithmic expression on each side of the equation and then exponentiate.

$$2\ln(x + 1) = \ln(1 - 2x) \quad \text{Given equation (Step 1 not needed)}$$
$$\ln(x + 1)^2 = \ln(1 - 2x) \quad \text{Power rule}$$
$$e^{\ln(x+1)^2} = e^{\ln(1-2x)} \quad \text{STEP 2: Exponentiate; base } e.$$
$$(x + 1)^2 = 1 - 2x \quad \text{STEP 3: Inverse property: } a^{\log_a k} = k$$
$$x^2 + 2x + 1 = 1 - 2x \quad \text{STEP 4: Expand the binomial.}$$
$$x^2 + 4x = 0 \quad \text{Combine terms.}$$
$$x(x + 4) = 0 \quad \text{Factor.}$$
$$x = 0 \text{ or } x = -4 \quad \text{Zero-product property}$$

Substituting $x = 0$ and $x = -4$ in the given equation shows that 0 is a solution but -4 is not a solution.

Now Try Exercises 61, 65, and 69

MAKING CONNECTIONS

Solving Exponential and Logarithmic Equations

At some point in the process of solving an exponential equation, we often take a logarithm of each side of the equation. Similarly, when solving a logarithmic equation, we often exponentiate each side of the equation.

EXAMPLE 12 **Solving various types of equations**

Solve each equation.

(a) $3x + 5 = 41$ **(b)** $3(7^x) + 5 = 41$ **(c)** $3\log x + 5 = 41$

(d) $3\ln x + 5 = 41$ **(e)** $3\ln(x + 5) = 41$

SOLUTION

(a) This is a linear equation.

$$3x + 5 = 41 \quad \text{Given equation}$$
$$3x = 36 \quad \text{Subtract 5.}$$
$$x = 12 \quad \text{Divide by 3.}$$

(b) This is an exponential equation. Start by isolating the expression 7^x.

$$\begin{aligned} 3(7)^x + 5 &= 41 && \text{Given equation} \\ 3(7)^x &= 36 && \text{Subtract 5.} \\ 7^x &= 12 && \text{Divide by 3.} \\ \ln 7^x &= \ln 12 && \text{Take natural logarithm.} \\ x \ln 7 &= \ln 12 && \text{Property 4: } \ln m^r = r \ln m \\ x &= \frac{\ln 12}{\ln 7} && \text{Divide by } \ln 7. \\ x &\approx 1.277 && \text{Approximate.} \end{aligned}$$

(c) This is a logarithmic equation. Start by isolating the expression $\log x$.

$$\begin{aligned} 3 \log x + 5 &= 41 && \text{Given equation} \\ 3 \log x &= 36 && \text{Subtract 5.} \\ \log x &= 12 && \text{Divide by 3.} \\ 10^{\log x} &= 10^{12} && \text{Exponentiate base-10.} \\ x &= 10^{12} && \text{Inverse property} \end{aligned}$$

(d) This is a logarithmic equation. Start by isolating the expression $\ln x$.

$$\begin{aligned} 3 \ln x + 5 &= 41 && \text{Given equation} \\ 3 \ln x &= 36 && \text{Subtract 5.} \\ \ln x &= 12 && \text{Divide by 3.} \\ e^{\ln x} &= e^{12} && \text{Exponentiate base-}e. \\ x &= e^{12} && \text{Inverse property} \\ x &\approx 162{,}755 && \text{Approximate.} \end{aligned}$$

(e) This is a logarithmic equation. Start by isolating the expression $\ln (x + 5)$.

$$\begin{aligned} 3 \ln (x + 5) &= 41 && \text{Given equation} \\ \ln (x + 5) &= \frac{41}{3} && \text{Divide by 3.} \\ e^{\ln(x+5)} &= e^{41/3} && \text{Exponentiate base-}e. \\ x + 5 &= e^{41/3} && \text{Inverse property} \\ x &= e^{41/3} - 5 && \text{Subtract 5.} \\ x &\approx 861{,}699 && \text{Approximate.} \end{aligned}$$

Now Try Exercise 73

5.6 Putting It All Together

The following table summarizes techniques that can be used to solve so[me] exponential and logarithmic equations symbolically.

CONCEPT	COMMENTS	EXAMPLES
Exponential equations	Typical form: $Ca^x = k$ Solve for a^x. Then take a base-a logarithm of each side. Use the inverse property: $\log_a a^x = x.$	$4e^x = 24$ $e^x = 6$ $\ln e^x = \ln 6$ $x = \ln 6 \approx 1.79$

CONCEPT	EXPLANATION	EXAMPLES
Logarithmic equations	***Equation 1:*** $C\log_a x = k$ Solve for $\log_a x$. Then exponentiate each side with base a. Use the inverse property: $$a^{\log_a x} = x.$$ ***Equation 2:*** $\log_a bx \pm \log_a cx = k$ When more than one logarithm with the same base occurs, use properties of logarithms to combine logarithms. *Be sure to check any solutions.*	**1.** $4\log x = 10$ $\log x = 2.5$ $10^{\log x} = 10^{2.5}$ $x = 10^{2.5} \approx 316$ **2.** $\log x + \log 4x = 2$ $\log 4x^2 = 2$ $4x^2 = 10^2$ $x^2 = 25$ $x = \pm 5$ The only solution is 5.

5.6 Exercises

Solving Exponential Equations

Exercises 1–4: The graphical and symbolic representations of f and g are shown.

(a) Use the graph to solve $f(x) = g(x)$.
(b) Solve $f(x) = g(x)$ symbolically.

1.

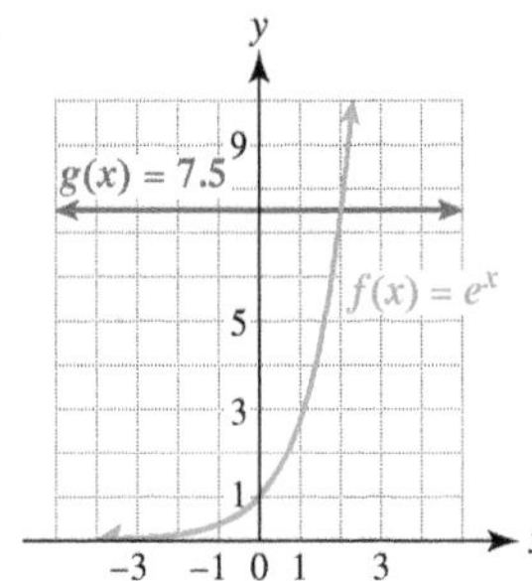

2.

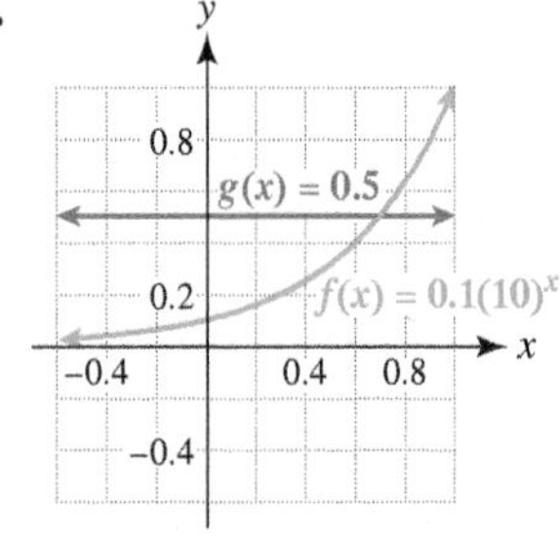

3.

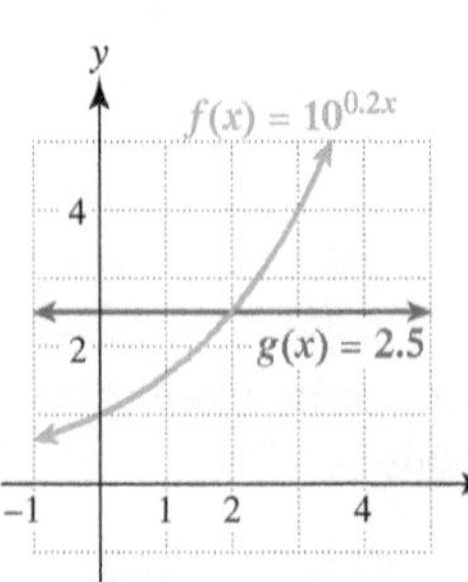

4.

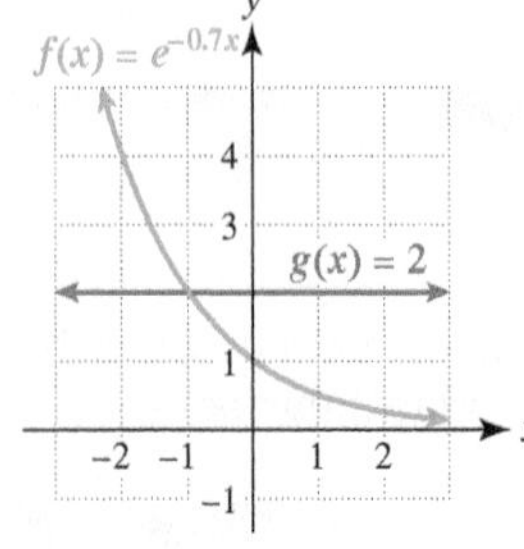

Exercises 5–32: Solve the exponential equation.

5. $4e^x = 5$ **6.** $2e^{-x} = 8$

7. $2(10)^x + 5 = 45$ **8.** $100 - 5(10)^x = 7$

9. $2.5e^{-1.2x} = 1$ **10.** $9.5e^{0.005x} = 19$

11. $1.2(0.9)^x = 0.6$ **12.** $0.05(1.15)^x = 5$

13. $4(1.1)^{x-1} = 16$ **14.** $3(2)^{x-2} = 99$

15. $5(1.2)^{3x-2} + 94 = 100$ **16.** $1.4(2)^{x+3} = 2.8$

17. $5^{3x} = 5^{1-2x}$ **18.** $7^{x^2} = 7^{4x-3}$

19. $10^{(x^2)} = 10^{3x-2}$ **20.** $e^{2x} = e^{5x-3}$

21. $\left(\frac{1}{5}\right)^x = -5$ **22.** $2^x = -4$

23. $\left(\frac{2}{5}\right)^{x-2} = \frac{1}{3}$ **24.** $\left(\frac{3}{2}\right)^{x+1} = \frac{7}{3}$

25. $4^{x-1} = 3^{2x}$ **26.** $3^{1-2x} = e^{0.5x}$

27. $e^{x-3} = 2^{3x}$ **28.** $6^{x+1} = 4^{2x-1}$

29. $3(1.4)^x - 4 = 60$ **30.** $2(1.05)^x + 3 = 10$

31. $5(1.015)^{x-1980} = 8$ **32.** $30 - 3(0.75)^{x-1} = 29$

Exercises 33–42: (Refer to Example 6.) Use the fact that $a^x = a^y$ implies $x = y$, to solve each equation.

33. $5^{2x} = 5^{x-3}$ **34.** $7^{-x} = 7^{2x+1}$

35. $e^{-x} = e^{x^2}$

36. $e^{x^2} = e^{2x+1}$

37. $2^{3x} = 8^{-x+2}$

38. $9^{2x} = 27^{1-x}$

39. $25^{2x} = 125^{2-x}$

40. $16^x = 4^{2-x}$

41. $32^{3x} = 16^{5x+3}$

42. $16^{x-5} = 64^{1-2x}$

Solving Logarithmic Equations

Exercises 43–72: Solve the logarithmic equation.

43. $3 \log x = 2$

44. $5 \ln x = 10$

45. $\ln 2x = 5$

46. $\ln 4x = 1.5$

47. $\log 2x^2 = 2$

48. $\log(2 - x) = 0.5$

49. $\log_2(3x - 2) = 4$

50. $\log_3(1 - x) = 1$

51. $\log(8 - 3x) = 3$

52. $\log(2x + 4) = 2$

53. $160 + 10 \log x = 50$

54. $160 + 10 \log x = 120$

55. $\ln x + \ln x^2 = 3$

56. $\log x^5 = 4 + 3 \log x$

57. $2 \log_2 x = 4.2$

58. $3 \log_2 3x = 1$

59. $\log x + \log 2x = 2$

60. $\ln 2x + \ln 3x = \ln 6$

61. $\log(2 - 3x) = 3$

62. $\log(x^2 + 1) = 2$

63. $\ln x + \ln(3x - 1) = \ln 10$

64. $\log x + \log(2x + 5) = \log 7$

65. $2 \ln x = \ln(2x + 1)$

66. $\log(x^2 + 3) = 2 \log(x + 1)$

67. $\log(x + 1) + \log(x - 1) = \log 3$

68. $\ln(x^2 - 4) - \ln(x + 2) = \ln(3 - x)$

69. $\log_2 2x = 4 - \log_2(x + 2)$

70. $\log_3 x + \log_3(x + 2) = \log_3 24$

71. $\ln(x + 1) + \ln(x - 1) = \ln 15$

72. $\log 4x - \log(x + 3) = \log x$

Solving Different Types of Equations

Exercises 73–78: (Refer to Example 12.) Solve each equation.

73. **(a)** $2x - 3 = 13$ **(b)** $2(3^x) - 3 = 13$
(c) $2 \log x - 3 = 13$ **(d)** $2 \ln x - 3 = 13$
(e) $2 \ln(x - 3) = 13$

74. **(a)** $4x + 1 = 21$ **(b)** $4(5^x) + 1 = 21$
(c) $4 \log x + 1 = 21$ **(d)** $4 \ln x + 1 = 21$
(e) $4 \ln(x + 1) = 21$

75. **(a)** $-5x + 4 = 29$ **(b)** $-5(6^x) + 4 = 29$
(c) $-5 \log x + 4 = 29$ **(d)** $-5 \ln x + 4 = 29$
(e) $-5 \ln(x + 4) = 29$

76. **(a)** $-x - 2 = 2$ **(b)** $-4^x - 2 = 2$
(c) $-\log x - 2 = 2$ **(d)** $-\ln x = 2$
(e) $-\ln(x - 2) = 2$

77. **(a)** $12 - 2x = 6$ **(b)** $12 - 2(5^x) = 6$
(c) $12 - 2 \log x = 6$ **(d)** $12 - 2 \ln x = 6$
(e) $-2 \ln(x + 12) = 6$

78. **(a)** $50 - 3x = 35$ **(b)** $50 - 3(2^x) = 35$
(c) $50 - 3 \log x = 35$ **(d)** $50 - 3 \ln x = 35$
(e) $-3 \ln(x + 50) = 35$

Solving Equations Graphically

Exercises 79–84: The following equations cannot be solved symbolically. Solve these equations graphically and round your answers to the nearest hundredth.

79. $2x + e^x = 2$

80. $xe^x - 1 = 0$

81. $x^2 - x \ln x = 2$

82. $x \ln|x| = -2$

83. $xe^{-x} + \ln x = 1$

84. $2^{x-2} = \log x^4$

Applications

85. **Population Growth** World population P in billions during year x can be modeled by $P(x) = 7(1.01)^{x-2011}$. Predict the year when world population might reach 7.5 billion.

86. **Population of Arizona** The population P of Arizona has been increasing at an annual rate of 2.3%. In 2010 the population of Arizona was 6.4 million.
(a) Write a formula for $P(x)$, where x is the years after 2010 and P is in millions.
(b) Estimate the population of Arizona in 2014.

87. Light Absorption When light passes through water, its intensity I decreases according to the formula $I(x) = I_0e^{-kx}$, where I_0 is the initial intensity of the light and x is the depth in feet. If $I_0 = 1000$ lumens per square meter and $k = 0.12$, determine the depth at which the intensity is 25% of I_0.

88. Light Absorption (Refer to Exercise 87.) Let $I(x) = 500e^{-0.2x}$ and determine the depth x at which the intensity I is 1% of $I_0 = 500$.

89. Moore's Law According to Moore's law the number of transistors that can be placed on an integrated circuit has doubled every 2 years. In 1971 there were only 2300 transistors on an integrated circuit.

(a) Find an exponential function $T(x) = Ca^x$ that gives the number of transistors on an integrated circuit x years after 1971.

(b) Evaluate $T(40)$ and interpret your result.

(c) Determine the year when integrated circuits first had 10 million transistors.

90. Electrical Efficiency (Refer to Example 4.) Use the formula $E(x) = 1000(2^{5/8})^x$ to determine when 1 billion computations could first be performed with 1 kilowatt-hour.

91. Corruption and Human Development There is a relationship between perceived corruption and human development in a country that can be modeled by $H(x) = 0.3 + 0.28\ln x$. In this formula x represents the Corruption Perception Index, where 1 is very corrupt and 10 is least corrupt. The output gives the Human Development Index, which is between 0.1 and 1 with 1 being the best for human development. (***Sources:*** Transparency International; UN Human Development Report.)

(a) For Britain $x = 8$. Evaluate $H(8)$ and interpret the result.

(b) The Human Development Index is 0.68 for China. Find the Corruption Perception Index for China.

92. Urbanization of Brazil The percentage of Brazil's population that lives in urban areas can be modeled by $U(x) = 72 + 4.33\ln x$, where $x \geq 1$ is the number of years after 1990.

(a) Evaluate $U(24)$ and interpret the result.

(b) Predict when urbanization will first reach 88%.

93. Bluefin Tuna The number of Atlantic bluefin tuna in thousands x years after 1974 can be modeled by $f(x) = 230(0.881)^x$. Estimate the year when the number of bluefin tuna reached 95 thousand.

94. Modeling Bacteria (Refer to Section 5.3 [Part II], Example 8.) The number N of *E. coli* bacteria in millions per milliliter after t minutes can be modeled by $N(t) = 0.5e^{0.014t}$. Determine symbolically the elapsed time required for the concentration of bacteria to reach 25 million per milliliter.

95. Population Growth In 2000 the population of India reached 1 billion, and in 2025 it is projected to be 1.4 billion. (***Source:*** Bureau of the Census.)

(a) Find values for C and a so that $P(x) = Ca^{x-2000}$ models the population of India in year x.

(b) Estimate India's population in 2010.

(c) Use P to determine the year when India's population might reach 1.5 billion.

96. Population of Pakistan In 2007 the population of Pakistan was 164 million, and it is expected to be 250 million in 2025. (***Source:*** United Nations.)

(a) Approximate C and a so that $P(x) = Ca^{x-2007}$ models these data, where P is in millions and x is the year.

(b) Estimate the population of Pakistan in 2015, and compare your estimate to the predicted value of 204 million.

(c) Estimate when this population could reach 212 million.

97. Newton's Law of Cooling A pan of boiling water with a temperature of 212°F is set in a bin of ice with a temperature of 32°F. The pan cools to 70°F in 30 minutes.

(a) Find T_0, D, and a so that $T(t) = T_0 + Da^t$ models the data, where t is in hours.

(b) Find the temperature of the pan after 10 minutes.

(c) How long did it take the pan to reach 40°F? Support your result graphically.

98. Warming an Object A pan of cold water with a temperature of 35°F is brought into a room with a temperature of 75°F. After 1 hour, the temperature of the pan of water is 45°F.

(a) Find T_0, D, and a so that $T(t) = T_0 + Da^t$ models the data, where t is in hours.

(b) Find the temperature of the water after 3 hours.

(c) How long would it take the water to reach 60°F?

99. Warming a Soda Can Suppose that a can of soda, initially at 5°C, warms to 18°C after 2 hours in a room that has a temperature of 20°C.

(a) Find the temperature of the soda can after 1.5 hours.

(b) How long did it take for the soda to warm to 15°C

100. Cooling a Soda Can A soda can at 80°F is put into a cooler containing ice at 32°F. The temperature of the soda after t minutes is given by $T(t) = 32 + 48(0.9)^t$.

(a) Evaluate $T(30)$ and interpret your results.

(b) How long did it take for the soda to cool to 50°F?

101. Caloric Intake (Refer to Example 10.) The formula

$$C(x) = 280 \ln(x + 1) + 1925$$

models the number of calories consumed daily by a person owning x acres of land in a developing country. Estimate the number of acres owned for which average intake is 2300 calories per day.

102. Salinity The salinity of the oceans changes with latitude and with depth. In the tropics, the salinity increases on the surface of the ocean due to rapid evaporation. In the higher latitudes, there is less evaporation and rainfall causes the salinity to be less on the surface than at lower depths. The function given by

$$S(x) = 31.5 + 1.1 \log(x + 1)$$

models salinity to depths of 1000 meters at a latitude of 57.5°N. The input x is the depth in meters and the output $S(x)$ is in grams of salt per kilogram of seawater. (***Source:*** D. Hartman, *Global Physical Climatology*.)

(a) Evaluate $S(500)$. Interpret your result.

(b) Graph S. Discuss any trends.

(c) Find the depth where the salinity equals 33.

103. Life Span In one study, the life spans of 129 robins were monitored over a 4-year period. The equation $y = \frac{2 - \log(100 - x)}{0.42}$ can be used to calculate the number of years y required for x percent of the robin population to die. For example, to find the time when 40% of the robins had died, substitute $x = 40$ into the equation. The result is $y \approx 0.53$, or about half a year. Find the percentage of the robins that had died after 2 years. (***Source:*** D. Lack, *The Life of a Robin*.)

104. Life Span of Sparrows (Refer to Exercise 103.) The life span of a sample of sparrows was studied. The equation $y = \frac{2 - \log(100 - x)}{0.37}$ calculates the number of years y required for x percent of the sparrows to die, where $0 \le x \le 95$.

(a) Find y when $x = 40$. Interpret your answer.

(b) Find x when $y = 1.5$. Interpret your answer.

105. Bacteria Growth The concentration of bacteria in a sample can be modeled by $B(t) = B_0e^{kt}$, where t is in hours and B is the concentration in billions of bacteria per liter.

(a) If the concentration increases by 15% in 6 hours, find k.

(b) If $B_0 = 1.2$, find B after 8.2 hours.

(c) By what percentage does the concentration increase each hour?

106. Voltage The voltage in a circuit can be modeled by $V(t) = V_0e^{kt}$, where t is in milliseconds.

(a) If the voltage decreases by 85% in 5 milliseconds, find k.

(b) If $V_0 = 4.5$ volts, find V after 2.3 milliseconds.

(c) By what percentage does the voltage decrease each millisecond?

Exercises 107 and 108: For the given annual interest rate r, estimate the time for P dollars to double.

107. $P = \$1000$, $r = 8.5\%$ compounded quarterly

108. $P = \$750$, $r = 2\%$ compounded continuously

Exercises 109 and 110: **Continuous Compounding** *Suppose that P dollars is deposited in a savings account paying 3% interest compounded continuously. After t years, the account will contain* $A(t) = Pe^{0.03t}$ *dollars.*

(a) Solve $A(t) = b$ *for the given values of P and b.*

(b) Interpret your results.

109. $P = 500$ and $b = 750$

110. $P = 1000$ and $b = 2000$

111. **Radioactive Carbon-14** The percentage P of radioactive carbon-14 remaining in a fossil after t years is given by $P = 100\left(\frac{1}{2}\right)^{t/5700}$. Suppose a fossil contains 35% of the carbon-14 that the organism contained when it was alive. Estimate the age of the fossil.

112. **Radioactive Radium-226** The amount A of radium in milligrams remaining in a sample after t years is given by $A(t) = 0.02\left(\frac{1}{2}\right)^{t/1600}$. How many years will it take for the radium to decay to 0.004 milligram?

113. **Traffic Flow** (Refer to Section 5.3 [Part II], Example 9.) The probability that a car will enter an intersection within a period of x minutes is given by $P(x) = 1 - e^{-0.5x}$. Determine symbolically the elapsed time x when there is a 50–50 chance that a car has entered the intersection. (*Hint:* Solve $P(x) = 0.5$.)

114. **Modeling Traffic Flow** Cars arrive randomly at an intersection with an average traffic volume of one car per minute. The likelihood, or probability, that at least one car enters the intersection during a period of x minutes can be estimated by $f(x) = 1 - e^{-x}$.
(a) What is the probability that at least one car enters the intersection during a 5-minute period?
(b) Determine the value of x that gives a 40% chance that at least one car enters the intersection during an interval of x minutes.

115. **Modeling Bacteria Growth** Suppose that the concentration of a bacteria sample is 100,000 bacteria per milliliter. If the concentration doubles every 2 hours, how long will it take for the concentration to reach 350,000 bacteria per milliliter?

116. **Modeling Bacteria Growth** Suppose that the concentration of a bacteria sample is 50,000 bacteria per milliliter. If the concentration triples in 4 days, how long will it take for the concentration to reach 85,000 bacteria per milliliter?

117. **Continuous Compounding** Suppose that \$2000 is deposited in an account and the balance increases to \$2300 after 4 years. How long will it take for the account to grow to \$3200? Assume continuous compounding.

118. **Modeling Radioactive Decay** Suppose that a 0.05-gram sample of a radioactive substance decays to 0.04 gram in 20 days. How long will it take for the sample to decay to 0.025 gram?

119. **Drug Concentrations** The concentration of a drug in a patient's bloodstream after t hours is modeled by the formula $C(t) = 11(0.72)^t$, where C is measured in milligrams per liter.
(a) What is the initial concentration of the drug?
(b) How long does it take for the concentration to decrease to 50% of its initial level?

120. **Reducing Carbon Emissions** When fossil fuels are burned, carbon is released into the atmosphere. Governments could reduce carbon emissions by placing a tax on fossil fuels. The **cost-benefit** equation

$$\ln(1 - P) = -0.0034 - 0.0053x$$

estimates the relationship between a tax of x dollars per ton of carbon and the percent P reduction in emissions of carbon, where P is in decimal form. Determine P when $x = 60$. Interpret the result (***Source:*** W. Clime, *The Economics of Global Warming.*)

121. **Investments** The formula $A = P\left(1 + \frac{r}{n}\right)^{nt}$ can be used to calculate the future value of an investment. Solve the equation for t.

122. **Decibels** The formula $D = 160 + 10\log x$ can be used to calculate loudness of a sound in decibels. Solve the equation for x.

Writing about Mathematics

123. Explain how to solve the equation $Ca^x = k$ symbolically for x. Demonstrate your method.

124. Explain how to solve the equation $b\log_a x = k$ symbolically for x. Demonstrate your method.

Extended and Discovery Exercise

1. **Exponential Functions** Show that any exponential function in the form $f(x) = Ca^x$ can be written as $f(x) = Ce^{kx}$. That is, write k in terms of a. Use your method to write $g(x) = 2^x$ in the form e^{kx} for some k.

CHECKING BASIC CONCEPTS FOR SECTIONS 5.5 AND 5.6

1. Use properties of logarithms to expand $\log \frac{x^2y^3}{\sqrt[3]{z}}$. Write your answer without exponents.

2. Combine the expression $\frac{1}{2}\ln x - 3\ln y + \ln z$ as a logarithm of a single expression.

3. Solve each equation.
   (a) $5(1.4)^x - 4 = 25$ **(b)** $4^{2-x} = 4^{2x+1}$

4. Solve each equation.
   (a) $5\log_2 2x = 25$

   (b) $\ln(x + 1) + \ln(x - 1) = \ln 3$

5. The temperature T of a cooling object in degrees Fahrenheit after x minutes is given by

$$T = 80 + 120(0.9)^x.$$

   (a) What happens to T after a long time?

   (b) After how long is the object's temperature 100°F?

5.7 Constructing Nonlinear Models

- **Find an exponential model**
- **Find a logarithmic model**
- **Find a logistic model**
- **Select a model**

Introduction

If data change at a constant rate, then they can be modeled with a linear function. However, real-life data often change at a nonconstant rate. For example, a tree grows slowly when it is small and then gradually grows faster as it becomes larger. Finally, when the tree is mature, its height begins to level off. This type of growth is nonlinear.

Three types of nonlinear data are shown in Figures 5.79–5.81 on the next page, where t represents time. In Figure 5.79 the data increase rapidly, and an *exponential function* might be an appropriate modeling function. In Figure 5.80 the data are growing, but at a slower rate than in Figure 5.79. These data could be modeled by a *logarithmic function*. Finally, in Figure 5.81 the data increase slowly, then increase faster, and finally level off. These data might represent the height of a tree over a 50-year period. To model these data, we need a new type of function called a *logistic function*.

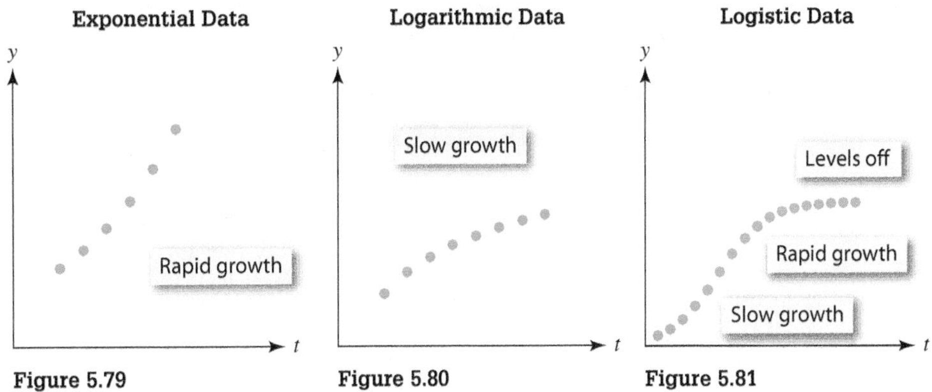

Figure 5.79 **Figure 5.80** **Figure 5.81**

Exponential Model

Both world population and bacteria growth can sometimes be modeled by an exponential function that *increases*. Exponential functions can also be used to model data that *decrease*. In the next example, an exponential function is used to model atmospheric pressure.

EXAMPLE 1 **Modeling atmospheric pressure**

As altitude increases, air pressure decreases. The atmospheric pressure P in millibars (mb) at a given altitude x in meters is listed in Table 5.24.

Altitude and Air Pressure

x (m)	0	5000	10,000	15,000	20,000	25,000	30,000
P (mb)	1013	541	265	121	55	26	12

Source: A. Miller and J. Thompson, *Elements of Meteorology*.

Table 5.24

(a) Make a scatterplot of the data. What type of function might model the data?
(b) Use regression to find an exponential function given by $f(x) = ab^x$. Graph the data and f in the same viewing rectangle.
(c) Use f to estimate the air pressure at an altitude of 23,000 feet.

Calculator Help
To find an equation of least-squares fit, see Appendix A (page AP-9). To copy a regression equation directly into Y_1, see Appendix A (page AP-11).

SOLUTION

(a) The data are shown in Figure 5.82. A *decreasing* exponential function might model the data.

NOTE It is possible for a different function, such as a portion of a polynomial graph, to model the data. Answers may vary.

(b) Figures 5.83 and 5.84 show that values of $a \approx 1104.9$ and $b \approx 0.99985$ are obtained from exponential regression, where $f(x) = ab^x$. Figure 5.85 illustrates that f models the data quite accurately.
(c) $f(23{,}000) = 1104.9(0.99985)^{23{,}000} \approx 35.1$ millibars

Plot the Data
[−5000, 35000, 5000] by [−100, 1200, 100]

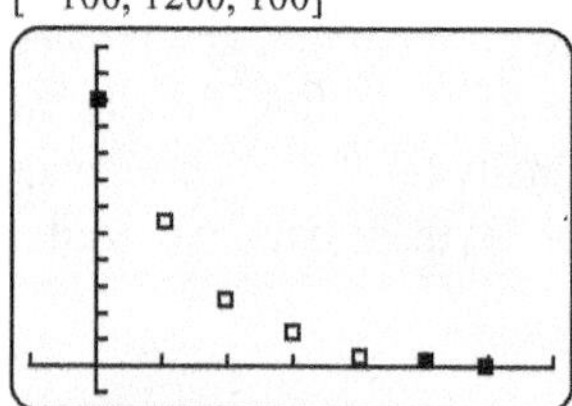

Figure 5.82

Select Exponential Regression

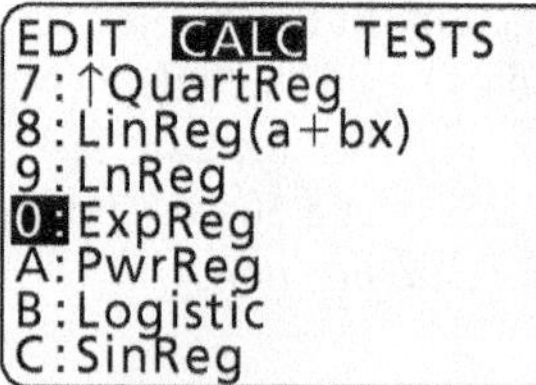

Figure 5.83

Exponential Function

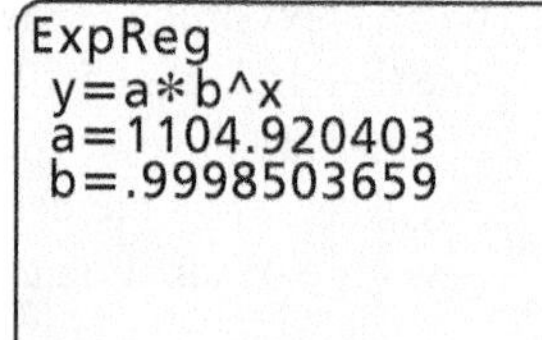

Figure 5.84

Graph Function with Data
[−5000, 35000, 5000] by [−100, 1200, 100]

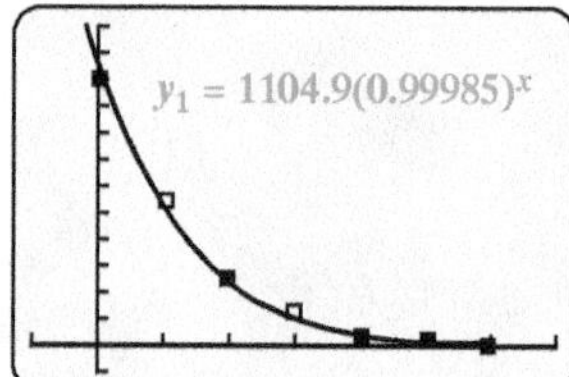

Figure 5.85

Now Try Exercise 15

Logarithmic Model

An investor buying a certificate of deposit (CD) usually gets a higher interest rate if the money is deposited for a longer period of time. However, the interest rate for a 9-month CD is not usually triple the rate for a 3-month CD. Instead, the rate of interest slowly increases with a longer-term CD. In the next example, we model interest rates with a logarithmic function.

EXAMPLE 2 **Modeling interest rates**

Table 5.25 lists the interest rates for certificates of deposit. Use the data to complete the following.

Yield on Certificates of Deposit

Time (months)	1	3	6	9	24	36	60
Yield (%)	0.25	0.39	0.74	0.80	1.25	1.40	1.50

Source: *USA Today.*

Table 5.25

(a) Make a scatterplot of the data. What type of function might model these data?
(b) Use least-squares regression to find a formula $f(x) = a + b\ln x$ that models the data.
(c) Graph f and the data in the same viewing rectangle.

SOLUTION

(a) Enter the data in Table 5.25 into your calculator. A scatterplot of the data is shown in Figure 5.86. The data increase but gradually level off. A logarithmic modeling function may be appropriate.
(b) In Figures 5.87 and 5.88 least-squares regression has been used to find a logarithmic function f given (approximately) by $f(x) = 0.143 + 0.334\ln x$.
(c) A graph of f and the data are shown in Figure 5.89.

Plot the Data

[0, 70, 10] by [0, 2, 0.5]

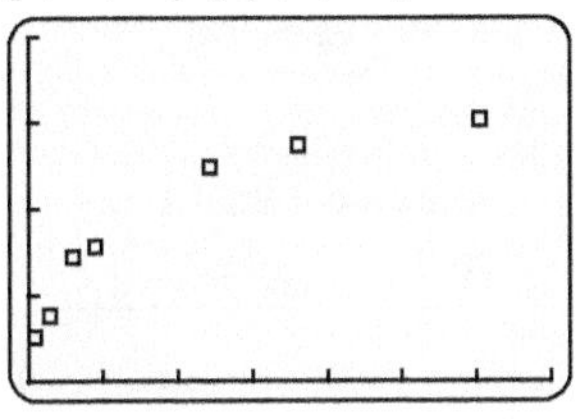

Figure 5.86

Select Logarithm Regression

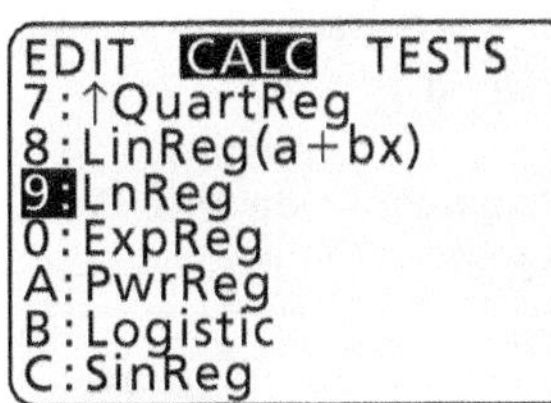

Figure 5.87

Regression Function

LnReg
y=a+blnx
a=.1426554975
b=.3343937622

Figure 5.88

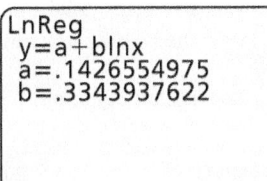

Graph Function with Data

[0, 70, 10] by [0, 2, 0.5]

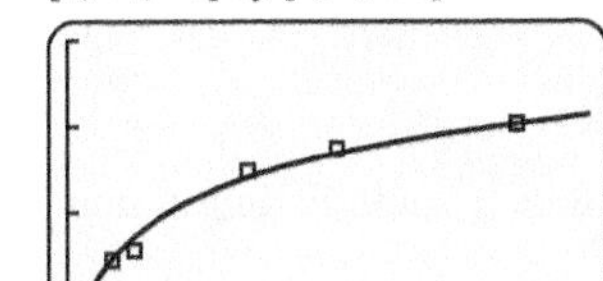

Figure 5.89

Now Try Exercise 13

Sigmoidal Curve

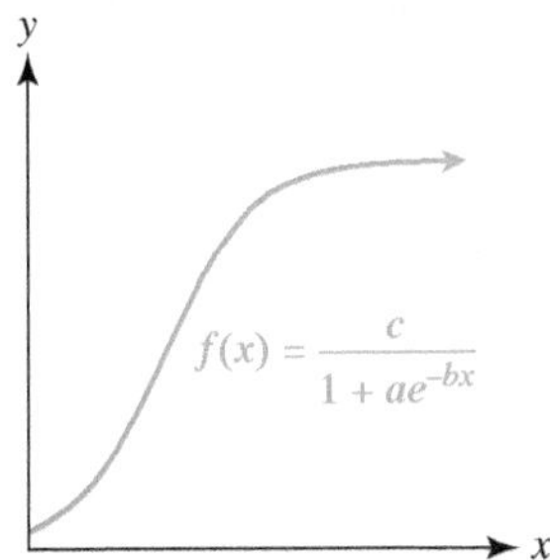

Figure 5.90

Logistic Model

In real life, populations of bacteria, insects, and animals do not continue to grow indefinitely. Initially, population growth may be slow. Then, as their numbers increase, so does the rate of growth. After a region has become heavily populated or saturated, the population usually levels off because of limited resources.

This type of growth may be modeled by a **logistic function** represented by $f(x) = \dfrac{c}{1 + ae^{-bx}}$, where a, b, and c are positive constants. A typical graph of a logistic function f is shown in Figure 5.90. The graph of f is referred to as a **sigmoidal curve.** The next example demonstrates how a logistic function can be used to describe the growth of a yeast culture.

EXAMPLE 3 Modeling logistic growth

One of the earliest studies about population growth was done in 1913 using yeast plants. A small amount of yeast was placed in a container with a fixed amount of nourishment. The units of yeast were recorded every 2 hours. The data are listed in Table 5.26.

Growth of Yeast Plants

Time	0	2	4	6	8	10	12	14	16	18
Yeast	9.6	29.0	71.1	174.6	350.7	513.3	594.8	640.8	655.9	661.8

Source: T. Carlson, *Biochem.;* D. Brown, *Models in Biology.*

Table 5.26

(a) Make a scatterplot of the data in Table 5.26. Describe the growth.
(b) Use least-squares regression to find a logistic function f that models the data.
(c) Graph f and the data in the same viewing rectangle.
(d) Approximate graphically the time when the amount of yeast was 200 units.

Plot the Data
$[-2, 20, 1]$ by $[-100, 800, 100]$

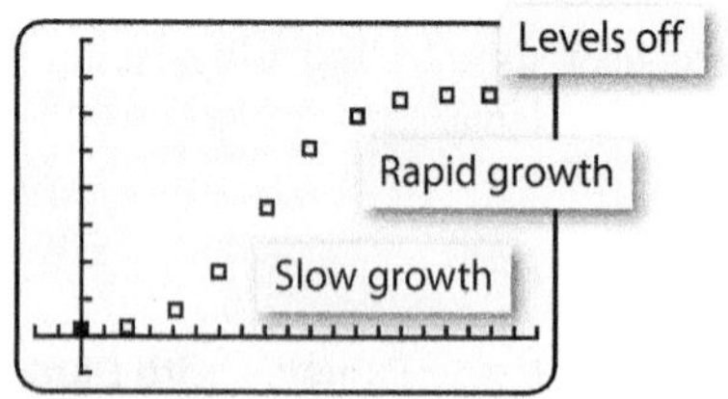

Figure 5.91

SOLUTION

(a) A scatterplot of the data is shown in Figure 5.91. The yeast increase slowly at first. Then they grow more rapidly until the amount of yeast gradually levels off. The limited amount of nourishment causes this leveling off.

(b) In Figure 5.92 and 5.93 we see least-squares regression being used to find a logistic function f given (approximately) by

$$f(x) = \frac{661.8}{1 + 74.46e^{-0.552x}}.$$

(c) In Figure 5.94 the data and f are graphed in the same viewing rectangle. The fit for the *real* data is remarkably good.

Select Logistic Regression

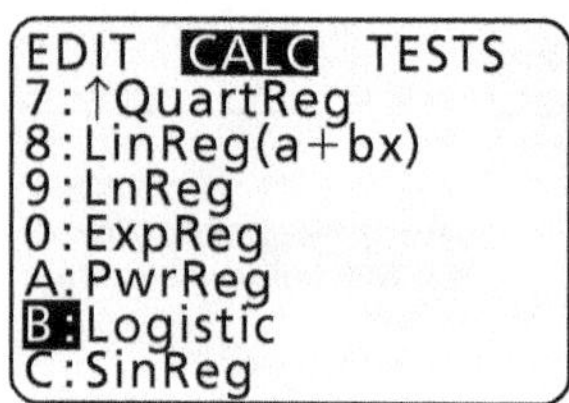

Figure 5.92

Regression Function

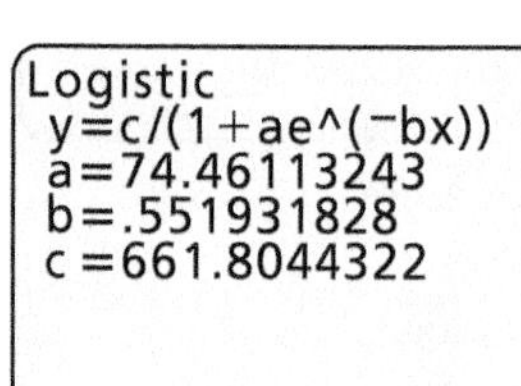

Figure 5.93

Graph Function with Data
$[-2, 20, 1]$ by $[-100, 800, 100]$

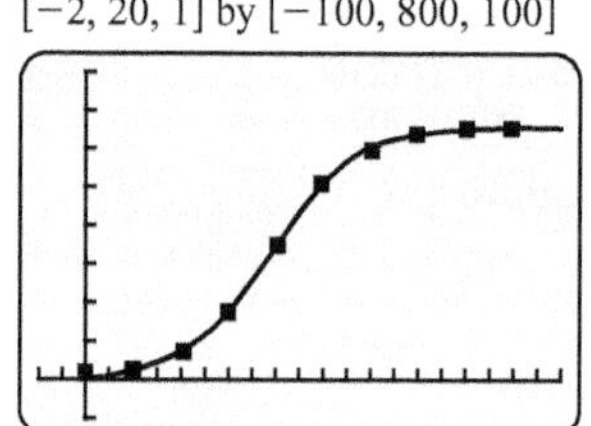

Figure 5.94

Graphical Solution
$[-2, 20, 1]$ by $[-100, 800, 100]$

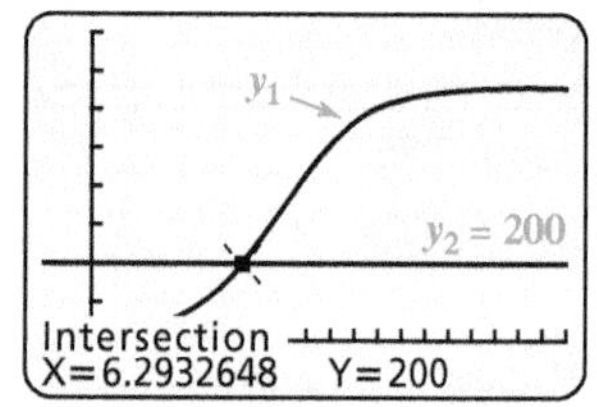

Figure 5.95

(d) The graphs of $Y_1 = f(x)$ and $Y_2 = 200$ intersect near (6.29, 200), as shown in Figure 5.95. The amount of yeast reached 200 units after about 6.29 hours.

Now Try Exercise 19

CLASS DISCUSSION

In Example 3, suppose that after 18 hours the experiment had been extended and more nourishment had been provided for the yeast plants. Sketch a possible graph of the amount of yeast.

MAKING CONNECTIONS

Logistic Functions and Horizontal Asymptotes If a logistic function is given by $f(x) = \frac{c}{1 + ae^{-bx}}$, where a, b, and c are positive constants, then the graph of f has a horizontal asymptote of $y = c$. (Try to explain why this is true.) In Example 3, the value of c was 661.8. This means that the amount of yeast leveled off at about 661.8 units.

Selecting a Model

In real-data applications, a modeling function is seldom given. Many times we must choose the type of modeling function and then find it using least-squares regression. Thus far in this section, we have used exponential, logarithmic, and logistic functions to model data. In the next two examples, we select a modeling function.

EXAMPLE 4 Modeling highway design

To allow enough distance for cars to pass on two-lane highways, engineers often calculate minimum sight distances between curves and hills. See the figure. Table 5.27 shows the minimum sight distance y in feet for a car traveling at x miles per hour.

Passing Distance

x (mph)	20	30	40	50	60	65	70
y (ft)	810	1090	1480	1840	2140	2310	2490

Source: L. Haefner, *Introduction to Transportation Systems.*

Table 5.27

(a) Find a modeling function for the data.
(b) Graph the data and your modeling function.
(c) Estimate the minimum sight distance for a car traveling at 43 miles per hour.

SOLUTION

Getting Started One strategy is to plot the data and then decide if the data are linear or nonlinear. If the data are approximately linear, use linear regression to find the modeling function. If the data are nonlinear, think about how the data increase or decrease. You may want to try several types of modeling functions, such as quadratic, cubic, power, exponential, or logarithmic, before making a final decision. ▶

(a) A scatterplot is shown in Figure 5.96. The data appear to be (nearly) linear, so linear regression has been used to obtain $f(x) = 33.93x + 113.4$. See Figure 5.97.
(b) The data and f are graphed in Figure 5.98. Function f gives a good fit.

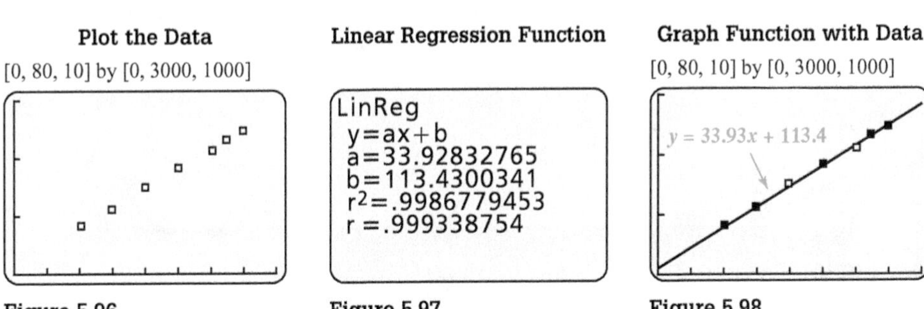

Figure 5.96 Figure 5.97 Figure 5.98

(c) $f(43) = 33.93(43) + 113.4 \approx 1572$ feet

Now Try Exercise 11

You may have seen or heard of asbestos being removed from buildings. Before 1960 people were generally unaware of its health hazards. As a result, insulation workers who worked with asbestos experienced higher rates of lung cancer. The following example models data from this era.

EXAMPLE 5 Modeling asbestos and cancer

Table 5.28 lists the number N of lung cancer cases occurring within a group of asbestos insulation workers with a cumulative total of 100,000 years of work experience, with their first date of employment x years ago.

Lung Cancer and Asbestos

x (years)	10	15	20	25	30
N (cases)	6.9	25.4	63.6	130	233

Years since employment began

Cases in a group with 100,000 years of work experience

Source: A. Walker, *Observation and Inference.*

Table 5.28

(a) Find a modeling function for the data.
(b) Graph the data and your modeling function.
(c) Estimate the number of lung cancer cases for $x = 23$ years. Interpret your answer.

SOLUTION

Getting Started The data are nonlinear and increasing, so there are a number of functions you can try. Three possibilities are quadratic, power, and exponential. ▶

(a) A scatterplot is shown in Figure 5.99. To model the data we have used a power function given by $f(x) = 0.004334x^{3.2}$. See Figure 5.100. (Answers may vary.)
(b) The data and f are graphed in Figure 5.101. Function f gives a good fit.

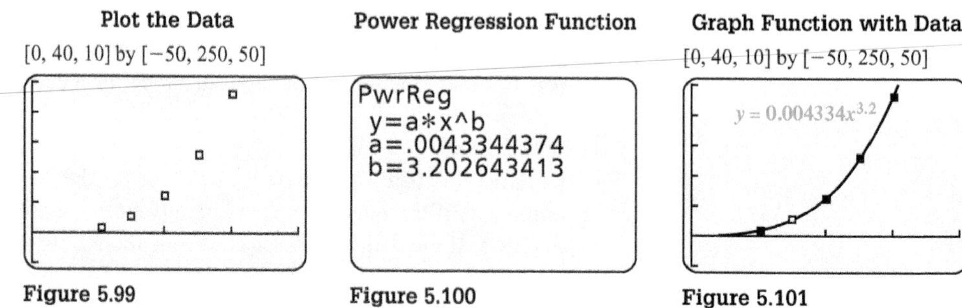

Figure 5.99 Figure 5.100 Figure 5.101

(c) $f(23) = 0.004334(23)^{3.2} \approx 99$ cases. If a group of asbestos workers began their employment 23 years earlier and had a cumulative work experience of 100,000 years, then the group experienced 99 cases of lung cancer.

Now Try Exercise 21

5.7 Putting It All Together

The following table summarizes the basics of exponential, logarithmic, and logistic models. Least-squares regression can be used to determine the constants *a*, *b*, *c*, and *C*.

CONCEPT	EXPLANATION	EXAMPLES
Exponential model	$f(x) = Ca^x$, $f(x) = ab^x$, or $A(t) = A_0e^{kt}$	Exponential functions can be used to model data that increase or decrease rapidly over time.
Logarithmic model	$f(x) = a + b\log x$ or $f(x) = a + b\ln x$	Logarithmic functions can be used to model data that increase gradually over time.
Logistic model	$f(x) = \dfrac{c}{1 + ae^{-bx}}$	Logistic functions can be used to model data that at first increase slowly, then increase rapidly, and finally level off.

5.7 Exercises

Note: Because different functions can be used to model the same data, your answers may vary from the given answers. You can check the validity of your answer by graphing the data and your modeling function in the same viewing rectangle.

Selecting a Model

Exercises 1–4: Select an appropriate type of modeling function for the data shown in the graph. Choose from the following.

i. Exponential ii. Logarithmic iii. Logistic

1. **2.**

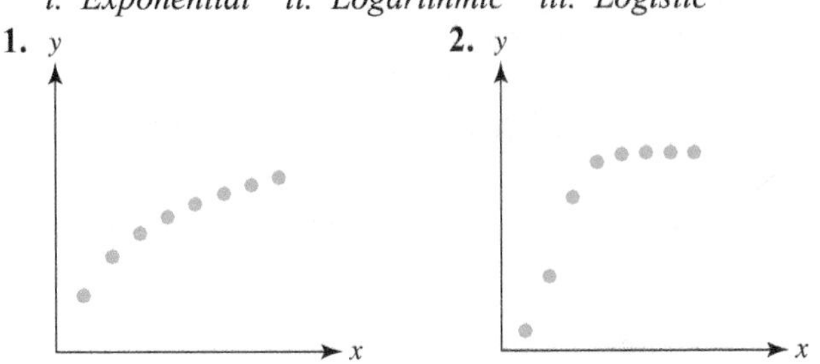

3. **4.**

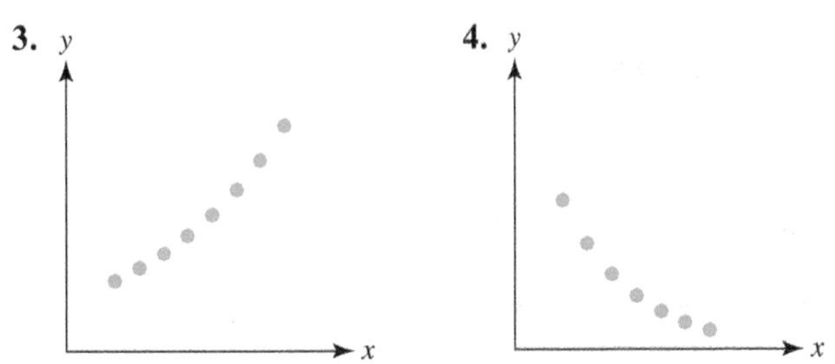

Exercises 5–10: Make a scatterplot of the data. Then find an exponential, logarithmic, or logistic function f that best models the data.

5.

x	1	2	3	4
y	2.04	3.47	5.90	10.02

6.

x	1	2	3	4	5
y	1.98	2.35	2.55	2.69	2.80

7.

x	1	2	3	4	5
y	1.1	3.1	4.3	5.2	5.8

8.

x	1	2	3	4	5	6
y	1	2	4	7	9	10

9.

x	0	1	2	3	4	5
y	0.3	1.3	4.0	7.5	9.3	9.8

10.

x	1	2	3	4	5
y	2.0	1.6	1.3	1.0	0.82

Applications

11. SlideShare Growth The following table shows the number of visitors in millions who visited the website SlideShare.

Year	2007	2008	2009	2010	2011
Visitors	1.5	6.3	17.0	33.2	60.1

Source: SlideShare.

(a) Choose a linear, quadratic, or logarithmic function $V(x)$ that best models the data, where x is years after 2007.

(b) Estimate the number of visitors in 2012.

12. Heart Disease Death Rates The following table contains heart disease death rates per 100,000 people for selected ages.

Age	30	40	50	60	70
Death rate	30.5	108.2	315	776	2010

Source: Department of Health and Human Services.

(a) Make a scatterplot of the data in the viewing rectangle [25, 75, 5] by [−100, 2100, 200].

(b) Find a function f that models the data.

(c) Estimate the heart disease death rate for people who are 80 years old.

13. Telecommuting In the past some workers used technology such as e-mail, computers, and multiple phone lines to work at home, rather than in the office. However, because of the need for teamwork and collaboration in the workplace, fewer employees telecommuted than expected. The table lists telecommuters T in millions during year x.

x	1997	1998	1999	2000	2001
T	9.2	9.6	10.0	10.4	10.6

x	2002	2003	2004	2005	2006
T	11.0	11.1	11.2	11.3	11.4

Source: *USA Today.*

Find a function f that models the data, where $x = 1$ corresponds to 1997, $x = 2$ to 1998, and so on.

14. Hurricanes The table shows the air pressure y in inches of mercury x miles from the eye of a hurricane.

x	2	4	8	15	30	100
y	27.3	27.7	28.04	28.3	28.7	29.3

Source: A. Miller and R. Anthes, *Meteorology*.

(a) Make a scatterplot of the data.

(b) Find a function f that models the data.

(c) Estimate the air pressure at 50 miles.

15. Atmospheric Density The table lists the atmospheric density y in kilograms per cubic meter (kg/m^3) at an altitude of x meters.

x (m)	0	5000	10,000	15,000	20,000	25,000	30,000
y (kg/m^3)	1.2250	0.7364	0.4140	0.1948	0.0889	0.0401	0.0184

Source: A. Miller.

(a) Find a function f that models the data.

(b) Predict the density at 7000 meters. (The actual value is 0.59 kg/m^3.)

16. Modeling Data Use the table to complete the following.

x	1	2	5	10
y	2.5	2.1	1.6	1.2

(a) Find a function f that models the data.

(b) Solve the equation $f(x) = 1.8$.

17. Insect Population The table shows the density y of a species of insect measured in thousands per acre after x days.

x	2	4	6	8	10	12	14
y	0.38	1.24	2.86	4.22	4.78	4.94	4.98

(a) Find a function f that models the data.

(b) Use f to estimate the insect density after a long time.

18. Heart Disease As age increases, so does the likelihood of coronary heart disease (CHD). The percentage P of people x years old with signs of CHD is shown in the table.

x	15	25	35	45	55	65	75
P(%)	2	7	19	43	68	82	87

Source: D. Hosmer and S. Lemeshow, *Applied Logistics Regression*.

(a) Evaluate $P(25)$ and interpret the answer.

(b) Find a function that models the data.

(c) Graph P and the data.

(d) At what age does a person have a 50% chance of having signs of CHD?

19. Mobile Phones in India The following table shows the number of cell phone subscriptions in India in billions for selected years.

Year	2005	2006	2007	2008	2009	2010	2011
Cell Phones	0.05	0.12	0.21	0.40	0.60	0.75	0.85

Source: Chetan Sharma Consulting.

(a) Find a function $C(x)$ that models the data, where x is years after 2005.

(b) Predict the number of cell phone subscriptions in 2014.

20. U.S. Radio Stations The numbers N of radio stations on the air for selected years x are listed in the table.

x	1970	1980	1990	2000	2010
$N(x)$	6760	8566	10,788	12,808	14,420

Source: M. Street Corporation.

(a) Find a function that models the data.

(b) Graph N and the data.

(c) Predict when the number of radio stations on the air might reach 16,000.

21. Wing Size Heavier birds tend to have larger wings than smaller birds. For one species of bird, the table lists the area A of the bird's wing in square inches if the bird weighs w pounds.

w (lb)	2	6	10	14	18
$A(w)$ (in^2)	160	330	465	580	685

Source: C. Pennycuick, *Newton Rules Biology*.

(a) Find a function that models the data.

(b) Graph A and the data.

(c) What weight corresponds to a wing area of 500 square inches?

22. Wing Span Heavier birds tend to have a longer wing span than smaller birds. For one species of bird, the table lists the length L of the bird's wing span in feet if the bird weighs w pounds.

w (lb)	0.22	0.88	1.76	2.42
$L(w)$ (ft)	1.38	2.19	2.76	3.07

Source: C. Pennycuick, *Newton Rules Biology*.

(a) Find a function that models the data.

(b) Graph L and the data.

(c) What weight corresponds to a wing span of 2 feet?

23. Tree Growth (Refer to the introduction to this section.) The height H of a tree in feet after x years is listed in the table.

x (yr)	1	5	10	20	30	40
$H(x)$ (ft)	1.3	3	8	32	47	50

(a) Evaluate $H(5)$ and interpret the answer.

(b) Find a function that models the data.

(c) Graph H and the data.

(d) What is the age of the tree when its height is 25 feet?

(e) Did your answer involve interpolation or extrapolation?

24. Bird Populations Near New Guinea there is a relationship between the number of bird species found on an island and the size of the island. The table lists the number of species of birds y found on an island with an area of x square kilometers.

x (km^2)	0.1	1	10	100	1000
y (species)	10	15	20	25	30

Source: B. Freedman, *Environmental Ecology.*

(a) Find a function f that models the data.

(b) Predict the number of bird species on an island of 5000 square kilometers.

(c) Did your answer involve interpolation or extrapolation?

25. Fertilizer Usage Between 1950 and 1980 the use of chemical fertilizers increased. The table lists worldwide average usage y in kilograms per hectare of cropland x years after 1950. (*Note:* 1 hectare $\approx$ 2.47 acres.)

x	0	13	22	29
y	12.4	27.9	54.3	77.1

Source: D. Grigg, *The World Food Problem.*

(a) Graph the data. Are the data linear?

(b) Find a function f that models the data.

(c) Predict fertilizer usage in 1989. The actual value was 98.7 kilograms per hectare. What does this indicate about usage of fertilizer during the 1980s?

26. Social Security If major reform occurs in the Social Security system, individuals might be able to invest some of their contributions into individual accounts. These accounts would be managed by financial firms, which often charge fees. The table lists the amount in billions of dollars that might be collected if fees are 0.93% of the assets each year.

Year	2005	2010	2015	2020
Fees ($ billions)	20	41	80	136

Source: Social Security Advisory Council.

(a) Use exponential regression to find a and b so that $f(x) = ab^x$ models the data x years after 2000.

(b) Graph f and the data.

(c) Estimate the fees in 2013.

(d) Did your answer involve interpolation or extrapolation?

Writing about Mathematics

27. How can you distinguish data that illustrate exponential growth from data that illustrate logarithmic growth?

28. Give an example of data that could be modeled by a logistic function and explain why.

Extended And Discovery Exercise

1. For medical reasons, dyes may be injected into the bloodstream to determine the health of internal organs. In one study involving animals, the dye BSP was injected to assess the blood flow in the liver. The results are listed in the table, where x represents the elapsed time in minutes and y is the concentration of the dye in the bloodstream in milligrams per milliliter.

x	1	2	3	4	5	7
y	0.102	0.077	0.057	0.045	0.036	0.023

x	9	13	16	19	22
y	0.015	0.008	0.005	0.004	0.003

Source: F. Harrison, "The measurement of liver blood flow in conscious calves."

(a) Find a function that models the data.

(b) Estimate the elapsed time when the concentration of the dye reaches 30% of its initial concentration of 0.133 mg/ml.

(c) Let $g(x) = 0.133(0.878(0.73^x) + 0.122(0.92^x))$. This formula was used by the researchers to model the data. Compare the accuracy of your formula to that of $g(x)$.

CHECKING BASIC CONCEPTS FOR SECTION 5.7

Exercises 1–4: Find a function that models the data. Choose from exponential, logarithmic, or logistic functions.

1.

x	2	3	4	5	6	7
y	0.72	0.86	1.04	1.24	1.49	1.79

2.

x	2	3	4	5	6	7
y	0.08	1.30	2.16	2.83	3.38	3.84

3.

x	2	3	4	5	6	7
y	0.25	0.86	2.19	3.57	4.23	4.43

4. **World Population** The table lists the actual or projected world population y (in billions) for selected years x.

x	1950	1960	2000	2050	2075
y	2.5	3.0	6.1	8.9	9.2

Source: U.N. Dept. of Economic and Social Affairs.

5 Summary

CONCEPT	EXPLANATION AND EXAMPLES
Section 5.1 Combining Functions	
Arithmetic Operations on Functions	Addition: $(f+g)(x) = f(x) + g(x)$ Subtraction: $(f-g)(x) = f(x) - g(x)$ Multiplication: $(fg)(x) = f(x) \cdot g(x)$ Division: $(f/g)(x) = \frac{f(x)}{g(x)}, g(x) \neq 0$ **Examples:** Let $f(x) = x^2 - 5, g(x) = x^2 - 4$. $(f+g)(x) = (x^2-5) + (x^2-4) = 2x^2 - 9$ $(f-g)(x) = (x^2-5) - (x^2-4) = -1$ $(fg)(x) = (x^2-5)(x^2-4) = x^4 - 9x^2 + 20$ $(f/g)(x) = \frac{x^2-5}{x^2-4}, x \neq 2, x \neq -2$
Composition of Functions	Composition: $(g \circ f)(x) = g(f(x))$ $(f \circ g)(x) = f(g(x))$ **Examples:** Let $f(x) = 3x + 2, g(x) = 2x^2 - 4x + 1$. $g(f(x)) = g(3x+2)$ $= 2(3x+2)^2 - 4(3x+2) + 1$ $f(g(x)) = f(2x^2 - 4x + 1)$ $= 3(2x^2 - 4x + 1) + 2$

CONCEPT	EXPLANATION AND EXAMPLES
Section 5.2 Inverse Functions and Their Representations (CONTINUED)	
Inverse Function	The inverse function of f is f^{-1} if $f^{-1}(f(x)) = x$ for every x in the domain of f and $f(f^{-1}(x)) = x$ for every x in the domain of f^{-1}. *Note:* If $f(a) = b$, then $f^{-1}(b) = a$. **Example:** Find the inverse function of $f(x) = 4x - 5$. $y = 4x - 5$ is equivalent to $\frac{y+5}{4} = x$. (Solve for x.) Thus $f^{-1}(x) = \frac{x+5}{4}$.
One-to-One Function	If different inputs always result in different outputs, then f is one-to-one. That is, $a \neq b$ implies $f(a) \neq f(b)$. (A function is also one-to-one if $f(a) = f(b)$ implies $a = b$.) *Note*: If f is one-to-one, then f has an inverse denoted f^{-1}. **Example:** $f(x) = x^2 + 1$ is not one-to-one because $f(2) = f(-2) = 5$.
Horizontal Line Test	If every horizontal line intersects the graph of a function f at most once, then f is a one-to-one function.
Section 5.3 Exponential Functions and Models (Part I)	
Exponential Function	$f(x) = Ca^x$, $a > 0$, $a \neq 1$, and $C > 0$ Exponential growth: $a > 1$; exponential decay: $0 < a < 1$ The base a is called the growth factor when $a > 1$ and the decay factor when $0 < a < 1$. If x represents time, then C is called the initial value. The initial value C corresponds to the y-intercept on the graph of f. **Examples:** $f(x) = 3(2)^x$ (growth); $f(x) = 1.2(0.5)^x$ (decay)
Exponential Data	For each unit increase in x, the y-values increase (or decrease) by a constant factor a. **Example:** The data in the table are modeled by $y = 5(2)^x$. x: 0, 1, 2, 3 y: 5, 10, 20, 40 The value of y when $x = 0$ is 5, so $C = 5$. The value of the base is $a = 2$ because consecutive x-values increase by 1 and the ratio of consecutive y-values equals 2.

CONCEPT	EXPLANATION AND EXAMPLES
Section 5.3 Exponential Functions and Models (Part I) (CONTINUED)	
Exponential Model	Data that can be described by a function f of the form $f(x) = Ca^x$ are said to be modeled by an exponential model. The initial value C and growth (or decay) factor a are determined by the given data.
Section 5.3 Exponential Functions and Models (Part II)	
Percentages	A percentage can be written in percent form or decimal form. **Example:** Fifteen percent can be written as 15% or 0.15.
Percent Change and Exponential Models	Suppose that an amount A changes by a given rate r (or percent expressed in decimal form) for each unit increase in x. Then the following hold. **1.** If $r > 0$, the constant growth factor is $a = 1 + r$ and $a > 1$. **2.** If $r < 0$, the constant decay factor is $a = 1 + r$ and $0 < a < 1$. **3.** If the initial amount is C, then the amount A after an x-unit increases in time is given by the exponential model $A(x) = C(1 + r)^x$, or $A(x) = Ca^x$. **Example:** A sample of 500 fish decreases in number by 2% each day. The decay factor is $a = 1 + r = 1 - 0.02 = 0.98$. The number of fish after x days is modeled by $f(x) = 500(0.98)^x$.
Natural Exponential Function	$f(x) = e^x$, where $e \approx 2.718282$
Compound Interest	$A = P\left(1 + \frac{r}{n}\right)^{nt}$, where P is the principal, r is the interest rate expressed as a decimal, n is the number of times interest is paid each year, and t is the number of years **Example:** $A = 2000\left(1 + \frac{0.10}{12}\right)^{12(4)} \approx \$2978.71$ calculates the future value of \$2000 invested at 10% compounded monthly for 4 years. $A = Pe^{rt}$, where P is the principal, r is the interest rate expressed as a decimal, and t is the number of years. **Example:** $A = 2000e^{0.10(4)} \approx \$2983.65$ calculates the future value of \$2000 invested at 10% compounded continuously for 4 years.

CONCEPT	EXPLANATION AND EXAMPLES
Section 5.3 Exponential Functions and Models (Part II) (CONTINUED)	
Continuously Compounded Interest	$A = Pe^{rt}$, where P is the principal, r is the interest rate expressed as a decimal, and t is the number of years. **Example:** $A = 2000e^{0.10(4)} \approx \$2983.65$ calculates the future value of \$2000 invested at 10% compounded continuously for 4 years.
Nominal and Effective Interest Rates	**Example:** If 8% annual interest interest is compounded continuously, then the nominal interest rate is 8%. To determine the effective interest rate let $P = 1$. Then after 1 year, $A = 1e^{0.08(1)} \approx 1.0833,$ so the effective interest rate is about 8.33%.
Natural Exponential Model	Exponential growth ($k > 0$) and decay ($k < 0$) can be modeled by $A(t) = A_0e^{kt}$. Any natural exponential model can be written in the form $f(x) = Ca^x$ by letting $C = A_0$ and $a = e^k$. **Example:** If the number of bacteria in millions after t hours is modeled by $A(t) = 300e^{0.03t}$, then there are initially 300 million bacteria that are increasing *continuously* at 3% per hour. This function could also be written approximately as $A(t) = 300(1.0305)^t$ because $e^{0.03} \approx 1.0305$.
Section 5.4 Logarithmic Functions and Models	
Common Logarithm	$\log x = k$ if and only if $x = 10^k$
Natural Logarithm	$\ln x = k$ if and only if $x = e^k$
General Logarithm	$\log_a x = k$ if and only if $x = a^k$ **Examples:** $\log 100 = 2$ because $100 = 10^2$. $\ln \sqrt{e} = \frac{1}{2}$ because $\sqrt{e} = e^{1/2}$. $\log_2 \frac{1}{8} = -3$ because $\frac{1}{8} = 2^{-3}$.
Inverse Properties	$\log 10^k = k,\quad 10^{\log k} = k,\ k > 0$ $\ln e^k = k,\quad e^{\ln k} = k,\ k > 0$ $\log_a a^k = k,\quad a^{\log_a k} = k,\ k > 0$ **Examples:** $10^{\log 100} = 100$; $e^{\ln 23} = 23$; $\log_4 64 = \log_4 4^3 = 3$

CONCEPT	EXPLANATION AND EXAMPLES
Section 5.4 Logarithmic Functions and Models (CONTINUED)	
Inverse Functions	The inverse function of $f(x) = a^x$ is $f^{-1}(x) = \log_a x$. **Examples:** If $f(x) = 10^x$, then $f^{-1}(x) = \log x$. If $f(x) = \ln x$, then $f^{-1}(x) = e^x$. If $f(x) = \log_5 x$, then $f^{-1}(x) = 5^x$.
Exponential and Logarithmic Forms	$\log_a x = k$ is equivalent to $x = a^k$. **Examples:** $\log_2 16 = 4$ is equivalent to $16 = 2^4$. $81 = 3^4$ is equivalent to $\log_3 81 = 4$.
Section 5.5 Properties of Logarithms	
Properties of Logarithms	**1.** $\log_a 1 = 0$ and $\log_a a = 1$ — Logarithms of 1 and of *a* **2.** $\log_a m + \log_a n = \log_a(mn)$ — Product rule **3.** $\log_a m - \log_a n = \log_a\left(\frac{m}{n}\right)$ — Quotient rule **4.** $\log_a(m^r) = r\log_a m$ — Power rule **Examples:** **1.** $\log_4 1 = 0$ and $\log_4 4 = 1$ **2.** $\log 2 + \log 5 = \log(2 \cdot 5) = \log 10 = 1$ **3.** $\log 500 - \log 5 = \log(500/5) = \log 100 = 2$ **4.** $\log_2 2^3 = 3\log_2 2 = 3(1) = 3$
Change of Base Formula	$\log_a x = \dfrac{\log_b x}{\log_b a}$ **Example:** $\log_3 23 = \dfrac{\log 23}{\log 3} \approx 2.854$
Section 5.6 Exponential and Logarithmic Equations	
Solving Exponential Equations	To solve an exponential equation we typically take the logarithm of each side. **Example:** $4e^x = 48$ — Given equation $e^x = 12$ — Divide by 4. $\ln e^x = \ln 12$ — Take the natural logarithm. $x = \ln 12$ — Inverse property $x \approx 2.485$ — Approximate.

CONCEPT	EXPLANATION AND EXAMPLES
Section 5.6 Exponential and Logarithmic Equations (CONTINUED)	
Solving Logarithmic Equations	To solve a logarithmic equation we typically need to exponentiate each side. **Example:** $5\log_3 x = 10$ Given equation $\log_3 x = 2$ Divide by 5. $3^{\log_3 x} = 3^2$ Exponentiate; base 3. $x = 9$ Inverse property
Section 5.7 Constructing Nonlinear Models	
Exponential Model	$f(x) = Ca^x$, $f(x) = ab^x$, or $A(t) = A_0e^{kt}$ Models data that increase or decrease rapidly
Logarithmic Model	$f(x) = a + b\ln x$ or $f(x) = a + b\log x$. Models data that increase slowly
Logistic Model	$f(x) = \frac{c}{1 + ae^{-bx}}$, where a, b, and c are positive constants. Models data that increase slowly at first, then increase more rapidly, and finally level off near the value of c. Its graph is a sigmoidal curve. See Figure 5.84.

5 Review Exercises

1. Use the tables to evaluate, if possible.

x	-1	0	1	3
$f(x)$	3	5	7	9

x	-1	0	1	3
$g(x)$	-2	0	1	9

(a) $(f + g)(1)$ **(b)** $(f - g)(3)$

(c) $(fg)(-1)$ **(d)** $(f/g)(0)$

2. Use the graph to evaluate each expression.
(a) $(f - g)(2)$ **(b)** $(fg)(0)$

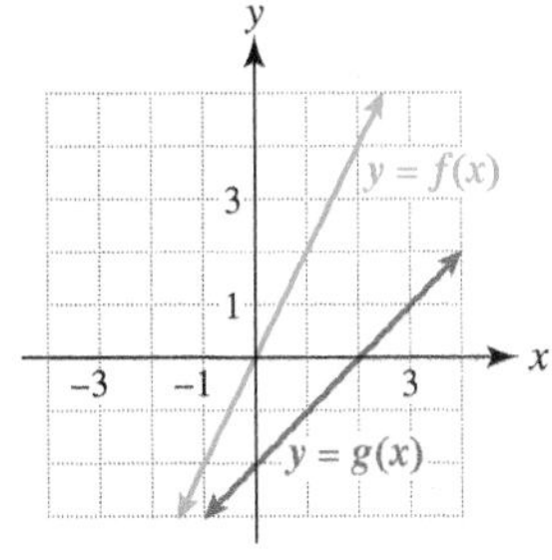

3. Let $f(x) = x^2$ and $g(x) = 1 - x$ and evaluate.
(a) $(f + g)(3)$ **(b)** $(f - g)(-2)$

(c) $(fg)(1)$ **(d)** $(f/g)(3)$

4. Use $f(x) = x^2 + 3x$ and $g(x) = x^2 - 1$ to find each expression. Identify its domain.
(a) $(f + g)(x)$ **(b)** $(f - g)(x)$

(c) $(fg)(x)$ **(d)** $(f/g)(x)$

5. Tables for f and g are given. Evaluate each expression.

x	-2	0	2	4
$f(x)$	1	4	3	2

x	1	2	3	4
$g(x)$	2	4	-2	0

(a) $(g \circ f)(-2)$ **(b)** $(f \circ g)(3)$ **(c)** $f^{-1}(3)$

6. Use the graph to evaluate each expression.
(a) $(f \circ g)(2)$ **(b)** $(g \circ f)(0)$ **(c)** $f^{-1}(1)$

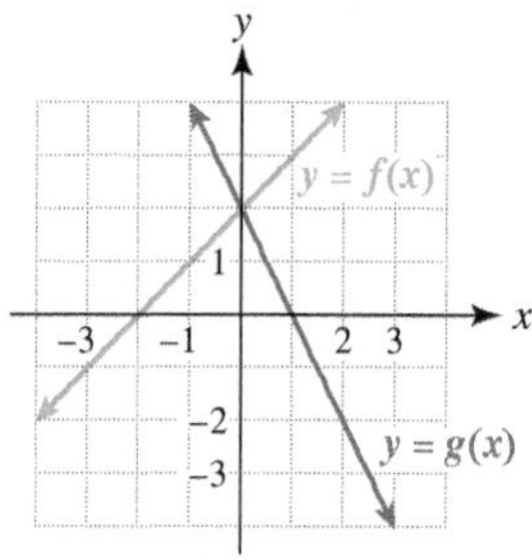

7. Let $f(x) = \sqrt{x}$ and $g(x) = x^2 + x$ and evaluate.
(a) $(f \circ g)(2)$ **(b)** $(g \circ f)(9)$

8. Use $f(x) = x^2 + 1$ and $g(x) = x^3 - x^2 + 2x + 1$ to find each expression.
(a) $(f \circ g)(x)$ **(b)** $(g \circ f)(x)$

Exercises 9–12: Find $(f \circ g)(x)$ and identify its domain.

9. $f(x) = x^3 - x^2 + 3x - 2$ $g(x) = x^{-1}$

10. $f(x) = \sqrt{x + 3}$ $g(x) = 1 - x^2$

11. $f(x) = \sqrt[3]{2x - 1}$ $g(x) = \frac{1}{2}x^3 + \frac{1}{2}$

12. $f(x) = \dfrac{2}{x - 5}$ $g(x) = \dfrac{1}{x + 1}$

Exercises 13 and 14: Find f and g so that $h(x) = (g \circ f)(x)$.

13. $h(x) = \sqrt{x^2 + 3}$ **14.** $h(x) = \dfrac{1}{(2x + 1)^2}$

Exercises 15 and 16: Describe the inverse operations of the given statement. Then express both the statement and its inverse symbolically.

15. Divide x by 10 and add 6.

16. Subtract 5 from x and take the cube root.

Exercises 17 and 18: Determine if f is one-to-one.

17. $f(x) = 3x - 1$ **18.** $f(x) = 3x^2 - 2x + 1$

Exercises 19 and 20: Determine if f is one-to-one.

19.

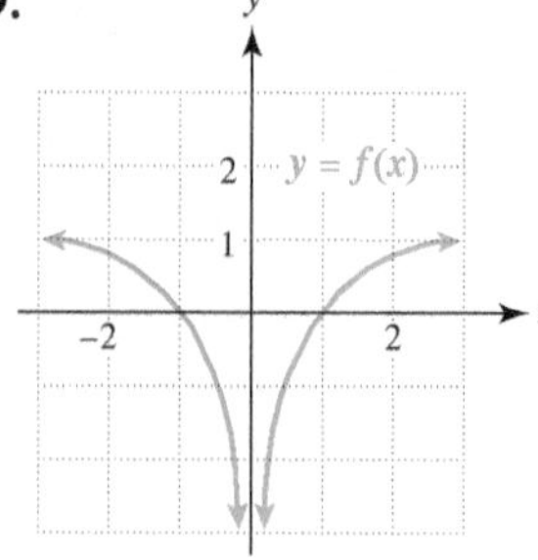

20.

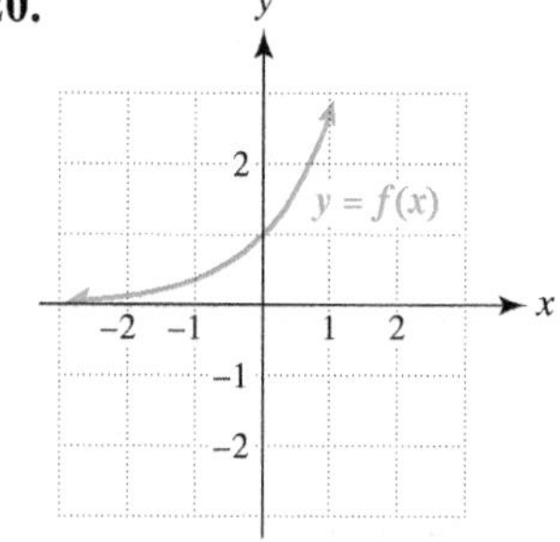

21. The table is a complete representation of f. Use the table of f to determine a table for f^{-1}. Identify the domains and ranges of f and f^{-1}.

x	−1	0	4	6
$f(x)$	6	4	3	1

22. Use the graph of f to sketch a graph of f^{-1}.

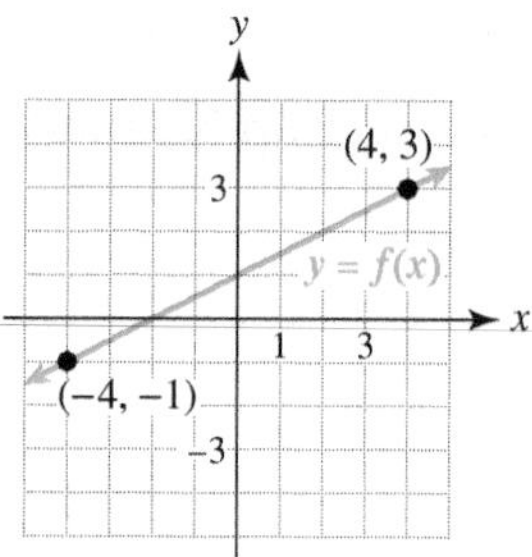

Exercises 23 and 24: Find $f^{-1}(x)$.

23. $f(x) = 3x - 5$ **24.** $f(x) = \frac{3x}{x + 7}$

25. Verify that $f(x) = 2x - 1$ and $f^{-1}(x) = \frac{x + 1}{2}$ are inverses.

26. Restrict the domain of $f(x) = 2(x - 4)^2 + 3$ so that f is one-to-one. Then find $f^{-1}(x)$.

Exercises 27 and 28: Use the tables to evaluate the given expression.

x	0	1	2	3
$f(x)$	4	3	2	1

x	0	1	2	3
$g(x)$	0	2	3	4

27. $(f \circ g^{-1})(4)$ **28.** $(g^{-1} \circ f^{-1})(1)$

29. Find $f^{-1}(x)$ if $f(x) = \sqrt{x + 1}, x \geq -1$. Identify the domain and range of f and of f^{-1}.

30. Simplify $e^x e^{-2x}$.

Exercises 31–34: Find an exponential model that describes each situation.

31. A sample of 9500 insects decreases in number by 35% per week.

32. A sample of 258 birds decreases in number by 5.1% per week.

33. A sample of 400 fish increases in number by 8% per month.

34. A mutual fund account contains \$500 and increases by 4.2% per year.

Exercises 35–38: For the given $f(x)$, state the initial value, the growth or decay factor, and percent change for each unit increase in x.

35. $f(x) = 3(1.05)^x$

36. $f(x) = 4.2(1.45)^x$

37. $f(x) = 0.23^x$

38. $f(x) = 7e^{x/3}$

Exercises 39 and 40: Find C and a so that $f(x) = Ca^x$ satisfies the given conditions.

39. $f(0) = 3$ and $f(3) = 24$

40. $f(-1) = 8$ and $f(1) = 2$

Exercises 41–44: Sketch a graph of $y = f(x)$. Identify the domain of f.

41. $f(x) = 4(2)^{-x}$

42. $f(x) = 3^{x-1}$

43. $f(x) = \log(-x)$

44. $f(x) = \log(x + 1)$

Exercises 45 and 46: Use the graph of $f(x) = Ca^x$ to determine values for C and a.

45.

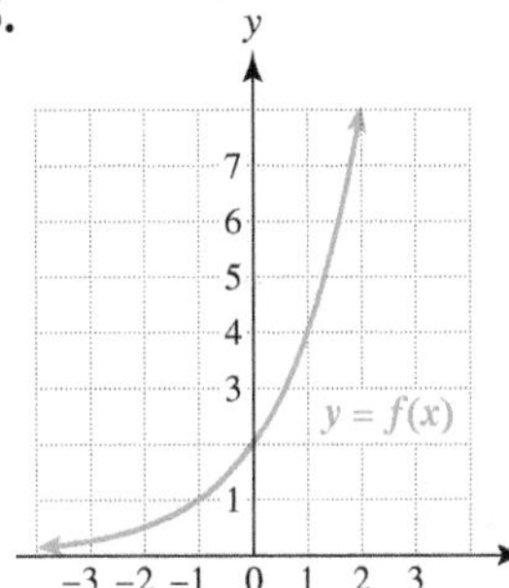

46.

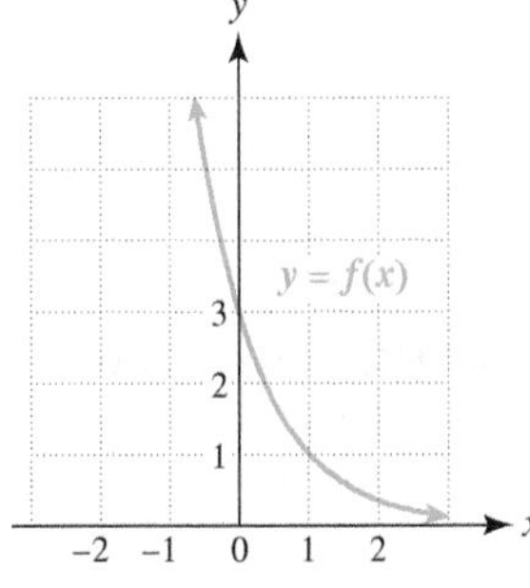

47. Determine the final value of \$1200 invested at 9% compounded semiannually for 3 years.

48. Determine the final value of \$500 invested at 6.5% compounded continuously for 8 years.

Exercises 49 and 50: For a nominal interest rate of 7.5%, determine the effective (annual) interest rate for each type of compounding. Round values to the nearest hundredth of a percent.

49. Monthly

50. Continuously

51. Solve $e^x = 19$ symbolically.

52. Solve $2^x - x^2 = x$ graphically. Round each solution to the nearest thousandth.

Exercises 53–56: Evaluate the expression without a calculator.

53. $\log 1000$

54. $\log 0.001$

55. $10 \log 0.01 + \log \frac{1}{10}$

56. $\log 100 + \log \sqrt[3]{10}$

Exercises 57–60: Evaluate the logarithm without a calculator.

57. $\log_3 9$

58. $\log_5 \frac{1}{25}$

59. $\ln e$

60. $\log_2 32$

Exercises 61 and 62: Approximate to the nearest thousandth.

61. $\log_3 18$

62. $\log_2 173$

Exercises 63–70: Solve the equation.

63. $10^x = 125$

64. $1.5^x = 55$

65. $e^{0.1x} = 5.2$

66. $4e^{2x} - 5 = 3$

67. $5^{-x} = 10$

68. $3(10)^{-x} = 6$

69. $50 - 3(0.78)^{x-10} = 21$

70. $5(1.3)^x + 4 = 104$

Exercises 71–76: Find either a linear or an exponential function that models the data in the table.

71.

x	0	1	2
y	1.5	3	6

72.

x	0	1	2
y	3	4.5	6

73.

x	4	7	10
y	12	6	0

74.

x	−2	0	2
y	0.375	3	24

75.

x	1	4	7
y	8	1	$\frac{1}{8}$

76.

x	−2	1	4
y	512	8	0.125

Exercises 77–80: Solve the equation.

77. $\log x = 1.5$

78. $\log_3 x = 4$

79. $\ln x = 3.4$

80. $4 - \ln(5 - x) = \frac{5}{2}$

Exercises 81–84: Use properties of logarithms to combine the expression as a logarithm of a single expression.

81. $\log 6 + \log 5x$

82. $\log \sqrt{3} - \log \sqrt[3]{3}$

83. Expand $\ln \frac{y}{x^2}$.

84. Expand $\log \frac{4x^3}{k}$.

Exercises 85–90: Solve the logarithmic equation.

85. $8 \log x = 2$

86. $\ln 2x = 2$

87. $2 \log 3x + 5 = 15$

88. $5 \log_2 x = 25$

89. $2 \log_5(x + 2) = \log_5(x + 8)$

90. $\ln(5 - x) - \ln(5 + x) = -\ln 9$

91. Suppose that b is the y-intercept on the graph of a one-to-one function f. What is the x-intercept on the graph of f^{-1}? Explain your reasoning.

92. Let $f(x) = ax + b$ with $a \neq 0$.
(a) Show that f^{-1} is also linear by finding $f^{-1}(x)$.

(b) How is the slope of the graph of f related to the slope of the graph of f^{-1}?

Applications

93. Bacteria Growth A sample of bacteria taken from a polluted lake has an initial concentration of 3.2 million bacteria per milliliter and its concentration quadruples each week.

(a) Find an exponential model that calculates the concentration in millions of bacteria per milliliter after x weeks.

(b) Estimate the concentration after 3.5 weeks.

94. Fish Population A fish population in a small lake is estimated to be 5500. Due to a change in water quality, this population is decreasing by one third each year.

(a) Find an exponential model that approximates the number of fish in the lake after x years.

(b) Estimate the fish population to nearest hundred after 1.4 years.

95. Bacteria Growth A population of bacteria increases by 15% every 9 hours. By what percentage does the sample increase in 13 hours?

96. Bird Population A population of birds decreases by 30% every 5 weeks. By what percentage does the population decrease in 3 weeks?

97. Pollution A pollutant in a river has an initial concentration of 5 parts per million and degrades at a rate of 2.5% per year. Approximate its concentration after 13 years.

98. Radioactive Half-Life A radioactive element decays to 50% of its original amount every 4 years. Find the percentage that remains after 8 years.

99. Bacteria Growth There are initially 4000 bacteria per milliliter in a sample, and after 1 hour their concentration increases to 6000 bacteria per milliliter. Assume exponential growth.

(a) How many bacteria are there after 2.5 hours?

(b) After how long are there 8500 bacteria per milliliter?

100. Newton's Law of Cooling A pan of boiling water with a temperature of 100°C is set in a room with a temperature of 20°C. The water cools to 50°C in 40 minutes.
(a) Find values for T_0, D, and a so that the formula $T(t) = T_0 + Da^t$ models the data, where t is in hours.

(b) Find the temperature of the water after 90 minutes.

(c) How long does it take the water to reach 30°C?

101. Combining Functions The total number of gallons of water passing through a pipe after x seconds is computed by $f(x) = 10x$. Another pipe delivers $g(x) = 5x$ gallons after x seconds. Find a function h that gives the volume of water passing through both pipes in x seconds.

102. Test Scores Let scores on a standardized test be modeled by $f(x) = 36e^{-(x-20)^2/49}$. The function f computes the number in thousands of people that received score x. Solve the equation $f(x) = 30$. Interpret your result.

103. Modeling Growth The function given by

$$W(x) = 175.6(1 - 0.66e^{-0.24x})^3$$

models the weight in milligrams of a small fish called the *Lebistes reticulatus* after x weeks, where $0 \leq x \leq 14$. Solve the equation $W(x) = 50$. Interpret the result. (***Source:*** D. Brown and P. Rothery, *Models in Biology*.)

104. Radioactive Decay After 23 days, a 10-milligram sample of a radioactive material decays to 5 milligrams. After how many days will there be 1 milligram of the material?

105. Tire Pressure A car tire has a small leak, and the tire pressure in pounds per square inch after t minutes is given by $P(t) = 32e^{-0.2t}$. After how many minutes is the pressure 15 pounds per square inch?

106. Converting Units The figures show graphs of a function f that converts fluid ounces to pints and a function g that converts pints to quarts. Evaluate each expression. Interpret the results.
(a) $(g \circ f)(32)$
(b) $f^{-1}(1)$
(c) $(f^{-1} \circ g^{-1})(1)$

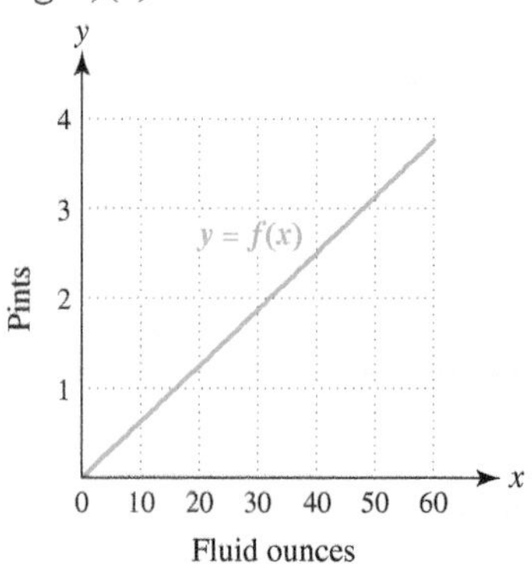

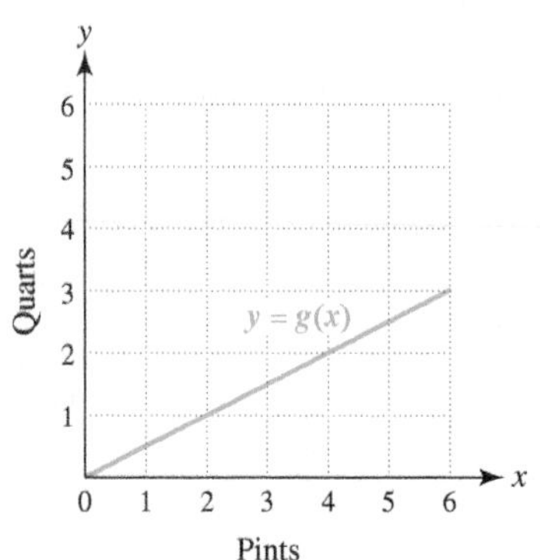

107. Modeling Epidemics In 1666 the village of Eyam, located in England, experienced an outbreak of the Great Plague. Out of 261 people in the community, only 83 people survived. The tables below show a function f that computes the number of people who were infected after x days.

x	0	15	30	45
$f(x)$	7	21	57	111

x	60	75	90	125
$f(x)$	136	158	164	178

Source: G. Raggett, "Modeling the Eyam plague."

Find a function f that models the given data. (Answers may vary.)

108. Greenhouse Gases Methane is a greenhouse gas that is produced when fossil fuels are burned. In 1600 methane had an atmospheric concentration of 700 parts per billion (ppb), whereas in 2000 its concentration was about 1700 ppb. (***Source:*** D. Wuebbles and J. Edmonds, *Primer on Greenhouse Gases.*)

(a) Find values for C and a so that $f(x) = Ca^x$ models the data, where x is the year.

(b) Solve $f(x) = 1000$ and interpret the answer.

109. Exponential Regression The data in the table can be modeled by $f(x) = ab^x$. Use regression to estimate the constants a and b. Graph f and the data.

x	1	2	3	4
y	2.59	1.92	1.42	1.05

110. Logarithmic Regression The data in the table can be modeled by $f(x) = a + b \ln x$. Use regression to estimate the constants a and b. Graph f and the data.

x	2	3	4	5
y	2.93	3.42	3.76	4.03

Extended and Discovery Exercises

1. Modeling Data with Power Functions There is a procedure to determine whether data can be modeled by $y = ax^b$, where a and b are constants. Start by taking the natural logarithm of each side of this equation.

$$\ln y = \ln(ax^b)$$

$$\ln y = \ln a + \ln x^b \qquad \ln(mn) = \ln m + \ln n$$

$$\ln y = \ln a + b \ln x \qquad \ln(m^r) = r \ln m$$

If we let $z = \ln y$, $d = \ln a$, and $w = \ln x$, then the equation $\ln y = \ln a + b \ln x$ becomes $z = d + bw$. Thus the data points $(w, z) = (\ln x, \ln y)$ lie on the line having a slope of b and y-intercept $d = \ln a$. The following steps provide a procedure for finding the constants a and b.

Modeling Data with the Equation $y = ax^b$

If a data set (x, y) can be modeled by the (power) equation $y = ax^b$, then the following procedure can be applied to determine the constants a and b.

STEP 1: Let $w = \ln x$ and $z = \ln y$ for each data point. Graph the points (w, z). If these data are not linear, then do *not* use this procedure.

STEP 2: Find an equation of a line in the form $z = bw + d$ that models the data points (w, z). (Linear regression may be used.)

STEP 3: The slope of the line equals the constant b. The value of a is given by $a = e^d$.

Apply this procedure to the table of data for the orbital distances and periods of the moons of Jupiter. Let the distance be x and the period be y.

Moons of Jupiter	Distance (10^3 km)	Period (days)
Metis	128	0.29
Almathea	181	0.50
Thebe	222	0.67
Io	422	1.77
Europa	671	3.55
Ganymede	1070	7.16
Callisto	1883	16.69

2. Climate Change Greenhouse gases such as carbon dioxide trap heat from the sun. Presently, the net incoming solar radiation reaching Earth's surface is approximately 240 watts per square meter (w/m^2). Any portion of this amount that is due to greenhouse gases is called *radiative forcing*. The table lists the estimated increase in radiative forcing R above the levels in 1750.

x (year)	1800	1850	1900	1950	2000
$R(x)$ (w/m^2)	0.2	0.4	0.6	1.2	2.4

Source: A. Nilsson, *Greenhouse Earth.*

(a) Estimate constants C and k so that $R(x) = Ce^{kx}$ models the data. Let $x = 0$ correspond to 1800.

(b) Estimate the year when the additional radiative forcing could reach 3 w/m^2.

*Exercises 3 and 4: Try to decide if the expression is precisely an integer. (*Hint: *Use computer software capable of calculating a large number of decimal places.)*

3. $\left(\frac{1}{\pi}\ln(640{,}320^3 + 744)\right)^2$

(***Source:*** I. J. Good, "What is the most amazing approximate integer in the universe?")

4. $e^{\pi\sqrt{163}}$ (***Source:*** W. Cheney and D. Kincaid, *Numerical Mathematics and Computing.*)

6 Systems of Equations and Inequalities

In 2000, less than 6% of the world's population had Internet access. Today, the majority of people on Earth are able to get online. It would be impossible for billions of people to download, post, tweet, and stream data, without the mathematics used to create and manage Internet networks. Systems of equations and matrices are vitally important to the success of social networks such as Facebook, Twitter, Spotify, and Pinterest.

Special types of graphs can be used to represent simple networks, and matrices can be used to summarize these graphs. With matrices it is possible to identify the connections between friends in a social network or to analyze web page links. (See Examples 2 and 9 in Section 6.5.)

In this chapter, we will see that mathematics can be used to solve systems of equations, compute movement in computer graphics, analyze web page links, and even represent social networks. Throughout history, many important discoveries have been based on the insights of a few people. The mathematicians who first worked with matrices and systems of equations could not have imagined the profound impact their work would have in the 21st century.

> Go deep enough into anything and you will find mathematics.
>
> —Dean Schlicter

Source: *Internet World Stats;* R. Hanneman and M. Riddle, *Introduction to Social Network Methods.*

6.1 Functions and Systems of Equations in Two Variables

- **Evaluate functions of two variables**
- **Understand basic concepts about systems of equations**
- **Recognize types of linear systems**
- **Apply the method of substitution**
- **Apply the elimination method**
- **Apply graphical and numerical methods**
- **Solve problems involving joint variation**

Introduction

Many quantities in everyday life depend on more than one variable.

- Finding the area of a rectangular room requires both its *length* and *width*.
- The heat index is a function of *temperature* and *humidity*.
- Grade point average is computed using *grades* and *credit hours*.

Quantities determined by more than one variable often are computed by a *function* of more than one variable. The mathematical concepts that we have already studied concerning functions of one input also apply to functions of more than one input. One unifying concept about every function is that it produces *at most one output* each time it is evaluated.

Functions of Two Variables

In order to perform addition, two numbers must be provided. The addition of x and y results in one output, z. The addition function f can be represented symbolically by

$$f(x, y) = x + y, \text{ where } z = f(x, y).$$

For example, the addition of 3 and 4 can be written as

$$z = f(3, 4) = 3 + 4 = 7.$$

In this case, $f(x, y)$ is a **function of two inputs** or a **function of two variables**. The **independent variables** are x and y, and z is the **dependent variable**. The output z depends on the inputs x and y. Other arithmetic operations can be defined similarly. For example, a division function can be defined by $g(x, y) = \frac{x}{y}$, where $z = g(x, y)$.

EXAMPLE 1 Evaluating functions of more than one input

For each function, evaluate the expression and interpret the result.

(a) $f(3, -4)$, where $f(x, y) = xy$ represents the multiplication function

(b) $M(120, 5)$, where $M(m, g) = \frac{m}{g}$ computes the gas mileage when traveling m miles on g gallons of gasoline

(c) $V(0.5, 2)$, where $V(r, h) = \pi r^2 h$ calculates the volume of a cylindrical barrel with radius r feet and height h feet. (See Figure 6.1.)

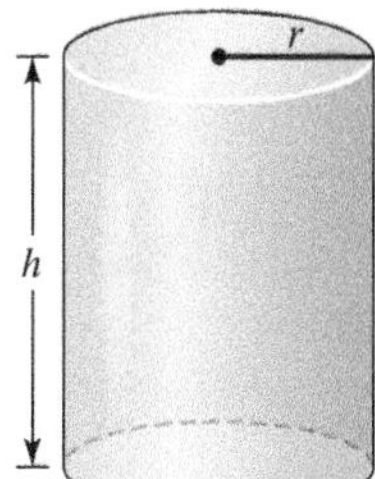

Figure 6.1

SOLUTION

(a) $f(3, -4) = (3)(-4) = -12$. The product of 3 and -4 is -12.

(b) $M(120, 5) = \frac{120}{5} = 24$. If a car travels 120 miles on 5 gallons of gasoline, its gas mileage is 24 miles per gallon.

(c) $V(0.5, 2) = \pi(0.5)^2(2) = 0.5\pi \approx 1.57$. If a barrel has a radius of 0.5 foot and a height of 2 feet, it holds about 1.57 cubic feet of liquid.

Now Try Exercises 1, 3, and 5

Systems of Equations in Two Variables

A **linear equation in two variables** can be written in the form

$$ax + by = k,$$

where a, b, and k are constants and a and b are not equal to 0. Examples of linear equations in two variables include

$$2x - 3y = 4, \qquad -x - 5y = 0, \qquad \text{and} \qquad 5x - y = 10.$$

Many situations involving two variables result in the need to determine values for x and y that satisfy *two* equations. For example, suppose that we would like to find a pair of numbers whose average is 10 and whose difference is 2. The function $f(x, y) = \frac{x + y}{2}$ calculates the average of two numbers, and $g(x, y) = x - y$ computes their difference. The solution can be found by solving two linear equations $f(x, y) = 10$ and $g(x, y) = 2$.

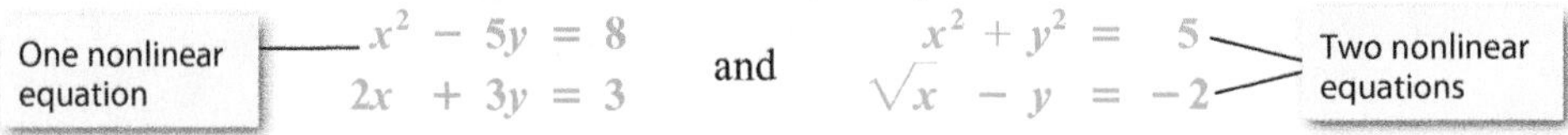

$$\frac{x + y}{2} = 10$$
$$x - y = 2$$

This pair of equations is called a **system of linear equations** because we are solving more than one linear equation at once. A **solution** to a system of equations in two variables consists of an x-value *and* a y-value that satisfy *both* equations simultaneously. The set of all solutions is called the **solution set**. Using trial and error, we see that $x = 11$ and $y = 9$ satisfy both equations. This is the only solution and it can be expressed as the *ordered pair* $(11, 9)$.

Systems of equations that have at least one nonlinear equation are called **nonlinear systems of equations.**

Nonlinear Systems of Equations

One nonlinear equation: $x^2 - 5y = 8$, $2x + 3y = 3$ and $x^2 + y^2 = 5$, $\sqrt{x} - y = -2$: Two nonlinear equations

Types of Linear Systems in Two Variables

CLASS DISCUSSION

Explain why a system of linear equations in two variables cannot have two or three solutions.

Any system of linear equations in two variables can be written in the form

$$a_1x + b_1y = c_1$$
$$a_2x + b_2y = c_2,$$

where a_1, b_1, c_1, a_2, b_2, and c_2 are constants. The graph of this system consists of *two* lines in the xy-plane. The following See the Concept summarizes the three possible types of linear systems. Note that **coincident lines** are identical lines and indicate that the two equations are equivalent and have the same graph. (See B below.)

See the Concept: Three Types of Linear Systems

One Solution	Infinitely Many Solutions	No Solutions
A Intersecting lines	B Coincident lines	C Parallel lines
Consistent System Independent Equations	Consistent System Dependent Equations	Inconsistent System
A The solution is given by the coordinates of the point of intersection.	B Every point on the coincident lines represents a solution.	C The distinct parallel lines have no points in common.

A **consistent system** of linear equations has either one solution, meaning the equations are **independent**, or infinitely many solutions, meaning the equations are **dependent.** An **inconsistent system** has no solutions.

EXAMPLE 2 Recognizing types of linear systems

Graph each system of equations and find any solutions. Identify the system as consistent or inconsistent. If the system is consistent, state whether the equations are dependent or independent.

(a) $x - y = 2$, $-x + y = 1$ **(b)** $4x - y = 2$, $x - 2y = -3$ **(c)** $2x - y = 1$, $-4x + 2y = -2$

SOLUTION

Getting Started Start by solving each equation for y. Use the resulting slope-intercept form to graph each line. Determine any points of intersection. ▶

(a) Graph $y = x - 2$ and $y = x + 1$, as shown in Figure 6.2. Their graphs (parallel lines) do not intersect, so there are no solutions. The system is inconsistent.

(b) Graph $y = 4x - 2$ and $y = \frac{1}{2}x + \frac{3}{2}$, as shown in Figure 6.3. Their graphs intersect at (1, 2). There is one solution, so the system is consistent and the equations are independent. Because graphical solutions can be approximate, we check this solution by substituting 1 for x and 2 for y in the given system.

$$4(1) - 2 = 2 \checkmark \quad \text{True}$$
$$(1) - 2(2) = -3 \checkmark \quad \text{True}$$

Because (1, 2) satisfies *both* equations, it is the solution.

(c) Solving the equations $2x - y = 1$ and $-4x + 2y = -2$ for y results in the same equation: $y = 2x - 1$. Therefore their graphs coincide, as shown in Figure 6.4. (Note that the second equation results when the first equation is multiplied by -2, so the equations are equivalent.) Any point on this line is a solution to both equations. Thus the system has infinitely many solutions of the form $\{(x, y) \mid 2x - y = 1\}$ and is consistent. The equations are dependent.

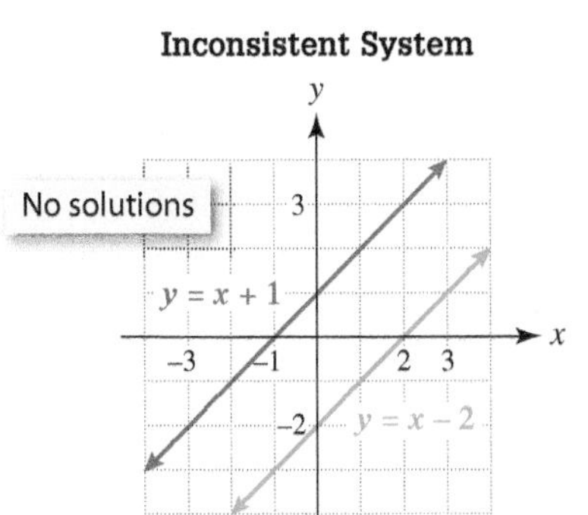

Figure 6.2

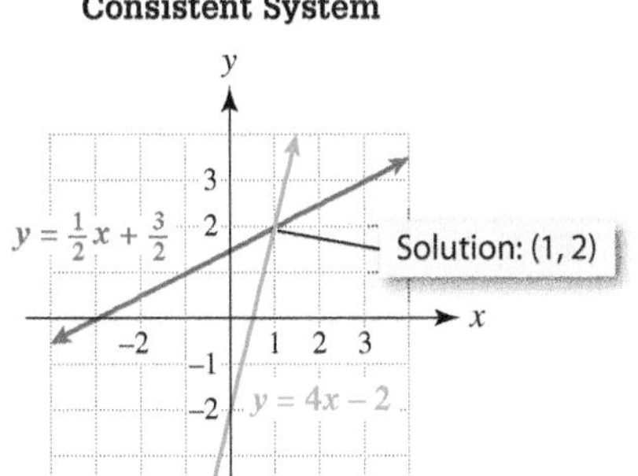

Figure 6.3

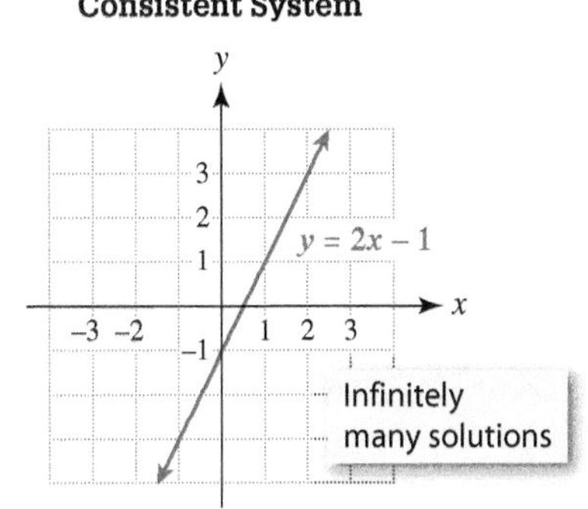

Figure 6.4

Now Try Exercises 31, 33, and 37

The Method of Substitution

The **method of substitution** is often used to solve systems of equations symbolically. It is summarized by the following steps.

THE METHOD OF SUBSTITUTION

To use the method of substitution to solve a system of two equations in two variables, perform the following steps.

STEP 1: Choose a variable in one of the two equations. Solve the equation for that variable.

STEP 2: Substitute the result from Step 1 into the other equation and solve for the remaining variable.

STEP 3: Use the value of the variable from Step 2 to determine the value of the other variable. To do this, you may want to use the equation you found in Step 1.

To check your answer, substitute the value of each variable into the *given* equations. These values should satisfy *both* equations.

An Application In the next example, we use the method of substitution to solve an example involving real data.

EXAMPLE 3 **Applying the method of substitution**

In the first quarter of 2011, Apple Corporation sold a combined total of 35.7 million iPods and iPhones. There were 3.3 million more iPods sold than iPhones. (***Source:*** Apple Corporation.)

(a) Write a system of equations whose solution gives the individual sales of iPods and of iPhones.

(b) Solve the system of equations. Interpret the results.

(c) Is your system consistent or inconsistent? If it is consistent, state whether the equations are dependent or independent.

SOLUTION

Getting Started When setting up a system of equations, it is important to identify what each variable represents. Then express the situation with equations. Finally, apply the method of substitution. ▶

(a) Let x be the number of iPods sold in millions and y be the number of iPhones sold in millions. The combined total is 35.7 million, so let $x + y = 35.7$. Because iPod sales exceeded iPhone sales by 3.3 million, let $x - y = 3.3$. Thus the system of equations is as follows.

$$x + y = 35.7 \quad \text{Total sales are 35.7 million.}$$
$$x - y = 3.3 \quad \text{iPod sales exceeded iPhone sales by 3.3 million.}$$

(b) **STEP 1:** With this system, we can solve for either variable in either equation. If we solve for x in the second equation, we obtain the equation $x = y + 3.3$.

STEP 2: Substitute $(y + 3.3)$ for x in the first equation, $x + y = 35.7$, and solve.

$$(y + 3.3) + y = 35.7 \quad \text{Substitute } (y + 3.3) \text{ for } x.$$
$$2y = 32.4 \quad \text{Subtract 3.3; combine terms.}$$
$$y = 16.2 \quad \text{Divide each side by 2.}$$

STEP 3: To find x, substitute 16.2 for y in the equation $x = y + 3.3$ from Step 1 to obtain $x = 16.2 + 3.3 = 19.5$. The solution is $(19.5, 16.2)$.

Thus, there were 19.5 million iPods and 16.2 million iPhones sold.

(c) There is one solution, so the system is consistent and the equations are independent.

Now Try Exercise 113

In the next example, we solve a system and check our result.

EXAMPLE 4 Using the method of substitution

Solve the system symbolically. Check your answer.

$$\begin{aligned} 5x - 2y &= -16 \\ x + 4y &= -1 \end{aligned}$$

SOLUTION

STEP 1: Begin by solving one of the equations for one of the variables. One possibility is to solve the second equation for x.

$$\begin{aligned} x + 4y &= -1 && \text{Second equation} \\ x &= -4y - 1 && \text{Subtract 4y from each side.} \end{aligned}$$

STEP 2: Next, substitute $(-4y - 1)$ for x in the first equation and solve the resulting equation for y.

$$\begin{aligned} 5x - 2y &= -16 && \text{First equation} \\ 5(-4y - 1) - 2y &= -16 && \text{Let } x = -4y - 1. \\ -20y - 5 - 2y &= -16 && \text{Distributive property} \\ -5 - 22y &= -16 && \text{Combine like terms.} \\ -22y &= -11 && \text{Add 5 to each side.} \\ y &= \frac{1}{2} && \text{Divide each side by } -22\text{; Simplify.} \end{aligned}$$

STEP 3: Now find the value of x by using the equation $x = -4y - 1$ from Step 1. Since $y = \frac{1}{2}$, it follows that $x = -4\left(\frac{1}{2}\right) - 1 = -3$. The solution can be written as an ordered pair: $\left(-3, \frac{1}{2}\right)$.

Check: Substitute $x = -3$ and $y = \frac{1}{2}$ in both given equations.

$$\begin{aligned} 5(-3) - 2\left(\frac{1}{2}\right) &\stackrel{?}{=} -16 \ \checkmark && \text{True} \\ -3 + 4\left(\frac{1}{2}\right) &\stackrel{?}{=} -1 \ \checkmark && \text{True} \end{aligned}$$

Both equations are satisfied, so the solution is $\left(-3, \frac{1}{2}\right)$.

Now Try Exercise 39

Nonlinear Systems of Equations The method of substitution can also be used to solve nonlinear systems of equations. In the next example, we solve a nonlinear system of equations having two solutions. In general, a nonlinear system of equations can have *any number of solutions*.

EXAMPLE 5 Solving a nonlinear system of equations

Solve the system symbolically.

$$\begin{aligned} 6x + 2y &= 10 \\ 2x^2 - 3y &= 11 \end{aligned}$$

SOLUTION

STEP 1: Begin by solving one of the equations for one of the variables. One possibility is to solve the first equation for y.

$$\begin{aligned} 6x + 2y &= 10 && \text{First equation} \\ 2y &= 10 - 6x && \text{Subtract 6x from each side.} \\ y &= 5 - 3x && \text{Divide each side by 2.} \end{aligned}$$

STEP 2: Next, substitute $(5 - 3x)$ for y in the second equation and solve the resulting quadratic equation for x.

Algebra Review
To review factoring, see Chapter R (pages R-22–R-23).

$$2x^2 - 3y = 11 \quad \text{Second equation}$$
$$2x^2 - 3(5 - 3x) = 11 \quad \text{Let } y = 5 - 3x.$$
$$2x^2 - 15 + 9x = 11 \quad \text{Distributive property}$$
$$2x^2 + 9x - 26 = 0 \quad \text{Subtract 11 from each side; rewrite.}$$
$$(2x + 13)(x - 2) = 0 \quad \text{Factor.}$$
$$x = -\frac{13}{2} \text{ or } x = 2 \quad \text{Zero-product property}$$

STEP 3: Now find the corresponding y-values for each x-value. From Step 1 we know that $y = 5 - 3x$, so it follows that $y = 5 - 3\left(-\frac{13}{2}\right) = \frac{49}{2}$ or $y = 5 - 3(2) = -1$. Thus the solutions are $\left(-\frac{13}{2}, \frac{49}{2}\right)$ and $(2, -1)$.

Now Try Exercise 51

EXAMPLE 6 **Solving a nonlinear system of equations**

Use the method of substitution to determine the points where the line $y = 2x$ intersects the circle $x^2 + y^2 = 5$. Sketch a graph that illustrates the solutions.

SOLUTION Substitute $(2x)$ for y in the equation $x^2 + y^2 = 5$.

$$x^2 + y^2 = 5 \quad \text{Second equation}$$
$$x^2 + (2x)^2 = 5 \quad y = 2x$$
$$x^2 + 4x^2 = 5 \quad \text{Square the expression.}$$
$$5x^2 = 5 \quad \text{Add like terms.}$$
$$x^2 = 1 \quad \text{Divide each side by 5.}$$
$$x = \pm 1 \quad \text{Square root property}$$

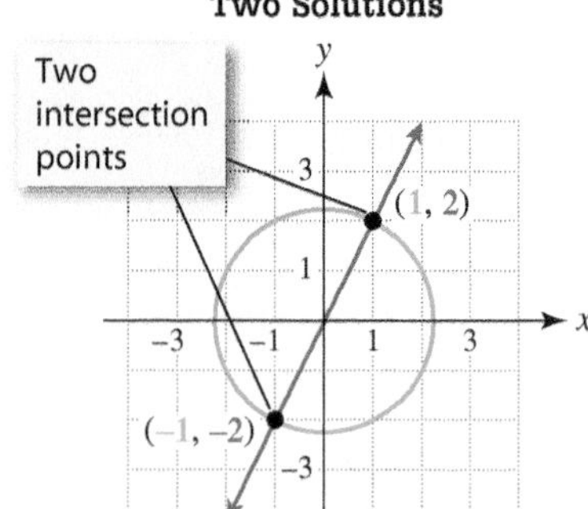

Figure 6.5

Since $y = 2x$ we see that when $x = 1, y = 2$ and when $x = -1, y = -2$. The graphs of $x^2 + y^2 = 5$ and $y = 2x$ intersect at the points $(1, 2)$ and $(-1, -2)$. This nonlinear system has two solutions, which are shown in Figure 6.5.

Now Try Exercise 99

EXAMPLE 7 **Identifying a system with zero or infinitely many solutions**

If possible, solve each system of equations.

(a) $x^2 + y = 1$
$x^2 - y = -2$

(b) $2x - 4y = 5$
$-x + 2y = -\frac{5}{2}$

SOLUTION

(a) STEP 1: Solve the second equation for y, which gives $y = x^2 + 2$.

STEP 2: Substitute $(x^2 + 2)$ for y in the first equation and then solve for x, if possible.

$$x^2 + y = 1 \quad \text{First equation}$$
$$x^2 + (x^2 + 2) = 1 \quad \text{Let } y = x^2 + 2.$$
$$2x^2 + 2 = 1 \quad \text{Combine like terms.}$$
$$2x^2 = -1 \quad \text{Subtract 2 from each side.}$$

Because $2x^2 \geq 0$, it follows that there are no real solutions and the system is inconsistent.

No Solutions

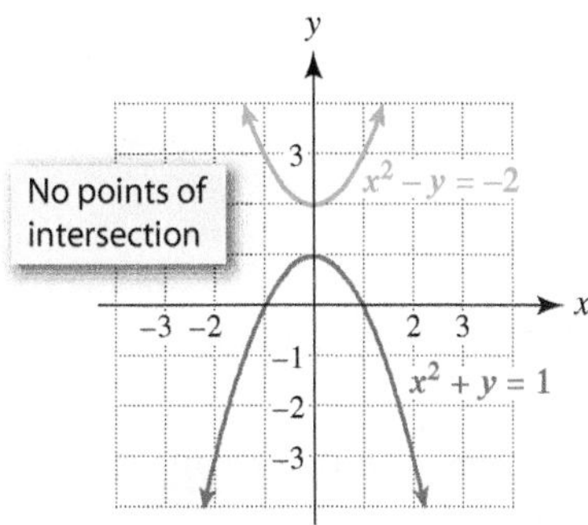

Figure 6.6

Infinitely Many Solutions

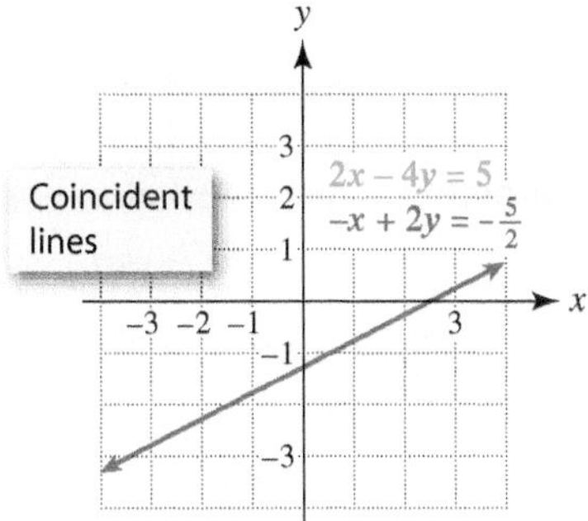

Figure 6.7

STEP 3: This step is not necessary because there are no real solutions for x. Figure 6.6 shows that the graphs, which are parabolas, do not intersect.

(b) STEP 1: First solve the second equation for x to obtain $x = 2y + \frac{5}{2}$.

STEP 2: Substitute $\left(2y + \frac{5}{2}\right)$ for x in the first equation and then solve for y.

$$2x - 4y = 5 \quad \text{First equation}$$
$$2\left(2y + \frac{5}{2}\right) - 4y = 5 \quad \text{Let } x = 2y + \tfrac{5}{2}.$$
$$4y + 5 - 4y = 5 \quad \text{Distributive property}$$
$$5 = 5 \quad \text{Combine like terms.}$$

The equation $5 = 5$ is an identity and indicates that there are infinitely many solutions. The system is consistent and the equations are dependent. Note that we can multiply each side of the second equation by -2 to obtain the first equation.

$$-2(-x + 2y) = -2\left(-\frac{5}{2}\right) \quad \text{Multiply second equation by } -2.$$
$$2x - 4y = 5 \quad \text{Distributive property}$$

STEP 3: In Figure 6.7 the graphs of the equations are identical lines. The solution set is $\{(x, y) \mid 2x - 4y = 5\}$ and includes all points on this line; $\left(0, -\frac{5}{4}\right)$ and $\left(2, -\frac{1}{4}\right)$ are examples of solutions to this system.

Now Try Exercises 45 and 57

The Elimination Method

The **elimination method** is another way to solve systems of equations symbolically. This method is based on the property that *equals added to equals are equal.* That is, if

$$a = b \quad \text{and} \quad c = d, \qquad \text{then} \qquad a + c = b + d.$$

The goal of this method is to obtain an equation where one of the two variables has been eliminated. This task is sometimes accomplished by adding two equations. The elimination method is demonstrated in the next example for three types of linear systems.

EXAMPLE 8 Using elimination to solve a system

Use elimination to solve each system of equations, if possible. Identify the system as consistent or inconsistent. If the system is consistent, state whether the equations are dependent or independent. Support your results graphically.

(a) $2x - y = -4$, $3x + y = -1$ **(b)** $4x - y = 10$, $-4x + y = -10$ **(c)** $x - y = 6$, $x - y = 3$

SOLUTION

(a) *Symbolic Solution* We can eliminate the y-variable by adding the equations.

$$2x - y = -4 \quad \text{First equation}$$
$$3x + y = -1 \quad \text{Second equation}$$
$$5x = -5 \text{ or } x = -1 \quad \text{Add equations.}$$

Now the y-variable can be determined by substituting $x = -1$ in either equation.

$$2x - y = -4 \quad \text{First equation}$$
$$2(-1) - y = -4 \quad \text{Let } x = -1.$$
$$-y = -2 \quad \text{Add 2.}$$
$$y = 2 \quad \text{Multiply by } -1.$$

One Solution

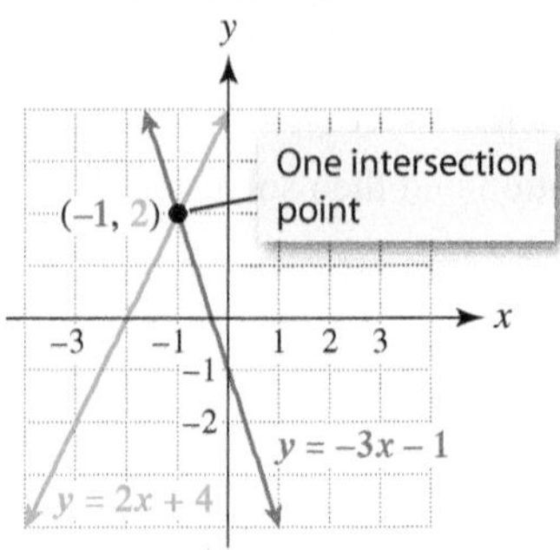

Figure 6.8

The solution is $(-1, 2)$. There is a unique solution so the system is consistent and the equations are independent.

Graphical Solution Start by solving each given equation for y.

$$2x - y = -4 \quad \text{is equivalent to} \quad y = 2x + 4.$$
$$3x + y = -1 \quad \text{is equivalent to} \quad y = -3x - 1.$$

The graphs of $y = 2x + 4$ and $y = -3x - 1$ intersect at the point $(-1, 2)$, as shown in Figure 6.8.

(b) *Symbolic Solution* If we add the equations, we obtain the following result.

$$\begin{aligned} 4x - y &= 10 && \text{First equation} \\ -4x + y &= -10 && \text{Second equation} \\ 0 &= 0 && \text{Add equations.} \end{aligned}$$

Infinitely Many Solutions

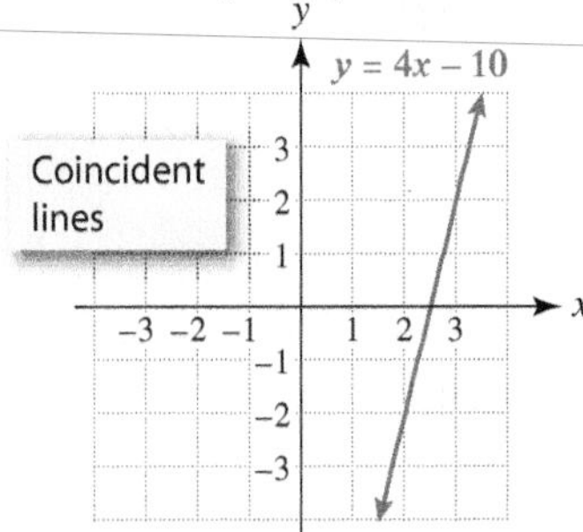

Figure 6.9

The equation $0 = 0$ is an identity. The two given equations are equivalent: if we multiply the first equation by -1, we obtain the second equation. Thus there are infinitely many solutions, and we can write the solution set in set-builder notation.

$$\{(x, y) \mid 4x - y = 10\}$$

Some examples of solutions are $(3, 2)$, $(4, 6)$, and $(1, -6)$. The system is consistent and the equations are dependent.

Graphical Solution For a graphical solution, start by solving each equation for y. Both equations are equivalent to $y = 4x - 10$. Their graphs are identical and coincide. The graph of $y = 4x - 10$ is shown in Figure 6.9. Any point on the line represents a solution to the system. For example, $(3, 2)$ is a solution.

(c) *Symbolic Solution* If we subtract the second equation from the first, we obtain the following result. (Note that subtracting the second equation from the first is equivalent to multiplying the second equation by -1 and then adding it to the first.)

$$\begin{aligned} x - y &= 6 \\ x - y &= 3 \\ \hline 0 &= 3 && \text{Subtract.} \end{aligned}$$

No Solutions

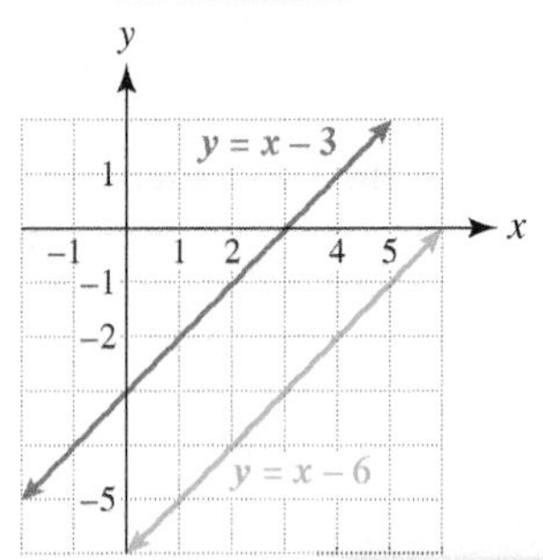

Figure 6.10

No points of intersection

The equation $0 = 3$ is a contradiction. Therefore there are no solutions, and the system is inconsistent.

Graphical Solution For a graphical solution, start by solving each equation for y to obtain $y = x - 6$ and $y = x - 3$. The graphs of $y = x - 6$ and $y = x - 3$, shown in Figure 6.10, are parallel lines that never intersect, so there are no solutions.

Now Try Exercises 71, 75, and 77

Sometimes multiplication is performed before elimination is used, as illustrated in the next example.

EXAMPLE 9 Multiplying before using elimination

Solve each system of equations by using elimination.

(a) $2x - 3y = 18$
$5x + 2y = 7$

(b) $5x + 10y = 10$
$x + 2y = 2$

SOLUTION

(a) If we multiply the first equation by 2 and the second equation by 3, then the y-coefficients become -6 and 6. Addition eliminates the y-variable.

$$\begin{aligned} 4x - 6y &= 36 && \text{Multiply first equation by 2.} \\ 15x + 6y &= 21 && \text{Multiply second equation by 3.} \\ \hline 19x \qquad &= 57, \text{ or } x = 3 && \text{Add equations.} \end{aligned}$$

Substituting $x = 3$ in $2x - 3y = 18$ (first equation) results in

$$2(3) - 3y = 18, \text{ or } y = -4.$$

The solution is $(3, -4)$.

(b) If the second equation is multiplied by -5, addition eliminates both variables.

$$\begin{aligned} 5x + 10y &= 10 && \text{First equation} \\ -5x - 10y &= -10 && \text{Multiply second equation by } -5. \\ 0 &= 0 && \text{Add equations.} \end{aligned}$$

The statement $0 = 0$ is an identity. The equations are dependent and there are infinitely many solutions. The solution set is $\{(x, y) | x + 2y = 2\}$.

Now Try Exercises 81 and 83

Elimination and Nonlinear Systems Elimination can also be used to solve some nonlinear systems of equations, as illustrated in the next example.

EXAMPLE 10 **Using elimination to solve a nonlinear system**

Solve the system of equations.

$$\begin{aligned} x^2 + y^2 &= 4 \\ 2x^2 - y &= 7 \end{aligned}$$

SOLUTION If we multiply each side of the first equation by 2, multiply each side of the second equation by -1, and then add the equations, the x variable is eliminated.

$$\begin{aligned} 2x^2 + 2y^2 &= 8 && \text{Multiply first equation by 2.} \\ -2x^2 + y &= -7 && \text{Multiply second equation by } -1. \\ 2y^2 + y &= 1 && \text{Add equations.} \end{aligned}$$

Next we solve $2y^2 + y - 1 = 0$ for y.

$$\begin{aligned} (2y - 1)(y + 1) &= 0 && \text{Factor.} \\ y = \frac{1}{2} \quad \text{or} \quad y &= -1 && \text{Solve.} \end{aligned}$$

Solving $x^2 + y^2 = 4$ for x results in $x = \pm\sqrt{4 - y^2}$. If $y = \frac{1}{2}$, then $x = \pm\sqrt{\frac{15}{4}}$, which can be written as $\pm\frac{\sqrt{15}}{2}$. If $y = -1$, then $x = \pm\sqrt{3}$. Thus there are four solutions: $\left(\pm\frac{\sqrt{15}}{2}, \frac{1}{2}\right)$ and $(\pm\sqrt{3}, -1)$.

A graph of the system of equations is shown in Figure 6.11. The four points of intersection correspond to the four solutions. In Figure 6.12 the four points of intersection are labeled.

Four Solutions to a Nonliner System

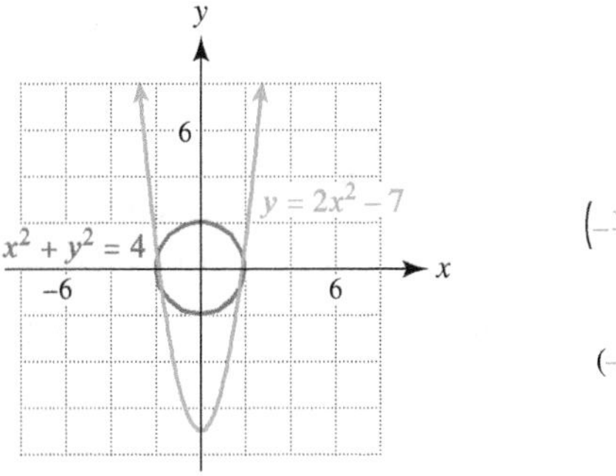

Figure 6.11

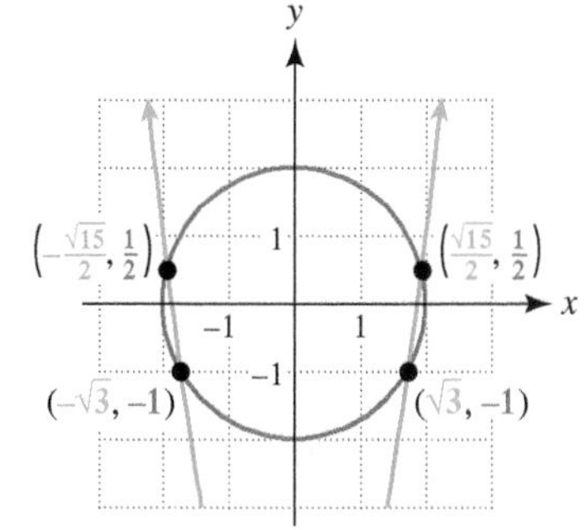

Figure 6.12

Now Try Exercise 93

Graphical and Numerical Methods

An Application The next example illustrates how a system with two variables can be solved symbolically, graphically, and numerically.

EXAMPLE 11 Modeling roof trusses

Linear systems occur in the design of roof trusses for homes and buildings. See Figure 6.13. One of the simplest types of roof trusses is an equilateral triangle. If a 200-pound force is applied to the peak of a truss, as shown in Figure 6.14, then the weights W_1 and W_2 exerted on each rafter of the truss are determined by the following system of linear equations. (***Source:*** R. Hibbeler, *Structural Analysis*.)

$$\begin{aligned} W_1 - W_2 &= 0 \\ \frac{\sqrt{3}}{2}(W_1 + W_2) &= 200 \end{aligned}$$

Estimate the solution symbolically, graphically, and numerically.

Equilateral Triangle Roof Trusses

Figure 6.13

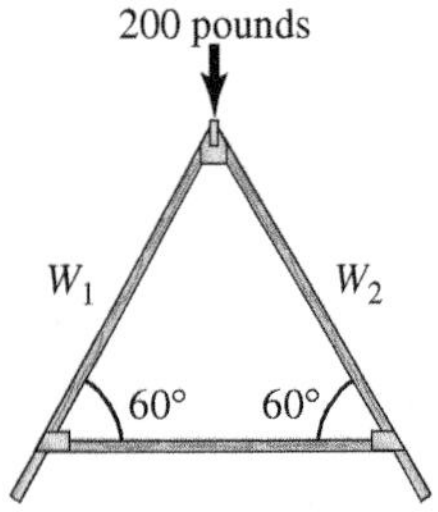

Figure 6.14

SOLUTION

Symbolic Solution The system of equations can be written as follows.

$$\begin{aligned} W_1 - W_2 &= 0 && \text{First equation} \\ \frac{\sqrt{3}}{2}W_1 + \frac{\sqrt{3}}{2}W_2 &= 200 && \text{Distributive property} \end{aligned}$$

We can apply elimination by multiplying the first equation by $\frac{\sqrt{3}}{2}$ and then adding.

$$\begin{aligned} \frac{\sqrt{3}}{2}W_1 - \frac{\sqrt{3}}{2}W_2 &= 0 && \text{Multiply by } \tfrac{\sqrt{3}}{2}. \\ \frac{\sqrt{3}}{2}W_1 + \frac{\sqrt{3}}{2}W_2 &= 200 \\ \hline \sqrt{3}\,W_1 &= 200 && \text{Add equations.} \end{aligned}$$

Dividing by $\sqrt{3}$ gives $W_1 = \frac{200}{\sqrt{3}} \approx 115.47$ pounds. From the first equation, it follows that $W_1 = W_2$, and so $W_2 \approx 115.47$ pounds.

Graphical Solution Begin by solving each equation for the variable W_2.

$$\begin{aligned} W_2 &= W_1 \\ W_2 &= \frac{400}{\sqrt{3}} - W_1 \end{aligned}$$

Solve each equation for W_2.

Graph the equations $y_1 = x$ and $y_2 = \frac{400}{\sqrt{3}} - x$. Their graphs intersect near the point (115.47, 115.47), as shown in Figure 6.15. This means that each rafter supports a weight of approximately 115 pounds.

Graphical Solution

[0, 200, 50] by [0, 200, 50]

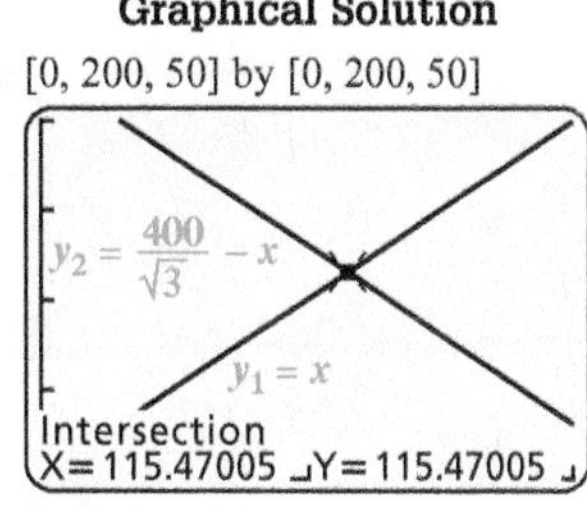

Figure 6.15

Numerical Solution

X	Y1	Y2
112	112	118.94
113	113	117.94
114	114	116.94
115	115	115.94
116	116	114.94
117	117	113.94
118	118	112.94

X=115

Figure 6.16

Numerical Solution In Figure 6.16, $y_1 \approx y_2$ for $x = 115$.

Now Try Exercise 115

EXAMPLE 12 **Determining the dimensions of a cylinder**

The volume V of a cylindrical container with a radius r and height h is computed by $V(r, h) = \pi r^2 h$. See Figure 6.17. The lateral surface area S of the container, *excluding* the circular top and bottom, is computed by $S(r, h) = 2\pi rh$.

Geometry Review
To review formulas related to cylinders, see Chapter R (page R-4).

Volume and Lateral Surface Area of a Cylinder

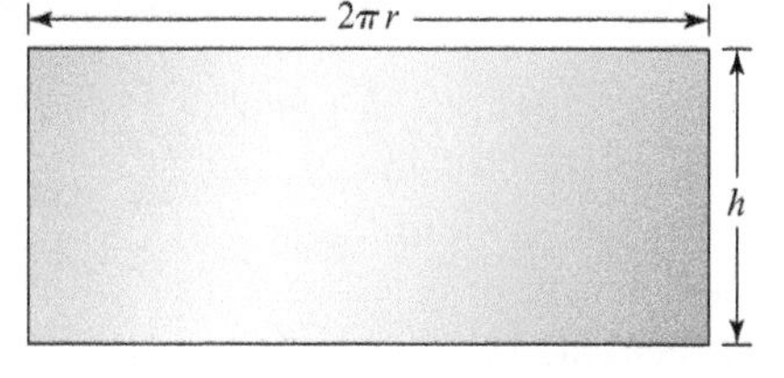

Figure 6.17

(a) Write a system of equations whose solution is the dimensions for a cylinder with a volume of 38 cubic inches and a lateral surface area of 63 square inches.

(b) Solve the system of equations graphically and symbolically.

SOLUTION

(a) The equations $V(r, h) = 38$ and $S(r, h) = 63$ must be satisfied. This results in the following system of nonlinear equations.

$$\pi r^2 h = 38 \quad \text{Volume}$$
$$2\pi rh = 63 \quad \text{Lateral surface area}$$

(b) *Graphical Solution* To find the solution graphically, we can solve each equation for h and then apply the intersection-of-graphs method.

$$h = \frac{38}{\pi r^2}$$
$$h = \frac{63}{2\pi r}$$

Solve each equation for h.

Graphical Solution

[0, 4, 1] by [0, 20, 5]

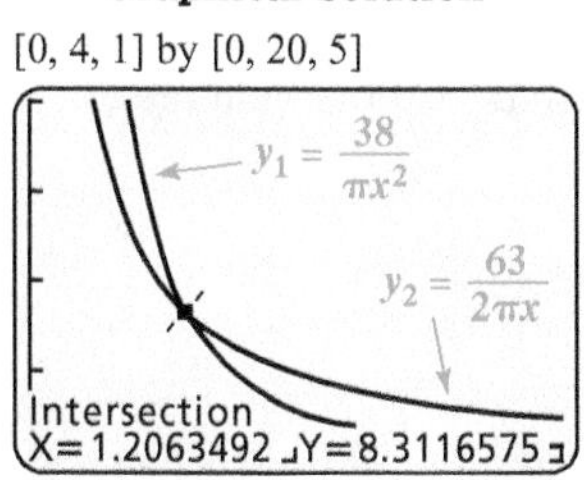

Figure 6.18

Let r correspond to x and h to y. Graph $y_1 = \frac{38}{\pi x^2}$ and $y_2 = \frac{63}{2\pi x}$. Their graphs intersect near the point (1.206, 8.312), as shown in Figure 6.18. Therefore a cylinder with a radius of $r \approx 1.206$ inches and height of $h \approx 8.312$ inches has a volume of 38 cubic inches and lateral surface area of 63 square inches.

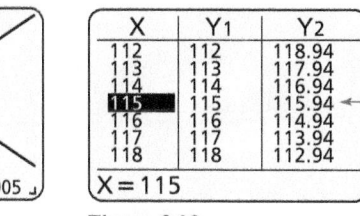

Symbolic Solution Because $h = \frac{38}{\pi r^2}$ and $h = \frac{63}{2\pi r}$, we can determine r by solving the following equation.

$$\frac{38}{\pi r^2} = \frac{63}{2\pi r} \quad \text{Equation to be solved}$$

$$2\pi r^2\left(\frac{38}{\pi r^2}\right) = 2\pi r^2\left(\frac{63}{2\pi r}\right) \quad \text{Multiply each side by the LCD, } 2\pi r^2.$$

$$76 = 63r \quad \text{Simplify.}$$

$$\frac{76}{63} = r \quad \text{Divide each side by 63.}$$

Because $r = \frac{76}{63} \approx 1.206$, $h = \frac{63}{2\pi r} = \frac{63}{2\pi(76/63)} \approx 8.312$; the symbolic result verifies our graphical result.

Now Try Exercise 117

An Example That Requires a Graphical Solution Sometimes it is either difficult or impossible to solve a nonlinear system of equations symbolically. However, it might be possible to solve such a system graphically.

EXAMPLE 13 **Solving a nonlinear system of equations graphically**

Solve the system graphically to the nearest thousandth.

$$2x^3 - y = 2$$
$$\ln x^2 - 3y = -1$$

SOLUTION Begin by solving both equations for y. The first equation becomes $y = 2x^3 - 2$. Solving the second equation for y gives the following results.

$$\ln x^2 - 3y = -1 \quad \text{Second equation}$$

$$\ln x^2 + 1 = 3y \quad \text{Add } 3y \text{ and 1 to each side.}$$

$$\frac{\ln x^2 + 1}{3} = y \quad \text{Divide each side by 3.}$$

Graphical Solution

[−6, 6, 1] by [−4, 4, 1]

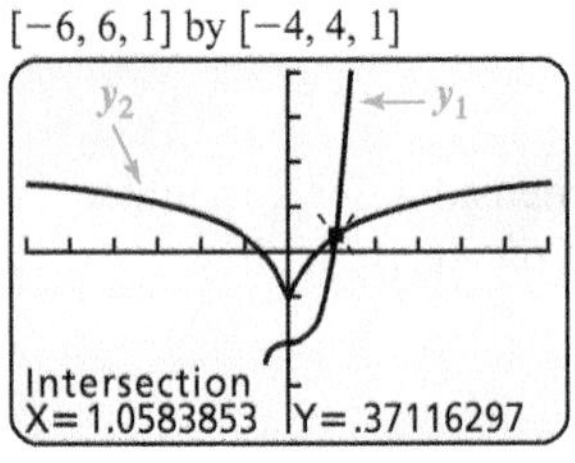

Figure 6.19

The graphs of $y_1 = 2x^3 - 2$ and $y_2 = \frac{\ln x^2 + 1}{3}$ in Figure 6.19 intersect at one point. To the nearest thousandth, the solution is (1.058, 0.371).

Now Try Exercise 107

Joint Variation

A quantity may depend on more than one variable. For example, the volume V of a cylinder is given by $V = \pi r^2 h$. We say that V *varies jointly* with h and the square of r. The *constant of variation* is π.

JOINT VARIATION

Let m and n be real numbers. Then z **varies jointly** with the mth power of x and the nth power of y if a nonzero real number k exists such that

$$z = kx^m y^n.$$

In the following example we use joint variation to determine the amount of timber in a tree with a specified diameter and height.

EXAMPLE 14 Modeling the amount of wood in a tree

To estimate the volume of timber in a given area of forest, formulas have been developed to find the amount of wood contained in a tree with height h in feet and diameter d in inches. See Figure 6.20. One study concluded that the volume V of wood in a tree varies jointly with the 1.12 power of h and the 1.98 power of d. (The diameter is measured 4.5 feet above the ground.) (***Source:*** B. Ryan, B. Joiner, and T. Ryan, *Minitab Handbook.*)

(a) Write an equation that relates V, h, and d.

(b) A tree with a 13.8-inch diameter and a 64-foot height has a volume of 25.14 cubic feet. Estimate the constant of variation k.

(c) Estimate the volume of wood in a tree with $d = 11$ inches and $h = 47$ feet.

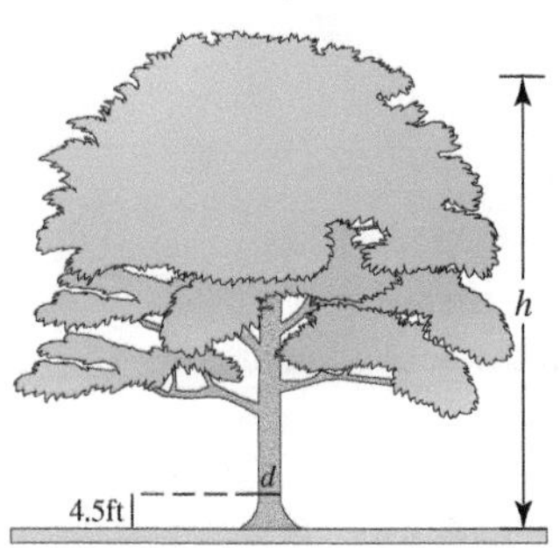

Figure 6.20

SOLUTION

(a) $V = kh^{1.12}d^{1.98}$, where k is the constant of variation.

(b) Substitute $d = 13.8$, $h = 64$, and $V = 25.14$ into the equation and solve for k.

$$25.14 = k(64)^{1.12}(13.8)^{1.98}$$

$$k = \frac{25.14}{(64)^{1.12}(13.8)^{1.98}} \approx 0.00132$$

Thus let $V = 0.00132\,h^{1.12}d^{1.98}$.

(c) $V = 0.00132(47)^{1.12}(11)^{1.98} \approx 11.4$ cubic feet

Now Try Exercise 143

6.1 Putting It All Together

The following table summarizes some mathematical concepts involved with functions and equations in two variables.

CONCEPT	COMMENTS	EXAMPLE
Function of two inputs or variables	$z = f(x, y)$ where x and y are inputs and z is the output.	$f(x, y) = x^2 + 5y$ $f(2, 3) = 2^2 + 5(3) = 19$
System of two linear equations	The equations can be written as $ax + by = k$. A solution is an ordered pair (x, y) that satisfies both equations.	$2x - 3y = 6$ $5x + 4y = -8$ Solution: $(0, -2)$
Nonlinear system of two equations	A system of equations that has at least one nonlinear equation is a nonlinear system. A solution is an ordered pair (x, y) that satisfies both equations. A nonlinear system of equations can have any number of solutions.	$5x^2 - 4xy = -3$ $\frac{5}{x} - 2y = 1$ Solutions: $(1, 2)$, $\left(-\frac{7}{5}, -\frac{16}{7}\right)$
Consistent system of linear equations in two variables	A consistent linear system has either one or infinitely many solutions. Its graph is either distinct, intersecting lines or identical lines.	$x + y = 10$ $x - y = 4$ $2x = 14$ Solution is given by $x = 7$ and $y = 3$. The equations are independent.
System of dependent linear equations in two variables	A system of dependent linear equations has infinitely many solutions. The graph consists of two identical lines.	$2x + 2y = 2$ and $x + y = 1$ are equivalent (dependent) equations. The solution set is $\{(x, y) \mid x + y = 1\}$.

continued on next page

CONCEPT	COMMENTS	EXAMPLE
Inconsistent system of linear equations in two variables	An inconsistent linear system has no solutions. The graph is two parallel lines.	$x + y = 1$ $x + y = 2$ Subtract. $0 = -1$ Always false
Method of substitution	Solve one equation for a variable. Then substitute the result in the second equation and solve.	$x - y = 1$ $x + y = 5$ If $x - y = 1$, then $x = 1 + y$. Substitute in the second equation: $(1 + y) + y = 5$. This results in $y = 2$ and $x = 3$. The solution is $(3, 2)$.
Elimination method	By performing arithmetic operations on a system, a variable is eliminated.	$2x + y = 5$ $x - y = 1$ Add. $3x = 6$ so $x = 2$ and $y = 1$.
Graphical method for two equations	Solve both equations for the same variable. Then apply the intersection-of-graphs method.	If $x + y = 3$, then $y = 3 - x$. If $4x - y = 2$, then $y = 4x - 2$. Graph and locate the point of intersection at $(1, 2)$.

6.1 Exercises

Functions of More than One Input

Exercises 1 and 2: Evaluate the function for the indicated inputs and interpret the result.

1. $A(5, 8)$, where $A(b, h) = \frac{1}{2}bh$ (A computes the area of a triangle with base b and height h.)

2. $A(20, 35)$, where $A(w, l) = wl$ (A computes the area of a rectangle with width w and length l.)

Exercises 3–8: Evaluate the expression for the given $f(x, y)$.

3. $f(2, -3)$ if $f(x, y) = x^2 + y^2$

4. $f(-1, 3)$ if $f(x, y) = 2x^2 - y^2$

5. $f(-2, 3)$ if $f(x, y) = 3x - 4y$

6. $f(5, -2)$ if $f(x, y) = 6y - \frac{1}{2}x$

7. $f\left(\frac{1}{2}, -\frac{7}{4}\right)$ if $f(x, y) = \frac{2x}{y + 3}$

8. $f(0.2, 0.5)$ if $f(x, y) = \frac{5x}{2y + 1}$

Exercises 9–12: Write a symbolic representation for $f(x, y)$ if the function f computes the following quantity.

9. The sum of y and twice x

10. The product of x^2 and y^2

11. The product of x and y divided by $1 + x$

12. The square root of the sum of x and y

Exercises 13–18: Solve the equation for x and then solve it for y.

13. $3x - 4y = 7$

14. $-x - 5y = 4$

15. $x - y^2 = 5$

16. $2x^2 + y = 4$

17. $\dfrac{2x - y}{3y} = 1$

18. $\dfrac{x + y}{x - y} = 2$

Solutions to Systems of Equations

Exercises 19–22: Determine which ordered pairs are solutions to the given system of equations. State whether the system is linear or nonlinear.

19. $(2, 1), (-2, 1), (1, 0)$
$$2x + y = 5$$
$$x + y = 3$$

20. $(3, 2), (3, -4), (5, 0)$
$$x - y = 5$$
$$2x + y = 10$$

21. $(4, -3), (0, 5), (4, 3)$
$$x^2 + y^2 = 25$$
$$2x + 3y = -1$$

22. $(4, 8), (8, 4), (-4, -8)$
$$xy = 32$$
$$x + y = 12$$

Exercises 23–26: The figure shows the graph of a system of two linear equations. Use the graph to estimate the solution to this system of equations. Then solve the system symbolically.

23.

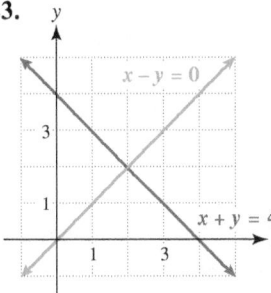

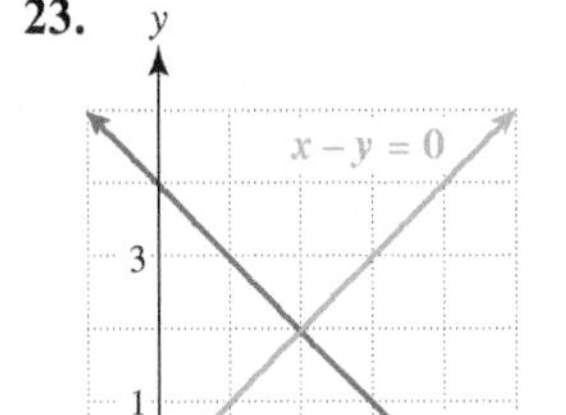

24.

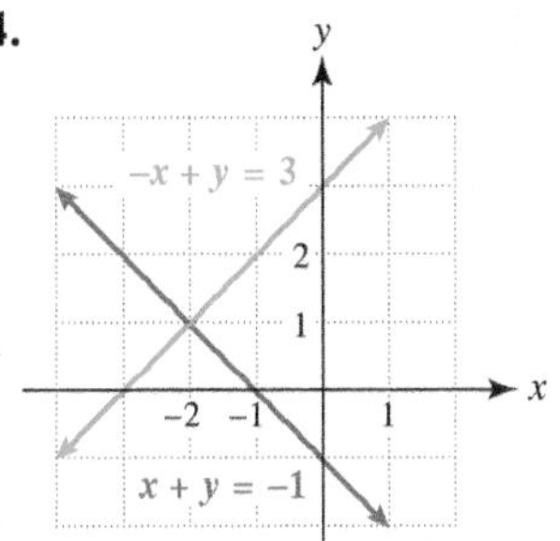

25.

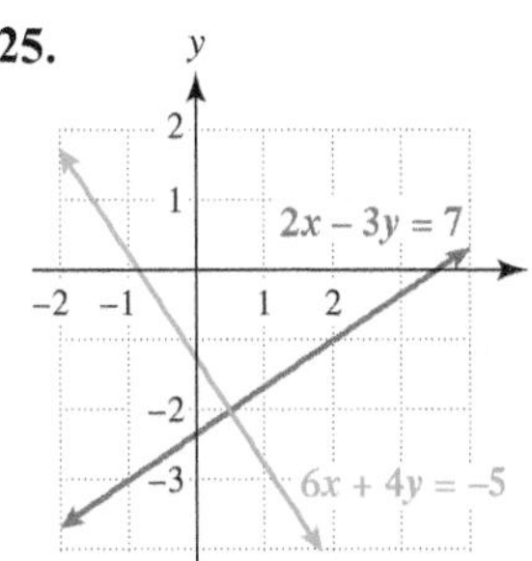

26.

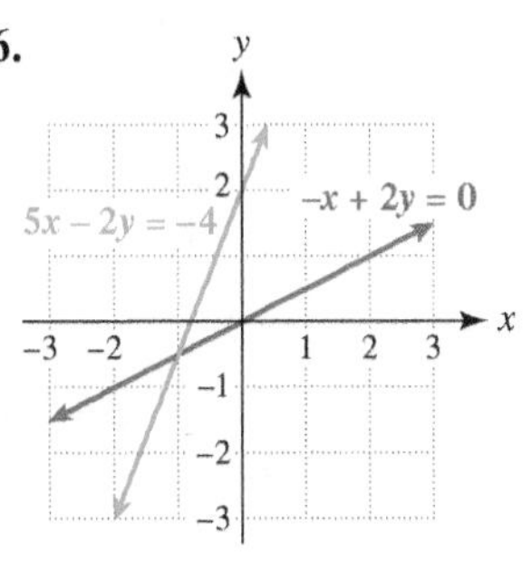

Consistent and Inconsistent Linear Systems

Exercises 27–30: The figure represents a system of linear equations. Classify the system as consistent or inconsistent. Solve the system graphically and symbolically, if possible.

27.

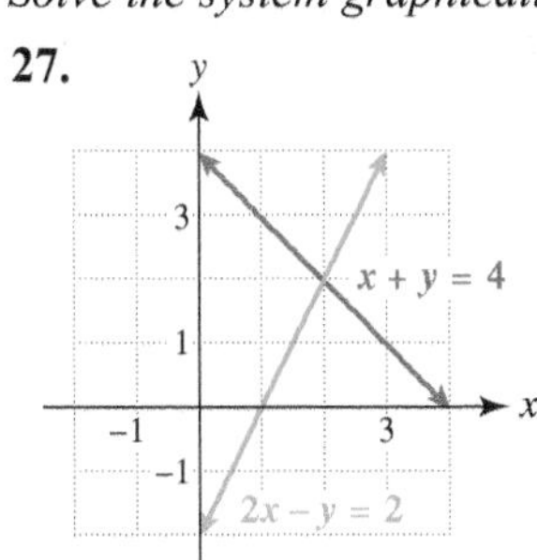

28.

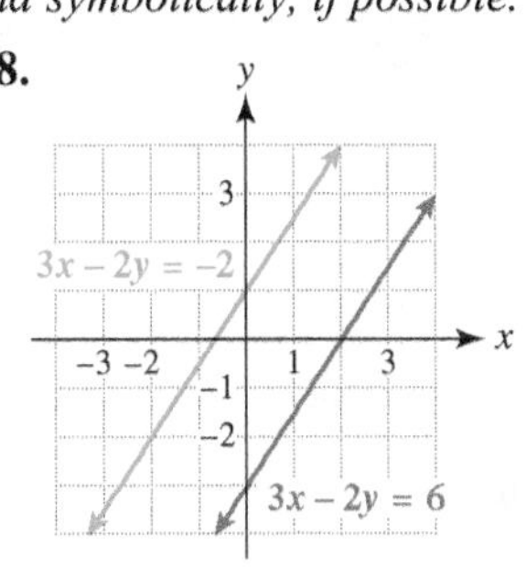

29. **30.**

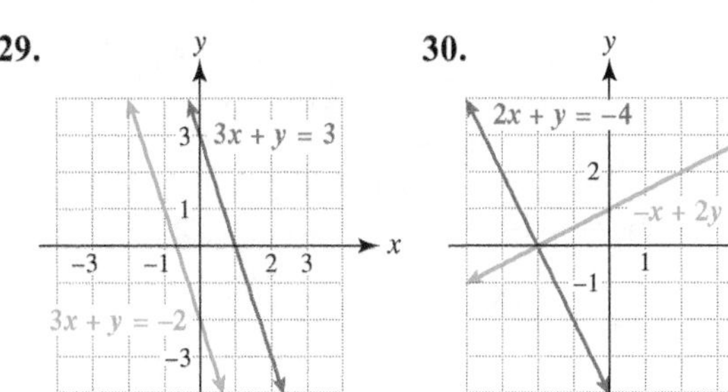

Exercises 31–38: Graph each system of equations and find any solutions. Check your answers. Identify the system as consistent or inconsistent. If the system is consistent, state whether the equations are dependent or independent.

31.
$$2x + y = 3$$
$$-2x - y = 4$$

32.
$$x - 4y = 4$$
$$2x - 8y = 4$$

33.
$$3x - y = 7$$
$$-2x + y = -5$$

34.
$$-x + 2y = 3$$
$$3x - y = 1$$

35.
$$x - 2y = -6$$
$$-2x + y = 6$$

36.
$$2x - 3y = 1$$
$$x + y = -2$$

37.
$$2x - y = -4$$
$$-4x + 2y = 8$$

38.
$$3x - y = -2$$
$$-3x + y = 2$$

The Method of Substitution

Exercises 39–50: If possible, solve the system of linear equations and check your answer.

39.
$$x + 2y = 0$$
$$3x + 7y = 1$$

40.
$$-2x - y = -2$$
$$3x + 4y = -7$$

41.
$$2x - 9y = -17$$
$$8x + 5y = 14$$

42.
$$3x + 6y = 0$$
$$4x - 2y = -5$$

43.
$$\tfrac{1}{2}x - y = -5$$
$$x + \tfrac{1}{2}y = 10$$

44.
$$-x - \tfrac{1}{3}y = -4$$
$$\tfrac{1}{3}x + 2y = 7$$

45.
$$3x - 2y = 5$$
$$-6x + 4y = -10$$

46.
$$\tfrac{1}{2}x - \tfrac{3}{4}y = \tfrac{1}{2}$$
$$\tfrac{1}{5}x - \tfrac{3}{10}y = \tfrac{1}{5}$$

47.
$$2x - 7y = 8$$
$$-3x + \tfrac{21}{2}y = 5$$

48.
$$0.6x - 0.2y = 2$$
$$-1.2x + 0.4y = 3$$

49.
$$0.2x - 0.1y = 0.5$$
$$0.4x + 0.3y = 2.5$$

50.
$$100x + 200y = 300$$
$$200x + 100y = 0$$

Exercises 51–64: If possible, solve the nonlinear system of equations.

51.
$$x^2 - y = 0$$
$$2x + y = 0$$

52.
$$x^2 - y = 3$$
$$x + y = 3$$

53.
$$xy = 8$$
$$x + y = 6$$

54.
$$2x - y = 0$$
$$2xy = 4$$

55.
$$x^2 + y^2 = 20$$
$$y = 2x$$

56.
$$x^2 + y^2 = 9$$
$$x + y = 3$$

57. $\sqrt{x} - 2y = 0$
$x - y = -2$

58. $x^2 + y^2 = 4$
$2x^2 + y = -3$

59. $2x^2 - y = 5$
$-4x^2 + 2y = -10$

60. $-6\sqrt{x} + 2y = -3$
$2\sqrt{x} - \frac{2}{3}y = 1$

61. $x^2 - y = 4$
$x^2 + y = 4$

62. $x^2 + x = y$
$2x^2 - y = 2$

63. $x^3 - x = 3y$
$x - y = 0$

64. $x^4 + y = 4$
$3x^2 - y = 0$

Exercises 65–68: Write a system of linear equations with two variables whose solution satisfies the problem. State what each variable represents. Then solve the system.

65. Screen Dimensions The screen of a rectangular television set is 2 inches wider than it is high. If the perimeter of the screen is 38 inches, find its dimensions.

66. Numbers The sum of two numbers is 300 and their difference is 8. Find the two numbers.

67. Tickets Admission prices to a movie are \$4 for children and \$7 for adults. If 75 tickets were sold for \$456, how many of each type of ticket were sold?

68. Coins A sample of 16 dimes and quarters has a value of \$2.65. How many of each type of coin are there?

Exercises 69 and 70: **Area and Perimeter** *The area of a rectangle with length l and width w is computed by $A(l, w) = lw$, and its perimeter is calculated by $P(l, w) = 2l + 2w$. Assume that $l > w$ and use the method of substitution to solve the system of equations for l and w.*

69. $A(l, w) = 35$
$P(l, w) = 24$

70. $A(l, w) = 300$
$P(l, w) = 70$

The Elimination Method

Exercises 71–80: Use elimination to solve the system of equations, if possible. Identify the system as consistent or inconsistent. If the system is consistent, state whether the equations are dependent or independent. Support your results graphically or numerically.

71. $x + y = 20$
$x - y = 8$

72. $2x + y = 15$
$x - y = 0$

73. $x + 3y = 10$
$x - 2y = -5$

74. $4x + 2y = 10$
$-2x - y = 10$

75. $x + y = 500$
$-x - y = -500$

76. $2x + 3y = 5$
$5x - 2y = 3$

77. $2x + 4y = 7$
$-x - 2y = 5$

78. $4x - 3y = 5$
$3x + 4y = 2$

79. $2x + 3y = 2$
$x - 2y = -5$

80. $x - 3y = 1$
$2x - 6y = 2$

Exercises 81–92: Solve the system, if possible.

81. $\frac{1}{2}x - y = 5$
$x - \frac{1}{2}y = 4$

82. $\frac{1}{2}x - \frac{1}{3}y = 1$
$\frac{1}{3}x - \frac{1}{2}y = 1$

83. $7x - 3y = -17$
$-21x + 9y = 51$

84. $-\frac{1}{3}x + \frac{1}{6}y = -1$
$2x - y = 6$

85. $\frac{2}{3}x + \frac{4}{3}y = \frac{1}{3}$
$-2x - 4y = 5$

86. $5x - 2y = 7$
$10x - 4y = 6$

87. $0.2x + 0.3y = 8$
$-0.4x + 0.2y = 0$

88. $2x - 3y = 1$
$3x - 2y = 2$

89. $2x + 3y = 7$
$-3x + 2y = -4$

90. $5x + 4y = -3$
$3x - 6y = -6$

91. $7x - 5y = -15$
$-2x + 3y = -2$

92. $-5x + 3y = -36$
$4x - 5y = 34$

Exercises 93–98: Use elimination to solve the nonlinear system of equations.

93. $x^2 + y = 12$
$x^2 - y = 6$

94. $x^2 + 2y = 15$
$2x^2 - y = 10$

95. $x^2 + y^2 = 25$
$x^2 + 7y = 37$

96. $x^2 + y^2 = 36$
$x^2 - 6y = 36$

97. $x^2 + y^2 = 4$
$2x^2 + y^2 = 8$

98. $x^2 + y^2 = 4$
$x^2 - y^2 = 4$

Using More Than One Method

Exercises 99–102: Solve the nonlinear system of equations (a) symbolically and (b) graphically.

99. $x^2 + y^2 = 16$
$x - y = 0$

100. $x^2 - y = 1$
$3x + y = -1$

101. $xy = 12$
$x - y = 4$

102. $x^2 + y^2 = 2$
$x^2 - y = 0$

Exercises 103–106: Solve the system of linear equations (a) graphically, (b) numerically, and (c) symbolically.

103. $2x + y = 1$
$x - 2y = 3$

104. $3x + 2y = -2$
$2x - y = -6$

105. $-2x + y = 0$
$7x - 2y = 3$

106. $x - 4y = 15$
$3x - 2y = 15$

Finding Approximate Solutions

Exercises 107–112: Approximate, to the nearest thousandth, any solutions to the nonlinear system of equations graphically.

107. $x^3 - 3x + y = 1$
$x^2 + 2y = 3$

108. $x^2 + y = 5$
$x + y^2 = 6$

109. $2x^3 - x^2 = 5y$
$2^{-x} - y = 0$

110. $x^4 - 3x^3 = y$
$\log x^2 - y = 0$

111. $e^{2x} + y = 4$
$\ln x - 2y = 0$

112. $3x^2 + y = 3$
$(0.3)^x + 4y = 1$

Applications

113. Population In 2010, the combined population of Minneapolis/St. Paul, Minnesota, was 670,000. The population of Minneapolis was 98,000 greater than the population of St. Paul. (*Source:* Census Bureau.)

(a) Write a system of equations whose solution gives the population of each city in thousands.

(b) Solve the system of equations.

(c) Is your system consistent or inconsistent? If it is consistent, state whether the equations are dependent or independent.

114. U.S. Energy Consumption In 2010, the United States consumed 94.58 quadrillion (10^{15}) Btu of energy from renewable and nonrenewable sources. It used 79.44 quadrillion Btu more from nonrenewable sources than from renewable sources. (*Source:* Department of Energy.)

(a) Write a system of equations whose solution gives the consumption of energy from renewable and nonrenewable sources (in quadrillion Btu).

(b) Solve the system of equations.

(c) Is your system consistent or inconsistent? If it is consistent, state whether the equations are dependent or independent.

115. Roof Truss (Refer to Example 11.) The weights W_1 and W_2 exerted on each rafter for the roof truss shown in the figure are determined by the system of linear equations. Solve the system.

$$W_1 + \sqrt{2}W_2 = 300$$
$$\sqrt{3}W_1 - \sqrt{2}W_2 = 0$$

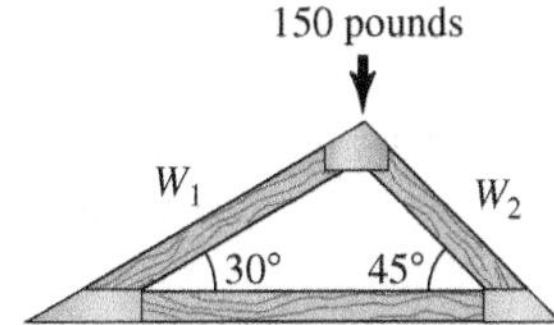

116. Time on the Internet From 2001 to 2010 the average number of hours that a user spent on the Internet each week increased by 180%. This percent increase amounted to 8 hours. Find the average number of hours that a user spent on the Internet each week in 2001 and 2010. (*Source:* eMarketer.)

117. Geometry (Refer to Example 12.) Find the radius and height of a cylindrical container with a volume of 50 cubic inches and a lateral surface area of 65 square inches.

118. Geometry (Refer to Example 12.) Determine if it is possible to construct a cylindrical container, *including* the top and bottom, with a volume of 38 cubic inches and a surface area of 38 square inches.

119. Dimensions of a Box A box has an *open* top, rectangular sides, and a square base. Its volume is 576 cubic inches, and its outside surface area is 336 square inches. Find the dimensions of the box.

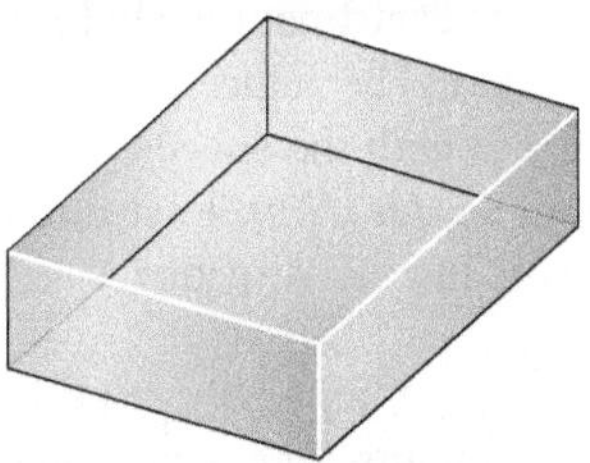

120. Dimensions of a Box A box has rectangular sides, and its rectangular top and base are twice as long as they are wide. Its volume is 588 cubic inches, and its outside surface area is 448 square inches. Find its dimensions.

121. Bank Theft The total incidences of bank theft in 2009 and 2010 was 11,693. There were 437 fewer incidences in 2009 than in 2010. (*Source:* FBI.)

(a) Write a system of equations whose solution represents the incidences of bank theft in each of these years.

(b) Solve the system symbolically.

(c) Solve the system graphically.

122. e-Waste The United States and China together produce 5.9 million tons of e-waste each year. About 0.7 million more tons are produced in the United States than in China.

(a) Write a system of equations whose solution represents the amount of e-waste produced in each country.

(b) Solve the system symbolically.

(c) Solve the system graphically.

123. Student Loans A student takes out two loans totaling $3000 to help pay for college expenses. One loan is at 8% interest, and the other is at 10%. Interest for both loans is compounded annually.

(a) If the first-year interest is $264, write a system of equations whose solution is the amount of each loan.

(b) Find the amount of each loan.

124. Student Loans (Refer to Exercise 123.) Suppose that both loans have an interest rate of 10% and the total first-year interest is $300. If possible, determine the amount of each loan. Interpret your results.

125. **Student Loans** (Refer to Exercises 123 and 124.) Suppose that both loans are at 10% and the total annual interest is \$264. If possible, determine the amount of each loan. Interpret your results.

126. **Investments** A student invests \$5000 at two annual interest rates, 5% and 7%. After 1 year the student receives a total of \$325 in interest. How much did the student invest at each interest rate?

127. **Air Speed** A jet airliner travels 1680 miles in 3 hours with a tail wind. The return trip, into the wind, takes 3.5 hours. Find both the speed of the jet with no wind and the wind speed. (*Hint*: First find the ground speed of the airplane in each direction.)

128. **River Current** A tugboat can pull a barge 60 miles upstream in 15 hours. The same tugboat and barge can make the return trip downstream in 6 hours. Determine the speed of the current in the river.

129. **Maximizing Area** Suppose a rectangular pen for a pet is to be made using 40 feet of fence. Let l represent its length and w its width, with $l \geq w$.
(a) Find l and w if the area is 91 square feet.
(b) Write a formula for the area A in terms of w.
(c) What is the maximum area possible for the pen? Interpret this result.

130. **The Toll of War** American battlefield deaths in World Wars I and II totaled about 345,000. There were about 5.5 times as many deaths in World War II as World War I. Find the number of American battlefield deaths in each war. Round your answers to the nearest whole number. (***Source:*** Defense Department.)

131. **Height and Weight** The relationship between a professional basketball player's height h in inches and weight w in pounds was modeled using two samples of players. The resulting modeling equations for the two samples were $w = 7.46h - 374$ and $w = 7.93h - 405$. Assume that $65 \leq h \leq 85$.
(a) Use each equation to predict the weight of a professional basketball player who is 6′11″.
(b) Determine graphically the height where the two models give the same weight.
(c) For each model, what change in weight is associated with a 1-inch increase in height?

132. **Heart Rate** In one study a group of athletes were exercised to exhaustion. Let x and y represent an athlete's heart rate 5 seconds and 10 seconds after stopping exercise, respectively. It was found that the maximum heart rate H for these athletes satisfied the following two equations.

$$H = 0.491x + 0.468y + 11.2$$
$$H = -0.981x + 1.872y + 26.4$$

If an athlete had a maximum heart rate of $H = 180$, determine x and y graphically. Interpret your answer. (***Source:*** V. Thomas, *Science and Sport*.)

133. **Surface Area and the Human Body** The surface area of the skin covering the human body is a function of more than one variable. A taller person tends to have a larger surface area, as does a heavier person. Both height and weight influence the surface area of a person's body. A formula used to determine the surface area of a person's body in square meters is given by

$$S(w, h) = 0.007184w^{0.425}h^{0.725},$$

where w is weight in kilograms and h is height in centimeters. Use S to estimate the surface area of a person who is 65 inches (165.1 centimeters) tall and weighs 154 pounds (70 kilograms). (***Source:*** H. Lancaster, *Quantitative Methods in Biological and Medical Sciences*.)

Exercises 134–136: **Skin and the Human Body** *(Refer to Exercise 133.) Estimate, to the nearest tenth, the surface area of a person with weight w and height h.*

134. $w = 86$ kilograms, $h = 185$ centimeters

135. $w = 132$ pounds, $h = 62$ inches

136. $w = 220$ pounds, $h = 75$ inches

Joint Variation

Exercises 137 and 138: Approximate the constant of variation to the nearest hundredth.

137. The variable z varies jointly with the second power of x and the third power of y. When $x = 2$ and $y = 2.5$, $z = 31.9$.

138. The variable z varies jointly with the 1.5 power of x and the 2.1 power of y. When $x = 4$ and $y = 3.5$, $z = 397$.

139. The variable z varies jointly with the square root of x and the cube root of y. If $z = 10.8$ when $x = 4$ and $y = 8$, find z when $x = 16$ and $y = 27$.

140. The variable z varies jointly with the third powers of x and y. If $z = 2160$ when $x = 3$ and $y = 4$, find z when $x = 2$ and $y = 5$.

141. **Wind Power** The electrical power generated by a windmill varies jointly with the square of the diameter of the area swept out by the blades and the cube of the wind velocity. If a windmill with an 8-foot diameter and a 10-mile-per-hour wind generates 2405 watts, how much power would be generated if the blades swept out an area 6 feet in diameter and the wind was 20 miles per hour?

142. **Strength of a Beam** The strength of a rectangular beam varies jointly with its width and the square of its thickness. If a beam 5.5 inches wide and 2.5 inches thick supports 600 pounds, how much can a similar beam that is 4 inches wide and 1.5 inches thick support?

143. **Volume of Wood** (Refer to Example 14.) One cord of wood contains 128 cubic feet. Estimate the number of cords in a tree that is 105 feet tall and has a diameter of 38 inches.

144. **Carpeting** The cost of carpet for a rectangular room varies jointly with its width and length. If a room 10 feet wide and 12 feet long costs $1560 to carpet, find the cost to carpet a room that is 11 feet by 23 feet. Interpret the constant of variation.

145. **Surface Area** Use the results of Exercise 133 to find a formula for $S(w, h)$ that calculates the surface area of a person if w is given in *pounds* and h is given in *inches*.

146. **Surface Area** Use the results of Exercise 145 to solve Exercises 135 and 136.

Writing about Mathematics

147. Give an example of a quantity occurring in everyday life that can be computed by a function of more than one input. Identify the inputs and the output.

148. Give an example of a system of linear equations with two variables. Explain how to solve the system graphically and symbolically

6.2 Systems of Inequalities in Two Variables

- **Solve inequalities in two variables graphically**
- **Solve systems of inequalities in two variables**
- **Learn basic properties of linear programming in two variables**

Introduction

For people who regularly consume caffeinated beverages, too much caffeine may cause "caffeine jitters," while too little caffeine may bring on a caffeine withdrawal headache. These caffeine amounts vary depending on an individual's weight. Figure 6.21 shows one possible relationship between a person's weight and the effects of caffeine, while Table 6.1 gives the caffeine content of selected beverages. To describe the middle shaded region in the figure, we need a *system of linear inequalities*. See Exercises 37–40. (***Source:*** Mayo Clinic)

Effects of Caffeine

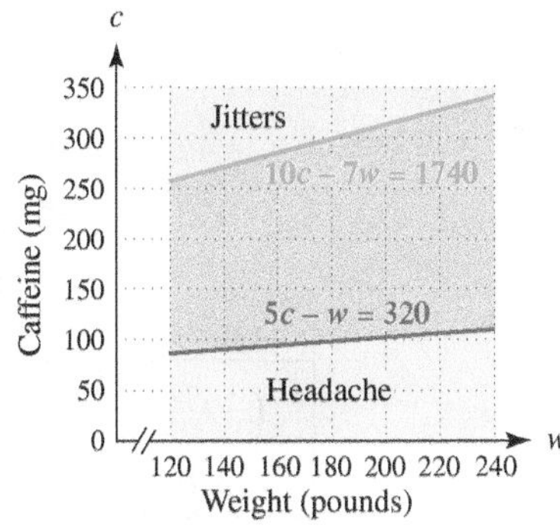

Figure 6.21

Beverage Caffeine Content

Beverage	Caffeine
7-Up: 12 oz	0 mg
Mt Dew: 12 oz	54 mg
Red Bull: 8.4 oz	80 mg
Brewed Coffee: 8 oz	108 mg
Monster: 16 oz	160 mg
Starbucks Tall Coffee: 12 oz	260 mg
All City NRG: 16 oz	300 mg

Source: Energy Fiend

Table 6.1

Systems of Linear and Nonlinear Inequalities

A linear inequality in two variables can be written as

$$ax + by \leq c,$$

where a, b, and c are constants with a and b not equal to zero. (The symbol $\leq$ can be replaced by $\geq$, $<$, or $>$.) If an ordered pair (x, y) makes the inequality a true statement, then (x, y) is a solution. The set of all solutions is called the *solution set.* The graph of an inequality includes all points (x, y) in the solution set.

The graph of a linear inequality is a (shaded) **half-plane,** which may include the boundary. To determine which half-plane to shade, select a **test point** that is not on the boundary. If the test point satisfies the given inequality, then shade the half-plane containing the test point. Otherwise, shade the other half-plane. For example, the following See the Concept demonstrates how to graph the solution to the inequality $3x - 2y \leq 6$.

See the Concept: Graphing a Linear Inequality

To graph $3x - 2y \leq 6$:

A Solve the inequality for y.

$$3x - 2y \leq 6$$
$$-2y \leq -3x + 6$$
$$y \geq \tfrac{3}{2}x - 3$$

B Graph the *equation* $y = \frac{3}{2}x - 3$.

C Choose a test point that is not on the line.

D Substitute the test point (0, 0) in the given inequality. Since $3(0) - 2(0) \leq 6$ is true, shade the half-plane containing the test point.

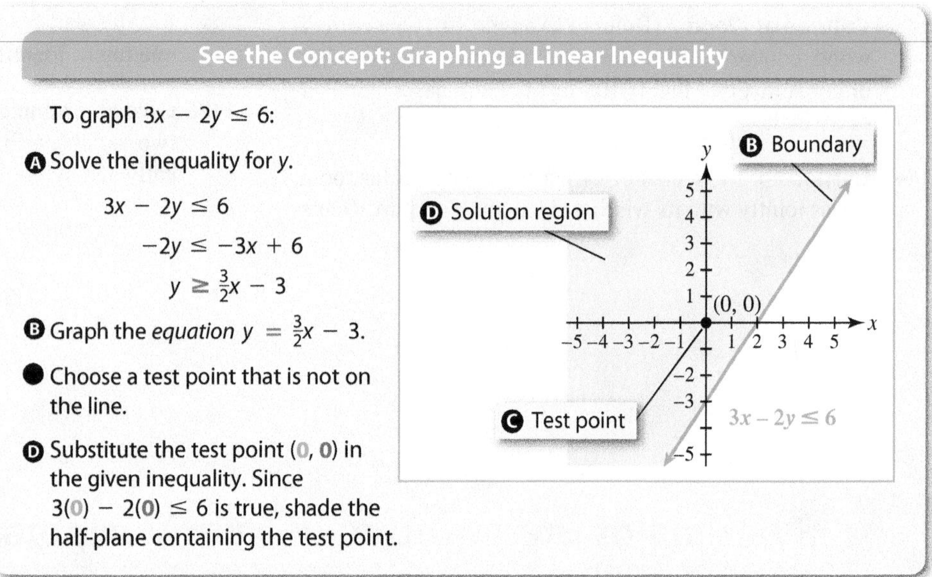

EXAMPLE 1 Graphing inequalities

Graph the solution set to each inequality.

(a) $2x - 3y \leq -6$ **(b)** $x^2 + y^2 < 9$

SOLUTION

(a) For $2x - 3y \leq -6$ start by graphing the line $2x - 3y = -6$, as in Figure 6.22. Note that this line is solid because equality is included. We can determine which side of the line to shade by using test points. For example, the test point $(-2, 2)$ lies above the line and the test point $(0, 0)$ lies below the line.

The Boundary

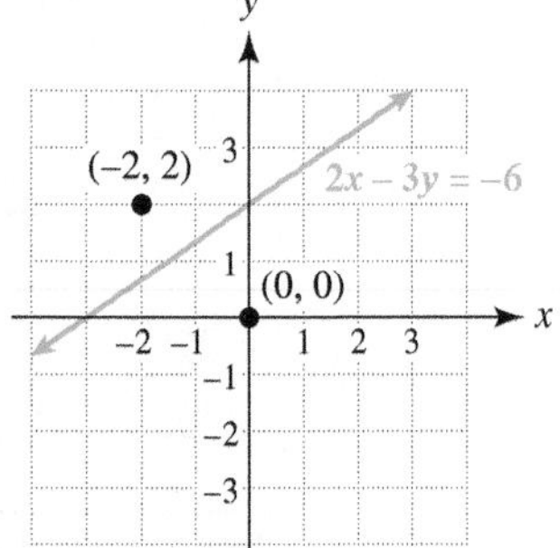

Figure 6.22

Checking Test Points

Test Point	$2x - 3y \leq -6$	True or False?
$(-2, 2)$	$2(-2) - 3(2) \overset{?}{\leq} -6$	True
$(0, 0)$	$2(0) - 3(0) \overset{?}{\leq} -6$	False

Table 6.2

In Table 6.2, the test point $(-2, 2)$ satisfies the given inequality, so shade the region above the line that contains the point $(-2, 2)$. See Figure 6.23.

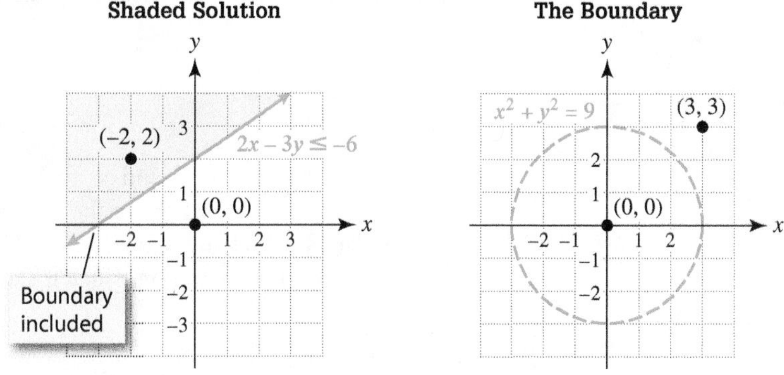

Figure 6.23

Figure 6.24

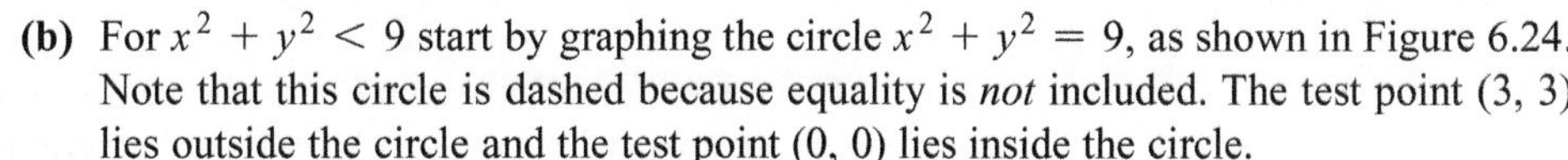

(b) For $x^2 + y^2 < 9$ start by graphing the circle $x^2 + y^2 = 9$, as shown in Figure 6.24. Note that this circle is dashed because equality is *not* included. The test point $(3, 3)$ lies outside the circle and the test point $(0, 0)$ lies inside the circle.

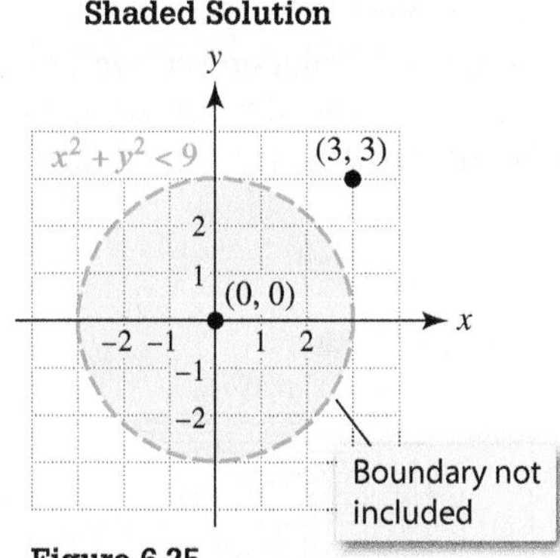

Figure 6.25

Checking Test Points

Test Point	$x^2 + y^2 < 9$	True or False?
(3, 3)	$3^2 + 3^2 \overset{?}{<} 9$	False
(0, 0)	$0^2 + 0^2 \overset{?}{<} 9$	True

Table 6.3

In Table 6.4, the test point $(0, 0)$ satisfies the given inequality, so shade the region inside the circle. The actual circle is not part of the solution set. See Figure 6.25.

Now Try Exercises 7 and 9

In Section 6.1, we saw that systems of equations could be linear or nonlinear. Similary, systems of inequalities can be linear or nonlinear. The next example illustrates a system of each type. Both are solved graphically.

EXAMPLE 2 **Solving systems of inequalities graphically**

Solve each system of inequalities by shading the solution set. Identify one solution.

(a) $\begin{aligned} y &> x^2 \\ x + y &< 4 \end{aligned}$ **(b)** $\begin{aligned} x + 3y &\le 9 \\ 2x - y &\le -1 \end{aligned}$

SOLUTION

(a) This is a nonlinear system. Graph the parabola $y = x^2$ and the line $y = 4 - x$. Since $y > x^2$ and $y < 4 - x$, the region satisfying the system lies above the parabola and below the line. It does not include the boundaries, which are shown using a dashed line and curve. See Figure 6.26.

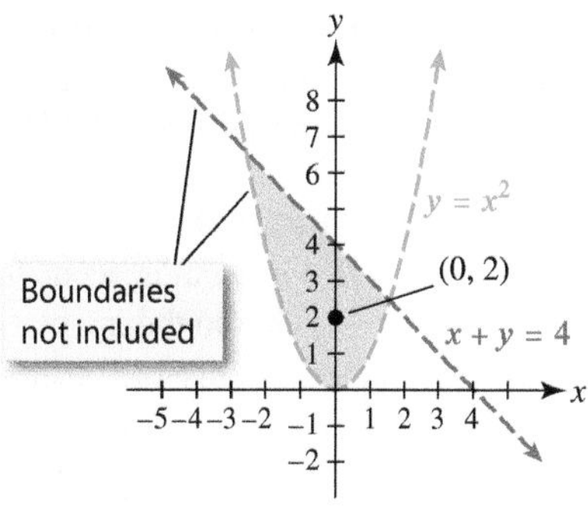

Figure 6.26

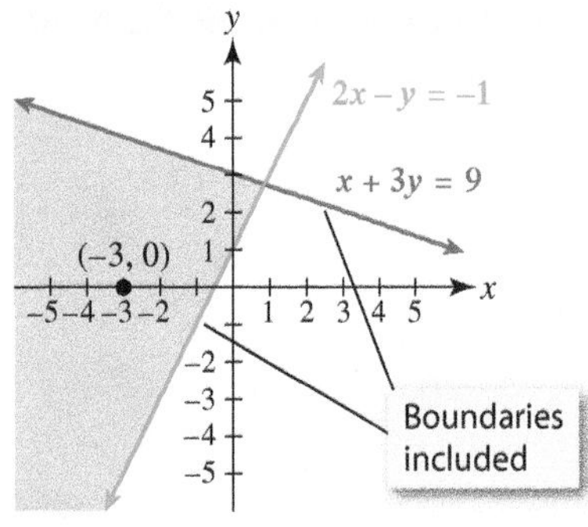

Figure 6.27

Any point in the shaded region represents a solution. For example, (0, 2) lies in the shaded region and is a solution, since $x = 0$ and $y = 2$ satisfy *both* inequalities.

(b) Begin by solving each linear inequality for y.

$$y \le -\frac{1}{3}x + 3$$

$$y \ge 2x + 1$$

Graph $y = -\frac{1}{3}x + 3$ and $y = 2x + 1$. The region satisfying the system is below the first (red) line and above the second (blue) line. Because equality is included, the boundaries, which are shown as solid lines in Figure 6.27, are part of the region. The point $(-3, 0)$ is a solution, since it satisfies both inequalities.

Now Try Exercises 17 and 19

Calculator Help
To shade a graph, see Appendix A (pages AP-10 and AP-12).

Graphing Calculators (Optional) Graphing calculators can be used to shade regions in the xy-plane. See Figure 6.28. The solution set shown in Figure 6.26 is also shown in Figure 6.29, where a graphing calculator has been used. However, the boundary is not dashed.

Figures 6.30 and 6.31 show a different method of shading a solution set; we have shaded the area below $y_1 = -\frac{1}{3}x + 3$ and above $y_2 = 2x + 1$. The solution set is the region shaded with both vertical *and* horizontal lines and corresponds to the shaded region in Figure 6.27.

Shading using the "Shade" Function
[−5, 5, 1] by [−2, 8, 1]

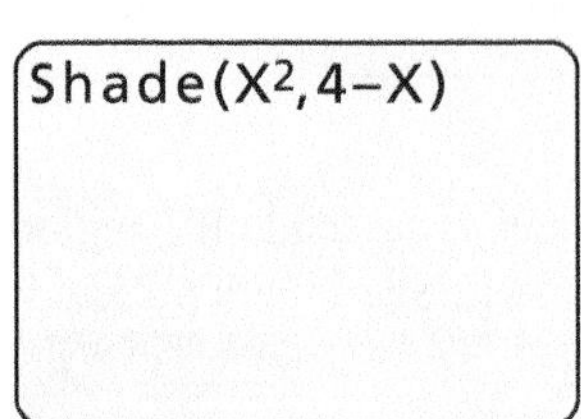

Figure 6.28

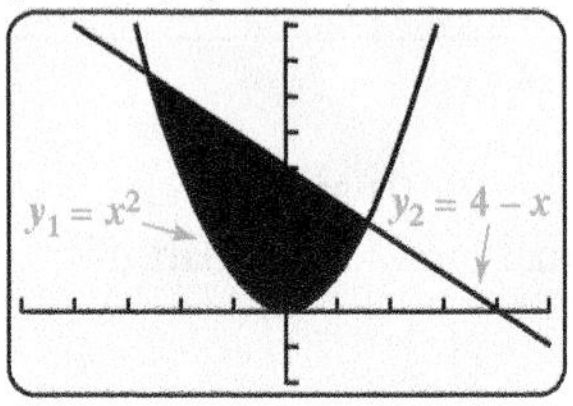

Figure 6.29

Shading using the Y= Menu
[−6, 6, 1] by [−6, 6, 1]

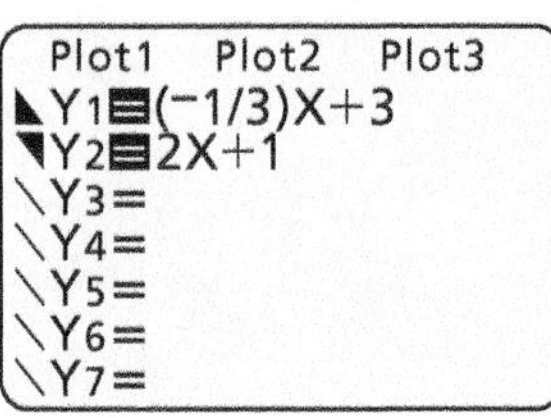

Figure 6.30

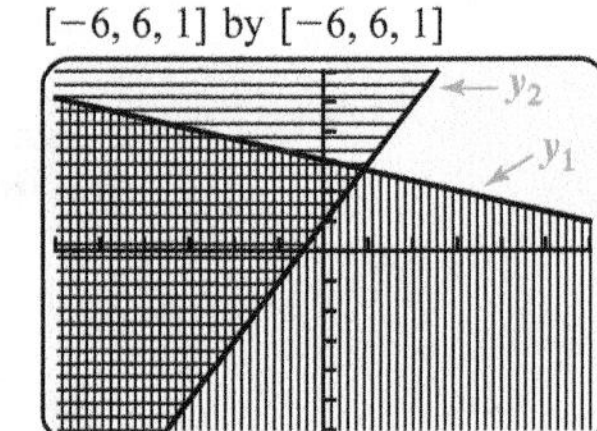

Figure 6.31

An Application of Inequalities The next example discusses how a system of inequalities can be used to determine where forests, grasslands, and deserts will occur.

EXAMPLE 3 Modeling plant growth

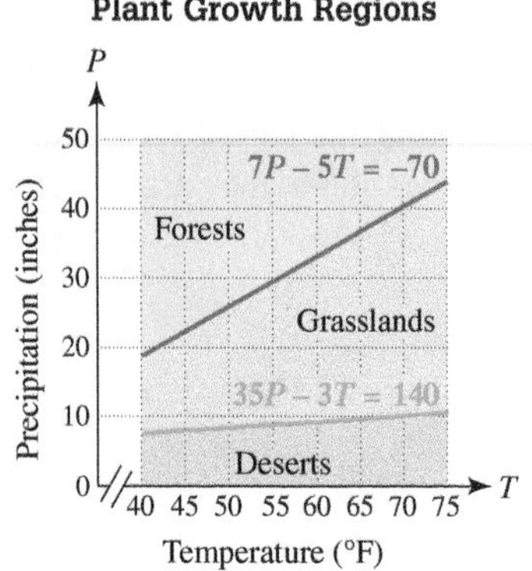

Figure 6.32

If a region has too little precipitation, it will be a desert. Forests tend to exist in regions where temperatures are relatively low and there is sufficient rainfall. At other levels of precipitation and temperature, grasslands may prevail. Figure 6.32 illustrates the relationship among forests, grasslands, and deserts, as suggested by annual average temperature T in degrees Fahrenheit and precipitation P in inches. (***Source:*** A. Miller and J. Thompson, *Elements of Meteorology*.)

(a) Determine a system of linear inequalities that describes where grasslands occur.

(b) Bismarck, North Dakota, has an annual average temperature of 40°F and precipitation of 15 inches. According to the graph, what type of plant growth would you expect near Bismarck? Do these values satisfy the system of inequalities from part (a)?

SOLUTION

(a) Grasslands occur for ordered pairs (T, P) lying between the two lines in Figure 6.32. The boundary between deserts and grasslands is determined by $35P - 3T = 140$. Solving for P (the variable on the vertical axis) results in

$$P = \frac{3}{35}T + \frac{140}{35}.$$

Grasslands grow where values of P are above the line. This region is described by $P > \frac{3}{35}T + \frac{140}{35}$, or equivalently, $35P - 3T > 140$. In a similar manner, the region below the boundary between grasslands and forests is represented by the inequality $7P - 5T < -70$. Thus grasslands satisfy the following system of inequalities.

$$35P - 3T > 140$$
$$7P - 5T < -70$$

Grasslands satisfy both inequalities.

(b) For Bismarck, $T = 40$ and $P = 15$. Figure 6.32 shows that the point $(40, 15)$ lies between the two lines, so the graph predicts that grasslands will exist around Bismarck. Substituting these values for T and P into the system of inequalities results in the following true statements.

$$35(15) - 3(40) = 405 > 140 \checkmark \quad \text{True}$$
$$7(15) - 5(40) = -95 < -70 \checkmark \quad \text{True}$$

The temperature and precipitation values for Bismarck satisfy the system of inequalities for grasslands.

Now Try Exercises 43 and 45

Linear Programming

Linear programming is a procedure used to optimize quantities such as cost and profit. It was developed during World War II as a method of efficiently allocating supplies. Linear programming applications frequently contain thousands of variables and are solved by computers. However, here we focus on problems involving two variables.

A linear programming problem consists of a linear **objective function** and a system of linear inequalities called **constraints**. The solution set for the system of linear inequalities is called the set of **feasible solutions**. The objective function describes a quantity that is to be optimized. For example, linear programming is often used to maximize profit or minimize cost. The following example illustrates these concepts.

EXAMPLE 4 Finding maximum profit

Suppose a small company manufactures two products—car radios and stereos. Each radio results in a profit of \$15, and each stereo provides a profit of \$35. Due to demand, the company must produce at least 5 and not more than 25 radios per day. The number of radios cannot exceed the number of stereos, and the number of stereos cannot exceed 30. How many of each should the company manufacture to obtain maximum profit?

SOLUTION Let x be the number of car radios produced daily and y be the number of stereos produced daily. Since the profit from x radios is $15x$ dollars and the profit from y stereos is $35y$ dollars, the total daily profit P is given by

$$P = 15x + 35y.$$

The company produces from 5 to 25 radios per day, so the inequalities

$$x \geq 5 \quad \text{and} \quad x \leq 25$$

must be satisfied. The requirements that the number of radios cannot exceed the number of stereos and the number of stereos cannot exceed 30 indicate that

$$x \leq y \quad \text{and} \quad y \leq 30.$$

Since the numbers of radios and stereos cannot be negative, we have

$$x \geq 0 \quad \text{and} \quad y \geq 0.$$

Listing all the constraints on production gives

$$x \geq 5, \quad x \leq 25, \quad y \leq 30, \quad x \leq y, \quad x \geq 0, \quad \text{and} \quad y \geq 0.$$

Graphing these constraints results in the shaded region shown in Figure 6.33. This shaded region is the set of feasible solutions. The vertices (or corners) of this region are (5, 5), (25, 25), (25, 30), and (5, 30).

It can be shown that maximum profit occurs at a vertex of the region of feasible solutions. Thus we evaluate P at each vertex, as shown in Table 6.4.

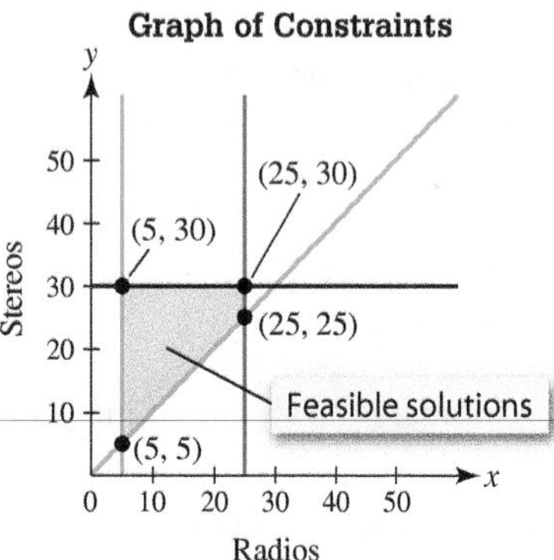

Figure 6.33

Checking Vertices in the Profit Equation

Vertex	$P = 15x + 35y$
(5, 5)	$15(5) + 35(5) = 250$
(25, 25)	$15(25) + 35(25) = 1250$
(25, 30)	$15(25) + 35(30) = 1425$ ← Maximum profit
(5, 30)	$15(5) + 35(30) = 1125$

Table 6.4

The maximum value of P is 1425 at vertex (25, 30). Thus the maximum profit is \$1425, and it occurs when 25 car radios and 30 stereos are manufactured.

Now Try Exercise 63

The following theorem holds for linear programming problems.

FUNDAMENTAL THEOREM OF LINEAR PROGRAMMING

If the optimal value for a linear programming problem exists, then it occurs at a vertex of the region of feasible solutions.

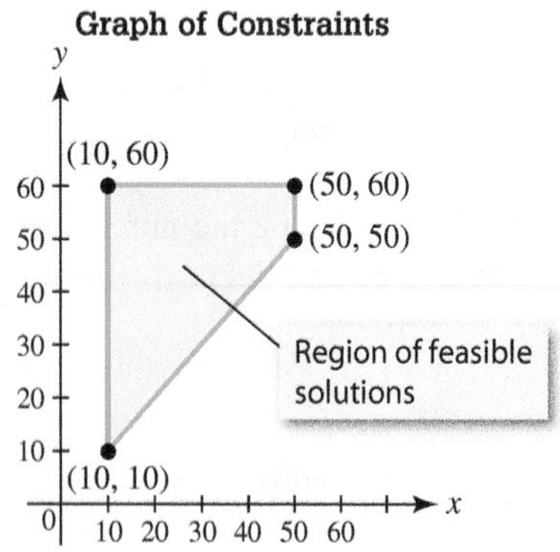

Figure 6.34

Justification of the Fundamental Theorem To better understand the fundamental theorem of linear programming, consider the following example. Suppose that we want to maximize $P = 30x + 70y$ subject to the following four constraints:

$$x \geq 10, \quad x \leq 50, \quad y \geq x, \quad \text{and} \quad y \leq 60.$$

The corresponding region of feasible solutions is shown in Figure 6.34.

Each value of P determines a unique line. For example, if $P = 7000$, then the equation for P becomes $30x + 70y = 7000$. The resulting line, shown in Figure 6.35, does not intersect the region of feasible solutions. Thus there are no values for x and y that lie in this region and result in a profit of 7000. Figure 6.35 also shows the lines that result from letting $P = 0$, 1000, and 3000. If $P = 1000$, then the line intersects the region of feasible solutions only at the vertex (10, 10). This means that if $x = 10$ and $y = 10$, then $P = 30(10) + 70(10) = 1000$. If $P = 3000$, then the line $30x + 70y = 3000$ intersects the region of feasible solutions infinitely many times. However, it appears that values greater than 3000 are possible for P.

In Figure 6.36 lines are drawn for $P = 5700$, 6300, and 7000. Notice that there are no points of intersection for $P = 6300$ or $P = 7000$, but there is one vertex in the region of feasible solutions at (50, 60) that gives $P = 5700$. Thus the maximum value of P is 5700 and this maximum occurs at a vertex of the region of feasible solutions. The fundamental theorem of linear programming generalizes this result.

CLASS DISCUSSION

What is the minimum value for P subject to the given constraints?

How the Objective Function Intersects the Region of Feasible Solutions

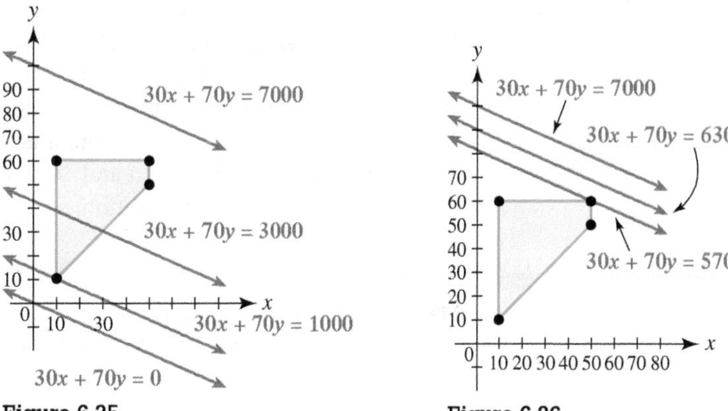

Figure 6.35

Figure 6.36

EXAMPLE 5 **Finding the minimum of an objective function**

Find the minimum value of $C = 2x + 3y$ subject to the following constraints.

$$x + y \geq 4$$
$$2x + y \leq 8$$
$$x \geq 0, \quad y \geq 0$$

SOLUTION Sketch the region determined by the constraints and find all vertices, as shown in Figure 6.37.

Evaluate the objective function C at each vertex, as shown in Table 6.5.

Graph of Constraints

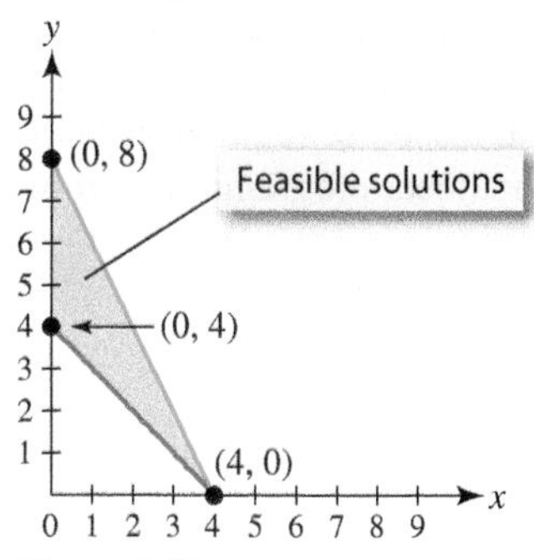

Figure 6.37

Checking Vertices in the Objective Function

Vertex	$C = 2x + 3y$
(4, 0)	$2(4) + 3(0) = 8$ — Minimum value
(0, 8)	$2(0) + 3(8) = 24$
(0, 4)	$2(0) + 3(4) = 12$

Table 6.5

The minimum value for C is 8 and it occurs at vertex (4, 0), or when $x = 4$ and $y = 0$.

Now Try Exercise 59

The following procedure describes how to solve a linear programming problem.

SOLVING A LINEAR PROGRAMMING PROBLEM

STEP 1: Read the problem carefully. Consider making a table to display the given information.

STEP 2: Use the table to write the objective function and all the constraints.

STEP 3: Sketch a graph of the region of feasible solutions. Identify all vertices, or corner points.

STEP 4: Evaluate the objective function at each vertex. A maximum (or a minimum) occurs at a vertex. If the region is unbounded, a maximum (or minimum) may not exist.

EXAMPLE 6 Minimizing cost

A breeder is buying two brands of food, A and B, for her animals. Each serving is a mixture of the two foods and should contain at least 40 grams of protein and at least 30 grams of fat. Brand A costs 90 cents per unit, and Brand B costs 60 cents per unit. Each unit of Brand A contains 20 grams of protein and 10 grams of fat, whereas each unit of Brand B contains 10 grams of protein and 10 grams of fat. Determine how much of each brand should be bought to obtain a minimum cost per serving.

SOLUTION

STEP 1: After reading the problem carefully, begin by listing the information, as illustrated in Table 6.6. (Your table may be different.)

Protein and Fat Content by Brand, with Cost

Brand	Units	Protein/Unit	Total Protein	Fat/Unit	Total Fat	Cost
A	x	20	$20x$	10	$10x$	$90x$
B	y	10	$10y$	10	$10y$	$60y$
		Minimum Total Protein	40		30	Minimum Total Fat

Table 6.6

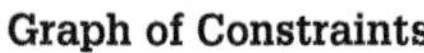

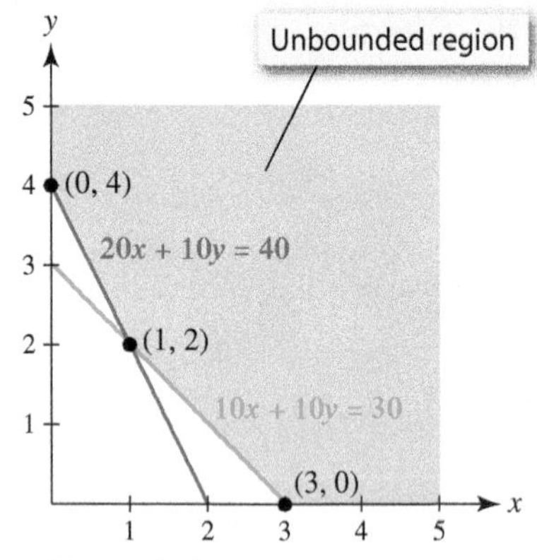

Figure 6.38

STEP 2: If x units of Brand A are purchased at 90¢ per unit and y units of Brand B are purchased at 60¢ per unit, then the cost C is given by $C = 90x + 60y$. Each serving requires at least 40 grams of protein. If x units of Brand A are bought (each containing 20 grams of protein), y units of Brand B are bought (each containing 10 grams of protein), and each serving requires at least 40 grams of protein, then we can write $20x + 10y \geq 40$. Similarly, since each serving requires at least 30 grams of fat, we can write $10x + 10y \geq 30$. The linear programming problem can be written as follows.

Minimize: $C = 90x + 60y$ Cost

Subject to: $20x + 10y \geq 40$ Protein

$10x + 10y \geq 30$ Fat

$x \geq 0, \quad y \geq 0$

STEP 3: The region of feasible solutions is unbounded and shown in Figure 6.38. The vertices for this region are (0, 4), (1, 2), and (3, 0).

STEP 4: Evaluate the objective function C at each vertex, as shown in Table 6.7.

Checking Vertices in the Cost Equation

Vertex	$C = 90x + 60y$	
(0, 4)	240	
(1, 2)	210	Minimum cost
(3, 0)	270	

Table 6.7

The minimum cost occurs when 1 unit of Brand A and 2 units of Brand B are mixed, at a cost of \$2.10 per serving.

Now Try Exercise 65

6.2 Putting It All Together

The following table summarizes some important mathematical concepts from this section.

CONCEPT	COMMENTS	EXAMPLE
Linear inequality in two variables	$ax + by \leq c$ ($\leq$ may be replaced by $<$, $>$, or $\geq$) The solution set is typically a shaded region in the xy-plane.	$2x - 3y \leq 12$ $-2x + y \leq 4$ 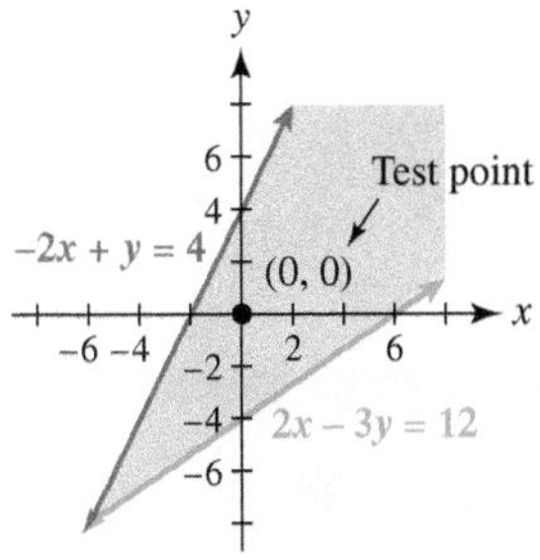
Linear programming	In a linear programming problem, the maximum or minimum of an objective function is found, subject to constraints. If a solution exists, it occurs at a vertex of the region of feasible solutions.	Maximize the objective function $P = 2x + 3y$ subject to the following constraints. $2x + y \leq 6$ $x + 2y \leq 6$ $x \geq 0, y \geq 0$ 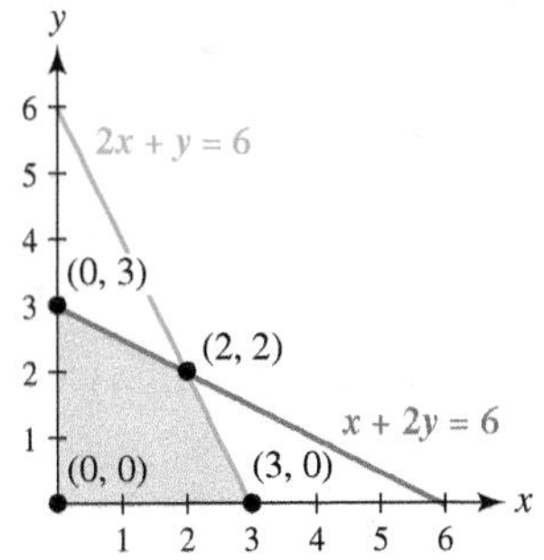 The maximum of $P = 10$ occurs at vertex (2, 2).

6.2 Exercises

Inequalities

Exercises 1–12: Graph the solution set to the inequality.

1. $x \geq y$

2. $y > -3$

3. $x < 1$

4. $y > 2x$

5. $x + y \leq 2$

6. $x + y > -3$

7. $2x + y > 4$

8. $2x + 3y \leq 6$

9. $x^2 + y^2 > 4$

10. $x^2 + y^2 \leq 1$

11. $x^2 + y \leq 2$

12. $2x^2 - y < 1$

Exercises 13–16: Match the system of inequalities with the appropriate graph (a–d). Use the graph to identify one solution.

13. $x + y \geq 2$
$x - y \leq 1$

14. $2x - y > 0$
$x - 2y \leq 1$

15. $\frac{1}{2}x^3 - y > 0$
$2x - y \leq 1$

16. $x^2 + y \leq 4$
$x^2 - y \leq 2$

a.

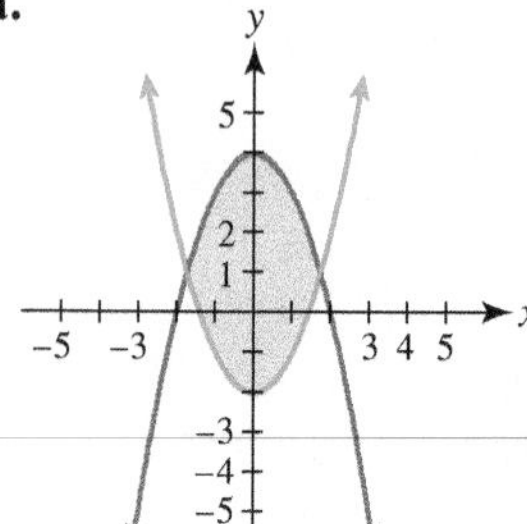

b.

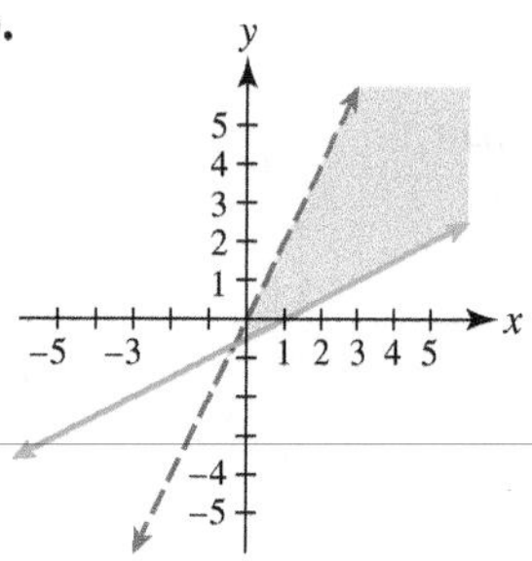

c.

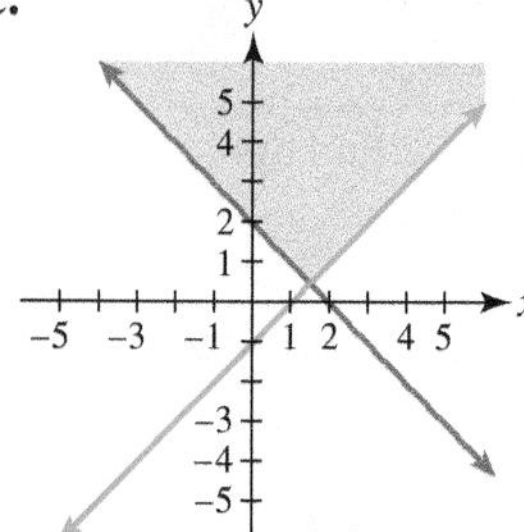

d.

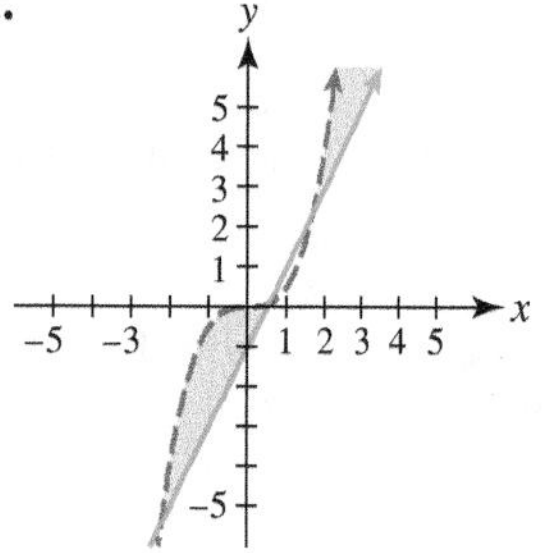

Exercises 17–24: Graph the solution set to the system of inequalities. Use the graph to identify one solution.

17. $y \geq x^2$
$x + y \leq 6$

18. $y \leq \sqrt{x}$
$y \geq 1$

19. $x + 2y > -2$
$x + 2y < 5$

20. $x - y \leq 3$
$x + y \leq 3$

21. $x^2 + y^2 \leq 16$
$x + y < 2$

22. $x^2 + y \leq 4$
$x^2 - y \leq 3$

23. $x^2 + y > 2$
$x^2 + y^2 \leq 9$

24. $x^2 + y^2 > 4$
$x^2 + y^2 < 16$

Exercises 25–36: Graph the solution set to the system of inequalities.

25. $x + 2y \leq 4$
$2x - y \geq 6$

26. $3x - y \leq 3$
$x + 2y \leq 2$

27. $3x + 2y < 6$
$x + 3y \leq 6$

28. $4x + 3y \geq 12$
$2x + 6y \geq 4$

29. $x - 2y \geq 0$
$x - 3y \leq 3$

30. $2x - 4y \geq 4$
$x + y \leq 0$

31. $x^2 + y^2 \leq 4$
$y \geq 1$

32. $x^2 - y \leq 0$
$x^2 + y^2 \leq 6$

33. $2x^2 + y \leq 0$
$x^2 - y \leq 3$

34. $x^2 + 2y \leq 4$
$x^2 - y \leq 0$

35. $x^2 + y^2 \leq 4$
$x^2 + 2y \leq 2$

36. $2x + 3y \leq 6$
$\frac{1}{2}x^2 - y \leq 2$

Applications

Exercises 37–40: **Caffeine Consumption** *(Refer to the introduction to this section.) The following graph shows one possible relationship between a person's weight and the effects of caffeine.* (***Source:*** Mayo Clinic)

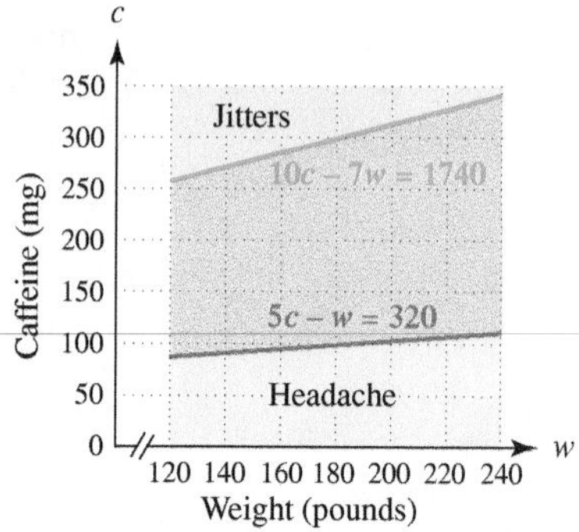

37. What does the graph indicate about the effects of caffeine on 140-pound person who has consumed 335 mg of caffeine?

38. Suppose a 180-pound person wishes to avoid both a headache and the jitters. What range of caffeine consumption is suggested?

39. (Refer to Table 6.1.) For what weights could a person drink a 16-ounce can of All City NRG without experiencing the jitters?

40. (Refer to Table 6.1.) According to this graph, does a single 12-ounce can of Mountain Dew contain enough caffeine for most people to avoid a headache?

41. **Traffic Control** The figure shows two intersections, labeled A and B, that involve one-way streets. The numbers and variables represent the average traffic flow rates measured in vehicles per hour. For example, an average of 500 vehicles per hour enter intersection A from the west, whereas 150 vehicles per hour enter this intersection from the north. A stoplight will control the unknown traffic flow denoted by the variables x and y. Use the fact that the number of vehicles entering an intersection must equal the number leaving to determine x and y.

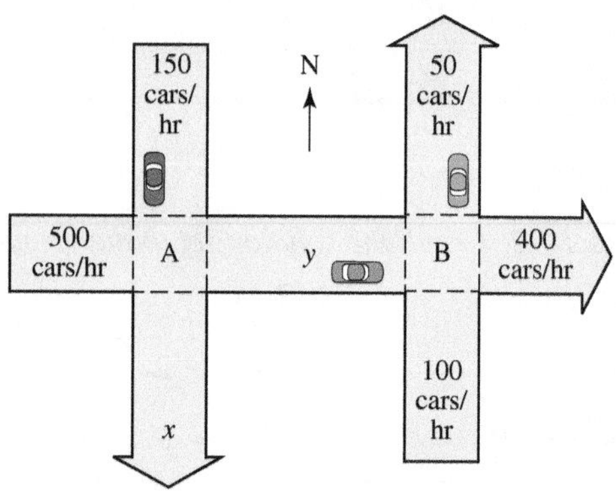

42. Traffic Control (Refer to Exercise 41.) Suppose that the number of vehicles entering intersection A from the west varies between 400 and 600. If all other traffic flows remain the same as in the figure, what effect does this have on the ranges of the values for x and y?

Exercises 43–46: **Weight and Height** *The following graph shows a weight and height chart. The weight w is listed in pounds and the height h in inches. The shaded area is a recommended region.* (***Source:*** Department of Agriculture.)

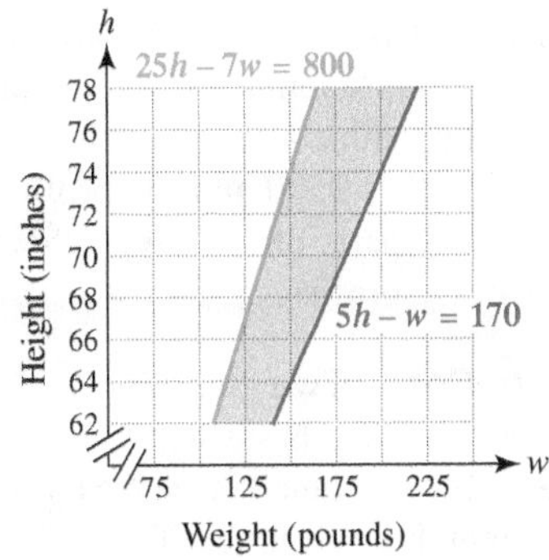

43. What does this chart indicate about an individual who weighs 125 pounds and is 70 inches tall?

44. Use the graph to estimate the recommended weight range for a person 74 inches tall.

45. Use the graph to find a system of linear inequalities that describes the recommended region.

46. Explain why inequalities are more appropriate than equalities for describing recommended weight and height combinations.

Linear Programming

Exercises 47–50: Shade the region of feasible solutions for the following constraints.

47. $x + y \le 4$
$x + y \ge 1$
$x \ge 0, y \ge 0$

48. $x + 2y \le 8$
$2x + y \ge 2$
$x \ge 0, y \ge 0$

49. $3x + 2y \le 12$
$2x + 3y \le 12$
$x \ge 0, y \ge 0$

50. $x + y \le 4$
$x + 4y \ge 4$
$x \ge 0, y \ge 0$

Exercises 51 and 52: The graph shows a region of feasible solutions for P. Find the maximum and minimum values of P.

51. $P = 3x + 5y$

52. $P = 6x + y$

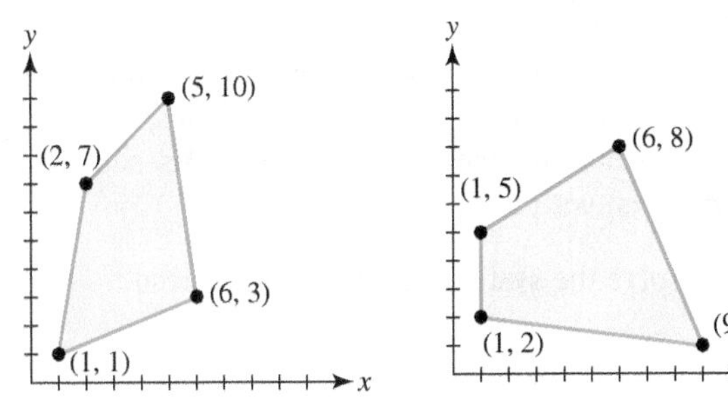

Exercises 53–56: The graph shows a region of feasible solutions for C. Find the maximum and minimum values of C.

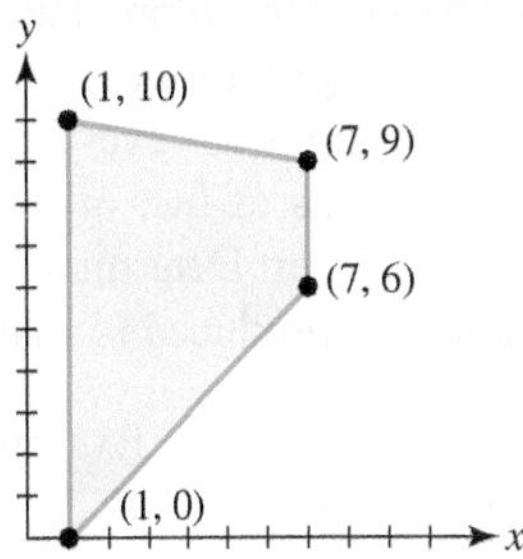

53. $C = 3x + 5y$

54. $C = 5x + 5y$

55. $C = 10y$

56. $C = 3x - y$

Exercises 57 and 58: Write a system of linear inequalities that describes the shaded region.

57. **58.**

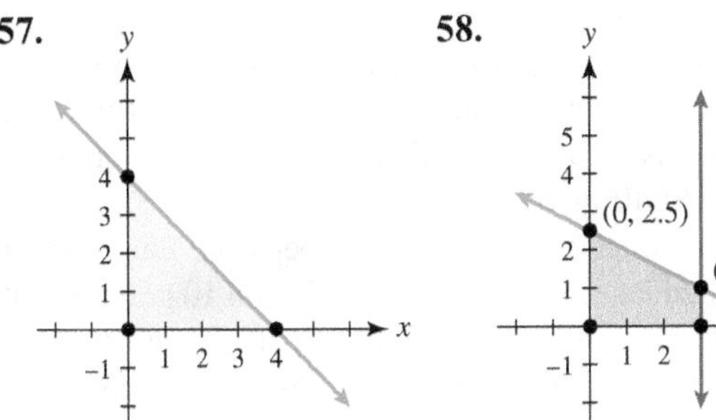

59. Find the minimum value of $C = 4x + 2y$ subject to the following constraints.

$$x + y \ge 3$$
$$2x + 3y \le 12$$
$$x \ge 0, y \ge 0$$

60. Find the maximum value of $P = 3x + 5y$ subject to the following constraints.

$$3x + y \le 8$$
$$x + 3y \le 8$$
$$x \ge 0, y \ge 0$$

Exercises 61 and 62: If possible, maximize and minimize z subject to the given constraints.

61. $z = 7x + 6y$

$$x + y \le 8$$
$$x + y \ge 4$$
$$x \ge 0, y \ge 0$$

62. $z = 8x + 3y$

$$4x + y \ge 12$$
$$x + 2y \ge 6$$
$$x \ge 0, y \ge 0$$

63. Maximizing Profit Rework Example 4 if the profit from each radio is \$20 and the profit from each CD player is \$15.

64. Maximizing Revenue A refinery produces both gasoline and fuel oil, and sells gasoline for \$4.00 per gallon and fuel oil for \$3.60 per gallon. The refinery can produce at most 600,000 gallons a day but must produce at least 2 gallons of fuel oil for every gallon of gasoline. At least 150,000 gallons of fuel oil must be made each day for the coming winter. Determine how much of each type of fuel should be produced to maximize revenue.

65. Minimizing Cost (Refer to Example 6.) A breeder is mixing Brand A and Brand B. Each serving should contain at least 60 grams of protein and 30 grams of fat. Brand A costs 80 cents per unit, and Brand B costs 50 cents per unit. Each unit of Brand A contains 15 grams of protein and 10 grams of fat, whereas each unit of Brand B contains 20 grams of protein and 5 grams of fat. Determine how much of each food should be bought to achieve a minimum cost per serving.

66. Pet Food Cost A pet owner is buying two brands of food, X and Y, for his animals. Each serving of the mixture of the two foods should contain at least 60 grams of protein and 40 grams of fat. Brand X costs 75 cents per unit, and Brand Y costs 50 cents per unit. Each unit of Brand X contains 20 grams of protein and 10 grams of fat, whereas each unit of Brand Y contains 10 grams of protein and 10 grams of fat. How much of each brand should be bought to obtain a minimum cost per serving?

67. Raising Animals A breeder can raise no more than 50 hamsters and mice and no more than 20 hamsters. If she sells the hamsters for \$15 each and the mice for \$10 each, find the maximum revenue produced.

68. Maximizing Storage A manager wants to buy filing cabinets. Cabinet X costs \$100, requires 6 square feet of floor space, and holds 8 cubic feet. Cabinet Y costs \$200, requires 8 square feet of floor space, and holds 12 cubic feet. No more than \$1400 can be spent, and the office has room for no more than 72 square feet of cabinets. The manager wants the maximum storage capacity within the limits imposed by funds and space. How many of each type of cabinet should be bought?

69. Maximizing Profit A business manufactures two parts, X and Y. Machines A and B are needed to make each part. To make part X, machine A is needed for 4 hours and machine B is needed for 2 hours. To make part Y, machine A is needed for 1 hour and machine B is needed for 3 hours. Machine A is available for 40 hours each week and machine B is available for 30 hours. The profit from part X is \$500 and the profit from part Y is \$600. How many parts of each type should be made to maximize weekly profit?

70. Minimizing Cost Two substances, X and Y, are found in pet food. Each substance contains the ingredients A and B. Substance X is 20% ingredient A and 50% ingredient B. Substance Y is 50% ingredient A and 30% ingredient B. The cost of substance X is \$2 per pound, and the cost of substance Y is \$3 per pound. The pet store needs at least 251 pounds of ingredient A and at least 200 pounds of ingredient B. If cost is to be minimal, how many pounds of each substance should be ordered? Find the minimum cost.

Writing about Mathematics

71. Give the general form of a system of linear inequalities in two variables. Discuss what distinguishes a system of linear inequalities from a nonlinear system of inequalities.

72. Discuss how to use test points to solve a linear inequality. Give an example.

CHECKING BASIC CONCEPTS FOR SECTIONS 6.1 AND 6.2

1. Evaluate $d(13, 18)$ if

$$d(x, y) = \sqrt{(x - 1)^2 + (y - 2)^2}.$$

2. Solve the nonlinear system of equations using the method of substitution.

$$\begin{aligned} 2x^2 - y &= 0 \\ 3x + 2y &= 7 \end{aligned}$$

3. Solve $z = x^2 + y^2$ for y.

4. Solve the system of linear equations by using elimination.

$$\begin{aligned} 3x - 2y &= 4 \\ -x + 6y &= 8 \end{aligned}$$

5. Graph the solution set to $3x - 2y \le 6$.

6. Graph the solution set to the system of inequalities. Use the graph to identify one solution.

$$\begin{aligned} x^2 - y &< 3 \\ x - y &\ge 1 \end{aligned}$$

7. HDTV Sales In 2010 there were 220 million HDTVs sold worldwide. For every 2 HDTVs sold with plasma screens, 9 HDTVs were sold with LCD screens. (***Source:*** Home Theater Review.)

(a) Write a linear system whose solution gives the number of HDTVs sold (in millions) with plasma screens and the number of HDTVs sold (in millions) with LCD screens.

(b) Solve the system and interpret the result.

Business Applications of Systems of Equations & Inequalities

1. A small T-shirt company has \$360 per month in fixed costs for a certain line of T-shirts and spends another \$4.50 per shirt. They sell these T-shirts for \$17.50 each.
   (a) Create the monthly cost C and revenue R equations for this line of T-shirts, where T represents the number of T-shirts produced and sold.

   (b) Determine the break-even point, where cost is equal to revenue. Round the number of T-shirts to the nearest whole number, and include units in your answer.

   (c) Graph the cost and revenue functions on the same coordinate plane. The region where revenue is greater than cost is the "profit region." Shade the profit region on your graph.

2. Two professors from a university reported that for a typical small-sized fertilizer plant in Florida, the fixed costs were \$250,000 and it cost \$220 to produce each ton of fertilizer.
   (a) If the company planned to sell the fertilizer at \$275 per ton, find the cost, C, and revenue, R, equations for x tons of fertilizer.

   (b) Find the break-even point. Round to the nearest whole ton, and be sure to give the units in your answer.

   (c) Graph the cost and revenue equations on the same coordinate plane. Shade the profit region on your graph.

3. Suppose that it costs \$186,000 to produce a master disc for a music video and \$1.19 to produce each copy, and that the music videos will be sold for \$16.69 each.
   (a) Find the cost function C that computes the cost of producing the master disc and x copies of the video.

   (b) Find the function R that outputs the revenue received from selling x music videos.

   (c) Determine the break-even point. Be sure to include the units in your answer.

   (d) Interpret (explain in words) the break-even point. Be specific, identifying what each coordinate of the break-even point means in context.

4. The quantity, Q, of pumpkins that would be demanded by consumers at Halloween time in a particular town is estimated to depend on the price, P, of a pumpkin by the demand equation: $Q = 25{,}000 - 2{,}000P$. Farmers in the region are not willing to plant pumpkins unless they can expect to earn a profit on them, but if they foresee getting a high price for their pumpkins they will plant more acres of pumpkins and produce more. The farmers' decision to produce a supply of pumpkins is captured by the supply equation: $Q = -10{,}000 + 10{,}000P$. Find the equilibrium point, that is, the point where the supply function is equal to the demand function. Be sure to include the units in your answer.

5. The supply and demand equations for a particular bicycle model relate price per bicycle, p (in dollars) and q, the number of bicycles (in thousands). The two equations are Supply: $p = 250 + 40q$ Demand: $p = 510 - 25q$

   Find the equilibrium point including any units.

6. John Parks is marketing director for the Burgerdelish restaurant chain. Burgerdelish has decided to have a cartoon-character doll made to sell at a premium price at participating Burgerdelish locations. The company can choose from several different versions of the doll that sell at different prices. Parks' problem is to decide which selling price will best suit the needs of Burgerdelish's customers and store managers. Parks has data from previous similar promotions to help him make a decision.

Selling Price of Each Doll	Number Supplied per Week per Store	Number Requested per Week per Store
\$1.00	35	530
\$2.00	130	400
\$4.00	320	140

   (a) Use two of the points given to find the equation for supply (S) as a function of price (P).

   (b) Use two of the points given to find the equation for demand (D) as a function of price (P).

   (c) Solve the system of supply-and-demand equations to find the price in exact equilibrium.

7. The daily cost to your company to print a paperback sci-fi novel is \$3.50 each, and your company has fixed costs of \$1200.
   (a) Write the daily cost function $C(x)$ for your company if C is measured in dollars, and x is measured in books (paperback sci-fi novels, to be precise).
   (b) Suppose that your publishing company sells sci-fi paperbacks to a large retailer for \$6.50 per book. Write the daily revenue function $R(x)$ for your company.
   (c) How many of these sci-fi books should you sell per day in order to break even?
   (d) Write the profit function $P(x)$ for these sci-fi novels.
   (e) How many sci-fi books must be produced and sold to make a profit of at least \$50,000?

8. The given graph shows the cost and revenue functions of a company that manufactures and sells beach chairs. Use the graph to answer the questions below.

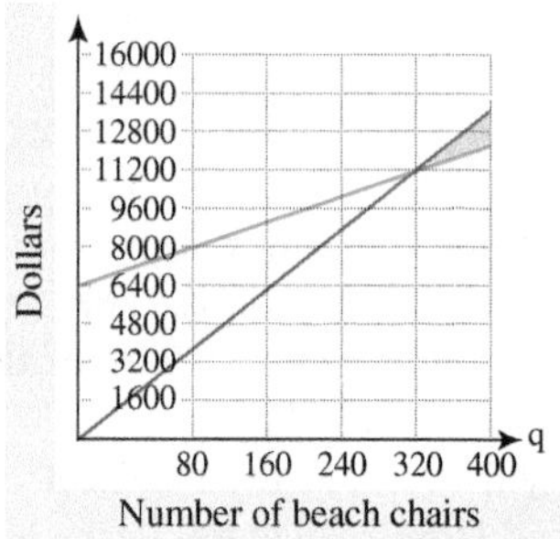

   (a) What are the company's fixed costs?
   (b) How much does it cost to make each beach chair?
   (c) What is the selling price of each beach chair?
   (d) Create a cost function $C(q)$ to represent the total cost of producing beach chairs.
   (e) Create a revenue function $R(q)$ to represent the total revenue received from selling q beach chairs.
   (f) Determine symbolically how many beach chairs the company must sell to break-even and compare the result to the given graph.

9. Corn is commonly used as animal feed. The price of corn is determined by the amount of corn consumers demand and the amount that corn producers are willing to supply. At a price of \$6.80 per bushel, consumer demand is 9.9 million bushels of corn, and producers are willing to supply 3.39 million bushels of corn. At a price of \$13 per bushel, consumer demand decreases to 5.25 million bushels of corn, and the amount producers are willing to supply increases to 8.35 million bushels of corn.
   (a) Use the information provided to find the demand equation, D (in millions of bushels of corn), as a function of the price, p (in dollars), per bushel of corn.
   (b) Use the information provided to find the supply equation, S (in millions of bushels of corn), as a function of the price, p (in dollars), per bushel of corn.
   (c) Solve the system of supply-and-demand equations to find the price per bushel of corn at equilibrium.
   (d) How many bushels of corn are supplied and demanded at this price?

10. A company is selling t-shirts. The company is examining the current demand for t-shirts to determine a price that will maximize their profit level. The company's cost function based on demand is given by $C(p) = 25{,}000 - 275p$ where $C(p)$ is in dollars and p is the price per t-shirt. The company's revenue function based on demand is given by $R(p) = -30p^2 + 2000p$, where $R(p)$ is in dollars and p is the price per t-shirt.
   (a) Graph the cost and revenue functions and determine the coordinates of the break-even points to the nearest hundredths place.
   (b) Use the cost and revenue functions to create a profit function as a function $M(p)$ of the price per t-shirt p.
   (c) Use the profit function to determine the price that will maximize the company's profit to the nearest hundredths place.
   (d) What is the company's projected profit at this price to the nearest hundredths place?
   (e) Based on your answer to part c, what price would you recommend the company charge per t-shirt? If your answer to part e is different from the result you obtained in part c, explain the reason for the difference in price.

Solutions to Business Applications of Systems

1. (a) $C = 360 + 4.50T$ and $R = 17.50T$;

   (b) (28 T-shirts, \$490);

   (c)

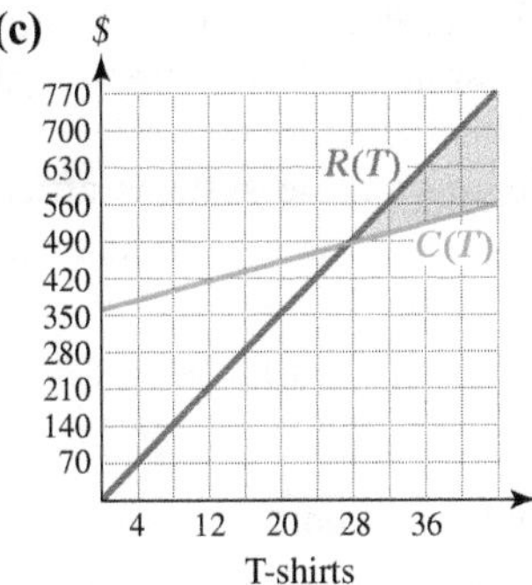

2. (a) $C + 250{,}000 + 220x$, $R = 275x$;

   (b) (4545 tons of fertilizer, \$1250000)

   (c)

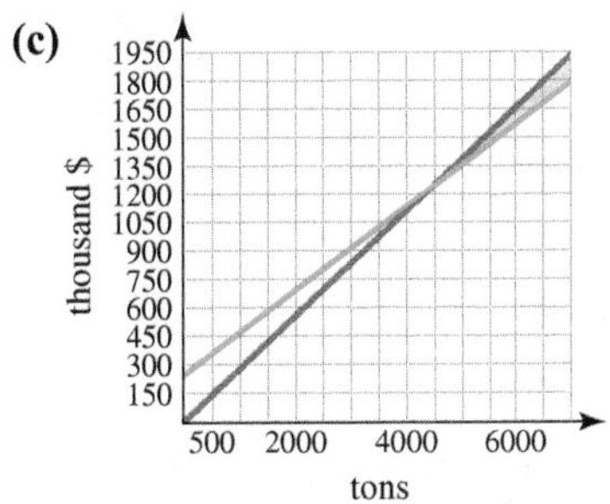

3. (a) $C = 186{,}000 + 1.19x$

   (b) $R = 16.69x$

   (c) (12000 videos, \$200280)

   (d) When 12000 videos are produced and sold, the cost and revenue will both be \$200280, so they break even.

4. (\$2.92, 19160 pumpkins)

5. (4000 bicycles, \$410)

6. (a) $S = 95P - 60$

   (b) $D = -130P + 660$

   (c) \$3.20

7. (a) $C(x) = 3.50x + 1200$

   (b) $R(x) = 6.50x$

   (c) 400 books

   (d) $P(x) = 3x - 1200$

   (e) 17,067 books

8. (a) \$6400

   (b) \$15

   (c) \$35

   (d) $C(q) = 15q + 6400$

   (e) $R(q) = 35q$

   (f) 320 beach chairs

9. (a) $D = -0.75p + 15$

   (b) $S = 0.8p - 2.05$

   (c) \$11 per bushel

   (d) 6.75 million bushels

10. (a) (13.33, 21333.33) and (62.50, 7812.50)

    (b) $M(p) = -30p^2 + 2275p - 25000$

    (c) \$37.92

    (d) \$18,130.12

    (e) *(answers will vary)* \$38.00, since it is more convenient to charge a whole dollar amount.

6.3 Systems of Linear Equations in Three Variables

- **Learn basic concepts about systems in three variables**
- **Solve systems using elimination and substitution**
- **Identify systems with no solutions**
- **Solve systems with infinitely many solutions**

Introduction

In Section 6.1 we discussed how to solve systems of linear equations in two variables. Systems of linear equations can have any number of variables. For example, Internet search sites such as Google, Yahoo!, and Bing use algorithms that involve linear systems with millions of variables. Computers are necessary to solve these systems efficiently. However, in this section we discuss solving systems of linear equations containing three variables by hand.

Basic Concepts

When writing systems of linear equations in three variables it is common, but not necessary, to use the variables x, y, and z. For example,

$$\left.\begin{aligned} 2x - 3y + 4z &= 4 \\ -y + 2z &= 0 \\ x + 5y - 6z &= 7 \end{aligned}\right\}$$ Linear System with three variables

represents a system of linear equations in three variables. The solution to this system is given by $x = 3$, $y = 2$, and $z = 1$ because each equation is satisfied when these values are substituted for the variables in the system of linear equations.

$$\begin{aligned} 2(3) - 3(2) + 4(1) &\stackrel{?}{=} 4 \ \checkmark \quad \text{True} \\ -(2) + 2(1) &\stackrel{?}{=} 0 \ \checkmark \quad \text{True} \\ (3) + 5(2) - 6(1) &\stackrel{?}{=} 7 \ \checkmark \quad \text{True} \end{aligned}$$

The solution to this system can be written as the **ordered triple** $(3, 2, 1)$. This system of linear equations has exactly one solution. In general, systems of linear equations can have zero, one, or infinitely many solutions.

EXAMPLE 1 Checking for solutions

Determine whether $(-1, -3, 2)$ or $(1, -10, -13)$ is a solution to the system of equations.

$$\begin{aligned} x - 4y + 2z &= 15 \\ 4x - y + z &= 1 \\ 6x - 2y - 3z &= -6 \end{aligned}$$

SOLUTION First substitute $x = -1$, $y = -3$, and $z = 2$ in the system of linear equations, and then substitute $x = 1$, $y = -10$, and $z = -13$.

$$\begin{aligned} (-1) - 4(-3) + 2(2) &\stackrel{?}{=} 15 \quad \text{True} \\ 4(-1) - (-3) + (2) &\stackrel{?}{=} 1 \quad \text{True} \\ 6(-1) - 2(-3) - 3(2) &\stackrel{?}{=} -6 \quad \text{True} \end{aligned}$$

$$\begin{aligned} (1) - 4(-10) + 2(-13) &\stackrel{?}{=} 15 \quad \text{True} \\ 4(1) - (-10) + (-13) &\stackrel{?}{=} 1 \quad \text{True} \\ 6(1) - 2(-10) - 3(-13) &\stackrel{?}{=} -6 \quad \text{False} \end{aligned}$$

The ordered triple $(-1, -3, 2)$ satisfies all three equations, so it is a solution to the system of equations. The ordered triple $(1, -10, -13)$ is not a solution to the system of equations because it satisfies only two of the three equations.

Now Try Exercise 7

Solving with Elimination and Substitution

We can solve systems of linear equations in three variables by hand. The following procedure uses substitution and elimination and assumes that the variables are x, y, and z.

SOLVING A SYSTEM OF LINEAR EQUATIONS IN THREE VARIABLES

STEP 1: Eliminate one variable, such as x, from two of the equations.

STEP 2: Apply the techniques discussed in Section 6.1 to solve the two resulting equations in two variables from Step 1. If x is eliminated, then solve these equations to find y and z.

If there are no solutions for y and z, then the given system also has no solutions. If there are infinitely many solutions for y and z, then write y in terms of z and proceed to Step 3.

STEP 3: Substitute the values for y and z in one of the given equations to find x. The solution is (x, y, z). If possible, check your answer as in Example 1.

EXAMPLE 2 **Solving a linear system in three variables**

Solve the following system.

$$\begin{aligned} x - y + 2z &= 6 \\ 2x + y - 2z &= -3 \\ -x - 2y + 3z &= 7 \end{aligned}$$

SOLUTION

STEP 1: We begin by eliminating the variable x from the second and third equations. To eliminate x from the second equation, we multiply the first equation by -2 and then add it to the second equation. To eliminate x from the third equation, we add the first and third equations.

$$\begin{aligned} -2x + 2y - 4z &= -12 && \text{First equation times } -2 \\ 2x + y - 2z &= -3 && \text{Second equation} \\ \hline 3y - 6z &= -15 && \text{Add.} \end{aligned}$$

$$\begin{aligned} x - y + 2z &= 6 && \text{First equation} \\ -x - 2y + 3z &= 7 && \text{Third equation} \\ \hline -3y + 5z &= 13 && \text{Add.} \end{aligned}$$

STEP 2: Take the two resulting equations from Step 1 and eliminate either variable. Here we add the two equations to eliminate y.

$$\begin{aligned} 3y - 6z &= -15 \\ -3y + 5z &= 13 \\ \hline -z &= -2 && \text{Add the equations.} \\ z &= 2 && \text{Multiply each side by } -1. \end{aligned}$$

Now we can use substitution to find the value of y. We let $z = 2$ in *either* equation used in Step 2 to find y.

$$\begin{aligned} 3y - 6z &= -15 && \text{Equation from Step 2} \\ 3y - 6(2) &= -15 && \text{Substitute } z = 2. \\ 3y - 12 &= -15 && \text{Multiply.} \\ 3y &= -3 && \text{Add 12 to each side.} \\ y &= -1 && \text{Divide each side by 3.} \end{aligned}$$

STEP 3: Finally, we substitute $y = -1$ and $z = 2$ in any of the *given* equations to find x.

$$\begin{aligned} x - y + 2z &= 6 && \text{First given equation} \\ x - (-1) + 2(2) &= 6 && \text{Let } y = -1 \text{ and } z = 2. \\ x + 1 + 4 &= 6 && \text{Simplify.} \\ x &= 1 && \text{Subtract 5 from each side.} \end{aligned}$$

The solution is $(1, -1, 2)$. Check this solution.

Now Try Exercise 11

In the next example, we determine numbers of tickets sold for a play.

EXAMPLE 3 Finding numbers of tickets sold

One thousand tickets were sold for a play, generating \$3800 in revenue. The prices of the tickets were \$3 for children, \$4 for students, and \$5 for adults. There were 100 fewer student tickets sold than adult tickets. Find the number of each type of ticket sold.

SOLUTION Let x be the number of tickets sold to children, y be the number of tickets sold to students, and z be the number of tickets sold to adults. The total number of tickets sold was 1000, so

$$x + y + z = 1000.$$

Each child's ticket costs \$3, so the revenue generated from selling x tickets is $3x$. Similarly, the revenue generated from students is $4y$, and the revenue from adults is $5z$. Total ticket sales were \$3800, so

$$3x + 4y + 5z = 3800.$$

The equation $z - y = 100$, or $y - z = -100$, must also be satisfied, because 100 fewer tickets were sold to students than adults.

To find the price of a ticket, we need to solve the following system of linear equations.

$$\begin{aligned} x + y + z &= 1000 && \text{Total number of tickets is 1000.} \\ 3x + 4y + 5z &= 3800 && \text{Total revenue is \$3800.} \\ y - z &= -100 && \text{100 fewer student tickets than adult tickets} \end{aligned}$$

STEP 1: We begin by eliminating the variable x from the first equation. To do this, we multiply the first equation by 3 and subtract the second equation.

$$\begin{aligned} 3x + 3y + 3z &= 3000 && \text{First given equation times 3} \\ 3x + 4y + 5z &= 3800 && \text{Second equation} \\ \hline -y - 2z &= -800 && \text{Subtract.} \end{aligned}$$

STEP 2: We then use the equation that resulted from Step 1 and the third given equation to eliminate y.

$$\begin{aligned} -y - 2z &= -800 && \text{Equation from Step 1} \\ y - z &= -100 && \text{Third given equation} \\ \hline -3z &= -900 && \text{Add the equations.} \end{aligned}$$

Thus $z = 300$. To find y, we can substitute $z = 300$ in the third equation.

$$\begin{aligned} y - z &= -100 && \text{Third given equation} \\ y - 300 &= -100 && \text{Let } z = 300. \\ y &= 200 && \text{Add 300.} \end{aligned}$$

STEP 3: Finally, we substitute $y = 200$ and $z = 300$ in the first equation.

$$\begin{aligned} x + y + z &= 1000 && \text{First given equation} \\ x + 200 + 300 &= 1000 && \text{Let } y = 200 \text{ and } z = 300. \\ x &= 500 && \text{Subtract 500.} \end{aligned}$$

Thus 500 tickets were sold to children, 200 to students, and 300 to adults. Check this answer.

Now Try Exercise 33

Systems with No Solutions

Regardless of the number of variables, a system of linear equations can have zero, one, or infinitely many solutions. In the next example, a system of linear equations has no solutions.

EXAMPLE 4 Identifying a system with no solutions

Three students buy lunch in the cafeteria. One student buys 2 hamburgers, 1 order of fries, and 1 soda for \$9. Another student buys 1 hamburger, 2 orders of fries, and 1 soda for \$8. The third student buys 3 hamburgers, 3 orders of fries, and 2 sodas for \$18. If possible, find the cost of each item. Interpret the results.

SOLUTION Let x be the cost of a hamburger, y be the cost of an order of fries, and z be the cost of a soda. Then the purchases of the three students can be expressed as a system of linear equations.

$$\begin{aligned} 2x + y + z &= 9 && \text{2 burgers, 1 order of fries, and 1 soda for \$9} \\ x + 2y + z &= 8 && \text{1 burger, 2 orders of fries, and 1 soda for \$8} \\ 3x + 3y + 2z &= 18 && \text{3 burgers, 3 orders of fries, and 2 sodas for \$18} \end{aligned}$$

STEP 1: We can eliminate z in the first equation by subtracting the second equation from the first equation. We can eliminate z in the third equation by subtracting twice the second equation from the third equation.

$$\begin{aligned} 2x + y + z &= 9 && \text{First equation} \\ x + 2y + z &= 8 && \text{Second equation} \\ \hline x - y &= 1 && \text{Subtract.} \end{aligned} \qquad \begin{aligned} 3x + 3y + 2z &= 18 && \text{Third equation} \\ 2x + 4y + 2z &= 16 && \text{Twice second equation} \\ \hline x - y &= 2 && \text{Subtract.} \end{aligned}$$

STEP 2: The equations $x - y = 1$ and $x - y = 2$ are *inconsistent* because the difference between two numbers cannot be both 1 and 2. Step 3 is not necessary—the system of equations has no solutions.

NOTE In this problem the third student bought the same amount of food as the first and second students bought together. Therefore the third student should have paid \$9 + \$8 = \$17 rather than \$18. *Inconsistent pricing* led to an *inconsistent system* of linear equations.

Now Try Exercise 35

Systems with Infinitely Many Solutions

Some systems of linear equations have infinitely many solutions. In this case, we say that the system of linear equations is consistent, but the equations are dependent. A system of dependent equations is solved in the next example.

EXAMPLE 5 Solving a system with infinitely many solutions

Solve the following system of linear equations.

$$\begin{aligned} x + y - z &= -2 \\ x + 2y - 2z &= -3 \\ y - z &= -1 \end{aligned}$$

SOLUTION

STEP 1: Because x does not appear in the third equation, begin by eliminating x from the first equation. To do this, subtract the second equation from the first equation.

$$\begin{aligned} x + y - z &= -2 && \text{First equation} \\ x + 2y - 2z &= -3 && \text{Second equation} \\ \hline -y + z &= 1 && \text{Subtract.} \end{aligned}$$

STEP 2: Adding the resulting equation from Step 1 and the third given equation gives the equation $0 = 0$, which indicates that there are infinitely many solutions.

$$\begin{aligned} -y + z &= 1 \\ y - z &= -1 \\ \hline 0 &= 0 \end{aligned}$$

Dependent equations: Solve either equation for *y*.

Add.

The variable y can be written in terms of z as $y = z - 1$.

STEP 3: To find x, substitute the results from Step 2 in the first given equation.

$$x + y - z = -2 \quad \text{First given equation}$$
$$x + (z - 1) - z = -2 \quad \text{Let } y = z - 1.$$
$$x = -1 \quad \text{Solve for } x.$$

Solutions to the given system are of the form $(-1, z - 1, z)$, where z is any real number. For example, if $z = 2$, then $(-1, 1, 2)$ is one possible solution.

Now Try Exercise 17

CLASS DISCUSSION

Three students buy lunch in the cafeteria. One student buys 1 hamburger, 1 order of fries, and 1 soda for \$5. Another student buys 2 hamburgers, 2 orders of fries, and 2 sodas for \$10. The third student buys 3 hamburgers, 3 orders of fries, and 3 sodas for \$15. Can you find the cost of each item? Interpret your answer.

6.3 Putting It All Together

In this section we discussed how to solve a system of three linear equations in three variables by hand. Systems of linear equations can have no solutions, one solution, or infinitely many solutions. The following table summarizes some of the important concepts presented in this section.

CONCEPT	EXPLANATION
System of linear equations in three variables	The following is a system of three linear equations in three variables. $x - 2y + z = 0$ $-x + y + z = 4$ $-y + 4z = 10$
Solution to a linear system in three variables	The solution to a linear system in three variables is an ordered triple, expressed as (x, y, z). The solution to the preceding system is $(1, 2, 3)$ because substituting $x = 1, y = 2$, and $z = 3$ in each equation results in a true statement. $(1) - 2(2) + (3) = 0$ ✓ True $-(1) + (2) + (3) = 4$ ✓ True $-(2) + 4(3) = 10$ ✓ True
Solving a linear system with substitution and elimination	Refer to Example 2. **STEP 1:** Eliminate one variable, such as x, from two of the equations. **STEP 2:** Apply the techniques discussed in Section 6.1 to solve the two resulting equations in two variables from Step 1. If x is eliminated, then solve these equations to find y and z. If there are no solutions for y and z, then the given system also has no solutions. If there are infinitely many solutions for y and z, then write y in terms of z and proceed to Step 3. **STEP 3:** Substitute the values for y and z in one of the given equations to find x. The solution is (x, y, z). If possible, check your answer.

6.3 Exercises

1. Can a system of linear equations have exactly three solutions?

2. Does the ordered triple $(1, 2, 3)$ satisfy the equation $3x + 2y + z = 10$?

3. To solve a system of linear equations in two variables, how many equations do you usually need?

4. To solve a system of linear equations in three variables, how many equations do you usually need?

5. If a system of linear equations has infinitely many solutions, are the equations dependent or independent?

6. If a system of linear equations is inconsistent, how many solutions does it have?

Exercises 7–10: Determine whether each ordered triple is a solution to the system of linear equations.

7. $(0, 2, -2), (-1, 3, -2)$

$$\begin{aligned} x + y - z &= 4 \\ -x + y + z &= 2 \\ x + y + z &= 0 \end{aligned}$$

8. $(5, 2, 2), (2, -1, 1)$

$$\begin{aligned} 2x - 3y + 3z &= 10 \\ x - 2y - 3z &= 1 \\ 4x - y + z &= 10 \end{aligned}$$

9. $\left(-\frac{5}{11}, \frac{20}{11}, -2\right), (1, 2, -1)$

$$\begin{aligned} x + 3y - 2z &= 9 \\ -3x + 2y + 4z &= -3 \\ -2x + 5y + 2z &= 6 \end{aligned}$$

10. $(1, 2, 3), (11, 16, -3)$

$$\begin{aligned} 4x - 2y + 2z &= 6 \\ 2x - 4y - 6z &= -24 \\ -3x + 3y + 2z &= 9 \end{aligned}$$

Exercises 11–32: If possible, solve the system.

11. $$\begin{aligned} x + y + z &= 6 \\ -x + 2y + z &= 6 \\ y + z &= 5 \end{aligned}$$

12. $$\begin{aligned} x - y + z &= -2 \\ x - 2y + z &= 0 \\ y - z &= 1 \end{aligned}$$

13. $$\begin{aligned} x + 2y + 3z &= 4 \\ 2x + y + 3z &= 5 \\ x - y + z &= 2 \end{aligned}$$

14. $$\begin{aligned} x - y + z &= 2 \\ 3x - 2y + z &= -1 \\ x + y &= -3 \end{aligned}$$

15. $$\begin{aligned} 3x + y + z &= 0 \\ 4x + 2y + z &= 1 \\ 2x - 2y - z &= 2 \end{aligned}$$

16. $$\begin{aligned} -x - 5y + 2z &= 2 \\ x + y + 2z &= 2 \\ 3x + y - 4z &= -10 \end{aligned}$$

17. $$\begin{aligned} x + 3y + z &= 6 \\ 3x + y - z &= 6 \\ x - y - z &= 0 \end{aligned}$$

18. $$\begin{aligned} 2x - y + 2z &= 6 \\ -x + y + z &= 0 \\ -x - 3z &= -6 \end{aligned}$$

19. $$\begin{aligned} x - 4y + 2z &= -2 \\ x + 2y - 2z &= -3 \\ x - y &= 4 \end{aligned}$$

20. $$\begin{aligned} 2x + y + 3z &= 4 \\ -3x - y - 4z &= 5 \\ x + y + 2z &= 0 \end{aligned}$$

21. $$\begin{aligned} 4a - b + 2c &= 0 \\ 2a + b - c &= -11 \\ 2a - 2b + c &= 3 \end{aligned}$$

22. $$\begin{aligned} a - 4b + 3c &= 2 \\ -a - 2b + 5c &= 9 \\ a + 2b + c &= 6 \end{aligned}$$

23. $$\begin{aligned} a + b + c &= 0 \\ a - b - c &= 3 \\ a + 3b + 3c &= 5 \end{aligned}$$

24. $$\begin{aligned} a - 2b + c &= -1 \\ a + 5b &= -3 \\ 2a + 3b + c &= -2 \end{aligned}$$

25. $$\begin{aligned} 3x + 2y + z &= -1 \\ 3x + 4y - z &= 1 \\ x + 2y + z &= 0 \end{aligned}$$

26. $$\begin{aligned} x - 2y + z &= 1 \\ x + y + 2z &= 2 \\ 2x + 3y + z &= 6 \end{aligned}$$

27. $$\begin{aligned} -x + 3y + z &= 3 \\ 2x + 7y + 4z &= 13 \\ 4x + y + 2z &= 7 \end{aligned}$$

28. $$\begin{aligned} x + 2y + z &= 0 \\ 3x + 2y - z &= 4 \\ -x + 2y + 3z &= -4 \end{aligned}$$

29. $$\begin{aligned} -x + 2z &= -9 \\ y + 4z &= -13 \\ 3x + y &= 13 \end{aligned}$$

30. $$\begin{aligned} x + y + z &= -1 \\ 2x + z &= -6 \\ 2y + 3z &= 0 \end{aligned}$$

31. $$\begin{aligned} \tfrac{1}{2}x - y + \tfrac{1}{2}z &= -4 \\ x + 2y - 3z &= 20 \\ -\tfrac{1}{2}x + 3y + 2z &= 0 \end{aligned}$$

32. $$\begin{aligned} \tfrac{3}{4}x + y + \tfrac{1}{2}z &= -3 \\ x + y - z &= -8 \\ \tfrac{1}{4}x - 2y + z &= -4 \end{aligned}$$

Applications

33. **Tickets Sold** Five hundred tickets were sold for a play, generating \$3560. The prices of the tickets were \$5 for children, \$7 for students, and \$10 for adults. There were 180 more student tickets sold than adult tickets. Find the number of each type of ticket sold.

34. **Tickets Sold** One thousand tickets were sold for a baseball game. There were one hundred more adult tickets sold than student tickets, and there were four times as many tickets sold to students as to children. How many of each type of ticket were sold?

35. **Buying Lunch** Three students buy lunch in the cafeteria. One student buys 2 hamburgers, 2 orders of fries, and 1 soda for \$9. Another student buys 1 hamburger, 1 order of fries, and 1 soda for \$5. The third student buys 1 hamburger and 1 order of fries for \$5. If possible, find the cost of each item. Interpret the results.

36. Cost of DVDs The table shows the total cost of purchasing various combinations of differently priced DVDs. The types of DVDs are labeled A, B, and C.

A	B	C	Total Cost
2	1	1	\$48
3	2	1	\$71
1	1	2	\$53

(a) Let a be the cost of a DVD of type A, b be the cost of a DVD of type B, and c be the cost of a DVD of type C. Write a system of three linear equations whose solution gives the cost of each type of DVD.

(b) Solve the system of equations and check your answer.

37. Geometry The largest angle in a triangle is 25° more than the smallest angle. The sum of the measures of the two smaller angles is 30° more than the measure of the largest angle.

(a) Let x, y, and z be the measures of the three angles from largest to smallest. Write a system of three linear equations whose solution gives the measure of each angle.

(b) Solve the system of equations and check your answer.

38. Geometry The perimeter of a triangle is 105 inches. The longest side is 22 inches longer than the shortest side. The sum of the lengths of the two shorter sides is 15 inches more than the length of the longest side. Find the lengths of the sides of the triangle.

39. Investment Mixture A sum of \$20,000 is invested in three mutual funds. In one year the first fund grew by 5%, the second by 7%, and the third by 10%. Total earnings for the year were \$1650. The amount invested in the third fund was four times the amount invested in the first fund. Find the amount invested in each fund.

40. Home Prices Prices of homes can depend on several factors such as size and age. The table shows the selling prices for three homes. In this table, price P is given in thousands of dollars, age A in years, and home size S in thousands of square feet. These data may be modeled by $P = a + bA + cS$.

Price (P)	Age (A)	Size (S)
190	20	2
320	5	3
50	40	1

(a) Write a system of linear equations whose solution gives a, b, and c.

(b) Solve this system of linear equations.

(c) Predict the price of a home that is 10 years old and has 2500 square feet.

41. Mixture Problem One type of lawn fertilizer consists of a mixture of nitrogen, N; phosphorus, P; and potassium, K. An 80-pound sample contains 8 more pounds of nitrogen and phosphorus than of potassium. There is nine times as much potassium as phosphorus.

(a) Write a system of three equations whose solution gives the amount of nitrogen, phosphorus, and potassium in this sample.

(b) Solve the system of equations.

42. Business Production A business has three machines that manufacture containers. Together they can make 100 containers per day, whereas the two fastest machines can make 80 containers per day. The fastest machine makes 34 more containers per day than the slowest machine.

(a) Let x, y, and z be the numbers of containers that the machines make from fastest to slowest. Write a system of three equations whose solution gives the number of containers each machine can make.

(b) Solve the system of equations.

Writing about Mathematics

43. When using elimination and substitution, explain how to recognize a system of linear equations that has no solutions.

44. When using elimination and substitution, explain how to recognize a system of linear equations that has infinitely many solutions.

6.4 Solutions to Linear Systems Using Matrices

- Represent systems of linear equations with matrices
- Learn row-echelon form
- Perform Gaussian elimination
- Learn reduced row-echelon form
- Perform Gauss-Jordan elimination
- Solve systems of linear equations with technology (optional)

Introduction

After its release in 2010, the iPad recorded remarkable quarterly sales growth. The three points plotted in Figure 6.39 give the *cumulative* sales y in millions of units, sold x quarters after the iPad's release. For example, the point (5, 29) indicates that Apple sold 29 million iPads by the end of the 5th quarter after its release. Because three distinct points (that are not collinear) determine the graph of a quadratic function, we can model these data by finding a unique parabola that passes though the given points, as illustrated in Figure 6.39. (***Source:*** Apple Corporation.)

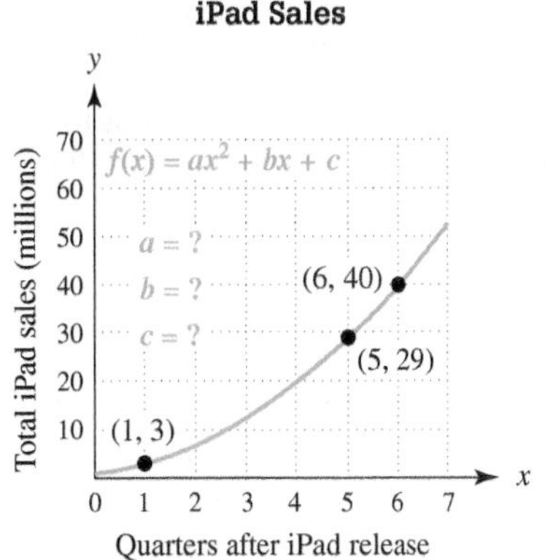

Figure 6.39

One way to accomplish this task is to set up a linear system of equations in three variables and solve it by using a matrix. This section discusses matrices and how they can be used to solve systems of linear equations. (See Example 11 and Exercise 87.)

Representing Systems of Linear Equations with Matrices

Arrays of numbers occur frequently in many different situations. Spreadsheets often make use of arrays, where data are displayed in a tabular format. A **matrix** is a rectangular array of elements. The following are examples of matrices whose elements are real numbers.

Examples of Matrices

$$\begin{bmatrix} 4 & -7 \\ -2 & 9 \end{bmatrix} \quad \begin{bmatrix} -1 & -5 & 3 \\ 1.2 & 0 & -1.3 \\ 4.1 & 5 & 7 \end{bmatrix} \quad \begin{bmatrix} -3 & -6 & 9 & 5 \\ \sqrt{2} & -8 & -8 & 0 \\ 3 & 0 & 19 & -7 \\ -11 & -3 & 7 & 8 \end{bmatrix} \quad \begin{bmatrix} 5 & -2 \\ -2 & \pi \\ 1 & -1 \end{bmatrix} \quad \begin{bmatrix} 1 & -0.5 & 9 \\ 5 & 0.4 & -3 \end{bmatrix}$$

2×2 $\qquad 3 \times 3$ $\qquad 4 \times 4$ $\qquad 3 \times 2$ $\qquad 2 \times 3$

The dimension of a matrix is given much like the dimensions of a rectangular room. We might say a room is m feet long and n feet wide. The **dimension** of a matrix is $m \times n$ (m by n) if it has m rows and n columns. For example, the last matrix has a dimension of 2×3 because it has 2 rows and 3 columns. If the numbers of rows and columns are equal, the matrix is a **square matrix.** The first three matrices are square matrices.

CLASS DISCUSSION

Give a general form of a system of linear equations with four equations and four variables. Write its augmented matrix.

Matrices are frequently used to represent systems of linear equations.

See the Concept: Representing a Linear System with a Matrix

A System of Three Equations

$$\begin{aligned} a_1x + b_1y + c_1z &= d_1 \\ a_2x + b_2y + c_2z &= d_2 \\ a_3x + b_3y + c_3z &= d_3 \end{aligned}$$

B Coefficient Matrix

$$\begin{bmatrix} a_1 & b_1 & c_1 \\ a_2 & b_2 & c_2 \\ a_3 & b_3 & c_3 \end{bmatrix}$$

C Augmented Matrix

$$\left[\begin{array}{ccc|c} a_1 & b_1 & c_1 & d_1 \\ a_2 & b_2 & c_2 & d_2 \\ a_3 & b_3 & c_3 & d_3 \end{array}\right]$$

- **A** The a_k, b_k, c_k, and d_k are constants and x, y, and z are variables.
- **B** The coefficients of the variables are represented in a square matrix called the **coefficient matrix** of the linear system.
- **C** The matrix is enlarged to include the constants d_k. The vertical line in this matrix corresponds to where the equals sign occurs in each equation. This matrix is commonly called an **augmented matrix.**

EXAMPLE 1 Representing a linear system with an augmented matrix

Express each linear system with an augmented matrix. State the dimension of the matrix.

(a) $\begin{aligned} 3x - 4y &= 6 \\ -5x + y &= -5 \end{aligned}$

(b) $\begin{aligned} 2x - 5y + 6z &= -3 \\ 3x + 7y - 3z &= 8 \\ x + 7y \quad\quad &= 5 \end{aligned}$

SOLUTION

(a) This system has two equations with two variables. It can be represented by an augmented matrix having dimension 2×3.

$$\left[\begin{array}{cc|c} 3 & -4 & 6 \\ -5 & 1 & -5 \end{array}\right] \qquad \begin{aligned} 3x - 4y &= 6 \\ -5x + y &= -5 \end{aligned}$$

(b) This system has three equations with three variables. Note that variable z does not appear in the third equation. A value of 0 is inserted for its coefficient.

$$\left[\begin{array}{ccc|c} 2 & -5 & 6 & -3 \\ 3 & 7 & -3 & 8 \\ 1 & 7 & 0 & 5 \end{array}\right] \qquad \begin{aligned} 2x - 5y + 6z &= -3 \\ 3x + 7y - 3z &= 8 \\ x + 7y \quad\quad &= 5 \end{aligned}$$

This matrix has dimension 3×4.

Now Try Exercises 7 and 9

EXAMPLE 2 Converting an augmented matrix into a linear system

Write the linear system represented by the augmented matrix. Let the variables be x, y, and z.

(a) $\left[\begin{array}{ccc|c} 1 & 0 & 2 & -3 \\ 2 & 2 & 10 & 3 \\ -1 & 2 & 3 & 5 \end{array}\right]$ **(b)** $\left[\begin{array}{ccc|c} 1 & 2 & 3 & -4 \\ 0 & 1 & -6 & 7 \\ 0 & 0 & 1 & 8 \end{array}\right]$

SOLUTION

Getting Started The first column corresponds to x, the second to y, and the third to z. When a 0 appears, the variable for that column does not appear in the equation. The vertical line gives the location of the equals sign. The last column represents the constant terms. ▶

$$\left[\begin{array}{rrr|r} 1 & 0 & 2 & -3 \\ 2 & 2 & 10 & 3 \\ -1 & 2 & 3 & 5 \end{array}\right]$$

(a) The augmented matrix (repeated in the margin) represents the following linear system.

$$\begin{aligned} x \quad\;\; + 2z &= -3 && \text{First row in the matrix} \\ 2x + 2y + 10z &= 3 && \text{Second row in the matrix} \\ -x + 2y + 3z &= 5 && \text{Third row in the matrix} \end{aligned}$$

$$\left[\begin{array}{rrr|r} 1 & 2 & 3 & -4 \\ 0 & 1 & -6 & 7 \\ 0 & 0 & 1 & 8 \end{array}\right]$$

(b) The augmented matrix (repeated in the margin) represents the following linear system.

$$\begin{aligned} x + 2y + 3z &= -4 && \text{First row in the matrix} \\ y - 6z &= 7 && \text{Second row in the matrix} \\ z &= 8 && \text{Third row in the matrix} \end{aligned}$$

Now Try Exercises 11 and 13

Row-Echelon Form

To solve a linear system with an augmented matrix, it is convenient to get the matrix in **row-echelon form.** The following matrices are in row-echelon form.

$$\begin{bmatrix} 1 & 3 & 0 & -1 \\ 0 & 1 & -6 & 1 \\ 0 & 0 & 1 & -2 \end{bmatrix} \quad \begin{bmatrix} 1 & 2 & 0 \\ 0 & 1 & 4 \end{bmatrix} \quad \begin{bmatrix} 1 & 3 & -1 & 5 \\ 0 & 1 & -1 & 3 \\ 0 & 0 & 1 & 0 \end{bmatrix} \quad \begin{bmatrix} 1 & 3 & -1 & 5 \\ 0 & 0 & 1 & 3 \\ 0 & 0 & 0 & 0 \end{bmatrix} \quad \begin{bmatrix} 1 & 3 & 5 \\ 0 & 0 & 1 \end{bmatrix}$$

The elements of the **main diagonal** are blue in each matrix. Scanning down the main diagonal of a matrix in row-echelon form, we see that this diagonal first contains only 1's, and then possibly 0's. The first nonzero element in any row is 1. Rows containing only 0's occur at the bottom of the matrix. All elements below the main diagonal are 0.

The next example demonstrates a technique called **backward substitution.** It can be used to solve linear systems represented by an augmented matrix in row-echelon form.

EXAMPLE 3 Solving a linear system with backward substitution

Solve the system of linear equations represented by the augmented matrix.

(a) $\left[\begin{array}{rrr|r} 1 & 1 & 3 & 12 \\ 0 & 1 & -2 & -4 \\ 0 & 0 & 1 & 3 \end{array}\right]$ **(b)** $\left[\begin{array}{rrr|r} 1 & -1 & 5 & 5 \\ 0 & 1 & 3 & 3 \\ 0 & 0 & 0 & 0 \end{array}\right]$

SOLUTION

(a) The matrix represents the following linear system.

$$\begin{aligned} x + y + 3z &= 12 && \text{First row in the matrix} \\ y - 2z &= -4 && \text{Second row in the matrix} \\ z &= 3 && \text{Third row in the matrix} \end{aligned}$$

Since $z = 3$, substitute this value in the second equation to find y.

Second equation with $z = 3$ — $y - 2(3) = -4, \quad \text{or} \quad y = 2$

Then $y = 2$ and $z = 3$ can be substituted in the first equation to determine x.

First equation with $y = 2$ and $z = 3$ — $x + 2 + 3(3) = 12, \quad \text{or} \quad x = 1$

The solution is given by $x = 1$, $y = 2$, and $z = 3$ and can be expressed as the *ordered triple* $(1, 2, 3)$.

(b) The matrix represents the following linear system.

$$\begin{aligned} x - y + 5z &= 5 && \text{First row in the matrix} \\ y + 3z &= 3 && \text{Second row in the matrix} \\ 0 &= 0 && \text{Third row in the matrix} \end{aligned}$$

The last equation, $0 = 0$, is an identity. Its presence usually indicates infinitely many solutions. Use the second equation to write y in terms of z.

Solve second equation for y. $\quad y = 3 - 3z$

Next, substitute $(3 - 3z)$ for y in the first equation and write x in terms of z.

$$x - (3 - 3z) + 5z = 5 \quad \text{Substitute } (3 - 3z) \text{ for } y$$

$$x - 3 + 3z + 5z = 5 \quad \text{Distributive property}$$

$$x = 8 - 8z \quad \text{Solve for } x.$$

All solutions can be written as the ordered triple $(8 - 8z, 3 - 3z, z)$, where z is any real number. There are infinitely many solutions. Sometimes we say that all solutions can be written in terms of the **parameter** z, where z is any real number. For example, if we let $z = 1$, then $y = 3 - 3(1) = 0$ and $x = 8 - 8(1) = 0$. Thus one solution to the system is $(0, 0, 1)$.

Now Try Exercises 21 and 23

Gaussian Elimination

The methods of elimination and substitution from Section 6.1 can be combined to create a state-of-the-art numerical method capable of solving systems of linear equations that contain thousands of variables. Even though this method, called *Gaussian elimination with backward substitution*, dates back to Carl Friedrich Gauss (1777–1855), it continues to be one of the most efficient methods for solving systems of linear equations.

If an augmented matrix is not in row-echelon form, it can be transformed into row-echelon form using *Gaussian elimination.* This method uses the following three basic matrix row transformations.

MATRIX ROW TRANSFORMATIONS

For any augmented matrix representing a system of linear equations, the following row transformations result in an equivalent system of linear equations.

1. Any two rows may be interchanged.
2. The elements of any row may be multiplied by a nonzero constant.
3. Any row may be changed by adding to (or subtracting from) its elements a multiple of the corresponding elements of another row.

When we transform a matrix into row-echelon form, we also are transforming a system of linear equations. The next two examples illustrate how Gaussian elimination with backward substitution is performed.

EXAMPLE 4 Transforming a matrix into row-echelon form

Use Gaussian elimination with backward substitution to solve the linear system of equations.

$$\begin{aligned} x + y + z &= 1 \\ -x + y + z &= 5 \\ y + 2z &= 5 \end{aligned}$$

SOLUTION

Getting Started The goal is to apply matrix row transformations that transform the given matrix into row-echelon form. Then we can perform backward substitution to determine the solution. ▶

The linear system is written to the right to illustrate how each row transformation affects the corresponding system of linear equations. Note that it is *not* necessary to write the system of equations to the right of the augmented matrix.

Augmented Matrix	***Linear System***
$\left[\begin{array}{rrr\|r} 1 & 1 & 1 & 1 \\ -1 & 1 & 1 & 5 \\ 0 & 1 & 2 & 5 \end{array}\right]$	$\begin{aligned} x + y + z &= 1 \\ -x + y + z &= 5 \\ y + 2z &= 5 \end{aligned}$

We can add the first equation to the second equation to obtain a 0 where the coefficient of x in the second row is highlighted. This row operation is denoted $R_2 + R_1$, and the result becomes the new row 2.

The row that is changing is written first.

$$R_2 + R_1 \rightarrow \left[\begin{array}{rrr|r} 1 & 1 & 1 & 1 \\ 0 & 2 & 2 & 6 \\ 0 & 1 & 2 & 5 \end{array}\right] \qquad \begin{aligned} x + y + z &= 1 \\ 2y + 2z &= 6 \\ y + 2z &= 5 \end{aligned}$$

To have the matrix in row-echelon form, we need the highlighted 2 in the second row to be a 1. Multiply each element in row 2 by $\frac{1}{2}$ and denote the operation $\frac{1}{2}R_2$.

Row 2 is changing.

$$\tfrac{1}{2}R_2 \rightarrow \left[\begin{array}{rrr|r} 1 & 1 & 1 & 1 \\ 0 & 1 & 1 & 3 \\ 0 & 1 & 2 & 5 \end{array}\right] \qquad \begin{aligned} x + y + z &= 1 \\ y + z &= 3 \\ y + 2z &= 5 \end{aligned}$$

Next, we need a 0 where the 1 is highlighted in row 3. Subtract row 2 from row 3 and denote the operation $R_3 - R_2$.

Row 3 is changing.

$$R_3 - R_2 \rightarrow \left[\begin{array}{rrr|r} 1 & 1 & 1 & 1 \\ 0 & 1 & 1 & 3 \\ 0 & 0 & 1 & 2 \end{array}\right] \qquad \begin{aligned} x + y + z &= 1 \\ y + z &= 3 \\ z &= 2 \end{aligned}$$

Because we have a 1 in the highlighted box, the matrix is now in row-echelon form, and we see that $z = 2$. Backward substitution may be applied now to find the solution. Substituting $z = 2$ in the second equation gives

$$y + 2 = 3, \quad \text{or} \quad y = 1.$$

Finally, let $y = 1$ and $z = 2$ in the first equation to determine x.

$$x + 1 + 2 = 1, \quad \text{or} \quad x = -2$$

The solution to the system is given by $x = -2$, $y = 1$, and $z = 2$, or $(-2, 1, 2)$.

Now Try Exercise 33

EXAMPLE 5 **Transforming a matrix into row-echelon form**

Use Gaussian elimination with backward substitution to solve the linear system of equations.

$$\begin{aligned} 2x + 4y + 4z &= 4 \\ x + 3y + z &= 4 \\ -x + 3y + 2z &= -1 \end{aligned}$$

SOLUTION The initial linear system and augmented matrix are written first.

Augmented Matrix	***Linear System***
$\left[\begin{array}{rrr\|r} 2 & 4 & 4 & 4 \\ 1 & 3 & 1 & 4 \\ -1 & 3 & 2 & -1 \end{array}\right]$	$\begin{aligned} 2x + 4y + 4z &= 4 \\ x + 3y + z &= 4 \\ -x + 3y + 2z &= -1 \end{aligned}$

First we obtain a 1 where the x-coefficient of 2 in the first row is highlighted. This can be accomplished by either multiplying the first equation by $\frac{1}{2}$ or interchanging rows 1 and 2. We multiply row 1 by $\frac{1}{2}$. This operation is denoted $\frac{1}{2}R_1$.

$$\begin{array}{r} \frac{1}{2}R_1 \rightarrow \\ \\ \\ \end{array} \left[\begin{array}{rrr|r} 1 & 2 & 2 & 2 \\ 1 & 3 & 1 & 4 \\ -1 & 3 & 2 & -1 \end{array}\right] \qquad \begin{aligned} x + 2y + 2z &= 2 \\ x + 3y + z &= 4 \\ -x + 3y + 2z &= -1 \end{aligned}$$

The next step is to eliminate the x-variable in rows 2 and 3 by obtaining zeros in the highlighted positions. To do this, subtract row 1 from row 2, and add row 1 to row 3.

$$\begin{array}{r} \\ R_2 - R_1 \rightarrow \\ R_3 + R_1 \rightarrow \end{array} \left[\begin{array}{rrr|r} 1 & 2 & 2 & 2 \\ 0 & 1 & -1 & 2 \\ 0 & 5 & 4 & 1 \end{array}\right] \qquad \begin{aligned} x + 2y + 2z &= 2 \\ y - z &= 2 \\ 5y + 4z &= 1 \end{aligned}$$

Since we have a 1 for the y-coefficient in the second row, the next step is to eliminate the y-variable in row 3 and obtain a zero where the y-coefficient of 5 is highlighted. Multiply row 2 by 5, and subtract the result from row 3.

$$\begin{array}{r} \\ \\ R_3 - 5R_2 \rightarrow \end{array} \left[\begin{array}{rrr|r} 1 & 2 & 2 & 2 \\ 0 & 1 & -1 & 2 \\ 0 & 0 & 9 & -9 \end{array}\right] \qquad \begin{aligned} x + 2y + 2z &= 2 \\ y - z &= 2 \\ 9z &= -9 \end{aligned}$$

Finally, make the z-coefficient of 9 in the third row equal 1 by multiplying row 3 by $\frac{1}{9}$.

$$\begin{array}{r} \\ \\ \frac{1}{9}R_3 \rightarrow \end{array} \left[\begin{array}{rrr|r} 1 & 2 & 2 & 2 \\ 0 & 1 & -1 & 2 \\ 0 & 0 & 1 & -1 \end{array}\right] \qquad \begin{aligned} x + 2y + 2z &= 2 \\ y - z &= 2 \\ z &= -1 \end{aligned}$$

The final matrix is in row-echelon form. Backward substitution may be applied to find the solution. Substituting $z = -1$ in the second equation gives

$$y - (-1) = 2, \qquad \text{or} \qquad y = 1.$$

Next, substitute $y = 1$ and $z = -1$ in the first equation to determine x.

$$x + 2(1) + 2(-1) = 2, \qquad \text{or} \qquad x = 2$$

The solution to the system is $(2, 1, -1)$.

Now Try Exercise 37

EXAMPLE 6 Transforming a system that has no solutions

Solve the system of linear equations, if possible.

$$\begin{aligned} x - 2y + 3z &= 2 \\ 2x + 3y + 2z &= 7 \\ 4x - y + 8z &= 8 \end{aligned}$$

SOLUTION Because it is not necessary to write the linear system next to the matrix, we write the matrices in a horizontal format in this example.

$$\left[\begin{array}{rrr|r} 1 & -2 & 3 & 2 \\ 2 & 3 & 2 & 7 \\ 4 & -1 & 8 & 8 \end{array}\right] \qquad \begin{array}{r} \\ R_2 - 2R_1 \rightarrow \\ R_3 - 4R_1 \rightarrow \end{array} \left[\begin{array}{rrr|r} 1 & -2 & 3 & 2 \\ 0 & 7 & -4 & 3 \\ 0 & 7 & -4 & 0 \end{array}\right] \qquad \begin{array}{r} \\ \\ R_3 - R_2 \rightarrow \end{array} \left[\begin{array}{rrr|r} 1 & -2 & 3 & 2 \\ 0 & 7 & -4 & 3 \\ 0 & 0 & 0 & -3 \end{array}\right]$$

The last row of the last matrix represents $0x + 0y + 0z = -3$, which has no solutions because $0 \neq -3$. There are no solutions.

Now Try Exercise 69

A Geometric Interpretation The graph of a single linear equation in three variables is a plane in three-dimensional space. For a system of three equations in three variables, the possible intersections of the planes are illustrated in Figure 6.40. The solution set of such a system may be either a single ordered triple (x, y, z), an infinite set of ordered triples (dependent equations), or the empty set (an inconsistent system).

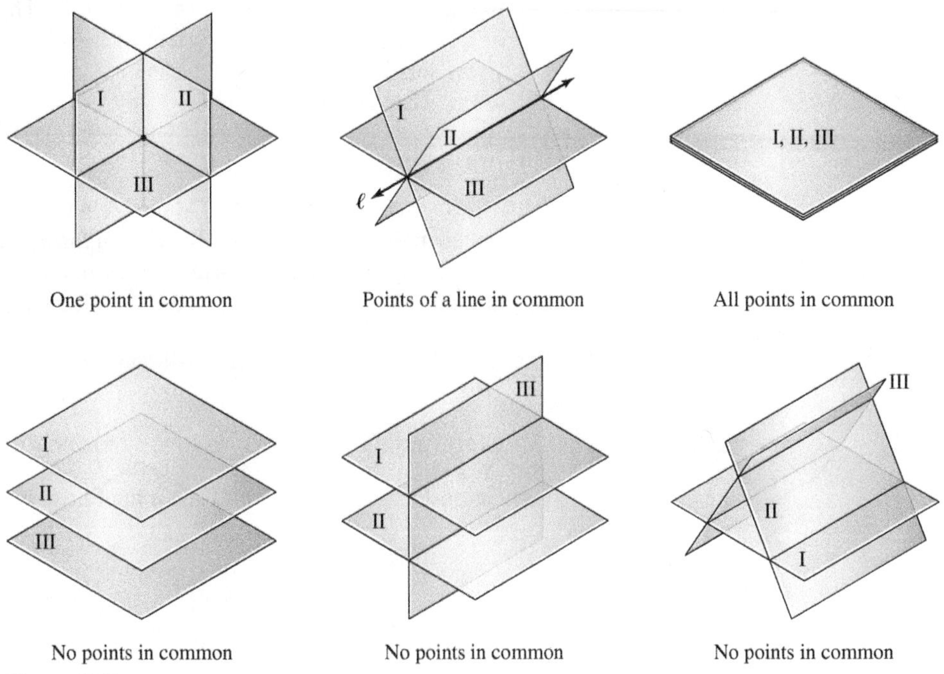

Figure 6.40

Reduced Row-Echelon Form Sometimes it is convenient to express a matrix in *reduced* row-echelon form. A matrix in row-echelon form is in **reduced row-echelon form** if every element above and below a 1 on the main diagonal is 0. The following matrices are examples of reduced row-echelon form.

$$\begin{bmatrix} 1 & 0 \\ 0 & 1 \end{bmatrix} \begin{bmatrix} 1 & 0 \\ 0 & 0 \end{bmatrix} \begin{bmatrix} 1 & 0 & 0 \\ 0 & 1 & 0 \\ 0 & 0 & 1 \end{bmatrix} \begin{bmatrix} 1 & 0 & 3 \\ 0 & 1 & -2 \end{bmatrix} \begin{bmatrix} 1 & 0 & 0 & 3 \\ 0 & 1 & 0 & 1 \\ 0 & 0 & 1 & -1 \end{bmatrix} \begin{bmatrix} 1 & 0 & 4 & 8 \\ 0 & 1 & -1 & 2 \\ 0 & 0 & 0 & 0 \end{bmatrix}$$

If an augmented matrix is in reduced row-echelon form, solving the system of linear equations is often straightforward.

EXAMPLE 7 **Determining a solution from a matrix in reduced row-echelon form**

Each matrix represents a system of linear equations. Find the solution.

(a) $\left[\begin{array}{cc|c} 1 & 0 & 6 \\ 0 & 1 & -5 \end{array}\right]$ **(b)** $\left[\begin{array}{ccc|c} 1 & 0 & 0 & 3 \\ 0 & 1 & 0 & -1 \\ 0 & 0 & 1 & 2 \end{array}\right]$

(c) $\left[\begin{array}{ccc|c} 1 & 0 & 0 & 4 \\ 0 & 1 & 0 & 3 \\ 0 & 0 & 0 & 2 \end{array}\right]$ **(d)** $\left[\begin{array}{ccc|c} 1 & 0 & -2 & -3 \\ 0 & 1 & 2 & 1 \\ 0 & 0 & 0 & 0 \end{array}\right]$

SOLUTION

(a) To see how the matrix in reduced row-echelon form provides immediate access to the solution to the related system of linear equations, we write the corresponding system of equations next to the given matrix.

Given Matrix	*Linear System*
$\left[\begin{array}{cc\|c} 1 & 0 & 6 \\ 0 & 1 & -5 \end{array}\right]$	$1x + 0y = 6$ or $x = 6$ $0x + 1y = -5$ or $y = -5$

The solution is $(6, -5)$.

(b) The top row represents $1x + 0y + 0z = 3$, or $x = 3$. Using similar reasoning for the second and third rows yields $y = -1$ and $z = 2$. The solution is $(3, -1, 2)$.

(c) The last row represents $0x + 0y + 0z = 2$, which has no solutions because $0 \neq 2$. Therefore there are no solutions to the system of equations.

(d) The last row simplifies to $0 = 0$, which is an identity and is always true. The second row gives $y + 2z = 1$, or $y = -2z + 1$. The first row represents $x - 2z = -3$, or $x = 2z - 3$. Thus this system of linear equations has infinitely many solutions. Every solution can be written as an ordered triple in the form $(2z - 3, -2z + 1, z)$, where z can be any real number.

Now Try Exercises 55, 57, 59, and 61

Gauss-Jordan Elimination Matrix row transformations can be used to transform an augmented matrix into reduced row-echelon form. This approach requires more effort than transforming a matrix into row-echelon form, but often eliminates the need for backward substitution. The technique is sometimes called **Gauss-Jordan elimination.**

EXAMPLE 8 **Transforming a matrix into reduced row-echelon form**

Use Gauss-Jordan elimination to solve the linear system.

$$\begin{aligned} 2x + y + 2z &= 10 \\ x \quad\;\; + 2z &= 5 \\ x - 2y + 2z &= 1 \end{aligned}$$

SOLUTION The linear system has been written to the right for illustrative purposes.

Augmented Matrix — *Linear System*

$$\left[\begin{array}{rrr|r} 2 & 1 & 2 & 10 \\ 1 & 0 & 2 & 5 \\ 1 & -2 & 2 & 1 \end{array}\right] \qquad \begin{aligned} 2x + y + 2z &= 10 \\ x \quad\;\; + 2z &= 5 \\ x - 2y + 2z &= 1 \end{aligned}$$

Obtain a 1 in the highlighted position in row 1 by interchanging rows 1 and 2.

$$\begin{array}{r} R_2 \rightarrow \\ R_1 \rightarrow \\ \\ \end{array} \left[\begin{array}{rrr|r} 1 & 0 & 2 & 5 \\ 2 & 1 & 2 & 10 \\ 1 & -2 & 2 & 1 \end{array}\right] \qquad \begin{aligned} x \quad\;\; + 2z &= 5 \\ 2x + y + 2z &= 10 \\ x - 2y + 2z &= 1 \end{aligned}$$

Next subtract 2 times row 1 from row 2. Then subtract row 1 from row 3. This eliminates the x-variable from the second and third equations.

$$\begin{array}{r} \\ R_2 - 2R_1 \rightarrow \\ R_3 - R_1 \rightarrow \end{array} \left[\begin{array}{rrr|r} 1 & 0 & 2 & 5 \\ 0 & 1 & -2 & 0 \\ 0 & -2 & 0 & -4 \end{array}\right] \qquad \begin{aligned} x \quad\;\; + 2z &= 5 \\ y - 2z &= 0 \\ -2y \quad\;\; &= -4 \end{aligned}$$

To eliminate the y-variable in row 3, add 2 times row 2 to row 3.

$$\begin{array}{r} \\ \\ R_3 + 2R_2 \rightarrow \end{array} \left[\begin{array}{rrr|r} 1 & 0 & 2 & 5 \\ 0 & 1 & -2 & 0 \\ 0 & 0 & -4 & -4 \end{array}\right] \qquad \begin{aligned} x \quad\;\; + 2z &= 5 \\ y - 2z &= 0 \\ -4z &= -4 \end{aligned}$$

To obtain a 1 in the highlighted position in row 3, multiply row 3 by $-\frac{1}{4}$.

$$\begin{array}{r} \\ \\ -\frac{1}{4}R_3 \rightarrow \end{array} \left[\begin{array}{rrr|r} 1 & 0 & 2 & 5 \\ 0 & 1 & -2 & 0 \\ 0 & 0 & 1 & 1 \end{array}\right] \qquad \begin{aligned} x \quad\;\; + 2z &= 5 \\ y - 2z &= 0 \\ z &= 1 \end{aligned}$$

Finally, the matrix can be transformed into reduced row-echelon form by subtracting 2 times row 3 from row 1, and adding 2 times row 3 to row 2.

$$\begin{array}{l} R_1 - 2R_3 \rightarrow \\ R_2 + 2R_3 \rightarrow \\ \\ \end{array} \left[\begin{array}{ccc|c} 1 & 0 & 0 & 3 \\ 0 & 1 & 0 & 2 \\ 0 & 0 & 1 & 1 \end{array}\right] \qquad \begin{array}{l} x = 3 \\ y = 2 \\ z = 1 \end{array}$$

This final matrix is in reduced row-echelon form. The solution is (3, 2, 1).

Now Try Exercise 65

Solving Systems of Linear Equations with Technology (Optional)

If the arithmetic at each step of Gaussian elimination is done exactly, then it may be thought of as an exact symbolic procedure. However, when calculators and computers are used to solve systems of equations, their solutions often are approximate. The next three examples use a graphing calculator to solve systems of linear equations.

EXAMPLE 9 **Solving a system of equations using technology**

Use a graphing calculator to solve the system of linear equations in Example 8.

SOLUTION To solve this system, enter the augmented matrix

$$A = \left[\begin{array}{ccc|c} 2 & 1 & 2 & 10 \\ 1 & 0 & 2 & 5 \\ 1 & -2 & 2 & 1 \end{array}\right],$$

as shown in Figures 6.41–6.43.

Calculator Help
To enter the elements of a matrix, see Appendix A (page AP-12).

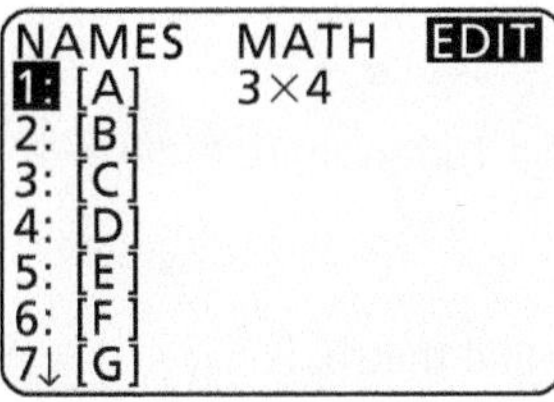

Figure 6.41

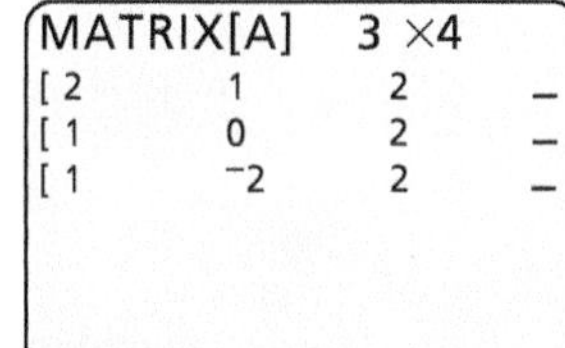

Figure 6.42

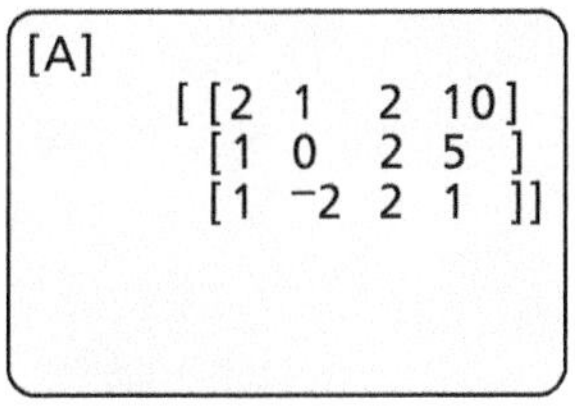

```
[A]
      [[2  1   2  10]
       [1  0   2  5 ]
       [1  ⁻2  2  1 ]]
```

Figure 6.43

A graphing calculator can transform matrix A into reduced row-echelon form, as illustrated in Figures 6.44 and 6.45. Notice that the reduced row-echelon form obtained from the graphing calculator agrees with our results from Example 8. The solution is (3, 2, 1).

Calculator Help
To transform a matrix into reduced row-echelon form, see Appendix A (page AP-13).

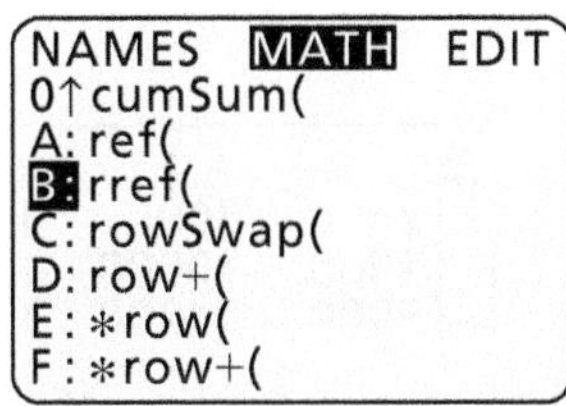

Figure 6.44

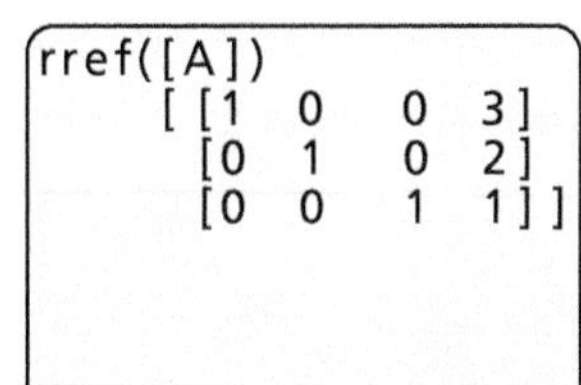

Figure 6.45

Now Try Exercise 71

EXAMPLE 10 Transforming a matrix into reduced row-echelon form

For three food shelters operated by a charitable organization, three different quantities are computed: monthly food costs F in dollars, number of people served per month N, and monthly charitable receipts R in dollars. The data are shown in Table 6.8.

Food Shelter Operations

Food Costs (F)	Number Served (N)	Charitable Receipts (R)
3000	2400	8000
4000	2600	10,000
8000	5900	14,000

Table 6.8

(a) Model these data by using $F = aN + bR + c$, where a, b, and c are constants.
(b) Predict the food costs for a shelter that serves 4000 people and receives charitable receipts of \$12,000. Round your answer to the nearest hundred dollars.

SOLUTION

(a) Getting Started Table 6.8 provides several values for F, N, and R in the equation $F = aN + bR + c$. The goal is to write a system of linear equations whose solution gives the values of a, b, and c. ▶

Since $F = aN + bR + c$, the constants a, b, and c satisfy the following equations.

$$\begin{aligned} 3000 &= a(2400) + b(8000) + c \\ 4000 &= a(2600) + b(10{,}000) + c \\ 8000 &= a(5900) + b(14{,}000) + c \end{aligned}$$

This system can be rewritten as

$$\begin{aligned} 2400a + 8000b + c &= 3000 \\ 2600a + 10{,}000b + c &= 4000 \\ 5900a + 14{,}000b + c &= 8000. \end{aligned}$$

The associated augmented matrix is

$$A = \left[\begin{array}{ccc|c} 2400 & 8000 & 1 & 3000 \\ 2600 & 10{,}000 & 1 & 4000 \\ 5900 & 14{,}000 & 1 & 8000 \end{array}\right].$$

Figure 6.46 shows the matrix A. The fourth column of A may be viewed by using the arrow keys. In Figure 6.47, A has been transformed into reduced row-echelon form where $a \approx 0.6897$, $b \approx 0.4310$, and $c \approx -2103$. Thus let $F = 0.6897N + 0.431R - 2103$.

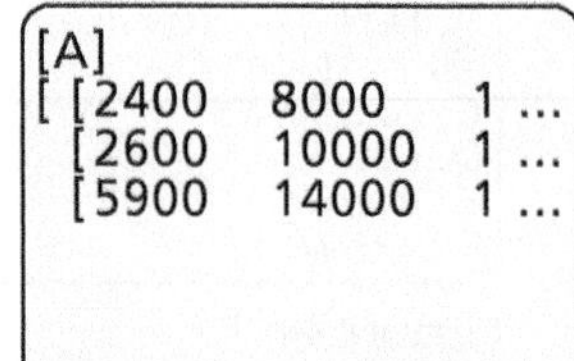

Figure 6.46

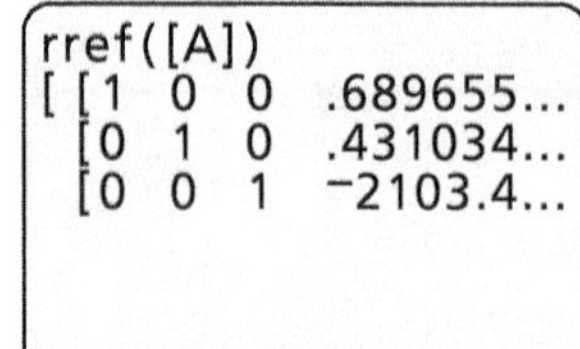

Figure 6.47

(b) To predict the food costs for a shelter that serves 4000 people and receives charitable receipts of $12,000, let $N = 4000$ and $R = 12{,}000$ and evaluate F.

$$F = 0.6897(4000) + 0.431(12{,}000) - 2103 = 5827.8.$$

This model predicts monthly food costs of about $5800.

Now Try Exercise 79

Determining a Quadratic Function The introduction to this section discussed how three points can be used to determine a quadratic function whose graph passes through these points. The next example illustrates this method.

EXAMPLE 11 **Determining a quadratic function**

More than half of private-sector employees cannot carry vacation days into a new year. The average number y of paid days off for full-time workers at medium to large companies after x years of employment is listed in Table 6.9.

Paid Days Off

x **(years)**	1	15	30
y **(days)**	9.4	18.8	21.9

Source: Bureau of Labor Statistics.

Table 6.9

(a) Determine the coefficients for $f(x) = ax^2 + bx + c$ so that f models these data.
(b) Graph f with the data in $[-4, 32, 5]$ by $[8, 23, 2]$.
(c) Estimate the number of paid days off after 3 years of employment. Compare it to the actual value of 11.2 days.

Calculator Help
To plot data and to graph an equation, see Appendix A (page AP-6).

SOLUTION

(a) For f to model the data, the equations $f(1) = 9.4$, $f(15) = 18.8$, and $f(30) = 21.9$ must be satisfied. See Table 6.9.

$$\begin{aligned} f(1) &= a(1)^2 + b(1) + c = 9.4 \\ f(15) &= a(15)^2 + b(15) + c = 18.8 \\ f(30) &= a(30)^2 + b(30) + c = 21.9 \end{aligned}$$

The associated augmented matrix is

$$\left[\begin{array}{ccc|c} 1^2 & 1 & 1 & 9.4 \\ 15^2 & 15 & 1 & 18.8 \\ 30^2 & 30 & 1 & 21.9 \end{array}\right].$$

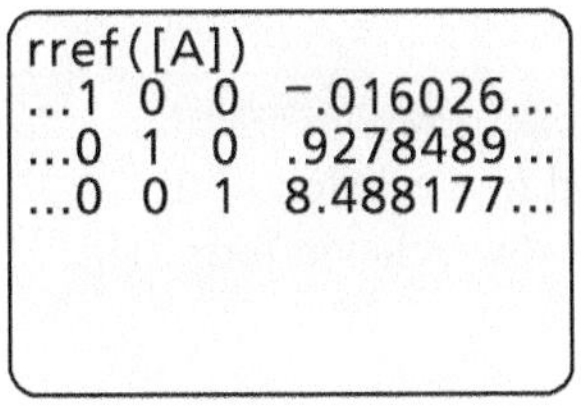

```
rref([A])
...1 0 0 -.016026...
...0 1 0 .9278489...
...0 0 1 8.488177...
```

Figure 6.48

Figure 6.48 shows a portion of the matrix represented in reduced row-echelon form. The solution is $a \approx -0.016026$, $b \approx 0.92785$, and $c \approx 8.4882$.

(b) Graph $y_1 = -0.016026x^2 + 0.92785x + 8.4882$ together with the points (1, 9.4), (15, 18.8), and (30, 21.9). The graph of f passes through the points. See Figure 6.49.

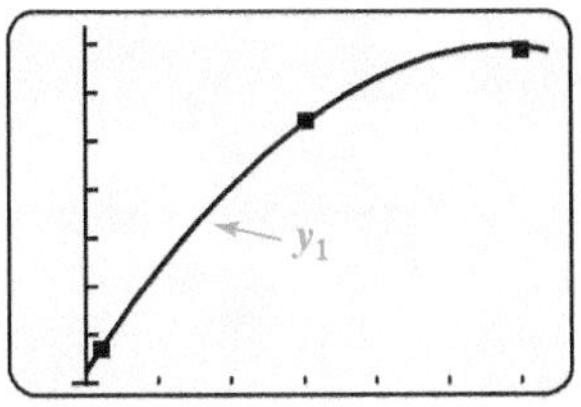

$[-4, 32, 5]$ by $[8, 23, 2]$

y_1

Figure 6.49

(c) To estimate the number of paid days off after 3 years of employment, evaluate $f(3)$.

$$f(3) = -0.016026(3)^2 + 0.92785(3) + 8.4882 \approx 11.1$$

This is quite close to the actual value of 11.2 days.

Now Try Exercise 87

6.4 Putting It All Together

Through a sequence of matrix row operations known as Gaussian elimination, an augmented matrix can be transformed into row-echelon form or reduced row-echelon form. Backward substitution is frequently used to find the solution when a matrix is in row-echelon form.

AUGMENTED MATRIX

A linear system can be represented by an augmented matrix.

$$\left[\begin{array}{rrr|r} 2 & 0 & -3 & 2 \\ -1 & 2 & -2 & -5 \\ 1 & -2 & -1 & 7 \end{array}\right] \qquad \begin{aligned} 2x \phantom{{}+2y} - 3z &= 2 \\ -x + 2y - 2z &= -5 \\ x - 2y - z &= 7 \end{aligned}$$

ROW-ECHELON FORM

The following matrices are in row-echelon form. They represent three possible situations: no solutions, one solution, and infinitely many solutions.

$$\left[\begin{array}{rrr|r} 1 & -2 & 1 & 0 \\ 0 & 1 & 2 & 3 \\ 0 & 0 & 0 & 1 \end{array}\right] \qquad \left[\begin{array}{rrr|r} 1 & -2 & 1 & 0 \\ 0 & 1 & 2 & 3 \\ 0 & 0 & 1 & 1 \end{array}\right] \qquad \left[\begin{array}{rrr|r} 1 & -2 & 1 & 0 \\ 0 & 1 & 2 & 3 \\ 0 & 0 & 0 & 0 \end{array}\right]$$

No solutions — *One solution* (1, 1, 1) — *Infinitely many solutions* $(6 - 5z, 3 - 2z, z)$

BACKWARD SUBSTITUTION

Backward substitution can be used to solve a system of linear equations represented by an augmented matrix in row-echelon form.

Augmented Matrix

$$\left[\begin{array}{rrr|r} 1 & -2 & 1 & 3 \\ 0 & 1 & -2 & -3 \\ 0 & 0 & 1 & 2 \end{array}\right]$$

From the last row, $z = 2$.

Substitute $z = 2$ in the second row: $y - 2(2) = -3$, or $y = 1$.

Let $z = 2$ and $y = 1$ in the first row: $x - 2(1) + 2 = 3$, or $x = 3$.

The solution is (3, 1, 2).

REDUCED ROW-ECHELON FORM

The Gauss-Jordan elimination method can be used to transform an augmented matrix into reduced row-echelon form, which often eliminates the need for backward substitution. The following matrices are in reduced row-echelon form. The solution is given below the matrix.

$$\left[\begin{array}{rrr|r} 1 & 0 & 0 & 4 \\ 0 & 1 & 0 & 5 \\ 0 & 0 & 0 & 2 \end{array}\right] \qquad \left[\begin{array}{rrr|r} 1 & 0 & 0 & 1 \\ 0 & 1 & 0 & 2 \\ 0 & 0 & 1 & 3 \end{array}\right] \qquad \left[\begin{array}{rrr|r} 1 & 0 & 3 & 2 \\ 0 & 1 & 2 & 3 \\ 0 & 0 & 0 & 0 \end{array}\right]$$

No solutions — *One solution* (1, 2, 3) — *Infinitely many solutions* $(2 - 3z, 3 - 2z, z)$

6.4 Exercises

Dimensions of Matrices and Augmented Matrices

Exercises 1–6: State the dimension of each matrix.

1. $\begin{bmatrix} 1 \\ 2 \\ 3 \end{bmatrix}$

2. $\begin{bmatrix} a & b & c \\ d & e & b \end{bmatrix}$

3. $\begin{bmatrix} 3 & 0 \\ 1 & -4 \end{bmatrix}$

4. $[-1 \quad 1]$

5. $\begin{bmatrix} 1 & -1 \\ 7 & 5 \\ -4 & 0 \end{bmatrix}$

6. $\begin{bmatrix} 1 & 3 & 8 & -3 \\ 1 & -1 & 1 & -2 \\ 4 & 5 & 0 & -1 \end{bmatrix}$

Exercises 7–10: Represent the linear system by an augmented matrix, and state the dimension of the matrix.

7. $\begin{aligned} 5x - 2y &= 3 \\ -x + 3y &= -1 \end{aligned}$

8. $\begin{aligned} 3x + y &= 4 \\ -x + 4y &= 5 \end{aligned}$

9. $\begin{aligned} -3x + 2y + z &= -4 \\ 5x - z &= 9 \\ x - 3y - 6z &= -9 \end{aligned}$

10. $\begin{aligned} x + 2y - z &= 2 \\ -2x + y - 2z &= -3 \\ 7x + y - z &= 7 \end{aligned}$

Exercises 11–14: Write the system of linear equations that the augmented matrix represents.

11. $\left[\begin{array}{cc|c} 3 & 2 & 4 \\ 0 & 1 & 5 \end{array}\right]$

12. $\left[\begin{array}{cc|c} -2 & 1 & 5 \\ 7 & 9 & 2 \end{array}\right]$

13. $\left[\begin{array}{ccc|c} 3 & 1 & 4 & 0 \\ 0 & 5 & 8 & -1 \\ 0 & 0 & -7 & 1 \end{array}\right]$

14. $\left[\begin{array}{ccc|c} 1 & -1 & 3 & 2 \\ -2 & 1 & 1 & -2 \\ -1 & 0 & -2 & 1 \end{array}\right]$

Row-Echelon Form

Exercises 15 and 16: Is the matrix in row-echelon form?

15. (a) $\left[\begin{array}{cc|c} 1 & 3 & 2 \\ 0 & 1 & -1 \end{array}\right]$
(b) $\left[\begin{array}{ccc|c} 1 & 4 & -1 & 0 \\ 0 & -1 & 1 & 3 \\ 0 & 2 & 1 & 7 \end{array}\right]$
(c) $\left[\begin{array}{ccc|c} 1 & 6 & -8 & 5 \\ 0 & 1 & 7 & 9 \\ 0 & 0 & 1 & 11 \end{array}\right]$

16. (a) $\left[\begin{array}{cc|c} 1 & 3 & 2 \\ 0 & -1 & -1 \end{array}\right]$
(b) $\left[\begin{array}{ccc|c} 1 & 3 & -1 & 8 \\ 0 & 1 & 5 & 3 \\ 0 & 0 & 0 & 0 \end{array}\right]$
(c) $\left[\begin{array}{ccc|c} 0 & 0 & 1 & 1 \\ 0 & 1 & 7 & 9 \\ 1 & 2 & -1 & 11 \end{array}\right]$

Exercises 17–26: The augmented matrix is in row-echelon form and represents a linear system. Solve the system by using backward substitution, if possible. Write the solution as either an ordered pair or an ordered triple.

17. $\left[\begin{array}{cc|c} 1 & 2 & 3 \\ 0 & 1 & -1 \end{array}\right]$

18. $\left[\begin{array}{cc|c} 1 & -5 & 6 \\ 0 & 0 & 1 \end{array}\right]$

19. $\left[\begin{array}{cc|c} 1 & -1 & 2 \\ 0 & 1 & 0 \end{array}\right]$

20. $\left[\begin{array}{cc|c} 1 & 4 & -2 \\ 0 & 1 & 3 \end{array}\right]$

21. $\left[\begin{array}{ccc|c} 1 & 1 & -1 & 4 \\ 0 & 1 & -1 & 2 \\ 0 & 0 & 1 & 1 \end{array}\right]$

22. $\left[\begin{array}{ccc|c} 1 & -2 & -1 & 0 \\ 0 & 1 & -3 & 1 \\ 0 & 0 & 1 & 2 \end{array}\right]$

23. $\left[\begin{array}{ccc|c} 1 & 2 & -1 & 5 \\ 0 & 1 & -2 & 1 \\ 0 & 0 & 0 & 0 \end{array}\right]$

24. $\left[\begin{array}{ccc|c} 1 & -1 & 2 & 8 \\ 0 & 1 & -4 & 2 \\ 0 & 0 & 0 & 0 \end{array}\right]$

25. $\left[\begin{array}{ccc|c} 1 & 2 & 1 & -3 \\ 0 & 1 & -3 & \frac{1}{2} \\ 0 & 0 & 0 & 4 \end{array}\right]$

26. $\left[\begin{array}{ccc|c} 1 & 0 & -4 & \frac{3}{4} \\ 0 & 1 & 2 & 1 \\ 0 & 0 & 0 & -3 \end{array}\right]$

Solving Systems with Gaussian Elimination

Exercises 27–30: Perform each row operation on the given matrix by completing the matrix at the right.

27. $\left[\begin{array}{ccc|c} 2 & -4 & 6 & 10 \\ -3 & 5 & 3 & 2 \\ 4 & 8 & 4 & -8 \end{array}\right] \begin{array}{l} \frac{1}{2}R_1 \rightarrow \\ \\ \frac{1}{4}R_3 \rightarrow \end{array} \left[\begin{array}{ccc|c} 1 & & & \\ -3 & 5 & 3 & 2 \\ & & 1 & \end{array}\right]$

28. $\left[\begin{array}{ccc|c} 1 & -2 & 1 & 3 \\ 1 & 4 & 0 & -1 \\ 2 & 0 & 1 & 5 \end{array}\right] \begin{array}{l} \\ R_2 - R_1 \rightarrow \\ R_3 - 2R_1 \rightarrow \end{array} \left[\begin{array}{ccc|c} 1 & -2 & 1 & 3 \\ & 6 & & \\ & & & -1 \end{array}\right]$

29. $\left[\begin{array}{ccc|c} 1 & -1 & 1 & 2 \\ -1 & 2 & -2 & 0 \\ 1 & 7 & 0 & 5 \end{array}\right] \begin{array}{l} \\ R_2 + R_1 \rightarrow \\ R_3 - R_1 \rightarrow \end{array} \left[\begin{array}{ccc|c} 1 & -1 & 1 & 2 \\ & & & \\ & & & \end{array}\right]$

30. $\left[\begin{array}{ccc|c} 1 & -2 & 3 & 6 \\ 2 & 1 & 4 & 5 \\ -3 & 5 & 3 & 2 \end{array}\right] \begin{array}{l} \\ R_2 - 2R_1 \rightarrow \\ R_3 + 3R_1 \rightarrow \end{array} \left[\begin{array}{ccc|c} 1 & -2 & 3 & 6 \\ & & & \\ & & & \end{array}\right]$

Exercises 31–42: Use Gaussian elimination with backward substitution to solve the system of linear equations. Write the solution as an ordered pair or an ordered triple whenever possible.

31. $\begin{aligned} x + 2y &= 3 \\ -x - y &= 7 \end{aligned}$

32. $\begin{aligned} 2x + 4y &= 10 \\ x - 2y &= -3 \end{aligned}$

33. $\begin{aligned} x + 2y + z &= 3 \\ x + y - z &= 3 \\ -x - 2y + z &= -5 \end{aligned}$

34. $\begin{aligned} x + y + z &= 6 \\ 2x + 3y - z &= 3 \\ x + y + 2z &= 10 \end{aligned}$

35. $\begin{aligned} x + 2y - z &= -1 \\ 2x - y + z &= 0 \\ -x - y + 2z &= 7 \end{aligned}$

36. $\begin{aligned} x + 3y - 2z &= -4 \\ 2x + 6y + z &= -3 \\ x + y - 4z &= -2 \end{aligned}$

37. $\begin{aligned} 3x + y + 3z &= 14 \\ x + y + z &= 6 \\ -2x - 2y + 3z &= -7 \end{aligned}$

38. $\begin{aligned} x + 3y - 2z &= 3 \\ -x - 2y + z &= -2 \\ 2x - 7y + z &= 1 \end{aligned}$

39. $\begin{aligned} 2x + 5y + z &= 8 \\ x + 2y - z &= 2 \\ 3x + 7y &= 5 \end{aligned}$

40. $\begin{aligned} x + y + z &= 3 \\ x + y + 2z &= 4 \\ 2x + 2y + 3z &= 7 \end{aligned}$

41. $\begin{aligned} -x + 2y + 4z &= 10 \\ 3x - 2y - 2z &= -12 \\ x + 2y + 6z &= 8 \end{aligned}$

42. $\begin{aligned} 4x - 2y + 4z &= 8 \\ 3x - 7y + 6z &= 4 \\ -x - 5y + 2z &= 7 \end{aligned}$

Exercises 43–54: Solve the system, if possible.

43. $\begin{aligned} x - y + z &= 1 \\ x + 2y - z &= 2 \\ y - z &= 0 \end{aligned}$

44. $\begin{aligned} x - y - 2z &= -11 \\ x - 2y - z &= -11 \\ -x + y + 3z &= 14 \end{aligned}$

45. $\begin{aligned} 2x - 4y + 2z &= 11 \\ x + 3y - 2z &= -9 \\ 4x - 2y + z &= 7 \end{aligned}$

46. $\begin{aligned} x - 4y + z &= 9 \\ 3y - 2z &= -7 \\ -x + z &= 0 \end{aligned}$

47. $\begin{aligned} 3x - 2y + 2z &= -18 \\ -x + 2y - 4z &= 16 \\ 4x - 3y - 2z &= -21 \end{aligned}$

48. $\begin{aligned} 2x - y - z &= 0 \\ x - y - z &= -2 \\ 3x - 2y - 2z &= -2 \end{aligned}$

49. $\begin{aligned} x - 4y + 3z &= 26 \\ -x + 3y - 2z &= -19 \\ -y + z &= 10 \end{aligned}$

50. $\begin{aligned} 4x - y - z &= 0 \\ 4x - 2y &= 0 \\ 2x + z &= 1 \end{aligned}$

51. $\begin{aligned} 5x + 4z &= 7 \\ 2x - 4y &= 6 \\ 3y + 3z &= 3 \end{aligned}$

52. $\begin{aligned} y + 2z &= -5 \\ 3x - 2z &= -6 \\ -x - 4y &= 11 \end{aligned}$

53. $\begin{aligned} 5x - 2y + z &= 5 \\ x + y - 2z &= -2 \\ 4x - 3y + 3z &= 7 \end{aligned}$

54. $\begin{aligned} 2x - 4y - z &= 2 \\ x + y - 3z &= 10 \\ -x - 7y + 8z &= 2 \end{aligned}$

Exercises 55–62: (Refer to Example 7.) The augmented matrix is in reduced row-echelon form and represents a system of linear equations. If possible, solve the system.

55. $\left[\begin{array}{cc|c} 1 & 0 & 12 \\ 0 & 1 & 3 \end{array}\right]$

56. $\left[\begin{array}{cc|c} 1 & -1 & 1 \\ 0 & 0 & 0 \end{array}\right]$

57. $\left[\begin{array}{ccc|c} 1 & 0 & 0 & -2 \\ 0 & 1 & 0 & 4 \\ 0 & 0 & 1 & \frac{1}{2} \end{array}\right]$

58. $\left[\begin{array}{ccc|c} 1 & 0 & 0 & 7 \\ 0 & 1 & 0 & -9 \\ 0 & 0 & 1 & 3 \end{array}\right]$

59. $\left[\begin{array}{ccc|c} 1 & 0 & 2 & 4 \\ 0 & 1 & -1 & -3 \\ 0 & 0 & 0 & 0 \end{array}\right]$

60. $\left[\begin{array}{ccc|c} 1 & 0 & 1 & -2 \\ 0 & 1 & 3 & 5 \\ 0 & 0 & 0 & 0 \end{array}\right]$

61. $\left[\begin{array}{ccc|c} 1 & 0 & 0 & \frac{3}{4} \\ 0 & 1 & 0 & -1 \\ 0 & 0 & 0 & \frac{2}{3} \end{array}\right]$

62. $\left[\begin{array}{ccc|c} 1 & 0 & 0 & 10 \\ 0 & 1 & 0 & 21 \\ 0 & 0 & 0 & -2 \end{array}\right]$

Exercises 63–70: **Reduced Row-Echelon Form** *Use Gauss-Jordan elimination to solve the system of equations.*

63. $\begin{aligned} x - y &= 1 \\ x + y &= 5 \end{aligned}$

64. $\begin{aligned} 2x + 3y &= 1 \\ x - 2y &= -3 \end{aligned}$

65. $\begin{aligned} x + 2y + z &= 3 \\ y - z &= -2 \\ -x - 2y + 2z &= 6 \end{aligned}$

66. $\begin{aligned} x + z &= 2 \\ x - y - z &= 0 \\ -2x + y &= -2 \end{aligned}$

67. $\begin{aligned} x - y + 2z &= 7 \\ 2x + y - 4z &= -27 \\ -x + y - z &= 0 \end{aligned}$

68. $\begin{aligned} 2x - 4y - 6z &= 2 \\ x - 3y + z &= 12 \\ 2x + y + 3z &= 5 \end{aligned}$

69. $\begin{aligned} 2x + y - z &= 2 \\ x - 2y + z &= 0 \\ x + 3y - 2z &= 4 \end{aligned}$

70. $\begin{aligned} -2x - y + z &= 3 \\ x + y - 3z &= 1 \\ x - 2y - 4z &= 2 \end{aligned}$

Exercises 71–76: **Technology** *Use technology to find the solution. Approximate values to the nearest thousandth.*

71. $\begin{aligned} 5x - 7y + 9z &= 40 \\ -7x + 3y - 7z &= 20 \\ 5x - 8y - 5z &= 15 \end{aligned}$

72. $\begin{aligned} 12x - 4y - 7z &= 8 \\ -8x - 6y + 9z &= 7 \\ 34x + 6y - 2z &= 5 \end{aligned}$

73. $\begin{aligned} 2.1x + 0.5y + 1.7z &= 4.9 \\ -2x + 1.5y - 1.7z &= 3.1 \\ 5.8x - 4.6y + 0.8z &= 9.3 \end{aligned}$

74. $\begin{aligned} 53x + 95y + 12z &= 108 \\ 81x - 57y - 24z &= -92 \\ -9x + 11y - 78z &= 21 \end{aligned}$

75. $\begin{aligned} 0.1x + 0.3y + 1.7z &= 0.6 \\ 0.6x + 0.1y - 3.1z &= 6.2 \\ 2.4y + 0.9z &= 3.5 \end{aligned}$

76. $\begin{aligned} 103x - 886y + 431z &= 1200 \\ -55x + 981y &= 1108 \\ -327x + 421y + 337z &= 99 \end{aligned}$

Applications

77. Pumping Water Three pumps are being used to empty a small swimming pool. The first pump is twice as fast as the second pump. The first two pumps can empty the pool in 8 hours, while all three pumps can empty it in 6 hours. How long would it take each pump to empty the pool individually? (*Hint:* Let x represent the fraction of the pool that the first pump can empty in 1 hour. Let y and z represent this fraction for the second and third pumps, respectively.)

78. Pumping Water Suppose in Exercise 77 that the first pump is three times as fast as the third pump, the first and second pumps can empty the pool in 6 hours, and all three pumps can empty the pool in 8 hours.

(a) Are these data realistic? Explain your reasoning.

(b) Make a conjecture about a solution to these data.

(c) Test your conjecture by solving the problem.

79. Food Shelters (Refer to Example 10.) For three food shelters, monthly food costs F in dollars, number of people served per month N, and monthly charitable receipts R in dollars are as shown in the table.

Food Costs (F)	Number Served (N)	Charitable Receipts (R)
1300	1800	5000
5300	3200	12,000
6500	4500	13,000

(a) Model these data using $F = aN + bR + c$, where a, b, and c are constants.

(b) Predict the food costs for a shelter that serves 3500 people and receives charitable receipts of \$12,500. Round your answer to the nearest hundred dollars.

80. Estimating the Weight of a Bear The following table shows the weight W, neck size N, and chest size C for a representative sample of black bears.

W (pounds)	N (inches)	C (inches)
100	17	27
272	25	36
381	30	43

Source: M. Triola, *Elementary Statistics*.

(a) Find values for a, b, and c so that the equation $W = a + bN + cC$ models these data.

(b) Estimate the weight of a bear with a 20-inch neck and a 31-inch chest size.

(c) Explain why it is reasonable for the coefficients b and c to be positive.

81. Electricity In the study of electrical circuits, the application of Kirchoff's rules frequently results in systems of linear equations. To determine the current I (in amperes) in each branch of the circuit shown in the figure, solve the system of linear equations. Round values to the nearest hundredth.

$$I_1 = I_2 + I_3$$
$$15 + 4I_3 = 14I_2$$
$$10 + 4I_3 = 5I_1$$

82. Electricity (Refer to Exercise 81.) Find the current (in amperes) in each branch of the circuit shown in the figure by solving the system of linear equations. Round values to the nearest hundredth.

$$I_1 = I_2 + I_3$$
$$20 = 4I_1 + 7I_3$$
$$10 + 7I_3 = 6I_2$$

83. Investment A sum of \$5000 is invested in three mutual funds that pay 8%, 11%, and 14% annual interest rates. The amount of money invested in the fund paying 14% equals the total amount of money invested in the other two funds, and the total annual interest from all three funds is \$595.

(a) Write a system of equations whose solution gives the amount invested in each mutual fund. Be sure to state what each variable represents.

(b) Solve the system of equations.

84. Investment A sum of \$10,000 is invested in three accounts that pay 3%, 4%, and 5% interest. Twice as much money is invested in the account paying 5% as in the account paying 3%, and the total annual interest from all three accounts is \$421.

(a) Write a system of equations whose solution gives the amount invested in each account. Be sure to state what each variable represents.

(b) Solve the system of equations.

Exercises 85 and 86: **Traffic Flow** *The figure shows three one-way streets with intersections* A, B, *and* C. *Numbers indicate the average traffic flow in vehicles per minute. The variables x, y, and z denote unknown traffic flows that need to be determined for timing of stoplights.*

(a) If the number of vehicles per minute entering an intersection must equal the number exiting an intersection, verify that the accompanying system of linear equations describes the traffic flow.

(b) Rewrite the system and solve.

(c) Interpret your solution.

85. A: $x + 5 = y + 7$
B: $z + 6 = x + 3$
C: $y + 3 = z + 4$

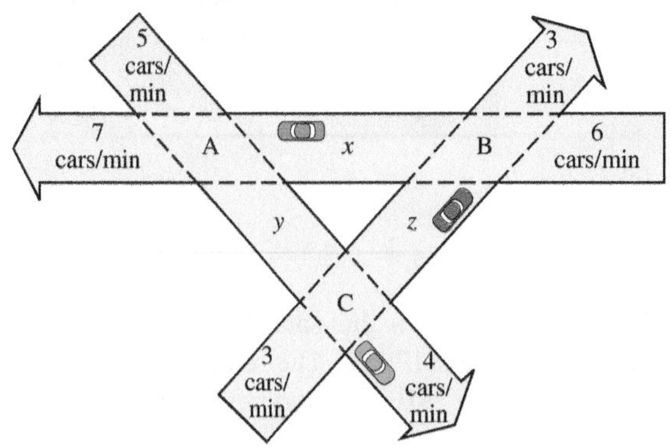

86. A: $x + 7 = y + 4$
B: $4 + 5 = x + z$
C: $y + 8 = 9 + 4$

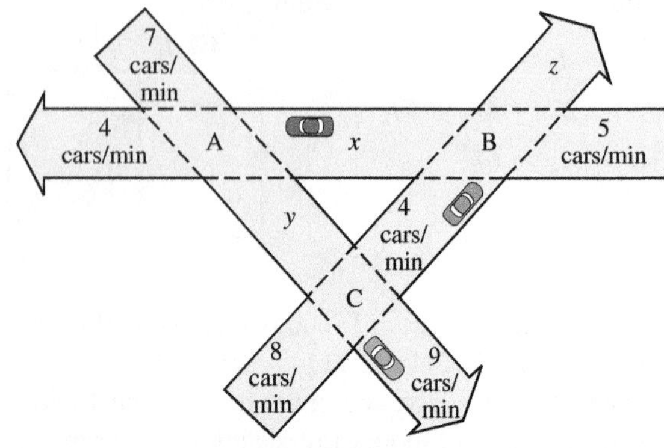

Exercises 87–90: Each set of data can be modeled by the quadratic function $f(x) = ax^2 + bx + c$.

(a) Write a linear system whose solution represents values of a, b, and c.
(b) Use technology to find the solution.
(c) Graph f and the data in the same viewing rectangle.
(d) Make your own prediction using f.

87. Estimating iPad Sales (Refer to the introduction to this section.) The table lists total iPad sales y in millions x quarters after its release.

x	1	5	6
y	3	29	40

Source: Apple Corporation.

88. Head Start Enrollment The table lists annual enrollment in thousands for the Head Start program x years after 1980.

x	0	10	26
y	376	541	909

Source: Dept. of Health and Human Services.

89. Chronic Health Care A large percentage of the U.S. population will require chronic health care in the coming decades. The average age of caregivers is 50–64, while the typical person needing chronic care is 85 or older. The ratio y of potential caregivers to those needing chronic health care will shrink in the coming years x, as shown in the table.

x	1990	2010	2030
y	11	10	6

Source: Robert Wood Johnson Foundation, *Chronic Care in America: A 21st Century Challenge.*

90. Carbon Dioxide Levels Carbon dioxide (CO_2) is a greenhouse gas. The table lists its concentration y in parts per million (ppm) measured at Mauna Loa, Hawaii, for three selected years x.

x	1958	1973	2003
y	315	325	376

Source: A. Nilsson, *Greenhouse Earth.*

Writing about Mathematics

91. A linear equation in three variables can be represented by a flat plane. Describe geometrically situations that can occur when a system of three linear equations has either no solution or an infinite number of solutions.

92. Give an example of an augmented matrix in row-echelon form that represents a system of linear equations that has no solution. Explain your reasoning.

Extended and Discovery Exercises

Exercises 1 and 2: Solve the system of four equations with four variables.

1.
$$\begin{aligned} w + x + 2y - z &= 4 \\ 2w + x + 2y + z &= 5 \\ -w + 3x + y - 2z &= -2 \\ 3w + 2x + y + 3z &= 3 \end{aligned}$$

2.
$$\begin{aligned} 2w - 5x + 3y - 2z &= -13 \\ 3w + 2x + 4y - 9z &= -28 \\ 4w + 3x - 2y - 4z &= -13 \\ 5w - 4x - 3y + 3z &= 0 \end{aligned}$$

CHECKING BASIC CONCEPTS FOR SECTIONS 6.3 AND 6.4

1. If possible, solve the system of linear equations.

(a)
$$\begin{aligned} x - 2y + z &= -2 \\ x + y + 2z &= 3 \\ 2x - y - z &= 5 \end{aligned}$$

(b)
$$\begin{aligned} x - 2y + z &= -2 \\ x + y + 2z &= 3 \\ 2x - y + 3z &= 1 \end{aligned}$$

(c)
$$\begin{aligned} x - 2y + z &= -2 \\ x + y + 2z &= 3 \\ 2x - y + 3z &= 5 \end{aligned}$$

2. Tickets Sold Two thousand tickets were sold for a play, generating \$19,700. The prices of the tickets were \$5 for children, \$10 for students, and \$12 for adults. There were 100 more adult tickets sold than student tickets. Find the number of each type of ticket sold.

3. Solve the system of linear equations using Gaussian elimination and backward substitution.

$$\begin{aligned} x \qquad + z &= 2 \\ x + y - z &= 1 \\ -x - 2y - z &= 0 \end{aligned}$$

4. Use technology to solve the system of linear equations in Exercise 3.

6.5 Properties and Applications of Matrices

- **Learn matrix notation**
- **Learn how matrices are used in social networks**
- **Find sums, differences, and scalar multiples of matrices**
- **Find matrix products**
- **Use technology (optional)**

Introduction

In the movie trilogy *The Matrix,* the reality that most humans perceive is nothing more than a simulated reality constructed by machines. Although these films are works of fiction, matrices make it possible for programmers to create popular, multiplayer virtual reality games for the Internet. Matrices are also vitally important in social networks and Internet browsing. In this section we discuss properties of matrices and some of their applications.

Matrix Notation

The following notation is used to denote elements in a matrix A.

$$\begin{bmatrix} a_{11} & a_{12} \\ a_{21} & a_{22} \end{bmatrix} \quad \begin{bmatrix} a_{11} & a_{12} & a_{13} \\ a_{21} & a_{22} & a_{23} \\ a_{31} & a_{32} & a_{33} \end{bmatrix} \quad \begin{bmatrix} a_{11} & a_{12} & a_{13} & a_{14} \\ a_{21} & a_{22} & a_{23} & a_{24} \\ a_{31} & a_{32} & a_{33} & a_{34} \\ a_{41} & a_{42} & a_{43} & a_{44} \end{bmatrix} \quad \begin{bmatrix} a_{11} & a_{12} \\ a_{21} & a_{22} \\ a_{31} & a_{32} \end{bmatrix} \quad \begin{bmatrix} a_{11} & a_{12} & a_{13} \\ a_{21} & a_{22} & a_{23} \end{bmatrix}$$

A general element is denoted by a_{ij}. This refers to the element in the ith row, jth column. For example, a_{23} would be the element of A located in the second row, third column. Two m by n matrices A and B are **equal** if corresponding elements are equal. If A and B have different dimensions, they cannot be equal. For example,

$$\begin{bmatrix} 3 & -3 & 7 \\ 2 & 6 & -2 \\ 4 & 2 & 5 \end{bmatrix} = \begin{bmatrix} 3 & -3 & 7 \\ 2 & 6 & -2 \\ 4 & 2 & 5 \end{bmatrix}$$ Equal matrices

because *all* corresponding elements are equal. However,

$$\begin{bmatrix} 1 & 4 \\ -3 & 2 \\ 4 & -7 \end{bmatrix} \neq \begin{bmatrix} 1 & 4 \\ -3 & 2 \\ 5 & -7 \end{bmatrix}$$ Unequal matrices: $a_{31} \neq b_{31}$

because $4 \neq 5$ in row 3 and column 1, and

$$\underset{2 \times 3}{\begin{bmatrix} 1 & 2 & 3 \\ 4 & 5 & 6 \end{bmatrix}} \neq \underset{2 \times 2}{\begin{bmatrix} 1 & 2 \\ 4 & 5 \end{bmatrix}}$$ Unequal matrices: different dimensions

because the matrices have different dimensions.

EXAMPLE 1 Determining matrix elements

Let a_{ij} denote a general element in A and b_{ij} a general element in B, where

$$A = \begin{bmatrix} 3 & -3 & 7 \\ 1 & 6 & -2 \\ 4 & 2 & 5 \end{bmatrix} \quad \text{and} \quad B = \begin{bmatrix} 3 & x & 7 \\ 1 & 6 & -2 \\ 4 & 5 & 2 \end{bmatrix}.$$

(a) Identify a_{12}, b_{32}, and a_{13}.
(b) Compute $a_{31}b_{13} + a_{32}b_{23} + a_{33}b_{33}$.
(c) Is there a value for x that will make the statement $A = B$ true?

SOLUTION

(a) The element a_{12} is located in the first row, second column of A. Thus, $a_{12} = -3$. In a similar manner, we find that $b_{32} = 5$ and $a_{13} = 7$.

(b) $a_{31}b_{13} + a_{32}b_{23} + a_{33}b_{33} = (4)(7) + (2)(-2) + (5)(2) = 34$

(c) No, since $a_{32} = 2 \neq 5 = b_{32}$ and $a_{33} = 5 \neq 2 = b_{33}$. Even if we let $x = -3$, other corresponding elements in A and B are not equal.

Now Try Exercise 1

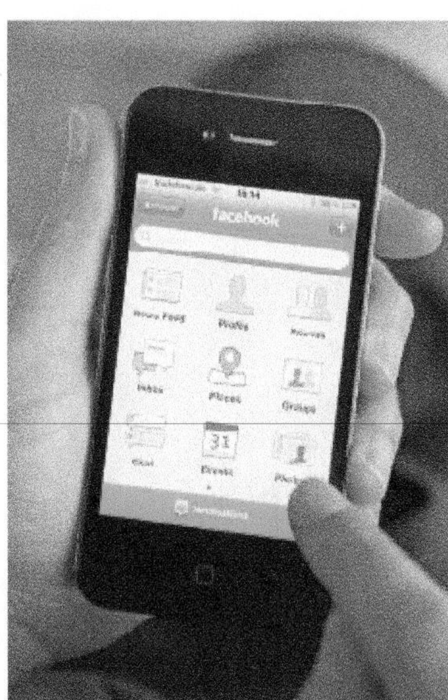

Matrices and Social Networks

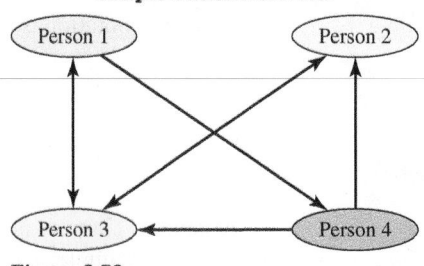

People with Internet access often choose to participate in at least one social network such as Facebook, Pinterest, or Twitter. Mathematics is essential to the success of these social networks, and matrices play an important role in processing social network data. Consider the diagram in Figure 6.50, which represents a simple social network of four people.

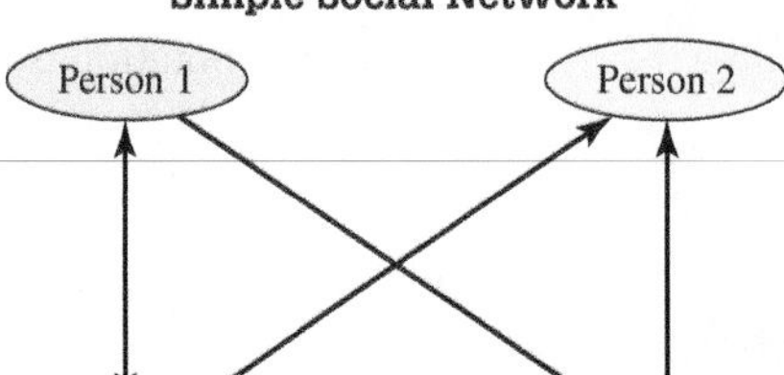

Figure 6.50

The arrows in Figure 6.50 show the social relationships among these people. For example, an arrow from Person 1 to Person 4 indicates that Person 1 likes Person 4. But Person 4 does not like Person 1 because there is no arrow pointing in the opposite direction. On the other hand Person 2 and Person 3 like each other, which is indicated by a double arrow between them. In the next example we see how a matrix can represent this social network.

EXAMPLE 2 Representing a social network with a matrix

Use a matrix to represent the social network shown in Figure 6.50.

SOLUTION A social network with four people can be represented by a 4×4 square matrix. Because Person 1 likes **Person 4**, we put a 1 in row 1 **column 4**. Similarly, Person 4 likes **Person 2**, so we put a **1** in row 4 **column 2**. When no arrow exists to indicate that one person likes another, we place a 0 in the appropriate row and column of the matrix. Using this process results in the following matrix.

$$\begin{bmatrix} 0 & 0 & 1 & 1 \\ 0 & 0 & 1 & 0 \\ 1 & 1 & 0 & 0 \\ 0 & 1 & 1 & 0 \end{bmatrix}$$

Now Try Exercise 53

Sums, Differences, and Scalar Multiples of Matrices

An Application As a result of an FCC mandate, all television stations are now required to broadcast digital signals. HDTVs can display digital images with a resolution up to 1920×1080 pixels. Matrices play an important role in processing digital images.

Matrix Addition and Subtraction To simplify the concept of a digital image, we reduce the resolution to 3×3 pixels and have just four gray levels, rather than colors.

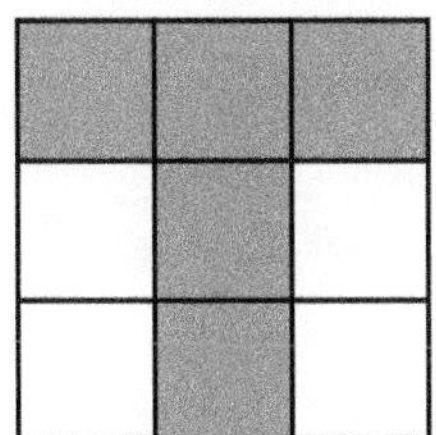
Figure 6.51

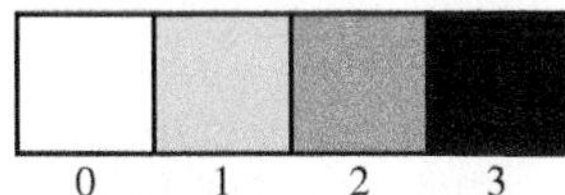

Figure 6.52 Gray Levels

We will let 0 represent white, 1 light gray, 2 dark gray, and 3 black. Suppose that we would like to digitize the letter T shown in Figure 6.51, using the gray levels shown in Figure 6.52. Since the T is dark gray and the background is white, Figure 6.51 can be represented by

$$A = \begin{bmatrix} 2 & 2 & 2 \\ 0 & 2 & 0 \\ 0 & 2 & 0 \end{bmatrix}.$$

Suppose that we want to make the entire picture darker. If we changed every element in A to 3, the entire picture would be black. A more acceptable solution would be to darken each pixel by one gray level. This corresponds to adding 1 to each element in the matrix A and can be accomplished efficiently using matrix notation.

Matrix Addition: Add Corresponding Elements

$$\begin{bmatrix} 2 & 2 & 2 \\ 0 & 2 & 0 \\ 0 & 2 & 0 \end{bmatrix} + \begin{bmatrix} 1 & 1 & 1 \\ 1 & 1 & 1 \\ 1 & 1 & 1 \end{bmatrix} = \begin{bmatrix} 2+1 & 2+1 & 2+1 \\ 0+1 & 2+1 & 0+1 \\ 0+1 & 2+1 & 0+1 \end{bmatrix} = \begin{bmatrix} 3 & 3 & 3 \\ 1 & 3 & 1 \\ 1 & 3 & 1 \end{bmatrix}$$

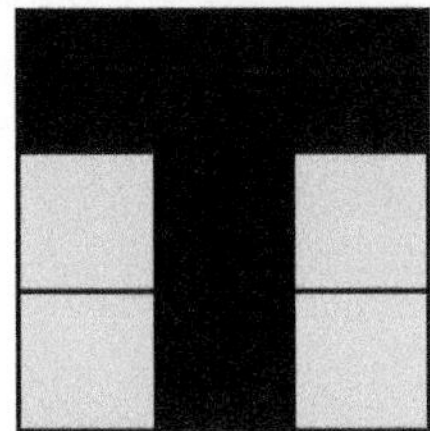
Figure 6.53

To add two matrices of equal dimension, add corresponding elements. The result is shown in picture form in Figure 6.53. Notice that the background is now light gray and the T is black. The entire picture is darker.

To lighten the picture in Figure 6.53, subtract 1 from each element. *To subtract two matrices of equal dimension, subtract corresponding elements.*

Matrix Subtraction: Subtract Corresponding Elements

$$\begin{bmatrix} 3 & 3 & 3 \\ 1 & 3 & 1 \\ 1 & 3 & 1 \end{bmatrix} - \begin{bmatrix} 1 & 1 & 1 \\ 1 & 1 & 1 \\ 1 & 1 & 1 \end{bmatrix} = \begin{bmatrix} 3-1 & 3-1 & 3-1 \\ 1-1 & 3-1 & 1-1 \\ 1-1 & 3-1 & 1-1 \end{bmatrix} = \begin{bmatrix} 2 & 2 & 2 \\ 0 & 2 & 0 \\ 0 & 2 & 0 \end{bmatrix}$$

EXAMPLE 3 Adding and subtracting matrices

If $A = \begin{bmatrix} 7 & 8 & -1 \\ 0 & -1 & 6 \end{bmatrix}$ and $B = \begin{bmatrix} 5 & -2 & 10 \\ -3 & 2 & 4 \end{bmatrix}$, find the following.

(a) $A + B$ **(b)** $B + A$ **(c)** $A - B$

SOLUTION

(a) $$A + B = \begin{bmatrix} 7 & 8 & -1 \\ 0 & -1 & 6 \end{bmatrix} + \begin{bmatrix} 5 & -2 & 10 \\ -3 & 2 & 4 \end{bmatrix}$$

$$= \begin{bmatrix} 7+5 & 8+(-2) & -1+10 \\ 0+(-3) & -1+2 & 6+4 \end{bmatrix}$$

$$= \begin{bmatrix} 12 & 6 & 9 \\ -3 & 1 & 10 \end{bmatrix}$$

(b) $$B + A = \begin{bmatrix} 5 & -2 & 10 \\ -3 & 2 & 4 \end{bmatrix} + \begin{bmatrix} 7 & 8 & -1 \\ 0 & -1 & 6 \end{bmatrix}$$

$$= \begin{bmatrix} 5+7 & -2+8 & 10+(-1) \\ -3+0 & 2+(-1) & 4+6 \end{bmatrix}$$

$$= \begin{bmatrix} 12 & 6 & 9 \\ -3 & 1 & 10 \end{bmatrix}$$

Notice that $A + B = B + A$. The commutative property for matrix addition holds in general, provided that A and B have the same dimension.

CLASS DISCUSSION

If matrices A and B have the same dimension, does $A - B = B - A$?

(c) $$A - B = \begin{bmatrix} 7 & 8 & -1 \\ 0 & -1 & 6 \end{bmatrix} - \begin{bmatrix} 5 & -2 & 10 \\ -3 & 2 & 4 \end{bmatrix}$$
$$= \begin{bmatrix} 7 - 5 & 8 - (-2) & -1 - 10 \\ 0 - (-3) & -1 - 2 & 6 - 4 \end{bmatrix}$$
$$= \begin{bmatrix} 2 & 10 & -11 \\ 3 & -3 & 2 \end{bmatrix}$$

Now Try Exercise 9

An Application Increasing the contrast in a digital image causes light areas to become lighter and dark areas to become darker. As a result, there are fewer pixels with intermediate gray levels. Changing contrast is different from making the entire picture lighter or darker.

EXAMPLE 4 **Applying matrix addition to a digital image**

Less Contrast

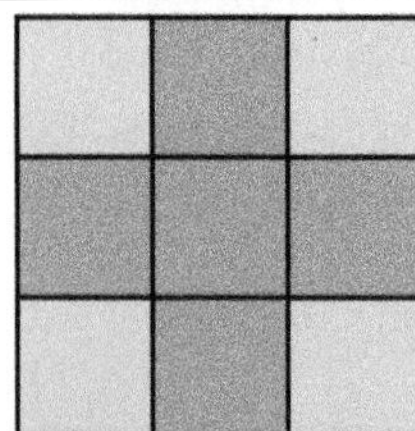

Figure 6.54

Increase the contrast of the + sign in Figure 6.54 by changing light gray to white and dark gray to black. Use matrices to represent this computation.

SOLUTION Figure 6.54 can be represented by the matrix A.

$$A = \begin{bmatrix} 1 & 2 & 1 \\ 2 & 2 & 2 \\ 1 & 2 & 1 \end{bmatrix}$$

To change the contrast, we reduce each 1 in matrix A to 0 and increase each 2 to 3. The addition of matrix B can accomplish this task.

Matrix Addition for Changing Contrast

$$A + B = \begin{bmatrix} 1 & 2 & 1 \\ 2 & 2 & 2 \\ 1 & 2 & 1 \end{bmatrix} + \begin{bmatrix} -1 & 1 & -1 \\ 1 & 1 & 1 \\ -1 & 1 & -1 \end{bmatrix} = \begin{bmatrix} 0 & 3 & 0 \\ 3 & 3 & 3 \\ 0 & 3 & 0 \end{bmatrix}$$

The picture corresponding to $A + B$ is shown in Figure 6.55.

More Contrast

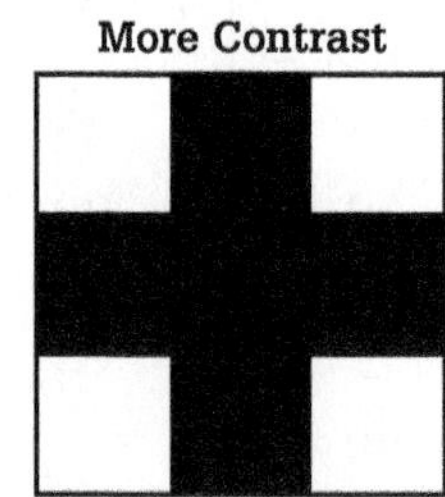

Figure 6.55

Now Try Exercises 23 and 25

Multiplication of a Matrix by a Scalar The matrix

$$B = \begin{bmatrix} 1 & 1 & 1 \\ 1 & 1 & 1 \\ 1 & 1 & 1 \end{bmatrix}$$

can be used to darken a digital picture. Suppose that a photograph is represented by a matrix A with gray levels 0 through 11. Every time matrix B is added to A, the picture becomes slightly darker. For example, if

$$A = \begin{bmatrix} 0 & 5 & 0 \\ 5 & 5 & 5 \\ 0 & 5 & 0 \end{bmatrix}$$

then the addition of $A + B + B$ would darken the picture by two gray levels and could be computed by

$$A + B + B = \begin{bmatrix} 0 & 5 & 0 \\ 5 & 5 & 5 \\ 0 & 5 & 0 \end{bmatrix} + \begin{bmatrix} 1 & 1 & 1 \\ 1 & 1 & 1 \\ 1 & 1 & 1 \end{bmatrix} + \begin{bmatrix} 1 & 1 & 1 \\ 1 & 1 & 1 \\ 1 & 1 & 1 \end{bmatrix} = \begin{bmatrix} 2 & 7 & 2 \\ 7 & 7 & 7 \\ 2 & 7 & 2 \end{bmatrix}.$$

A simpler way to write the expression $A + B + B$ is $A + 2B$. Multiplying B by 2 to obtain $2B$ is called **scalar multiplication.**

Scalar Multiplication: Multiply Each Element by the Scalar

Scalar

$$2B = 2\begin{bmatrix} 1 & 1 & 1 \\ 1 & 1 & 1 \\ 1 & 1 & 1 \end{bmatrix} = \begin{bmatrix} 2(1) & 2(1) & 2(1) \\ 2(1) & 2(1) & 2(1) \\ 2(1) & 2(1) & 2(1) \end{bmatrix} = \begin{bmatrix} 2 & 2 & 2 \\ 2 & 2 & 2 \\ 2 & 2 & 2 \end{bmatrix}$$

Every element of B is multiplied by the real number (scalar) 2.

Sometimes a matrix B is denoted $B = [b_{ij}]$, where b_{ij} represents the element in the ith row, jth column. In this way, we could write $2B$ as $2[b_{ij}] = [2b_{ij}]$. This indicates that to calculate $2B$, multiply each b_{ij} by 2. In a similar manner, a matrix A is sometimes denoted by $[a_{ij}]$.

Some operations on matrices are now summarized.

OPERATIONS ON MATRICES

Matrix Addition

The sum of two $m \times n$ matrices A and B is the $m \times n$ matrix $A + B$, in which each element is the sum of the corresponding elements of A and B. This is written as $A + B = [a_{ij}] + [b_{ij}] = [a_{ij} + b_{ij}]$. If A and B have different dimensions, then $A + B$ is undefined.

Matrix Subtraction

The difference of two $m \times n$ matrices A and B is the $m \times n$ matrix $A - B$, in which each element is the difference of the corresponding elements of A and B. This is written as $A - B = [a_{ij}] - [b_{ij}] = [a_{ij} - b_{ij}]$. If A and B have different dimensions, then $A - B$ is undefined.

Multiplication of a Matrix by a Scalar

The product of a scalar (real number) k and an $m \times n$ matrix A is the $m \times n$ matrix kA, in which each element is k times the corresponding element of A. This is written as $kA = k[a_{ij}] = [ka_{ij}]$.

EXAMPLE 5 Performing scalar multiplication

If $A = \begin{bmatrix} 2 & 7 & 11 \\ -1 & 3 & -5 \\ 0 & 9 & -12 \end{bmatrix}$, find $-4A$.

SOLUTION

$$-4A = -4\begin{bmatrix} 2 & 7 & 11 \\ -1 & 3 & -5 \\ 0 & 9 & -12 \end{bmatrix} = \begin{bmatrix} -4(2) & -4(7) & -4(11) \\ -4(-1) & -4(3) & -4(-5) \\ -4(0) & -4(9) & -4(-12) \end{bmatrix} = \begin{bmatrix} -8 & -28 & -44 \\ 4 & -12 & 20 \\ 0 & -36 & 48 \end{bmatrix}$$

Now Try Exercise 11(*b*)

EXAMPLE 6 Performing operations on matrices

If possible, perform the indicated operations using

$$A = \begin{bmatrix} 4 & -2 \\ 3 & 5 \end{bmatrix},\ B = \begin{bmatrix} 0 & 1 \\ -2 & 3 \end{bmatrix},\ C = \begin{bmatrix} 1 & -1 \\ 0 & 7 \\ -4 & 2 \end{bmatrix},\ \text{and } D = \begin{bmatrix} -1 & -3 \\ 9 & -7 \\ 1 & 8 \end{bmatrix}.$$

(a) $A + 3B$ **(b)** $A - C$ **(c)** $-2C - 3D$

SOLUTION

(a)
$$A + 3B = \begin{bmatrix} 4 & -2 \\ 3 & 5 \end{bmatrix} + 3\begin{bmatrix} 0 & 1 \\ -2 & 3 \end{bmatrix}$$
$$= \begin{bmatrix} 4 & -2 \\ 3 & 5 \end{bmatrix} + \begin{bmatrix} 0 & 3 \\ -6 & 9 \end{bmatrix} = \begin{bmatrix} 4 & 1 \\ -3 & 14 \end{bmatrix}$$

(b) $A - C$ is undefined because the dimension of A is 2×2 and unequal to the dimension of C, which is 3×2.

(c)
$$-2C - 3D = -2\begin{bmatrix} 1 & -1 \\ 0 & 7 \\ -4 & 2 \end{bmatrix} - 3\begin{bmatrix} -1 & -3 \\ 9 & -7 \\ 1 & 8 \end{bmatrix}$$
$$= \begin{bmatrix} -2 & 2 \\ 0 & -14 \\ 8 & -4 \end{bmatrix} - \begin{bmatrix} -3 & -9 \\ 27 & -21 \\ 3 & 24 \end{bmatrix} = \begin{bmatrix} 1 & 11 \\ -27 & 7 \\ 5 & -28 \end{bmatrix}$$

Now Try Exercises 13 and 15

Matrix Products

Addition, subtraction, and multiplication can be performed on numbers, variables, and functions. The same operations apply to matrices. Matrix multiplication is different from scalar multiplication.

Credits Taken

	College A	College B
Student 1	10	7
Student 2	11	4

Table 6.10

Credit Cost

	Cost per Credit
College A	\$60
College B	\$80

Table 6.11

An Application Suppose two students are taking day classes at one college and night classes at another, in order to graduate on time. Tables 6.10 and 6.11 list the number of credits taken by the students and the cost per credit at each college.

The cost of tuition is computed by multiplying the number of credits and the cost of each credit. Student 1 is taking 10 credits at \$60 each and 7 credits at \$80 each. The total tuition for Student 1 is 10(\$60) + 7(\$80) = \$1160. In a similar manner, the tuition for Student 2 is given by 11(\$60) + 4(\$80) = \$980. The information in these tables can be represented by matrices. Let A represent Table 6.10 and B represent Table 6.11. B is called a **column matrix** because it has exactly one column.

$$A = \begin{bmatrix} 10 & 7 \\ 11 & 4 \end{bmatrix} \quad \text{and} \quad B = \begin{bmatrix} 60 \\ 80 \end{bmatrix}$$ — Column matrix

The matrix product AB calculates total tuition for each student.

Matrix Multiplication

$$AB = \begin{bmatrix} 10 & 7 \\ 11 & 4 \end{bmatrix}\begin{bmatrix} 60 \\ 80 \end{bmatrix} = \begin{bmatrix} 10(60) + 7(80) \\ 11(60) + 4(80) \end{bmatrix} = \begin{bmatrix} 1160 \\ 980 \end{bmatrix}$$

Generalizing from this example provides the following definition of matrix multiplication.

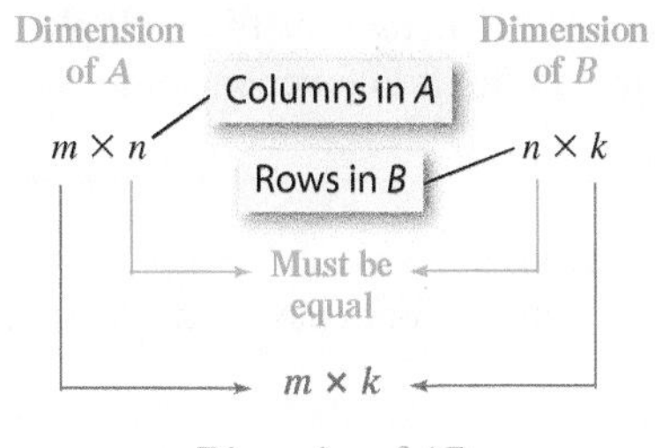

Figure 6.56

MATRIX MULTIPLICATION

The **product** of an $m \times n$ matrix A and an $n \times k$ matrix B is the $m \times k$ matrix AB, which is computed as follows. To find the element of AB in the ith row and jth column, multiply each element in the ith row of A by the corresponding element in the jth column of B. The sum of these products will give the element in row i, column j of AB.

NOTE In order to compute the product of two matrices, the number of columns in the first matrix must equal the number of rows in the second matrix, as illustrated in Figure 6.56.

EXAMPLE 7 **Multiplying matrices**

If possible, compute each product using

$$A = \begin{bmatrix} 1 & -1 \\ 0 & 3 \\ 4 & -2 \end{bmatrix}, B = \begin{bmatrix} -1 \\ -2 \end{bmatrix}, C = \begin{bmatrix} 1 & 2 & 3 \\ 4 & 5 & 6 \end{bmatrix}, \text{ and } D = \begin{bmatrix} 1 & -1 & 2 \\ 0 & 3 & -2 \\ -3 & 4 & 5 \end{bmatrix}.$$

(a) AB **(b)** CA **(c)** DC **(d)** CD

SOLUTION

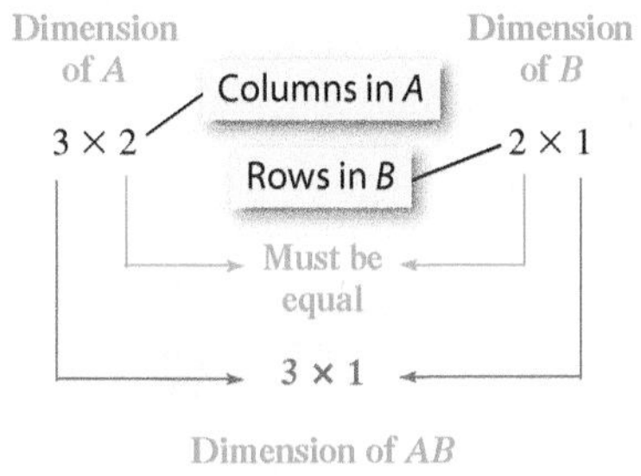

(a) The dimension of A is 3×2 and the dimension of B is 2×1. The dimension of AB is 3×1, as shown in Figure 6.57. The product AB is found as follows.

Dimension of A | Dimension of B | Columns in A | 3×2 | 2×1 | Rows in B | Must be equal | 3×1 | Dimension of AB

Figure 6.57

$$AB = \begin{bmatrix} 1 & -1 \\ 0 & 3 \\ 4 & -2 \end{bmatrix} \begin{bmatrix} -1 \\ -2 \end{bmatrix} = \begin{bmatrix} (1)(-1) + (-1)(-2) \\ (0)(-1) + \quad (3)(-2) \\ (4)(-1) + (-2)(-2) \end{bmatrix} = \begin{bmatrix} 1 \\ -6 \\ 0 \end{bmatrix}$$

(b) The dimension of C is 2×3 and the dimension of A is 3×2. Thus CA is 2×2.

$$CA = \begin{bmatrix} 1 & 2 & 3 \\ 4 & 5 & 6 \end{bmatrix} \begin{bmatrix} 1 & -1 \\ 0 & 3 \\ 4 & -2 \end{bmatrix}$$

$$= \begin{bmatrix} 1(1) + 2(0) + 3(4) & 1(-1) + 2(3) + 3(-2) \\ 4(1) + 5(0) + 6(4) & 4(-1) + 5(3) + 6(-2) \end{bmatrix}$$

$$= \begin{bmatrix} 13 & -1 \\ 28 & -1 \end{bmatrix}$$

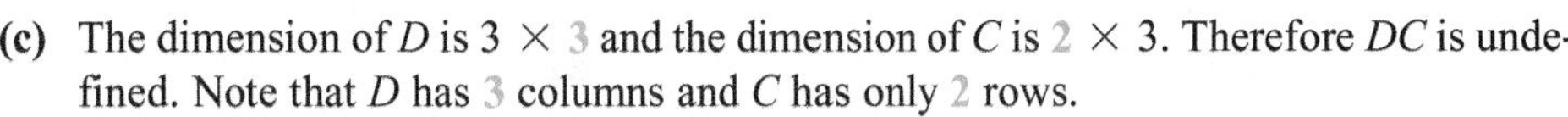

(c) The dimension of D is 3×3 and the dimension of C is 2×3. Therefore DC is undefined. Note that D has 3 columns and C has only 2 rows.

(d) The dimension of C is 2×3 and the dimension of D is 3×3. Thus CD is 2×3.

$$CD = \begin{bmatrix} 1 & 2 & 3 \\ 4 & 5 & 6 \end{bmatrix} \begin{bmatrix} 1 & -1 & 2 \\ 0 & 3 & -2 \\ -3 & 4 & 5 \end{bmatrix}$$

$$= \begin{bmatrix} 1(1) + 2(0) + 3(-3) & 1(-1) + 2(3) + 3(4) & 1(2) + 2(-2) + 3(5) \\ 4(1) + 5(0) + 6(-3) & 4(-1) + 5(3) + 6(4) & 4(2) + 5(-2) + 6(5) \end{bmatrix}$$

$$= \begin{bmatrix} -8 & 17 & 13 \\ -14 & 35 & 28 \end{bmatrix}$$

Now Try Exercises 27, 31, 33, and 43

MAKING CONNECTIONS

The Commutative Property and Matrix Multiplication Example 7 shows that $CD \neq DC$. Unlike multiplication of numbers, variables, and functions, matrix multiplication is *not* commutative. Instead, matrix multiplication is similar to function composition, where for a general pair of functions $f \circ g \neq g \circ f$.

Square matrices have the same number of rows as columns and have dimension $n \times n$ for some natural number n. When we multiply two square matrices, both having dimension $n \times n$, the resulting matrix also has dimension $n \times n$.

EXAMPLE 8 **Multiplying square matrices**

If $A = \begin{bmatrix} 1 & 0 & 7 \\ 3 & 2 & -1 \\ -5 & -2 & 5 \end{bmatrix}$ and $B = \begin{bmatrix} 4 & -6 & 7 \\ 8 & 9 & 10 \\ 0 & 1 & -3 \end{bmatrix}$, find AB.

SOLUTION

$$AB = \begin{bmatrix} 1 & 0 & 7 \\ 3 & 2 & -1 \\ -5 & -2 & 5 \end{bmatrix}\begin{bmatrix} 4 & -6 & 7 \\ 8 & 9 & 10 \\ 0 & 1 & -3 \end{bmatrix}$$

$$= \begin{bmatrix} 1(4) + 0(8) + 7(0) & 1(-6) + 0(9) + 7(1) & 1(7) + 0(10) + 7(-3) \\ 3(4) + 2(8) - 1(0) & 3(-6) + 2(9) - 1(1) & 3(7) + 2(10) - 1(-3) \\ -5(4) - 2(8) + 5(0) & -5(-6) - 2(9) + 5(1) & -5(7) - 2(10) + 5(-3) \end{bmatrix}$$

$$= \begin{bmatrix} 4 & 1 & -14 \\ 28 & -1 & 44 \\ -36 & 17 & -70 \end{bmatrix}$$

Now Try Exercise 37

An Application People can navigate from one web page to another by clicking a link. Figure 6.58 shows the links connecting four web pages. An arrow from one web page to another indicates a link. For example, it is possible to navigate from Page 1 to Page 3 in a single click, but it is not possible to navigate from Page 2 to Page 4 in a single click.

Web Page Links

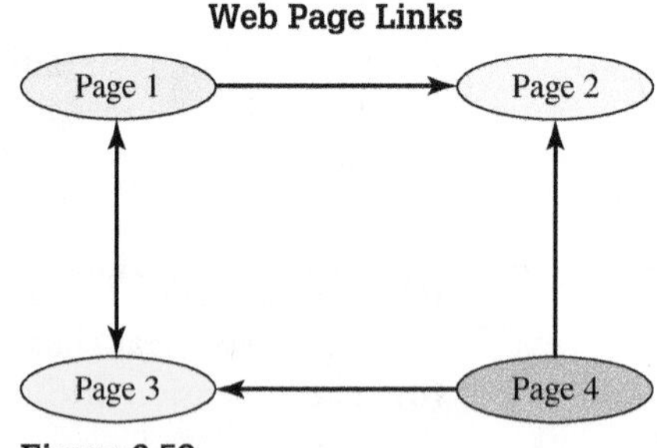

Figure 6.58

These web page links can be represented by a 4×4 square matrix. Because there is a link from Page 1 to **Page 2**, we put a 1 in row 1 **column 2**. Similarly, a link exists from Page 4 to **Page 3**, so we put a **1** in row 4 **column 3**. When no link exists from one web page to another, we place a 0 in the appropriate row and column of the matrix. Using this process results in the following matrix.

$$A = \begin{bmatrix} 0 & 1 & 1 & 0 \\ 0 & 0 & 0 & 0 \\ 1 & 0 & 0 & 0 \\ 0 & 1 & 1 & 0 \end{bmatrix}$$

In the next example we use matrix multiplication to find all of the 2-click paths between web pages.

EXAMPLE 9 **Finding 2-click paths between web pages**

Use matrix multiplication to find all 2-click paths among the web pages in Figure 6.58 on the previous page.

SOLUTION
The computation A^2 can be used to determine if it is possible to get from web page i to web page j in 2 clicks (links).

$$A^2 = \begin{bmatrix} 0 & 1 & 1 & 0 \\ 0 & 0 & 0 & 0 \\ 1 & 0 & 0 & 0 \\ 0 & 1 & 1 & 0 \end{bmatrix} \cdot \begin{bmatrix} 0 & 1 & 1 & 0 \\ 0 & 0 & 0 & 0 \\ 1 & 0 & 0 & 0 \\ 0 & 1 & 1 & 0 \end{bmatrix} = \begin{bmatrix} 1 & 0 & 0 & 0 \\ 0 & 0 & 0 & 0 \\ 0 & 1 & 1 & 0 \\ 1 & 0 & 0 & 0 \end{bmatrix}$$

The 1 in row 3 column 2 of A^2 indicates that there is a 2-click path from Page 3 to Page 2 (Page 3 to Page 1 to Page 2.) The other 1's in A^2 can be interpreted similarly.

Now Try Exercises 77, 79

NOTE In Example 9, computing A^3 would give all 3-click paths between the web pages. Similar statements can be made for A^n, where n is a positive integer.

Real numbers satisfy the commutative, associative, and distributive properties for various arithmetic operations. Matrices also satisfy some of these properties, provided that their dimensions are valid so the resulting expressions are defined.

PROPERTIES OF MATRICES

Let A, B, and C be matrices. Assume that each matrix operation is defined.

1. $A + B = B + A$	Commutative property for matrix addition (No commutative property for matrix multiplication)
2. $(A + B) + C = A + (B + C)$	Associative property for matrix addition
3. $(AB)C = A(BC)$	Associative property for matrix multiplication
4. $A(B + C) = AB + AC$	Distributive property

Technology and Matrices (Optional)

Computing arithmetic operations on large matrices by hand can be a difficult task. Many graphing calculators have the capability to perform addition, subtraction, multiplication, and scalar multiplication with matrices, as the next two examples demonstrate.

EXAMPLE 10 **Multiplying matrices with technology**

Use a graphing calculator to find the product AB from Example 8.

SOLUTION First enter the matrices A and B into your calculator, as illustrated in Figures 6.59 and 6.60. Then find their product on the home screen, as shown in Figure 6.61. Notice that the answer agrees with our results from Example 8.

Calculator Help
To enter the elements of a matrix, see Appendix A (page AP-12). To multiply two matrices, see Appendix A (page AP-13).

```
MATRIX[A]   3 ×3
[1    0    7   ]
[3    2    ⁻1  ]
[⁻5   ⁻2   5   ]
```

Figure 6.59

```
MATRIX[B]   3 ×3
[4    ⁻6   7   ]
[8    9    10  ]
[0    1    ⁻3  ]
```

Figure 6.60

```
[A]∗[B]
 [[4     1    ⁻14]
  [28   ⁻1    44 ]
  [⁻36  17   ⁻70]]
```

Figure 6.61

Now Try Exercise 45

EXAMPLE 11 Using technology to evaluate a matrix expression

Evaluate the expression $2A + 3B^3$, where

$$A = \begin{bmatrix} 3 & -1 & 2 \\ -1 & 6 & -1 \\ 2 & -1 & 9 \end{bmatrix} \quad \text{and} \quad B = \begin{bmatrix} 1 & -2 & 5 \\ 3 & 1 & -1 \\ 5 & 2 & 1 \end{bmatrix}.$$

```
2[A]+3[B]^3
 [[300   -32   322]
  [133    63    73 ]
  [358    28   348]]
```

Figure 6.62

SOLUTION In the expression $2A + 3B^3$, B^3 is equal to BBB. Enter each matrix into a calculator and evaluate the expression. Figure 6.62 shows the result of this computation.

Now Try Exercise 47

6.5 Putting It All Together

Addition, subtraction, and multiplication can be performed on numbers, variables, and functions. In this section we looked at how these operations also apply to matrices. The following table provides examples of these operations.

MATRIX ADDITION

$$\begin{bmatrix} 1 & 2 & 3 \\ 5 & 6 & 7 \end{bmatrix} + \begin{bmatrix} -1 & 0 & 8 \\ 9 & -2 & 10 \end{bmatrix} = \begin{bmatrix} 1 + (-1) & 2 + 0 & 3 + 8 \\ 5 + 9 & 6 + (-2) & 7 + 10 \end{bmatrix} = \begin{bmatrix} 0 & 2 & 11 \\ 14 & 4 & 17 \end{bmatrix}$$

The matrices must have the same dimension for their sum to be defined.

MATRIX SUBTRACTION

$$\begin{bmatrix} 1 & -4 \\ -3 & 4 \\ 2 & 7 \end{bmatrix} - \begin{bmatrix} 5 & 1 \\ 3 & 6 \\ 8 & -9 \end{bmatrix} = \begin{bmatrix} 1 - 5 & -4 - 1 \\ -3 - 3 & 4 - 6 \\ 2 - 8 & 7 - (-9) \end{bmatrix} = \begin{bmatrix} -4 & -5 \\ -6 & -2 \\ -6 & 16 \end{bmatrix}$$

The matrices must have the same dimension for their difference to be defined.

SCALAR MULTIPLICATION

$$3\begin{bmatrix} 3 & -2 \\ 0 & 1 \end{bmatrix} = \begin{bmatrix} 3(3) & 3(-2) \\ 3(0) & 3(1) \end{bmatrix} = \begin{bmatrix} 9 & -6 \\ 0 & 3 \end{bmatrix}$$

MATRIX MULTIPLICATION

$$\begin{bmatrix} 0 & 1 \\ 2 & -3 \end{bmatrix}\begin{bmatrix} 3 & -5 \\ 4 & 6 \end{bmatrix} = \begin{bmatrix} 0(3) + 1(4) & 0(-5) + 1(6) \\ 2(3) + (-3)(4) & 2(-5) + (-3)(6) \end{bmatrix} = \begin{bmatrix} 4 & 6 \\ -6 & -28 \end{bmatrix}$$

For a matrix product to be defined, the number of columns in the first matrix must equal the number of rows in the second matrix. Matrix multiplication is not commutative. That is, $AB \neq BA$ in general.

6.5 Exercises

Elements of Matrices

Exercises 1 and 2: Let a_{ij} and b_{ij} be general elements for the given matrices A and B.

(a) Identify a_{12}, b_{32}, and b_{22}.
(b) Compute $a_{11}b_{11} + a_{12}b_{21} + a_{13}b_{31}$.
(c) If possible, find a value for x that makes $A = B$.

1. $A = \begin{bmatrix} 1 & 3 & -4 \\ 3 & 0 & 7 \\ x & 1 & -1 \end{bmatrix}$, $B = \begin{bmatrix} 1 & x & -4 \\ 3 & 0 & 7 \\ 3 & 1 & -1 \end{bmatrix}$

2. $A = \begin{bmatrix} 0 & -1 & 6 \\ 2 & x & -1 \\ 9 & -2 & 1 \end{bmatrix}$, $B = \begin{bmatrix} 0 & -1 & x \\ 2 & 6 & -1 \\ 7 & -2 & 1 \end{bmatrix}$

Exercises 3–6: If possible, find values for x and y so that the matrices A and B are equal.

3. $A = \begin{bmatrix} x & 2 \\ -2 & 1 \end{bmatrix}$, $B = \begin{bmatrix} 1 & 2 \\ -2 & y \end{bmatrix}$

4. $A = \begin{bmatrix} 1 & x+y & 3 \\ 4 & -1 & 6 \\ 3 & 7 & -2 \end{bmatrix}$, $B = \begin{bmatrix} 1 & 2 & 3 \\ 4 & -1 & 6 \\ 3 & y & -2 \end{bmatrix}$

5. $A = \begin{bmatrix} x & 3 \\ 6 & -2 \end{bmatrix}$, $B = \begin{bmatrix} 1 & y & 0 \\ 6 & -2 & 0 \\ 0 & 0 & 0 \end{bmatrix}$

6. $A = \begin{bmatrix} 4 & -2 \\ 3 & -4 \\ x & y \end{bmatrix}$, $B = \begin{bmatrix} 4 & -2 & -2 \\ 3 & -4 & -4 \\ 7 & 8 & 8 \end{bmatrix}$

Addition, Subtraction, and Scalar Multiplication

Exercises 7–10: For the given matrices A and B find each of the following.
(a) $A + B$ (b) $B + A$ (c) $A - B$

7. $A = \begin{bmatrix} 4 & -1 \\ -1 & 4 \end{bmatrix}$, $B = \begin{bmatrix} -1 & 4 \\ 4 & -1 \end{bmatrix}$

8. $A = \begin{bmatrix} 2 & -4 \\ -1 & \frac{1}{2} \\ 3 & -2 \end{bmatrix}$, $B = \begin{bmatrix} 5 & 0 \\ 3 & \frac{1}{2} \\ -1 & 1 \end{bmatrix}$

9. $A = \begin{bmatrix} 3 & 4 & -1 \\ 0 & -3 & 2 \\ -2 & 5 & 10 \end{bmatrix}$, $B = \begin{bmatrix} 11 & 5 & -2 \\ 4 & -7 & 12 \\ 6 & 6 & 6 \end{bmatrix}$

10. $A = \begin{bmatrix} 1 & 6 & 1 & -2 \\ 0 & 1 & 3 & 5 \\ 0 & 0 & 1 & -2 \end{bmatrix}$, $B = \begin{bmatrix} 1 & 0 & 0 & 9 \\ 3 & 1 & 0 & 3 \\ -1 & 4 & 1 & -2 \end{bmatrix}$

Exercises 11–16: If possible, find each of the following.
(a) $A + B$ (b) $3A$ (c) $2A - 3B$

11. $A = \begin{bmatrix} 2 & -6 \\ 3 & 1 \end{bmatrix}$, $B = \begin{bmatrix} -1 & 0 \\ -2 & 3 \end{bmatrix}$

12. $A = \begin{bmatrix} 1 & -2 & 5 \\ 3 & -4 & -1 \end{bmatrix}$, $B = \begin{bmatrix} 0 & -1 & -5 \\ -3 & 1 & 2 \end{bmatrix}$

13. $A = \begin{bmatrix} 1 & -1 & 0 \\ 1 & 5 & 9 \\ -4 & 8 & -5 \end{bmatrix}$, $B = \begin{bmatrix} 2 & 8 & -1 \\ 6 & -1 & 3 \end{bmatrix}$

14. $A = \begin{bmatrix} 6 & 2 & 9 \\ 3 & -2 & 0 \\ -1 & 4 & 8 \end{bmatrix}$, $B = \begin{bmatrix} 1 & 0 & -1 \\ 3 & 0 & 7 \\ 0 & -2 & -5 \end{bmatrix}$

15. $A = \begin{bmatrix} -2 & -1 \\ -5 & 1 \\ 2 & -3 \end{bmatrix}$, $B = \begin{bmatrix} 2 & -1 \\ 3 & 1 \\ 7 & -5 \end{bmatrix}$

16. $A = \begin{bmatrix} 0 & 1 \\ 3 & 2 \\ 4 & -9 \end{bmatrix}$, $B = \begin{bmatrix} 5 & 2 & -7 \\ 8 & -2 & 0 \end{bmatrix}$

Exercises 17–22: Evaluate the matrix expression.

17. $2\begin{bmatrix} 2 & -1 \\ 5 & 1 \\ 0 & 3 \end{bmatrix} + \begin{bmatrix} 5 & 0 \\ 7 & -3 \\ 1 & 1 \end{bmatrix} - \begin{bmatrix} 9 & -4 \\ 4 & 4 \\ 1 & 6 \end{bmatrix}$

18. $-3\begin{bmatrix} 3 & 8 \\ -1 & -9 \end{bmatrix} + 5\begin{bmatrix} 4 & -8 \\ 1 & 6 \end{bmatrix}$

19. $\begin{bmatrix} 4 & 6 \\ 3 & -7 \end{bmatrix} - 2\begin{bmatrix} 1 & 0 \\ -4 & 1 \end{bmatrix}$

20. $\begin{bmatrix} 5 & -1 & 6 \\ -2 & 10 & 12 \\ 5 & 2 & 9 \end{bmatrix} - \begin{bmatrix} -1 & 2 & 2 \\ 2 & -1 & 2 \\ 2 & 2 & -1 \end{bmatrix}$

21. $2\begin{bmatrix} 2 & -1 & -1 \\ -1 & 2 & -1 \\ -1 & -1 & 2 \end{bmatrix} + 3\begin{bmatrix} 1 & 2 & 3 \\ 2 & 1 & 3 \\ 2 & 3 & 1 \end{bmatrix}$

22. $3\begin{bmatrix} 1 & 0 & 3 & -1 \\ 0 & 1 & 2 & -1 \\ 1 & 0 & -3 & 1 \end{bmatrix} - 4\begin{bmatrix} -1 & 0 & 0 & 4 \\ 0 & -1 & 3 & 2 \\ 2 & 0 & 1 & -1 \end{bmatrix}$

Matrices and Digital Photography

Exercises 23–26: **Digital Photography** *(Refer to the discussion of digital images in this section.) Consider the following simplified digital image, which has a 3 × 3 grid with four gray levels numbered from 0 to 3. It shows the number 1 in dark gray on a light gray background. Let A be the 3 × 3 matrix that represents this image digitally.*

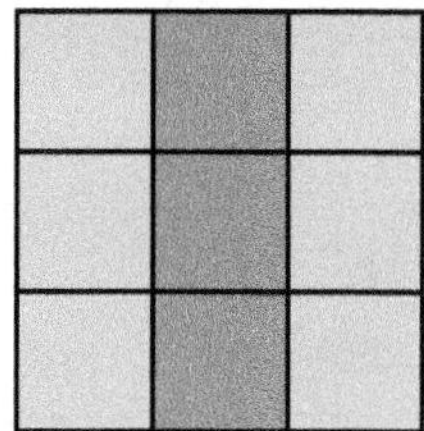

23. Find the matrix A.

24. Find a matrix B such that adding B to A will cause the entire image to become one gray level darker. Evaluate the expression $A + B$.

25. (Refer to Example 4.) Find a matrix B such that adding B to A will enhance the contrast of A by one gray level. Evaluate $A + B$.

26. Find a matrix B such that subtracting B from A will cause the entire image to become lighter by one gray level. Evaluate the expression $A - B$.

Matrix Multiplication

Exercises 27–44: If possible, find AB and BA.

27. $A = \begin{bmatrix} 1 & -1 \\ 2 & 0 \end{bmatrix}$, $B = \begin{bmatrix} -2 & 3 \\ 1 & 2 \end{bmatrix}$

28. $A = \begin{bmatrix} -3 & 5 \\ 2 & 7 \end{bmatrix}$, $B = \begin{bmatrix} -1 & 2 \\ 0 & 7 \end{bmatrix}$

29. $A = \begin{bmatrix} 5 & -7 & 2 \\ 0 & 1 & 5 \end{bmatrix}$, $B = \begin{bmatrix} 9 & 8 & 7 \\ 1 & -1 & -2 \end{bmatrix}$

30. $A = \begin{bmatrix} 2 & 1 & -1 \\ 0 & 2 & 1 \\ 3 & 2 & -1 \end{bmatrix}$, $B = \begin{bmatrix} 1 & 0 \\ 2 & -1 \\ 3 & 1 \end{bmatrix}$

31. $A = \begin{bmatrix} 3 & -1 \\ 1 & 0 \\ -2 & -4 \end{bmatrix}$, $B = \begin{bmatrix} -2 & 5 & -3 \\ 9 & -7 & 0 \end{bmatrix}$

32. $A = \begin{bmatrix} -1 & 0 & -2 \\ 4 & -2 & 1 \end{bmatrix}$, $B = \begin{bmatrix} 2 & -2 \\ 5 & -1 \\ 0 & 1 \end{bmatrix}$

33. $A = \begin{bmatrix} 1 & -1 & 0 \\ 2 & -1 & 5 \\ 6 & 1 & -4 \end{bmatrix}$, $B = \begin{bmatrix} -1 & 3 & -1 \\ 7 & -7 & 1 \end{bmatrix}$

34. $A = \begin{bmatrix} 2 & -1 & -5 \\ 4 & -1 & 6 \\ -2 & 0 & 9 \end{bmatrix}$, $B = \begin{bmatrix} 1 & 2 \\ -1 & -1 \\ 2 & 0 \end{bmatrix}$

35. $A = \begin{bmatrix} 2 & -3 \\ 5 & 3 \end{bmatrix}$, $B = \begin{bmatrix} -3 \\ 4 \\ 1 \end{bmatrix}$

36. $A = \begin{bmatrix} 3 & -1 \\ 2 & -2 \\ 0 & 4 \end{bmatrix}$, $B = \begin{bmatrix} 1 & -4 & 0 \\ -1 & 3 & 2 \end{bmatrix}$

37. $A = \begin{bmatrix} 2 & -1 & 3 \\ 0 & 1 & 0 \\ 2 & -2 & 3 \end{bmatrix}$, $B = \begin{bmatrix} 1 & 5 & -1 \\ 0 & 1 & 3 \\ -1 & 2 & 1 \end{bmatrix}$

38. $A = \begin{bmatrix} 1 & -2 & 5 \\ 1 & 0 & -2 \\ 1 & 3 & 2 \end{bmatrix}$, $B = \begin{bmatrix} -1 & 4 & 2 \\ -3 & 0 & 1 \\ 5 & 1 & 0 \end{bmatrix}$

39. $A = \begin{bmatrix} 2 & -1 \\ 3 & 1 \end{bmatrix}$, $B = \begin{bmatrix} 1 \\ 3 \end{bmatrix}$

40. $A = [5 \quad -3]$, $B = \begin{bmatrix} 1 \\ 3 \end{bmatrix}$

41. $A = \begin{bmatrix} -3 & 1 \\ 2 & -4 \end{bmatrix}$, $B = \begin{bmatrix} 1 & 0 & -2 \\ -4 & 8 & 1 \end{bmatrix}$

42. $A = \begin{bmatrix} 6 & 1 & 0 \\ -2 & 5 & 1 \\ 4 & -7 & 10 \end{bmatrix}$, $B = \begin{bmatrix} 10 \\ 20 \\ 30 \end{bmatrix}$

43. $A = \begin{bmatrix} 1 & 0 & -2 \\ 3 & -4 & 1 \\ 2 & 0 & 5 \end{bmatrix}$, $B = \begin{bmatrix} 1 \\ -1 \\ 3 \end{bmatrix}$

44. $A = \begin{bmatrix} 1 & -1 & 3 & -2 \\ 1 & 0 & 3 & 4 \\ 2 & -2 & 0 & 8 \end{bmatrix}$, $B = \begin{bmatrix} 1 & -1 \\ 0 & 5 \\ 2 & 3 \\ -5 & 4 \end{bmatrix}$

Technology and Matrices

Exercises 45–48: Use the given A and B to evaluate each expression.

$$A = \begin{bmatrix} 3 & -2 & 4 \\ 5 & 2 & -3 \\ 7 & 5 & 4 \end{bmatrix}, \quad B = \begin{bmatrix} 1 & 1 & -5 \\ -1 & 0 & -7 \\ -6 & 4 & 3 \end{bmatrix}$$

45. AB

46. BA

47. $3A^2 + 2B$

48. $B^2 - 3A$

Exercises 49–52: **Properties of Matrices** *Use a graphing calculator to evaluate the expression with the given matrices A, B, and C. Compare your answers for parts (a) and (b). Then interpret the results.*

$$A = \begin{bmatrix} 2 & -1 & 3 \\ 1 & 3 & -5 \\ 0 & -2 & 1 \end{bmatrix}, B = \begin{bmatrix} 6 & 2 & 7 \\ 3 & -4 & -5 \\ 7 & 1 & 0 \end{bmatrix},$$

$$C = \begin{bmatrix} 1 & 4 & -3 \\ 8 & 1 & -1 \\ 4 & 6 & -2 \end{bmatrix}$$

49. **(a)** $A(B + C)$ **(b)** $AB + AC$

50. **(a)** $(A - B)C$ **(b)** $AC - BC$

51. **(a)** $(A - B)^2$ **(b)** $A^2 - AB - BA + B^2$

52. **(a)** $(AB)C$ **(b)** $A(BC)$

Applications

Exercises 53–56: **Social Networks** *(Refer to Example 2.) The following graph shows a simple social network.*

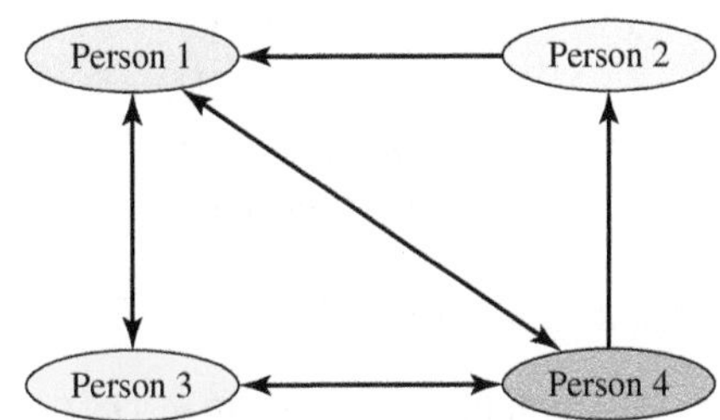

53. Use a matrix to represent this social network.

54. Which person is the most liked person in the network?

55. Which person is the least liked person in the network?

56. Which person likes the most people in the network?

Exercises 57–60: **Social Networks** *(Refer to the previous four exercises.) The following matrix represents a simple social network.*

$$\begin{bmatrix} 0 & 0 & 1 & 0 \\ 0 & 0 & 0 & 0 \\ 1 & 1 & 0 & 0 \\ 1 & 0 & 1 & 0 \end{bmatrix}$$

57. Draw a graph of this network.

58. Row 2 in the matrix contains only 0's. What does this tell us about Person 2?

59. Column 4 in the matrix contains only 0's. What does this tell us about Person 4?

60. If a column of a social network matrix contains only 1's (except on the main diagonal), what can be said about the person represented by that column?

61. **Negative Image** The negative image of a picture interchanges black and white. The number 1 is represented by the matrix A. Determine a matrix B such that $B - A$ represents the negative image of the picture represented by A. Evaluate $B - A$.

$$A = \begin{bmatrix} 0 & 3 & 0 \\ 0 & 3 & 0 \\ 0 & 3 & 0 \end{bmatrix}$$

62. **Negative Image** (Refer to the previous exercise.) Matrix A represents a digital photograph. Find a matrix B that represents the negative image of this picture.

$$A = \begin{bmatrix} 0 & 3 & 0 \\ 1 & 3 & 1 \\ 2 & 3 & 2 \end{bmatrix}$$

Exercises 63 and 64: **Digital Photography** *The digital image represents the letter F using 20 pixels in a 5 × 4 grid. Assume that there are four gray levels from 0 to 3.*

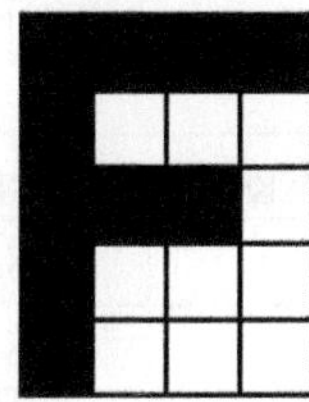

63. Find a matrix A that represents this digital image of the letter F.

64. (Continuation of Exercise 63)

(a) Find a matrix B such that $B - A$ represents the negative image of the picture represented by A.

(b) Find a matrix C such that $A + C$ represents a decrease in the contrast of A by one gray level.

Exercises 65–68: **Digitizing Letters** *(Refer to Exercise 61.) Complete the following.*

(a) Design a matrix A with dimension 4 × 4 that represents a digital image of the given letter. Assume that there are four gray levels from 0 to 3.

(b) Find a matrix B such that B − A represents the negative image of the picture represented by matrix A from part (a).

65. Z **66.** N

67. L **68.** O

Exercises 69–72: **Tuition Costs** *(Refer to the discussion after Example 6.)*

(a) Find a matrix A and a column matrix B that describe the following tables.

(b) Find the matrix product AB, and interpret the result.

69.

	College A	College B
Student 1	12	4
Student 2	8	7

	Cost per Credit
College A	\$55
College B	\$70

70.

	College A	College B
Student 1	15	2
Student 2	12	4

	Cost per Credit
College A	\$90
College B	\$75

71.

	College A	College B
Student 1	10	5
Student 2	9	8
Student 3	11	3

	Cost per Credit
College A	\$60
College B	\$70

72.

	College A	College B	College C
Student 1	6	0	3
Student 2	11	3	0
Student 3	0	12	3

	Cost per Credit
College A	\$50
College B	\$65
College C	\$60

73. **Auto Parts** A store owner makes two separate orders for three types of auto parts: I, II, and III. The numbers of parts ordered are represented by the matrix A.

$$A = \begin{array}{c} \begin{matrix} \text{I} & \text{II} & \text{III} \end{matrix} \\ \begin{bmatrix} 3 & 4 & 8 \\ 5 & 6 & 2 \end{bmatrix} \end{array} \begin{matrix} \text{Order 1} \\ \text{Order 2} \end{matrix}$$

For example, Order 1 called for 4 parts of type II. The cost in dollars of each part can be represented by the matrix B.

$$B = \begin{array}{c} \text{Cost} \\ \begin{bmatrix} 10 \\ 20 \\ 30 \end{bmatrix} \end{array} \begin{matrix} \text{Part I} \\ \text{Part II} \\ \text{Part III} \end{matrix}$$

Find AB and interpret the result.

74. **Car Sales** Two car dealers buy four different makes of cars: I, II, III, and IV. The number of each make of automobile bought by each dealer is represented by the matrix A.

$$A = \begin{array}{c} \begin{matrix} \text{I} & \text{II} & \text{III} & \text{IV} \end{matrix} \\ \begin{bmatrix} 1 & 3 & 8 & 4 \\ 3 & 5 & 7 & 0 \end{bmatrix} \end{array} \begin{matrix} \text{Dealer 1} \\ \text{Dealer 2} \end{matrix}$$

For example, Dealer 2 bought 7 cars of type III. The cost in thousands of dollars of each type of car can be represented by the matrix B.

$$B = \begin{array}{c} \text{Cost} \\ \begin{bmatrix} 15 \\ 21 \\ 28 \\ 38 \end{bmatrix} \end{array} \begin{matrix} \text{Make I} \\ \text{Make II} \\ \text{Make III} \\ \text{Make IV} \end{matrix}$$

Find AB and interpret the result.

Exercises 75–80: **Web Page Links** *(Refer to Example 9 and the application preceding it.) The following graph shows web page links.*

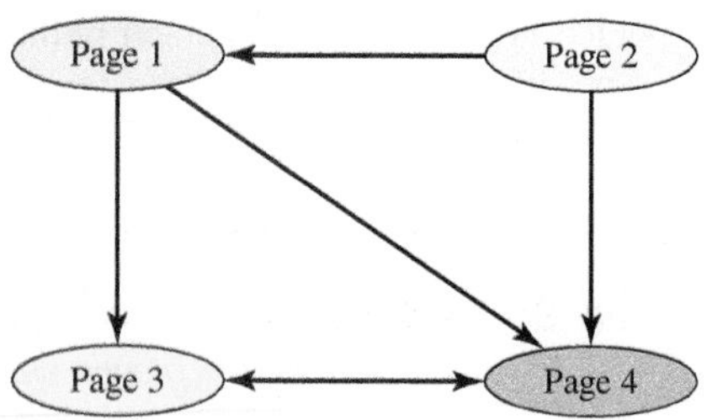

75. Create a matrix A that represents this situation.

76. Which page can be reached in a single click from every other page in the network?

77. Compute A^2.

78. Which two pages cannot be reached using a 2-click path from any other page in the network?

79. There is a 2 in row 2 column 3 of A^2. What does this tell us?

80. There is a 1 in row 4 column 4 of A^2. What does this tell us?

Writing about Mathematics

81. Discuss whether matrix multiplication is more like multiplication of functions or composition of functions. Explain your reasoning.

82. Describe one application of matrices.

Extended and Discovery Exercises

Exercises 1–4: **Representing Colors** *Colors for computer monitors are often described using ordered triples. One model, called the RGB system, uses red, green, and blue to generate all colors. The figure describes the relationships of these colors in this system. Red is* $(1, 0, 0)$, *green is* $(0, 1, 0)$, *and blue is* $(0, 0, 1)$. *Since equal amounts of red and green combine to form yellow, yellow is represented by* $(1, 1, 0)$. *Similarly, magenta (a deep reddish purple) is a mixture of blue and red and is represented by* $(1, 0, 1)$. *Cyan is* $(0, 1, 1)$, *since it is a mixture of blue and green.*

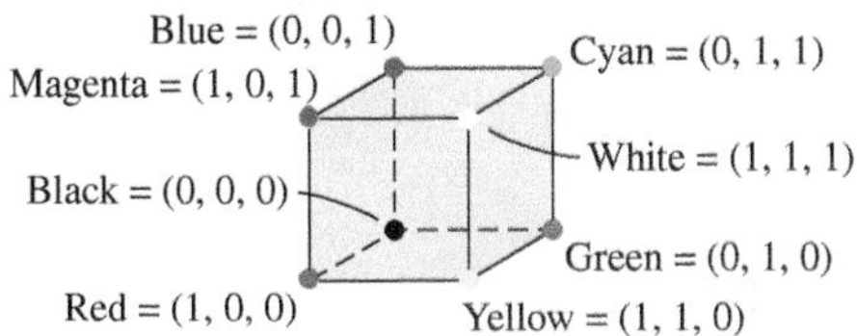

Another color model uses cyan, magenta, and yellow. Referred to as the CMY model, it is used in the four-color printing process for textbooks like this one. In this system, cyan is $(1, 0, 0)$, *magenta is* $(0, 1, 0)$, *and yellow is* $(0, 0, 1)$.

In the CMY model, red is created by mixing magenta and yellow. Thus, red is $(0, 1, 1)$ *in this system. To convert ordered triples in the RGB model to ordered triples in the CMY model, we can use the following matrix equation. In both of these systems, color intensities vary between 0 and 1.* (***Sources:*** I. Kerlow, *The Art of 3-D Computer Animation and Imaging;* R. Wolff.)

$$\begin{bmatrix} C \\ M \\ Y \end{bmatrix} = \begin{bmatrix} 1 \\ 1 \\ 1 \end{bmatrix} - \begin{bmatrix} R \\ G \\ B \end{bmatrix}$$

1. In the RGB model, aquamarine is (0.631, 1, 0.933). Use the matrix equation to determine the mixture of cyan, magenta, and yellow that makes aquamarine in the CMY model.

2. In the RGB model, rust is (0.552, 0.168, 0.066). Use the matrix equation to determine the mixture of cyan, magenta, and yellow that makes rust in the CMY model.

3. Use the given matrix equation to find a matrix equation that changes colors represented by ordered triples in the CMY model into ordered triples in the RGB model.

4. In the CMY model, (0.012, 0, 0.597) is a cream color. Use the matrix equation from Exercise 3 to determine the mixture of red, green, and blue that makes a cream color in the RGB model.

6.6 Inverses of Matrices

- **Understand matrix inverses and the identity matrices**
- **Find inverses symbolically**
- **Represent linear systems with matrix equations**
- **Solve linear systems with matrix inverses**

Introduction

Section 5.2 discussed how the inverse function f^{-1} will undo or cancel the computation performed by the function f. Like functions, some matrices have inverses. The inverse of a matrix A will undo or cancel the computation performed by A. For example, in computer graphics, if a matrix A rotates a figure on the screen 90° clockwise, then the inverse matrix will rotate the figure 90° counterclockwise. Similarly, if a matrix B translates a figure 3 units right, then B^{-1} will restore the figure to its original position by translating it 3 units left. This section discusses matrix inverses and some of their applications.

Understanding Matrix Inverses

An Application In computer graphics, the matrix

$$A = \begin{bmatrix} 1 & 0 & h \\ 0 & 1 & k \\ 0 & 0 & 1 \end{bmatrix} \quad \text{Matrix for translating a point}$$

is used to translate a point (x, y) horizontally h units and vertically k units. The translation is to the right if $h > 0$ and to the left if $h < 0$. Similarly, the translation is upward if

$k > 0$ and downward if $k < 0$. A point (x, y) is represented by the 3×1 *column matrix*

$$X = \begin{bmatrix} x \\ y \\ 1 \end{bmatrix}. \quad \text{Column matrix}$$

Translating a Point

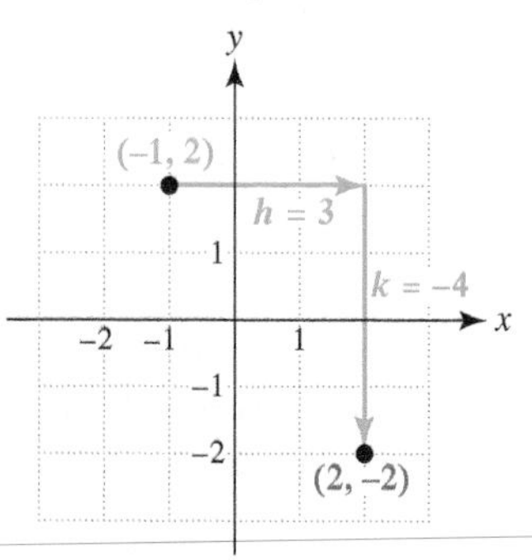

Figure 6.63

The third element in X is always equal to 1. For example, the point $(-1, 2)$ could be translated 3 units right and 4 units downward by computing the following matrix product.

Translating (−1, 2) Right 3 Units and Downward 4 Units

$$AX = \begin{bmatrix} 1 & 0 & 3 \\ 0 & 1 & -4 \\ 0 & 0 & 1 \end{bmatrix}\begin{bmatrix} -1 \\ 2 \\ 1 \end{bmatrix} = \begin{bmatrix} 2 \\ -2 \\ 1 \end{bmatrix} = Y$$

Its new location is $(2, -2)$. In the matrix A, $h = 3$ and $k = -4$. See Figure 6.63. (***Source:*** C. Pokorny and C. Gerald, *Computer Graphics*.)

If A translates a point 3 units right and 4 units downward, then the inverse matrix translates a point 3 units left and 4 units upward. This would return a point to its original position after being translated by A. Therefore the *inverse matrix of A*, denoted A^{-1}, is given by

$$A^{-1} = \begin{bmatrix} 1 & 0 & -3 \\ 0 & 1 & 4 \\ 0 & 0 & 1 \end{bmatrix}. \quad \text{Inverse matrix}$$

In A^{-1}, $h = -3$ and $k = 4$. The matrix product $A^{-1}Y$ results in

Translating (2, −2) Left 3 Units and Upward 4 Units

$$A^{-1}Y = \begin{bmatrix} 1 & 0 & -3 \\ 0 & 1 & 4 \\ 0 & 0 & 1 \end{bmatrix}\begin{bmatrix} 2 \\ -2 \\ 1 \end{bmatrix} = \begin{bmatrix} -1 \\ 2 \\ 1 \end{bmatrix} = X.$$

The matrix A^{-1} translates $(2, -2)$ to its original coordinates of $(-1, 2)$. The two translations acting on the point $(-1, 2)$ can be represented by the following computation.

$$A^{-1}AX = \begin{bmatrix} 1 & 0 & -3 \\ 0 & 1 & 4 \\ 0 & 0 & 1 \end{bmatrix}\begin{bmatrix} 1 & 0 & 3 \\ 0 & 1 & -4 \\ 0 & 0 & 1 \end{bmatrix}\begin{bmatrix} -1 \\ 2 \\ 1 \end{bmatrix} = \begin{bmatrix} 1 & 0 & 0 \\ 0 & 1 & 0 \\ 0 & 0 & 1 \end{bmatrix}\begin{bmatrix} -1 \\ 2 \\ 1 \end{bmatrix} = \begin{bmatrix} -1 \\ 2 \\ 1 \end{bmatrix} = X$$

That is, the action of A followed by A^{-1} on the point $(-1, 2)$ results in $(-1, 2)$. In a similar manner, if we reverse the order of A^{-1} and A to compute $AA^{-1}X$, the result is again X.

$$AA^{-1}X = \begin{bmatrix} 1 & 0 & 3 \\ 0 & 1 & -4 \\ 0 & 0 & 1 \end{bmatrix}\begin{bmatrix} 1 & 0 & -3 \\ 0 & 1 & 4 \\ 0 & 0 & 1 \end{bmatrix}\begin{bmatrix} -1 \\ 2 \\ 1 \end{bmatrix} = \begin{bmatrix} 1 & 0 & 0 \\ 0 & 1 & 0 \\ 0 & 0 & 1 \end{bmatrix}\begin{bmatrix} -1 \\ 2 \\ 1 \end{bmatrix} = \begin{bmatrix} -1 \\ 2 \\ 1 \end{bmatrix} = X$$

Notice that both matrix products $A^{-1}A$ and AA^{-1} resulted in a matrix with 1's on its main diagonal and 0's elsewhere.

The Identity Matrix

An $n \times n$ matrix with 1's on its main diagonal and 0's elsewhere is called the $n \times n$ *identity matrix*. This matrix is important because its product with any $n \times n$ matrix A always equals A.

THE $n \times n$ IDENTITY MATRIX

The **$n \times n$ identity matrix,** denoted I_n, has only 1's on its main diagonal and 0's elsewhere.

Some examples of identity matrices are shown here.

Identity Matrices

$$I_2 = \begin{bmatrix} 1 & 0 \\ 0 & 1 \end{bmatrix}, \quad I_3 = \begin{bmatrix} 1 & 0 & 0 \\ 0 & 1 & 0 \\ 0 & 0 & 1 \end{bmatrix}, \quad \text{and} \quad I_4 = \begin{bmatrix} 1 & 0 & 0 & 0 \\ 0 & 1 & 0 & 0 \\ 0 & 0 & 1 & 0 \\ 0 & 0 & 0 & 1 \end{bmatrix}$$

If A is any $n \times n$ matrix, then $I_nA = A$ and $AI_n = A$. For instance, if

$$A = \begin{bmatrix} 2 & 3 \\ 4 & 5 \end{bmatrix},$$

then

$$I_2A = \begin{bmatrix} 1 & 0 \\ 0 & 1 \end{bmatrix}\begin{bmatrix} 2 & 3 \\ 4 & 5 \end{bmatrix} = \begin{bmatrix} 2 & 3 \\ 4 & 5 \end{bmatrix} = A \quad \text{and}$$

$$AI_2 = \begin{bmatrix} 2 & 3 \\ 4 & 5 \end{bmatrix}\begin{bmatrix} 1 & 0 \\ 0 & 1 \end{bmatrix} = \begin{bmatrix} 2 & 3 \\ 4 & 5 \end{bmatrix} = A.$$

Matrix Inverses

Next we formally define the inverse of an $n \times n$ matrix A, whenever it exists.

INVERSE OF A SQUARE MATRIX

Let A be an $n \times n$ matrix. If there exists an $n \times n$ matrix, denoted A^{-1}, that satisfies

$$A^{-1}A = I_n \quad \text{and} \quad AA^{-1} = I_n,$$

then A^{-1} is the **inverse** of A.

If A^{-1} exists, then A is **invertible** or **nonsingular.** On the other hand, if a matrix A is not invertible, then it is **singular.** Not every matrix has an inverse. For example, the **zero matrix** with dimension 3×3 is given by

$$O_3 = \begin{bmatrix} 0 & 0 & 0 \\ 0 & 0 & 0 \\ 0 & 0 & 0 \end{bmatrix}. \quad \text{Zero matrix}$$

The matrix O_3 does not have an inverse. The product of O_3 with any 3×3 matrix B would be O_3, rather than the identity matrix I_3.

EXAMPLE 1 **Verifying an inverse**

Determine if B is the inverse of A, where

$$A = \begin{bmatrix} 5 & 3 \\ -3 & -2 \end{bmatrix} \quad \text{and} \quad B = \begin{bmatrix} 2 & 3 \\ -3 & -5 \end{bmatrix}.$$

SOLUTION For B to be the inverse of A, it must satisfy $AB = I_2$ and $BA = I_2$.

$$AB = \begin{bmatrix} 5 & 3 \\ -3 & -2 \end{bmatrix}\begin{bmatrix} 2 & 3 \\ -3 & -5 \end{bmatrix} = \begin{bmatrix} 1 & 0 \\ 0 & 1 \end{bmatrix} = I_2$$

$$BA = \begin{bmatrix} 2 & 3 \\ -3 & -5 \end{bmatrix}\begin{bmatrix} 5 & 3 \\ -3 & -2 \end{bmatrix} = \begin{bmatrix} 1 & 0 \\ 0 & 1 \end{bmatrix} = I_2$$

Thus B is the inverse of A. That is, $B = A^{-1}$.

Now Try Exercise 1

An Application The next example discusses the significance of an inverse matrix in computer graphics.

EXAMPLE 2 **Interpreting an inverse matrix**

The matrix A can be used to rotate a point 90° clockwise about the origin, where

$$A = \begin{bmatrix} 0 & 1 & 0 \\ -1 & 0 & 0 \\ 0 & 0 & 1 \end{bmatrix} \quad \text{and} \quad A^{-1} = \begin{bmatrix} 0 & -1 & 0 \\ 1 & 0 & 0 \\ 0 & 0 & 1 \end{bmatrix}.$$

(a) Use A to rotate the point $(-2, 0)$ clockwise 90° about the origin.
(b) Make a conjecture about the effect of A^{-1} on the resulting point.
(c) Test this conjecture.

SOLUTION

(a) First, let the point $(-2, 0)$ be represented by the column matrix

$$X = \begin{bmatrix} -2 \\ 0 \\ 1 \end{bmatrix}.$$

Then compute

$$AX = \begin{bmatrix} 0 & 1 & 0 \\ -1 & 0 & 0 \\ 0 & 0 & 1 \end{bmatrix}\begin{bmatrix} -2 \\ 0 \\ 1 \end{bmatrix} = \begin{bmatrix} 0 \\ 2 \\ 1 \end{bmatrix} = Y.$$

If the point $(-2, 0)$ is rotated 90° clockwise about the origin, its new location is $(0, 2)$. See Figure 6.64.

Rotating a Point About the Origin

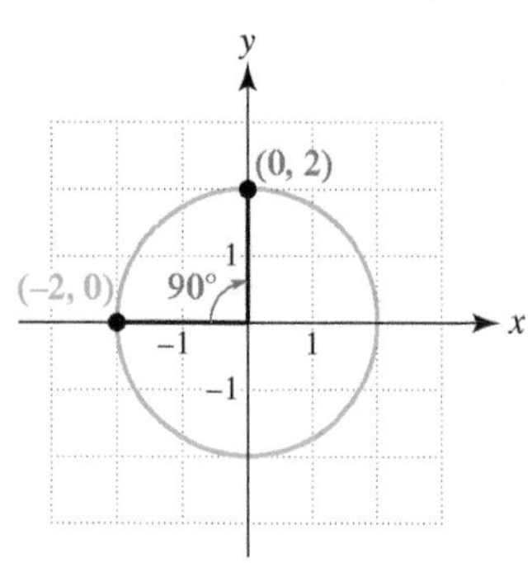

Figure 6.64

(b) Since A^{-1} represents the inverse operation of A, A^{-1} will rotate the point located at $(0, 2)$ counterclockwise 90°, back to $(-2, 0)$.

(c) This conjecture is correct, since

$$A^{-1}Y = \begin{bmatrix} 0 & -1 & 0 \\ 1 & 0 & 0 \\ 0 & 0 & 1 \end{bmatrix}\begin{bmatrix} 0 \\ 2 \\ 1 \end{bmatrix} = \begin{bmatrix} -2 \\ 0 \\ 1 \end{bmatrix} = X.$$

Now Try Exercise 67

CLASS DISCUSSION

What will the results be of the computations AAX and $A^{-1}A^{-1}X$?

Finding Inverses Symbolically

The inverse matrix of an $n \times n$ matrix A can be found symbolically by first forming the augmented matrix $[A \,|\, I_n]$ and then performing matrix row operations, until the left side of the augmented matrix becomes the identity matrix. The resulting augmented matrix can be written as $[I_n \,|\, A^{-1}]$, where the right side of the matrix is A^{-1}.

In the next example, we find A^{-1} from Example 2 by hand.

EXAMPLE 3 **Finding an inverse symbolically**

Find A^{-1} if

$$A = \begin{bmatrix} 0 & 1 & 0 \\ -1 & 0 & 0 \\ 0 & 0 & 1 \end{bmatrix}.$$

SOLUTION

Getting Started Begin by forming the following 3×6 augmented matrix with the 3×3 identity matrix on the right half.

Augmented Matrix $[A|I_3]$

$$\left[\begin{array}{ccc|ccc} 0 & 1 & 0 & 1 & 0 & 0 \\ -1 & 0 & 0 & 0 & 1 & 0 \\ 0 & 0 & 1 & 0 & 0 & 1 \end{array}\right]$$

Next use row transformations to obtain the 3×3 identity on the left side. ▶

To obtain a 1 in the first row and first column, we negate the elements in row 2 and then interchange row 1 and row 2. The same row transformations are also applied to the right side of the augmented matrix.

$$\left[\begin{array}{ccc|ccc} 0 & 1 & 0 & 1 & 0 & 0 \\ -1 & 0 & 0 & 0 & 1 & 0 \\ 0 & 0 & 1 & 0 & 0 & 1 \end{array}\right] \begin{array}{c} -R_2 \rightarrow \\ R_1 \rightarrow \\ R_3 \rightarrow \end{array} \left[\begin{array}{ccc|ccc} 1 & 0 & 0 & 0 & -1 & 0 \\ 0 & 1 & 0 & 1 & 0 & 0 \\ 0 & 0 & 1 & 0 & 0 & 1 \end{array}\right]$$

Because the left side of the augmented matrix is now the 3×3 identity, we stop. The right side of the augmented matrix is A^{-1}. Thus

$$A^{-1} = \begin{bmatrix} 0 & -1 & 0 \\ 1 & 0 & 0 \\ 0 & 0 & 1 \end{bmatrix}, \quad \text{Inverse matrix}$$

and our result agrees with the information in Example 2.

Now Try Exercise 21

Many times finding inverses requires several steps of row transformations. In the next two examples, we find the inverse of a 2×2 matrix and a 3×3 matrix.

EXAMPLE 4 **Finding the inverse of a 2×2 matrix symbolically**

Find A^{-1} if

$$A = \begin{bmatrix} 1 & 4 \\ 2 & 9 \end{bmatrix}.$$

SOLUTION Begin by forming a 2×4 augmented matrix. Perform matrix row operations to obtain the identity matrix on the left side, and perform the same operation on the right side of this matrix.

$$\left[\begin{array}{cc|cc} 1 & 4 & 1 & 0 \\ 2 & 9 & 0 & 1 \end{array}\right] \underset{R_2 - 2R_1 \rightarrow}{} \left[\begin{array}{cc|cc} 1 & 4 & 1 & 0 \\ 0 & 1 & -2 & 1 \end{array}\right] \overset{R_1 - 4R_2 \rightarrow}{} \left[\begin{array}{cc|cc} 1 & 0 & 9 & -4 \\ 0 & 1 & -2 & 1 \end{array}\right]$$

Since the 2×2 identity matrix appears on the left side, it follows that the right side equals A^{-1}. That is,

$$A^{-1} = \begin{bmatrix} 9 & -4 \\ -2 & 1 \end{bmatrix}.$$

Furthermore, it can be verified that $A^{-1}A = I_2 = AA^{-1}$.

Now Try Exercise 15

EXAMPLE 5 **Finding the inverse of a 3 × 3 matrix symbolically**

Find A^{-1} if

$$A = \begin{bmatrix} 1 & 0 & 1 \\ 2 & 1 & 3 \\ -1 & 1 & 1 \end{bmatrix}.$$

SOLUTION Begin by forming the following 3 × 6 augmented matrix. Perform matrix row operations to obtain the identity matrix on the left side, and perform the same operation on the right side of this matrix.

$$\left[\begin{array}{rrr|rrr} 1 & 0 & 1 & 1 & 0 & 0 \\ 2 & 1 & 3 & 0 & 1 & 0 \\ -1 & 1 & 1 & 0 & 0 & 1 \end{array}\right] \quad \begin{array}{r} \\ R_2 - 2R_1 \rightarrow \\ R_3 + R_1 \rightarrow \end{array} \left[\begin{array}{rrr|rrr} 1 & 0 & 1 & 1 & 0 & 0 \\ 0 & 1 & 1 & -2 & 1 & 0 \\ 0 & 1 & 2 & 1 & 0 & 1 \end{array}\right]$$

$$\begin{array}{r} \\ \\ R_3 - R_2 \rightarrow \end{array} \left[\begin{array}{rrr|rrr} 1 & 0 & 1 & 1 & 0 & 0 \\ 0 & 1 & 1 & -2 & 1 & 0 \\ 0 & 0 & 1 & 3 & -1 & 1 \end{array}\right] \quad \begin{array}{r} R_1 - R_3 \rightarrow \\ R_2 - R_3 \rightarrow \\ \\ \end{array} \left[\begin{array}{rrr|rrr} 1 & 0 & 0 & -2 & 1 & -1 \\ 0 & 1 & 0 & -5 & 2 & -1 \\ 0 & 0 & 1 & 3 & -1 & 1 \end{array}\right]$$

The right side is equal to A^{-1}. That is,

$$A^{-1} = \begin{bmatrix} -2 & 1 & -1 \\ -5 & 2 & -1 \\ 3 & -1 & 1 \end{bmatrix}.$$

It can be verified that $A^{-1}A = I_3 = AA^{-1}$.

Now Try Exercise 25

NOTE If it is not possible to obtain the identity matrix on the left side of the augmented matrix by using matrix row operations, then A^{-1} does *not* exist.

Representing Linear Systems with Matrix Equations

In Section 6.4 linear systems were solved using Gaussian elimination with backward substitution. This method used an augmented matrix to represent a system of linear equations. A system of linear equations can also be represented by a matrix equation.

$$\begin{aligned} 3x - 2y + 4z &= 5 \\ 2x + y + 3z &= 9 \\ -x + 5y - 2z &= 5 \end{aligned}$$

Let A, X, and B be matrices defined as

Coefficient Matrix **Variable Matrix** **Constant Matrix**

$$A = \begin{bmatrix} 3 & -2 & 4 \\ 2 & 1 & 3 \\ -1 & 5 & -2 \end{bmatrix}, \quad X = \begin{bmatrix} x \\ y \\ z \end{bmatrix}, \quad \text{and} \quad B = \begin{bmatrix} 5 \\ 9 \\ 5 \end{bmatrix}.$$

The matrix product AX is given by

$$AX = \begin{bmatrix} 3 & -2 & 4 \\ 2 & 1 & 3 \\ -1 & 5 & -2 \end{bmatrix} \begin{bmatrix} x \\ y \\ z \end{bmatrix} = \begin{bmatrix} 3x + (-2)y + 4z \\ 2x + 1y + 3z \\ (-1)x + 5y + (-2)z \end{bmatrix} = \begin{bmatrix} 3x - 2y + 4z \\ 2x + y + 3z \\ -x + 5y - 2z \end{bmatrix}.$$

Thus the matrix equation $AX = B$ simplifies to

$$\begin{bmatrix} 3x - 2y + 4z \\ 2x + y + 3z \\ -x + 5y - 2z \end{bmatrix} = \begin{bmatrix} 5 \\ 9 \\ 5 \end{bmatrix}.$$

This matrix equation $AX = B$ is equivalent to the original system of linear equations. Any system of *linear* equations can be represented by a matrix equation.

EXAMPLE 6 **Representing linear systems with matrix equations**

Represent each system of linear equations in the form $AX = B$.

(a) $\begin{aligned} 3x - 4y &= 7 \\ -x + 6y &= -3 \end{aligned}$ **(b)** $\begin{aligned} x - 5y &= 2 \\ -3x + 2y + z &= -7 \\ 4x + 5y + 6z &= 10 \end{aligned}$

SOLUTION

(a) This linear system comprises two equations and two variables. The equivalent matrix equation is

$$AX = \begin{bmatrix} 3 & -4 \\ -1 & 6 \end{bmatrix}\begin{bmatrix} x \\ y \end{bmatrix} = \begin{bmatrix} 7 \\ -3 \end{bmatrix} = B.$$

(b) The equivalent matrix equation is

$$AX = \begin{bmatrix} 1 & -5 & 0 \\ -3 & 2 & 1 \\ 4 & 5 & 6 \end{bmatrix}\begin{bmatrix} x \\ y \\ z \end{bmatrix} = \begin{bmatrix} 2 \\ -7 \\ 10 \end{bmatrix} = B.$$

Now Try Exercises 39 and 43

Solving Linear Systems with Inverses

The matrix equation $AX = B$ can be solved by using A^{-1}, if it exists.

$$\begin{aligned} AX &= B && \text{Linear system} \\ A^{-1}AX &= A^{-1}B && \text{Multiply each side by } A^{-1}. \\ I_nX &= A^{-1}B && A^{-1}A = I_n \\ X &= A^{-1}B && I_nX = X \text{ for any } n \times 1 \text{ matrix } X \end{aligned}$$

To solve a linear system, multiply each side of the matrix equation $AX = B$ by A^{-1}, if it exists. The solution to the system is unique and can be written as $X = A^{-1}B$.

NOTE Since matrix multiplication is not commutative, it is essential to multiply each side of the equation on the *left* by A^{-1}. That is, $X = A^{-1}B \neq BA^{-1}$ in general.

EXAMPLE 7 **Solving a linear system using the inverse of a 2 × 2 matrix**

Write the linear system as the matrix equation $AX = B$. Find A^{-1} and solve for X.

$$\begin{aligned} x + 4y &= 3 \\ 2x + 9y &= 5 \end{aligned}$$

SOLUTION The linear system can be written as

$$AX = \begin{bmatrix} 1 & 4 \\ 2 & 9 \end{bmatrix}\begin{bmatrix} x \\ y \end{bmatrix} = \begin{bmatrix} 3 \\ 5 \end{bmatrix} = B.$$

The matrix A^{-1} was found in Example 4. Thus we can solve for X as follows.

$$X = A^{-1}B = \begin{bmatrix} 9 & -4 \\ -2 & 1 \end{bmatrix}\begin{bmatrix} 3 \\ 5 \end{bmatrix} = \begin{bmatrix} 7 \\ -1 \end{bmatrix}$$

The solution to the system is $(7, -1)$. Check this.

Now Try Exercise 47

Technology and Inverse Matrices (Optional) In the next two examples, we use technology to solve the system of linear equations. Technology is especially helpful when finding A^{-1}.

EXAMPLE 8 **Solving a linear system using the inverse of a 3 × 3 matrix**

Write the linear system as the matrix equation $AX = B$. Find A^{-1} and solve for X.

$$\begin{aligned} x + 3y - z &= 6 \\ -2y + z &= -2 \\ -x + y - 3z &= 4 \end{aligned}$$

SOLUTION The linear system can be written as

$$AX = \begin{bmatrix} 1 & 3 & -1 \\ 0 & -2 & 1 \\ -1 & 1 & -3 \end{bmatrix} \begin{bmatrix} x \\ y \\ z \end{bmatrix} = \begin{bmatrix} 6 \\ -2 \\ 4 \end{bmatrix} = B.$$

The matrix A^{-1} can be found by hand or with a graphing calculator, as shown in Figure 6.65. The solution to the system is given by $x = 4.5$, $y = -0.5$, and $z = -3$. See Figure 6.66.

Calculator Help
To find the inverse of a matrix, see Appendix A (page AP-14). To solve a linear system with a matrix inverse, see Appendix A (page AP-14).

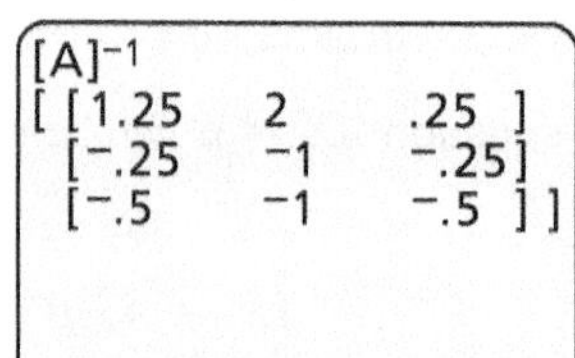

Figure 6.65

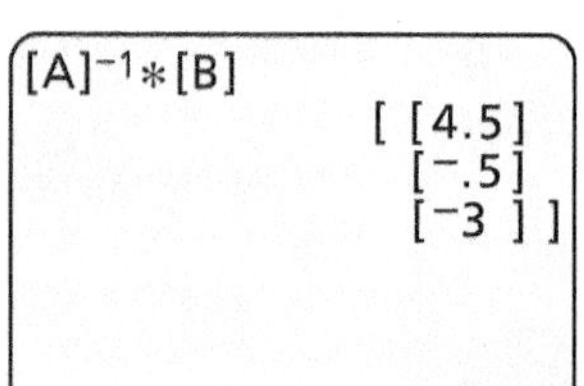

Figure 6.66

Now Try Exercise 59

EXAMPLE 9 **Modeling blood pressure**

In one study of adult males, the effect of both age A in years and weight W in pounds on systolic blood pressure P was found to be modeled by $P(A, W) = a + bA + cW$, where a, b, and c are constants. Table 6.12 lists three individuals with representative blood pressures.

(a) Use Table 6.12 to approximate values for the constants a, b, and c.

(b) Estimate a typical systolic blood pressure for an individual who is 55 years old and weighs 175 pounds.

P	*A*	*W*
113	39	142
138	53	181
152	65	191

Table 6.12

SOLUTION

(a) Determine the constants a, b, and c in $P(A, W) = a + bA + cW$ by solving the following three equations.

$$\begin{aligned} P(39, 142) &= a + b(39) + c(142) = 113 \\ P(53, 181) &= a + b(53) + c(181) = 138 \\ P(65, 191) &= a + b(65) + c(191) = 152 \end{aligned}$$

These three equations can be rewritten as follows.

$$\begin{aligned} a + 39b + 142c &= 113 \\ a + 53b + 181c &= 138 \\ a + 65b + 191c &= 152 \end{aligned}$$

```
[A]-1*[B]
 [[32.7804878  ]
  [.9024390244 ]
  [.3170731707 ]]
```

Figure 6.67

This system can be represented by the matrix equation $AX = B$.

$$AX = \begin{bmatrix} 1 & 39 & 142 \\ 1 & 53 & 181 \\ 1 & 65 & 191 \end{bmatrix} \begin{bmatrix} a \\ b \\ c \end{bmatrix} = \begin{bmatrix} 113 \\ 138 \\ 152 \end{bmatrix} = B$$

The solution, $X = A^{-1}B$, is shown in Figure 6.67. The values for the constants are $a \approx 32.78$, $b \approx 0.9024$, and $c \approx 0.3171$. Thus it follows that P is given by the equation $P(A, W) = 32.78 + 0.9024A + 0.3171W$.

(b) Evaluate $P(55, 175) = 32.78 + 0.9024(55) + 0.3171(175) \approx 137.9$. This model predicts that a typical (male) individual 55 years old, weighing 175 pounds, has a systolic blood pressure of approximately 138. Clearly, this could vary greatly among individuals.

Now Try Exercise 73

6.6 Putting It All Together

The following table summarizes some of the mathematical concepts presented in this section.

CONCEPT	COMMENTS	EXAMPLES
Identity matrix	The $n \times n$ identity matrix I_n has only 1's on the main diagonal and 0's elsewhere. When it is multiplied by any $n \times n$ matrix A, the result is A.	$\begin{bmatrix} 1 & 0 \\ 0 & 1 \end{bmatrix}\begin{bmatrix} 2 & 3 \\ 4 & 5 \end{bmatrix} = \begin{bmatrix} 2 & 3 \\ 4 & 5 \end{bmatrix}$ and $\begin{bmatrix} 2 & 3 \\ 4 & 5 \end{bmatrix}\begin{bmatrix} 1 & 0 \\ 0 & 1 \end{bmatrix} = \begin{bmatrix} 2 & 3 \\ 4 & 5 \end{bmatrix}$, where $I_2 = \begin{bmatrix} 1 & 0 \\ 0 & 1 \end{bmatrix}$.
Matrix inverse	If an $n \times n$ matrix A has an inverse, it is unique, is denoted A^{-1}, and satisfies the equations $AA^{-1} = I_n$ and $A^{-1}A = I_n$. Matrix inverses can be found by using technology. They can also be found with pencil and paper by performing matrix row operations on the augmented matrix $[A \mid I_n]$ until it is transformed to $[I_n \mid A^{-1}]$.	If $A = \begin{bmatrix} 2 & 3 \\ 3 & 5 \end{bmatrix}$, then $A^{-1} = \begin{bmatrix} 5 & -3 \\ -3 & 2 \end{bmatrix}$ because $AA^{-1} = \begin{bmatrix} 2 & 3 \\ 3 & 5 \end{bmatrix}\begin{bmatrix} 5 & -3 \\ -3 & 2 \end{bmatrix} = \begin{bmatrix} 1 & 0 \\ 0 & 1 \end{bmatrix} = I_2$ $A^{-1}A = \begin{bmatrix} 5 & -3 \\ -3 & 2 \end{bmatrix}\begin{bmatrix} 2 & 3 \\ 3 & 5 \end{bmatrix} = \begin{bmatrix} 1 & 0 \\ 0 & 1 \end{bmatrix} = I_2$.
Matrix equations	Systems of linear equations can be written by using the matrix equation $AX = B$. If A is invertible, then there will be a unique solution given by $X = A^{-1}B$. If A is not invertible, then there could be either no solution or infinitely many solutions. In the latter case, Gaussian elimination should be applied.	The linear system $2x - y = 3$, $x + 2y = 4$ can be written as $AX = B$, where $A = \begin{bmatrix} 2 & -1 \\ 1 & 2 \end{bmatrix}$, $X = \begin{bmatrix} x \\ y \end{bmatrix}$, and $B = \begin{bmatrix} 3 \\ 4 \end{bmatrix}$. The solution to the system is given by $X = A^{-1}B = \begin{bmatrix} 0.4 & 0.2 \\ -0.2 & 0.4 \end{bmatrix}\begin{bmatrix} 3 \\ 4 \end{bmatrix} = \begin{bmatrix} 2 \\ 1 \end{bmatrix}$. The solution is (2, 1).

6.6 Exercises

Inverse and Identity Matrices

Exercises 1–6: Determine if B is the inverse matrix of A by calculating AB and BA.

1. $A = \begin{bmatrix} 4 & 3 \\ 5 & 4 \end{bmatrix}, \quad B = \begin{bmatrix} 4 & -3 \\ -5 & 4 \end{bmatrix}$

2. $A = \begin{bmatrix} -1 & 2 \\ -3 & 8 \end{bmatrix}, \quad B = \begin{bmatrix} -4 & 1 \\ -2 & 0.5 \end{bmatrix}$

3. $A = \begin{bmatrix} 1 & -1 & 2 \\ 0 & 1 & -1 \\ 1 & 0 & 2 \end{bmatrix}, \quad B = \begin{bmatrix} 2 & 2 & -1 \\ -1 & 0 & 1 \\ -1 & -1 & 1 \end{bmatrix}$

4. $A = \begin{bmatrix} 2 & 1 & 1 \\ -1 & 0 & -1 \\ 0 & 2 & -1 \end{bmatrix}, \quad B = \begin{bmatrix} 2 & 3 & -1 \\ -1 & -2 & 1 \\ -2 & -4 & 1 \end{bmatrix}$

5. $A = \begin{bmatrix} 2 & 1 & -1 \\ 3 & 0 & 2 \\ -1 & 0 & 1 \end{bmatrix}, \quad B = \begin{bmatrix} 0 & 1 & -2 \\ 1 & -3 & 7 \\ 0 & -1 & 3 \end{bmatrix}$

6. $A = \begin{bmatrix} 1 & -1 & 1 \\ 0 & 1 & 0 \\ 1 & 1 & 2 \end{bmatrix}, \quad B = \begin{bmatrix} 2 & 3 & -1 \\ 0 & 1 & 0 \\ -1 & -2 & 1 \end{bmatrix}$

Exercises 7–10: Find the value of the constant k in A^{-1}.

7. $A = \begin{bmatrix} 1 & 1 \\ 1 & 2 \end{bmatrix}, \quad A^{-1} = \begin{bmatrix} 2 & -1 \\ -1 & k \end{bmatrix}$

8. $A = \begin{bmatrix} -2 & 2 \\ 1 & -2 \end{bmatrix}, \quad A^{-1} = \begin{bmatrix} -1 & k \\ -0.5 & -1 \end{bmatrix}$

9. $A = \begin{bmatrix} 1 & 3 \\ -1 & -5 \end{bmatrix}, \quad A^{-1} = \begin{bmatrix} k & 1.5 \\ -0.5 & -0.5 \end{bmatrix}$

10. $A = \begin{bmatrix} -2 & 5 \\ -3 & 4 \end{bmatrix}, \quad A^{-1} = \begin{bmatrix} \frac{4}{7} & -\frac{5}{7} \\ k & -\frac{2}{7} \end{bmatrix}$

Exercises 11–14: Predict the results of I_nA and AI_n. Then verify your prediction.

11. $I_2 = \begin{bmatrix} 1 & 0 \\ 0 & 1 \end{bmatrix}, \quad A = \begin{bmatrix} 1 & -2 \\ 4 & 3 \end{bmatrix}$

12. $I_3 = \begin{bmatrix} 1 & 0 & 0 \\ 0 & 1 & 0 \\ 0 & 0 & 1 \end{bmatrix}, \quad A = \begin{bmatrix} 1 & -4 & 3 \\ 1 & 9 & 5 \\ 3 & -5 & 0 \end{bmatrix}$

13. $I_3 = \begin{bmatrix} 1 & 0 & 0 \\ 0 & 1 & 0 \\ 0 & 0 & 1 \end{bmatrix}, \quad A = \begin{bmatrix} 0 & 0 & 0 \\ 0 & 0 & 0 \\ 0 & 0 & 0 \end{bmatrix}$

14. $I_4 = \begin{bmatrix} 1 & 0 & 0 & 0 \\ 0 & 1 & 0 & 0 \\ 0 & 0 & 1 & 0 \\ 0 & 0 & 0 & 1 \end{bmatrix}, \quad A = \begin{bmatrix} 5 & -2 & 6 & -3 \\ 0 & 1 & 4 & -1 \\ -5 & 7 & 9 & 8 \\ 0 & 0 & 3 & 1 \end{bmatrix}$

Calculating Inverses

Exercises 15–28: (Refer to Examples 3–5.) Let A be the given matrix. Find A^{-1} without a calculator.

15. $\begin{bmatrix} 1 & 2 \\ 1 & 3 \end{bmatrix}$

16. $\begin{bmatrix} 1 & 0 \\ 1 & -1 \end{bmatrix}$

17. $\begin{bmatrix} -1 & 2 \\ 3 & -5 \end{bmatrix}$

18. $\begin{bmatrix} 1 & 3 \\ 2 & 5 \end{bmatrix}$

19. $\begin{bmatrix} 8 & 5 \\ 2 & 1 \end{bmatrix}$

20. $\begin{bmatrix} -2 & 4 \\ -5 & 9 \end{bmatrix}$

21. $\begin{bmatrix} 0 & 0 & 1 \\ 1 & 0 & 0 \\ 0 & 1 & 0 \end{bmatrix}$

22. $\begin{bmatrix} 1 & 0 & 0 \\ 1 & 1 & 0 \\ 0 & 1 & 1 \end{bmatrix}$

23. $\begin{bmatrix} 1 & 0 & 1 \\ 2 & 1 & 3 \\ -1 & 1 & 1 \end{bmatrix}$

24. $\begin{bmatrix} -2 & 1 & 0 \\ 1 & 0 & 1 \\ -1 & 1 & 0 \end{bmatrix}$

25. $\begin{bmatrix} 1 & 2 & -1 \\ 2 & 5 & 0 \\ -1 & -1 & 2 \end{bmatrix}$

26. $\begin{bmatrix} 2 & -2 & 1 \\ 1 & 3 & 2 \\ 4 & -2 & 4 \end{bmatrix}$

27. $\begin{bmatrix} -2 & 1 & -3 \\ 0 & 1 & 2 \\ 1 & -2 & 1 \end{bmatrix}$

28. $\begin{bmatrix} 1 & -1 & 1 \\ -1 & 2 & 1 \\ 0 & 2 & 1 \end{bmatrix}$

Exercises 29–38: Let A be the given matrix. Find A^{-1}.

29. $\begin{bmatrix} 0.5 & -1.5 \\ 0.2 & -0.5 \end{bmatrix}$

30. $\begin{bmatrix} -0.5 & 0.5 \\ 3 & 2 \end{bmatrix}$

31. $\begin{bmatrix} 1 & 2 & 0 \\ -1 & 4 & -1 \\ 2 & -1 & 0 \end{bmatrix}$

32. $\begin{bmatrix} -2 & 0 & 1 \\ 5 & -4 & 1 \\ 1 & -2 & 0 \end{bmatrix}$

33. $\begin{bmatrix} 2 & -2 & 1 \\ 0 & 5 & 8 \\ 0 & 0 & -1 \end{bmatrix}$

34. $\begin{bmatrix} 2 & 0 & 2 \\ 1 & 5 & 0 \\ -1 & 0 & 2 \end{bmatrix}$

35. $\begin{bmatrix} 3 & -1 & -1 \\ -1 & 3 & -1 \\ -1 & -1 & 3 \end{bmatrix}$

36. $\begin{bmatrix} 2 & -3 & 1 \\ 5 & -6 & 3 \\ 3 & 2 & 0 \end{bmatrix}$

37. $\begin{bmatrix} 1 & -1 & 0 & 0 \\ -1 & 5 & -1 & 0 \\ 0 & -1 & 5 & -1 \\ 0 & 0 & -1 & 1 \end{bmatrix}$

38. $\begin{bmatrix} 3 & 1 & 0 & 0 \\ 1 & 3 & 1 & 0 \\ 0 & 1 & 3 & 1 \\ 0 & 0 & 1 & 3 \end{bmatrix}$

Matrices and Linear Systems

Exercises 39–46: Represent the system of linear equations in the form $AX = B$.

39. $\begin{aligned} 2x - 3y &= 7 \\ -3x - 4y &= 9 \end{aligned}$

40. $\begin{aligned} -x + 3y &= 10 \\ 2x - 6y &= -1 \end{aligned}$

41. $\begin{aligned} \tfrac{1}{2}x - \tfrac{3}{2}y &= \tfrac{1}{4} \\ -x + 2y &= 5 \end{aligned}$

42. $\begin{aligned} -1.1x + 3.2y &= -2.7 \\ 5.6x - 3.8y &= -3.0 \end{aligned}$

43. $\begin{aligned} x - 2y + z &= 5 \\ 3y - z &= 6 \\ 5x - 4y - 7z &= 0 \end{aligned}$

44. $\begin{aligned} 4x - 3y + 2z &= 8 \\ -x + 4y + 3z &= 2 \\ -2x - 5z &= 2 \end{aligned}$

45. $\begin{aligned} 4x - y + 3z &= -2 \\ x + 2y + 5z &= 11 \\ 2x - 3y &= -1 \end{aligned}$

46. $\begin{aligned} x - 2y + z &= 12 \\ 4y + 3z &= 13 \\ -2x + 7y &= -2 \end{aligned}$

Solving Linear Systems

Exercises 47–54: Complete the following.

(a) Write the system in the form $AX = B$.
(b) Solve the system by finding A^{-1} and then using the equation $X = A^{-1}B$. (Hint: Some of your answers from Exercises 15–28 may be helpful.)

47. $\begin{aligned} x + 2y &= 3 \\ x + 3y &= 6 \end{aligned}$

48. $\begin{aligned} 2x + y &= 4 \\ -x + 2y &= -1 \end{aligned}$

49. $\begin{aligned} -x + 2y &= 5 \\ 3x - 5y &= -2 \end{aligned}$

50. $\begin{aligned} x + 3y &= -3 \\ 2x + 5y &= -2 \end{aligned}$

51. $\begin{aligned} x + z &= -7 \\ 2x + y + 3z &= -13 \\ -x + y + z &= -4 \end{aligned}$

52. $\begin{aligned} -2x + y &= -5 \\ x + z &= -5 \\ -x + y &= -4 \end{aligned}$

53. $\begin{aligned} x + 2y - z &= 2 \\ 2x + 5y &= -1 \\ -x - y + 2z &= 0 \end{aligned}$

54. $\begin{aligned} 2x - 2y + z &= 1 \\ x + 3y + 2z &= 3 \\ 4x - 2y + 4z &= 4 \end{aligned}$

Exercises 55–62: Complete the following for the given system of linear equations.

(a) Write the system in the form $AX = B$.
(b) Solve the linear system by computing $X = A^{-1}B$ with a calculator. Approximate the solution to the nearest hundredth when appropriate.

55. $\begin{aligned} 1.5x + 3.7y &= 0.32 \\ -0.4x - 2.1y &= 0.36 \end{aligned}$

56. $\begin{aligned} 31x + 18y &= 64.1 \\ 5x - 23y &= -59.6 \end{aligned}$

57. $\begin{aligned} 0.08x - 0.7y &= -0.504 \\ 1.1x - 0.05y &= 0.73 \end{aligned}$

58. $\begin{aligned} -231x + 178y &= -439 \\ 525x - 329y &= 2282 \end{aligned}$

59. $\begin{aligned} 3.1x + 1.9y - z &= 1.99 \\ 6.3x - 9.9z &= -3.78 \\ -x + 1.5y + 7z &= 5.3 \end{aligned}$

60. $\begin{aligned} 17x - 22y - 19z &= -25.2 \\ 3x + 13y - 9z &= 105.9 \\ x - 2y + 6.1z &= -23.55 \end{aligned}$

61. $\begin{aligned} 3x - y + z &= 4.9 \\ 5.8x - 2.1y &= -3.8 \\ -x + 2.9z &= 3.8 \end{aligned}$

62. $\begin{aligned} 1.2x - 0.3y - 0.7z &= -0.5 \\ -0.4x + 1.3y + 0.4z &= 0.9 \\ 1.7x + 0.6y + 1.1z &= 1.3 \end{aligned}$

Interpreting Inverses

Exercises 63 and 64: **Translations** *(Refer to the discussion in this section about translating a point.) The matrix product AX performs a translation on the point (x, y), where*

$$A = \begin{bmatrix} 1 & 0 & h \\ 0 & 1 & k \\ 0 & 0 & 1 \end{bmatrix} \text{ and } X = \begin{bmatrix} x \\ y \\ 1 \end{bmatrix}.$$

(a) Predict the new location of the point (x, y) when it is translated by A. Compute $Y = AX$ to verify your prediction.
(b) Make a conjecture as to what $A^{-1}Y$ represents. Find A^{-1} and calculate $A^{-1}Y$ to test your conjecture.
(c) What will AA^{-1} and $A^{-1}A$ equal?

63. $A = \begin{bmatrix} 1 & 0 & 2 \\ 0 & 1 & 3 \\ 0 & 0 & 1 \end{bmatrix}$, $(x, y) = (0, 1)$, and $X = \begin{bmatrix} 0 \\ 1 \\ 1 \end{bmatrix}$

64. $A = \begin{bmatrix} 1 & 0 & -4 \\ 0 & 1 & 5 \\ 0 & 0 & 1 \end{bmatrix}$, $(x, y) = (4, 2)$, and $X = \begin{bmatrix} 4 \\ 2 \\ 1 \end{bmatrix}$

Exercises 65 and 66: **Translations** *(Refer to the discussion in this section about translating a point.) Find a 3×3 matrix A that performs the following translation of a point (x, y) represented by X. Find A^{-1} and describe what it computes.*

65. 3 units to the left and 5 units downward

66. 6 units to the right and 1 unit upward

67. **Rotation** (Refer to Example 2.) The matrix B rotates the point (x, y) clockwise about the origin 45°, where

$$B = \begin{bmatrix} \frac{1}{\sqrt{2}} & \frac{1}{\sqrt{2}} & 0 \\ -\frac{1}{\sqrt{2}} & \frac{1}{\sqrt{2}} & 0 \\ 0 & 0 & 1 \end{bmatrix} \text{ and } B^{-1} = \begin{bmatrix} \frac{1}{\sqrt{2}} & -\frac{1}{\sqrt{2}} & 0 \\ \frac{1}{\sqrt{2}} & \frac{1}{\sqrt{2}} & 0 \\ 0 & 0 & 1 \end{bmatrix}.$$

(a) Let X represent the point $(-\sqrt{2}, -\sqrt{2})$. Compute $Y = BX$.

(b) Find $B^{-1}Y$. Interpret what B^{-1} computes.

68. Rotation (Refer to Exercise 67.) Predict the result of the computations $BB^{-1}X$ and $B^{-1}BX$ for any point (x, y) represented by X. Explain this result geometrically.

69. Translations The matrix A translates a point to the right 4 units and downward 2 units, and the matrix B translates a point to the left 3 units and upward 3 units, where

$$A = \begin{bmatrix} 1 & 0 & 4 \\ 0 & 1 & -2 \\ 0 & 0 & 1 \end{bmatrix} \quad \text{and} \quad B = \begin{bmatrix} 1 & 0 & -3 \\ 0 & 1 & 3 \\ 0 & 0 & 1 \end{bmatrix}.$$

(a) Let X represent the point $(1, 1)$. Predict the result of $Y = ABX$. Check your prediction.

(b) Find AB mentally, and then compute AB.

(c) Would you expect $AB = BA$? Verify your answer.

(d) Find $(AB)^{-1}$ mentally. Explain your reasoning.

70. Rotation (Refer to Exercises 63 and 67 for A and B.)

(a) Let X represent the point $(0, \sqrt{2})$. If this point is rotated about the origin 45° clockwise and then translated 2 units to the right and 3 units upward, determine its new coordinates geometrically.

(b) Compute $Y = ABX$, and explain the result.

(c) Is ABX equal to BAX? Interpret your answer.

(d) Find a matrix that translates Y back to X.

Applications

71. Cost of CDs A music store marks its compact discs A, B, or C to indicate one of three selling prices. The last column in the table shows the total cost of a purchase. Use this information to determine the cost of one CD of each type by setting up a matrix equation and solving it with an inverse.

A	B	C	Total
2	3	4	\$120.91
1	4	0	\$62.95
2	1	3	\$79.94

72. Traffic Flow (Refer to Exercises 85 and 86 in Section 6.4.) The figure at the top of the next column shows four one-way streets with intersections A, B, C, and D. Numbers indicate the average traffic flow in vehicles per minute. The variables x_1, x_2, x_3, and x_4 denote unknown traffic flows.

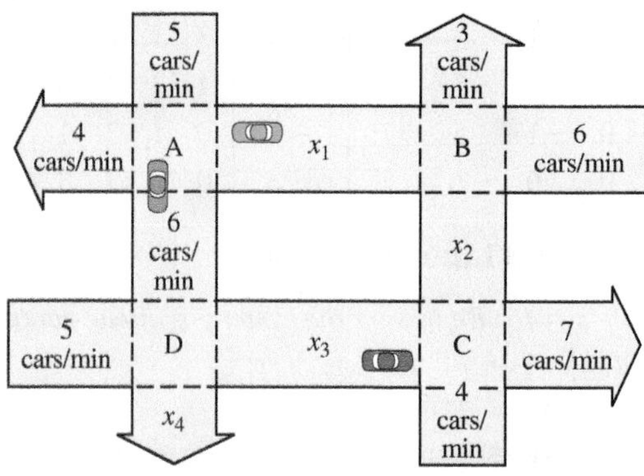

(a) The number of vehicles per minute entering an intersection equals the number exiting an intersection. Verify that the given system of linear equations describes the traffic flow.

A: $x_1 + 5 = 4 + 6$ B: $x_2 + 6 = x_1 + 3$
C: $x_3 + 4 = x_2 + 7$ D: $6 + 5 = x_3 + x_4$

(b) Write the system as $AX = B$ and solve using A^{-1}.

(c) Interpret your results.

73. Home Prices The table contains data on sales of three homes. Price P is measured in thousands of dollars, home size S is in square feet, and condition C is rated on a scale from 1 to 10, where 10 represents excellent condition. The variables were found to be related by the equation $P = a + bS + cC$.

P	*S*	*C*
122	1500	8
130	2000	5
158	2200	10

(a) Use the table to write a system of linear equations whose solution gives a, b, and c. Solve this system of linear equations.

(b) Estimate the selling price of a home with 1800 square feet and a condition of 7.

74. Tire Sales A study investigated the relationship among annual tire sales T in thousands, automobile registrations A in millions, and personal disposable income I in millions of dollars. Representative data for three different years are shown in the table. The data were modeled by $T = aA + bI + c$, where a, b, and c are constants. (***Source:*** J. Jarrett, *Business Forecasting Methods*.)

T	*A*	*I*
10,170	113	308
15,305	133	622
21,289	155	1937

continued on next page

(a) Use the data to write a system of linear equations whose solution gives a, b, and c.

(b) Solve this linear system. Write a formula for T, as $T = aA + bI + c$.

(c) If $A = 118$ and $I = 311$, predict T. (The actual value for T was 11,314.)

75. Leontief Economic Model Suppose that a closed economic region has three industries: service, electrical power, and tourism. The service industry uses 20% of its own production, 40% of the electrical power, and 80% of the tourism. The power company uses 40% of the service industry, 20% of the electrical power, and 10% of the tourism. The tourism industry uses 40% of the service industry, 40% of the electrical power, and 10% of the tourism.

(a) Let S, E, and T be the numbers of units produced by the service, electrical, and tourism industries, respectively. The following system of linear equations can be used to determine the relative number of units each industry needs to produce. (This model assumes that all production is consumed by the region.)

$$0.2S + 0.4E + 0.8T = S$$
$$0.4S + 0.2E + 0.1T = E$$
$$0.4S + 0.4E + 0.1T = T$$

Solve the system and write the solution in terms of T.

(b) If tourism produces 60 units, how many units should the service and electrical industries produce?

76. Plate Glass Sales Plate glass sales G can be affected by the number of new building contracts B issued and the number of automobiles A produced, since plate glass is used in buildings and cars. To forecast sales, a plate glass company in California collected data for three consecutive years, shown in the table. All units are in millions. The data were modeled by $G = aA + bB + c$, where a, b, and c are constants. (***Source:*** S. Makridakis and S. Wheelwright, *Forecasting Methods for Management*.)

G	A	B
603	5.54	37.1
657	6.93	41.3
779	7.64	45.6

(a) Write a system of linear equations whose solution gives a, b, and c.

(b) Solve this linear system. Write a formula for G.

(c) For the following year, it was estimated that $A = 7.75$ and $B = 47.4$. Predict G. (The actual value for G was 878.)

Writing about Mathematics

77. Discuss how to solve the matrix equation $AX = B$ if A^{-1} exists.

78. Give an example of a 2×2 matrix A with only nonzero elements that does not have an inverse. Explain what happens if one attempts to find A^{-1} symbolically.

CHECKING BASIC CONCEPTS FOR SECTIONS 6.5 AND 6.6

1. Perform the operations on the given matrices A and B.

$$A = \begin{bmatrix} 1 & 0 & 1 \\ -1 & 1 & 2 \\ 1 & 3 & 0 \end{bmatrix}, \quad B = \begin{bmatrix} -1 & 1 & 2 \\ 0 & 4 & 1 \\ 1 & -2 & 0 \end{bmatrix}$$

(a) $A + B$ (b) $2A - B$ (c) AB

2. Find the inverse of the matrix A by hand.

$$A = \begin{bmatrix} 0 & 0 & 1 \\ 1 & 1 & 0 \\ 1 & 0 & 1 \end{bmatrix}$$

3. Write each system of linear equations as a matrix equation $AX = B$. Solve the system utilizing A^{-1}.

(a) $\begin{aligned} x - 2y &= 13 \\ 2x + 3y &= 5 \end{aligned}$

(b) $\begin{aligned} x - y + z &= 2 \\ -x + y + z &= 4 \\ y - z &= -1 \end{aligned}$

(c) $\begin{aligned} 3.1x - 5.3y &= -2.682 \\ -0.1x + 1.8y &= 0.787 \end{aligned}$

4. Find A^{-1} if $A = \begin{bmatrix} 2 & -3 & 5 \\ 4 & -3 & 2 \\ 1 & 5 & -4 \end{bmatrix}$.

6.7 Determinants

- **Define and calculate determinants**
- **Apply Cramer's rule**
- **Use determinants to find areas of regions**

Introduction

Determinants are used in mathematics for theoretical purposes. However, they also are used to test if a matrix is invertible and to find the area of certain geometric figures, such as triangles. A *determinant* is a real number associated with a square matrix. We begin our discussion by defining a determinant for a 2×2 matrix.

Definition and Calculation of Determinants

Finding the determinant of a matrix with dimension 2×2 is a straightforward arithmetic calculation.

DETERMINANT OF A 2 × 2 MATRIX

The **determinant** of

$$A = \begin{bmatrix} a & b \\ c & d \end{bmatrix}$$

is a real number defined by

$$\det A = ad - cb.$$

Later we define determinants for any $n \times n$ matrix. The following theorem can be used to determine if a matrix has an inverse.

INVERTIBLE MATRIX

A square matrix A is invertible if and only if $\det A \neq 0$.

EXAMPLE 1 Determining if a 2 × 2 matrix is invertible

Determine if A^{-1} exists by computing the determinant of the matrix A.

(a) $A = \begin{bmatrix} 3 & -4 \\ -5 & 9 \end{bmatrix}$ **(b)** $A = \begin{bmatrix} 52 & -32 \\ 65 & -40 \end{bmatrix}$

SOLUTION

(a) The determinant of the 2×2 matrix A is calculated as follows.

$$\det A = \det \begin{bmatrix} 3 & -4 \\ -5 & 9 \end{bmatrix} = (3)(9) - (-5)(-4) = 7$$

Since $\det A = 7 \neq 0$, the matrix A is invertible and A^{-1} exists.

(b) Similarly,

$$\det A = \det \begin{bmatrix} 52 & -32 \\ 65 & -40 \end{bmatrix} = (52)(-40) - (65)(-32) = 0.$$

Since $\det A = 0$, A^{-1} does not exist. Try finding A^{-1}. What happens?

Now Try Exercises 1 and 3

We can use determinants of 2×2 matrices to find determinants of larger square matrices. In order to do this, we first define the concepts of a *minor* and a *cofactor*.

MINORS AND COFACTORS

The **minor**, denoted by M_{ij}, for element a_{ij} in the square matrix A is the real number computed by performing the following steps.

STEP 1: Delete the ith row and jth column from the matrix A.

STEP 2: Compute the determinant of the resulting matrix, which is equal to M_{ij}.

The **cofactor**, denoted A_{ij}, for a_{ij} is defined by $A_{ij} = (-1)^{i+j}M_{ij}$.

EXAMPLE 2 **Calculating minors and cofactors**

Find the following minors and cofactors for the matrix A.

$$A = \begin{bmatrix} 2 & -3 & 1 \\ -2 & 1 & 0 \\ 0 & -1 & 4 \end{bmatrix}$$

(a) M_{11} and M_{21} **(b)** A_{11} and A_{21}

SOLUTION

(a) To obtain the minor M_{11}, begin by crossing out the first row and first column of A.

$$A = \begin{bmatrix} 2 & -3 & 1 \\ -2 & 1 & 0 \\ 0 & -1 & 4 \end{bmatrix}$$

For M_{11}, cross out row 1 and column 1.

The remaining elements form the 2×2 matrix

$$B = \begin{bmatrix} 1 & 0 \\ -1 & 4 \end{bmatrix}.$$

The minor M_{11} is equal to $\det B = (1)(4) - (-1)(0) = 4$.

M_{21} is found by crossing out the second row and first column of A.

$$A = \begin{bmatrix} 2 & -3 & 1 \\ -2 & 1 & 0 \\ 0 & -1 & 4 \end{bmatrix}$$

For M_{21}, cross out row 2 and column 1.

The resulting matrix is

$$B = \begin{bmatrix} -3 & 1 \\ -1 & 4 \end{bmatrix}.$$

Thus $M_{21} = \det B = (-3)(4) - (-1)(1) = -11$.

(b) Since $A_{ij} = (-1)^{i+j} M_{ij}$, A_{11} and A_{21} can be computed as follows.

$$A_{11} = (-1)^{1+1}M_{11} = (-1)^2(4) = 4$$
$$A_{21} = (-1)^{2+1}M_{21} = (-1)^3(-11) = 11$$

Now Try Exercise 5

Using the concept of a cofactor, we can calculate the determinant of *any* square matrix.

DETERMINANT OF A SQUARE MATRIX USING COFACTORS

For a square matrix A, multiply each element in any row or column of the matrix by its cofactor. The sum of the products is equal to the determinant of A.

To compute the determinant of a 3×3 matrix A, begin by selecting either a row or a column.

$$A = \begin{bmatrix} a_{11} & a_{12} & a_{13} \\ a_{21} & a_{22} & a_{23} \\ a_{31} & a_{32} & a_{33} \end{bmatrix}$$

For example, if the *second row* of A is selected, the elements are a_{21}, a_{22}, and a_{23}. Then

$$\det A = a_{21}A_{21} + a_{22}A_{22} + a_{23}A_{23}.$$

On the other hand, utilizing the elements of a_{11}, a_{21}, and a_{31} in the *first column* gives

$$\det A = a_{11}A_{11} + a_{21}A_{21} + a_{31}A_{31}.$$

Regardless of the row or column selected, the value of det A is the same. The calculation is easier if some elements in the selected row or column equal 0.

EXAMPLE 3 Evaluating the determinant of a 3×3 matrix

Find det A if

$$A = \begin{bmatrix} 2 & -3 & 1 \\ -2 & 1 & 0 \\ 0 & -1 & 4 \end{bmatrix}.$$

SOLUTION To find the determinant of A, we can select any row or column. If we begin *expanding* about the first column of A, then

$$\det A = a_{11}A_{11} + a_{21}A_{21} + a_{31}A_{31}.$$

In the first column, $a_{11} = 2$, $a_{21} = -2$, and $a_{31} = 0$. In Example 2, the cofactors A_{11} and A_{21} were computed as 4 and 11, respectively. Since A_{31} is multiplied by $a_{31} = 0$, we do not need to calculate its value. Thus

$$\begin{aligned} \det &= a_{11}A_{11} + a_{21}A_{21} + a_{31}A_{31} \\ &= 2(4) + (-2)(11) + (0)A_{31} \quad \text{First column of } A \\ &= -14. \end{aligned}$$

We could also have expanded about the second row.

$$\begin{aligned} \det A &= a_{21}A_{21} + a_{22}A_{22} + a_{23}A_{23} \\ &= (-2)A_{21} + (1)A_{22} + (0)A_{23} \quad \text{Second row of } A \end{aligned}$$

To complete this computation we need to determine only A_{22}, since A_{21} is known to be 11 and A_{23} is multiplied by 0. To compute A_{22}, delete the second row and column of A to obtain M_{22}.

$$M_{22} = \det \begin{bmatrix} 2 & 1 \\ 0 & 4 \end{bmatrix} = 8 \quad \text{and} \quad A_{22} = (-1)^{2+2}(8) = 8$$

Thus $\det A = (-2)(11) + (1)(8) + (0)A_{23} = -14$. The same value for det A is obtained in both calculations.

Now Try Exercise 17

CLASS DISCUSSION

If a row or column in matrix A contains only zeros, what is det A?

Instead of calculating $(-1)^{i+j}$ for each cofactor, we can use the following **sign matrix** to find determinants of 3×3 matrices. The checkerboard pattern can be expanded to include larger square matrices.

Sign Matrix

$$\begin{bmatrix} + & - & + \\ - & + & - \\ + & - & + \end{bmatrix}$$

For example, if

$$A = \begin{bmatrix} 2 & 3 & 7 \\ -3 & -2 & -1 \\ 4 & 0 & 2 \end{bmatrix},$$

we can compute $\det A$ by expanding about the second column to take advantage of the 0. The second column contains $-$, $+$, and $-$ signs. Therefore

$$\begin{aligned} \det A &= -(3) \det \begin{bmatrix} -3 & -1 \\ 4 & 2 \end{bmatrix} + (-2) \det \begin{bmatrix} 2 & 7 \\ 4 & 2 \end{bmatrix} - (0) \det \begin{bmatrix} 2 & 7 \\ -3 & -1 \end{bmatrix} \\ &= -3(-2) + (-2)(-24) - (0)(19) \\ &= 54. \end{aligned}$$

NOTE We could have computed $\det A$ by expanding about *any* row or column. However, computation can be simplified by taking advantage of any 0's in the matrix. For the matrix above, the 0 can be used by expanding about either the second column or the third row.

Graphing calculators can evaluate determinants, as shown in the next example.

EXAMPLE 4 Using technology to find a determinant

Find the determinant of A.

(a) $A = \begin{bmatrix} 2 & -3 & 1 \\ -2 & 1 & 0 \\ 0 & -1 & 4 \end{bmatrix}$ **(b)** $A = \begin{bmatrix} 2 & -3 & 1 & 5 \\ 7 & 1 & -8 & 0 \\ 5 & 4 & 9 & 7 \\ -2 & 3 & 3 & 0 \end{bmatrix}$

SOLUTION

(a) The determinant of this matrix was calculated in Example 3 by hand. To use technology, enter the matrix and evaluate its determinant, as shown in Figure 6.68. The result is $\det A = -14$, which agrees with our earlier calculation.

Calculator Help
To calculate a determinant, see Appendix A (page AP-15).

Finding Determinants with a Calculator

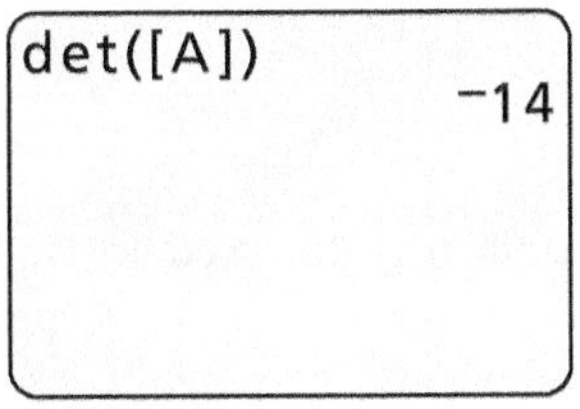

```
det([A])
            -14
```

Figure 6.68

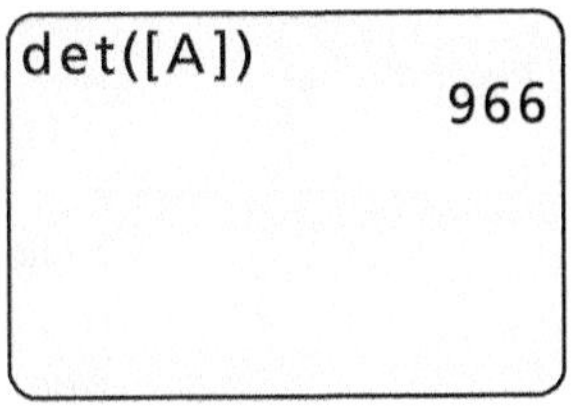

```
det([A])
            966
```

Figure 6.69

(b) The determinant of a 4×4 matrix can be computed using cofactors. However, it is considerably easier to use technology. From Figure 6.69 we see that $\det A = 966$.

Now Try Exercises 23 and 24

Cramer's Rule

We can solve *linear* systems in two variables using determinants and a method called **Cramer's rule.** Cramer's rule for linear systems in *three* variables is discussed in the Extended and Discovery Exercises at the end of this section. Although Cramer's rule can be used to solve linear systems with more than three variables, it is not practical to do so.

CRAMER'S RULE FOR LINEAR SYSTEMS IN TWO VARIABLES

The solution to the linear system

$$a_1x + b_1y = c_1$$
$$a_2x + b_2y = c_2$$

is given by $x = \frac{E}{D}$ and $y = \frac{F}{D}$, where

$$E = \det\begin{bmatrix} c_1 & b_1 \\ c_2 & b_2 \end{bmatrix}, \quad F = \det\begin{bmatrix} a_1 & c_1 \\ a_2 & c_2 \end{bmatrix}, \quad \text{and} \quad D = \det\begin{bmatrix} a_1 & b_1 \\ a_2 & b_2 \end{bmatrix} \neq 0.$$

NOTE If $D = 0$, then the system does not have a unique solution. There are either no solutions or infinitely many solutions.

EXAMPLE 5 **Using Cramer's rule to solve a linear system in two variables**

Use Cramer's rule to solve the linear system

$$4x + y = 146$$
$$9x + y = 66.$$

SOLUTION In this system $a_1 = 4$, $b_1 = 1$, $c_1 = 146$, $a_2 = 9$, $b_2 = 1$, and $c_2 = 66$. By Cramer's rule, the solution can be found as follows.

$$E = \det\begin{bmatrix} c_1 & b_1 \\ c_2 & b_2 \end{bmatrix} = \det\begin{bmatrix} 146 & 1 \\ 66 & 1 \end{bmatrix} = (146)(1) - (66)(1) = 80$$

$$F = \det\begin{bmatrix} a_1 & c_1 \\ a_2 & c_2 \end{bmatrix} = \det\begin{bmatrix} 4 & 146 \\ 9 & 66 \end{bmatrix} = (4)(66) - (9)(146) = -1050$$

$$D = \det\begin{bmatrix} a_1 & b_1 \\ a_2 & b_2 \end{bmatrix} = \det\begin{bmatrix} 4 & 1 \\ 9 & 1 \end{bmatrix} = (4)(1) - (9)(1) = -5$$

The solution is

$$x = \frac{E}{D} = \frac{80}{-5} = -16 \quad \text{and} \quad y = \frac{F}{D} = \frac{-1050}{-5} = 210.$$

Now Try Exercise 25

Area of Regions

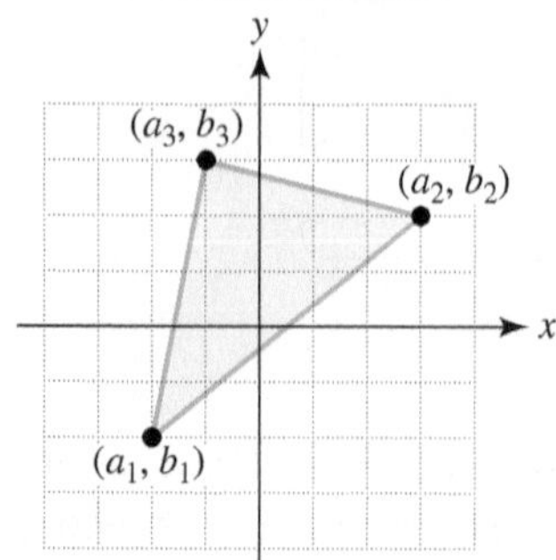

Figure 6.70

Determinants may be used to find the area of a triangle. If a triangle has vertices (a_1, b_1), (a_2, b_2), and (a_3, b_3), as shown in Figure 6.70, then its area is equal to the *absolute value* of D, where

$$D = \frac{1}{2}\det\begin{bmatrix} a_1 & a_2 & a_3 \\ b_1 & b_2 & b_3 \\ 1 & 1 & 1 \end{bmatrix}.$$

If the vertices are entered into the columns of D in a *counterclockwise* direction, then D will be positive. (***Source:*** W. Taylor, *The Geometry of Computer Graphics*.)

EXAMPLE 6 **Computing the area of a parallelogram**

Use determinants to calculate the area of the parallelogram in Figure 6.71.

SOLUTION To find the area of the parallelogram, we view the parallelogram as comprising two triangles. One triangle has vertices at (0, 0), (4, 2), and (1, 2), and the other triangle has vertices at (4, 2), (5, 4), and (1, 2). The area of the parallelogram is equal to the sum of the areas of the two triangles. Since these triangles are congruent, we can calculate the area of one triangle and double it. The area of one triangle is equal to D.

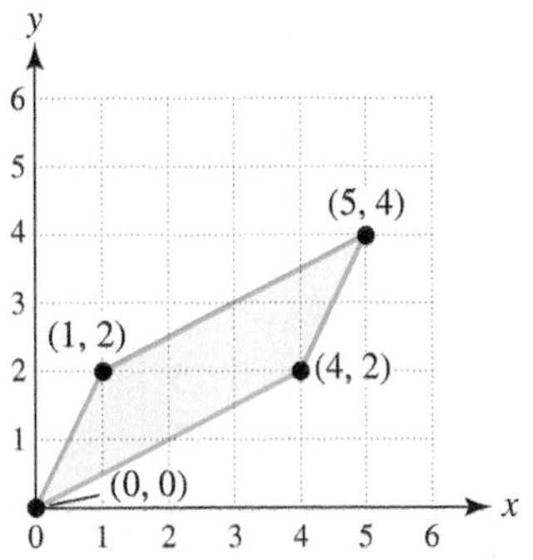

Figure 6.71

$$D = \frac{1}{2}\det\begin{bmatrix} 0 & 4 & 1 \\ 0 & 2 & 2 \\ 1 & 1 & 1 \end{bmatrix} = \frac{1}{2}(6) = 3$$

Since the vertices were entered in a counterclockwise direction, D is positive. The area of one triangle is equal to 3 square units. Therefore the area of the parallelogram is twice this value, or 6 square units.

Now Try Exercise 35

CLASS DISCUSSION

Suppose we are given three distinct vertices and $D = 0$. What must be true about the three points?

6.7 Putting It All Together

The determinant of a square matrix A is a real number, denoted $\det A$. If $\det A \neq 0$, then the matrix A is invertible. The following table summarizes the calculation of 2×2 and 3×3 determinants by hand.

DETERMINANTS OF 2 × 2 MATRICES

The determinant of a 2×2 matrix A is given by

$$\det A = \det\begin{bmatrix} a & b \\ c & d \end{bmatrix} = ad - cb.$$

Example: $\det\begin{bmatrix} 6 & -2 \\ 3 & 7 \end{bmatrix} = (6)(7) - (3)(-2) = 48$

DETERMINANTS OF 3 × 3 MATRICES

Finding the determinant of a 3×3 matrix A can be reduced to calculating the determinants of three 2×2 matrices. This calculation can be performed using cofactors.

$$\det A = \det\begin{bmatrix} a_1 & b_1 & c_1 \\ a_2 & b_2 & c_2 \\ a_3 & b_3 & c_3 \end{bmatrix}$$

$$= a_1 \det\begin{bmatrix} b_2 & c_2 \\ b_3 & c_3 \end{bmatrix} - a_2 \det\begin{bmatrix} b_1 & c_1 \\ b_3 & c_3 \end{bmatrix} + a_3 \det\begin{bmatrix} b_1 & c_1 \\ b_2 & c_2 \end{bmatrix}$$

Example: $\det\begin{bmatrix} 1 & -2 & 3 \\ 4 & 5 & -1 \\ -3 & 7 & 8 \end{bmatrix} = (1)\det\begin{bmatrix} 5 & -1 \\ 7 & 8 \end{bmatrix} - (4)\det\begin{bmatrix} -2 & 3 \\ 7 & 8 \end{bmatrix} + (-3)\det\begin{bmatrix} -2 & 3 \\ 5 & -1 \end{bmatrix}$

$$= (1)(47) - 4(-37) - 3(-13) = 234$$

6.7 Exercises

Calculating Determinants

Exercises 1–4: Determine if the matrix A is invertible by calculating det A.

1. $A = \begin{bmatrix} 4 & 3 \\ 5 & 4 \end{bmatrix}$

2. $A = \begin{bmatrix} 1 & -3 \\ 2 & 6 \end{bmatrix}$

3. $A = \begin{bmatrix} -4 & 6 \\ -8 & 12 \end{bmatrix}$

4. $A = \begin{bmatrix} 10 & -20 \\ -5 & 10 \end{bmatrix}$

Exercises 5–8: Find the specified minor and cofactor for A.

5. M_{12} and A_{12} if $A = \begin{bmatrix} 1 & -1 & 3 \\ 2 & 3 & -2 \\ 0 & 1 & 5 \end{bmatrix}$

6. M_{23} and A_{23} if $A = \begin{bmatrix} 1 & 2 & -1 \\ 4 & 6 & -3 \\ 2 & 3 & 9 \end{bmatrix}$

7. M_{22} and A_{22} if $A = \begin{bmatrix} 7 & -8 & 1 \\ 3 & -5 & 2 \\ 1 & 0 & -2 \end{bmatrix}$

8. M_{31} and A_{31} if $A = \begin{bmatrix} 0 & 0 & -1 \\ 6 & -7 & 1 \\ 8 & -9 & -1 \end{bmatrix}$

Exercises 9–12: Let A be the given matrix. Find det A by expanding about the first column. State whether A^{-1} exists.

9. $\begin{bmatrix} 1 & 4 & -7 \\ 0 & 2 & -3 \\ 0 & -1 & 3 \end{bmatrix}$

10. $\begin{bmatrix} 0 & 2 & 8 \\ -1 & 3 & 5 \\ 0 & 4 & 1 \end{bmatrix}$

11. $\begin{bmatrix} 5 & 1 & 6 \\ 0 & -2 & 0 \\ 0 & 4 & 0 \end{bmatrix}$

12. $\begin{bmatrix} 3 & 2 & 3 \\ 2 & 2 & 2 \\ 1 & 3 & 1 \end{bmatrix}$

Exercises 13–20: Let A be the given matrix. Find det A by using the method of cofactors.

13. $\begin{bmatrix} 2 & 0 & 0 \\ 0 & 3 & 0 \\ 0 & 0 & 5 \end{bmatrix}$

14. $\begin{bmatrix} 0 & 0 & 2 \\ 0 & 3 & 0 \\ 5 & 0 & 0 \end{bmatrix}$

15. $\begin{bmatrix} 0 & 0 & 0 \\ -8 & 3 & -9 \\ 15 & 5 & 9 \end{bmatrix}$

16. $\begin{bmatrix} 1 & 1 & 5 \\ -3 & -3 & 0 \\ 7 & 0 & 0 \end{bmatrix}$

17. $\begin{bmatrix} 3 & -1 & 2 \\ 0 & 5 & 7 \\ 1 & 0 & -1 \end{bmatrix}$

18. $\begin{bmatrix} 3 & 0 & -1 \\ 2 & 3 & -4 \\ 6 & -5 & 1 \end{bmatrix}$

19. $\begin{bmatrix} 1 & -5 & 2 \\ -7 & 1 & 3 \\ 0 & 4 & -2 \end{bmatrix}$

20. $\begin{bmatrix} 1 & -1 & 2 \\ -2 & 0 & 1 \\ 1 & 1 & -1 \end{bmatrix}$

Exercises 21–24: Let A be the given matrix. Use technology to calculate det A.

21. $\begin{bmatrix} 11 & -32 \\ 1.2 & 55 \end{bmatrix}$

22. $\begin{bmatrix} 17 & -4 & 3 \\ 11 & 5 & -15 \\ 7 & -9 & 23 \end{bmatrix}$

23. $\begin{bmatrix} 2.3 & 5.1 & 2.8 \\ 1.2 & 4.5 & 8.8 \\ -0.4 & -0.8 & -1.2 \end{bmatrix}$

24. $\begin{bmatrix} 1 & -1 & 3 & 7 \\ 9 & 2 & -7 & -4 \\ 5 & -7 & 1 & -9 \\ 7 & 1 & 3 & 6 \end{bmatrix}$

Cramer's Rule

Exercises 25–32: Use Cramer's rule to solve the system of linear equations.

25. $\begin{aligned} -x + 2y &= 5 \\ 3x + 3y &= 1 \end{aligned}$

26. $\begin{aligned} 2x + y &= -3 \\ -4x - 6y &= -7 \end{aligned}$

27. $\begin{aligned} -2x + 3y &= 8 \\ 4x - 5y &= 3 \end{aligned}$

28. $\begin{aligned} 5x - 3y &= 4 \\ -3x - 7y &= 5 \end{aligned}$

29. $\begin{aligned} 7x + 4y &= 23 \\ 11x - 5y &= 70 \end{aligned}$

30. $\begin{aligned} -7x + 5y &= 8.2 \\ 6x + 4y &= -0.4 \end{aligned}$

31. $\begin{aligned} 1.7x - 2.5y &= -0.91 \\ -0.4x + 0.9y &= 0.423 \end{aligned}$

32. $\begin{aligned} -2.7x + 1.5y &= -1.53 \\ 1.8x - 5.5y &= -1.68 \end{aligned}$

Calculating Area

Exercises 33–36: Use a determinant to find the area of the shaded region.

33.

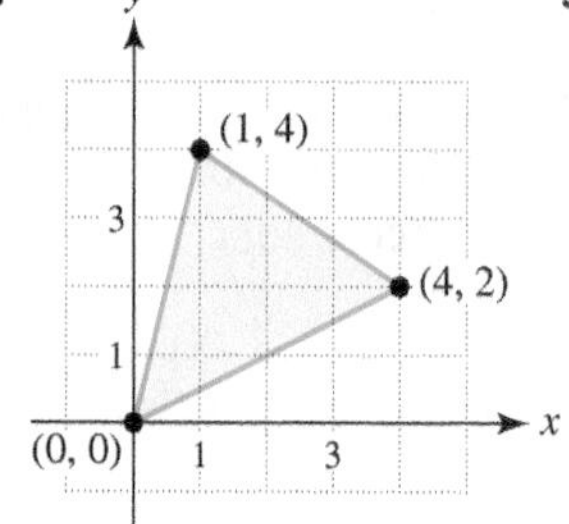

34.

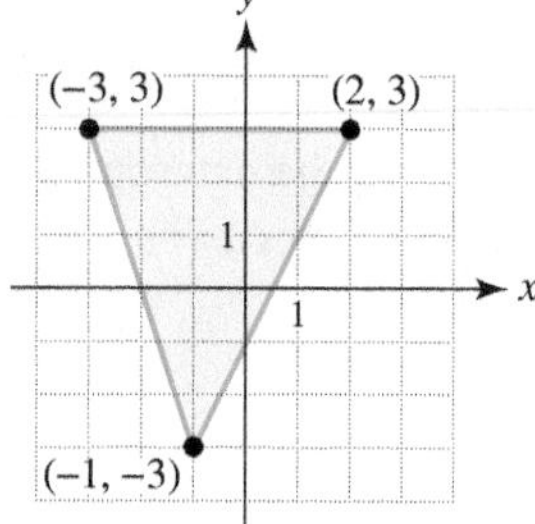

35.

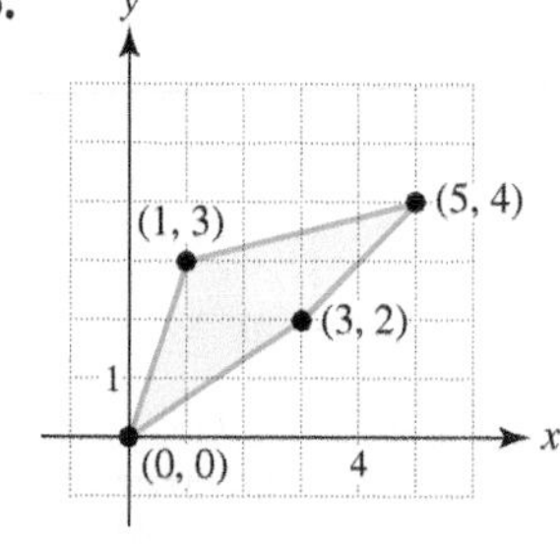

36.

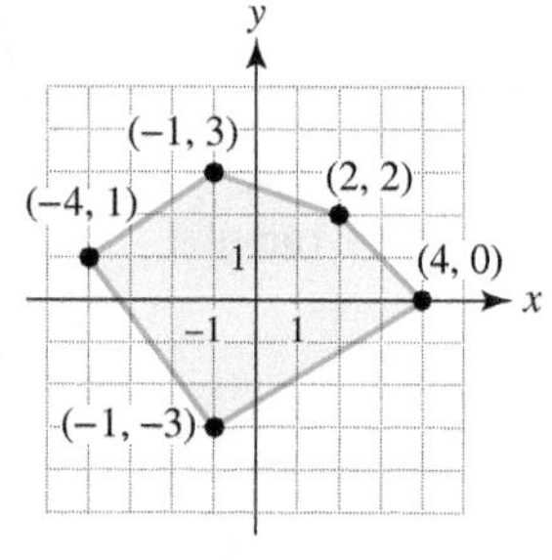

Applying a Concept

Exercises 37–40: Use the concept of the area of a triangle to determine if the three points are collinear.

37. $(1, 3), (-3, 11), (2, 1)$

38. $(3, 6), (-1, -6), (5, 11)$

39. $(-2, -5), (4, 4), (2, 3)$

40. $(4, -5), (-2, 10), (6, -10)$

Equations of Lines

Exercises 41–44: If a line passes through the points (x_1, y_1) and (x_2, y_2), then an equation of this line can be found by calculating the determinant.

$$\det\begin{bmatrix} x & y & 1 \\ x_1 & y_1 & 1 \\ x_2 & y_2 & 1 \end{bmatrix} = 0$$

Find the standard form $ax + by = c$ of the line passing through the given points.

41. $(2, 1)$ and $(-1, 4)$

42. $(-1, 3)$ and $(4, 2)$

43. $(6, -7)$ and $(4, -3)$

44. $(5, 1)$ and $(2, -2)$

Writing about Mathematics

45. Choose two matrices A and B with dimension 2×2. Calculate $\det A$, $\det B$, and $\det(AB)$. Repeat this process until you are able to discover how these three determinants are related. Summarize your results.

46. Calculate both $\det A$ and $\det A^{-1}$ for several different matrices. Compare the determinants. Try to generalize your results.

Extended and Discovery Exercises

Exercises 1–6: **Cramer's Rule** *Cramer's rule can be applied to systems of three linear equations in three variables. For the system of equations*

$$\begin{aligned} a_1x + b_1y + c_1z &= d_1 \\ a_2x + b_2y + c_2z &= d_2 \\ a_3x + b_3y + c_3z &= d_3, \end{aligned}$$

the solution can be written as follows.

$$D = \det\begin{bmatrix} a_1 & b_1 & c_1 \\ a_2 & b_2 & c_2 \\ a_3 & b_3 & c_3 \end{bmatrix}, \quad E = \det\begin{bmatrix} d_1 & b_1 & c_1 \\ d_2 & b_2 & c_2 \\ d_3 & b_3 & c_3 \end{bmatrix}$$

$$F = \det\begin{bmatrix} a_1 & d_1 & c_1 \\ a_2 & d_2 & c_2 \\ a_3 & d_3 & c_3 \end{bmatrix}, \quad G = \det\begin{bmatrix} a_1 & b_1 & d_1 \\ a_2 & b_2 & d_2 \\ a_3 & b_3 & d_3 \end{bmatrix}$$

If $D \neq 0$, a unique solution exists and is given by

$$x = \frac{E}{D}, \quad y = \frac{F}{D}, \quad z = \frac{G}{D}.$$

Use Cramer's rule to solve the system of equations.

1. $$\begin{aligned} x + y + z &= 6 \\ 2x + y + 2z &= 9 \\ y + 3z &= 9 \end{aligned}$$

2. $$\begin{aligned} y + z &= 1 \\ 2x - y - z &= -1 \\ x + y - z &= 3 \end{aligned}$$

3. $$\begin{aligned} x \quad + z &= 2 \\ x + y \quad &= 0 \\ y + 2z &= 1 \end{aligned}$$

4. $$\begin{aligned} x + y + 2z &= 1 \\ -x - 2y - 3z &= -2 \\ y - 3z &= 5 \end{aligned}$$

5. $$\begin{aligned} x \quad + 2z &= 7 \\ -x + y + z &= 5 \\ 2x - y + 2z &= 6 \end{aligned}$$

6. $$\begin{aligned} x + 2y + 3z &= -1 \\ 2x - 3y - z &= 12 \\ x + 4y - 2z &= -12 \end{aligned}$$

Exercises 7–10: **Equations of Circles** *Given three distinct points on a circle (x_1, y_1), (x_2, y_2), and (x_3, y_3), we can find the equation of the circle by using the following determinant.*

$$\det\begin{bmatrix} x^2 + y^2 & x & y & 1 \\ x_1^2 + y_1^2 & x_1 & y_1 & 1 \\ x_2^2 + y_2^2 & x_2 & y_2 & 1 \\ x_3^2 + y_3^2 & x_3 & y_3 & 1 \end{bmatrix} = 0$$

Find the equation of the circle through the given points.

7. $(0, 2)$ $(2, 0)$, and $(-2, 0)$

8. $(0, 0)$, $(4, 0)$, and $(2, -2)$

9. $(0, 1)$, $(1, -1)$, and $(2, 2)$

10. $(1, 0)$, $(-1, 2)$, and $(3, 2)$

CHECKING BASIC CONCEPTS FOR SECTION 6.7

1. Find the determinant of the matrix A by using the method of cofactors. Is A invertible?

$$A = \begin{bmatrix} 1 & -1 & 2 \\ 2 & 3 & 1 \\ 0 & -2 & 5 \end{bmatrix}$$

2. Use Cramer's rule to solve the system of equations.

$$\begin{aligned} 3x - 4y &= 7 \\ -4x + 3y &= 5 \end{aligned}$$

6 Summary

CONCEPT	EXPLANATION AND EXAMPLES
Section 6.1 Functions and Systems of Equations in Two Variables	
Functions of Two Variables	$z = f(x, y)$, where x and y are inputs to f **Example:** $f(x, y) = 2x - 3y$ $f(4, -1) = 2(4) - 3(-1) = 11$
System of Linear Equations in Two Variables	*General form:* $a_1x + b_1y = c_1$ $a_2x + b_2y = c_2$ A linear system can have zero, one, or infinitely many solutions. A solution can be written as an ordered pair. A linear system may be solved symbolically, graphically, or numerically. **Example:** $x - y = 2$ $2x + y = 7$ Solution: (3, 1)
Types of Linear Systems with Two Variables	*Consistent system:* Has either one solution (independent equations) or infinitely many solutions (dependent equations) *Inconsistent system:* Has no solutions

One Solution

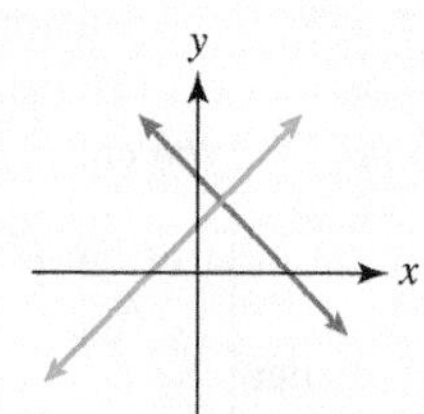

Consistent System
Independent Equations

Infinitely Many Solutions

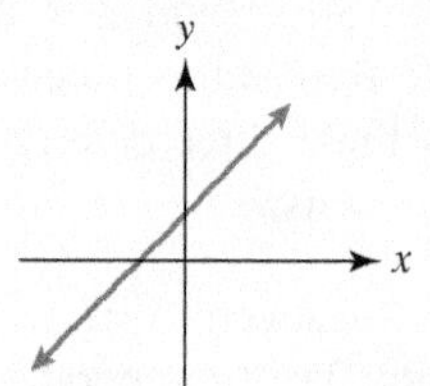

Consistent System
Dependent Equations

No Solution

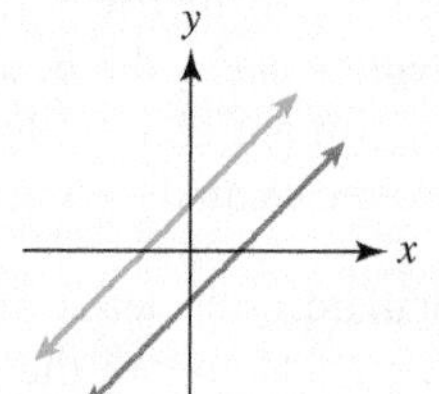

Inconsistent System

CONCEPT	EXPLANATION AND EXAMPLES
Method of Substitution for Two Equations	Can be used to solve systems of linear or nonlinear equations **Example:** $x - y = -3$ $x + 4y = 17$ Solve the first equation for x to obtain $x = y - 3$. Substitute this result in the second equation and solve for y. $(y - 3) + 4y = 17$ implies that $y = 4$. Then $x = 4 - 3 = 1$ and the solution is (1, 4).
Method of Elimination	Can be used to solve systems of linear or nonlinear equations **Example:** $2x - 3y = 4$ $x + 3y = 11$ $3x = 15$, or $x = 5$ Add. Substituting $x = 5$ in the first equation gives $y = 2$. The solution is (5, 2).

CONCEPT	EXPLANATION AND EXAMPLES
Section 6.1 Functions and Systems of Equations in Two Variables (CONTINUED)	
Joint Variation	Let m and n be real numbers. Then z *varies jointly* with the mth power of x and the nth power of y if a nonzero real number k exists such that $z = kx^m y^n$. **Example:** The area of a triangle varies jointly with the base b and the height h because $A = \frac{1}{2}bh$. Note that $k = \frac{1}{2}$, $m = 1$, and $n = 1$ in this example.
Section 6.2 Systems of Inequalities in Two Variables	
System of Inequalities in Two Variables	The solution set is often a shaded region in the xy-plane. **Example:** $x + y \le 4$ $y \ge 0$ $x \ge 0$ (0, 4) (4, 0) (0, 0)
Linear Programming	Method for maximizing (or minimizing) an objective function subject to a set of constraints **Example:** Maximize $P = 2x + 4y$, subject to $x + y \le 4, x \ge 0, y \ge 0.$ The maximum of $P = 16$ occurs at the vertex (0, 4), in the region of feasible solutions. See the figure above.
Section 6.3 Systems of Linear Equations in Three Variables	
Solution to a System of Linear Equations in Three Variables	An ordered triple (x, y, z) that satisfies *every* equation **Example:** $x - 2y + 3z = 6$ $-x + 3y + 4z = 17$ $3x + 4y - 5z = -4$ The solution is (1, 2, 3) because the values $x = 1, y = 2$, and $z = 3$ satisfy all three equations. (Check this fact.)
Elimination and Substitution	Systems of linear equations in three variables can be solved by using elimination and substitution. The following three steps outline this process. **STEP 1:** Eliminate one variable, such as x, from two of the equations. **STEP 2:** Apply the techniques discussed in Section 6.1 to solve the two equations in two variables resulting from Step 1. If x is eliminated, then solve these equations to find y and z. If there are no solutions for y and z, then the given system has no solutions. If there are infinitely many solutions for y and z, then write y in terms of z and go to Step 3. **STEP 3:** Substitute the values for y and z in one of the given equations to find x. The solution is (x, y, z). If possible, check your solution.

CONCEPT	EXPLANATION AND EXAMPLES
Section 6.4 Solutions to Linear Systems Using Matrices	
Matrices and Systems of Linear Equations	An augmented matrix can be used to represent a system of linear equations. **Example:** $\begin{aligned} x - 2y + z &= 0 \\ -x + 4y - z &= 4 \\ 2x + y - 3z &= -5 \end{aligned}$ **Augmented Matrix** $\left[\begin{array}{rrr\|r} 1 & -2 & 1 & 0 \\ -1 & 4 & -1 & 4 \\ 2 & 1 & -3 & -5 \end{array}\right]$
Row-Echelon Form	**Examples:** $\begin{bmatrix} 1 & 2 & -1 \\ 0 & 1 & 2 \end{bmatrix}$ $\left[\begin{array}{rrr\|r} 1 & 3 & -2 & 7 \\ 0 & 1 & 4 & 5 \\ 0 & 0 & 1 & -3 \end{array}\right]$
Gaussian Elimination with Backward Substitution	Gaussian elimination can be used to transform a matrix representing a system of linear equations into row-echelon form. Then backward substitution can be used to solve the resulting system of linear equations. (Graphing calculators can also be used to solve systems of equations.)
Section 6.5 Properties and Applications of Matrices	
Operations on Matrices	Matrices can be added, subtracted, and multiplied, but there is *no* division of matrices.
Addition	$\begin{bmatrix} 2 & 4 \\ 5 & 6 \end{bmatrix} + \begin{bmatrix} -2 & 1 \\ 7 & 3 \end{bmatrix} = \begin{bmatrix} 0 & 5 \\ 12 & 9 \end{bmatrix}$
Subtraction	$\begin{bmatrix} -3 & 0 \\ 4 & -4 \end{bmatrix} - \begin{bmatrix} 1 & 2 \\ 6 & -7 \end{bmatrix} = \begin{bmatrix} -4 & -2 \\ -2 & 3 \end{bmatrix}$
Scalar Multiplication	$3\begin{bmatrix} 5 & 1 & 6 & -1 \\ 0 & -2 & 3 & 2 \end{bmatrix} = \begin{bmatrix} 15 & 3 & 18 & -3 \\ 0 & -6 & 9 & 6 \end{bmatrix}$
Multiplication	$\begin{bmatrix} 2 & -1 \\ 0 & 3 \\ -7 & 1 \end{bmatrix}\begin{bmatrix} 1 & -1 & 0 \\ 3 & -5 & -4 \end{bmatrix} = \begin{bmatrix} -1 & 3 & 4 \\ 9 & -15 & -12 \\ -4 & 2 & -4 \end{bmatrix}$
Section 6.6 Inverses of Matrices	
Matrix Inverses	The inverse of an $n \times n$ matrix A, denoted A^{-1}, satisfies $A^{-1}A = I_n$ and $AA^{-1} = I_n$, where I_n is the $n \times n$ identity matrix. The inverse of a matrix can be found by hand or with technology. **Example:** $A = \begin{bmatrix} 5 & 2 \\ 2 & 1 \end{bmatrix}$ and $A^{-1} = \begin{bmatrix} 1 & -2 \\ -2 & 5 \end{bmatrix}$ $\begin{bmatrix} 5 & 2 \\ 2 & 1 \end{bmatrix}\begin{bmatrix} 1 & -2 \\ -2 & 5 \end{bmatrix} = \begin{bmatrix} 1 & 0 \\ 0 & 1 \end{bmatrix} = I_2$ $\begin{bmatrix} 1 & -2 \\ -2 & 5 \end{bmatrix}\begin{bmatrix} 5 & 2 \\ 2 & 1 \end{bmatrix} = \begin{bmatrix} 1 & 0 \\ 0 & 1 \end{bmatrix} = I_2$

CONCEPT	EXPLANATION AND EXAMPLES
Section 6.6 Inverses of Matrices (CONTINUED)	
Matrix Equations	A system of linear equations can be written as the matrix equation $AX = B$. **Example:** $2x - 2y = 3$ $-3x + 4y = 2$ $AX = \begin{bmatrix} 2 & -2 \\ -3 & 4 \end{bmatrix}\begin{bmatrix} x \\ y \end{bmatrix} = \begin{bmatrix} 3 \\ 2 \end{bmatrix} = B$ The solution can be found as follows. $X = A^{-1}B = \begin{bmatrix} 2 & 1 \\ 1.5 & 1 \end{bmatrix}\begin{bmatrix} 3 \\ 2 \end{bmatrix} = \begin{bmatrix} 8 \\ 6.5 \end{bmatrix}$ The solution is (8, 6.5).
Section 6.7 Determinants	
Determinant of a 2 × 2 Matrix	$\det A = \det \begin{bmatrix} a & b \\ c & d \end{bmatrix} = ad - cb$ **Example:** $\det \begin{bmatrix} 1 & 4 \\ 3 & 5 \end{bmatrix} = (1)(5) - (3)(4) = -7$
Determinant of a 3 × 3 Matrix	Finding a 3×3 determinant can be reduced to calculating the determinants of three 2×2 matrices by using cofactors. If $\det A \neq 0$, then A^{-1} exists. **Example:** $\det \begin{bmatrix} 3 & 1 & -1 \\ 2 & 2 & 0 \\ 0 & 1 & -3 \end{bmatrix}$ $= 3\begin{bmatrix} 2 & 0 \\ 1 & -3 \end{bmatrix} - 2\begin{bmatrix} 1 & -1 \\ 1 & -3 \end{bmatrix} + 0\begin{bmatrix} 1 & -1 \\ 2 & 0 \end{bmatrix}$ $= 3(-6) - 2(-2) + 0(2)$ $= -14$
Cramer's Rule	Cramer's rule makes use of determinants to solve systems of linear equations. However, Gaussian elimination with backward substitution is usually more efficient.

6 Review Exercises

Exercises 1 and 2: Evaluate the function for the inputs.

1. $A(3, 6)$, where $A(b, h) = \frac{1}{2}bh$

2. $V(2, 5)$, where $V(r, h) = \pi r^2 h$

Exercises 3 and 4: The figure in the next column shows the graph of a system of two linear equations. Use the graph to estimate the solution to the system of equations. Then solve the system symbolically.

3. **4.**

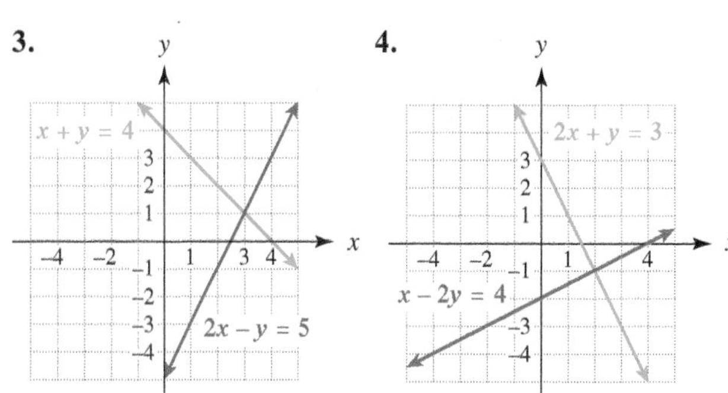

Exercises 5 and 6: Solve the system of equations

(a) graphically and (b) symbolically.

5. $3x + y = 1$
$2x - 3y = 8$

6. $x^2 - y = 1$
$x + y = 1$

Exercises 7–10: Use the elimination method to solve each system of linear equations, if possible. Identify the system as consistent or inconsistent.

7. $2x + y = 7$
$x - 2y = -4$

8. $3x + 3y = 15$
$-x - y = -4$

9. $6x - 15y = 12$
$-4x + 10y = -8$

10. $3x - 4y = -10$
$4x + 3y = -30$

Exercises 11 and 12: Use elimination to solve the nonlinear system of equations.

11. $x^2 - 3y = 3$
$x^2 + 2y^2 = 5$

12. $2x - 3y = 1$
$2x^2 + y = 1$

Exercises 13 and 14: Graph the solution set to the inequality.

13. $y \geq -1$

14. $2x - y < 4$

Exercises 15 and 16: Graph the solution set to the system of inequalities. Use the graph to find one solution.

15. $x^2 + y^2 < 9$
$x + y > 3$

16. $x + 3y \geq 3$
$x + y \leq 4$

Exercises 17–20: If possible, solve the system.

17. $x - y + z = -2$
$x + 2y - z = 2$
$2y + 3z = 7$

18. $x - 3y + 2z = -10$
$2x - y + 3z = -9$
$-x - y + z = -1$

19. $-x + 2y + 2z = 9$
$x + y - 3z = 6$
$3y - z = 8$

20. $2x - y - 3z = -9$
$x - 8z = -23$
$-3x + 2y - 2z = -5$

Exercises 21–24: The augmented matrix represents a system of linear equations. Solve the system.

21. $\left[\begin{array}{cc|c} 1 & 5 & 6 \\ 0 & 1 & 3 \end{array}\right]$

22. $\left[\begin{array}{ccc|c} 1 & 2 & -2 & 8 \\ 0 & 1 & 1 & 5 \\ 0 & 0 & 0 & 0 \end{array}\right]$

23. $\left[\begin{array}{ccc|c} 1 & 0 & 0 & -2 \\ 0 & 1 & 0 & 3 \\ 0 & 0 & 1 & 0 \end{array}\right]$

24. $\left[\begin{array}{ccc|c} 1 & 0 & 0 & -5 \\ 0 & 1 & -4 & 1 \\ 0 & 0 & 0 & 5 \end{array}\right]$

Exercises 25 and 26: Use Gaussian elimination with backward substitution to solve the system of linear equations.

25. $2x - y + 2z = 10$
$x - 2y + z = 8$
$3x - y + 2z = 11$

26. $x - 2y + z = 1$
$2x - 5y + 3z = 4$
$2x - 3y + z = 0$

Exercises 27 and 28: Let a_{ij} denote the general term for the matrix A. Find each of the following.

(a) $a_{12} + a_{22}$ *(b)* $a_{11} - 2a_{23}$

27. $A = \begin{bmatrix} -2 & 3 & -1 \\ 5 & 2 & 4 \end{bmatrix}$

28. $\begin{bmatrix} -1 & 2 & 5 \\ 1 & -3 & 7 \\ 0 & 7 & -2 \end{bmatrix}$

Exercises 29 and 30: Evaluate the following.

(a) $A + 2B$ *(b)* $A - B$ *(c)* $-4A$

29. $A = \begin{bmatrix} 1 & -3 \\ 2 & -1 \end{bmatrix}$, $B = \begin{bmatrix} 3 & 2 \\ -5 & 1 \end{bmatrix}$

30. $A = \begin{bmatrix} 4 & 0 & 1 \\ -2 & 8 & 9 \end{bmatrix}$, $B = \begin{bmatrix} -5 & 3 & 2 \\ -4 & 0 & 7 \end{bmatrix}$

Exercises 31–34: If possible, find AB and BA.

31. $A = \begin{bmatrix} 2 & 0 \\ -5 & 3 \end{bmatrix}$, $B = \begin{bmatrix} -1 & -2 \\ 4 & 7 \end{bmatrix}$

32. $A = \begin{bmatrix} 1 & -2 \\ 2 & 3 \end{bmatrix}$, $B = \begin{bmatrix} 1 & 0 & 2 \\ -1 & 3 & 4 \end{bmatrix}$

33. $A = \begin{bmatrix} 2 & -1 & 3 \\ 2 & 4 & 0 \end{bmatrix}$, $B = \begin{bmatrix} 1 & 0 \\ -1 & 2 \\ 0 & 3 \end{bmatrix}$

34. $A = \begin{bmatrix} 1 & -1 & 2 \\ 0 & 3 & 4 \\ 1 & 0 & 2 \end{bmatrix}$, $B = \begin{bmatrix} -1 & 0 & 0 \\ 2 & 0 & -1 \\ 1 & 4 & 2 \end{bmatrix}$

Exercises 35 and 36: Determine if B is the inverse matrix of A by evaluating AB and BA.

35. $A = \begin{bmatrix} 8 & 5 \\ 6 & 4 \end{bmatrix}$, $B = \begin{bmatrix} 2 & -2.5 \\ -3 & 4 \end{bmatrix}$

36. $A = \begin{bmatrix} -1 & 1 & 2 \\ 1 & 0 & -1 \\ 0 & 1 & 2 \end{bmatrix}$, $B = \begin{bmatrix} -1 & 0 & 1 \\ 2 & 2 & -1 \\ -1 & -1 & -1 \end{bmatrix}$

Exercises 37 and 38: Let A be the given matrix. Find A^{-1}.

37. $\begin{bmatrix} 1 & -2 \\ -1 & 1 \end{bmatrix}$

38. $\begin{bmatrix} 1 & 0 & 1 \\ 1 & 1 & 1 \\ 0 & 1 & -1 \end{bmatrix}$

Exercises 39 and 40: Complete the following.

(a) Write the system in the form $AX = B$.

(b) Solve the linear system by computing $X = A^{-1}B$.

39. $x - 3y = 4$
$2x - y = 3$

40. $x - 2y + z = 0$
$2x + y + 2z = 10$
$y + z = 3$

41. Solve the system using technology.

$$\begin{aligned} 12x + 7y - 3z &= 14.6 \\ 8x - 11y + 13z &= -60.4 \\ -23x \quad\quad + 9z &= -14.6 \end{aligned}$$

42. If possible, graphically approximate the solution of each system of equations to the nearest thousandth. Identify each system as consistent or inconsistent. If the system is consistent, determine if the equations are dependent or independent.

(a) $3.1x + 4.2y = 6.4$
$1.7x - 9.1y = 1.6$

(b) $6.3x - 5.1y = 9.3$
$4.2x - 3.4y = 6.2$

(c) $0.32x - 0.64y = 0.96$
$-0.08x + 0.16y = -0.72$

Exercises 43 and 44: Let A be the given matrix. Find det A by using the method of cofactors.

43. $\begin{bmatrix} 2 & 1 & 3 \\ 0 & 3 & 4 \\ 1 & 0 & 5 \end{bmatrix}$ **44.** $\begin{bmatrix} 3 & 0 & 2 \\ 1 & 3 & 5 \\ -5 & 2 & 0 \end{bmatrix}$

Exercises 45 and 46: Let A be the given matrix. Use technology to find det A. State whether A is invertible.

45. $\begin{bmatrix} 13 & 22 \\ 55 & -57 \end{bmatrix}$ **46.** $\begin{bmatrix} 6 & -7 & -1 \\ -7 & 3 & -4 \\ 23 & 54 & 77 \end{bmatrix}$

Applications

47. Area and Perimeter Let l represent the length of a rectangle and w its width, where $l \geq w$. Then its area can be computed by $A(l, w) = lw$ and its perimeter by $P(l, w) = 2l + 2w$. Solve the system of equations determined by $A(l, w) = 77$ and $P(l, w) = 36$.

48. Cylinder Approximate the radius r and height h of a cylindrical container with a volume V of 30 cubic inches and a lateral (side) surface area S of 45 square inches.

49. Student Loans A student takes out two loans totaling \$2000 to help pay for college expenses. One loan is at 7% interest, and the other is at 9%. Interest for both loans is compounded annually.

(a) If the combined total interest for the first year is \$156, find the amount of each loan symbolically.

(b) Determine the amount of each loan graphically or numerically.

50. Dimensions of a Screen The screen of a rectangular television set is 3 inches wider than it is high. If the perimeter of the screen is 42 inches, find its dimensions by writing a system of linear equations and solving.

51. CD Prices A music store marks its compact discs A or B to indicate one of two selling prices. Each row in the table represents a purchase. Determine the cost of each type of CD by using a matrix inverse.

A	B	Total
1	2	\$37.47
2	3	\$61.95

52. Digital Photography Design a 3×3 matrix A that represents a digital photograph of the letter T in black on a white background. Find a matrix B such that adding B to A darkens only the white background by one gray level.

53. Area Use a determinant to find the area of the triangle whose vertices are (0, 0), (5, 2), and (2, 5).

54. Voter Turnout The table shows the percent y of voter turnout in the United States for the presidential election in year x, where $x = 0$ corresponds to 1900. Find a quadratic function defined by $f(x) = ax^2 + bx + c$ that models these data. Graph f together with the data.

x	24	60	96
y	48.9	62.8	48.8

Source: Committee for the Study of the American Electorate.

55. Joint Variation Suppose P varies jointly with the square of x and the cube of y. If $P = 432$ when $x = 2$ and $y = 3$, find P when $x = 3$ and $y = 5$.

56. Linear Programming Find the maximum value of $P = 3x + 4y$ subject to the following constraints.

$$\begin{aligned} x + 3y &\leq 12 \\ 3x + y &\leq 12 \\ x \geq 0, y &\geq 0 \end{aligned}$$

Extended and Discovery Exercises

1. To form the **transpose** of a matrix A, denoted A^T, let the first row of A be the first column of A^T, the second row of A be the second column of A^T, and so on, for each row of A. The following are examples of A and A^T. If A has dimension $m \times n$, then A^T has dimension $n \times m$.

$$A = \begin{bmatrix} 3 & -3 & 7 \\ 1 & 6 & -2 \\ 4 & 2 & 5 \end{bmatrix}, \quad A^T = \begin{bmatrix} 3 & 1 & 4 \\ -3 & 6 & 2 \\ 7 & -2 & 5 \end{bmatrix}$$

$$A = \begin{bmatrix} 1 & 2 \\ 3 & 4 \\ 5 & 6 \end{bmatrix}, \quad A^T = \begin{bmatrix} 1 & 3 & 5 \\ 2 & 4 & 6 \end{bmatrix}$$

Find the transpose of each matrix A.

(a) $A = \begin{bmatrix} 3 & -3 \\ 2 & 6 \\ 4 & 2 \end{bmatrix}$ **(b)** $A = \begin{bmatrix} 0 & 1 & -2 \\ 2 & 5 & 4 \\ -4 & 3 & 9 \end{bmatrix}$

(c) $A = \begin{bmatrix} 5 & 7 \\ 1 & -7 \\ 6 & 3 \\ -9 & 2 \end{bmatrix}$

Exercises 2 and 3: **Least-Square Models** *The table shows the average cost of tuition and fees y in dollars at 4-year public colleges. In this table $x = 0$ represents 1980 and $x = 20$ corresponds to 2000.*

x	0	5	10	15	20
y	804	1318	1908	2860	3487

Source: The College Board.

These data can be modeled by using linear regression. Ideally, we would like $f(x) = ax + b$ to satisfy the following five equations.

$$\begin{aligned} f(0) &= a(0) + b = 804 \\ f(5) &= a(5) + b = 1318 \\ f(10) &= a(10) + b = 1908 \\ f(15) &= a(15) + b = 2860 \\ f(20) &= a(20) + b = 3487 \end{aligned}$$

Since the data points are not collinear, it is impossible for the graph of a line to pass through all five points. These five equations can be written as

$$AX = \begin{bmatrix} 0 & 1 \\ 5 & 1 \\ 10 & 1 \\ 15 & 1 \\ 20 & 1 \end{bmatrix} \begin{bmatrix} a \\ b \end{bmatrix} = \begin{bmatrix} 804 \\ 1318 \\ 1908 \\ 2860 \\ 3487 \end{bmatrix} = B.$$

The least-squares solution is found by solving the ***normal equations***

$$A^{T}AX = A^{T}B$$

for X. The solution is $X = (A^{T}A)^{-1}A^{T}B$. Using technology, we find $a = 138.16$ and $b = 693.8$. Thus f is given by the formula $f(x) = 138.16x + 693.8$. The function f and the data can be graphed. See the figure.

```
([A]T[A])-1[A]T[B
]
         [[138.16]
          [693.8 ]]
```

[−5, 25, 5] by [0, 4000, 1000]

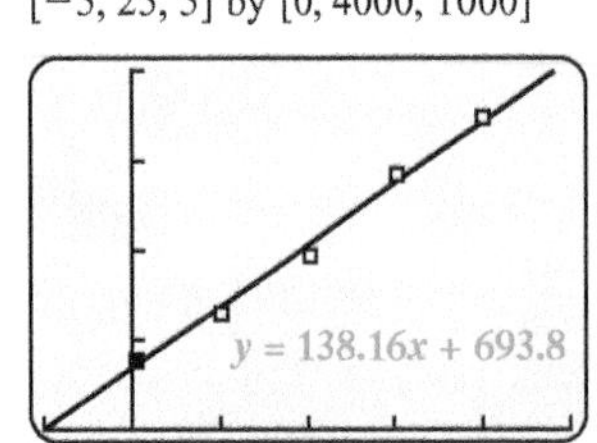

Solve the normal equations to model the data with the line determined by $f(x) = ax + b$. Plot the data and f in the same viewing rectangle.

2. **Tuition and Fees** The table shows average cost of tuition and fees y in dollars at private 4-year colleges. In this table $x = 0$ corresponds to 1980 and $x = 20$ to 2000.

x	0	5	10	15	20
y	3617	6121	9340	12,216	16,233

Source: The College Board.

3. **Early Satellite TV** The table lists the number of satellite television subscribers y in millions. In this table $x = 0$ corresponds to 1995 and $x = 5$ to the year 2000.

x	0	1	2	3	4	5
y	2.2	4.5	7.9	10.5	13	15

Source: *USA Today.*

4. **Cryptography** Businesses and government agencies frequently send classified messages in code. One such cryptographic technique that involves matrices is the **polygraphic system**. In this system each letter in the alphabet is associated with a number between 1 and 26. The following table gives a common example.

A	B	C	D	E	F	G	H	I	J
1	2	3	4	5	6	7	8	9	10
K	**L**	**M**	**N**	**O**	**P**	**Q**	**R**	**S**	**T**
11	12	13	14	15	16	17	18	19	20
U	**V**	**W**	**X**	**Y**	**Z**				
21	22	23	24	25	26				

Source: A. Sinkov, *Elementary Cryptanalysis: A Mathematical Approach.*

For example, the word MATH is coded as 13 1 20 8. Enter these numbers in a 2×2 matrix B.

$$B = \begin{bmatrix} 13 & 20 \\ 1 & 8 \end{bmatrix}$$

To encrypt these letters, a 2×2 matrix, such as

$$A = \begin{bmatrix} 2 & 1 \\ -5 & -2 \end{bmatrix},$$

is multiplied times B to form the product AB.

$$AB = \begin{bmatrix} 2 & 1 \\ -5 & -2 \end{bmatrix} \begin{bmatrix} 13 & 20 \\ 1 & 8 \end{bmatrix} = \begin{bmatrix} 27 & 48 \\ -67 & -116 \end{bmatrix}$$

Since the resulting elements of AB are less than 1 or greater than 26, they may be scaled between 1 and 26 by adding or subtracting multiples of 26.

$$27 - 1(26) = 1 \qquad 48 - 1(26) = 22$$
$$-67 + 3(26) = 11 \qquad -116 + 5(26) = 14$$

Thus the word MATH is coded as **1 11 22 14,** or AKVN. The advantage of this coding technique is that a particular letter is not always coded the same each time. Use the matrix A to code the following words.

(a) HELP **(b)** LETTER

5. Decoding a Message (Refer to Exercise 4.) To decode a message we reverse the process by using A^{-1}. Decode each of the following.

(a) UBNL **(b)** QNABMV

1-6 Cumulative Review Exercises

1. Write 125,000 in scientific notation and 4.67×10^{-3} in standard notation.

2. Find the midpoint of the line segment connecting the points $(-3, 2)$ and $(-1, 6)$.

3. Express the domain and range of f in set-builder or interval notation. Then evaluate $f(-0.5)$.

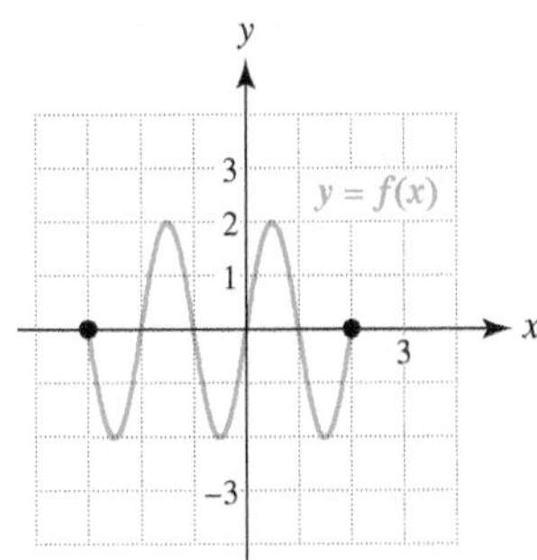

4. Graph $y = g(x)$ by hand.

(a) $g(x) = 2x - 3$ **(b)** $g(x) = |x + 2|$

(c) $g(x) = \ln x$ **(d)** $g(x) = \sqrt{x - 2}$

Exercises 5 and 6: Complete the following.

(a) Determine the domain of f.
(b) Evaluate $f(-1)$ and $f(2a)$.

5. $f(x) = \sqrt{4 - x}$ **6.** $\dfrac{x - 2}{4x^2 - 16}$

7. The graph of a linear function f is shown in the next column.

(a) Identify the slope, y-intercept, and x-intercept.

(b) Write a formula for $f(x)$.

(c) Evaluate $f(-2)$ symbolically and graphically.

(d) Find any zeros of f.

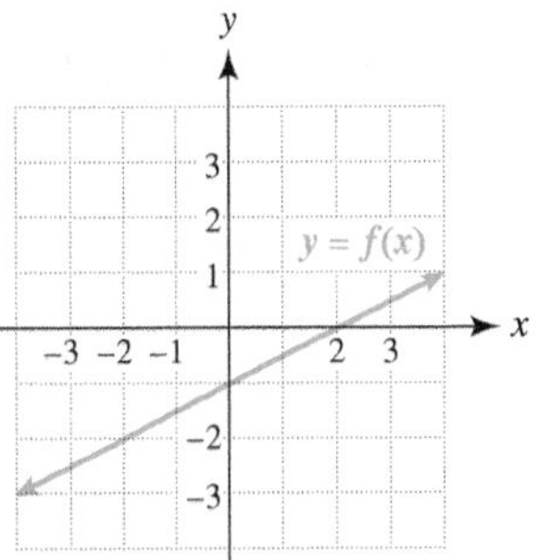

8. Write the slope-intercept form of a line that passes through $(2, -3)$ and is parallel to the line $2x + 3y = 6$.

9. Determine the x- and y-intercepts on the graph of the equation $-2x + 5y = 20$.

10. If $R(x) = \frac{1}{2}x + 2$ calculates the amount of rainfall in inches x hours past midnight, interpret the numbers $\frac{1}{2}$ and 2 in the formula for $R(x)$.

11. Solve each equation.

(a) $2(1 - 2x) = 5 - (4 - x)$ **(b)** $2e^x - 1 = 27$

(c) $\sqrt{2x - 1} = x - 2$ **(d)** $2x^2 + x = 1$

(e) $x^3 - 3x^2 + 2x = 0$ **(f)** $x^4 + 8 = 6x^2$

(g) $\dfrac{x}{x - 2} = \dfrac{2x - 1}{x + 1}$ **(h)** $|4 - 5x| = 8$

12. Graph f. Is f continuous on its domain? Evaluate $f(1)$.

$$f(x) = \begin{cases} 1 - x & \text{if } -4 \le x \le -1 \\ -2x & \text{if } -1 < x < 2 \\ \frac{1}{2}x^2 & \text{if } \ 2 \le x \le 4 \end{cases}$$

13. Solve the inequality. Write the solution set in set-builder or interval notation.
(a) $-3(2 - x) < 4 - (2x + 1)$ (b) $-3 \leq 4 - 3x < 6$
(c) $|4x - 3| \geq 9$ (d) $x^2 - 5x + 4 \leq 0$
(e) $t^3 - t > 0$ (f) $\frac{1}{t + 2} - 3 \geq 0$

14. Use the graph of f to solve each equation or inequality. Write the solution set for each inequality in set-builder or interval notation.
(a) $f(x) = 0$
(b) $f(x) > 0$
(c) $f(x) \leq 0$

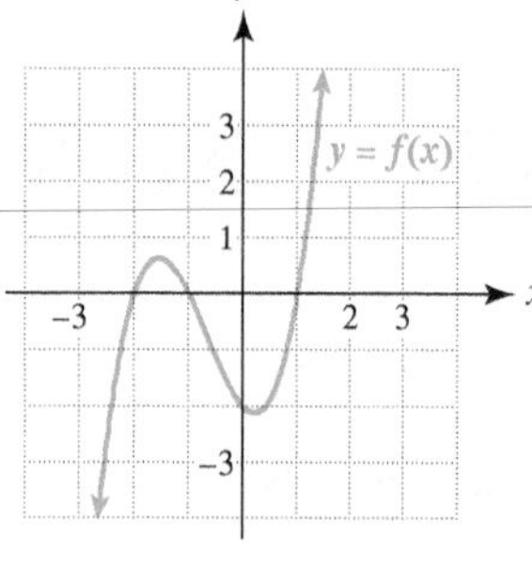

15. Write $f(x) = -2x^2 + 6x - 1$ in the vertex form given by $f(x) = a(x - h)^2 + k$.

16. Solve $2x^2 + 4x = 1$ by completing the square.

17. Use the given graph of $y = f(x)$ to sketch a graph of each equation.
(a) $y = f(x - 1) + 2$
(b) $y = \frac{1}{2}f(x)$
(c) $y = -f(-x)$
(d) $y = f(2x)$

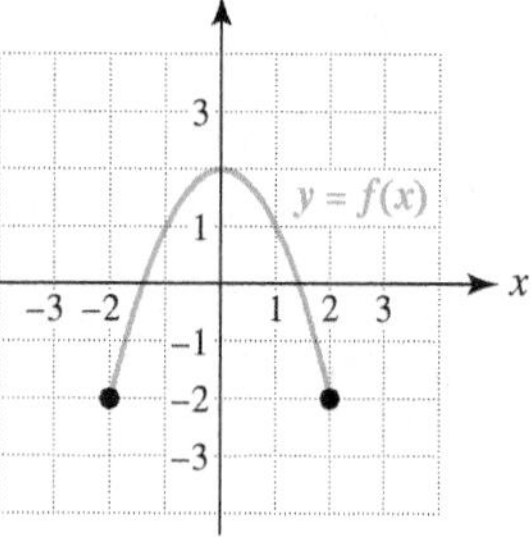

18. Divide each expression.
(a) $\frac{5a^4 - 2a^2 + 4}{2a^2}$ (b) $\frac{x^4 + 2x^3 - 2x}{x - 1}$

19. Write the complete factored form for the polynomial given by $f(x) = 2x^3 + x^2 - 8x - 4$.

20. Find all zeros, real or imaginary, of

$$f(x) = x^3 - x^2 + 4x - 4$$

given that one zero is $2i$.

21. Use the tables for f and g to evaluate each expression, if possible.
(a) $(f + g)(2)$
(b) $(g/f)(4)$
(c) $(f \circ g)(3)$
(d) $(f^{-1} \circ g)(1)$

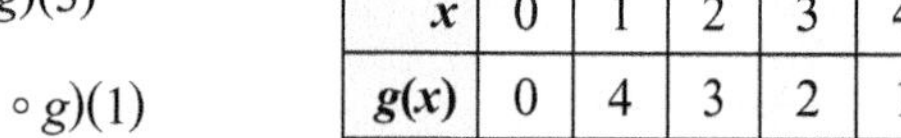

x	0	1	2	3	4
$f(x)$	4	3	2	1	0

x	0	1	2	3	4
$g(x)$	0	4	3	2	1

22. Use the graphs of f and g to complete the following.
(a) $(f - g)(-1)$
(b) $(fg)(2)$
(c) $(g \circ f)(0)$
(d) $(g^{-1} \circ f)(2)$

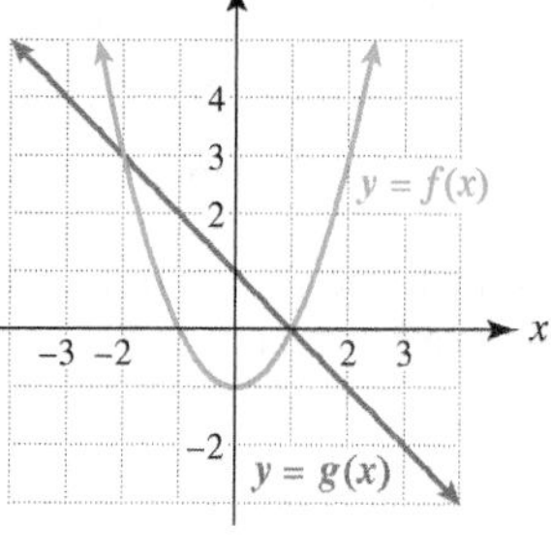

23. Let $f(x) = x^2 + 3x - 2$ and $g(x) = x - 2$. Find the following.
(a) $(f + g)(2)$ (b) $(g \circ f)(1)$
(c) $(f - g)(x)$ (d) $(f \circ g)(x)$

24. Find $f^{-1}(x)$ if $f(x) = 2\sqrt[3]{x} + 1$.

25. Find either a linear or an exponential function f that models the data in the table.

x	0	1	2	3	4
$f(x)$	9	6	4	$\frac{8}{3}$	$\frac{16}{9}$

26. There are initially 2000 bacteria and this number doubles every 3 hours. Find C and a so that $f(x) = Ca^x$ models the number of bacteria after x hours.

27. Use the graph to determine values for C and a.

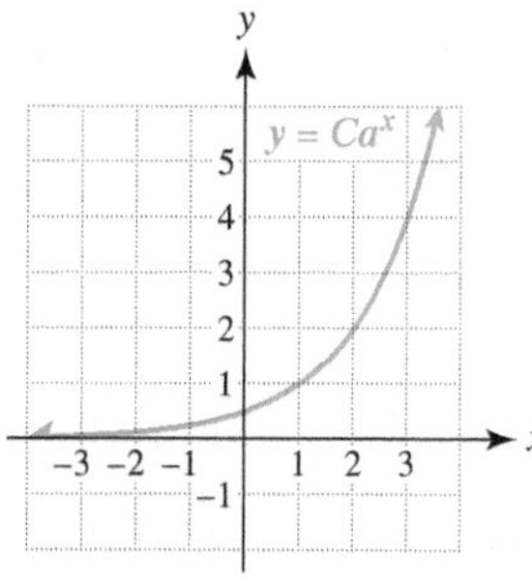

28. Five hundred dollars is deposited in an account that pays 5% annual interest compounded monthly. Find the amount in the account after 10 years.

29. Simplify each logarithm by hand.
(a) $\log 100$ (b) $\log_2 16$
(c) $\ln \frac{1}{e^2}$ (d) $\log_6 24 - \log_6 4$

30. Write $3 \log x - 4 \log y + \frac{1}{2} \log z$ as a logarithm of a single expression.

31. Expand the expression $\log_2 \frac{\sqrt[3]{x^2 - 4}}{\sqrt{x^2 + 4}}$.

32. Solve each equation.

(a) $3(2)^{-2x} + 4 = 100$ **(b)** $2 \log_3 (3x) = 4$

33. Evaluate $f(3, 4)$ if $f(x, y) = x^2 + y^2$.

34. If possible, solve each system of equations. Check your answer.

(a) $\begin{aligned} 3x - 2y &= 5 \\ 2x - 3y &= 0 \end{aligned}$ **(b)** $\begin{aligned} -x + \tfrac{3}{4}y &= 1 \\ 4x - 3y &= 4 \end{aligned}$

(c) $\begin{aligned} x^2 + y^2 &= 13 \\ 2x - 3y &= 0 \end{aligned}$ **(d)** $\begin{aligned} -x + \tfrac{3}{4}y &= 1 \\ 4x - 3y &= -4 \end{aligned}$

(e) $\begin{aligned} x - 4y + z &= 2 \\ x + 5y - z &= 0 \\ 2x - 7y + 3z &= 5 \end{aligned}$ **(f)** $\begin{aligned} 2x + y - 3z &= 3 \\ -x + 2y + z &= 3 \\ 3x - y - 4z &= 0 \end{aligned}$

35. The variable z varies jointly with the square of x and the square root of y. If $z = 7.2$ when $x = 3$ and $y = 16$, find z when $x = 5$ and $y = 4$.

36. Graph the solution set.

(a) $y \le -2$ **(b)** $3x - 4y > 12$

(c) $\begin{aligned} x + 2y &< -2 \\ 2x - 3y &> -3 \end{aligned}$ **(d)** $\begin{aligned} x^2 - 2y &\le 4 \\ 2 - x^2 &\ge y \end{aligned}$

37. Solve the system of linear equations.

$$\begin{aligned} x - y - z &= -2 \\ -x + y - z &= 0 \\ y - 2z &= -6 \end{aligned}$$

38. Find $A - 3B$ and AB if

$$A = \begin{bmatrix} -2 & 3 & 4 \\ -5 & 1 & 5 \\ 7 & -1 & 0 \end{bmatrix} \text{ and } B = \begin{bmatrix} 3 & 0 & -2 \\ 5 & -1 & 4 \\ -2 & 6 & -5 \end{bmatrix}.$$

39. Find A^{-1} if $A = \begin{bmatrix} 4 & -5 \\ 1 & -3 \end{bmatrix}$.

40. Calculate the determinant of each matrix.

(a) $\begin{bmatrix} -2 & 3 \\ 3 & 5 \end{bmatrix}$ **(b)** $\begin{bmatrix} 1 & -1 & 3 \\ 4 & -5 & 0 \\ 0 & 3 & 6 \end{bmatrix}$

Applications

41. Dimensions of an Aluminum Can The volume V of an aluminum can is given by $V = \pi r^2 h$, where r is the radius and h is the height. If an aluminum can has a volume of 12 cubic inches and a diameter of 2 inches, find the height of the can to the nearest hundredth of an inch.

42. Distance from Home The graph shows the distance that the driver of a car on a straight highway is from home. Find the slope of each line segment and interpret each slope.

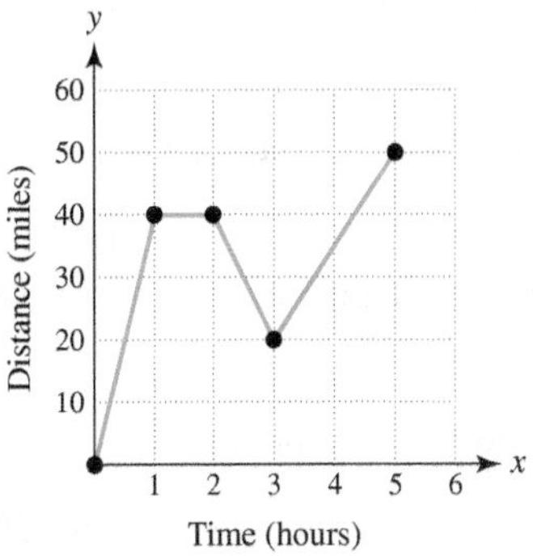

43. Average Rate of Change The total distance D in feet that an object has fallen after t seconds is given by $D(t) = 16t^2$ for $0 \le t \le 3$.

(a) Find the average rate of change of D from 0 to 1 and from 1 to 2.

(b) Interpret these average rates of change.

(c) Find the difference quotient of D.

44. Working Together Suppose one person can mow a large lawn in 4 hours and another person can mow the same lawn in 6 hours. How long will it take to mow the lawn if they work together?

45. Inverse Variation The force of gravity F varies inversely with the square of the distance d from the *center* of Earth. If a person weighs 150 pounds on the surface of Earth ($d = 4000$ miles), how much would this person weigh 10,000 miles from the center of Earth?

46. Linear Programming Find the minimum value of $C = 3x + y$ subject to the following constraints.

$$\begin{aligned} x + y &\ge 1 \\ 2x + 3y &\le 6 \\ x \ge 0&, y \ge 0 \end{aligned}$$

47. Hotel Rooms Rooms at a hotel are regularly \$110, but the cost of every room is reduced by \$2 for each additional room rented.

(a) Write a quadratic function C that gives the total cost of renting x rooms.

(b) Solve $C(x) = 1470$ and interpret the result.

(c) Find the absolute maximum for C and interpret your result.

48. Volume of a Balloon The radius r in inches of a spherical balloon after t seconds is given by $r = \sqrt{t}$.
(a) Is the radius increasing or decreasing?

(b) Write a formula for a function V that calculates the volume of the sphere after t seconds.

(c) Evaluate $V(4)$ and interpret the result.

49. Inverse Function The formula $f(x) = \frac{5}{9}(x - 32)$ converts degrees Fahrenheit to degrees Celsius.
(a) Find $f^{-1}(x)$.

(b) What does f^{-1} compute?

50. Bacteria Growth There are initially 200,000 bacteria per milliliter in a sample. The number of bacteria reaches 300,000 per milliliter after 3 hours.
(a) Use the formula $N(t) = N_0e^{kt}$ to model the concentration of bacteria after t hours.
(b) Evaluate $N(5)$ and interpret the result.

(c) After how long did the concentration reach 500,000 per milliliter?

51. Interest Formula Solve $A = P\left(1 + \frac{r}{n}\right)^{nt}$ for t.

52. Dimensions of a Rectangle A rectangle has a perimeter of 60 inches and an area of 209 square inches. Find its dimensions.

53. Student Loans A student takes out two loans totaling \$5000 to help pay for college expenses. One loan is at 4% interest and the other is at 3% interest. If the total interest is \$173 after 1 year, how much did the student borrow at each interest rate?

54. Tickets Sold Nine hundred tickets are sold for a concert, generating \$7500 in revenue. The prices of the tickets are \$6 for children, \$7 for students, and \$10 for adults. One hundred and fifty more adult tickets are sold than student tickets. How many of each type of ticket are sold?

55. Modeling Data Determine a, b, and c so that the formula $f(x) = ax^2 + bx + c$ models the data in the table *exactly*. (*Hint:* Use a system of equations.)

x	-1	1	3
$f(x)$	-8	6	-4

56. Area of a Triangle Use a determinant to find the area of the triangle with vertices $(-1, 2)$, $(2, 4)$, and $(3, -3)$.

R Reference: Basic Concepts from Algebra and Geometry

Throughout the text there are algebra and geometry review notes that direct students to "see Chapter R." This reference chapter contains seven sections, which provide a review of important topics from algebra and geometry. Students can refer to these sections for more explanation or extra practice. Instructors can use these sections to emphasize a variety of mathematical skills.

R.1 Formulas from Geometry

- **Use formulas for shapes in a plane**
- **Find sides of right triangles by applying the Pythagorean theorem**
- **Apply formulas to three-dimensional objects**
- **Use similar triangles to solve problems**

Geometric Shapes in a Plane

This subsection discusses formulas related to rectangles, triangles, and circles.

Rectangles The distance around the boundary of a geometric shape in a plane is called its **perimeter**. The perimeter of a rectangle equals the sum of the lengths of its four sides. For example, the perimeter of the rectangle shown in Figure R.1 is $5 + 4 + 5 + 4 = 18$ feet. The perimeter P of a rectangle with length L and width W is $P = 2L + 2W$.

Rectangle

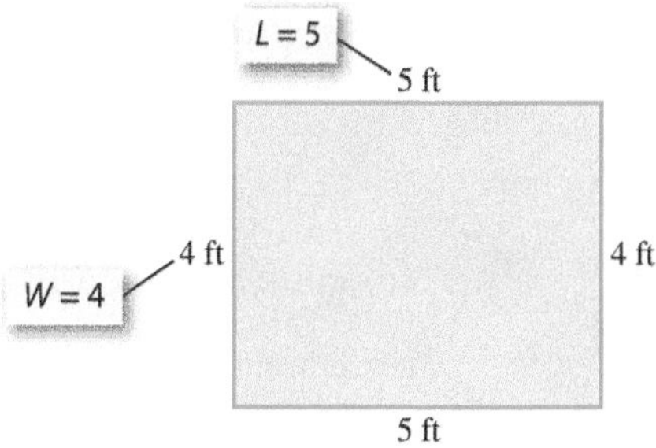

Figure R.1

The area A of a rectangle equals the product of its length and width: $A = LW$. So the rectangle in Figure R.1 has an area of $5 \cdot 4 = 20$ square feet.

Many times the perimeter or area of a rectangle is written in terms of variables, as demonstrated in the next example.

EXAMPLE 1 Finding the perimeter and area of a rectangle

The length of a rectangle is three times greater than its width. If the width is x inches, write expressions that give the perimeter and area.

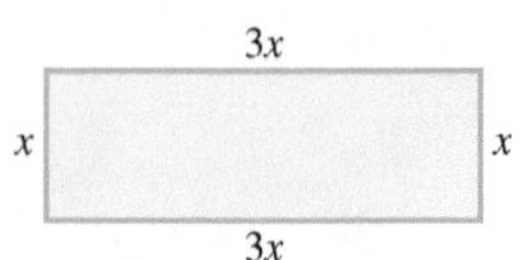

Figure R.2

SOLUTION The width of the rectangle is x inches, so its length is $3x$ inches. A sketch is shown in Figure R.2. The perimeter is

$$\begin{aligned} P &= 2L + 2W \\ &= 2(3x) + 2(x) \\ &= 8x \text{ inches.} \end{aligned}$$

Write the length in terms of the width.

The area is $A = LW = 3x \cdot x = 3x^2$ square inches.

Now Try Exercise 7

Triangle

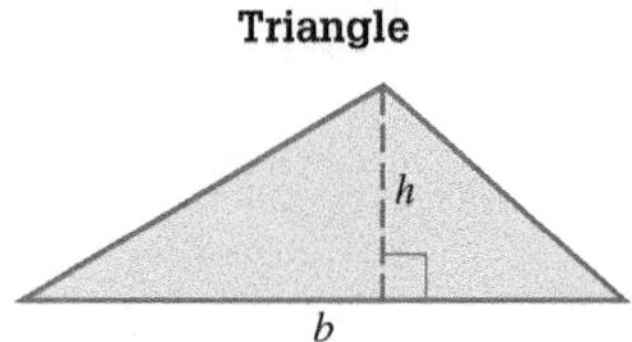

Figure R.3

Triangles If the base of a triangle is b and its height is h, as illustrated in Figure R.3, then the area A of the triangle is given by

$$A = \frac{1}{2}bh.$$

EXAMPLE 2 **Finding the area of a triangle**

Calculate the area of the triangle.

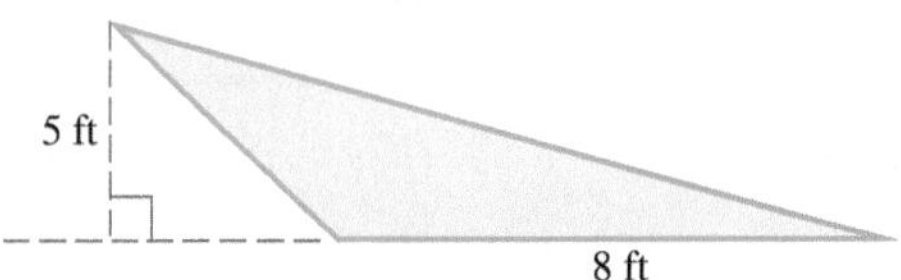

SOLUTION The triangle has a base of 8 feet and a height of 5 feet. Therefore its area is

$$A = \frac{1}{2}bh = \frac{1}{2} \cdot 8 \cdot 5 = 20 \text{ square feet.}$$

Now Try Exercise 11

Circle

r

$C = 2\pi r$
$A = \pi r^2$

Figure R.4

Circles The perimeter of a circle is called its **circumference** C and is given by $C = 2\pi r$, where r is the radius of the circle. The area A of a circle is $A = \pi r^2$. See Figure R.4.

EXAMPLE 3 **Finding the circumference and area of a circle**

A circle has a radius of 12.5 inches. Approximate its circumference and area.

SOLUTION

Circumference: $C = 2\pi r = 2\pi(12.5) = 25\pi \approx 78.5$ inches

Area: $A = \pi r^2 = \pi(12.5)^2 = 156.25\pi \approx 490.9$ square inches

Now Try Exercise 21

Pythagorean Theorem

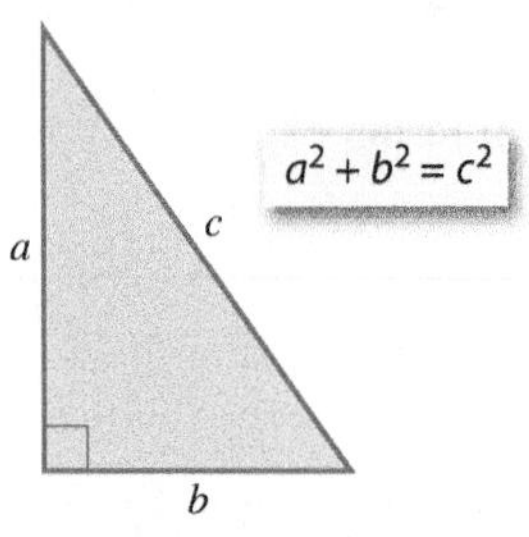

Figure R.5

The Pythagorean Theorem

One of the most famous theorems in mathematics is the Pythagorean theorem. It states that a triangle with legs a and b and hypotenuse c is a right triangle if and only if

$$a^2 + b^2 = c^2,$$

as illustrated in Figure R.5.

EXAMPLE 4 **Finding the perimeter of a right triangle**

One Side Unknown

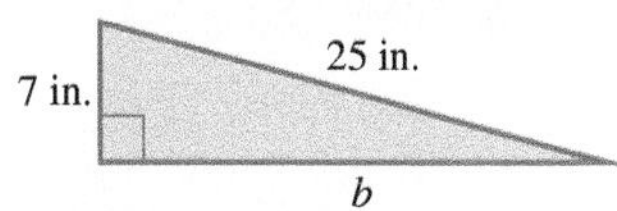

Figure R.6

Find the perimeter of the triangle shown in Figure R.6.

SOLUTION Given one leg and the hypotenuse of a right triangle, we can use the Pythagorean theorem to find the other leg. Let $a = 7$, $c = 25$, and find b.

$$a^2 + b^2 = c^2 \qquad \text{Pythagorean theorem}$$

$$b^2 = c^2 - a^2 \qquad \text{Subtract } a^2.$$

$$b^2 = 25^2 - 7^2 \qquad \text{Let } a = 7 \text{ and } c = 25.$$

$$b^2 = 576 \qquad \text{Simplify.}$$

$$b = 24 \qquad \text{Solve for } b > 0.$$

The perimeter of the triangle is

$$a + b + c = 7 + 24 + 25 = 56 \text{ inches.}$$

Now Try Exercise 29

Three-Dimensional Objects

Rectangular Box

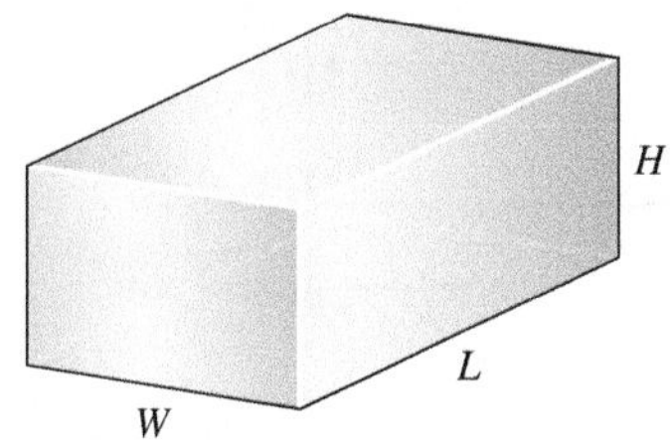

Figure R.7

Objects that occupy space have both volume and surface area. This subsection discusses rectangular boxes, spheres, cylinders, and cones.

Rectangular Boxes The volume V of a rectangular box with length L, width W, and height H equals $V = LWH$. See Figure R.7. The surface area S of the box equals the sum of the areas of the six sides: $S = 2LW + 2WH + 2LH$.

EXAMPLE 5 **Finding the volume and surface area of a box**

The box in Figure R.8 has dimensions x by $2x$ by y. Find its volume and surface area.

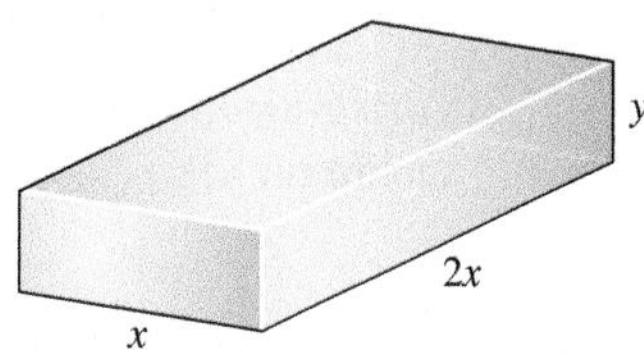

Figure R.8

SOLUTION

Volume: $LWH = 2x \cdot x \cdot y = 2x^2y$ cubic units

Surface Area: Base and top: $2x \cdot x + 2x \cdot x = 4x^2$
Front and back: $xy + xy = 2xy$
Left and right sides: $2xy + 2xy = 4xy$
Total surface area: $4x^2 + 2xy + 4xy = 4x^2 + 6xy$ square units

Find the area of each side and add.

Now Try Exercise 41

Sphere

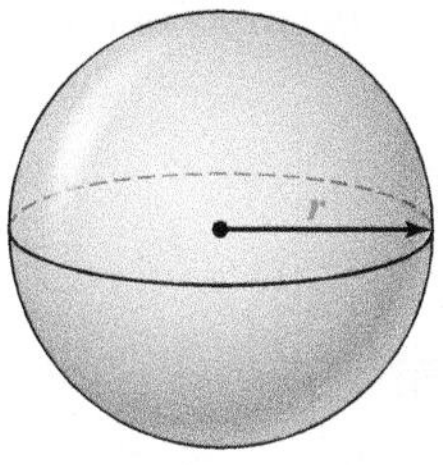

Figure R.9

Spheres The volume V of a sphere with radius r is $V = \frac{4}{3}\pi r^3$, and its surface area S is $S = 4\pi r^2$. See Figure R.9.

EXAMPLE 6 Finding the volume and surface area of a sphere

Estimate, to the nearest tenth, the volume and surface area of a sphere with a radius of 5.1 feet.

SOLUTION

Volume: $V = \frac{4}{3}\pi r^3 = \frac{4}{3}\pi(5.1)^3 \approx 555.6$ cubic feet

Surface Area: $S = 4\pi r^2 = 4\pi(5.1)^2 \approx 326.9$ square feet

Now Try Exercise 47

Cylinders The volume of a cylinder with radius r and height h is $V = \pi r^2 h$. See Figure R.10. To find the total surface area of a cylinder, we add the area of the top and bottom to the area of the side. Figure R.11 illustrates a cylinder cut open to determine its surface area. The top and bottom are circular with areas of πr^2 each, and the side has a surface area of $2\pi rh$. The total surface area is $S = 2\pi r^2 + 2\pi rh$. The side surface area is called the **lateral surface area.**

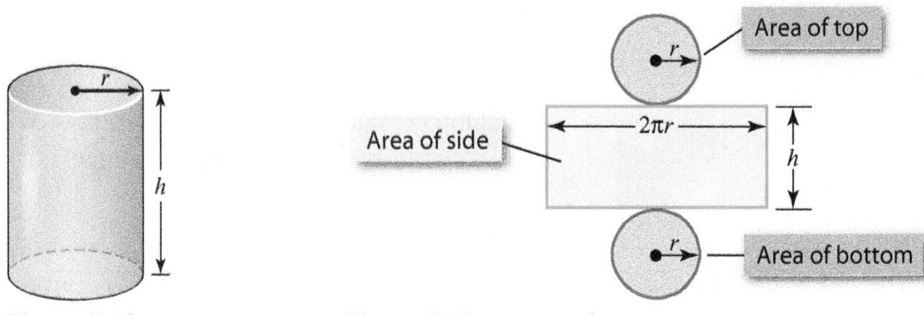

Figure R.10 Figure R.11

EXAMPLE 7 Finding the volume and surface area of a cylinder

A cylinder has radius $r = 3$ inches and height $h = 2.5$ feet. Find its volume and total surface area to the nearest tenth.

SOLUTION

Begin by changing 2.5 feet to 30 inches so that all units are in inches.

Volume: $V = \pi r^2 h = \pi(3)^2(30) = 270\pi \approx 848.2$ cubic inches

Total Surface Area: $S = 2\pi r^2 + 2\pi rh = 2\pi(3)^2 + 2\pi(3)(30) = 198\pi \approx 622.0$ square inches

Now Try Exercise 51

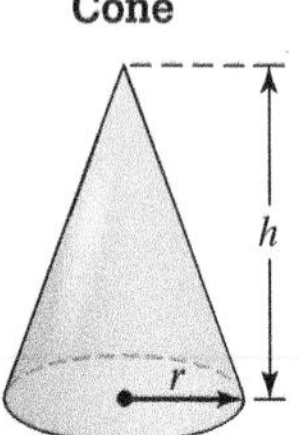

Figure R.12

Cones The volume of a cone with radius r and height h is $V = \frac{1}{3}\pi r^2 h$, as shown in Figure R.12. (Compare this formula with the formula for the volume of a cylinder.) Excluding the bottom of the cone, the side (or lateral) surface area is $S = \pi r\sqrt{r^2 + h^2}$. The bottom of the cone is circular and has a surface area of πr^2.

EXAMPLE 8 Finding the volume and surface area of a cone

Approximate, to the nearest tenth, the volume and surface area (side only) of a cone with a radius of 1.45 inches and a height of 5.12 inches.

SOLUTION

Volume: $V = \frac{1}{3}\pi r^2 h = \frac{1}{3}\pi(1.45)^2(5.12) \approx 11.3$ cubic inches

Surface Area (side only): $S = \pi r\sqrt{r^2 + h^2} = \pi(1.45)\sqrt{(1.45)^2 + (5.12)^2} \approx 24.2$ square inches

Now Try Exercise 55

Similar Triangles

The corresponding angles of **similar triangles** have equal measure, but similar triangles are not necessarily the same size. Two similar triangles are shown in Figure R.13. Notice that both triangles have angles of 30°, 60°, and 90°. Corresponding sides are not equal in length; however, corresponding ratios are equal. For example, in triangle ABC the ratio of the shortest leg to the hypotenuse equals $\frac{2}{4} = \frac{1}{2}$, and in triangle DEF this ratio is $\frac{3}{6} = \frac{1}{2}$.

Similar Triangles

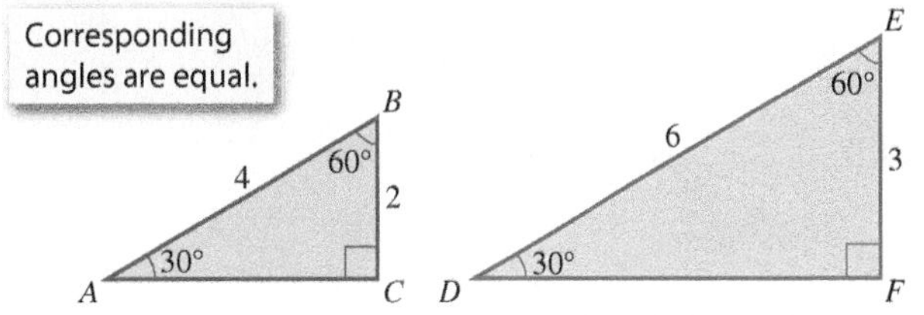

Corresponding angles are equal.

Figure R.13

EXAMPLE 9 Using similar triangles

Find the length of BC in Figure R.14.

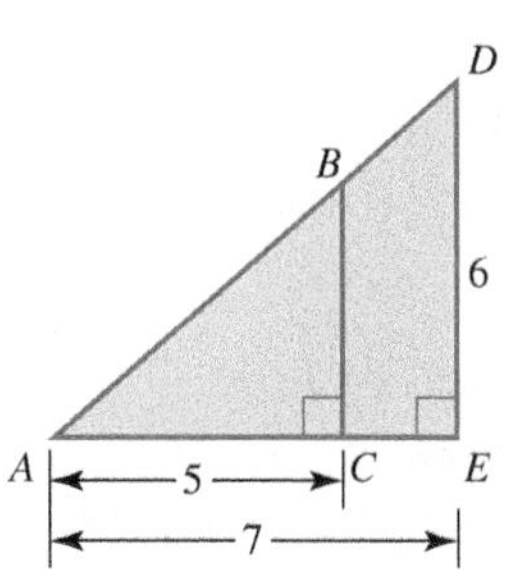

Figure R.14

SOLUTION Notice that triangle ABC and triangle ADE are both right triangles. These triangles share an angle at vertex A. Therefore triangles ABC and ADE have two corresponding angles that are congruent. Because the sum of the angles in a triangle equals 180°, all three corresponding angles in these two triangles are congruent. Thus triangles ABC and ADE are similar.

Since corresponding ratios are equal, we can find BC as follows.

$$\frac{BC}{AC} = \frac{DE}{AE}$$ Corresponding ratios are equal.

$$\frac{BC}{5} = \frac{6}{7}$$

Solving this equation for BC gives $BC = \frac{30}{7} \approx 4.3$.

Now Try Exercise 61

NOTE For a summary of these formulas, see the back endpapers of this text.

R.1 Exercises

Rectangles

Exercises 1–6: Find the area and perimeter of the rectangle with length L and width W.

1. $L = 15$ feet, $W = 7$ feet
2. $L = 16$ inches, $W = 10$ inches
3. $L = 100$ meters, $W = 35$ meters
4. $L = 80$ yards, $W = 13$ yards
5. $L = 3x$, $W = y$
6. $L = a + 5$, $W = a$

Exercises 7–10: Find the area and perimeter of the rectangle in terms of the width W.

7. The width W is half the length.
8. Triple the width W minus 3 equals the length.
9. The length equals the width W plus 5.
10. The length is 2 less than twice the width W.

Triangles

Exercises 11 and 12: Find the area of the triangle shown in the figure.

11.

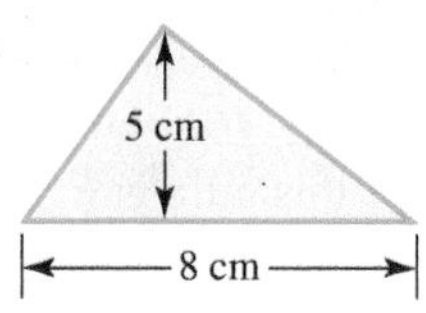

12.

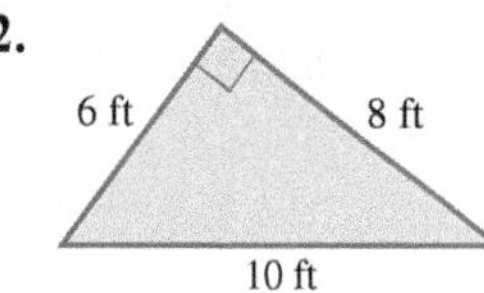

Exercises 13–20: Find the area of the triangle with base b and height h.

13. $b = 5$ inches, $h = 8$ inches

14. $b = 24$ inches, $h = 9$ feet

15. $b = 10.1$ meters, $h = 730$ meters

16. $b = 52$ yards, $h = 102$ feet

17. $b = 2x, h = 6x$

18. $b = x, h = x + 4$

19. $b = z, h = 5z$

20. $b = y + 1, h = 2y$

Circles

Exercises 21–26: Find the circumference and area of the circle. Approximate each value to the nearest tenth when appropriate.

21. $r = 4$ meters

22. $r = 1.5$ feet

23. $r = 19$ inches

24. $r = 22$ miles

25. $r = 2x$

26. $r = 5z$

Pythagorean Theorem

Exercises 27–32: Use the Pythagorean theorem to find the missing side of the right triangle with legs a and b and hypotenuse c. Then calculate the perimeter. Approximate values to the nearest tenth when appropriate.

27. $a = 60$ feet, $b = 11$ feet

28. $a = 21$ feet, $b = 11$ yards

29. $a = 5$ centimeters, $c = 13$ centimeters

30. $a = 6$ meters, $c = 15$ meters

31. $b = 7$ millimeters, $c = 10$ millimeters

32. $b = 1.2$ miles, $c = 2$ miles

Exercises 33–36: Find the area of the right triangle that satisfies the conditions. Approximate values to the nearest tenth when appropriate.

33. Legs with lengths 3 feet and 6 feet

34. Hypotenuse 10 inches and leg 6 inches

35. Hypotenuse 15 inches and leg 11 inches

36. Shorter leg 40 centimeters and hypotenuse twice the shorter leg

Rectangular Boxes

Exercises 37–44: Find the volume and surface area of a rectangular box with length L, width W, and height H.

37. $L = 4$ feet, $W = 3$ feet, $H = 2$ feet

38. $L = 6$ meters, $W = 4$ meters, $H = 1.5$ meters

39. $L = 4.5$ inches, $W = 4$ inches, $H = 1$ foot

40. $L = 9.1$ yards, $W = 8$ yards, $H = 6$ feet

41. $L = 3x, W = 2x, H = x$

42. $L = 6z, W = 5z, H = 7z$

43. $L = x, W = 2y, H = 3z$

44. $L = 8x, W = y, H = z$

Exercises 45 and 46: Find the volume of the rectangular box in terms of the width W.

45. The length is twice the width W, and the height is half the width.

46. The width W is three times the height and one-third of the length.

Spheres

Exercises 47–50: Find the volume and surface area of the sphere satisfying the given condition, where r is the radius and d is the diameter. Approximate values to the nearest tenth.

47. $r = 3$ feet

48. $r = 4.1$ inches

49. $d = 6.4$ meters

50. $d = 16$ feet

Cylinders

Exercises 51–54: Find the volume, the surface area of the side, and the total surface area of the cylinder that satisfies the given conditions, where r is the radius and h is the height. Approximate values to the nearest tenth.

51. $r = 0.5$ foot, $h = 2$ feet

52. $r = \frac{1}{3}$ yard, $h = 2$ feet

53. $r = 12$ millimeters, and h is twice r

54. r is one-fourth of h, and $h = 2.1$ feet

Cones

Exercises 55–60: Approximate, to the nearest tenth, the volume and surface area (side only) of the cone satisfying the given conditions, where r is the radius and h is the height.

55. $r = 5$ centimeters, $h = 6$ centimeters

56. $r = 8$ inches, $h = 30$ inches

57. $r = 24$ inches, $h = 3$ feet

58. $r = 100$ centimeters, $h = 1.3$ meters

59. Three times r equals h, and $r = 2.4$ feet

60. Twice h equals r, and $h = 3$ centimeters

Similar Triangles

Exercises 61–64: Use the fact that triangles ABC and DEF are similar to find the value of x.

61.

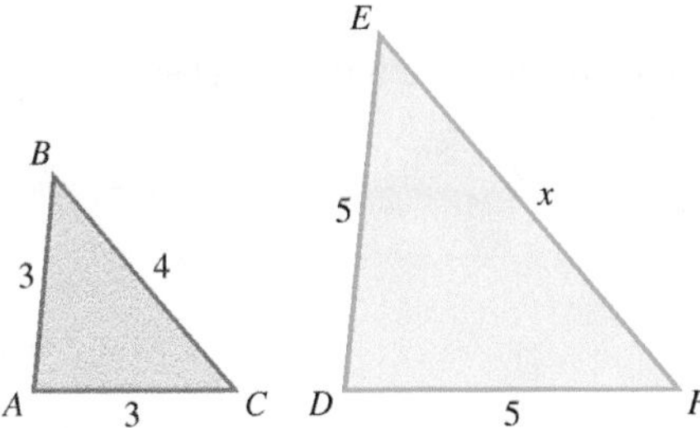

62.

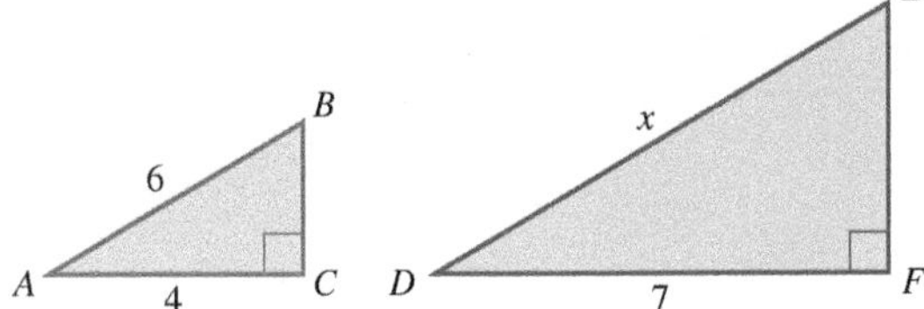

63.

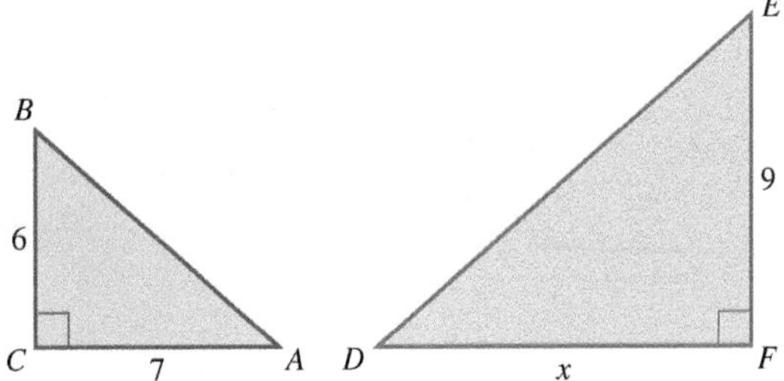

64.

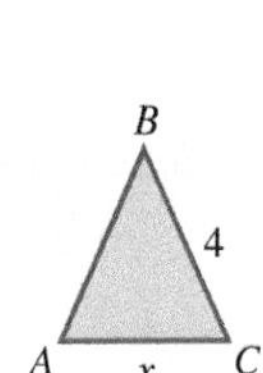

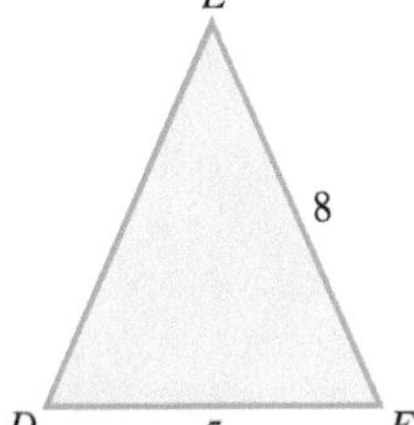

R.2 Integer Exponents

- **Use bases and exponents**
- **Use zero and negative exponents**
- **Apply the product, quotient, and power rules**

Bases and Positive Exponents

The expression 8^2 is an exponential expression with base 8 and exponent 2. Table R.1 contains examples of other exponential expressions.

Exponential Expressions

Equal Expressions	Base	Exponent
$2 \cdot 2 \cdot 2 = 2^3$	2	3
$6 \cdot 6 \cdot 6 \cdot 6 = 6^4$	6	4
$7 = 7^1$	7	1
$0.5 \cdot 0.5 = 0.5^2$	0.5	2
$x \cdot x \cdot x = x^3$	x	3

Table R.1

We read 0.5^2 as "0.5 squared," 2^3 as "2 cubed," and 6^4 as "6 to the fourth power."

EXAMPLE 1 Writing numbers in exponential notation

Use the given base to write each number as an exponential expression. Check your results with a calculator.

(a) 10,000 (base 10) **(b)** 27 (base 3) **(c)** 32 (base 2)

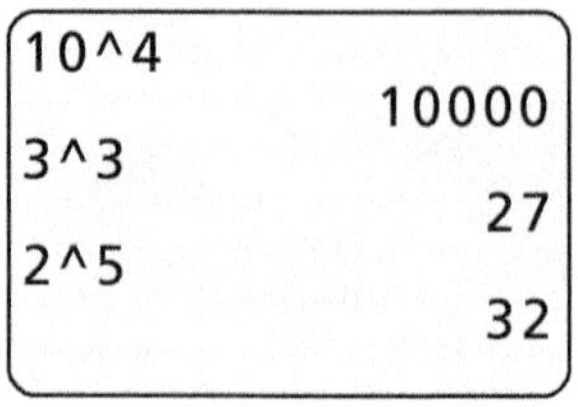

```
10^4
        10000
3^3
           27
2^5
           32
```

Figure R.15

SOLUTION

(a) $10{,}000 = 10 \cdot 10 \cdot 10 \cdot 10 = 10^4$ **(b)** $27 = 3 \cdot 3 \cdot 3 = 3^3$

(c) $32 = 2 \cdot 2 \cdot 2 \cdot 2 \cdot 2 = 2^5$

These values are supported in Figure R.15, where exponential expressions are evaluated with a calculator, using the ^ key.

Now Try Exercises 11 and 13

Zero and Negative Exponents

Exponents can be defined for any integer. The following box lists some properties for integer exponents.

INTEGER EXPONENTS

Let a and b be nonzero real numbers and m and n be positive integers. Then

1. $a^n = a \cdot a \cdot a \cdot \cdots \cdot a$ (n factors of a)
2. $a^0 = 1$ (*Note:* 0^0 is undefined.)
3. $a^{-n} = \dfrac{1}{a^n}$ and $\dfrac{1}{a^{-n}} = a^n$
4. $\dfrac{a^{-n}}{b^{-m}} = \dfrac{b^m}{a^n}$
5. $\left(\dfrac{a}{b}\right)^{-n} = \left(\dfrac{b}{a}\right)^n$

EXAMPLE 2 **Evaluating expressions**

Evaluate each expression.

(a) 3^{-4} **(b)** $\dfrac{1}{2^{-3}}$ **(c)** $\left(\dfrac{5}{7}\right)^{-2}$ **(d)** $\dfrac{1}{(xy)^{-1}}$ **(e)** $\dfrac{2^{-2}}{3t^{-3}}$

SOLUTION

(a) $3^{-4} = \dfrac{1}{3^4} = \dfrac{1}{3 \cdot 3 \cdot 3 \cdot 3} = \dfrac{1}{81}$ **(b)** $\dfrac{1}{2^{-3}} = 2^3 = 2 \cdot 2 \cdot 2 = 8$

(c) $\left(\dfrac{5}{7}\right)^{-2} = \left(\dfrac{7}{5}\right)^2 = \dfrac{7}{5} \cdot \dfrac{7}{5} = \dfrac{49}{25}$ **(d)** $\dfrac{1}{(xy)^{-1}} = (xy)^1 = xy$

Base is xy.

(e) Note that only t, not $3t$, is raised to the power of -3.

$$\frac{2^{-2}}{3t^{-3}} = \frac{t^3}{3(2^2)} = \frac{t^3}{3 \cdot 4} = \frac{t^3}{12}$$

Base is t.

Now Try Exercises 27, 29, 31, 65, and 67

Product, Quotient, and Power Rules

We can calculate products and quotients of exponential expressions *provided their bases are the same.* For example,

$$3^2 \cdot 3^3 = \overbrace{(3 \cdot 3) \cdot (3 \cdot 3 \cdot 3)}^{\text{5 factors of 3}} = 3^5.$$

This expression has a total of $2 + 3 = 5$ factors of 3, so the result is 3^5. To multiply exponential expressions with *like bases*, add exponents.

THE PRODUCT RULE

For any nonzero number a and integers m and n,

$$a^m \cdot a^n = a^{m+n}.$$

The product rule holds for negative exponents. For example,

$$10^5 \cdot 10^{-2} = 10^{5+(-2)} = 10^3.$$

Product rule: add exponents.

EXAMPLE 3 Using the product rule

Multiply and simplify.

(a) $7^3 \cdot 7^{-4}$ **(b)** $x^3x^{-2}x^4$ **(c)** $(3y^2)(2y^{-4})$

SOLUTION

(a) $7^3 \cdot 7^{-4} = 7^{3+(-4)} = 7^{-1} = \frac{1}{7}$ **(b)** $x^3x^{-2}x^4 = x^{3+(-2)+4} = x^5$

(c) $(3y^2)(2y^{-4}) = 3 \cdot 2 \cdot y^2 \cdot y^{-4} = 6y^{2+(-4)} = 6y^{-2} = \frac{6}{y^2}$

Note that 6 is not raised to the power of -2 in the expression $6y^{-2}$.

Now Try Exercises 35, 37, and 39

Consider division of exponential expressions using the following example.

$$\frac{6^5}{6^3} = \frac{6 \cdot 6 \cdot \not{6} \cdot \not{6} \cdot \not{6}}{\not{6} \cdot \not{6} \cdot \not{6}} = 6 \cdot 6 = 6^2$$

After simplifying, there are two 6s left in the numerator. The result is $6^{5-3} = 6^2 = 36$. To divide exponential expressions with *like bases*, subtract exponents.

THE QUOTIENT RULE

For any nonzero number a and integers m and n,

$$\frac{a^m}{a^n} = a^{m-n}.$$

```
2^(-6)/2^(-4)
                .25
.25▶Frac
                1/4
```

Figure R.16

The quotient rule holds true for negative exponents. For example,

$$\frac{2^{-6}}{2^{-4}} = 2^{-6-(-4)} = 2^{-2} = \frac{1}{2^2} = \frac{1}{4}.$$

Quotient rule: subtract exponents.

This result is supported by Figure R.16.

EXAMPLE 4 Using the quotient rule

Simplify the expression. Use positive exponents.

(a) $\frac{10^4}{10^6}$ **(b)** $\frac{x^5}{x^2}$ **(c)** $\frac{15x^2y^3}{5x^4y}$

SOLUTION

(a) $\frac{10^4}{10^6} = 10^{4-6} = 10^{-2} = \frac{1}{10^2} = \frac{1}{100}$ **(b)** $\frac{x^5}{x^2} = x^{5-2} = x^3$

(c) $\frac{15x^2y^3}{5x^4y} = \frac{15}{5} \cdot \frac{x^2}{x^4} \cdot \frac{y^3}{y^1} = 3 \cdot x^{(2-4)}y^{(3-1)} = 3x^{-2}y^2 = \frac{3y^2}{x^2}$

Now Try Exercises 45, 49, and 51

How should we evaluate $(4^3)^2$? To answer this question, consider

$$(4^3)^2 = \underbrace{4^3 \cdot 4^3}_{} = 4^{3+3} = 4^6.$$

2 factors of 4^3

Similarly,

$$(x^4)^3 = \underbrace{x^4 \cdot x^4 \cdot x^4}_{} = x^{4+4+4} = x^{12}.$$

3 factors of x^4

These results suggest that to raise a power to a power, we must multiply the exponents.

RAISING POWERS TO POWERS

For any nonzero real number a and integers m and n,

$$(a^m)^n = a^{mn}.$$

EXAMPLE 5 Raising powers to powers

Simplify each expression. Use positive exponents.
(a) $(5^2)^3$ **(b)** $(2^4)^{-2}$ **(c)** $(b^{-7})^5$

SOLUTION

(a) $(5^2)^3 = 5^{2 \cdot 3} = 5^6 = 15{,}625$ **(b)** $(2^4)^{-2} = 2^{4(-2)} = 2^{-8} = \frac{1}{2^8} = \frac{1}{256}$

(c) $(b^{-7})^5 = b^{-7 \cdot 5} = b^{-35} = \frac{1}{b^{35}}$

Multiply exponents.

Now Try Exercises 55 and 57

How can we simplify the expression $(2x)^3$? Consider the following.

$$(2x)^3 = 2x \cdot 2x \cdot 2x = \underbrace{(2 \cdot 2 \cdot 2)}_{\text{3 factors}} \cdot \underbrace{(x \cdot x \cdot x)}_{\text{3 factors}} = 2^3x^3$$

This result suggests that to cube a product, we can cube each factor.

RAISING PRODUCTS TO POWERS

For any nonzero real numbers a and b and integer n,

$$(ab)^n = a^n b^n.$$

EXAMPLE 6 Raising products to powers

Simplify each expression. Use positive exponents.
(a) $(6y)^2$ **(b)** $(x^2y)^{-2}$ **(c)** $(2xy^3)^4$

SOLUTION

(a) $(6y)^2 = 6^2y^2 = 36y^2$ **(b)** $(x^2y)^{-2} = (x^2)^{-2}y^{-2} = x^{-4}y^{-2} = \frac{1}{x^4y^2}$

(c) $(2xy^3)^4 = 2^4x^4(y^3)^4 = 16x^4y^{12}$

Now Try Exercises 59 and 73

To simplify a power of a quotient, use the following rule.

RAISING QUOTIENTS TO POWERS

For nonzero numbers a and b and any integer n,

$$\left(\frac{a}{b}\right)^n = \frac{a^n}{b^n}.$$

EXAMPLE 7 Raising quotients to powers

Simplify each expression. Use positive exponents.

(a) $\left(\frac{3}{x}\right)^3$ **(b)** $\left(\frac{1}{2^3}\right)^{-2}$ **(c)** $\left(\frac{3x^{-3}}{y^2}\right)^4$

SOLUTION

(a) $\left(\frac{3}{x}\right)^3 = \frac{3^3}{x^3} = \frac{27}{x^3}$ **(b)** $\left(\frac{1}{2^3}\right)^{-2} = \frac{1^{-2}}{(2^3)^{-2}} = \frac{1}{2^{-6}} = 2^6 = 64$

(c) $\left(\frac{3x^{-3}}{y^2}\right)^4 = \frac{3^4(x^{-3})^4}{(y^2)^4} = \frac{81x^{-12}}{y^8} = \frac{81}{x^{12}y^8}$

Now Try Exercises 61, 63, and 81

In the next example, we use several properties of exponents to simplify expressions.

EXAMPLE 8 **Simplifying expressions**

Write each expression using positive exponents. Simplify the result completely.

(a) $\left(\frac{x^2y^{-3}}{3z^{-4}}\right)^{-2}$ **(b)** $\frac{(rt^3)^{-3}}{(r^2t^3)^{-2}}$

SOLUTION

(a) $\left(\frac{x^2y^{-3}}{3z^{-4}}\right)^{-2} = \left(\frac{3z^{-4}}{x^2y^{-3}}\right)^2$

$= \left(\frac{3y^3}{x^2z^4}\right)^2$

$= \frac{9y^6}{x^4z^8}$

(b) $\frac{(rt^3)^{-3}}{(r^2t^3)^{-2}} = \frac{(r^2t^3)^2}{(rt^3)^3}$

$= \frac{r^4t^6}{r^3t^9}$

$= \frac{r}{t^3}$

Now Try Exercises 77 and 79

R.2 Exercises

Concepts

1. Are the expressions 2^3 and 3^2 equal? Explain your answer.

2. Are the expressions -4^2 and $(-4)^2$ equal? Explain your answer.

3. $7^{-n} =$ ____

4. $6^m \cdot 6^n =$ ____

5. $\frac{5^m}{5^n} =$ ____

6. $(3x)^k =$ ____

7. $(2^m)^k =$ ____

8. $\left(\frac{x}{y}\right)^m =$ ____

9. $5 \times 10^3 =$ ____

10. $5 \times 10^{-3} =$ ____

Properties of Exponents

Exercises 11–16: (Refer to Example 1.) Write the number as an exponential expression, using the base shown. Check your result with a calculator.

11. 8 (base 2)

12. 1000 (base 10)

13. 256 (base 4)

14. $\frac{1}{64}$ (base 4)

15. 1 (base 3)

16. $\frac{1}{49}$ (base 7)

Exercises 17–34: Evaluate the expression by hand. Check your result with a calculator.

17. 5^3

18. 5^{-3}

19. -2^4

20. $(-2)^4$

21. 5^0

22. $\left(-\frac{2}{3}\right)^{-3}$

23. $\left(\frac{2}{3}\right)^3$

24. $\frac{1}{4^{-2}}$

25. $\left(-\frac{1}{2}\right)^4$

26. $\left(-\frac{3}{4}\right)^3$

27. 4^{-3}

28. 10^{-4}

29. $\frac{1}{2^{-4}}$

30. $\frac{1}{3^{-2}}$

31. $\left(\frac{3}{4}\right)^{-3}$

32. $\left(\frac{1}{2}\right)^0$

33. $\frac{3^{-2}}{2^{-3}}$

34. $\frac{10^{-4}}{4^{-3}}$

Exercises 35–44: Use the product rule to simplify.

35. $6^3 \cdot 6^{-4}$

36. $10^2 \cdot 10^5 \cdot 10^{-3}$

37. $2x^2 \cdot 3x^{-3} \cdot x^4$

38. $3y^4 \cdot 6y^{-4} \cdot y$

39. $10^0 \cdot 10^6 \cdot 10^2$

40. $y^3 \cdot y^{-5} \cdot y^4$

41. $5^{-2} \cdot 5^3 \cdot 2^{-4} \cdot 2^3$

42. $2^{-3} \cdot 3^4 \cdot 3^{-2} \cdot 2^5$

43. $(2a^3)(b^2)(a^{-4})(4b^{-5})$

44. $(3x^{-4})(2x^2)(5y^4)(y^{-3})$

Exercises 45–54: Use the quotient rule to simplify the expression. Use positive exponents to write your answer.

45. $\frac{5^4}{5^2}$

46. $\frac{6^2}{6^{-7}}$

47. $\frac{a^{-3}}{a^2 \cdot a}$

48. $\frac{y^0 \cdot y \cdot y^5}{y^{-2} \cdot y^{-3}}$

49. $\frac{24x^3}{6x}$

50. $\frac{10x^5}{5x^{-3}}$

51. $\frac{12a^2b^3}{18a^4b^2}$

52. $\frac{-6x^7y^3}{3x^2y^{-5}}$

53. $\frac{21x^{-3}y^4}{7x^4y^{-2}}$

54. $\frac{32x^3y}{-24x^5y^{-3}}$

Exercises 55–64: Use the power rules to simplify the expression. Use positive exponents to write your answer.

55. $(5^{-1})^3$

56. $(-4^2)^3$

57. $(y^4)^{-2}$

58. $(x^2)^4$

59. $(4y^2)^3$

60. $(-2xy^3)^{-4}$

61. $\left(\frac{4}{x}\right)^3$

62. $\left(\frac{-3}{x^3}\right)^2$

63. $\left(\frac{2x}{z^4}\right)^{-5}$

64. $\left(\frac{2xy}{3z^5}\right)^{-1}$

Exercises 65–90: Use rules of exponents to simplify the expression. Use positive exponents to write your answer.

65. $\frac{2}{(ab)^{-1}}$

66. $\frac{5a^2}{(xy)^{-1}}$

67. $\frac{2^{-3}}{2t^{-2}}$

68. $\frac{t^{-3}}{2t^{-1}}$

69. $\frac{6a^2b^{-3}}{4ab^{-2}}$

70. $\frac{20a^{-2}b}{4a^{-2}b^{-1}}$

71. $\frac{5r^2st^{-3}}{25rs^{-2}t^2}$

72. $\frac{36r^{-1}(st)^2}{9(rs)^2t^{-1}}$

73. $(3x^2y^{-3})^{-2}$

74. $(-2x^{-3}y^{-2})^3$

75. $\frac{(d^3)^{-2}}{(d^{-2})^3}$

76. $\frac{(b^2)^{-1}}{(b^{-4})^3}$

77. $\left(\frac{3t^2}{2t^{-1}}\right)^3$

78. $\left(\frac{-2t}{4t^{-2}}\right)^{-1}$

79. $\frac{(-m^2n^{-1})^{-2}}{(mn)^{-1}}$

80. $\frac{(-mn^4)^{-1}}{(m^2n)^{-3}}$

81. $\left(\frac{2a^3}{6b}\right)^4$

82. $\left(\frac{-3a^2}{9b^3}\right)^4$

83. $\frac{8x^{-3}y^{-2}}{4x^{-2}y^{-4}}$

84. $\frac{6x^{-1}y^{-1}}{9x^{-2}y^3}$

85. $\frac{(r^2t^2)^{-2}}{(r^3t)^{-1}}$

86. $\frac{(2rt)^2}{(rt^4)^{-2}}$

87. $\frac{4x^{-2}y^3}{(2x^{-1}y)^2}$

88. $\frac{(ab)^3}{a^4b^{-4}}$

89. $\left(\frac{15r^2t}{3r^{-3}t^4}\right)^3$

90. $\left(\frac{4(xy)^2}{(2xy^{-2})^3}\right)^{-2}$

R.3 Polynomial Expressions

- **Perform addition and subtraction on monomials**
- **Perform addition and subtraction on polynomials**
- **Apply the distributive property**
- **Perform multiplication on polynomials**
- **Find the product of a sum and difference**
- **Square a binomial**

Addition and Subtraction of Monomials

A **term** is a number, a variable, or a *product* of numbers and variables raised to powers. Examples of terms include

$$-15, \quad y, \quad x^4, \quad 3x^3z, \quad x^{-1/2}y^{-2}, \quad \text{and} \quad 6x^{-1}y^3.$$

Terms

If the variables in a term have only *nonnegative integer* exponents, the term is called a *monomial*. Examples of monomials include

$$-4, \quad 5y, \quad x^2, \quad 5x^2z^6, \quad -xy^7, \quad \text{and} \quad 6xy^3.$$

Monomials

If two terms contain the same variables raised to the same powers, we call them **like terms**. We can add or subtract *like* terms, but not *unlike* terms. For example, the terms

$x^3 + y^3$ Unlike terms cannot be combined.

cannot be combined because they are *unlike terms.* However,

$$x^3 + 3x^3 = (1 + 3)x^3 = 4x^3$$ Like terms can be combined.

because x^3 and $3x^3$ are *like terms*. To add or subtract monomials, we simply combine like terms, as illustrated in the next example.

EXAMPLE 1 **Adding and subtracting monomials**

Simplify each of the following expressions by combining like terms.
(a) $8x^2 - 4x^2 + x^3$ **(b)** $9x - 6xy^2 + 2xy^2 + 4x$

SOLUTION
(a) The terms $8x^2$ and $-4x^2$ are like terms, so they may be combined.

$$\begin{aligned} 8x^2 - 4x^2 + x^3 &= (8 - 4)x^2 + x^3 && \text{Combine like terms.} \\ &= 4x^2 + x^3 && \text{Subtract.} \end{aligned}$$

Unlike terms cannot be combined.

(b) The terms $9x$ and $4x$ may be combined, as may $-6xy^2$ and $2xy^2$.

$$\begin{aligned} 9x - 6xy^2 + 2xy^2 + 4x &= 9x + 4x - 6xy^2 + 2xy^2 && \text{Commutative property} \\ &= (9 + 4)x + (-6 + 2)xy^2 && \text{Combine like terms.} \\ &= 13x - 4xy^2 && \text{Add.} \end{aligned}$$

Now Try Exercises 5 and 11

Addition and Subtraction of Polynomials

A polynomial is either a monomial or a sum (or difference) of monomials. Examples of polynomials include

$5x^4z^2$, $9x^4 - 5$, $4x^2 + 5xy - y^2$, and $4 - y^2 + 5y^4 + y^5$.

1 term *2 terms* *3 terms* *4 terms*

Polynomials containing one variable are called polynomials of one variable. The second and fourth polynomials shown above are examples of polynomials of one variable. The leading coefficient of a polynomial of one variable is the coefficient of the monomial with highest degree. The degree of a polynomial with one variable equals the exponent of the monomial with the highest power. Table R.2 shows several polynomials of one variable along with their degrees and leading coefficients. A polynomial of degree 1 is a *linear* polynomial, a polynomial of degree 2 is a *quadratic* polynomial, and a polynomial of degree 3 is a *cubic* polynomial.

Characterizing Polynomials

Polynomial	Degree	Leading Coefficient	Type
-98	0	-98	Constant
$2x - 7$	1	2	Linear
$-5z + 9z^2 + 7$	2	9	Quadratic
$-2x^3 + 4x^2 + x - 1$	3	-2	Cubic
$7 - x + 4x^2 + x^5$	5	1	Fifth Degree

Table R.2

To add two polynomials, we combine like terms.

EXAMPLE 2 Adding polynomials

Simplify.

(a) $(2x^2 - 3x + 7) + (3x^2 + 4x - 2)$ **(b)** $(z^3 + 4z + 8) + (4z^2 - z + 6)$

SOLUTION

(a) $$\begin{aligned}(2x^2 - 3x + 7) + (3x^2 + 4x - 2) &= 2x^2 + 3x^2 - 3x + 4x + 7 - 2\\ &= (2 + 3)x^2 + (-3 + 4)x + (7 - 2)\\ &= 5x^2 + x + 5\end{aligned}$$

(b) $$\begin{aligned}(z^3 + 4z + 8) + (4z^2 - z + 6) &= z^3 + 4z^2 + 4z - z + 8 + 6\\ &= z^3 + 4z^2 + (4 - 1)z + (8 + 6)\\ &= z^3 + 4z^2 + 3z + 14\end{aligned}$$

Now Try Exercises 21 and 27

To subtract integers, we add the first integer and the **opposite,** or **additive inverse,** of the second integer. For example, to evaluate $3 - 5$, we perform the following operations.

Subtracting integers

$$\begin{aligned}3 - 5 &= 3 + (-5) && \text{Add the opposite.}\\ &= -2 && \text{Simplify.}\end{aligned}$$

Similarly, to subtract two polynomials, we add the first polynomial and the opposite, or additive inverse, of the second polynomial. To find the opposite of a polynomial, we simply negate each term. Table R.3 shows three polynomials and their opposites.

Finding the Additive Inverse

Polynomial	Opposite
$9 - x$	$-9 + x$
$5x^2 + 4x - 1$	$-5x^2 - 4x + 1$
$-x^4 + 5x^3 - x^2 + 5x - 1$	$x^4 - 5x^3 + x^2 - 5x + 1$

Table R.3

EXAMPLE 3 Subtracting polynomials

Simplify.

(a) $(y^5 + 3y^3) - (-y^4 + 2y^3)$ **(b)** $(5x^3 + 9x^2 - 6) - (5x^3 - 4x^2 - 7)$

SOLUTION

(a) The opposite of $(-y^4 + 2y^3)$ is $(y^4 - 2y^3)$.

Add the opposite.

$$\begin{aligned}(y^5 + 3y^3) - (-y^4 + 2y^3) &= (y^5 + 3y^3) + (y^4 - 2y^3)\\ &= y^5 + y^4 + (3 - 2)y^3\\ &= y^5 + y^4 + y^3\end{aligned}$$

(b) The opposite of $(5x^3 - 4x^2 - 7)$ is $(-5x^3 + 4x^2 + 7)$.

$$\begin{aligned}(5x^3 + 9x^2 - 6) - (5x^3 - 4x^2 - 7) &= (5x^3 + 9x^2 - 6) + (-5x^3 + 4x^2 + 7)\\ &= (5 - 5)x^3 + (9 + 4)x^2 + (-6 + 7)\\ &= 0x^3 + 13x^2 + 1\\ &= 13x^2 + 1\end{aligned}$$

Now Try Exercises 39 and 41

Distributive Properties

Distributive properties are used frequently in the multiplication of polynomials. For all real numbers a, b, and c,

$$a(b + c) = ab + ac \qquad \text{and}$$
$$a(b - c) = ab - ac.$$

In the next example, we use these distributive properties to multiply expressions.

EXAMPLE 4 **Using distributive properties**

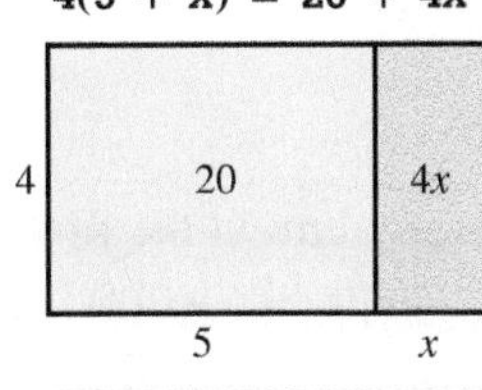

Figure R.17

Multiply.

(a) $4(5 + x)$ **(b)** $-3(x - 4y)$ **(c)** $(2x - 5)(6)$

SOLUTION

(a) $4(5 + x) = 4 \cdot 5 + 4 \cdot x = 20 + 4x$

(b) $-3(x - 4y) = -3 \cdot x - (-3) \cdot (4y) = -3x + 12y$

(c) $(2x - 5)(6) = 2x \cdot 6 - 5 \cdot 6 = 12x - 30$

Now Try Exercises 47, 51, and 53

You can visualize the product in part (a) of Example 4 by using areas of rectangles. If a rectangle has width 4 and length $5 + x$, its area is $20 + 4x$, as shown in Figure R.17.

Multiplying Polynomials

A polynomial with two terms is a **binomial**, and a polynomial with three terms is a **trinomial**. Examples are shown in Table R.4.

Types of Polynomials

One term	**Monomials**	$2x^2$	$-3x^4$	9
Two terms	**Binomials**	$3x - 1$	$2x^3 - x$	$x^2 + 5$
Three terms	**Trinomials**	$x^2 - 3x + 5$	$5x^2 - 2x + 10$	$2x^3 - x^2 - 2$

Table R.4

In the next example, we multiply two binomials.

EXAMPLE 5 **Multiplying binomials**

Multiply $(x + 1)(x + 3)$.

SOLUTION To multiply $(x + 1)(x + 3)$, we apply the distributive property.

$$\begin{aligned}(x + 1)(x + 3) &= (x + 1)(x) + (x + 1)(3) \\ &= x \cdot x + 1 \cdot x + x \cdot 3 + 1 \cdot 3 \\ &= x^2 + x + 3x + 3 \\ &= x^2 + 4x + 3\end{aligned}$$

Now Try Exercise 55

To multiply the bionomials $(x + 1)$ and $(x + 3)$, we multiplied every term in $x + 1$ by every term in $x + 3$. That is,

$$\begin{aligned}(x + 1)(x + 3) &= x^2 + 3x + x + 3 \\ &= x^2 + 4x + 3.\end{aligned}$$

NOTE This process of multiplying binomials is called *FOIL*. You may use the name to remind yourself to multiply the first terms (F), outside terms (O), inside terms (I), and last terms (L).

Multiply the *First terms* to obtain x^2. $(x + 1)(x + 3)$ F

Multiply the *Outside terms* to obtain $3x$. $(x + 1)(x + 3)$ O

Multiply the *Inside terms* to obtain x. $(x + 1)(x + 3)$ I

Multiply the *Last terms* to obtain 3. $(x + 1)(x + 3)$ L

The following box summarizes how to multiply two polynomials in general.

MULTIPLYING POLYNOMIALS

The product of two polynomials may be found by multiplying every term in the first polynomial by every term in the second polynomial and then combining like terms.

EXAMPLE 6 **Multiplying binomials**

Multiply each binomial.

(a) $(2x - 1)(x + 2)$ **(b)** $(1 - 3x)(2 - 4x)$ **(c)** $(x^2 + 1)(5x - 3)$

SOLUTION

(a)
$$\begin{aligned}(2x - 1)(x + 2) &= 2x \cdot x + 2x \cdot 2 - 1 \cdot x - 1 \cdot 2\\ &= 2x^2 + 4x - x - 2\\ &= 2x^2 + 3x - 2\end{aligned}$$

(b)
$$\begin{aligned}(1 - 3x)(2 - 4x) &= 1 \cdot 2 - 1 \cdot 4x - 3x \cdot 2 + 3x \cdot 4x\\ &= 2 - 4x - 6x + 12x^2\\ &= 2 - 10x + 12x^2\end{aligned}$$

(c)
$$\begin{aligned}(x^2 + 1)(5x - 3) &= x^2 \cdot 5x - x^2 \cdot 3 + 1 \cdot 5x - 1 \cdot 3\\ &= 5x^3 - 3x^2 + 5x - 3\end{aligned}$$

Now Try Exercises 57, 59, and 77

EXAMPLE 7 **Multiplying polynomials**

Multiply each expression.

(a) $3x(x^2 + 5x - 4)$ **(b)** $-x^2(x^4 - 2x + 5)$ **(c)** $(x + 2)(x^2 + 4x - 3)$

SOLUTION

(a)
$$\begin{aligned}3x(x^2 + 5x - 4) &= 3x \cdot x^2 + 3x \cdot 5x - 3x \cdot 4\\ &= 3x^3 + 15x^2 - 12x\end{aligned}$$

(b)
$$\begin{aligned}-x^2(x^4 - 2x + 5) &= -x^2 \cdot x^4 + x^2 \cdot 2x - x^2 \cdot 5\\ &= -x^6 + 2x^3 - 5x^2\end{aligned}$$

(c)
$$\begin{aligned}(x + 2)(x^2 + 4x - 3) &= x \cdot x^2 + x \cdot 4x - x \cdot 3 + 2 \cdot x^2 + 2 \cdot 4x - 2 \cdot 3\\ &= x^3 + 4x^2 - 3x + 2x^2 + 8x - 6\\ &= x^3 + 6x^2 + 5x - 6\end{aligned}$$

Now Try Exercises 67, 69, and 73

Some Special Products

Sum and Difference The following special product often occurs in mathematics.

Product of a sum of two numbers and their difference

$$
\begin{aligned}
(a + b)(a - b) &= a \cdot a - a \cdot b + b \cdot a - b \cdot b \\
&= a^2 - ab + ba - b^2 \\
&= a^2 - b^2
\end{aligned}
$$

That is, the product of a sum of two numbers and their difference equals the difference of their squares: $(a + b)(a - b) = a^2 - b^2$.

EXAMPLE 8 Finding the product of a sum and difference

Multiply.

(a) $(x - 3)(x + 3)$ **(b)** $(5 + 4x^2)(5 - 4x^2)$

SOLUTION

(a) If we let $a = x$ and $b = 3$, we can apply $(a - b)(a + b) = a^2 - b^2$. Thus

$$
\begin{aligned}
(x - 3)(x + 3) &= (x)^2 - (3)^2 \\
&= x^2 - 9.
\end{aligned}
$$

Product is the difference of the squares of x and 3.

(b) Similarly,

$$
\begin{aligned}
(5 + 4x^2)(5 - 4x^2) &= (5)^2 - (4x^2)^2 \\
&= 25 - 16x^4.
\end{aligned}
$$

Now Try Exercises 79 and 95

Squaring a Binomial Two other special products involve *squaring a binomial:*

$$
\begin{aligned}
(a + b)^2 &= (a + b)(a + b) \\
&= a^2 + ab + ba + b^2 \\
&= a^2 + 2ab + b^2
\end{aligned}
$$

and

$$
\begin{aligned}
(a - b)^2 &= (a - b)(a - b) \\
&= a^2 - ab - ba + b^2 \\
&= a^2 - 2ab + b^2.
\end{aligned}
$$

Note that to obtain the middle term, we multiply the two terms in the binomial and double the result.

EXAMPLE 9 Squaring a binomial

Multiply.

(a) $(x + 5)^2$ **(b)** $(3 - 2x)^2$

SOLUTION

(a) If we let $a = x$ and $b = 5$, we can apply $(a + b)^2 = a^2 + 2ab + b^2$. Thus

$$
\begin{aligned}
(x + 5)^2 &= (x)^2 + 2(x)(5) + (5)^2 \\
&= x^2 + 10x + 25.
\end{aligned}
$$

(b) Applying the formula $(a - b)^2 = a^2 - 2ab + b^2$, we find

$$
\begin{aligned}
(3 - 2x)^2 &= (3)^2 - 2(3)(2x) + (2x)^2 \\
&= 9 - 12x + 4x^2.
\end{aligned}
$$

Now Try Exercises 85 and 91

R.3 Exercises

Monomials and Polynomials

Exercises 1–12: Combine like terms whenever possible.

1. $3x^3 + 5x^3$
2. $-9z + 6z$
3. $5y^7 - 8y^7$
4. $9x - 7x$
5. $5x^2 + 8x + x^2$
6. $5x + 2x + 10x$
7. $9x^2 - x + 4x - 6x^2$
8. $-y^2 - \frac{1}{2}y^2$
9. $x^2 + 9x - 2 + 4x^2 + 4x$
10. $6y + 4y^2 - 6y + y^2$
11. $7y + 9x^2y - 5y + x^2y$
12. $5ab - b^2 + 7ab + 6b^2$

Exercises 13–18: Identify the degree and leading coefficient of the polynomial.

13. $5x^2 - 4x + \frac{3}{4}$
14. $-9y^4 + y^2 + 5$
15. $5 - x + 3x^2 - \frac{2}{5}x^3$
16. $7x + 4x^4 - \frac{4}{3}x^3$
17. $8x^4 + 3x^3 - 4x + x^5$
18. $5x^2 - x^3 + 7x^4 + 10$

Exercises 19–28: Add the polynomials.

19. $(5x + 6) + (-2x + 6)$
20. $(5y^2 + y^3) + (12y^2 - 5y^3)$
21. $(2x^2 - x + 7) + (-2x^2 + 4x - 9)$
22. $(x^3 - 5x^2 + 6) + (5x^2 + 3x + 1)$
23. $(4x) + (1 - 4.5x)$
24. $(y^5 + y) + \left(5 - y + \frac{1}{3}y^2\right)$
25. $(x^4 - 3x^2 - 4) + \left(-8x^4 + x^2 - \frac{1}{2}\right)$
26. $(3z + z^4 + 2) + (-3z^4 - 5 + z^2)$
27. $(2z^3 + 5z - 6) + (z^2 - 3z + 2)$
28. $(z^4 - 6z^2 + 3) + (5z^3 + 3z^2 - 3)$

Exercises 29–34: Find the opposite of the polynomial.

29. $7x^3$
30. $-3z^8$
31. $19z^5 - 5z^2 + 3z$
32. $-x^2 - x + 6$
33. $z^4 - z^2 - 9$
34. $1 - 8x + 6x^2 - \frac{1}{6}x^3$

Exercises 35–42: Subtract the polynomials.

35. $(5x - 3) - (2x + 4)$
36. $(10x + 5) - (-6x - 4)$
37. $(x^2 - 3x + 1) - (-5x^2 + 2x - 4)$
38. $(-x^2 + x - 5) - (x^2 - x + 5)$
39. $(4x^4 + 2x^2 - 9) - (x^4 - 2x^2 - 5)$
40. $(8x^3 + 5x^2 - 3x + 1) - (-5x^3 + 6x - 11)$
41. $(x^4 - 1) - (4x^4 + 3x + 7)$
42. $(5x^4 - 6x^3 + x^2 + 5) - (x^3 + 11x^2 + 9x - 3)$

Exercises 43–54: Apply the distributive property.

43. $5x(x - 5)$
44. $3x^2(-2x + 2)$
45. $-5(3x + 1)$
46. $-(-3x + 1)$
47. $5(y + 2)$
48. $4(x - 7)$
49. $-2(5x + 9)$
50. $-3x(5 + x)$
51. $(y - 3)6y$
52. $(2x - 5)8x^3$
53. $-4(5x - y)$
54. $-6(3y - 2x)$

Exercises 55–66: Multiply the binomials.

55. $(y + 5)(y - 7)$
56. $(3x + 1)(2x + 1)$
57. $(3 - 2x)(3 + x)$
58. $(7x - 3)(4 - 7x)$
59. $(-2x + 3)(x - 2)$
60. $(z - 2)(4z + 3)$
61. $\left(x - \frac{1}{2}\right)\left(x + \frac{1}{4}\right)$
62. $\left(z - \frac{1}{3}\right)\left(z - \frac{1}{6}\right)$
63. $(x^2 + 1)(2x^2 - 1)$
64. $(x^2 - 2)(x^2 + 4)$
65. $(x + y)(x - 2y)$
66. $(x^2 + y^2)(x - y)$

Exercises 67–78: Multiply the polynomials.

67. $3x(2x^2 - x - 1)$
68. $-2x(3 - 2x + 5x^2)$
69. $-x(2x^4 - x^2 + 10)$
70. $-2x^2(5x^3 + x^2 - 2)$
71. $(2x^2 - 4x + 1)(3x^2)$
72. $(x - y + 5)(xy)$
73. $(x + 1)(x^2 + 2x - 3)$
74. $(2x - 1)(3x^2 - x + 6)$
75. $(2 - 3x)(5 - 2x)(x^2 - 1)$
76. $(3 + z)(6 - 4z)(4 + 2z^2)$
77. $(x^2 + 2)(3x - 2)$
78. $(4 + x)(2x^2 - 3)$

Exercises 79–96: Multiply the expressions.

79. $(x - 7)(x + 7)$

80. $(x + 9)(x - 9)$

81. $(3x + 4)(3x - 4)$

82. $(9x - 4)(9x + 4)$

83. $(2x - 3y)(2x + 3y)$

84. $(x + 2y)(x - 2y)$

85. $(x + 4)^2$

86. $(z + 9)^2$

87. $(2x + 1)^2$

88. $(3x + 5)^2$

89. $(x - 1)^2$

90. $(x - 7)^2$

91. $(2 - 3x)^2$

92. $(5 - 6x)^2$

93. $3x(x + 1)(x - 1)$

94. $-4x(3x - 5)^2$

95. $(2 - 5x^2)(2 + 5x^2)$

96. $(6y - x^2)(6y + x^2)$

R.4 Factoring Polynomials

- **Use common factors**
- **Factor by grouping**
- **Factor $x^2 + bx + c$**
- **Factor trinomials by grouping**
- **Factor trinomials with FOIL**
- **Factor the difference of two squares**
- **Factor perfect square trinomials**
- **Factor the sum and difference of two cubes**

Common Factors

When factoring a polynomial, we first look for factors that are common to each term in an expression. By applying a distributive property, we can write a polynomial as two factors. For example, each term in $2x^2 + 4x$ contains a factor of $2x$.

$$2x^2 = 2x \cdot x$$
$$4x = 2x \cdot 2$$

Factor $2x$ out of each term.

Thus the polynomial $2x^2 + 4x$ can be factored as follows.

$$2x^2 + 4x = 2x(x + 2)$$

Apply a distributive property to factor.

EXAMPLE 1 Finding common factors

Factor.

(a) $6z^3 - 2z^2 + 4z$ **(b)** $4x^3y^2 + x^2y^3$

SOLUTION

(a) Each of the terms $6z^3$, $2z^2$, and $4z$ contains a common factor of $2z$. That is,

$$6z^3 = 2z \cdot 3z^2, \quad 2z^2 = 2z \cdot z, \quad \text{and} \quad 4z = 2z \cdot 2.$$

Thus $6z^3 - 2z^2 + 4z = 2z(3z^2 - z + 2)$.

(b) Both $4x^3y^2$ and x^2y^3 contain a common factor of x^2y^2. That is,

$$4x^3y^2 = x^2y^2 \cdot 4x \quad \text{and} \quad x^2y^3 = x^2y^2 \cdot y.$$

Thus $4x^3y^2 + x^2y^3 = x^2y^2(4x + y)$.

Now Try Exercises 5 and 15

Many times we factor out the *greatest common factor*. For example, the polynomial $15x^4 - 5x^2$ has a common factor of $5x$. We could write this polynomial as

$$15x^4 - 5x^2 = 5x(3x^3 - x).$$

However, we can also factor out $5x^2$ to obtain

$$15x^4 - 5x^2 = 5x^2(3x^2 - 1).$$

Because $5x^2$ is the common factor with the highest degree and largest coefficient, we say that $5x^2$ is the **greatest common factor** (GCF) of $15x^4 - 5x^2$.

EXAMPLE 2 Factoring greatest common factors

Factor.

(a) $6m^3n^2 - 3mn^2 + 9m$ **(b)** $-9x^4 + 6x^3 - 3x^2$

SOLUTION

(a) The GCF of $6m^3n^2$, $3mn^2$, and $9m$ is $3m$.

$$6m^3n^2 = 3m \cdot 2m^2n^2, \quad 3mn^2 = 3m \cdot n^2, \quad \text{and} \quad 9m = 3m \cdot 3$$

Thus $6m^3n^2 - 3mn^2 + 9m = 3m(2m^2n^2 - n^2 + 3)$.

(b) Rather than factoring out $3x^2$, we can factor out $-3x^2$ and make the leading coefficient of the remaining expression positive.

$$-9x^4 = -3x^2 \cdot 3x^2, \quad 6x^3 = -3x^2 \cdot -2x, \quad \text{and} \quad -3x^2 = -3x^2 \cdot 1$$

Thus $-9x^4 + 6x^3 - 3x^2 = -3x^2(3x^2 - 2x + 1)$.

Now Try Exercises 11 and 17

Factoring by Grouping

Factoring by grouping is a technique that makes use of the associative and distributive properties. The next example illustrates the first step in this factoring technique.

Consider the cubic polynomial

$$3t^3 + 6t^2 + 2t + 4.$$

We can factor this polynomial by first grouping it into two binomials.

$$(3t^3 + 6t^2) + (2t + 4) \qquad \text{Associative property}$$
$$3t^2(t + 2) + 2(t + 2) \qquad \text{Factor out common factors.}$$
$$(3t^2 + 2)(t + 2). \qquad \text{Factor out } (t + 2).$$

The following steps summarize factoring four terms by grouping.

FACTORING BY GROUPING

STEP 1: Use parentheses to group the terms into binomials with common factors. Begin by writing the expression with a plus sign between the binomials.

STEP 2: Factor out the common factor in each binomial.

STEP 3: Factor out the common binomial. If there is no common binomial, try a different grouping or a different method of factoring.

EXAMPLE 3 Factoring by grouping

Factor each polynomial.

(a) $12x^3 - 9x^2 - 8x + 6$ **(b)** $2x - 2y + ax - ay$

SOLUTION

(a)
$$\begin{aligned} 12x^3 - 9x^2 - 8x + 6 &= (12x^3 - 9x^2) + (-8x + 6) && \text{Write with a plus sign between binomials.} \\ &= 3x^2(4x - 3) - 2(4x - 3) && \text{Factor out } 3x^2 \text{ and } -2. \\ &= (3x^2 - 2)(4x - 3) && \text{Factor out } 4x - 3. \end{aligned}$$

(b)
$$\begin{aligned} 2x - 2y + ax - ay &= (2x - 2y) + (ax - ay) && \text{Group terms.} \\ &= 2(x - y) + a(x - y) && \text{Factor out 2 and } a. \\ &= (2 + a)(x - y) && \text{Factor out } x - y. \end{aligned}$$

Now Try Exercises 21 and 31

Factoring $x^2 + bx + c$

The product $(x + 3)(x + 4)$ can be found as follows.

Multiply using FOIL.

$$(x + 3)(x + 4) = x^2 + 4x + 3x + 12$$
$$= x^2 + 7x + 12$$

The middle term $7x$ is found by calculating the sum $4x + 3x$, and the last term is found by calculating the product $3 \cdot 4 = 12$.

When we factor polynomials, we are *reversing* the process of multiplication. To factor $x^2 + 7x + 12$, we must find m and n that satisfy

$$x^2 + 7x + 12 = (x + m)(x + n).$$

Factor Pairs for 12

Factors	1, 12	2, 6	3, 4
Sum	13	8	7

Table R.5

Because

$$(x + m)(x + n) = x^2 + (m + n)x + mn,$$

it follows that $mn = 12$ and $m + n = 7$. To determine m and n, we list factors of 12 and their sum, as shown in Table R.5.

Because $3 \cdot 4 = 12$ and $3 + 4 = 7$, we can write the factored form as

$$x^2 + 7x + 12 = (x + 3)(x + 4).$$

This result can always be checked by multiplying the two binomials.

$$(x + 3)\ (x + 4) = x^2 + 7x + 12$$

3x
+4x
7x ⟵ The middle term checks.

FACTORING $x^2 + bx + c$

To factor the trinomial $x^2 + bx + c$, find integers m and n that satisfy

$$m \cdot n = c \qquad \text{and} \qquad m + n = b.$$

Then $x^2 + bx + c = (x + m)(x + n)$.

EXAMPLE 4 Factoring the form $x^2 + bx + c$

Factor each trinomial.

(a) $x^2 + 10x + 16$ **(b)** $x^2 + 7x - 30$

SOLUTION

(a) We need to find a factor pair for 16 whose sum is 10. From Table R.6 the required factor pair is $m = 2$ and $n = 8$. Thus

$$x^2 + 10x + 16 = (x + 2)(x + 8).$$

Factor Pairs for 16

Factors	1, 16	2, 8	4, 4
Sum	17	10	8

Table R.6

(b) Factors of -30 whose sum equals 7 are -3 and 10. Thus

$$x^2 + 7x - 30 = (x - 3)(x + 10).$$

Now Try Exercises 33 and 37

EXAMPLE 5 Removing common factors first

Factor completely.

(a) $3x^2 + 15x + 18$ **(b)** $5x^3 + 5x^2 - 60x$

SOLUTION

(a) If we first factor out the common factor of 3, the resulting trinomial is easier to factor.

$$3x^2 + 15x + 18 = 3(x^2 + 5x + 6)$$

Now we find m and n such that $mn = 6$ and $m + n = 5$. These numbers are 2 and 3.

$$\begin{aligned} 3x^2 + 15x + 18 &= 3(x^2 + 5x + 6) \\ &= 3(x + 2)(x + 3) \end{aligned}$$

(b) First, we factor out the common factor of $5x$. Then we factor the resulting trinomial.

$$\begin{aligned} 5x^3 + 5x^2 - 60x &= 5x(x^2 + x - 12) \\ &= 5x(x - 3)(x + 4) \end{aligned}$$

Now Try Exercises 51 and 53

Factoring Trinomials by Grouping

In this subsection we use grouping to factor trinomials in the form $ax^2 + bx + c$ with $a \neq 1$. For example, one way to factor $3x^2 + 14x + 8$ is to find two numbers m and n such that $mn = 3 \cdot 8 = 24$ and $m + n = 14$. Because $2 \cdot 12 = 24$ and $2 + 12 = 14$, we let $m = 2$ and $n = 12$. Using grouping, we can now factor this trinomial.

$$\begin{aligned} 3x^2 + 14x + 8 &= 3x^2 + 2x + 12x + 8 && \text{Write } 14x \text{ as } 2x + 12x. \\ &= (3x^2 + 2x) + (12x + 8) && \text{Associative property} \\ &= x(3x + 2) + 4(3x + 2) && \text{Factor out } x \text{ and } 4. \\ &= (x + 4)(3x + 2) && \text{Distributive property} \end{aligned}$$

Writing the polynomial as $3x^2 + 12x + 2x + 8$ would also work.

FACTORING $ax^2 + bx + c$ BY GROUPING

To factor $ax^2 + bx + c$, perform the following steps. (Assume that a, b, and c have no factor in common.)

1. Find numbers m and n such that $mn = ac$ and $m + n = b$. This step may require trial and error.
2. Write the trinomial as $ax^2 + mx + nx + c$.
3. Use grouping to factor this expression as two binomials.

EXAMPLE 6 Factoring $ax^2 + bx + c$ by grouping

Factor each trinomial.

(a) $12y^2 + 5y - 3$ **(b)** $6r^2 - 19r + 10$

SOLUTION

(a) In this trinomial $a = 12$, $b = 5$, and $c = -3$. Because $mn = ac$ and $m + n = b$, the numbers m and n satisfy $mn = -36$ and $m + n = 5$. Thus $m = 9$ and $n = -4$.

$$\begin{aligned} 12y^2 + 5y - 3 &= 12y^2 + 9y - 4y - 3 && \text{Write } 5y \text{ as } 9y - 4y. \\ &= (12y^2 + 9y) + (-4y - 3) && \text{Associative property} \\ &= 3y(4y + 3) - 1(4y + 3) && \text{Factor out } 3y \text{ and } -1. \\ &= (3y - 1)(4y + 3) && \text{Distributive property} \end{aligned}$$

(b) In this trinomial $a = 6$, $b = -19$, and $c = 10$. Because $mn = ac$ and $m + n = b$, the numbers m and n satisfy $mn = 60$ and $m + n = -19$. Thus $m = -4$ and $n = -15$.

$$\begin{aligned} 6r^2 - 19r + 10 &= 6r^2 - 4r - 15r + 10 && \text{Write } -19r \text{ as } -4r - 15r. \\ &= (6r^2 - 4r) + (-15r + 10) && \text{Associative property} \\ &= 2r(3r - 2) - 5(3r - 2) && \text{Factor out } 2r \text{ and } -5. \\ &= (2r - 5)(3r - 2) && \text{Distributive property} \end{aligned}$$

Now Try Exercises 41 and 43

Factoring Trinomials with FOIL

An alternative to factoring trinomials by grouping is to use FOIL in *reverse*. For example, the factors of $3x^2 + 7x + 2$ are two binomials.

$$3x^2 + 7x + 2 \stackrel{?}{=} (\_\_ + \_\_)(\_\_ + \_\_)$$

The expressions to be placed in the four blanks are yet to be found. By the FOIL method, we know that the product of the first terms is $3x^2$. Because $3x^2 = 3x \cdot x$, we can write

$$3x^2 + 7x + 2 \stackrel{?}{=} (\underline{3x} + \_\_)(\underline{x} + \_\_).$$

The product of the last terms in each binomial must equal 2. Because $2 = 1 \cdot 2$, we can put the 1 and 2 in the blanks, but we must be sure to place them correctly so that the product of the *outside terms* plus the product of the *inside terms* equals $7x$.

$$(3x + 1)(x + 2) = 3x^2 + 7x + 2$$

Determine where to place the 1 and 2 and then check the middle term.

$1x$
$+6x$
$7x$ ← Middle term checks. — Correct

If we had interchanged the 1 and 2, we would have obtained an incorrect result.

$$(3x + 2)(x + 1) = 3x^2 + 5x + 2$$

$2x$
$+3x$
$5x$ ← Middle term is not $7x$. — Incorrect

In the next example, we factor expressions of the form $ax^2 + bx + c$, where $a \neq 1$. In this situation, we may need to *guess and check* or use *trial and error* a few times to find the correct factors.

EXAMPLE 7 Factoring the form $ax^2 + bx + c$

Factor each trinomial.

(a) $6x^2 - x - 2$ **(b)** $4x^3 - 14x^2 + 6x$

SOLUTION

(a) The factors of $6x^2$ are either $2x$ and $3x$ or $6x$ and x. The factors of -2 are either -1 and 2 or 1 and -2. To obtain a middle term of $-x$, we use the following factors.

$$(3x - 2)(2x + 1) = 6x^2 - x - 2$$

$-4x$
$+3x$
$-x$ ← It checks.

To find the correct factorization, we may need to guess and check a few times.

(b) Each term contains a common factor of $2x$, so we do the following step first.

$$4x^3 - 14x^2 + 6x = 2x(2x^2 - 7x + 3)$$

Next we factor $2x^2 - 7x + 3$. The factors of $2x^2$ are $2x$ and x. Because the middle term is negative, we use -1 and -3 for factors of 3.

$$\begin{aligned} 4x^3 - 14x^2 + 6x &= 2x(2x^2 - 7x + 3) \\ &= 2x(2x - 1)(x - 3) \end{aligned}$$

Now Try Exercises 55 and 57

Difference of Two Squares

When we factor polynomials, we are *reversing* the process of multiplying polynomials. In Section R.3 we discussed the equation

$$(a - b)(a + b) = a^2 - b^2.$$

We can use this equation to factor a difference of two squares.

DIFFERENCE OF TWO SQUARES

For any real numbers a and b,

$$a^2 - b^2 = (a - b)(a + b).$$

NOTE The sum of two squares *cannot* be factored (using real numbers). For example, $x^2 + y^2$ cannot be factored, whereas $x^2 - y^2$ can be factored. It is important to remember that $x^2 + y^2 \neq (x + y)^2$.

EXAMPLE 8 Factoring the difference of two squares

Factor each polynomial, if possible.

(a) $9x^2 - 64$ **(b)** $4x^2 + 9y^2$ **(c)** $4a^3 - 4a$

SOLUTION

(a) Note that $9x^2 = (3x)^2$ and $64 = 8^2$.

$$\begin{aligned} 9x^2 - 64 &= (3x)^2 - (8)^2 && \text{Factor difference of two squares.} \\ &= (3x - 8)(3x + 8) \end{aligned}$$

(b) Because $4x^2 + 9y^2$ is the *sum* of two squares, it *cannot* be factored.

(c) Start by factoring out the common factor of $4a$.

$$\begin{aligned} 4a^3 - 4a &= 4a(a^2 - 1) \\ &= 4a(a - 1)(a + 1) \end{aligned}$$

Now Try Exercises 61, 65, and 69

EXAMPLE 9 Applying the difference of two squares

Factor each expression.

(a) $x^4 - y^4$ **(b)** $6r^2 - 24t^4$

SOLUTION

(a) Use $a^2 - b^2 = (a - b)(a + b)$, with $a = x^2$ and $b = y^2$.

$$\begin{aligned} x^4 - y^4 &= (x^2)^2 - (y^2)^2 && \text{Write as difference of squares.} \\ &= (x^2 - y^2)(x^2 + y^2) && \text{Difference of squares} \\ &= (x - y)(x + y)(x^2 + y^2) && \text{Difference of squares} \end{aligned}$$

(b) Start by factoring out the common factor of 6.

$$\begin{aligned} 6r^2 - 24t^4 &= 6(r^2 - 4t^4) && \text{Factor out 6.} \\ &= 6\left(r^2 - (2t^2)^2\right) && \text{Write as difference of squares.} \\ &= 6(r - 2t^2)(r + 2t^2) && \text{Difference of squares} \end{aligned}$$

Now Try Exercises 66 and 67

Perfect Square Trinomials

In Section R.3 we expanded $(a + b)^2$ and $(a - b)^2$ as follows.

$$(a + b)^2 = a^2 + 2ab + b^2 \quad \text{and} \quad (a - b)^2 = a^2 - 2ab + b^2$$

The expressions $a^2 + 2ab + b^2$ and $a^2 - 2ab + b^2$ are called **perfect square trinomials**. We can use the following formulas to factor them.

PERFECT SQUARE TRINOMIALS

For any real numbers a and b,

$$a^2 + 2ab + b^2 = (a + b)^2 \quad \text{and}$$
$$a^2 - 2ab + b^2 = (a - b)^2.$$

EXAMPLE 10 Factoring perfect square trinomials

Factor each expression.

(a) $x^2 + 6x + 9$ **(b)** $81x^2 - 72x + 16$

SOLUTION

(a) Let $a^2 = x^2$ and $b^2 = 3^2$. In a perfect square trinomial, the middle term is $2ab$.

$$2ab = 2(x)(3) = 6x,$$

which equals the given middle term. Thus $a^2 + 2ab + b^2 = (a + b)^2$ implies

$$\underbrace{x^2 + 6x + 9}_{\text{Perfect square trinomial}} = (x + 3)^2.$$

(b) Let $a^2 = (9x)^2$ and $b^2 = 4^2$. In a perfect square trinomial, the middle term is $2ab$.

$$2ab = 2(9x)(4) = 72x,$$

which equals the given middle term. Thus $a^2 - 2ab + b^2 = (a - b)^2$ implies

$$81x^2 - 72x + 16 = (9x - 4)^2.$$

Now Try Exercises 77 and 81

EXAMPLE 11 Factoring perfect square trinomials

Factor $25a^3 + 10a^2b + ab^2$.

SOLUTION Start by factoring out the common factor of a. Then factor the resulting perfect square trinomial.

$$25a^3 + 10a^2b + ab^2 = a(\underbrace{25a^2 + 10ab + b^2}_{\text{Perfect square trinomial}})$$
$$= a(5a + b)^2$$

Now Try Exercise 89

Sum and Difference of Two Cubes

The sum or difference of two cubes may be factored. This fact is justified by the following two equations.

$$(a + b)(a^2 - ab + b^2) = a^3 + b^3 \quad \text{and}$$
$$(a - b)(a^2 + ab + b^2) = a^3 - b^3$$

These equations can be verified by multiplying the left side to obtain the right side. For example,

$$(a + b)(a^2 - ab + b^2) = a \cdot a^2 - a \cdot ab + a \cdot b^2 + b \cdot a^2 - b \cdot ab + b \cdot b^2$$
$$= a^3 - a^2b + ab^2 + a^2b - ab^2 + b^3$$
$$= a^3 + b^3.$$

SUM AND DIFFERENCE OF TWO CUBES

For any real numbers a and b,

$$a^3 + b^3 = (a + b)(a^2 - ab + b^2) \quad \text{and}$$
$$a^3 - b^3 = (a - b)(a^2 + ab + b^2).$$

EXAMPLE 12 Factoring the sum and difference of two cubes

Factor each polynomial.

(a) $x^3 + 8$ **(b)** $27x^3 - 64y^3$ **(c)** $27p^9 - 8q^6$

SOLUTION

(a) Because $x^3 = (x)^3$ and $8 = 2^3$, we let $a = x$, $b = 2$ and factor. Substituting in

$$a^3 + b^3 = (a + b)(a^2 - ab + b^2)$$

gives

$$x^3 + 2^3 = (x + 2)(x^2 - x \cdot 2 + 2^2)$$
$$= (x + 2)(x^2 - 2x + 4).$$

Note that the quadratic expression does not factor further.

(b) Here, $27x^3 = (3x)^3$ and $64y^3 = (4y)^3$, so

$$27x^3 - 64y^3 = (3x)^3 - (4y)^3.$$

Substituting $a = 3x$ and $b = 4y$ in

$$a^3 - b^3 = (a - b)(a^2 + ab + b^2)$$

gives

$$(3x)^3 - (4y)^3 = (3x - 4y)((3x)^2 + 3x \cdot 4y + (4y)^2)$$
$$= (3x - 4y)(9x^2 + 12xy + 16y^2).$$

(c) Let $a^3 = (3p^3)^3$ and $b^3 = (2q^2)^3$. Then $a^3 - b^3 = (a - b)(a^2 + ab + b^2)$ implies

$$27p^9 - 8q^6 = (3p^3 - 2q^2)(9p^6 + 6p^3q^2 + 4q^4).$$

Now Try Exercises 93, 95, and 99

R.4 Exercises

Greatest Common Factor

Exercises 1–18: Factor out the greatest common factor.

1. $10x - 15$
2. $32 - 16x$
3. $2x^3 - 5x$
4. $3y - 9y^2$
5. $8x^3 - 4x^2 + 16x$
6. $-5x^3 + x^2 - 4x$
7. $5x^4 - 15x^3 + 15x^2$
8. $28y + 14y^3 - 7y^5$
9. $15x^3 + 10x^2 - 30x$
10. $14a^4 - 21a^2 + 35a$
11. $6r^5 - 8r^4 + 12r^3$
12. $15r^6 + 20r^4 - 10r^3$
13. $8x^2y^2 - 24x^2y^3$
14. $36xy - 24x^3y^3$
15. $18mn^2 - 12m^2n^3$
16. $24m^2n^3 + 12m^3n^2$
17. $-4a^2 - 2ab + 6ab^2$
18. $-5a^2 + 10a^2b^2 - 15ab$

Factoring by Grouping

Exercises 19–32: Use grouping to factor the polynomial.

19. $x^3 + 3x^2 + 2x + 6$
20. $4x^3 + 3x^2 + 8x + 6$
21. $6x^3 - 4x^2 + 9x - 6$
22. $x^3 - 3x^2 - 5x + 15$
23. $z^3 - 5z^2 + z - 5$
24. $y^3 - 7y^2 + 8y - 56$
25. $y^4 + 2y^3 - 5y^2 - 10y$
26. $4z^4 + 4z^3 + z^2 + z$
27. $2x^3 - 3x^2 + 2x - 3$
28. $8x^3 - 2x^2 + 12x - 3$
29. $2x^4 - x^3 + 4x - 2$
30. $2x^4 - 5x^3 + 10x - 25$
31. $ab - 3a + 2b - 6$
32. $2ax - 6bx - ay + 3by$

Factoring Trinomials

Exercises 33–58: Factor the expression completely.

33. $x^2 + 7x + 10$ **34.** $x^2 + 3x - 10$

35. $x^2 + 8x + 12$ **36.** $x^2 - 8x + 12$

37. $z^2 + z - 42$ **38.** $z^2 - 9z + 20$

39. $z^2 + 11z + 24$ **40.** $z^2 + 15z + 54$

41. $24x^2 + 14x - 3$ **42.** $25x^2 - 5x - 6$

43. $6x^2 - x - 2$ **44.** $10x^2 + 3x - 1$

45. $1 + x - 2x^2$ **46.** $3 - 5x - 2x^2$

47. $20 + 7x - 6x^2$ **48.** $4 + 13x - 12x^2$

49. $5x^3 + x^2 - 6x$ **50.** $2x^3 + 8x^2 - 24x$

51. $3x^3 + 12x^2 + 9x$ **52.** $12x^3 - 8x^2 - 20x$

53. $2x^2 - 14x + 20$ **54.** $7x^2 + 35x + 42$

55. $60t^4 + 230t^3 - 40t^2$ **56.** $24r^4 + 8r^3 - 80r^2$

57. $4m^3 + 10m^2 - 6m$ **58.** $30m^4 + 3m^3 - 9m^2$

Difference of Two Squares

Exercises 59–76: Factor the expression completely, if possible.

59. $x^2 - 25$ **60.** $z^2 - 169$

61. $4x^2 - 25$ **62.** $36 - y^2$

63. $36x^2 - 100$ **64.** $9x^2 - 4y^2$

65. $64z^2 - 25z^4$ **66.** $100x^3 - x$

67. $16x^4 - y^4$ **68.** $x^4 - 9y^2$

69. $a^2 + 4b^2$ **70.** $9r^4 + 25t^4$

71. $4 - r^2t^2$ **72.** $25 - x^4y^2$

73. $(x - 1)^2 - 16$ **74.** $(y + 2)^2 - 1$

75. $4 - (z + 3)^2$ **76.** $64 - (t - 3)^2$

Perfect Square Trinomials

Exercises 77–90: Factor the expression.

77. $x^2 + 2x + 1$ **78.** $x^2 - 6x + 9$

79. $4x^2 + 20x + 25$ **80.** $x^2 + 10x + 25$

81. $x^2 - 12x + 36$ **82.** $16z^4 - 24z^3 + 9z^2$

83. $9z^3 - 6z^2 + z$ **84.** $49y^2 + 42y + 9$

85. $9y^3 + 30y^2 + 25y$ **86.** $25y^3 - 20y^2 + 4y$

87. $4x^2 - 12xy + 9y^2$ **88.** $25a^2 + 60ab + 36b^2$

89. $9a^3b - 12a^2b + 4ab$ **90.** $16a^3 + 8a^2b + ab^2$

Sum and Difference of Two Cubes

Exercises 91–102: Factor the expression.

91. $x^3 - 1$ **92.** $x^3 + 1$

93. $y^3 + z^3$ **94.** $y^3 - z^3$

95. $8x^3 - 27$ **96.** $8 - z^3$

97. $x^4 + 125x$ **98.** $3x^4 - 81x$

99. $8r^6 - t^3$ **100.** $125r^6 + 64t^3$

101. $10m^9 - 270n^6$ **102.** $5t^6 + 40r^3$

General Factoring

Exercises 103–158: Factor the expression completely.

103. $16x^2 - 25$ **104.** $25x^2 - 30x + 9$

105. $x^3 - 64$ **106.** $1 + 8y^3$

107. $x^2 + 16x + 64$ **108.** $12x^2 + x - 6$

109. $5x^2 - 38x - 16$ **110.** $125x^3 - 1$

111. $x^4 + 8x$ **112.** $2x^3 - 12x^2 + 18x$

113. $64x^3 + 8y^3$ **114.** $54 - 16x^3$

115. $3x^2 - 5x - 8$ **116.** $15x^2 - 11x + 2$

117. $7a^3 + 20a^2 - 3a$ **118.** $b^3 - b^2 - 2b$

119. $2x^3 - x^2 + 6x - 3$ **120.** $3x^3 - 5x^2 + 3x - 5$

121. $2x^4 - 5x^3 - 25x^2$ **122.** $10x^3 + 28x^2 - 6x$

123. $2x^4 + 5x^2 + 3$ **124.** $2x^4 + 2x^2 - 4$

125. $x^3 + 3x^2 + x + 3$ **126.** $x^3 + 5x^2 + 4x + 20$

127. $5x^3 - 5x^2 + 10x - 10$

128. $5x^4 - 20x^3 + 10x - 40$

129. $ax + bx - ay - by$ **130.** $ax - bx - ay + by$

131. $18x^2 + 12x + 2$

132. $-3x^2 + 30x - 75$

133. $-4x^3 + 24x^2 - 36x$

134. $18x^3 - 60x^2 + 50x$

135. $27x^3 - 8$

136. $27x^3 + 8$

137. $-x^4 - 8x$

138. $x^5 - 27x^2$

139. $x^4 - 2x^3 - x + 2$

140. $x^4 + 3x^3 + x + 3$

141. $r^4 - 16$

142. $r^4 - 81$

143. $25x^2 - 4a^2$

144. $9y^2 - 16z^2$

145. $2x^4 - 2y^4$

146. $a^4 - b^4$

147. $9x^3 + 6x^2 - 3x$

148. $8x^3 + 28x^2 - 16x$

149. $(z - 2)^2 - 9$

150. $(y + 2)^2 - 4$

151. $3x^5 - 27x^3 + 3x^2 - 27$

152. $2x^5 - 8x^3 - 16x^2 + 64$

153. $(x + 2)^2(x + 4)^4 + (x + 2)^3(x + 4)^3$

154. $(x - 3)(2x + 1)^3 + (x - 3)^2(2x + 1)^2$

155. $(6x + 1)(8x - 3)^4 - (6x + 1)^2(8x - 3)^3$

156. $(2x + 3)^4(x + 1)^4 - (2x + 3)^3(x + 1)^5$

157. $4x^2(5x - 1)^5 + 2x(5x - 1)^6$

158. $x^4(7x + 3)^3 + x^5(7x + 3)^2$

R.5 Rational Expressions

- **Simplify rational expressions**
- **Multiply and divide fractions**
- **Perform multiplication and division on rational expressions**
- **Find least common multiples and denominators**
- **Add and subtract fractions**
- **Perform addition and subtraction on rational expressions**
- **Clear fractions from equations**
- **Simplify complex fractions**

Simplifying Rational Expressions

When simplifying fractions, we sometimes use the **basic principle of fractions**, which states that

$$\frac{a \cdot c}{b \cdot c} = \frac{a}{b}.$$

This principle holds because $\frac{c}{c} = 1$ and $\frac{a}{b} \cdot 1 = \frac{a}{b}$. It can be used to simplify a fraction.

$$\frac{6}{44} = \frac{3 \cdot 2}{22 \cdot 2} = \frac{3}{22}$$

Factor out 2 in the numerator and denominator and simplify.

This same principle can also be used to simplify rational expressions.

SIMPLIFYING RATIONAL EXPRESSIONS

The following principle can be used to simplify rational expressions, where A, B, and C are polynomials.

$$\frac{A \cdot C}{B \cdot C} = \frac{A}{B}, \quad B \text{ and } C \text{ are nonzero.}$$

EXAMPLE 1 Simplifying rational expressions

Simplify each expression.

(a) $\dfrac{9x}{3x^2}$ **(b)** $\dfrac{2z^2 - 3z - 9}{z^2 + 2z - 15}$ **(c)** $\dfrac{a^2 - b^2}{a + b}$

SOLUTION

(a) First factor out the greatest common factor, $3x$, in the numerator and denominator.

$$\frac{9x}{3x^2} = \frac{3 \cdot 3x}{x \cdot 3x} = \frac{3}{x} \cdot 1 = \frac{3}{x}$$

(b) Start by factoring the numerator and denominator.

$$\frac{2z^2 - 3z - 9}{z^2 + 2z - 15} = \frac{(2z + 3)(z - 3)}{(z + 5)(z - 3)} = \frac{2z + 3}{z + 5}$$

(c) Start by factoring the numerator as the difference of squares.

$$\frac{a^2 - b^2}{a + b} = \frac{(a - b)(a + b)}{a + b} = a - b$$

Now Try Exercises 1, 5, and 11

Review of Multiplication and Division of Fractions

Recall that to multiply two fractions we use the property

$$\frac{a}{b} \cdot \frac{c}{d} = \frac{ac}{bd}.$$

For example, $\frac{2}{5} \cdot \frac{3}{7} = \frac{2 \cdot 3}{5 \cdot 7} = \frac{6}{35}$.

EXAMPLE 2 **Multiplying fractions**

Multiply and simplify the product.

(a) $\frac{4}{9} \cdot \frac{3}{8}$ **(b)** $\frac{2}{3} \cdot \frac{3}{4} \cdot \frac{5}{6}$

SOLUTION

(a) $\frac{4}{9} \cdot \frac{3}{8} = \frac{4 \cdot 3}{9 \cdot 8} = \frac{12}{72} = \frac{1 \cdot 12}{6 \cdot 12} = \frac{1}{6}$ **(b)** $\frac{2}{3} \cdot \frac{3}{4} \cdot \frac{5}{6} = \frac{6 \cdot 5}{12 \cdot 6} = \frac{5}{12}$

Now Try Exercises 15 and 17

Recall that to divide two fractions we "invert and multiply." That is, we change a division problem to a multiplication problem. For example,

$$\frac{3}{4} \div \frac{5}{4} = \frac{3}{4} \cdot \frac{4}{5} = \frac{3 \cdot 4}{5 \cdot 4} = \frac{3}{5}.$$

Multiplication and Division of Rational Expressions

Multiplying and dividing rational expressions is similar to multiplying and dividing fractions.

PRODUCTS AND QUOTIENTS OF RATIONAL EXPRESSIONS

To multiply two rational expressions, multiply numerators and multiply denominators.

$$\frac{A}{B} \cdot \frac{C}{D} = \frac{AC}{BD}, \quad B \text{ and } D \text{ are nonzero.}$$

To divide two rational expressions, multiply by the reciprocal of the divisor.

$$\frac{A}{B} \div \frac{C}{D} = \frac{A}{B} \cdot \frac{D}{C}, \quad B, C, \text{ and } D \text{ are nonzero.}$$

EXAMPLE 3 **Multiplying rational expressions**

Multiply.

(a) $\frac{1}{x} \cdot \frac{2x}{x + 1}$ **(b)** $\frac{x - 1}{x} \cdot \frac{x - 1}{x + 2}$

SOLUTION

(a) $\frac{1}{x} \cdot \frac{2x}{x + 1} = \frac{1 \cdot 2x}{x(x + 1)} = \frac{2}{x + 1}$ **(b)** $\frac{x - 1}{x} \cdot \frac{x - 1}{x + 2} = \frac{(x - 1)(x - 1)}{x(x + 2)}$

Now Try Exercises 33 and 37

EXAMPLE 4 Dividing two rational expressions

Divide and simplify.

(a) $\dfrac{2}{x} \div \dfrac{2x - 1}{4x}$ **(b)** $\dfrac{x^2 - 1}{x^2 + x - 6} \div \dfrac{x - 1}{x + 3}$

SOLUTION

(a)
$$\frac{2}{x} \div \frac{2x - 1}{4x} = \frac{2}{x} \cdot \frac{4x}{2x - 1} \quad \text{"Invert and multiply."}$$
$$= \frac{8x}{x(2x - 1)} \quad \text{Multiply.}$$
$$= \frac{8}{2x - 1} \quad \text{Simplify.}$$

(b)
$$\frac{x^2 - 1}{x^2 + x - 6} \div \frac{x - 1}{x + 3} = \frac{x^2 - 1}{x^2 + x - 6} \cdot \frac{x + 3}{x - 1} \quad \text{"Invert and multiply."}$$
$$= \frac{(x + 1)(x - 1)}{(x - 2)(x + 3)} \cdot \frac{x + 3}{x - 1} \quad \text{Factor.}$$
$$= \frac{(x + 1)(x - 1)(x + 3)}{(x - 2)(x - 1)(x + 3)} \quad \text{Commutative property}$$
$$= \frac{x + 1}{x - 2} \quad \text{Simplify.}$$

Now Try Exercises 45 and 53

Least Common Multiples and Denominators

To add or subtract fractions and rational expressions, we need to find a common denominator. The **least common denominator** (LCD) is equivalent to the **least common multiple** (LCM) of the denominators. The following procedure can be used to find the least common multiple.

FINDING THE LEAST COMMON MULTIPLE

The least common multiple (LCM) of two polynomials can be found as follows.

STEP 1: Factor each polynomial completely.

STEP 2: List each factor the greatest number of times that it occurs in either factorization.

STEP 3: Find the product of this list of factors. The result is the LCM.

The next example illustrates how to use this procedure.

EXAMPLE 5 Finding least common multiples

Find the least common multiple for each pair of expressions.

(a) $4x, 5x^3$ **(b)** $x^2 + 4x + 4, x^2 + 3x + 2$

SOLUTION

(a) STEP 1: Factor each polynomial completely.

$$4x = 2 \cdot 2 \cdot x \quad \text{and} \quad 5x^3 = 5 \cdot x \cdot x \cdot x$$

STEP 2: The factor 2 occurs twice, the factor 5 occurs once, and the factor x occurs at most three times. The list then is 2, 2, 5, x, x, and x.

STEP 3: The LCM is the product $2 \cdot 2 \cdot 5 \cdot x \cdot x \cdot x$, or $20x^3$.

(b) **STEP 1:** Factor each polynomial as follows.

$$x^2 + 4x + 4 = (x + 2)(x + 2) \quad \text{and} \quad x^2 + 3x + 2 = (x + 1)(x + 2)$$

STEP 2: The factor $(x + 1)$ occurs once, and $(x + 2)$ occurs at most twice.
STEP 3: The LCM is the product $(x + 1)(x + 2)^2$, which is left in factored form.

Now Try Exercises 61 and 65

EXAMPLE 6 **Finding a least common denominator**

Find the LCD for the expressions $\dfrac{1}{x^2 + 4x + 4}$ and $\dfrac{5}{x^2 + 3x + 2}$.

SOLUTION From Example 5(b), the LCM for $x^2 + 4x + 4$ and $x^2 + 3x + 2$ is

$$(x + 1)(x + 2)^2.$$

Therefore the LCD is *also* $(x + 1)(x + 2)^2$.

The LCD is the same as the LCM of the denominators.

Now Try Exercise 69

Review of Addition and Subtraction of Fractions

Recall that to add two fractions we use the property $\frac{a}{c} + \frac{b}{c} = \frac{a + b}{c}$. This property requires *like* denominators. For example, $\frac{1}{5} + \frac{3}{5} = \frac{1 + 3}{5} = \frac{4}{5}$. When the denominators are not alike, we must find a common denominator. Before adding two fractions, such as $\frac{2}{3}$ and $\frac{1}{4}$, we write them with 12 as their common denominator. That is, we multiply each fraction by 1 written in an appropriate form. For example, to write $\frac{2}{3}$ with a denominator of 12, we multiply $\frac{2}{3}$ by 1, written as $\frac{4}{4}$.

$$\frac{2}{3} = \frac{2}{3} \cdot \frac{4}{4} = \frac{8}{12} \quad \text{and} \quad \frac{1}{4} = \frac{1}{4} \cdot \frac{3}{3} = \frac{3}{12}$$

1. Write each fraction with a common denominator.

Once the fractions have a common denominator, we can add them, as in

$$\frac{2}{3} + \frac{1}{4} = \frac{8}{12} + \frac{3}{12} = \frac{11}{12}.$$

2. Add numerators. Keep the common denominator.

The *least common denominator* (LCD) for $\frac{2}{3}$ and $\frac{1}{4}$ is equal to the *least common multiple* (LCM) of 3 and 4. Thus the least common denominator is 12.

EXAMPLE 7 **Adding fractions**

Simplify $\dfrac{3}{5} + \dfrac{2}{7}$.

SOLUTION The LCD is 35.

$$\frac{3}{5} + \frac{2}{7} = \frac{3}{5} \cdot \frac{7}{7} + \frac{2}{7} \cdot \frac{5}{5} = \frac{21}{35} + \frac{10}{35} = \frac{31}{35}$$

Now Try Exercise 27

Recall that subtraction is similar to addition. To subtract two fractions with *like* denominators, we use the property $\frac{a}{c} - \frac{b}{c} = \frac{a - b}{c}$. For example, $\frac{3}{11} - \frac{7}{11} = \frac{3 - 7}{11} = -\frac{4}{11}$.

EXAMPLE 8 **Subtracting fractions**

Simplify $\dfrac{3}{8} - \dfrac{5}{6}$.

SOLUTION The LCD is 24.

Multiply each fraction by 1 in the appropriate form.

$$\frac{3}{8} - \frac{5}{6} = \frac{3}{8} \cdot \frac{3}{3} - \frac{5}{6} \cdot \frac{4}{4} = \frac{9}{24} - \frac{20}{24} = -\frac{11}{24}$$

Now Try Exercise 29

Addition and Subtraction of Rational Expressions

Addition and subtraction of rational expressions with like denominators are performed in the following manner.

SUMS AND DIFFERENCES OF RATIONAL EXPRESSIONS

To add (or subtract) two rational expressions with like denominators, add (or subtract) their numerators. The denominator does not change.

$$\frac{A}{C} + \frac{B}{C} = \frac{A + B}{C}$$

$$\frac{A}{C} - \frac{B}{C} = \frac{A - B}{C}, \quad C \neq 0$$

NOTE If the denominators are not alike, begin by writing each rational expression, using a common denominator. The LCD equals the LCM of the denominators.

EXAMPLE 9 Adding rational expressions

Add the expressions.

(a) $\frac{x}{x + 2} + \frac{3x + 1}{x + 2}$ **(b)** $\frac{1}{x - 1} + \frac{2x}{x + 1}$

SOLUTION

(a) The denominators are alike, so we add the numerators and keep the same denominator.

$$\frac{x}{x + 2} + \frac{3x + 1}{x + 2} = \frac{x + 3x + 1}{x + 2} \qquad \text{Add numerators.}$$

$$= \frac{4x + 1}{x + 2} \qquad \text{Combine like terms.}$$

(b) The LCM for $x - 1$ and $x + 1$ is their product, $(x - 1)(x + 1)$.

$$\frac{1}{x - 1} + \frac{2x}{x + 1} = \frac{1}{x - 1} \cdot \frac{x + 1}{x + 1} + \frac{2x}{x + 1} \cdot \frac{x - 1}{x - 1} \qquad \text{Change to a common denominator.}$$

$$= \frac{x + 1}{(x - 1)(x + 1)} + \frac{2x(x - 1)}{(x + 1)(x - 1)} \qquad \text{Multiply.}$$

$$= \frac{x + 1 + 2x^2 - 2x}{(x - 1)(x + 1)} \qquad \text{Add numerators; distributive property}$$

$$= \frac{2x^2 - x + 1}{(x - 1)(x + 1)} \qquad \text{Combine like terms.}$$

Now Try Exercises 73 and 81

Subtraction of rational expressions is similar.

EXAMPLE 10 Subtracting rational expressions

Subtract the expressions: $\frac{x - 1}{x} - \frac{5}{x + 5}$.

SOLUTION The LCD is $x(x + 5)$.

$$\frac{x - 1}{x} - \frac{5}{x + 5} = \frac{x - 1}{x} \cdot \frac{x + 5}{x + 5} - \frac{5}{x + 5} \cdot \frac{x}{x} \qquad \text{Change to a common denominator.}$$

$$= \frac{(x - 1)(x + 5)}{x(x + 5)} - \frac{5x}{x(x + 5)} \qquad \text{Multiply.}$$

$$= \frac{(x - 1)(x + 5) - 5x}{x(x + 5)} \qquad \text{Subtract numerators.}$$

$$= \frac{x^2 + 4x - 5 - 5x}{x(x + 5)} \qquad \text{Multiply binomials.}$$

$$= \frac{x^2 - x - 5}{x(x + 5)} \qquad \text{Combine like terms.}$$

Now Try Exercise 79

Clearing Fractions

To solve rational equations, it is sometimes advantageous to multiply each side by the LCD to clear fractions. For example, the LCD for the equation $\frac{1}{x+2} + \frac{1}{x-2} = 0$ is $(x+2)(x-2)$. Multiplying each side by the LCD results in the following.

$$(x+2)(x-2)\left(\frac{1}{x+2} + \frac{1}{x-2}\right) = 0 \qquad \text{Multiply each side by LCD.}$$

$$\frac{(x+2)(x-2)}{x+2} + \frac{(x+2)(x-2)}{x-2} = 0 \qquad \text{Distributive property}$$

$$(x-2) + (x+2) = 0 \qquad \text{Simplify.}$$

$$x = 0 \qquad \text{Combine like terms and solve.}$$

This technique is applied in the next example.

EXAMPLE 11 **Clearing fractions**

Clear fractions from the equation and solve.

$$\frac{3}{x} + \frac{x}{x^2-1} - \frac{4}{x+1} = 0$$

SOLUTION The LCD is $x(x^2-1) = x(x-1)(x+1)$.

$$x(x^2-1)\left(\frac{3}{x} + \frac{x}{x^2-1} - \frac{4}{x+1}\right) = x(x^2-1)\cdot 0$$

$$\frac{3x(x^2-1)}{x} + \frac{x(x)(x^2-1)}{x^2-1} - \frac{4x(x^2-1)}{x+1} = 0$$

$$\frac{3x(x^2-1)}{x} + \frac{x^2(x^2-1)}{x^2-1} - \frac{4x(x-1)(x+1)}{x+1} = 0$$

$$3(x^2-1) + x^2 - 4x(x-1) = 0$$

$$3x^2 - 3 + x^2 - 4x^2 + 4x = 0$$

$$4x - 3 = 0$$

$$x = \frac{3}{4}$$

The solution is $\frac{3}{4}$. Check this answer. **Now Try Exercise 111**

Complex Fractions

A complex fraction is a rational expression that contains fractions in its numerator, denominator, or both. One strategy for simplifying a complex fraction is to multiply the numerator and denominator by the LCD of the fractions in the numerator and denominator. For example, the LCD for the complex fraction

$$\frac{1 - \frac{1}{x}}{1 + \frac{1}{2x}}$$

is $2x$. To simplify, multiply the complex fraction by 1, expressed in the form $\frac{2x}{2x}$.

$$\frac{\left(1 - \frac{1}{x}\right)\cdot 2x}{\left(1 + \frac{1}{2x}\right)\cdot 2x} = \frac{2x - \frac{2x}{x}}{2x + \frac{2x}{2x}} \qquad \text{Distributive property}$$

$$= \frac{2x-2}{2x+1} \qquad \text{Simplify.}$$

In the next example, we simplify a complex fraction.

EXAMPLE 12 **Simplifying a complex fraction**

Simplify the complex fraction.

$$\frac{\dfrac{3}{x-1} - \dfrac{2}{x}}{\dfrac{1}{x-1} + \dfrac{3}{x}}$$

SOLUTION The LCD is the product, $x(x - 1)$. Multiply the expression by $\frac{x(x-1)}{x(x-1)}$.

$$\frac{\left(\dfrac{3}{x-1} - \dfrac{2}{x}\right)}{\left(\dfrac{1}{x-1} + \dfrac{3}{x}\right)} \cdot \frac{x(x-1)}{x(x-1)} = \frac{\dfrac{3x(x-1)}{x-1} - \dfrac{2x(x-1)}{x}}{\dfrac{x(x-1)}{x-1} + \dfrac{3x(x-1)}{x}} \quad \text{Distributive property}$$

$$= \frac{3x - 2(x-1)}{x + 3(x-1)} \quad \text{Simplify.}$$

$$= \frac{3x - 2x + 2}{x + 3x - 3} \quad \text{Distributive property}$$

$$= \frac{x+2}{4x-3} \quad \text{Combine like terms.}$$

Now Try Exercise 115

R.5 Exercises

Simplifying Rational Expressions

Exercises 1–14: Simplify the expression.

1. $\frac{10x^3}{5x^2}$
2. $\frac{24t^3}{6t^2}$
3. $\frac{(x-5)(x+5)}{x-5}$
4. $-\frac{5-a}{a-5}$
5. $\frac{x^2-16}{x-4}$
6. $\frac{(x+5)(x-4)}{(x+7)(x+5)}$
7. $\frac{x+3}{2x^2+5x-3}$
8. $\frac{2x^2-9x+4}{6x^2+7x-5}$
9. $-\frac{z+2}{4z+8}$
10. $\frac{x^2-25}{x^2+10x+25}$
11. $\frac{x^2+2x}{x^2+3x+2}$
12. $\frac{x^2-3x-10}{x^2-6x+5}$
13. $\frac{a^3+b^3}{a+b}$
14. $\frac{a^3-b^3}{a-b}$

Review of Fractions

Exercises 15–32: Simplify.

15. $\frac{5}{8} \cdot \frac{4}{15}$
16. $\frac{7}{2} \cdot \frac{4}{21}$
17. $\frac{5}{6} \cdot \frac{3}{10} \cdot \frac{8}{3}$
18. $\frac{9}{5} \cdot \frac{10}{3} \cdot \frac{1}{27}$
19. $\frac{4}{7} \div \frac{8}{7}$
20. $\frac{5}{12} \div \frac{10}{9}$
21. $\frac{1}{2} \div \frac{3}{4} \div \frac{5}{6}$
22. $\frac{3}{4} \div \frac{7}{8} \div \frac{5}{14}$
23. $\frac{3}{8} + \frac{5}{8}$
24. $\frac{5}{9} + \frac{2}{9}$
25. $\frac{3}{7} - \frac{4}{7}$
26. $\frac{8}{11} - \frac{9}{11}$
27. $\frac{2}{3} + \frac{5}{11}$
28. $\frac{9}{13} + \frac{3}{2}$

29. $\frac{4}{5} - \frac{1}{10}$

30. $\frac{3}{4} - \frac{7}{12}$

31. $\frac{1}{3} + \frac{3}{4} - \frac{3}{7}$

32. $\frac{6}{11} - \frac{1}{2} + \frac{3}{8}$

Multiplication and Division of Rational Expressions

Exercises 33–58: Simplify. Leave numerators and denominators in factored form when appropriate.

33. $\frac{1}{x^2} \cdot \frac{3x}{2}$

34. $\frac{6a}{5} \cdot \frac{5}{12a^2}$

35. $\frac{5x}{3} \div \frac{10x}{6}$

36. $\frac{2x^2 + x}{3x + 9} \div \frac{x}{x + 3}$

37. $\frac{x + 1}{2x - 5} \cdot \frac{x}{x + 1}$

38. $\frac{4x + 8}{2x} \cdot \frac{x^2}{x + 2}$

39. $\frac{(x - 5)(x + 3)}{3x - 1} \cdot \frac{x(3x - 1)}{(x - 5)}$

40. $\frac{b^2 + 1}{b^2 - 1} \cdot \frac{b - 1}{b + 1}$

41. $\frac{x^2 - 2x - 35}{2x^3 - 3x^2} \cdot \frac{x^3 - x^2}{2x - 14}$

42. $\frac{2x + 4}{x + 1} \cdot \frac{x^2 + 3x + 2}{4x + 2}$

43. $\frac{6b}{b + 2} \div \frac{3b^4}{2b + 4}$

44. $\frac{5x^5}{x - 2} \div \frac{10x^3}{5x - 10}$

45. $\frac{3a + 1}{a^7} \div \frac{a + 1}{3a^8}$

46. $\frac{x^2 - 16}{x + 3} \div \frac{x + 4}{x^2 - 9}$

47. $\frac{x + 5}{x^3 - x} \div \frac{x^2 - 25}{x^3}$

48. $\frac{x^2 + x - 12}{2x^2 - 9x - 5} \div \frac{x^2 + 7x + 12}{2x^2 - 7x - 4}$

49. $\frac{x - 2}{x^3 - x} \div \frac{x^2 - 2x}{x^2 - 1}$

50. $\frac{x^2 + 3x + 2}{2x^2 + 7x + 3} \div \frac{x^2 - 4}{2x^2 - x - 1}$

51. $\frac{x^2 - 3x + 2}{x^2 + 5x + 6} \div \frac{x^2 + x - 2}{x^2 + 2x - 3}$

52. $\frac{2x^2 + x - 1}{6x^2 + x - 2} \div \frac{2x^2 + 5x + 3}{6x^2 + 13x + 6}$

53. $\frac{x^2 - 4}{x^2 + x - 2} \div \frac{x - 2}{x - 1}$

54. $\frac{x^2 + 2x + 1}{x - 2} \div \frac{x + 1}{2x - 4}$

55. $\frac{3y}{x^2} \div \frac{y^2}{x} \div \frac{y}{5x}$

56. $\frac{x + 1}{y - 2} \div \frac{2x + 2}{y - 2} \div \frac{x}{y}$

57. $\frac{x - 3}{x - 1} \div \frac{x^2}{x - 1} \div \frac{x - 3}{x}$

58. $\frac{2x}{x - 2} \div \frac{x + 2}{x} \div \frac{7x}{x^2 - 4}$

Least Common Multiples

Exercises 59–66: Find the least common multiple.

59. 12, 18

60. 9, 15

61. $5a^3, 10a$

62. $6a^2, 9a^5$

63. $z^2 - 4z, (z - 4)^2$

64. $z^2 - 1, z^2 + 2z + 1$

65. $x^2 - 6x + 9, x^2 - 5x + 6$

66. $x^2 - 4, x^2 - 4x + 4$

Common Denominators

Exercises 67–72: Find the LCD for the rational expressions.

67. $\frac{1}{x + 1}, \frac{1}{7}$

68. $\frac{1}{2x - 1}, \frac{1}{x + 1}$

69. $\frac{1}{x + 4}, \frac{1}{x^2 - 16}$

70. $\frac{4}{2x^2}, \frac{1}{2x + 2}$

71. $\frac{3}{2}, \frac{x}{2x + 1}, \frac{x}{2x - 4}$

72. $\frac{1}{x}, \frac{1}{x^2 - 4x}, \frac{1}{2x}$

Addition and Subtraction of Rational Expressions

Exercises 73–102: Simplify. Leave numerators and denominators in factored form when appropriate.

73. $\frac{4}{x + 1} + \frac{3}{x + 1}$

74. $\frac{2}{x^2} + \frac{5}{x^2}$

75. $\frac{2}{x^2 - 1} - \frac{x + 1}{x^2 - 1}$

76. $\frac{2x}{x^2 + x} - \frac{2x}{x + 1}$

77. $\frac{x}{x + 4} - \frac{x + 1}{x(x + 4)}$

78. $\frac{4x}{x + 2} + \frac{x - 5}{x - 2}$

79. $\frac{2}{x^2} - \frac{4x - 1}{x}$

80. $\frac{2x}{x - 5} - \frac{x}{x + 5}$

81. $\frac{x + 3}{x - 5} + \frac{5}{x - 3}$

82. $\frac{x}{2x - 1} + \frac{1 - x}{3x}$

83. $\dfrac{3}{x-5} - \dfrac{1}{x-3} - \dfrac{2x}{x-5}$

84. $\dfrac{2x+1}{x-1} - \dfrac{3}{x+1} + \dfrac{x}{x-1}$

85. $\dfrac{x}{x^2-9} + \dfrac{5x}{x-3}$

86. $\dfrac{a^2+1}{a^2-1} + \dfrac{a}{1-a^2}$

87. $\dfrac{b}{2b-4} - \dfrac{b-1}{b-2}$

88. $\dfrac{y^2}{2-y} - \dfrac{y}{y^2-4}$

89. $\dfrac{2x}{x-5} + \dfrac{2x-1}{3x^2-16x+5}$

90. $\dfrac{x+3}{2x-1} + \dfrac{3}{10x^2-5x}$

91. $\dfrac{x}{(x-1)^2} - \dfrac{1}{(x-1)(x+3)}$

92. $\dfrac{3}{x^2-x-6} - \dfrac{2}{x^2+5x+6}$

93. $\dfrac{x}{x^2-5x+4} + \dfrac{2}{x^2-2x-8}$

94. $\dfrac{3}{x^2-2x+1} + \dfrac{1}{x^2-3x+2}$

95. $\dfrac{x}{x^2-4} - \dfrac{1}{x^2+4x+4}$

96. $\dfrac{3x}{x^2+2x-3} + \dfrac{1}{x^2-2x+1}$

97. $\dfrac{3x}{x-y} - \dfrac{3y}{x^2-2xy+y^2}$

98. $\dfrac{4c}{ab} + \dfrac{3b}{ac} - \dfrac{2a}{bc}$

99. $x + \dfrac{1}{x-1} - \dfrac{1}{x+1}$

100. $5 - \dfrac{6}{n^2-36} + \dfrac{3}{n-6}$

101. $\dfrac{6}{t-1} + \dfrac{2}{t-2} + \dfrac{1}{t}$

102. $\dfrac{3}{x-5} - \dfrac{1}{x-3} - \dfrac{2x}{x-5}$

Clearing Fractions

Exercises 103–112: (Refer to Example 11.) Clear fractions and solve. Check your answers.

103. $\dfrac{1}{x} + \dfrac{3}{x^2} = 0$

104. $\dfrac{1}{x-2} + \dfrac{3}{x+1} = 0$

105. $\dfrac{1}{x} + \dfrac{3x}{2x-1} = 0$

106. $\dfrac{x}{2x-5} + \dfrac{4}{x} = 0$

107. $\dfrac{2x}{9-x^2} + \dfrac{1}{3-x} = 0$

108. $\dfrac{1}{1-x^2} + \dfrac{1}{1+x} = 0$

109. $\dfrac{1}{2x} + \dfrac{1}{2x^2} - \dfrac{1}{x^3} = 0$

110. $\dfrac{1}{x^2-16} + \dfrac{4}{x+4} - \dfrac{5}{x-4} = 0$

111. $\dfrac{1}{x} - \dfrac{2}{x+5} + \dfrac{1}{x-5} = 0$

112. $\dfrac{1}{x-2} + \dfrac{1}{x-3} - \dfrac{2}{x} = 0$

Complex Fractions

Exercises 113–124: Simplify. Leave numerators and denominators in factored form when appropriate.

113. $\dfrac{1+\frac{1}{x}}{1-\frac{1}{x}}$

114. $\dfrac{\frac{1}{2}-x}{\frac{1}{x}-2}$

115. $\dfrac{\frac{1}{x-5}}{\frac{4}{x}-\frac{1}{x-5}}$

116. $\dfrac{1+\frac{1}{x-3}}{\frac{1}{x-3}-1}$

117. $\dfrac{\frac{1}{x}+\frac{2-x}{x^2}}{\frac{3}{x^2}-\frac{1}{x}}$

118. $\dfrac{\frac{1}{x-1}+\frac{2}{x}}{2-\frac{1}{x}}$

119. $\dfrac{\frac{1}{x+3}+\frac{2}{x-3}}{2-\frac{1}{x-3}}$

120. $\dfrac{\frac{1}{x}+\frac{2}{x}}{\frac{1}{x-1}+\frac{x}{2}}$

121. $\dfrac{\frac{4}{x-5}}{\frac{1}{x+5}+\frac{1}{x}}$

122. $\dfrac{\frac{2}{x-4}}{1-\frac{1}{x+4}}$

123. $\dfrac{\frac{1}{2a}-\frac{1}{2b}}{\frac{1}{a^2}-\frac{1}{b^2}}$

124. $\dfrac{\frac{1}{2x^2}-\frac{1}{2y^2}}{\frac{1}{3y^2}+\frac{1}{3x^2}}$

R.6 Radical Notation and Rational Exponents

- Use radical notation
- Apply rational exponents
- Use properties of rational exponents

Radical Notation

Square Root Recall the definition of the **square root** of a number a.

SQUARE ROOT

The number b is a *square root* of a if $b^2 = a$.

Every positive number a has two square roots, one positive and one negative. For example, the square roots of 100 are 10 and -10. Recall that the *positive square root* is called the **principal square root** and is denoted $\sqrt{a}$. The *negative square root* is denoted $-\sqrt{a}$. To identify both square roots, we write $\pm\sqrt{a}$. The symbol $\pm$ is read "plus or minus." The symbol $\sqrt{}$ is called the **radical sign**. The expression under the radical sign is called the **radicand**, and an expression containing a radical sign is called a **radical expression**. Examples of radical expressions include

$$\sqrt{6}, \quad 5 + \sqrt{x+1}, \quad \text{and} \quad \sqrt{\frac{3x}{2x-1}}.$$

Radical sign Radicand

Radical Expressions

EXAMPLE 1 Finding principal square roots

Find the principal square root of each expression.

(a) 25 **(b)** 17 **(c)** $\frac{4}{9}$ **(d)** $c^2, c > 0$

SOLUTION

(a) Because $5 \cdot 5 = 25$, the principal, or positive, square root of 25 is $\sqrt{25} = 5$.

(b) The principal square root of 17 is $\sqrt{17}$. This value is not an integer, but we can approximate it. Figure R.18 shows that $\sqrt{17} \approx 4.12$, rounded to the nearest hundredth. Note that calculators do not give *exact* answers when approximating many radical expressions; they give decimal *approximations*.

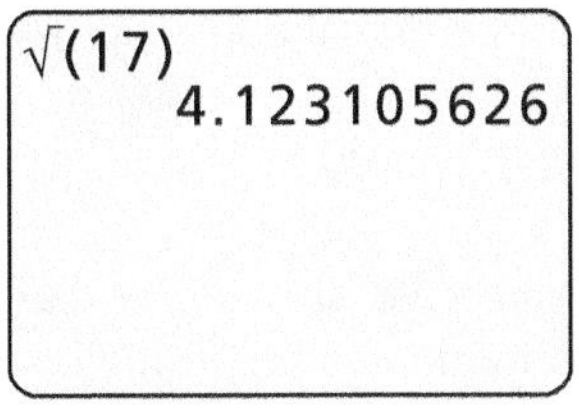

(c) Because $\frac{2}{3} \cdot \frac{2}{3} = \frac{4}{9}$, the principal square root of $\frac{4}{9}$ is $\sqrt{\frac{4}{9}} = \frac{2}{3}$.

(d) The principal square root of c^2 is $\sqrt{c^2} = c$, as it is given that c is positive.

Now Try Exercises 7, 9, 11 and 13

√(17)
4.123105626

Figure R.18

Cube Root Another common radical expression is the **cube root** of a number a, denoted $\sqrt[3]{a}$.

CUBE ROOT

The number b is a *cube root* of a if $b^3 = a$.

Although the square root of a negative number is not a real number, the cube root of a negative number is a negative real number. *Every real number has one real cube root.*

EXAMPLE 2 Finding cube roots

Find the cube root of each expression.

(a) 8 **(b)** -27 **(c)** 16 **(d)** $\frac{1}{64}$ **(e)** d^6

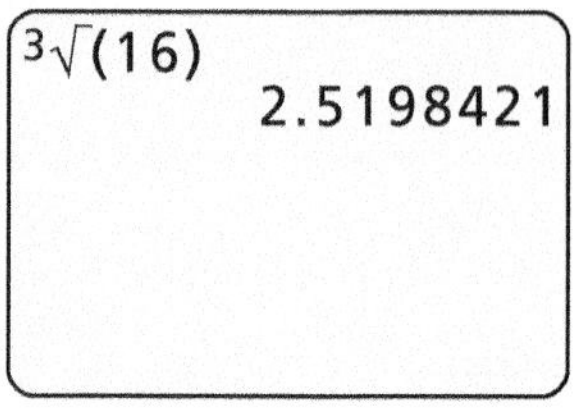

```
3√(16)
            2.5198421
```

Figure R.19

SOLUTION

(a) $\sqrt[3]{8} = 2$ because $2^3 = 2 \cdot 2 \cdot 2 = 8$.

(b) $\sqrt[3]{-27} = -3$ because $(-3)^3 = (-3)(-3)(-3) = -27$.

(c) $\sqrt[3]{16}$ is not an integer. Figure R.19 shows that $\sqrt[3]{16} \approx 2.52$.

(d) $\sqrt[3]{\frac{1}{64}} = \frac{1}{4}$ because $\left(\frac{1}{4}\right)^3 = \frac{1}{4} \cdot \frac{1}{4} \cdot \frac{1}{4} = \frac{1}{64}$.

(e) $\sqrt[3]{d^6} = d^2$ because $(d^2)^3 = d^2 \cdot d^2 \cdot d^2 = d^{2+2+2} = d^6$.

Now Try Exercises 15, 17, 19, 21, and 31

***n*th Root** We can generalize square roots and cube roots to include the *n*th root of a number *a*. The number *b* is an ***n*th root** of *a* if $b^n = a$, where *n* is a positive integer, and the **principal *n*th root** is denoted $\sqrt[n]{a}$. The number *n* is called the **index**. For the square root, the index is 2, although we usually write $\sqrt{a}$ rather than $\sqrt[2]{a}$. When *n* is odd, we are finding an **odd root**, and when *n* is even, we are finding an **even root**. The square root $\sqrt{a}$ is an example of an even root, and the cube root $\sqrt[3]{a}$ is an example of an odd root.

NOTE An odd root of a negative number is a negative number, but the even root of a negative number is *not* a real number. For example, $\sqrt[3]{-8} = -2$, whereas $\sqrt[4]{-81}$ is *not* a real number.

EXAMPLE 3 Finding *n*th roots

Find each root.

(a) $\sqrt[4]{16}$ **(b)** $\sqrt[5]{-32}$

SOLUTION

(a) $\sqrt[4]{16} = 2$ because $2^4 = 2 \cdot 2 \cdot 2 \cdot 2 = 16$. Note that when *n* is even the principal *n*th root is positive.

(b) $\sqrt[5]{-32} = -2$ because $(-2)^5 = (-2)(-2)(-2)(-2)(-2) = -32$.

Now Try Exercises 37 and 38

Rational Exponents

When *m* and *n* are integers, the product rule states that $a^m a^n = a^{m+n}$. This rule can be extended to include exponents that are fractions. For example,

$$4^{1/2} \cdot 4^{1/2} = 4^{1/2+1/2} = 4^1 = 4.$$

That is, if we multiply $4^{1/2}$ by itself, the result is 4. Because we also know that $\sqrt{4} \cdot \sqrt{4} = 4$, this discussion suggests that $4^{1/2} = \sqrt{4}$ and motivates the following definition.

THE EXPRESSION $a^{1/n}$

If *n* is an integer greater than 1, then

$$a^{1/n} = \sqrt[n]{a}.$$

If $a < 0$ and *n* is an even positive integer, then $a^{1/n}$ is not a real number.

The next two examples show how to interpret rational exponents.

EXAMPLE 4 Interpreting rational exponents

Write each expression in radical notation. Then evaluate the expression (to the nearest hundredth when appropriate).

(a) $36^{1/2}$ **(b)** $23^{1/5}$ **(c)** $(5x)^{1/2}$

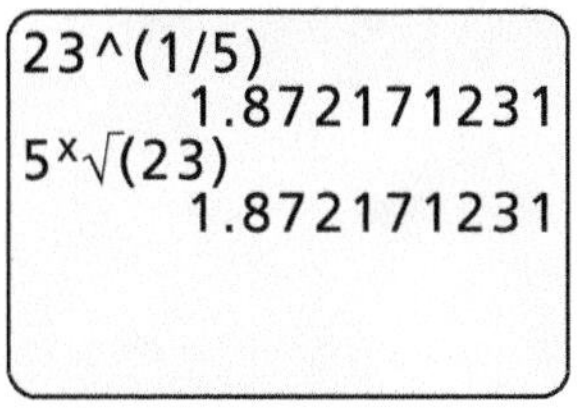

```
23^(1/5)
         1.872171231
5x√(23)
         1.872171231
```

Figure R.20

SOLUTION

(a) The exponent $\frac{1}{2}$ indicates a square root. Thus $36^{1/2} = \sqrt{36}$, which evaluates to 6.

(b) The exponent $\frac{1}{5}$ indicates a fifth root. Thus $23^{1/5} = \sqrt[5]{23}$, which is not an integer. Figure R.20 shows this expression approximated in both exponential and radical notation. In either case $23^{1/5} \approx 1.87$.

(c) The exponent $\frac{1}{2}$ indicates a square root, so $(5x)^{1/2} = \sqrt{5x}$.

Now Try Exercises 39, 43, and 55

Suppose that we want to define the expression $8^{2/3}$. On the one hand, using properties of exponents we have

$$8^{1/3} \cdot 8^{1/3} = 8^{1/3+1/3} = 8^{2/3}.$$

On the other hand, we have

$$8^{1/3} \cdot 8^{1/3} = \sqrt[3]{8} \cdot \sqrt[3]{8} = 2 \cdot 2 = 4.$$

Thus $8^{2/3} = 4$, and that value is obtained whether we interpret $8^{2/3}$ as either

$$8^{2/3} = (8^2)^{1/3} = \sqrt[3]{8^2} = \sqrt[3]{64} = 4$$

or

$$8^{2/3} = (8^{1/3})^2 = (\sqrt[3]{8})^2 = 2^2 = 4.$$

This result illustrates that $8^{2/3} = \sqrt[3]{8^2} = \left(\sqrt[3]{8}\right)^2 = 4$ and suggests the following definition.

THE EXPRESSION $a^{m/n}$

If m and n are positive integers with $\frac{m}{n}$ in lowest terms, then

$$a^{m/n} = \sqrt[n]{a^m} = \left(\sqrt[n]{a}\right)^m.$$

If $a < 0$ and n is an even integer, then $a^{m/n}$ is not a real number.

EXAMPLE 5 **Interpreting rational exponents**

Write each expression in radical notation. Then evaluate the expression when the result is an integer.

(a) $(-27)^{2/3}$ **(b)** $12^{3/5}$

SOLUTION

(a) The exponent $\frac{2}{3}$ indicates either that we take the **cube root** of -27 and then square it or that we square -27 and then take the cube root. In either case the result will be the same. Thus

$$(-27)^{2/3} = (\sqrt[3]{-27})^2 = (-3)^2 = 9$$

or

$$(-27)^{2/3} = \sqrt[3]{(-27)^2} = \sqrt[3]{729} = 9.$$

(b) The exponent $\frac{3}{5}$ indicates either that we take the fifth root of 12 and then cube it or that we cube 12 and then take the fifth root. Thus

$$12^{3/5} = (\sqrt[5]{12})^3 \quad \text{or} \quad 12^{3/5} = \sqrt[5]{12^3}.$$

This result is not an integer. **Now Try Exercises 47 and 61**

From properties of exponents we know that $a^{-n} = \frac{1}{a^n}$, where n is a positive integer. We now define this property for negative rational exponents.

THE EXPRESSION $a^{-m/n}$

If m and n are positive integers with $\frac{m}{n}$ in lowest terms, then

$$a^{-m/n} = \frac{1}{a^{m/n}}, \qquad a \neq 0.$$

EXAMPLE 6 Interpreting negative rational exponents

Write each expression in radical notation and then evaluate.
(a) $(64)^{-1/3}$ **(b)** $(81)^{-3/4}$

SOLUTION

(a) $(64)^{-1/3} = \frac{1}{64^{1/3}} = \frac{1}{\sqrt[3]{64}} = \frac{1}{4}$

(b) $(81)^{-3/4} = \frac{1}{81^{3/4}} = \frac{1}{(\sqrt[4]{81})^3} = \frac{1}{3^3} = \frac{1}{27}$

Now Try Exercises 51 and 53

Properties of Rational Exponents

Any rational number can be written as a ratio of two integers. That is, if p is a rational number, then $p = \frac{m}{n}$, where m and n are integers. Properties for integer exponents also apply to rational exponents—with one exception. If n is even in the expression $a^{m/n}$ and $\frac{m}{n}$ is written in lowest terms, then a must be nonnegative (not negative) for the result to be a real number.

PROPERTIES OF EXPONENTS

Let p and q be rational numbers written in lowest terms. For all real numbers a and b for which the expressions are real numbers, the following properties hold.

1. $a^p \cdot a^q = a^{p+q}$ — Product rule for exponents
2. $a^{-p} = \frac{1}{a^p}$, $\frac{1}{a^{-p}} = a^p$ — Negative exponents
3. $\left(\frac{a}{b}\right)^{-p} = \left(\frac{b}{a}\right)^p$ — Negative exponents for quotients
4. $\frac{a^p}{a^q} = a^{p-q}$ — Quotient rule for exponents
5. $(a^p)^q = a^{pq}$ — Power rule for exponents
6. $(ab)^p = a^p b^p$ — Power rule for products
7. $\left(\frac{a}{b}\right)^p = \frac{a^p}{b^p}$ — Power rule for quotients

In the next example, we apply these properties.

EXAMPLE 7 Applying properties of exponents

Write each expression using rational exponents and simplify. Write the answer with a positive exponent. Assume that all variables are positive numbers.

(a) $\sqrt{x} \cdot \sqrt[3]{x}$ **(b)** $\sqrt[3]{27x^2}$ **(c)** $\left(\frac{x^2}{81}\right)^{-1/2}$

SOLUTION

(a)
$$\begin{aligned} \sqrt{x} \cdot \sqrt[3]{x} &= x^{1/2} \cdot x^{1/3} && \text{Use rational exponents.} \\ &= x^{1/2+1/3} && \text{Product rule for exponents} \\ &= x^{5/6} && \text{Simplify.} \end{aligned}$$

(b)
$$\begin{aligned} \sqrt[3]{27x^2} &= (27x^2)^{1/3} && \text{Use rational exponents.} \\ &= 27^{1/3}(x^2)^{1/3} && \text{Power rule for products} \\ &= 3x^{2/3} && \text{Power rule for exponents} \end{aligned}$$

(c) $\left(\frac{x^2}{81}\right)^{-1/2} = \left(\frac{81}{x^2}\right)^{1/2}$ Negative exponents for quotients

$= \frac{(81)^{1/2}}{(x^2)^{1/2}}$ Power rule for quotients

$= \frac{9}{x}$ Power rule for exponents; simplify.

Now Try Exercises 81, 89, and 99

R.6 Exercises

Square Roots and Cube Roots

Exercises 1–6: Find the square roots of the number. Approximate your answers to the nearest hundredth whenever appropriate.

1. 25 **2.** 49

3. $\frac{16}{25}$ **4.** $\frac{64}{81}$

5. 11 **6.** 17

Exercises 7–14: Find the principal square root of the number. Approximate your answer to the nearest hundredth whenever appropriate.

7. 144 **8.** 100

9. 23 **10.** 45

11. $\frac{4}{49}$ **12.** $\frac{16}{121}$

13. $b^2, b < 0$ **14.** $(xy)^2, xy > 0$

Exercises 15–22: Find the cube root of the number.

15. 27 **16.** 64

17. -8 **18.** -125

19. $\frac{1}{27}$ **20.** $-\frac{1}{64}$

21. b^9 **22.** $8x^6$

Radical Notation

Exercises 23–40: If possible, simplify the expression by hand. If you cannot, approximate the answer to the nearest hundredth. Variables represent any real number.

23. $\sqrt{9}$ **24.** $\sqrt{121}$

25. $-\sqrt{5}$ **26.** $\sqrt{11}$

27. $\sqrt[3]{27}$ **28.** $\sqrt[3]{64}$

29. $\sqrt[3]{-64}$ **30.** $-\sqrt[3]{-1}$

31. $\sqrt[3]{5}$ **32.** $\sqrt[3]{-13}$

33. $-\sqrt[3]{x^9}$ **34.** $\sqrt[3]{(x+1)^6}$

35. $\sqrt[3]{(2x)^6}$ **36.** $\sqrt[3]{9x^3}$

37. $\sqrt[4]{81}$ **38.** $\sqrt[5]{-1}$

39. $\sqrt[5]{-7}$ **40.** $\sqrt[4]{6}$

Rational Exponents

Exercises 41–46: Write the expression in radical notation.

41. $6^{1/2}$ **42.** $7^{1/3}$

43. $(xy)^{1/2}$ **44.** $x^{2/3}y^{1/5}$

45. $y^{-1/5}$ **46.** $\left(\frac{x}{y}\right)^{-2/7}$

Exercises 47–54: Write the expression in radical notation. Then evaluate the expression when the result is an integer.

47. $27^{2/3}$ **48.** $8^{4/3}$

49. $(-1)^{4/3}$ **50.** $81^{3/4}$

51. $8^{-1/3}$ **52.** $16^{-3/4}$

53. $13^{-3/5}$ **54.** $23^{-1/2}$

Exercises 55–76: Evaluate the expression by hand. Approximate the answer to the nearest hundredth when appropriate.

55. $16^{1/2}$ **56.** $8^{1/3}$

57. $256^{1/4}$ **58.** $4^{3/2}$

59. $32^{1/5}$ **60.** $(-32)^{1/5}$

61. $(-8)^{4/3}$ **62.** $(-1)^{3/5}$

63. $2^{1/2} \cdot 2^{2/3}$ **64.** $5^{3/5} \cdot 5^{1/10}$

65. $\left(\frac{4}{9}\right)^{1/2}$ **66.** $\left(\frac{27}{64}\right)^{1/3}$

67. $\frac{4^{2/3}}{4^{1/2}}$ **68.** $\frac{6^{1/5} \cdot 6^{3/5}}{6^{2/5}}$

69. $4^{-1/2}$ **70.** $9^{-3/2}$

71. $(-8)^{-1/3}$ **72.** $49^{-1/2}$

73. $\left(\frac{1}{16}\right)^{-1/4}$

74. $\left(\frac{16}{25}\right)^{-3/2}$

75. $(2^{1/2})^3$

76. $(5^{6/5})^{-1/2}$

Exercises 77–106: Simplify the expression and write it with rational exponents. Assume that all variables are positive.

77. $(x^2)^{3/2}$

78. $(y^4)^{1/2}$

79. $(x^2y^8)^{1/2}$

80. $(y^{10}z^4)^{1/4}$

81. $\sqrt[3]{x^3y^6}$

82. $\sqrt{16x^4}$

83. $\sqrt{\dfrac{y^4}{x^2}}$

84. $\sqrt[3]{\dfrac{x^{12}}{z^6}}$

85. $\sqrt{y^3} \cdot \sqrt[3]{y^2}$

86. $\left(\dfrac{x^6}{81}\right)^{1/4}$

87. $\left(\dfrac{x^6}{27}\right)^{2/3}$

88. $\left(\dfrac{1}{x^8}\right)^{-1/4}$

89. $\left(\dfrac{x^2}{y^6}\right)^{-1/2}$

90. $\dfrac{\sqrt{x}}{\sqrt[3]{27x^6}}$

91. $\sqrt{\sqrt{y}}$

92. $\sqrt{\sqrt[3]{(3x)^2}}$

93. $(a^{-1/2})^{4/3}$

94. $(x^{-3/2})^{2/3}$

95. $(a^3b^6)^{1/3}$

96. $(64x^3y^{18})^{1/6}$

97. $\dfrac{(k^{1/2})^{-3}}{(k^2)^{1/4}}$

98. $\dfrac{(b^{3/4})^4}{(b^{4/5})^{-5}}$

99. $\sqrt{b} \cdot \sqrt[4]{b}$

100. $\sqrt[3]{t} \cdot \sqrt[5]{t}$

101. $\sqrt{z} \cdot \sqrt[3]{z^2} \cdot \sqrt[4]{z^3}$

102. $\sqrt{b} \cdot \sqrt[3]{b} \cdot \sqrt[5]{b}$

103. $p^{1/2}(p^{3/2} + p^{1/2})$

104. $d^{3/4}(d^{1/4} - d^{-1/4})$

105. $\sqrt[3]{x}(\sqrt{x} - \sqrt[3]{x^2})$

106. $\frac{1}{2}\sqrt{x}(\sqrt{x} + \sqrt[4]{x^2})$

R.7 Radical Expressions

- Apply the product rule
- Simplify radical expressions
- Apply the quotient rule
- Perform addition, subtraction, and multiplication on radical expressions
- Rationalize the denominator

Product Rule for Radical Expressions

The product of two (like) roots is equal to the root of their product.

PRODUCT RULE FOR RADICAL EXPRESSIONS

Let a and b be real numbers, where $\sqrt[n]{a}$ and $\sqrt[n]{b}$ are both defined. Then

$$\sqrt[n]{a} \cdot \sqrt[n]{b} = \sqrt[n]{a \cdot b}.$$

NOTE The product rule works only when the radicals have the *same* index.

We apply the product rule in the next two examples.

EXAMPLE 1 Multiplying radical expressions

Multiply each pair of radical expressions.

(a) $\sqrt{5} \cdot \sqrt{20}$ **(b)** $\sqrt[3]{-3} \cdot \sqrt[3]{9}$

SOLUTION

(a) $\sqrt{5} \cdot \sqrt{20} = \sqrt{5 \cdot 20} = \sqrt{100} = 10$

(b) $\sqrt[3]{-3} \cdot \sqrt[3]{9} = \sqrt[3]{-3 \cdot 9} = \sqrt[3]{-27} = -3$

Now Try Exercises 3 and 5

EXAMPLE 2 Multiplying radical expressions containing variables

Multiply each pair of radical expressions. Assume that all variables are positive.

(a) $\sqrt{x} \cdot \sqrt{x^3}$ **(b)** $\sqrt[3]{2a} \cdot \sqrt[3]{5a}$ **(c)** $\sqrt[5]{\dfrac{2x}{y}} \cdot \sqrt[5]{\dfrac{16y}{x}}$

SOLUTION

(a) $\sqrt{x} \cdot \sqrt{x^3} = \sqrt{x \cdot x^3} = \sqrt{x^4} = x^2$

(b) $\sqrt[3]{2a} \cdot \sqrt[3]{5a} = \sqrt[3]{2a \cdot 5a} = \sqrt[3]{10a^2}$

(c) $\sqrt[5]{\frac{2x}{y}} \cdot \sqrt[5]{\frac{16y}{x}} = \sqrt[5]{\frac{2x}{y} \cdot \frac{16y}{x}}$ Product rule

$= \sqrt[5]{\frac{32xy}{xy}}$ Multiply fractions.

$= \sqrt[5]{32}$ Simplify.

$= 2$ $2^5 = 32$

Now Try Exercises 27, 33, and 35

Simplifying Radicals An integer a is a **perfect nth power** if there exists an integer b such that $b^n = a$. Thus 36 is a **perfect square** because $6^2 = 36$, 8 is a **perfect cube** because $2^3 = 8$, and 81 is a *perfect fourth power* because $3^4 = 81$.

The product rule for radicals can be used to simplify radical expressions. For example, because the largest perfect square factor of 50 is 25, the expression $\sqrt{50}$ can be simplified as

25 is a perfect square.

$$\sqrt{50} = \sqrt{25 \cdot 2} = \sqrt{25} \cdot \sqrt{2} = 5\sqrt{2}.$$

This procedure is generalized as follows.

SIMPLIFYING RADICALS (nth ROOTS)

STEP 1: Determine the largest perfect nth power factor of the radicand.

STEP 2: Use the product rule to factor out and simplify this perfect nth power.

EXAMPLE 3 **Simplifying radical expressions**

Simplify each expression.

(a) $\sqrt{300}$ **(b)** $\sqrt[3]{16}$ **(c)** $\sqrt[4]{512}$

SOLUTION

(a) First note that $300 = 100 \cdot 3$ and that 100 is the largest perfect square factor of 300.

$$\sqrt{300} = \sqrt{100} \cdot \sqrt{3} = 10\sqrt{3}$$

(b) The largest perfect cube factor of 16 is 8. Thus $\sqrt[3]{16} = \sqrt[3]{8} \cdot \sqrt[3]{2} = 2\sqrt[3]{2}$.

(c) $\sqrt[4]{512} = \sqrt[4]{256} \cdot \sqrt[4]{2} = 4\sqrt[4]{2}$ because $4^4 = 256$.

Now Try Exercises 37, 39, and 41

NOTE To simplify a cube root of a negative number, we usually factor out the negative of the largest perfect cube factor. For example, because $-16 = -8 \cdot 2$, it follows that $\sqrt[3]{-16} = \sqrt[3]{-8} \cdot \sqrt[3]{2} = -2\sqrt[3]{2}$. This procedure can be used with any odd root of a negative number.

EXAMPLE 4 **Simplifying radical expressions**

Simplify each expression. Assume that all variables are positive.

(a) $\sqrt{25x^4}$ **(b)** $\sqrt{32n^3}$ **(c)** $\sqrt[3]{-16x^3y^5}$ **(d)** $\sqrt[3]{2a} \cdot \sqrt[3]{4a^2b}$

SOLUTION

(a) $\sqrt{25x^4} = 5x^2$ $\quad (5x^2)^2 = 25x^4$

(b) $\sqrt{32n^3} = \sqrt{(16n^2)2n}$ $\quad$ $16n^2$ is the largest perfect square factor.

$= \sqrt{16n^2} \cdot \sqrt{2n}$ $\quad$ Product rule

$= 4n\sqrt{2n}$ $\quad (4n)^2 = 16n^2$

(c) $\sqrt[3]{-16x^3y^5} = \sqrt[3]{(-8x^3y^3)2y^2}$ $\quad$ $8x^3y^3$ is the largest perfect cube factor.

$= \sqrt[3]{-8x^3y^3} \cdot \sqrt[3]{2y^2}$ $\quad$ Product rule

$= -2xy\sqrt[3]{2y^2}$ $\quad (-2xy)^3 = -8x^3y^3$

(d) $\sqrt[3]{2a} \cdot \sqrt[3]{4a^2b} = \sqrt[3]{(2a)(4a^2b)}$ $\quad$ Product rule

$= \sqrt[3]{(8a^3)b}$ $\quad$ $8a^3$ is the largest perfect cube factor.

$= \sqrt[3]{8a^3} \cdot \sqrt[3]{b}$ $\quad$ Product rule

$= 2a\sqrt[3]{b}$ $\quad (2a)^3 = 8a^3$

Now Try Exercises 45, 47, 49, and 51

The product rule for radical expressions cannot be used if the radicals do not have the same indexes. In this case we use rational exponents, as illustrated in the next example.

EXAMPLE 5 **Multiplying radicals with different indexes**

Simplify each expression. Write your answer in radical notation.

(a) $\sqrt{2} \cdot \sqrt[3]{4}$ **(b)** $\sqrt[3]{x} \cdot \sqrt[4]{x}$

SOLUTION

(a) First note that $\sqrt[3]{4} = \sqrt[3]{2^2} = 2^{2/3}$. Thus

$$\sqrt{2} \cdot \sqrt[3]{4} = 2^{1/2} \cdot 2^{2/3} = 2^{1/2+2/3} = 2^{7/6}.$$

In radical notation, $2^{7/6} = \sqrt[6]{2^7} = \sqrt[6]{2^6 \cdot 2^1} = \sqrt[6]{2^6} \cdot \sqrt[6]{2} = 2\sqrt[6]{2}$.

(b) $\sqrt[3]{x} \cdot \sqrt[4]{x} = x^{1/3} \cdot x^{1/4} = x^{7/12} = \sqrt[12]{x^7}$

Now Try Exercises 57 and 59

Quotient Rule for Radical Expressions

The root of a quotient is equal to the quotient of the roots.

QUOTIENT RULE FOR RADICAL EXPRESSIONS

Let a and b be real numbers, where $\sqrt[n]{a}$ and $\sqrt[n]{b}$ are both defined and $b \neq 0$. Then

$$\sqrt[n]{\frac{a}{b}} = \frac{\sqrt[n]{a}}{\sqrt[n]{b}}.$$

EXAMPLE 6 **Simplifying quotients**

Simplify each radical expression. Assume that all variables are positive.

(a) $\sqrt[3]{\frac{5}{8}}$ **(b)** $\sqrt{\frac{16}{y^2}}$

SOLUTION

(a) $\sqrt[3]{\frac{5}{8}} = \frac{\sqrt[3]{5}}{\sqrt[3]{8}} = \frac{\sqrt[3]{5}}{2}$ $\quad$ Quotient rule

(b) $\sqrt{\frac{16}{y^2}} = \frac{\sqrt{16}}{\sqrt{y^2}} = \frac{4}{y}$ because $y > 0$.

Now Try Exercises 7 and 21

EXAMPLE 7 Simplifying radical expressions

Simplify each radical expression. Assume that all variables are positive.

(a) $\dfrac{\sqrt{40}}{\sqrt{10}}$ **(b)** $\sqrt[4]{\dfrac{16x^3}{y^4}}$ **(c)** $\sqrt{\dfrac{5a^2}{8}} \cdot \sqrt{\dfrac{5a^3}{2}}$

SOLUTION

(a) $\dfrac{\sqrt{40}}{\sqrt{10}} = \sqrt{\dfrac{40}{10}} = \sqrt{4} = 2$

(b) $\sqrt[4]{\dfrac{16x^3}{y^4}} = \dfrac{\sqrt[4]{16x^3}}{\sqrt[4]{y^4}} = \dfrac{\sqrt[4]{16} \cdot \sqrt[4]{x^3}}{\sqrt[4]{y^4}} = \dfrac{2\sqrt[4]{x^3}}{y}$

(c) To simplify this expression, we use both the product and quotient rules.

$$\sqrt{\frac{5a^2}{8}} \cdot \sqrt{\frac{5a^3}{2}} = \sqrt{\frac{25a^5}{16}} \qquad \text{Product rule}$$

$$= \frac{\sqrt{25a^5}}{\sqrt{16}} \qquad \text{Quotient rule}$$

$$= \frac{\sqrt{25a^4} \cdot \sqrt{a}}{\sqrt{16}} \qquad \text{Factor out largest perfect square.}$$

$$= \frac{5a^2\sqrt{a}}{4} \qquad (5a^2)^2 = 25a^4$$

Now Try Exercises 13, 19, and 53

Addition and Subtraction

We can add $2x^2$ and $5x^2$ to obtain $7x^2$ because they are *like* terms. That is,

$$2x^2 + 5x^2 = (2 + 5)x^2 = 7x^2.$$

We can add and subtract **like radicals**, which have the same index and the same radicand. For example, we can add $3\sqrt{2}$ and $5\sqrt{2}$ because they are like radicals.

$$3\sqrt{2} + 5\sqrt{2} = (3 + 5)\sqrt{2} = 8\sqrt{2}$$

Sometimes two radical expressions that are not alike can be added by changing them to like radicals. For example, $\sqrt{20}$ and $\sqrt{5}$ are unlike radicals. However,

$$\sqrt{20} = \sqrt{4 \cdot 5} = \sqrt{4} \cdot \sqrt{5} = 2\sqrt{5},$$

so it follows that

$$\sqrt{20} + \sqrt{5} = 2\sqrt{5} + \sqrt{5} = 3\sqrt{5}.$$

Write $\sqrt{20}$ as a multiple of $\sqrt{5}$.

We cannot combine $x + x^2$ because they are unlike terms. Similarly, we cannot combine $\sqrt{2} + \sqrt{5}$ because they are unlike radicals.

EXAMPLE 8 Adding radical expressions

Add the expressions and simplify.

(a) $10\sqrt{11} + 4\sqrt{11}$ **(b)** $5\sqrt[3]{6} + \sqrt[3]{6}$ **(c)** $\sqrt{12} + 7\sqrt{3}$

SOLUTION

(a) $10\sqrt{11} + 4\sqrt{11} = (10 + 4)\sqrt{11} = 14\sqrt{11}$

(b) $5\sqrt[3]{6} + \sqrt[3]{6} = (5 + 1)\sqrt[3]{6} = 6\sqrt[3]{6}$

(c) $\sqrt{12} + 7\sqrt{3} = \sqrt{4 \cdot 3} + 7\sqrt{3}$

$$= \sqrt{4} \cdot \sqrt{3} + 7\sqrt{3}$$

$$= 2\sqrt{3} + 7\sqrt{3}$$

$$= 9\sqrt{3}$$

Now Try Exercises 63, 67, and 69

EXAMPLE 9 Adding radical expressions

Add the expressions and simplify. Assume that all variables are positive.

(a) $-2\sqrt{4x} + \sqrt{x}$ **(b)** $3\sqrt{3k} + 5\sqrt{12k} + 9\sqrt{48k}$

SOLUTION

(a) Note that $\sqrt{4x} = \sqrt{4} \cdot \sqrt{x} = 2\sqrt{x}$.

$$-2\sqrt{4x} + \sqrt{x} = -2(2\sqrt{x}) + \sqrt{x} = -4\sqrt{x} + \sqrt{x} = -3\sqrt{x}$$

(b) Note that $\sqrt{12k} = \sqrt{4} \cdot \sqrt{3k} = 2\sqrt{3k}$ and that $\sqrt{48k} = \sqrt{16} \cdot \sqrt{3k} = 4\sqrt{3k}$.

$$\begin{aligned} 3\sqrt{3k} + 5\sqrt{12k} + 9\sqrt{48k} &= 3\sqrt{3k} + 5(2\sqrt{3k}) + 9(4\sqrt{3k}) \\ &= (3 + 10 + 36)\sqrt{3k} \\ &= 49\sqrt{3k} \end{aligned}$$

Now Try Exercises 77 and 83

Subtraction of radical expressions is similar to addition of radical expressions, as illustrated in the next example.

EXAMPLE 10 Subtracting radical expressions

Subtract and simplify. Assume that all variables are positive.

(a) $3\sqrt[3]{xy^2} - 2\sqrt[3]{xy^2}$ **(b)** $\sqrt{16x^3} - \sqrt{x^3}$

SOLUTION

(a) $3\sqrt[3]{xy^2} - 2\sqrt[3]{xy^2} = (3 - 2)\sqrt[3]{xy^2} = \sqrt[3]{xy^2}$

(b)

$$\begin{aligned} \sqrt{16x^3} - \sqrt{x^3} &= \sqrt{16} \cdot \sqrt{x^3} - \sqrt{x^3} \\ &= 4\sqrt{x^3} - \sqrt{x^3} \\ &= 3\sqrt{x^3} \\ &= 3x\sqrt{x} \end{aligned}$$

Now Try Exercises 75 and 81

Multiplication

Some types of radical expressions can be multiplied like binomials. The next example demonstrates this technique.

EXAMPLE 11 Multiplying radical expressions

Multiply and simplify.

(a) $(\sqrt{b} - 4)(\sqrt{b} + 5)$ **(b)** $(4 + \sqrt{3})(4 - \sqrt{3})$

SOLUTION

(a) This expression can be multiplied and then simplified.

$$\begin{aligned} (\sqrt{b} - 4)(\sqrt{b} + 5) &= \sqrt{b} \cdot \sqrt{b} + 5\sqrt{b} - 4\sqrt{b} - 4 \cdot 5 \\ &= b + \sqrt{b} - 20 \end{aligned}$$

(Compare this product to $(b - 4)(b + 5) = b^2 + b - 20$.)

(b) This expression is in the form $(a + b)(a - b)$, which equals $a^2 - b^2$.

$$\begin{aligned} (4 + \sqrt{3})(4 - \sqrt{3}) &= (4)^2 - (\sqrt{3})^2 \\ &= 16 - 3 \\ &= 13 \end{aligned}$$

Now Try Exercises 89 and 95

Rationalizing the Denominator

Quotients containing radical expressions can appear to be different but actually be equal. For example, $\frac{1}{\sqrt{3}}$ and $\frac{\sqrt{3}}{3}$ represent the same real number even though they do not look equal. To show this fact, we multiply the first quotient by 1 in the form $\frac{\sqrt{3}}{\sqrt{3}}$.

$$\frac{1}{\sqrt{3}} \cdot \frac{\sqrt{3}}{\sqrt{3}} = \frac{1 \cdot \sqrt{3}}{\sqrt{3} \cdot \sqrt{3}} = \frac{\sqrt{3}}{3}$$

NOTE $\sqrt{b} \cdot \sqrt{b} = \sqrt{b^2} = b$ for any *positive* number b.

One way to standardize radical expressions is to remove any radical expressions from the denominator. This process is called **rationalizing the denominator**. The next example demonstrates how to rationalize the denominator of two quotients.

EXAMPLE 12 **Rationalizing the denominator**

Rationalize each denominator. Assume that all variables are positive.

(a) $\frac{3}{5\sqrt{3}}$ **(b)** $\sqrt{\frac{x}{24}}$

SOLUTION

(a) We multiply this expression by 1 in the form $\frac{\sqrt{3}}{\sqrt{3}}$.

$$\frac{3}{5\sqrt{3}} \cdot \frac{\sqrt{3}}{\sqrt{3}} = \frac{3\sqrt{3}}{5\sqrt{9}} = \frac{3\sqrt{3}}{5 \cdot 3} = \frac{\sqrt{3}}{5}$$

(b) Because $\sqrt{24} = \sqrt{4} \cdot \sqrt{6} = 2\sqrt{6}$, we start by simplifying the expression.

$$\sqrt{\frac{x}{24}} = \frac{\sqrt{x}}{\sqrt{24}} = \frac{\sqrt{x}}{2\sqrt{6}}$$

To rationalize the denominator, we multiply this expression by 1 in the form $\frac{\sqrt{6}}{\sqrt{6}}$.

$$\frac{\sqrt{x}}{2\sqrt{6}} = \frac{\sqrt{x}}{2\sqrt{6}} \cdot \frac{\sqrt{6}}{\sqrt{6}} = \frac{\sqrt{6x}}{12}$$

Now Try Exercises 99 and 101

If the denominator consists of two terms, at least one of which contains a radical expression, then the **conjugate** of the denominator is found by changing a + sign to a − sign or vice versa. For example, the conjugate of $\sqrt{2} + \sqrt{3}$ is $\sqrt{2} - \sqrt{3}$, and the conjugate of $\sqrt{3} - 1$ is $\sqrt{3} + 1$. In the next example, we multiply the numerator and denominator by the conjugate of the *denominator* to rationalize the denominator of fractions that contain radicals.

EXAMPLE 13 **Rationalizing the denominator**

Rationalize the denominator. Assume that all variables are positive.

(a) $\frac{3 + \sqrt{5}}{2 - \sqrt{5}}$ **(b)** $\frac{\sqrt{x}}{\sqrt{x} - 2}$

SOLUTION

(a) The conjugate of the denominator $2 - \sqrt{5}$ is $2 + \sqrt{5}$.

$$\frac{3 + \sqrt{5}}{2 - \sqrt{5}} = \frac{(3 + \sqrt{5})}{(2 - \sqrt{5})} \cdot \frac{(2 + \sqrt{5})}{(2 + \sqrt{5})} \quad \text{Multiply by } \frac{\text{conjugate}}{\text{conjugate}}.$$

$$= \frac{6 + 3\sqrt{5} + 2\sqrt{5} + (\sqrt{5})^2}{(2)^2 - (\sqrt{5})^2} \quad \text{Multiply.}$$

$$= \frac{11 + 5\sqrt{5}}{4 - 5} \quad \text{Combine terms.}$$

$$= -11 - 5\sqrt{5} \quad \text{Simplify.}$$

(b) The conjugate of the denominator $\sqrt{x} - 2$ is $\sqrt{x} + 2$.

$$\frac{\sqrt{x}}{\sqrt{x}-2} = \frac{\sqrt{x}}{(\sqrt{x}-2)} \cdot \frac{(\sqrt{x}+2)}{(\sqrt{x}+2)} \quad \text{Multiply by } \frac{\text{conjugate}}{\text{conjugate}}.$$

$$= \frac{x + 2\sqrt{x}}{x - 4} \quad \text{Multiply.}$$

Now Try Exercises 103 and 109

R.7 Exercises

Multiplying and Dividing

Exercises 1–36: Simplify the expression. Assume that all variables are positive.

1. $\sqrt{3} \cdot \sqrt{3}$
2. $\sqrt{2} \cdot \sqrt{18}$
3. $\sqrt{2} \cdot \sqrt{50}$
4. $\sqrt[3]{-2} \cdot \sqrt[3]{-4}$
5. $\sqrt[3]{4} \cdot \sqrt[3]{16}$
6. $\sqrt[3]{x} \cdot \sqrt[3]{x^2}$
7. $\sqrt{\frac{9}{25}}$
8. $\sqrt[3]{\frac{x}{8}}$
9. $\sqrt{\frac{1}{2}} \cdot \sqrt{\frac{1}{8}}$
10. $\sqrt{\frac{5}{3}} \cdot \sqrt{\frac{1}{3}}$
11. $\sqrt{\frac{x}{2}} \cdot \sqrt{\frac{x}{8}}$
12. $\sqrt{\frac{4}{y}} \cdot \sqrt{\frac{y}{5}}$
13. $\frac{\sqrt{45}}{\sqrt{5}}$
14. $\frac{\sqrt{7}}{\sqrt{28}}$
15. $\sqrt[4]{9} \cdot \sqrt[4]{9}$
16. $\sqrt[5]{16} \cdot \sqrt[5]{-2}$
17. $\frac{\sqrt[5]{64}}{\sqrt[5]{-2}}$
18. $\frac{\sqrt[4]{324}}{\sqrt[4]{4}}$
19. $\sqrt{\frac{36}{z^4}}$
20. $\frac{\sqrt{4xy^2}}{\sqrt{x}}$
21. $\sqrt[3]{\frac{x^3}{8}}$
22. $\frac{\sqrt{a^2b}}{\sqrt{b}}$
23. $\sqrt{4x^4}$
24. $\sqrt[3]{-8y^3}$
25. $\sqrt[4]{16x^4y}$
26. $\sqrt[3]{8xy^3}$
27. $\sqrt{3x} \cdot \sqrt{12x}$
28. $\sqrt{6x^5} \cdot \sqrt{6x}$
29. $\sqrt[3]{8x^6y^3z^9}$
30. $\sqrt{16x^4y^6}$
31. $\sqrt[4]{\frac{3}{4}} \cdot \sqrt[4]{\frac{27}{4}}$
32. $\sqrt[5]{\frac{4}{-9}} \cdot \sqrt[5]{\frac{8}{-27}}$
33. $\sqrt[4]{25z} \cdot \sqrt[4]{25z}$
34. $\sqrt[5]{3z^2} \cdot \sqrt[5]{7z}$
35. $\sqrt[5]{\frac{7a}{b^2}} \cdot \sqrt[5]{\frac{b^2}{7a^6}}$
36. $\sqrt[3]{\frac{8m}{n}} \cdot \sqrt[3]{\frac{n^4}{m^2}}$

Exercises 37–54: Simplify the radical expression by factoring out the largest perfect nth power. Assume that all variables are positive.

37. $\sqrt{200}$
38. $\sqrt{72}$
39. $\sqrt[3]{81}$
40. $\sqrt[3]{256}$
41. $\sqrt[4]{64}$
42. $\sqrt[5]{27 \cdot 81}$
43. $\sqrt[5]{-64}$
44. $\sqrt[3]{-81}$
45. $\sqrt{8n^3}$
46. $\sqrt{32a^2}$
47. $\sqrt{12a^2b^5}$
48. $\sqrt{20a^3b^2}$
49. $\sqrt[3]{-125x^4y^5}$
50. $\sqrt[3]{-81a^5b^2}$
51. $\sqrt[3]{5t} \cdot \sqrt[3]{125t}$
52. $\sqrt[4]{4bc^3} \cdot \sqrt[4]{64ab^3c^2}$
53. $\sqrt[4]{\frac{9t^5}{r^8}} \cdot \sqrt[4]{\frac{9r}{5t}}$
54. $\sqrt[5]{\frac{4t^6}{r}} \cdot \sqrt[5]{\frac{8t}{r^6}}$

Exercises 55–62: Simplify the expression. Assume that all variables are positive and write your answer in radical notation.

55. $\sqrt{3} \cdot \sqrt[3]{3}$
56. $\sqrt{5} \cdot \sqrt[3]{5}$
57. $\sqrt[4]{8} \cdot \sqrt[3]{4}$
58. $\sqrt[5]{16} \cdot \sqrt{2}$
59. $\sqrt[4]{x^3} \cdot \sqrt[3]{x}$
60. $\sqrt[4]{x^3} \cdot \sqrt{x}$
61. $\sqrt[4]{rt} \cdot \sqrt[3]{r^2t}$
62. $\sqrt[3]{a^3b^2} \cdot \sqrt{a^2b}$

Exercises 63–88: Simplify the expression. Assume that all variables are positive.

63. $2\sqrt{3} + 7\sqrt{3}$
64. $8\sqrt{7} + 2\sqrt{7}$
65. $\sqrt{x} + \sqrt{x} - \sqrt{y}$
66. $\sqrt{xy^2} - \sqrt{x}$
67. $2\sqrt[3]{6} + 7\sqrt[3]{6}$
68. $18\sqrt[3]{3} + 3\sqrt[3]{3}$

69. $3\sqrt{28} + 3\sqrt{7}$

70. $9\sqrt{18} - 2\sqrt{8}$

71. $\sqrt{44} - 4\sqrt{11}$

72. $\sqrt[4]{5} + 2\sqrt[4]{5}$

73. $2\sqrt[3]{16} + \sqrt[3]{2} - \sqrt{2}$

74. $5\sqrt[3]{x} - 3\sqrt[3]{x}$

75. $\sqrt[3]{xy} - 2\sqrt[3]{xy}$

76. $3\sqrt{x^3} - \sqrt{x}$

77. $\sqrt{4x + 8} + \sqrt{x + 2}$

78. $\sqrt{2a + 1} + \sqrt{8a + 4}$

79. $\dfrac{15\sqrt{8}}{4} - \dfrac{2\sqrt{2}}{5}$

80. $\dfrac{23\sqrt{11}}{2} - \dfrac{\sqrt{44}}{8}$

81. $20\sqrt[3]{b^4} - 4\sqrt[3]{b}$

82. $2\sqrt[4]{64} - \sqrt[4]{324} + \sqrt[4]{4}$

83. $2\sqrt{3z} + 3\sqrt{12z} + 3\sqrt{48z}$

84. $\sqrt{64x^3} - \sqrt{x} + 3\sqrt{x}$

85. $\sqrt[4]{81a^5b^5} - \sqrt[4]{ab}$

86. $\sqrt[4]{xy^5} + \sqrt[4]{x^5y}$

87. $5\sqrt[3]{\dfrac{n^4}{125}} - 2\sqrt[3]{n}$

88. $\sqrt[3]{\dfrac{8x}{27}} - \dfrac{2\sqrt[3]{x}}{3}$

Exercises 89–96: Multiply and simplify.

89. $(3 + \sqrt{7})(3 - \sqrt{7})$

90. $(5 - \sqrt{5})(5 + \sqrt{5})$

91. $(\sqrt{x} + 8)(\sqrt{x} - 8)$

92. $(\sqrt{ab} - 3)(\sqrt{ab} + 3)$

93. $(\sqrt{ab} - \sqrt{c})(\sqrt{ab} + \sqrt{c})$

94. $(\sqrt{2x} + \sqrt{3y})(\sqrt{2x} - \sqrt{3y})$

95. $(\sqrt{x} - 7)(\sqrt{x} + 8)$

96. $(\sqrt{ab} - 1)(\sqrt{ab} - 2)$

Exercises 97–112: Rationalize the denominator.

97. $\dfrac{4}{\sqrt{3}}$

98. $\dfrac{8}{\sqrt{2}}$

99. $\dfrac{5}{3\sqrt{5}}$

100. $\dfrac{6}{11\sqrt{3}}$

101. $\sqrt{\dfrac{b}{12}}$

102. $\sqrt{\dfrac{5b}{72}}$

103. $\dfrac{1}{3 - \sqrt{2}}$

104. $\dfrac{1}{\sqrt{3} - 2}$

105. $\dfrac{\sqrt{2}}{\sqrt{5} + 2}$

106. $\dfrac{\sqrt{3} - 1}{\sqrt{3} + 1}$

107. $\dfrac{1}{\sqrt{7} - \sqrt{6}}$

108. $\dfrac{1}{\sqrt{8} - \sqrt{7}}$

109. $\dfrac{\sqrt{z}}{\sqrt{z} - 3}$

110. $\dfrac{2\sqrt{z}}{2 - \sqrt{z}}$

111. $\dfrac{\sqrt{a} + \sqrt{b}}{\sqrt{a} - \sqrt{b}}$

112. $\dfrac{1}{\sqrt{a + 1} + \sqrt{a}}$

Appendix A: Using the Graphing Calculator

Overview of the Appendix

The intent of this appendix is to provide instruction in the TI-83, TI-83 Plus, and TI-84 Plus graphing calculators that may be used in conjunction with this textbook. It includes specific keystrokes needed to work several examples from the text. Students are also advised to consult the *Graphing Calculator Guidebook* provided by the manufacturer.

The following is a listing of the topics covered in this appendix.

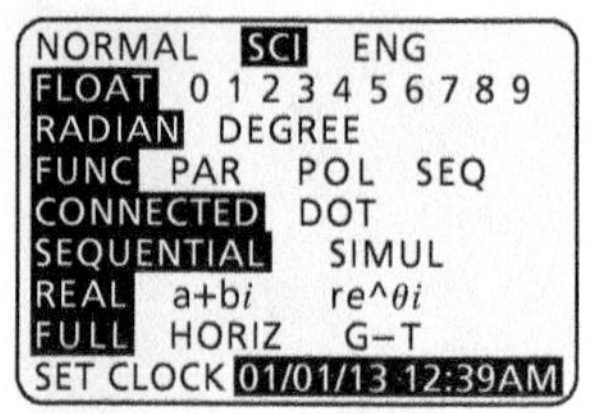

Figure A.1

Displaying Numbers in Scientific Notation

To display numbers in scientific notation when the calculator is in normal mode, set the graphing calculator in scientific mode (SCI) by using the following keystrokes. See Figure A.1.

(MODE) (▷) (ENTER) (2nd) (MODE [QUIT])

Figure A.2 shows the numbers 5432 and 0.00001234 displayed in scientific notation.

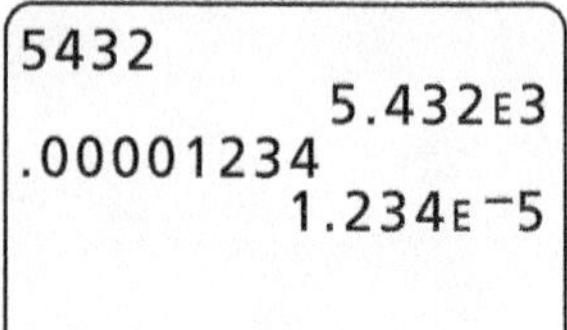

Figure A.2

SUMMARY: SETTING SCIENTIFIC MODE

If your calculator is in normal mode, it can be set in scientific mode by pressing

(MODE) (▷) (ENTER) (2nd) (MODE [QUIT])

These keystrokes return the graphing calculator to the home screen.

Entering Numbers in Scientific Notation

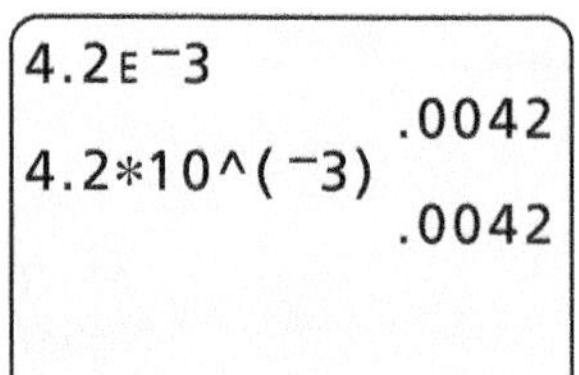

Figure A.3 Normal Mode

Numbers can be entered in scientific notation. For example, to enter 4.2×10^{-3} in scientific notation, use the following keystrokes. (Be sure to use the negation key (−) rather than the subtraction key.)

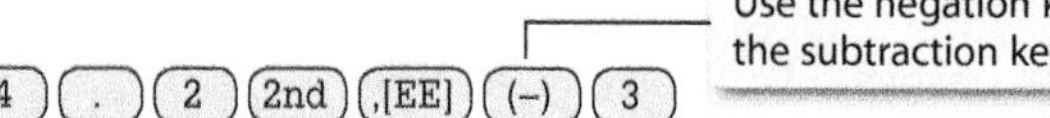

This number can also be entered using the following keystrokes. See Figure A.3.

SUMMARY: ENTERING NUMBERS IN SCIENTIFIC NOTATION

One way to enter a number in scientific notation is to use the keystrokes

(2nd) (,[EE])

to access an exponent (EE) of 10.

Entering Mathematical Expressions

Several expressions are evaluated in Example 7, Section 1.1. To evaluate $\sqrt[3]{131}$, use the following keystrokes from the home screen.

(MATH) (4) (1) (3) (1) ()) (ENTER)

To calculate $\pi^3 + 1.2^2$, use the following keystrokes. (Do *not* use 3.14 for π.)

(2nd) (^[π]) (^) (3) (+) (1) (.) (2) (x^2) (ENTER)

To calculate $|\sqrt{3} - 6|$, use the following keystrokes.

(MATH) (▷) (1) (2nd) (x^2[√]) (3) ()) (−) (6) ()) (ENTER)

SUMMARY: ENTERING COMMON MATHEMATICAL EXPRESSIONS

To calculate a cube root, use the keystrokes (MATH) (4).

To access the number π, use the keystrokes (2nd) (^[π]).

To access the absolute value, use the keystrokes (MATH) (▷) (1).

To access the square root, use the keystrokes (2nd) (x^2[√]).

Setting the Viewing Rectangle

In Example 12, Section 1.2, there are at least two ways to set the standard viewing rectangle to [−10, 10, 1] by [−10, 10, 1]. The first method involves pressing (ZOOM) followed by (6). (See Figure A.4.) The second method is to press (WINDOW) and enter the following keystrokes. (See Figure A.5.)

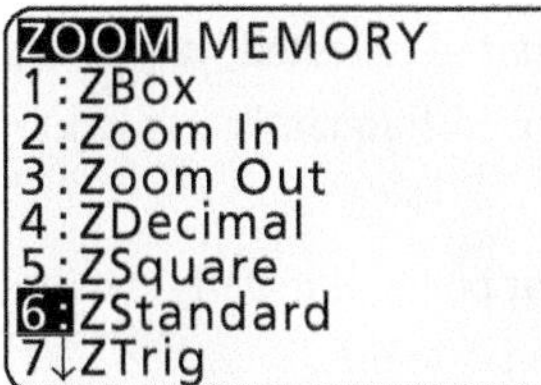

Figure A.4

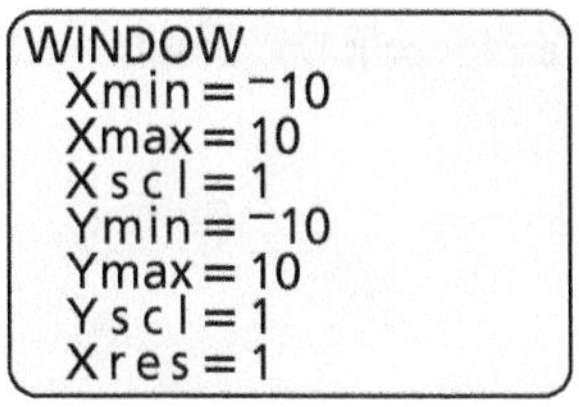

WINDOW
Xmin = −10
Xmax = 10
Xscl = 1
Ymin = −10
Ymax = 10
Yscl = 1
Xres = 1

Figure A.5

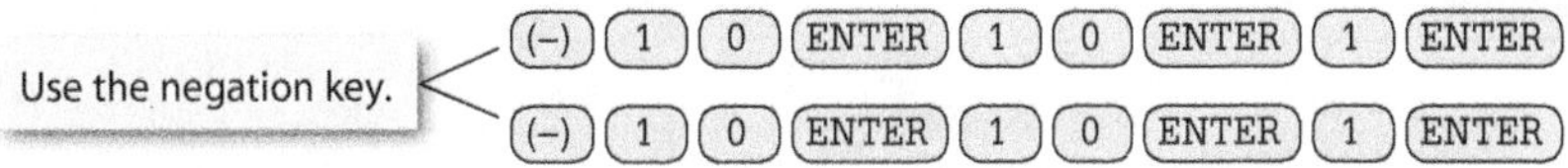

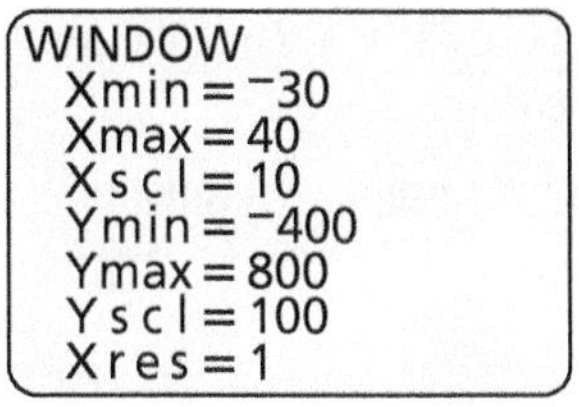

(Be sure to use the negation key (−) rather than the subtraction key.) The viewing rectangle [−30, 40, 10] by [−400, 800, 100] can be set in a similar manner, as shown in Figure A.6. To see the viewing rectangle, press (GRAPH).

WINDOW
Xmin = −30
Xmax = 40
Xscl = 10
Ymin = −400
Ymax = 800
Yscl = 100
Xres = 1

Figure A.6

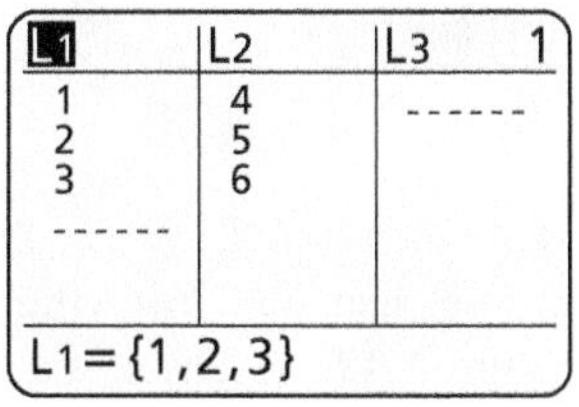

SUMMARY: SETTING THE VIEWING RECTANGLE

To set the standard viewing rectangle, press (ZOOM) (6). To set any viewing rectangle, press (WINDOW) and enter the necessary values. To see the viewing rectangle, press (GRAPH).

Note: You do not need to change "Xres".

Making a Scatterplot or a Line Graph

In Example 13, Section 1.2, we are asked to make a scatterplot with (−5, −5), (−2, 3), (1, −7), and (4, 8). Begin this task by following these steps.

1. Press (STAT) followed by (1).
2. If list L1 is not empty, use the arrow keys to place the cursor on L1, as shown in Figure A.7. Then press (CLEAR) followed by (ENTER). This deletes all elements in the list. Similarly, if L2 is not empty, clear the list.
3. Input each x-value into list L1, followed by (ENTER). Input each y-value into list L2, followed by (ENTER). See Figure A.8.

L1	L2	L3 1
1	4	------
2	5	
3	6	

L1 = {1,2,3}

Figure A.7

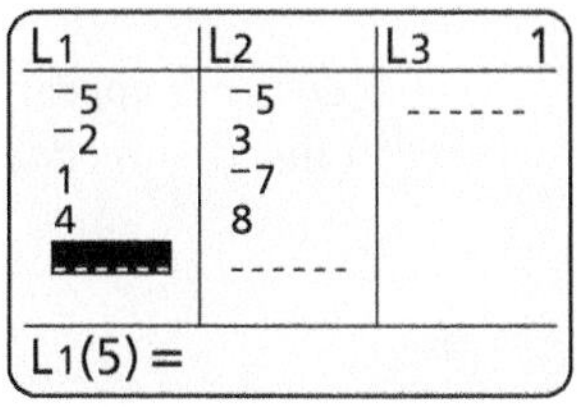

L1	L2	L3 1
−5	−5	------
−2	3	
1	−7	
4	8	
------	------	

L1(5) =

Figure A.8

It is essential that both lists have the same number of values—otherwise an error message will appear when a scatterplot is attempted. Before these four points can be plotted, STATPLOT must be turned on. It is accessed by pressing

(2nd) (Y=[STAT PLOT])

as shown in Figure A.9.

There are three possible STATPLOTS, numbered 1, 2, and 3. Any one of the three can be selected. The first plot is selected by pressing (1). Next, place the cursor over "On" and press (ENTER) to turn Plot1 on. There are six types of plots that can be selected. The first type is a *scatterplot* and the second type is a *line graph*, so place the cursor over the first type of plot and press (ENTER) to select a scatterplot. (To make the line graph in Example 14, Section 1.2, be sure to select the line graph.) The x-values are stored in list L1, so select L1 for "Xlist" by pressing (2nd) (1). Similarly, press (2nd) (2) for "Ylist," since the y-values are stored in list L2. Finally, there are three styles of marks that can be used to show data points in the graph. We usually use the first, because it is largest and shows up the best. Make the screen appear as in Figure A.10. Before plotting the four data points, be sure to set an appropriate viewing rectangle. Then press (GRAPH). The data points will appear as in Figure A.11 on the next page.

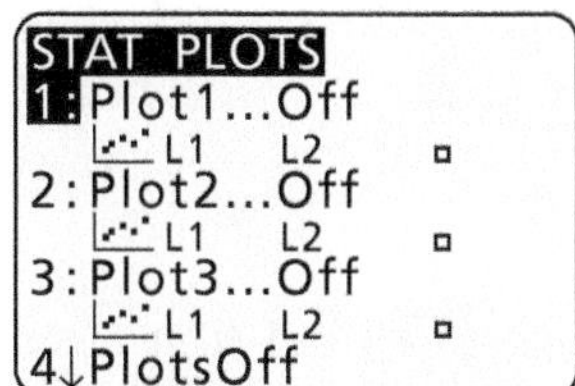

Figure A.9

Figure A.10

NOTE 1 A fast way to set the viewing rectangle for any scatterplot is to select the ZOOMSTAT feature by pressing (ZOOM) (9). This feature automatically scales the viewing rectangle so that all data points are shown.

[−10, 10, 1] by [−10, 10, 1]

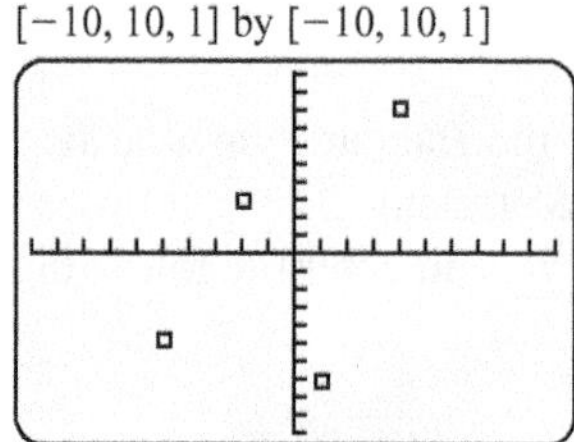

Figure A.11

NOTE 2 If an equation has been entered into the Y= menu and selected, it will be graphed with the data. Throughout this textbook, this feature is used frequently in modeling data.

NOTE 3 When the error message "ERR: DIM MISMATCH" appears, it usually means that there are not equal numbers of x-values and y-values in lists L1 and L2.

SUMMARY: MAKING A SCATTERPLOT OR A LINE GRAPH

The following are basic steps necessary to make either a scatterplot or a line graph.

STEP 1: Use STAT 1 to access lists L1 and L2.

STEP 2: If list L1 is not empty, place the cursor on L1 and press CLEAR ENTER. Repeat for list L2 if it is not empty.

STEP 3: Enter the x-values into list L1 and the y-values into list L2.

STEP 4: Use 2nd Y = [STAT PLOT] to set the appropriate parameters for the scatterplot or line graph.

STEP 5: Either set an appropriate viewing rectangle or press ZOOM 9. This feature automatically sets the viewing rectangle and plots the data.

Note: ZOOM 9 *cannot* be used to set a viewing rectangle for the graph of a function.

Deleting and Inserting a List A list, such as L2, can be deleted. Press STAT 1 and then place the cursor on L2 and press DEL. If you want to insert a deleted list, press STAT 1 and then place the cursor where you want to insert the list. For example, to insert L2, place the cursor on L3. Press 2nd DEL [INS] 2nd 2[L2] ENTER.

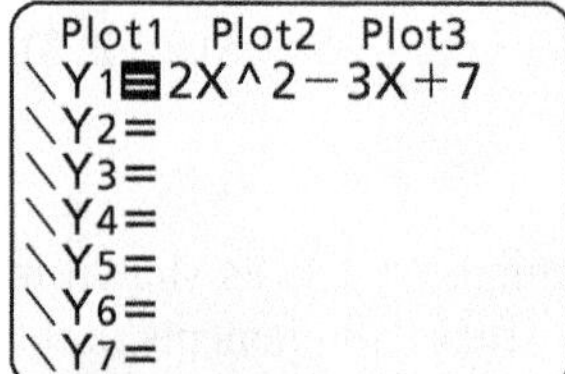

Figure A.12

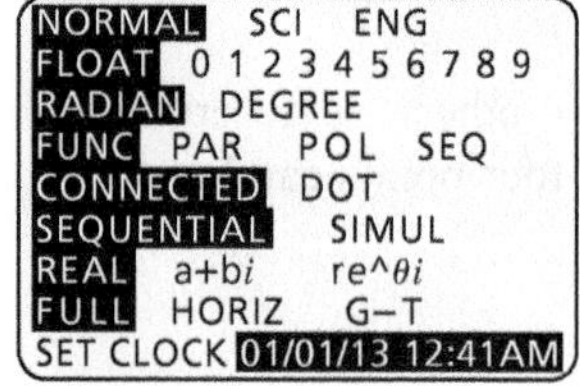

Figure A.13

Entering a Formula for a Function

To enter the formula for a function f, press Y=. For example, use the following keystrokes after "Y_1 = " to enter $f(x) = 2x^2 - 3x + 7$. See Figure A.12.

Y= CLEAR 2 X,T,θ,n ^ 2 − 3 X,T,θ,n + 7

Note that there is a built-in key for entering the variable X. If "Y_1 = " does not appear after you press Y=, press MODE and make sure the calculator is set in function mode, denoted "Func". See Figure A.13.

SUMMARY: ENTERING A FORMULA FOR A FUNCTION

To enter the formula for a function, press Y=. To delete an existing formula, press CLEAR. Then enter the symbolic representation for the function.

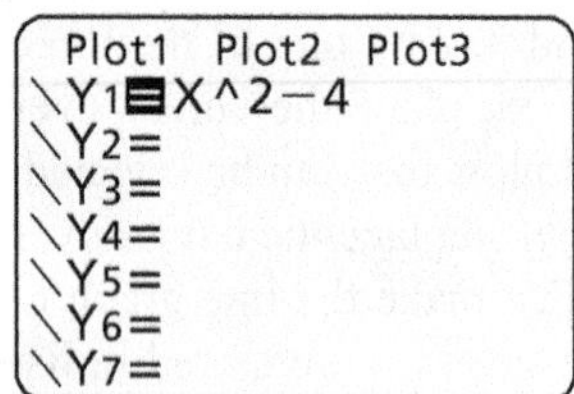

Figure A.14

[−10, 10, 1] by [−10, 10, 1]

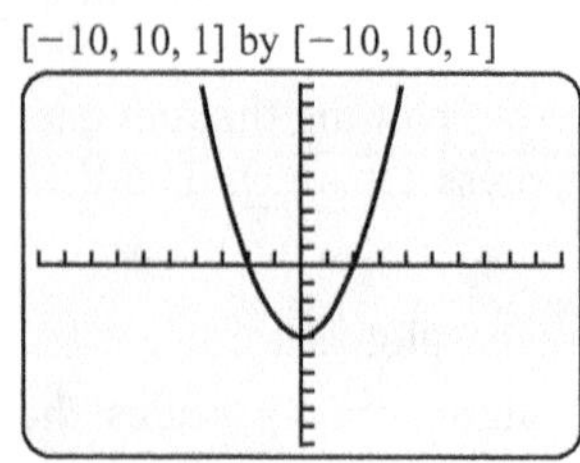

Figure A.15

Graphing a Function

To graph a function such as $f(x) = x^2 - 4$, start by pressing Y= and then enter Y_1 = X^2 − 4. If there is an equation already entered, remove it by pressing CLEAR. The equals sign in "Y_1 = " should be in reverse video (a dark rectangle surrounding a white equals sign), which indicates that the equation will be graphed. If the equals sign is not in reverse video, place the cursor over it and press ENTER. Set an appropriate viewing rectangle and then press GRAPH. The graph of f will appear in the specified viewing rectangle. See Figures A.14 and A.15.

NOTE If the error message "ERR: DIM MISMATCH" appears when you try to graph a function, check to see if one of the STATPLOTS is turned on. If it is, turn it off and then try graphing the function.

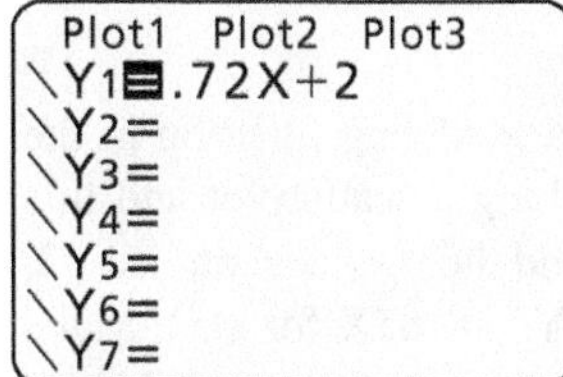

Plot1 Plot2 Plot3
\Y1■.72X+2
\Y2=
\Y3=
\Y4=
\Y5=
\Y6=
\Y7=
Figure A.16

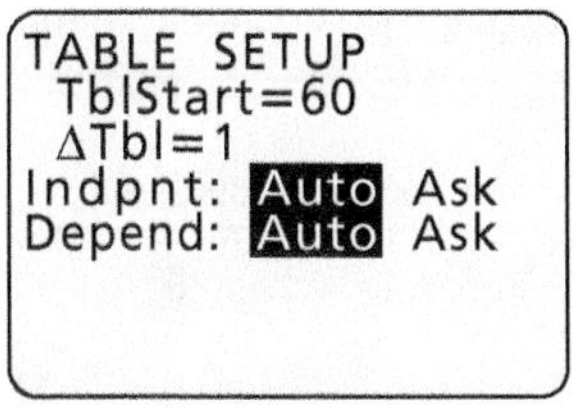

TABLE SETUP
TblStart=60
ΔTbl=1
Indpnt: Auto Ask
Depend: Auto Ask
Figure A.17

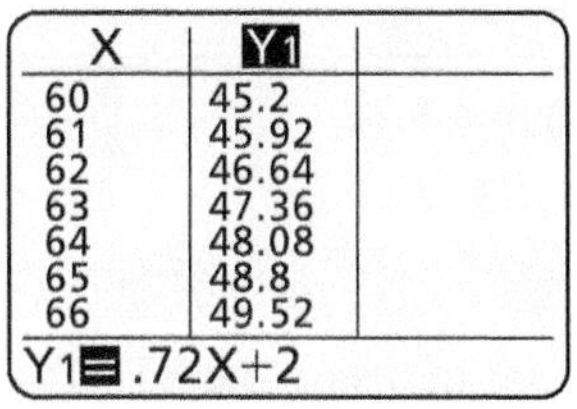

X
Y1
60 45.2
61 45.92
62 46.64
63 47.36
64 48.08
65 48.8
66 49.52
Y1■.72X+2
Figure A.18

SUMMARY: GRAPHING A FUNCTION

Use the Y= menu to enter the formula for the function and the WINDOW menu to set an appropriate viewing rectangle. Then press GRAPH.

ZoomFit The ZoomFit feature can be used to find an appropriate window when graphing a function. ZoomFit leaves the current Xmin and Xmax settings unchanged and adjusts the current Ymin and Ymax values so that they are equal to the smallest and largest y-values on the graph of the function between Xmin and Xmax. To use ZoomFit, press ZOOM 0.

Making a Table

To make a table of values for a function, such as $f(x) = 0.72x + 2$, start by pressing Y= and then entering the formula $Y_1 = .72X + 2$, as shown in Figure A.16. To set the table parameters, use the following keystrokes. (See Figure A.17.)

2nd WINDOW [TBLSET] 6 0 ENTER 1

These keystrokes specify a table that starts at $x = 60$ and increments the x-values by 1. Therefore the values of Y_1 at $x = 60, 61, 62, \ldots$ appear in the table. To create this table, press the following keys.

2nd GRAPH [TABLE]

One can scroll through x- and y-values by using the arrow keys. See Figure A.18. Note that there is no first or last x-value in the table.

SUMMARY: MAKING A TABLE OF A FUNCTION

Enter the formula for the function using Y=. Then press

2nd WINDOW [TBLSET]

to set the starting x-value and the increment between x-values appearing in the table. Create the table by pressing

2nd GRAPH [TABLE].

Squaring a Viewing Rectangle

In a square viewing rectangle, the graph of $y = x$ is a line that makes a 45° angle with the positive x-axis, a circle appears circular, and all sides of a square have the same length. An approximately square viewing rectangle can be set if the distance along the x-axis is 1.5 times the distance along the y-axis. Examples of viewing rectangles that are (approximately) square include

$$[-6, 6, 1] \text{ by } [-4, 4, 1] \quad \text{and} \quad [-9, 9, 1] \text{ by } [-6, 6, 1].$$

Square viewing rectangles can be set automatically by pressing either

ZOOM 4 or ZOOM 5.

ZOOM 4 provides a decimal window, which is discussed later. See Figure A.19.

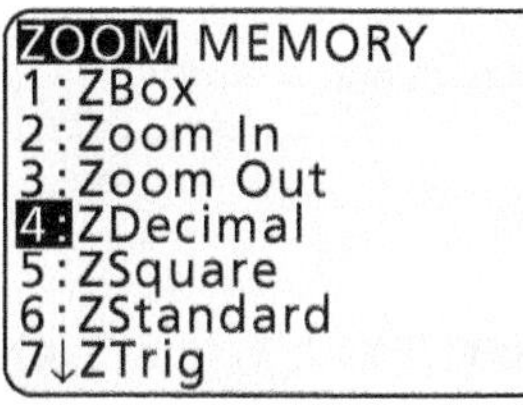

ZOOM MEMORY
1:ZBox
2:Zoom In
3:Zoom Out
4:ZDecimal
5:ZSquare
6:ZStandard
7↓ZTrig
Figure A.19

SUMMARY: SQUARING A VIEWING RECTANGLE

Either ZOOM 4 or ZOOM 5 may be used to produce a square viewing rectangle. An (approximately) square viewing rectangle has the form

$$[-1.5k, 1.5k, 1] \text{ by } [-k, k, 1],$$

where k is a positive number.

Plotting Data and an Equation

L1	L2	L3 1
240	150	------
360	230	
680	435	
800	510	
------	------	

L1(5)=

Figure A.20

In Example 3, Section 2.4, we are asked to plot data and graph a modeling function in the same xy-plane. (You may want to refer to the subsection on making a scatterplot and line graph in this appendix.) Start by entering the x-values into list L1 and the y-values into list L2, as shown in Figure A.20. Then press (Y=) and enter the formula $Y_1 = .65X$ for $f(x)$. Make sure that STATPLOT is on, and set an appropriate viewing rectangle. See Figures A.21 and A.22, and note that Figure A.21 shows "Plot1" in reverse video, which indicates that the scatterplot is on. Now press (GRAPH) to have both the scatterplot and the graph of Y_1 appear in the same viewing rectangle, as shown in Figure A.23.

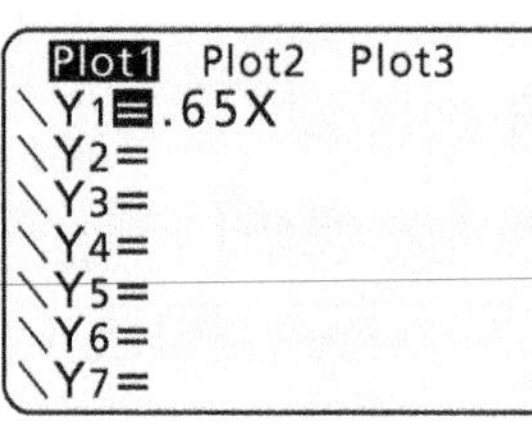

Figure A.21

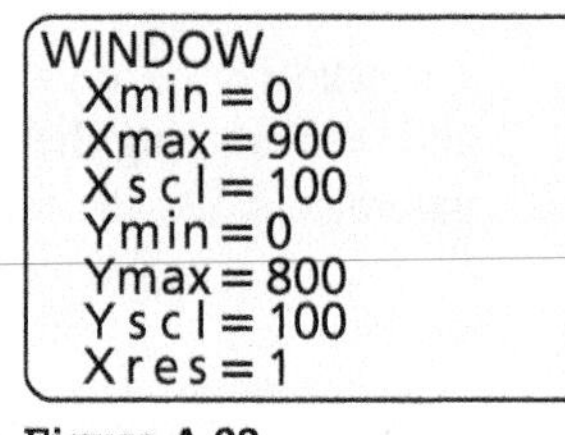

Figure A.22

[0, 900, 100] by [0, 800, 100]

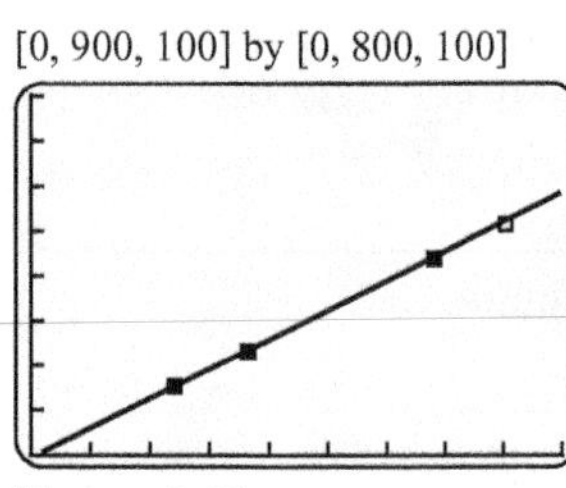

Figure A.23

SUMMARY: PLOTTING DATA AND AN EQUATION

STEP 1: Enter the x-values into list L1 and the y-values into list L2 using the STAT EDIT menu. Turn on Plot1 so that the scatterplot appears.

STEP 2: Use the (Y=) menu to enter the equation to be graphed.

STEP 3: Use (WINDOW) or (ZOOM) to set an appropriate viewing rectangle.

STEP 4: Press (GRAPH) to graph both the scatterplot and the equation in the same viewing rectangle.

Accessing the Greatest Integer Function

MATH NUM CPX PRB
1:abs(
2:round(
3:iPart(
4:fPart(
5:int(
6:min(
7↓max(

Figure A.24

To access the greatest integer function, enter the following keystrokes from the home screen.

(MATH) (▷) (5)

See Figure A.24.

SUMMARY: ACCESSING THE GREATEST INTEGER FUNCTION

STEP 1: Press (MATH).

STEP 2: Position the cursor over "NUM".

STEP 3: Press (5) to select the greatest integer function, which is denoted "int(".

Finding the Line of Least-Squares Fit

In Example 11, Section 2.1, the line of least-squares fit for the points (1, 1), (2, 3), and (3, 4) is found. Begin by entering the points in the same way as for a scatterplot. See Figure 2.14, where the x-values are in list L1 and the y-values are in list L2.

After the data have been entered, perform the following keystrokes from the home screen.

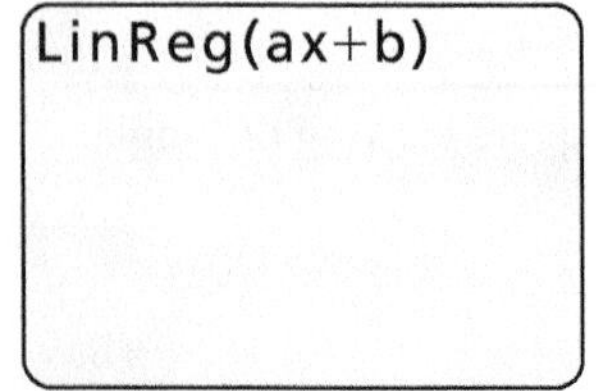

Figure A.25

(See Figure 2.15.) This causes "LinReg(ax+b)" to appear on the home screen, as shown in Figure A.25. The graphing calculator assumes that the x-values are in list L1 and the y-values are in list L2. Now press (ENTER). The result is shown in Figure 2.16.

If the correlation coefficient r does not appear, enter the keystrokes

2nd 0 [CATALOG]

and scroll down until you find "DiagnosticsOn". Press ENTER twice. See Figures A.26 and A.27. The graphs of the data and the least-squares regression line are shown in Figure 2.17.

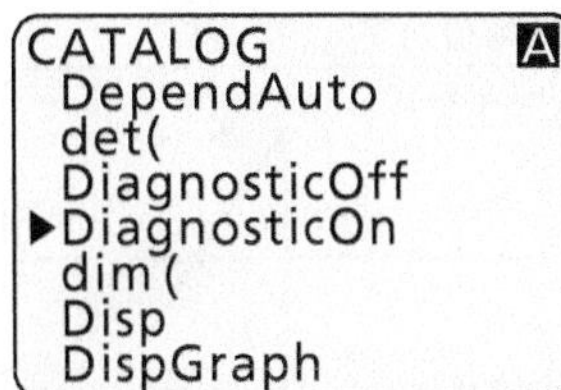

Figure A.26

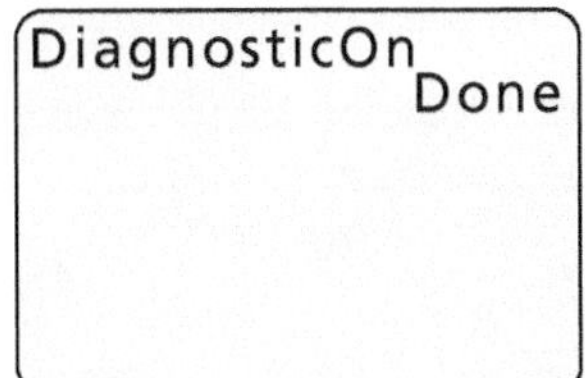

Figure A.27

SUMMARY: LINEAR LEAST-SQUARES FIT

STEP 1: Enter the data using STAT 1, as is done for a scatterplot. Input the x-values into list L1 and the y-values into list L2.

STEP 2: Press STAT ▷ 4 from the home screen to access the least-squares regression line. Press ENTER to start the computation. See page AP-11 to learn how to copy a regression equation into Y_1.

Locating a Point of Intersection

In Example 8, Section 2.2, we are asked to find the point of intersection for two lines. To find the point of intersection for the graphs of

$$f(x) = 5.91x + 13.7 \quad \text{and} \quad g(x) = -4.71x + 64.7,$$

start by entering Y_1 and Y_2, as shown in Figure A.28. Set the viewing rectangle to [0, 12, 2] by [0, 100, 10], and graph both equations in the same viewing rectangle, as shown in Figure 2.24. Then press the following keys to find the intersection point.

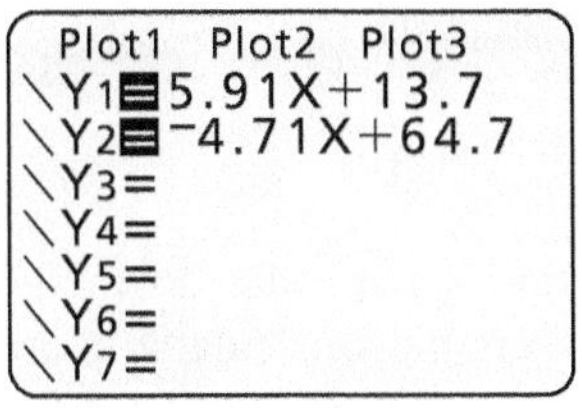

Plot1 Plot2 Plot3
\Y1=5.91X+13.7
\Y2=⁻4.71X+64.7
\Y3=
\Y4=
\Y5=
\Y6=
\Y7=

Figure A.28

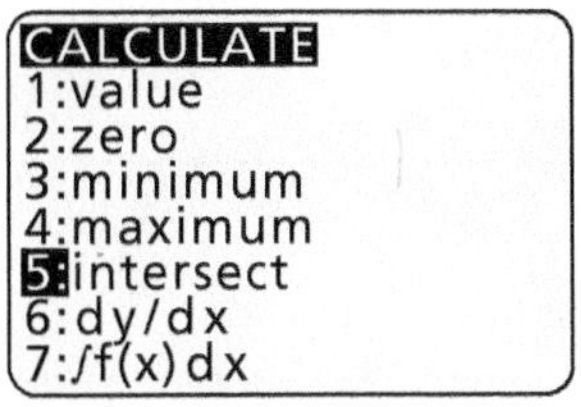

2nd TRACE [CALC] 5

CALCULATE
1:value
2:zero
3:minimum
4:maximum
5:intersect
6:dy/dx
7:∫f(x)dx

Figure A.29

See Figure A.29, where the intersect utility is being selected. The calculator prompts for the first curve, as shown in Figure A.30. Use the arrow keys to locate the cursor near the point of intersection and press ENTER. Repeat these steps for the second curve, as shown in Figure A.31. Finally the calculator prompts for a guess. For each of the three prompts, place the free-moving cursor near the point of intersection and press ENTER. The approximate coordinates of the point of intersection are shown in Figure 2.25.

[0, 12, 2] by [0, 100, 10]

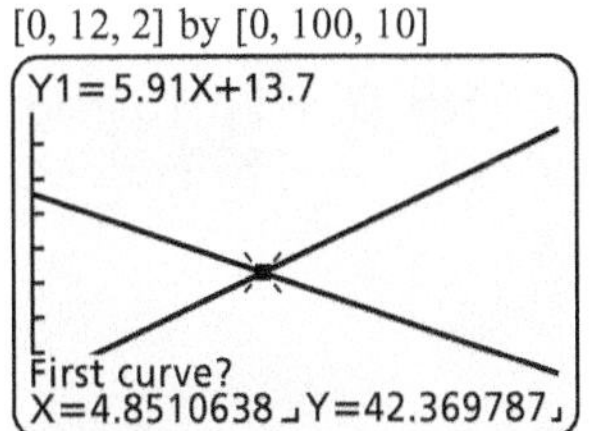

Figure A.30

SUMMARY: FINDING A POINT OF INTERSECTION

STEP 1: Graph the two functions in an appropriate viewing rectangle.

STEP 2: Press 2nd TRACE [CALC] 5.

STEP 3: Use the arrow keys to select an approximate location for the point of intersection. Press ENTER to make the three selections for "First curve?", "Second curve?", and "Guess?". (If the cursor is near the point of intersection, you usually do not need to move the cursor for each selection. Just press ENTER three times.)

[0, 12, 2] by [0, 100, 10]

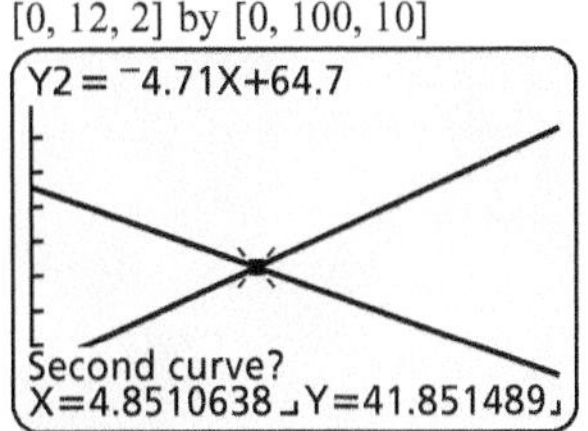

Figure A.31

Locating a Zero of a Function

In Example 4, Section 2.3, we are asked to locate an x-intercept, or *zero*, of the function f given by $f(x) = 1 - x - \frac{1}{2}x + 2$. Start by entering $Y_1 = 1 - X - .5X + 2$ into the Y= menu. Set the viewing rectangle to $[-6, 6, 1]$ by $[-4, 4, 1]$ and graph Y_1. Afterwards, press the following keys to invoke the zero finder. (See Figure A.32.)

2nd TRACE [CALC] 2

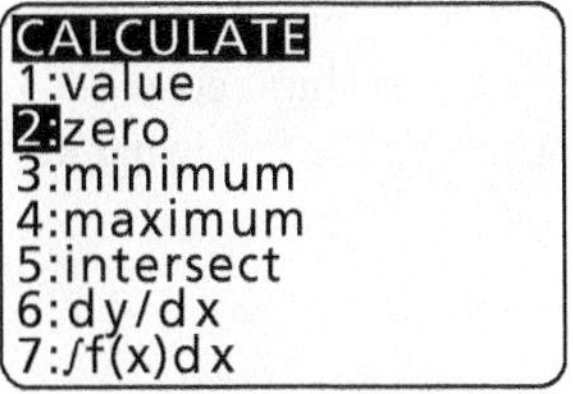

Figure A.32

The calculator prompts for a left bound. Use the arrow keys to set the cursor to the left of the x-intercept and press ENTER. The calculator then prompts for a right bound. Set the cursor to the right of the x-intercept and press ENTER. Finally the calculator prompts for a guess. Set the cursor roughly at the x-intercept and press ENTER. See Figures A.33–A.35 on the next page. The calculator then approximates the x-intercept, or zero, automatically, as shown in Figure 2.35(b).

[−6, 6, 1] by [−4, 4, 1]

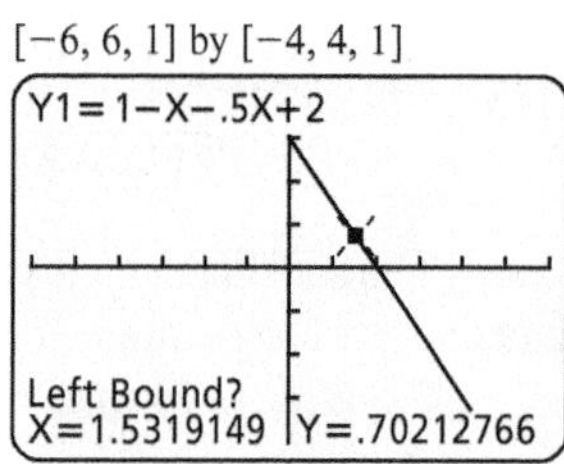

Figure A.33

[−6, 6, 1] by [−4, 4, 1]

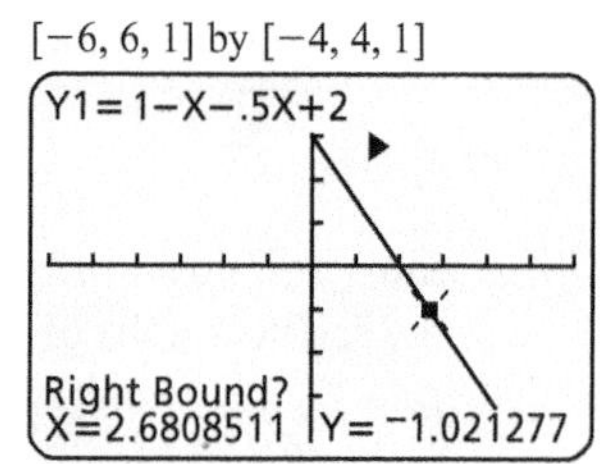

Figure A.34

[−6, 6, 1] by [−4, 4, 1]

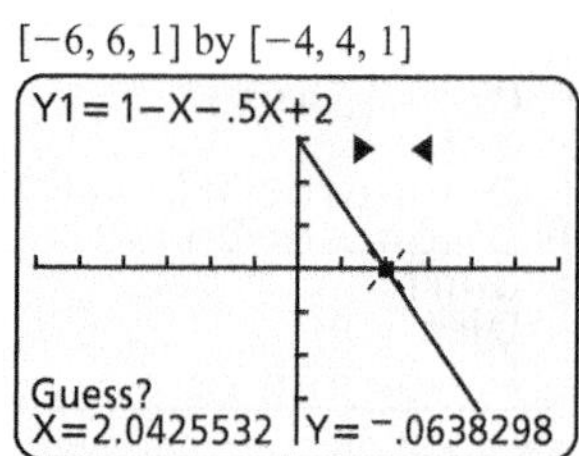

Figure A.35

SUMMARY: LOCATING A ZERO OF A FUNCTION

STEP 1: Graph the function in an appropriate viewing rectangle.

STEP 2: Press (2nd) (TRACE [CALC]) (2).

STEP 3: Select the left and right bounds, followed by a guess. Press (ENTER) after each selection. The calculator then approximates the zero.

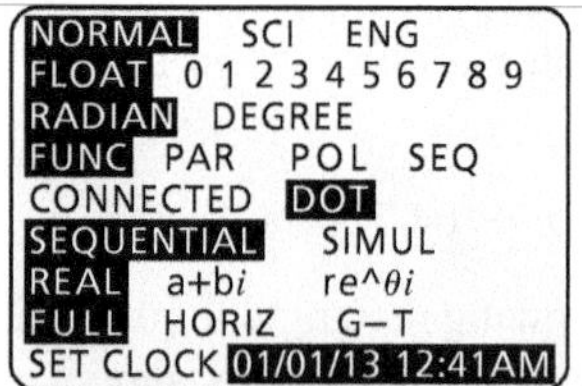

Figure A.36

Setting Connected and Dot Mode

In Figure 2.48 of Section 2.4 a form of the greatest integer function is graphed in dot mode, and in Figure 2.49 it is graphed in connected mode. To set your graphing calculator in dot mode, press (MODE), position the cursor over "Dot", and press (ENTER). See Figure A.36. Graphs will now appear in dot mode rather than connected mode.

SUMMARY: SETTING CONNECTED OR DOT MODE

STEP 1: Press (MODE).

STEP 2: Position the cursor over "Connected" or "Dot". Press (ENTER).

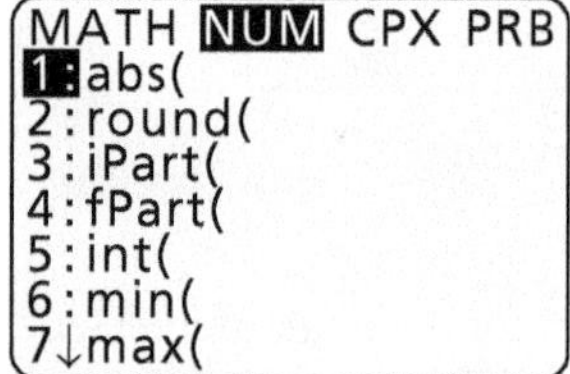

Figure A.37

Accessing the Absolute Value

In Example 1, Section 2.5, the absolute value is used to graph $f(x) = |x + 2|$. To graph f, begin by entering $Y_1 = \text{abs}(X + 2)$. The absolute value (abs) is accessed by pressing

(MATH) (▷) (1).

See Figure A.37.

SUMMARY: ACCESSING THE ABSOLUTE VALUE

STEP 1: Press (MATH).

STEP 2: Position the cursor over "NUM".

STEP 3: Press (1) to select the absolute value.

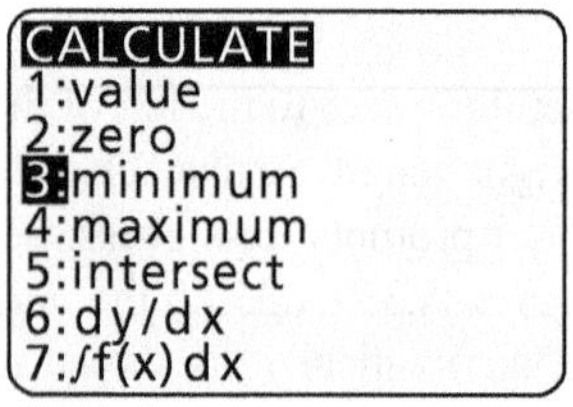

CALCULATE
1:value
2:zero
3:minimum
4:maximum
5:intersect
6:dy/dx
7:∫f(x)dx

Figure A.38

Finding Extrema (Minima and Maxima)

To find a minimum point (or vertex) on a graph, such as $f(x) = 1.5x^2 - 6x + 4$, start by entering $Y_1 = 1.5X\text{^}2 - 6X + 4$ into the (Y=) menu. Set the viewing rectangle to [−4.7, 4.7, 1] by [−3.1, 3.1, 1] by entering (ZOOM) (4). Then perform the following keystrokes to find the minimum y-value.

(2nd) (TRACE [CALC]) (3)

See Figure A.38.

[−4.7, 4.7, 1] by [−3.1, 3.1, 1]

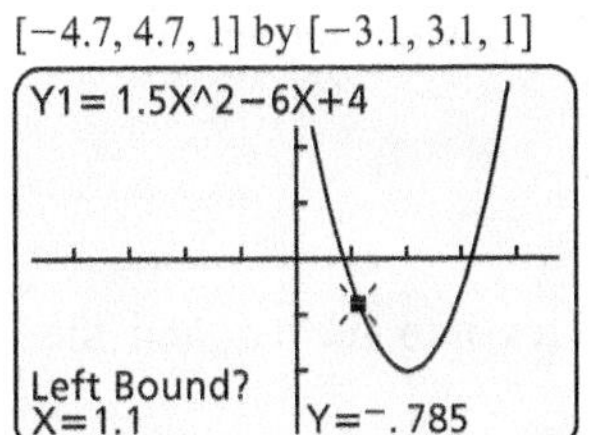

Figure A.39

[−4.7, 4.7, 1] by [−3.1, 3.1, 1]

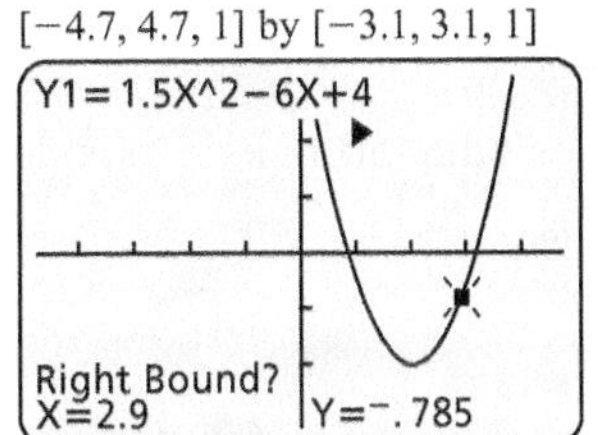

Figure A.40

[−4.7, 4.7, 1] by [−3.1, 3.1, 1]

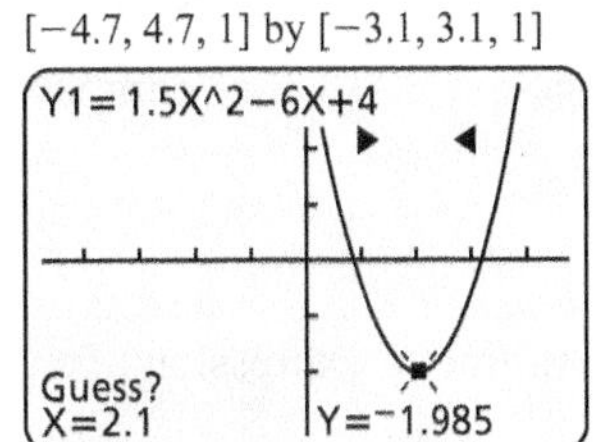

Figure A.41

[−4.7, 4.7, 1] by [−3.1, 3.1, 1]

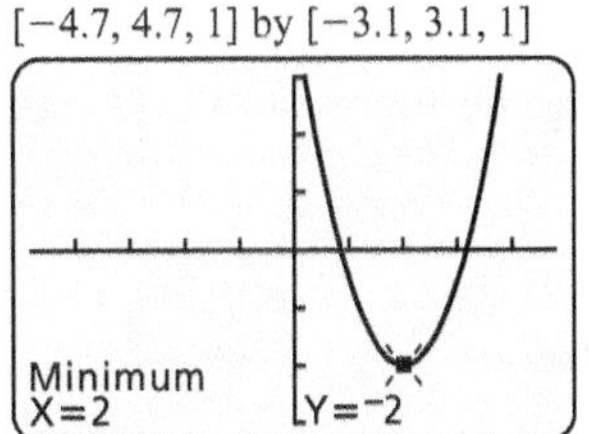

Figure A.42

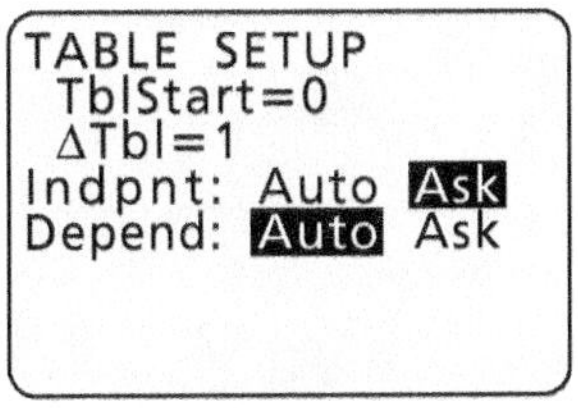

TABLE SETUP
TblStart=0
ΔTbl=1
Indpnt: Auto **Ask**
Depend: **Auto** Ask

Figure A.43

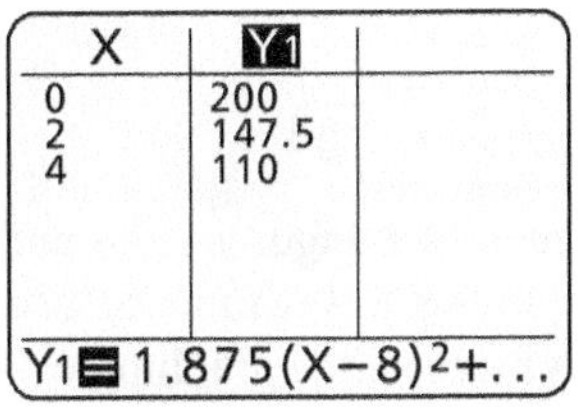

X	Y1
0	200
2	147.5
4	110

Y1=1.875(X−8)2+...

Figure A.44

The calculator prompts for a left bound. Use the arrow keys to position the cursor to the left of the vertex and press ENTER. Similarly, position the cursor to the right of the vertex for the right bound and press ENTER. Finally the calculator asks for a guess between the left and right bounds. Place the cursor near the minimum point and press ENTER. See Figures A.39–A.41. The minimum point (or vertex) is shown in Figure A.42.

To find a maximum of the function f on an interval, use a similar approach, except enter

2nd TRACE [CALC] 4.

The calculator prompts for left and right bounds, followed by a guess. Press ENTER after the cursor has been located appropriately for each prompt. An example of a maximum point is displayed in Figure 3.17 in Section 3.1.

SUMMARY: FINDING EXTREMA (MAXIMA AND MINIMA)

STEP 1: Graph the function in an appropriate viewing rectangle.

STEP 2: Press 2nd TRACE [CALC] 3 to find a minimum point or 2nd TRACE [CALC] 4 to find a maximum point.

STEP 3: Use the arrow keys to locate the left and right x-bounds, followed by a guess. Press ENTER to select each position of the cursor.

Using the Ask Table Feature

In Example 10, Section 3.1, a table with x-values of 0, 2, 4, 6, and 8 is created. Start by entering $Y_1 = 1.875(X - 8)^2 + 80$. To obtain the table shown in Figure 3.20, use the Ask feature rather than the Auto feature for the independent variable (Indpnt:). Press 2nd GRAPH [TABLE]. Whenever an x-value is entered, the corresponding y-value is calculated automatically. See Figures A.43 and A.44.

SUMMARY: USING THE ASK FEATURE FOR A TABLE

STEP 1: Enter the formula for $f(x)$ into Y_1 by using the Y= menu.

STEP 2: Press 2nd WINDOW [TBLSET] to access "TABLE SETUP" and then select "Ask" for the independent variable (Indpnt:). "TblStart" and "ΔTbl" do not need to be set.

STEP 3: Enter x-values of your choice. The corresponding y-values will be calculated automatically.

Finding a Nonlinear Function of Least-Squares Fit

In Example 11, Section 3.1, a quadratic function of least-squares fit is found in a manner similar to the way a linear function of least-squares fit is found. To solve Example 11, start by pressing STAT 1 and then enter the data points from Table 3.4, as shown in Figure 3.22. Input the x-values into list L1 and the y-values into list L2. To find the equation for a quadratic polynomial of least-squares fit, perform the following keystrokes from the home screen.

CLEAR STAT ▷ 5

This causes "Quadreg" to appear on the home screen. The calculator assumes that the x-values are in list L1 and the y-values are in list L2, unless otherwise designated. Press ENTER to obtain the quadratic regression equation, as shown in Figure 3.24. Graphs of the data and the regression equation are shown in Figure 3.25.

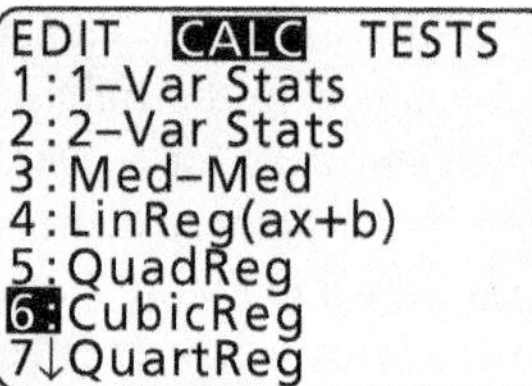

Figure A.45

Other types of regression equations, such as cubic, quartic, power, and exponential, can be selected from the STAT CALC menu. See Figure A.45.

SUMMARY: NONLINEAR LEAST-SQUARES FIT

STEP 1: Enter the data using (STAT)(1). Input the x-values into list L1 and the y-values into list L2, as is done for a scatterplot.

STEP 2: From the home screen, press (STAT)(▷) and select a type of least-squares modeling function from the menu. Press (ENTER) to initiate the computation.

Evaluating Complex Arithmetic

Complex arithmetic can be performed in much the same way as other arithmetic expressions are evaluated. The imaginary unit i is obtained by entering

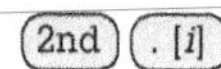

from the home screen. For example, to add the numbers $(-2 + 3i) + (4 - 6i)$, perform the following keystrokes on the home screen.

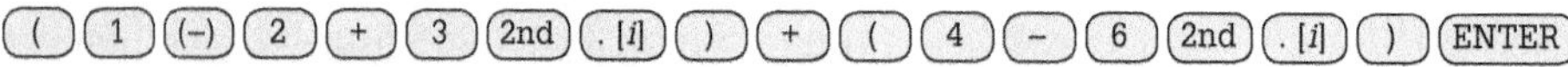

The result is shown in the first two lines of Figure 3.37 in Section 3.3. Other complex arithmetic operations are done similarly.

SUMMARY: EVALUATING COMPLEX ARITHMETIC

Enter a complex expression in the same way as any other arithmetic expression. To obtain the complex number i, use (2nd)(. [i]).

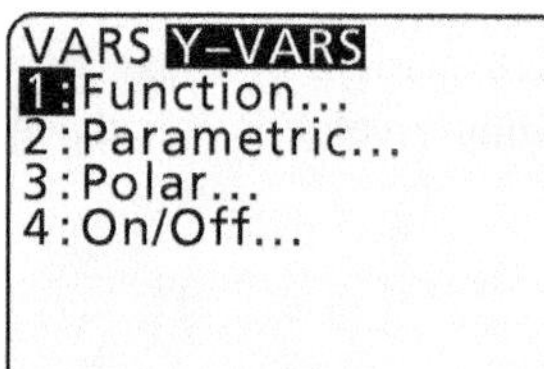

Figure A.46

Accessing the Variable Y_1

In Figure 3.78, Section 3.5, the expressions $-Y_1$ and $Y_1(-X)$ in the (Y=) menu are used to graph reflections. The Y_1 variable can be found by pressing the following keys. (See Figures A.46 and A.47.)

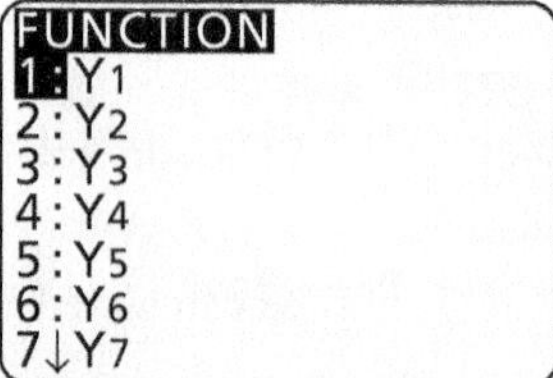

Figure A.47

SUMMARY: ACCESSING THE VARIABLE Y_1

STEP 1: Press (VARS).

STEP 2: Position the cursor over "Y-VARS".

STEP 3: Press (1) twice.

These keystrokes will make Y_1 appear on the screen.

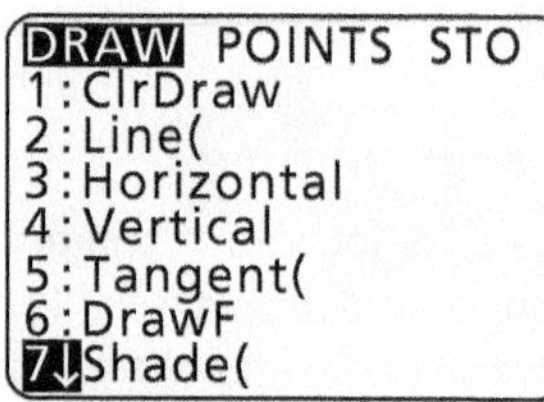

Figure A.48

Shading between Two Graphs

In Example 9, Section 3.5, the region below the graph of $f(x) = -0.4x^2 + 4$ is shaded to make it look like a mountain, as illustrated in Figure 3.97. One way to shade below the graph of f is to begin by entering $Y_1 = -.4X^\wedge 2 + 4$ after pressing (Y=). Then use the following keystrokes from the home screen.

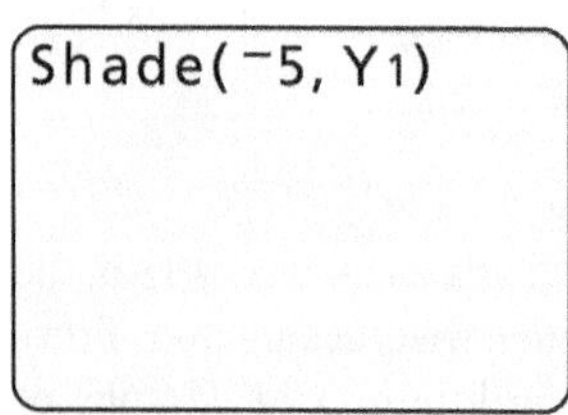

Figure A.49

The expression Shade$(-5, Y_1)$ should appear on your home screen. See Figures A.48 and A.49. The shading utility, accessed from the DRAW menu, requires a lower function and then an upper function, separated by a comma. When (ENTER) is pressed, the graphing calculator shades between the graph of the lower function and the graph of the upper function.

For the lower function we have arbitrarily selected $y = -5$ because its graph lies below the graph of f and does not appear in the viewing rectangle in Figure 3.97. Instead of entering the variable Y_1, we could enter the formula $-.4X\text{^}2 + 4$ for the upper function.

SUMMARY: SHADING A GRAPH

STEP 1: Press (2nd) (PRGM [DRAW]) (7) from the home screen.

STEP 2: Enter a formula or a variable such as Y_1 for the lower function, followed by a comma.

STEP 3: Enter a formula or a variable such as Y_2 for the upper function, followed by a right parenthesis.

STEP 4: Set an appropriate viewing rectangle.

STEP 5: Press (ENTER). The region between the two graphs will be shaded.

Copying a Regression Equation into Y_1 =

In Example 8, Section 4.2, we are asked to use cubic regression to model real data. The resulting formula for the cubic function, shown in Figure 4.54, is quite complicated and tedious to enter into Y_1 = by hand. A graphing calculator has the capability to copy this equation into Y_1 automatically. To do this, clear the equation for Y_1 = . Then enter Y_1 after "CubicReg", as shown in Figure A.50. When (ENTER) is pressed, the regression equation will be calculated and then copied into Y_1 = , as shown in Figure A.51. The following keystrokes may be used from the home screen. (Be sure to enter the data into lists L1 and L2.)

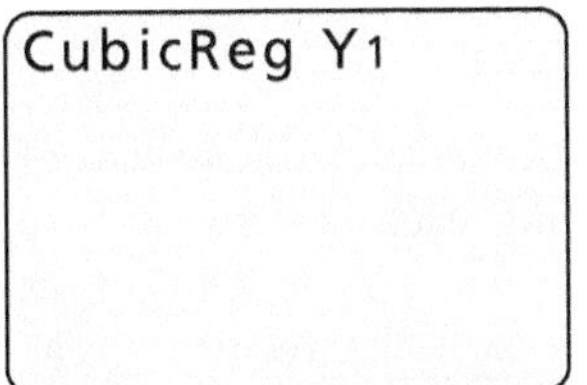

Figure A.50

Figure A.51

SUMMARY: COPYING A REGRESSION EQUATION INTO Y_1 =

STEP 1: Clear Y_1 in the (Y =) menu if an equation is present. Return to the home screen.

STEP 2: Select a type of regression from the STAT CALC menu.

STEP 3: Press (VARS) (▷) (1) (1) (ENTER).

Setting a Decimal Window

In Example 1, Section 4.7, a decimal (or friendly) window is used to trace the graph of f. With a decimal window, the cursor stops on convenient x-values. In the decimal window $[-9.4, 9.4, 1]$ by $[-6.2, 6.2, 1]$, the cursor stops on x-values that are multiples of 0.2. If we reduce the viewing rectangle to $[-4.7, 4.7, 1]$ by $[-3.1, 3.1, 1]$, the cursor stops on x-values that are multiples of 0.1. To set this smaller window automatically, press (ZOOM) (4). See Figure A.52. Decimal windows are useful when graphing rational functions with asymptotes in connected mode.

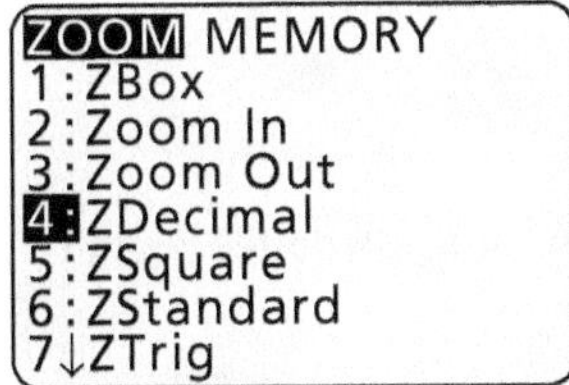

Figure A.52

SUMMARY: SETTING A DECIMAL WINDOW

Press (ZOOM) (4) to set the viewing rectangle $[-4.7, 4.7, 1]$ by $[-3.1, 3.1, 1]$. A convenient larger decimal window is $[-9.4, 9.4, 1]$ by $[-6.2, 6.2, 1]$.

Graphing an Inverse Function

In Example 7, Section 5.2, the inverse function of $f(x) = x^3 + 2$ is graphed. A graphing calculator can graph the inverse of a function without a formula for $f^{-1}(x)$. Begin by entering $Y_1 = X\text{^}3 + 2$ into the (Y =) menu. Then return to the home screen by pressing

(2nd) (MODE [QUIT]).

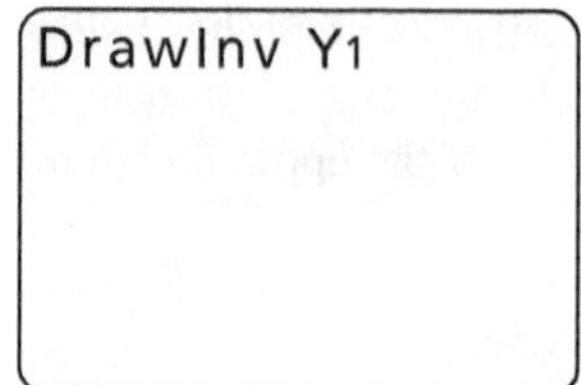

Figure A.53

[−6, 6, 1] by [−4, 4, 1]

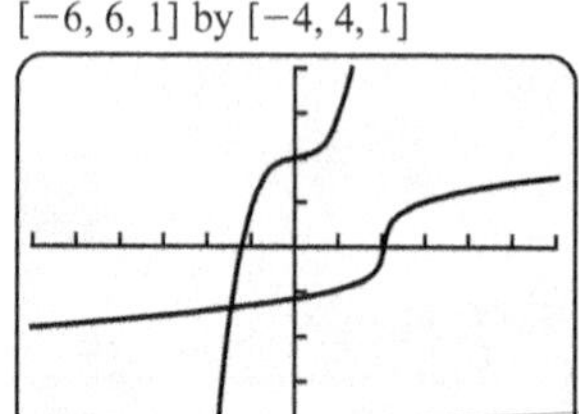

Figure A.54

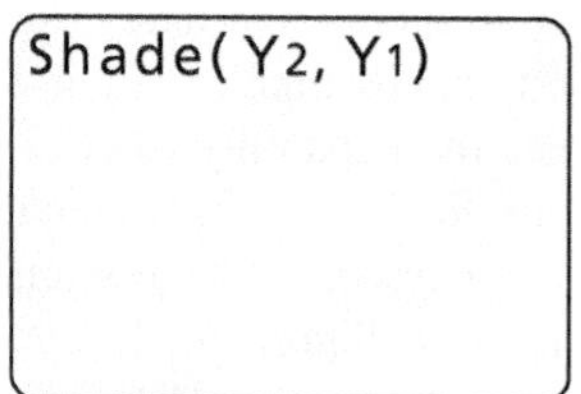

Figure A.55

[−6, 6, 1] by [−6, 6, 1]

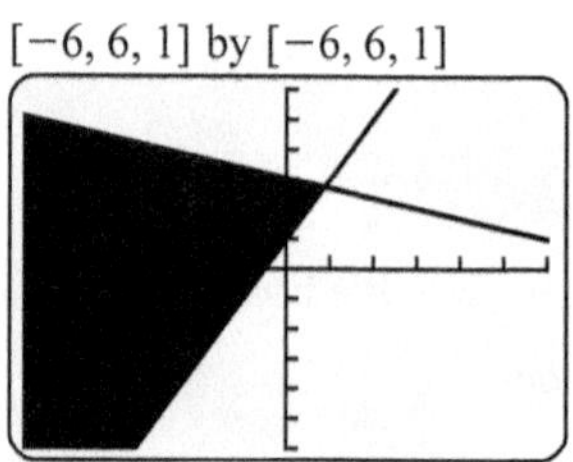

Figure A.56

The DrawInv utility may be accessed by pressing

2nd PRGM [DRAW] 8,

followed by

VARS ▷ 1 1

to obtain the variable Y_1. See A.53. Pressing ENTER causes both Y_1 and its inverse to be graphed, as shown in A.54.

SUMMARY: GRAPHING AN INVERSE FUNCTION

STEP 1: Enter the formula for $f(x)$ into Y_1 using the Y= menu.

STEP 2: Set an appropriate viewing rectangle by pressing WINDOW.

STEP 3: Return to the home screen by pressing 2nd MODE [QUIT].

STEP 4: Press 2nd PRGM [DRAW] 8 VARS ▷ 1 1 ENTER to create the graphs of f and f^{-1}.

Shading a System of Inequalities

In Example 2(b), Section 6.2, we are asked to shade the solution set for the system of linear inequalities $x + 3y \le 9$, $2x - y \le -1$. Begin by solving each system for y to obtain $y \le -\frac{1}{3}x + 3$ and $y \ge 2x + 1$. Then let $Y_1 = -X/3 + 3$ and $Y_2 = 2X + 1$, as shown in Figure 6.30. Position the cursor to left of Y_1 and press ENTER three times. The triangle that appears indicates that the calculator will shade the region below the graph of Y_1. Next locate the cursor to the left of Y_2 and press ENTER twice. This triangle indicates that the calculator will shade the region above the graph of Y_2. After setting the viewing rectangle to [−6, 6, 1] by [−6, 6, 1], press GRAPH. The result is shown in Figure 6.31. The solution set could also be shaded using Shade(Y_2, Y_1) from the home screen. See Figures A.55 and A.56.

SUMMARY: SHADING A SYSTEM OF INEQUALITIES

STEP 1: Solve each inequality for y.

STEP 2: Enter the formulas as Y_1 and Y_2 in the Y= menu.

STEP 3: Locate the cursor to the left of Y_1 and press ENTER two or three times, to shade either above or below the graph of Y_1. Repeat for Y_2.

STEP 4: Set an appropriate viewing rectangle.

STEP 5: Press GRAPH.

Note: The Shade utility under the DRAW menu can also be used to shade the region *between* two graphs.

Entering the Elements of a Matrix

In Example 9, Section 6.4, the augmented matrix A is given by

$$A = \left[\begin{array}{ccc|c} 2 & 1 & 2 & 10 \\ 1 & 0 & 2 & 5 \\ 1 & -2 & 2 & 1 \end{array}\right].$$

On the TI-83 Plus and TI-84 Plus, use the following keystrokes to define a matrix A with dimension 3×4. (On the TI-83 graphing calculator, the matrix menu is found by pressing MATRIX.)

2nd x^{-1} [MATRIX] ▷ ▷ 1 3 ENTER 4 ENTER

See Figures 6.41 and 6.42. Then input the 12 elements of the matrix A, row by row, as shown in Figure 6.42. Finish each entry by pressing (ENTER). After these elements have been entered, press

(2nd) (MODE [QUIT])

to return to the home screen. To display the matrix A, press

(2nd) (x^{-1} [MATRIX]) (1) (ENTER).

See Figure 6.43.

SUMMARY: ENTERING THE ELEMENTS OF A MATRIX A

STEP 1: Begin by accessing the matrix A by pressing (2nd) (x^{-1} [MATRIX]) (▷) (▷) (1).

STEP 2: Enter the dimension of A by pressing (m) (ENTER) (n) (ENTER), where the dimension of the matrix is $m \times n$.

STEP 3: Input each element of the matrix, row by row. Finish each entry by pressing (ENTER). Use (2nd) (MODE [QUIT]) to return to the home screen.

Note: On the TI-83, replace the keystrokes (2nd) (x^{-1} [MATRIX]) with (MATRIX).

Reduced Row-Echelon Form

In Example 9, Section 6.4, the reduced row-echelon form of a matrix is found. To find this reduced row-echelon form on the TI-83 Plus and TI-84 Plus, use the following keystrokes from the home screen. (See Figure 6.44.)

(2nd) (x^{-1} [MATRIX]) (▷) (ALPHA) (APPS [B]) (2nd) (x^{-1} [MATRIX]) (1) ( )) (ENTER)

The resulting matrix is shown in Figure 6.45. On the TI-83 graphing calculator, use the following keystrokes to find the reduced row-echelon form.

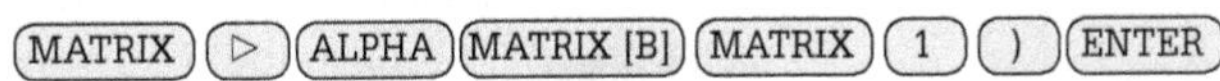

SUMMARY: FINDING THE REDUCED ROW-ECHELON FORM OF A MATRIX

STEP 1: To make rref([A]) appear on the home screen, use the following keystrokes.

(2nd) (x^{-1} [MATRIX]) (▷) (ALPHA) (APPS [B]) (2nd) (x^{-1} [MATRIX]) (1) ( )) (ENTER)

STEP 2: Press (ENTER) to calculate the reduced row-echelon form. Use arrow keys to access elements that do not appear on the screen.

Note: On the TI-83, replace the keystrokes (2nd) (x^{-1} [MATRIX]) with (MATRIX) and (APPS [B]) with (MATRIX [B]).

Performing Arithmetic Operations on Matrices

In Example 10, Section 6.5, the matrices A and B are multiplied. Begin by entering the elements for the matrices A and B. The following keystrokes can be used to define a matrix A with dimension 3×3.

(2nd) (x^{-1} [MATRIX]) (▷) (▷) (1) (3) (ENTER) (3) (ENTER)

Next input the 9 elements in the matrix A, row by row. Finish each entry by pressing (ENTER). See Figure 6.59. Repeat this process to define a matrix B with dimension 3×3.

(2nd) (x^{-1} [MATRIX]) (▷) (▷) (2) (3) (ENTER) (3) (ENTER)

Enter the 9 elements in B. See Figure 6.60. After the elements of A and B have been entered, press

(2nd) (MODE [QUIT])

to return to the home screen. To multiply the expression AB, use the following keystrokes from the home screen.

(2nd) (x^{-1} [MATRIX]) (1) (×) (2nd) (x^{-1} [MATRIX]) (2) (ENTER)

The result is shown in Figure 6.61.

SUMMARY: PERFORMING ARITHMETIC OPERATIONS ON MATRICES

STEP 1: Enter the elements of each matrix, beginning with the keystrokes

(2nd) (x^{-1} [MATRIX]) (▷) (▷) (k) (m) (ENTER) (n) (ENTER),

where k is the menu number of the matrix and the dimension of the matrix is $m \times n$.

STEP 2: Return to the home screen by pressing (2nd) (MODE [QUIT]).

STEP 3: Enter the matrix expression, followed by (ENTER). Use the keystrokes

(2nd) (x^{-1} [MATRIX]) (k)

to access the matrix with menu number k.

Note: On the TI-83, replace the keystrokes (2nd) (x^{-1} [MATRIX]) with (MATRIX).

Finding the Inverse of a Matrix

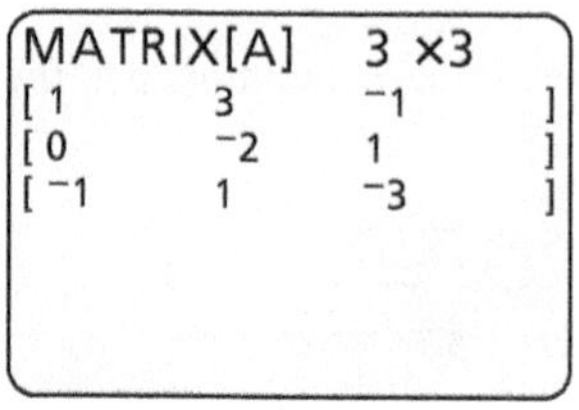

```
MATRIX[A]   3 ×3
[1     3    ⁻1   ]
[0    ⁻2     1   ]
[⁻1    1    ⁻3   ]
```

Figure A.57

In Example 8, Section 6.6, the inverse of A, denoted A^{-1}, is displayed in Figure 6.65. To calculate A^{-1}, start by entering the elements of the matrix A, as shown in Figure A.57. To compute A^{-1}, perform the following keystrokes from the home screen.

(2nd) (x^{-1} [MATRIX]) (1) (x^{-1}) (ENTER)

The results are shown in Figure 6.65.

SUMMARY: FINDING THE INVERSE OF A SQUARE MATRIX

STEP 1: Enter the elements of the square matrix A.

STEP 2: Return to the home screen by pressing

(2nd) (MODE [QUIT]).

STEP 3: Perform the following keystrokes from the home screen to display A^{-1}.

(2nd) (x^{-1} [MATRIX]) (1) (x^{-1}) (ENTER)

Note: On the TI-83, replace the keystrokes (2nd) (x^{-1} [MATRIX]) with (MATRIX).

Solving a Linear System with a Matrix Inverse

In Example 8, Section 6.6, the solution to a system of equations is found. The matrix equation $AX = B$ has the solution $X = A^{-1}B$, provided A^{-1} exists, and is given by

$$AX = \begin{bmatrix} 1 & 3 & -1 \\ 0 & -2 & 1 \\ -1 & 1 & -3 \end{bmatrix} \begin{bmatrix} x \\ y \\ z \end{bmatrix} = \begin{bmatrix} 6 \\ -2 \\ 4 \end{bmatrix} = B.$$

To solve this equation, start by entering the elements of the matrices A and B. To compute the solution $A^{-1}B$, perform the following keystrokes from the home screen.

(2nd) (x^{-1} [MATRIX]) (1) (x^{-1}) (×) (2nd) (x^{-1} [MATRIX]) (2) (ENTER)

The results are shown in Figure 6.66.

SUMMARY: SOLVING A LINEAR SYSTEM WITH A MATRIX INVERSE

STEP 1: Write the system of equations as $AX = B$.

STEP 2: Enter the elements of the matrices A and B.

STEP 3: Return to the home screen by pressing

(2nd) (MODE [QUIT]).

STEP 4: Perform the following keystrokes.

(2nd) (x^{-1} [MATRIX]) (1) (x^{-1}) (×) (2nd) (x^{-1} [MATRIX]) (2) (ENTER)

Note: On the TI-83, replace the keystrokes with (2nd) (x^{-1} [MATRIX]) with (MATRIX).

Evaluating a Determinant

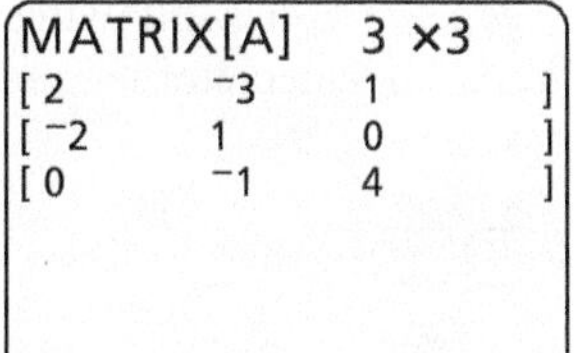

Figure A.58

In Example 4(a), Section 6.7, a graphing calculator is used to evaluate a determinant of a matrix. Start by entering the 9 elements of the 3×3 matrix A, as shown in Figure A.58. To compute det A, perform the following keystrokes from the home screen.

(2nd) (x^{-1} [MATRIX]) (▷) (1) (2nd) (x^{-1} [MATRIX]) (1) ( )) (ENTER)

The results are shown in Figure 6.68.

SUMMARY: EVALUATING A DETERMINANT OF A SQUARE MATRIX

STEP 1: Enter the elements of the matrix A.

STEP 2: Return to the home screen by pressing

(2nd) (MODE [QUIT]).

STEP 3: Perform the following keystrokes.

(2nd) (x^{-1} [MATRIX]) (▷) (1) (2nd) (x^{-1} [MATRIX]) (1) ( )) (ENTER)

Note: On the TI-83, replace the keystrokes (2nd) (x^{-1} [MATRIX]) with (MATRIX).

Creating a Sequence

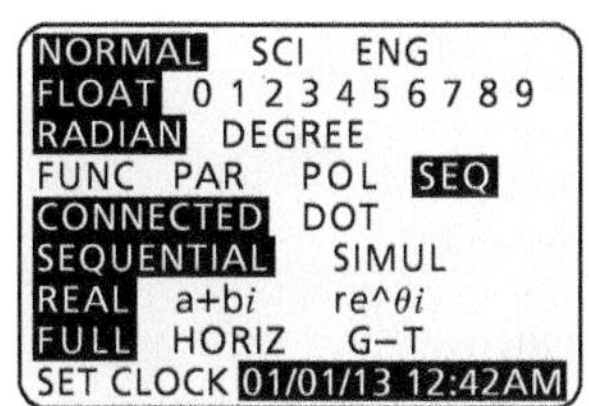

Figure A.59

A graphing calculator can be used to calculate the terms of the sequence given by $f(n) = 2n - 5$ for $n = 1, 2, 3, 4$. Start by setting the mode of the calculator to sequence ("Seq") using the following keystrokes. (See Figure A.59.)

Then enter the following from the home screen.

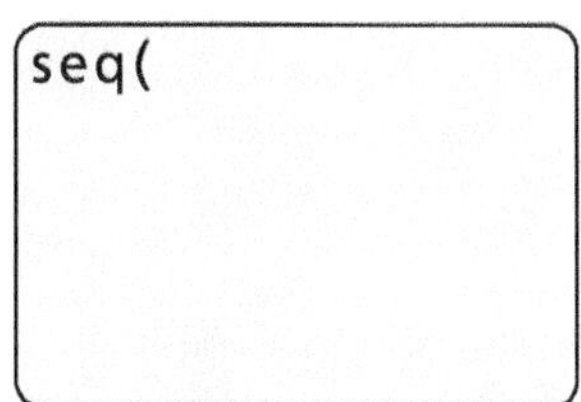

Figure A.60

On the home screen, "seq(" will appear, as shown in Figure A.60. This sequence utility requires that four things be entered—all separated by commas. They are the formula, the variable, the subscript of the first term, and the subscript of the last term. Use the following keystrokes to obtain the first four terms (a_1, a_2, a_3, a_4) of the sequence $a_n = 2n - 5$,

(2) (X, T, θ, n) (−) (5) (,) (X, T, θ, n) (,) (1) (,) (4) ()) (ENTER)

SUMMARY: CREATING A SEQUENCE

STEP 1: To create a sequence, use the keystrokes

(2nd) (STAT [LIST]) (▷) (5).

STEP 2: Enter the formula, the variable, the subscript of the first term, and the subscript of the last term—all separated by commas. For example, if you want the first 10 terms ($a_1, a_2, a_3, \ldots, a_{10}$) of $a_n = n^2$, enter seq$(n^2, n, 1, 10)$. Be sure to set your calculator in sequence mode.

STEP 3: Press (ENTER) to get the terms of the sequence to appear.

Entering, Tabling, and Graphing a Sequence

A table and a graph of a sequence are created with a graphing calculator. The calculator should be set to sequence mode by entering the following keystrokes.

(MODE) (▽) (▽) (▽) (▷) (▷) (▷) (ENTER)

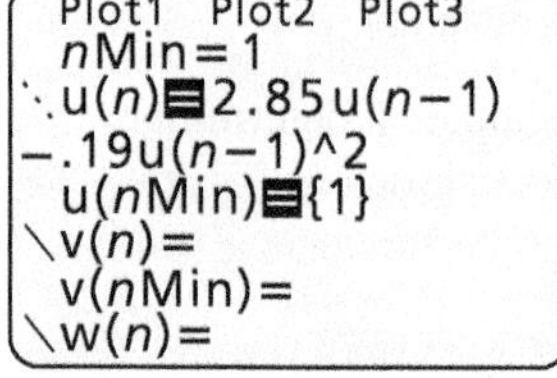

Figure A.61

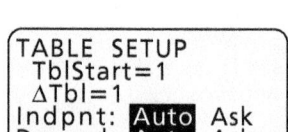

To enter the formula for a sequence, press (Y=). See Figure A.61. Let nMin = 1, since the initial value of n is equal to 1. To enter $a_n = 2.85a_{n-1} - .19a_{n-1}^2$, use the following keystrokes, after clearing out any old formula. (Notice that the graphing calculator uses u instead of a to denote a term of the sequence.)

(2) (.) (8) (5) (2nd) (7[u]) (() (X, T, θ, n) (−) (1) ()) (−) (.) (1) (9)

(2nd) (7[u]) (() (X, T, θ, n) (−) (1) ()) (^) (2) (ENTER)

Since $a_1 = 1$, let $u(n\text{Min}) = \{1\}$. This can be done as follows. See Figure A.61.

(CLEAR) (2nd) (() (1) (2nd) ())

TABLE SETUP
TblStart=1
ΔTbl=1
Indpnt: Auto Ask
Depend: Auto Ask

Figure A.62

To create a table for this sequence, starting with a_1 and incrementing n by 1, perform the following keystrokes. See Figure A.62 and Figure 8.7.

(2nd) (WINDOW [TBLSET]) (1) (ENTER) (1) (2nd) (GRAPH [TABLE])

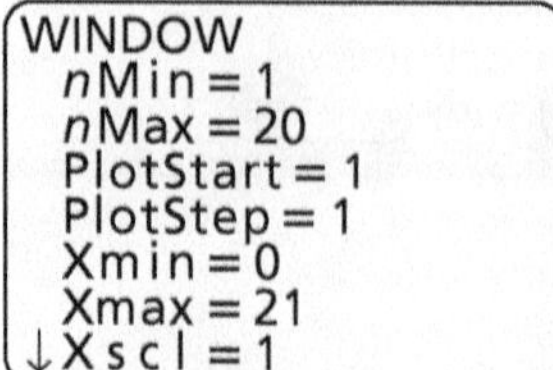

Figure A.63

To graph the first 20 terms of this sequence, start by selecting (WINDOW). Since we want the first 20 terms plotted, let nMin = 1, nMax = 20, PlotStart = 1, and PlotStep = 1. The window can be set as [0, 21, 1] by [0, 14, 1]. See Figure A.63. To graph the sequence, press (GRAPH). The resulting graph uses dot mode.

SUMMARY: ENTERING, TABLING, AND GRAPHING A SEQUENCE

STEP 1: Set the mode to "Seq" by using the (MODE) menu.

STEP 2: Enter the formula for the sequence by pressing (Y=).

STEP 3: To create a table of a sequence, set the start and increment values with

(2nd) (WINDOW [TBLSET])

and then press

(2nd) (GRAPH [TABLE]).

STEP 4: To graph a sequence, set the viewing rectangle by using (WINDOW) and then press (GRAPH). Be sure to use dot mode.

Summing a Series

The sum of the series $\sum_{n=1}^{50}\left(\frac{1}{n^4}\right)$ is found by using a graphing calculator. Use the following keystrokes from the home screen.

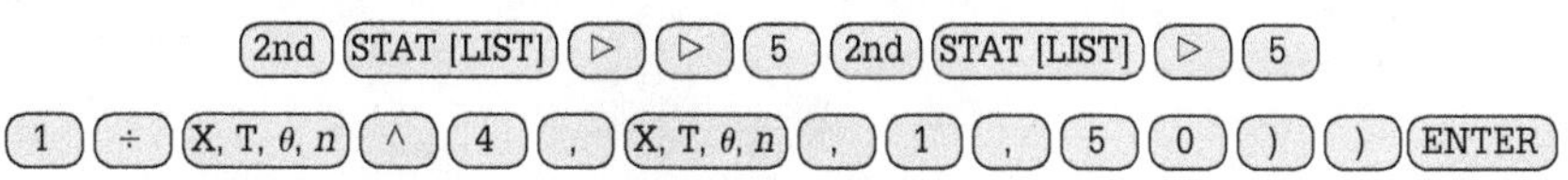

SUMMARY: SUMMING A SERIES

STEP 1: Use (2nd) (STAT [LIST]) (▷) (▷) (5) to access the sum utility.

STEP 2: Use (2nd) (STAT [LIST]) (▷) (5) to access the sequence utility. (To use the sequence utility, see "Creating a Sequence" in this appendix.)

Calculating Factorial Notation

Factorial notation is evaluated with a graphing calculator. The factorial utility is found under the MATH PRB menus. To calculate 8!, use the following keystrokes from the home screen.

SUMMARY: CALCULATING FACTORIAL NOTATION

To calculate n factorial, use the following keystrokes.

(n) (MATH) (▷) (▷) (▷) (4) (ENTER)

The value of n should be entered as a number, not a variable.

Calculating Permutations and Combinations

The permutation $P(7, 3)$ is evaluated. To perform this calculation, use the following keystrokes from the home screen.

(7) (MATH) (▷) (▷) (▷) (2) (3) (ENTER)

The combination $C(7, 3)$ can be calculated by using the following keystrokes.

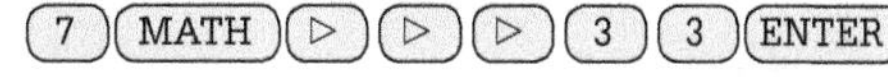

SUMMARY: CALCULATING PERMUTATIONS AND COMBINATIONS

STEP 1: To calculate $P(n, r)$, use (MATH) and select "PRB" followed by (2).

STEP 2: To calculate $C(n, r)$, use (MATH) and select "PRB" followed by (3).

B

Appendix B: A Library of Functions

Basic Functions

The following are symbolic, numerical, and graphical representations of several functions used in algebra. Their domains D and ranges R are given in interval notation.

Identity Function: $f(x) = x$

x	-2	-1	0	1	2
$y = x$	-2	-1	0	1	2

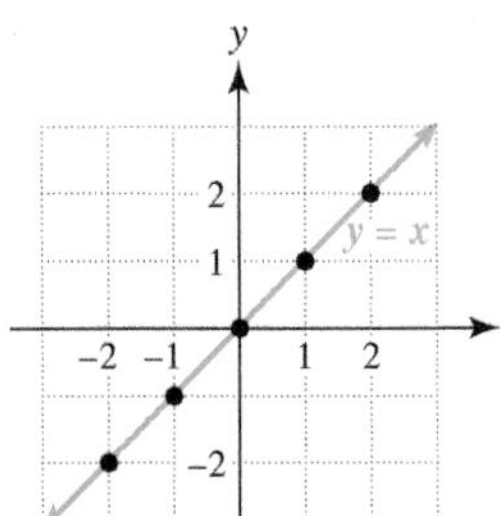

$D = (-\infty, \infty)$

$R = (-\infty, \infty)$

Square Function: $f(x) = x^2$

x	-2	-1	0	1	2
$y = x^2$	4	1	0	1	4

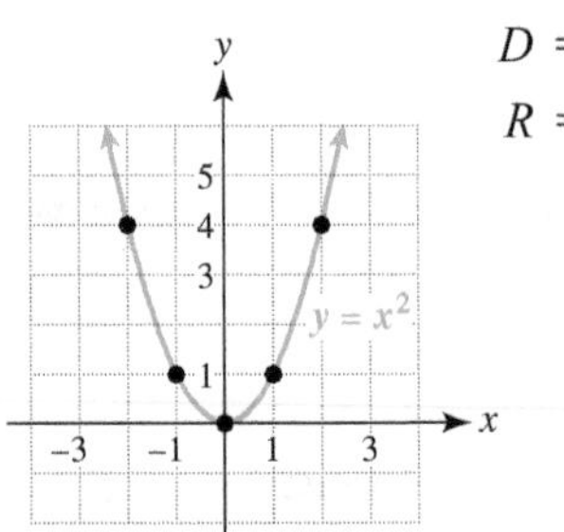

$D = (-\infty, \infty)$

$R = [0, \infty)$

Square Root Function: $f(x) = \sqrt{x}$

x	0	1	4	9
$y = \sqrt{x}$	0	1	2	3

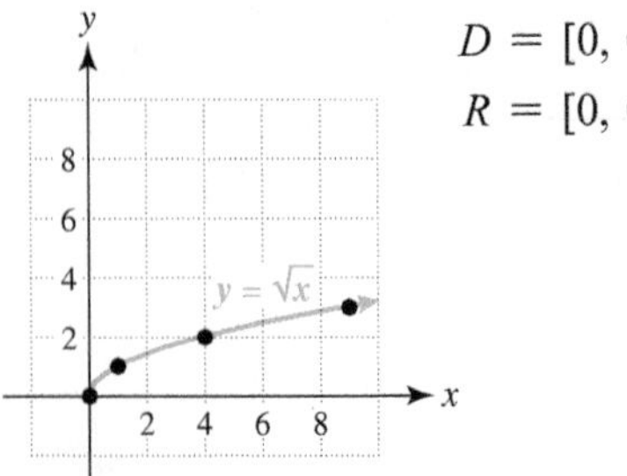

$D = [0, \infty)$

$R = [0, \infty)$

Absolute Value Function: $f(x) = |x|$

x	-2	-1	0	1	2
$y = \|x\|$	2	1	0	1	2

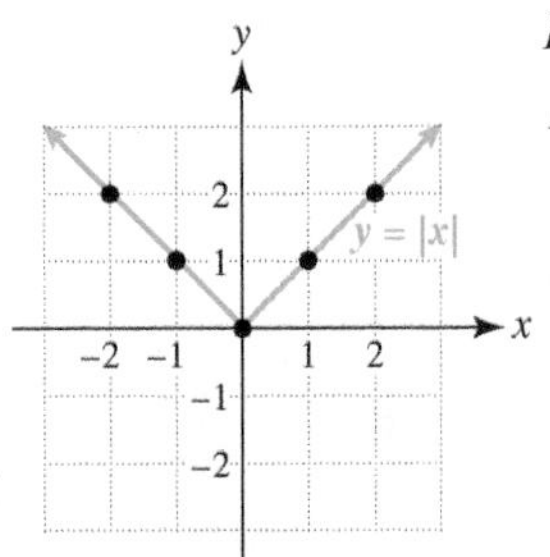

$D = (-\infty, \infty)$

$R = [0, \infty)$

Cube Function: $f(x) = x^3$

x	-2	-1	0	1	2
$y = x^3$	-8	-1	0	1	8

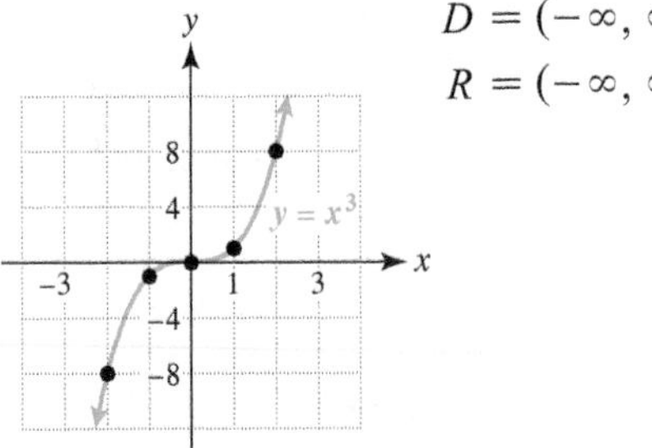

$D = (-\infty, \infty)$

$R = (-\infty, \infty)$

Cube Root Function: $f(x) = \sqrt[3]{x}$

x	-8	-1	0	1	8
$y = \sqrt[3]{x}$	-2	-1	0	1	2

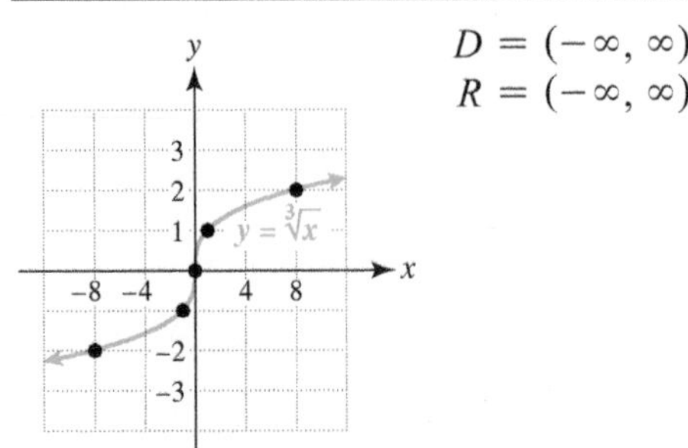

$D = (-\infty, \infty)$

$R = (-\infty, \infty)$

Greatest Integer Function: $f(x) = [\![x]\!]$

x	-2.5	-1.5	0	1.5	2.5
$y = [\![x]\!]$	-3	-2	0	1	2

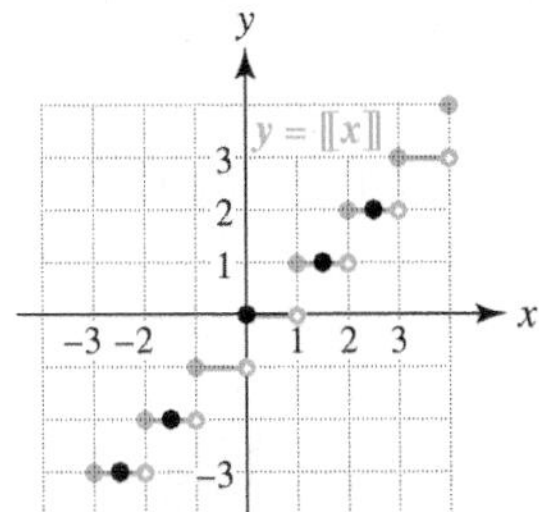

$D = (-\infty, \infty)$
$R =$ Integers

Reciprocal Function: $f(x) = \frac{1}{x}$

x	-2	-1	0	1	2
$y = \frac{1}{x}$	$-\frac{1}{2}$	-1	—	1	$\frac{1}{2}$

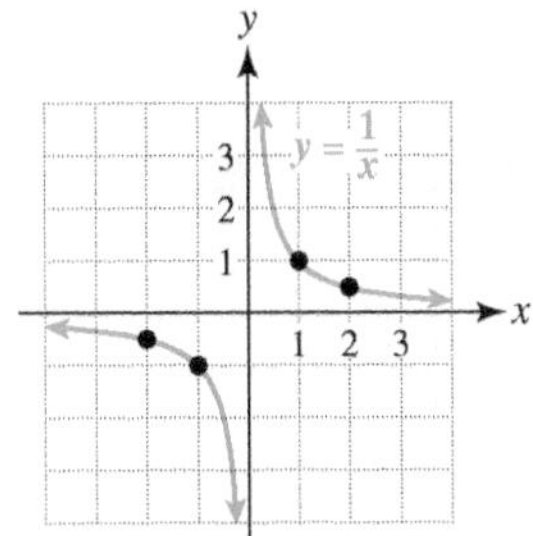

$D = (-\infty, 0) \cup (0, \infty)$
$R = (-\infty, 0) \cup (0, \infty)$

Base-2 Exponential Function: $f(x) = 2^x$

x	-2	-1	0	1	2
$y = 2^x$	$\frac{1}{4}$	$\frac{1}{2}$	1	2	4

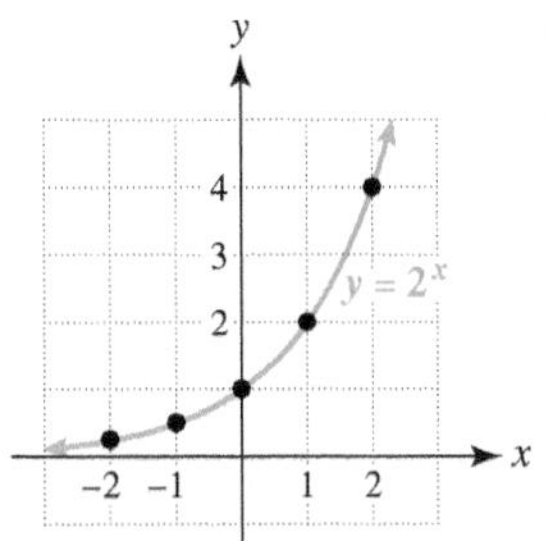

$D = (-\infty, \infty)$
$R = (0, \infty)$

Natural Exponential Function: $f(x) = e^x$

x	-2	-1	0	1	2
$y = e^x$	e^{-2}	e^{-1}	1	e^1	e^2

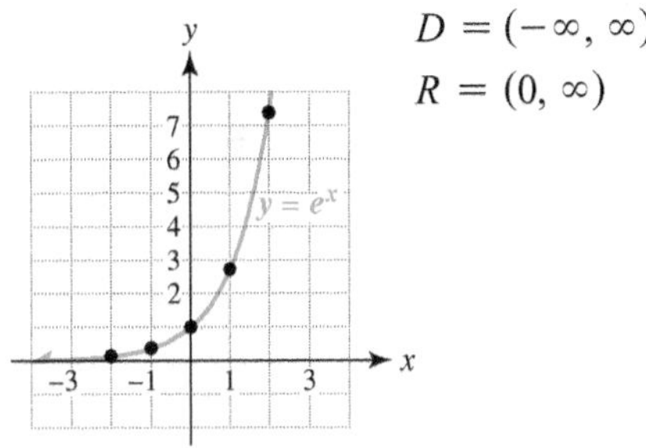

$D = (-\infty, \infty)$
$R = (0, \infty)$

Common Logarithmic Function: $f(x) = \log x$

x	0.1	1	4	7	10
$y = \log x$	-1	0	$\log 4$	$\log 7$	1

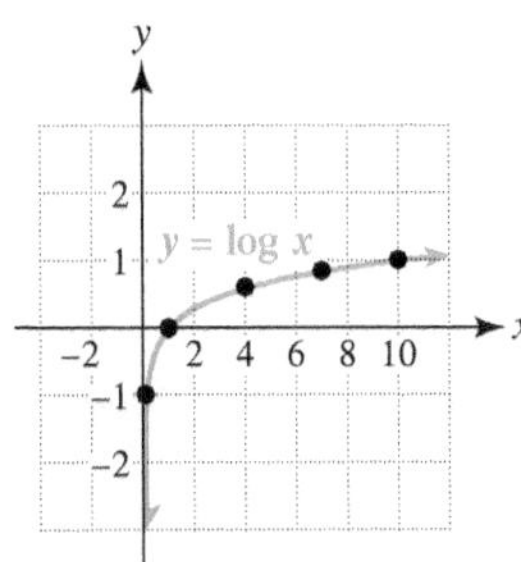

$D = (0, \infty)$
$R = (-\infty, \infty)$

Natural Logarithmic Function: $f(x) = \ln x$

x	$\frac{1}{2}$	1	2	e	e^2
$y = \ln x$	$\ln \frac{1}{2}$	0	$\ln 2$	1	2

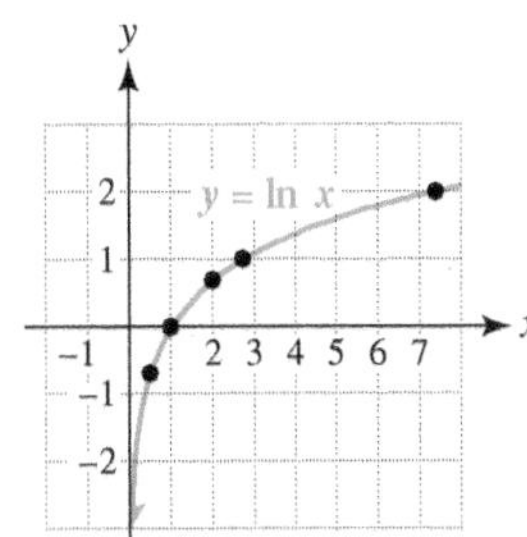

$D = (0, \infty)$
$R = (-\infty, \infty)$

Families of Functions

This subsection shows the formulas and graphs of some families of functions, such as linear, quadratic, and exponential. Notice that the appearance of the graphs of these functions depends on the value of k, m, or a.

Constant Functions: $f(x) = k$

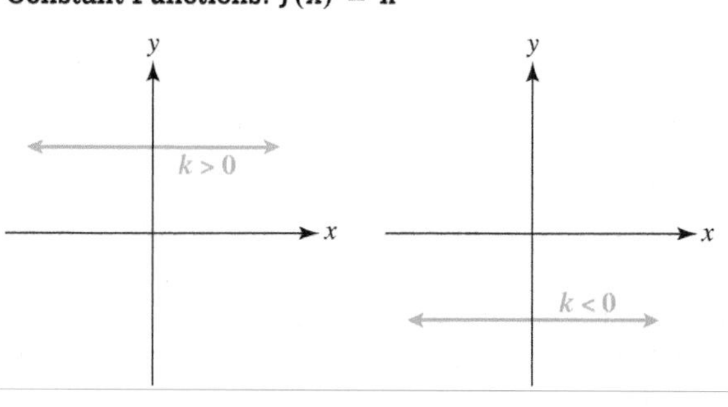

Linear Functions: $f(x) = mx + b$

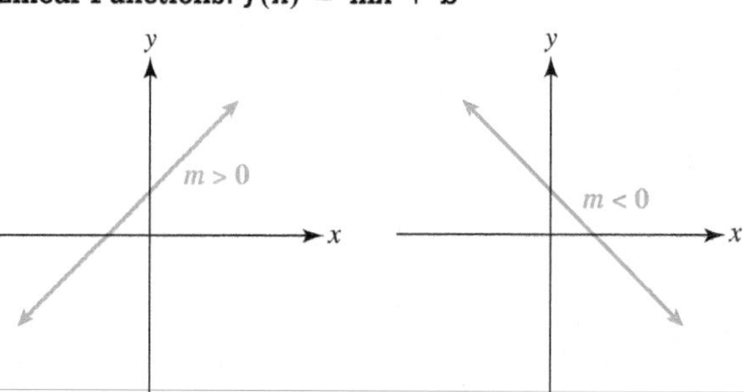

Quadratic Functions: $f(x) = ax^2 + bx + c$

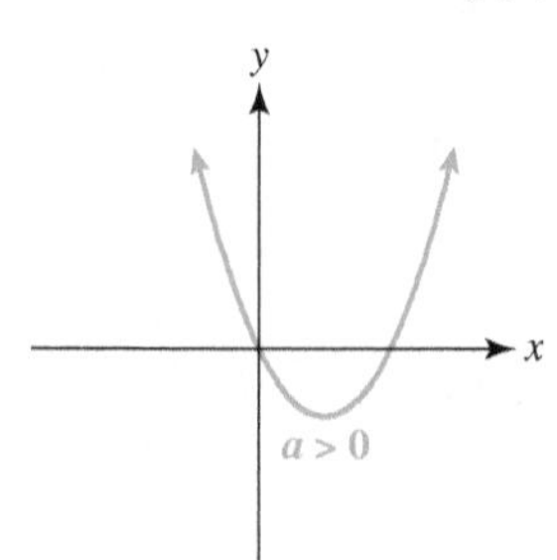

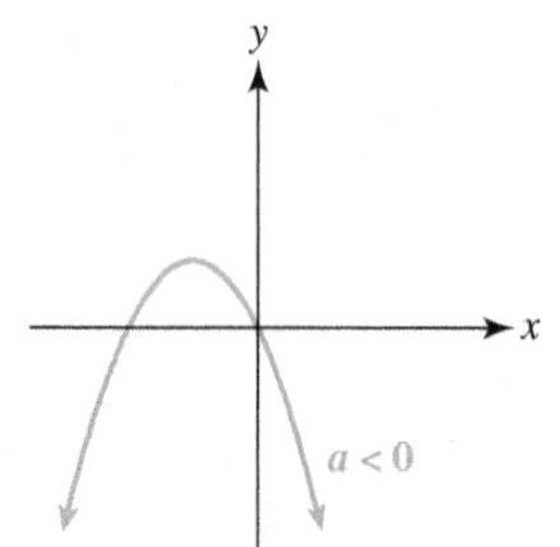

Cubic Functions: $f(x) = ax^3 + bx^2 + cx + d$

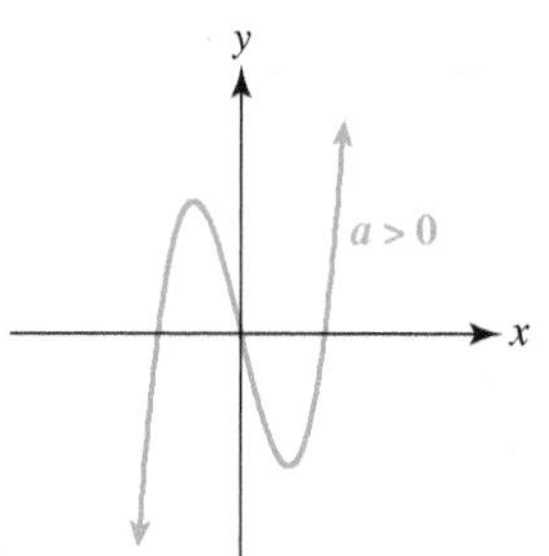

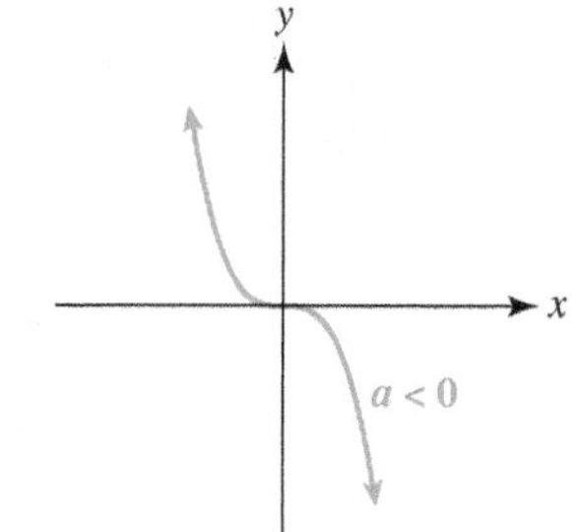

Quartic Functions: $f(x) = ax^4 + bx^3 + cx^2 + dx + e$

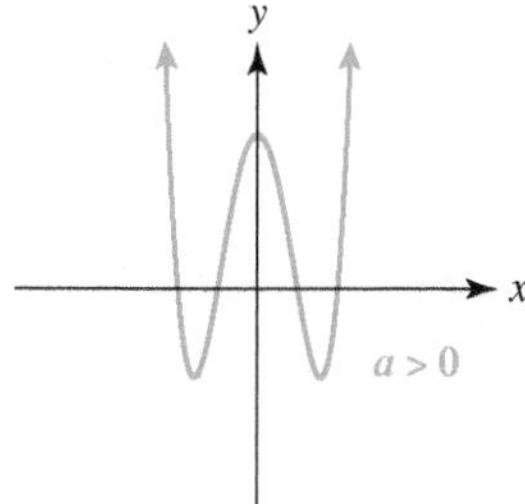

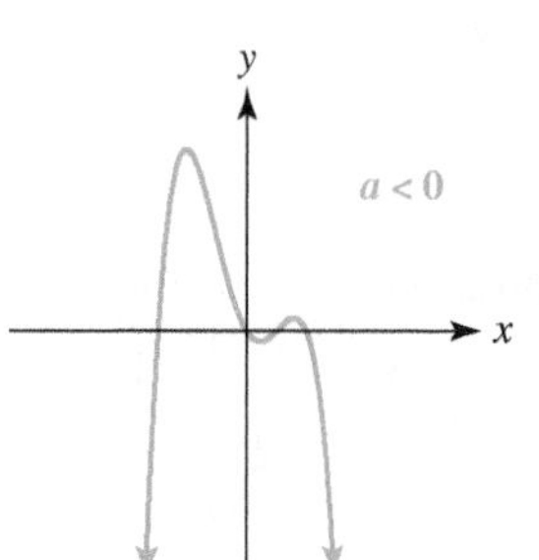

Power Functions: $f(x) = x^a, x > 0$

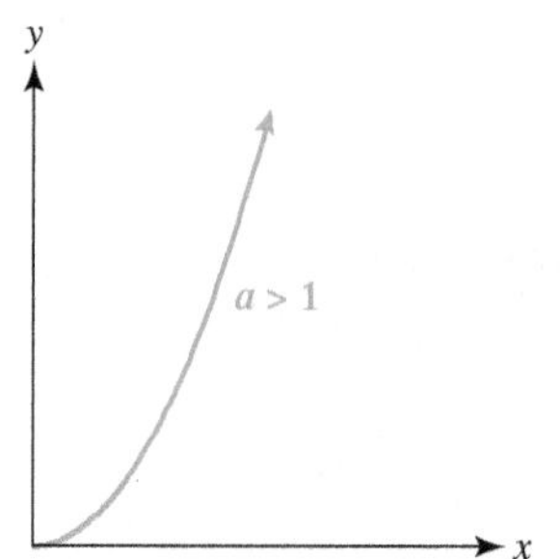

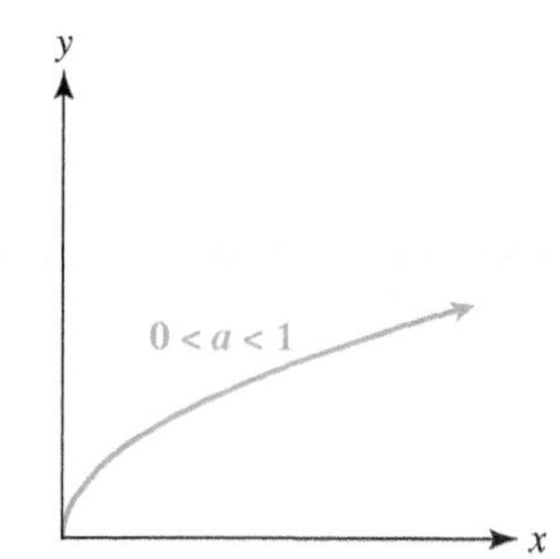

Exponential Functions: $f(x) = Ca^x, C > 0$

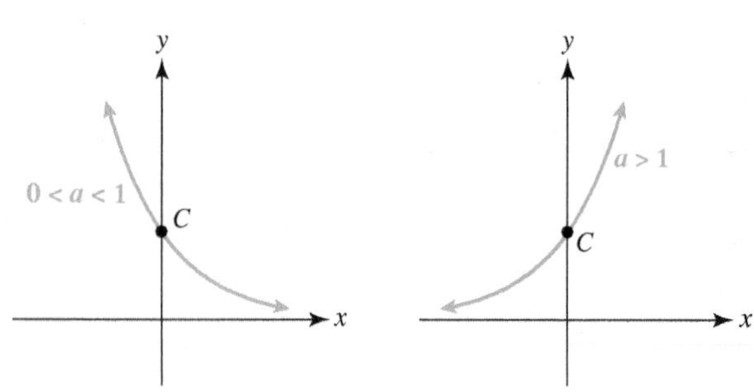

Logarithmic Functions: $f(x) = \log_a x$

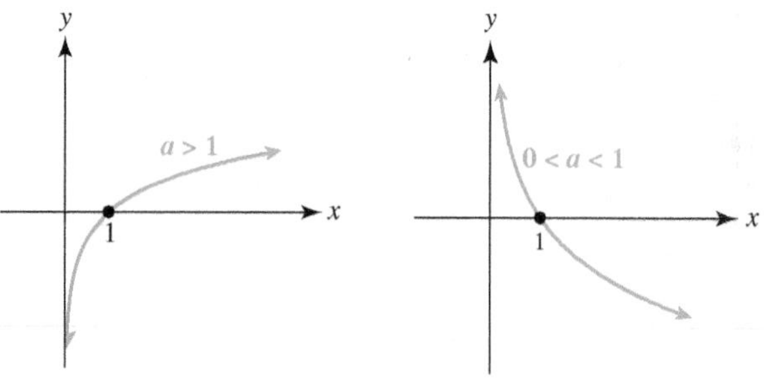

C Percent Change and Exponential Functions

Percentages and Percent Change

Percentages A percentage can be written either in **percent form** or in **decimal form**. For example, the percent form of 15% can be also written in decimal form as 0.15. To change a percent form $R\%$ to a decimal form r we divide R by 100. That is, $r = \frac{R}{100}$.

EXAMPLE 1 **Writing percentages as decimals**

Write each percentage as a decimal.

(a) 45% **(b)** 0.03% **(c)** 420% **(d)** -1.45% **(e)** $\frac{2}{5}\%$

SOLUTION

(a) Let $R = 45$. Then $r = \frac{45}{100} = 0.45$.

(b) Let $R = 0.03$. Then $r = \frac{0.03}{100} = 0.0003$.

(c) Let $R = 420$. Then $r = \frac{420}{100} = 4.2$.

(d) Let $R = -1.45$. Then $r = \frac{-1.45}{100} = -0.0145$. A negative percentage generally corresponds to a quantity decreasing rather than increasing.

(e) Let $R = \frac{2}{5}$. Then $r = \frac{\frac{2}{5}}{100} = \frac{2}{500} = 0.004$.

Now Try Exercise 1

NOTE Dividing a number by 100 is equivalent to moving the decimal point two places to the *left*.

In a similar manner a decimal form r can be changed to a percent form R by using the formula $R = 100r$. For example, the decimal form 0.047 has the percent form

$$R = 100r = 100(0.047) = 4.7\%.$$

In this calculation the decimal point is moved 2 places to the *right*.

Percent Change When an amount A_1 changes to a new amount A_2, then the **percent change** is

$$\frac{A_2 - A_1}{A_1} \times 100. \qquad \text{Percent change}$$

We multiply by 100 to change decimal form to percent form.

EXAMPLE 2 **Finding percent change**

Complete the following.

(a) Find the percent change if an account increases from \$1200 to \$1500.

(b) Find the percent change if an account decreases from \$1500 to \$1200.

(c) Comment on your results from parts (a) and (b).

SOLUTION

(a) Let $A_1 = 1200$ and $A_2 = 1500$.

$$\frac{1500 - 1200}{1200} \times 100 = \frac{300}{1200} \times 100$$
$$= \frac{1}{4} \times 100$$
$$= 25\%$$

The percent change (increase) is 25%.

(b) Let $A_1 = 1500$ and $A_2 = 1200$.

$$\frac{1200 - 1500}{1500} \times 100 = -\frac{300}{1500} \times 100$$
$$= -\frac{1}{5} \times 100$$
$$= -20\%$$

The percent change (decrease) is -20%.

(c) Notice that the account increased by 25% and then decreased by 20% to return to its initial value. Because the initial amount of $A_1 = \$1500$ in part (b) is larger than the initial amount $A_1 = \$1200$ in part (a), the amount of \$1500 only needs to decrease by 20% or \$300, to return to the original \$1200.

Now Try Exercise 9

Suppose a child's weight increases from 20 pounds to 60 pounds over a period of years. The percent increase is

$$\frac{60 - 20}{20} \times 100 = 2 \times 100 = 200\%.$$

Notice that the child's weight *tripled* and the percent change is 200%, *not* 300%. The actual *increase* in weight is 40 pounds and can be found by taking 200% of 20 pounds.

$$200\% \text{ of } 20 = 2.00 \times 20 = 40 \text{ pounds} \qquad \text{Change 200\% to decimal form.}$$

If we want to find the percent change, expressed in *decimal form*, of an amount A_1 changing to an amount A_2, then we do not need to multiply by 100. Thus

$$r = \frac{A_2 - A_1}{A_1}.$$

We can solve this equation for A_2.

$$r = \frac{A_2 - A_1}{A_1} \qquad \text{Percent change in decimal form}$$
$$rA_1 = A_2 - A_1 \qquad \text{Multiply each side by } A_1.$$
$$A_1 + rA_1 = A_2 \qquad \text{Add } A_1 \text{ to each side.}$$
$$A_2 = A_1 + rA_1 \qquad \text{Rewrite the equation.}$$

Thus, if the percent increase in an amount A_1 is given by r in *decimal form*, then the *increase* (or *decrease*) in A_1 is given by rA_1 and the *final amount* is given by $A_1 + rA_1$, or $A_1(1 + r)$. The initial amount A_1 changes by the *factor* $1 + r$.

For example, if a \$100,000 budget decreases by 12%, then

$$rA_1 = -0.12(100{,}000) = -\$12{,}000$$

and the budget decrease is \$12,000. Also,

$$A_1 + rA_1 = 100{,}000 + (-0.12)(100{,}000) = \$88{,}000$$

and the new budget decreased to \$88,000. The budget changed by a factor of

$$1 + r = 1 + (-0.12) = 0.88,$$

or the budget is now 88% of the original budget.

EXAMPLE 3 **Analyzing the increase in an account**

An account that contains \$5000 increases in value by 150%.

(a) Find the increase in value of the account.

(b) Find the final value of the account.

(c) By what factor did the account increase?

SOLUTION

(a) Let $A_1 = 5000$ and $r = 1.50$ (150% in decimal form). The increase is

$$rA_1 = 1.50(5000) = 7500.$$

The account increased in value by \$7500.

(b) The final value of the account is $A_1 + rA_1 = 5000 + 7500 = \$12{,}500$.

(c) The account increased in value by a factor of $1 + r = 1 + 1.50 = 2.5$. Note that $5000(2.5) = 12{,}500$.

Now Try Exercise 15

More Exponential Functions and Models

Section 5.3 discussed how an exponential function results when the *initial value* C is multiplied by a *constant factor* a for each unit increase in x. For example, if an initial value of $C = 3$ is multiplied by a *constant growth factor* of $a = 2$ for each unit increase in x, then the exponential function

$$f(x) = 3(2)^x \qquad \text{Initial value} = 3\text{, growth factor} = 2$$

models this growth. This concept can be used to describe exponential functions and models in terms of *constant percent change*.

Suppose that an initial population of a country is $P_0 = 10$ million and the population increases by 1.2% in 1 year. Then the increase is

$$rP_0 = 0.012(10) = 0.12 \text{ million,} \qquad \text{1.2\% equals 0.012 in decimal form.}$$

and after 1 year the new population is

$$P_0(1 + r)^1 = 10(1.012)^1 = 10.12 \text{ million.}$$

After 1 year the population has increased by a *growth factor* of $1 + r$, or 1.012. If the rate of growth were to remain constant in future years, then after x years the population would be

$$P_0(1 + r)^x = 10(1.012)^x$$

with initial value $C = 10$ and *growth* factor $a = 1.012$.

EXAMPLE 4 **Finding exponential models**

A sample of 10,000 insects is decreasing in number by 8% per week. Find an exponential model $f(x)$ that describes this population after x weeks.

SOLUTION The initial value is $C = 10{,}000$, the rate of decrease is $r = -0.08$, and the *decay* factor is

$$a = 1 + r = 1 + (-0.08) = 0.92.$$

Thus the sample of insects contains

$$f(x) = 10{,}000(0.92)^x$$

insects after x weeks.

Now Try Exercise 21

These concepts are summarized in the following box.

PERCENT CHANGE AND EXPONENTIAL FUNCTIONS

Suppose that an amount A changes by R percent (or r expressed in decimal form) for each unit increase in x. Then the following hold.

1. $r = \dfrac{R}{100}$ and $R = 100r$.
2. If $r > 0$, the **constant growth factor** is $a = 1 + r$ and $a > 1$.
3. If $r < 0$, the **constant decay factor** is $a = 1 + r$ and $0 < a < 1$.
4. If the initial amount is C, then the amount A after an x-unit increase in time is given by the exponential model

$$A(x) = C(1 + r)^x, \quad \text{or} \quad A(x) = Ca^x.$$

EXAMPLE 5 Analyzing constant percent change

For each $f(x)$, give the initial value, the growth or decay factor, and percent change for each unit increase in x.

(a) $f(x) = 5(1.034)^x$ **(b)** $f(x) = 10(0.45)^x$ **(c)** $f(x) = 3^x$

SOLUTION

(a) For $f(x) = 5(1.034)^x$ the initial value is $C = 5$ and the growth factor is $a = 1.034$. Because $a = 1 + r$, it follows that

$$r = a - 1 = 1.034 - 1 = 0.034.$$

The percent change for each unit increase in x is 3.4%.

(b) For $f(x) = 10(0.45)^x$ the initial value is $C = 10$ and the decay factor is $a = 0.45$. The percent change for each unit increase in x is

$$r = a - 1 = 0.45 - 1 = -0.55, \text{ or } -55\%.$$

(c) For $f(x) = 3^x$ the initial value is $C = 1$ and the growth factor is $a = 3$. The percent change for each unit increase in x is $r = a - 1 = 3 - 1 = 2$, or 200%.

Now Try Exercises 27, 29, and 31

Growth and Decay Models If an initial quantity A_0 either grows or decays by a factor of b each k units of time, then the amount A after t units of time is given by the exponential model

$$A(t) = Ab^{t/k}.$$

For example, if 700 bacteria triple every 5 days, the formula

$$A(t) = 700(3)^{t/5}$$

gives the number of bacteria after t days.

EXAMPLE 6 Applying an exponential model

The population of a city is currently 239,000 and is increasing at a constant rate of 8.5% every 4 years. Find the population of this city after 7 years.

SOLUTION The population of the city is 239,000 and increasing by a factor of 1.085 every 4 years. Thus $A_0 = 239{,}000$, $b = 1.085$, $k = 4$, and

$$A(t) = 239{,}000(1.085)^{t/4}.$$

After 7 years the population is

$$A(7) = 239{,}000(1.085)^{7/4} \approx 275{,}677.$$

Now Try Exercise 37

Rule of 70 The **rule of 70** can be used to quickly estimate the number of years it takes for an investment to double. If R is the interest rate (in percent form) and T is the number of years for a quantity to double, then

$$RT = 70. \quad \text{Rule of 70}$$

Interest rate (%) — Years to double

This formula is most accurate for continuous compounding, but it can also be applied to other types of compound interest. For example, if we deposit an amount of money at 5% interest compounded continuously, then it will require about

$$T = \frac{70}{R} = \frac{70}{5} = 14 \text{ years}$$

to double. Similarly, if a city's population doubles in 35 years, then its annual growth rate is about

$$R = \frac{70}{T} = \frac{70}{35} = 2\%.$$

See Exercises 45–50.

C Exercises

Percentages

Exercises 1–4: Write each percentage in decimal form.

1. (a) 35% (b) −0.07% (c) 721% (d) $\frac{3}{10}\%$

2. (a) 95% (b) 0.321% (c) −175% (d) $\frac{4}{5}\%$

3. (a) −5.5% (b) −1.54% (c) 120% (d) $\frac{3}{20}\%$

4. (a) −4.7% (b) −0.01% (c) 500% (d) $\frac{1}{40}\%$

Exercises 5–8: Write each decimal form in percent form.

5. (a) 0.37 (b) −0.095 (c) 1.9 (d) $\frac{7}{20}$

6. (a) 0.97 (b) −0.04 (c) 10 (d) $\frac{9}{10}$

7. (a) −0.121 (b) 1.4 (c) 3.2 (d) $-\frac{1}{4}$

8. (a) 0.001 (b) 12 (c) 1.01 (d) $-\frac{1}{8}$

Percent Change

Exercises 9–14: For the given amounts A and B, find each of the following. Round values to the nearest hundredth when appropriate.

(a) The percent change if A changes to B
(b) The percent change if B changes to A

9. $A = \$500, B = \$1000$ **10.** $A = \$500, B = \$200$

11. $A = \$1.27, B = \$1.30$ **12.** $A = 15, B = 5$

13. $A = 45, B = 65$ **14.** $A = 75, B = 50$

Exercises 15–20: An account contains A dollars and increases/decreases by R percent. For each A and R, complete the following.

(a) Find the increase/decrease in value of the account.
(b) Find the final value of the account.
(c) By what factor did the account value increase/decrease?

15. $A = \$1500, R = 120\%$

16. $A = \$3500, R = 210\%$

17. $A = \$4000, R = -55\%$

18. $A = \$6000, R = -75\%$

19. $A = \$7500, R = -60\%$

20. $A = \$9000, R = 85\%$

Exponential Models

Exercises 21–26: Find an exponential model $f(x)$ that describes each situation.

21. A sample of 9500 insects decreases in number by 35% per week

22. A sample of 5000 insects increases in number by 120% per day

23. A sample of 2500 fish increases in number by 5% per month

24. A sample of 152 birds decreases in number by 3.4% per week

25. A mutual fund account contains $1000 and decreases by 6.5% per year

26. A mutual fund account contains $2500 and increases by 2.1% per year

Exercises 27–36: For the given $f(x)$, state the initial value, the growth or decay factor, and percent change for each unit increase in x.

27. $f(x) = 8(1.12)^x$ **28.** $f(x) = 9(1.005)^x$

29. $f(x) = 1.5(0.35)^x$

30. $f(x) = 100(1.23)^x$

31. $f(x) = 0.55^x$

32. $f(x) = 0.4^x$

33. $f(x) = 7e^x$

34. $f(x) = 91e^{x/2}$

35. $f(x) = 6(3^{-x})$

36. $f(x) = 9(4^{-x})$

Exercises 37–44: (Refer to Example 6.) Write a formula for $f(t)$ that models the situation and then answer the question.

37. The population of a city is currently 35,000 and is increasing at a constant rate of 9.8% every 2 years. What is the population after 5 years?

38. A savings account contains $2500 and increases by 10% in 3 years. How much is in the account after 8 years?

39. A sample of 1000 bacteria triples in number every 7 hours. How many bacteria are there after 11 hours?

40. A sample of 5 million insects decreases in number by $\frac{2}{3}$ every 10 days. In millions, how many insects are there after 65 days?

41. The intensity I_0 of a light passing through colored glass decreases by $\frac{1}{3}$ for each 2 millimeters in thickness of the glass. What is the intensity of the light in terms of I_0 after passing through 4.3 millimeters of colored glass?

42. The intensity I_0 of a sound passing through the atmosphere decreases 20% for each 100 feet of distance. What is the intensity of the sound in terms of I_0 after traveling a distance of 450 feet?

43. An investment of $5000 will quadruple every 35 years. How much is the investment worth after 8 years?

44. An investment of $2500 increases by a factor of 1.2 every 4 years. How much is the investment worth after 9 years?

Exercises 45–50: **Rule of 70** *Use the rule of 70 to estimate the time required for the given principal P to double at the annual percent interest rate R. Check your answer by using the continuously compounded interest formula.*

45. $P = \$2000, R = 7\%$ **46.** $P = \$1200, R = 14\%$

47. $P = \$500, R = 20\%$ **48.** $P = \$9000, R = 10\%$

49. $P = \$1500, R = 25\%$ **50.** $P = \$5000, R = 8\%$

Exercises 51–56: **Rule of 70** *Use the rule of 70 to estimate the annual percent rate of growth for a city whose population P doubles in time T.*

51. $P = 150{,}000, T = 40$ years

52. $P = 400{,}000, T = 25$ years

53. $P = 1{,}500{,}000$, $T = 35$ years

54. $P = 20{,}000$, $T = 10$ years

55. $P = 750{,}000$, $T = 70$ years

56. $P = 80{,}000$, $T = 50$ years

Applications

57. **Bacteria Growth** A population of bacteria increases by 6% every 8 hours. By what percentage does the sample increase in 3 hours?

58. **Bacteria Growth** A population of bacteria decreases by 40% every 4 hours. By what percentage does the sample decrease in 7 hours?

59. **Percent Change** The number of cell phone subscribers to a company increases by 25% during the first year and then decreases by 20% the second year. Compare the number of subscribers at the beginning of the first year with the number of subscribers at the end of the second year.

60. **Wage Increase** If your wages are \$8 per hour and you receive a 300% raise for excellent work, determine your new wages.

61. **Wages** If a wage of \$9.81 decreases by 9% each year, what is the new wage after 3 years?

62. **Pollution** A pollutant in a river has an initial concentration of 3 parts per million and degrades at a rate of 3% every 2 years. Approximate its concentration after 20 years.

63. **Radioactive Half-Life** A radioactive element decays to 40% of its original amount every 2 years. Approximate the percentage that remains after 8 years.

64. **Radioactive Half-Life** A radioactive element decays to 80% of its original amount every 3 years. Approximate the percentage that remains after 8 years.

Bibliography

Battan, L. *Weather in Your Life.* San Francisco: W. H. Freeman, 1983.

Beckmann, P. *A History of Pi.* New York: Barnes and Noble, 1993.

Bell, D. *Fundamentals of Electric Circuits*, Reston, Va.: Reston Publishing Company, 1981.

Brearley, J., and A. Nicholas. *This Is the Bichon Frise.* Hong Kong: TFH Publication, 1973.

Brown, D., and P. Rothery. *Models in Biology: Mathematics, Statistics and Computing.* West Sussex, England: John Wiley and Sons, 1993.

Carlson, T. "Über Geschwindigkeit und Grösse der Hefevermehrung in Würze." *Biochem. A.* 57:313–334.

Cheney, W., and D. Kincaid. *Numerical Mathematics and Computing.* 3rd ed. Pacific Grove, Calif.: Brooks/Cole Publishing Company, 1994.

Clime, W. *The Economics of Global Warming.* Washington, D.C.: Institute for International Economics, 1992.

Cotton, W., and R. Pielke. *Human Impacts on Weather and Climate.* Geophysical Science Series, vol. 2. Fort Collins, Colo.: *ASTeR Press, 1992.

Eves, H. *An Introduction to the History of Mathematics.* 5th ed. Philadelphia: Saunders College Publishing, 1983.

Foster, R., and J. Bates. "Use of mussels to monitor point source industrial discharges." *Environ. Sci. Technol.* 12:958–962.

Freedman, B. *Environmental Ecology: The Ecological Effects of Pollution, Disturbance, and Other Stresses.* 2nd ed. San Diego: Academic Press, 1995.

Garber, N., and L. Hoel. *Traffic and Highway Engineering.* Boston, Mass.: PWS Publishing Co., 1997.

Good, I. J. "What is the most amazing approximate integer in the universe?" *Pi Mu Epsilon Journal* 5 (1972): 314–315.

Grigg, D. *The World Food Problem.* Oxford: Blackwell Publishers, 1993.

Haber-Schaim, U., J. Cross, G. Abegg, J. Dodge, and J. Walter. *Introductory Physical Science.* Englewood Cliffs, N.J.: Prentice Hall, 1972.

Haefner, L. *Introduction to Transportation Systems.* New York: Holt, Rinehart and Winston, 1986.

Harrison, F., F. Hills, J. Paterson, and R. Saunders. "The measurement of liver blood flow in conscious calves." *Quarterly Journal of Experimental Physiology* 71:235–247.

Hartman, D. *Global Physical Climatology.* San Diego: Academic Press, 1994.

Heinz-Otto, P., H. Jürgens, and D. Saupe. *Chaos and Fractals: New Frontiers in Science.* New York: Springer-Verlag, 1993.

Hibbeler, R. *Structural Analysis.* Englewood Cliffs, N.J.: Prentice-Hall, 1995.

Hines, A., T. Ghosh, S. Loyalka, and R. Warder, Jr. *Indoor Air Quality and Control.* Englewood Cliffs, N.J.: Prentice-Hall, 1993.

Hoggar, S. *Mathematics for Computer Graphics.* New York: Cambridge University Press, 1993.

Hoppensteadt, F., and C. Peskin. *Mathematics in Medicine and the Life Sciences.* New York: Springer-Verlag, 1992.

Hosmer, D., and S. Lemeshow. *Applied Logistic Regression.* New York: John Wiley and Sons, 1989.

Howatson, A. *Electrical Circuits and Systems.* New York: Oxford University Press, 1996.

Howells, G. *Acid Rain and Acid Waters.* 2nd ed. New York: Ellis Horwood, 1995.

Huffman, R. *Atmospheric Ultraviolet Remote Sensing.* San Diego: Academic Press, 1992.

Huxley, J. *Problems of Relative Growth.* London: Methuen and Co., 1932.

Jarrett, J. *Business Forecasting Methods.* Oxford: Basil Blackwell, 1991.

Karttunen, H., P. Kroger, H. Oja, M. Poutanen, and K. Donner, eds. *Fundamental Astronomy.* 2nd ed. New York: Springer-Verlag, 1994.

Kerlow, I. *The Art of 3-D Computer Animation and Imaging.* New York: Van Nostrand Riehold, 1996.

Kline, M. *The Loss of Certainty.* New York: Oxford University Press, 1980.

Kraljic, M. *The Greenhouse Effect.* New York: The H. W. Wilson Company, 1992.

Kress, S. *Bird Life—A Guide to the Behavior and Biology of Birds.* Racine, Wisc.: Western Publishing Company, 1991.

Lack, D. *The Life of a Robin.* London: Collins, 1965.

Lancaster, H. *Quantitative Methods in Biological and Medical Sciences: A Historical Essay.* New York: Springer-Verlag, 1994.

Loh, W. *Dynamics and Thermodynamics of Planetary Entry.* Englewood Cliffs, N.J.: Prentice-Hall, 1963.

Makridakis, S., and S. Wheelwright. *Forecasting Methods for Management.* New York: John Wiley and Sons, 1989.

Mannering, F., and W. Kilareski. *Principles of Highway Engineering and Traffic Analysis.* New York: John Wiley and Sons, 1990.

Mar, J., and H. Liebowitz. *Structure Technology for Large Radio and Radar Telescope Systems.* Cambridge, Mass.: The MIT Press, 1969.

Mason, C. *Biology of Freshwater Pollution.* New York: Longman and Scientific and Technical, John Wiley and Sons, 1991.

Mehrotra, A. *Cellular Radio: Analog and Digital Systems.* Boston: Artech House, 1994.

Miller, A., and J. Thompson. *Elements of Meteorology.* 2nd ed. Columbus, Ohio: Charles E. Merrill Publishing Company, 1975.

Miller, A., and R. Anthes. *Meteorology.* 5th ed. Columbus, Ohio: Charles E. Merrill Publishing Company, 1985.

Mortenson, M. *Computer Graphics: An Introduction to Mathematics and Geometry.* New York: Industrial Press Inc., 1989.

Motz, L., and J. Weaver. *The Story of Mathematics.* New York: Plenum Press, 1993.

National Council of Teachers of Mathematics. *Historical Topics for the Mathematics Classroom, Thirty-first Yearbook,* 1969.

Navarra, J. *Atmosphere, Weather and Climate.* Philadelphia: W. B. Saunders, 1979.

Nilsson, A. *Greenhouse Earth.* New York: John Wiley and Sons, 1992.

Pennycuick, C. *Newton Rules Biology.* New York: Oxford University Press, 1992.

Pielou, E. *Population and Community Ecology: Principles and Methods.* New York: Gordon and Breach Science Publishers, 1974.

Pokorny, C., and C. Gerald. *Computer Graphics: The Principles behind the Art and Science.* Irvine, Calif.: Franklin, Beedle, and Associates, 1989.

Raggett, G. "Modeling the Eyam plague." *The Institute of Mathematics and Its Applications* 18: 221–226.

Rist, Curtis. "The Physics of Foul Shots." *Discover,* October 2000.

Robert Wood Johnson Foundation. *Chronic Care in America: A 21st Century Challenge,* 1996.

Rodricks, J. *Calculated Risk.* New York: Cambridge University Press, 1992.

Rogers, E., and T. Kostigen. *The Green Book.* New York: Random House, 2007.

Ronan, C. *The Natural History of the Universe.* New York: MacMillan Publishing Company, 1991.

Ryan, B., B. Joiner, and T. Ryan. *Minitab Handbook.* Boston: Duxbury Press, 1985.

Semat, H., and J. Albright. *Introduction to Atomic and Nuclear Physics.* Austin, Tex.: Holt, Rinehart and Winston, 1972.

Sharov, A., and I. Novikov. *Edwin Hubble: The Discoverer of the Big Bang Universe.* New York: Cambridge University Press, 1993.

Sinkov, A. *Elementary Cryptanalysis: A Mathematical Approach.* New York: Random House, 1968.

Socolow, R., and S. Pacala. "A Plan to Keep Carbon in Check." *Scientific American,* September 2006.

Stent, G. S. *Molecular Biology of Bacterial Viruses.* San Francisco: W. H. Freeman, 1963.

Thomas, D. *Swimming Pool Operators Handbook.* Washington, D.C.: National Swimming Pool Foundation, 1972.

Thomas, R. *The Old Farmer's 2012 Almanac.* Dublin, N.H.: The Old Farmer's Almanac, 2011.

Thomas, V. *Science and Sport.* London: Faber and Faber, 1970.

Thomson, W. *Introduction to Space Dynamics.* New York: John Wiley and Sons, 1961.

Triola, M. *Elementary Statistics.* Pearson Education, 2012.

Tucker, A., A. Bernat, W. Bradley, R. Cupper, and G. Scragg. *Fundamentals of Computing 1. Logic: Problem Solving, Programs, and Computers.* New York: McGraw-Hill, 1995.

Turner, R. K., D. Pierce, and I. Bateman. *Environmental Economics: An Elementary Approach.* Baltimore: The Johns Hopkins University Press, 1993.

Varley, G., and G. Gradwell. "Population models for the winter moth." *Symposium of the Royal Entomological Society of London* 4:132–142.

Walker, A. *Observation and Inference: An Introduction to the Methods of Epidemiology.* Newton Lower Falls, Mass.: Epidemiology Resources, 1991.

Wang, Z. "Self-Powered Nanotech." *Scientific American,* January 2008.

Watt, A. *3D Computer Graphics.* Reading, Mass.: Addison-Wesley Publishing Company, 1993.

Weidner, R., and R. Sells. *Elementary Classical Physics,* vol. 2. Boston: Allyn and Bacon, 1965.

Williams, J. *The Weather Almanac 1995.* New York: Vintage Books, 1994.

Wolff, R., and L. Yaeger. *Visualization of Natural Phenomena.* New York: Springer-Verlag, 1993.

Wuebbles, D., and J. Edmonds. *Primer on Greenhouse Gases.* Chelsea, Mich.: Lewis Publishers, 1991.

Zeilik, M., S. Gregory, and D. Smith. *Introductory Astronomy and Astrophysics.* 3rd ed. Philadelphia: Saunders College Publishers, 1992.

Answers to Selected Exercises

CHAPTER 1: Introduction to Functions and Graphs

SECTION 1.1 (pp. 8–10)

1. Rational number, real number **3.** Rational number, real number **5.** Real number **7.** Natural number: $\sqrt{9}$; integers: $-3, \sqrt{9}$; rational numbers: $-3, \frac{2}{9}, \sqrt{9}, 1.\overline{3}$; irrational numbers: $\pi, -\sqrt{2}$ **9.** Natural numbers: none; integer: $-\sqrt{4}$; rational numbers: $\frac{1}{3}$, 5.1×10^{-6}, -2.33, $0.\overline{7}$, $-\sqrt{4}$; irrational number: $\sqrt{13}$ **11.** Rational numbers **13.** Natural numbers **15.** Integers **17.** 51 **19.** -84 **21.** 0 **23.** 5 **25.** 8 **27.** -32 **29.** 4×10^1 **31.** 3.65×10^{-3} **33.** 2.45×10^3 **35.** 5.6×10^{-1} **37.** -8.7×10^{-3} **39.** 2.068×10^2 **41.** 0.000001 **43.** 200,000,000 **45.** 156.7 **47.** 500,000 **49.** 4500 **51.** 67,000 **53.** 8×10^8; 800,000,000 **55.** 3.5×10^{-1}; 0.35 **57.** 2.1×10^{-3}; 0.0021 **59.** 5×10^{-3}; 0.005 **61.** 4.24×10^{19} **63.** 8.72×10^4 **65.** 7.67×10^{11} **67.** 5.769 **69.** 0.058 **71.** 0.419 **73.** -1.235 **75.** 15.819 **77.** 1.4×10^{-1} watt **79.** About 53,794 miles per hour **81. (a)** 1.4% **(b)** 3.9% **83. (a)** 45,000,000 ft **(b)** Yes **85. (a)** $7.436\pi \approx 23.4$ in^3 **(b)** Yes

1.1 EXTENDED AND DISCOVERY EXERCISES (p. 11)

1. 2.9×10^{-4} cm **3.** 0.25 feet, or 3 inches

SECTION 1.2 (pp. 22–25)

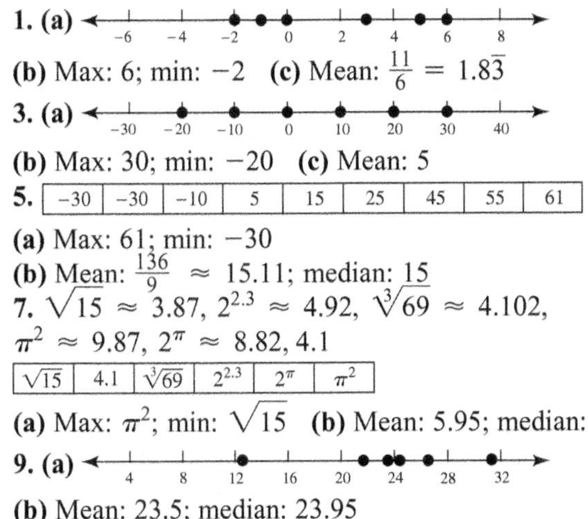

1. (a) (number line: −6, −4, −2, 0, 2, 4, 6, 8)

(b) Max: 6; min: -2 **(c)** Mean: $\frac{11}{6} = 1.8\overline{3}$

3. (a) (number line: −30, −20, −10, 0, 10, 20, 30, 40)

(b) Max: 30; min: -20 **(c)** Mean: 5

5.

−30	−30	−10	5	15	25	45	55	61

(a) Max: 61; min: -30
(b) Mean: $\frac{136}{9} \approx 15.11$; median: 15

7. $\sqrt{15} \approx 3.87$, $2^{2.3} \approx 4.92$, $\sqrt[3]{69} \approx 4.102$, $\pi^2 \approx 9.87$, $2^{\pi} \approx 8.82$, 4.1

$\sqrt{15}$	4.1	$\sqrt[3]{69}$	$2^{2.3}$	2^{π}	π^2

(a) Max: π^2; min: $\sqrt{15}$ **(b)** Mean: 5.95; median: 4.51

9. (a) (number line: 4, 8, 12, 16, 20, 24, 28, 32)

(b) Mean: 23.5; median: 23.95
The average area of the six largest lakes is 23,500 square miles. Half of these lakes have areas below 23,950 square miles and half have areas above. **(c)** Lake Superior

11. 16, 18, 26; no

13. (a) $S = \{(-1, 5), (2, 2), (3, -1), (5, -4), (9, -5)\}$
(b) $D = \{-1, 2, 3, 5, 9\}$, $R = \{-5, -4, -1, 2, 5\}$
15. (a) $S = \{(1, 5), (4, 5), (5, 6), (4, 6), (1, 5)\}$
(b) $D = \{1, 4, 5\}$, $R = \{5, 6\}$
17. (a) $D = \{-3, -2, 0, 7\}$, $R = \{-5, -3, 0, 4, 5\}$
(b) x-min: -3; x-max: 7; y-min: -5; y-max: 5
(c) & (d)

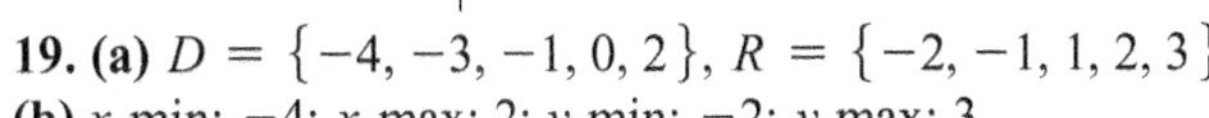

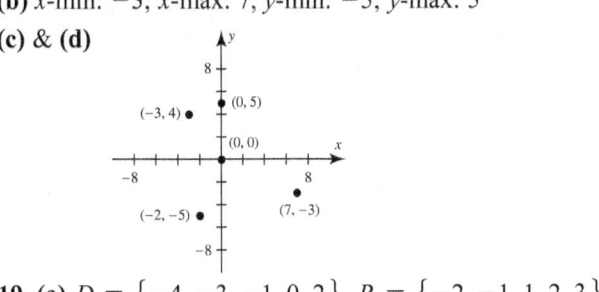

19. (a) $D = \{-4, -3, -1, 0, 2\}$, $R = \{-2, -1, 1, 2, 3\}$
(b) x-min: -4; x-max: 2; y-min: -2; y-max: 3
(c) & (d)

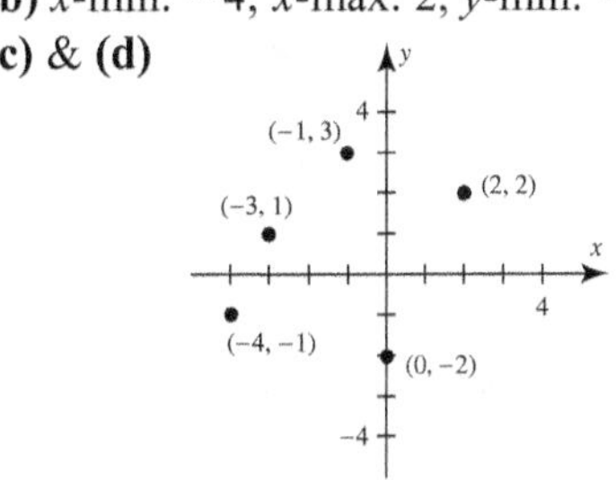

21. (a) $D = \{-35, -25, 0, 10, 75\}$, $R = \{-55, -25, 25, 45, 50\}$
(b) x-min: -35; x-max: 75; y-min: -55; y-max: 50
(c) & (d)

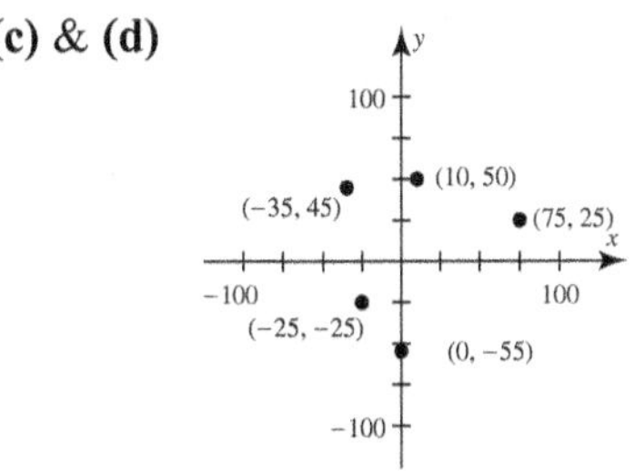

23. Scatterplot / Line graph

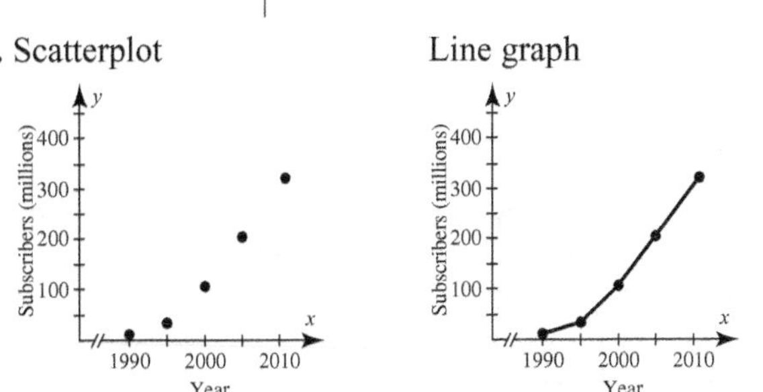

25. 5 **27.** $\sqrt{29} \approx 5.39$ **29.** $\sqrt{41.49} \approx 6.44$ **31.** 8
33. $\frac{\sqrt{17}}{4} \approx 1.03$ **35.** $\frac{\sqrt{2}}{2} \approx 0.71$ **37.** 130 **39.** $\sqrt{a^2 + b^2}$
41. Yes
43. (a)

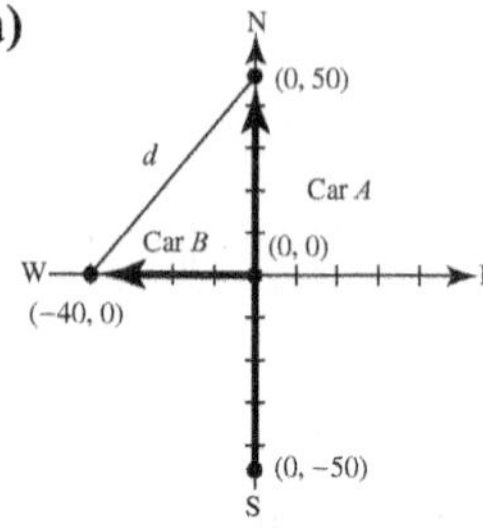

(b) $d = \sqrt{4100} \approx 64.0$ miles
45. 27 million units **47.** 9.5 seconds **49.** $(3, -0.5)$
51. $(10, 10)$ **53.** $(-2.1, -0.35)$ **55.** $(\sqrt{2}, 0)$ **57.** $(0, 2b)$
59. Center: $(0, 0)$; radius: 5 **61.** Center: $(0, 0)$; radius: $\sqrt{7}$
63. Center: $(2, -3)$; radius: 3 **65.** Center: $(0, -1)$; radius: 10
67. $(x - 1)^2 + (y + 2)^2 = 1$
69. $(x + 2)^2 + (y - 1)^2 = 4$
71. $(x - 3)^2 + (y + 5)^2 = 64$ **73.** $(x - 3)^2 + y^2 = 49$
75. $(x - 3)^2 + (y + 5)^2 = 50$
77. $(x + 2)^2 + (y + 3)^2 = 25$
79. $\left(x - \frac{7}{2}\right)^2 + (y - 3)^2 = \frac{25}{4}$

81.

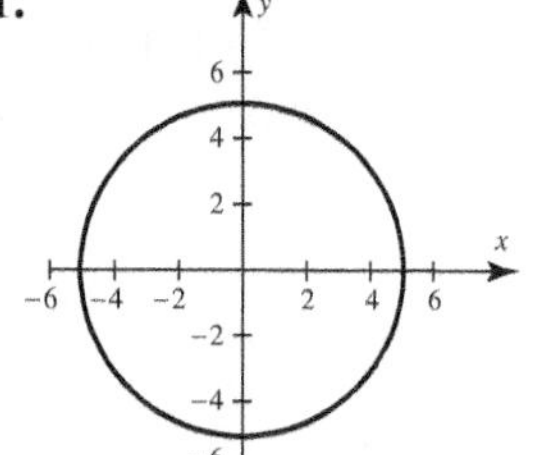

83.

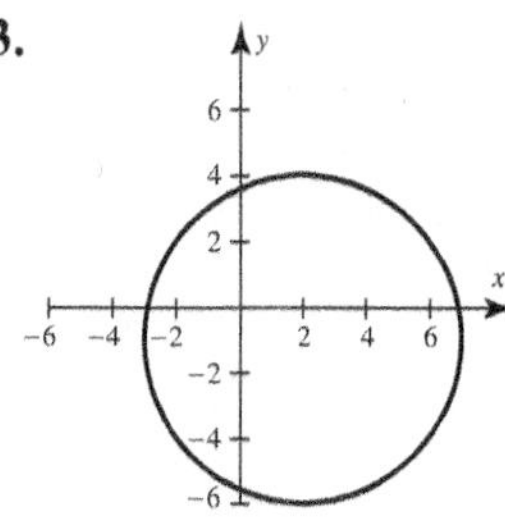

85.

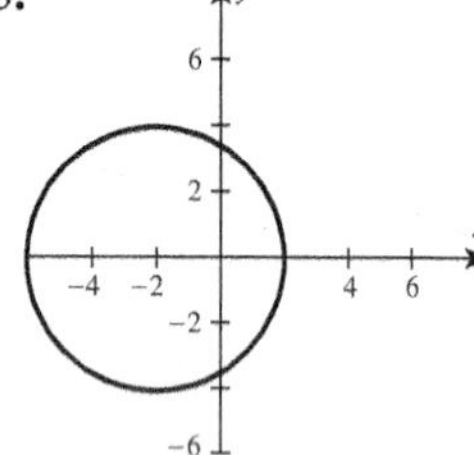

87.

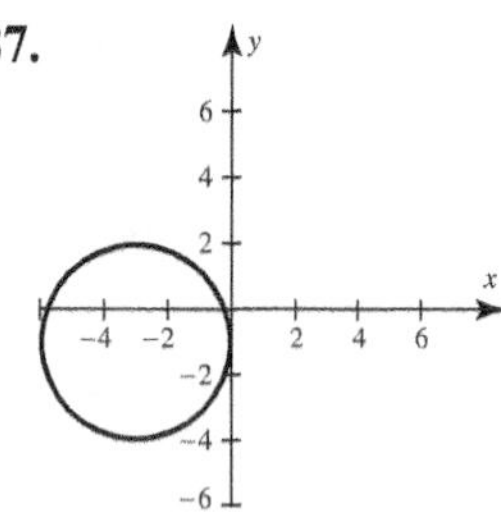

89.

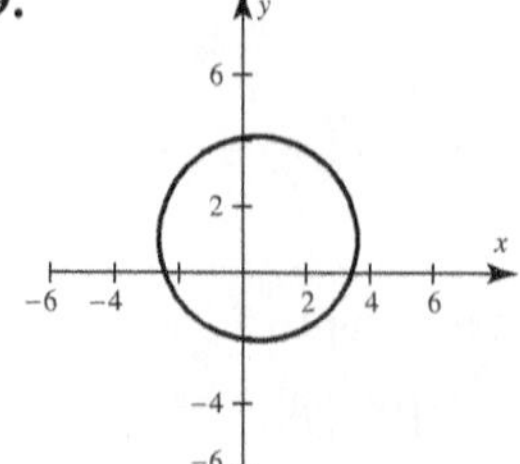

91. x-axis: 10; y-axis: 10 **93.** x-axis: 10; y-axis: 5

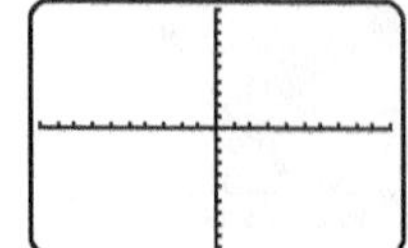

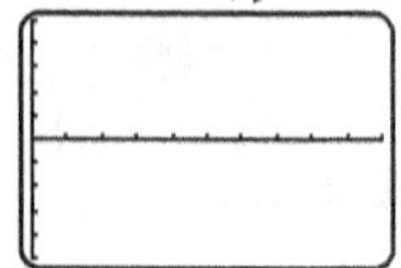

95. x-axis: 16; y-axis: 5

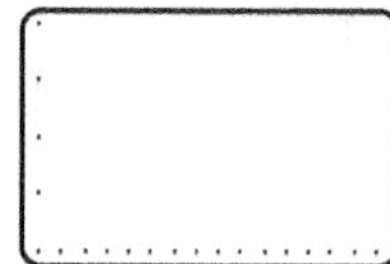

97. b **99.** a

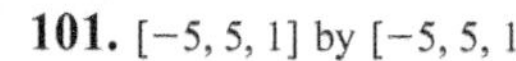

101. $[-5, 5, 1]$ by $[-5, 5, 1]$

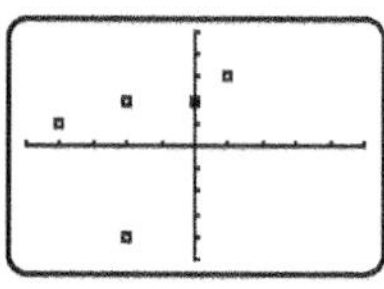

103. $[-100, 100, 10]$ by $[-100, 100, 10]$

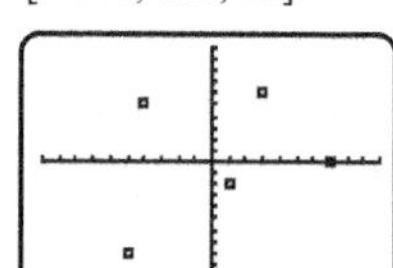

105. (a) x-min: 2006; x-max: 2010; y-min: 6.1; y-max: 19.4
(b) [2005, 2011, 1] by [5, 20, 5] (answers may vary)
(c)

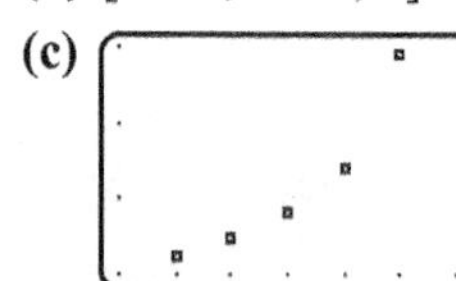

(d)

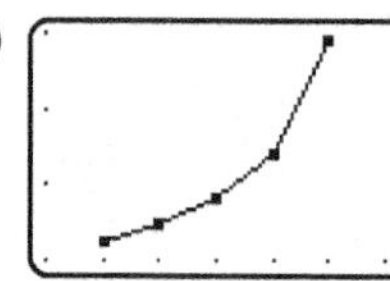

107. (a) x-min: 2006; x-max: 2011; y-min: 180; y-max: 590
(b) [2005, 2012, 1] by [150, 600, 50] (answers may vary)
(c)

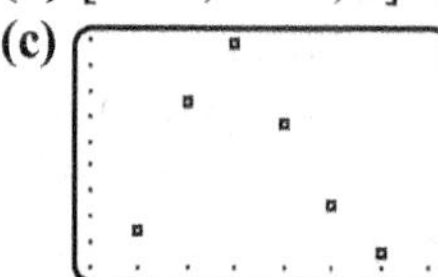

(d)

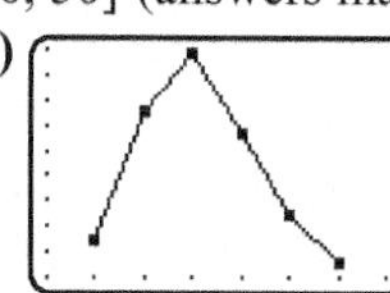

CHECKING BASIC CONCEPTS FOR SECTIONS 1.1 AND 1.2 (p. 25)

1. (a) 9.88 **(b)** 1.28
3. (a) 3.485×10^8 **(b)** -1.2374×10^3 **(c)** 1.98×10^{-3}
5. $\left(1, \frac{5}{2}\right)$ **7.** Mean $= 10{,}762.75$; median $= 12{,}941.5$

SECTION 1.3 (pp. 38–41)

1. $(-2, 3)$ **3.** $f(7) = 8$
5.

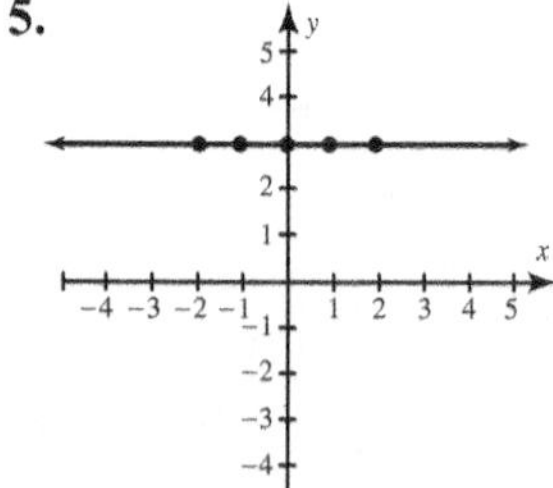

7.

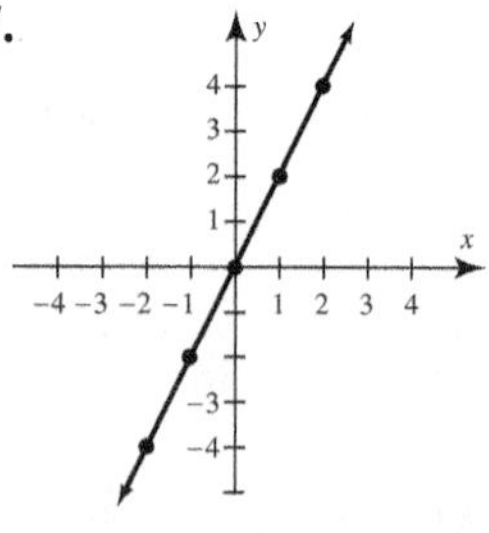

9.

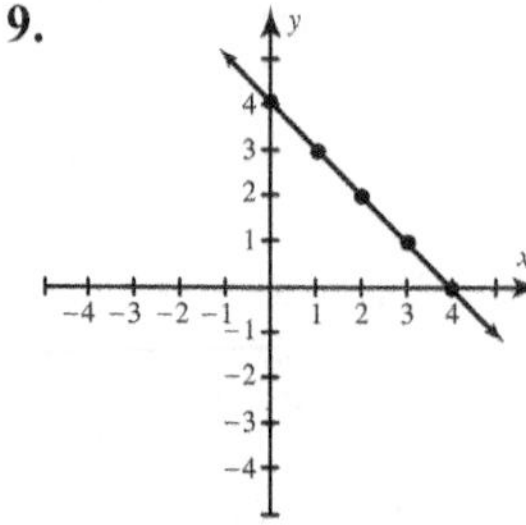

11.

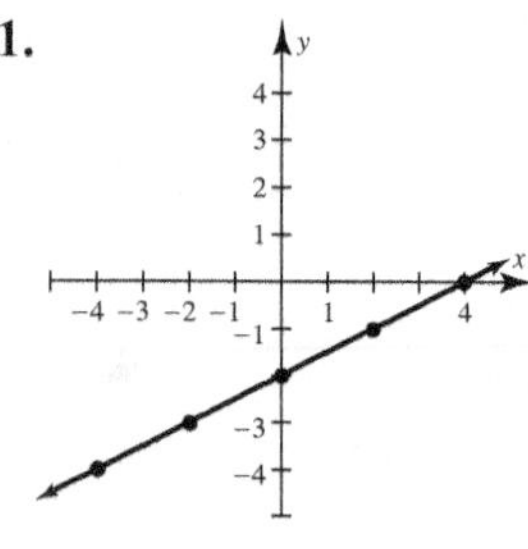

13.
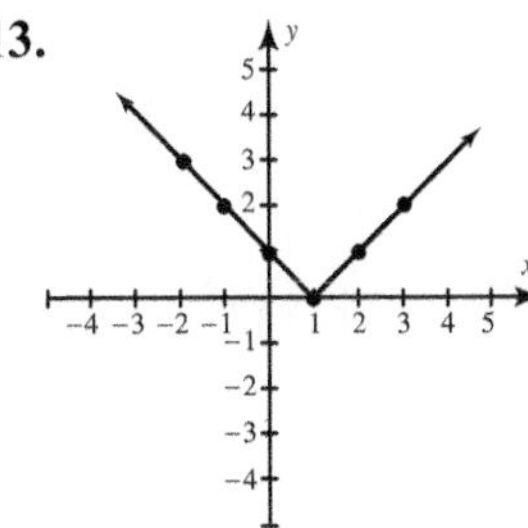

15.
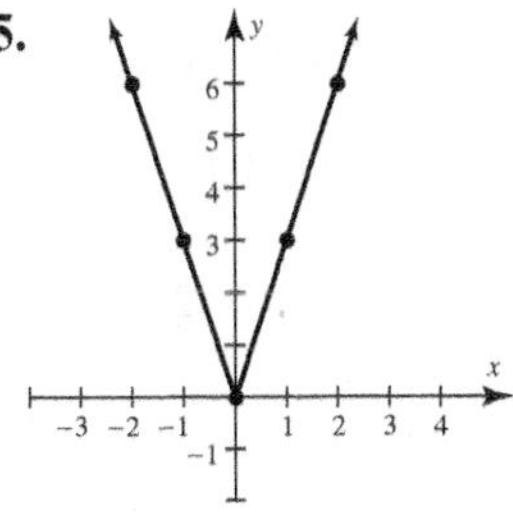

17.
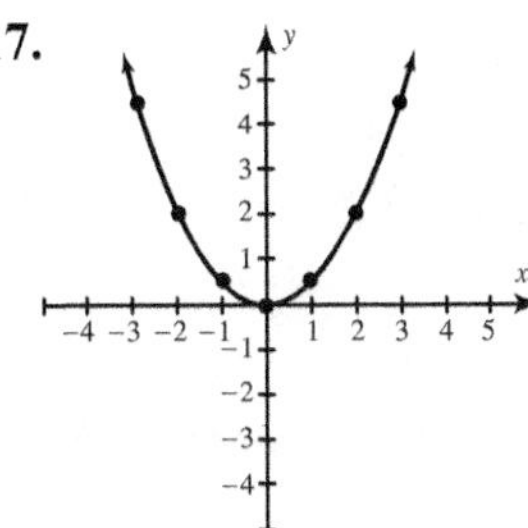

19.
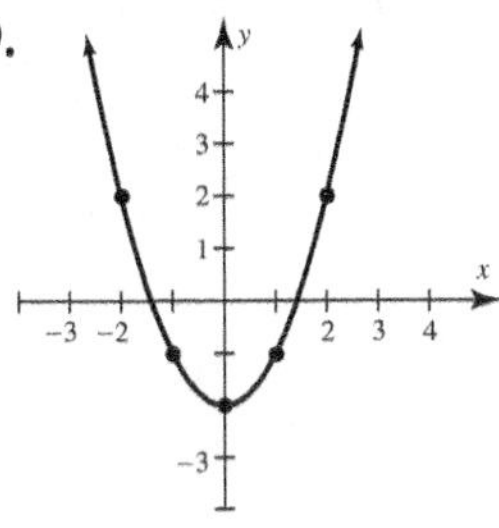

21. (a) $g = \{(-1, 0), (2, -2), (5, 7)\}$
(b) $D = \{-1, 2, 5\}, R = \{-2, 0, 7\}$
23. (a) $g = \{(1, 8), (2, 8), (3, 8)\}$
(b) $D = \{1, 2, 3\}, R = \{8\}$
25. (a) $g = \{(-1, 2), (0, 4), (1, -3), (2, 2)\}$
(b) $D = \{-1, 0, 1, 2\}, R = \{-3, 2, 4\}$
27. (a) $f(-2) = -8, f(5) = 125$ **(b)** All real numbers
29. (a) $f(-1)$ is undefined, $f(a + 1) = \sqrt{a + 1}$
(b) Nonnegative real numbers
31. (a) $f(-1) = 9, f(a + 1) = 3 - 3a$
(b) All real numbers
33. (a) $f(-1) = -2, f(a) = \frac{3a - 5}{a + 5}$ **(b)** $\{x \mid x \neq -5\}$
35. (a) $f(4) = \frac{1}{16}, f(-7) = \frac{1}{49}$ **(b)** $\{x \mid x \neq 0\}$
37. (a) $D =$ All real numbers; $R =$ All real numbers
(b) $g(-1) = -3; g(2) = 3$ **(c)** $g(-1) = -3; g(2) = 3$
39. (a) $D =$ All real numbers; $R = \{y \mid y \leq 2\}$
(b) $g(-1) = 1; g(2) = -2$ **(c)** $g(-1) = 1; g(2) = -2$
41. (a) $D = \{x \mid -2 \leq x \leq 2\}; R = \{y \mid -3 \leq y \leq 1\}$
(b) $g(-1) = -2; g(2) = 1$ **(c)** $g(-1) = -2; g(2) = 1$
43. $D = \{x \mid -3 \leq x \leq 3\}, R = \{y \mid 0 \leq y \leq 3\};$
$f(0) = 3$
45. $D =$ all real numbers, $R = \{y \mid y \leq 2\}; f(0) = 2$
47. $D = \{x \mid x \geq -1\}, R = \{y \mid y \leq 2\}; f(0) = 0$
49. (a) $f(2) = 7$ **(b)** $f = \{(1, 7), (2, 7), (3, 8)\}$
(c) $D = \{1, 2, 3\}, R = \{7, 8\}$
51. (a) $[-4.7, 4.7, 1]$ by $[-3.1, 3.1, 1]$ **(b)** $f(2) = 1$
(c)

X	Y1
-3	2.25
-2	1
-1	.25
0	0
1	.25
2	1
3	2.25

Y1=.25X²

53. (a) $[-4.7, 4.7, 1]$ by $[-3.1, 3.1, 1]$ **(b)** $f(2) = 2$
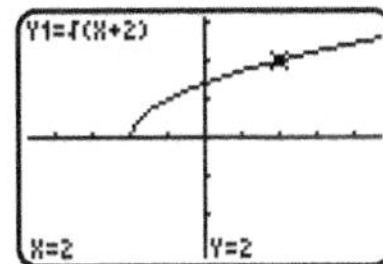
(c)

X	Y1
-3	ERROR
-2	0
-1	1
0	1.4142
1	1.7321
2	2
3	2.2361

Y1=√(X+2)

55. Verbal: Square the input x.
Graphical:
$[-10, 10, 1]$ by $[-10, 10, 1]$
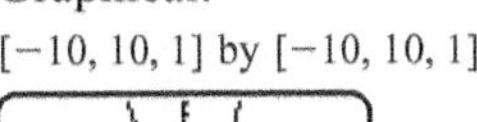
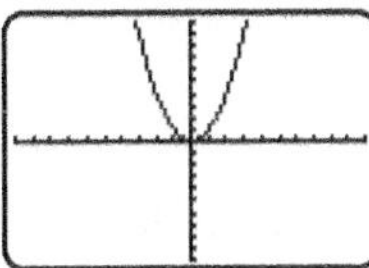
$f(2) = 4$
Numerical:

x	−2	−1	0	1	2
y	4	1	0	1	4

57. Verbal: Multiply the input by 2, add 1, and then take the absolute value.
Graphical:
$[-6, 6, 1]$ by $[-4, 4, 1]$
$f(2) = 5$
Numerical:

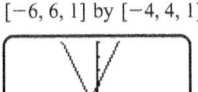

x	−2	−1	0	1	2
y	3	1	1	3	5

59. Verbal: Subtract x from 5.
Graphical:
$[-10, 10, 1]$ by $[-10, 10, 1]$
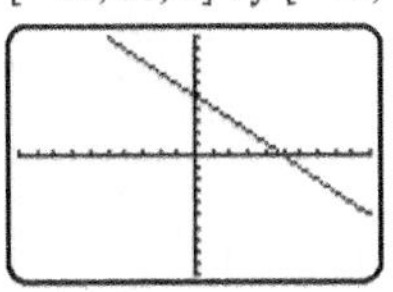
$f(2) = 3$
Numerical:

x	−2	−1	0	1	2
y	7	6	5	4	3

61. Verbal: Add 1 to the input and then take the square root of the result.
Graphical:
$[-6, 6, 1]$ by $[-4, 4, 1]$
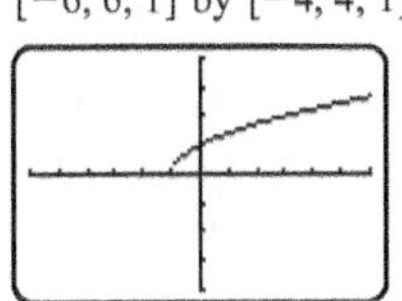
$f(2) = \sqrt{3}$
Numerical:

x	−2	−1	0	1	2
y	—	0	1	$\sqrt{2}$	$\sqrt{3}$

63. Symbolic: $f(x) = 0.50x$
Graphical:
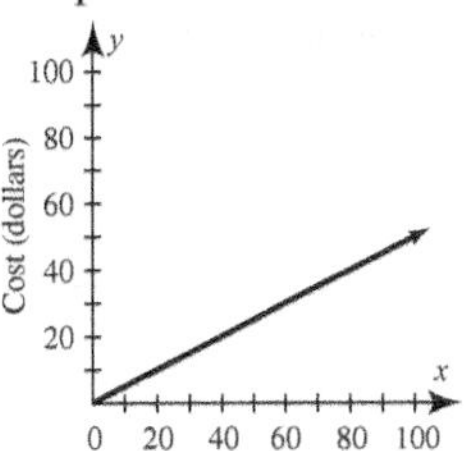

Numerical:

Miles	1	2	3	4	5	6
Cost	0.50	1.00	1.50	2.00	2.50	3.00

65. Yes. Domain and range include all real numbers.
67. No
69. Yes. $D: \{x \mid -4 \leq x \leq 4\}; R: \{y \mid 0 \leq y \leq 4\}$
71. (a) Yes
(b) Each real number has exactly one real cube root.
73. (a) No
(b) More than one student could have score x.
75. Yes, because IDs are unique. **77.** No **79.** Yes **81.** No
83. No **85.** Yes **87.** No **89.** Yes
91. $g(x) = 12x; g(10) = 120$; there are 120 inches in 10 feet.
93. $g(x) = \frac{x}{4}$; $g(10) = 2.5$; there are 2.5 dollars in 10 quarters.
95. $g(x) = 86{,}400x; g(10) = 864{,}000$; there are 864,000 seconds in 10 days.

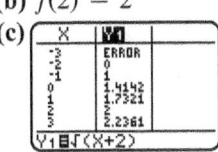

97. (a) $V = \{(R, 37), (N, 30), (S, 17)\}$
(b) $D = \{N, R, S\}$, $R = \{17, 30, 37\}$
99. 200; 200 million tons of electronic waste will accumulate after 5 years.
101. $N(x) = 2200x$; $N(3) = 6600$; in 3 years the average person uses 6600 napkins.
103. Verbal: Multiply the input x by -5.8 to obtain the change in temperature.
Symbolic: $f(x) = -5.8x$.
Graphical: [0, 3, 1] by [−20, 20, 5]

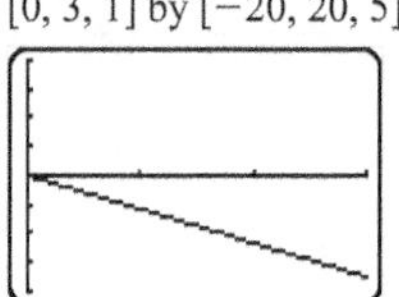

Numerical:

X	Y1
0	0
.5	-2.9
1	-5.8
1.5	-8.7
2	-11.6
2.5	-14.5
3	-17.4

Y1 = -5.8X

79. Incr: $(1, \infty)$, $(\{x \mid x > 1\})$; decr: never
81. Incr: $(-3, \infty)$, $(\{x \mid x > -3\})$; decr: $(-\infty, -3)$, $(\{x \mid x < -3\})$
83. Incr: $(-\infty, \infty)$, $(\{x \mid -\infty < x < \infty\})$; decr: never
85. Incr: $(-\infty, -2)$, $(2, \infty)$, $(\{x \mid x < -2\}, \{x \mid x > 2\})$; decr: $(-2, 2)$, $(\{x \mid -2 < x < 2\})$
87. Incr: $(-\infty, -1)$, $(0, 2)$, $(\{x \mid x < -1\}, \{x \mid 0 < x < 2\})$; decr: $(-1, 0)$, $(2, \infty)$, $(\{x \mid -1 < x < 0\}, \{x \mid x > 2\})$
89. $(0, 2.4)$, $(8.7, 14.7)$, $(21, 27)$, $(\{x \mid 0 < x < 2.4\}, \{x \mid 8.7 < x < 14.7\}, \{x \mid 21 < x < 27\})$
91. From -3 to -1: 1.2; from 1 to 3: -1.2
93. (a) 3 **(b)**

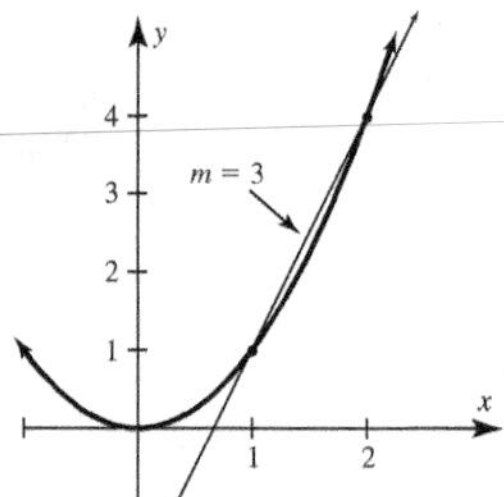

SECTION 1.4 (pp. 57–61)

1. $m = -2, b = 5$ **3.** $m = -8, b = 0$ **5.** $\frac{1}{2}$ **7.** -1
9. 0 **11.** -1 **13.** -8 **15.** Undefined
17. $-\frac{39}{35} \approx -1.1143$
19. Slope $= 2$; the graph rises 2 units for every unit increase in x.
21. Slope $= -\frac{3}{4}$; the graph falls $\frac{3}{4}$ unit for every unit increase in x, or equivalently, the line falls 3 units for every 4-unit increase in x.
23. Slope $= -1$; the graph falls 1 unit for every unit increase in x.
25. (a) Zero square feet of carpet would cost \$0.
(b) Slope $= 20$ **(c)** The carpet costs \$20 per square foot.
27. (a) $D(5) = 50$; after 5 hours the train is 50 miles from the station **(b)** -20; the train is traveling *toward* the station at 20 miles per hour.
29. (a) 150 miles **(b)** Slope $= 75$; the car is traveling *away* from the rest stop at 75 miles per hour.
31. Linear, but not constant **33.** Linear and constant
35. Nonlinear **37.** Nonlinear **39.** Yes, $m = 4$ **41.** No
43. (a) Slope: 2; y-int: -1; x-int: 0.5 **(b)** $f(x) = 2x - 1$
(c) 0.5
45. (a) Slope: $-\frac{1}{3}$; y-int: 2; x-int: 6 **(b)** $f(x) = -\frac{1}{3}x + 2$
(c) 6
47. $f(x) = -\frac{3}{4}x + \frac{1}{3}$ **49.** $f(x) = 15x$ **51.** $[5, \infty)$
53. $[4, 19)$ **55.** $[-1, \infty)$ **57.** $(-\infty, 1) \cup [3, \infty)$
59. $(-3, 5]$ **61.** $(-\infty, -2)$ **63.** $(-\infty, -2) \cup [1, \infty)$
65. Incr: never; decr: $(-\infty, \infty)$, $(\{x \mid -\infty < x < \infty\})$
67. Incr: $(2, \infty)$, $(\{x \mid x > 2\})$; decr: $(-\infty, 2)$, $(\{x \mid x < 2\})$
69. Incr: $(-\infty, -2)$, $(1, \infty)$, $(\{x \mid x < -2\}, \{x \mid x > 1\})$; decr: $(-2, 1)$, $(\{x \mid -2 < x < 1\})$
71. Incr: $(-8, 0)$, $(8, \infty)$, $(\{x \mid -8 < x < 0\}, \{x \mid x > 8\})$; decr: $(-\infty, -8)$, $(0, 8)$, $(\{x \mid x < -8\}, \{x \mid 0 < x < 8\})$
73. Incr: $(-\infty, \infty)$, $(\{x \mid -\infty < x < \infty\})$; decr: never
75. Incr: $(0, \infty)$, $(\{x \mid x > 0\})$; decr: $(-\infty, 0)$, $(\{x \mid x < 0\})$
77. Incr: $(-\infty, 1)$, $(\{x \mid x < 1\})$; decr: $(1, \infty)$, $(\{x \mid x > 1\})$

95. 7 **97.** 0.62 **99. (a)** From 1900 to 1940: 4.475; from 1940 to 1980: 11.25; from 1980 to 2010: about -10.57.
(b) From 1900 to 1940 cigarette consumption increased by 4.475 billion cigarettes per year, on average. The other rates may be interpreted similarly.
101.

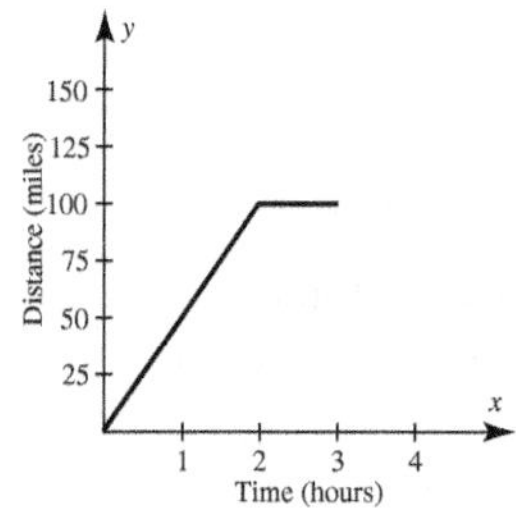

103. Answers may vary.

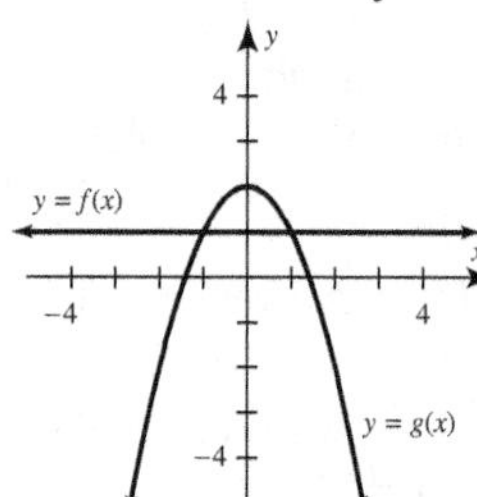

105. (a) 3 **(b)** 0 **107. (a)** $2x + 2h + 1$ **(b)** 2
109. (a) $3x^2 + 6xh + 3h^2 + 1$ **(b)** $6x + 3h$
111. (a) $-x^2 - 2xh - h^2 + 2x + 2h$ **(b)** $-2x - h + 2$
113. (a) $2x^2 + 4xh + 2h^2 - x - h + 1$ **(b)** $4x + 2h - 1$
115. (a) $x^3 + 3x^2h + 3h^2x + h^3$ **(b)** $3x^2 + 3hx + h^2$
117. (a) $8t^2 + 16th + 8h^2$ **(b)** $16t + 8h$
(c) 64.4; the average speed of the car from 4 to 4.05 seconds is 64.4 feet per second.

1.4 EXTENDED AND DISCOVERY EXERCISES (p. 61)

1. (a) Yes; 2π inches per second **(b)** No; because the area function depends on the radius squared, the area function is not a linear function and does not increase at a constant rate.

CHECKING BASIC CONCEPTS FOR SECTIONS 1.3 AND 1.4 (p. 61)

1. Symbolic: $f(x) = 5280x$
Numerical:

x	1	2	3	4	5
$f(x)$	5280	10,560	15,840	21,120	26,400

Graphical:

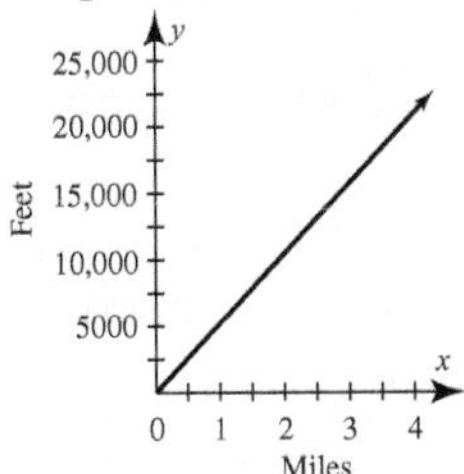

3. $-\frac{3}{2}$ **5. (a)** $(-\infty, 5]$ **(b)** $[1, 6)$ **7.** -7

CHAPTER 1 REVIEW EXERCISES (pp. 70–73)

1. Natural number: $\sqrt{16}$; integers: $-2, 0, \sqrt{16}$; rational numbers: $-2, \frac{1}{2}, 0, 1.23, \sqrt{16}$; real numbers: $-2, \frac{1}{2}, 0, 1.23, \sqrt{7}, \sqrt{16}$

3. 1.891×10^6 **5.** 15,200 **7. (a)** 32.07 **(b)** 2.62 **(c)** 5.21 **(d)** 49.12 **9.** -41

11.

−23	−5	8	19	24

(a) Max: 24; min: -23 **(b)** Mean: 4.6; median: 8

13. (a) $S = \{(-15, -3), (-10, -1), (0, 1), (5, 3), (20, 5)\}$ **(b)** $D = \{-15, -10, 0, 5, 20\}$, $R = \{-3, -1, 1, 3, 5\}$

15. Not a function

$[-50, 50, 10]$ by $[-50, 50, 10]$

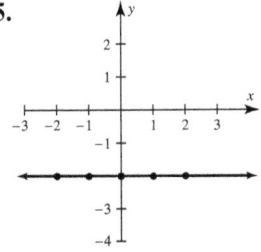

17. 10 **19.** $\left(2, -\frac{3}{2}\right)$ **21.** Yes

23. $(x - 2)^2 + (y - 5)^2 = 17$

25. **27.**

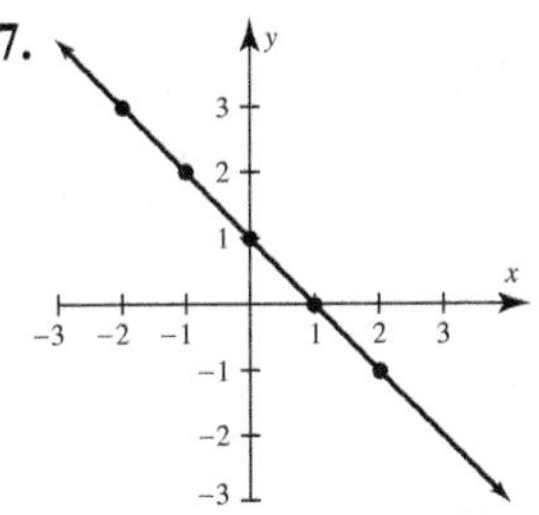

29.

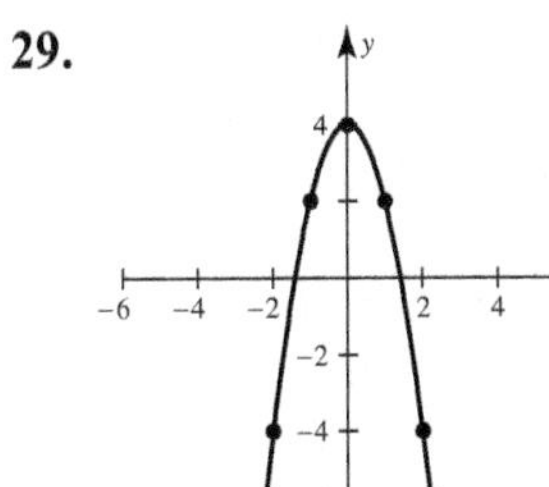

31.

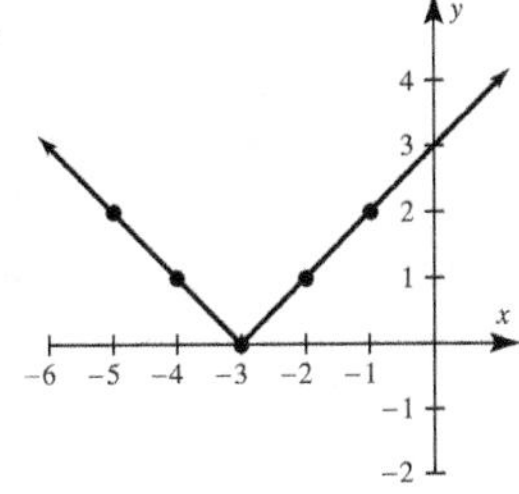

33. $f(x) = 16x$

$[0, 100, 10]$ by $[0, 1800, 300]$

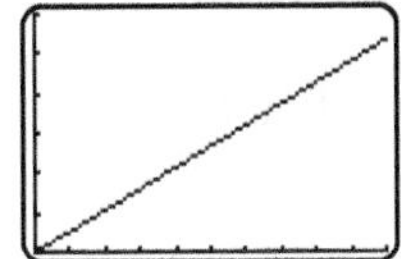

x	0	25	50	75	100
$f(x)$	0	400	800	1200	1600

35. (a) $f(-3) = 5$, $f(1.5) = 5$ **(b)** All real numbers

37. (a) $f(-10) = 97$, $f(a + 2) = a^2 + 4a + 1$ **(b)** All real numbers

39. (a) $f(-3) = -\frac{1}{7}$, $f(a + 1) = \frac{1}{a - 3}$ **(b)** $D = \{x \mid x \neq 4\}$

41. No **43. (a)** Slope: -2; y-int: 6; x-int: 3 **(b)** $f(x) = -2x + 6$ **(c)** 3

45. Yes **47.** Yes **49.** 0 **51.** $-\frac{3}{4}$ **53.** 0 **55.** Linear

57. Nonlinear

59.

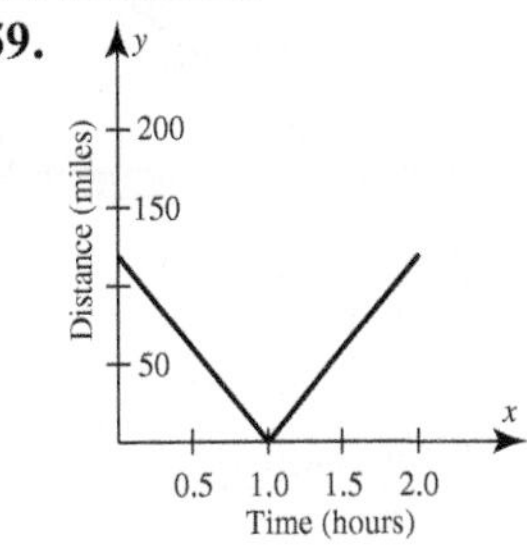

61. Yes; -4 **63.** 5 **65.** 760 seconds

67. (a) 198 feet **(b)** 1044 sq ft

69. (a) The data decrease rapidly, indicating a very high mortality rate during the first year.

$[-1, 5, 1]$ by $[0, 110, 10]$

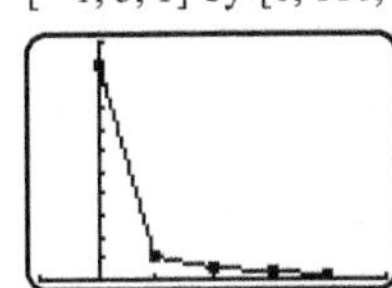

(b) Yes **(c)** From 0 to 1: -90; from 1 to 2: -4; from 2 to 3: -3; from 3 to 4: -1. During the first year the population decreased, on average, by 90 birds. The other average rates of change can be interpreted similarly.

71. (a) $[1, 5, 1]$ by $[40, 70, 5]$

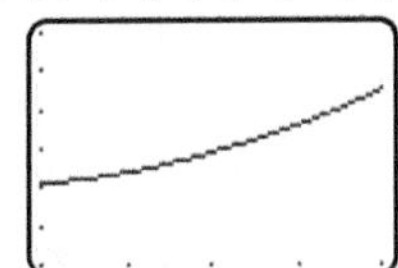

Nonlinear

(b) 2.5 **(c)** The average rate of change in outside temperature from 1 P.M. to 4 P.M. was 2.5°F per hour.

CHAPTER 1 EXTENDED AND DISCOVERY EXERCISES (pp. 73–74)

1. About 7.17 km

3. About 3.862

$[-3, 3, 1]$ by $[-2, 2, 1]$

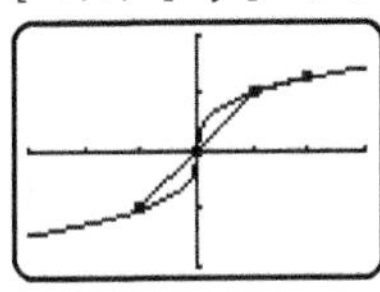

5. About 4.039

$[-3, 3, 1]$ by $[-1, 3, 1]$

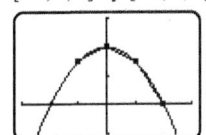

7. About 3.16; estimates will be less than the true value.

9. (a) Determine the number of square miles of Earth's surface that are covered by the oceans. Then divide the total volume of the water from the ice cap by the surface area of the oceans to get the rise in sea level. **(b)** About 25.7 feet **(c)** Since the average elevations of Boston, New Orleans, and San Diego are all less than 25 feet, these cities would be under water without some type of dike system. **(d)** About 238 feet

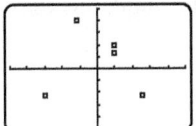

CHAPTER 2: Linear Functions and Equations

SECTION 2.1 (pp. 88–93)

1. $y = -2(x - 1) + 2$ **3.** $y = \frac{3}{4}(x + 3) - 1$

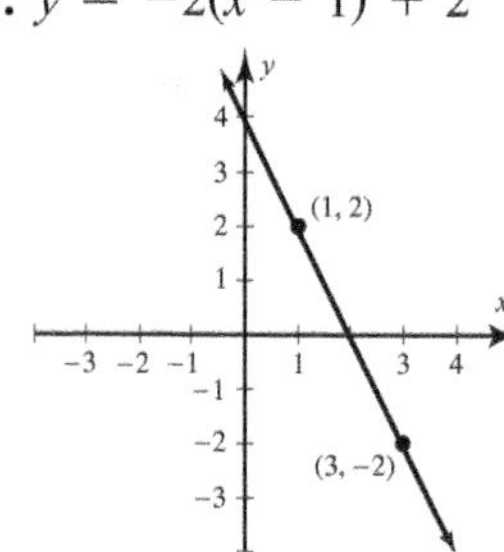

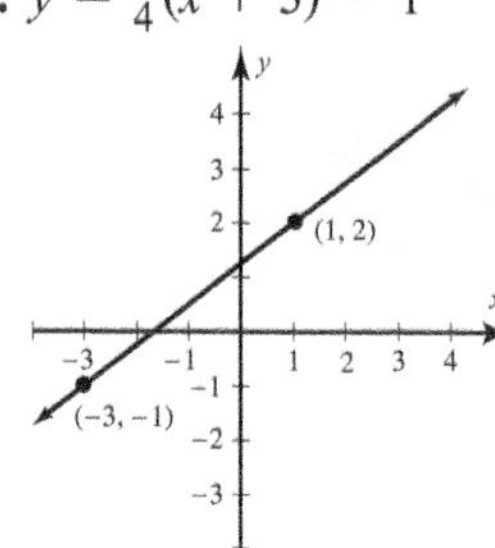

5. $y = -2.4(x - 4) + 5$; $y = -2.4x + 14.6$; $f(x) = -2.4x + 14.6$
7. $y = -\frac{1}{2}(x - 1) - 2$; $y = -\frac{1}{2}x - \frac{3}{2}$; $f(x) = -\frac{1}{2}x - \frac{3}{2}$
9. $y = \frac{3}{4}(x - 4) + 0$; $y = \frac{3}{4}x - 3$; $f(x) = \frac{3}{4}x - 3$
11. $y = \frac{2}{3}x - 1$ **13.** $y = -\frac{3}{5}x + \frac{3}{5}$ **15.** c
17. b **19.** e **21.** $y = 3x - 1$ **23.** $y = \frac{8}{3}x - \frac{17}{3}$
25. $y = -7.8x + 5$ **27.** $y = -\frac{1}{2}x + 45$
29. $y = -3x + 5$ **31.** $y = \frac{3}{2}x - 6$ **33.** $y = \frac{5}{18}x + \frac{11}{18}$
35. $y = 4x + 9$ **37.** $y = \frac{3}{2}x - 2960$ **39.** $y = \frac{2}{3}x - 2.1$
41. $y = \frac{1}{2}x + 6$ **43.** $y = x - 20$
45. $y = \frac{1}{2}x + \frac{9}{2}$ **47.** $y = -12x - 20$
49. $x = -5$; not possible **51.** $y = 6$, $f(x) = 6$
53. $x = 4$; not possible **55.** $x = 19$; not possible
57. x-int: 5; y-int: -4 **59.** x-int: 7; y-int: -7

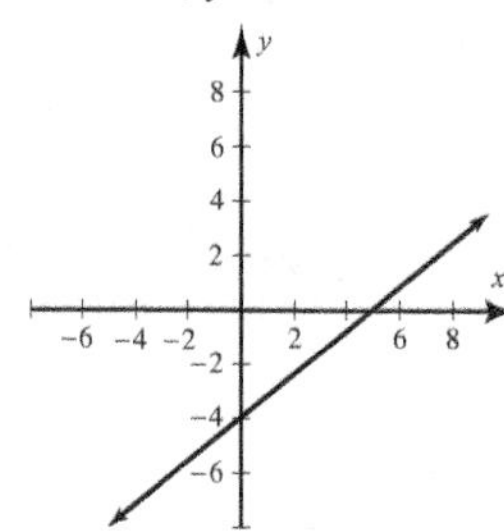

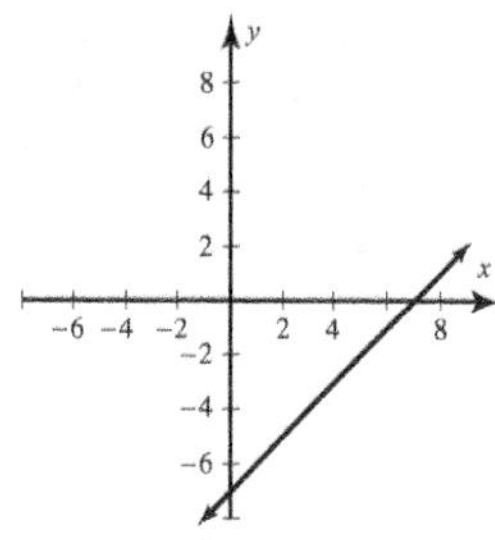

61. x-int: -7; y-int: 6 **63.** x-int: $-\frac{7}{3}$; y-int: 7

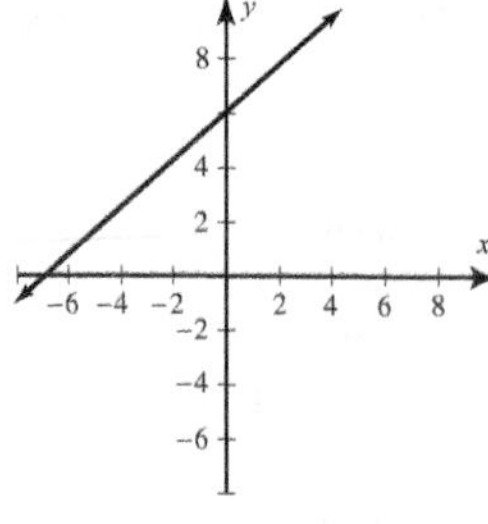

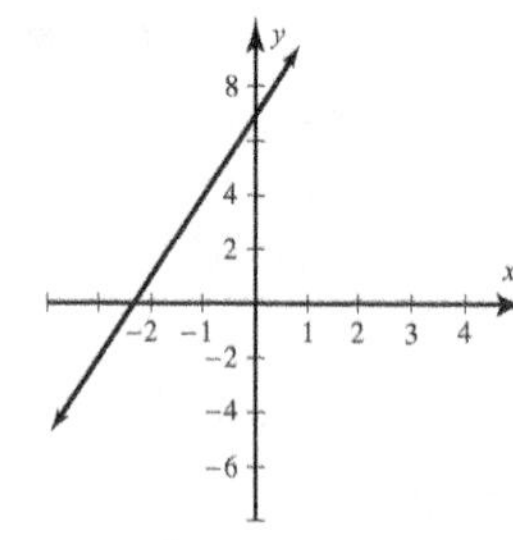

65. x-int: 4; y-int: 2 **67.** x-int: $\frac{5}{8}$; y-int: -5

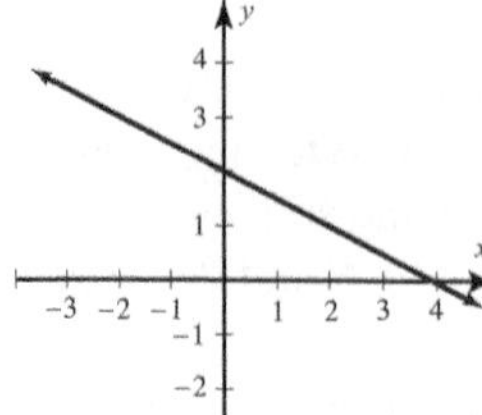

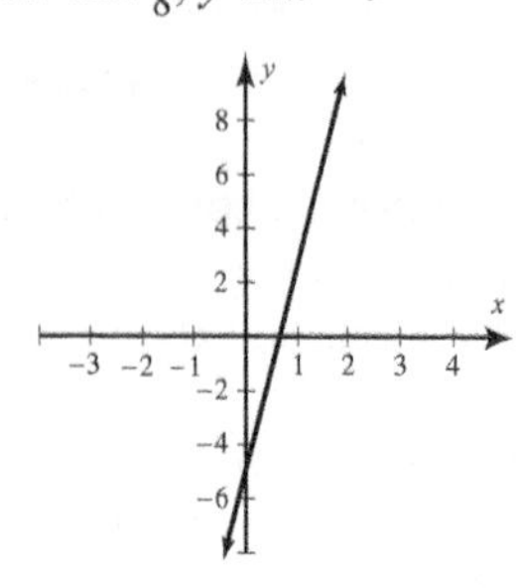

69. x-int: 5; y-int: 7; a and b represent the x- and y-intercepts, respectively.
71. x-int: $\frac{3}{2}$; y-int: $\frac{5}{4}$; a and b represent the x- and y-intercepts, respectively. **73.** $\frac{x}{5} + \frac{y}{9} = 1$
75. (a) $y = 1.5x - 3.2$ **(b)** When $x = -2.7$, $y = -7.25$ (interpolation); when $x = 6.3$, $y = 6.25$ (extrapolation)
77. (a) $y = -2.1x + 105.2$ **(b)** When $x = -2.7$, $y = 110.87$ (extrapolation); when $x = 6.3$, $y = 91.97$ (interpolation).
79. (a) $f(x) = 7(x - 2008) + 3$, or $f(x) = 7x - 14{,}053$ (answers may vary); approximate **(b)** -4%
(c) Extrapolation; the result is negative, which is not possible.
81. (a) $y = \frac{12{,}000}{7}(x - 2003) + 25{,}000$, or $y = \frac{12{,}000}{7}(x - 2010) + 37{,}000$; the cost of attending a private college or university is increasing by $\frac{12{,}000}{7} \approx \$1714$ per year, on average. **(b)** About \$31,857
83. (a) Leaving; 70 gallons **(b)** x-int: 10, the tank is empty after 10 minutes; y-int: 100, the tank held 100 gallons initially. **(c)** $y = -10x + 100$; the slope is -10, so the water is being drained at a rate of 10 gal/min. **(d)** 5
85. (a) $y = -\frac{3}{7}(x - 1999) + 15$ or $y = -\frac{3}{7}(x - 2013) + 9$ **(b)** Sales decreased, on average, by $\frac{3}{7} \approx \$0.43$ billion per year. **(c)** \$11.1 billion; this estimate is \$0.7 billion high; interpolation
87. (a) [2005, 2011, 1] by [150, 450, 50]

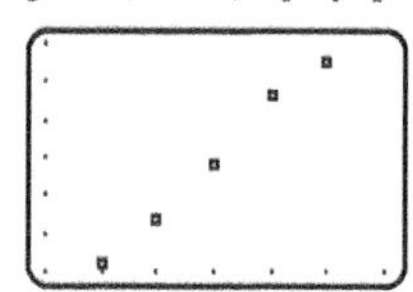

(b) Using the first and last points gives $f(x) = 66.25(x - 2006) + 160$ (answers may vary).
(c) [2005, 2011, 1] by [150, 450, 50]

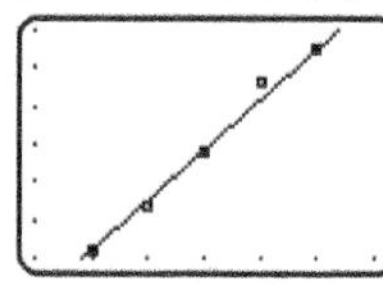

(d) The number of bankruptcies increased, on average, by 66,250 per year.
(e) 690,000 (answers may vary); extrapolation
89. (a) $y = -10.25x + 2000$ (answers may vary)
(b) Hours worked decreased, on average, by 10.25 hours per year. **(c)** About 1549 hours (answers may vary)
91. [0, 3, 1] by [−2, 2, 1]

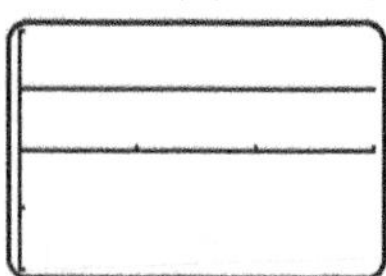

(a) No, the slope is not zero. **(b)** The resolution of most calculator screens is not high enough to show the slight increase in the y-values.
93. (a) They do not appear to be perpendicular in the standard viewing rectangle (answers may vary for different calculators).

(b) In $[-15, 15, 1]$ by $[-10, 10, 1]$ and $[-3, 3, 1]$ by $[-2, 2, 1]$ they appear to be perpendicular.

$[-10, 10, 1]$ by $[-10, 10, 1]$

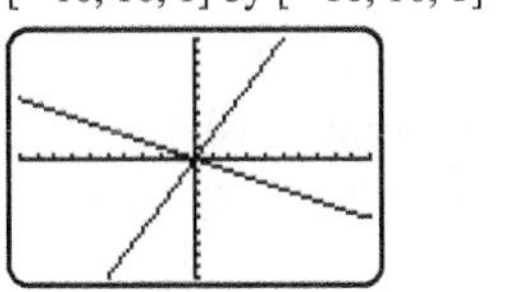

$[-15, 15, 1]$ by $[-10, 10, 1]$

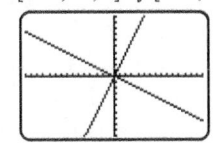

$[-10, 10, 1]$ by $[-3, 3, 1]$

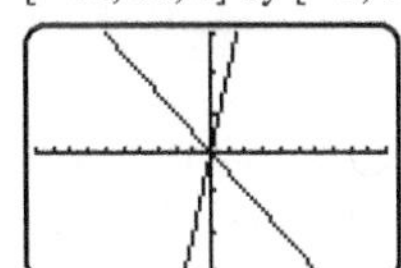

$[-3, 3, 1]$ by $[-2, 2, 1]$

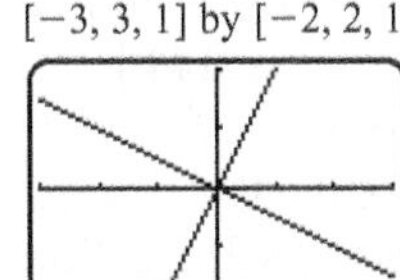

(c) The lines appear perpendicular when the distance shown along the x-axis is approximately 1.5 times the distance along the y-axis.
95. $y_1 = x, y_2 = -x, y_3 = x + 2, y_4 = -x + 4$
97. $y_1 = x + 4, y_2 = x - 4, y_3 = -x + 4, y_4 = -x - 4$
99. $y \approx -0.789x + 0.526; r \approx -0.993$

$[-3, 4, 1]$ by $[-3, 3, 1]$

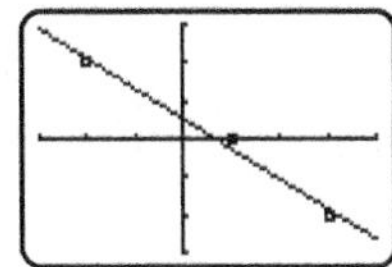

101. (a) Positive **(b)** $y = ax + b$, where $a = 3.25$ and $b = -2.45; r \approx 0.9994$ **(c)** $y = 5.35$
103. (a) Negative **(b)** $y = ax + b$, where $a \approx -3.8857$ and $b \approx 9.3254; r \approx -0.9996$ **(c)** $y \approx -0.00028$ (because of rounding, answers may vary slightly)
105. (a) $[-100, 1800, 100]$ by $[-1000, 28000, 1000]$

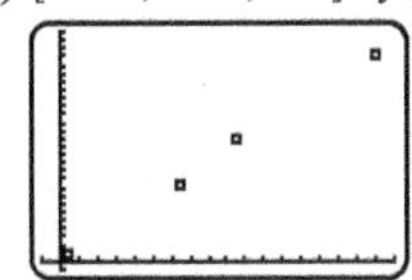

(b) $y = ax + b$, where $a \approx 14.680$ and $b \approx 277.82$
(c) 2500 light-years
107. (a) Positive

$[-5, 45, 5]$ by $[0, 6, 1]$

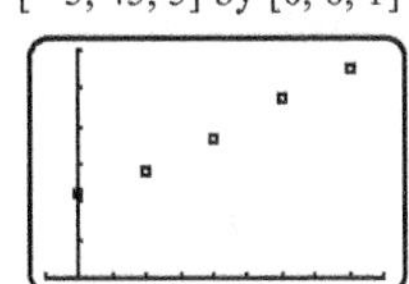

(b) $f(x) \approx 0.085x + 2.08$
(c) The number of passenger miles increased by about 0.085 trillion per year, on average.

$[-5, 45, 5]$ by $[0, 6, 1]$

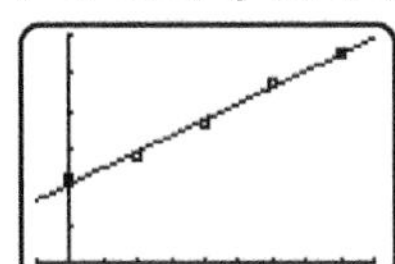

(d) About 5.9 trillion

SECTION 2.2 (pp. 107–111)

1. One **3.** $4x - 1$ **5.** They are equal. **7.** Linear **9.** Nonlinear **11.** Linear **13.** 4 **15.** -4
17. $\frac{32}{3}$ **19.** 4 **21.** 3 **23.** $\frac{1}{3}$ **25.** $\frac{4}{7}$ **27.** $-\frac{2}{19}$
29. -5 **31.** $\frac{17}{10}$ **33.** $\frac{7}{32}$ **35.** $\frac{5}{17}$ **37.** $\frac{400}{7}$
39. (a) No solutions **(b)** Contradiction
41. (a) $\frac{8}{3}$ **(b)** Conditional
43. (a) All real numbers **(b)** Identity
45. (a) No solutions **(b)** Contradiction
47. (a) All real numbers **(b)** Identity
49. 3 **51. (a)** 4 **(b)** 2 **(c)** -2
53. -1 **55.** 1 **57.** 4 **59.** 1.3 **61.** 0.675
63. 3.621 **65.** 2.294 **67.** 3 **69.** 8.6
71. 0.2 **73.** -1.2 **75.** 1 **77.** -4 **79.** 0.8
81. 2 **83.** $W = \frac{A}{L}$ **85.** $L = \frac{1}{2}P - W$
87. $y = 4 - \frac{3}{2}x$ **89.** $x = \frac{1}{4}y + \frac{3}{2}$
91. (a) $y = -2x + 8$ **(b)** $f(x) = -2x + 8$
93. (a) $y = \frac{1}{2}x + \frac{1}{4}$ **(b)** $f(x) = \frac{1}{2}x + \frac{1}{4}$
95. (a) $y = \frac{9}{8}x + \frac{9}{8}$ **(b)** $f(x) = \frac{9}{8}x + \frac{9}{8}$
97. 1989 **99.** About 1987
101. (a) For the graph of A, the percentage of people *against* legalization was decreasing at a rate of 1.6% per year. For the graph of F, the percentage of people *for* legalization was increasing at a rate of 1.5% per year.
(b) About 2011
103. $f(x) = 0.75x$; \$42.18
105. (a) $0.048x$ **(b)** About 1,583,000
107. (a) About 2 hours (answers may vary)
(b) $\frac{15}{8} = 1.875$ hours
109. 3.2 hours at 55 mi/hr and 2.8 hours at 70 mi/hr
111. $\frac{1}{9}$ hour, or $6\frac{2}{3}$ minutes **113.** 41.25 feet
115. About 36.4 cubic feet **117.** About 8.33 liters
119. 36 inches by 54 inches
121. (a) $S(x) = 19x - 38{,}017$ **(b)** Sales increased, on average, by \$19 billion per year. **(c)** 2013
123. $-40°$F is equivalent to $-40°$C.
125. (a) f is linear because the amount of oil is mixed at a constant rate. **(b)** 0.48 pint; 0.48 pint of oil should be added to 3 gallons of gasoline to get the correct mixture. **(c)** 12.5 gallons **127.** $\frac{80}{9} \approx 8.89$

2.2 EXTENDED AND DISCOVERY EXERCISES (p. 111)

1. (a) Yes; since multiplication distributes over addition, doubling the lengths gives double the sum of the lengths. **(b)** No; for example, in the case of a square (a type of rectangle), the square of twice a side is four times the square of the side.
3. (a) $f(x) = 14{,}000x$ **(b)** About 1.9 hours

CHECKING BASIC CONCEPTS FOR SECTIONS 2.1 AND 2.2 (p. 112)

1. $y = -\frac{3}{4}x + \frac{7}{4}$; parallel: $y = -\frac{3}{4}x$; perpendicular: $y = \frac{4}{3}x$ (answers may vary)
3. $y = -\frac{3}{2}x + \frac{1}{2}$ **5.** $-\frac{5}{3}$
7. (a) 2.5 **(b)** 2.5 **(c)** 2.5; The results are the same.

SECTION 2.3 (pp. 122–125)

1. $(-\infty, 2)$ **3.** $[-1, \infty)$ **5.** $[1, 8)$ **7.** $(-\infty, 1]$
9. $\{x \mid x \geq 2\}$, or $[2, \infty)$

11. $\{x \mid x < 10.5\}$, or $(-\infty, 10.5)$
13. $\{x \mid x \geq 13\}$, or $[13, \infty)$ **15.** $\{x \mid x < 0\}$, or $(-\infty, 0)$
17. $\{x \mid x \geq -10\}$, or $[-10, \infty)$
19. $\{x \mid x > 1\}$, or $(1, \infty)$
21. $\{x \mid x > \frac{7}{3}\}$, or $\left(\frac{7}{3}, \infty\right)$
23. $\{x \mid \frac{3}{2} < x \leq 3\}$, or $\left(\frac{3}{2}, 3\right]$
25. $\{x \mid -16 \leq x \leq 1\}$, or $[-16, 1]$
27. $\{x \mid -20.75 < x \leq 12.5\}$, or $(-20.75, 12.5]$
29. $\{x \mid -4 < x < 1\}$, or $(-4, 1)$
31. $\{x \mid \frac{9}{2} \leq x \leq \frac{21}{2}\}$, or $\left[\frac{9}{2}, \frac{21}{2}\right]$
33. $\{x \mid x \geq \frac{5}{3}\}$, or $\left[\frac{5}{3}, \infty\right)$
35. $\{x \mid -\frac{1}{2} < x \leq -\frac{1}{4}\}$, or $\left(-\frac{1}{2}, -\frac{1}{4}\right]$
37. $\{z \mid z \leq \frac{21}{19}\}$, or $\left(-\infty, \frac{21}{19}\right]$
39. $\{x \mid x \leq 2\}$ **41.** $\{x \mid x > 3\}$
43. $\{x \mid 0 \leq x \leq 2\}$ **45.** $\{x \mid -1 < x \leq 4\}$
47. (a) 2 **(b)** $\{x \mid x < 2\}$, or $(-\infty, 2)$
(c) $\{x \mid x \geq 2\}$, or $[2, \infty)$
49. (a) -2 **(b)** $\{x \mid x > -2\}$, or $(-2, \infty)$
(c) $\{x \mid x \leq -2\}$, or $(-\infty, -2]$
51. $\{x \mid x \leq 2\}$, or $(-\infty, 2]$
53. $\{x \mid x > 1\}$, or $(1, \infty)$
55. $\{x \mid x > 2.8\}$ **57.** $\{x \mid x \leq 1987.5\}$
59. $\{x \mid x > -1.82\}$
61. $\{x \mid 4 \leq x < 6.4\}$, or $[4, 6.4)$
63. $\{x \mid 4.6 \leq x \leq 15.2\}$, or $[4.6, 15.2]$
65. $\{x \mid 1 < x < 5.5\}$, or $(1, 5.5)$
67. (a) 8 **(b)** $\{x \mid x < 8\}$
69. $\{x \mid x < 4\}$; $\{x \mid x \geq 4\}$
71. $\{x \mid x < -\frac{3}{2}\}$, or $\left(-\infty, -\frac{3}{2}\right)$
73. $\{x \mid 1 \leq x \leq 4\}$, or $[1, 4]$
75. $\{x \mid -\frac{1}{20} \leq x < \frac{17}{20}\}$, or $\left[-\frac{1}{20}, \frac{17}{20}\right)$
77. $\{x \mid x \leq 31.4\}$, or $(-\infty, 31.4]$
79. $\{x \mid x > \frac{13}{2}\}$, or $\left(\frac{13}{2}, \infty\right)$
81. $\{x \mid x \leq 1.534\}$, or $(-\infty, 1.534]$
83. (a) Car A is traveling faster since its graph has the greater slope. **(b)** 2.5 hours; 225 miles
(c) $0 \leq x < 2.5$
85. (a) $T(x) = 65 - 19x$ **(b)** $D(x) = 50 - 5.8x$
(c) Below 1.14 miles (approximately)
(d) Below 1.14 miles (approximately)
87. (a) Revenue increased, on average, by $0.86 billion per year. **(b)** From 2012 to 2015
89. (a) $U(x) = 225x + 100$ **(b)** 2010 and after
91. (a) $V(x) = 7.6x - 15{,}212.6$
(b) About 2007 to 2009
93. About day 110 (April 19) to day 119 (April 28)
95. $3.98\pi \leq C \leq 4.02\pi$
97. (a) $f(x) = 3x - 1.5$ **(b)** $x > 1.25$
99. (a) $P(x) = 0.658x - 1290.76$ **(b)** Between 1989 and 2005 **(c)** Interpolation

2.3 EXTENDED AND DISCOVERY EXERCISES (p. 125)

1. $a < b \Rightarrow 2a < a + b < 2b \Rightarrow a < \frac{a+b}{2} < b$

SECTION 2.4 (pp. 135–141)

1. (a) $f(x) = \frac{x}{16}$ **(b)** $f(x) = 10x$
(c) $f(x) = 0.06x + 6.50$ **(d)** $f(x) = 500$
3. $f(x) = -\frac{1}{2}x + 3$ **5.** $f(x) = 2x + 5$ **7.** d **9.** c
11. $B(t) = 1.2t + 27$; t represents years after 2010; $D = \{t \mid 0 \leq t \leq 4\}$ **13.** $T(t) = 0.5t + 0.4$; t represents months after January; $D = \{t \mid 0 \leq t \leq 11\}$
15. $P(t) = 21.5 + 0.6t$; t represents years after 1900; $D = \{t \mid 0 \leq t \leq 111\}$
17. (a) $W(t) = -10t + 300$ **(b)** 230 gal
(c) x-int: 30, the tank is empty after 30 minutes; y-int: 300, the tank contains 300 gallons of water initially.
(d) $D = \{t \mid 0 \leq t \leq 30\}$

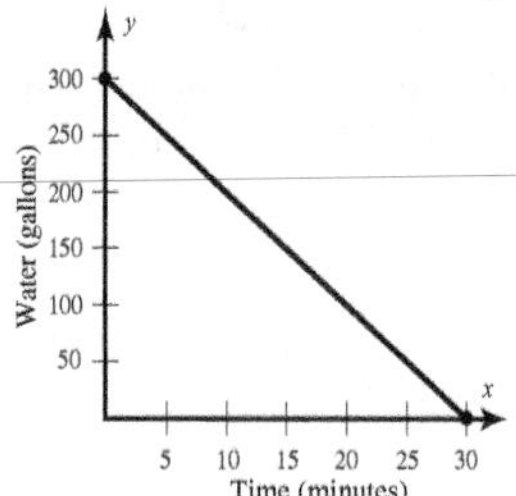

19. (a) $f(x) = 0.04x + 1.2$ **(b)** 1,480,000
21. (a) $f(x) = 0.25x + 0.5$ **(b)** 1.125 inches
23. (a) 17; 17.2; 16.6 **(b)** $f(x) = 17x$
(c) The vehicle is getting 17 miles per gallon.

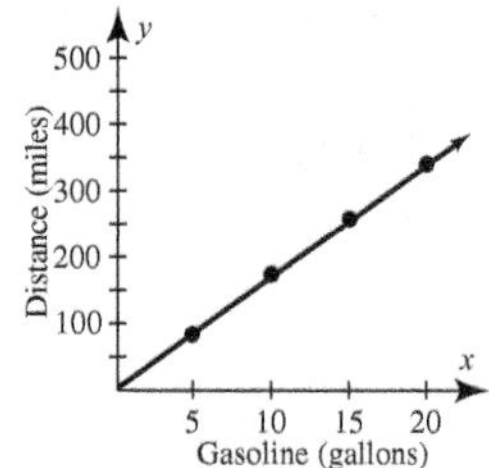

(d) $f(30) = 510$; the vehicle travels 510 miles on 30 gallons of gas.
25. (a) Max: 55 mi/hr; min: 30 mi/hr **(b)** 12 miles
(c) $f(4) = 40$, $f(12) = 30$, $f(18) = 55$
(d) $x = 4, 6, 8, 12$, and 16. The speed limit changes at each discontinuity.
27. (a) $P(1.5) = 1.10$, $P(3) = 1.30$; it costs $1.10 to mail 1.5 ounces and $1.30 to mail 3 ounces.
(b) $D = \{x \mid 0 < x \leq 5\}$

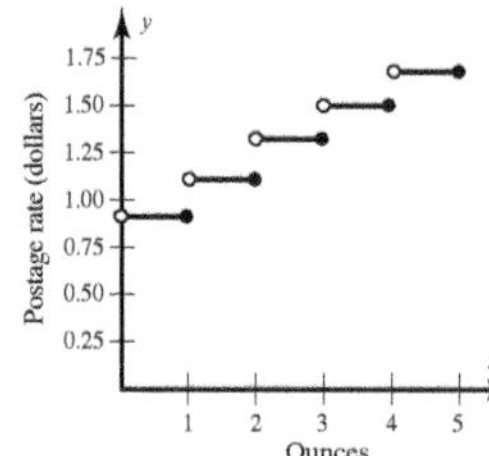

(c) $x = 1, 2, 3, 4$
29. (a) $f(1.5) = 30$; $f(4) = 10$
(b) $m_1 = 20$ indicates that the car is moving away from home at 20 mi/hr; $m_2 = -30$ indicates that the car is moving toward home at 30 mi/hr; $m_3 = 0$ indicates that the car is not moving; $m_4 = -10$ indicates that the car is moving toward home at 10 mi/hr. **(c)** The driver starts at home and

drives away from home at 20 mi/hr for 2 hours until the car is 40 miles from home. The driver then travels toward home at 30 mi/hr for 1 hour until the car is 10 miles from home. Then the car does not move for 1 hour. Finally, the driver returns home in 1 hour at 10 mi/hr.
(d) Incr: $0 < x < 2$; decr: $2 < x < 3$ or $4 < x < 5$; const: $3 < x < 4$
31. (a) $-5 \le x \le 5$
(b) $f(-2) = 2, f(0) = 3, f(3) = 6$
(c) **(d)** f is continuous.

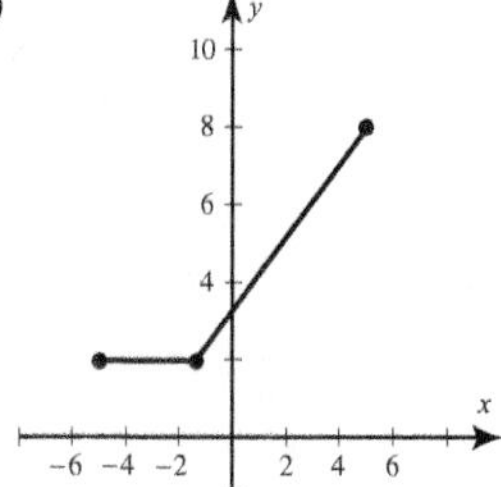

33. (a) $-1 \le x \le 2$
(b) $f(-2) =$ undefined, $f(0) = 0$, $f(3) =$ undefined
(c) **(d)** f is not continuous.

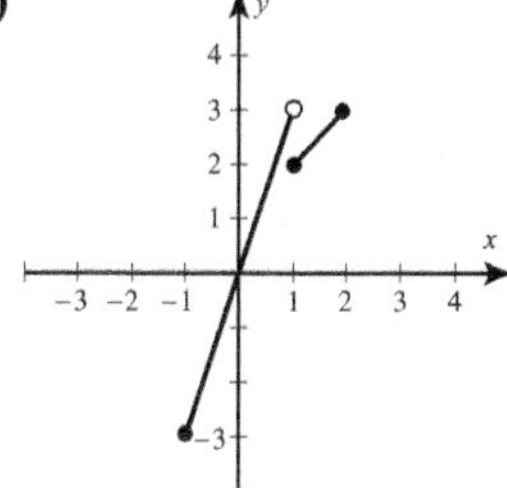

35. (a) $-3 \le x \le 3$
(b) $f(-2) = -2, f(0) = 1, f(3) = -1$
(c) **(d)** f is not continuous.

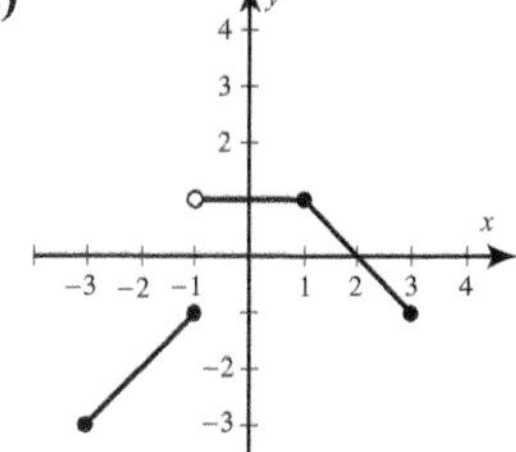

37.

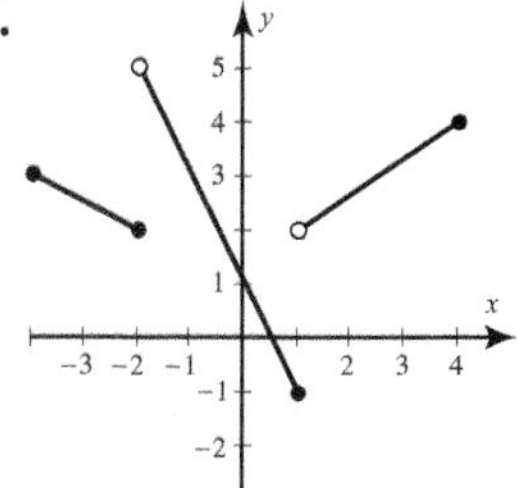

39. (a) $f(-3) = -10, f(1) = 4, f(2) = 4, f(5) = 1$
(b) [1, 3] **(c)** f is not continuous.

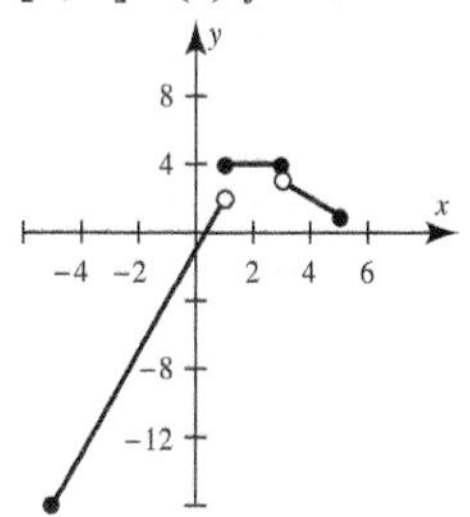

41. $xf(x) = \begin{cases} \frac{3}{4}x + 3, & \text{if } -4 \le x < 0 \\ -\frac{2}{3}x + 2, & \text{if } 0 \le x \le 3 \end{cases}$

43. (a)

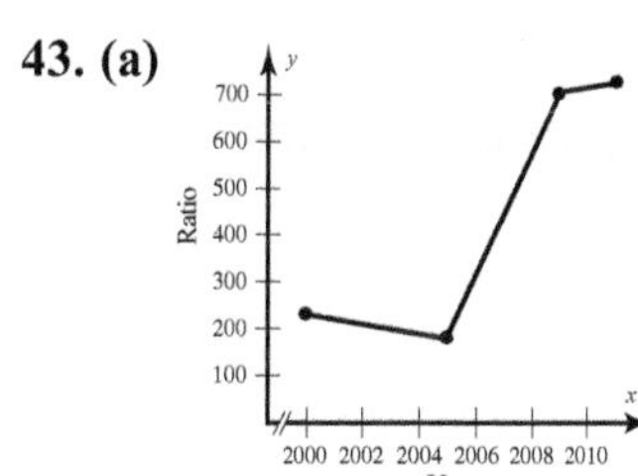

(b) 700; there were 700 people for each housing start in 2009; small values **(c)** Yes
(d) Increasing: (2005, 2011); decreasing: (2000, 2005); constant: never

(e) $R(x) = \begin{cases} -9x + 18{,}225, & \text{if } 2000 \le x \le 2005 \\ 130x - 260{,}470, & \text{if } 2005 < x \le 2009 \\ 13.5x - 26{,}421.5, & \text{if } 2009 < x \le 2011 \end{cases}$

45. (a) [−10, 10, 1] by [−10, 10, 1]

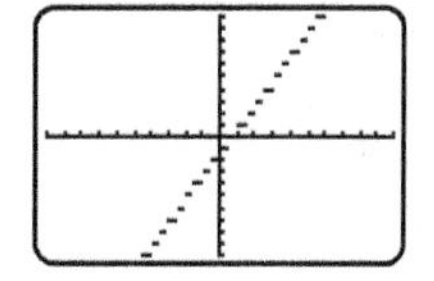

(b) $f(-3.1) = -8, f(1.7) = 2$
47. (a) [−10, 10, 1] by [−10, 10, 1]

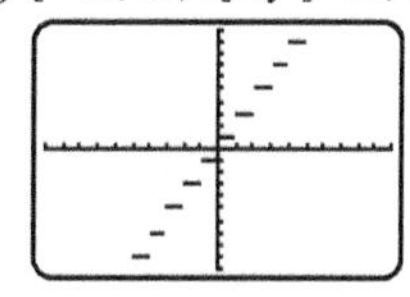

(b) $f(-3.1) = -7, f(1.7) = 3$
49. (a) $f(x) = 0.8[\![x/2]\!]$ for $6 \le x \le 18$
(b) [6, 18, 1] by [0, 8, 1]

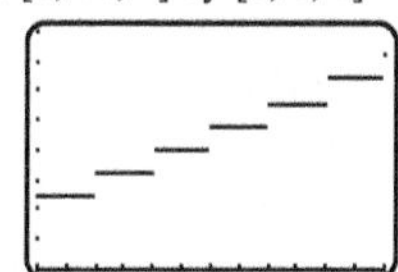

(c) $f(8.5) = \$3.20, f(15.2) = \$5.60$
51. 2.5 **53.** $\frac{9}{8}$ **55.** $k = 2.5, y = 20$ when $x = 8$
57. $k = 0.06, x = \$85$ when $y = \$5.10$
59. \$1048, $k = 65.5$ **61. (a)** $k = 0.01$ **(b)** 1.1 mm
63. (a) $k = \frac{15}{8}$ **(b)** $13\frac{1}{3}$ inches
65. (a) For (150, 26), $\frac{F}{x} \approx 0.173$; for (180, 31), $\frac{F}{x} \approx 0.172$; for (210, 36), $\frac{F}{x} \approx 0.171$; for (320, 54), $\frac{F}{x} \approx 0.169$; the ratios give the force needed to push a 1-pound box. **(b)** $k \approx 0.17$ (answers may vary)
(c) [125, 350, 25] by [0, 75, 5]

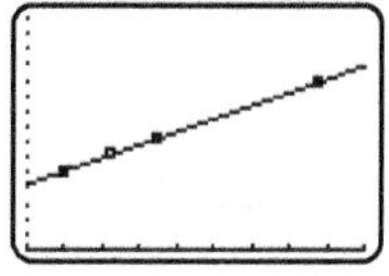

(d) 46.75 pounds

67. (a) $S(x) \approx 3.974x - 14.479$ (answers may vary)
(b) About 5.15 cm
69. (a) $f(x) \approx 0.12331x - 244.75$ (answers may vary)
(b) \$3.0 million; interpolation **(c)** About 2017

2.4 EXTENDED AND DISCOVERY EXERCISES (p. 141)

1. About 615 fish
3. Answers will vary.
5. (a) $[1.580, 1.584, 0.001]$ by $[-6.252, -6.248, 0.001]$

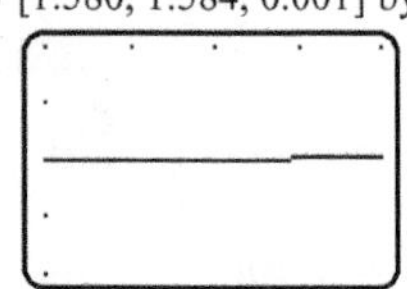

(b) A linear function would be a good approximation over a small interval.

CHECKING BASIC CONCEPTS FOR SECTIONS 2.3 AND 2.4 (p. 141)

1. $\{x \mid x > 3\}$
3. (a) 3 **(b)** $\{x \mid x > 3\}$ or $(3, \infty)$
(c) $\{x \mid x \le 3\}$ or $(-\infty, 3]$
5. $f(t) = 60t + 50$, where t is in hours

SECTION 2.5 (pp. 150–152)

1. $-3, 3$ **3.** $x < -3$ or $x > 3$, or $(-\infty, -3) \cup (3, \infty)$
5. It is V-shaped with the vertex on the x-axis. **7.** $|6a|$
9.

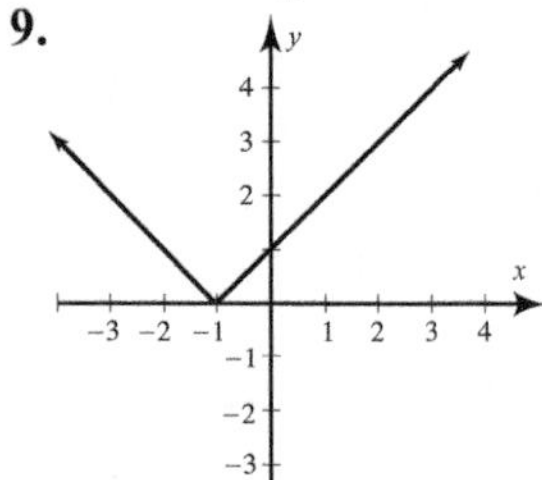

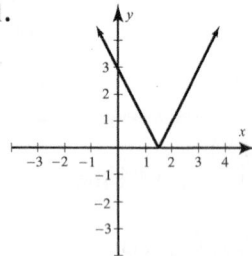

(a) -1 **(b)** Incr: $x > -1$, or $(-1, \infty)$; decr: $x < -1$, or $(-\infty, -1)$
11.

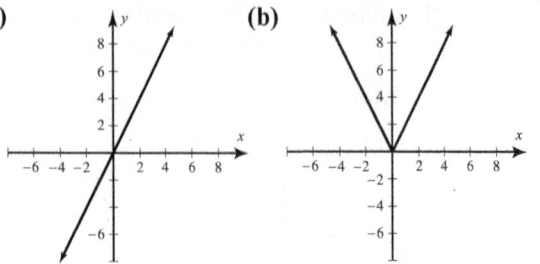

(a) $\frac{3}{2}$ **(b)** Incr: $x > \frac{3}{2}$, or $\left(\frac{3}{2}, \infty\right)$; decr: $x < \frac{3}{2}$, or $\left(-\infty, \frac{3}{2}\right)$
13. (a) **(b)**

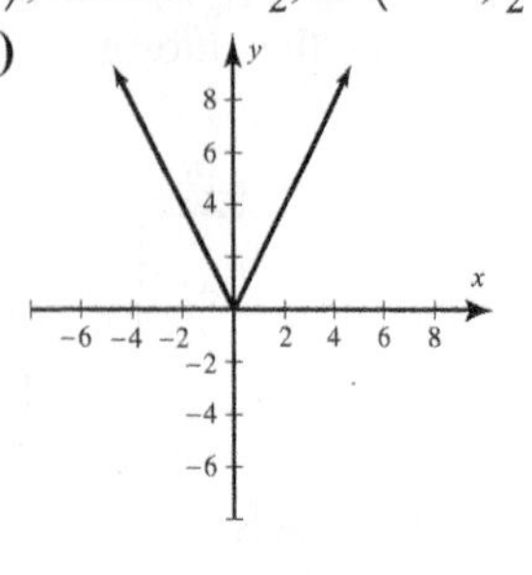

(c) 0

15. (a) **(b)**

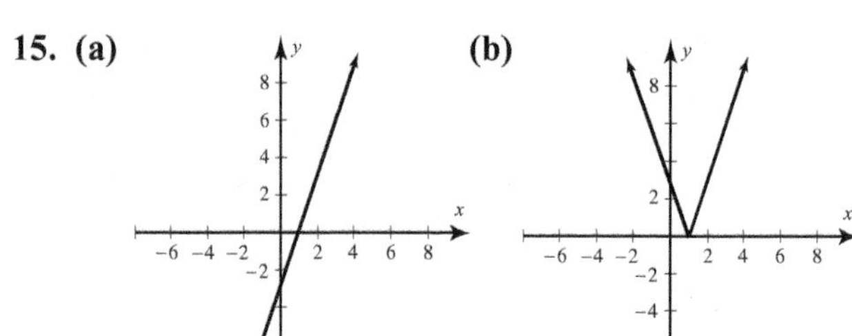

(c) 1
17. (a) **(b)**

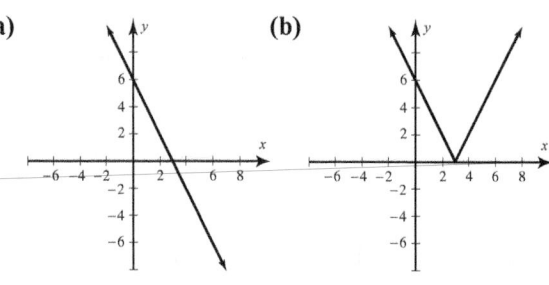

(c) 3
19. $-2, 2$ **21.** $1, \frac{9}{5}$ **23.** $-\frac{1}{2}, 2$ **25.** $-\frac{1}{3}$ **27.** $\frac{7}{16}$
29. No solutions **31.** $-\frac{23}{12}, \frac{19}{4}$ **33.** No solutions
35. $-1, \frac{17}{5}$ **37.** $-1, 1$ **39.** $-3, 2$
41. (a) $-1, 7$ **(b)** $-1 < x < 7$, or $(-1, 7)$
(c) $x < -1$ or $x > 7$, or $(-\infty, -1) \cup (7, \infty)$
43. (a) $1, 2$ **(b)** $1 < x < 2$, or $(1, 2)$
(c) $x < 1$ or $x > 2$, or $(-\infty, 1) \cup (2, \infty)$
45. $-\frac{5}{2}, \frac{15}{2}$; $-\frac{5}{2} < x < \frac{15}{2}$, or $\left(-\frac{5}{2}, \frac{15}{2}\right)$
47. $\frac{7}{3}, 1$; $x < 1$ or $x > \frac{7}{3}$, or $(-\infty, 1) \cup \left(\frac{7}{3}, \infty\right)$
49. $-\frac{17}{21}, \frac{31}{21}$; $x \le -\frac{17}{21}$ or $x \ge \frac{31}{21}$, or $\left(-\infty, -\frac{17}{21}\right] \cup \left[\frac{31}{21}, \infty\right)$
51. $-\frac{1}{3}, \frac{1}{3}$; $x < -\frac{1}{3}$ or $x > \frac{1}{3}$, or $\left(-\infty, -\frac{1}{3}\right) \cup \left(\frac{1}{3}, \infty\right)$
53. There are no solutions for the equation or inequality.
55. $\left(-\frac{7}{3}, 3\right)$, or $-\frac{7}{3} < x < 3$
57. $\left[-1, \frac{9}{2}\right]$, or $-1 \le x \le \frac{9}{2}$
59. $\left(-\frac{5}{2}, \frac{11}{2}\right)$, or $-\frac{5}{2} < x < \frac{11}{2}$
61. $(-\infty, 1) \cup (2, \infty)$, or $x < 1$ or $x > 2$
63. $\left(-\infty, \frac{5}{3}\right] \cup \left[\frac{11}{3}, \infty\right)$, or $x \le \frac{5}{3}$ or $x \ge \frac{11}{3}$
65. $(-\infty, -8) \cup (16, \infty)$, or $x < -8$ or $x > 16$
67. 6 **69.** $[-2, 4]$ **71.** $[0, \infty)$
73. Max: 75 mi/hr; min: 40 mi/hr
75. (a) $\frac{48}{19} \le x \le \frac{80}{19}$ **(b)** $\left|x - \frac{64}{19}\right| \le \frac{16}{19}$
77. (a) $19 \le T \le 67$ **(b)** The monthly average temperatures in Marquette vary between a low of 19°F and a high of 67°F. The monthly averages are always within 24 degrees of 43°F.
79. (a) $28 \le T \le 72$ **(b)** The monthly average temperatures in Boston vary between a low of 28°F and a high of 72°F. The monthly averages are always within 22 degrees of 50°F.
81. (a) $49 \le T \le 74$ **(b)** The monthly average temperatures in Buenos Aires vary between a low of 49°F (possibly in July) and a high of 74°F (possibly in January). The monthly averages are always within 12.5 degrees of 61.5°F.

83. **(a)** $|T - 10.5| < 0.5$ **(b)** $10.45 < T < 10.55$; The actual thickness must be greater than 10.45 mm and less than 10.55 mm.
85. **(a)** $|D - 2.118| \le 0.007$ **(b)** $2.111 \le D \le 2.125$; D must be greater than or equal to 2.111 inches and less than or equal to 2.125 inches.
87. $34.3 \le Q \le 35.7$

2.5 EXTENDED AND DISCOVERY EXERCISES (p. 152)

1. $|x - c| < \delta$

CHECKING BASIC CONCEPTS FOR SECTION 2.5 (p. 153)

1. $|2x|$ **3.** **(a)** $-2, 3$ **(b)** $[-2, 3]$, or $-2 \le x \le 3$; $(-\infty, -2) \cup (3, \infty)$, or $x < -2$ or $x > 3$ **5.** $-\frac{1}{3}, 1$

CHAPTER 2 REVIEW EXERCISES (pp. 156–160)

1. $y = \frac{1}{5}(x + 3) + 4$
3. $y = -\frac{7}{5}(x + 5) + 6$; $y = -\frac{7}{5}x - 1$; $f(x) = -\frac{7}{5}x - 1$
5. $y = \frac{2}{5}(x - 5) + 0$; $y = \frac{2}{5}x - 2$; $f(x) = \frac{2}{5}x - 2$
7. $f(x) = -2x - 1$
9. $y = 7x + 30$ **11.** $y = -3x + 2$
13. $y = -\frac{31}{57}x - \frac{368}{57}$
15. $x = 6$ **17.** $y = 3$ **19.** $x = 2.7$
21. x-int: 4; y-int: -5

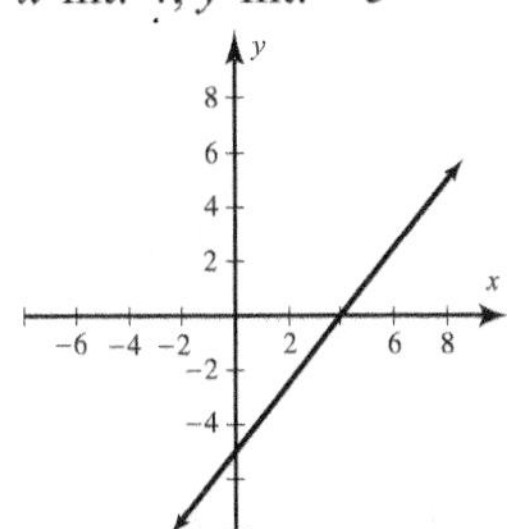

23. 6.4 **25.** $\frac{15}{7} \approx 2.143$ **27.** $\frac{5}{\pi} \approx 1.592$ **29.** -2.9
31. **(a)** All real numbers **(b)** Identity
33. **(a)** -3 **(b)** Conditional
35. $(-3, \infty)$ **37.** $\left[-2, \frac{3}{4}\right)$
39. $\{x \mid x \le 3\}$, or $(-\infty, 3]$
41. $\{x \mid -\infty < x < \infty\}$, or $(-\infty, \infty)$
43. $\{x \mid -1 < x \le \frac{7}{2}\}$, or $\left(-1, \frac{7}{2}\right]$
45. $\{x \mid x > -1\}$, or $(-1, \infty)$
47. **(a)** 2 **(b)** $x > 2$ **(c)** $x < 2$
49. **(a)** $f(-2) = 4$, $f(-1) = 6$, $f(2) = 3$, $f(3) = 4$
(b) f is continuous. **(c)** $x = -\frac{5}{2}$ or 2

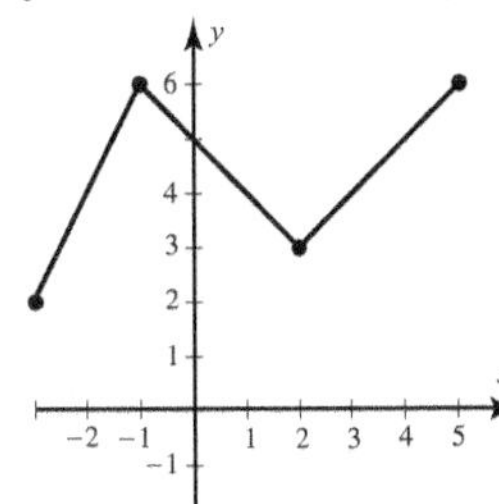

51. $-2, 7$ **53.** No solutions
55. ± 3; $x < -3$ or $x > 3$, or $(-\infty, -3) \cup (3, \infty)$
57. $\frac{17}{3}, -1$; $x < -1$ or $x > \frac{17}{3}$, or $(-\infty, -1) \cup \left(\frac{17}{3}, \infty\right)$
59. $-3 < x < 6$, or $(-3, 6)$
61. $x \le -\frac{5}{2}$ or $x \ge \frac{7}{2}$, or $\left(-\infty, -\frac{5}{2}\right] \cup \left[\frac{7}{2}, \infty\right)$
63. **(a)** $f(x) = 1060x + 17{,}700$ **(b)** Slope 1060 means that median income increased, on average, by about \$1060 per year; y-intercept 17,700 means that in 1980 median income was \$17,700 **(c)** \$30,420; they are approximately equal. **(d)** About 2020; extrapolation
65. **(a)** $f(x) = 42.5x + 524$ **(b)** Slope 42.5 means that spending increased, on average, by about \$42.5 billion per year; y-intercept 524 means that in 2010 spending was \$524 billion. **(c)** \$779 billion; interpolation **(d)** From 2014 to 2018
67. Initially the car is at home. After traveling 30 mi/hr for 1 hour, the car is 30 miles away from home. During the second hour the car travels 20 mi/hr until it is 50 miles away. During the third hour the car travels toward home at 30 mi/hr until it is 20 miles away. During the fourth hour the car travels away from home at 40 mi/hr until it is 60 miles away from home. During the last hour the car travels 60 miles at 60 mi/hr until it arrives home.
69. 155,590 **71.** 18.75 minutes
73. 0.9 hour at 7 mi/hr and 0.9 hour at 8 mi/hr
75. **(a)** $y = -1.2x + 3$
(b) $y = 4.8$ when $x = -1.5$, interpolation; $y = -1.2$ when $x = 3.5$, extrapolation **(c)** $\frac{17}{12}$
77. When $0 \le x \le 3$, the slope is 5, which means the inlet pipe is open and the outlet pipe is closed; when $3 < x \le 5$, the slope is 2, which means both pipes are open; when $5 < x \le 8$, the slope is 0, which means both pipes are closed; when $8 < x \le 10$, the slope is -3, which means the inlet pipe is closed and the outlet pipe is open.
79. The distance above the ground is between $1\frac{2}{3}$ kilometers and $3\frac{1}{3}$ kilometers.
81. Between 52.1431 feet and 52.4569 feet

CHAPTER 2 EXTENDED AND DISCOVERY EXERCISES (pp. 160)

1. **(a)** 62.8 inches
(b) [7, 15, 1] by [45, 75, 5] [7, 15, 1] by [45, 75, 5]

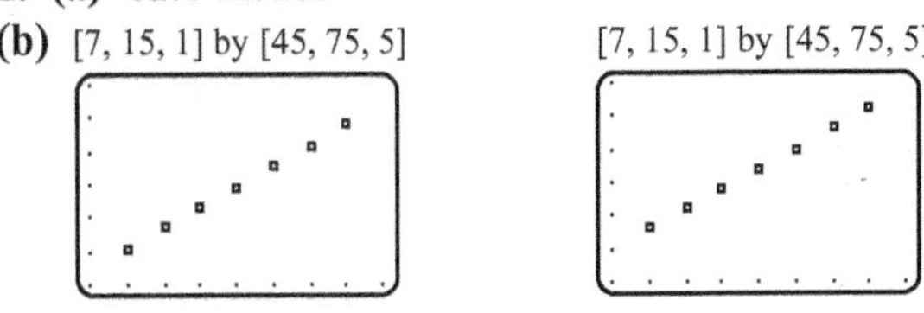

Both sets of data are linear.
(c) Female: 3.1 inches; male: 3.0 inches
(d) $f(x) = 3.1(x - 8) + 50.4$; $g(x) = 3.0(x - 8) + 53$
(e) $55.67 \le$ female height ≤ 56.91; $58.1 \le$ male height ≤ 59.3
3. 3 miles

CHAPTERS 1–2 CUMULATIVE REVIEW EXERCISES (pp. 160–162)

1. 1.23×10^5; 5.1×10^{-3} **3.** 2.09
5. $(x + 2)^2 + (y - 3)^2 = 49$ **7.** $\sqrt{89}$

9. **(a)** $D = \{x \mid -\infty < x < \infty\}, R = \{y \mid y \geq -2\}$; $f(-1) = -1$
(b) $D = \{x \mid -3 \leq x \leq 3\}, R = \{y \mid -3 \leq y \leq 2\}$; $f(-1) = -\frac{1}{2}$
11. **(a)** $f(2) = 7$; $f(a - 1) = 5a - 8$
(b) $D = \{x \mid -\infty < x < \infty\}$
13. No. The graph does not pass the vertical line test.
15. 1 **17.** **(a)** $\frac{2}{3}$; -2; 3 **(b)** $f(x) = \frac{2}{3}x - 2$ **(c)** 3
19. $y = -\frac{11}{8}x - \frac{29}{8}$
21. $x = -1$ **23.** $y = 2x + 11$
25. x-int: -3; y-int: 2

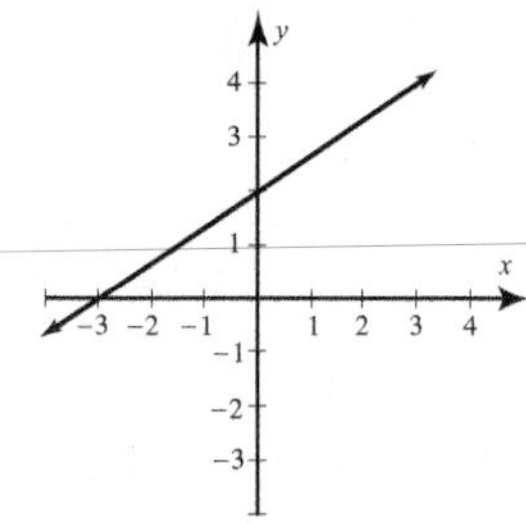

27. 1 **29.** $-\frac{24}{17}$ **31.** 3 **33.** $(-\infty, 5)$
35. $(-\infty, -2) \cup (2, \infty)$
37. $\{x \mid x \leq \frac{5}{8}\}$, or $\left(-\infty, \frac{5}{8}\right]$
39. **(a)** 2 **(b)** $x < 2$ **(c)** $x \geq 2$
41. $-6, 4$ **43.** $-7, 7$
45. $\{x \mid 0 \leq x \leq 5\}$, or $[0, 5]$
47. **(a)** 770,000; it costs $770,000 to manufacture 1500 computers. **(b)** 500; each additional computer costs $500 to manufacture; fixed costs are $20,000.
49. **(a)** 9°F per hour **(b)** On average, the temperature increased by 9°F per hour over this 2-hour period.
51. $\frac{60}{17} \approx 3.53$ hours
53. **(a)** $f(x) = \frac{28}{9}(x - 2001) + 56$ or $f(x) = \frac{28}{9}(x - 2010) + 84$ **(b)** About 100 pounds

CHAPTER 3: Quadratic Functions and Equations

SECTION 3.1 (pp. 175–180)

1. Quadratic; leading coefficient: 3; $f(-2) = 17$
3. Neither linear nor quadratic **5.** Linear
7. **(a)** $a > 0$ **(b)** $(1, 0)$ **(c)** $x = 1$
(d) Incr: $x > 1$, or $(1, \infty)$; decr: $x < 1$, or $(-\infty, 1)$
(e) $D = (-\infty, \infty)$; $R = [0, \infty)$
9. **(a)** $a < 0$ **(b)** $(-3, -2)$ **(c)** $x = -3$
(d) Incr: $x < -3$, or $(-\infty, -3)$; decr: $x > -3$, or $(-3, \infty)$
(e) $D = (-\infty, \infty)$; $R = (-\infty, -2]$
11. The graph of g is narrower than the graph of f.
13. The graph of g is wider than the graph of f and opens downward rather than upward.
15. Vertex: $(1, 2)$; leading coefficient: -3; $f(x) = -3x^2 + 6x - 1$
17. Vertex: $(4, 5)$; leading coefficient: -2; $f(x) = -2x^2 + 16x - 27$
19. Vertex: $\left(-5, -\frac{7}{4}\right)$; leading coefficient: $\frac{3}{4}$; $f(x) = \frac{3}{4}x^2 + \frac{15}{2}x + 17$
21. $f(x) = (x - 2)^2 - 2$ **23.** $f(x) = \frac{1}{2}(x - 2)^2 - 3$
25. $f(x) = -2(x + 1)^2 + 3$ **27.** $f(x) = -3(x - 2)^2 + 6$
29. $f(x) = (x + 2)^2 - 9$; vertex: $(-2, -9)$
31. $f(x) = \left(x - \frac{3}{2}\right)^2 - \frac{9}{4}$; vertex: $\left(\frac{3}{2}, -\frac{9}{4}\right)$
33. $f(x) = 2\left(x - \frac{5}{4}\right)^2 - \frac{1}{8}$; vertex: $\left(\frac{5}{4}, -\frac{1}{8}\right)$
35. $f(x) = \frac{1}{3}\left(x + \frac{3}{2}\right)^2 + \frac{1}{4}$; vertex: $\left(-\frac{3}{2}, \frac{1}{4}\right)$
37. $f(x) = 2(x - 2)^2 - 9$; vertex: $(2, -9)$
39. $f(x) = -3(x + 1.5)^2 + 8.75$; vertex: $(-1.5, 8.75)$
41. **(a)** $(0, 6)$ **(b)** Incr: $x < 0$, or $(-\infty, 0)$; decr: $x > 0$, or $(0, \infty)$
43. **(a)** $(3, -9)$ **(b)** Incr: $x > 3$, or $(3, \infty)$; decr: $x < 3$, or $(-\infty, 3)$
45. **(a)** $(1, -1)$ **(b)** Incr: $x > 1$, or $(1, \infty)$; decr: $x < 1$, or $(-\infty, 1)$
47. **(a)** $(0, 10)$ **(b)** Incr: $x > 0$, or $(0, \infty)$; decr: $x < 0$, or $(-\infty, 0)$
49. **(a)** $\left(\frac{1}{3}, -\frac{35}{12}\right)$ **(b)** Incr: $x < \frac{1}{3}$, or $\left(-\infty, \frac{1}{3}\right)$; decr: $x > \frac{1}{3}$, or $\left(\frac{1}{3}, \infty\right)$
51. **(a)** $\left(-\frac{1}{4}, \frac{15}{8}\right)$ **(b)** Incr: $x < -\frac{1}{4}$, or $\left(-\infty, -\frac{1}{4}\right)$; decr: $x > -\frac{1}{4}$, or $\left(-\frac{1}{4}, \infty\right)$
53. -6 **55.** $\frac{2}{3}$ **57.** $\frac{11}{4}$ **59.** $\frac{1}{4}$ **61.** $\frac{25}{4}$ **63.** $\frac{1}{3}$

65.

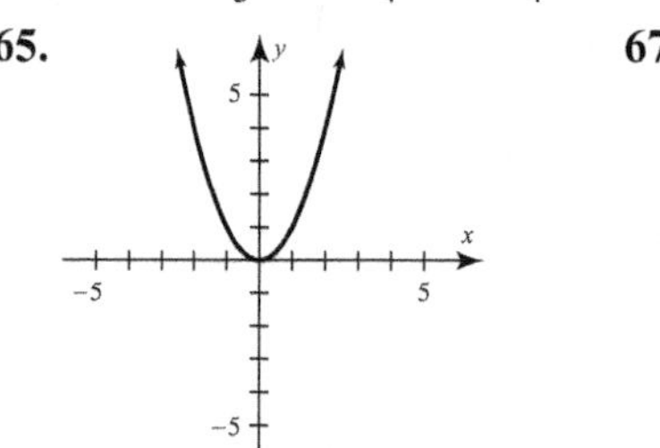

67.

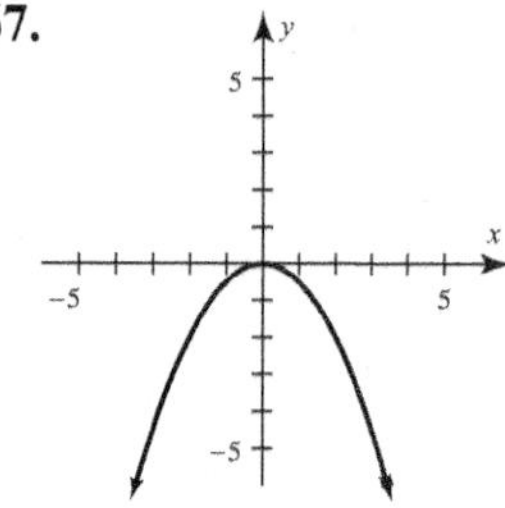

69.

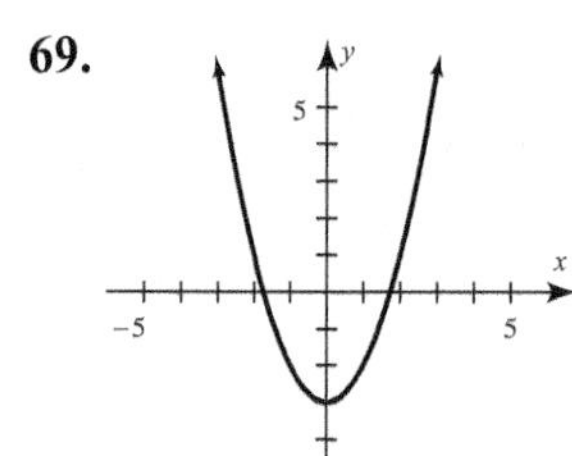

71.

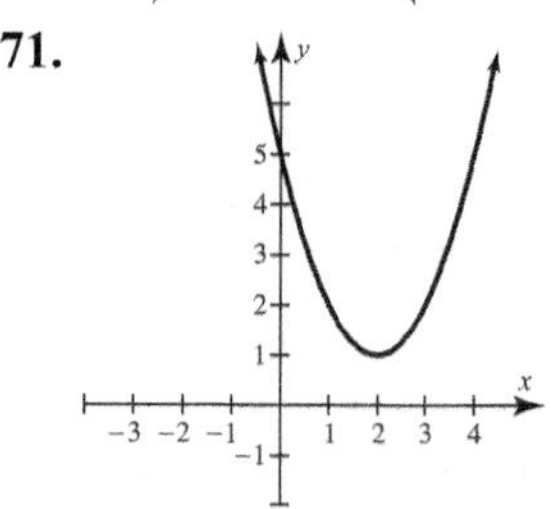

73.

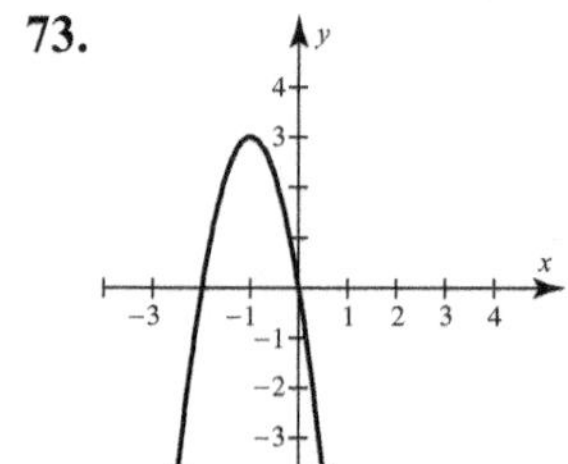

75.

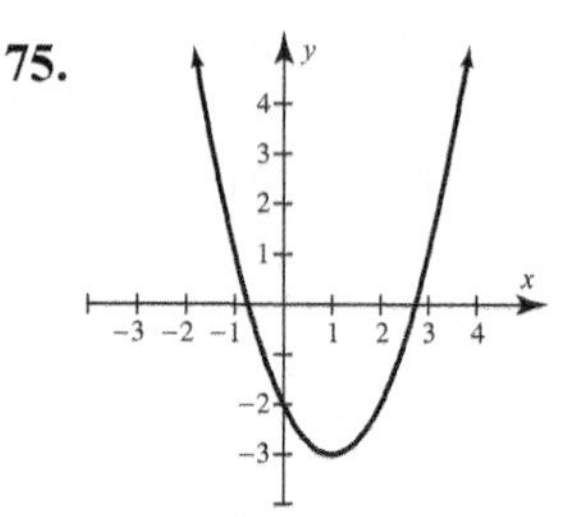

77.

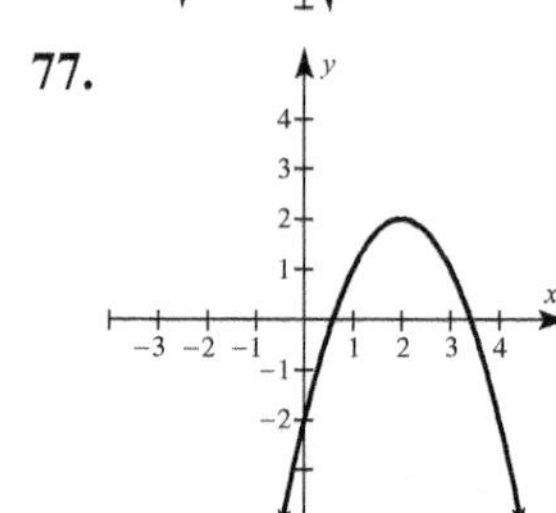

79.

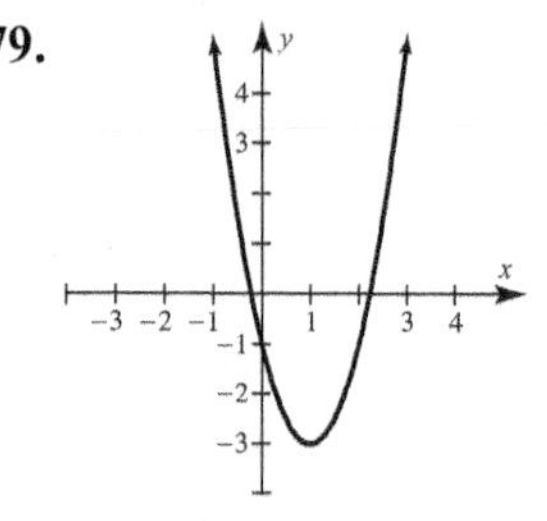

81.

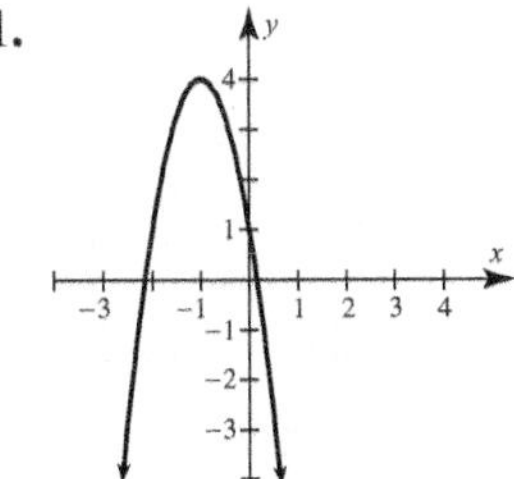

83.

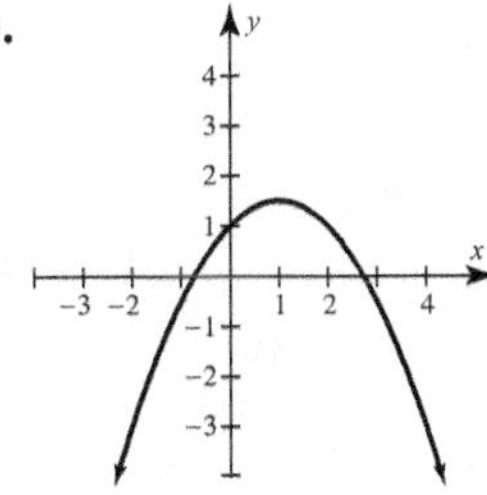

85. -7 **87.** $6x + 3h - 2$ **89.** $f(x) = 2(x - 3)^2 + 1$
91. d **93.** a **95.** 250 ft by 250 ft
97. (a) $R(2) = 72$; the company receives \$72,000 for producing 2000 DVD players. **(b)** 10,000 **(c)** \$200,000
99. (a) It is a parabola that opens upward. **(b)** About 3.5¢ per copy when 7796 copies are made.
101. (a) 32 ft **(b)** 34.25 ft
103. (a) $s(t) = -16t^2 - 66t + 120$
(b) Yes, because $s(2) < 0$.
105. 40 ft by 80 ft **107.** 146 ft after 2.75 sec
109. 323 ft after 6.77 sec
111. $f(x) = \frac{1}{225}x^2 + 20$, or $f(x) \approx 0.0044x^2 + 20$
113. $f(x) = 2(x - 1)^2 - 3$
115. (a) $H(t) = 2(t - 4)^2 + 90$; $D = \{t \mid 0 \le t \le 4\}$
(b) $H(1.5) = 102.5$ beats per minute
117. (a) $V(x) = 3.66x^2 + 1.5$ **(b)** 93 million
119. (a) $f(x) = 3.06(x - 1982)^2 + 1.6$ (answers may vary)
(b) [1980, 1996, 2] by [−50, 500, 100]

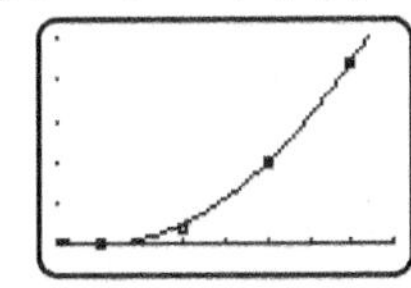

(c) About 250; by 1991 a total of about 250 thousand AIDS cases had been reported.
121. $f(x) = 3.125x^2 + 2.05x - 0.9$; $f(3.5) \approx 44.56$
123. (a) $f(x) \approx 0.055562x^2 - 220.05x + 217{,}886$
(b) About 49 thouand, which is 2 thousand too low
125. (a) $f(x) \approx 0.59462x^2 - 2350.82x + 2{,}323{,}895$
(b) About 454 thousand

3.1 EXTENDED AND DISCOVERY EXERCISES (p. 180)

1. (a)

x	1	2	3	4	5
$f(x)$	−2	1	6	13	22

(b) 3; 5; 7; 9 **(c)** $2x + h$; $2x + 1$
(d) 3; 5; 7; 9; the results are the same.

3. (a)

x	1	2	3	4	5
$f(x)$	0	−3	−10	−21	−36

(b) -3; -7; -11; -15
(c) $-4x + 3 - 2h$; $-4x + 1$
(d) -3; -7; -11; -15; the results are the same.

SECTION 3.2 (pp. 191–195)

1. $-4, 3$ **3.** $0, 2$ **5.** $0, \frac{7}{3}$ **7.** $-1, \frac{15}{2}$ **9.** -3
11. $\frac{1}{2}$ **13.** $-5, \frac{1}{3}$ **15.** $\frac{1}{2}, \frac{5}{6}$ **17.** $-3 \pm \sqrt{5}$
19. $\pm\frac{\sqrt{13}}{2}$ **21.** No real solutions **23.** $3 \pm 2\sqrt{2}$
25. $\frac{-1 \pm \sqrt{13}}{3}$ **27.** $\frac{1}{5}$ **29.** $\frac{5 \pm \sqrt{85}}{30}$ **31.** $-2, -1$
33. x-intercepts: $-\frac{5}{2}, \frac{1}{3}$; y-intercept: -5
35. x-intercept: $\frac{3}{2}$; y-intercept: -9
37. x-intercepts: $\frac{2}{3}, 3$; y-intercept: -6
39. $-2, 0$ **41.** $-2, 3$ **43.** $\pm\sqrt{3} \approx \pm 1.7$ **45.** 1.5
47. $-0.75, 0.2$ **49.** $0.7, 1.2$ **51.** $-2 \pm \sqrt{10}$
53. $-\frac{5}{2} \pm \frac{1}{2}\sqrt{41}$ **55.** $1 \pm \frac{\sqrt{15}}{3}$ **57.** $4 \pm \sqrt{26}$
59. $\frac{3 \pm \sqrt{17}}{2}$ **61.** $\frac{3 \pm \sqrt{17}}{4}$ **63.** $\frac{-1 \pm \sqrt{97}}{12}$
65. $\{x \mid x \ne \sqrt{5}, x \ne -\sqrt{5}\}$
67. $\{t \mid t \ne -1, t \ne 2\}$ **69.** $y = \frac{-12x^2 + 1}{8}$; yes
71. $y = \frac{x}{5}$; yes **73.** $y = 3 \pm \sqrt{9 - x^2}$; no
75. $y = \pm\frac{\sqrt{12 - 3x^2}}{2}$; no **77.** $r = \pm\sqrt{\frac{3V}{\pi h}}$
79. $v = \pm\sqrt{\frac{2K}{m}}$ **81.** $b = \pm\sqrt{c^2 - a^2}$
83. $t = \frac{25 \pm \sqrt{625 - 4s}}{8}$
85. (a) $3x^2 - 12 = 0$ **(b)** $b^2 - 4ac = 144 > 0$. There are two real solutions. **(c)** ± 2
87. (a) $x^2 - 2x + 1 = 0$ **(b)** $b^2 - 4ac = 0$. There is one real solution. **(c)** 1
89. (a) $x^2 - 4x = 0$ **(b)** $b^2 - 4ac = 16 > 0$. There are two real solutions. **(c)** 0, 4
91. (a) $x^2 - x + 1 = 0$ **(b)** $b^2 - 4ac = -3 < 0$. There are no real solutions.
93. (a) $2x^2 + 5x - 12 = 0$ **(b)** $b^2 - 4ac = 121 > 0$. There are two real solutions. **(c)** $-4, \frac{3}{2}$
95. (a) $9x^2 - 36x + 36 = 0$ **(b)** $b^2 - 4ac = 0$. There is one real solution. **(c)** 2
97. (a) $\frac{1}{2}x^2 + x + \frac{13}{2} = 0$ **(b)** $b^2 - 4ac = -12 < 0$. There are no real solutions.
99. (a) $3x^2 + x - 1 = 0$
(b) $b^2 - 4ac = 13 > 0$. There are two real solutions.
(c) $\frac{-1 \pm \sqrt{13}}{6}$
101. (a) $a > 0$ **(b)** $-6, 2$ **(c)** Positive
103. (a) $a > 0$ **(b)** -4 **(c)** Zero
105. 2.2 seconds **107.** 2009 **109.** 8.5 in. by 11 in.; yes
111. 15 in. by 25 in. **113.** About 1.49 in.
115. About 18.23 in.
117. 86 shirts **119. (a)** $s(t) = -16t^2 + 160t + 32$
(b) About 10.2 sec
121. (a) $B(x) = 5.2(x - 1995)^2 + 180$ **(b)** 2005
123. (a) $I(x) = -2.277x^2 + 11.71x + 40.4$
(b) About 2005 and 2012
125. (a) $E(15) = 1.4$; in 2002 there were 1.4 million Walmart employees.
(b) $f(x) \approx 0.00474x^2 + 0.00554x + 0.205$ (answers may vary)
(c) [0, 25, 5] by [0, 2.6, 0.2]

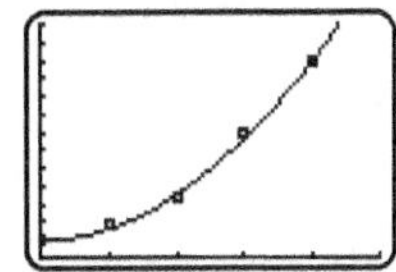

(d) About 2011 (answers may vary)

3.2 EXTENDED AND DISCOVERY EXERCISES (pp. 195–196)

1. $676 = 26^2$; yes; $-\frac{5}{2}, \frac{3}{4}$ **3.** 69; no; $\frac{3 \pm \sqrt{69}}{10}$
7. $x^2 = k \Rightarrow \sqrt{x^2} = \sqrt{k} \Rightarrow |x| \Rightarrow \sqrt{k} \Rightarrow x = \pm\sqrt{k}$

CHECKING BASIC CONCEPTS FOR SECTIONS 3.1 AND 3.2 (p. 196)

1. Vertex; $(1, -4)$; axis of symmetry: $x = 1$; x-intercepts: $-1, 3$

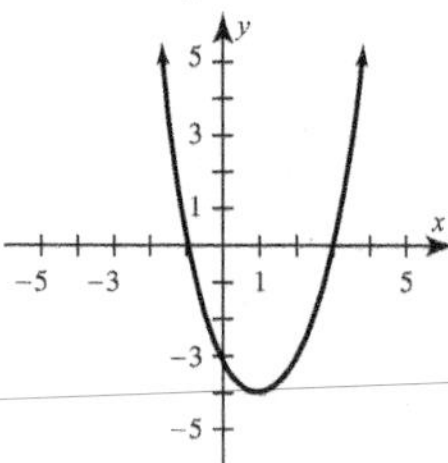

3. $f(x) = 2(x + 1)^2 + 3$
5. $f(x) = (x + 2)^2 - 7; (-2, -7); -7$
7. 11 in. by 15 in.

SECTION 3.3 (pp. 203–204)

1. $2i$ **3.** $10i$ **5.** $i\sqrt{23}$ **7.** $2i\sqrt{3}$ **9.** $3i\sqrt{6}$
11. $2 \pm 2i$ **13.** $-2 \pm 2i\sqrt{2}$ **15.** -5 **17.** -6
19. $-3\sqrt{2}$ **21.** $8i$ **23.** $-2 - i$ **25.** $5 - 21i$
27. $-1 + 6i$ **29.** $4 + 8i$ **31.** $5 - i$ **33.** $4 - 7i$
35. $-5 - 12i$ **37.** 4 **39.** $\frac{1}{2} - \frac{1}{2}i$ **41.** $\frac{19}{26} + \frac{9}{26}i$
43. $-\frac{2}{25} + \frac{4}{25}i$ **45.** $3i$ **47.** $\frac{1}{2} + i$
49. $-18.5 + 87.4i$ **51.** $8.7 - 6.7i$
53. $-117.27 + 88.11i$ **55.** $-0.921 - 0.236i$
57. -1 **59.** $-i$ **61.** 1 **63.** i
65. $\pm i\sqrt{5}$ **67.** $\pm i\sqrt{\frac{1}{2}}$ **69.** $\frac{3}{10} \pm \frac{i\sqrt{11}}{10}$ **71.** $2 \pm i$
73. $\frac{3}{2} \pm \frac{i\sqrt{11}}{2}$ **75.** $-1 \pm i\sqrt{3}$ **77.** $1 \pm \frac{i\sqrt{2}}{2}$
79. $\frac{5}{4} \pm \frac{i\sqrt{7}}{4}$ **81.** $\frac{11}{8} \pm \frac{i\sqrt{7}}{8}$
83. (a) Two real zeros **(b)** $-1, \frac{3}{2}$
85. (a) Two imaginary zeros **(b)** $-\frac{1}{2} \pm \frac{i\sqrt{7}}{2}$
87. (a) Two imaginary zeros **(b)** $\pm i\sqrt{2}$
89. $Z = 10 + 6i$ **91.** $V = 11 + 2i$ **93.** $I = 1 + i$

3.3 EXTENDED AND DISCOVERY EXERCISE (p. 204)

1. (a) $i^1 = i, i^2 = -1, i^3 = -i, i^4 = 1, i^5 = i, i^6 = -1, i^7 = -i, i^8 = 1$, and so on. **(b)** Divide n by 4. If the remainder is r, then $i^n = i^r$, where $i^0 = 1, i^1 = i, i^2 = -1$, and $i^3 = -i$.

SECTION 3.4 (pp. 211–214)

1. (a) $(-\infty, -1) \cup (1, \infty)$, or $\{x \mid x < -1 \text{ or } x > 1\}$
(b) $(-1, 1)$, or $\{x \mid -1 < x < 1\}$
3. (a) $[-4, 4]$, or $\{x \mid -4 \le x \le 4\}$
(b) $(-\infty, -4] \cup [4, \infty)$, or $\{x \mid x \le -4 \text{ or } x \ge 4\}$
5. (a) $(-2, 2)$, or $\{x \mid -2 < x < 2\}$
(b) $(-\infty, -2) \cup (2, \infty)$, or $\{x \mid x < -2 \text{ or } x > 2\}$
7. (a) $-3, 4$ **(b)** $(-3, 4)$, or $\{x \mid -3 < x < 4\}$
(c) $(-\infty, -3) \cup (4, \infty)$, or $\{x \mid x < -3 \text{ or } x > 4\}$
9. (a) $\pm\sqrt{5}$ **(b)** $[-\sqrt{5}, \sqrt{5}]$, or $\{x \mid -\sqrt{5} \le x \le \sqrt{5}\}$
(c) $(-\infty, -\sqrt{5}] \cup [\sqrt{5}, \infty)$, or $\{x \mid x \le -\sqrt{5} \text{ or } x \ge \sqrt{5}\}$
11. (a) $-\frac{8}{3}, 0$ **(b)** $[-\frac{8}{3}, 0]$, or $\{x \mid -\frac{8}{3} \le x \le 0\}$
(c) $(-\infty, -\frac{8}{3}] \cup [0, \infty)$, or $\{x \mid x \le -\frac{8}{3} \text{ or } x \ge 0\}$
13. (a) $\frac{3}{2}$ **(b)** $(-\infty, \frac{3}{2}) \cup (\frac{3}{2}, \infty)$, or $\{x \mid x < \frac{3}{2} \text{ or } x > \frac{3}{2}\}$
(c) No solutions
15. (a) $\frac{2}{3}, \frac{5}{4}$ **(b)** $[\frac{2}{3}, \frac{5}{4}]$, or $\{x \mid \frac{2}{3} \le x \le \frac{5}{4}\}$
(c) $(-\infty, \frac{2}{3}] \cup [\frac{5}{4}, \infty)$, or $\{x \mid x \le \frac{2}{3} \text{ or } x \ge \frac{5}{4}\}$
17. (a) $-1 \pm \sqrt{2}$ **(b)** $(-1 - \sqrt{2}, -1 + \sqrt{2})$, or $\{x \mid -1 - \sqrt{2} < x < -1 + \sqrt{2}\}$
(c) $(-\infty, -1 - \sqrt{2}) \cup (-1 + \sqrt{2}, \infty)$, or $\{x \mid x < -1 - \sqrt{2} \text{ or } x > -1 + \sqrt{2}\}$
19. (a) $-3 < x < 2$ **(b)** $x \le -3$ or $x \ge 2$
21. (a) $x = -2$ **(b)** $x \ne -2$
23. (a) No solutions **(b)** All real numbers
25. (a) $-\frac{5}{2}, -\frac{1}{2}$ **(b)** $(-\frac{5}{2}, -\frac{1}{2})$, or $\{x \mid -\frac{5}{2} < x < -\frac{1}{2}\}$
(c) $(-\infty, -\frac{5}{2}) \cup (-\frac{1}{2}, \infty)$, or $\{x \mid x < -\frac{5}{2} \text{ or } x > -\frac{1}{2}\}$
27. (a) $-1, \frac{7}{5}$ **(b)** $(-\infty, -1) \cup (\frac{7}{5}, \infty)$, or $\{x \mid x < -1 \text{ or } x > \frac{7}{5}\}$ **(c)** $(-1, \frac{7}{5})$, or $\{x \mid -1 < x < \frac{7}{5}\}$
29. (a) $x < -1$ or $x > 1$ **(b)** $-1 \le x \le 1$
31. (a) $-6 < x < -2$ **(b)** $x \le -6$ or $x \ge -2$
33. $-2 \le x \le -0.5$ **35.** $x < -3$ or $x > 2$
37. $-2 \le x \le 2$ **39.** All real numbers
41. $x \le -2$ or $x \ge 3$ **43.** $-\frac{1}{3} < x < \frac{1}{2}$
45. $-4 \le x \le 10$ **47.** No solutions
49. All real numbers except $\frac{2}{3}$ **51.** $x \le 0$ or $x \ge 1$
53. $x \le -2$ or $x \ge 3$ **55.** $-\sqrt{5} \le x \le \sqrt{5}$
57. $x \le \frac{23}{7}$ or $x \ge 22.4$ **59.** $2 \le x \le 7$
61. $x \le -2$ or $x \ge 5$ **63.** All real numbers
65. $x < -2 - \sqrt{7}$ or $x > -2 + \sqrt{7}$
67. About 35 mi/hr, but not more than 38 mi/hr
69. $2 \le r \le 3$ (inches)
71. (a) $f(0) = 160$, $f(2) = 131.2$; initially the heart rate is 160 bpm, and after 2 minutes it is about 131 bpm.
(b) About $2.9 \le x \le 5$ (minutes)
73. From 1989 to 1992
75. From 2007 to 2008 and from 2009 to 2010

CHECKING BASIC CONCEPTS FOR SECTIONS 3.3 AND 3.4 (p. 214)

1. (a) $5i$ **(b)** $-3\sqrt{6}$ **(c)** $\frac{1}{2} \pm \frac{i\sqrt{2}}{2}$
3. (a) $[-3, 0]$, or $\{x \mid -3 \le x \le 0\}$; $(-\infty, -3) \cup (0, \infty)$, or $\{x \mid x < -3 \text{ or } x > 0\}$
(b) $(-\infty, \infty)$, or $\{x \mid -\infty < x < \infty\}$; no solutions
5. (a) $(-\infty, -6] \cup [6, \infty)$, or $\{x \mid x \le -6 \text{ or } x \ge 6\}$
(b) $(-\infty, \infty)$, or $\{x \mid -\infty < x < \infty\}$
(c) $\left[\frac{1 - \sqrt{5}}{2}, \frac{1 + \sqrt{5}}{2}\right]$, or $\left\{x \mid \frac{1 - \sqrt{5}}{2} \le x \le \frac{1 + \sqrt{5}}{2}\right\}$

SECTION 3.5 (pp. 228–231)

1. $y = (x + 2)^2$ **3.** $y = \sqrt{x + 3}$
5. $y = |x + 2| - 1$
7. $y = \sqrt{x + 2} - 3$

9. $y = (x - 2)^2 - 3$
$[-10, 10, 1]$ by $[-10, 10, 1]$

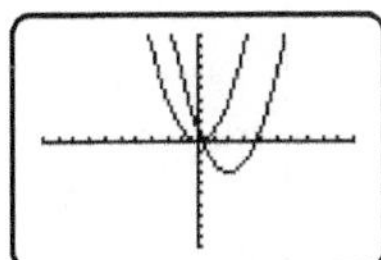

11. $y = (x + 6)^2 - 4(x + 6) + 5$
$[-10, 10, 1]$ by $[-10, 10, 1]$

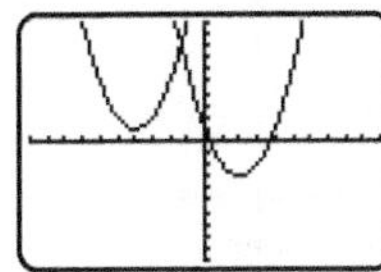

13. $y = \frac{1}{2}(x + 3)^2 + 2(x + 3) - 3$
$[-10, 10, 1]$ by $[-10, 10, 1]$

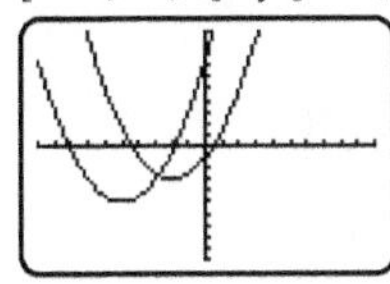

15. (a) $g(x) = 3(x + 3)^2 + 2(x + 3) - 5$
(b) $g(x) = 3x^2 + 2x - 9$
17. (a) $g(x) = 2(x - 2)^2 + 4$
(b) $g(x) = 2(x + 8)^2 - 5$
19. (a) $g(x) = 3(x - 2000)^2 - 3(x - 2000) + 72$
(b) $g(x) = 3(x + 300)^2 - 3(x + 300) - 28$
21. (a) $g(x) = -\sqrt{x - 4}$ **(b)** $g(x) = \sqrt{-x + 2}$
23. $(x - 3)^2 + (y + 4)^2 = 4$; center: $(3, -4)$; $r = 2$
25. $(x + 5)^2 + (y - 3)^2 = 5$;
center: $(-5, 3)$; $r = \sqrt{5}$

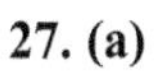

27. (a)

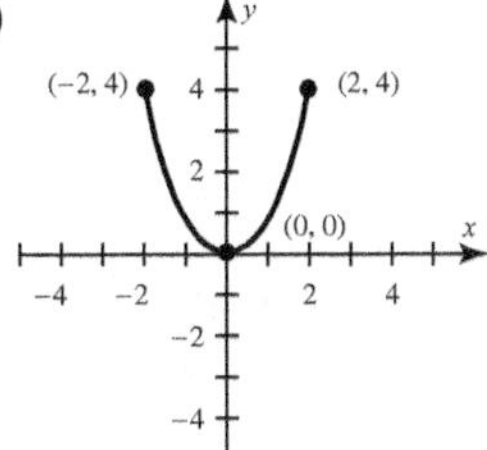

(b)

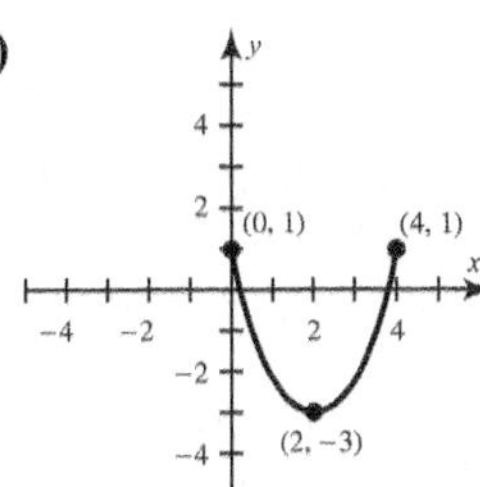

(c)

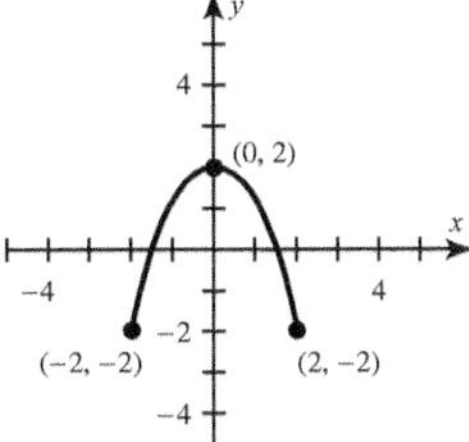

29. (a)

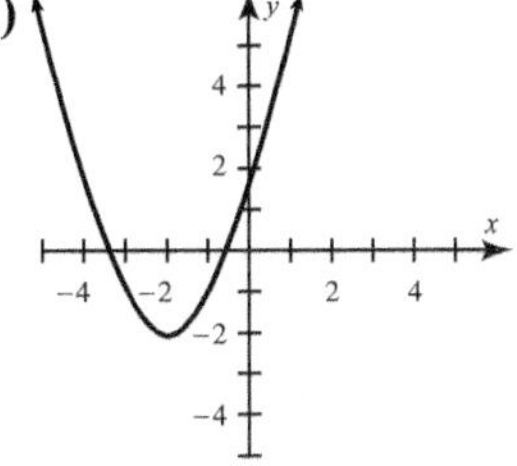

(b)

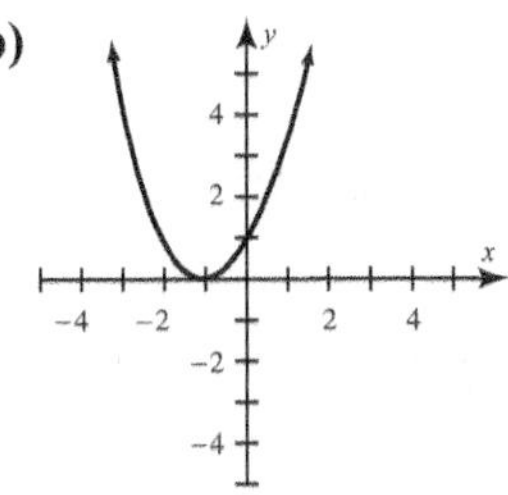

(c)

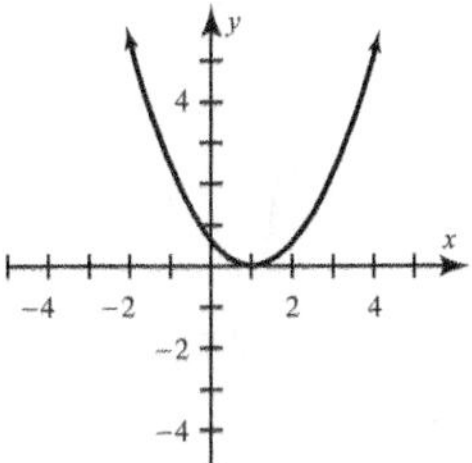

31. (a)

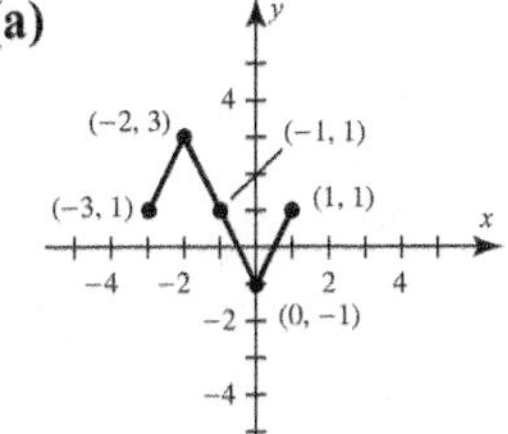

(b)

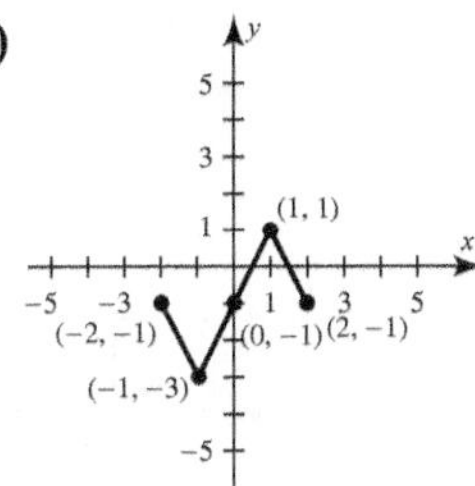

(c)

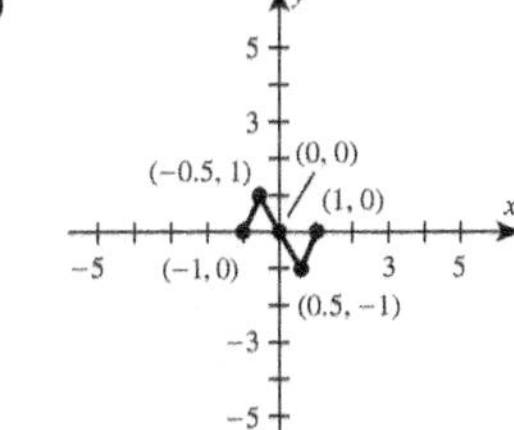

33. (a)

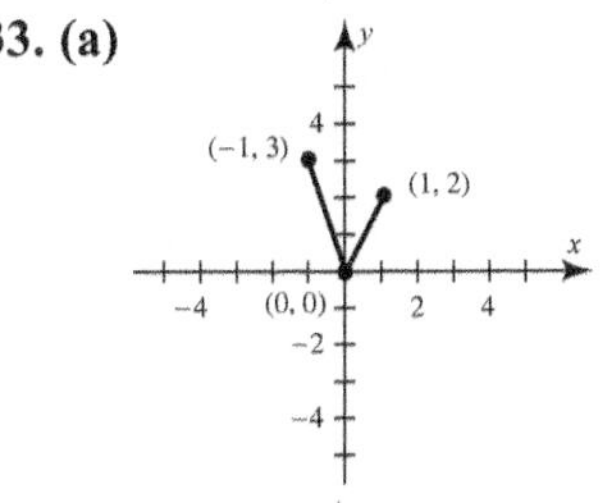

(b)

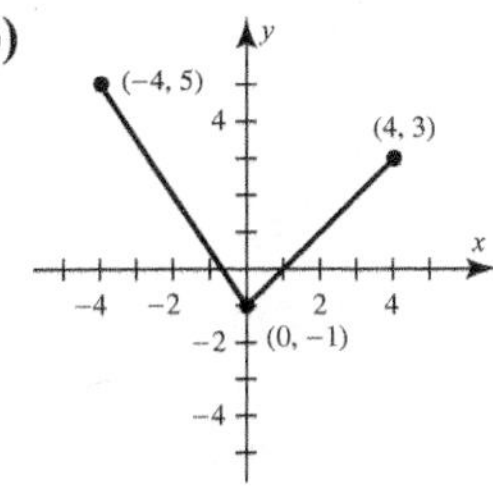

(c)

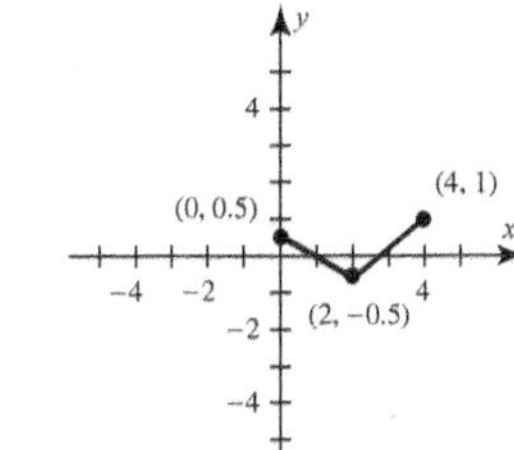

35. $y = -\sqrt{x} - 1$

Given function

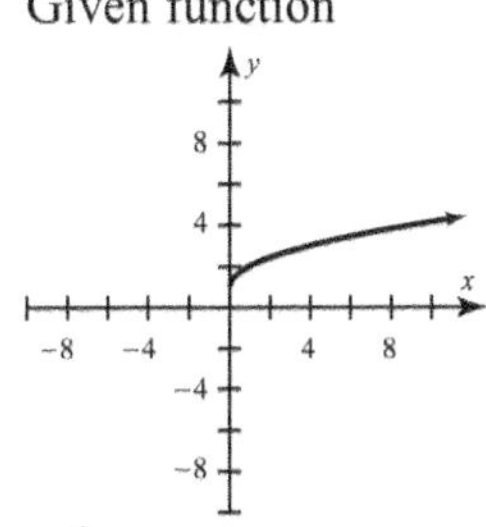

x-axis reflection

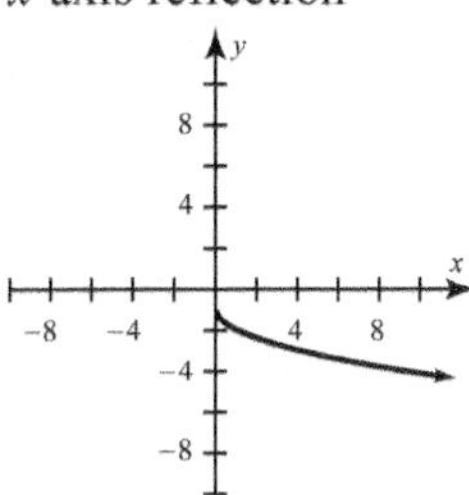

37. $y = x^2 + x$

Given function

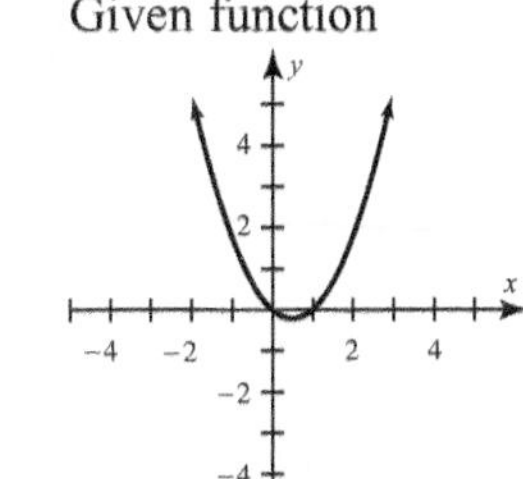

y-axis reflection

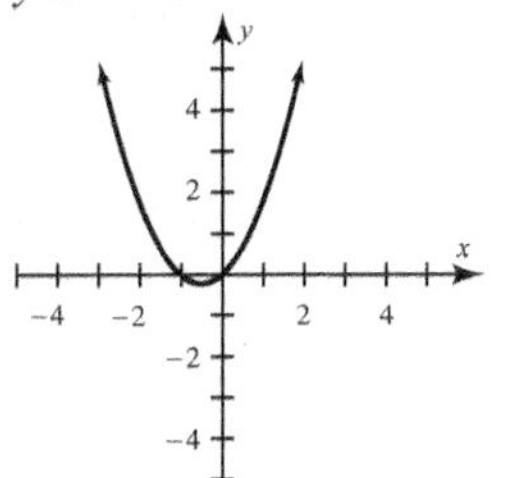

39. x-axis:

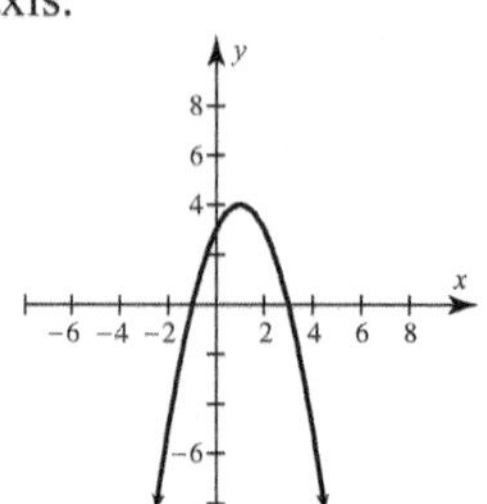

y-axis:

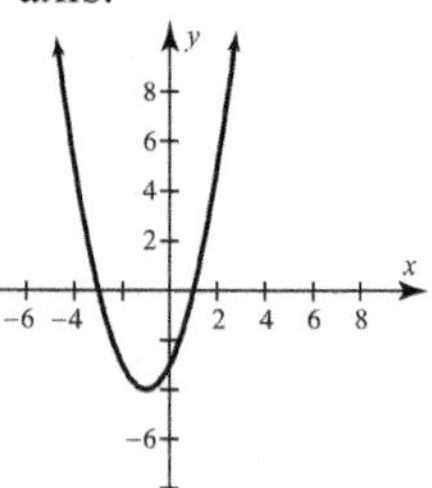

41. x-axis:

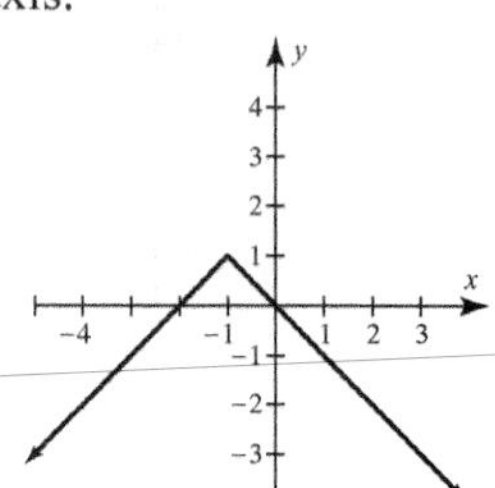

y-axis:

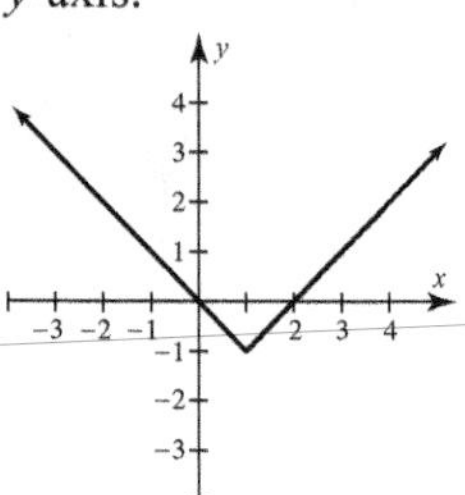

43. x-axis:

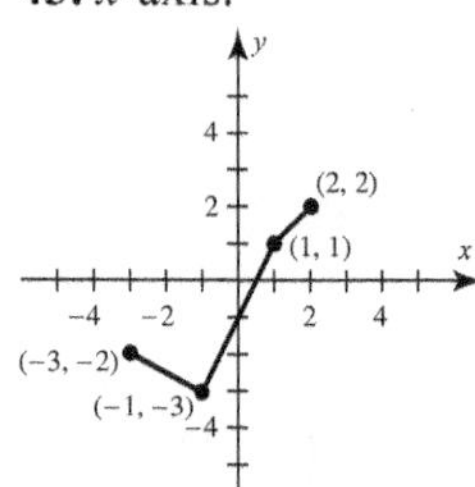

y-axis:

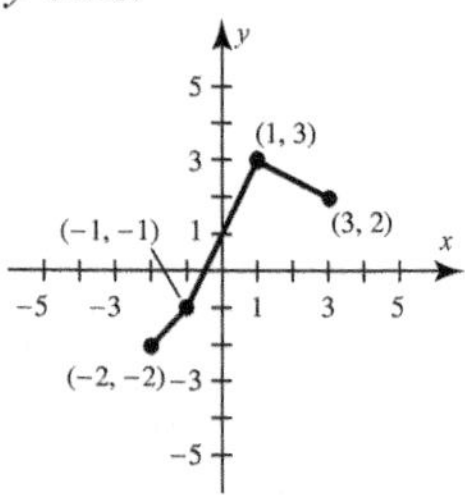

45. Shift the graph of $y = x^2$ right 3 units and upward 1 unit.
47. Shift the graph of $y = x^2$ left 1 unit and vertically shrink it with factor $\frac{1}{4}$.
49. Reflect the graph of $y = \sqrt{x}$ across the x-axis and shift it left 5 units.
51. Reflect the graph of $y = \sqrt{x}$ across the y-axis and vertically stretch it with factor 2.
53. Reflect the graph of $y = |x|$ across the y-axis and shift it left 1 unit.

55.

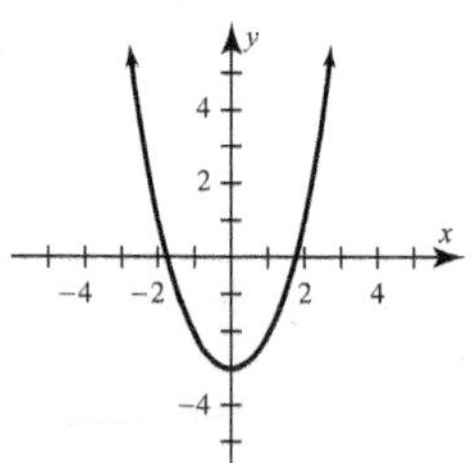

57.

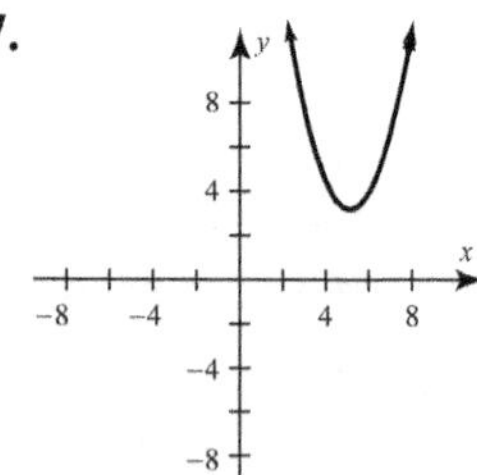

59.

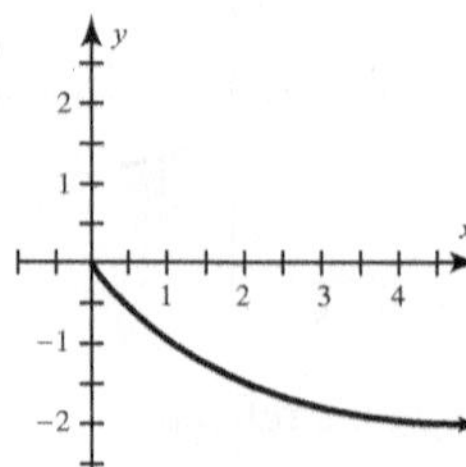

61.

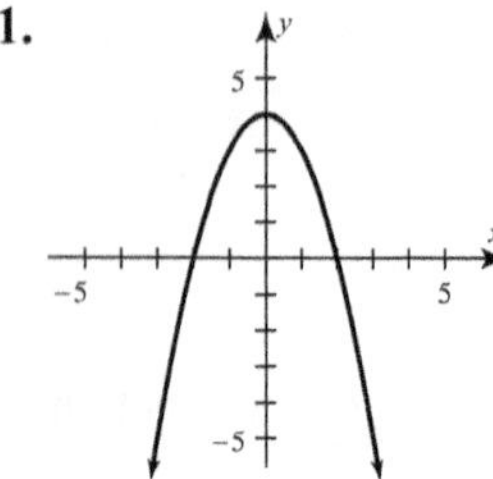

63.

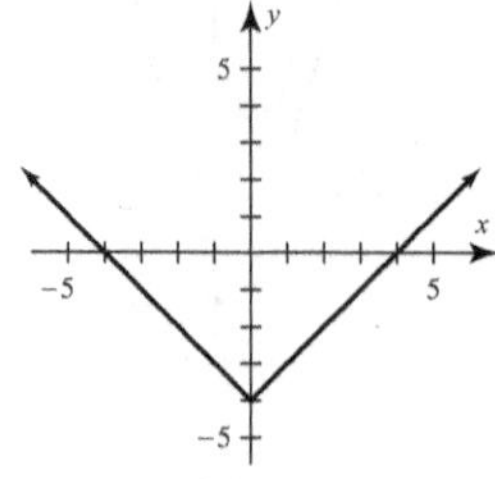

65.

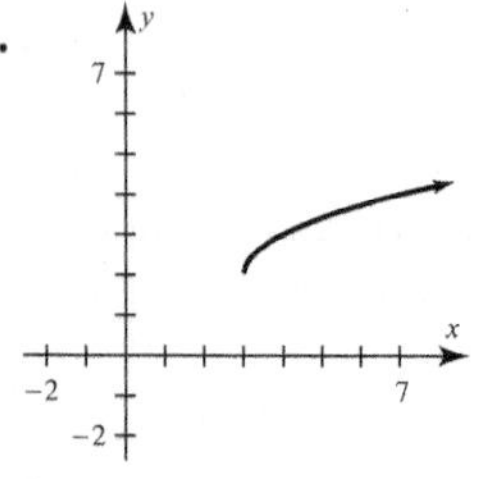

67.

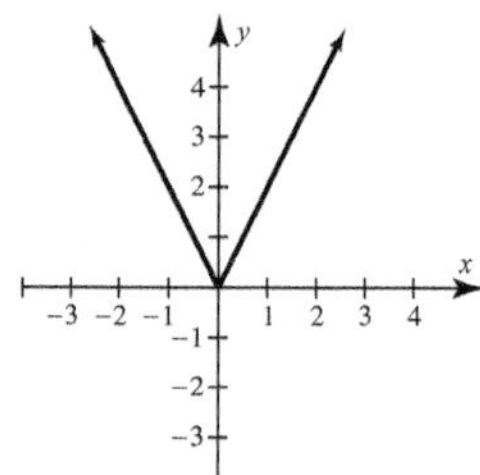

69.

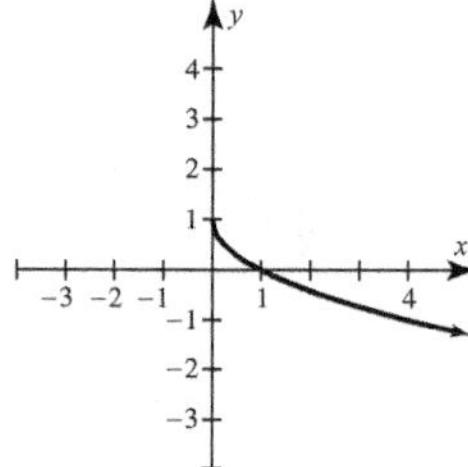

71.

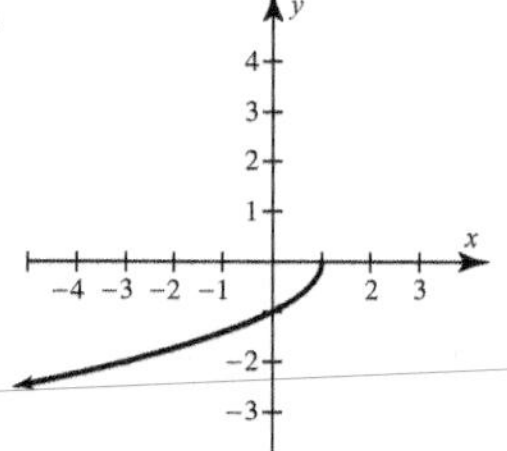

73.

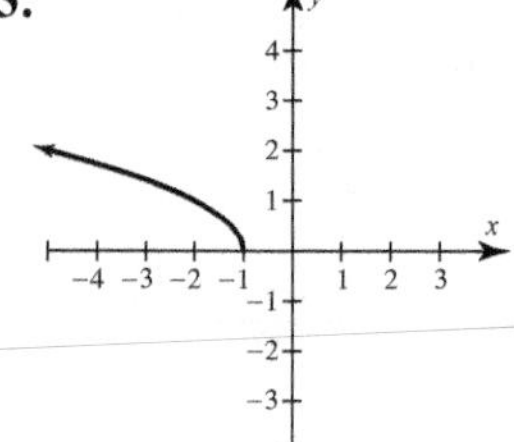

75.

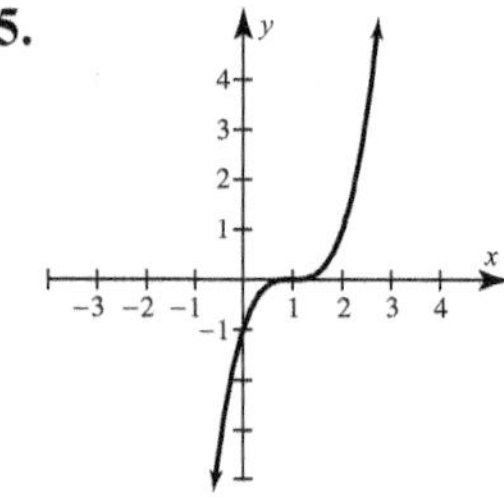

77.

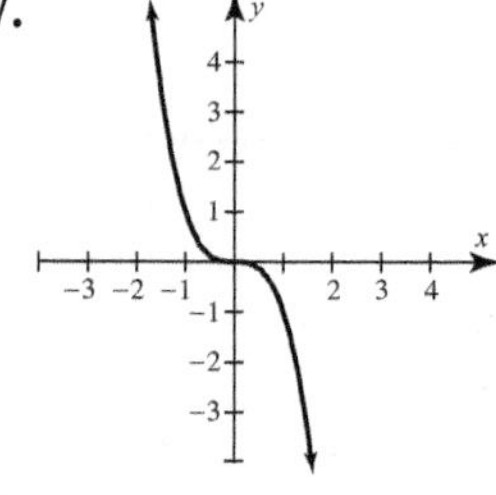

79.

x	1	2	3	4	5	6
$g(x)$	12	8	13	9	14	16

81.

x	−2	0	2	4	6
$g(x)$	5	2	−3	−5	−9

83.

x	0	1	2	3	4	5
$g(x)$	0	2	1	5	6	8

85.

x	−2	−1	0	1	2
$g(x)$	0	3	6	9	12

87. $(-12, 8)$, $(0, 10)$, and $(8, -2)$
89. $(-10, 7)$, $(2, 9)$, and $(10, -3)$
91. $(-12, -3)$, $(0, -4)$, and $(8, 2)$
93. $(6, 6)$, $(0, 8)$, and $(-4, -4)$
95. $f(x) = 7(x - 2008)^2 + 11.6$
97. $f(x) = 1.8(x - 2008)^2 + 22$
99. $g(x) = 0.00075(x - 1990)^2 + 0.17(x - 1990) + 44$
101. $y = -0.4(x - 3)^2 + 4$ (mountain)
$[-4, 4, 1]$ by $[0, 6, 1]$

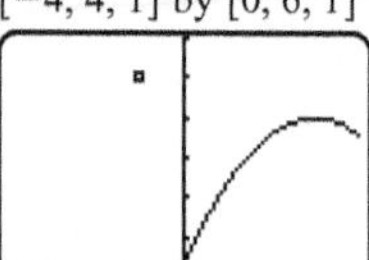

103. (a) $y = \frac{1}{20}x^2 - 1.6$
$[-15, 15, 1]$ by $[-10, 10, 1]$

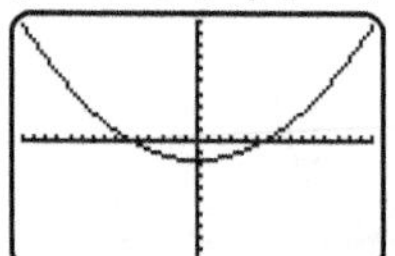

(b) $y = \frac{1}{20}(x - 2.1)^2 - 2.5$.
The front has reached Columbus by midnight.
$[-15, 15, 1]$ by $[-10, 10, 1]$

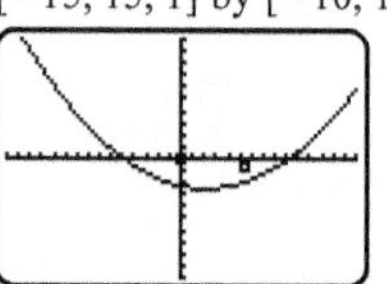

CHECKING BASIC CONCEPTS FOR SECTION 3.5 (p. 232)

1. (a) Shifted 4 units to the left
(b) Shifted 3 units down
(c) Shifted 5 units to the right and 3 units up
3. (a) $y = (x - 3)^2 - 4$ **(b)** $y = -x^2$
(c) $y = (-x + 6)^2$ **(d)** $y = (-(x + 6))^2$

5. (a)

x	-2	0	2	4	6
$g(x)$	4	6	9	11	12

(b)

x	-5	-3	-1	1	3
$h(x)$	-2	-6	-12	-16	-18

CHAPTER 3 REVIEW EXERCISES (pp. 236–237)

1. (a) $a < 0$ **(b)** $(2, 4)$ **(c)** $x = 2$
(d) Incr: $x < 2$, or $(-\infty, 2)$; Decr: $x > 2$, or $(2, \infty)$
3. $f(x) = -2x^2 + 20x - 49$; leading coefficient: -2
5. $f(x) = -(x + 1)^2 + 2$
7. $f(x) = (x + 3)^2 - 10$; vertex: $(-3, -10)$ **9.** $\left(\frac{1}{3}, -\frac{11}{3}\right)$

11.

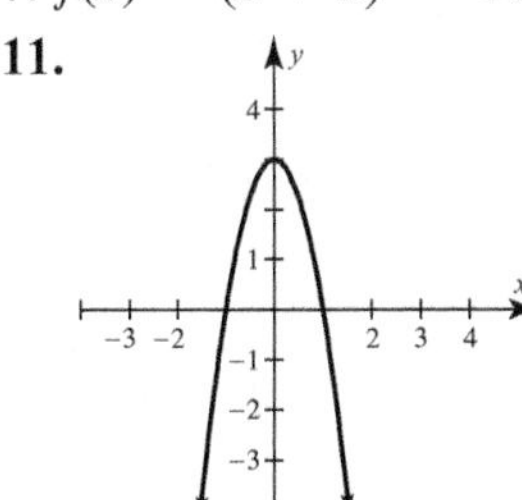

13.

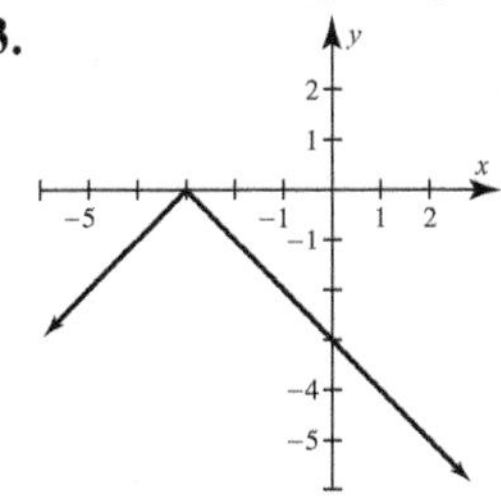

15. -29 **17.** $-4, 5$ **19.** $\pm\frac{\sqrt{7}}{2}$ **21.** $-\frac{7}{2}, 2$ **23.** $-2, 5$
25. $-1 \pm \sqrt{6}$ **27.** $\frac{3 \pm \sqrt{11}}{2}$ **29.** $y = \pm\sqrt{\frac{2x^2 - 6}{3}}$; no
31. (a) $4i$ **(b)** $4i\sqrt{3}$ **(c)** $-5\sqrt{3}$
33. (a) $-\frac{5}{2}, \frac{1}{2}$ **(b)** $-\frac{5}{2}, \frac{1}{2}$ **35.** $\pm\frac{3}{2}i$
37. (a) $-3 < x < 2$, or $(-3, 2)$
(b) $x \le -3$ or $x \ge 2$, or $(-\infty, -3] \cup [2, \infty)$
39. $\{x \mid 1 \le x \le 2\}$, or $[1, 2]$
41. $\{x \mid x \le -3 \text{ or } x \ge 5\}$, or $(-\infty, -3] \cup [5, \infty)$
43. $y = -f(x)$ $y = f(-x)$

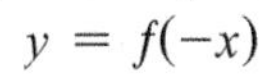

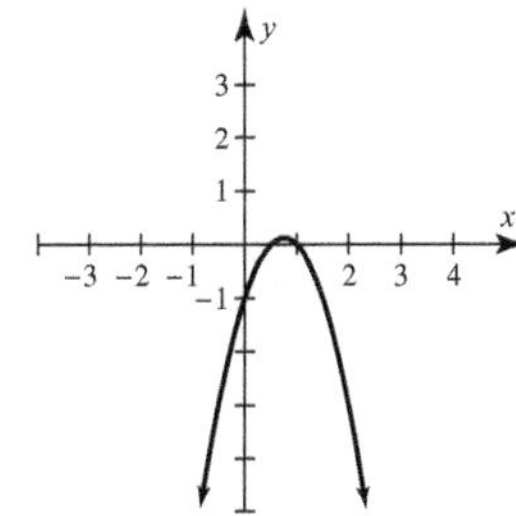

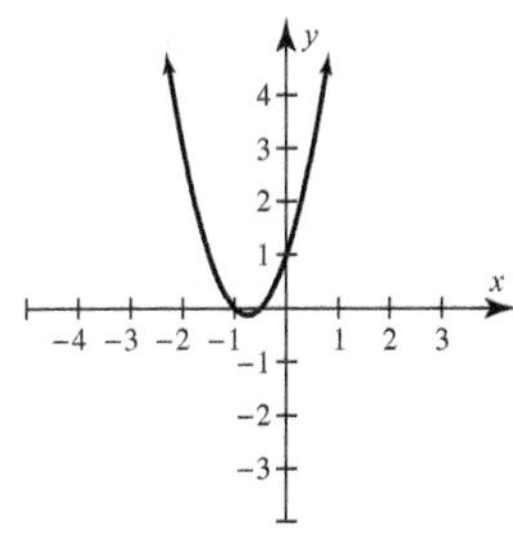

45.

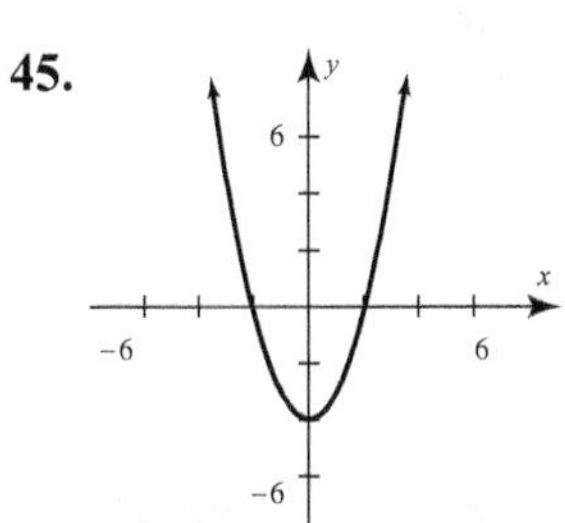

47.

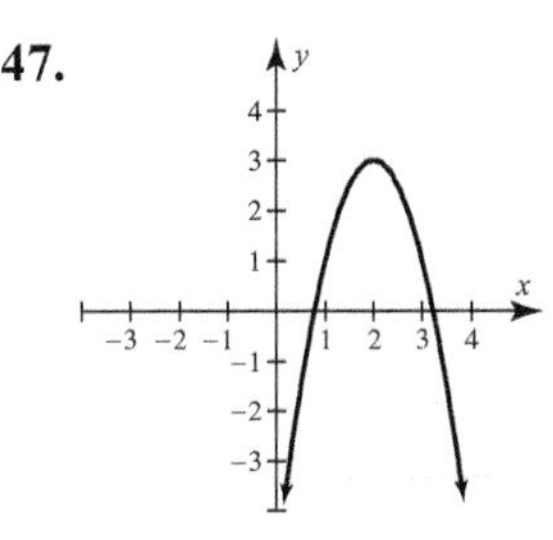

49. 11 ft by 22 ft

51. (a) $h(0) = 5$; the stone was 5 ft above the ground when it was released. **(b)** 117 ft **(c)** 126 ft
(d) After 2 seconds and 3.5 seconds
53. 11 in. by 15 in.
55. $M(x) = 30(x - 2007)^2 + 60$

CHAPTER 3 EXTENDED AND DISCOVERY EXERCISES (p. 238)

1. (a) 23.32 ft/sec
(b) $[-1, 16, 1]$ by $[-1, 16, 1]$ Yes **(c)** 12.88 ft

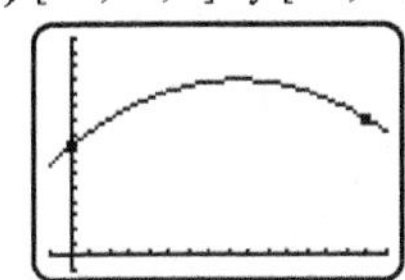

3. (a) $[-1, 8, 1]$ by $[-4, 4, 1]$

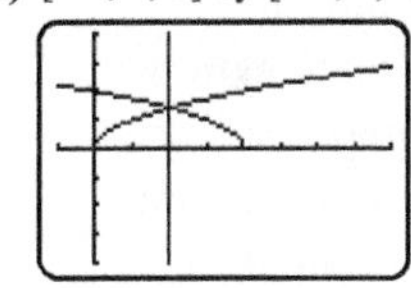

(b) The graph of $y = f(2k - x) = f(4 - x)$ is a reflection of $y = f(x)$ across the line $x = 2$.
5. (a) $[-15, 3, 1]$ by $[-3, 9, 1]$

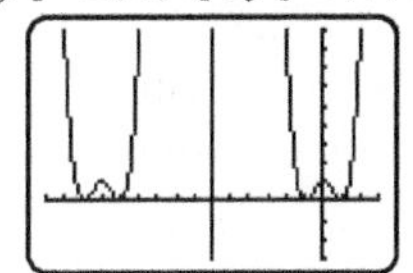

(b) The graph of $f(2k - x) = f(-12 - x)$ is a reflection of $y = f(x)$ across the line $x = -6$.
7. (a) $[0, 1200, 100]$ by $[-800, 0, 100]$

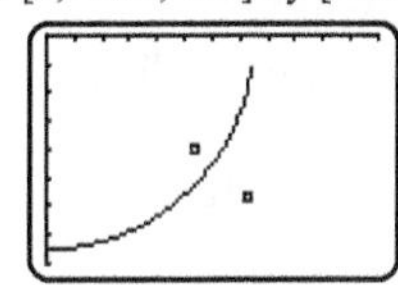

The front reached St. Louis, but not Nashville.
(b) $g(x) = -\sqrt{750^2 - (x - 160)^2} - 110$
(c) $[0, 1200, 100]$ by $[-800, 0, 100]$

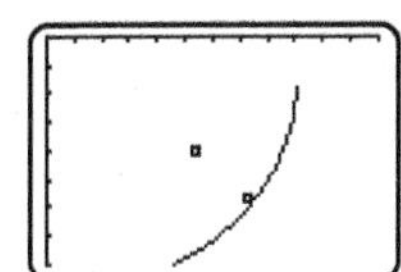

The cold front reached both cities in less than 12 hours.

CHAPTER 4: More Nonlinear Functions and Equations

SECTION 4.1 (pp. 246–250)

1. Yes; degree: 3; a: 2 **3.** No
5. Yes; degree: 4; a: -5 **7.** No
9. Yes; degree: 0; a: 22
11. (a) Local maximum: approximately 5.5; local minimum: approximately -5.5 **(b)** No absolute extrema
13. (a) Local maxima: approximately 17 and 27; local minima: approximately -10 and 24 **(b)** No absolute extrema

15. **(a)** Local maxima: approximately 0.5 and 2.8; local minimum: approximately 0 **(b)** Absolute maximum: 2.8; no absolute minimum
17. **(a)** Local maximum: 0; local minimum: approximately -1000 **(b)** No absolute maximum; absolute minimum: -1000
19. **(a)** Local maximum: 1; local minimum: -1 **(b)** Absolute maximum: 1; absolute minimum: -1
21. **(a)** No local maxima; local minimum: approximately -3.2 **(b)** Absolute maximum: 3; absolute minimum: approximately -3.2
23. **(a)** Local maxima: approximately 0.5 and 2; local minima: approximately -2 and -0.5 **(b)** Absolute maximum: 2; absolute minimum: -2
25. **(a)** No local maxima; local minimum: -2 **(b)** No absolute maximum; absolute minimum: -2
27. **(a)** No local extrema **(b)** No absolute extrema
29. **(a)** Local minimum: 1; no local maxima **(b)** Absolute minimum: 1; no absolute maximum
31. **(a)** Local maximum: 4; no local minima **(b)** Absolute maximum: 4; no absolute minimum
33. **(a)** Local minimum: $-\frac{1}{8}$; no local maxima **(b)** Absolute minimum: $-\frac{1}{8}$; no absolute maximum
35. **(a)** Local minimum: 0; no local maxima **(b)** Absolute minimum: 0; no absolute maximum
37. **(a)** No local extrema **(b)** No absolute extrema
39. (a) Local minimum: -2; local maximum: 2 **(b)** No absolute extrema
41. **(a)** Local maxima: 19, -8; local minimum: -13 **(b)** Absolute maximum: 19; no absolute minimum
43. **(a)** Local minimum: -8; local maximum: 4.5 **(b)** Absolute minimum: -8; no absolute maximum
45. **(a)** Local maximum: 8; no local minima **(b)** Absolute maximum: 8; no absolute minimum
47. Neither **49.** Even
51. Odd **53.** Neither **55.** Even **57.** Even
59. Odd **61.** Neither **63.** Even
65. Even **67.** Even **69.** Neither **71.** Odd
73. Note that $f(0)$ can be any number.

x	-3	-2	-1	0	1	2	3
$f(x)$	21	-12	-25	1	-25	-12	21

75. $f(5) = 6$; $f(3) = -4$
77. Answers may vary.

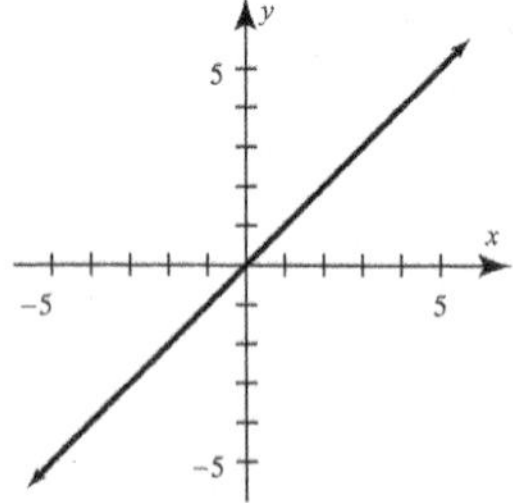

79. No. If (2, 5) is on the graph of an odd function f, then so is $(-2, -5)$. Since f would pass through $(-3, -4)$ and then $(-2, -5)$, it could not always be increasing.

81. Answers may vary.

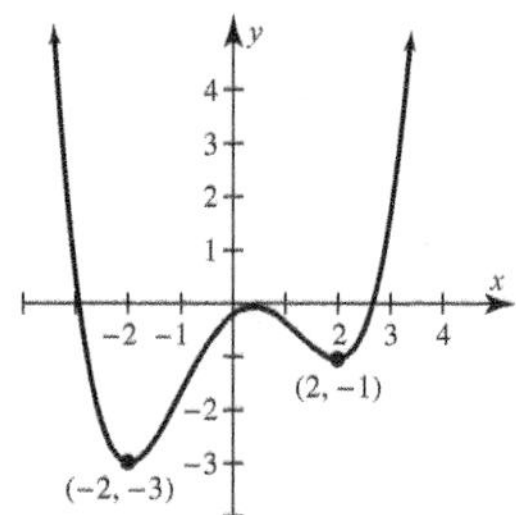

83. Answers may vary; yes, but it does not have to be quadratic.

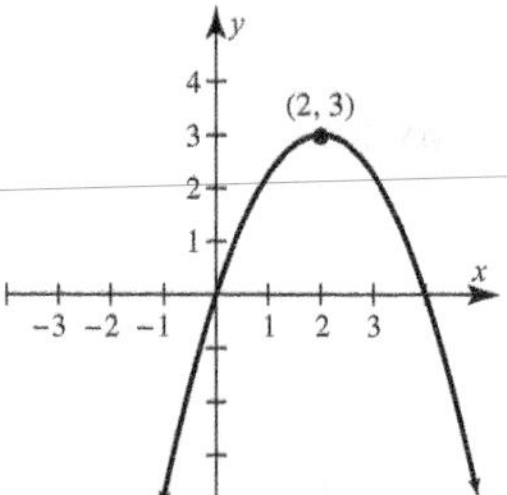

85.

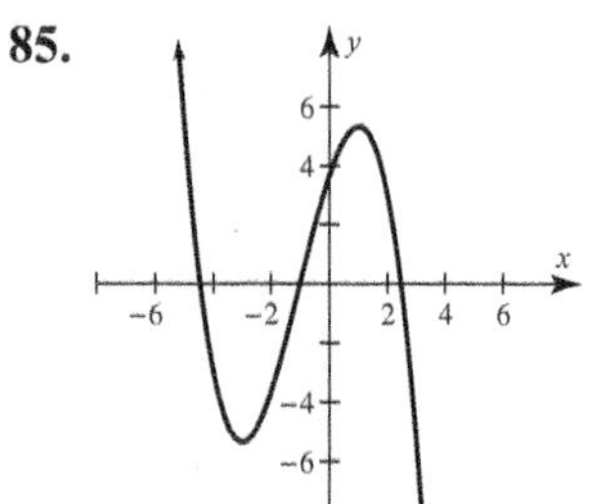

87.

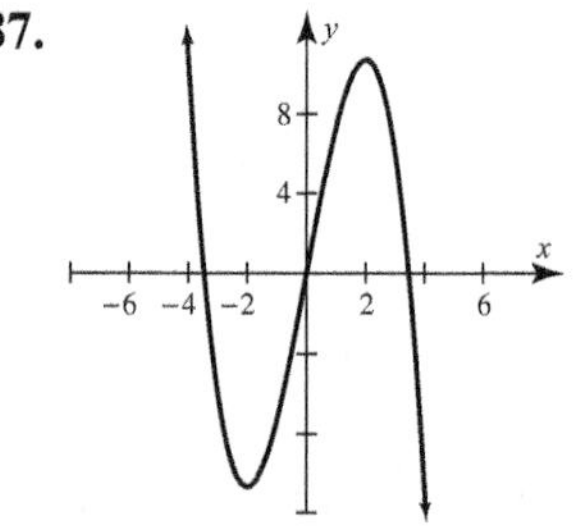

89. On (0, 3); on (3, 6)
91. **(a)** Absolute maximum: 84°F; absolute minimum: 63°F; the high temperature was 84°F and the low was 63°F. **(b)** Local maxima: approximately 78°F and 84°F; local minima: approximately 63°F and 72°F **(c)** $1.6 < x < 2.9$; $3.8 < x < 5$ (approximate)
93. **(a)** $F(1) \approx 69$; in January 2009, Facebook had about 69 million unique users. $F(12) \approx 132$; in December 2009, Facebook had about 132 million unique users. **(b)** No, F has no real extrema.

[0, 13, 2] by [0, 150, 25]

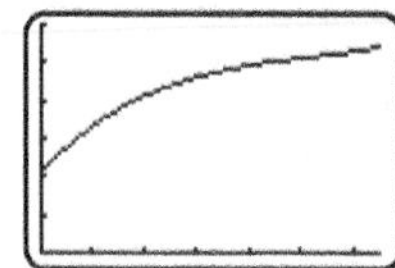

(c) (1, 12) or $\{x \mid 1 < x < 12\}$
95. **(a)** Possible absolute maximum in January and absolute minimum in July **(b)** Absolute maximum: \$140; absolute minimum: \$15; the maximum cost, \$140, occurs in January and the minimum cost, \$15, occurs in July.

[1, 12, 1] by [0, 150, 10]

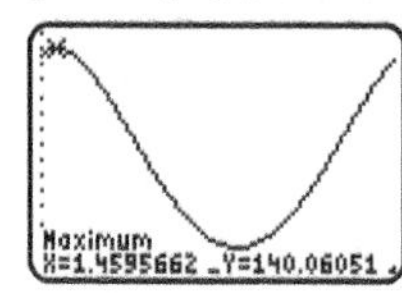

[1, 12, 1] by [0, 150, 10]

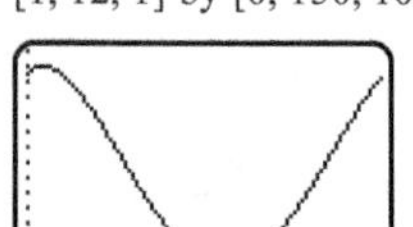

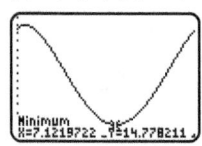

97. (a) Even **(b)** 83°F **(c)** They are equal. **(d)** Monthly average temperatures are symmetric about July. July has the highest average and January the lowest. The pairs June-August, May-September, April-October, March-November, and February-December have approximately the same average temperatures.

4.1 EXTENDED AND DISCOVERY EXERCISES (pp. 250–251)

1. The maximum area occurs when the figure is a rectangle with length about 4.24 and height about 2.12.
3. (a) About 1 hour 54 minutes **(b)** About 2 hours 8 minutes **(c)** About 1 hour 46 minutes

SECTION 4.2 (pp. 261–266)

1. (a) The turning points are approximately (1.6, 3.6), (3, 1.2), (4.4, 3.6). **(b)** After 1.6 minutes, the runner is 360 feet from the starting line. The runner turns and jogs toward the starting line. After 3 minutes, the runner is 120 feet from the starting line. The runner turns and jogs away from the starting line. After 4.4 minutes, the runner is again 360 feet from the starting line. The runner turns and jogs back to the starting line.
3. (a) 0; 0.5 **(b)** $a > 0$ **(c)** 1
5. (a) 3; -6, -1, and 6 **(b)** $a < 0$ **(c)** 4
7. (a) 4; -3, -1, 0, 1, and 2 **(b)** $a > 0$ **(c)** 5
9. (a) 2; -3 **(b)** $a > 0$ **(c)** 3
11. (a) 1; -1 and 2 **(b)** $a > 0$ **(c)** 2
13. (a) d **(b)** (1, 0) **(c)** 1 **(d)** No local maxima; local minimum: 0 **(e)** No absolute maxima; absolute minimum: 0
15. (a) b **(b)** $(-3, 27)$, $(1, -5)$ **(c)** $x \approx -4.9$, $x = 0$, $x \approx 1.9$ **(d)** Local maximum: 27; local minimum: -5 **(e)** No absolute maximum; no absolute minimum
17. (a) a **(b)** $(-2, 16)$, $(0, 0)$, $(2, 16)$ **(c)** $x \approx -2.8$, $x = 0$, $x \approx 2.8$ **(d)** Local maximum: 16; local minimum: 0 **(e)** Absolute maximum: 16; no absolute minimum
19. (a) $[-10, 10, 1]$ by $[-10, 10, 1]$

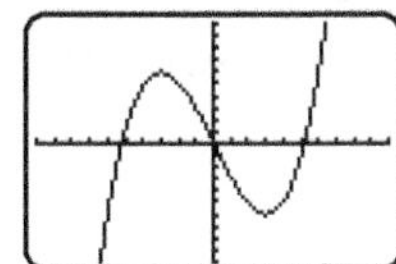

(b) $(-3, 6)$, $(3, -6)$ **(c)** Local minimum: -6; local maximum: 6
21. (a) $[-10, 10, 1]$ by $[-10, 10, 1]$

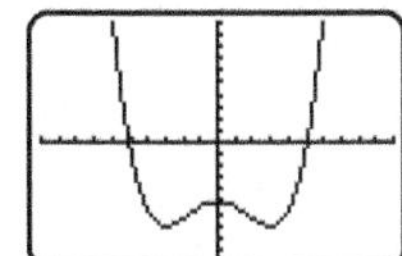

(b) There are three turning points located at $(-3, -7.025)$, $(0, -5)$, and $(3, -7.025)$.
(c) Local minimum: -7.025; local maximum: -5
23. (a) $[-10, 10, 1]$ by $[-10, 10, 1]$

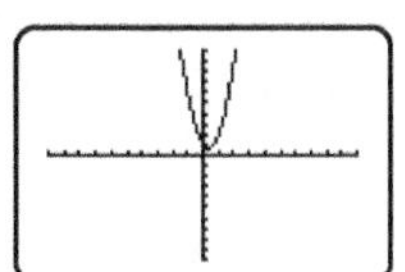

(b) $\left(\frac{1}{3}, \frac{2}{3}\right) \approx (0.333, 0.667)$
(c) Local minimum: $\frac{2}{3} \approx 0.667$; no local maximum
25. (a) $[-10, 10, 1]$ by $[-10, 10, 1]$

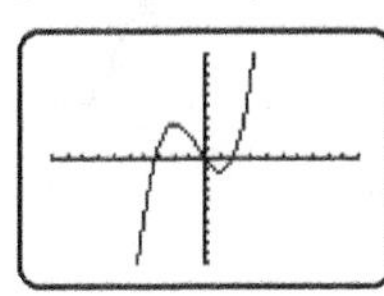

(b) $\left(-2, \frac{10}{3}\right) \approx (-2, 3.333)$, $\left(1, -\frac{7}{6}\right) \approx (1, -1.167)$
(c) Local minimum: $-\frac{7}{6} \approx -1.167$; local maximum: $\frac{10}{3} \approx 3.333$
27. (a) Degree: 1; leading coefficient: -2
(b) Up on left end, down on right end; $f(x) \to \infty$ as $x \to -\infty$, $f(x) \to -\infty$ as $x \to \infty$
29. (a) Degree: 2; leading coefficient: 1 **(b)** Up on both ends; $f(x) \to \infty$ as $x \to -\infty$, $f(x) \to \infty$ as $x \to \infty$
31. (a) Degree: 3; leading coefficient: -2
(b) Up on left end, down on right end; $f(x) \to \infty$ as $x \to -\infty$, $f(x) \to -\infty$ as $x \to \infty$
33. (a) Degree: 3; leading coefficient: -1
(b) Up on left end, down on right end; $f(x) \to \infty$ as $x \to -\infty$, $f(x) \to -\infty$ as $x \to \infty$
35. (a) Degree: 5; leading coefficient: 0.1
(b) Down on left end, up on right end; $f(x) \to -\infty$ as $x \to -\infty$, $f(x) \to \infty$ as $x \to \infty$
37. (a) Degree: 2; leading coefficient: $-\frac{1}{2}$ **(b)** Down on both ends; $f(x) \to -\infty$ as $x \to -\infty$, $f(x) \to -\infty$ as $x \to \infty$
39. (a)

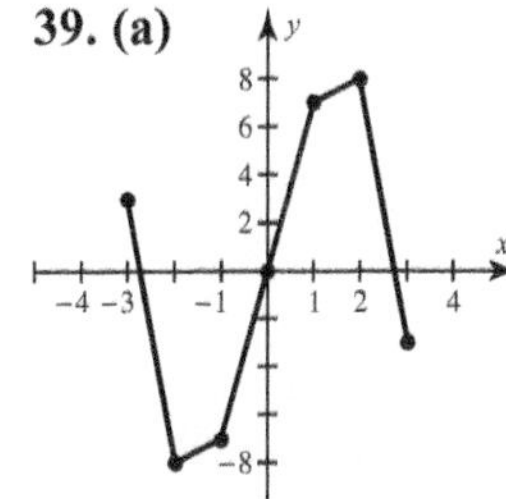

(b) Degree 3 **(c)** $a < 0$ **(d)** $f(x) = -x^3 + 8x$
41. (a)

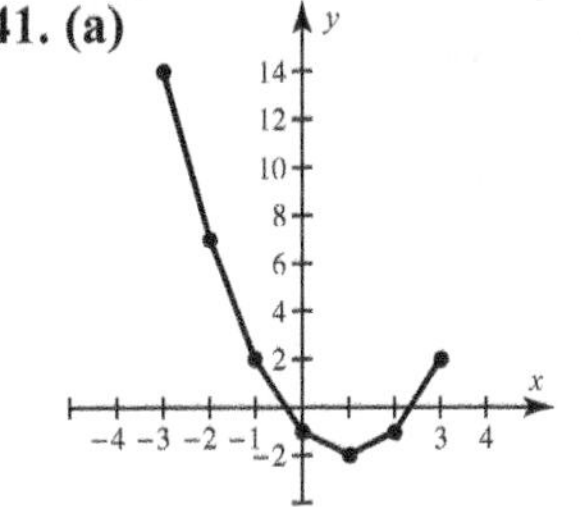

(b) Degree 2 **(c)** $a > 0$ **(d)** $f(x) = x^2 - 2x - 1$
43. (a)

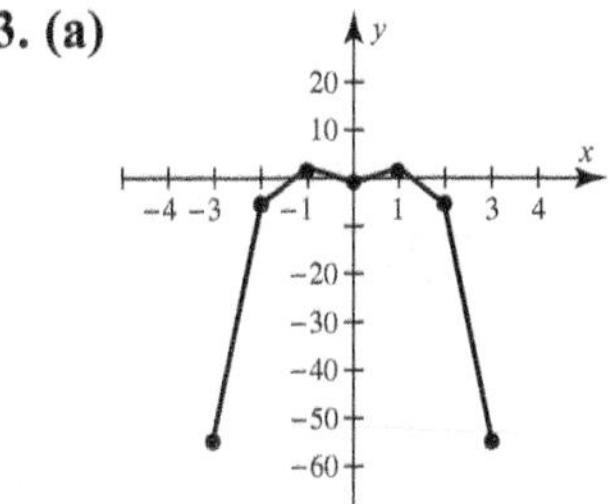

(b) Degree 4 **(c)** $a < 0$ **(d)** $f(x) = -x^4 + 3x^2 - 1$

45. Answers may vary.

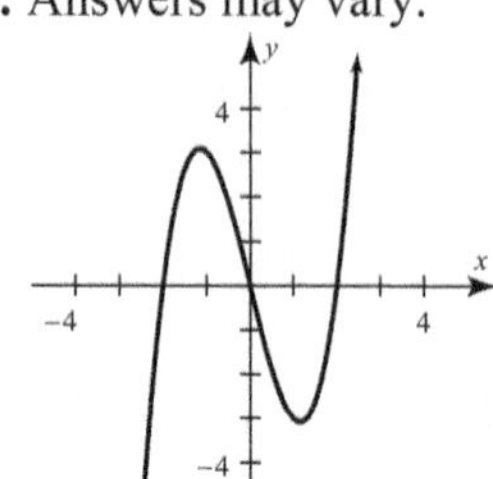

47. Answers may vary.

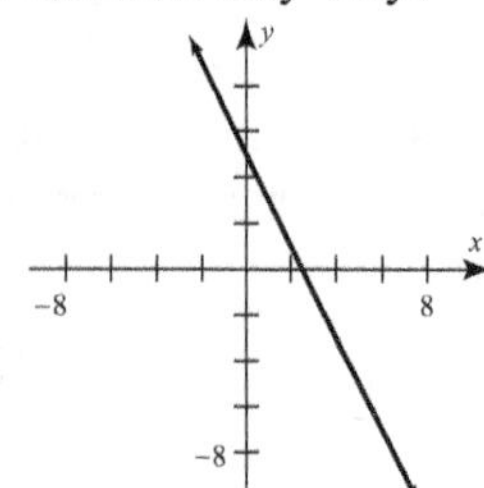

49. Not possible

51. Not possible

53. Answers may vary.

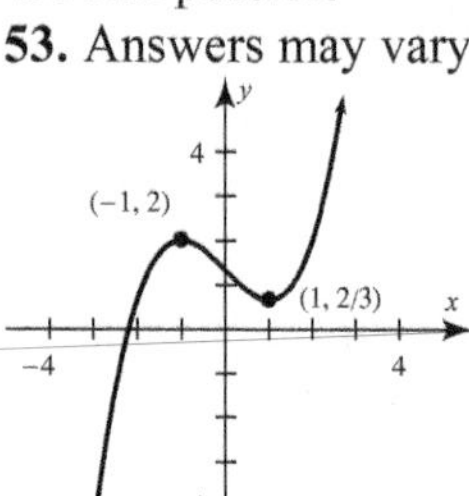

55.

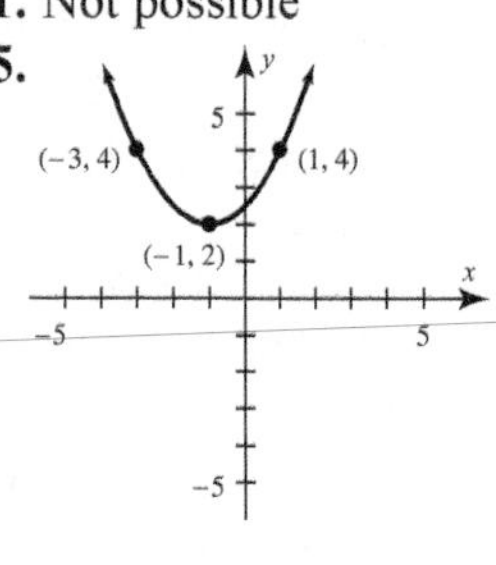

57. As the viewing rectangle increases in size, the graphs begin to look alike. Each formula contains the term $2x^4$, which determines the end behavior of the graph for large values of $|x|$.

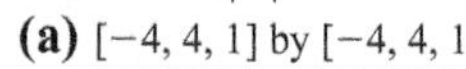

(a) $[-4, 4, 1]$ by $[-4, 4, 1]$ **(b)** $[-10, 10, 1]$ by $[-100, 100, 10]$

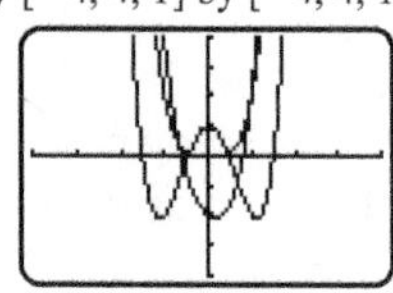

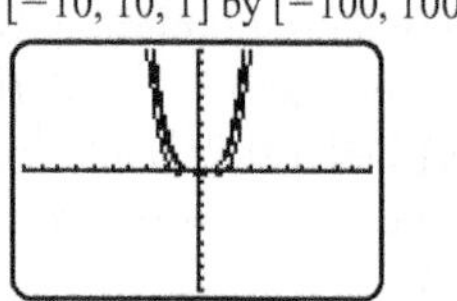

(c) $[-100, 100, 10]$ by $[-10^6, 10^6, 10^5]$

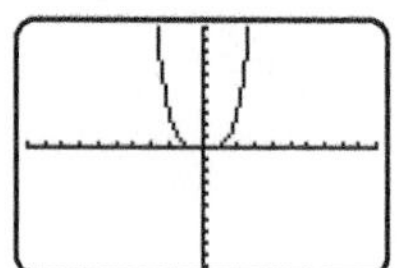

59. For f: 1; for g: 0.5; for h: 0.25. On the interval $[0, 0.5]$, the higher the degree of the function, the smaller the average rate of change.

61. (a) 12.01 **(b)** 12.0001 **(c)** 12.000001
The average rate of change is approaching 12.

63. (a) $4.01\overline{6}$ **(b)** $4.0001\overline{6}$ **(c)** $4.000001\overline{6}$
The average rate of change is approaching 4.

65. $9x^2 + 9xh + 3h^2$ **67.** $-3x^2 - 3xh - h^2 + 1$

69. $f(-2) \approx 5, f(1) \approx 0$

71. $f(-1) \approx -1, f(1) \approx 1, f(2) \approx -2$

73. $f(-3) = -63, f(1) = 3, f(4) = 10$

75. $f(-2) = 6, f(1) = 7, f(2) = 9$

77. (a)

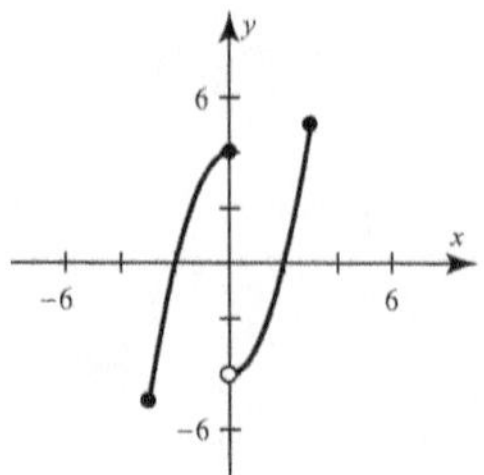

(b) f is not continuous. **(c)** ± 2

79. (a)

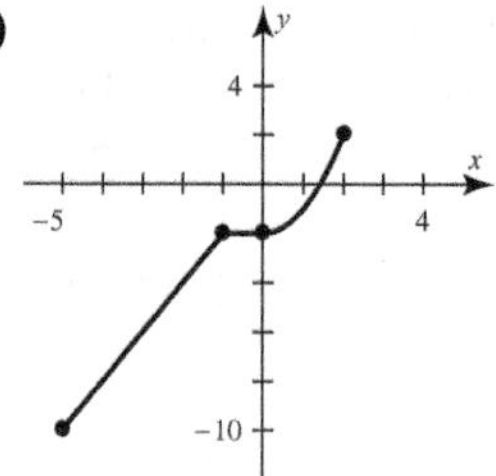

(b) f is continuous. **(c)** $\sqrt{2}$

81. (a)

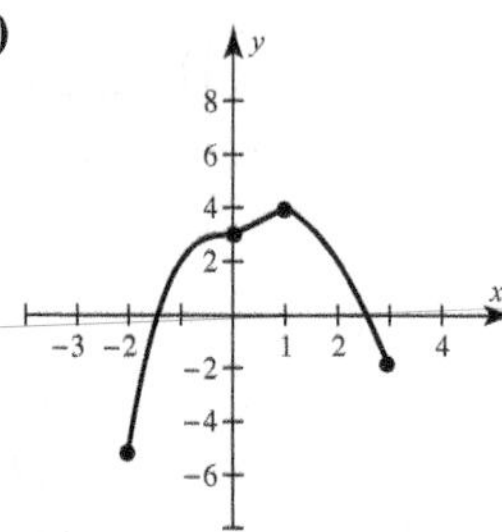

(b) f is continuous. **(c)** $-\sqrt[3]{3}, \frac{\sqrt{17} + 1}{2}$

83. (a) $F(3) = 6$; 300 boats are able to harvest 6 thousand tons of fish. **(b)** Absolute max: 12; 12 thousand tons of fish is the maximum that can be caught.

85. (a) $H(-2) = 0$; $H(0) = 1$; $H(3.5) = 1$

(b)

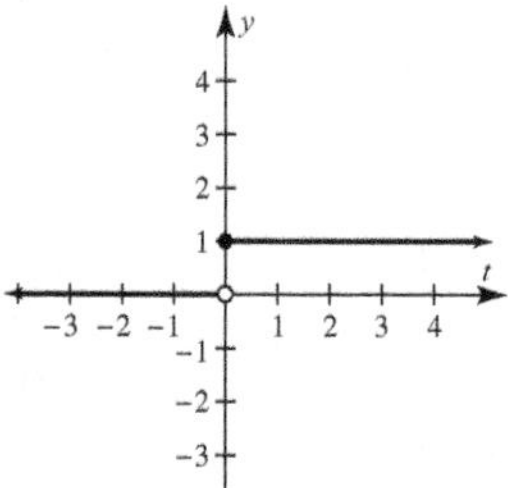

87. (a) Approximately (1, 13) and (7, 72) **(b)** The low monthly average temperature of 13°F occurs in January. The high monthly average temperature of 72°F occurs in July.

89. (a) 4 seconds **(b)** From 0 to 4 seconds; from 4 to 7 seconds **(c)** $m = 36, a = -16, b = 144$
(d) $x \approx 2.8$ or $x \approx 5.7$; the height is 100 feet at about 2.8 seconds and at about 5.7 seconds.

91. (a) $f(x) \approx -0.0006296x^3 + 0.06544x^2 - 0.368x + 2.8$
(b) $[-5, 60, 10]$ by $[0, 80, 20]$

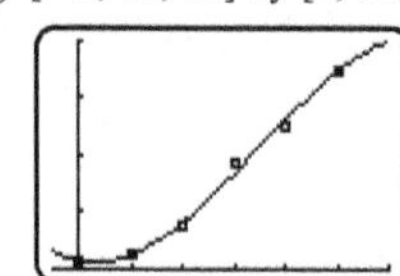

(c) $f(34) \approx 41.2$; $f(60) \approx 80.3$ **(d)** 1994 ($x = 34$), interpolation; 2020 ($x = 60$), extrapolation

4.2 EXTENDED AND DISCOVERY EXERCISES (pp. 266–267)

1. (a) $D = [0, 10]$, or $\{x | 0 \leq x \leq 10\}$
(b) $A(1) = 405$; after 1 min, the tank contains 405 gal of water. **(c)** Degree: 2; leading coefficient: 5 **(d)** No, more than half; yes, because the water will drain faster at first.

3. Conc. down: $(-\infty, \infty)$
5. Conc. up: $(1, \infty)$; conc. down: $(-\infty, 1)$
7. Conc. up: $(-2, 2)$; conc. down: $(-\infty, -2)$, $(2, \infty)$

CHECKING BASIC CONCEPTS FOR SECTIONS 4.1 AND 4.2 (p. 267)

1. (a) Incr: $(-2, 1)$, $(3, \infty)$, or $\{x \mid -2 < x < 1\}$, $\{x \mid x > 3\}$; decr: $(-\infty, -2)$, $(1, 3)$, or $\{x \mid x < -2\}$, $\{x \mid 1 < x < 3\}$
(b) Local maximum: approximately 3; local minima: approximately -13 and -2
(c) No absolute maximum; absolute minimum: approximately -13 **(d)** Approximately -3.1, 0, 2.2, and 3.6; they are the same values.
3. (a) Not possible
(b) Answers may vary.

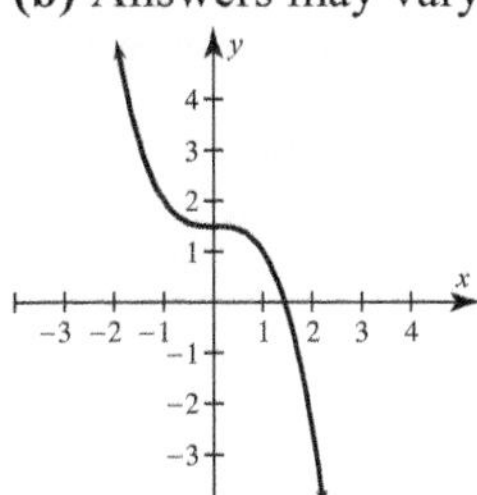

(c) Answers may vary.

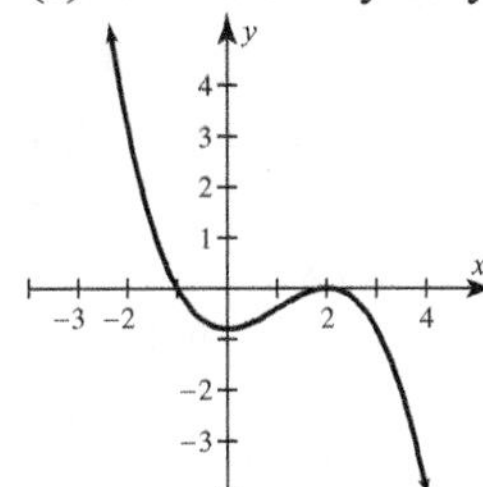

(d) Not possible
5. $f(x) \approx -1.01725x^4 + 10.319x^2 - 10$

SECTION 4.3 (pp. 274–275)

1. $\frac{x^3}{2} - \frac{3}{2x}$ **3.** $x - \frac{2}{3x} - \frac{1}{3x^3}$ **5.** $-\frac{1}{x^3} + \frac{1}{4}$ **7.** $5x - 10 + \frac{5}{3x}$
9. Quotient: $x^2 + x - 2$; remainder: 0
11. Quotient: $2x^3 - 9x^2 + 4x - 23$; remainder: 40
13. Quotient: $3x^2 + 3x - 4$; remainder: 6
15. $x^3 - 1$ **17.** $4x^2 + 3x - 2 + \frac{4}{x - 1}$ **19.** $x^2 - x + 1$
21. $3x^2 + 4x - 2 + \frac{2}{2x - 1}$ **23.** $x^3 + 2 + \frac{-2}{3x - 7}$
25. $5x^2 - 12 + \frac{30}{x^2 + 2}$ **27.** $4x + 5$
29. $x^2 - 2x + 4 + \frac{-1}{2x^2 + 3x + 2}$ **31.** $x^3 - 8x^2 + 15x - 6$
33. $(x - 2)(x - 1) - 1$ **35.** $(2x + 1)(x^2 - 1) + 1$
37. $(x^2 + 1)(x - 1) + 2$ **39.** $x^2 - 3x - 2$
41. $3x^2 + 4x + \frac{3}{x - 5}$ **43.** $x^3 - x^2 - 6x$
45. $2x^4 - 2x^3 + 4 + \frac{1}{x + 0.5}$ **47.** 3 **49.** -42
51. $L = 4x + 3$; 43 ft

SECTION 4.4 (pp. 286–290)

1. $(x + 2)$, $(x + 1)$, $(x - 1)$
3. $(x + 2)$, $(x + 1)$, $(x - 1)$, $(x - 2)$
5. $f(x) = 2\left(x - \frac{11}{2}\right)(x - 7)$
7. $f(x) = (x + 2)(x - 1)(x - 3)$
9. $f(x) = -2(x + 5)\left(x - \frac{1}{2}\right)(x - 6)$
11. $f(x) = 7(x + 3)(x - 2)$
13. $f(x) = -2x(x + 1)(x - 1)$
15. $f(x) = (x + 4)(x - 2)(x - 8)$
17. $f(x) = -1(x + 8)(x + 4)(x + 2)(x - 4)$
19. $f(x) = \frac{1}{2}(x + 1)(x - 2)(x - 3)$
21. $f(x) = \frac{1}{2}(x + 1)(x - 1)(x - 2)$
23. $f(x) = -2(x + 2)(x + 1)(x - 1)(x - 2)$
25. $f(x) = 10(x + 2)\left(x - \frac{3}{10}\right)$
27. $f(x) = -3x(x - 2)(x + 3)$
29. $f(x) = x(x + 1)(x + 3)\left(x - \frac{3}{2}\right)$
31. $f(x) = (x - 1)(x - 3)(x - 5)$
33. $f(x) = -4(x + 4)\left(x - \frac{3}{4}\right)(x - 3)$
35. $f(x) = 2x(x + 2)\left(x + \frac{1}{2}\right)(x - 3)$
37. Yes **39.** No
41. -2 (odd), 4 (even); minimum degree: 5
43. $f(x) = (x + 1)^2(x - 6)$
45. $f(x) = (x - 2)^3(x - 6)$
47. $f(x) = (x + 2)^2(x - 4)$
49. $f(x) = -1(x + 3)^2(x - 3)^2$
51. $f(x) = 2(x + 1)^2(x - 1)^3$
53. (a) x-int: $-2, -1$; y-int: 4
(b) -2 has multiplicity 1; -1 has multiplicity 2
(c)

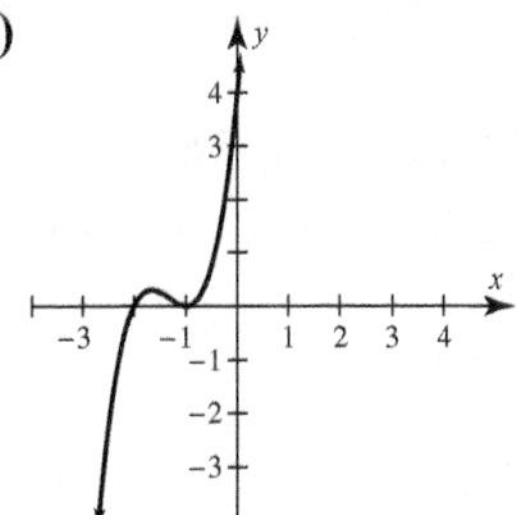

55. (a) x-int: $-2, 0, 2$; y-int: 0
(b) 0 has multiplicity 2; -2 and 2 each have multiplicity 1
(c)

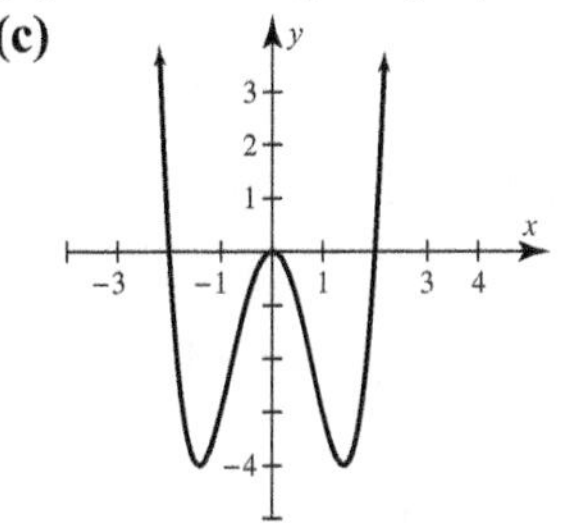

57. (a) $-3, \frac{1}{2}, 1$ **(b)** $f(x) = 2(x + 3)\left(x - \frac{1}{2}\right)(x - 1)$
59. (a) $-2, -1, 1, \frac{3}{2}$
(b) $f(x) = 2(x + 2)(x + 1)(x - 1)\left(x - \frac{3}{2}\right)$
61. (a) $\frac{1}{3}, 1, 4$ **(b)** $f(x) = 3\left(x - \frac{1}{3}\right)(x - 1)(x - 4)$
63. (a) 1 **(b)** $f(x) = \left(x + \sqrt{7}\right)(x - 1)\left(x - \sqrt{7}\right)$
65. Possible: 0 or 2 positive, 1 negative; actual: 0 positive, 1 negative
67. Possible: 1 positive, 1 negative; actual: 1 positive, 1 negative
69. Possible: 0 or 2 positive, 1 or 3 negative; actual: 0 positive, 1 negative
71. $-3, 0, 2$ **73.** $-1, 1$ **75.** $-2, 0, 2$ **77.** $-5, 0, 5$
79. ± 2 **81.** $-3, 0, 6$ **83.** 0, 1 **85.** $-\frac{1}{4}, 0, \frac{5}{3}$
87. $\pm\frac{2}{3}, \pm 1$ **89.** $-1, \pm\frac{\sqrt{3}}{2}$ **91.** $\pm 2, \frac{1}{2}$ **93.** $\pm\frac{3}{2}, \pm\frac{\sqrt{6}}{2}$
95. $-2, 3$ **97.** $-2.01, 0.12, 2.99$ **99.** $-4.05, -0.52, 1.71$
101. $-2.69, -1.10, 0.55, 3.98$
103. Because $f(2) = -1 < 0$ and $f(3) = 4 > 0$, the intermediate value property states that there exists an x-value between 2 and 3 where $f(x) = 0$.
105. Because $f(0) = -1 < 0$ and $f(1) = 1 > 0$, the intermediate value property states that there exists an x-value between 0 and 1 where $f(x) = 0$.

107. 4, 32; yes, by the intermediate value property
109. 12 A.M., 2 A.M., 4 A.M.
111. Approximately 11.34 cm
113. June 2, June 22, and July 12
115. (a) $f(x) \approx -0.184(x + 6.01)(x - 2.15)(x - 11.7)$
(b) The zero of -6.01 has no significance. The zeros of $2.15 \approx 2$ and $11.7 \approx 12$ indicate that during February and December the average temperature is 0°F.
117. (a) As x increases, C decreases.
(b) $C(x) \approx -0.000068x^3 + 0.0099x^2 - 0.653x + 23$
(c) [0, 70, 10] by [0, 22, 5]

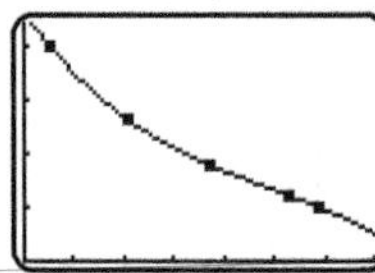

(d) $0 \le x < 32.1$ (approximately)

4.4 EXTENDED AND DISCOVERY EXERCISES (p. 290)

1. Dividing $P(x)$ by $x - 2$ synthetically results in the following bottom row: 1 1 5 2 12.
Since $2 > 0$ and the bottom row values are all nonnegative, there is no real zero greater than 2.
3. Dividing $P(x)$ by $x + 2$ synthetically results in the following bottom row: 1 −1 1 −2 7.
Since $-2 < 0$ and the bottom row values alternate in sign, there is no real zero less than -2.
5. Dividing $P(x)$ by $x - 1$ synthetically results in the following bottom row: 3 5 1 2 1.
Since $1 > 0$ and the bottom row values are all nonnegative, there is no real zero greater than 1.

CHECKING BASIC CONCEPTS FOR SECTIONS 4.3 AND 4.4 (p. 291)

1. $x^2 - 2x + 1$ **3.** $f(x) = -\frac{1}{2}(x + 2)^2(x - 1)$;
-2 has multiplicity 2; 1 has multiplicity 1.
5. The zeros are $-4, -1, 2$, and 4;
$f(x) = (x + 4)(x + 1)(x - 2)(x - 4)$.

SECTION 4.5 (pp. 296–297)

1. Two imaginary zeros
3. One real zero; two imaginary zeros
5. Two real zeros; two imaginary zeros
7. Three real zeros; two imaginary zeros
9. (a) $f(x) = (x - 6i)(x + 6i)$ **(b)** $f(x) = x^2 + 36$
11. (a) $f(x) = -1(x + 1)(x - 2i)(x + 2i)$
(b) $f(x) = -x^3 - x^2 - 4x - 4$
13. (a) $f(x) = 10(x - 1)(x + 1)(x - 3i)(x + 3i)$
(b) $f(x) = 10x^4 + 80x^2 - 90$
15. (a) $f(x) = \frac{1}{2}(x + i)(x - i)(x + 2i)(x - 2i)$
(b) $f(x) = \frac{1}{2}x^4 + \frac{5}{2}x^2 + 2$
17. (a) $f(x) = -2(x - (1 - i))(x - (1 + i))(x - 3)$
(b) $f(x) = -2x^3 + 10x^2 - 16x + 12$
19. $\frac{5}{3}, \pm 5i$ **21.** $\pm 3i, \frac{1}{4} \pm \frac{i\sqrt{7}}{4}$
23. (a) $\pm 5i$ **(b)** $f(x) = (x - 5i)(x + 5i)$
25. (a) $0, \pm i$ **(b)** $f(x) = 3(x - 0)(x - i)(x + i)$, or $f(x) = 3x(x - i)(x + i)$
27. (a) $\pm i, \pm 2i$
(b) $f(x) = (x - i)(x + i)(x - 2i)(x + 2i)$
29. (a) $-2, \pm 4i$ **(b)** $f(x) = (x + 2)(x + 4i)(x - 4i)$
31. $0, \pm i$ **33.** $2, \pm i\sqrt{7}$ **35.** $0, \pm i\sqrt{5}$
37. $0, \frac{1}{2} \pm \frac{i\sqrt{15}}{2}$ **39.** $-2, 1, \pm i\sqrt{8}$ **41.** $-2, \frac{1}{3} \pm \frac{i\sqrt{8}}{3}$

SECTION 4.6 (pp. 310–313)

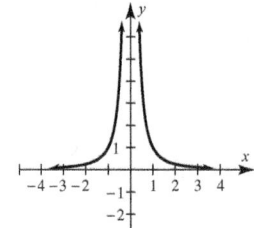

1. Yes; $D = \{x \mid x \neq \frac{5}{4}\}$
3. Yes; $D =$ all real numbers
5. No; $D = \{x \mid x \neq -1\}$
7. Yes; $D =$ all real numbers
9. No; $D = \{x \mid x \neq -1, x \neq 0\}$
11. Yes; $D = \{x \mid x \neq -1\}$
13. Horizontal: $y = 4$; vertical: $x = 2$; $D = \{x \mid x \neq 2\}$
15. Horizontal: $y = -4$; vertical: $x = \pm 2$; $D = \{x \mid x \neq 2, x \neq -2\}$
17. Horizontal: $y = 0$; vertical: none; $D =$ all real numbers
19. $y = 3$ **21.** Horizontal: $y = 2$; vertical: $x = 3$
23. Horizontal: $y = 0$; vertical: $x = \pm\sqrt{5}$
25. Horizontal: none; vertical: $x = -5$ or 2
27. Horizontal: $y = \frac{1}{2}$; vertical: $x = \frac{5}{2}$
29. Horizontal: $y = 3$; vertical: $x = 1$
31. Horizontal: none; vertical: none, since $f(x) = x - 3$ for $x \neq -3$ **33.** b **35.** d
37. $f(x) = \frac{x + 1}{x + 3}$ (answers may vary)
39. $f(x) = \frac{1}{x^2 - 9}$ (answers may vary)
41. Horizontal: $y = 0$; vertical: $x = 0$
43. Horizontal: $y = 0$ vertical: $x = 0$

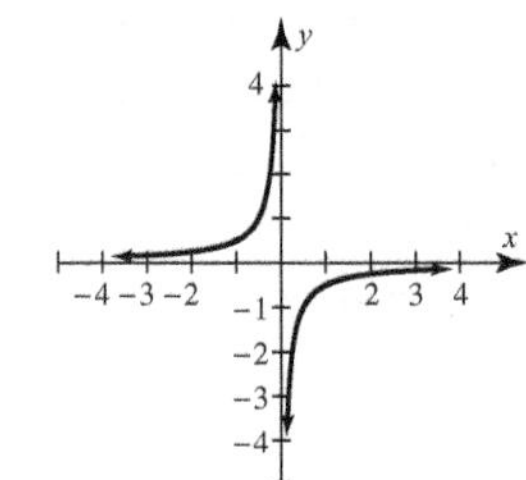

45. $g(x) = f(x - 3)$

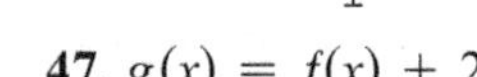

47. $g(x) = f(x) + 2$

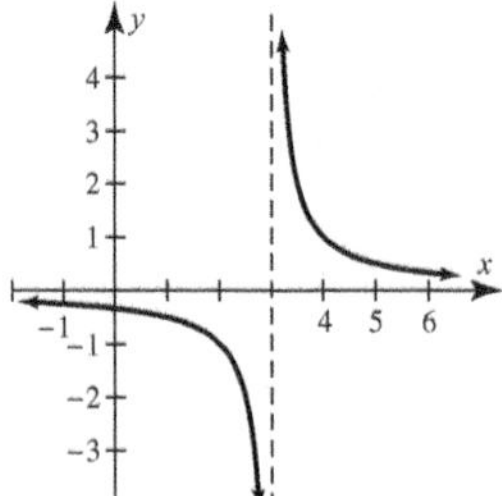

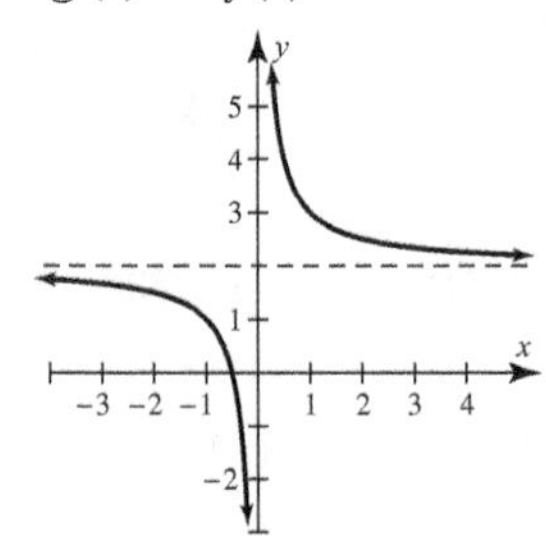

49. $g(x) = f(x + 1) - 2$

51. $g(x) = -2h(x - 1)$

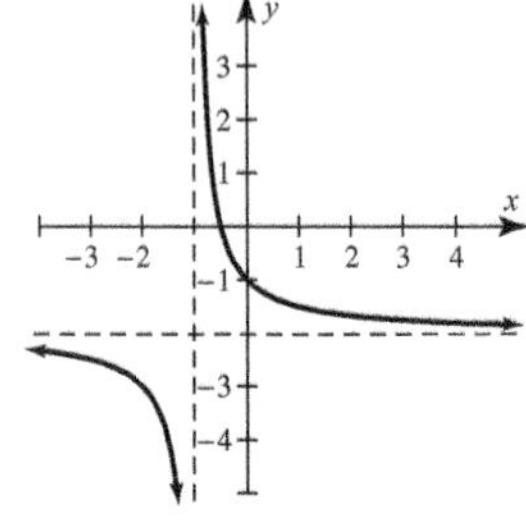

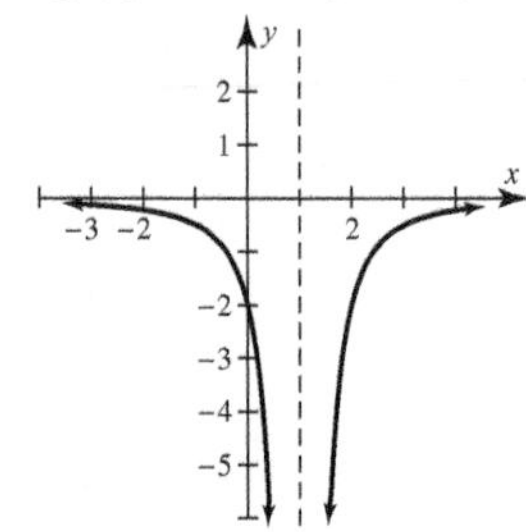

53. $g(x) = h(x + 1) - 2$

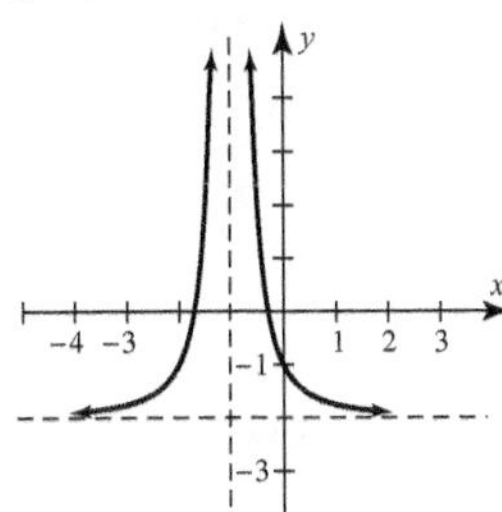

55. **(a)** $D = \{x | x \neq 2\}$
(b) $[-9.4, 9.4, 1]$ by $[-6.2, 6.2, 1]$
(c) Horizontal: $y = 1$; vertical: $x = 2$
(d)

57. **(a)** $D = \{x | x \neq 2, x \neq -2\}$
(b) $[-9.4, 9.4, 1]$ by $[-6.2, 6.2, 1]$

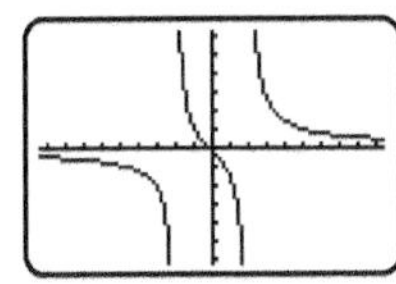

(c) Horizontal: $y = 0$; vertical: $x = \pm 2$
(d)

59. **(a)** $D = \{x | x \neq 2, x \neq -2\}$
(b) $[-9.4, 9.4, 1]$ by $[-9.3, 9.3, 1]$

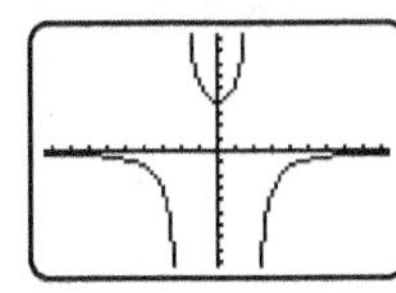

(c) Horizontal: $y = 0$; vertical: $x = \pm 2$
(d)

61. **(a)** $D = \{x | x \neq 2\}$
(b) $[-4.7, 4.7, 1]$ by $[-6.2, 6.2, 1]$

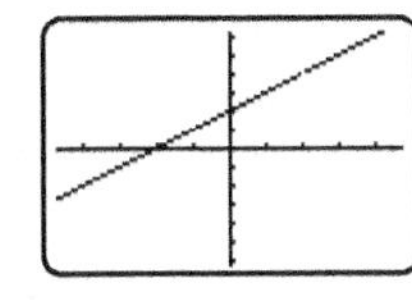

(c) Horizontal: none; vertical: none, since $f(x) = x + 2$ for $x \neq 2$
(d)

63.

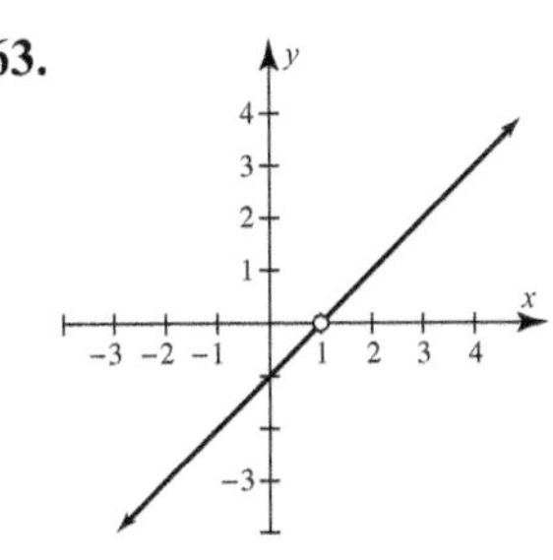

65.

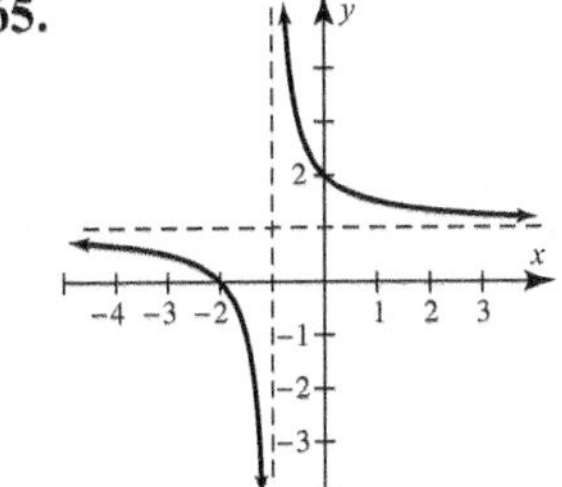

67.

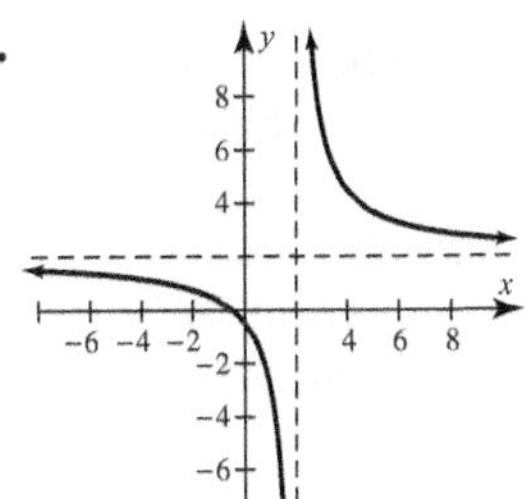

69.

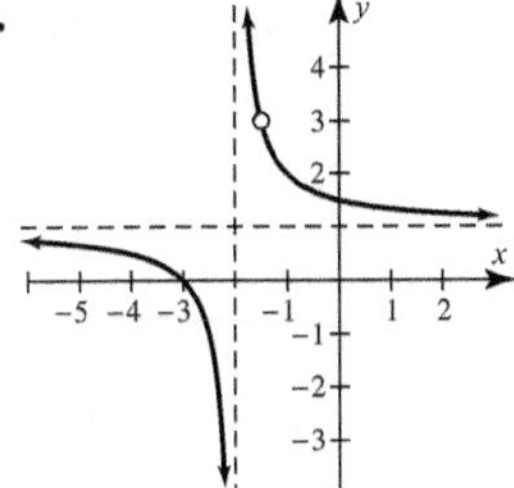

71.

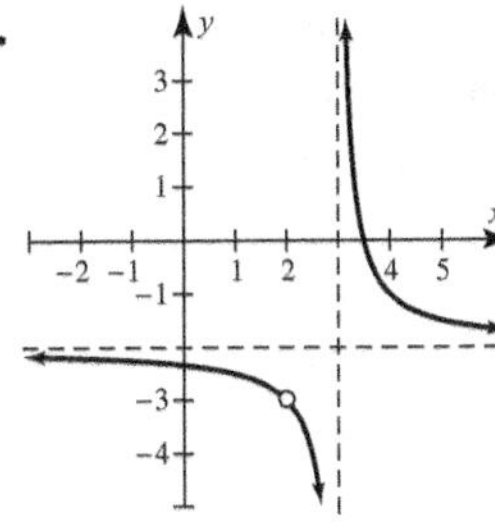

73. **(a)** Slant: $y = x - 1$; vertical: $x = -1$
(b)

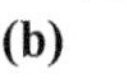

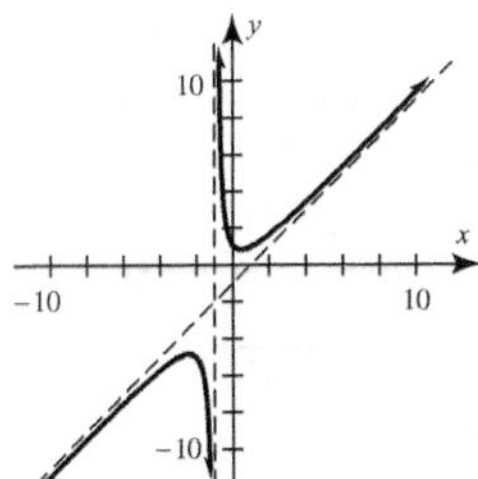

75. **(a)** Slant: $y = \frac{1}{2}x - 3$; vertical: $x = -2$
(b)

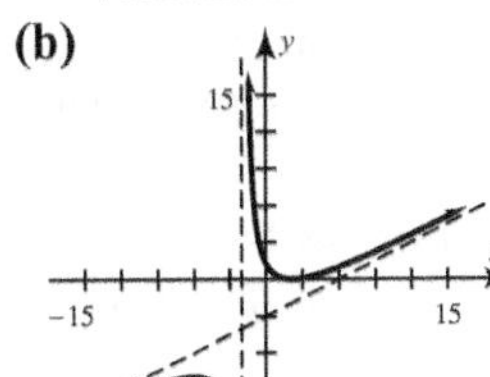

77. **(a)** Slant: $y = x + 3$; vertical: $x = 1$
(b)

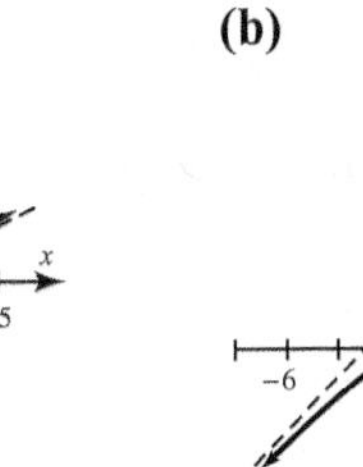

79. **(a)** Slant: $y = 2x + 1$; vertical: $x = \frac{1}{2}$
(b)

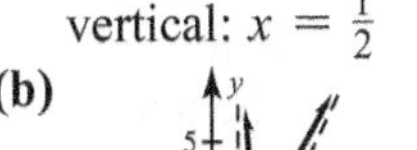

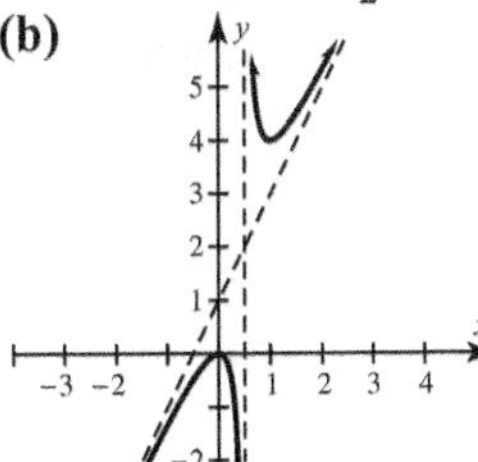

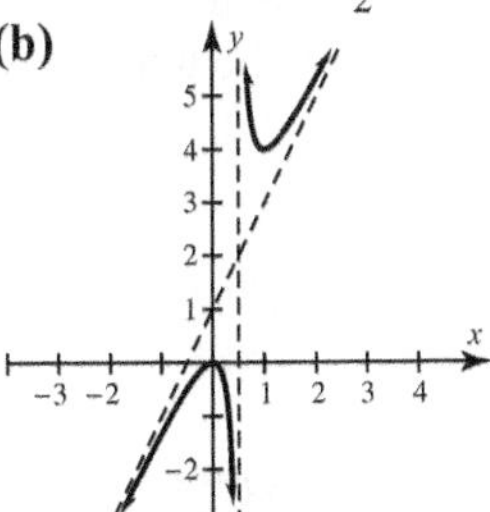

81. -3 **83.** 1 **85.** $-\frac{1}{2}$

87.

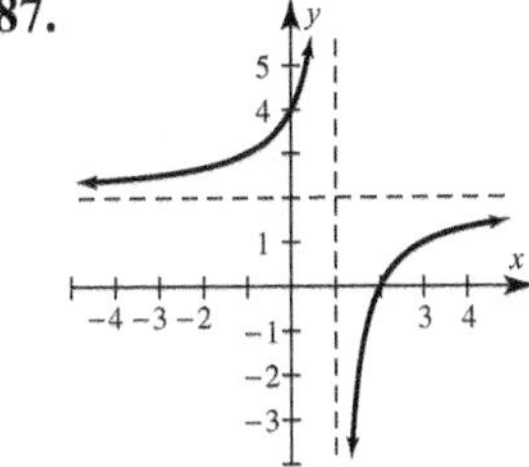

89.

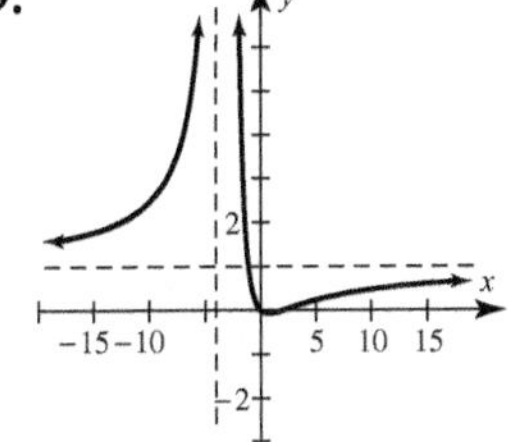

91.

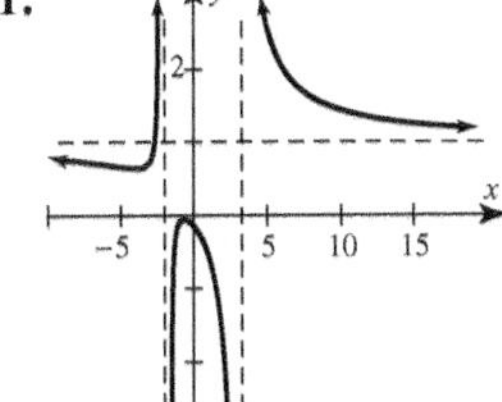

93. (a) About 33%; the least active 98% post $\frac{1}{3}$ of the postings. **(b)** About 67%; the most active 2% post $\frac{2}{3}$ of the postings.
95. (a) 5%; at 1 second, there is a 5% chance that the visitor is abandoning the website. **(b)** About 1.8%; at 60 seconds, there is a 1.8% chance that the visitor is abandoning the website.
97. (a) $T(4) = 0.25$; when vehicles leave the ramp at an average rate of 4 vehicles per minute, the wait is 0.25 minute or 15 seconds. $T(7.5) = 2$; when vehicles leave the ramp at an average rate of 7.5 vehicles per minute, the wait is 2 minutes. **(b)** The wait increases dramatically.
99. (a) $N(20) = 0.5$, $N(39) \approx 38$
(b) It increases dramatically. **(c)** $x = 40$
101. (a) $y = 10$

[0, 14, 1] by [0, 14, 1]

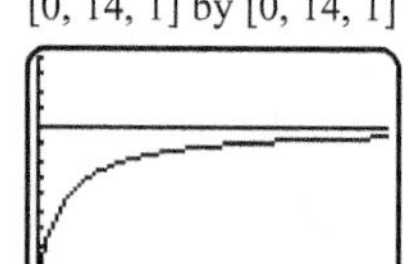

(b) When $x = 0$, there are 1 million insects. **(c)** It starts to level off at 10 million. **(d)** The horizontal asymptote $y = 10$ represents the limiting population after a long time.
103. (a) $f(400) = \frac{2540}{400} = 6.35$ inches. A curve designed for 60 miles per hour with a radius of 400 ft should have the outer rail elevated 6.35 in. **(b)** As the radius x of the curve increases, the elevation of the outer rail decreases.

[0, 600, 100] by [0, 50, 5]

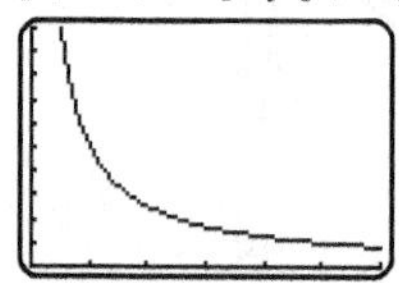

(c) The horizontal asymptote is $y = 0$. As the radius of the curve increases without bound ($x \to \infty$), the tracks become straight and no elevation or banking ($y \to 0$) is necessary.
(d) 200 ft

4.6 EXTENDED AND DISCOVERY EXERCISES (p. 313)

1. $-\frac{1}{3}$; $-\frac{1}{x(x + h)}$ **3.** $-\frac{1}{2}$; $-\frac{3}{2x(x + h)}$

CHECKING BASIC CONCEPTS FOR SECTIONS 4.5 AND 4.6 (pp. 313–314)

1. $f(x) = 3(x - 4i)(x + 4i) = 3x^2 + 48$
3. $f(x) = (x - 1)(x - 2i)(x + 2i)$
5. (a) $D = \{x \mid x \neq 1\}$ **(b)** Vertical asymptote: $x = 1$; horizontal asymptote: $y = 2$
(c)

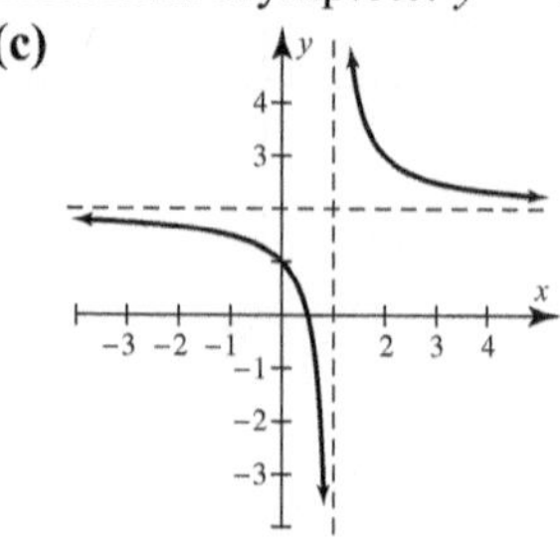

7. (a)

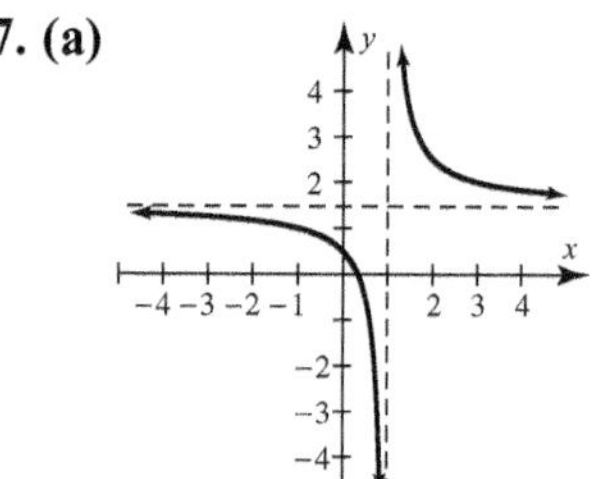

(b)

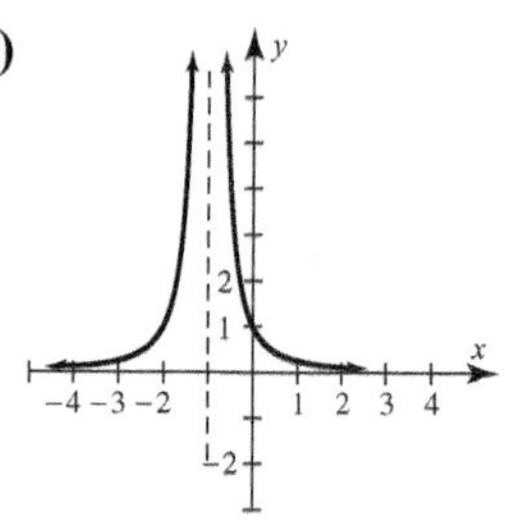

(c)

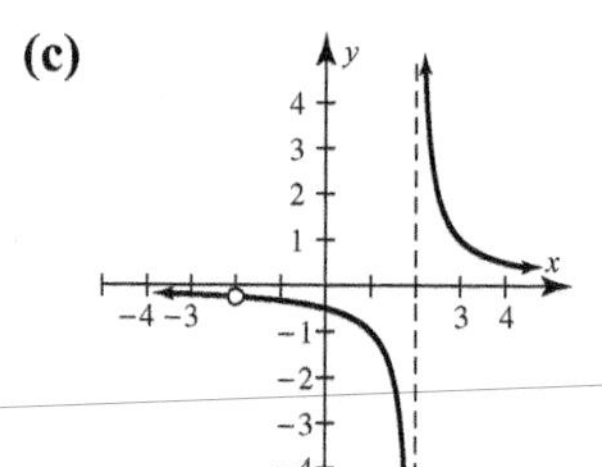

(d)

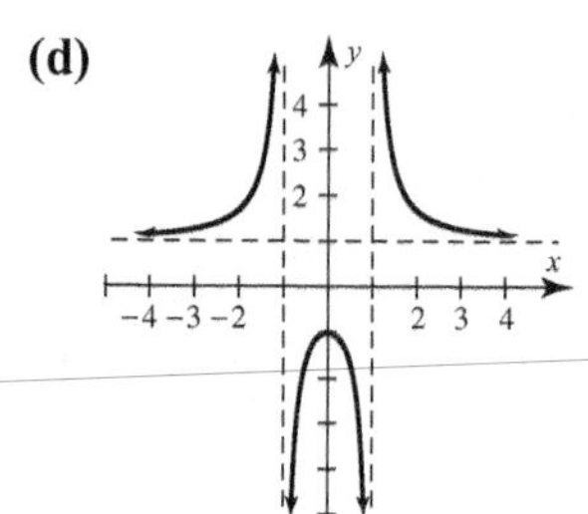

SECTION 4.7 (pp. 325–330)

1. -3 **3.** $\frac{1}{2}, 2$ **5.** $\frac{1}{2}$ **7.** -1 **9.** $\frac{13}{8}$ **11.** $\pm\sqrt{2}$ **13.** No real solutions **15.** $0, \pm 2$ **17.** $-\frac{5}{3}, \frac{7}{5}$ **19.** -14
21. No real solutions (extraneous: 2)
23. -3 (extraneous: 1) **25.** 1 (extraneous: -2)
27. No real solutions (extraneous: 1)
29. (a) $-4, -2$, or 2
(b) $(-4, -2) \cup (2, \infty)$, or $\{x \mid -4 < x < -2 \text{ or } x > 2\}$
(c) $(-\infty, -4) \cup (-2, 2)$, or $\{x \mid x < -4 \text{ or } -2 < x < 2\}$
31. (a) $-4, -2, 0$, or 2
(b) $(-4, -2) \cup (0, 2)$, or $\{x \mid -4 < x < -2 \text{ or } 0 < x < 2\}$
(c) $(-\infty, -4) \cup (-2, 0) \cup (2, \infty)$, or $\{x \mid x < -4 \text{ or } -2 < x < 0 \text{ or } x > 2\}$
33. (a) $-2, 1$, or 2 **(b)** $(-\infty, -2) \cup (-2, 1)$, or $\{x \mid x < -2 \text{ or } -2 < x < 1\}$
(c) $(1, 2) \cup (2, \infty)$, or $\{x \mid 1 < x < 2 \text{ or } x > 2\}$
35. (a) 0 **(b)** $(-\infty, 0) \cup (0, \infty)$, or $\{x \mid x < 0 \text{ or } x > 0\}$
(c) No solutions
37. (a) 0 or 1 **(b)** $(-\infty, 0) \cup (1, \infty)$, or $\{x \mid x < 0 \text{ or } x > 1\}$
(c) $(0, 1)$, or $\{x \mid 0 < x < 1\}$
39. (a) $-2, 0$, or 2
(b) $(-\infty, -2) \cup (2, \infty)$, or $\{x \mid x < -2 \text{ or } x > 2\}$
(c) $(-2, 0) \cup (0, 2)$, or $\{x \mid -2 < x < 0 \text{ or } 0 < x < 2\}$
41. $(-1, 0) \cup (1, \infty)$, or $\{x \mid -1 < x < 0 \text{ or } x > 1\}$
43. $[-2, 0] \cup [1, \infty)$, or $\{x \mid -2 \le x \le 0 \text{ or } x \ge 1\}$
45. $(-3, -2) \cup (2, 3)$, or $\{x \mid -3 < x < -2 \text{ or } 2 < x < 3\}$
47. $(-\infty, -\sqrt{2}) \cup (\sqrt{2}, \infty)$, or $\{x \mid x < -\sqrt{2} \text{ or } x > \sqrt{2}\}$
49. $[-2, 1] \cup [2, \infty)$, or $\{x \mid -2 \le x \le 1 \text{ or } x \ge 2\}$
51. $[-3, 2]$, or $\{x \mid -3 \le x \le 2\}$
53. $(-\infty, 1] \cup [2, 4]$, or $\{x \mid x \le 1 \text{ or } 2 \le x \le 4\}$
55. $(-\infty, -1) \cup \left(0, \frac{4}{3}\right) \cup (2, \infty)$, or $\left\{x \mid x < -1 \text{ or } 0 < x < \frac{4}{3} \text{ or } x > 2\right\}$
57. $(-\infty, 0)$, or $\{x \mid x < 0\}$
59. $(-3, \infty)$, or $\{x \mid x > -3\}$
61. $(-2, 2)$, or $\{x \mid -2 < x < 2\}$
63. $(-\infty, 2)$, or $\{x \mid x < 2\}$

65. $(-\infty, -1) \cup \left(\frac{3}{2}, \infty\right)$, or $\left\{x \mid x < -1 \text{ or } x > \frac{3}{2}\right\}$
67. $(-\infty, -3) \cup (-1, 2)$, or $\{x \mid x < -3 \text{ or } -1 < x < 2\}$
69. $(-1, 1) \cup \left[\frac{5}{2}, \infty\right)$, or $\left\{x \mid -1 < x < 1 \text{ or } x \ge \frac{5}{2}\right\}$
71. $(3, \infty)$, or $\{x \mid x > 3\}$
73. $(-\infty, 0) \cup \left(0, \frac{1}{2}\right] \cup [2, \infty)$, or $\left\{x \mid x < 0 \text{ or } 0 < x \le \frac{1}{2} \text{ or } x \ge 2\right\}$
75. $(-2, 0) \cup [2, \infty)$, or $\{x \mid -2 < x < 0 \text{ or } x \ge 2\}$
77. **(a)** About 12.4 cars per minute **(b)** 3
79. Two possible solutions: width $= 7$ in., length $= 14$ in., height $= 2$ in.; width ≈ 2.266 in., length ≈ 4.532 in., height ≈ 19.086 in.
81. **(a)** $A(x) = \frac{x^2}{144} + \frac{3}{x}$ **(b)** $C(x) = 0.1\left(\frac{x^2}{144} + \frac{3}{x}\right)$
(c) 6 in. $\times$ 6 in. $\times$ 3 in.
83. **(a)** $D(0.05) \approx 238$; the braking distance for a car traveling at 50 miles per hour on a 5% uphill grade is about 238 ft. **(b)** As the uphill grade x increases, the braking distance decreases, which agrees with driving experience.
(c) $x = \frac{13}{165} \approx 0.079$, or 7.9%
85. **(a)** $x \le 36$ (approximately) **(b)** The average line length is less than or equal to 8 cars when the average arrival rate is about 36 cars per hour or less.
87. **(a)** The braking distance increases. **(b)** $0 < x \le 0.3$
89. $\sqrt[3]{212.8} \le x \le \sqrt[3]{213.2}$, or (approximately) $5.97022 \le x \le 5.97396$ inches
91. $k = 6$ **93.** $k = 8$ **95.** $T = 160$ **97.** $y = 2$
99. Becomes half as much **101.** Becomes 27 times as much
103. $k = 0.5, n = 2$ **105.** $k = 3, n = 1$
107. 1.18 grams **109.** $\sqrt{50} \approx 7$ times as far
111. $\frac{2}{9}$ ohm **113.** F decreases by a factor of $\frac{\sqrt{2}}{2}$

SECTION 4.8 (pp. 341–344)

1. 4 **3.** $\frac{1}{8}$ **5.** -9 **7.** 27 **9.** 2 **11.** 9 **13.** $-\frac{1}{243}$
15. 16 **17.** $\frac{9}{4}$ **19.** $(2x)^{1/2}$ **21.** $z^{5/3}$ **23.** $\frac{1}{y^{3/4}}$
25. $x^{5/6}$ **27.** $y^{3/4}$ **29.** $\frac{\sqrt{b}}{\sqrt[4]{a^3}}$ **31.** $\sqrt{\sqrt{a} + \sqrt{b}}$
33. 4 **35.** 64 **37.** 5 **39.** -2

41.

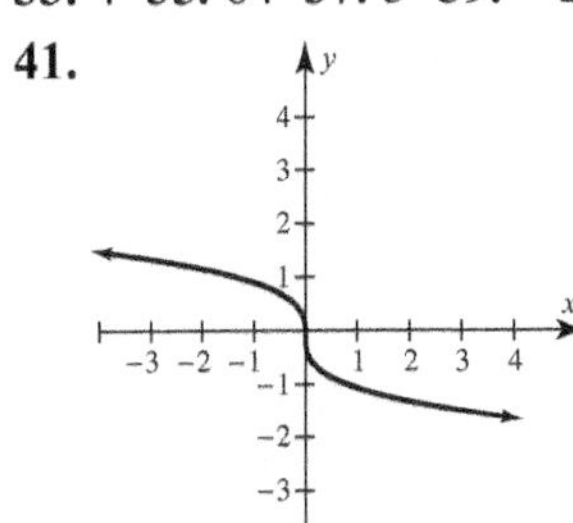

43.

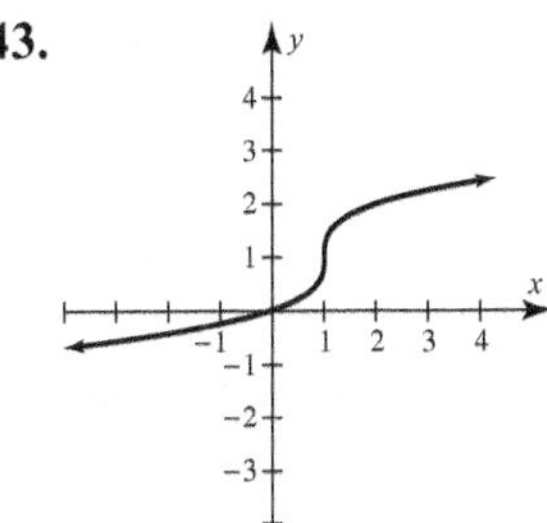

45.

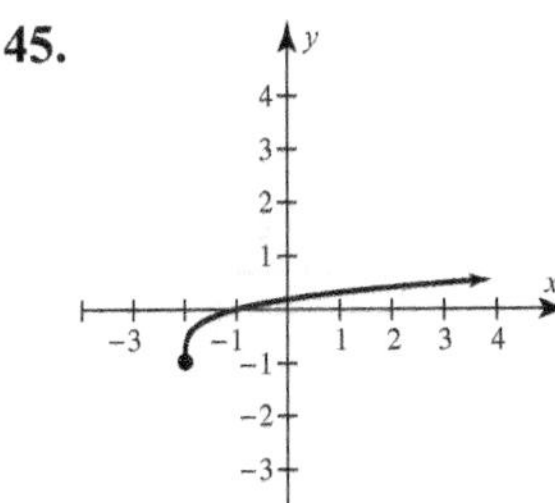

47.

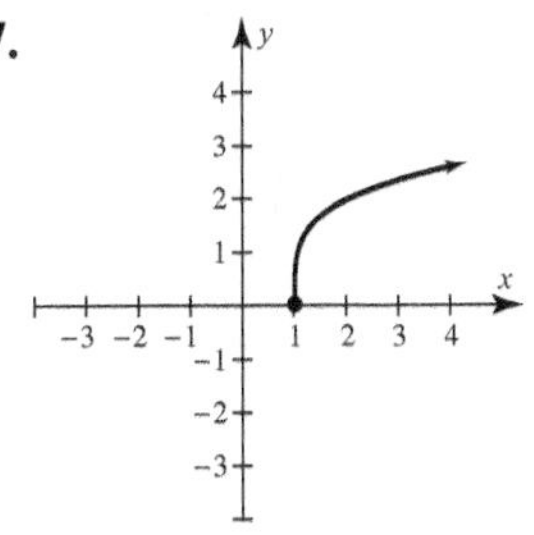

49.

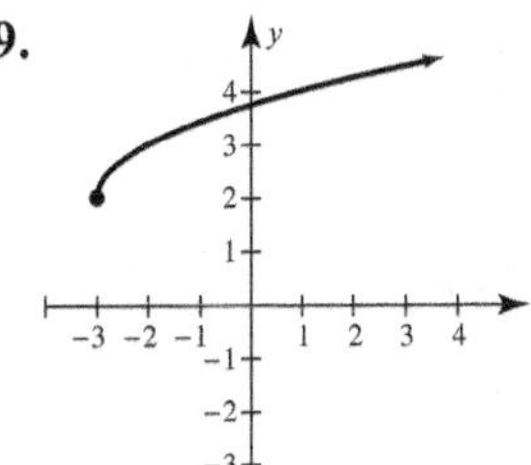

51.

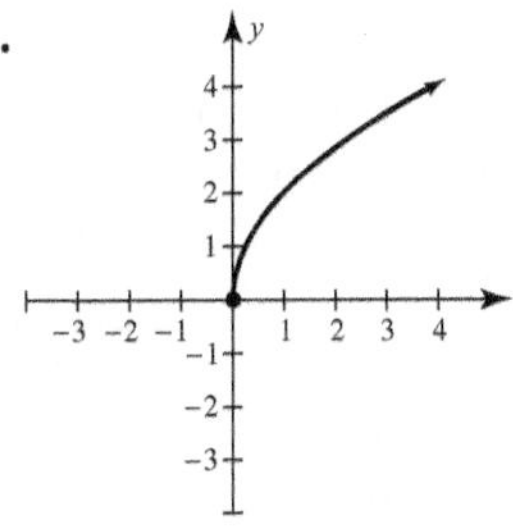

53. 7 **55.** -1 **57.** 2, 3 **59.** 4 **61.** 15 **63.** 8
65. -28 **67.** 2 **69.** 65,538
71. $50^{3/2} - 50^{1/2} \approx 346.48$ **73.** b

75.

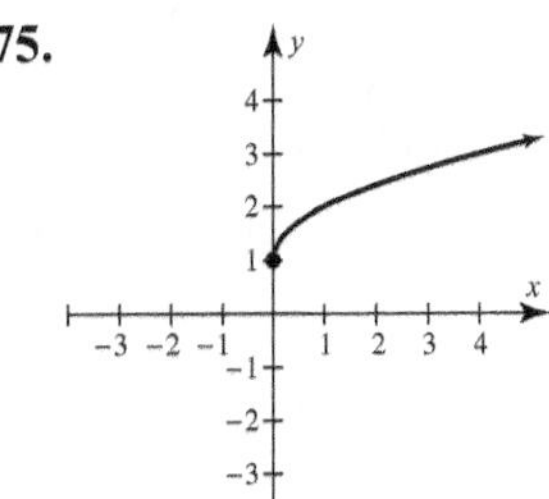

77.

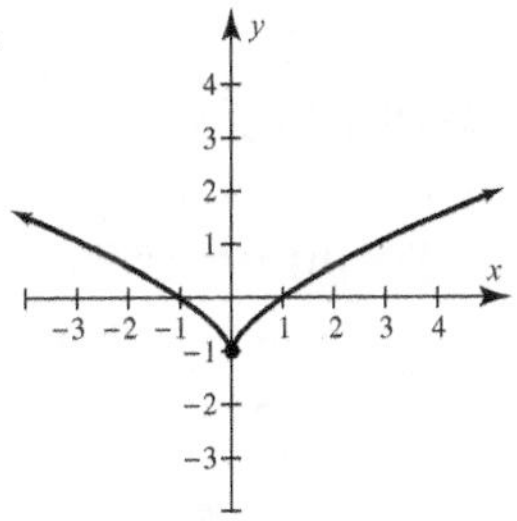

79.

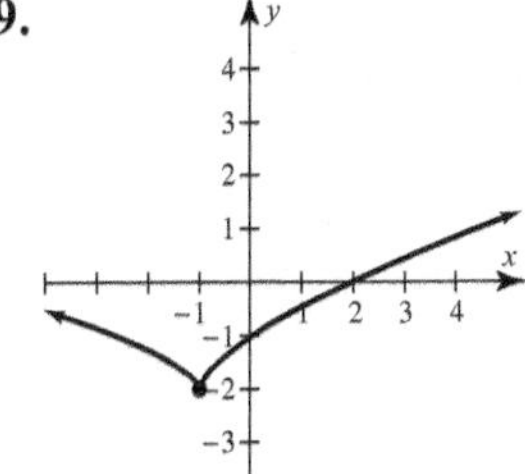

81. 2 **83.** 81 **85.** ± 32 **87.** ± 8 **89.** $\sqrt[3]{16}$
91. $-1, -\frac{1}{2}$ **93.** $-\frac{1}{4}, \frac{5}{7}$ **95.** $-8, 27$ **97.** $\frac{1}{8}, \frac{64}{27}$
99. 1 **101.** $-1, \frac{1}{27}$
103. About 3.5; average speed is about 3.5 mi/hr.
105. $w \approx 3.63$ lb**107.** About 58.1 yr
109. **(a)** $a = 1960$ **(b)** $b \approx -1.2$
(c) $f(4) = 1960(4)^{-1.2} \approx 371$. If the zinc ion concentration reaches 371 milligrams per liter, a rainbow trout will survive, on average, 4 minutes.
111. **(a)** $f(2) \approx 1.06$ grams
(b) & **(c)** Approximately 1.1 grams
113. $a \approx 3.20, b \approx 0.20$

[1, 9, 1] by [0, 6, 1]

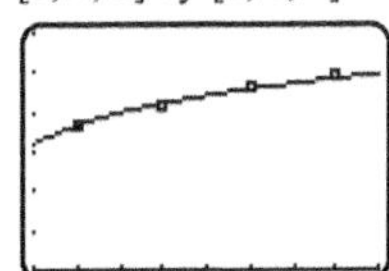

115. **(a)** $f(x) = 0.005192x^{1.7902}$ (Answers may vary.)
(b) About 2.6 million; too high; extrapolation
(c) About 1999
117. $a \approx 874.54, b \approx -0.49789$

4.8 EXTENDED AND DISCOVERY EXERCISES (p. 344)

1. The graph of an odd root function (not shown) is always increasing; the function is negative for $x < 0$, positive for $x > 0$, and zero at $x = 0$. It is an odd function.

3. $\dfrac{1}{\sqrt{x+h}+\sqrt{x}}$ **5.** $\dfrac{x+1}{x^{5/3}}$ **7.** $\dfrac{2-x}{3x^{1/3}(x+1)^2}$

9. (a) $20-x$

(b) $AP=\sqrt{x^2+12^2}$; $BP=\sqrt{(20-x)^2+16^2}$

(c) $f(x)=\sqrt{x^2+12^2}+\sqrt{(20-x)^2+16^2}$, $0<x<20$

(d) [0, 20, 5] by [0, 50, 10] **(e)** 8.57 ft; 34.41 ft

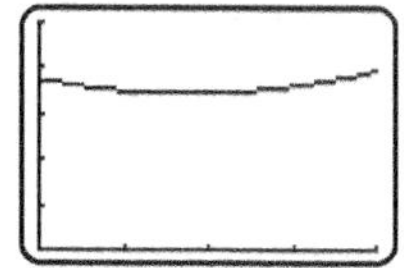

39. $f(x)=(x+i)(x-i)\left(x-\left(-\frac{1}{2}+\frac{i\sqrt{3}}{2}\right)\right)\times\left(x-\left(-\frac{1}{2}-\frac{i\sqrt{3}}{2}\right)\right)$

41. Horizontal: $y=\frac{2}{3}$; vertical: $x=\frac{1}{3}$

43.

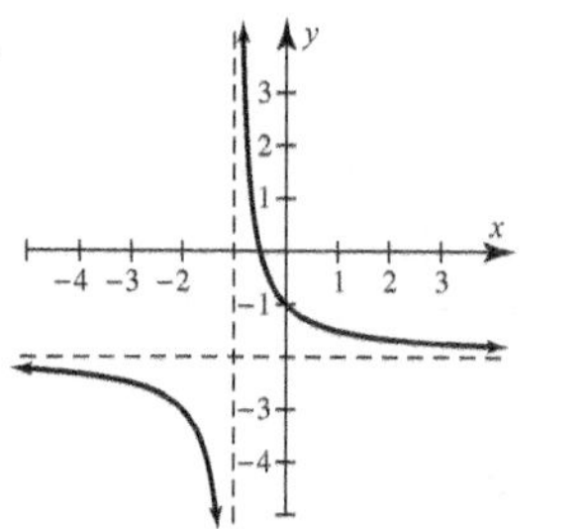

45.

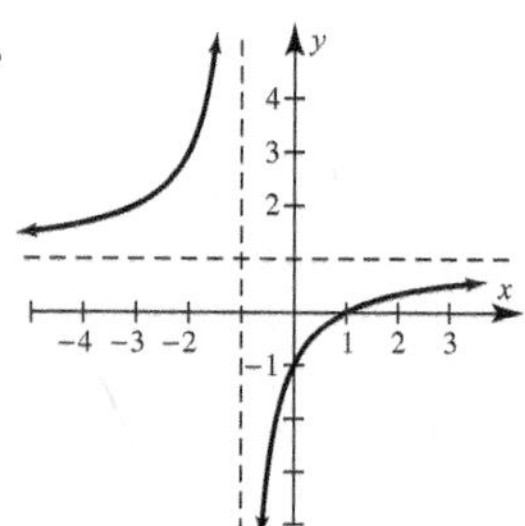

CHECKING BASIC CONCEPTS FOR SECTIONS 4.7 AND 4.8 (p. 344)

1. (a) $\frac{1}{2}$ **(b)** $-5, \frac{7}{3}$
(c) No real solutions (extraneous: –2)
3. $(-2,-1]\cup[1,\infty)$, or $\{x\mid -2<x\le -1 \text{ or } x\ge 1\}$
5. (a) -8 **(b)** $\frac{1}{4}$ **(c)** 9 **7.** 8 (extraneous: 1)
9. $a=2, b=\frac{1}{2}$

CHAPTER 4 REVIEW EXERCISES (pp. 353–356)

1. Degree: 3; leading coefficient: -7
3. (a) Local minimum: -2; local maximum: 4.1
(b) No absolute minimum; no absolute maximum
5. Even **7.** Odd **9.** Odd
11. Answers may vary.

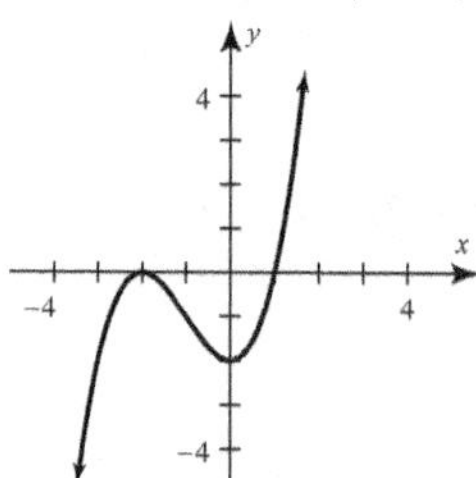

13. (a) 2; $-2, 0, 1$ **(b)** $a<0$ **(c)** 3
15. Up on left end, down on right end;
$f(x)\to\infty$ as $x\to-\infty$; $f(x)\to-\infty$ as $x\to\infty$
17. 7
19. (a)

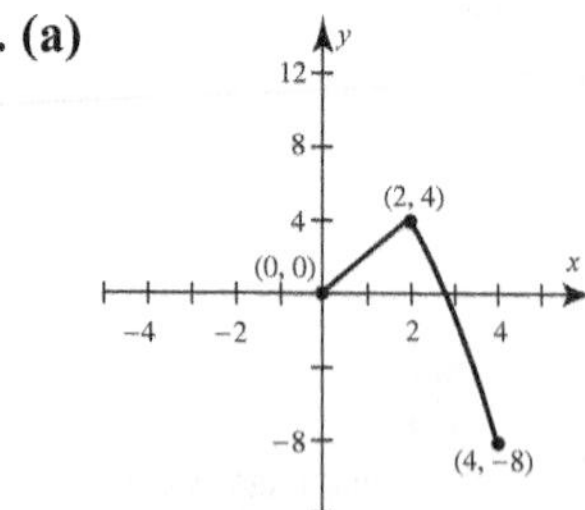

f is continuous.

(b) $f(1)=2$; $f(3)=-1$ **(c)** $1, \sqrt{6}$
21. $2x^2-3x-1$ **23.** $2x^2-3x+1+\frac{1}{2x+3}$
25. $f(x)=\frac{1}{2}(x-1)(x-2)(x-3)$
27. $f(x)=\frac{1}{2}(x+2)(x-1)(x-3)$
29. $-3, \frac{1}{2}, 2$ **31.** $0, \pm\sqrt{3}$ **33.** $-1.88, 0.35, 1.53$
35. $0, \pm i$ **37.** $f(x)=4(x-1)(x-3i)(x+3i)$; $f(x)=4x^3-4x^2+36x-36$;

47. Answers may vary.

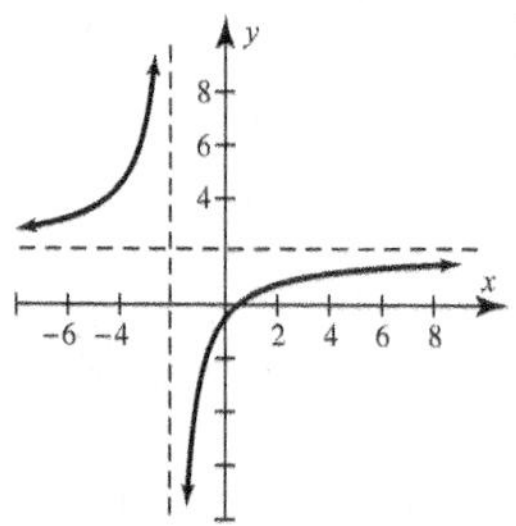

49. 4 **51.** No real solutions (extraneous: 2)
53. (a) $(-\infty,-4)\cup(-2,3)$, or $\{x\mid x<-4 \text{ or } -2<x<3\}$
(b) $(-4,-2)\cup(3,\infty)$, or $\{x\mid -4<x<-2 \text{ or } x>3\}$
55. $(-3,0)\cup(2,\infty)$, or $\{x\mid -3<x<0 \text{ or } x>2\}$
57. $(-\infty,-2)\cup\left(\frac{1}{2},\infty\right)$, or $\left\{x\mid x<-2 \text{ or } x>\frac{1}{2}\right\}$
59. 216 **61.** 8 **63.** $x^{4/3}$ **65.** $y^{1/2}$
67. $D=\{x\mid x\ge 0\}$; $f(3)\approx 15.59$
69. 4 **71.** 6 **73.** $\frac{81}{16}$ **75.** 15 **77.** $-2, \frac{1}{3}$ **79.** $-1, 125$
81. (a) Dog: 148; person: 69 **(b)** 6.4 in.
83. (a) 81.5°F **(b)** 87.3; the ocean reaches a maximum temperature of about 87.3°F in late July. **85.** 4 sec

CHAPTER 4 EXTENDED AND DISCOVERY EXERCISES (pp. 356–357)

1. (a)

$f(t)=t^2$	$t_1=10$, $t_2=11$	$t_1=10$, $t_2=10.1$	$t_1=10$, $t_2=10.01$	$t_1=10$, $t_2=10.001$
average velocity (ft/sec)	21	20.1	20.01	20.001

(b) The velocity of the bike rider is 20 ft/sec at 10 sec.
3. (a)

f_1 in [−10, 10, 1] by [−10, 10, 1]

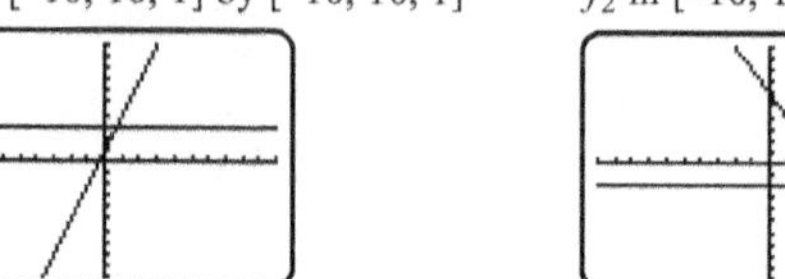

f_2 in [−10, 10, 1] by [−10, 10, 1]

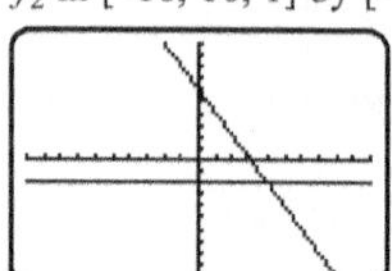

f_3 in [−10, 10, 1] by [−10, 10, 1]

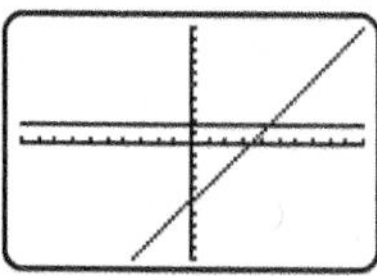

f_4 in [−10, 10, 1] by [−10, 10, 1]

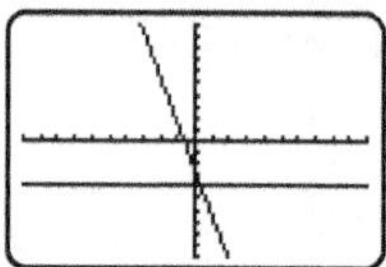

(b) Neither the graph of each linear function nor the graph of its average rate of change has any turning points.

CHAPTER 5: Exponential and Logarithmic Functions

SECTION 5.1 (pp. 371–377)

1. 7 **3.** $4x^3$ **5.** The cost of x square yards of carpet
7. **(a)** -5 **(b)** -5 **(c)** -3 **(d)** $-\frac{1}{3}$
9. **(a)** $\frac{11}{2}$ **(b)** 0 **(c)** $\frac{9}{4}$ **(d)** Undefined
11. **(a)** $(f + g)(x) = 2x + x^2$; all real numbers
(b) $(f - g)(x) = 2x - x^2$; all real numbers
(c) $(fg)(x) = 2x^3$; all real numbers
(d) $(f/g)(x) = \frac{2}{x}$; $D = \{x \mid x \neq 0\}$
13. **(a)** $(f + g)(x) = 2x^2$; all real numbers
(b) $(f - g)(x) = -2$; all real numbers
(c) $(fg)(x) = x^4 - 1$; all real numbers
(d) $(f/g)(x) = \frac{x^2 - 1}{x^2 + 1}$; all real numbers
15. **(a)** $(f + g)(x) = 2x$; $D = \{x \mid x \geq 1\}$
(b) $(f - g)(x) = -2\sqrt{x - 1}$; $D = \{x \mid x \geq 1\}$
(c) $(fg)(x) = x^2 - x + 1$; $D = \{x \mid x \geq 1\}$
(d) $(f/g)(x) = \frac{x - \sqrt{x - 1}}{x + \sqrt{x - 1}}$; $D = \{x \mid x \geq 1\}$
17. **(a)** $(f + g)(x) = 2\sqrt{x}$; $D = \{x \mid x \geq 0\}$
(b) $(f - g)(x) = -2$; $D = \{x \mid x \geq 0\}$
(c) $(fg)(x) = x - 1$; $D = \{x \mid x \geq 0\}$
(d) $(f/g)(x) = \frac{\sqrt{x} - 1}{\sqrt{x} + 1}$; $D = \{x \mid x \geq 0\}$
19. **(a)** $(f + g)(x) = \frac{4}{x + 1}$; $D = \{x \mid x \neq -1\}$
(b) $(f - g)(x) = -\frac{2}{x + 1}$; $D = \{x \mid x \neq -1\}$
(c) $(fg)(x) = \frac{3}{(x + 1)^2}$; $D = \{x \mid x \neq -1\}$
(d) $(f/g)(x) = \frac{1}{3}$; $D = \{x \mid x \neq -1\}$
21. **(a)** $(f + g)(x) = \frac{x + 1}{2x - 4}$; $D = \{x \mid x \neq 2\}$
(b) $(f - g)(x) = \frac{1 - x}{2x - 4}$; $D = \{x \mid x \neq 2\}$
(c) $(fg)(x) = \frac{x}{(2x - 4)^2}$; $D = \{x \mid x \neq 2\}$
(d) $(f/g)(x) = \frac{1}{x}$; $D = \{x \mid x \neq 0, x \neq 2\}$
23. **(a)** $(f + g)(x) = x^2 - 1 + |x + 1|$; all real numbers
(b) $(f - g)(x) = x^2 - 1 - |x + 1|$; all real numbers
(c) $(fg)(x) = (x^2 - 1)|x + 1|$; all real numbers
(d) $(f/g)(x) = \frac{x^2 - 1}{|x + 1|}$; $D = \{x \mid x \neq -1\}$
25. **(a)** $(f + g)(x) = \frac{(x - 1)(2x^2 - 2x + 5)}{(x + 1)(x - 2)}$;
$D = \{x \mid x \neq -1, x \neq 2\}$
(b) $(f - g)(x) = \frac{-3(x - 1)(2x - 1)}{(x + 1)(x - 2)}$;
$D = \{x \mid x \neq -1, x \neq 2\}$
(c) $(fg)(x) = (x - 1)^2$; $D = \{x \mid x \neq -1, x \neq 2\}$
(d) $(f/g)(x) = \frac{(x - 2)^2}{(x + 1)^2}$;
$D = \{x \mid x \neq 1, x \neq -1, \text{and } x \neq 2\}$
27. **(a)** $(f + g)(x) = \frac{x^2 + 4x - 1}{(x - 1)^2 (x + 1)}$;
$D = \{x \mid x \neq 1, x \neq -1\}$
(b) $(f - g)(x) = \frac{-x^2 - 3}{(x - 1)^2 (x + 1)}$;
$D = \{x \mid x \neq 1, x \neq -1\}$
(c) $(fg)(x) = \frac{2}{(x - 1)^3}$; $D = \{x \mid x \neq 1, x \neq -1\}$
(d) $(f/g)(x) = \frac{2(x - 1)}{(x + 1)^2}$; $D = \{x \mid x \neq 1, x \neq -1\}$
29. **(a)** $(f + g)(x) = x^{1/2}(x^2 - x + 1)$; $D = \{x \mid x \geq 0\}$
(b) $(f - g)(x) = x^{1/2}(x^2 - x - 1)$; $D = \{x \mid x \geq 0\}$
(c) $(fg)(x) = x^2(x - 1)$; $D = \{x \mid x \geq 0\}$
(d) $(f/g)(x) = x(x - 1)$; $D = \{x \mid x > 0\}$
31. **(a)** 2 **(b)** 4 **(c)** 0 **(d)** $-\frac{1}{3}$
33. **(a)** 2 **(b)** -3 **(c)** 2 **(d)** -2
35. **(a)** -5 **(b)** -2 **(c)** 0 **(d)** Undefined
37. **(a)** 5 **(b)** 5 **(c)** 0 **(d)** Undefined
39.

x	-2	0	2	4
$(f + g)(x)$	6	5	5	15
$(f - g)(x)$	-6	5	9	5
$(fg)(x)$	0	0	-14	50
$(f/g)(x)$	0	—	-3.5	2

41. **(a)** $g(-3) = -5$ **(b)** $g(b) = 2b + 1$
(c) $g(x^3) = 2x^3 + 1$ **(d)** $g(2x - 3) = 4x - 5$
43. **(a)** $g(-3) = -4$ **(b)** $g(b) = 2(b + 3)^2 - 4$
(c) $g(x^3) = 2(x^3 + 3)^2 - 4$
(d) $g(2x - 3) = 8x^2 - 4$
45. **(a)** $g(-3) = -\frac{11}{2}$ **(b)** $g(b) = \frac{1}{2}b^2 + 3b - 1$
(c) $g(x^3) = \frac{1}{2}x^6 + 3x^3 - 1$ **(d)** $g(2x - 3) = 2x^2 - \frac{11}{2}$
47. **(a)** $g(-3) = 1$ **(b)** $g(b) = \sqrt{b + 4}$
(c) $g(x^3) = \sqrt{x^3 + 4}$ **(d)** $g(2x - 3) = \sqrt{2x + 1}$
49. **(a)** $g(-3) = 14$ **(b)** $g(b) = |3b - 1| + 4$
(c) $g(x^3) = |3x^3 - 1| + 4$
(d) $g(2x - 3) = |6x - 10| + 4$
51. **(a)** $g(-3)$ is undefined. **(b)** $g(b) = \frac{4b}{b + 3}$
(c) $g(x^3) = \frac{4x^3}{x^3 + 3}$ **(d)** $g(2x - 3) = \frac{2(2x - 3)}{x}$
53. **(a)** 3 **(b)** 4 **55.** **(a)** 18 **(b)** 23
57. **(a)** $(f \circ g)(x) = (x^2 + 3x - 1)^3$; all real numbers
(b) $(g \circ f)(x) = x^6 + 3x^3 - 1$; all real numbers
(c) $(f \circ f)(x) = x^9$; all real numbers
59. **(a)** $(f \circ g)(x) = x^4 + x^2 - 3x - 2$; all real numbers
(b) $(g \circ f)(x) = (x + 2)^4 + (x + 2)^2 - 3(x + 2) - 4$; all real numbers **(c)** $(f \circ f)(x) = x + 4$; all real numbers
61. **(a)** $(f \circ g)(x) = 2 - 3x^3$; all real numbers
(b) $(g \circ f)(x) = (2 - 3x)^3$; all real numbers
(c) $(f \circ f)(x) = 9x - 4$; all real numbers
63. **(a)** $(f \circ g)(x) = \frac{1}{5x + 1}$; $D = \{x \mid x \neq -\frac{1}{5}\}$
(b) $(g \circ f)(x) = \frac{5}{x + 1}$; $D = \{x \mid x \neq -1\}$
(c) $(f \circ f)(x) = \frac{x + 1}{x + 2}$; $D = \{x \mid x \neq -1, x \neq -2\}$
65. **(a)** $(f \circ g)(x) = \sqrt{4 - x^2} + 4$;
$D = \{x \mid -2 \leq x \leq 2\}$
(b) $(g \circ f)(x) = \sqrt{4 - (x + 4)^2}$;
$D = \{x \mid -6 \leq x \leq -2\}$
(c) $(f \circ f)(x) = x + 8$; all real numbers
67. **(a)** $(f \circ g)(x) = \sqrt{3x - 1}$; $D = \{x \mid x \geq \frac{1}{3}\}$
(b) $(g \circ f)(x) = 3\sqrt{x - 1}$; $D = \{x \mid x \geq 1\}$
(c) $(f \circ f)(x) = \sqrt{\sqrt{x - 1} - 1}$; $D = \{x \mid x \geq 2\}$
69. **(a)** $(f \circ g)(x) = x$; all real numbers
(b) $(g \circ f)(x) = x$; all real numbers
(c) $(f \circ f)(x) = 25x - 4$; all real numbers
71. **(a)** $(f \circ g)(x) = x$; $D = \{x \mid x \neq 0\}$
(b) $(g \circ f)(x) = x$; $D = \{x \mid x \neq 0\}$
(c) $(f \circ f)(x) = x$; $D = \{x \mid x \neq 0\}$

73. **(a)** −4 **(b)** 2 **(c)** −4
75. **(a)** −3 **(b)** −2 **(c)** 0
77. **(a)** 5 **(b)** Undefined **(c)** 4 **79.** 4; 2
Answers may vary for Exercises 81–93.
81. $f(x) = x - 2, g(x) = \sqrt{x}$
83. $f(x) = x + 2, g(x) = \frac{1}{x}$
85. $f(x) = 2x + 1, g(x) = 4x^3$
87. $f(x) = x^3 - 1, g(x) = x^2$
89. $f(x) = x + 2, g(x) = -4|x| - 3$
91. $f(x) = x - 1, g(x) = \frac{1}{x^2}$
93. $f(x) = x^{1/4}, g(x) = x^3 - x$
95. $P(x) = 10x - 12{,}000$; $P(3000) = \$18{,}000$
97. **(a)** $I(x) = 36x$ **(b)** $C(x) = 2.54x$
(c) $F(x) = (C \circ I)(x)$ **(d)** $F(x) = 91.44x$
99. **(a)** $s(x) = \frac{11}{6}x + \frac{1}{9}x^2$ **(b)** $s(60) = 510$; it takes 510 feet to stop when traveling 60 mi/hr.
101. **(a)** $(g \circ f)(1) = 5.25$; a 1% decrease in the ozone layer could result in a 5.25% increase in skin cancer.
(b) Not possible using the given tables
103. **(a)** 4.5% **(b)** $(g \circ f)(x)$ computes the percent increase in peak electrical demand during year x.
105. **(a)** $(g \circ f)(1960) = 1.98$
(b) $(g \circ f)(x) = 0.165(x - 1948)$
(c) f, g, and $g \circ f$ are all linear functions.
107. **(a)** $(g \circ f)(2) \approx 25°\text{C}$ **(b)** $(g \circ f)(x)$ computes the Celsius temperature after x hours.
109. **(a)** $A(4s) = 16\frac{\sqrt{3}}{4}s^2 = 16A(s)$; if the length of a side is quadrupled, the area increases by a factor of 16.
(b) $A(s + 2) = \frac{\sqrt{3}}{4}(s^2 + 4s + 4) = A(s) + \sqrt{3}(s + 1)$; if the length of a side increases by 2, the area increases by $\sqrt{3}(s + 1)$.
111. $A = 36\pi t^2$
113. **(a)**

x	1990	2000	2010	2020	2030
$h(x)$	32	35.5	39	42.5	46

(b) $h(x) = f(x) + g(x)$
115. $h(x) = 0.35x - 664.5$
117. **(a)** $M(20) = 50$; $N(20) = 140$; the median income was \$50 thousand in 2010, while the 90th percentile was \$140 thousand.
(b) $D(x) = -0.15x^2 + 3.9x + 72$; $D(x)$ gives the household income difference between the 90th percentile and the median.
(c) $D(20) = 90$; the household income difference between the 90th percentile and the median in 2010 was \$90 thousand.
119. Let $f(x) = ax + b$ and $g(x) = cx + d$. Then $f(x) + g(x) = (ax + b) + (cx + d) = (a + c)x + (b + d)$, which is linear.
121. **(a)** $(f \circ g)(x) = k$; a constant function
(b) $(g \circ f)(x) = ak + b$; a constant function

SECTION 5.2 (pp. 387–391)

1. Closing a window
3. Closing a book, standing up, and walking out of the classroom
5. Subtract 2 from x; $x + 2$ and $x - 2$
7. Divide x by 3 and then add 2; $3(x - 2)$ and $\frac{x}{3} + 2$
9. Subtract 1 from x and cube the result; $\sqrt[3]{x} + 1$ and $(x - 1)^3$ **11.** Take the reciprocal of x; $\frac{1}{x}$ and $\frac{1}{x}$
13. One-to-one **15.** Not one-to-one
17. Not one-to-one
19. Not one-to-one; does not have an inverse
21. One-to-one; does have an inverse
23. One-to-one **25.** Not one-to-one
27. Not one-to-one **29.** Not one-to-one
31. Not one-to-one **33.** Not one-to-one
35. One-to-one **37.** No **39.** Yes
41. $f^{-1}(x) = x^3$ **43.** $f^{-1}(x) = -\frac{1}{2}x + 5$
45. $f^{-1}(x) = \frac{x + 1}{3}$ **47.** $f^{-1}(x) = \sqrt[3]{\frac{x + 5}{2}}$
49. $f^{-1}(x) = \sqrt{x + 1}$ **51.** $f^{-1}(x) = \frac{1}{2x}$
53. $f^{-1}(x) = -\frac{2(x - 3)}{5}$ **55.** $f^{-1}(x) = -\frac{2x}{x - 1}$
57. $f^{-1}(x) = \frac{x + 1}{x - 2}$ **59.** $f^{-1}(x) = \frac{1}{x + 3}$
61. $f^{-1}(x) = \sqrt[3]{\frac{1 + x}{x}}$
63. If the domain of f is restricted to $x \geq 0$, then $f^{-1}(x) = \sqrt{4 - x}$.
65. If the domain of f is restricted to $x \geq 2$, then $f^{-1}(x) = 2 + \sqrt{x - 4}$.
67. If the domain of f is restricted to $x \geq 0$, then $f^{-1}(x) = (x - 1)^{3/2}$.
69. If the domain of f is restricted to $0 \leq x \leq \frac{3}{\sqrt{2}}$, then $f^{-1}(x) = \sqrt{\frac{9 - x^2}{2}}$.
71. $f^{-1}(x) = \frac{x + 15}{5}$; D and R are all real numbers.
73. $f^{-1}(x) = x^3 + 5$; D and R are all real numbers.
75. $f^{-1}(x) = 4x + 5$; D and R are all real numbers.
77. $f^{-1}(x) = x^2 + 5$; $D = \{x | x \geq 0\}$ and $R = \{y | y \geq 5\}$
79. $f^{-1}(x) = \frac{1}{x} - 3$; $D = \{x | x \neq 0\}$ and $R = \{y | y \neq -3\}$
81. $f^{-1}(x) = \sqrt[3]{\frac{x}{2}}$; D and R are all real numbers.
83. $f^{-1}(x) = \sqrt{x}$; D and R include all nonnegative real numbers.
85.

x	5	7	9
$f^{-1}(x)$	1	2	3

For f: $D = \{1, 2, 3\}$, $R = \{5, 7, 9\}$;
for f^{-1}: $D = \{5, 7, 9\}$, $R = \{1, 2, 3\}$
87.

x	0	4	16
$f^{-1}(x)$	0	2	4

For f: $D = \{0, 2, 4\}$, $R = \{0, 4, 16\}$;
for f^{-1}: $D = \{0, 4, 16\}$, $R = \{0, 2, 4\}$
89.

x	0	2	4	6
$f^{-1}(x)$	0	$\frac{1}{2}$	1	$\frac{3}{2}$

91. 1 **93.** 3 **95.** 5 **97.** 1
99. **(a)** $f(1) \approx 110$ dollars **(b)** $f^{-1}(110) \approx 1$ year
(c) $f^{-1}(160) \approx 5$ years; $f^{-1}(x)$ computes the years necessary for the account to accumulate x dollars.
101. **(a)** 2 **(b)** 3 **(c)** 1 **(d)** 3
103. **(a)** 4 **(b)** 0 **(c)** 9 **(d)** 4

105.

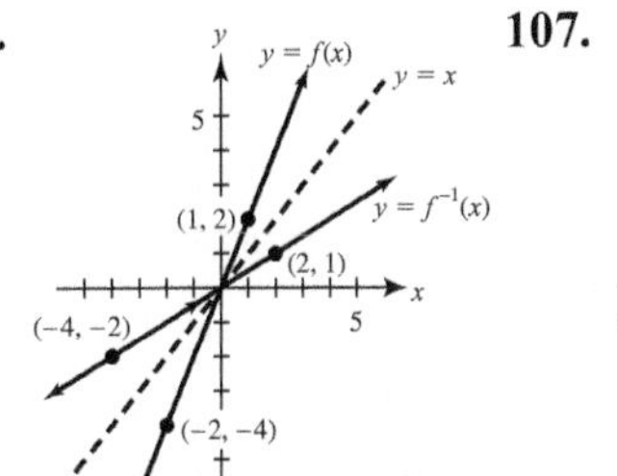

107.

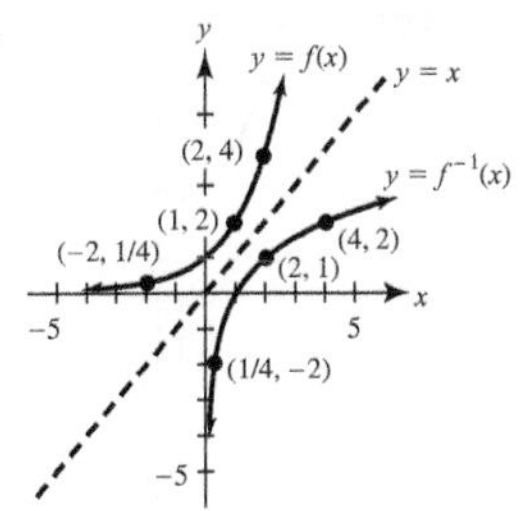

109.

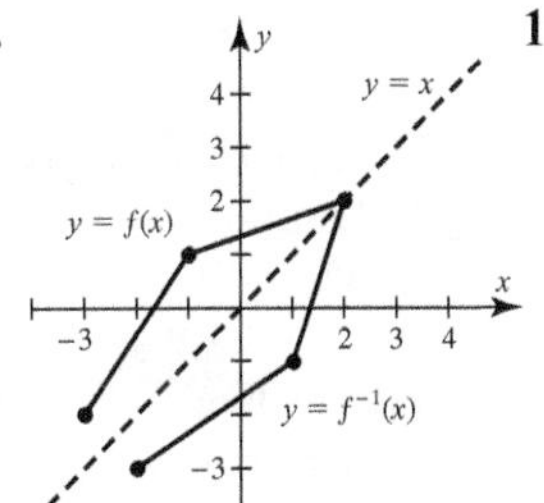

111.

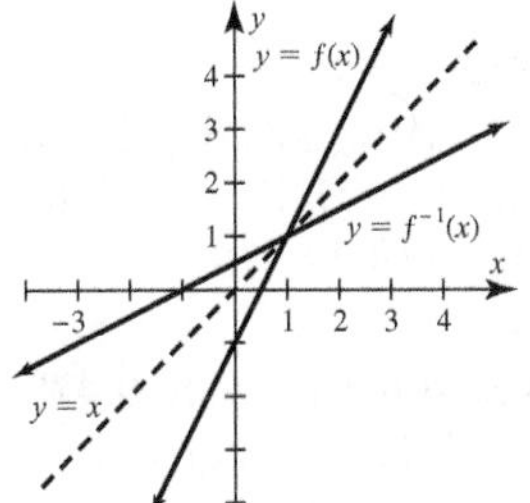

113.

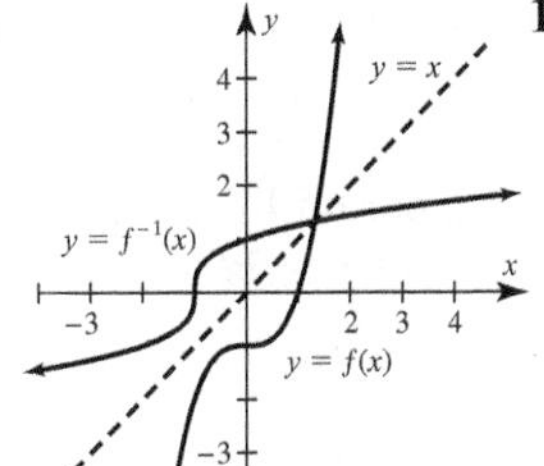

115.

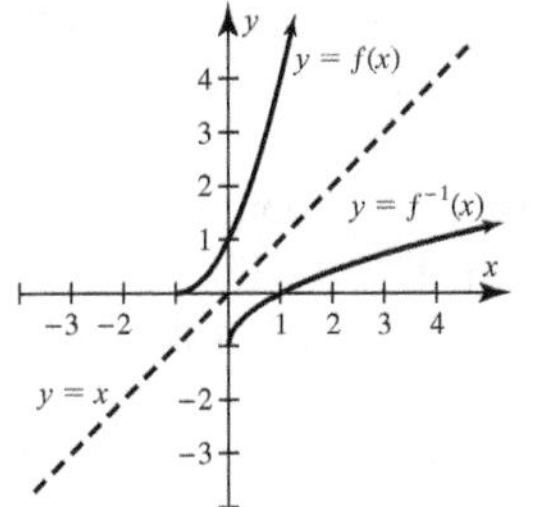

117. $Y_1 = 3X - 1$, $Y_2 = (X + 1)/3$, $Y_3 = X$
$[-4.7, 4.7, 1]$ by $[-3.1, 3.1, 1]$

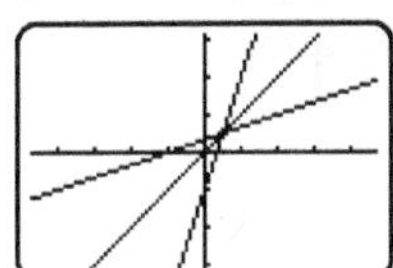

119. $Y_1 = X\wedge 3/3 - 1$, $Y_2 = \sqrt[3]{(3X + 3)}$, $Y_3 = X$
$[-4.7, 4.7, 1]$ by $[-3.1, 3.1, 1]$

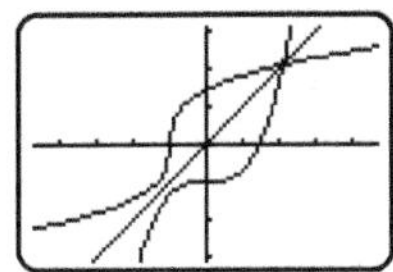

121. (a) Yes **(b)** The radius r of a sphere with volume V **(c)** $r = \sqrt[3]{\frac{3V}{4\pi}}$ **(d)** No. If V and r were interchanged, then r would represent the volume and V would represent the radius. **123. (a)** 135.7 pounds **(b)** Yes **(c)** $h = \frac{7}{25}\left(W + \frac{800}{7}\right) = \frac{7}{25}W + 32$ **(d)** 74; the maximum recommended height for a person weighing 150 lb is 74 in. **(e)** The inverse formula computes the maximum recommended height for a person of a given weight.
125. (a) $(F \circ Y)(2) = 10{,}560$ represents the number of feet in 2 miles. **(b)** $F^{-1}(26{,}400) = 8800$ represents the number of yards in 26,400 ft. **(c)** $(Y^{-1} \circ F^{-1})(21{,}120) = 4$ represents the number of miles in 21,120 ft.
127. (a) $(Q \circ C)(96) = 1.5$ represents the number of quarts in 96 tbsp. **(b)** $Q^{-1}(2) = 8$ represents the number of cups in 2 qt. **(c)** $(C^{-1} \circ Q^{-1})(1.5) = 96$ represents the number of tablespoons in 1.5 qt.

5.2 EXTENDED AND DISCOVERY EXERCISES (p. 391)

1. (a) $f^{-1}(x)$ computes the elapsed time in seconds when the rocket was x ft above the ground. **(b)** The solution to the equation $f(x) = 5000$ is the elapsed time in seconds when the rocket reached 5000 ft above the ground. **(c)** Evaluate $f^{-1}(5000)$.

CHECKING BASIC CONCEPTS FOR SECTIONS 5.1 AND 5.2 (p. 392)

1. (a) $(f + g)(1) = 1$ **(b)** $(f - g)(-1) = 3$ **(c)** $(fg)(0) = 2$ **(d)** $(f/g)(2)$ is undefined. **(e)** $(f \circ g)(2) = -2$ **(f)** $(g \circ f)(-2) = -1$
3. (a) $(f + g)(x) = x^2 + 6x - 3$
(b) $(f/g)(x) = \frac{x^2 + 3x - 2}{3x - 1}, x \neq \frac{1}{3}$
(c) $(f \circ g)(x) = 9x^2 + 3x - 4$
5. (a) Yes; yes; $f^{-1}(x) = x - 1$ **(b)** No; no
7. (a) 0 **(b)** 2

SECTION 5.3 (PART I) (pp. 405–408)

1. $\frac{1}{8}$ **3.** 6 **5.** -18 **7.** 2 **9.** 1
11. 5 **13.** Linear; $f(x) = -1.2x + 2$
15. Exponential; $f(x) = 8\left(\frac{1}{2}\right)^x$
17. Exponential; $f(x) = 5(2^x)$
19. Linear; $f(x) = 3.5x - 2$
21. Exponential; $f(x) = 81\left(\frac{1}{3}\right)^x$
23. $f(x) = 4x + 4$; $g(x) = 4(2)^x$
25. $f(x) = -3.5x + 5$; $g(x) = 3\left(\frac{1}{2}\right)^x$
27. $f(x) = -2x + 5$; $g(x) = 3\left(\frac{1}{\sqrt{3}}\right)^x$
29. $f(x) = 2^x$ **31.** $f(x) = 2x + 1$
33. $C = 5, a = 1.5$ **35.** $C = 10, a = 2$
37. $C = 3, a = 3$ **39.** $C = \frac{1}{2}, a = \frac{1}{3}$
41. $f(x) = 5000(2^x)$; x represents time in hours.
43. $f(x) = 200{,}000(0.95^x)$; x represents the number of years after 2000.
45. About 11 pounds per square inch

47.

49.

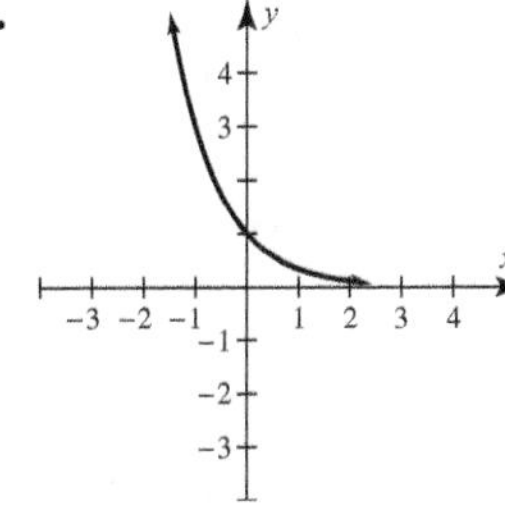

51.

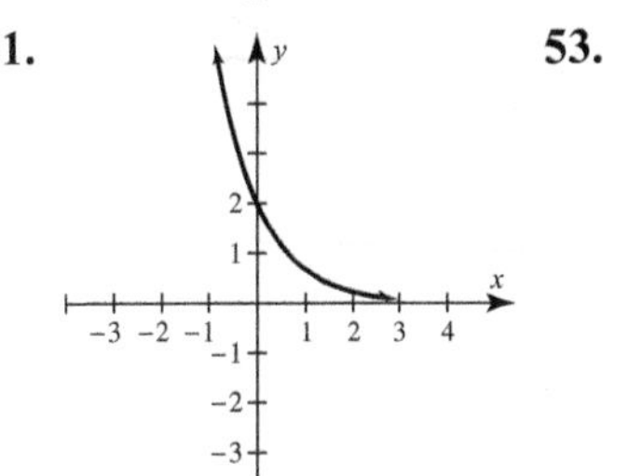

53.

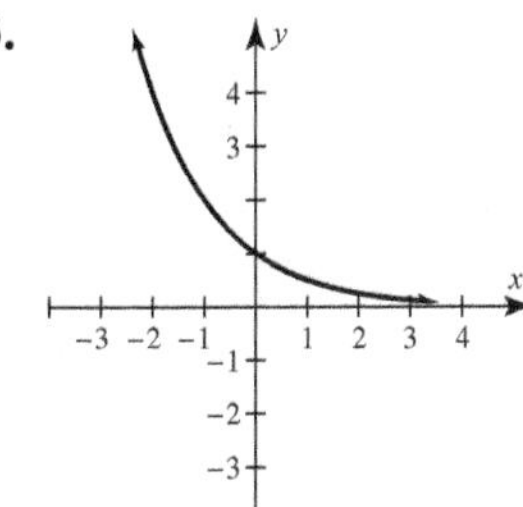

55. $C = 1, a = \frac{1}{2}$ **57.** $C = \frac{1}{2}, a = 4$

59. **(a)** D: $(-\infty, \infty)$ or $\{x \mid -\infty < x < \infty\}$; R: $(0, \infty)$ or $\{x \mid x > 0\}$ **(b)** Decreasing **(c)** $y = 0$
(d) y-intercept: 7; no x-intercept **(e)** Yes; yes
61. **(i)** b **(ii)** d **(iii)** a **(iv)** c
63. **(a)** $f(x) = 2.5(3)^x$
(b) About 13 million bacteria per milliliter
65. **(a)** About 1.5 watts per square meter
(b) The y-intercept is 300 and equals C and the initial value.

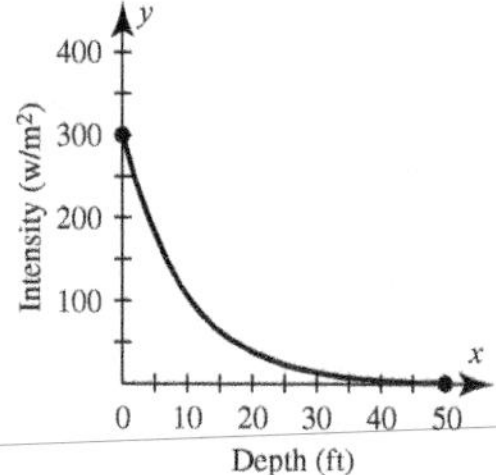

67. **(a)** $C \approx 0.72$, $a \approx 1.041$ (answers may vary)
(b) 1.21 ppb (answers may vary)
69. About 18,935 yr
71. About 27.3%
73. **(a)** $C = 2.5$, $a = 0.7$ **(b)** 1.225 ppm
(c) About 1.4 days
75. **(a)** $H(30) \approx 0.42$; about 0.42 horsepower is required for each ton pulled at 30 mi/hr.
(b) About 2100 horsepower **(c)** 2
77. $T(t) = 100(\frac{1}{2})^{t/2.8}$; $T(5.5) \approx 25.6\%$
79. **(a)** $P(x) = 95(0.9)^x$ **(b)** About 11.5%
(c) About 6.6 feet
81. $A(t) = 1000(3)^{t/7}$; about 5620 bacteria
83. $I(t) = I_0(\frac{1}{3})^{t/2}$; about $0.094\ I_0$
85. $A(t) = 5000(4)^{t/35}$; about \$6864.10

SECTION 5.3 (PART II) (pp. 418–421)

1. $f(x) = 9500(0.65)^x$
3. $f(x) = 2500(1.05)^x$
5. $f(x) = 1000(0.935)^x$
7. $C = 8$, $a = 1.12$, $r = 0.12$, or 12%
9. $C = 1.5$, $a = 0.35$, $r = -0.65$, or -65%
11. $C = 1$, $a = 0.55$, $r = -0.45$, or -45%
13. $C = 7$, $a = e$, $r = e - 1$, or about 171.8%
15. $C = 6$, $a = \frac{1}{3}$, $r = -\frac{2}{3}$, or about -66.7%
17. 71.2571
19. -0.7586
21. **(i)** b **(ii)** d **(iii)** a **(iv)** c
23. **(a)** **(b)**

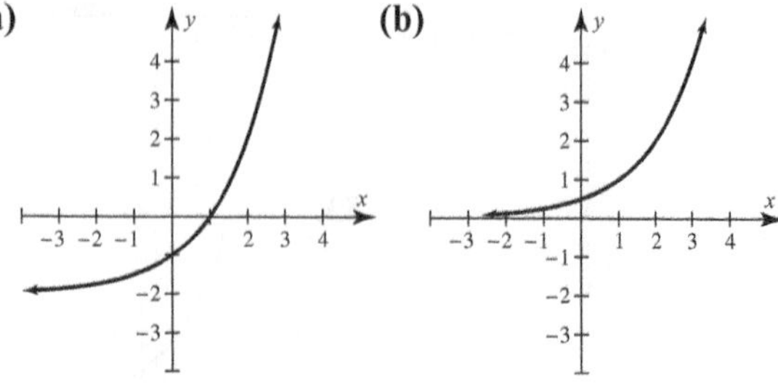

(c) **(d)**

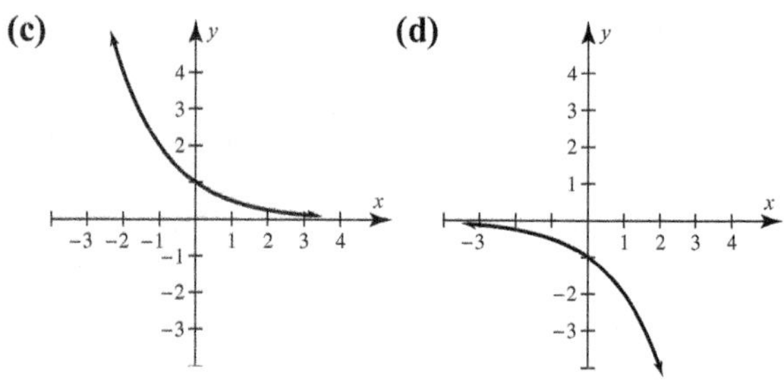

25. \$841.53 **27.** \$1730.97 **29.** \$4451.08
31. \$2072.76
33. 10%: \$14,656.15; 13%: \$26,553.58; a 13% rate results in \$11,897.43 more interest than a 10% rate.
35. \$14,326.78 **37.** Annually at 6.3%
39. 5.641% **41.** 5.654% **43.** About 4.34%
45. 4.07% **47.** 9.42% **49.** About 2.21%
51. They are equal. **53.** \$11.41 **55.** 6.25%
57. **(a)** \$9074.47 **(b)** The last 10 years
59. About \$1288 billion, or \$1.288 trillion
61. \$19,870.65
63. $A(x) = Pe^{-0.0325x}$, where P is the initial value
65. **(a)** About 6,214,000 bacteria per milliliter
(b) There will be 10 million *E. coli* bacteria per milliliter after about 214 min, or about 3.6 hr.
67. **(a)** About 92% **(b)** About 0.83 min
69. **(a)** 31.7 mg; the half-life is less than 50 yr. **(b)** 30.2 yr

5.3 (PART II) EXTENDED AND DISCOVERY EXERCISES (pp. 421–422)

1. The formulas are equivalent. **3.** \$12,914.64
5. **(a)** About 1.0005 **(b)** 1
(c) They are very similar.
7. **(a)** About 0.6068 **(b)** About 0.6065
(c) They are very similar.
9. The average rate of change near x and the value of the function at x are approximately equal.

SECTION 5.4 (pp. 434–438)

1.

x	10^0	10^4	10^{-8}	$10^{1.26}$
$\log x$	0	4	–8	1.26

3. **(a)** Undefined **(b)** -2 **(c)** $-\frac{1}{2}$ **(d)** 0
5. **(a)** 1 **(b)** 4 **(c)** -20 **(d)** -2
7. **(a)** 2 **(b)** $\frac{1}{2}$ **(c)** 3 **(d)** Undefined
9. **(a)** $n = 1, \log 79 \approx 1.898$
(b) $n = 2, \log 500 \approx 2.699$ **(c)** $n = 0, \log 5 \approx 0.699$
(d) $n = -1, \log 0.5 \approx -0.301$
11. **(a)** $\frac{3}{2}$ **(b)** $\frac{1}{3}$ **(c)** $-\frac{1}{5}$ **(d)** -1
13. $\{x \mid x > -3\}$, or $(-3, \infty)$
15. $\{x \mid x < -1 \text{ or } x > 1\}$, or $(-\infty, -1) \cup (1, \infty)$
17. $\{x \mid -\infty < x < \infty\}$, or $(-\infty, \infty)$
19. $\{x \mid x < 2\}$, or $(-\infty, 2)$
21. -5.7 **23.** $2x, x > 0$ **25.** 64
27. -4 **29.** π **31.** $x - 1$ for $x > 1$
33. 6 **35.** $\frac{1}{2}$ **37.** -3 **39.** 2 **41.** –2 **43.** -2

45. -1 **47.** 0 **49.** -4

51.

x	6	15	105
$f(x)$	0	2	4

53. **(a)** $4x = \log 4$ **(b)** $x = \ln 7$ **(c)** $x = \log_c b$
55. **(a)** $x = 10^3$ **(b)** $2 + x = e^5$ **(c)** $b = k^c$
57. **(a)** -2 **(b)** $\log 7 \approx 0.85$ **(c)** No solutions
59. **(a)** -2 **(b)** $\ln 2 \approx 0.69$ **(c)** 3
61. **(a)** 0 **(b)** $\frac{1}{2}$ **(c)** $\frac{1}{3}$
63. $-\ln 3 \approx -1.10$ **65.** 2 **67.** $\frac{2}{3}$
69. $\frac{\log 13}{4} \approx 0.28$ **71.** $\ln 4 \approx 1.39$ **73.** $\ln 23 \approx 3.14$
75. $\ln 14 \approx 2.64$ **77.** $\ln\left(\frac{18}{5}\right) \approx 1.28$ **79.** 8
81. **(a)** $10^2 = 100$ **(b)** $10^{-3} = 0.001$
(c) $10^{1.2} \approx 15.8489$
83. **(a)** $e^6 \approx 403.4288$ **(b)** $e^{-2} \approx 0.1353$ **(c)** $e^2 \approx 7.3891$
85. $10^{1.2} \approx 15.8489$ **87.** $\frac{49}{2}$ **89.** 1000 **91.** 20
93. $e^{3/4} \approx 2.1170$ **95.** $e^{7/5} \approx 4.0552$ **97.** 16
99. $\frac{1}{2}e^{6/5} \approx 1.6601$ **101.** 50 **103.** $a = 5, b = 2$
105. $f^{-1}(x) = \ln x$

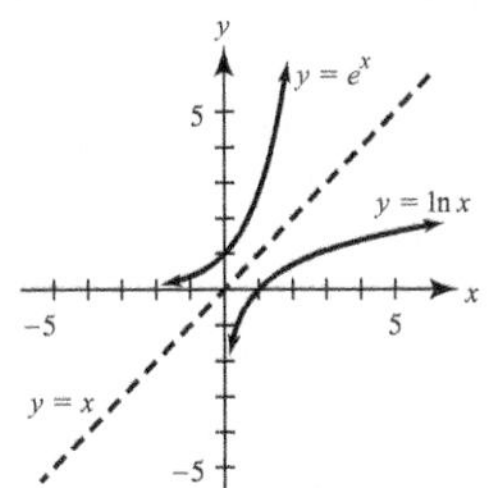

107. $f^{-1}(x) = 2^x$

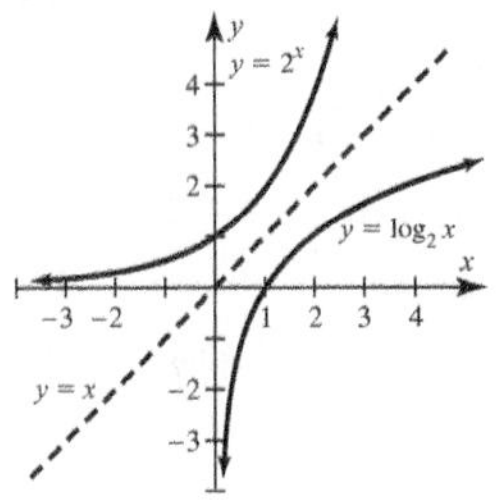

109. Decreasing

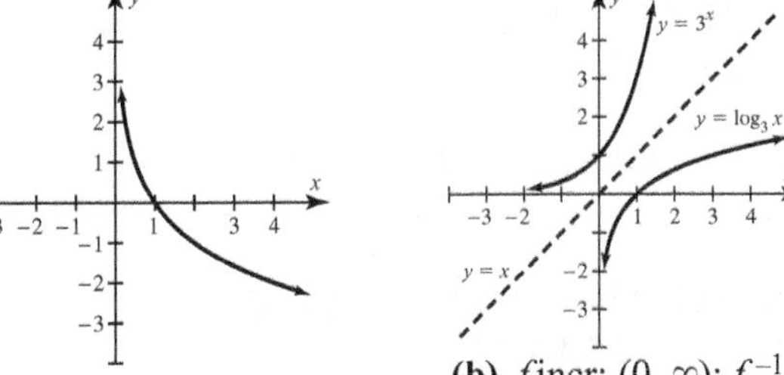

111. **(a)**

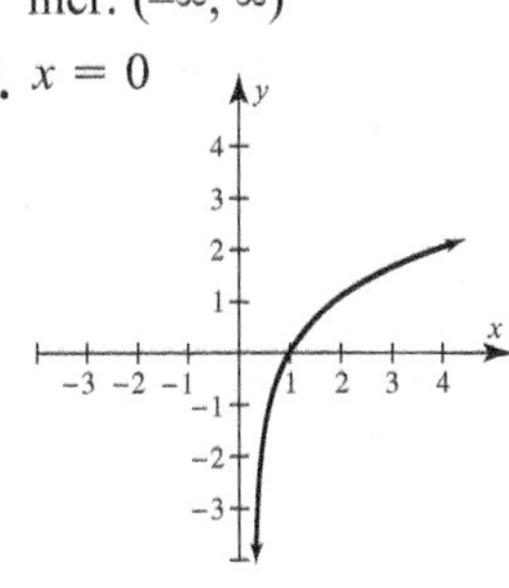

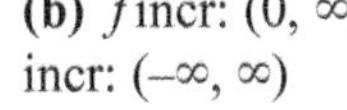

(b) f incr: $(0, \infty)$; f^{-1} incr: $(-\infty, \infty)$

113. $x = 2$

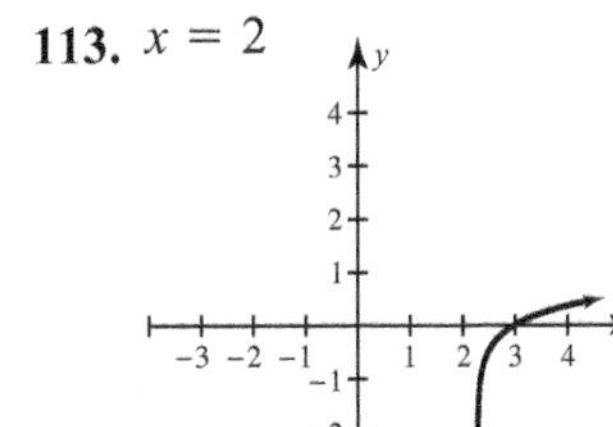

115. $x = 0$

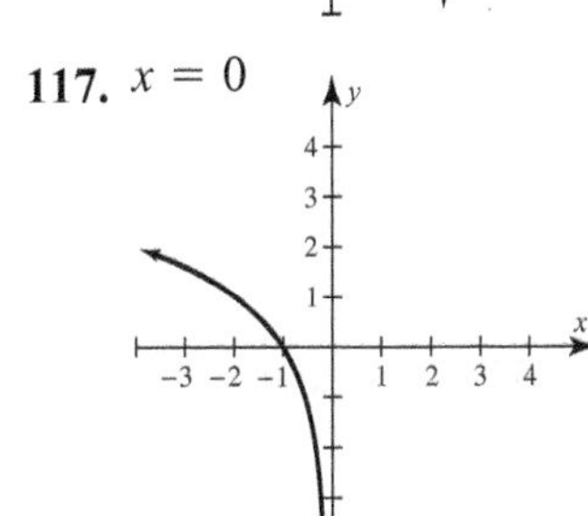

117. $x = 0$

119. $x = 1$

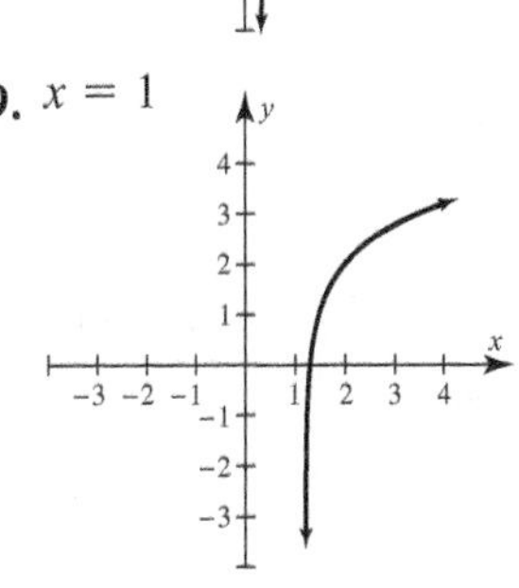

121. $D = \{x | x > -1\}$
$[-6, 6, 1]$ by $[-4, 4, 1]$

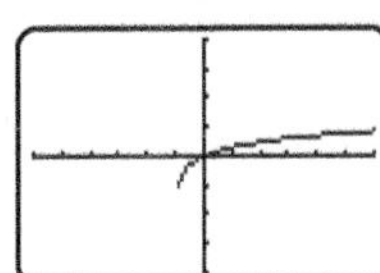

123. $D = \{x | x < 0\}$
$[-6, 6, 1]$ by $[-4, 4, 1]$

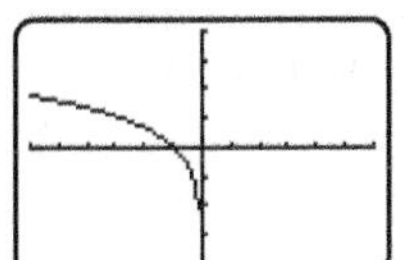

125. 120 dB **127.** **(a)** $L(100) = 6$; a 100-thousand-pound plane needs 6000 feet of runway. **(b)** No. It increases by 3000 ft. **(c)** If the weight increases tenfold, the runway length increases by 3000 ft.
129. **(a)** 4.7 **(b)** $10^{3.5} \approx 3162$
131. **(a)** Yugoslavia: $x = 1{,}000{,}000$; Indonesia: $x = 100{,}000{,}000$ **(b)** 100
133. **(a)** $f(0) = 27$, $f(100) \approx 29.2$. At the eye, the barometric air pressure is 27 in.; 100 mi away, it is 29.2 in.
(b) The air pressure increases rapidly at first and then starts to level off.
$[0, 250, 50]$ by $[25, 30, 1]$

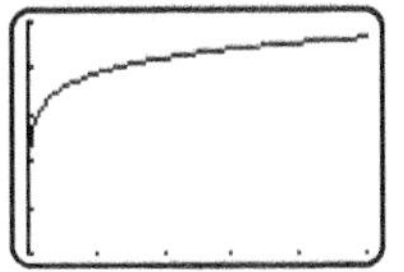

(c) About 7 miles
135. **(a)** About 49.4°C **(b)** About 0.69 hr, or 41.4 min
137. **(a)** About 0.189, or an 18.9% chance
(b) $x = -3\ln(0.3) \approx 3.6$ min
139. $a = 7, b = 4$; about 178 km^2
141. **(a)** $C = 3, a = 2$ **(b)** After about 2.4 days

5.4 EXTENDED AND DISCOVERY EXERCISES (p. 438)

1. **(a)** 1.00 **(b)** 0.50 **(c)** 0.33 **(d)** 0.25
3. **(a)** $T(x) = 6.5\ln(1.3 \cdot 1.005^x)$; $T(100) \approx 4.95$. The average global temperature may increase by 4.95°F by the year 2100.
(b) $[0, 200, 50]$ by $[0, 1000, 100]$

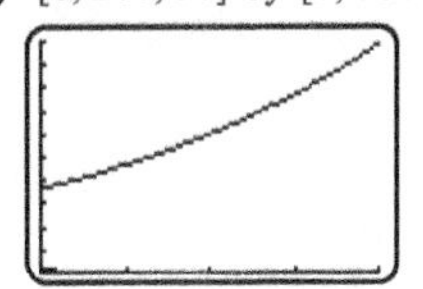

$[0, 200, 50]$ by $[0, 10, 1]$

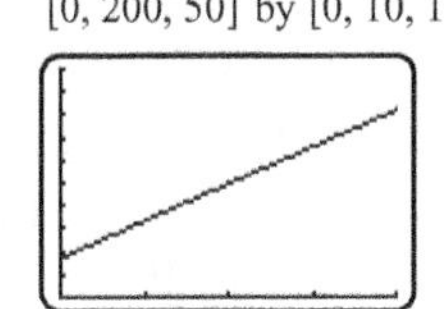

The carbon dioxide level graph is exponential, whereas the average global temperature graph is linear. **(c)** Average global temperature rises by a constant amount each year.

CHECKING BASIC CONCEPTS FOR SECTIONS 5.3 AND 5.4 (pp. 438–439)

1. \$1752.12; \$1754.74
3. $\log_2 15$ represents the exponent k such that $2^k = 15$. No.
5. **(a)** $\ln 5 \approx 1.609$ **(b)** $\log 25 \approx 1.398$
(c) $10^{1.5} \approx 31.623$ **7.** **(a)** About 38.1 million; in 2012 California's population was about 38.1 million. **(b)** 37.3; in 2010 California's population was about 37.3 million. **(c)** About 1% **(d)** 2017

SECTION 5.5 (pp. 445–446)

1. 1.447; Product rule **3.** 2.197; Quotient rule **5.** 3.010; Power rule **7.** $\log a + \log b$ **9.** $\ln 7 + 4\ln a$ **11.** $\log 6 - \log z$ **13.** $2\log x - \log 3$ **15.** $\ln 2 + 7\ln x - \ln 3 - \ln k$ **17.** $\log 4 + 2\log k + 3\log x$ **19.** $\log 25 + 3\log x - 4\log y$ **21.** $4\ln x - 2\ln y - \frac{3}{2}\ln z$ **23.** $\log 0.25 + 3\log(x + 2)$ **25.** $3\ln x - 4\ln(x - 4)$ **27.** $\frac{1}{2}\log x - 2\log z$ **29.** $\frac{1}{3}\ln(2x + 6) - \frac{5}{3}\ln(x + 1)$ **31.** $\frac{1}{3}\log(x^2 - 1) - \frac{1}{2}\log(1 + x^2)$ **33.** $\log 6$ **35.** $\ln 5^{-3/2}$ **37.** $\log 2$ **39.** $\log 6$ **41.** $\ln 5k^2$ **43.** $\ln x^3$ **45.** $\log x^{3/2}$ **47.** $\ln\frac{x^3z^4}{\sqrt{y^3}}$ **49.** $\ln\frac{2}{e}$ **51.** $\ln\frac{x^2\sqrt{z}}{y^4}$ **53.** $\log(4\sqrt{x^5})$ **55.** $\log\frac{(x^2 - 1)^2(x - 2)^4}{\sqrt{y}}$ **57. (a)** Yes **(b)** By the product rule: $\log 3x + \log 2x = \log(3x \cdot 2x) = \log 6x^2$ **59. (a)** Yes **(b)** By the quotient rule: $\ln 2x^2 - \ln x = \ln\left(\frac{2x^2}{x}\right) = \ln 2x$ **61. (a)** Yes **(b)** By the power rule: $\ln x^4 - \ln x^2 = 4\ln x - 2\ln x = 2\ln x$

63. **65.**

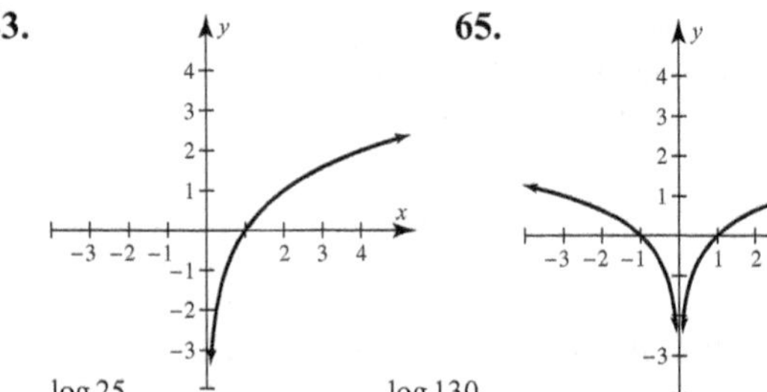

67. $\frac{\log 25}{\log 2} \approx 4.644$ **69.** $\frac{\log 130}{\log 5} \approx 3.024$ **71.** $\frac{\log 5}{\log 2} + \frac{\log 7}{\log 2} \approx 5.129$ **73.** $\sqrt{\frac{\log 46}{\log 4}} \approx 1.662$ **75.** $\frac{\log 12/\log 2}{\log 3/\log 2} = \frac{\log 12}{\log 3} \approx 2.262$ **77.** 215.111 **79.** ± 2.035 **81.** $L(x) = \frac{3\ln x}{\ln 10}$; $L(50) \approx 5.097$; yes **83.** 10 decibels **85.** $I = I_0 e^{-kx}$ **87. (a)** $x = 100\ln\frac{P}{37.3}$ **(b)** About 7; the population is expected to reach 40 million during 2017. **89.** $t = \frac{\ln\frac{A}{P}}{r}$ **91.** $\log(1 \cdot 2^2 \cdot 3^3 \cdot 4^4 \cdot 5^5) = \log 86{,}400{,}000$

SECTION 5.6 (pp. 456–460)

1. (a) About 2 **(b)** $\ln 7.5 \approx 2.015$ **3. (a)** About 2 **(b)** $5\log 2.5 \approx 1.990$ **5.** $\ln 1.25 \approx 0.2231$ **7.** $\log 20 \approx 1.301$ **9.** $-\frac{5}{6}\ln 0.4 \approx 0.7636$ **11.** $\frac{\ln 0.5}{\ln 0.9} \approx 6.579$ **13.** $1 + \frac{\log 4}{\log 1.1} \approx 15.55$ **15.** 1 **17.** $\frac{1}{5}$ **19.** 1, 2 **21.** No solutions **23.** $2 + \frac{\log(1/3)}{\log(2/5)} \approx 3.199$ **25.** $\frac{\log 4}{\log 4 - 2\log 3} \approx -1.710$ **27.** $\frac{3}{1 - 3\ln 2} \approx -2.779$ **29.** $\frac{\log(64/3)}{\log 1.4} \approx 9.095$ **31.** $1980 + \frac{\log(8/5)}{\log 1.015} \approx 2012$ **33.** -3 **35.** 0, -1 **37.** 1 **39.** $\frac{6}{7}$ **41.** $-\frac{12}{5}$ **43.** $10^{2/3} \approx 4.642$ **45.** $\frac{1}{2}e^5 \approx 74.207$ **47.** $\pm\sqrt{50} \approx \pm 7.071$ **49.** 6 **51.** $-\frac{992}{3}$ **53.** 10^{-11} **55.** $e \approx 2.718$ **57.** $2^{2.1} \approx 4.287$ **59.** $\sqrt{50} \approx 7.071$ **61.** $-\frac{998}{3}$ **63.** 2 (extraneous $-\frac{5}{3}$) **65.** $1 + \sqrt{2} \approx 2.414$ (extraneous $1 - \sqrt{2}$) **67.** 2 (extraneous -2) **69.** 2 (extraneous -4) **71.** 4 (extraneous -4) **73. (a)** 8 **(b)** $\frac{\ln 8}{\ln 3}$ **(c)** 10^8 **(d)** e^8 **(e)** $e^{13/12} + 3$ **75. (a)** –5 **(b)** No solutions **(c)** 10^{-5} **(d)** e^{-5} **(e)** $e^{-29/5} - 4$ **77. (a)** 3 **(b)** $\frac{\ln 3}{\ln 5}$ **(c)** 10^3 **(d)** e^3 **(e)** $e^{-3} - 12$ **79.** 0.31 **81.** 1.71 **83.** 2.10 **85.** 2018 **87.** $\frac{\ln 0.25}{-0.12} \approx 11.55$ ft **89. (a)** $T(x) = 2300(2)^{x/2}$ **(b)** $T(40) \approx 2{,}411{,}724{,}800$; in 2011 there were about 2.4 billion transistors on an integrated circuit. **(c)** About 1995 **91. (a)** About 0.88; the Human Development Index is 0.88. **(b)** 3.9 **93.** About 1981 **95. (a)** $C = 1, a \approx 1.01355$ **(b)** $P(2010) \approx 1.14$ billion **(c)** About 2030 **97. (a)** $T_0 = 32, D = 180, a \approx 0.045$ **(b)** About 139°F **(c)** About 1 hr **99. (a)** About 16.7°C **(b)** About 1.09 hr **101.** About 2.8 acres **103.** $100 - 10^{1.16} \approx 85.5\%$ **105. (a)** $\frac{\ln 1.15}{6} \approx 0.0233$ **(b)** About 1.45 billion per liter **(c)** About 2.36% **107.** 8.25 yr **109. (a)** $\frac{\ln 1.5}{0.03} \approx 13.5$ **(b)** \$500 invested at 3% compounded continuously results in \$750 after 13.5 years. **111.** About 8633 yr **113.** $-2\ln 0.5 \approx 1.39$ min **115.** About 3.6 hr **117.** About 13.5 yr **119. (a)** 11 milligrams/liter **(b)** About 2.11 hr **121.** $t = \frac{\log(A/P)}{n\log(1 + r/n)}$

5.6 EXTENDED AND DISCOVERY EXERCISE (p. 460)

1. $f(x) = Ce^{x\ln a}$ and $g(x) = e^{x\ln 2}$; that is, $k = \ln a$.

CHECKING BASIC CONCEPTS FOR SECTIONS 5.5 AND 5.6 (p. 461)

1. $2\log x + 3\log y - \frac{1}{3}\log z$ **3. (a)** $\frac{\log(29/5)}{\log(1.4)} \approx 5.224$ **(b)** $\frac{1}{3}$ **5. (a)** It levels off at 80°F. **(b)** 17 min

SECTION 5.7 (pp. 467–469)

1. Logarithmic **3.** Exponential **5.** Exponential: $f(x) = 1.2(1.7)^x$ **7.** Logarithmic: $f(x) = 1.088 + 2.937\ln x$ **9.** Logistic: $f(x) = \frac{9.96}{1 + 30.6e^{-1.51x}}$ **11. (a)** Quadratic: $V(x) = 3.55x^2 + 0.21x + 1.9$ **(b)** 91.7 million **13.** $f(x) = 9.02 + 1.03\ln x$ **15. (a)** $f(x) = 1.4734(0.99986)^x$ **(b)** Approximately 0.55 kg/m^3 **17. (a)** $f(x) = \frac{4.9955}{1 + 49.7081e^{-0.6998x}}$ **(b)** About 5 thousand per acre **19. (a)** $C(x) = \frac{0.94}{1 + 17.97e^{-0.862x}}$ **(b)** About 0.93 billion **21. (a)** $A(w) = 101w^{0.662}$

(b) [0, 20, 2] by [100, 700, 50]

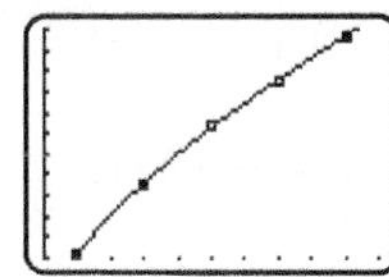

(c) About 11.2 lb

23. (a) 3 ft; after 5 years, the tree is 3 feet tall.
(b) $H(x) = \frac{50.2}{1 + 47.4e^{-0.221x}}$
(c) [0, 45, 5] by [0, 55, 5]

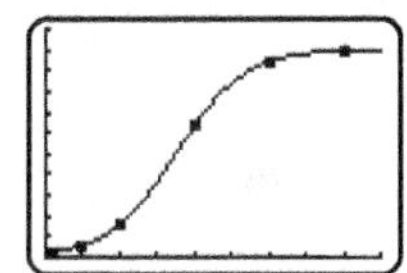

(d) About 17.4 yr **(e)** Interpolation

25. (a) The data are not linear.
[−2, 32, 5] by [0, 80, 10]

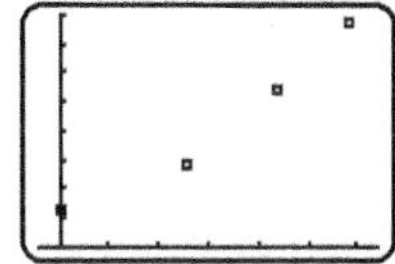

(b) $f(x) = 12.42(1.066)^x$ **(c)** $f(39) \approx 150$; fertilizer use increased but at a slower rate than predicted by f.

5.7 EXTENDED AND DISCOVERY EXERCISE (p. 469)

1. (a) $f(x) = 0.0904(0.844)^x$ (regression) or $f(x) \approx 0.128(0.777)^x$ (trial and error)
(b) About 4.6 min **(c)** Answers may vary.

CHECKING BASIC CONCEPTS FOR SECTION 5.7 (p. 470)

1. Exponential: $f(x) = 0.5(1.2)^x$
3. Logistic: $f(x) = \frac{4.5}{1 + 277e^{-1.4x}}$

CHAPTER 5 REVIEW EXERCISES (pp. 475–479)

1. (a) 8 **(b)** 0 **(c)** −6 **(d)** Undefined
3. (a) 7 **(b)** 1 **(c)** 0 **(d)** $-\frac{9}{2}$
5. (a) 2 **(b)** 1 **(c)** 2 **7. (a)** $\sqrt{6}$ **(b)** 12
9. $(f \circ g)(x) = \left(\frac{1}{x}\right)^3 - \left(\frac{1}{x}\right)^2 + 3\left(\frac{1}{x}\right) - 2$; $D = \{x \mid x \neq 0\}$
11. $(f \circ g)(x) = x$; all real numbers
13. $f(x) = x^2 + 3$, $g(x) = \sqrt{x}$ (answers may vary)
15. Subtract 6 from x and then multiply the result by 10; $\frac{x}{10} + 6$ and $10(x - 6)$ **17.** f is one-to-one. **19.** f is not one-to-one.
21.

x	6	4	3	1
$f^{-1}(x)$	−1	0	4	6

For f: $D = \{-1, 0, 4, 6\}$ and $R = \{1, 3, 4, 6\}$; for f^{-1}: $D = \{1, 3, 4, 6\}$ and $R = \{-1, 0, 4, 6\}$

23. $f^{-1}(x) = \frac{x + 5}{3}$

25. $(f \circ f^{-1})(x) = f\left(\frac{x+1}{2}\right) = 2\left(\frac{x+1}{2}\right) - 1 = x$;
$(f^{-1} \circ f)(x) = f^{-1}(2x - 1) = \frac{(2x - 1) + 1}{2} = x$

27. 1 **29.** $f^{-1}(x) = x^2 - 1, x \geq 0$;
for f: $D = \{x \mid x \geq -1\}$ and $R = \{y \mid y \geq 0\}$;
for f^{-1}: $D = \{x \mid x \geq 0\}$ and $R = \{y \mid y \geq -1\}$
31. $f(x) = 9500(0.65)^x$ **33.** $f(x) = 400(1.08)^x$
35. $C = 3$, $a = 1.05$, $r = 0.05$, or 5%
37. $C = 1$, $a = 0.23$, $r = -0.77$, or −77%
39. $C = 3$, $a = 2$
41. **43.**

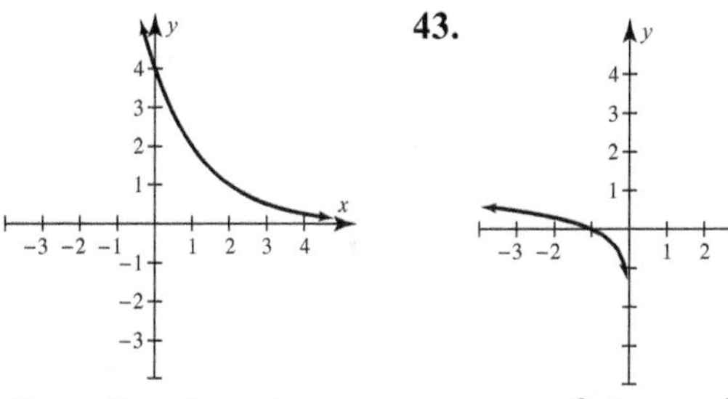

45. $C = 2$, $a = 2$ **47.** \$1562.71 **49.** 7.76%
51. $\ln 19 \approx 2.9444$ **53.** 3 **55.** −21 **57.** 2 **59.** 1
61. 2.631 **63.** $\log 125 \approx 2.097$ **65.** $10 \ln 5.2 \approx 16.49$
67. $-\frac{1}{\log 5} \approx -1.431$ **69.** $10 + \frac{\log(29/3)}{\log(0.78)} \approx 0.869$
71. $f(x) = 1.5(2)^x$ **73.** $f(x) = 20 - 2x$ **75.** $f(x) = 16\left(\frac{1}{2}\right)^x$
77. $10^{1.5} \approx 31.62$ **79.** $e^{3.4} \approx 29.96$ **81.** $\log 30x$
83. $\ln y - 2 \ln x$ **85.** $10^{1/4} \approx 1.778$
87. $\frac{100{,}000}{3} \approx 33{,}333$ **89.** 1 (extraneous −4)
91. The x-intercept is b. If $(0, b)$ is on the graph of f, then $(b, 0)$ is on the graph of f^{-1}.
93. (a) $f(x) = 3.2(4)^x$ **(b)** About 410 million bacteria per milliliter
95. About 22.37% **97.** About 3.6 ppm
99. (a) 11,022/mL **(b)** About 1.86 hr **101.** $h(x) = 15x$
103. $x \approx 2.74$; the fish weighs 50 milligrams at about 3 weeks. **105.** About 3.8 min
107. Logistic: $f(x) = \frac{171.4}{1 + 18.4e^{-0.0744x}}$
109. $a \approx 3.50$, $b \approx 0.74$

[0, 5, 1] by [0, 3, 1]

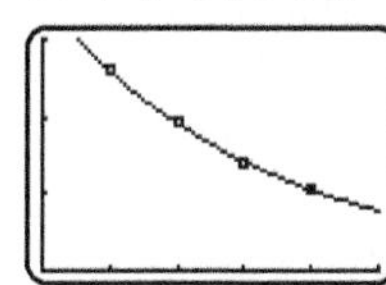

CHAPTER 5 EXTENDED AND DISCOVERY EXERCISES (p. 479)

1. The data points $(\ln x, \ln y)$ seem to be almost linear. Using linear regression gives the equation $y = 1.5x - 8.5$. Since $b = 1.5$ and $a = e^{-8.5} \approx 0.0002$, we get the power function $f(x) = 0.0002x^{1.5}$.
3. (a) 163.000000000000000000000000000232; it is not an integer.

CHAPTER 6: Systems of Equations and Inequalities

SECTION 6.1 (pp. 494–499)

1. 20; the area of a triangle with base 5 and height 8 is 20. **3.** 13 **5.** -18 **7.** $\frac{4}{5}$ **9.** $f(x, y) = y + 2x$
11. $f(x, y) = \frac{xy}{1 + x}$ **13.** $x = \frac{4y + 7}{3}$; $y = \frac{3x - 7}{4}$
15. $x = y^2 + 5$; $y = \pm\sqrt{x - 5}$ **17.** $x = 2y$; $y = \frac{x}{2}$
19. (2, 1); linear **21.** $(4, -3)$; nonlinear **23.** (2, 2)
25. $\left(\frac{1}{2}, -2\right)$ **27.** Consistent with solution (2, 2)
29. Inconsistent; no solutions

31.

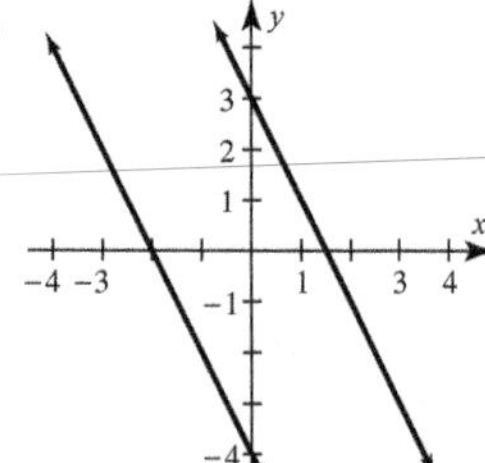

No solutions; inconsistent

33.

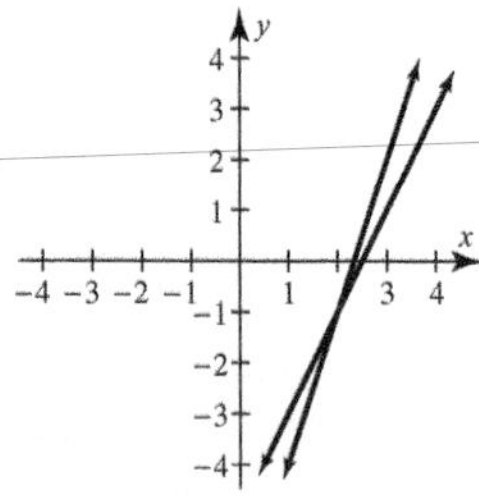

$(2, -1)$; consistent, independent

35.

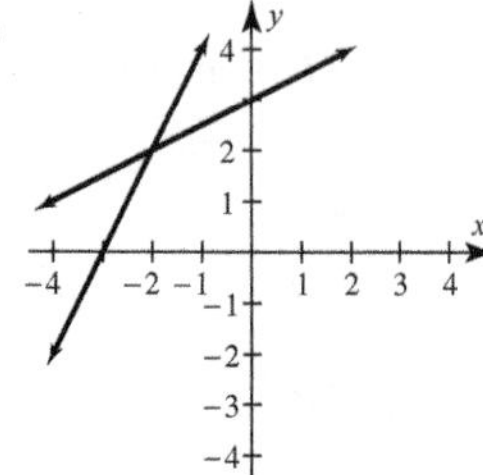

$(-2, 2)$; consistent, independent

37.

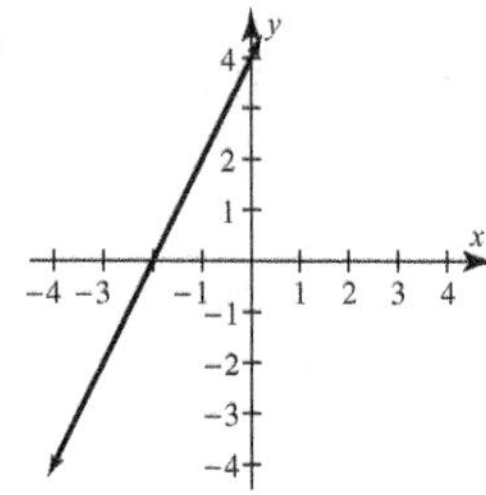

$\{(x, y) \mid 2x - y = -4\}$; consistent, dependent

39. $(-2, 1)$ **41.** $\left(\frac{1}{2}, 2\right)$ **43.** (6, 8)
45. $\{(x, y) \mid 3x - 2y = 5\}$ **47.** No solutions **49.** (4, 3)
51. $(-2, 4)$, (0, 0) **53.** (2, 4), (4, 2) **55.** (2, 4), $(-2, -4)$
57. No real solutions **59.** $\{(x, y) \mid 2x^2 - y = 5\}$
61. $(-2, 0)$, (2, 0) **63.** $(-2, -2)$, (0, 0), (2, 2)
65. $x - y = 2$, $2x + 2y = 38$, where x is width and y is height; 10.5 in. wide, 8.5 in. high
67. $x + y = 75$, $4x + 7y = 456$, where x is the number of child tickets and y is the number of adult tickets; 23 child tickets, 52 adult tickets **69.** $l = 7$, $w = 5$ **71.** (14, 6); consistent, independent **73.** (1, 3); consistent, independent
75. $\{(x, y) \mid x + y = 500\}$; consistent, dependent
77. No solutions; inconsistent
79. $\left(-\frac{11}{7}, \frac{12}{7}\right)$; consistent, independent
81. $(2, -4)$ **83.** $\{(x, y) \mid 7x - 3y = -17\}$
85. No solutions **87.** (10, 20) **89.** (2, 1)
91. $(-5, -4)$ **93.** (3, 3), $(-3, 3)$
95. (4, 3), $(-4, 3)$, (3, 4), $(-3, 4)$ **97.** (2, 0), $(-2, 0)$
99. $(-\sqrt{8}, -\sqrt{8})$, $(\sqrt{8}, \sqrt{8})$ **101.** (6, 2), $(-2, -6)$
103. $(1, -1)$ **105.** (1, 2)
107. $(-1.588, 0.239)$, (0.164, 1.487), $(1.924, -0.351)$
109. (1.220, 0.429) **111.** $(0.714, -0.169)$
113. **(a)** $x + y = 670$, $x - y = 98$
(b) (384, 286) **(c)** Consistent; independent
115. $W_1 = \frac{300}{1 + \sqrt{3}} \approx 109.8$ lb,
$W_2 = \frac{300\sqrt{3}}{\sqrt{6} + \sqrt{2}} \approx 134.5$ lb
117. $r \approx 1.538$ in., $h \approx 6.724$ in.
119. 12 by 12 by 4 in. or 9.10 by 9.10 by 6.96 in.
121. **(a)** $x + y = 11{,}693$, $x - y = 437$
(b) & (c) (6065, 5628)
123. **(a)** $x + y = 3000$, $0.08x + 0.10y = 264$
(b) \$1800 at 8%; \$1200 at 10%
125. There are no solutions. If loans totaling \$3000 are at 10%, then the interest must be \$300.
127. Airplane: 520 mi/hr; wind speed: 40 mi/hr
129. **(a)** $l = 13$ ft, $w = 7$ ft **(b)** $A = 20w - w^2$
(c) 100 ft^2; a square pen will provide the largest area.
131. **(a)** First model: about 245 lb; second model: about 253 lb **(b)** Models agree when $h \approx 65.96$ in.
(c) First model: 7.46 lb; second model: 7.93 lb
133. About 1.77 m^2 **135.** $S(60, 157.48) \approx 1.6$ m^2
137. 0.51 **139.** 32.4 **141.** Approximately 10,823 watts
143. Approximately 2.54 cords
145. $S(w, h) = 0.0101w^{0.425}h^{0.725}$

SECTION 6.2 (pp. 507–510)

1.

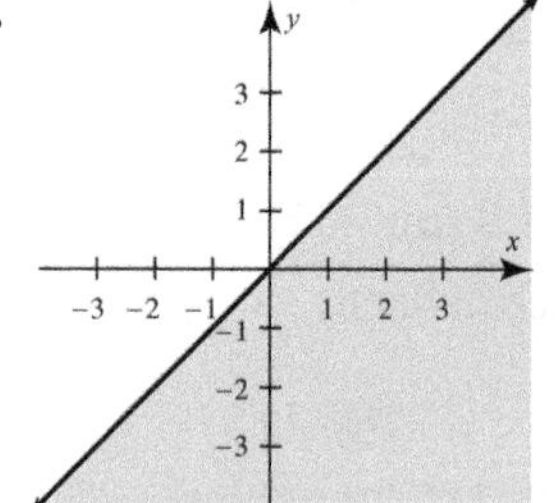

3.

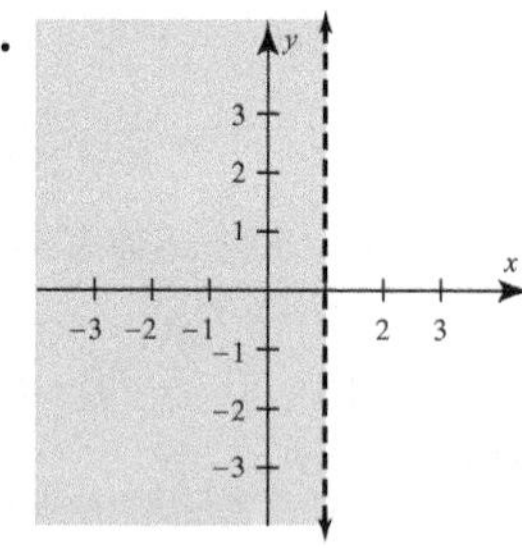

5.

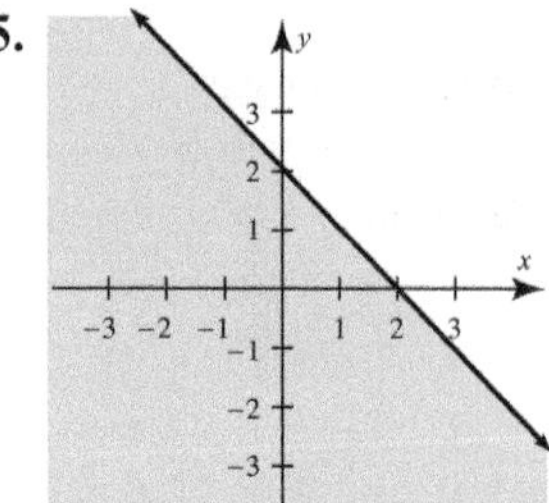

7.

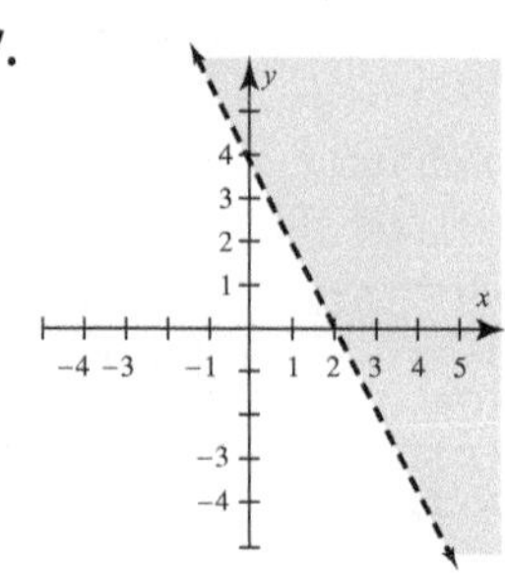

9.

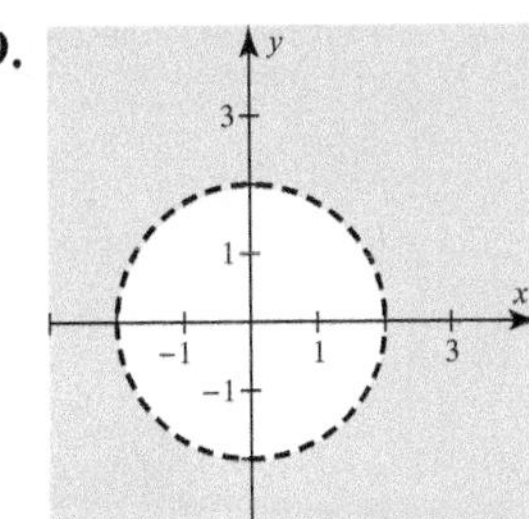

11.

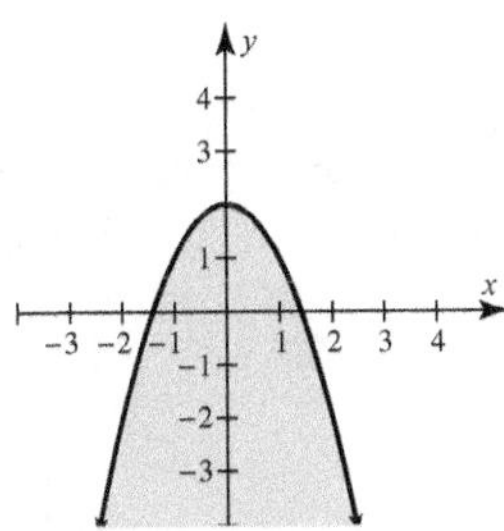

13. c; (2, 3) (answers may vary)
15. d; $(-1, -1)$ (answers may vary)

17. (0, 2)
(answers may vary)

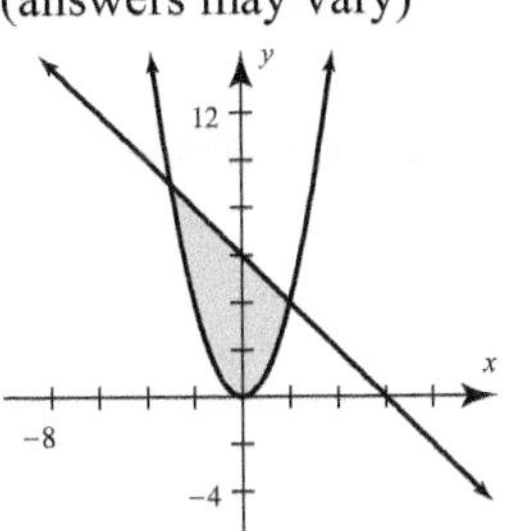

19. (0, 0)
(answers may vary)

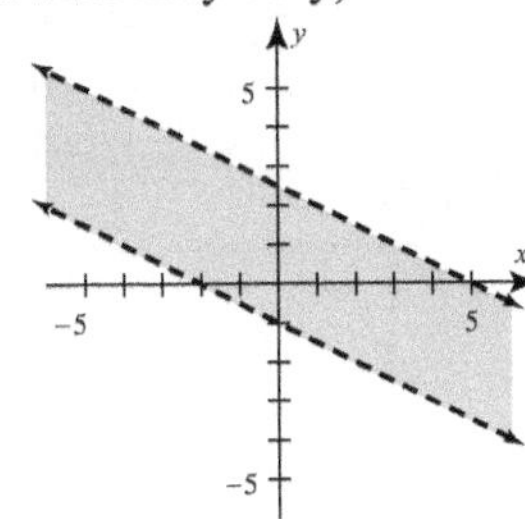

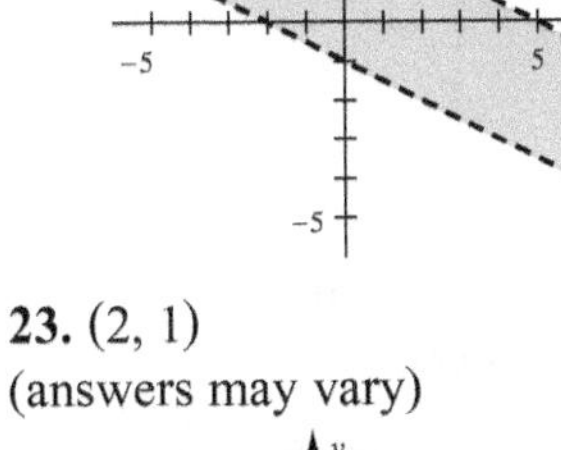

21. $(-1, 1)$
(answers may vary)

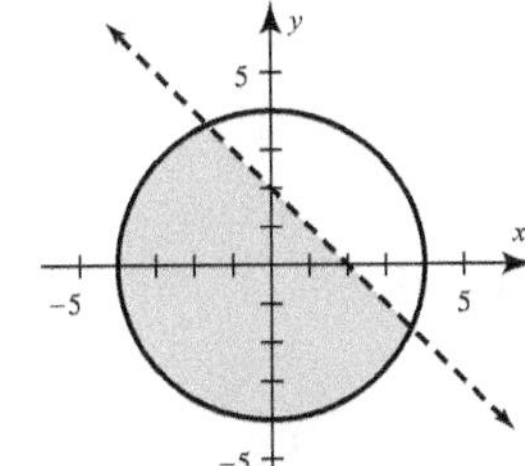

23. (2, 1)
(answers may vary)

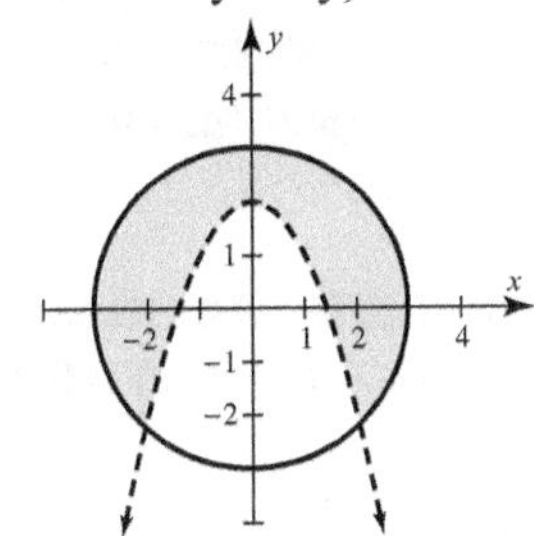

25.

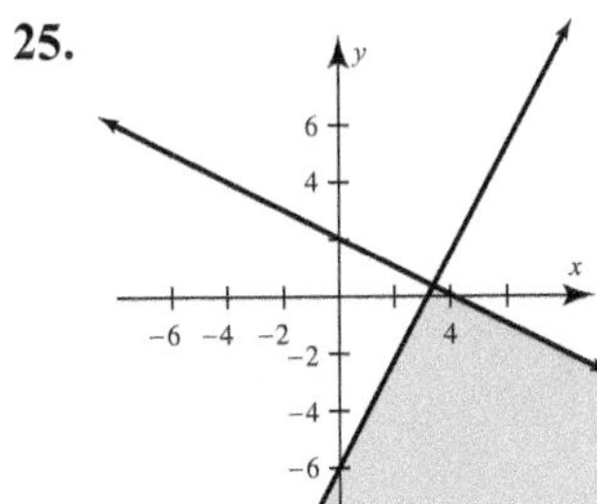

27.

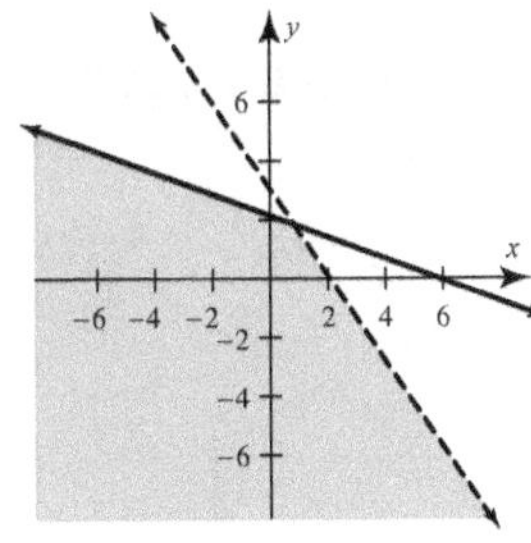

29.

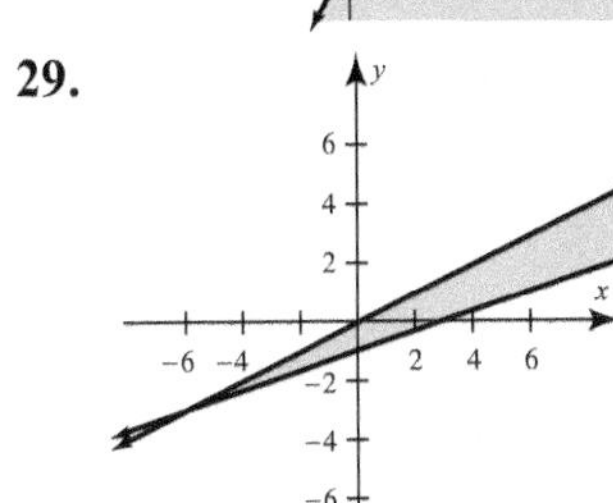

31.

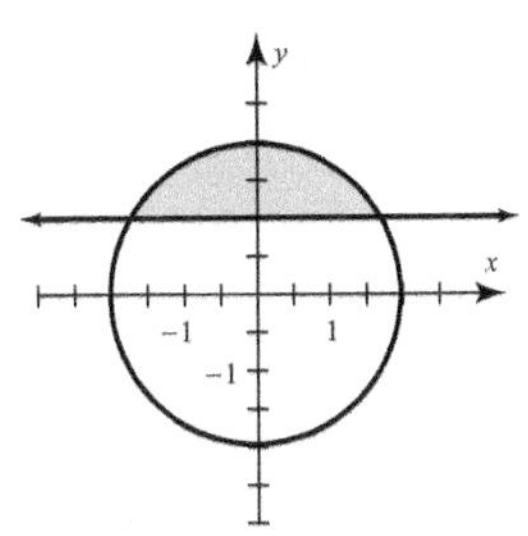

33.

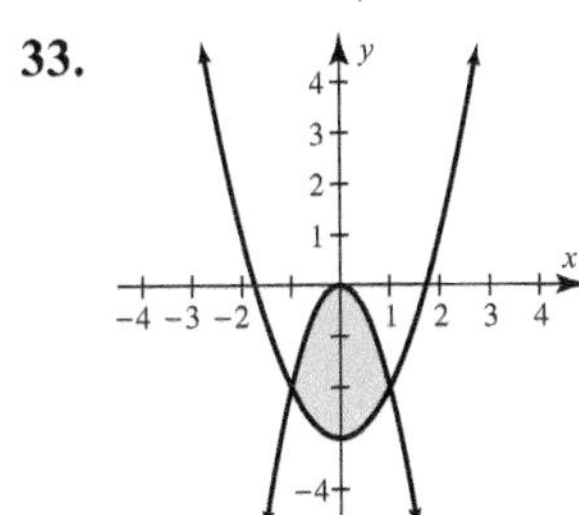

35.

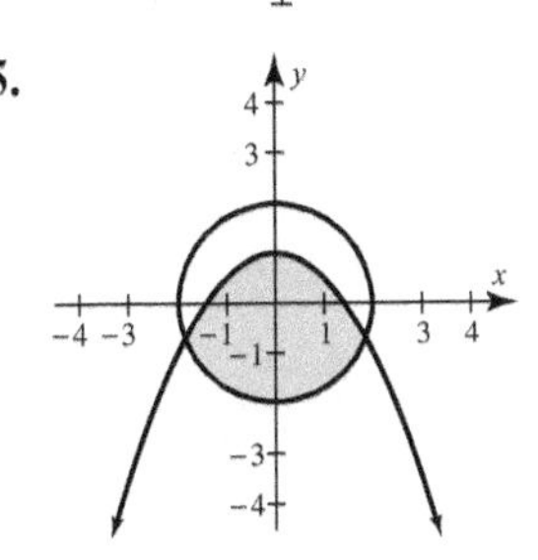

37. Jitters **39.** 180 pounds or more
41. $x = 300, y = 350$
43. This individual weighs less than recommended for his or her height.
45. $25h - 7w \le 800,\ 5h - w \ge 170$

47.

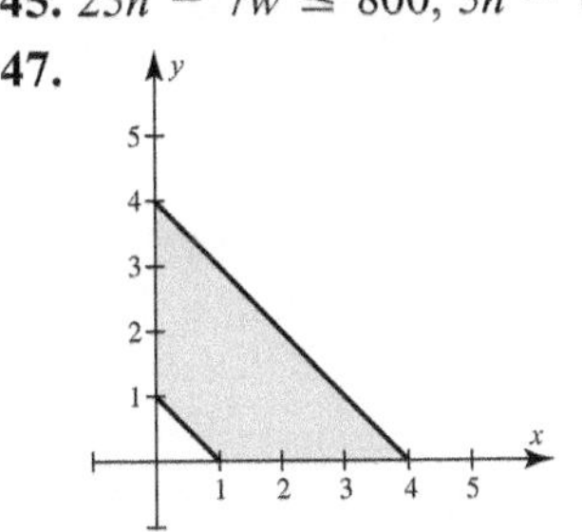

49.

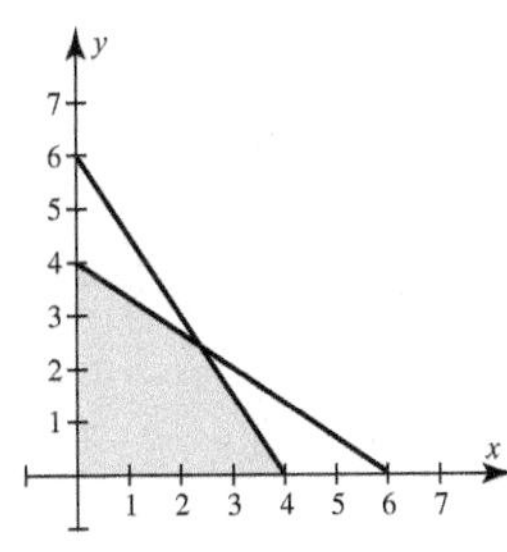

51. Maximum: 65; minimum: 8
53. Maximum: 66; minimum: 3
55. Maximum: 100; minimum: 0
57. $x + y \le 4, x \ge 0, y \ge 0$
59. Minimum: 6
61. Maximum: $z = 56$; minimum: $z = 24$
63. 25 radios, 30 CD players
65. 2.4 units of Brand A, 1.2 units of Brand B
67. \$600 **69.** Part X: 9, part Y: 4

CHECKING BASIC CONCEPTS FOR SECTIONS 6.1 AND 6.2 (p. 510)

1. $d(13, 18) = 20$ **3.** $y = \pm\sqrt{z - x^2}$

5.

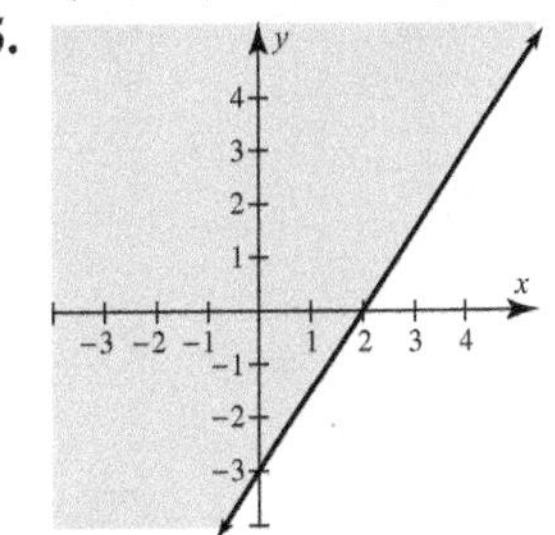

7. (a) $x + y = 220,\ 4.5x - y = 0$
(b) (40, 180); in 2010 40 million HDTVs were sold with plasma screens and 180 million were sold with LCD screens.

SECTION 6.3 (pp. 519–520)

1. No **3.** 2 **5.** Dependent
7. $(0, 2, -2)$ is not, but $(-1, 3, -2)$ is a solution.
9. Both are solutions. **11.** (1, 2, 3) **13.** (1, 0, 1)
15. $\left(\frac{1}{2}, \frac{1}{2}, -2\right)$ **17.** $\left(\frac{z+3}{2}, \frac{-z+3}{2}, z\right)$
19. No solutions **21.** $\left(-\frac{5}{2}, -2, 4\right)$ **23.** No solutions
25. $\left(-\frac{1}{2}, \frac{1}{2}, -\frac{1}{2}\right)$ **27.** $\left(\frac{-5z+18}{13}, \frac{-6z+19}{13}, z\right)$
29. $\left(8, -11, -\frac{1}{2}\right)$ **31.** $(2, 3, -4)$
33. 120 child, 280 student, and 100 adult tickets
35. No solutions; at least one student was charged incorrectly.
37. (a)
$$\begin{aligned} x + y + z &= 180 \\ x \quad\; - z &= 25 \\ -x + y + z &= 30 \end{aligned}$$
(b) 75°, 55°, 50°

39. \$2500 at 5%, \$7500 at 7%, \$10,000 at 10%
41. (a) $N + P + K = 80$
$N + P - K = 8$
$9P - K = 0$
(b) (40, 4, 36); 40 lb of nitrogen, 4 lb of phosphorus, 36 lb of potassium

SECTION 6.4 (pp. 533–536)

1. 3×1 **3.** 2×2 **5.** 3×2

7. Dimension: 2×3
$$\left[\begin{array}{rr|r} 5 & -2 & 3 \\ -1 & 3 & -1 \end{array}\right]$$

9. Dimension: 3×4
$$\left[\begin{array}{rrr|r} -3 & 2 & 1 & -4 \\ 5 & 0 & -1 & 9 \\ 1 & -3 & -6 & -9 \end{array}\right]$$

11. $3x + 2y = 4$
$y = 5$

13. $3x + y + 4z = 0$
$5y + 8z = -1$
$-7z = 1$

15. (a) Yes **(b)** No **(c)** Yes **17.** $(5, -1)$ **19.** $(2, 0)$
21. $(2, 3, 1)$ **23.** $(3 - 3z, 1 + 2z, z)$ **25.** No solutions

27. $\left[\begin{array}{rrr|r} 1 & -2 & 3 & 5 \\ -3 & 5 & 3 & 2 \\ 1 & 2 & 1 & -2 \end{array}\right]$ **29.** $\left[\begin{array}{rrr|r} 1 & -1 & 1 & 2 \\ 0 & 1 & -1 & 2 \\ 0 & 8 & -1 & 3 \end{array}\right]$

31. $(-17, 10)$ **33.** $(0, 2, -1)$ **35.** $(-1, 2, 4)$
37. $(3, 2, 1)$ **39.** No solutions
41. $\left(-1 - z, \frac{9 - 5z}{2}, z\right)$ **43.** $(1, 1, 1)$
45. $\left(\frac{1}{2}, -\frac{1}{2}, 4\right)$ **47.** $(-2, 5, -1)$
49. No solutions **51.** $(-1, -2, 3)$
53. $\left(\frac{3z + 1}{7}, \frac{11z - 15}{7}, z\right)$ **55.** $(12, 3)$
57. $\left(-2, 4, \frac{1}{2}\right)$ **59.** $(4 - 2z, z - 3, z)$
61. No solutions **63.** $(3, 2)$ **65.** $(-2, 1, 3)$
67. $(-2, 5, 7)$ **69.** No solutions
71. $(-9.226, -9.167, 2.440)$
73. $(5.211, 3.739, -4.655)$
75. $(7.993, 1.609, -0.401)$
77. Pump 1: 12 hours; pumps 2 and 3: 24 hours
79. (a) $F = 0.5714N + 0.4571R - 2014$ **(b)** \$5700
81. $(3.53, 1.62, 1.91)$
83. (a) $x + y + z = 5000$
$x + y - z = 0$
$0.08x + 0.11y + 0.14z = 595,$
where x is amount invested at 8%, y is amount invested at 11%, and z is amount invested at 14%
(b) \$1000 at 8%; \$1500 at 11%; \$2500 at 14%
85. (a) At intersection A, incoming traffic is equal to $x + 5$. The outgoing traffic is given by $y + 7$. Therefore, $x + 5 = y + 7$. The other equations can be justified in a similar way.
(b) The three equations can be written as
$x - y = 2$
$x - z = 3$
$y - z = 1$
The solution can be written as $\{(z + 3, z + 1, z) \mid z \geq 0\}$.
(c) There are infinitely many solutions, since some cars could be driving around the block continually.

87. (a) $a + b + c = 3$
$25a + 5b + c = 29$
$36a + 6b + c = 40$
(b) $f(x) = 0.9x^2 + 1.1x + 1$
(c) $[-0.5, 10, 1]$ by $[-5, 90, 10]$

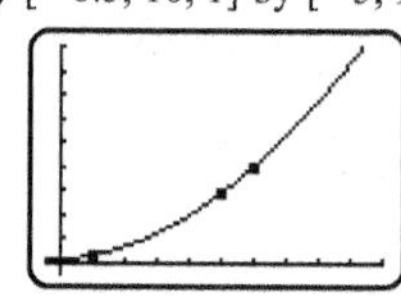

(d) After 9 quarters predicted sales are $f(9) = 83.8$ million (answers may vary).
89. (a) $1990^2a + 1990b + c = 11$
$2010^2a + 2010b + c = 10$
$2030^2a + 2030b + c = 6$
(b) $f(x) = -0.00375x^2 + 14.95x - 14{,}889.125$
(c) $[1985, 2035, 5]$ by $[5, 12, 1]$

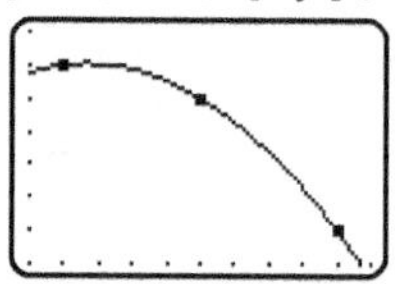

(d) In 2015 the predicted ratio is $f(2015) \approx 9.3$ (answers may vary).

6.4 EXTENDED AND DISCOVERY EXERCISES (p. 536)

1. $(1, -1, 2, 0)$

CHECKING BASIC CONCEPTS FOR SECTIONS 6.3 AND 6.4 (p. 536)

1. (a) $(3, 2, -1)$ **(b)** $\left(\frac{4 - 5z}{3}, \frac{5 - z}{3}, z\right)$ **(c)** No solutions
3. $(2, -1, 0)$

SECTION 6.5 (pp. 547–551)

1. (a) $a_{12} = 3, b_{32} = 1, b_{22} = 0$ **(b)** -2 **(c)** $x = 3$
3. $x = 1, y = 1$ **5.** Not possible

7. (a) $A + B = \begin{bmatrix} 3 & 3 \\ 3 & 3 \end{bmatrix}$ **(b)** $B + A = \begin{bmatrix} 3 & 3 \\ 3 & 3 \end{bmatrix}$

(c) $A - B = \begin{bmatrix} 5 & -5 \\ -5 & 5 \end{bmatrix}$

9. (a) $A + B = \begin{bmatrix} 14 & 9 & -3 \\ 4 & -10 & 14 \\ 4 & 11 & 16 \end{bmatrix}$

(b) $B + A = \begin{bmatrix} 14 & 9 & -3 \\ 4 & -10 & 14 \\ 4 & 11 & 16 \end{bmatrix}$

(c) $A - B = \begin{bmatrix} -8 & -1 & 1 \\ -4 & 4 & -10 \\ -8 & -1 & 4 \end{bmatrix}$

11. (a) $A + B = \begin{bmatrix} 1 & -6 \\ 1 & 4 \end{bmatrix}$ **(b)** $3A = \begin{bmatrix} 6 & -18 \\ 9 & 3 \end{bmatrix}$

(c) $2A - 3B = \begin{bmatrix} 7 & -12 \\ 12 & -7 \end{bmatrix}$

13. (a) $A + B$ is undefined.

(b) $3A = \begin{bmatrix} 3 & -3 & 0 \\ 3 & 15 & 27 \\ -12 & 24 & -15 \end{bmatrix}$

(c) $2A - 3B$ is undefined.

15. (a) $A + B = \begin{bmatrix} 0 & -2 \\ -2 & 2 \\ 9 & -8 \end{bmatrix}$ **(b)** $3A = \begin{bmatrix} -6 & -3 \\ -15 & 3 \\ 6 & -9 \end{bmatrix}$

(c) $2A - 3B = \begin{bmatrix} -10 & 1 \\ -19 & -1 \\ -17 & 9 \end{bmatrix}$

17. $\begin{bmatrix} 0 & 2 \\ 13 & -5 \\ 0 & 1 \end{bmatrix}$ **19.** $\begin{bmatrix} 2 & 6 \\ 11 & -9 \end{bmatrix}$

21. $\begin{bmatrix} 7 & 4 & 7 \\ 4 & 7 & 7 \\ 4 & 7 & 7 \end{bmatrix}$ **23.** $A = \begin{bmatrix} 1 & 2 & 1 \\ 1 & 2 & 1 \\ 1 & 2 & 1 \end{bmatrix}$

25. $B = \begin{bmatrix} -1 & 1 & -1 \\ -1 & 1 & -1 \\ -1 & 1 & -1 \end{bmatrix}$, $A + B = \begin{bmatrix} 0 & 3 & 0 \\ 0 & 3 & 0 \\ 0 & 3 & 0 \end{bmatrix}$

27. $AB = \begin{bmatrix} -3 & 1 \\ -4 & 6 \end{bmatrix}$, $BA = \begin{bmatrix} 4 & 2 \\ 5 & -1 \end{bmatrix}$

29. AB and BA are undefined.

31. $AB = \begin{bmatrix} -15 & 22 & -9 \\ -2 & 5 & -3 \\ -32 & 18 & 6 \end{bmatrix}$, $BA = \begin{bmatrix} 5 & 14 \\ 20 & -9 \end{bmatrix}$

33. AB is undefined. $BA = \begin{bmatrix} -1 & -3 & 19 \\ -1 & 1 & -39 \end{bmatrix}$

35. AB and BA are undefined.

37. $AB = \begin{bmatrix} -1 & 15 & -2 \\ 0 & 1 & 3 \\ -1 & 14 & -5 \end{bmatrix}$, $BA = \begin{bmatrix} 0 & 6 & 0 \\ 6 & -5 & 9 \\ 0 & 1 & 0 \end{bmatrix}$

39. $AB = \begin{bmatrix} -1 \\ 6 \end{bmatrix}$, BA is undefined.

41. $AB = \begin{bmatrix} -7 & 8 & 7 \\ 18 & -32 & -8 \end{bmatrix}$, BA is undefined.

43. $AB = \begin{bmatrix} -5 \\ 10 \\ 17 \end{bmatrix}$, BA is undefined.

45. $\begin{bmatrix} -19 & 19 & 11 \\ 21 & -7 & -48 \\ -22 & 23 & -58 \end{bmatrix}$ **47.** $\begin{bmatrix} 83 & 32 & 92 \\ 10 & -63 & -8 \\ 210 & 56 & 93 \end{bmatrix}$

49. They both equal $\begin{bmatrix} 36 & 36 & 8 \\ -15 & -38 & -4 \\ -11 & 13 & 10 \end{bmatrix}$. The distributive property appears to hold for matrices.

51. They both equal $\begin{bmatrix} 50 & 3 & 12 \\ -6 & 55 & 8 \\ 27 & -3 & 29 \end{bmatrix}$. Matrices appear to conform to rules of algebra except that $AB \neq BA$.

53. $\begin{bmatrix} 0 & 0 & 1 & 1 \\ 1 & 0 & 0 & 0 \\ 1 & 0 & 0 & 1 \\ 1 & 1 & 1 & 0 \end{bmatrix}$

55. Person 2

57.

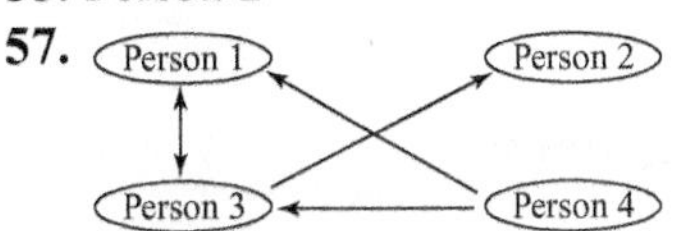

59. No one likes Person 4.

61. $B = \begin{bmatrix} 3 & 3 & 3 \\ 3 & 3 & 3 \\ 3 & 3 & 3 \end{bmatrix}$, $B - A = \begin{bmatrix} 3 & 0 & 3 \\ 3 & 0 & 3 \\ 3 & 0 & 3 \end{bmatrix}$

63. $A = \begin{bmatrix} 3 & 3 & 3 & 3 \\ 3 & 0 & 0 & 0 \\ 3 & 3 & 3 & 0 \\ 3 & 0 & 0 & 0 \\ 3 & 0 & 0 & 0 \end{bmatrix}$

65. (a) One possibility is $A = \begin{bmatrix} 3 & 3 & 3 & 3 \\ 0 & 0 & 3 & 0 \\ 0 & 3 & 0 & 0 \\ 3 & 3 & 3 & 3 \end{bmatrix}$.

(b) $B = \begin{bmatrix} 3 & 3 & 3 & 3 \\ 3 & 3 & 3 & 3 \\ 3 & 3 & 3 & 3 \\ 3 & 3 & 3 & 3 \end{bmatrix}$

67. (a) One possibility is $A = \begin{bmatrix} 3 & 0 & 0 & 0 \\ 3 & 0 & 0 & 0 \\ 3 & 0 & 0 & 0 \\ 3 & 3 & 3 & 3 \end{bmatrix}$.

(b) $B = \begin{bmatrix} 3 & 3 & 3 & 3 \\ 3 & 3 & 3 & 3 \\ 3 & 3 & 3 & 3 \\ 3 & 3 & 3 & 3 \end{bmatrix}$

69. (a) $A = \begin{bmatrix} 12 & 4 \\ 8 & 7 \end{bmatrix}$, $B = \begin{bmatrix} 55 \\ 70 \end{bmatrix}$

(b) $AB = \begin{bmatrix} 940 \\ 930 \end{bmatrix}$. Tuition for Student 1 is \$940, and tuition for Student 2 is \$930.

71. (a) $A = \begin{bmatrix} 10 & 5 \\ 9 & 8 \\ 11 & 3 \end{bmatrix}$, $B = \begin{bmatrix} 60 \\ 70 \end{bmatrix}$

(b) $AB = \begin{bmatrix} 950 \\ 1100 \\ 870 \end{bmatrix}$. Tuition for Student 1 is \$950, for Student 2 it is \$1100, and for Student 3 it is \$870.

73. $AB = \begin{bmatrix} 350 \\ 230 \end{bmatrix}$. The total cost of order 1 is \$350, and the total cost of order 2 is \$230.

75. $\begin{bmatrix} 0 & 0 & 1 & 1 \\ 1 & 0 & 0 & 1 \\ 0 & 0 & 0 & 1 \\ 0 & 0 & 1 & 0 \end{bmatrix}$ **77.** $\begin{bmatrix} 0 & 0 & 1 & 1 \\ 0 & 0 & 2 & 1 \\ 0 & 0 & 1 & 0 \\ 0 & 0 & 0 & 1 \end{bmatrix}$

79. There are two different 2-click paths from Page 2 to Page 3

6.5 EXTENDED AND DISCOVERY EXERCISES (p. 551)

1. Aquamarine is represented by (0.369, 0, 0.067) in CMY.

3. $\begin{bmatrix} R \\ G \\ B \end{bmatrix} = \begin{bmatrix} 1 \\ 1 \\ 1 \end{bmatrix} - \begin{bmatrix} C \\ M \\ Y \end{bmatrix}$

SECTION 6.6 (pp. 560–563)

1. Yes **3.** Yes **5.** No **7.** $k = 1$ **9.** $k = 2.5$ **11.** A **13.** A

15. $\begin{bmatrix} 3 & -2 \\ -1 & 1 \end{bmatrix}$ **17.** $\begin{bmatrix} 5 & 2 \\ 3 & 1 \end{bmatrix}$ **19.** $\begin{bmatrix} -\frac{1}{2} & \frac{5}{2} \\ 1 & -4 \end{bmatrix}$

21. $\begin{bmatrix} 0 & 1 & 0 \\ 0 & 0 & 1 \\ 1 & 0 & 0 \end{bmatrix}$ **23.** $\begin{bmatrix} -2 & 1 & -1 \\ -5 & 2 & -1 \\ 3 & -1 & 1 \end{bmatrix}$

25. $\begin{bmatrix} -10 & 3 & -5 \\ 4 & -1 & 2 \\ -3 & 1 & -1 \end{bmatrix}$ **27.** $\begin{bmatrix} -1 & -1 & -1 \\ -\frac{2}{5} & -\frac{1}{5} & -\frac{4}{5} \\ \frac{1}{5} & \frac{3}{5} & \frac{2}{5} \end{bmatrix}$

29. $\begin{bmatrix} -10 & 30 \\ -4 & 10 \end{bmatrix}$ **31.** $\begin{bmatrix} 0.2 & 0 & 0.4 \\ 0.4 & 0 & -0.2 \\ 1.4 & -1 & -1.2 \end{bmatrix}$

33. $\begin{bmatrix} 0.5 & 0.2 & 2.1 \\ 0 & 0.2 & 1.6 \\ 0 & 0 & -1 \end{bmatrix}$ **35.** $\begin{bmatrix} 0.5 & 0.25 & 0.25 \\ 0.25 & 0.5 & 0.25 \\ 0.25 & 0.25 & 0.5 \end{bmatrix}$

37. $\begin{bmatrix} 1.2\overline{6} & 0.2\overline{6} & 0.0\overline{6} & 0.0\overline{6} \\ 0.2\overline{6} & 0.2\overline{6} & 0.0\overline{6} & 0.0\overline{6} \\ 0.0\overline{6} & 0.0\overline{6} & 0.2\overline{6} & 0.2\overline{6} \\ 0.0\overline{6} & 0.0\overline{6} & 0.2\overline{6} & 1.2\overline{6} \end{bmatrix}$

39. $AX = \begin{bmatrix} 2 & -3 \\ -3 & -4 \end{bmatrix}\begin{bmatrix} x \\ y \end{bmatrix} = \begin{bmatrix} 7 \\ 9 \end{bmatrix} = B$

41. $AX = \begin{bmatrix} \frac{1}{2} & -\frac{3}{2} \\ -1 & 2 \end{bmatrix}\begin{bmatrix} x \\ y \end{bmatrix} = \begin{bmatrix} \frac{1}{4} \\ 5 \end{bmatrix} = B$

43. $AX = \begin{bmatrix} 1 & -2 & 1 \\ 0 & 3 & -1 \\ 5 & -4 & -7 \end{bmatrix}\begin{bmatrix} x \\ y \\ z \end{bmatrix} = \begin{bmatrix} 5 \\ 6 \\ 0 \end{bmatrix} = B$

45. $AX = \begin{bmatrix} 4 & -1 & 3 \\ 1 & 2 & 5 \\ 2 & -3 & 0 \end{bmatrix}\begin{bmatrix} x \\ y \\ z \end{bmatrix} = \begin{bmatrix} -2 \\ 11 \\ -1 \end{bmatrix} = B$

47. **(a)** $AX = \begin{bmatrix} 1 & 2 \\ 1 & 3 \end{bmatrix}\begin{bmatrix} x \\ y \end{bmatrix} = \begin{bmatrix} 3 \\ 6 \end{bmatrix} = B$ **(b)** $X = \begin{bmatrix} -3 \\ 3 \end{bmatrix}$

49. **(a)** $AX = \begin{bmatrix} -1 & 2 \\ 3 & -5 \end{bmatrix}\begin{bmatrix} x \\ y \end{bmatrix} = \begin{bmatrix} 5 \\ -2 \end{bmatrix} = B$

(b) $X = \begin{bmatrix} 21 \\ 13 \end{bmatrix}$

51. **(a)** $AX = \begin{bmatrix} 1 & 0 & 1 \\ 2 & 1 & 3 \\ -1 & 1 & 1 \end{bmatrix}\begin{bmatrix} x \\ y \\ z \end{bmatrix} = \begin{bmatrix} -7 \\ -13 \\ -4 \end{bmatrix} = B$

(b) $X = \begin{bmatrix} 5 \\ 13 \\ -12 \end{bmatrix}$

53. **(a)** $AX = \begin{bmatrix} 1 & 2 & -1 \\ 2 & 5 & 0 \\ -1 & -1 & 2 \end{bmatrix}\begin{bmatrix} x \\ y \\ z \end{bmatrix} = \begin{bmatrix} 2 \\ -1 \\ 0 \end{bmatrix} = B$

(b) $X = \begin{bmatrix} -23 \\ 9 \\ -7 \end{bmatrix}$

55. **(a)** $AX = \begin{bmatrix} 1.5 & 3.7 \\ -0.4 & -2.1 \end{bmatrix}\begin{bmatrix} x \\ y \end{bmatrix} = \begin{bmatrix} 0.32 \\ 0.36 \end{bmatrix} = B$

(b) $X = \begin{bmatrix} 1.2 \\ -0.4 \end{bmatrix}$

57. **(a)** $AX = \begin{bmatrix} 0.08 & -0.7 \\ 1.1 & -0.05 \end{bmatrix}\begin{bmatrix} x \\ y \end{bmatrix} = \begin{bmatrix} -0.504 \\ 0.73 \end{bmatrix} = B$

(b) $X = \begin{bmatrix} 0.7 \\ 0.8 \end{bmatrix}$

59. **(a)** $AX = \begin{bmatrix} 3.1 & 1.9 & -1 \\ 6.3 & 0 & -9.9 \\ -1 & 1.5 & 7 \end{bmatrix}\begin{bmatrix} x \\ y \\ z \end{bmatrix} = \begin{bmatrix} 1.99 \\ -3.78 \\ 5.3 \end{bmatrix} = B$

(b) $X = \begin{bmatrix} 0.5 \\ 0.6 \\ 0.7 \end{bmatrix}$

61. **(a)** $AX = \begin{bmatrix} 3 & -1 & 1 \\ 5.8 & -2.1 & 0 \\ -1 & 0 & 2.9 \end{bmatrix}\begin{bmatrix} x \\ y \\ z \end{bmatrix} = \begin{bmatrix} 4.9 \\ -3.8 \\ 3.8 \end{bmatrix} = B$

(b) $X \approx \begin{bmatrix} 9.26 \\ 27.39 \\ 4.50 \end{bmatrix}$

63. **(a)** (2, 4) **(b)** It will translate (2, 4) to the left 2 units and downward 3 units, back to (0, 1);

$A^{-1} = \begin{bmatrix} 1 & 0 & -2 \\ 0 & 1 & -3 \\ 0 & 0 & 1 \end{bmatrix}$ **(c)** I_3

65. $A = \begin{bmatrix} 1 & 0 & -3 \\ 0 & 1 & -5 \\ 0 & 0 & 1 \end{bmatrix}$ and $A^{-1} = \begin{bmatrix} 1 & 0 & 3 \\ 0 & 1 & 5 \\ 0 & 0 & 1 \end{bmatrix}$.

A^{-1} will translate a point 3 units to the right and 5 units upward.

67. (a) $BX = \begin{bmatrix} -2 \\ 0 \\ 1 \end{bmatrix} = Y$ **(b)** $B^{-1}Y = \begin{bmatrix} -\sqrt{2} \\ -\sqrt{2} \\ 1 \end{bmatrix} = X$.

B^{-1} rotates the point represented by Y counterclockwise 45° about the origin.

69. (a) $ABX = \begin{bmatrix} 2 \\ 2 \\ 1 \end{bmatrix} = Y$ **(b)** The net result of A and B is to translate a point 1 unit to the right and 1 unit upward.

$AB = \begin{bmatrix} 1 & 0 & 1 \\ 0 & 1 & 1 \\ 0 & 0 & 1 \end{bmatrix}$. **(c)** Yes **(d)** Since AB translates a point 1 unit right and 1 unit upward, the inverse of AB would translate a point 1 unit left and 1 unit downward. Therefore

$$(AB)^{-1} = \begin{bmatrix} 1 & 0 & -1 \\ 0 & 1 & -1 \\ 0 & 0 & 1 \end{bmatrix}.$$

71. A: \$10.99; B: \$12.99; C: \$14.99

73. (a)

$$\begin{aligned} a + 1500b + 8c &= 122 \\ a + 2000b + 5c &= 130 \\ a + 2200b + 10c &= 158 \end{aligned}$$

$a = 30, b = 0.04, c = 4$

(b) \$130,000 **75. (a)** $\left(\frac{17}{12}T, \frac{5}{6}T, T\right)$

(b) Service: 85 units; electrical: 50 units

CHECKING BASIC CONCEPTS FOR SECTIONS 6.5 AND 6.6 (p. 563)

1. (a) $A + B = \begin{bmatrix} 0 & 1 & 3 \\ -1 & 5 & 3 \\ 2 & 1 & 0 \end{bmatrix}$

(b) $2A - B = \begin{bmatrix} 3 & -1 & 0 \\ -2 & -2 & 3 \\ 1 & 8 & 0 \end{bmatrix}$

(c) $AB = \begin{bmatrix} 0 & -1 & 2 \\ 3 & -1 & -1 \\ -1 & 13 & 5 \end{bmatrix}$

3. (a) $AX = \begin{bmatrix} 1 & -2 \\ 2 & 3 \end{bmatrix}\begin{bmatrix} x \\ y \end{bmatrix} = \begin{bmatrix} 13 \\ 5 \end{bmatrix} = B; X = \begin{bmatrix} 7 \\ -3 \end{bmatrix}$

(b) $AX = \begin{bmatrix} 1 & -1 & 1 \\ -1 & 1 & 1 \\ 0 & 1 & -1 \end{bmatrix}\begin{bmatrix} x \\ y \\ z \end{bmatrix} = \begin{bmatrix} 2 \\ 4 \\ -1 \end{bmatrix} = B; X = \begin{bmatrix} 1 \\ 2 \\ 3 \end{bmatrix}$

(c) $AX = \begin{bmatrix} 3.1 & -5.3 \\ -0.1 & 1.8 \end{bmatrix}\begin{bmatrix} x \\ y \end{bmatrix} = \begin{bmatrix} -2.682 \\ 0.787 \end{bmatrix} = B;$

$X = \begin{bmatrix} -0.13 \\ 0.43 \end{bmatrix}$

SECTION 6.7 (pp. 570–571)

1. $\det A = 1 \neq 0$. A is invertible.
3. $\det A = 0$. A is not invertible.
5. $M_{12} = 10, A_{12} = -10$
7. $M_{22} = -15, A_{22} = -15$
9. $\det A = 3 \neq 0$. A^{-1} exists.
11. $\det A = 0$. A^{-1} does not exist.
13. 30 **15.** 0 **17.** −32 **19.** 0
21. 643.4 **23.** −4.484 **25.** $\left(-\frac{13}{9}, \frac{16}{9}\right)$ **27.** $\left(\frac{49}{2}, 19\right)$
29. (5, −3) **31.** (0.45, 0.67) **33.** 7 square units
35. 6.5 square units **37.** The points are collinear.
39. The points are not collinear.
41. $x + y = 3$ **43.** $2x + y = 5$

6.7 EXTENDED AND DISCOVERY EXERCISES (p. 571)

1. (1, 3, 2) **3.** (1, −1, 1) **5.** (−1, 0, 4)
7. $x^2 + y^2 - 4 = 0$ **9.** $5x^2 + 5y^2 - 15x - 5y = 0$

CHECKING BASIC CONCEPTS FOR SECTION 6.7 (p. 571)

1. $\det A = 19$; A is invertible.

CHAPTER 6 REVIEW EXERCISES (pp. 575–577)

1. $A(3, 6) = 9$ **3.** (3, 1) **5.** (1, −2)
7. (2, 3); consistent
9. $\{(x, y) \mid 2x - 5y = 4\}$; consistent
11. $\left(\frac{3\sqrt{2}}{2}, \frac{1}{2}\right), \left(-\frac{3\sqrt{2}}{2}, \frac{1}{2}\right)$

13. **15.** (2, 2) (answers may vary)

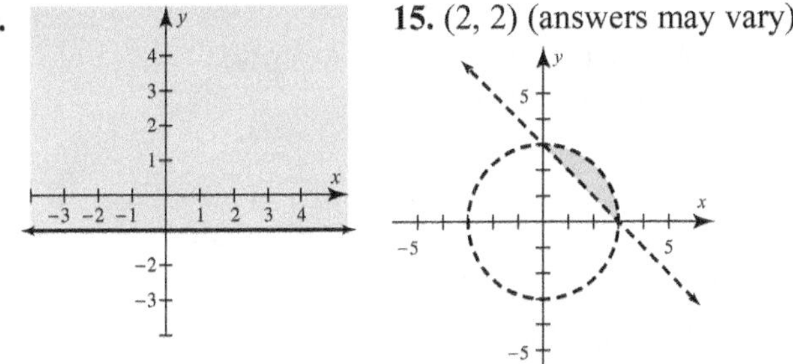

17. (−1, 2, 1) **19.** No solutions **21.** (−9, 3) **23.** (−2, 3, 0)
25. (1, −2, 3) **27. (a)** 5 **(b)** −10

29. (a) $A + 2B = \begin{bmatrix} 7 & 1 \\ -8 & 1 \end{bmatrix}$

(b) $A - B = \begin{bmatrix} -2 & -5 \\ 7 & -2 \end{bmatrix}$ **(c)** $-4A = \begin{bmatrix} -4 & 12 \\ -8 & 4 \end{bmatrix}$

31. $AB = \begin{bmatrix} -2 & -4 \\ 17 & 31 \end{bmatrix}, BA = \begin{bmatrix} 8 & -6 \\ -27 & 21 \end{bmatrix}$

33. $AB = \begin{bmatrix} 3 & 7 \\ -2 & 8 \end{bmatrix}, BA = \begin{bmatrix} 2 & -1 & 3 \\ 2 & 9 & -3 \\ 6 & 12 & 0 \end{bmatrix}$ **35.** Yes

37. $\begin{bmatrix} -1 & -2 \\ -1 & -1 \end{bmatrix}$

39. (a) $AX = \begin{bmatrix} 1 & -3 \\ 2 & -1 \end{bmatrix}\begin{bmatrix} x \\ y \end{bmatrix} = \begin{bmatrix} 4 \\ 3 \end{bmatrix} = B$

(b) $X = \begin{bmatrix} 1 \\ -1 \end{bmatrix}$

41. $(-0.5, 1.7, -2.9)$
43. $\det A = 25$ **45.** $\det A = -1951 \neq 0$. A is invertible.
47. $l = 11, w = 7$
49. Both methods yield \$1200 at 7%, \$800 at 9%.
51. A: \$11.49; B: \$12.99
53. 10.5 square units **55.** 4500

CHAPTER 6 EXTENDED AND DISCOVERY EXERCISES (pp. 577–578)

1. (a) $A^T = \begin{bmatrix} 3 & 2 & 4 \\ -3 & 6 & 2 \end{bmatrix}$ **(b)** $A^T = \begin{bmatrix} 0 & 2 & -4 \\ 1 & 5 & 3 \\ -2 & 4 & 9 \end{bmatrix}$

(c) $A^T = \begin{bmatrix} 5 & 1 & 6 & -9 \\ 7 & -7 & 3 & 2 \end{bmatrix}$

3. $f(x) = 2.6314x + 2.2714$
$[-1, 6, 1]$ by $[0, 18, 2]$

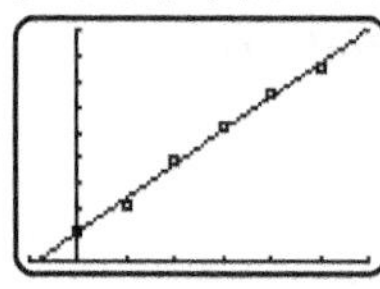

5. (a) UBNL is decoded as the word HELP.
(b) QNABMV is decoded as the word DIVIDE.

CHAPTERS 1–6 CUMULATIVE REVIEW EXERCISES (pp. 579–582)

1. 1.25×10^5; 0.00467
3. $D = \{x \mid -3 \le x \le 2\}$, or $[-3, 2]$;
$R = \{x \mid -2 \le x \le 2\}$, or $[-2, 2]$; $f(-0.5) = -2$
5. (a) $D = \{x \mid x \le 4\}$, or $(-\infty, 4]$
(b) $f(-1) = \sqrt{5}$; $f(2a) = \sqrt{4 - 2a}$
7. (a) $m = \frac{1}{2}$; y-int: -1; x-int: 2
(b) $f(x) = \frac{1}{2}x - 1$ **(c)** -2 **(d)** 2
9. x-int: -10; y-int: 4
11. (a) $\frac{1}{5}$ **(b)** $\ln 14 \approx 2.64$ **(c)** 5 (extraneous: 1)
(d) $-1, \frac{1}{2}$ **(e)** 0, 1, 2 **(f)** $\pm 2, \pm\sqrt{2}$ **(g)** $3 \pm \sqrt{7}$
(h) $-\frac{4}{5}, \frac{12}{5}$ **13. (a)** $\{x \mid x < \frac{9}{5}\}$, or $(-\infty, \frac{9}{5})$
(b) $\{x \mid -\frac{2}{3} < x \le \frac{7}{3}\}$, or $(-\frac{2}{3}, \frac{7}{3}]$
(c) $\{x \mid x \le -\frac{3}{2} \text{ or } x \ge 3\}$, or $(-\infty, -\frac{3}{2}] \cup [3, \infty)$
(d) $\{x \mid 1 \le x \le 4\}$, or $[1, 4]$
(e) $\{t \mid -1 < t < 0 \text{ or } t > 1\}$ or $(-1, 0) \cup (1, \infty)$
(f) $\{t \mid -2 < t \le -\frac{5}{3}\}$, or $(-2, -\frac{5}{3}]$

15. $f(x) = -2\left(x - \frac{3}{2}\right)^2 + \frac{7}{2}$

17. (a) (b)

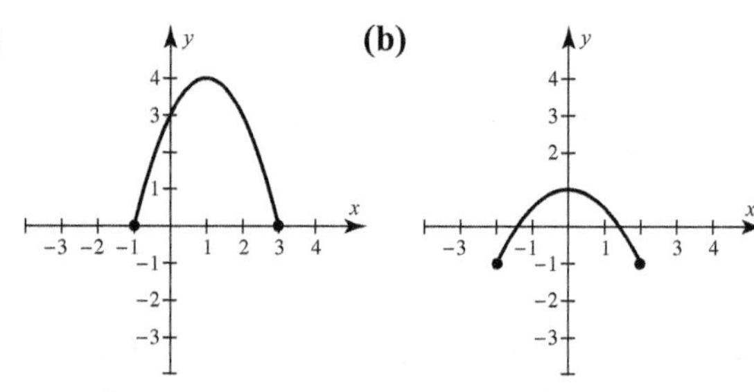

(c) (d)

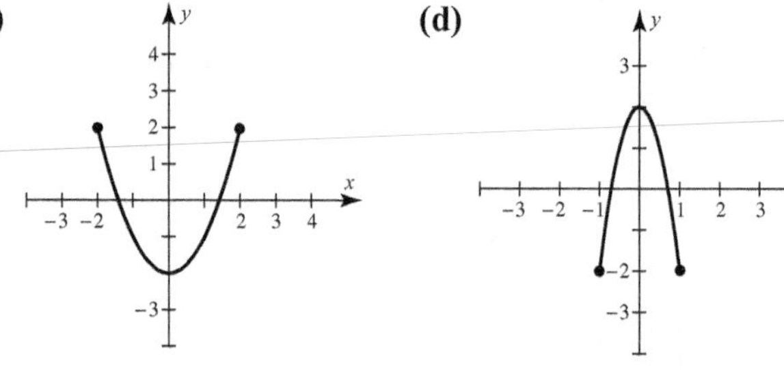

19. $f(x) = 2(x - 2)(x + 2)\left(x + \frac{1}{2}\right)$ or
$f(x) = (x - 2)(x + 2)(2x + 1)$
21. (a) 5 **(b)** Undefined **(c)** 2 **(d)** 0
23. (a) 8 **(b)** 0 **(c)** $(f - g)(x) = x^2 + 2x$
(d) $(f \circ g)(x) = x^2 - x - 4$
25. $f(x) = 9\left(\frac{2}{3}\right)^x$ **27.** $C = \frac{1}{2}, a = 2$
29. (a) 2 **(b)** 4 **(c)** -2 **(d)** 1
31. $\frac{1}{3}\log_2(x + 2) + \frac{1}{3}\log_2(x - 2) - \frac{1}{2}\log_2(x^2 + 4)$
33. 25 **35.** 10
37. $(-5, -4, 1)$ **39.** $\begin{bmatrix} \frac{3}{7} & -\frac{5}{7} \\ \frac{1}{7} & -\frac{4}{7} \end{bmatrix}$
41. $h = \frac{12}{\pi} \approx 3.82$ in.
43. (a) 16 ft/sec; 48 ft/sec **(b)** During the first second, the average speed is 16 ft/sec. During the next second, the average speed is 48 ft/sec. The object is speeding up.
(c) $32t + 16h$ **45.** 24 lb
47. (a) $C(x) = x(112 - 2x) = 112x - 2x^2$
(b) 21 or 35; the total cost is \$1470 when either 21 or 35 rooms are rented. **(c)** 1568; a maximum cost of \$1568 occurs when 28 rooms are rented.
49. (a) $f^{-1}(x) = \frac{9}{5}x + 32$
(b) f^{-1} converts degrees Celsius to degrees Fahrenheit.

51. $t = \dfrac{\ln\left(\frac{A}{P}\right)}{n \ln\left(1 + \frac{r}{n}\right)}$

53. \$2300 at 4%; \$2700 at 3%
55. $a = -3, b = 7, c = 2$

CHAPTER R: Reference: Basic Concepts from Algebra and Geometry

SECTION R.1 (pp. R-5–R-7)

1. Area: 105 ft^2; perimeter: 44 ft **3.** Area: 3500 m^2; perimeter: 270 m **5.** Area: $3xy$; perimeter: $6x + 2y$ **7.** Area: $2W^2$; perimeter: $6W$ **9.** Area: $W(W + 5)$; perimeter: $4W + 10$ **11.** 20 cm^2 **13.** 20 in^2 **15.** 3686.5 m^2 **17.** $6x^2$ **19.** $\frac{5}{2}z^2$ **21.** Circumference: $8\pi \approx 25.1$ m; area: $16\pi \approx 50.3$ m^2 **23.** Circumference: $38\pi \approx 119.4$ in.; area: $361\pi \approx 1134.1$ in^2 **25.** Circumference: $4\pi x$; area: $4\pi x^2$ **27.** $c = 61$ ft; perimeter: 132 ft **29.** $b = 12$ cm; perimeter: 30 cm **31.** $a = \sqrt{51} \approx 7.1$ mm; perimeter: $17 + \sqrt{51} \approx 24.1$ mm **33.** Area: 9 ft^2 **35.** Area: $\frac{11}{2}\sqrt{104} \approx 56.1$ in^2 **37.** Volume: 24 ft^3; surface area: 52 ft^2 **39.** Volume: 216 in^3; surface area: 240 in^2 **41.** Volume: $6x^3$; surface area: $22x^2$ **43.** Volume: $6xyz$; surface area: $4xy + 6xz + 12yz$ **45.** W^3 **47.** Volume: $36\pi \approx 113.1$ ft^3; surface area: $36\pi \approx 113.1$ ft^2 **49.** Volume: $43.7\pi \approx 137.3$ m^3; surface area: $41.0\pi \approx 128.8$ m^2 **51.** Volume: $\frac{1}{2}\pi \approx 1.6$ ft^3; side surface area: $2\pi \approx 6.3$ ft^2; total surface area: $\frac{5}{2}\pi \approx 7.9$ ft^2 **53.** Volume: $3456\pi \approx 10{,}857.3$ mm^3; side surface area: $576\pi \approx 1809.6$ mm^2; total surface area: $864\pi \approx 2714.3$ mm^2 **55.** Volume: 157.1 cm^3; side surface area: 122.7 cm^2 **57.** Volume: 12.6 ft^3; side surface area: 22.7 ft^2 **59.** Volume: 43.4 ft^3; side surface area: 57.2 ft^2 **61.** $x = \frac{20}{3} \approx 6.7$ **63.** $x = \frac{21}{2} = 10.5$

SECTION R.2 (pp. R-11–R-12)

1. No; $2^3 = 8$ and $3^2 = 9$. **3.** $\frac{1}{7^n}$ **5.** 5^{m-n} **7.** 2^{mk} **9.** 5000 **11.** 2^3 **13.** 4^4 **15.** 3^0 **17.** 125 **19.** -16 **21.** 1 **23.** $\frac{8}{27}$ **25.** $\frac{1}{16}$ **27.** $\frac{1}{64}$ **29.** 16 **31.** $\frac{64}{27}$ **33.** $\frac{8}{9}$ **35.** $6^{-1} = \frac{1}{6}$ **37.** $6x^3$ **39.** $10^8 = 100{,}000{,}000$ **41.** $\frac{5}{2}$ **43.** $8a^{-1}b^{-3} = \frac{8}{ab^3}$ **45.** $5^2 = 25$ **47.** $\frac{1}{a^6}$ **49.** $4x^2$ **51.** $\frac{2b}{3a^2}$ **53.** $\frac{3y^6}{x^7}$ **55.** $\frac{1}{5^3} = \frac{1}{125}$ **57.** $\frac{1}{y^8}$ **59.** $4^3y^6 = 64y^6$ **61.** $\frac{4^3}{x^3} = \frac{64}{x^3}$ **63.** $\frac{z^{20}}{2^5x^5} = \frac{z^{20}}{32x^5}$ **65.** $2ab$ **67.** $\frac{t^2}{16}$ **69.** $\frac{3a}{2b}$ **71.** $\frac{rs^3}{5t^5}$ **73.** $\frac{y^6}{9x^4}$ **75.** 1 **77.** $\frac{27t^9}{8}$ **79.** $\frac{n^3}{m^3}$ **81.** $\frac{a^{12}}{81b^4}$ **83.** $\frac{2y^2}{x}$ **85.** $\frac{1}{rt^3}$ **87.** y **89.** $\frac{125r^{15}}{t^9}$

SECTION R.3 (pp. R-18–R-19)

1. $8x^3$ **3.** $-3y^7$ **5.** $6x^2 + 8x$ **7.** $3x^2 + 3x$ **9.** $5x^2 + 13x - 2$ **11.** $10x^2y + 2y$ **13.** Degree: 2; leading coefficient: 5 **15.** Degree: 3; leading coefficient: $-\frac{2}{5}$ **17.** Degree: 5; leading coefficient: 1 **19.** $3x + 12$ **21.** $3x - 2$ **23.** $-0.5x + 1$ **25.** $-7x^4 - 2x^2 - \frac{9}{2}$ **27.** $2z^3 + z^2 + 2z - 4$ **29.** $-7x^3$ **31.** $-19z^5 + 5z^2 - 3z$ **33.** $-z^4 + z^2 + 9$ **35.** $3x - 7$ **37.** $6x^2 - 5x + 5$ **39.** $3x^4 + 4x^2 - 4$ **41.** $-3x^4 - 3x - 8$ **43.** $5x^2 - 25x$ **45.** $-15x - 5$ **47.** $5y + 10$ **49.** $-10x - 18$ **51.** $6y^2 - 18y$ **53.** $-20x + 4y$ **55.** $y^2 - 2y - 35$ **57.** $-2x^2 - 3x + 9$ **59.** $-2x^2 + 7x - 6$ **61.** $x^2 - \frac{1}{4}x - \frac{1}{8}$ **63.** $2x^4 + x^2 - 1$ **65.** $x^2 - xy - 2y^2$ **67.** $6x^3 - 3x^2 - 3x$ **69.** $-2x^5 + x^3 - 10x$ **71.** $6x^4 - 12x^3 + 3x^2$ **73.** $x^3 + 3x^2 - x - 3$ **75.** $6x^4 - 19x^3 + 4x^2 + 19x - 10$ **77.** $3x^3 - 2x^2 + 6x - 4$ **79.** $x^2 - 49$ **81.** $9x^2 - 16$ **83.** $4x^2 - 9y^2$ **85.** $x^2 + 8x + 16$ **87.** $4x^2 + 4x + 1$ **89.** $x^2 - 2x + 1$ **91.** $4 - 12x + 9x^2$ **93.** $3x^3 - 3x$ **95.** $4 - 25x^4$

SECTION R.4 (pp. R-26–R-28)

1. $5(2x - 3)$ **3.** $x(2x^2 - 5)$ **5.** $4x(2x^2 - x + 4)$ **7.** $5x^2(x^2 - 3x + 3)$ **9.** $5x(3x^2 + 2x - 6)$ **11.** $2r^3(3r^2 - 4r + 6)$ **13.** $8x^2y^2(1 - 3y)$ **15.** $6mn^2(3 - 2mn)$ **17.** $-2a(2a + b - 3b^2)$ **19.** $(x + 3)(x^2 + 2)$ **21.** $(3x - 2)(2x^2 + 3)$ **23.** $(z - 5)(z^2 + 1)$ **25.** $y(y + 2)(y^2 - 5)$ **27.** $(x^2 + 1)(2x - 3)$ **29.** $(x^3 + 2)(2x - 1)$ **31.** $(b - 3)(a + 2)$ **33.** $(x + 2)(x + 5)$ **35.** $(x + 2)(x + 6)$ **37.** $(z - 6)(z + 7)$ **39.** $(z + 3)(z + 8)$ **41.** $(4x + 3)(6x - 1)$ **43.** $(2x + 1)(3x - 2)$ **45.** $(1 - x)(1 + 2x)$ **47.** $(5 - 2x)(4 + 3x)$ **49.** $x(x - 1)(5x + 6)$ **51.** $3x(x + 3)(x + 1)$ **53.** $2(x - 5)(x - 2)$ **55.** $10t^2(t + 4)(6t - 1)$ **57.** $2m(m + 3)(2m - 1)$ **59.** $(x - 5)(x + 5)$ **61.** $(2x - 5)(2x + 5)$ **63.** $4(3x - 5)(3x + 5)$ **65.** $z^2(8 - 5z)(8 + 5z)$ **67.** $(2x - y)(2x + y)(4x^2 + y^2)$ **69.** Does not factor **71.** $(2 - rt)(2 + rt)$ **73.** $(x - 5)(x + 3)$ **75.** $-(z + 1)(z + 5)$ **77.** $(x + 1)^2$ **79.** $(2x + 5)^2$ **81.** $(x - 6)^2$ **83.** $z(3z - 1)^2$ **85.** $y(3y + 5)^2$ **87.** $(2x - 3y)^2$ **89.** $ab(3a - 2)^2$ **91.** $(x - 1)(x^2 + x + 1)$ **93.** $(y + z)(y^2 - yz + z^2)$ **95.** $(2x - 3)(4x^2 + 6x + 9)$ **97.** $x(x + 5)(x^2 - 5x + 25)$ **99.** $(2r^2 - t)(4r^4 + 2r^2t + t^2)$ **101.** $10(m^3 - 3n^2)(m^6 + 3m^3n^2 + 9n^4)$ **103.** $(4x - 5)(4x + 5)$ **105.** $(x - 4)(x^2 + 4x + 16)$ **107.** $(x + 8)^2$ **109.** $(x - 8)(5x + 2)$ **111.** $x(x + 2)(x^2 - 2x + 4)$ **113.** $8(2x + y)(4x^2 - 2xy + y^2)$ **115.** $(x + 1)(3x - 8)$ **117.** $a(a + 3)(7a - 1)$ **119.** $(x^2 + 3)(2x - 1)$ **121.** $x^2(x - 5)(2x + 5)$ **123.** $(x^2 + 1)(2x^2 + 3)$ **125.** $(x^2 + 1)(x + 3)$ **127.** $5(x^2 + 2)(x - 1)$ **129.** $(a + b)(x - y)$ **131.** $2(3x + 1)^2$ **133.** $-4x(x - 3)^2$ **135.** $(3x - 2)(9x^2 + 6x + 4)$ **137.** $-x(x + 2)(x^2 - 2x + 4)$ **139.** $(x - 1)(x - 2)(x^2 + x + 1)$ **141.** $(r - 2)(r + 2)(r^2 + 4)$ **143.** $(5x - 2a)(5x + 2a)$ **145.** $2(x - y)(x + y)(x^2 + y^2)$ **147.** $3x(3x - 1)(x + 1)$ **149.** $(z - 5)(z + 1)$

151. $3(x + 1)(x^2 - x + 1)(x - 3)(x + 3)$
153. $2(x + 2)^2(x + 4)^3(x + 3)$
155. $2(6x + 1)(8x - 3)^3(x - 2)$
157. $2x(5x - 1)^5(7x - 1)$

SECTION R.5 (pp. R-34–R-36)

1. $2x$ **3.** $x + 5$ **5.** $x + 4$ **7.** $\frac{1}{2x - 1}$ **9.** $-\frac{1}{4}$
11. $\frac{x}{x + 1}$ **13.** $a^2 - ab + b^2$ **15.** $\frac{1}{6}$ **17.** $\frac{2}{3}$ **19.** $\frac{1}{2}$
21. $\frac{4}{5}$ **23.** 1 **25.** $-\frac{1}{7}$ **27.** $\frac{37}{33}$ **29.** $\frac{7}{10}$ **31.** $\frac{55}{84}$
33. $\frac{3}{2x}$ **35.** 1 **37.** $\frac{x}{2x - 5}$ **39.** $x(x + 3)$
41. $\frac{(x - 1)(x + 5)}{2(2x - 3)}$ **43.** $\frac{4}{b^3}$ **45.** $\frac{3a(3a + 1)}{a + 1}$
47. $\frac{x^2}{(x - 5)(x^2 - 1)}$ **49.** $\frac{1}{x^2}$ **51.** $\frac{(x - 2)(x - 1)}{(x + 2)^2}$
53. 1 **55.** $\frac{15}{y^2}$ **57.** $\frac{1}{x}$ **59.** 36 **61.** $10a^3$
63. $z(z - 4)^2$ **65.** $(x - 2)(x - 3)^2$ **67.** $7(x + 1)$
69. $(x + 4)(x - 4)$ **71.** $2(2x + 1)(x - 2)$ **73.** $\frac{7}{x + 1}$
75. $-\frac{1}{x + 1}$ **77.** $\frac{x^2 - x - 1}{x(x + 4)}$ **79.** $\frac{-4x^2 + x + 2}{x^2}$
81. $\frac{x^2 + 5x - 34}{(x - 5)(x - 3)}$ **83.** $\frac{-2(x^2 - 4x + 2)}{(x - 5)(x - 3)}$ **85.** $\frac{x(5x + 16)}{(x - 3)(x + 3)}$
87. $-\frac{1}{2}$ **89.** $\frac{6x^2 - 1}{(x - 5)(3x - 1)}$ **91.** $\frac{(x + 1)^2}{(x - 1)^2(x + 3)}$
93. $\frac{x^2 + 4x - 2}{(x - 4)(x - 1)(x + 2)}$ **95.** $\frac{x^2 + x + 2}{(x - 2)(x + 2)^2}$
97. $\frac{3(x^2 - xy - y)}{(x - y)^2}$ **99.** $\frac{x^3 - x + 2}{(x - 1)(x + 1)}$ **101.** $\frac{9t^2 - 17t + 2}{t(t - 2)(t - 1)}$
103. -3 **105.** $-1, \frac{1}{3}$ **107.** -1 **109.** $-2, 1$ **111.** $\frac{5}{3}$
113. $\frac{x + 1}{x - 1}$ **115.** $\frac{x}{3x - 20}$ **117.** $\frac{2}{3 - x}$
119. $\frac{3(x + 1)}{(x + 3)(2x - 7)}$ **121.** $\frac{4x(x + 5)}{(x - 5)(2x + 5)}$ **123.** $\frac{ab}{2(a + b)}$

SECTION R.6 (pp. R-41–R-42)

1. $-5, 5$ **3.** $-\frac{4}{5}, \frac{4}{5}$ **5.** $-3.32, 3.32$ **7.** 12 **9.** 4.80
11. $\frac{2}{7}$ **13.** $-b$ **15.** 3 **17.** -2 **19.** $\frac{1}{3}$ **21.** b^3
23. 3 **25.** -2.24 **27.** 3 **29.** -4 **31.** 1.71
33. $-x^3$ **35.** $4x^2$ **37.** 3 **39.** -1.48 **41.** $\sqrt{6}$
43. $\sqrt{xy}$ **45.** $\frac{1}{\sqrt[5]{y}}$ **47.** $\sqrt[3]{27^2}$, or $(\sqrt[3]{27})^2$; 9
49. $\sqrt[3]{(-1)^4}$, or $(\sqrt[3]{-1})^4$; 1 **51.** $\frac{1}{\sqrt[3]{8}}; \frac{1}{2}$
53. $\frac{1}{\sqrt[5]{13^3}}$, or $\frac{1}{(\sqrt[5]{13})^3}$ **55.** 4 **57.** 4 **59.** 2 **61.** 16
63. $2^{7/6} \approx 2.24$ **65.** $\frac{2}{3}$ **67.** $4^{1/6} \approx 1.26$ **69.** $\frac{1}{2}$
71. $-\frac{1}{2}$ **73.** 2 **75.** $2^{3/2} \approx 2.83$ **77.** x^3 **79.** xy^4
81. xy^2 **83.** $\frac{y^2}{x}$ **85.** $y^{13/6}$ **87.** $\frac{x^4}{9}$ **89.** $\frac{y^3}{x}$ **91.** $y^{1/4}$
93. $\frac{1}{a^{2/3}}$ **95.** ab^2 **97.** $\frac{1}{k^2}$ **99.** $b^{3/4}$ **101.** $z^{23/12}$
103. $p^2 + p$ **105.** $x^{5/6} - x$

SECTION R.7 (pp. R-48–R-49)

1. 3 **3.** 10 **5.** 4 **7.** $\frac{3}{5}$ **9.** $\frac{1}{4}$ **11.** $\frac{x}{4}$ **13.** 3
15. 3 **17.** -2 **19.** $\frac{6}{z^2}$ **21.** $\frac{x}{2}$ **23.** $2x^2$ **25.** $2x\sqrt[4]{y}$
27. $6x$ **29.** $2x^2yz^3$ **31.** $\frac{3}{2}$ **33.** $5\sqrt{z}$ **35.** $\frac{1}{a}$
37. $10\sqrt{2}$ **39.** $3\sqrt[3]{3}$ **41.** $2\sqrt{2}$ **43.** $-2\sqrt[5]{2}$
45. $2n\sqrt{2n}$ **47.** $2ab^2\sqrt{3b}$ **49.** $-5xy\sqrt[3]{xy^2}$
51. $5\sqrt[3]{5t^2}$ **53.** $\frac{3t}{r\sqrt[4]{5r^3}}$ **55.** $\sqrt[6]{3^5}$ **57.** $2\sqrt[12]{2^5}$
59. $x\sqrt[12]{x}$ **61.** $\sqrt[12]{r^{11}t^7}$ **63.** $9\sqrt{3}$ **65.** $2\sqrt{x} - \sqrt{y}$
67. $9\sqrt[3]{6}$ **69.** $9\sqrt{7}$ **71.** $-2\sqrt{11}$ **73.** $5\sqrt[3]{2} - \sqrt{2}$
75. $-\sqrt[3]{xy}$ **77.** $3\sqrt{x + 2}$ **79.** $\frac{71\sqrt{2}}{10}$
81. $4\sqrt[3]{b}(5b - 1)$ **83.** $20\sqrt{3z}$ **85.** $(3ab - 1)\sqrt[4]{ab}$
87. $(n - 2)\sqrt[3]{n}$ **89.** 2 **91.** $x - 64$ **93.** $ab - c$
95. $x + \sqrt{x} - 56$ **97.** $\frac{4\sqrt{3}}{3}$ **99.** $\frac{\sqrt{5}}{3}$ **101.** $\frac{\sqrt{3b}}{6}$
103. $\frac{3 + \sqrt{2}}{7}$ **105.** $\sqrt{10} - 2\sqrt{2}$ **107.** $\sqrt{7} + \sqrt{6}$
109. $\frac{z + 3\sqrt{z}}{z - 9}$ **111.** $\frac{a + 2\sqrt{ab} + b}{a - b}$

APPENDIX C: Percent Change and Exponential Functions (pp. AP-25–AP-27)

1. **(a)** 0.35 **(b)** -0.0007 **(c)** 7.21 **(d)** 0.003
3. **(a)** -0.055 **(b)** -0.0154 **(c)** 1.2 **(d)** 0.0015
5. **(a)** 37% **(b)** -9.5% **(c)** 190% **(d)** 35%
7. **(a)** -12.1% **(b)** 140% **(c)** 320% **(d)** -25%
9. **(a)** 100% **(b)** -50%
11. **(a)** 2.36% **(b)** -2.31%
13. **(a)** 44.44% **(b)** -30.77%
15. **(a)** \$1800 **(b)** \$3300 **(c)** 2.2
17. **(a)** $-\$2200$ **(b)** \$1800 **(c)** 0.45
19. **(a)** $-\$4500$ **(b)** \$3000 **(c)** 0.4
21. $f(x) = 9500(0.65)^x$ **23.** $f(x) = 2500(1.05)^x$
25. $f(x) = 1000(0.935)^x$
27. $C = 8, a = 1.12, r = 0.12$ or 12%
29. $C = 1.5, a = 0.35, r = -0.65$ or -65%
31. $C = 1, a = 0.55, r = -0.45$ or -45%
33. $C = 7, a = e, r = e - 1$ or about 171.8%
35. $C = 6, a = \frac{1}{3}, r = -\frac{2}{3}$ or about -66.7%
37. $f(t) = 35{,}000(1.098)^{t/2}$; about 44,215
39. $f(t) = 1000(3)^{t/7}$; about 5620
41. $f(t) = I_0\left(\frac{2}{3}\right)^{t/2}$; about $0.418I_0$
43. $f(t) = 5000(4)^{t/35}$; \$6864.10
45. 10 years; \$4027.51 **47.** 3.5 years; \$1006.88
49. 2.8 years; \$3020.63 **51.** 1.75% **53.** 2% **55.** 1%
57. About 2.21% **59.** They are equal. **61.** \$7.39
63. About 2.56%

Photo Credits

First front endsheet: **upper left,** Pixelbully/Alamy **upper right,** Frio Canyon Photography/Alamy **lower left,** Shutterstock **lower right,** Peter Dean/Alamy ***Second front endsheet:*** **upper left,** Fotoflirt Creative/Alamy **upper right,** Corbis Premium RF/Alamy **lower left,** Shutterstock **lower right,** Fotolia **iv,** Sommai/Shutterstock **1,** PCN Photography/Alamy **2,** Sandy Young/Alamy **4,** Courtesy of Wendy Rockswold **10,** Courtesy of Wendy Rockswold **11 (top),** Courtesy of Wendy Rockswold **11 (bottom),** Pressmaster/Fotolia **12,** Courtesy of Wendy Rockswold **13,** Steve Hamblin/Alamy **26,** Leonid Tit/Fotolia **44,** David Pearson/Alamy **47,** Marc Xavier/Fotolia **72,** U.S. Fish and Wildlife Service **74,** Andrew Watson/Fotolia **75,** Fotolia **76,** Stefan Sollfors/Alamy **79,** Kevin Foy/Alamy **84,** Iain Masterton/Alamy **94,** Fotolia **112,** Frio Canyon Photography/Alamy **118,** Courtesy of Wendy Rockswold **119,** Courtesy of Wendy Rockswold **124 (left),** Vera Bogaerts/Shutterstock **124 (right),** EPA European Pressphoto Agency B.V./Alamy **126,** Fotolia **129,** Corbis Premium RF/Alamy **130,** Courtesy of Wendy Rockswold **132,** Courtesy of Wendy Rockswold **142,** Peter Dean/Alamy **148,** Stanca Sanda/Alamy **163 (top),** Tannen Maury/Newscom **163 (bottom),** Walter Iooss Jr./NBAE/Getty Images **164,** ZUMA Wire Service/Alamy **173,** Alex Segre/Alamy **180,** Fotolia **186,** Fotolia **193,** Paul Sakuma/AP Images **196,** Shutterstock **205,** Shutterstock **213,** Fotolia **214,** Ilene MacDonald/Alamy **220,** Shutterstock **225,** Shutterstock **239,** Fotolia **240,** Courtesy of Wendy Rockswold **243,** Shutterstock **251,** Shutterstock **259,** Shutterstock **268,** Shutterstock **275,** Shutterstock **291,** Shutterstock **297,** Shutterstock **299,** Jeff Greenberg/Alamy **314,** Corbis Premium RF/Alamy **329,** NASA **330,** Shutterstock **333,** Shutterstock **334,** Fotolia **335,** Courtesy of Wendy Rockswold **360,** Newscom **361,** Keith Shuttlewood/Alamy **364,** UpperCut Images/Alamy **369,** Courtesy of Wendy Rockswold **377,** Cultura Creative/Alamy **423,** Shutterstock **439,** NASA **447,** Shutterstock **448,** Shutterstock **449,** Alex Segre/Alamy **458,** Shutterstock **461,** Courtesy of Wendy Rockswold **480,** Pixelbully/Alamy **481,** Fotolia **499,** Shutterstock **514,** Alex Segre/Alamy **521,** David Young-Wolf/Alamy **537,** Everett Collection **538,** Cyberstock/Alamy **551,** MIRA/Alamy **564,** Aardvark/Alamy

Index of Applications

Index

Note: Page numbers preceded by AP indicate appendices; those preceded by R indicate the Reference chapter.

S

Psychiatric Mental Health Nursing

An Introduction to Theory and Practice

Psychiatric Mental Health Nursing: An Introduction to Theory and Practice, Second Edition drives comprehension through various strategies that meet the learning needs of students, while also generating enthusiasm about the topic. This interactive approach addresses different learning styles, making this the ideal text to ensure mastery of key concepts. The pedagogical aids that appear in most chapters include the following:

Learning Objectives

Each chapter includes learning objectives that help you to identify and discuss important concepts from the text. Learning objectives can also be found on the companion website at http://go.jblearning.com/mentalhealth.

Key Terms

Important terms and vocabulary are highlighted in the opening of each chapter and bolded throughout. The "www" icon directs you to the companion website http://go.jblearning.com/mentalhealth to see these terms in an interactive glossary and to use flashcards and word puzzles to master the definitions.

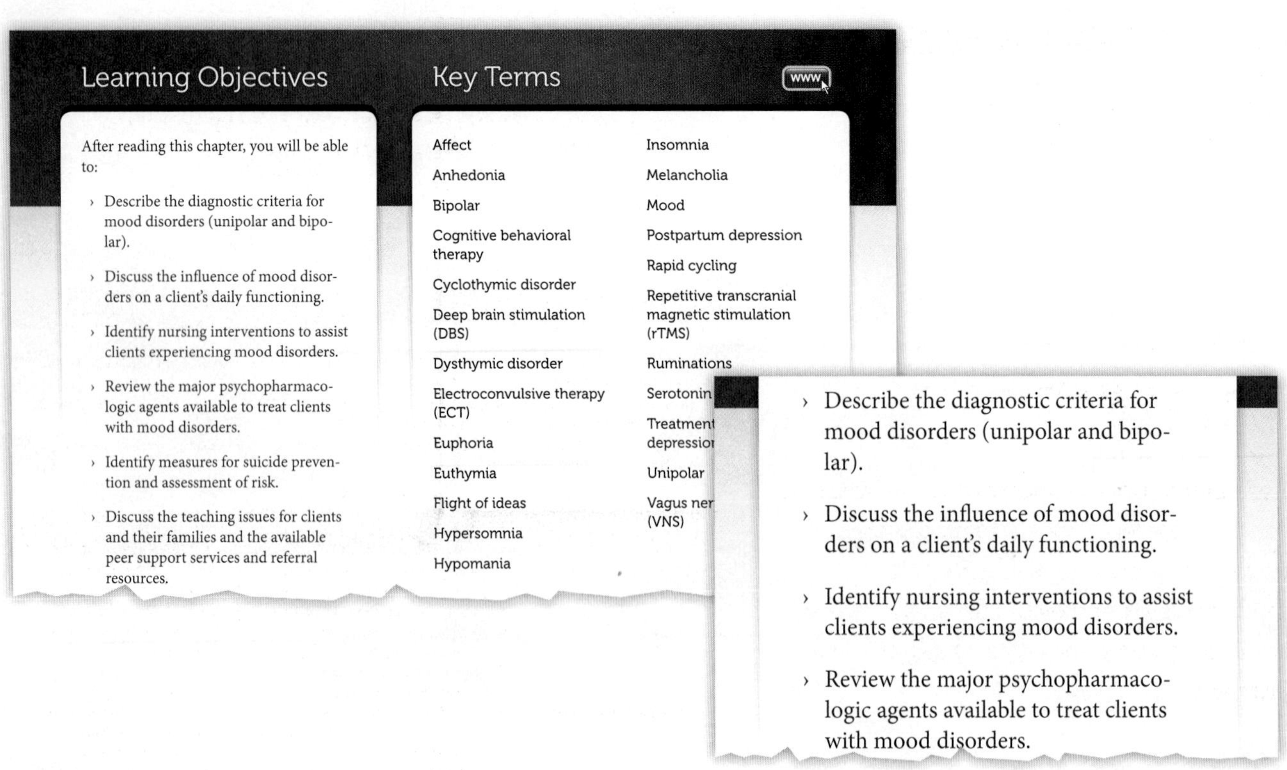
Learning Objectives
After reading this chapter, you will be able to:
› Describe the diagnostic criteria for mood disorders (unipolar and bipolar).
› Discuss the influence of mood disorders on a client's daily functioning.
› Identify nursing interventions to assist clients experiencing mood disorders.
› Review the major psychopharmacologic agents available to treat clients with mood disorders.
› Identify measures for suicide prevention and assessment of risk.
› Discuss the teaching issues for clients and their families and the available peer support services and referral resources.
Key Terms
www
Affect
Anhedonia
Bipolar
Cognitive behavioral therapy
Cyclothymic disorder
Deep brain stimulation (DBS)
Dysthymic disorder
Electroconvulsive therapy (ECT)
Euphoria
Euthymia
Flight of ideas
Hypersomnia
Hypomania
Insomnia
Melancholia
Mood
Postpartum depression
Rapid cycling
Repetitive transcranial magnetic stimulation (rTMS)
Ruminations
› Describe the diagnostic criteria for mood disorders (unipolar and bipolar).
› Discuss the influence of mood disorders on a client's daily functioning.
› Identify nursing interventions to assist clients experiencing mood disorders.
› Review the major psychopharmacologic agents available to treat clients with mood disorders.

http://go.jblearning.com/mentalhealth 

Critical Thinking Questions

Each chapter includes critical thinking questions that students can work on individually or in a group after reading through the material. The "www" icon directs students to the companion website http://go.jblearning.com/mentalhealth to delve deeper into concepts by completing these exercises online.

Critical Thinking Question 

When obtaining a medication history, why is it important to obtain information on medications for mood disorders, other medical conditions, and over-the-counter medications that a client may be taking?

Clinical Examples

By offering real-life examples that nursing students may encounter in practice, the subject matter becomes tangible and more applicable with clinical examples included in each chapter.

Clinical Example 

Fifty-eight-year-old Pearl has been living with bipolar I disorder since her mid-teens. Every few months she experiences significant mood fluctuations—periods of euphoria, increased energy, and greatly reduced sleep. She has been known to bake hundreds of cookies for local workers such as the police, firefighters, and postal workers, showing up at odd times of the day or night to distribute her baked goods. On her last admission to the crisis unit, Pearl took off all of her clothes and marched down the hallway singing, "Let Me Love You" while approaching other clients and staff in an overtly

Nursing Care Plans

These plans provide information on what type of care should be administered based on the nursing assessment, and they provide examples of care plans that should be given to patients based on their diagnoses.

Nursing Care Plan **Major Depressive Disorder**

Nursing Diagnosis 1: Risk for self-directed violence related to depressed mood, as evidenced by appearance, self-reporting, and yearning for death

Nursing Diagnosis 2: Self-care deficit related to lack of energy and interest in caring for oneself or family, as evidenced by unkempt appearance, lack of attention to self, and loss of weight

Nursing Diagnosis 3: Low self-esteem related to perceived role inadequacy, as evidenced by stated guilt regarding inability to care for children, home, or self

Expected Outcomes	Nursing Interventions	Evaluations
Short term:		
• Will take medication as prescribed.	• Administer prescribed medications such as escitalopram 20 mg, one every morning, and trazodone 50 mg, 1 hour after bedtime if unable to sleep. • Regularly review medication regimen and repeat medication education from the beginning of hospital stay.	• The client is able to correctly repeat information about taking her medication, is compliant with regimen, and can report changes in symptoms.
• Will remain free of self-harm.	• Demonstrate an empathetic, caring relationship with client, letting her know your concern for her safety and gentle optimism for her future progression.	• The client states she no longer wishes to be dead. "I want to be the mother for my boys." • She also states that her spiritual

The Pedagogy

Case Studies

Case studies encourage active learning and promote critical thinking skills in learners. Students can ask questions, analyze the situation they are presented with, and solve problems so they can learn how the information in the text applies to everyday practice online at http://go.jblearning.com/mentalhealth.

Suicide and Mood Disorders 431

CASE STUDIES Mr. M.

Mr. M. is a 31-year-old professor of Italian at a major university. He is single, lives alone, and his family lives out of state. He became depressed during the past year while he was applying for tenure. The psychiatrist he saw treated him with sertraline (Zoloft). The medication was very effective in relieving his depression, but after about 8 months, he became hypomanic with increasing disturbances in his behavior. Prior to this he had not experienced any signs of mental illness. He had received an award as an outstanding professor with an impressive list of publications to his credit.

Mr. M. was brought to the ER by his girlfriend and admitted to the crisis unit. His girlfriend noted that his behavior had been escalating for several weeks. She reported the following behaviors:

- He had slept only a few hours in the past week, experiencing high energy levels with no desire to rest.
- His behavior had become uncontrolled and potentially dangerous, including drinking much more than usual and driving recklessly.
- He had recently been reported for being too friendly with several female students and assistant instructors, with two women filing sexual harassment charges against him.

...day and declared that he was ...essage from God and that he ...ace to the world.

- He had also been spending money furiously, buying venture stocks with some inheritance money, and using his credit cards to buy Italian wines by the case to stock his wine cellar.
- He was calling old friends and colleagues on the phone at all hours of the night.

On the night he was brought to the ER, he was loud and intrusive to other patrons in a restaurant and demanded to be given the special attention deserved by someone of his notoriety. After only two drinks he started singing loudly and swinging around a decorative column. Four staff members struggled to get him out the front door. It was all his girlfriend could do to get him to the car. Against his wishes, she drove him straight to the hospital, yet upon arrival he did agree to sign for a voluntary admission.

The girlfriend told the staff before leaving that she was concerned for Mr. M., especially since he just learned that week that his tenure had been denied, but she was really getting weary of struggling with their relationship. Mr. M. appeared unshaven, with very wrinkled clothes, yet bursting with energy and unable to sit down for his intake interview.

Mr. M. had a *DSM-IV-TR*, Axis I diagnosis of bipolar I, most recent episode manic. Some nursing diagnoses that apply to this client are identified in the following nursing care plan.

CASE STUDIES Mr. M.

Mr. M. is a 31-year-old professor of Italian at a major university. He is single, lives alone, and his family lives out of state. He became depressed during the past year while he was applying for tenure. The psychiatrist he saw treated him with sertraline (Zoloft). The medication was very effective in relieving his depression, but after about 8 months, he became hypomanic with increasing disturbances in his behavior. Prior to this he had not experienced any signs of mental illness. He had received an award as an outstanding professor with an impressive list of publications to his credit.

Mr. M. was brought to the ER by his girlfriend and admitted to the crisis unit. His girlfriend noted that his behavior had been escalating for several weeks. She reported the following behaviors:

- He had also been spending money ... venture stocks with some inheritance ... his credit cards to buy Italian wines b... his wine cellar.
- He was calling old friends and collea... at all hours of the night.

On the night he was brought to the ER, ... intrusive to other patrons in a restaurant ... be given the special attention deserved b... notoriety. After only two drinks he start... and swinging around a decorative column... bers struggled to get him out the front d... girlfriend could do to get him to the car. ... she drove him straight to the hospital, ...

...d just because the client ...e taught about nutrition ...ake can greatly affect the Clients and family mem- ...d how to seek help from and their ongoing support ...se is often the practitioner ...ent and the needed com-

...uestion

...loyer that she or he has a bipolar disorder? How can such a decision impact the client's work situation?

Suicide and Mood Disorders

Suicide takes the lives of over 30,000 Americans a year—nearly twice the number of homicides—and worldwide, suicide is the leading cause of violent death, outnumbering homicide and war-related deaths. It is the 11th leading cause of death of all Americans; the 8th leading cause of death for all U.S. men, and the 3rd leading cause of death among young people 15–24 years of age. More than four times as many men as women die by suicide, although women attempt suicide three times as often as men. Native American youth are 3–4 times more likely to die by suicide than white or black youth. There are 25 attempts for every completed suicide, with approxi-

Evidence-Based Practice Boxes

Learn how EBP impacts psychiatric-mental health nursing with these in-text features.

Evidence-Based Practice

Among persons with mental illness, the prevalence of smoking is twice that of the general public, and in addition, mental illness is associated higher levels of smoking among smokers (Lawrence, Mitrou, & Zubrick, 2009). Smoking may well contribute to the significantly shortened life expectancy among persons with mental illness. Given the serious health consequences associated with smoking, the American Psychiatric Nurses Association (APNA) has taken the position that failure by nurses to act on tobacco dependence equals harm (2008). The standard of care is that nurses assess and offer tobacco dependence treatment to all consumers and document the approach and outcome (APNA, 2010).

The U.S. Public Health Service provides evidence-based approaches for use by health professionals to assist clients with smoking cessation, including those with psychiatric and substance abuse disorders (Fiore, Jaén, Baker, Bailey, Benowitz, Curry, et al., 2009). Strategies include asking all clients about tobacco use, assessing readiness to learn, educating smokers and nonsmokers about the dangers of tobacco use, assisting with quit efforts, and referring for further treatment.

Findings from systematic reviews and original research were examined using strength of evidence and, consistent with previous studies, showed that (a) school-based prevention interventions have short-term (but not long-term) effects on adolescents; (b) multicomponent approaches, including telephone counseling, increase the number of users who attempt to quit; (c) self-help strategies alone are ineffective, but counseling and pharmacotherapy used either alone or in combination can improve success rates of quit attempts (Ranney, Melvin, Lux, McClain, & Lohr, 2006). Using effective smoking treatments was strongly encouraged for all populations, especially those with high and heavy rates of smok-

http://go.jblearning.com/mentalhealth 

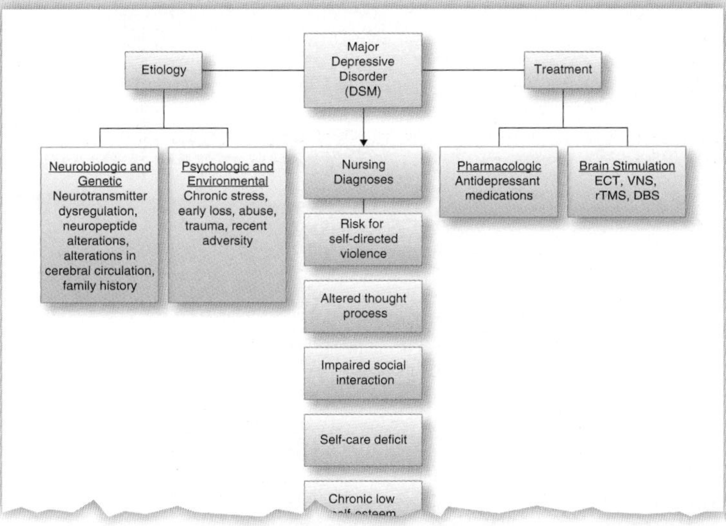

Concept Maps

Concept maps help students to recognize relationships among the field of mental health, disorders, client behaviors, nursing diagnoses and care planning. Students can analyze real-life scenarios and develop their own concept maps using the "Additional Case Studies" feature on the companion website at http://go.jblearning.com/mentalhealth.

Table 17-5 Nursing Interventions for Clients with Mood Disorders

Nursing Diagnoses	Nursing Interventions	Rationales
Risk for suicide	Determine the severity of the risk for suicidal acts and the level of suicide precautions needed.	A client at high risk for self-directed vi needs a carefully completed assessme supervision, and a safe environment.
Disturbed thought processes	Use simple, concrete words. Identify the client's previous level of cognitive functioning. Permit the client time to think and frame responses.	A client with a thought disturbance w thinking and difficulty concentrating. Establishing a baseline of previous fu for evaluation of the client's progress. When a client has slowed thinking, tin to formulate a response.
Impaired social interaction	Provide an environment with less stimulation. Involve the client in one-to-one activities. Gradually increase the client's contact with others.	Minimal distractions promote the abil Permits the client to focus and increas for successful interactions. Distracts the client from self and such socialization decreases the client's feelings of isolation.
Self-care deficit	Monitor intake, output, and vital signs.	This will ensure adequate fluid and calorie intake,

Table 17-5 Nursing Interventions for Clients with Mood Disorders

Nursing Diagnoses	Nursing Interventions	Rationales
Risk for suicide	Determine the severity of the risk for suicidal acts and the level of suicide precautions needed.	A client at high risk for self-directed violence (suicide) needs a carefully completed assessment, constant supervision, and a safe environment.
Disturbed thought processes	Use simple, concrete words. Identify the client's previous level of cognitive functioning. Permit the client time to think and frame responses.	A client with a thought disturbance will have slowed thinking and difficulty concentrating. Establishing a baseline of previous functioning allows for evaluation of the client's progress. When a client has slowed thinking, time will be needed to formulate a response.
Impaired social interaction	Provide an environment with less stimulation. Involve the client in one-to-one activities.	Minimal distractions promote the ability to focus. Permits the client to focus and increases the potential

Nursing Interventions and Rationales Boxes

These boxes feature the skills and tools nursing students need to know regarding how and why to intervene in a client's care. They include nursing diagnoses common for clients with the specific mental disorder covered in each chapter, and then provide examples of nursing interventions and rationales.

In 1792, Philippe Pinel introduced moral therapy. Attendants were required to treat patients kindly and keep them busy with various activities.

During the Middle Ages, mentally ill persons (the insane) were believed to be possessed by devils.

The inhumane treatment of insane persons reached its peak in the 17th century wh...

History

Society has always adopted measures designed to change the behavior of persons with mental illness. In prehistoric times, those measures were likely to have been tribal rites that, if unsuccessful, probably led to the abandonment of the ill person. During the Greek and Roman eras, the sick were treated in the temples, and treatment ranged from humane care to flogging, bleeding, and purging.

The plight of mentally ill persons continued to be poor in the Middle Ages, when their care was determined by mistaken religious beliefs such as be-

ity on the streets of London; the Be Shakespeare's *King Lear* were based ers (Taylor, 1994).

The 18th and 19th Cen

In the 18th century, Europe, parti underwent political and social re Philippe Pinel, the medical directo asylum outside Paris, introduced a regimen termed **moral therapy**, b lief that mental illness was related t faulty upbringing and that a therapeu could correct these weaknesses. Inste

Margin Notes

Margin notes throughout each chapter enhance content and emphasize critical points.

Second Edition

Psychiatric Mental Health Nursing

An Introduction to Theory and Practice

Patricia G. O'Brien, PhD, RN, PMHCNS-BC, PMHNP-BC
Associate Professor
Long Island University, School of Nursing
Brooklyn, New York

Winifred Z. Kennedy, MSN, RN, PMHCNS-BC
Senior Nurse Clinician Consultation and Emergency Psychiatry Service
Maimonides Medical Center
Brooklyn, New York

Karen A. Ballard, MA, RN, FAAN
Adjunct Associate Professor
Lienhard School of Nursing, Pace University
Pleasantville, New York
Adjunct Faculty
College of Nursing, New York University
New York, New York

JONES & BARTLETT
LEARNING

World Headquarters
Jones & Bartlett Learning
5 Wall Street
Burlington, MA 01803
978-443-5000
info@jblearning.com
www.jblearning.com

Jones & Bartlett Learning books and products are available through most bookstores and online booksellers. To contact Jones & Bartlett Learning directly, call 800-832-0034, fax 978-443-8000, or visit our website, www.jblearning.com.

Substantial discounts on bulk quantities of Jones & Bartlett Learning publications are available to corporations, professional associations, and other qualified organizations. For details and specific discount information, contact the special sales department at Jones & Bartlett Learning via the above contact information or send an email to specialsales@jblearning.com.

Additional credits appear on page 739, which constitutes a continuation of the copyright page.

Production Credits
Publisher: Kevin Sullivan
Acquisitions Editor: Amanda Harvey
Editorial Assistant: Sara Bempkins
Associate Production Editor: Cindie Bryan
Marketing Manager: Elena McAnespie
Associate Marketing Manager: Katie Hennessy
V.P., Manufacturing and Inventory Control: Therese Connell
Composition: Publishers' Design and Production Services, Inc.
Cover and Interior Design: Timothy Dziewit
Cover Image: © Subbotina Anna/ShutterStock, Inc.
Printing and Binding: Courier Kendallville
Cover Printing: Courier Kendallville

To order this product, use ISBN: 978-1-4496-5174-9

Library of Congress Cataloging-in-Publication Data
Psychiatric mental health nursing : an introduction to theory and practice / [edited by] Patricia O'Brien, Winifred Kennedy, Karen Ballard. -- 2nd ed.
p. ; cm.
Includes bibliographical references and index.
ISBN-13: 978-1-4496-4608-0 (pbk.)
ISBN-10: 1-4496-4608-5 (pbk.)
I. O'Brien, Patricia G. II. Kennedy, Winifred Z. III. Ballard, Karen A.
[DNLM: 1. Mental Disorders--nursing. 2. Nursing Theory. 3. Psychiatric Nursing--methods. WY 160]
616.89'0231--dc23

2011034752

6048

Printed in the United States of America
16 15 14 13 12 10 9 8 7 6 5 4 3 2 1

Introduction

Psychiatric Mental Health Nursing: An Introduction to Theory and Practice, Second Edition is intended as a basic text for the undergraduate nursing student and as a care plan reference for both the psychiatric nurse and the nurse in a nonpsychiatric setting who is caring for a client with a psychiatric diagnosis. The book is also an excellent educational resource for the nurse who is making a transition from another specialty into psychiatric-mental health nursing. The content applies to nursing practice in a range of clinical settings, including acute and chronic care facilities, the client's home, or community settings.

Nursing interventions and rationales are identified for each of the mental health disorders. These interventions are linked to nursing diagnoses and client behaviors and are the foundation for outcome-focused care plans. The content is presented in a concise manner and provides essential information related to the theory and practice of psychiatric-mental health nursing, without overwhelming the novice practitioner. This text offers a practical alternative to lengthier introductory texts without sacrificing essential content. The editors and publisher carefully considered the learning features and the content in order to achieve this focused presentation.

Each chapter includes:

- Learning objectives to guide and focus study as students move through each topic
- Key terms that list and define the most essential words and phrases
- Margin notes to enhance content and provide emphasis of critical points
- Critical thinking questions to help students process and expand upon the material they are reading and absorbing
- Annotated references that offer complete information on each reference
- Additional resources, also annotated, for the student who wishes to pursue a subject in greater length

The chapters in Part II and Part III include the following student aids:

- Clinical examples—concise vignettes—that provide realistic illustrations of specific content
- Case studies that offer detailed depictions of psychiatric disorders including the client's situation and symptoms and 3-part nursing diagnosis
- Nursing care plans that provide expected outcomes, interventions, and evaluation in relation to the client presented in the corresponding case study
- Diagnostic criteria from the *DSM-IV-TR*
- Considerations for client and family education that contain detailed instructions for teaching information to clients and their families
- Evidence-based practice boxes that highlight recent studies or journal articles that provide research-based evidence for specific nursing interventions

New features introduced in this edition include:

- Tables that provide examples of nursing interventions and rationales corresponding to a variety of nursing diagnoses
- Concept maps in some chapters that help the student visually understand symptoms, etiology, treatment, and nursing diagnoses for specific mental disorders
- Where applicable, changes in diagnostic criteria for certain disorders that are currently proposed for the latest edition of the American Psychiatric Association's *Diagnostic and Statistical Manual of Mental Disorders,* the *DSM-5*, to be published in 2013.

Part I: Overview of Psychiatric-Mental Health Nursing is a summary of the history and fundamentals of psychiatric-mental health nursing.

Chapter 1 traces the development of psychiatric nursing, and introduces concepts fundamental to mental health, including personality development, ego defense mechanisms, and interpersonal nursing. The chapter discusses the major treatment modalities utilized in psychiatric-mental health nursing practice.

Chapter 2 covers the scope and standards of nursing practice, including the nursing process, nursing diagnosis, evidence-based practice, and client and family education. Issues and trends that affect client access to treatment, including cultural factors, insurance and reimbursement, and practice settings are discussed.

Chapter 3 provides an introduction into therapeutic communication and the nurse–client relationship including the characteristics and phases of the relationship. The concepts of transference and countertransference and the essentials of communication techniques are explored.

Chapter 4 describes the psychiatric nursing evaluation in a way that supports and delineates the nurse's role in client assessment. It guides the student through the steps of taking a biopsychosocial history and conducting a mental status examination. It gives practical advice to guide the client interview, such as what questions to ask. Finally, it covers the steps from data collection to nursing diagnosis, outcomes identification, and planning of care.

Chapter 5 provides a clear, in-depth understanding of neurobiologic theories of mental disorders, with down-to-earth examples illustrating these processes. The unique role that the sections and chemicals of the brain play in mental disorders and conditions is explored.

Chapter 6 combines up-to-date information on psychopharmacologic agents with a discussion of the nurse's role in medication administration and client education, with expanded information on drug actions and the management of side effects. The most recent evidence-based guidelines for the use of antipsychotic medications are summarized. Easy-to-read tables help the student to organize and learn actions, dosages, and side effects of the medications.

Chapter 7 introduces the principles of crisis intervention and provides direction to guide the nurse's actions in response to psychiatric emergencies. The principles are applied to a variety of clinical situations, including acute trauma, agitation and aggression, and disasters. Discussion includes alternatives to restraints or seclusion, as well as considerations for client and staff safety when these interventions are used.

Legal and ethical considerations of psychiatric-mental health nursing are discussed in Chapter 8, including issues related to the client's right to treatment and the right to refuse treatment and/or medication, the use of seclusion and restraint, informed consent, client confidentiality, and sexual misconduct.

Chapter 9 provides an introduction to group therapy with a focus on self-help groups and the role of the client in the therapeutic healing process.

The use of an experiential format in Chapter 10 allows the student to be actively involved in learning about the application of complementary therapies to meet the biologic, psychologic, and spiritual needs of clients in the context of holistic nursing practice. Scripts are provided to encourage the student nurse to use various forms of relaxation therapy with clients.

Chapter 11 addresses violence in the family, including the issues of intimate partner violence, child, and elder abuse.

Part II: Mental Health Disorders and Conditions addresses specific mental health disorders in a way that is consistent with both the *DSM-IV-TR* classification, the official nomenclature used by multidisciplinary teams treating psychiatric clients, and the utilization of NANDA-I diagnoses. Additionally, information is provided regarding proposed changes for classification of mental disorders in the anticipated publication of the *DSM-5*. As members of the treatment team, nurses must be familiar with the process used to diagnose and assess mental disorders as well as be conversant in the language and terminology used by the team.

The format for each chapter includes a general description of the specific disorder; information on incidence and prevalence; etiology and physiology, including neurobiology and genetics; clinical presentation, course, and complications; differential diagnoses; management and treatment; nursing interventions with rationales; considerations for client and family education, a chapter summary; and annotated references. The application of a 3-part nursing diagnosis is demonstrated via case studies accompanied by complete nursing care plans.

Part III: Nursing Management of Special Populations provides information on the nursing management of unique populations. These client groups were selected based on the unique challenges associated with providing care specific to their needs. Topics include age-related issues associated with the care of children, adolescents, and the aging client with mental disorders. Individual chapters are devoted to the special needs of clients with intellectual and developmental disabilities, and chronic mental illness.

The appendices include:

- Appendix I—The most current American Nurses Association's scope and standards of practice for psychiatric-mental health nursing.
- Appendix II—Aligns the *DSM-IV-TR* disorders with possibly relevant NANDA-I nursing diagnoses. This appendix assists the student to identify client needs and areas for nursing intervention. A table containing the complete NANDA-I taxonomy II domains, classes, and diagnoses (2012–2014) is also provided.

Ancillary Package

A full companion website has been designed to accompany *Psychiatric-Mental Health Nursing: An Introduction to Theory and Practice, Second Edition*, found at **http://go.jblearning.com/mentalhealth**. The special features here are designed to complement and expand upon concepts provided in the main text and through faculty-assisted, classroom instruction. Designed to be as simple, yet as useful as possible, the features on the website can be accessed either by chapter number or by type of feature (e.g., flashcards or Web Links).

Students

The student features can be used to supplement individual study time by the reader or as assigned by the instructor. They include the following:

- Interactive glossary, crossword puzzles, and flash cards to test knowledge of key terminology and concepts
- Additional case studies similar to those in the textbook give students the opportunity to acquire skill in developing individualized nursing care plans with clients based on clinical case scenarios
- Web Links to psychiatric and mental health nursing resources for further information on specific topics
- NCLEX-RN® review questions that provide overall review of psychiatric-mental health nursing content and help to prepare students for the NCLEX-RN® examination

Instructors

Instructors will have access to the student resources on the website and will also have a secure right of entry to the following resources that are designed to assist the instructor in developing course content:

- PowerPoint slides outlining each chapter's content for classroom presentation
- Instructor's manual containing suggestions for classroom discussions, activities, group work, assignments, and lectures
- Test bank of questions for use in creating examinations and quizzes

Preface

This book has been designed to guide nursing faculty in their important role of introducing nursing students and novice nurses to the basics of psychiatric-mental health nursing. The organization of the content recognizes the need to provide the nursing student with a clear understanding of what psychiatric-mental health nursing is and the context in which it is practiced. The editors are very aware of the special challenge that faculty confront in introducing a significant volume of new and complicated information within limited didactic and clinical semester hours. Therefore, we have made an effort to present essential content in a way that provides sufficient substance, without overwhelming the novice.

In the late 1990s, when the authors collaborated on an earlier textbook, we made a decision to present the nursing interventions in the framework of the American Psychiatric Association's (APA) *Diagnostic and Statistical Manual of Mental Disorders (DSM-IV*; 1994). Other psychiatric nursing books have since followed a similar format. We think this confirms our belief that modern psychiatric-mental health nurses must learn the common language of the multidisciplinary team that is so integral to the delivery of mental health services. We have updated the information on mental disorders to be consistent with the revised *DSM-IV-TR* (2000) and have made some comments regarding the APA's proposed changes for the *DSM-5*.

The NANDA-I (2012) nursing diagnoses are identified for each of the *DSM* diagnostic categories. This is in keeping with our belief that psychiatric-mental health nursing must be grounded in nursing theory. Each editor has extensive experience as an advanced practice registered nurse. Our collective backgrounds, including teaching and mentoring nursing students and as psychiatric-mental health nurses, has informed our approach to this textbook. We retained features of previous versions of the text that faculty, nursing students, and novice nurses found helpful and included new features to bring clinical situations to life, promote critical thinking, and structure the course content.

Throughout the book, care plans and nursing interventions reference nursing diagnostic terminology developed by NANDA-I. Disturbed sensory perception and disturbed thought processes are among the nursing diagnoses that have been recently retired by NANDA-I. These diagnoses have been used by psychiatric nurses to refer to hallucinations and delusions, respectively. In the absence of alternative nursing diagnoses, these continue to be used throughout the text. They meet a need and are familiar to psychiatric nurses. We note, however, that they are not currently among the NANDA-I–approved nursing diagnoses.

The content has been organized to promote incremental learning and to accommodate both discrete psychiatric nursing courses and integrated nursing curricula. Part I: Overview of Psychiatric-Mental Health Nursing introduces nursing students and novice psychiatric-mental health nurses to the general knowledge and specific skills that are applicable to learning the nursing care of clients with specific mental disorders and conditions. The student traces the development of psychiatric-mental health nursing, learns about the nursing theorists who have had the most influence on the specialty, compares the *DSM-IV* nomenclature with NANDA-I, and reviews the phases and components of therapeutic communication, neurobiology, psychopharmacology, and psychiatric emergencies. Ethical concerns, including client competence, are introduced. There is a brief overview of the types of therapies offered to clients with psychiatric illness, including group therapy, somatic therapies, and cognitive behavioral therapy.

New to this edition, is a dedicated chapter on therapeutic communication and the nurse-client relationship. The presentation of group theory and practice has been expanded beyond self-help groups. A focus on self-help groups is retained in response to positive feedback.

The content on psychiatric nursing assessment builds on the nursing process that the nursing student is already familiar with and then takes the student through the steps of obtaining a biopsychosocial history and conducting a mental status examination. It gives practical advice to guide the client interview, such as what questions to ask, and covers the nursing diagnosis and development of an outcome-focused nursing care plan.

We have heard from faculty about the increased emphasis on teaching documentation relevant to psychiatric-mental health nursing. A comprehensive list of what should be included in nursing documentation provides a handy reference for both nursing students and novice nurses and can be easily utilized in the clinical setting.

The various categories of psychotropic medications are discussed in detail in the psychopharmacology chapter (Chapter 6) and are also reviewed in the chapters on specific disorders and conditions. The medications are discussed in both text and presented in table format with dosage, intended actions, interactions, and side effects. The tables are designed to organize a significant amount of information in a manner that will promote learning.

All of the fundamental knowledge and skills that are presented in Part I of the text are applied to specific disorders in Part II: Mental Health Disorders and Conditions. A uniform format is followed with each disorder: description; incidence and prevalence; etiology and physiology, including neurobiolgy and genetics; clinical presentation; differential diagnosis; clinical course and complications; management and treatment; and nursing interventions and rationales. Concept maps are introduced in this edition to visually display relationships among symptoms, nursing diagnoses, and the mental disorders.

Each chapter has a special section on client and family education because we consider this to be a major nursing intervention. The theoretical content is enriched with clinical examples, case studies, and outcome-focused nursing care plans. Throughout each chapter there are margin notes to highlight important and interesting facts, as well as critical thinking questions that can trigger classroom or postclinical discussions. Evidence-based practice is highlighted through the presentation of recent research. Again, all content is organized, concise, and complete.

Part III: Nursing Management of Special Populations covers special populations and lends itself to a community-based mental health nursing curriculum or courses on the nursing care of specific age groups, such as child, adult, or geriatric clients with mental health disorders. Chapters are devoted to the special needs of clients diagnosed with intellectual and developmental disabilities, and chronic mental illness.

We hope our readers, both faculty and students, find this book to be readable, interesting, and a resource that you can utilize in the practice of any nursing specialty. Of course, we would be pleased if this introduction to psychiatric-mental health nursing inspires some nursing students to pursue careers as psychiatric-mental health nurses. But, regardless of where one practices, there will be clients who are living with mental illness. We are confident that this text will provide a knowledge and skill base necessary for the nursing student and novice nurse to meet the psychiatric-mental health nursing needs of clients and families in any setting.

Note from the Publisher

The editors bring to this project extensive experience in the practice of psychiatric-mental health nursing. The combined experiences, specialized knowledge, and interests of the editors were enriched by those of the contributors. The resulting efforts communicate the spirit of discovery and hope associated with current advances in understanding the etiologies and treatments of mental disorders and conditions. As remarkable as these scientific advances are, they do not lessen the significance of the interpersonal component of nursing care. Communication skills, so much the essence of nursing, will continue to be valued. This text provides nursing students and nurses with the fundamental knowledge to contribute to the care of clients and their families living with mental disorders.

The editors wish to thank the psychiatric-mental health nurse educators and clinicians who have been our mentors throughout our professional careers. You continue to inspire us, and we are indebted to you for your wisdom, your patience, your friendship, and your belief in us.

We extend our appreciation to our expert contributors who, by sharing their knowledge and insight into psychiatric-mental health nursing and the care of clients and their families, have made this book possible and a unique resource in the specialty.

We are grateful to our nurse colleagues, the nurses with whom we work, who continue every day to define and expand the practice of psychiatric-mental health nursing As educators, we also want to thank our students. They are constant reminders of why we chose nursing as a profession, of the difference a nurse can make, and of the need to continually learn.

We extend love and appreciation to our families and friends who have supported and encouraged us throughout this challenging process. Thank you for your enthusiasm, understanding, and love.

We wish to express our appreciation for the editorial, production, and marketing direction and support of Kevin Sullivan, Cindie Bryan, Amanda Harvey, Sara Bempkins, Janet Kiefer, and their assistants.

Jeanne Anselmo, BSN, RN, BCIAC-SF, HN-BC
Holistic Nursing Consultant
Sea Cliff, NY

Karen A. Ballard, MA, RN, FAAN
Adjunct Associate Professor
Lienhard School of Nursing, Pace University
Pleasantville, New York
Adjunct Faculty
College of Nursing, New York University
New York, NY

Blaine R. Beemer, BSc(Hons), RN, MN, CPMHN(C)
University of Calgary
Calgary, Alberta, Canada

Donna R. Falvo, PhD, RN, CRC
Clinical Professor (Retired)

Loraine Fleming, MA, APRN, PMHCNS-BC, PMHNP-BC
Director of Behavioral Health, Orthopedics, Rehabilitation and Surgical Inpatient Services
The Queen's Medical Center
Honolulu, HI
Assistant Professor
College of Nursing and Health Sciences
Hawaii Pacific University
Honolulu, HI
DNP candidate
Massachusetts General Hospital Institute of Health Professionals
Boston, MA

Sherry Goertz, PhD, RN, PMHCNS-BC
Nursing Faculty
Pennsylvania State University
Mont Alto, PA

Beth Harris, MA, RN, PMHCNS-BC
Health Education Coordinator
New York-Presbyterian Hospital
White Plains, NY

Beverley E. Holland, PhD, ARNP
Bellarmine University
Louisville, KY

Winifred Z. Kennedy, MSN, RN, PMHCNS-BC
Senior Nurse Clinician Consultation and Emergency Psychiatry Service
Maimonides Medical Center
Brooklyn, NY

Karan Kverno, PhD, RN, PMHNP-BC
Department of Family and Community Health
University of Maryland School of Nursing
Baltimore, MD

Edward J. Madara, MS
American & N.J. Self-Help Group Clearinghouses
Cedar Knolls, NJ

Valerie N. Markley, MSN, RN, PMHCNS-BC
Assistant Professor Emerita of Nursing
Indiana University School of Nursing
Bloomington, IN
Adjunct Faculty
Indiana Wesleyan University

Joan C. Masters, EdD, MBA, APRN, PMHNP-BC
Associate Professor of Nursing, Bellarmine University
Louisville, KY

Claudia Mitzeliotis, MS, APRN-BC, CASAC
Psychiatric Clinical Nurse Specialist
Veterans Administration, New York Harbor Healthcare System
New York, NY

Christine Carniaux Moran, LCSW, RN(C)
Vice President for Behavioral Health Services
South Oaks Hospital
Amityville, NY

Bethany A. Murray, MSN, RN, PMHCNS-BC
Center for Behavioral Health
Bloomington, IN

Patricia G. O'Brien, PhD, RN, PMHCNS-BC, PMHNP-BC
Associate Professor
Long Island University, School of Nursing
Brooklyn, NY

Cecelia M. Taylor, PhD, RN
Professor Emerita of Nursing
The College of St. Scholastica
Duluth, MN

Amy Wysoker, PhD, RN, PMHCNS-BC
Professor
C.W. Post Campus of Long Island University
School of Health Professions and Nursing
Department of Nursing
Brookville, NY

Part I

Overview of Psychiatric-Mental Health Nursing

Learning Objectives

After reading this chapter, you will be able to:

- Describe the evolution of psychiatric-mental health nursing practice.
- Explain two key concepts from each of the major theories of personality development including the psychoanalytic, interpersonal, and behavioral conceptual models.
- Discuss the impact on psychiatric-mental health nursing of nursing theorists and their conceptual models.
- Describe the characteristics of individual therapy, family therapy, group therapy, milieu therapy, crisis intervention, and somatic therapies.
- Identify the members of the contemporary multidisciplinary mental health treatment team and describe their distinctive abilities and responsibilities.

Key Terms

Anticipatory guidance
Anxiety
Apathy
Behavioral model
Classical conditioning
Cognitive behavioral therapy (CBT)
Cognitive model
Conceptual model
Coping mechanisms
Crisis
Developmental crises
Dynamisms
Ego defense mechanisms
Extinction
Family systems therapy
Genogram
Group therapy
Hierarchy of needs
Individual therapy
Levels of consciousness
Milieu therapy
Moral therapy
Multidisciplinary treatment team
Need for satisfaction
Need for security
Negative reinforcement
Neurobiologic model
Nurse–patient relationship
Operant conditioning
Positive reinforcement
Preoccupation
Psychoanalytic model
Psychodynamic nursing
Psychosexual theory of personality development
Punishment
Rational emotive behavioral therapy
Response cost
Security operations
Selective inattention
Self-actualization
Self-care deficit
Self-concept
Situational crises
Somatic therapies
Somnolent detachment
Structural family therapy
Structure of the personality
Therapeutic community

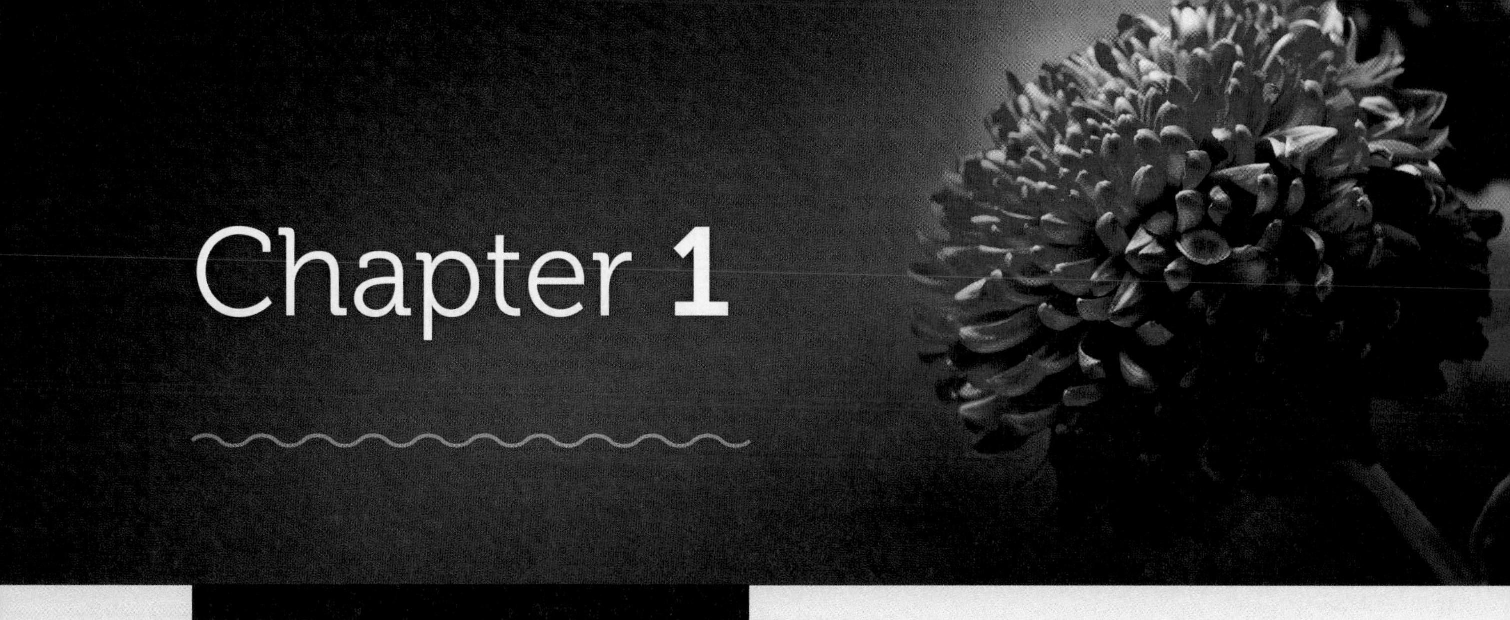

Introduction to Psychiatric-Mental Health Nursing

Cecelia M. Taylor and Karen A. Ballard

The use of the term *patient* in the first half of this chapter reflects historical usage.

http://go.jblearning.com/mentalhealth 

For a full suite of assignments and additional learning activities, use the access code located in the front of your book to visit this exclusive website: http://go.jblearning.com/mentalhealth. If you do not have an access code, you can obtain one at the site.

History

In 1792, Philippe Pinel introduced moral therapy. Attendants were required to treat patients kindly and keep them busy with various activities. During the Middle Ages, mentally ill persons (the insane) were believed to be possessed by devils.

The inhumane treatment of insane persons reached its peak in the 17th century when almshouses, a combination of a jail and an asylum, confined both criminals and those who were mentally ill.

Benjamin Rush (1745–1813) is considered the "father of American psychiatry." The first public psychiatric hospital in America was built in Williamsburg, Virginia, in 1773 and is still in operation today as Eastern State Hospital.

Society has always adopted measures designed to change the behavior of persons with mental illness. In prehistoric times, those measures were likely to have been tribal rites that, if unsuccessful, probably led to the abandonment of the ill person. During the Greek and Roman eras, the sick were treated in the temples, and treatment ranged from humane care to flogging, bleeding, and purging.

The plight of mentally ill persons continued to be poor in the Middle Ages, when their care was determined by mistaken religious beliefs such as being possessed by devils that could be exorcised by whippings and starvation. When the church stopped treating mentally ill persons during the 16th century, they were imprisoned in almshouses, which were a combination of a jail and an asylum. Those who were violent and delusional were placed in jails and dungeons. King Henry VIII officially dedicated Bethlehem Hospital in London as a lunatic asylum, and it soon became known as the notorious "Bedlam," whose hideous practices were immortalized by Hogarth, the famous cartoonist (**Figure 1-1**). The more harmless inmates were forced to seek charity on the streets of London; the Bedlam beggars of Shakespeare's *King Lear* were based on these prisoners (Taylor, 1994).

Figure 1-1 Bedlam, as depicted by William Hogarth. Note the well-dressed ladies, who made social visits to the prison to view the spectacle of the inmates as entertainment.

The 18th and 19th Centuries

In the 18th century, Europe, particularly France, underwent political and social reform. In 1792, Philippe Pinel, the medical director of the Bicêtre asylum outside Paris, introduced a new treatment regimen termed **moral therapy**, based on the belief that mental illness was related to immorality or faulty upbringing and that a therapeutic environment could correct these weaknesses. Instead of harsh confinement, patients were kept busy with work, music, or other diversions. Moral therapy required that attendants treat patients with kindness and keep them involved in the treatment program (Wasserbauer & Brodie, 1992). The Quakers established the York Retreat and brought about the same dramatic reforms in England. The development of moral therapy and its reliance on attendants were the beginnings of current psychiatric nursing care.

The first place identified as a "poorhouse, workhouse, and house of correction" in the United States opened in 1736 in New York City. In 1756, under the guidance of Benjamin Franklin, the Pennsylvania Hospital was completed. One of the first two patients admitted was described as a lunatic. Although patients with a mental illness were relegated to the cellar, they were assured clean bedding and warm rooms. Benjamin Rush (1745–1813), a humanitarian and the father of American psychiatry, began working at Pennsylvania Hospital in 1783. The first public psychiatric hospital in America was built in Williamsburg, Virginia, in 1773 and is known today as Eastern State Hospital. Most states, even as late as 1830, did not have facilities for treatment of the mentally ill, although a number of excellent private hospitals existed, such as the Hartford Retreat, founded in 1818.

Dorothea Lynde Dix (1802–1887) was a schoolteacher who volunteered to tutor individuals confined to jails and poorhouses. She was horrified by the conditions in these facilities, and in 1841 began a campaign to convince state legislatures that suitable hospitals, not jails, were required for those with mental illnesses. Twenty states in the United States and the Canadian government responded directly to her appeals by authorizing the construction of large institutions for the mentally ill. This was the beginning of the state hospital system in the United States.

The original intent of the state hospital system was to treat those with mental illness and then discharge them to the community or the care of their families. Because so little was known about mental illness at that time, the goals of treatment and discharge were not able to be achieved. Consequently, state hospitals rapidly became overcrowded with chronically mentally ill patients. Paradoxically, the same state hospitals that were supposed to alleviate the suffering of violent persons who were previously imprisoned contributed to the ultimate demise of moral therapy, because this treatment could not be implemented in overcrowded settings.

In 1844, the Association of Medical Superintendents was formed as psychiatry began to develop as a profession and as physicians became increasingly responsible for the administration of asylums. This organization became the American Medico-Psychological Association in 1851, and was renamed the American Psychiatric Association (APA) in 1921. It was founded by medical superintendents from 13 asylums in the United States (Wasserbauer & Brodie, 1992).

By the 1870s, asylums were considered abysmal institutions with a terrible public image. Searching for ways to improve care, psychiatrists adopted the strategies already in use at general hospitals to improve patient services. These improvements included incorporating effective therapies that had a scientific basis and using graduate nurses instead of attendants. However, asylums were unable to attract enough nurses to improve patient care, so schools of nursing in asylums were established. The first school of this type was established at the McLean Asylum in Massachusetts in 1882 (Wasserbauer & Brodie, 1992).

The 20th Century

At the beginning of the 20th century, treatment was still limited to restraints, isolation, water bath treatments, dietary regimens, and, eventually, early sedative drugs and shock treatments. Noticeable changes occurred in the state hospital system in 1908 when Clifford Beers, a psychiatric patient who was hospitalized several times, wrote a book about his experiences titled *A Mind That Found Itself*. The book's revelations led to the founding of the National Committee for Mental Hygiene. The committee was the first organization that espoused the prevention of mental illness and early intervention.

The most significant psychiatric revolution in the early 20th century was a direct result of the work of Sigmund Freud (1856–1939). Freud made great contributions to the understanding of human behavior. Before his theories were introduced, human behavior, particularly the behavior of persons with mental illnesses, was shrouded in superstition, secrecy, and stigma. Freud brought the subject of human behavior to the public's attention. His theories served as a springboard for the scientific study of human behavior. Although much of Freudian theory is no longer embraced in scientific circles, some of his concepts have become so integrated into the mainstream that they have become part of everyday language (e.g., ego, conscience, unconscious).

The National Mental Health Act, passed in 1946, was one of the most progressive actions addressing mental illness the United States has ever taken. The legislation stemmed from the nation's concerns about the mental health of its citizens as a result of experiences during World War II. More men in the armed forces were disabled from mental disorders than from all other health problems related to military action. Immediately after the National Mental Health Act was passed, the National Institute of Mental Health (NIMH) was established in 1946. The NIMH provided funding to support research into the causes of mental illness and to provide tuition and stipends for education in the four core mental health disciplines: psychiatry, psychology, psychiatric nursing, and psychiatric social work. Major strides were made in increasing the number of mental health professionals as a result of this funding. For example, in the 1940s, only five to seven graduate programs in psychiatric nursing existed; these numbers expanded greatly in the 1950s and 1960s as a result of NIMH funding.

Psychiatric nursing underwent a major change when *Interpersonal Relations in Nursing* by Hildegard Peplau, EdD, RN, FAAN was published in 1952, emphasizing the significance of the relationship between the patient and nurse as a treatment modality. Integrating the theories of psychiatrist Harry Stack Sullivan into nursing theory, Dr. Peplau is considered the mother of modern psychiatric nursing. An extensive internet-based biography on Dr. Peplau, including audio and video information, is available (http://publish.uwo.ca/~cforchuk/peplau/hpcb.html).

The master's programs in psychiatric nursing have graduated hundreds of clinical nurse specialists (CNSs) in psychiatric nursing. These individuals assumed leadership positions in organized nursing and lobbied for recognition as autonomous practitioners of mental health care, specifically psychotherapy. Currently, many states authorize certified psychiat-

Sigmund Freud brought the need to understand human behavior to the attention of the scientific community and public. Before him, it was shrouded in superstition, secrecy, and stigma.

Dorothea Lynde Dix (1802–1887), an early advocate for the mentally ill, convinced state legislatures that suitable hospitals, not jails, were required for those with mental illnesses.

One of the most progressive actions ever taken by the United States in response to mental illness was the passage of the National Mental Health Act in 1946 and the subsequent establishment of the NIMH.

A movement began in the 1870s to use graduate nurses instead of attendants in state hospitals. The first school of nursing at a state asylum was founded in 1882 at the McLean Asylum in Massachusetts.

A major turning point in psychiatric nursing was the publication of *Interpersonal Relations in Nursing* by Hildegard Peplau. This book emphasized the significance of the relationship between patient and nurse as a treatment modality.

A Mind That Found Itself, by Clifford Beers, led to the founding of the National Committee for Mental Hygiene, which espoused the prevention of mental illness and early intervention.

ric clinical nurse specialists and certified psychiatric nurse practitioners to prescribe psychopharmaceuticals, and Medicare, Medicaid, and most insurance plans reimburse them for their services.

In 1953, the National League for Nursing required the inclusion of psychiatric nursing experience and coursework in the basic nursing curricula for all nursing students.

In 1953, the National League for Nursing (NLN), the accreditation agency for schools of nursing, required the inclusion of psychiatric nursing clinical experience and coursework in all basic curricula and required that these subjects be taught by nursing faculty. Thus, all nursing students have some exposure to the practice and theory of psychiatric nursing. In 1955, the U.S. Congress passed the Mental Health Study Act. This act provided funds for a 5-year study of the problem of mental illness in the United States. As a result, the Joint Commission on Mental Illness was established. The commission's report, *Action for Mental Health*, provided the stimulus for developing more effective services for people in need of psychiatric care.

The Mental Health Study Act of 1955 led to the establishment of the Joint Commission on Mental Illness; the commission's report, *Action for Mental Health*, provided a nationwide stimulus to develop more effective services for people in need of psychiatric care.

A revolution in care occurred in the late 1950s when the first effective antipsychotic medication, chlorpromazine (Thorazine), became widely available. Although many other, more effective, medications are currently available, none have had the impact of chlorpromazine when it was first introduced. This medication controlled many of the most distressing symptoms experienced by patients, resulting in their becoming more amenable to other forms of treatment and being able to function better both in and out of hospitals.

The care of persons with mental illness was revolutionized in the late 1950s when chlorpromazine (Thorazine) first became available for widespread use.

On February 5, 1963, President John F. Kennedy addressed the Congress on mental illness and mental retardation, emphasizing the goal of community care for persons with mental illnesses. In that same year, Congress authorized the Community Mental Health Centers Construction Act, which was followed in 1965 by amendments to provide for staffing in the centers (P.L. 89-105). These acts sought to revolutionize mental health care by emphasizing prevention and decentralized, local community treatment over institutional care, even for persons with the most severe psychiatric difficulties. The first federally funded centers opened in 1966, initiating the deinstitutionalization of persons with mental illness.

The 1963 Community Mental Health Centers Construction Act and its 1965 staffing amendments sought to revolutionize the provision of mental health care by emphasizing prevention and decentralized, local community treatment.

In the late 1980s, NIMH shifted its focus and funding from education and service delivery to research. This legislative shift resulted, in part, from intense lobbying by the National Alliance for the Mentally Ill (NAMI), an advocacy group of families of mentally ill persons who demanded increased research into the cause and treatment of mental illness. Deinstitutionalization of the mentally Ill was finally achieved in the late 1980s and early 1990s as a result of economic constraints and the availability of medications and services that enabled patients to function in the community. Currently, persons with mental illness who require hospitalization are likely to be admitted to a freestanding private hospital or a psychiatric unit in a general hospital. The nature of treatment has also changed. An individual admitted to the hospital no longer has to remain for months, with most staying for less than 2 weeks (Taylor, 1994).

Critical Thinking Question

What are the advantages and disadvantages for clients, families, communities, and healthcare practitioners when short-term hospitalization is deemed necessary?

Many of the most severe forms of mental illness most likely have a neurobiologic basis. As a result, treatment is based on the use of psychopharmaceuticals (i.e., drug therapy).

Finally, a major paradigm shift has occurred in understanding the causes of major mental illness, and this shift has altered the nature of psychiatric treatment. As a result of increasingly sophisticated technology, scientists have proposed that many of the most severe forms of mental illness have a neurobiologic basis (see Chapter 5). As a result, treatment relies heavily on the ever-expanding array of psychopharmaceuticals as a single treatment modality or in conjunction with the more traditional "talking" therapies (individual psychotherapy, group therapy, family therapy; **Figure 1-2**). Furthermore, because of these findings, many graduate programs in psychiatric nursing have revised their curricula to emphasize neurobiology and psychopharmacology.

The 21st Century

The understanding of the causes and treatment of mental illness has increased dramatically over the centuries. The availability of increasingly sophisticated technology ensures even more dramatic advances in knowledge. Because of the increasing scope and complexity of this burgeoning knowledge, it is necessary for the **multidisciplinary treatment team** to work closely together to achieve the goals of preventing mental illness and effectively treating those who are ill. Therefore, the psychiatric nurse in the 21st century works collaboratively in the community with other healthcare practitioners, clients, and their families, each an integral part of the multidisciplinary treatment team utilizing a variety of treatments. Recognition of the patient as an integral member of the treatment team is reflected in the con-

Figure 1-2 An individual psychotherapy session.

temporary use of the term *client* rather than *patient* when referring to the person in need of professional mental health services.

In addition to clients and their families, the multidisciplinary treatment team includes the psychiatrist, clinical psychologist, psychiatric mental health nurse, psychiatric social worker, and activities therapists, who teach, for example, life skills, art, and music. All mental health professionals share a common knowledge of and skill in interpersonal relationships and a deep appreciation of the inextricable relationships between mind and body and between genetics and the environment. Each professional discipline has a distinctive knowledge base and skills that enrich the treatment team.

Psychiatrists are physicians with several years of supervised residency training in the medical specialty of psychiatry. The psychiatrist prescribes medications and administers other somatic therapies, such as electroconvulsive therapy. Psychiatrists are particularly skilled in identifying and treating persons whose problems have highly interrelated emotional physiological components.

Clinical psychologists have advanced education in the study of mental processes and the treatment of mental disorders. They have particular expertise in the use of inferential tools designed to assist in the diagnostic process and assessment of treatment effects. An example of such a tool is the Rorschach test, commonly known as the inkblot test (**Figure 1-3**).

Psychiatric-mental health nurse generalists and advanced practice psychiatric nurses work collaboratively in outpatient and inpatient treatment settings. According to the Society for Education and Research in Psychiatric-Mental Health Nursing, psychiatric-mental health nurses are registered nurses who are educationally prepared in nursing, licensed to practice in their individual states, and qualified to practice in the psychiatric-mental health nursing specialty at one of two levels: basic or advanced. All nurses bring expertise in assessing the client's ability to engage in activities of daily living and to assist the client to cope as necessary. The nurse in an inpatient setting is responsible for establishing and maintaining an environment that is therapeutic for the client population as a whole. It is believed that the therapeutic nurse–client relationship is the hallmark of psychiatric nursing.

Psychiatric social workers are prepared at the master's degree level and have particular skill in assessing familial, environmental, and social factors that contribute to the problems of clients and their

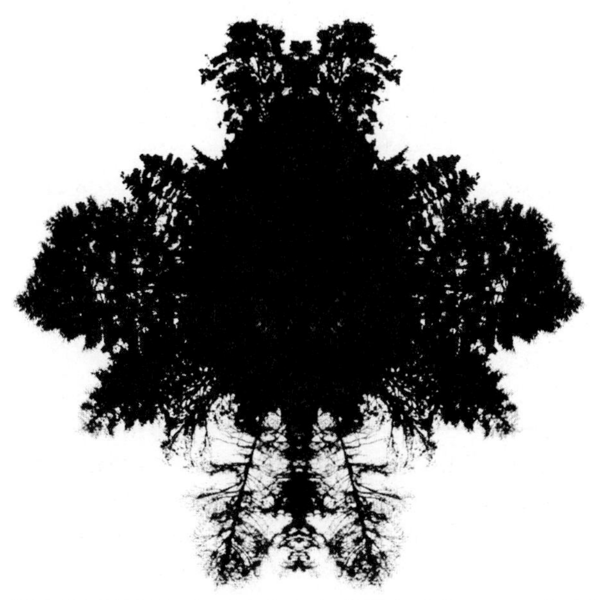

Figure 1-3 A sample Rorschach "ink blot."

families. They are also major contributors to discharge planning and the follow-up care of the client.

Activity therapists have at least a bachelor's degree, and increasingly a master's degree is required in their specialty field. The basis of activity therapy is the belief that persons can benefit from engaging in activities that focus outside of the self, such as exercise, crafts, writing, music, or painting (**Figure 1-4**). These activities can be done either alone or in conjunction with other clients. Therefore, the activity therapist is skilled in the development, implementation, and evaluation of a highly individualized activity regimen designed to meet the needs of the person for whom it is designed.

The founder of the psychoanalytic model is Sigmund Freud. Key Freudian concepts include levels of consciousness, structure of the personality, and psychosexual development.

Theories of Personality Development and Conceptual Models

A conceptual model is a framework of related concepts. Most mental health practitioners use a variety of approaches to assist clients in achieving mental health.

A **conceptual model** is a framework of related concepts. Conceptual models used by mental health practitioners address the bases for behavior in order to direct interventions. Although some mental health practitioners adhere strictly to one conceptual model, most practitioners in the United States use an eclectic approach in which they employ one or more approaches from several models. The most important conceptual models are the psychoanalytic, interpersonal, behavioral, cognitive, developmental, and neurobiologic models. We will review all the models in this chapter, but the last three models are discussed in more detail in other chapters of this book.

The three levels of consciousness are the conscious, the preconscious, and the unconscious; the three aspects of the personality are the id, the ego, and the superego.

Figure 1-4 A client engaged in painting.

Critical Thinking Question

Why would most mental health practitioners choose to use an eclectic approach to treatment? What are the advantages of this practice? Are there any disadvantages to this approach?

Psychoanalytic Model

Sigmund Freud is the founder of the **psychoanalytic model**. An Austrian neurologist, he developed an elaborate theory of human behavior based primarily on his work with persons suffering from disabling anxiety. Key Freudian concepts include levels of consciousness, structure of the personality, and psychosexual development. The treatment approach derived from his theories is termed psychoanalysis.

Three Levels of Consciousness

Freud believed in three **levels of consciousness**. The first level is the conscious mind, the part that is aware of the present and functions only when the person is awake. It represents the smallest part of the mind and directs an individual's rational, thoughtful behavior.

The second level of consciousness is the preconscious (subconscious), the part of the mind in which thoughts, feelings, and sensations are stored. Although materials stored in the preconscious mind are outside of awareness, they can be brought to the conscious mind with the proper stimulus, such as a direct question.

The third level of consciousness is the unconscious, the largest part of the mind and the storehouse for all of the thoughts, feelings, and sensations experienced during the individual's lifetime. The individual is rarely aware of the unconscious mind, except when it demonstrates its presence through dreams, slips of the tongue, unexplained behavior, jokes, and lapses of memory (Taylor, 1994). Belief in the existence of the unconscious is the basis for the saying, "All behavior has meaning."

Structure of the Personality

The second major concept developed by Freud is the **structure of the personality**, consisting of three aspects—the id, the ego, and the superego. The id is part of and derived from the unconscious. It is unlearned, primitive, and selfish and does not have a sense of right and wrong, ruthlessly insisting on immediate satisfaction of its impulses and desires, which are geared toward avoiding pain and experiencing pleasure. The other parts of the personality are responsible for keeping the id under control.

The ego develops as a result of the infant's interaction with its environment. It establishes an acceptable compromise between the crude, pleasure-seeking strivings of the id and the inhibitions of the superego through reality testing, a process that ascertains the likely consequences of behavior. The ego is the practical part of the personality. As an individual matures, the ego becomes the rational, reasonable, conscious part of the personality and strives to integrate the total personality into a smoothly functioning, coherent whole (Taylor, 1994).

Chronologically, the superego develops last, acting as the moral judge of the individual based on what the person has learned from significant others, such as parents and teachers. It operates mostly at the unconscious level and controls the id. The two aspects of the superego are the conscience, which punishes individuals through guilt and anxiety when their behavior deviates from the strict standards of the superego, and the ego ideal, which rewards individuals with feelings of well-being when their behavior achieves those standards believed desirable by the superego (Taylor, 1994).

Freud believed that when id impulses unacceptable to the superego threaten to emerge, the individual experiences anxiety. **Anxiety** is a diffuse, vague sense of impending doom, and it is always perceived as a negative emotion. Therefore, the person experiencing anxiety works to get rid of this feeling, often through the use of **ego defense mechanisms**, mental mechanisms derived from the ego that are designed to effect a compromise between the demands of the id and the superego to relieve anxiety. Ego defense mechanisms operate on the unconscious level, although an objective observer may be able to discern when others are using them. For example, a student who perceives herself as very intelligent but who fails a test may rationalize this otherwise anxiety-producing outcome by telling herself and others that the test was not important. Persons with whom she shares this belief may be very aware that she is using the ego defense mechanism of rationalization. **Table 1-1** details commonly used defense mechanisms.

In contrast to the unconscious nature of defense mechanisms, **coping mechanisms** are conscious mental strategies or behaviors an individual employs to lower anxiety. Coping mechanisms are categorized as short term or long term and are as plentiful as the creativity and resourcefulness of human beings.

Short-term coping mechanisms are designed to address an immediate problem. For example, a person experiencing a great deal of work-related stress may drink alcohol as a means of coping. Although this action may relieve the immediate anxiety, it does not address the source of the stress or prevent the anxiety from reemerging. In contrast, long-term coping mechanisms address the cause of the anxiety and are likely to benefit the individual more than short-term coping mechanisms. Some examples are relaxation techniques, biofeedback, exercise, assertiveness training, setting goals, clarifying communications, visualization and guided imagery, meditation, yoga, seeking out peer support, and self-hypnosis.

Psychosexual Theory of Personality Development

Freud also defined the developmental stages of personality. His theory of personality development is termed the **psychosexual theory of personality development**. Freud maintained that personality is a dynamic, evolving process that develops from birth through young adulthood. Freud's stages of psychosexual development are oral (birth to 18 months), anal (18 months to 3 years), phallic (3 to 6 years), and genital (13 years to adulthood).

Freud developed the psychosexual theory of personality development. He claimed that personality develops in stages (oral, anal, phallic, latency, and genital) from birth through young adulthood.

Anxiety is a diffuse, vague sense of impending doom and is perceived by the individual as a negative emotion.

Although specific portions of Freud's theory are now viewed as an outgrowth of the Victorian era in which he lived, his theories provided the foundation for the work of subsequent theorists. Erik Erikson expanded Freud's theory of personality development to include the entire life span and emphasized the importance of culture as a major determinant of personality development. Erikson's theory of psychosocial development is called the Eight Ages of Man and encompasses trust versus mistrust (infancy, 0 to 1 year), autonomy versus shame and doubt (early childhood, 1 to 3 years), initiative versus guilt (preschool, 3 to 6 years), industry versus inferiority (school age, 6 to 12 years), identity versus role confusion (adolescence, 12 to 18 years), intimacy versus isolation (young adulthood, 18 to 25 years), generativity versus stagnation (adulthood, 25 to 45 years), and ego integrity versus despair (older adulthood, 45 years to death).

Erik Erikson expanded Freud's theory of personality development to include the entire life span from a psychosocial framework. Erikson's theory is known as the Eight Ages of Man—trust versus mistrust, autonomy versus shame and doubt, initiative versus guilt, industry versus inferiority, identity versus role confusion, intimacy versus isolation, generativity versus stagnation, and ego integrity versus despair.

Interpersonal Model

The interpersonal model was first developed by an American-born psychiatrist, Harry Stack Sullivan

Table 1-1 Ego Defense Mechanisms

Defense Mechanism	Definition	Example
Compensation	Exaggerating one trait to make up for feelings of inadequacy or inferiority in another dimension.	A physically small man verbally bullies his employees.
Conversion	Expressing unconscious emotional conflicts through a physical symptom with no demonstrable organic basis.	A young woman wakes up paralyzed from the waist down on the morning of her wedding day.
Denial	Failing to perceive some threatening object or event in the external world.	A woman sets a place for dinner for her husband, who has just been killed.
Displacement	Attributing feelings to a person or object that are really directed at another person or object.	A young woman kicks her cat after a telephone argument with her boss.
Fixation	Remaining stuck in a developmental stage.	A husband depends totally on his wife for most of his activities of daily living.
Identification	Integrating desired attributes of an admired person to compensate for perceived inadequacy.	A shy adolescent girl styles her hair identically to that of a popular rock star.
Introjection	Incorporating another person to avoid the threat posed by the person or by one's own urges.	A psychotically depressed woman attempts suicide to kill her mother, whom she states is in her stomach.
Isolation	Severing the connection between the thoughts and feelings associated with an event so the event can remain conscious without undue anxiety.	A single parent talks unemotionally about her only child's recent diagnosis of a malignant brain tumor.
Projection	Attributing to others an objectionable trait or feeling that really emanates from oneself.	"My husband is cheating on me."
Rationalization	Substituting a fictitious, socially acceptable reason for the genuine, unacceptable reason for one's wishes or actions.	"I would have helped you if I could, but I had to take my dog to the vet."
Reaction formation	Substituting directly opposite wishes for one's true wishes.	An adult who grew up in a very messy home is compulsively neat in his or her own home.
Regression	Returning to patterns of behavior characteristic of a less anxiety-producing stage of development.	A 6-year-old girl begins to wet the bed at night after her mother's remarriage.
Repression	Forcibly dismissing anxiety-producing thoughts, feelings, or events from consciousness.	A woman is unable to remember being raped by her brother when she was 10 years old.
Sublimation	Redirecting socially unacceptable urges into socially acceptable behavior.	An angry, hostile young man becomes a boxer.
Symbolization and condensation	Using a neutral idea or object to represent an unacceptable idea or object.	A 40-year-old man has unconscious feelings of inadequacy as a male and spends all his money on guns and all his time polishing and cleaning them.
Undoing	Engaging in certain thoughts and actions so as to cancel out or atone for threatening thoughts or actions that have previously occurred.	A business executive studies to become a nursery school teacher after having an abortion.

Source: Taylor, C. M. (1994). *Essentials of psychiatric nursing* (p. 211). St. Louis, MO: Mosby Yearbook. Reprinted with permission.

(1892–1949). Sullivan believed the most critical factor in the development of the individual's personality, and thus his or her behavior, is the person's relationship with significant others.

Sullivan believed that all human behavior is goal directed toward the fulfillment of two needs—the need for satisfaction and the need for security. The **need for satisfaction** derives from the person's biologic needs for air, food, sex, shelter, and so on. The **need for security** derives from a person's emotional needs for feeling states such as interpersonal intimacy, status, and self-esteem. When these needs are perceived, internal tension results and the individual employs a variety of methods to meet them and thereby reduce the tension. Sullivan termed these methods **dynamisms**. He emphasized that dynamisms are age specific, which helps to explain the characteristics of each stage of personality development, from infancy (birth to 18 months), childhood (18 months to 6 years), juvenile (6 to 9 years), preadolescence (9 to 12 years), early adolescence (12 to 14 years), and late adolescence (14 to 21 years). During infancy, the oral cavity is used almost exclusively to meet the needs for satisfaction (by crying to be fed) and the needs for security (by crying to be held). Therefore, the stage of infancy is characterized by the oral dynamism, because it is the means through which the individual establishes interpersonal contact to meet needs and reduce tension (Taylor, 1994).

The concept of anxiety is central to Sullivan's theory. He postulated that anxiety is a response to feelings of disapproval from a significant adult. These feelings of disapproval may or may not be based on reality, and the adult whose disapproval is feared may be real or a symbolic representation. Sullivan believed that people defend against such anxiety by using **security operations**, including apathy, somnolent detachment, selective inattention, and preoccupation. Individuals use **apathy** by not allowing themselves to feel the emotion associated with an anxiety-producing event. **Somnolent detachment** is a primitive defense in which an individual falls asleep when confronted by a highly threatening, anxiety-producing experience. More common is **selective inattention**, in which anxiety-producing aspects of a situation are not allowed into awareness, enabling the individual to maintain a sense of stability. **Preoccupation** manifests as a consuming interest in a person, thought, or event to the exclusion of the anxiety-producing reality.

Sullivan defined the **self-concept** as the result of reflected appraisals of significant others. He believed that the development of the self-concept begins in the stage of infancy and is closely related to the quality of the infant's feeding experiences. If infants frequently experience satisfaction and security from the mothering they receive during the feeding process, they begin to see themselves as worthwhile individuals; they start to develop what Sullivan refers to as "good me" self-concepts. However, if their needs for satisfaction and security often are not met, anxiety results and infants believe they are not worthwhile; this lays the foundation for the development of "bad me" self-concepts. In extreme cases where infants are severely deprived or when the majority of interpersonal relationships are fraught with great threats to their existence, infants defend themselves by dissociating the anxiety-generating experiences. As a result, because they cannot develop a sense of self from reflected appraisals, infants develop a "not me" self-concept, which may lead to severe emotional problems.

The interpersonal model is based on relationships. Harry Stack Sullivan believed that all human behavior is goal directed toward the fulfillment of two needs—the need for satisfaction and the need for security. When these needs are perceived, internal tension results, and the individual uses dynamisms to relieve the tension.

Once developed, the self-concept tends to self-perpetuate because people behave in a manner consistent with their self-concept and elicit interpersonal responses from others that reinforce their self-concept. Anxiety occurs when others' responses are incongruent with a person's self-concept. People deal with this anxiety by utilizing security operations that enable them to ignore differing input. This theory helps to explain why some persons succeed against all odds and others fail despite all advantages.

Behavioral Models

Unlike the psychoanalytic and interpersonal models, **behavioral models** are concerned with the here and now, not with how or why people developed the behavior they currently exhibit. Ivan Pavlov (1849–1936) was the first behavioral researcher. His work on classical conditioning is well known to all students of psychology. **Classical conditioning** focuses on involuntary behaviors, such as blinking and salivation. In classical conditioning, a person has a reaction to a neutral event because the reaction and the event have become associated. For example, a person who exhibits the involuntary symptoms of anxiety (pounding heart, rapid respirations) when he or she sees a picture of a tall building somehow has learned to associate tall buildings or heights with danger.

The theory of **operant conditioning** has been credited to B. F. Skinner (1904–1990) and his associates. Operant conditioning is concerned with the relationship between voluntary behavior and the environment. Skinner demonstrated that behaviors are influenced by their consequences; those behaviors

People defend against anxiety by using the security operations of apathy, somnolent detachment, selective inattention, and preoccupation.

Ivan Pavlov developed the theory of classical conditioning in which events and reactions become associated. B. F. Skinner developed the theory of operant conditioning, which addresses the relationship between voluntary behavior and the environment.

The self-concept is the result of reflected appraisals of significant others and may include "good me," "bad me," and "not me."

that have a positive consequence increase in strength and are likely to be repeated, whereas behaviors that result in negative consequences are weakened and are less likely to be repeated (McLeod, 2007).

A desired behavior can be increased through positive and negative reinforcement. Behavior is decreased through punishment, response cost, and extinction.

Increasing a desired behavior is achieved through positive and negative reinforcement. **Positive reinforcement** rewards the desired behavior. For example, a person who receives a pay raise because he or she produced more widgets is likely to continue trying to produce even more widgets, assuming that he or she values an increase in pay. **Negative reinforcement** increases the frequency of a behavior by reinforcing the behavior's power to control a negative stimulus. For example, children quickly learn which behaviors are likely to prevent their parents from yelling at them.

Decreasing behavior is a more difficult task. It is achieved through punishment, response cost, and extinction. **Punishment** is an aversive stimulus that occurs after the behavior and serves to decrease its future occurrence. For example, a child whose parents make him take a time out by standing in the corner every time he uses a swear word is likely to decrease his use of swear words after several time outs. In **response cost**, a person experiences a loss or penalty as a consequence of engaging in a certain behavior. The teenager who is grounded 1 day for every 5 minutes she is late coming home from a date is likely to arrive home on time after several experiences of being grounded. **Extinction** is the process of eliminating a behavior by ignoring or not rewarding it. Repeatedly ignoring a child's temper tantrums is an example of extinction. Efforts to increase or decrease behavior require a plan of treatment that is consistently implemented and avoids unintended secondary gains, such as getting much-desired attention (McLeod, 2007).

Cognitive frameworks address mental processes such as memory, attention, perception, thinking, problem solving, decision making, and communication as demonstrated in cognitive behavior and rational emotive behavioral therapies.

Self-Actualization Model

Abraham Maslow, an American psychologist, first published his book, *Towards a Psychology of Being*, in 1962, postulating a theory of quality of life. He described his theory as a psychology of **self-actualization** based on a concept of meeting various human needs. Maslow identified a **hierarchy of needs** that motivate individuals moving from the most basic to the highest level of need, often described as a pyramid of progressive needs. In order, these needs are (Maslow, 2011):

- *Biological and physiological needs:* Air, food, water, shelter, warmth, sexuality, sleep, homeostasis, freedom from pain
- *Safety needs:* Protection from the elements, harm, loss, and assurance of security, order, law, limits, and stability
- *Belonging and love needs:* Acceptance in meaningful groups (family, peers, and workplace), affection, commitment, and relationships
- *Esteem needs:* Self-respect, achievement, mastery, independence, status, workplace responsibility
- *Self-actualization needs:* Realizing personal potential, self-fulfillment, morality, creativity, problem-solving, lack of prejudice, seeking personal growth

Some theorists have postulated an additional level called transcendence needs, helping others to achieve their own self-actualization. Increasingly, healthcare practitioners are understanding that when a client's diseases and/or health status do not improve in spite of the best medical and nursing care, that the key lies in the client's feelings of empowerment and ability to achieve his or her hierarchy of needs.

Cognitive Models

Cognitive models address mental processes such as memory, attention, perception, thinking, problem solving, decision making and communication. During the 1st decade of the 21st century, the National Institute of Mental Health has been supporting research on how the many facets of cognition relate to mental disorders.

Two pioneers in cognitive therapy were Aaron Beck, a psychiatrist and researcher, and Albert Ellis, a psychologist and psychotherapist. Dr. Beck's early research focused on increasing depressed patients' objectivity regarding their misinterpretations (cognitive distortions) of situations, sensations, or feelings. His cognitive therapy focused on teaching patients how to modify their cognitive distortions and cope more effectively with their psychological and interpersonal behaviors. He discovered that the content of patients' thoughts was mainly focused on negative ideas about themselves, the world, and the future. He was able to demonstrate that patients with psychiatric disorders (especially depression, bipolar disorder, panic disorder, and schizophrenia) who participated in cognitive therapy in conjunction with psychopharmacology had more successful outcomes. Currently, **cognitive behavioral therapy** continues to prove to be an effective modality (Beck, 2011).

Dr. Ellis developed the ABC cognitive model based on a belief that dysfunctional emotions and behaviors come from underlying beliefs in how patients appraise events, persons, and their inner world. Irrational beliefs produce dysfunctional emotions while rational beliefs culminate in functional emotions. He encouraged his patients to identify the "Activating event," explore the "Belief" or expectation, and understand the "Consequences." He developed a method of short-term therapy (**Rational Emotive Behavior Therapy**) that had patients focusing on what was happening in their lives and taking immediate action to change their behavior (Ellis & Dryden, 1997).

Developmental Models

There is a variety of developmental models offered by theorists that assist one in understanding how growth and development impact upon an individual's mental health. These include:

- An attachment model (John Bowlby, 1907–1990) based on the establishment of trust, bonding, and attachment as essential to the survival of the human species.
- A behavior modification model postulated by Fritz Redl (1902–1988) and David Wineman in which children are taught how to establish controls from within and that there are consequences (natural, logical, and unrelated) to one's behavior.
- A psychosocial model (Erik Erikson, 1902–1994) based on the importance of trust as a basic building block for normal psychological development that includes eight stages of developmental growth (see Chapter 27).
- A developmental model (Jean Piaget, 1896–1980), focused on the process involved in a child's ability to know and understand. He was the first theorist to postulate the different maturation cycles involved in how children gain an awareness of self through cognitive abilities. His stages of cognitive development include sensorimotor (birth to 18 months), preoperational (2 to 7 years), concrete operations (6 to 12 years), and formal operations (12 years to adulthood). For more on this topic, see Chapter 27.

Neurobiologic Model

In the late 20th century, it became apparent that an understanding of the brain and the nervous system is basic to understanding the symptoms, processes, and treatment of mental illnesses and disorders. Molecular biology is the foundation for molecular psychiatry.

Psychiatric-mental health nurses and other clinicians are increasingly challenged to understand neurons, neuronal transmitter brain receptors, ion channel variants, and intercellular neuronal molecules and their effect on neural circuits, and ultimately, the behavior of individuals. The **neurobiologic model** and its associated psychopharmacologic treatments are driving forces in modern psychiatric interventions. For most clients, pharmacologic treatment controls the main symptoms of the mental illness or disorder and is used in conjunction with supportive therapies such as individual psychotherapy, group therapy, family therapy, and self-help groups.

The neurobiologic model and its associated psychopharmacologic treatments are the driving forces in the modern era of psychiatric-mental health care.

Stress Adaptation Model

Hans Selye, the father of modern stress theory (1907–1982), pioneered the concept of biological stress (general adaptation stress). More recently, researchers have explored the role of corticotropin-releasing factor (CRF) signaling pathways in the endocrine, behavioral, autonomic, and immune responses of individuals. Researchers have been particularly studying the relationships among early childhood traumas, socioeconomic status, family environment, and genetic predispositions as stressors on these major regulatory systems, culminating in adverse mental and physical health outcomes in adults (Taylor, Way, & Seeman, 2010). While there appears to be a strong correlation between early childhood trauma and neurobiological changes in the brain, there is also evidence that maladaptive behaviors related to these alterations can be changed by evidence-based interventions from mental health practitioners (Rich & Douglas, 2007).

Jean Piaget was the first theorist to use a developmental model to describe cognitive abilities (sensorimotor, preoperational, concrete operations, and formal operations).

Interpersonal Theory of Psychiatric Nursing Practice

The practice of professional nursing has a long history of various nursing philosophies (including those of Florence Nightingale, Jean Watson, and Patricia Benner); nursing models (behavioral, systems, **self-care deficit**, adaptation), and theories (interpersonal, role modeling, cultural diversity, and nursing process). Nurse theorists and psychiatric-mental health nursing specialists have stressed the interpersonal dimension of nursing in their various conceptual models and their shared understanding that some form of personal interaction with patients or clients is the basis of the practice of the nursing profession.

The Dynamic Nurse–Patient Relationship: Function, Process and Principles of Professional Nursing Practice, written by Ida Jean Orlando and published in 1961, emphasizes the reciprocal relationship between patient and nurse.

Hildegard Peplau, as a nurse educator, clinician, and researcher, has had the greatest impact on the development and practice of psychiatric nursing. Although Peplau held a number of significant positions, she is best known for initiating and developing the graduate program in psychiatric nursing at Rutgers University, where she was the director for 20 years. Her textbook, *Interpersonal Relations in Nursing*, first published in 1952, significantly changed psychiatric nursing from a medical model to an interpersonal model in which the nurse has a major role in therapeutic interventions. It was empowering to nurses and the nursing profession at a critical time when their contributions to the care of mentally ill patients were not recognized. Furthermore, her theories were widely applicable to the practice of nursing in all settings and with all types of patients. The major concepts of Peplau's theories are **psychodynamic nursing**, the **nurse–patient relationship**, and nursing roles.

No other nurse has had a greater impact on the development and practice of psychiatric nursing than Hildegard Peplau. The major concepts of Peplau's theories are psychodynamic nursing, the nurse–patient relationship, and nursing roles.

As described by Marriner-Tomey, "Psychodynamic nursing is being able to understand one's own behavior to help others identify felt difficulties, and to apply principles of human relations to the problems that arise at all levels of experience" (1998, p. 327). The therapeutic nurse–patient relationship is the concept for which Peplau is best known; it is considered the hallmark of psychiatric-mental health nursing. She describes an interaction between the nurse and patient as having four distinct yet overlapping phases: orientation, identification, exploitation, and resolution. In the orientation phase there is a felt need, and the patient seeks professional assistance. Identification occurs after the patient has clarified the situation and begins to respond selectively to the various healthcare practitioners. In the exploitation phase, the patient has identified with a specific nurse and makes full use of all offered services. The resolution phase occurs as the patient gradually relinquishes identification with the caregivers (nurses and others) and is once again independent (Peplau, 1952).

The therapeutic relationship between the nurse and client is a hallmark of psychiatric-mental health nursing.

Finally, Peplau describes six different nursing roles that emerge in the various phases of the nurse–patient relationship: stranger, resource person, teacher, leader, surrogate, and counselor. The roles change with the patients and the circumstances. Peplau emphasized that skill in these roles is developed only through practice and with ongoing, competent supervision.

Individual therapy focuses on the person. Almost all conceptual models are now implemented as types of individual therapy.

With support from the National Institute of Mental Health, Ida Jean Orlando (Pelletier) was able to develop a theory that clearly described what nurses consider to be good and bad nursing practice (Alligood & Tomey, 2006). In 1961 in *The Dynamic Nurse–Patient Relationship: Function, Process and Principles of Professional Nursing Practice*, Orlando described the reciprocal relationship between patient and nurse; this description has had great impact on psychiatric nursing. Equally significant in her theory is the importance of the nurse's mind in the process and nurse's recognition of the need to acquire new knowledge in many different domains (physiological, psychosocial, research based, administrative, and political) to address differing patient situations (Alligood & Tomey, 2006). She was one of the first leaders of nursing to emphasize the elements of the nursing process and the critical importance of the patient's participation during the nursing process (Marriner-Tomey, 1998). Additionally, Josephine Paterson and Loretta Zderad have developed a humanistic theory that defines nursing as a nurturing response aimed at achieving well-being. Their framework incorporates the importance of practice, education, and research into clinical nursing practice (O'Connor, 1993). As with Peplau's theory, the theories of Orlando, and Paterson and Zderad have been demonstrated to apply to all nurse–patient interactions.

Critical Thinking Question www

Which of the previously described nursing models do you think would be most useful in the practice of psychiatric-mental health nursing, and why?

Treatment Modalities

Based on the conceptual models used by the therapist and an assessment of the needs of the client, a treatment modality is selected, implemented, and evaluated. The following briefly describes the most commonly used treatments.

Individual Therapy

Individual therapy focuses on the person and includes other aspects of a person's life only as they relate to the individual. Psychoanalysis was the original form of individual therapy, although almost all conceptual models are now implemented as types of individual therapy. Individual therapy continues to be the most commonly used form of mental health therapy, although most therapists agree that treating individuals in the absence of their social support groups is not optimal.

Family Therapy

Although all nurses are concerned with the family's impact on the client, only those educated as advanced practice psychiatric nurses function as family therapists. Family therapy is based on the belief that the person identified as ill, the identified client, exhibits symptoms that emanate from problems within the family system. Therefore, treatment of the identified client in isolation from his or her family is doomed to failure. Two of the theoretical bases of family therapy are family systems therapy and structural family therapy.

Family systems therapy was developed by Murray Bowen in the 1950s and is based on the belief that families are systems in which change in one aspect of the system affects the entire system. Therefore, when there is a change in the functioning of one family member, the entire family is affected. Family systems theory consists of seven interlocking concepts. Three concepts apply to overall characteristics of family systems: differentiation of self, triangles, and the nuclear family emotional system. The other four concepts are related to the central family characteristics: multigenerational transmission process, family projection process, sibling position, and emotional cutoff (Stuart, 2008).

Bowen believes that a member's movement toward either increased emotional closeness or distance is reflexive and predictable. The higher the level of differentiation, the higher the level of functioning. Differentiating the self from "we-ness" is the ultimate goal of treatment (Stuart, 2008). Family genograms are commonly used to depict the familial emotional system through generations (**Figure 1-5**). A **genogram** is a diagram or map of multiple generations of a family indicating family relationships, life events, family functioning, and significant developmental events. Men are represented by boxes, and women are represented by circles. Other symbols and lines represent births, deaths, marriages, cohabitation, children, pregnancies, adoptions, divorces and separations, ethnic and religious origin, health and illness, risk factors, and geographic locations.

Structural family therapy was developed by family therapist Salvatore Minuchin. It is based on understanding the individual within a social context. Minuchin postulated that behavior is a consequence

Family therapy is based on the belief that the person who is identified as ill exhibits symptoms that emanate from problems within the family system.

Family systems therapy is based on the belief that families are systems in which change in one aspect of the system affects the entire system.

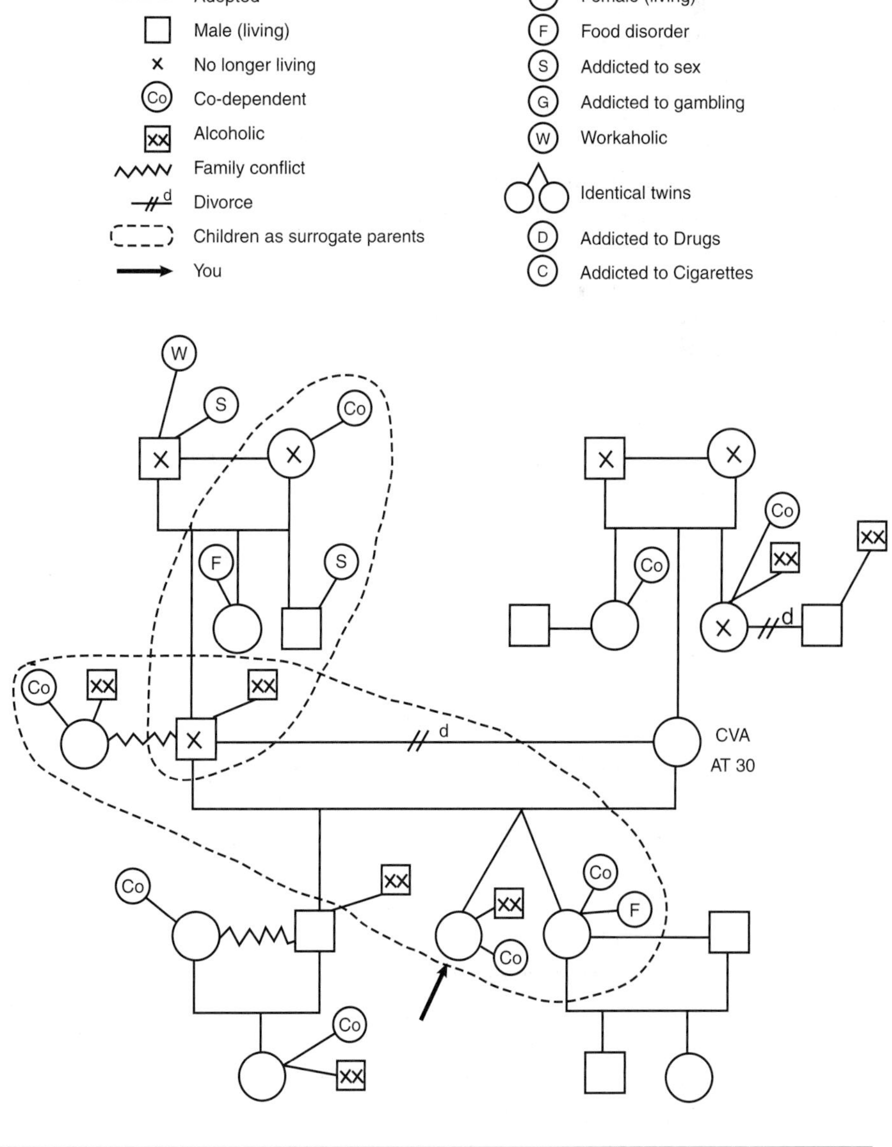

Figure 1-5 **An example of a genogram.**

Group theorist Irvin D. Yalom identified 11 operative factors that influence the therapeutic efficacy of groups.

Structural family therapy is based on understanding the individual within a social context.

Milieu therapy is the use of the environment as a therapeutic tool.

The therapeutic group differs from a social group because its goal is to assist individuals to alter their behavior patterns and to develop new and more effective ways of dealing with the stressors of daily living.

There are four developmental phases for all groups: the preaffiliation phase, the power and control phase, the working phase, and the termination phase.

of the family's organization and the interactional patterns between members. Changing the family organization and the feedback processes between members changes the context in which a person functions. Thus, a person's inner processes and behavior change (Stuart, 2008).

Critical Thinking Question

What do you think is the impact of the nurse–patient reciprocal relationship on the practice of psychiatric-mental health nursing?

Group Therapy

Group therapy became a standard intervention for the treatment of persons diagnosed with a mental illness during and immediately after World War II. A group is an identifiable system composed of three or more individuals who engage in certain tasks to achieve a common goal. The therapeutic group differs from a social group because its goal is to assist individuals to alter their behavior patterns and to develop new and more effective ways of dealing with the stressors of daily living. This goal may be achieved through many forms of group therapy, including task groups, socialization groups, self-help groups, psychotherapy groups, teaching and learning groups, and supportive therapy groups.

Regardless of their type, all groups go through four developmental phases, and certain group behaviors characterize each phase. The first phase is the preaffiliation phase, during which members become acquainted with each other and develop trust in one another and in the group leader. Some groups are never able to move beyond this first phase. If the group is successful in achieving trust, it enters the second phase, termed the power and control phase. During this phase, intragroup conflict is experienced as members test each other and the group leader. If this phase is successfully negotiated, the group enters the third phase, termed the working phase. During this phase, the goal of the group is addressed directly. For example, in a task group, the members are able to address the task the group was formed to accomplish.

The final phase is the termination phase. Group members integrate what they have learned about themselves and the behavioral changes they have made so that they can use these skills in the future. The success of the group is determined to some extent by the skill of the group leader or coleaders whose interventions must be appropriate to the group's development. For example, the question, "What is our purpose?" in the first phase is likely to be an attempt to set boundaries and orient group members. Therefore, a direct, factual answer is most appropriate. The same question asked during the next stage of group development is likely to represent a testing behavior and is best answered by reflecting the question back to the group as a whole.

Group theorist Irvin D. Yalom has identified 11 operative factors that appear to account for the therapeutic efficacy of groups: the imparting of information, the instillation of hope, universality, altruism, corrective recapitulation of the primary family group, development of socializing techniques, imitative behavior, interpersonal learning, existential factors, catharsis, and group cohesion (Yalom & Leszcz, 2005).

Milieu Therapy

Milieu therapy is the use of the environment as a therapeutic tool. The basis of milieu therapy is the belief that all human beings are affected by their physical, social, and emotional climate. Therefore, the physical, social, and emotional climate may be structured to help those who have a mental illness. For example, research has documented that clients who are acutely ill respond best to a structured, consistent, and nonstimulating environment. In contrast, individuals with a mental illness who are well enough to live in the community often benefit from treatment environments they have actively helped to create and maintain (Taylor, 1994). Therapeutic treatment settings have the following characteristics:

- The client's physical needs are met.
- The client is respected as an individual with rights, needs, and opinions and is encouraged to express them.
- Decision-making authority is clearly defined and distributed appropriately among clients and staff.
- The client is protected from injury from self and others, but only those restrictions necessary to afford such protection are imposed.
- The client is afforded increasing opportunities for freedom of choice, commensurate with his or her ability to make decisions.
- The staff remains essentially constant.
- The environment provides a testing ground for the establishment of new patterns of behavior.

- Emphasis is placed on social interaction between and among clients and staff, and the environment's physical structure and appearance facilitate this interaction.
- Programming is structured but flexible.

The **therapeutic community** is a type of milieu therapy that strives to involve clients in their therapy, restore their self-confidence by providing many opportunities for decision making, increase their self-awareness, and focus their attention and concern away from the self and toward the needs of others. This treatment modality has been most successful with groups of clients who are in contact with reality (Taylor, 1994).

Crisis Intervention

A **crisis** is a "state of disequilibrium resulting from the interaction of an event with the individual's or family's coping mechanisms, which are inadequate to meet the demands of the situation, combined with the individual's or family's perception of the meaning of the event" (Taylor, 1994, p. 456). Thus, not every untoward event precipitates a crisis state in all individuals and families. Crisis intervention is of great interest to mental health professionals, because it provides a specific opportunity to prevent mental illness and to promote mental health. Research has documented that there are three potential outcomes to a crisis state: (1) the individual or family may reintegrate at a lower or less healthy level of functioning than the one before the crisis; (2) the individual or family may reintegrate at the same level of functioning as previously; or (3) the individual or family may reintegrate at a higher, healthier level of functioning than the level before the crisis experience. This last potential outcome promotes mental health and is most likely to be achieved with skilled intervention.

There are two types of crises—developmental and situational. The events that precipitate **developmental crises** are predictable and occur in conjunction with normal developmental transitions with which the individual and family are not prepared to cope. For example, the demands placed on a young couple by the birth of their first child may precipitate a crisis state if their idea of parenthood was fashioned by romantic notions of baby powder and teething biscuits. Developmental crises may be averted by **anticipatory guidance**, an educative process in which individuals and families are prepared for the normal life changes expected at each stage of development and are told about successful coping strategies. Self-help groups and books are common sources of anticipatory guidance.

In contrast, **situational crises** are precipitated by unpredictable events for which people cannot prepare, such as the sudden death of a child. Whereas the death of one's parent is a normal developmental event, the sudden death of one's child is an untoward event for which no one can be prepared. In such events, parents have no recourse other than general coping strategies, such as their religious faith and family cohesiveness. If these are adequate, a crisis state may be averted. If these or similar strategies do not exist or are insufficient, a crisis state occurs.

The goal of crisis intervention is to assist the individual and family to seek new and useful adaptive mechanisms within the context of the social support system. The steps of crisis intervention are deceptively simple: clients must achieve an accurate perception of the event that precipitated the crisis state, become aware of the human and material resources available to assist them, and learn how to manage their feelings. Even though these three steps seem simple, the crisis intervention counselor often spends hours helping clients tell and retell their experiences to identify the significance of the events and to identify and plan the use of resources. This process often must be repeated several times, but the reward of promoting the mental health of clients more than justifies the amount of time spent and the flexibility required.

The therapeutic community is a particular type of therapeutic environment that has been very successful for clients who are in contact with reality.

A crisis results when the individual's or family's coping mechanisms are inadequate to deal with the demands of a particular event, causing a state of disequilibrium.

The goal of crisis intervention is to assist the individual and family to seek new and useful adaptive mechanisms within the context of the social support system.

Somatic Therapies

Somatic therapies are physiologically based interventions designed to produce behavioral change. Somatic therapies are based on the belief that an inextricable relationship exists between the mind and the body. In other words, the dichotomy between mind and body and between mental and physical illnesses is false. The most commonly used somatic therapies are pharmacologic therapy and brain stimulation therapies (ECT). These interventions are discussed in depth in Chapters 6 and 17.

Somatic therapies are physiologically based interventions designed to produce behavioral change. The most commonly used somatic therapies are electroconvulsive therapy and pharmacologic therapy.

There are three potential outcomes to a crisis state and two types of crises—developmental and situational.

Summary

Historically, mentally ill persons have been poorly treated by society, suffering abandonment, beatings, starvation, and imprisonment. More humane models of treatment were short lived until the recent advent of therapeutic models of care and the availability of reliable psychopharmaceuticals. Because of the current scope and complexity of the burgeoning knowledge about the causes and treatment of mental illness, it is necessary for the multidisciplinary treatment team to work closely together to achieve the goals of preventing mental illness and effectively treating those who are ill.

The major conceptual models are the psychoanalytic, interpersonal, behavioral, cognitive, developmental, and neurobiologic models. These models of care are supplemented by Peplau's interpersonal theory of psychiatric nursing practice. The therapeutic nurse–patient or nurse–client relationship is the hallmark of psychiatric nursing. The treatment modalities commonly utilized include individual, family, group, milieu, and somatic therapies, with consideration of the need for crisis intervention.

Annotated References

Alligood, M. R., & Tomey, A. M. (2006). *Nursing theory: Utilization & application* (3rd ed.). St. Louis, MO: Mosby/Elsevier.
This edition demonstrates how nursing philosophies, models, and theories guide critical thinking and decision making in the practice of the nursing profession.

Beck, J. (2011). *Cognitive behavior therapy: Basics & beyond* (2nd ed.). New York, NY: Guilford Press.
This is a modern interpretation of a classic work on cognition, behavior, mental disorders, and therapy.

Beers, C. (1923). *A mind that found itself.* New York, NY: Doubleday.
This is Beers's autobiographical account of his mental illness, hospitalizations, treatment, and recovery.

Ellis, A., & Dryden, W. (1997). *The practice of rational emotive behavior therapy.* New York, NY: Springer Publishing.
This is an insightful description of this form of cognitive therapy by its founder, Dr. Ellis, and one of his disciples.

Marriner-Tomey, A. (1998). *Nursing theorists and their work.* St. Louis, MO: Mosby-Yearbook.
This text presents a discussion of the theories of all major nurse theorists. A lengthy reference list for each theorist is included.

Maslow, A. (2011). *Toward a psychology of being* (3rd ed.). New York, NY: Wilder Publications.
This new edition of this classic book brings Professor Maslow's ideas to a whole new generation of psychology and management readers, as well as anyone interested in the study of human behavior.

McLeod, S. (2007). Skinner: Operant conditioning. *Simply Psychology.* Retrieved from www.simplypsychology.org/operant-conditioning.html
This piece contains review of the contributions of B.F. Skinner to the laws of effect and conditioning of research subjects.

O'Connor, N. (1993). *Paterson & Zderad: Humanistic nursing theory.* Newbury, CA: Sage Publications.
This is one of Sage's nursing theory treatises in its Notes on Nursing Theories series.

Peplau, H. (1952). *Interpersonal relations in nursing.* New York, NY: G. P. Putnam.
This classic psychiatric nursing textbook provides the basic concepts to guide professional nurses in establishing mature therapeutic relationships with clients (patients) with all types of conditions and in all settings.

Redl, F. & Wineman, D. (1965). *Controls from within: Techniques for the treatment of the aggressive child.* New York, NY: Free Press.
A classic work in the field, the authors describe the personality and behavior problems they encountered dealing with boys in Pioneer House and methods for establishing control over aberrant behaviors.

Rich, S., & Douglas, D. H. (2007, April). Neurobiological effects of childhood abuse. *Journal of Psychosocial Nursing and Mental Health Services, 45*(4), 47–54.
This article discusses the correlation between early childhood abuse and neurobiological changes in specific regions of the brain, often reflected in psychopathology and lifelong maladaptive behaviors.

Stuart, G. W. (2008). *Principles & practice of psychiatric nursing* (9th ed.). St. Louis, MO: Mosby-Elsevier.
This comprehensive textbook on psychiatric nursing is useful for the practicing nurse as well as for the beginning student.

Taylor, C. M. (1994). *Essentials of psychiatric nursing.* St. Louis, MO: Mosby-Yearbook.
This classic text was designed for the beginning student. It includes many approaches to dealing with problem situations.

Taylor, S. E., Way, B. M., & Seeman, T. E. (2010, August 23). Early adversity and adult health outcomes. *Development and Psychopathology, 3*, 939–954.
The authors examine early childhood socioeconomic status, family environment, and genetic predispositions as antecedents to socio-emotional functioning and psychological distress and physical health outcomes.

Wasserbauer, L. I., & Brodie, B. (1992). Early precursors of psychiatric nursing, 1838–1907. *Nursing Connections, 5*, 19–25.
This article provides an excellent description of the conditions and events contributing to the development of contemporary psychiatric nursing.

Yalom, I. D., & Leszcz, M. (2005). *The theory and practice of group psychotherapy*. New York, NY: Basic Books.
This standard text about group psychotherapy covers all aspects of group psychotherapy with helpful hints for addressing difficult situations.

Additional Resources

Albert Ellis Institute. http://www.rebt.org

Beck Institute for Cognitive and Behavioral Therapy. http://beckinstitute.org

Carter, E., Peplau, H. E., & Sills, G. M. (1997). The ins and outs of psychiatric-mental health nursing and the American Nurses Association. *Journal of the American Psychiatric Nurses Association, 3*, 10–16.
This article describes the profound influence of the American Nurses Association on the development of psychiatric-mental health nursing.

Joint Commission on Mental Illness. (1961). *Action for mental health*. New York, NY: Basic Books.
This is the final report of the commission's recommendation for the development of more effective mental health services for the nation.

King, I. (1971). *Toward a theory for nursing: General concepts of human behavior*. New York, NY: John Wiley.
In this book, King's first publication, she proposes a theory for nursing practice based on systems theory.

Olson, T. (1996). Fundamental and special: The dilemma of psychiatric-mental health nursing. *Archives of Psychiatric Nursing, 10*, 3–10.
This article explores the tension between defining psychiatric-mental health nursing as fundamental to the discipline yet also special. The formative works of Hildegard Peplau, Dorothy Mereness, and Claire Fagin are cited.

Orem, D. (2001). *Nursing: Concepts of practice*. St. Louis, MO: Mosby-Yearbook.
First published in 1980, Orem's basic book explains her self-care deficit nursing theory.

Orlando, I. J. (1961). *The dynamic nurse-client relationship: Function, process, and principles of professional nursing practices*. New York, NY: Putnam.
This book, Orlando's first publication, explores the nurse–client relationship.

Pickens, J. (1998). Formal and informal care of people with psychiatric disorders: Historical perspectives and current trends. *Journal of Psychosocial Nursing and Mental Health Services, 36*, 37–43.
This article describes the historical context and current trends in the care of people with psychiatric disorders.

Smoyak, S. (1993). American psychiatric nursing. *AAOHN Journal, 41*, 316–322.
This article provides a broad view of the work of psychiatric nurses in the United States during the previous century.

Smoyak, S. A., & Rouslin, S. (1982). *A collection of classics in psychiatric nursing literature*. Thorofare, NJ: Charles B. Stock.
This book is a compilation of 36 articles written by leaders in psychiatric nursing prior to 1963. It provides a unique perspective on the roots of the specialty.

Internet Resources

For a full suite of assignments and additional learning activities, use the access code located in the front of your book to visit this exclusive website: http://go.jblearning.com/mentalhealth. If you do not have an access code, you can obtain one at the site.

Learning Objectives

After reading this chapter, you will be able to:

- Discuss the applicability of standards of practice to psychiatric-mental health nursing.
- Explain the differences in primary, secondary, and tertiary prevention in the field of mental health.
- Describe the application of the nursing process to psychiatric-mental health nursing.
- Identify the various treatment settings available to clients.
- Contrast the differences and similarities in the practice of psychiatric-mental health registered nurses and psychiatric-mental health advanced practice registered nurses.

Key Terms

Advanced practice registered nurse (APRN)

Assertive community treatment (ACT)

Behavioral health

Case management

Clubhouse model

Diagnostic and Statistical Manual of Mental Disorders

Discharge planning

Evidence-based practice (EBP)

Managed care

Mental disorder or illness

Mental health

Mental health parity

Neurosis

Nurse practice acts

Nursing diagnosis

Nursing documentation

Nursing process

Outcomes of care

Partial hospitalization program

Primary mental health care

Primary, secondary, and tertiary prevention

Psychiatric rehabilitation

Psychosis

Residential treatment setting

Standards of practice

Standards of professional performance

Third-party reimbursement

Chapter 2

Psychiatric-Mental Health Nursing: Practice Issues

Karen A. Ballard

http://go.jblearning.com/mentalhealth 

For a full suite of assignments and additional learning activities, use the access code located in the front of your book to visit this exclusive website: http://go.jblearning.com/mentalhealth. If you do not have an access code, you can obtain one at the site.

Introduction

Psychiatric-mental health nursing is an integral part of the continuum of nursing practice. The American Nurses Association (ANA) describes psychiatric-mental health nursing as "a specialized area of nursing practice committed to promoting mental health through the assessment, diagnosis, and treatment of human responses to mental health problems and psychiatric disorders" (ANA, 2007, p. 1). As a core mental health profession, psychiatric-mental health nursing "employs a purposeful use of self as its art and a wide range of nursing, psychosocial, and neurobiological theories and research evidence as its science" (ANA, 2007, p. 1). The practice of psychiatric-mental health registered nurses includes the provision of "comprehensive, patient-centered mental health and psychiatric care and treatment and outcome evaluation in a variety of settings across the entire continuum of care" (ANA, 2007, p. 14).

Classification of mental disorders should not be seen as classification of people, but of the disorders that can affect people.

Mental Health Definitions

Karl Menninger described the state of **mental health** as "the adjustment of human beings to each other and to the world around them with a maximum of effectiveness and happiness" (1945, p. 1). Others see mental health as the individual's ability to be, to act, to grow, to master, and to become whatever the person wants to be. The ANA views mental health as "emotional and psychological wellness; the capacity to interact with others, deal with ordinary stress, and perceive one's surroundings realistically" (ANA, 2007, p. 67).

A mental disorder or illness is a disturbance in thoughts or mood that causes maladaptive behavior, inability to cope with normal stresses, and impaired functioning.

A **mental disorder or illness** can be defined as "a disturbance in thoughts or mood that causes maladaptive behavior, inability to cope with normal stresses, and/or impaired functioning. Etiology may include genetic, physical, chemical, biologic, psychological, or sociocultural factors" (ANA, 2007, p. 67). Mental illnesses have been traditionally categorized as neuroses or psychoses. A **neurosis** is a mental disorder usually characterized by anxiety and other uncomfortable and distressing symptoms for the individual while reality testing remains intact. A **psychosis** is a mental disorder in which the individual experiences gross impairment of reality testing, severe personality disintegration, and impairment in meeting the ordinary demands of everyday life.

What physically affects the body often has a mental component, and many mental disorders may manifest physically. It is important, always, to see the individual from a holistic perspective.

The American Psychiatric Association (APA) offers the following definition of a mental disorder:

> a clinically significant behavioral or psychological syndrome or pattern that occurs in an individual and that is associated with present distress (e.g., a painful symptom) or disability (i.e., impairment in one or more important areas of functioning) or with a significantly increased risk of suffering, death, pain, disability or an important loss of freedom. . . . It must currently be considered a manifestation of a behavioral, psychological, or biological dysfunction in the individual (2000, p. i).

The classification of mental disorders should not be seen as a classification of people, but of the disorders that people manifest. Individuals should never be referred to as "the manic depressive," "the alcoholic," or "the schizophrenic," but as "the client or individual with schizophrenia, manic-depressive episodes, or alcohol dependence." It is equally incorrect to view individuals as "the cardiac" or "the gallbladder." Such labeling reduces the person to a condition or disease and ignores his or her individuality and humanity.

In this era of managed care, the term **behavioral health** is increasingly being used instead of *psychiatric* or *mental health care*. It appears to some to be more acceptable and less stigmatizing terminology. Behavioral health care blends prevention and treatment of mental health disorders with substance abuse disorders (drug and alcohol) for the purpose of providing comprehensive services to the client.

Critical Thinking Question

Describe how you think a person would feel and/or react to being labeled as "the schizophrenic," "the case with meningitis," "the manic nursing student," or the "alcoholic mother." How does such labeling potentially impact upon an individual's ability to function?

Mental Health Parity

Health insurance plans such as traditional indemnity plans, self-insured plans, government programs, and managed care plans have a history of bias against covering mental health treatment. For decades, such plans used expense as a rationale for not providing mental health coverage.

As a result of the federal Mental Health Parity Act of 1996, employer-sponsored health plans were required to provide equivalent annual and lifetime limits for both medical–surgical benefits and mental health benefits. The employer could choose to not provide mental health benefits. However, if mental health benefits were offered in a plan, **mental health parity** became mandatory. The 1996 legislation did not cover substance abuse services and allowed higher deductible charges for mental health services than for medical or surgical services. The Mental Health Parity and Addiction Equity Act of 2007 extended coverage to substance abuse services, and banned differences in limits, co-payments, and deductibles for mental health, substance abuse, and medical-surgical services. Parity or equality in benefits helps to increase access to mental health and addiction services. Many analysts now indicate that parity adds little to total health costs and may even save money, especially if the mental health benefit is provided through a managed care plan.

Critical Thinking Question 

How does inadequate access to mental health services impact upon the health of the individual, family, and community?

Nurse Practice Acts

Registered nurses are guided in both general and specialty practice by individual state **nurse practice acts** that establish the authority for professional nursing practice and the rules and regulations for each state. Most state nurse practice acts provide a general description of what constitutes the legally protected scope of practice in the state for registered professional nurses (RNs) and licensed practical nurses (LPNs). RNs are independent practitioners of nursing, whereas LPNs are dependent practitioners who deliver nursing care under the direction or supervision of a registered professional nurse, physician, or other legally authorized healthcare practitioner. Some states also describe the scope of practice of **advanced practice registered nurses (APRNs)** or advanced practice nurses (APNs) such as nurse practitioners, clinical nurse specialists, certified nurse midwives, and certified registered nurse anesthetists.

All nurses are responsible for knowing the statutes, rules, and regulations for nursing practice in the states in which they are licensed to practice. In specialties such as psychiatric-mental health nursing, nurses are responsible for acquiring and maintaining competency through appropriate education, knowledge, training, and experience.

Scope and Standards of Practice

Nurses receive direction for both general and specialty practice from such documents as the ANA's *Nursing's Social Policy Statement, Code of Ethics for Nurses, Nursing: Scope and Standards of Practice*, and various statements and standards related to psychiatric-mental health nursing, child and adolescent psychiatric nursing, psychiatric consultation liaison nursing, addictions nursing, and intellectual and developmental disabilities nursing. The phenomena of concern specific to psychiatric-mental health nursing (**Table 2-1**) include actual or potential mental health problems.

Critical Thinking Question 

How are the psychiatric-mental health phenomena of concern manifested by clients in an inpatient psychiatric unit?

ANA's *Psychiatric-Mental Health Nursing: Scope and Standards of Practice* (2007) was collaboratively written by representatives of the American Nurses Association, American Psychiatric Nurses Association (APNA), and the International Society of Psychiatric-Mental Health Nurses and can be found in Appendix I. The standards are authoritative statements describing the responsibilities for which nurses are accountable, reflect the values and priorities of the profession, provide direction for professional nursing practice, provide a framework for the evaluation of nursing practice, define the profession's accountability to the public, and identify the client outcomes for which nurses are responsible (ANA, 2007). Based on the generic *Nursing: Scope and Standards of Practice*, the specialty-specific *Psychiatric-Mental Health Nursing: Scope and Standards of Practice* is divided into **standards of practice** and **standards of professional performance**.

The standards of practice address the care that the client receives from the psychiatric-mental health registered nurse and are based on the **nursing process**. These standards cover assessment, diagnosis, outcome identification, planning, implementation (coordination of care, health teaching and promotion, milieu therapy, and pharmacological, biological,

Mental health parity means that the annual and lifetime limits in health plans for mental health benefits are equal to the plan's medical and surgical benefits.

The phenomena of concern specific to psychiatric-mental health nursing include actual or potential health problems related to mental disorders and conditions.

Nurse practice acts provide a general description of what constitutes the legally protected scopes of practice of the RN, the LPN, and, in some states, different categories of APRNs.

The *Psychiatric-Mental Health Nursing: Scope and Standards of Practice* includes standards of practice and standards of professional performance. Standards of practice address the care that the mental health client receives and are based on the nursing process. Standards of professional performance address the nurse's behavior in the professional role of a psychiatric-mental health nurse.

Advanced practice registered nurse (APRN) is an umbrella classification used to describe the four nurse specialist categories:
Certified registered nurse anesthetist (CRNA)
Certified nurse midwife (CNM)
Nurse practitioner (NP)
Clinical nurse specialist (CNS)

Standards are authoritative statements reflecting the values and priorities of the profession. They provide direction and a framework for practice while addressing client outcomes and the nurse's accountability.

Table 2-1 Psychiatric-Mental Health Nursing Phenomena of Concern

The promotion of optimal health and well-being and the prevention of mental illness
Impaired ability to function related to psychiatric, emotional, and physiological distress
Alterations in thinking, perceiving, and communicating due to psychiatric disorders or mental health problems
Behaviors and mental states that indicate potential danger to self or others
Emotional stress related to illness, pain, disability, and loss
Symptom management, side effects, and toxicities associated with self-administered drugs, psychopharmacological intervention, and other treatment modalities
Barriers to treatment efficacy and recovery posed by alcohol and substance abuse and dependence
Self-concept and body image changes, developmental issues, life process changes, and end-of-life issues
Physical symptoms that occur along with altered physiological status
Psychological symptoms that occur along with altered physiological status
Interpersonal, organizational, sociocultural, spiritual, or environmental circumstances and events that affect the mental and emotional well-being of the individual, family, or community
Elements of recovery including the ability to maintain housing, employment, and social support that help individuals reengage in the seeking of meaningful lives

Source: American Nurses Association. (2007). *Psychiatric-mental health nursing: Scope and standards of practice.* Washington, DC: Author. pp. 15–16.

and complementary interventions), and evaluation. Additional standards of practice for APRNs include prescriptive authority and treatment, psychotherapy, and consultation. The standards of professional performance address the psychiatric-mental health registered nurse's professional functioning. These standards include quality of practice, education, evaluation, collegiality, collaboration, ethics, research, resource utilization, and leadership (ANA, 2007, p. vi).

In addition to standards, the ANA provides measurement criteria for each of the standards, which should be reviewed by all nurses interested in the specialty. For example, under the diagnosis standard, the psychiatric-mental health registered nurse "derives the diagnoses or problems from the assessment data," and under the quality of practice standard, the psychiatric-mental health registered nurse "incorporates new knowledge to initiate changes in nursing practice if desired outcomes are not achieved" (ANA, 2007, pp. 29, 45). These standards and accompanying measurement criteria apply to the practice of psychiatric-mental health registered nurses in all settings and with all clients—individuals, families, groups, communities, or populations.

Psychiatric-Mental Health Registered Nurses

According to the Society for Education and Research in Psychiatric-Mental Health Nursing (SERPN, 1996), psychiatric-mental health nurses are registered nurses who are educationally prepared in nursing, are licensed to practice in their individual states, and are qualified to practice in the psychiatric-mental health nursing specialty at one of two levels: basic or advanced. These levels of practice are differentiated by the nurse's level of educational preparation, the complexity of the nurse's practice, and the performance of certain specialty nursing functions.

The psychiatric-mental health registered nurse, whose practice skills are generalized, provides interventions such as health promotion and health maintenance, intake screening and evaluation, case management, provision of milieu therapy, promotion of self-care activities, assisting with psychobiological interventions, health teaching, counseling, crisis care, and psychiatric rehabilitation. These nurses combine unique skills to address the mental health client's physical, mental, emotional, social, and spiritual needs. They work in many diverse settings such as hospitals, ambulatory clinics, walk-in clinics, residential settings, halfway houses, occupational health offices, employee assistance programs, and schools (ANA, 2007). Depending upon the individual nurse's level of practice, education, and special training, psychiatric-mental health nurses can utilize counseling; group therapy; milieu therapy; art, music, dance, and other expressive therapies; and alternative and complementary therapies such as imagery, therapeutic touch, and journaling. To achieve professional certification, in addition to meeting the educational requirements, the psychiatric-mental health registered nurse (RN-BC) must have spent a specified time in the practice of psychiatric-mental health nursing, have participated in continuing education, and have successfully completed a national certifying examination administered by the American Nurses Credentialing Center (ANCC).

Psychiatric-Mental Health Advanced Practice Registered Nurses

APRNs in the psychiatric-mental health specialty hold either master's or doctoral degrees in a psychiatric-mental health nursing specialty. These, advanced practice registered nurses are either NPs or CNSs. Some states require APRNs to have a second license whereas others issue certificates authorizing such advanced practice, and other states do not even address advanced practice as a separate category. States may recognize the practice of all four advanced practice categories or selectively recognize particular ones. Almost all the states have laws, regulations, or guidelines for advanced nursing practice.

The movement for separate recognition of the different categories of APRNs was driven by the fears and beliefs that advanced nursing practice without separate authorization was illegal, the desire for prescriptive privileges, and the need for nurses in private practice to qualify for direct third-party reimbursement from traditional indemnity insurance plans, federal and state reimbursement plans, and managed care plans. Even the titles of APRN and APN were created to uniformly recognize and refer to these nurses because in some states and insurance programs the various specialty titles were unclear and often were used to refer to more than one category of practitioner, especially that of NP and CNS.

APRNs in psychiatric-mental health nursing may become certified specialists, as clinical nurse specialists (PMHCNS-BC) or nurse practitioners (PMHNP-BC), through the American Nurses Credentialing Center. There are specific requirements for educational preparation, including a master's degree, post-master's degree or doctorate from an appropriately accredited program, that includes specific course work in health assessment, pharmacology, pathophysiology, as well as a minimum number of faculty-supervised clinical hours, with clinical training in at least two psychotherapeutic treatment modalities.

Psychiatric-mental health APRNs may work in individual or group practices with other nurse specialists or mental health professionals. They practice psychotherapy and psychoanalysis; may prescribe psychotropic medications and supervise medication regimens; act as consultants, educators, and clinical liaisons; and provide direct clinical supervision for psychiatric nurses and other APRNs. The areas of subspecialization in psychiatric-mental health nursing include adult, child, and adolescent; geriatric; addictions; chronically mentally ill; consultation-liaison; forensic; marital and family; home care; and case management.

Critical Thinking Question

What are some specific differences in the scopes of practice of a psychiatric-mental health registered nurse and a psychiatric-mental health advanced practice registered nurse?

Third-Party Reimbursement

Third-party reimbursement for the services of APRNs in psychiatric-mental health care may be reimbursed through traditional indemnity insurance plans; self-insured plans constructed by employers and other groups; managed care plans; and state and federal government plans such as Medicare and Medicaid. From the 1970s through the 1990s, the ANA on a federal level, the state nurses associations on a local level, and the psychiatric nursing specialty organizations advocated in the states and in Congress for the inclusion of the services of psychiatric-mental health APRNs in all appropriate plans where mental health services were covered. Examples of some of these federal initiatives include four demonstration projects establishing community nursing organizations providing community-based nursing and ambulatory care services under the direction of RNs (Bower, 1992). A significant reimbursement victory for nurses involved the legislation of Medicare reimbursement for CNSs and NPs in all specialty areas, regardless of geographic setting, in the 1997 federal Balanced Budget Act. As of January 1, 1998, if a service is covered under Medicare Part B and can be provided within the legal scope of practice of an NP or CNS, that service is reimbursable directly to the nurse, or, if the nurse agrees, the facility, physician, or group that employs the NP or CNS. In 2010, in the Patient Protection and Affordable Care Act, all APRNs were recognized as providers for services within their scope of nursing practice for covered healthcare services identified within the legislation.

Managed care is both a delivery system and a reimbursement system; it is a healthcare system that aims to combine cost-effectiveness with quality care.

Managed care is both a delivery system and a reimbursement system; this dual role has created implementation problems. It is difficult to concentrate on managing a client's care and addressing health needs while focusing on controlling costs and payments. Ultimately, concerns arise about the type of care being delivered, who is receiving it, under what circumstances, and by which provider. Concern has been raised whether managed care, with its focus on cost containment and financing arrangements, puts at risk the traditional values of nursing such as patient advocacy, holistic care, and addressing the individual's specific health needs (ANA, 1998).

Managed care has been described as "a health care system that combines cost-effectiveness with quality care" (Klainberg, Holzemer, Leonard, & Arnold, 1998, p. 392). Increasingly, APRNs have been able to receive admission as clinicians on the treatment panels of managed care organizations. Some examples of managed care entities are health maintenance organizations (HMOs), preferred provider organizations (PPOs), and point of service (POS) plans. Some terms that nurses encounter in managed care include *alternate delivery system* (services outside of the hospital), *capitation* (a method of providing a set payment per month per covered member to a provider), *case mix* (the frequency and intensity of the health needs of a population), *gatekeeper* (a practitioner who controls access to health care), *paneled provider* (a practitioner who can provide care in a payment system), *integrated delivery system* (networks of providers joined for purposes of mutual benefit), and *seamless care* (coordinated care as the client moves along the health services continuum). To be identified as a managed care plan, a plan must comprise certain components: restricted service networks, control of payment for services, benefits designed to maximize services, aggressive care and case management, an active quality improvement program, and data gathering and dissemination of information on the health of the population being served by the plan (Al-Assaf, 1998).

Some managed care buzzwords are *alternative delivery system, capitation, case mix, gatekeeper, paneled provider, integrated delivery system*, and *seamless care*.

The Nursing Process and Classification Systems

The nursing process is a systematic and interactive problem-solving approach that includes individualized client assessment, diagnosis, outcomes identification, planning, implementation, and evaluation.

The nursing process "encompasses significant actions taken by registered nurses and forms the foundation of the nurse's decision-making" (ANA, 2010 p. 9). When applied to psychiatric-mental health nursing, the nursing process involves the following areas: assessment, diagnosis, outcomes identification, planning, implementation and evaluation.

Assessment

During the assessment interview and in subsequent interactions, the psychiatric-mental health registered nurse collects both subjective (client history) and objective data (mental status evaluation), including observations made during the interview. These may include: the main complaint or problem; general physical, mental, and emotional health status; personal and family history; support systems in the family, social group, or community; activities of daily living (ADLs); health habits and beliefs; substance use or abuse; use of prescription medications; interpersonal relationships; risk of injury to self and others; coping patterns; spiritual beliefs and values; client's interest in changing behaviors; and any other factors that may influence the client's ability to function and respond to treatment. Family, significant others, social workers and other clinicians, and individuals who have interacted with the client (e.g., emergency room personnel, law enforcement officers, shelter staff, and clergy) can be consulted to confirm, contradict, or add to the assessment data.

Nursing Diagnosis

The psychiatric-mental health registered nurse uses the assessment data to identify the actual or potential problems. Depending on the nurse's level of practice and skill, the data are organized into an acceptable framework using one or more of the common classification systems. These systems are the North American Nursing Diagnosis Association's (NANDA) *Nursing Diagnosis Classification*, which includes appropriate psychiatric nursing diagnoses, and the APA's ***Diagnostic and Statistical Manual of Mental Disorders,*** which defines criteria for the diagnosis of mental disorders.

A **nursing diagnosis** is composed of the problem or unmet need, its etiology or cause (expressed as "related to"), and the objective and subjective supporting data (expressed as "evidenced by"). An example for a client with anorexia nervosa would be the following: Disturbed body image related to morbid fear of obesity as evidenced by self-destructive behaviors (refusal to eat, vomiting, and abuse of laxatives).

Nursing diagnoses are the basis for choosing goals, outcomes, and nursing interventions.

Outcomes Identification

Outcomes reflect the desired changes to be achieved by the client as a result of the planned nursing interventions. They provide direction for the client's care and should be both attainable and measurable. The psychiatric mental health nurse sets both short- and long-term goals, ideally with the client, that move the client toward attaining the desired outcomes. *Nursing Outcomes Classification (NOC)* is a text that presents standardized terminology and measures for nursing-sensitive patient outcomes that result from nursing interventions; it includes 385 research-based outcomes (Moorhead, Swanson, Johnson, & Maas, 2008). Each diagnosis should have at least one outcome with corresponding goal(s).

Planning

The psychiatric-mental health registered nurse develops an individualized plan of care for the client, clearly identifying the evidence-based interventions that should be used to meet the expected outcomes. Interventions should be safe, appropriate, effective, and individualized for the client. Each outcome should have at least one corresponding goal. Goals (short and long term) should be measurable, realistic, understandable, and prioritized within an established time frame. This plan of care is developed in collaboration with the client, family, and other clinicians. It provides continuity of care and should reflect current and evidence-based psychiatric nursing practice.

Implementation

Nursing activities or actions are identified and implemented to help the client meet the planned goals. The implementation interventions utilized by psychiatric-mental health nurses and APRNs, depending upon the nurse's education, experience, and authorization, may include counseling, milieu therapy, self-care activities, medications, health education, health promotion, health maintenance, and case management; and, for APRNS, consultation and referrals, psychopharmacology, and psychotherapy.

Evaluation

Evaluation is an ongoing process and should occur throughout the client's course of treatment in order to allow for necessary adjustments to the nursing diagnoses, outcomes, goals, and interventions as needed. This critical step in the nursing process is often considered the most overlooked and undervalued step in the process. The psychiatric-mental health registered nurse determines whether the goals and expected outcomes were met and whether the interventions were effective. If they were not, the nurse should reconsider all steps of the process and consider changes in the plan and interventions. The ANA standards clearly state that psychiatric-mental health registered nurses must identify expected outcomes, develop plans of care to attain expected outcomes, and evaluate the client's progress in attaining expected outcomes. This participation is an integral part of psychiatric-mental health nursing practice (ANA, 2007).

Utilization of the North American Nursing Diagnosis Association (NANDA) and The Diagnostic and Statistical Manual-IV-Text Revised (*DSM-IV-TR*) Classification Systems

A nursing diagnosis states the actual or potential nursing problems based on the nurse's critical appraisal and analysis of the assessment data, including responses and stressors, as they apply to individuals, families, and groups (Reighley, 1988). Formulating a correct nursing diagnosis is a critical step in the nursing process. In writing the nursing diagnosis, the psychiatric-mental health registered nurse utilizes the NANDA-I taxonomy, identifies the problem and its etiology, and describes the specific signs and symptoms particular to the client. Some nursing diagnoses are specific to mental health problems. The taxonomy itself uses a multiaxial structure (see Appendix II). Many resources are available to students and instructors regarding nursing diagnoses and their use in the delivery of nursing care. These should be reviewed and used when constructing nursing care plans for clients with particular psychiatric-mental health problems.

A nursing diagnosis states the actual or potential nursing problems based on the nurse's critical appraisal and analysis of the assessment data, including responses and stressors, as they apply to individuals, families, and groups.

A variety of practitioners provide mental health services to clients, so the most frequently used diagnostic nomenclature utilized by the multidisciplinary team is the *DSM-IV-TR*, a manual, compiled by the American Psychiatric Association (APA). This manual is revised periodically, and the APA is currently reviewing the mental disorders and related diagnostic criteria in preparation for a new edition, the *DSM-5*, scheduled for publication in May 2013. In addition to the *DSM*, some APRNs in psychiatric mental health nursing use the *International Classification of Diseases* (*ICD-9-CM*) to identify and record diagnoses.

Interventions, Outcomes, and Research

Primary, Secondary, and Tertiary Prevention

There are three levels of preventive intervention: primary, secondary, and tertiary. In the United States, more emphasis is placed on secondary and tertiary prevention.

There are three levels of preventive intervention: **primary, secondary, and tertiary prevention.** Currently, in the United States, more emphasis is placed on secondary and tertiary prevention than on primary prevention. Continued interest by the healthcare professions, consumers, insurance plans, and government in health promotion and disease prevention should provide more support for activities that emphasize primary prevention.

Primary prevention focuses on reducing the incidence of mental disorders or the rates at which new cases develop by identifying the causes of specific mental health disorders and offering early intervention programs. These programs include health promotion and education, growth and development classes, parenting classes, stress management, biofeedback, relaxation techniques, and community or political activities.

Secondary prevention focuses on reducing the prevalence of mental disorders by decreasing the number of existing cases through screening and evaluating clients, identifying health needs and health problems, and providing crisis and emergency intervention, medication treatment, case management, and early treatment when symptoms are identified.

There are three categories of indicators for tracking the quality of nursing care: structure, process, and outcome.

Tertiary prevention focuses on reducing the severity of a mental disorder and its associated disabilities through such activities as rehabilitation programs, educational programs that increase understanding of how to manage the symptoms of the disorder and medications, case management, social skills training, aftercare, vocational counseling, and job training (Klainberg et al., 1998; Krupnick & Wade, 1993; Worley, 1997).

Primary mental health care is holistic and addresses the needs and strengths of the whole person.

Primary mental health care from a nursing viewpoint is "a mode of service delivery that is initiated at the first point of contact with the mental health care system." It involves the "continuous and comprehensive mental health services necessary for promotion of optimal mental health, prevention of mental illness, and intervention, health maintenance, and rehabilitation" (ANA, 2007, p. 15). Increasingly, individuals with mental health conditions have been treated with interdisciplinary care. Therapists from the various disciplines of psychiatry; psychology; nursing; social work; art, dance, and music therapy; and more recently philosophical counseling are administering care interchangeably. Ideally, interdisciplinary care should focus on a team approach, with the overlapping strengths and knowledge of the various healthcare professionals matched to the needs of the client, family, group, or community and, as a result of this planned synergy, the **outcomes of care** are enhanced and more comprehensive (ANA, 2007).

Quality of Care

There is increasing pressure on the healthcare industry to measure the quality of outcomes of care, including psychiatric-mental health care. It is often difficult to isolate the particular nursing interventions that produce specific client outcomes. Indicators are qualitative measures used in evaluating and monitoring outcomes; outcomes are measurable changes.

Dramatic shifts in the nursing workforce and concerns among nursing professionals regarding quality of care and client safety resulted in the formation of the National Database of Nursing Quality Indicators (NDNQI) (https://www.nursingquality.org/) in the ANA's National Center for Nursing Quality. The initiative is a national program tracking the quality of nursing care and addresses the following three categories of indicators:

- *Structure of care indicators:* Focus on the organization and delivery of nursing care (supply of nursing staff, skill mix, and educational levels)
- *Process of care indicators:* Focus on the nature and amount of care provided (assessment, intervention, RN work satisfaction)
- *Outcome indicators:* Focus on the effects of interactions between nursing staff and clients (occurrence of pressure ulcers, falls, restraints prevalence, assaults)

Although directed toward acute care, many of the indicators apply to all nursing specialties and clinical settings. Some of the indicators currently being studied include nosocomial infection rates, client injury rate, client satisfaction with nursing care, client satisfaction with educational information, maintenance of skin integrity, staff mix (RN, licensed practical nurse, nursing assistants), total nursing care hours provided per client day, and psychiatric, physical, and sexual assaults. The federal government established the Agency for Healthcare Research and Quality (AHRQ) to study the effectiveness of health care and produce guidelines to support best practices (http://www.ahrq.gov). Some examples of this agency's early work include the management of depression in primary care, acute pain management, and the recognition of early Alzheimer's disease and related dementia. It has established evidence-based practice centers to produce evidence reports on clinical conditions (http://www.ahrq.gov/clinic/epc/).

Evidence-Based Practice

Evidence-based practice (EBP) has been defined as "the integration of the best possible research to evidence with clinical expertise and with patient needs" (Malloch & Porter-O'Grady, 2006, p. 1) and "a problem solving approach to practice that involves the conscientious use of current best evidence in making decisions about patient care" (Melnyk & Fineout-Overholt, 2005, p. 587). In order for evidence-based practice to truly work and to impact upon today's health care and mental health delivery systems, it must arise from the practice setting, include the actual practitioners involved in the delivery of care, and represent the aggregation and integration of applied clinical experiences (Breslin & Lucas, 2003; Malloch & Porter-O'Grady, 2006).

Interest in utilizing evidence-based practice in the delivery of medical, nursing, and health care has increased in the last decade, buoyed by the incredible changes in technology that are available to researchers. Health care as an industry has been slow in utilizing these technologies in the practice setting at the point of care. Also, nurses and other health-care practitioners can be reluctant to try something new and are often distracted from participating in a new approach by the ongoing problems (organizational problems, staffing, lack of support from peers and/or management) encountered in the practice setting.

Stuart (2000) has identified levels of evidence that can be incorporated into evidence-based nursing practice (EBNP). In ascending order of the importance and reliability of these levels, they include the following:

- opinions of reviewers based on their experience and knowledge
- opinions promulgated by well-known experts and respected authorities, and
- results of research studies

Within the research studies, nonrandomized controlled studies provide the weakest evidence, small randomized controlled trials provide stronger evidence, and evidence from large randomized controlled trials and meta-analysis of studies supply the strongest evidence upon which to base practice and interventions (Stuart, 2000; Zauszniewski & Suresky, 2004).

Any evidence only becomes meaningful when it is successfully integrated into nursing practice. Evidence-based practice is critically needed in order to provide quality care for mental health clients. Therefore, throughout this book, the reader will see examples of evidence-based practice and how it can influence psychiatric nursing interventions and client care.

Research

Nurse researchers need to conduct ongoing research regarding the effectiveness of psychiatric nursing interventions and the various mental health treatment modalities, including conventional therapies and complementary and alternative therapies. Additionally, research is required to successfully combine psychodynamic, psychosocial, and psychobiological interventions with psychiatric-mental health nursing practice. Nurse researchers need to clearly identify and interpret for psychiatric-mental health nurses the research findings that have been adequately studied and are applicable to clinical practice. In addition, nurse researchers need to collaborate with nurse administrators so that there is an organizational culture that supports both conducting and implementing nursing research, especially when such research involves nursing interventions.

More research is required to successfully combine psychodynamic, psychosocial, and psychobiologic interventions with psychiatric-mental health nursing practice.

Documentation and Client and Family Education

Documentation

An accurate record of the client's care is required for legal reasons, for regulatory agencies, for accrediting organizations, for institutional requirements, for staffing requirements, and, most important, to provide an accurate and comprehensive care plan for the client. Psychiatric-mental health registered nurses are

Psychiatric-mental health nurses are required to document all information, outcomes, goals, plans, and interventions in an understandable and retrievable manner that can be accessed as needed by all members of the healthcare team.

required by state laws and regulations, facility policies, and standards of practice to document all information, plans, interventions, and outcomes in an understandable and retrievable manner that can be accessed as needed by all members of the healthcare team. Health care continues to use multiple methods for documenting care, from traditional paper charts to concept mapping to electronic health records.

In the process of recording client care, two types of plans are generally used in psychiatric-mental health settings—nursing plans and multidisciplinary treatment plans. The latter is a record reflecting the care delivered by members of the treatment team and are termed treatment action plans, case management plans, or interdisciplinary care plans depending on the treatment setting (Rowland & Rowland, 1997). Nursing plans of care (e.g., standardized care plans, computerized records, concept mapping, care maps, clinical pathways, charting by exception, clinical protocols, critical paths, flow sheets, nursing interventions lists, and practice guidelines) provide documentation of the delivery of nursing care by establishing a record of the nursing assessment, identified problems, nursing diagnoses, expected client outcomes with short- and long-term goals, suggested and implemented nursing interventions, and discharge planning. The increased utilization of concept mapping in clinical practice settings should result in less paperwork, enhance the nurse's critical thinking skills and clinical reasoning, and assist in identifying priorities and determining critical relationships in the clinical data (Schuster, 2000).

Typical charting or documentation rules that generally apply in many settings include writing neatly and legibly, using proper spelling and grammar, utilizing only institutionally approved abbreviations, and transcribing orders carefully. The nurse should also punctually document complete information about medication administration, never chart nursing care or observations ahead of time; clearly identify care that was given by another member of the healthcare team, and never leave blank spaces on charts or forms. Additionally, the nurse must correctly identify late or supplemental entries, correct mistaken entries properly, and avoid sounding tentative. The nurse should never tamper with a record, never criticize the actions of other healthcare team members in the chart, and must eliminate personal biases from the written descriptions of the client. Finally, the nurse precisely documents information reported to the physician or other team members and carefully records any client actions that might negatively influence the outcome of care (Frank-Stromberg, Christensen, & Do, 2001; Iyer, 1991a, 1991b).

Examples of types of specific observations, behaviors, and outcomes of care that should be included in **nursing documentation** include the following (Eggland, 1997; Finkelman, 1997; Menenberg, 1995):

- Behaviors specific to the presenting problems
- New behaviors
- Nutrition and ADLs
- Interactions with other clients, staff, and family
- Family response to and involvement in the treatment plan
- Positive responses to medications
- Medication side effects (e.g., tardive dyskinesia, fluid retention, dystonia, and oculogyric crisis)
- Client and family educational needs and responses to teaching
- Comments on mood, affect, anxiety levels, reality testing, orientation, suicidal thoughts, or periods of aggression
- Symptom relief
- Improved ability to function
- Specific expressions of feelings
- Substance abuse
- Failure to comply with treatment plan
- Restraints and seclusion
- Aggression and potential for violence
- Life events

As the electronic health record (EHR) becomes increasingly utilized in mental healthcare settings, nurses need to have the appropriate computer skills and expertise. Regardless of the format of the documentation, the professional nurse retains responsibility for the accurate recording of the client's nursing care. Like all nurses, psychiatric-mental health nurses are ethically and legally responsible for maintaining the confidentiality of the client's record and information. Under the Health Insurance Portability and Accountability Act of 1996 (HIPAA), the federal government established more stringent regulations regarding the security and privacy of health data and new national standards for electronic healthcare transactions.

Critical Thinking Question

When reviewing a client's healthcare record, you discover what appear to be major discrepancies in the observations and information recorded by medicine, nursing, and social work. What would be appropriate actions for you to take in this situation?

Education for Clients and Families

Psychoeducation has proven to reduce relapse rates and support the recovery of persons with mental illnesses. It has been established that the components of an effective client/family psychoeducation program include education, supportive resources during crisis periods, assistance with problem-solving skills, and emotional support (Dixon et al., 2001).

Clients and their families and significant others require basic knowledge of the mental disorder, the treatment plan, medications, and any support services or advocacy groups (e.g., the National Alliance on Mental Illness [NAMI]) that might be involved. Such education promotes understanding and adherence to the mental health plan. Positive treatment outcomes are directly related to the client's and the family's willingness to be engaged in the treatment process. If the client does not understand the mental health condition, the treatment plan, any medication regimen, and expectations for changes in behavior, the result will be poor outcomes of care. Psychoeducation can benefit clients by establishing a clear understanding of the treatment plan, increasing client motivation, improving compliance with medical and behavioral recommendations, and increasing the client's and family's overall satisfaction with the healthcare experience (O'Donohue & Levensky, 2006).

Case Management and Discharge Planning

Treatment for clients with mental illnesses can occur in a variety of settings, such as inpatient behavioral health units, partial hospitalization programs, residential settings, community mental health clinics, home care, and psychiatric rehabilitation programs. Regardless of the setting, case management and discharge planning are critical to supporting the client's adjustment and response.

As clients are placed in less restrictive settings, psychiatric-mental health nurses will be increasingly required to move throughout the community, offering mental health services wherever clients are, including their homes, alternative treatment centers, congregate housing, soup kitchens, homeless shelters, single-room-occupancy hotels, adult homes, and assisted living arrangements. Psychiatric-mental health nurses will have to combine multiple nursing skills to meet clients' increasingly complex and interdependent physical and mental health needs in a variety of living arrangements. Individualized case management and careful discharge planning will be the major determinants for the success of maintaining clients with mental health needs in these new settings. For information on clients' rights to treatment, to the least restrictive environment, to refuse treatment, and to refuse medication, as well as to confidentiality and privileged communication, see Chapter 8.

Community-based psychiatric-mental health nurses must combine multiple nursing skills to meet the increasingly complex and interdependent physical and mental health needs of clients living in a variety of alternative living arrangements.

Case Management

Case management may be a role, a technology, a process, a service, and a system. According to Bower (1992, p. 3), "The fundamental focus of case management is to integrate, coordinate, and advocate for individuals, families, and groups requiring extensive services. . . . The goal is to achieve planned care outcomes by brokering services across the health care continuum." Case management is unique in that "it is episode-focused, viewing health issues and responding to the care needs of clients along the illness and/or care continuum often across multiple settings" (Bower, p. 4). It is especially effective when used with selected populations such as frail and chronically disabled clients, clients with long-term, medically complex problems, and clients who are severely compromised by an acute episode of illness or an exacerbation of a chronic condition. The goals of case management are to assist the client in gaining access to appropriate resources and to help the client make personal healthcare and other choices. Increased exposure to case management appears to result in an improved quality of life in veterans experiencing the trauma of war (Jinnett, Alexander, & Ullman, 2001). There is also strong evidence showing the benefit of care coordination interventions for patients who have severe mental illness or depression (McDonald et al., 2007). Registered nurses typically have the special knowledge and skills that are appropriate to the case management field. Nurses are able to recognize the signs and symptoms of physical illness and mental health disorders, are taught to be good communicators, and understand group and family dynamics and the use and abuse of psychotropic medications. In psychiatric-mental health nursing, case management involves "population-specific nursing knowledge coupled with research, knowledge of the social and legal systems related to mental health, and expertise to engage a wide range of services for

Case management is a method of assigning the coordination of a client's care; it may be a role, a technology, a process, a service, and a system. The goals of case management are to do the following:
Assist the client in gaining access to appropriate resources
Assist the client in making choices
Support the client in making personal healthcare choices

Treatment settings for clients with mental disorders can include behavioral health units, partial hospitalization, residential settings, community health settings, home care, and psychiatric rehabilitation.

the patient, regardless of setting . . . [these] activities may be with a single client or with a designated population such as the seriously and persistent mentally ill" (ANA, 2007, p. 15).

The psychiatric-mental health registered nurse can provide case management to coordinate the client's comprehensive health services and ensure continuity of care. According to Cohen and Cesta,

> By emphasizing care that is patient-centered, the nursing case management approach embraces techniques of business in which the patient is seen as a valuable consumer who has the right to demand the best in health care. . . . Placing the patient at the core of nursing's power base authorizes the profession to reconfirm its commitment to society. (1997, p. 18)

Discharge Planning

Discharge planning refers to the coordinated activities of the multidisciplinary mental health team that facilitate a client's movement from one healthcare setting to another or to home. It ideally should begin on admission and its goal is to enhance the continuity of the client's care. It is a collaborative process with the client, family, and treatment team. It includes options for continuing treatment, referral to other programs for services or housing accommodations, contact with other agencies to ensure that the client has access to the necessary services, and support for the client and family during the process. For a discussion of the legal and ethical issues associated with discharge planning, see Chapter 8.

Treatment Settings

Inpatient Behavioral Health Units

The inpatient, hospital-based, behavioral health unit for clients with mental health disorders functions as a structured treatment environment offering medical management, nursing care, psychotherapy, group therapy, occupational and recreational therapy, mental health education, and psychiatric case management. Hospitalization may be necessary during the acute phase of the mental disorder or if the client is a danger to self or to others with the units being locked or open, depending upon the needs of the clients. During hospitalization, the client receives a complete medical evaluation and psychiatric assessment, which facilitates establishment of a diagnosis and a treatment regimen. There is generally a strong emphasis on relapse prevention and a successful discharge from the inpatient unit that results in the client maintaining an optimal level of well-being. The psychiatric-mental health nurse on an inpatient unit, as in all treatment settings, is responsible for maintaining a safe, therapeutic milieu for the client; establishing a nursing plan of care; assessing the client on an ongoing basis, and documenting all objective and subjective findings regarding the client, including, but not limited to identifying stressors that trigger symptoms in the client; assessing the effects of psychopharmacology on the client; documenting the client's compliance or noncompliance with the treatment plan; and observing and documenting the client's interactions with treatment staff, other clients, and family members and visitors. The psychiatric-mental health nurse participates in the treatment team meetings providing a nursing viewpoint on the client's progress and assisting with the coordination of care and discharge planning.

Psychiatric Partial Hospitalization Programs

A **partial hospitalization program** or day treatment is an option on the continuum of care to treat clients with mental illnesses. It is generally an outpatient program of less than 24-hour daily care, usually provided by a hospital, specifically designed for the diagnosis or active treatment of a serious mental disorder when there is a reasonable expectation for improvement or when it is necessary to maintain a patient's functional level and prevent relapse or full hospitalization (NAPPH & AAPH, 1990). Such programs can be a step-down level of care for those who have been hospitalized while transitioning back to home, or they can be used to provide patients with an intensive level of intervention and services in an effort to prevent hospitalization. Clients generally participate 6–8 hours a day. The units can be for clients with different mental disorders or be specific to clients with a certain problem such as eating disorders, addictions, or bipolar disorders. Clients usually have access to the same types of supportive services available on the inpatient unit including daily group and individual therapy.

Residential Treatment Settings

A **residential treatment setting** is a therapeutic community with varying levels of supportive care built into the client's daily life. There are many types of these communities; they are generally transitional care communities (treatment-based care center), group residential communities (group homes, halfway houses, congregate living), and apartment-based communities (foster home, boarding home, independent living programs). The nature and degree of clinical treatment varies in these settings. For some clients, living in these types of residences minimizes the stigma of having a mental disorder. The success of these programs is dependent on the availability of therapeutic activities and support services to the client and family including individual, group and family therapy, crisis intervention, medication management, medical care, job training, close access to a therapeutic community meeting place, and planned leisure time activities. The availability of trained mental health practitioners is also crucial as the level and quality of staffing varies considerably in these settings.

Community Mental Health Centers (CMHC)

In 1963, the Congress authorized the Community Mental Health Centers Act, which sought to revolutionize mental health care by emphasizing prevention and decentralized, local community treatment over institutionalized care, even for clients with severe psychiatric problems. The first funded clinics opened in 1966, initiating the nation's movement towards the deinstitutionalization of persons with mental illness. The CMHCs had mixed success. As clients were discharged into the communities, there were often gaps in services and inadequate funding with some clients becoming homeless with exacerbations of their disorders. Today, the challenge is to integrate clients into their communities while providing appropriate community-based care and preventing relapse. Some necessary interventions include medication management and education; symptom education, especially regarding signs of impeding relapse; treatment continuity; social skills training; daily living assistance; daily structure; and the addressing of family issues.

Assertive Community Treatment Team

In community-based care, the psychiatric-mental health nurse delivers care "in partnership with patients in their homes, work sites, mental health clinics and programs, health maintenance organizations, shelters and clinics for the homeless, crisis centers, senior centers, group homes, and other community settings" (ANA, 2007, p. 25). One method is the **assertive community treatment (ACT)** model, which is "an interdisciplinary team approach to the care of people with severe mental illness. It provides services in the individual's natural setting, including homeless shelters" (ANA, 2007, p. 25). In addition to psychiatric services and case management, ACT teams (psychiatry, nursing, social work, rehabilitation, and counseling) provide employment and housing assistance, family support and education, substance abuse services, and other services as needed to maintain the client in the community.

The Assertive Community Treatment (ACT) model is an interdisciplinary team approach to the care of people with severe mental illness providing services in the individual's own natural setting, regardless of place.

The ACT's goals are "to help patients meet the requirements of community living after discharge from another more restrictive form of care, and to reduce recurrences of hospitalization" (ANA, 2007, p. 25). ACT services are available 24 hours a day, 365 days a year. A goal of the National Alliance on Mental Illness (NAMI) is to make high-quality ACT teams available to all who need them and to educate others about the effectiveness of this model (2007). Clients in ACT programs have fewer episodes of homelessness, lower arrest rates and less jail time, and fewer instances of rehospitalization (NAMI, 2007).

Home Care

Offering psychiatric-mental health services to clients in their homes is a cost-effective method of providing services to this population. Psychiatric clients receiving services through home care agencies or similar outreach programs often have complex physical health problems in addition to the presenting mental disorder (often depression, anxiety, or difficulty coping with life situations). Most psychiatric home care is short-term care. Clients may be receiving multiple home healthcare services, have family caregivers on site, or have no readily available support systems. The family members need to be involved in the plan of care and be provided with counseling and support services to facilitate the reintegration of the client into the family. More information is needed on the

In psychiatric home care, many individuals have persistent mental disorders, are elderly, have significant medical conditions, and are homebound.

specific psychiatric-mental health nursing interventions that are helpful to these clients and their caregivers (Horton-Deutsch, Farran, Loukissa, & Fogg, 1997). Increasing numbers of elderly clients, individuals with persistent mental disorders, clients with significant medical illnesses in addition to the mental disorder, and clients who are essentially homebound are receiving psychiatric home care.

According to Peplau (1995), psychiatric-mental health nurses are uniquely able to provide the multiple appropriate services needed by clients in a home setting, are able to integrate assessment of both physical and psychiatric needs into a treatment plan, can provide health education, can coordinate care, can supervise home health aides, and can integrate the family and significant others into a support system for the client. The mental illness of the individual is a family problem. The family may thus fear that the mental health practitioner blames them for the family member's illness. This fear can negatively impact what should be a positive collaboration between the practitioner and the family (Peplau, 1995).

Psychiatric Rehabilitation

Psychiatric rehabilitation encompasses relearning skills and competencies needed for successful interpersonal, social, and vocational functioning.

Psychiatric rehabilitation consists of two intervention strategies: one is individual centered, focused on developing the client's skills in interacting with a stressful environment, and the second is an ecological one, focused on accessing resources to reduce potential stressors (Rossler, 2006). Farkas (2006) discusses that the overall purpose of psychiatric rehabilitation services is to assist the client in achieving recovery and taking back a meaningful life. The fundamental values of psychiatric rehabilitation include empowerment and choice, partnership, hope, a focus on the client's strengths, interests, and limitations, and an outcomes orientation in the provision of services (Farkas, 2006). This form of rehabilitation can occur in a variety of community-based settings; unfortunately, it is not a mental health service that is usually reimbursed by healthcare plans, which becomes a barrier for the client.

According to the U.S. Psychiatric Rehabilitation Association (USPRA), psychiatric rehabilitation services promote "recovery, full community integration and improved quality of life for persons who have been diagnosed with any mental health condition that seriously impairs functioning" (2007, p. 1). This association promulgates 15 core principles (**Table 2-2**).

An example of a community-based resource is the **clubhouse model**, which is "first and foremost a local community center that offers people who have mental illness hope and opportunities to achieve their full potential. Much more than simply a program or a social service, a Clubhouse is most importantly a community of people who are working together to achieve a common goal" (ICCD, 2011). The word *clubhouse* was originally used to describe the work of Fountain House (1948), a support system in New York City for people living with mental illness; it was the first, and model for, future clubhouses. The word has been embraced around the world to describe similar programs that communicate the message of membership, belonging and inclusion—the very heart of the clubhouse movement (ICCD, 2011). Members are provided with opportunities to build long-term relationships that support them in obtaining employment, education, and housing.

Cultural Issues and Mental Health

An estimated 6–8 million immigrants entered the United States in the last decade of the 20th century. The United States is a diverse country with strong immigrant roots, and the nation's diversity will continue to expand, with significant increases in African, Hispanic, and Asian populations. Psychiatric-mental health nurses will encounter clients of many different racial, ethnic, and cultural backgrounds. It is important that there be positive interactions among the culture of the healthcare practitioner, the culture of the client, and the culture of the setting (Dienemann, 1997).

Psychiatric-mental health nurses need to be both culturally sensitive and culturally competent.

Psychiatric-mental health nurses need to be both culturally sensitive and culturally competent. Cultural sensitivity refers to the psychiatric-mental health nurse's "ability to be aware of and respect the client's values and lifestyles even when these differ from the nurse's own"; cultural competence refers to "a multidimensional concept involving various aspects of knowledge, attitude and skills" (Louie, 1996, p. 572). Clients from diverse backgrounds have different ideas about the causes of mental illness and their acceptance of the illness. Some cultures believe that disorders may be caused by evil spirits, events in previous lives, bad thoughts or curses from other people, racism, or divine retribution. The nurse should carefully evaluate unusual or unexpected behaviors for

Table 2-2 Fifteen Core Principles of Psychiatric Rehabilitation

1. Recovery is the ultimate goal of psychiatric rehabilitation. Interventions must facilitate the process of recovery.
2. Psychiatric rehabilitation practices help people reestablish normal roles in the community and their reintegration into community life.
3. Psychiatric rehabilitation practices facilitate the development of personal support networks.
4. Psychiatric rehabilitation practices facilitate an enhanced quality of life for each person receiving services.
5. All people have the capacity to learn and grow.
6. People receiving services have the right to direct their own affairs, including those that are related to their psychiatric disability.
7. All people are to be treated with respect and dignity.
8. Psychiatric rehabilitation practitioners make conscious and consistent efforts to eliminate labeling and discrimination, particularly discrimination based upon a disabling condition.
9. Culture and/or ethnicity play an important role in recovery. They are sources of strength and enrichment for the person and the services.
10. Psychiatric rehabilitation interventions build on the strengths of each person.
11. Psychiatric rehabilitation services are to be coordinated, accessible, and available as long as needed.
12. All services are to be designed to address the unique needs of each individual, consistent with the individual's cultural values and norms.
13. Psychiatric rehabilitation practices actively encourage and support the involvement of persons in normal community activities, such as school and work, throughout the rehabilitation process.
14. The involvement and partnership of persons receiving services and family members is an essential ingredient of the process of rehabilitation and recovery.
15. Psychiatric rehabilitation practitioners should constantly strive to improve the services they provide.

Source: U.S. Psychiatric Rehabilitation Association. (2007). *Psychiatric rehabilitation principles*. Available at www.uspra.org

cultural influences and the client's acceptance of the behavior before assuming the behaviors are intrinsic to a mental disorder. Language differences must be accommodated by using competent and sensitive translators according to federal and state requirements and the policies of the treatment setting.

Clients may seek to replace conventional therapies or use them in conjunction with cultural therapies and complementary or alternative treatments. Such therapies include the treatment of herbalists, folk healers, and family healers; invocations of the good spirits; imagery; religious ceremonies; the use of magical, life-giving objects; healing touch; and communing with the spirit world for guidance and assistance. The psychiatric-mental health nurse must understand and appreciate the influence of culture on the client, family, and community support system. The nurse should learn to incorporate these cultural therapies into the plan of care to achieve the best outcomes.

Professional Psychiatric Nursing Organizations

The two major professional psychiatric nursing organizations are the American Psychiatric Nurses Association (APNA) and the International Society of Psychiatric-Mental Health Nurses (ISPN), which has four divisions—the Association of Child and Adolescent Psychiatric Nurses (ACAPN), the Adult and Geropsychiatric-Mental Health Nurses (AGPN), the International Society of Psychiatric-Consultation Liaison Nurses (ISPCLN), and the Society for Education and Research in Psychiatric-Mental Health Nursing (SERPN).

Founded in 1987, APNA provides national leadership on psychiatric-mental health nursing issues. An organizational affiliate of the ANA, APNA works closely with the ANA on legislation, practice standards, certification of psychiatric nurses as generalists and specialists, and provision of continuing nursing education in the specialty. In 1997, the ANA, APNA, and many other mental health advocacy groups signed a bill of rights for individuals seeking treatment for psychiatric and substance-abuse disorders. This bill of rights includes the following:

- The individual's right to know what mental health benefits are included in an insurance plan

- The right to receive full information concerning the professional expertise of the treating practitioner
- The right to know if there are contractual arrangements between the treating practitioners and a third-party payer
- The right to receive information concerning how to submit complaints or grievances about care
- The right to guaranteed confidentiality
- The right to choose any duly licensed or certified mental health professional for care
- The right to receive mental health care
- Other rights related to discrimination, including receiving mental health services, the structure of mental health benefits plans, treatment review, and accountability

ACAPN was founded in 1971 and has focused on meeting the professional needs of nurses specializing in the mental health care of children and adolescents. In 1998, the ACAPN, ISPCLN, and SERPN agreed to form the International Society of Psychiatric Mental Health Nurses (ISPN). The purposes of the new alliance were to unite and strengthen the presence and impact of specialized psychiatric-mental health nurses, to work together on major issues affecting the nursing profession, to impact health policy, and to promote equitable and quality care for individuals and families with mental health problems.

Summary

Many issues and trends influence the practice of psychiatric-mental health nursing. The chapter began with a look at definitions of mental health, mental disorders, and psychiatric-mental health nursing practice. The independent and dependent legal authorizations for practice in states' nurse practice acts and the profession's scope and standards of practice and psychiatric-mental health nursing practice were discussed. The nursing process (assessment, diagnosis, outcomes identification, planning, implementation, and evaluation) and its application to psychiatric-mental health nursing were described. Documentation specific to psychiatric-mental health nursing was identified, including client behaviors, new behaviors, interactions, responses to medications, symptom relief, substance abuse, restraints and seclusion, and life events. The need for research on psychiatric nursing interventions and the types of client outcomes related to psychiatric nursing practice (client satisfaction, return to functional status, response to educational interventions) were discussed. The unique role of managed care in the delivery of mental health services, the utilization of case management, and the need for mental health parity were reviewed. Treatment settings including inpatient behavioral health units, partial hospitalization programs, residential settings, community health settings, home care, and psychiatric rehabilitation programs were described. The roles and contributions of registered nurses and advanced practice registered nurses to the care of the mental health client were discussed, and the missions of the various professional psychiatric nursing organizations were presented.

Annotated References

Al-Assaf, A. F. (Ed.). (1998). *Managed care quality: A practical guide*. New York, NY: CRC Press.

This book provides a historical review of managed care and numerous discussions of achieving quality in a managed care system.

American Nurses Association. (1998). Nursing's values challenged by managed care. *Nursing Trends and Issues, 3*(1), 1–8.

This article is a thoughtful discussion of nursing's traditional ethical values and principles in relation to a managed health care environment.

American Nurses Association. (2007). *Psychiatric-mental health nursing: Scope and standards of practice*. Washington, DC: Author.

This is an authoritative statement on the clinical aspects of psychiatric-mental health nursing practice, including the scope and standards of practice in keeping with the contemporary and future needs of clients. This document was a collaborative effort of the ANA, APNA, and International Society of Psychiatric-Mental Health Nurses.

American Nurses Association. (2010). *Nursing: Scope and standards of practice*. (2nd ed.). Silver Spring, MD: Nursesbooks.

This is a foundational document that articulates a single scope of practice specifying the who, what, where, when, why, and how of nursing practice. Each standard of professional practice is now measurable by specific competencies that serve as evidence of compliance.

American Psychiatric Association. (2000). *Diagnostic and statistical manual of mental disorders* (4th ed., text revision). Washington, DC: Author.

This is the fourth edition with text revision of the American Psychiatric Association's official nomenclature of psychiatric conditions and disorders. It provides a systematic listing of the official codes and categories, a description of the multiaxial system for diagnosis, and diagnostic criteria for each of the disorders. This book is used by psychiatrists, physicians, psychologists, registered nurses, social workers, therapists, and other mental health workers in all clinical settings.

Bower, K. (1992). *Case management by nurses.* Washington, DC: American Nurses.
This publication provides a guide for the continued development and expansion of case management practice.

Breslin, E., & Lucas, V. (2003). *Women's health nursing: Towards evidence based practice.* Chicago, IL: W. B. Saunders.
This book utilizes evidence-based practice as it explores women's health problems across the life span, highlighting key phenomena. It discusses foundational concepts essential to the care of women, and it covers health history, screening and diagnostic tests, and physical examinations.

Cohen, E., & Cesta, T. (1997). *Nursing case management.* St. Louis, MO: C. V. Mosby.
This book examines nursing case management by explaining its historical roots and current and future challenges.

Dienemann, J. (1997). *Cultural diversity in nursing: Issues, strategies and outcomes.* Washington, DC: American Academy of Nursing.
This monograph promotes culturally competent teamwork. It explores types of cultures, the cultural competence of U.S. nurses, intercultural counseling, and training for cultural sensitivity.

Dixon, L., McFarlane, W. R., Lefley, H., Lucksted, A., Cohen, M., Falloon I., . . . Sondheimer, D. (2001). Evidence based practices for services to families of people with psychiatric disabilities. *Psychiatric Services, 52*(7), 903–910.
This article examines the evidence-based practice that supports family psychoeducation that has been shown to reduce relapse rates and facilitate recovery of persons with psychiatric disabilities.

Eggland, E. (1997). Charting tips: Documenting psychiatric and behavioral outcomes. *Nursing 97, 27*(4), 25.
This article provides a brief listing of specific suggestions for documenting nursing outcomes in psychiatric care.

Farkas, M. (2006, October). Identifying psychiatric rehabilitation interventions: An evidence and valued based practice. *World Psychiatry, 5*(3), 161–162.
The author explains that psychiatric rehabilitation services should be those that are effective in facilitating success and satisfaction in valued roles through a process clearly congruent with accepted rehabilitation values.

Finkelman, A. W. (1997). *Psychiatric home care.* Gaithersberg, MD: Aspen.
This book provides a complete review of the care of the psychiatric client in a home care setting. Topics discussed include psychiatric rehabilitation, the family and significant others, psychoeducation, psychopharmacology, case management, and specific clinical problems.

Frank-Stromberg, M., Christensen, A., & Do, D. E. (2001). Nurse documentation: Not done or worse, done the wrong way—part II. *Oncology Nursing Forum, 28*(5), 841–846.
Educating nurses about the principles of documentation and the importance of implementing risk-reduction practices will help guard against liability and ultimately improve patient care.

Horton-Deutsch, S., Farran, C., Loukissa, D., & Fogg, L. (1997). Who are these patients and what services do they receive? *Home Healthcare Nurse, 15*(12), 847–854.
This article presents an interesting description of the psychiatric client in home care.

International Center for Clubhouse Development (ICCD). (2011). *What is a clubhouse?* Retrieved from http://www.iccd.org/whatis.html#origin
Comprehensive description of the clubhouse model of community support for persons with mental illness.

Iyer, P. (1991a). Six more charting rules: To keep you legally safe. *Nursing 91, 21*(7), 35–39.
This article focuses on what should not be documented in a chart and how to record clients' actions that contribute to personal injury.

Iyer, P. (1991b). Thirteen charting rules: To keep you legally safe. *Nursing 91, 21*(6), 40–44.
This article discusses the recommended mechanics of charting and documentation.

Jinnett, K., Alexander, J. A., & Ullman, E. (2001, April). Case management and quality of life: Assessing treatment and outcomes for clients with chronic and persistent mental illness. *Health Services Research, 36*(1 Pt. 1), 61–90.
The study findings provide managers, clinicians, and policy makers a fuller understanding of how this mode of service delivery—case manage-

ment—affects several domains of quality of life for clients with chronic illnesses.

Klainberg, M., Holzemer, S., Leonard, M., & Arnold, J. (1998). *Community health nursing: An alliance for health.* New York, NY: McGraw-Hill.
This concise textbook provides a focused and thorough introduction to community health nursing.

Krupnick, S., & Wade, A. (1993). *Psychiatric care planning.* Springhouse, PA: Springhouse.
This excellent reference includes specific suggestions for planning the care of psychiatric clients including psychiatric diagnostic categories, nursing diagnoses, outcome criteria, and discharge planning.

Louie, K. (1996). Cultural issues in psychiatric-mental health nursing. In S. Lego (Ed.), *Psychiatric nursing: A comprehensive reference* (2nd ed., pp. 572–575). Philadelphia, PA: J. B. Lippincott.
This chapter identifies the changing demographics of the U.S. population and discusses cultural sensitivity, assessment, and competence in psychiatric-mental health nursing practice.

Malloch, K., & Porter-O'Grady, T. (2006). *Introduction to evidence based practice in nursing and health care.* Sudbury, MA: Jones and Bartlett.
This introduction to the use of evidence-based practice in nursing and health care provides an excellent orientation to the basic principles of evidence-based practice and explores barriers and strengths within organizations seeking to implement such a process.

McDonald, K. M., Sundaram, V., Bravata, D. M., Lewis, R., Lin, N., Kraft, S. A., . . . Owens, D. K. (2007, June). *Closing the quality gap: A critical analysis of quality improvement strategies (Vol. 7: care coordination).* Report No. 04(07)-0051-7. Rockville, MD: Agency for Healthcare Research and Quality (US).
Care coordination interventions represent a wide range of approaches at the service delivery and systems level. Their effectiveness is most likely dependent upon appropriate matching between intervention and care coordination problem.

Melnyk, B., & Fineout-Overholt, E. (2005). *Evidence based practice in nursing and healthcare.* Philadelphia, PA: Lippincott, Williams & Wilkins.
This text clarifies misperceptions about evidence-based practice and provides readers with practical strategies for implementing evidence-based practice.

Menenberg, S. (1995). Standards of care in documentation of psychiatric nursing care. *Clinical Nurse Specialist, 9*(3), 140–148.
This article discusses the multiple factors that require careful documentation of psychiatric care and the need to coordinate all aspects of the interdisciplinary care record.

Menninger, K. A. (1945). *The human mind* (3rd ed.). New York, NY: Alfred Knopf.
This classic, early psychiatric textbook describes mental conditions and related behaviors.

Moorhead, S., Swanson, E., Johnson, M., & Maas, M. L. (2008). *Nursing Outcomes Classification (NOC)* (4th ed.). St. Louis, MO: Mosby.
This is a text that presents standardized terminology and measures for nursing-sensitive patient outcomes that result from nursing interventions; it includes 385 research-based outcomes.

National Alliance on Mental Illness (NAMI). (2007). *Assertive community treatment: Investment yields outcomes.* Available at http://www.nami.org
This is a fact sheet explaining the various aspects of assertive community treatment.

National Association of Private Psychiatric Hospitals (NAPPH) and the American Association for Partial Hospitalization (AAPH). (1990, Spring). Definition of partial hospitalization. *The Psychiatric Hospital, 21*(2), 89–90.
The article provides a discussion of the acceptance of the definition included in the federal regulations on partial hospitalization for clients with mental illnesses.

O'Donohue, W., & Levensky, E. R. (2006). *Promoting treatment adherence.* Thousand Oaks, CA: Sage.
This practical handbook for clinicians offers comprehensive information and strategies for understanding and promoting treatment compliance.

Peplau, H. (1995). Some unresolved issues in the era of biopsychosocial nursing. *Journal of the American Psychiatric Nurses Association, 1*(3), 92–96.
Four unresolved issues of importance to psychiatric-mental health nurses are explored in this article: biology versus environment, community and family nursing, primary care and advanced practice, and external versus internal regulation of nursing.

Reighley, J. (1988). *Nursing care planning guides for mental health.* Baltimore, MD: Williams & Wilkins.

This classic reference guides the planning of nursing care for clients with mental health conditions through the application of a nursing diagnosis framework.

Rossler, W. (2006, October). Psychiatric rehabilitation today: An overview. *World Psychiatry, 5*(3), 151–157.

The author presents an overview of psychiatric rehabilitation, stressing that it has reached a point where it should be made readily available for every disabled person.

Rowland, H., & Rowland, B. (1997). *Nursing administration handbook* (4th ed.). Gaithersberg, MD: Aspen.

This comprehensive overview of the field of nursing administration can be used as a hands-on tool by nurse managers. It explains leadership skills, problem solving and decision making, the overall working environment, finances and budgeting, technology and informatics, the operation of a nursing service, human resources, research, and the impact of today's healthcare environment on the nurse manager.

Schuster, P. M. (2000). Concept mapping: Reducing clinical care plan paperwork and increasing learning. *Nurse Educator, 25*(2), 76–81.

The authors discuss how concept mapping reduces paperwork and enhances nursing students' critical thinking skills and clinical reasoning.

Society for Education and Research in Psychiatric-Mental Health Nursing. (1996). *The Society for Education and Research in Psychiatric-Mental Health Nursing (SERPN) Division.* Retrieved from http://www.ispn-psych.org/html/serpn.html

SERPN focuses on graduate education in psychiatric nursing and the evolving research base for psychiatric nursing practice. Its members include nurse educators, researchers, and advanced practice registered nurses—all dedicated to addressing the mental health needs of the consumers via the education and development of the advanced practice workforce, research, and innovative practice models.

Stuart, G. W. (2000). Evidence based psychiatric nursing practice. In G. W. Stuart & M. T. Laraia (Eds.), *Principles and practices of psychiatric nursing* (7th ed., pp. 76–85). St. Louis, MO: Mosby.

An excellent psychiatric-mental health nursing textbook from one of the specialty's most competent and compelling educators.

U.S. Psychiatric Rehabilitation Association. (2007). *Psychiatric rehabilitation principles.* Available at www.uspra.org

This association is a membership organization supporting mental health recovery through psychiatric rehabilitation. It brings together mental health practitioners, clients, and families.

Worley, N. (1997). *Mental health nursing in the community.* St. Louis, MO: C. V. Mosby.

This book presents psychiatric-mental health nursing concepts with a focus on practicing in the community.

Zauszniewski, J. A., & Suresky, J. (2004). Evidence for psychiatric nursing practice: An analysis of three years of published research. *Online Journal of Issues in Nursing, 9*(1). Available at: www.nursingworld.org/MainMenuCategories/ANAMarketplace/ANAPeriodicals/OJIN/TableofContents/Volume92004/No1Jan04/HirshArticle/EvidenceforPsychiatricNursingPractice.aspx

This state of the evidence review analyzed 227 data-based studies published in the five most commonly read U.S. psychiatric nursing journals from January 2000 through December 2002.

Additional Resources

American Nurses Association. (2010). *Nursing's social policy statement* (3rd ed.). Silver Spring, MD: ANA.

This document describes nursing care and its knowledge base, the scope of practice, and methods by which the profession is regulated.

Cesta, T., & Cunningham, B. (2009). *Overview: Core skills for the hospital case manager.* Boston, MA: HCPro, Inc.

This text is an orientation and training manual for nurses transitioning into case management, an easy-to-read reference guide for new case managers, and a source of inspiration, tools, and resources for seasoned professionals.

Internet Resources

For a full suite of assignments and additional learning activities, use the access code located in the front of your book to visit this exclusive website: http://go.jblearning.com/mentalhealth. If you do not have an access code, you can obtain one at the site.

Learning Objectives

After reading this chapter, you will be able to:

- Describe characteristics of the nurse–client relationship.
- Explain the tasks associated with each phase of the nurse–client relationship.
- Define the conditions that are conducive to the development of a therapeutic relationship.
- Describe strategies for managing issues unique to the professional nature of the nurse–client relationship.
- Identify therapeutic and nontherapeutic communication techniques.

Key Terms

Active listening
Assertive communication
Countertransference
Emotional intelligence
Empathy
Genuineness
Nurse–client relationship
Self-disclosure
Transference

The Nurse–Client Relationship and Therapeutic Communication

Patricia G. O'Brien

http://go.jblearning.com/mentalhealth 

For a full suite of assignments and additional learning activities, use the access code located in the front of your book to visit this exclusive website: http://go.jblearning.com/mentalhealth. If you do not have an access code, you can obtain one at the site.

Introduction

The therapeutic relationship between the nurse and client is the hallmark of psychiatric-mental health nursing.

The therapeutic relationship between nurse and client is the hallmark of psychiatric nursing. In 1952, the publication of *Interpersonal Relations in Nursing*, by Hildegard E. Peplau, essentially revolutionized the teaching and practice of psychiatric nursing in the United States. At a time when the introduction of psychotropic medications was changing the treatment of psychiatric illness, Peplau emphasized the interpersonal relationship of the nurse and client. Peplau defined nursing as "a human relationship between an individual who is sick, or in need of health services, and a nurse especially educated to recognize and to respond to the need for help" (1952, p. 5–6). This chapter will explore the multiple factors that contribute to the development and success of the nurse–client relationship, including the use of therapeutic communication techniques.

Nurses need to understand the difference between professional and social relationships. A relationship exists between the client and nurse only when they become significant to each other.

Critical Thinking Question

What factors contribute to making the therapeutic relationship between the psychiatric nurse and the client the hallmark of psychiatric nursing?

The Nurse–Client Relationship

The **nurse–client relationship** is the context in which the nursing process occurs and is the primary means of providing nursing care. This is true for all nursing practice, not just psychiatric nursing. According to Peplau, nursing's unique focus is the reactions of clients to the circumstances of their illness or health situation. Illness provides an opportunity for learning and growth. The nurse, through careful observation and thoughtfully guided communication, assists the client to identify needs and develop new intellectual and interpersonal skills. The competency of the nurse will substantially affect the quality of the client's experience and the outcome of care. Nursing competence goes beyond the mastery and application of scientific knowledge and technical skills. The vehicle for all nursing action is the nurse–client relationship, and it is the basis for a successful and fulfilling nursing practice as well as for all nursing actions.

Characteristics of the Therapeutic Nurse–Client Relationship

All intentional interactions with clients that are helpful are considered therapeutic. However, not all nurse–client interactions constitute a relationship. A relationship exists between the client and the nurse only when they become significant to each other (i.e., the opinion of the other makes a difference in how one views oneself). When this occurs, the potential for corrective emotional experiences exists. If it is achieved, the relationship becomes therapeutic. There are several characteristics that define the therapeutic nurse–client relationship. They include the following:

- To be therapeutic, the nurse–client relationship must be based on mutual respect.
- The relationship is client focused and designed to meet the client's needs. The emotional needs of the nurse cannot interfere with this process.
- The interactions are goal oriented.
- Goals are mutually established by both the client and the nurse.
- The relationship is collaborative, with both the client and the nurse contributing to the healing, growth, and problem solving.
- The client and nurse engage in shared decision making.
- The relationship promotes the client's independence to the maximum extent possible. The nurse *works with* the client and does *not do for* the client.
- The relationship promotes the expression of the client's feelings.

At the beginning of the relationship, an agreement or contract between the nurse and client should be established. This is an excellent opportunity to establish the rules and behaviors or boundaries that are expected between the nurse and client, such as the time and frequency of meetings; reimbursement for services; contact with family members, significant others, and other therapists; and prohibition against socialization. Nurses need to be aware that boundaries are critical in maintaining a professional therapeutic relationship. Ideally, the nurse and client develop a collaborative and dynamic relationship in which both learn and grow.

Identifying goals and boundaries early in the relationship helps to define the professional nature of the relationship. The nurse does not relate to the client

Table 3-1 Comparison of Professional and Social Relationships

Professional Relationships	Social Relationships
Client focused	Shared focus
Structured	Unstructured
Purposeful and time limited	Open with respect to content and time
Mutually determined goals	No specific goals
Intimate, personal information restricted	Exchange of information not restricted
Nurse is responsible to guide the interaction and meet client's needs	Shared responsibility for the interaction

in the same way as one relates in a social situation. There are clear differences between a professional and a social relationship (**Table 3-1**). If one is angry with a friend, one can choose to ignore the person, argue with the person, or even become verbally loud or aggressive. The nurse does not have these options in the professional nurse–client relationship. The nurse must honor the implicit contract to help the client. Therefore, if something in the client's behavior raises feelings of anger in the nurse, the nurse must recognize and try to understand the response, set firm limits in a calm manner, help identify the client's need at the moment, and help the client meet the need in an acceptable way. This is a large task, and it requires strong communication skills.

Because the relationship is collaborative, the nurse partners with the client in establishing goals, planning interventions, and making decisions about the client's care. Early in psychiatric nursing, the nurse was cast in a custodial role and was seen as taking care of the client. This had the effect of fostering dependency. Rather, in a therapeutic relationship, the nurse encourages the client's participation and growth towards independence. At times, the client's fears, anger, anxiety, or expectations may impede participation in treatment. Through the purposeful use of therapeutic communication techniques, the nurse can promote the client's understanding and acceptance of the situation. **Table 3-2** shows the application and effectiveness of Peplau's interpersonal nursing model in a medical-surgical setting.

There are four phases of the nurse–client relationship: the preinteraction phase, the orientation phase, the working phase, and the termination phase.

Phases of the Nurse–Client Relationship

The nurse and client come to the nurse–client relationship as strangers, and the trust and respect essential to the therapeutic process develops over time and

Table 3-2 Application of Peplau's Interpersonal Nursing Model to a Clinical Situation

Situation: The nurse is caring for a client who has a new colostomy.

Without the Model	With Interpersonal Model
The client appears tense about caring for her colostomy. The nurse lightens the mood through distraction in an attempt to make the client feel more comfortable. The client smiles and appears more relaxed.	The nurse recognizes both her own anxieties related to colostomy care, and the client's anxieties, evidenced by the client's efforts to avoid caring for her colostomy.
Recognizing the client's discomfort, the nurse proceeds by taking care of the colostomy for the client.	The nurse uses therapeutic communication techniques to assist the client to explore her feelings about having and caring for the colostomy.
Result: The client's inadequate coping is reinforced.	The nurse openly prompts the client to talk about her concerns during care of the colostomy.
On subsequent days the nurse continues to "help" by taking care of the colostomy for the client, thereby promoting increased dependency.	The nurse encourages the client to look at, touch, and care for the colostomy. Gradually, the client assumes independent care of the colostomy.

Source: Adapted from Sparks, A. (2009). *Peplau Interpersonal Relations* (PowerPoint presentation). Available at www.slideshare.net

progresses through stages. There are various frameworks for viewing the stages of the nurse–client relationship. As presented in Chapter 1, Peplau identified four phases: orientation, identification, exploitation, and resolution, with specific outcomes associated with each phase. An alternative framework that identifies the four phases as preinteraction, orientation, working, and termination is presented next, along with the expected goals and tasks that are expected to occur during each stage of the relationship.

Preinteraction Phase

The preinteraction phase begins before the nurse and client meet. At this stage, the nurse prepares for the interaction by reviewing available data and considers personal feelings and thoughts that may relate to the client.

A review of available data may include a medical record, a verbal report, or other source of introductory information. The nurse uses this information to construct an initial plan for assessment and intervention. For example, the nurse who knows that a client who is being admitted has suicidal thoughts will plan for necessary safety measures, including adequate staffing should 1:1 supervision be indicated.

During this phase, the nurse examines any preconceived attitudes or beliefs that may interfere with providing therapeutic care to the particular client. If the client has negative feelings about people with addictions or a history of criminal behaviors, it is important for the nurse to acknowledge these feelings. This issue relates to the concept of countertransference, which is discussed later in the chapter.

Orientation Phase

The orientation phase is the getting acquainted or introductory phase, which begins when the nurse and client have their initial encounter. The tasks of this phase are to develop trust and to establish the nurse as a significant other to the client, establish a verbal contract or understanding of the nature and boundaries of the relationship, collect data as part of completing a nursing assessment, formulate a nursing diagnosis, establish mutually acceptable goals, and develop an initial plan of care.

The client's first impression of the nurse can be critical to the relationship. The client learns to trust the nurse only if the nurse is able to convey acceptance of the client (as a parent would of a child) and exhibit consistent behavior. The client identifies strengths as well as relevant concerns, and the nurse facilitates the process. During this phase, the nurse and client agree on a mutually acceptable contract that establishes the relationship's parameters. Although consistency and acceptance are desirable during all phases of the relationship, these behaviors are essential during the orientation phase.

Working Phase

The working phase, as indicated by the term, is the period during which much of the work is done. Therapeutic tasks during this phase may include acquiring knowledge, implementing problem-solving interventions, understanding the relationship of feelings to behaviors, and learning new behaviors and skills. The nurse collaborates with the client to promote insight and acceptance.

This phase is characterized by the highly individualized nature of the problems being addressed. During this phase the nurse is aware that the client may experience an increase in anxiety that can lead to resistance or reluctance to continue the work that is under way. Often without awareness of the underlying anxiety, the client may miss appointments or become angry during this stage of the relationship. The nurse helps the client understand this behavior and move past this anxiety. To accomplish this, it is necessary to maintain trust and rapport. Evaluation of progress towards the identified goals is made at intervals and adjustments are made, if indicated.

Termination Phase

Termination marks the ending of the nurse–client relationship. Tasks during this phase include evaluating outcomes, expressing feelings about ending the relationship, summarizing achievements, and transitioning to the next level of care, if applicable. The goal of this phase for both the client and nurse is to integrate helpful experiences so that what has been learned may be used in future relationships.

Ideally, termination of the relationship occurs when the goals have been met. At other times, termination may be related to discharge from one level of care, with plans for continued treatment with another nurse or therapist in a different setting, or it could be related to a change in nurse assignment, such as vacation or the end of a student's rotation. In these situations, because the termination is anticipated, the nurse and client will have time to prepare for and carry out the tasks associated with termination. If, for an unexpected reason, the relationship ends abruptly, attention must be given to assisting the nurse and client with feelings about the termination.

Termination can be difficult for both the nurse and the client. Paradoxically, the more successful the relationship, the more emotionally painful is the termination. As a result, both the nurse and client are tempted to deny the inevitable and pretend that their parting is only temporary. They may use phrases such as, "Keep in touch," "I'm sure we'll run into each other," and, "See you later." These strategies are comforting in the short term but do not help either in the long run. It is better to acknowledge the end of the relationship. In response to ambivalence about termination, the client may regress and exhibit behaviors that were part of the original treatment goal, or the client may verbalize uncertainty about readiness for discharge. These behaviors are understandable, and their occurrence provides an opportunity for the nurse to help the client explore these feelings, review the client's achievements and strengths, and identify other sources of support that will be available to the client.

Essential Characteristics of the Nurse in a Therapeutic Relationship

Several qualities are recognized as significant to the development of a helping relationship.

Respect

Psychologist Carl Rogers (1951) referred to respect as unconditional positive regard or the ability to accept another's beliefs even if they differ from one's own feelings and beliefs. This concept is the foundation for an accepting and nonjudgmental attitude. It communicates to clients that their personal beliefs and values are important. The nurse does not need to agree, but, at the same time, does not impose personal values on the client. Rather, the nurse attempts to understand the client's perspective. When the client feels understood, a rapport or affinity develops between the client and the nurse. An accepting and respectful attitude is likely to promote client comfort and facilitate the client's honest expression of symptoms, beliefs, thoughts, feelings, and concerns.

Ways to foster respect include asking clients how they prefer to be addressed, spending time with the client, being honest in all communications, providing for privacy, maintaining confidentiality, collaborating with clients on treatment planning, providing information, and answering questions.

Trust

Trust is the foundation of all interpersonal relationships and the first task in Erikson's developmental hierarchy. The client's ability to trust will be influenced by how well this developmental task was accomplished during early interactions with parents and caregivers. In describing trust, Erikson (1963) used the terms *consistent*, *familiar*, and *predictable*. The client needs to know that the nurse is reliable, honest, and dependable. Trust is particularly important, given the vulnerable position of clients with healthcare needs. Trust does not happen immediately but evolves or, more correctly, is earned over the course of the relationship. Every interaction with the nurse will either support or shake the development of trust on the part of the client.

Nurse actions that promote trust include following through on promises, showing kindness, treating the client fairly, and presenting a confident manner.

Genuineness

The nurse's ability to be oneself, or to be real, when interacting with clients is referred to as **genuineness**. By acting in a genuine way, the nurse helps the client to see the shared humanity between client and nurse. Genuineness implies congruence between what the nurse is feeling and the expression of that feeling. The nurse must learn appropriate use of self-disclosure. The nurse would not share all personal experiences, even if relevant, nor would the nurse express judgments that are critical of the client or the client's values. Still, there are many ways that the nurse can show his or her humanity when interacting with the client. The nurse may laugh at a funny joke told by the client or express understanding about a difficulty the client is having, or share that the nurse finds meditation to be a helpful form of relaxation. A novice nurse may try to disguise his or her inexperience from the client out of concern that the client will think less of the nurse. In fact, clients can easily detect a lack of genuineness and are more likely to respect the nurse for honestly acknowledging limitations. The quality of genuineness, or the authentic representation of the self, will greatly enrich the nurse–client experience.

Critical Thinking Question

How would you feel if, as a novice nurse, a client asked how long you had worked as a psychiatric nurse? What would you be thinking? How would you reply?

Empathy

Empathy is the ability to put oneself in another's place and see the world as the other person does. This objective understanding of the client's emotions allows the nurse to be sensitive to the client's feelings without experiencing the emotions. This is in contrast to sympathy, a subjective experience, in which there is an actual sharing of experienced emotions. Sympathy can interfere with the nurse–client relationship in a couple of ways: the nurse can become overwhelmed by the emotions and be unable to help the client; the nurse who shares an experience with the client as a way of saying "I know how you feel" risks shifting the focus of the interaction away from the client. The nurse's intention may be to support the client, but the action is not effective. Empathy promotes sensitivity to the client's feelings and needs. The nurse must communicate this understanding to the client in a way that the client can understand. This will contribute to the client's experience of being understood, thus building trust.

Transference and Countertransference

Transference and countertransference are unconscious processes that can interfere with communication in the nurse–client relationship. It is important for the nurse to recognize behaviors that suggest transference or countertransference so it can be addressed with the client or in supervision.

Transference consists of realistic and unrealistic feelings that the client has toward the nurse.

Countertransference refers to the feelings the nurse has toward the client.

Transference

Transference is traditionally defined as a client's projection or displacement of unconscious feelings, desires, and actions from a person in his or her life onto the nurse or other therapist (APA, 2007). The concept of transference includes a realistic appreciation for the role that the therapeutic relationship plays in determining the client's response to treatment and attitude toward the nurse or healthcare worker. For example, a minority client who has been the victim of prejudice may be appropriately apprehensive about disclosing information to a nurse of the same ethnic background as his or her oppressors. The rationale for the client's feelings towards the nurse is outside of conscious awareness. In another example, the nurse may remind the client of a punitive parent and the client may then act towards the nurse with anger or with behaviors that challenge the nurse's authority.

Countertransference

The healthcare professional's feelings and reactions toward the client are known as **countertransference**. The nurse or healthcare worker displaces or projects unconscious feelings, desires, or actions from a person in his or her life onto the client (APA, 2007). The countertransference feelings can be based on positive or negative associations. In either case, they can interfere with the therapeutic relationship. For example, a nurse who cared for her grandmother during the final months of her illness may value the experience and remember the appreciation and love she received from her grandmother. The nurse may transfer feelings for her grandmother to a female client and attempt to take care of the woman, doing for her things that the woman can manage independently. This has the nontherapeutic effect of fostering dependence.

The following behaviors should alert the nurse to the possibility of countertransference: inappropriate or exaggerated emotional responses toward the client, feelings of exhaustion, stereotyped or fixed responses regardless of what the client is saying, impulses to treat the client in a special way, and extreme over- or underinvolvement with the client.

Education, supervision, and consultation with colleagues are essential for the nurse to use the countertransference productively. Appropriately analyzed, countertransference may offer important clues to a client's diagnosis or symptoms. For example, a nurse's feelings of extreme anger during an interview may identify the client's hidden rage.

Power Disparity

One important source of transference and countertransference is the power disparity between the nurse and the client. The nurse assumes the responsibility for moving the interaction forward to achieve a goal, while the client passively answers questions.

Clinical Example 

Leo is a 15-year-old male admitted to a residential treatment center for the treatment of oppositional defiant disorder. Immediately upon his arrival to the unit, the admitting nurse sat down with Leo to complete a four-page nursing assessment form. When the rest of the residents lined up to go to the cafeteria for dinner, Leo promptly got up to join them. The nurse shouted at Leo to sit back down because the assessment was not yet complete and he had not asked for permission to join the group. Leo cursed at the nurse and stated that he was hungry. The nurse shouted back to Leo that she—and not Leo—was in charge of the unit, and that if he kept it up she would ban him from the cafeteria for the rest of the week. The supervisor arrived on the scene and quickly recognized that a power struggle had developed between the nurse and the new resident, who were demonstrating countertransference and transference, respectively. The supervisor asked another nurse to go over the rule book with Leo and to inform him that food would soon be brought to the unit for him, while the supervisor discussed the problematic transaction privately with the admitting nurse.

This situation often results in a transference, which for the client represents a repetition of feelings and reactions from past experiences with authority figures. Depending upon the client's history and current symptoms, the client may be overly compliant with the interviewer (e.g., tell the interviewer exactly what the interviewer wants to hear) or overly oppositional (e.g., assert that the professional has no right to ask such personal questions). For the nurse, the power disparity may cause feelings of omnipotence and fantasies of being able to save the client. The nurse may fail to involve the client in the treatment plan and may feel anger toward noncompliant clients as well.

Conditions That Influence the Nurse–Client Relationship

Client Factors

Religion and Culture

Styles of communication vary across cultures and religions. It is helpful for the nurse to be familiar with the beliefs, values, customs, and preferences of the groups most often served in the community. Even with knowledge of general beliefs and practices, the nurse should not assume that the client fits that expectation. Therefore, the nurse should clarify personal preferences with each client. Consideration should be given to the proper pronunciation of the client's name, the need for an interpreter, the role of the family, and preferences or religious requirements regarding interaction with persons of the opposite gender. Cultural variances may include the use of eye contact, the acceptable distance between persons while communicating, posture, and other nonverbal communication. The nurse needs to be sensitive to these differences and respectful to the client.

Age or Developmental Level

The nurse must have knowledge of the client's developmental level and be aware of the client's ability to communicate. This understanding will shape the way the nurse relates to the client. Communication must be appropriate to the client's level of comprehension. The nurse will need to be aware of the client's nonverbal communication and open to alternative ways of communicating, such as play. Children can express feelings, fears, and concerns through play.

Nurse Factors

Self-Awareness

Self-awareness literally means understanding the self. The nurse has a responsibility to examine personal feelings, thoughts, behaviors, attitudes, and intentions. This ongoing monitoring requires openness and an ability to be self-critical. The nurse's emotional responses and actions have a significant impact on the client. The nurse must be sensitive to this effect. Self-awareness allows the nurse to separate personal feelings from the client's responses. This ability to control and manage personal emotions and respond appropriately to others is called emotional competency or **emotional intelligence**. The personal growth that comes through self-awareness will enrich the therapeutic relationship.

Even with knowledge of general customs and practices, the nurse should not assume that the client fits that expectation. Therefore, the nurse should clarify personal preferences with each client.

Boundaries

Boundaries are limits that help establish and maintain the nurse and client roles in the relationship. To be truly helpful to clients, nurses need to understand the difference between professional and social relationships. Social relationships are interactions in which the needs of both persons are of equal importance. In contrast, professional relationships are those in which the needs of the client are paramount. This principle guides the nurse's decisions on handling difficult situations with clients.

Self-Disclosure. One area of boundaries involves self-disclosure. **Self-disclosure** refers to revealing personal information about oneself, with the goal of benefiting the client and the therapeutic process. It is not always easy to know if the information will help the client. Self-disclosure can reverse the nurse–client dynamic and sever the client from the role of information giver. The focus of the nurse–client relationship is always the client. With experience, the nurse is better able to determine what information may be shared without compromising the relationship. In the following example, the nurse balances genuineness with maintaining a professional relationship.

Self-disclosure is a controversial intervention that should only be used to benefit the client and the therapeutic process, never for selfish reasons.

Example:

Client: "I think I have to place my mother in a nursing facility. She is becoming very forgetful and needs help with her personal care. What do you think I should do?"

Nurse: "That is something you will have to decide. I have an elderly parent, and I can imagine how difficult this is for you."

The nurse should never reveal intimate information or answer questions that raise feelings of discomfort.

Example:

Client: "May I have your phone number so I can stay in touch after I leave the hospital?"

Nurse: "I cannot give my phone number. Are you concerned about who to call if you have questions or concerns after you are discharged?"

In this example, the nurse appropriately refuses to give personal information and counters the client's possible feelings of rejection by showing concern and a willingness to help.

Because decisions about what information is appropriate to share with the client are difficult, the nurse should seek guidance from an experienced nurse or colleague.

One piece of information important to disclose to the client to protect the client's rights is the nurse's name, title, and position. As mentioned earlier, students and beginning practitioners may be reluctant to divulge their novice status. Clients, however, may pick up on an interviewer's newness. Thus, denying that you are new in the field may cause a lack of trust. Clients who seem distressed by the nurse's lack of experience should be encouraged to discuss this with the nurse and may be referred to the nurse's supervisor for reassurance if necessary. Psychiatric clients who have had previous experience with new nurses and students often come to expect this as the norm; certain clients actually take pride in "training" new nurses.

Touch. The use of touch is another area that is influenced by the importance of maintaining appropriate boundaries. Touch is commonly used to convey caring, provide comfort, or offer support. Touch is essential to carry out physical care or treatments. However, touch can be interpreted differently by clients, and at times may be misinterpreted. Touch may not be welcomed based on cultural or religious preferences. Clients who are experiencing paranoia or psychoses may be threatened by touch, and clients with sexual preoccupation may misinterpret the nurse's touch as sexual. Inpatient settings often have a general rule of no touching as a way of reducing incidents related to such misinterpretations. This rule is helpful to students and novice practitioners, since it often takes experience to recognize when touch can present serious risks. In the absence of a rule,

Clinical Example 

A client is going through a bad breakup of a relationship. The nurse may feel tempted to tell the client of a similar experience (e.g., "I know how you feel. My boyfriend and I just split up."). The nurse may feel good revealing this; however, a client in acute distress may feel that the nurse is not understanding his or her unique feelings and circumstances.

the nurse should use touch cautiously and inform clients before touching them for physical care, such as taking a blood pressure.

Critical Thinking Question 

What personal information might you share with a client? How and in what context would you disclose this information? What personal information would you not disclose to a client?

Communication Techniques

Active Listening

Active listening is an interactive process between the nurse and the client with the goal of understanding and being understood, involving hearing the message, understanding the message, and giving feedback about what was heard (Sheldon, 2009). Active listening requires vast energy, self-control, patience, genuine interest, and concentration (Antai-Otong, 2007). Active listening fosters trust and establishes a dialogue for the expression of the client's feelings. **Table 3-3** lists actions that promote active listening.

Table 3-3 Actions to Promote Active Listening

Sit upright facing the client
Lean slightly forward toward the client
Maintain an open posture (arms and legs not crossed)
Make eye contact; keep gaze comfortable; do not stare
Relax
Be attentive; block out distractions
Nod or make encouraging overtures, e.g., "Go on."
Avoid interruptions

Source: Adapted from Sheldon, L. K. (2009). *Communication for nurses, talking with patients* (2nd ed.). Sudbury, MA: Jones and Bartlett Publishers; and Antai-Otong, D. A. (2007). *Nurse-client communication, a life span approach*. Sudbury, MA: Jones and Bartlett Publishers.

Active listening requires vast energy, self-control, patience, genuine interest, and concentration.

Nonverbal Techniques

Facial Expression

Facial expression can communicate a variety of emotions. Tears communicate sadness, while a smile can communicate warmth or happiness. While the nurse may interpret the client's feeling or mood based on the facial expression, it is important to validate the interpretation with the client. It is significant to note if the client's facial expression is incongruent with the stated feeling. Incongruence or an absence of facial expression can be related to certain physical or mental disorders.

Eye Contact

Eye contact varies greatly across cultures. In the American culture, direct eye contact communicates interest, openness, and trustworthiness. In other cultures, this may be considered disrespectful or even hostile. An averted gaze may be interpreted as shyness, disinterest, or avoidance. However, in some cultures, it is a sign of respect. Eye contact is a form of communication, but the meaning must be validated with each individual.

Posture

A person's body posture communicates how the person feels about him or herself, and, if engaged in an interaction, posture also communicates feelings towards the other person. Standing tall communicates confidence and self esteem. Hands on the hips or clasped behind the head conveys superiority. The person with slumped shoulders, staring at the floor, suggests low self esteem. Tapping fingers or feet indicate nervousness or impatience. A closed posture, that is crossed arms and legs, indicates the person is closed to communication. In contrast, an open posture, with hands on lap, legs uncrossed, signals an openness or receptivity to communication. The nurse must validate the meaning of the client's posture. Knowing that posture is a way of communicating, the nurse must be aware and sensitive to the messages sent by his or her own posture.

Verbal Techniques

Therapeutic Techniques

To be effective, the nurse depends on skillful communication. In addition to the qualities of self-awareness, empathy, genuineness, and a positive self-image, the nurse needs to apply constructive strategies for obtaining and conveying information. The nurse selects specific strategies based on the goal of the interaction or the type of response being elicited. **Table 3-4** matches common goals of the nurse's communication with techniques best suited to soliciting the desired response.

Table 3-4 Therapeutic Versus Nontherapeutic Communication Techniques

Goals	Therapeutic Techniques and Examples	Nontherapeutic Techniques and Examples
To engage the client in treatment	Offering self: "I will stay here with you for a while." Suggested collaboration: "Let's work together to see if we can identify when your problems began."	Giving false reassurance: "Don't worry; everything will be fine." Using platitudes: "Keep your chin up; tomorrow is another day."
To get the client to open up and share information, thoughts, and feelings	Judiciously using silence. Using broad, open-ended questions such as, "Tell me about your family." Actively listening by nodding and leaning toward the client. Using encouraging verbalizations such as "yes" and "I understand." Offering general leads such as "please continue" or "I am interested in hearing more about that."	Asking questions that yield only "yes" or "no" answers. Asking incessant closed-ended questions, so that the conversation seems like an interrogation.
To convey to the client that you understand	Summarizing the content. Restating content: *Client*: "I am so depressed that I cannot even eat." *Nurse*: "So your depression has caused you to lose your appetite." Reflecting on process: "You seem anxious." or "It seems difficult for you to talk about this."	Using premature interpretations that deny the client's feelings: "You're not really angry with your mother; you're just looking for attention." Inappropriately using self-disclosure: "I know just how you feel, because my boyfriend just broke up with me, too."
To get the client more actively involved in treatment	Reflecting the client's questions back to him or her: *Client*: "What should I tell people at work about my hospitalization?" *Nurse*: "What are you thinking about telling them?" Encouraging comparison: "What have you done in the past when faced with such a difficult situation?" Encouraging decision making: "What will you do the next time that you find yourself in a similar situation?"	Overtly agreeing or disagreeing with the client: "What you did was definitely the right (or wrong) thing to do." Giving advice: "I think that you should . . ."
To explore a topic in more detail	Exploring: "Could you tell me more about that issue?" Focusing: "Let's go back and discuss that topic further."	Bombarding the client with multiple closed-ended questions on a topic.
To diffuse a client's nonpsychotic anger	Agreeing with the grain of truth in the client's complaint: *Client:* "I hate this hospital. It's like a jail." *Nurse:* "I can see how you would feel that way, with all of the rules and the locked door. Let's talk about how you can be more comfortable here."	Denying the client's reality: *Client:* "I hate this hospital. It's like a jail." *Nurse:* "You know that this is not a jail."

Table 3-4 **Therapeutic Versus Nontherapeutic Communication Techniques *(Continued)***

Goals	Therapeutic Techniques and Examples	Nontherapeutic Techniques and Examples
To help the client control aggressive behavior	Limit-setting: "I will not be able to continue to talk with you if you continue to act in a threatening manner." Giving positive reinforcement for calm behavior. Decreasing stimuli: Placing the client in a quiet area until he or she is calmer.	Punishing the client: "You are going to have to stay in your room for 1 hour because you cursed at me" (choosing an arbitrary time period, unrelated to the client's behavior).
To clarify information	Asking for clarification: "Could you explain that to me again?" "Let's see if I have this straight." Placing events in sequence: "Did you start to drink alcohol before or after becoming depressed?"	Jumping to conclusions about the meaning of a client's statement, instead of seeking clarification.
To determine causes of problems or behaviors	Nonjudgmentally exploring: "What is it that gets in the way of your getting up to make it to work on time?"	Asking confrontational "why" questions: "Why are you unable to get to work on time?"
To effectively address delusional content	Focusing on the feeling content of delusions: *Client:* "People are trying to kill me!" *Nurse:* "You must be very frightened."	Directly challenging a client's belief system: *Client*: "Laser beams are irradiating me!" *Nurse:* "There is no way that laser beams are being sent through you—that's impossible."
To move to another topic of discussion	Transitioning gently: "What you are saying is very important, and I want to give it proper attention when we have more time. Right now, however, we need to move on."	Rejecting a client's topic or abruptly changing the subject: "It's not necessary to go into that right now. Let's talk about your hallucinations instead."

Nontherapeutic Techniques

Table 3-4 also provides examples of nontherapeutic communication techniques, or strategies that are likely to impede successful communication. Students often express a fear of saying the wrong thing to a client. More important than the words used, is the intention to help and a caring, respectful manner. If the nurse notes an unexpected or unfavorable response from the client, it is important to clarify what the client heard and restate the nurse's message and intent. The nurse will only become skilled in the art of communication through practice and review. The effort will be worth the rewards.

Assertive Communication

Assertive communication is a style that effectively expresses the person's thoughts and feelings in a way that respects the needs and rights of others. Assertive communication promotes the use of *I* statements, which allow the client to own the feeling. In assertive communication, the client is encouraged to make clear what he or she wants from the other person. This clarity, and a respectful manner, maximizes the chances that the person's needs will be recognized and met in a satisfactory way. By avoiding anger, assertiveness helps to preserve relationships. Assertive communication avoids the use of *you* statements, which can sound angry or accusatory and put people on the defensive. This style of communication would be called aggressive. Assertive communication is also in contrast with the passive style, which is apologetic and in which the client subjugates his or her own needs in deference to the feelings or needs of another person. A comparison of these styles is presented in **Table 3-5.**

Assertive communication is a skill that clients can learn and apply to a range of situations, such as expressing feelings, asking for help, and saying no to requests that cause stress or discomfort. Most impor-

Table 3-5 Assertive Versus Passive and Aggressive Communication

Assertive	Effectively communicates personal needs, thoughts, and feelings while respecting the rights of others; uses *I* statements.	"I lose my train of thought when you come into class late. I expect all students to be here when class starts."
Passive	Personal needs are secondary to others; style is apologetic or complaining.	"I hate to bring this up, but could you try to come to class on time?"
Aggressive	Expresses needs but in a way that is disrespectful to others; manner is hostile, angry, accusatory; uses *you* statements.	"You are always late. Your behavior is unacceptable and will not be tolerated."

tantly, the nurse should model effective communication by the practice of assertive communication.

Critical Thinking Question

A colleague asks you to switch weekends and you don't want to make the change. Using principles of assertive communication, how would you refuse this request?

Summary

The nurse–client relationship is the hallmark of psychiatric nursing and the context in which all nursing is practiced. The nurse–client relationship is focused on meeting the needs of the client, is collaborative in nature, and has identified goals. There are four phases to the nurse–client relationship—the preinteraction phase, the orientation phase, the working phase, and the termination phase, each with expected tasks and goals. Essential characteristics of the nurse in a helping relationship include respect, trust, genuineness, and empathy. The unconscious processes of transference and countertransference can interfere with the nurse–client relationship and must be addressed. The client's beliefs and values, which are associated with religion and culture, as well as his or her developmental level, affect communication. The nurse must validate interpretations of behavior with each individual. Self-awareness allows the nurse to separate personal feelings from the client's responses. The use of therapeutic communication techniques and the avoidance of nontherapeutic techniques can help the nurse to guide the nurse-client interaction. Assertive communication skills are important for both the nurse and client as an aid to effective communication of needs.

Annotated References

American Psychological Association (APA). (2007). *APA dictionary of psychology*. Washington, DC: Author.
The dictionary provides definitions of psychology terms and encompasses all areas of research and application, concepts, processes, and therapies.

Antai-Otong, D. A. (2007). *Nurse–client communication, a life span approach*. Sudbury, MA: Jones and Bartlett Publishers.
This book presents an overview of effective communication and its influence on therapeutic relationships across the life span.

Erikson, E. (1963). *Childhood and society* (2nd ed.). New York, NY: W. W. Norton & Company.
This pioneering work regarding the evolution of personality over one's lifetime is easy to understand and apply to practice. Development is put into historical and sociological perspective, and the role of the child in society is also explored.

Peplau, H. (1952). *Interpersonal relations in nursing*. New York, NY: G. P. Putnam.
This classic psychiatric nursing textbook provides the basic concepts to guide professional nurses in establishing mature therapeutic relationships with clients (patients) with all types of conditions and in all settings.

Rogers, C. (1951). *Client-centered therapy*. Boston, MA: Houghton Mifflin Company.
A classic book defining the Rogerian approach to psychotherapy.

Sheldon, L. K. (2009). *Communication for nurses, talking with patients* (2nd ed.). Sudbury, MA: Jones and Bartlett Publishers.
This book presents communication techniques to enhance the nurse-client relationship with different client groups and across a variety of situations.

Additional Resources

Hays, J. S., & Larson, K. H. (1963). *Interacting with patients.* New York, NY: Macmillan.

Travelbee, J. (1969). *Intervention in psychiatric nursing: Process in the one-to-one relationship.* Philadelphia, PA: F. A. Davis Company.

This classic primer by one of the pioneers of psychiatric nursing is rich in clear explanations and clinical examples of the practice of psychiatric nursing.

Williams, C. L. (2008). *Therapeutic interaction in nursing* (2nd ed.). Sudbury, MA: Jones and Bartlett Publishers.

This book addresses communication issues relevant to a variety of nurse–client interactions and provides many clinical examples as well as exercises for the learner.

Internet Resources

For a full suite of assignments and additional learning activities, use the access code located in the front of your book to visit this exclusive website: http://go.jblearning.com/mentalhealth. If you do not have an access code, you can obtain one at the site.

Learning Objectives

After reading this chapter, you will be able to:

- Describe the components of a holistic assessment, including mental status examination.
- Correctly use psychiatric terminology to describe a client's symptoms.
- Apply appropriate interviewing techniques to gather information for a holistic assessment.
- Discuss the role of psychological testing and rating scales in assessment.
- Describe each of the five axes in a *DSM-IV-TR* diagnosis.

Key Terms

Affect

Biopsychosocial history

Chief complaint

Collateral history

Concrete thought process

Coping skills

Delusions

Diagnostic and Statistical Manual of Mental Disorders, 4th ed., text revision (*DSM-IV-TR*)

Differential diagnosis

Empathy

Global Assessment of Functioning (GAF) scale

Hallucinations

History of present illness (HPI)

Holistic psychiatric assessment

Homicidal thoughts

Impulse control

Insight

Judgment

Mental status examination

Mood

Multiaxial *DSM-IV-TR* diagnosis

Physical assessment

Psychiatric nursing interview

Psychological tests

Resistance

Suicidal thoughts

Therapeutic contract

Chapter 4

The Psychiatric Nursing Assessment

Christine Carniaux Moran

http://go.jblearning.com/mentalhealth 

For a full suite of assignments and additional learning activities, use the access code located in the front of your book to visit this exclusive website: http://go.jblearning.com/mentalhealth. If you do not have an access code, you can obtain one at the site.

Introduction

The evaluation of psychiatric clients is a multifaceted endeavor, most effectively performed by an interdisciplinary team of mental health professionals. A comprehensive, **holistic psychiatric assessment** examines the physical, psychological, intellectual, social, and spiritual aspects of the individual. The **physical assessment** may include a physical examination, a study of the client's biologic life stage and genetic predisposition, laboratory tests, and diagnostic tests such as magnetic resonance imaging (MRI) and electroencephalography (EEG). The psychological evaluation surveys childhood experiences, personality, and current objective and subjective symptoms of psychiatric illness. This information is gathered by interviewing the client and family, performing a **mental status examination**, and administering specific **psychological tests** and rating scales.

Cognitive functioning is best assessed by utilizing a standard measure such as the Mini-Mental Status examination. The social assessment consists of an exploration of cultural, environmental, and familial influences on the expression and experience of illness, and the spiritual assessment is an exploration of the client's religious and spiritual dimensions (**Table 4-1**).

The psychiatric nursing evaluation covers the assessment, diagnosis, outcome identification, and planning stages of the nursing process. The evaluation is ongoing; as more of the client's history and new **insights** into his or her issues come to light, the diagnosis and treatment plan evolve accordingly.

Table 4-1 Holistic Psychiatric Nursing Assessment

Assessment Tool	Component Parts	Dimension Addressed
Biopsychosocial history	Chief complaint	Psychological
	History of present illness	Psychological
	Psychiatric history	Psychological
	Alcohol and substance use history	Psychological
	Medical history	Physical
	Family history	Psychological, physical, social
	Developmental history	Psychological, physical, social
	Social history	Social
	Occupational/educational history	Social
	Culture	Social
	Spirituality	Spiritual
	Coping skills	Psychological
Mental status examination	Behavior and appearance	Psychological, physical, social
	Emotions: mood and affect	Psychological
	Speech	Psychological, physical, social, intellectual
	Thought process and content	Psychological, social, intellectual, spiritual
	Perceptual disturbances	Psychological, physical
	Impulse control	Psychological, physical
	Cognition and sensorium	Intellectual, physical
	Knowledge, insight, and judgment	Intellectual, psychological
Psychological tests	Multiple tools, including rating scales	Psychological, intellectual
Physical assessment	Physical examination	Physical
	Assessment of activities of daily living	Physical
	Laboratory tests	Physical
	CT scans/other diagnostic tests	Physical

Assessment

The ability to assess clients is one of the psychiatric nurse's most important skills. The assessment, the first step in the nursing process, defines the client's problem and allows the nurse and client to establish a relationship. A thorough nursing assessment is a prerequisite for formulating an appropriate nursing diagnosis and plan of care. Assessment data also provide a baseline level of functioning that is used to evaluate, change, and respond to the treatment plan.

Data used for assessment are gathered not only from the client, but also from other sources. The client's self-assessment usually differs from the perception of family, coworkers, other clients in the hospital, and members of the treatment team; those views also vary between groups. Additionally, anyone's perception of the client will change over time.

Assessment guidelines vary according to the specific dimensions of the client being evaluated; however, the need for a structured interview and a data collection tool is widely accepted. Enough data must be collected in order to effectively diagnose and treat the patient, but not so much information that the assessment process becomes overwhelming to both patient and nurse. Data collection is focused on information that is most relevant for the patient and setting. It is the quality and not the quantity of the assessment data that matters. The following guidelines for a holistic psychiatric nursing assessment should be tailored to meet the specific needs of the nurse, client, and situation. These guidelines provide instructions for conducting a **psychiatric nursing interview** to obtain data for a **biopsychosocial history** and mental status examination.

Psychiatric Nursing Interview

An interview is a conversation with a deliberate purpose that ideally is mutually accepted by the participants. It differs from a social conversation in that one participant (the nurse) is responsible for the content and flow of the interaction, while the other participant (the client) is the focus of the discussion. The interview must take place within a specific time frame. The purpose of the psychiatric nursing interview is to gather the information necessary to understand and treat the client.

The content and process of the interview vary according to the state of the participants and the context in which the interview takes place. For example, suppose an agitated client has just been admitted to an acute psychiatric unit of a teaching hospital. The client's severe impairment, the nurse's need to budget time, and the busy nature of the setting indicate that a series of brief, structured interviews is the most practical approach. The members of the interdisciplinary treatment team (psychiatrist, nurse, social worker, and other specialists) share the responsibility for data collection, and effective communication of this information among the professionals is the key to avoiding omissions in the assessment process that might otherwise lead to medical errors (Nance, 2008). With consent, family or significant others may be approached to elucidate the client's story. The content of the initial interview should focus on eliciting information to help the staff provide a safe environment for the client and others (i.e., the client's potential for suicidal and violent behavior is assessed).

Assessment guidelines and data collection tools should be individualized for each client during the psychiatric evaluation.

The content of the psychiatric nursing interview focuses on the client's biopsychosocial history and current mental status.

Content of the Psychiatric Nursing Interview: Biopsychosocial History

Biopsychosocial history is a comprehensive assessment of the client's lifetime biologic, psychological, and social functioning.

Identifying Data

A written biopsychosocial history begins with a succinct summary of the client's demographics: name, age, gender, marital status, ethnicity, religion, occupation, education, and current living situation.

Chief Complaint

The client's **chief complaint** is the reason for current contact with the mental health system. The chief complaint should be obtained in the client's own words. Because of the nature of the illness, the client's statement may differ greatly from the family's or evaluator's assessment of the situation (e.g., an inpatient insists that she is in the hospital for a medical checkup following her abduction by aliens).

The chief complaint provides valuable data concerning the client's illness.

History of Present Illness

The chief complaint should be obtained in the client's own words.

The **history of present illness (HPI)** is a chronologic account of the events leading up to the current contact with the mental health professional. The HPI includes a description of the evolution of the client's symptoms that covers the onset, duration, and change of symptoms over time. Attendant changes in somatic functioning (sleep pattern, appetite, cognitive ability, sexual functioning) should also be noted. Exacerbating and ameliorating factors of the current psychological distress must be explored, and the nurse should delineate factors that may have precipitated the current episode. These stressful events may be negative (e.g., job loss) or positive (e.g., job promotion). For clients with preexisting psychiatric illness, the precipitant may be related to ineffectiveness of his or her current treatment regimen. Compiling a list of the client's current medications, dosing, and adherence is essential. The information obtained in the psychiatric HPI is similar to that obtained when clients are evaluated for nonpsychiatric medical illnesses (see **Table 4-2**).

A high level of comorbidity exists between mental illness and alcohol or substance abuse, and there is evidence that both may have a genetic or familial component.

Psychiatric History

Information concerning past psychiatric illness and treatment must be obtained to understand the current episode, to make an accurate diagnosis, and to make a prognosis. Psychiatric illness may be a single event, chronic, or intermittent; and the course of the illness may improve or deteriorate over time.

Alcohol and Substance Use History

Studies have shown high comorbidity of mental illness and alcohol or substance abuse. Causality is difficult to discern, because alcohol and drug abuse may precipitate an episode of mental illness or may represent a client's attempt to cope with a preexisting mental disorder. Research has shown that drug and alcohol use in the mentally ill adversely affects the course of their illness (Sadock, Sadock, & Ruiz, 2009).

The nurse should obtain a history of the client's caffeine and nicotine use; both are prevalent in

Table 4-2 Comparison of Assessment for Physical and Mental Disorders

Chief Complaint		
	Angina	**Depression**
Quality	"Chest tightening, with pain radiating down my left arm."	"Emotional pain that feels like I am going to die."
Severity	"Severe—a 9 on a scale of 1 to 10."	"Severe—a 9 on a scale of 1 to 10."
Timing	"It lasts about 5 minutes."	"It is constant."
History of Present Illness		
	Angina	**Depression**
Factors that aggravate	Exercise, emotional stress, and meals	Stress at work, arguments with family members, and morning hours
Factors that alleviate	Rest and nitroglycerine tablets	Social contact, activities, and antidepressant medication
Associated symptoms	Dyspnea, nausea, and sweating	Anhedonia (chronic inability to experience pleasure), diminished appetite, and insomnia
Chronology	Started with chest pain on exertion 1 year ago; getting increasingly more severe and frequent	Started with a sad mood and feeling overwhelmed after a job promotion 6 months ago; getting increasingly more incapacitating and unrelated to life events over time

psychiatric clients. Caffeine may supply energy to depressed and schizophrenic clients; caffeine and caffeine withdrawal may cause agitation as well. Nicotine use may increase attention span and memory in clients with schizophrenia but may decrease the efficacy of neuroleptics. Nicotine withdrawal may lead to agitation or depression (American Psychiatric Association [APA], 2000).

Medical History

The nurse should ascertain significant illnesses, injuries, and treatments received. The client must be assessed for allergies and past and present side effects from medication. An Abnormal Involuntary Movement Scale (AIMS)(Guy, 1976) examination may be done to measure psychotropic medication–induced motor side effects. In performing an AIMS examination, the nurse observes for abnormal muscle movement while the client performs a series of simple motor tasks. See Chapter 6 for a copy of the Abnormal Involuntary Movement Scale.

Women should be questioned concerning their menstrual cycles, pregnancies, and menopause; hormonal changes may have a significant impact on the client's mental health. The nurse should evaluate the client's risk for falling and skin breakdown and take note of assistive devices the client requires (e.g., eyeglasses, hearing aids, dentures, canes, or a walker).

Family History

Obtaining information regarding family history of mental illness can be helpful in diagnosing the client, because many of these disorders are hereditary. Bipolar and unipolar mood disorders, schizophrenia, and attention deficit disorder (ADD) have significant genetic components. The client's response to specific interventions (e.g., certain medications) may be inherited as well and should be included in the family history (Sadock et al., 2009).

Developmental History

The developmental history is an account of the client's infancy, childhood, and adolescence. It may provide clues to the origin of current behaviors and aid in the diagnosis. Erikson (1963) created a developmental timetable to identify the psychosocial adaptation required during each stage of life. All stages, beginning with birth and extending through senescence, are characterized by developmental tasks. The successful completion of these tasks, crucial to both happiness and success with subsequent tasks, represents optimal adaptation at a given stage. In contrast, failure at these tasks may lead to difficulty completing future tasks and may stifle psychosocial growth. Self-esteem, self-control, and independence emerge during toddlerhood, peak during the industry-versus-inferiority stage (6 years of age through puberty), and represent key issues in assessing an adult's ability to cope with, for example, the stress of illness (**Table 4-3**).

Childhood mental disorders, temperament, and style of interpersonal relationships may remain with the client into adulthood. Additionally, psychic trauma (e.g., neglect or abuse, loss of parent) experienced by a client during childhood may adversely affect brain development, leading to **impulse control** problems, personality disorder, posttraumatic stress disorder (PTSD), depression, other psychiatric illness, and physical illnesses (Bloom, 1999; Felitti et al., 1998). It is estimated that 25% of children under age 16 will experience some kind of trauma (National Child Traumatic Stress Network, 2004). Data show that 34–53% of the mentally ill population report childhood sexual or physical abuse, with a 29–43% rate of PTSD among the seriously mentally ill (Kessler et al., 1995).

Clinical Example

Jerry is a 34-year-old male diagnosed with chronic paranoid schizophrenia who was brought to the hospital by the police after threatening to harm passersby on the street. Jerry became enraged when he discovered that the hospital was a smoke-free environment; he had been smoking one to two packs of cigarettes per day for 15 years. Jerry was offered treatment with a nicotine patch or gum; however, he adamantly refused this treatment. Jerry required physical restraint on one occasion and medication on several other occasions due to psychotic agitation that was exacerbated by nicotine withdrawal. Jerry was stabilized on psychotropic medications and was discharged within 2 weeks. Upon discharge, Jerry resumed smoking and had a relapse of psychotic symptoms. His psychiatrist attributed the outpatient decompensation to the diminished efficacy of the antipsychotic medication, because the medication dose had been titrated in the hospital while Jerry was nicotine free. Jerry's condition was stabilized with an increase in dose.

Table 4-3 Erikson's Stages of Psychosocial Growth and Development

Age Group	Developmental Stage Task	Characteristics
Infancy	Trust vs. mistrust	The goal is the development of a sense of trust. Consistent attention to physical needs within a reasonable time period builds trust.
Toddlerhood	Autonomy vs. shame and doubt	The goal is the achievement of autonomy. An environment in which the child is able to explore surroundings in a safe way engenders autonomy. Successful toilet training plays a key role.
Preschool age	Initiative vs. guilt	The goal is the development of a sense that the child's actions produce outcomes through opportunity to try to do things on one's own.
School age	Industry vs. inferiority	The goal is a feeling of self-worth, gained by mastering schoolwork, sports, and other competitive activities.
Adolescence	Identity vs. role confusion	The goal is to establish a unique identity, first by rejecting adults and identifying with peer group and later by developing individuality.
Young adulthood	Intimacy vs. isolation	Establishment of close relationships with members of both sexes.
Middle adulthood	Generativity vs. stagnation	The goal is a feeling of giving back to the younger generation or society, through successfully adjusting to changing roles in marriage, parenting, and career.
Late adulthood	Integrity vs. despair	The goals are to attain a sense of continuity of past, present, and future, of meaning in one's life as it was, and of acceptance of death. This is achieved through life review and reminiscence.

Social History

A client's ability to make and sustain relationships indicates the ability to utilize the therapeutic relationship and aids in the diagnosis. Larger social networks are correlated with decreased severity of mental illness and a more thorough recovery. It is often difficult to ascertain whether a client's social problems have precipitated or resulted from the mental illness.

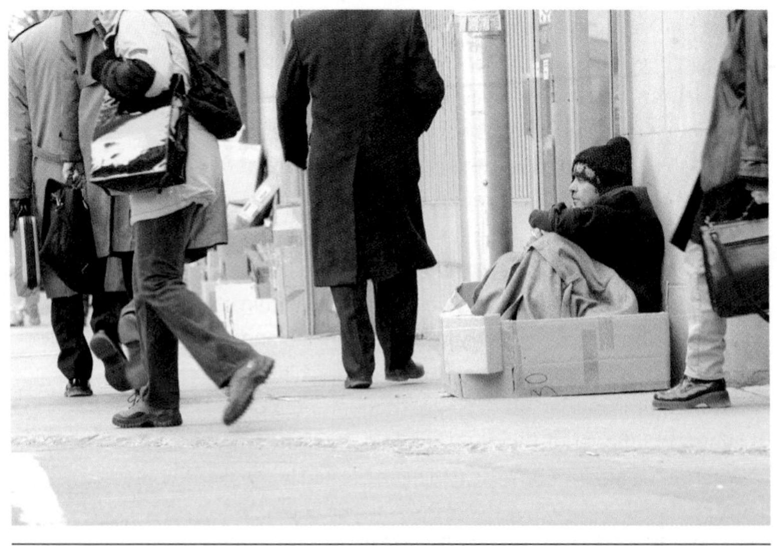

Figure 4-1 Homelessness is a severe social stressor.

The psychiatric nurse should inquire about the client's family and household members. How have family and significant others responded to the client's illness? Often, coping with a family member's mental illness is extremely stressful and may be disruptive to the family system (Zauszniewski, Bekhet, & Suresky, 2010). Seek the client's permission to involve family members and significant others in the assessment and treatment process, unless this involvement would be counterproductive. Ascertain a history of the client's friendships and sexual partners.

The nurse should have the client describe these relationships or lack thereof. Is the client satisfied with his or her social role at this point in life? For example, some persons become distressed when they fail to accomplish social milestones such as marriage by a certain age. Assess the client's wider social network, including religious organizations, community centers, and clubs. The client's living situation is also integral to the assessment, because many of the client's stressors are environmental in origin. Homelessness, for example, is a severe social stressor (**Figure 4-1**).

Occupational and Educational History

It is essential to establish a client's past and present level of function in work and school. A sporadic or chaotic employment history may indicate personality disorder or frequent episodes of mental decompensation. Work- or school-related stress may have precipitated the illness. Assess the impact that hospitalization or treatment may have on the client's function at work or school. The client's level of education partially determines how the nurse can most effectively communicate with and educate the client. Low socioeconomic status has been correlated with a relatively high rate of symptoms of mental illness (Gresenz, Sturm, & Tang, 2001).

Culture

Ethnicity, race, social class, degree of acculturation, and language should be included in the cultural assessment. Culture can significantly influence the development, expression, and reporting of mental disorders; thereby affecting diagnosis. A clinician who is unfamiliar with the nuances of an individual's culture may see psychopathology when a behavior or experience may actually be a normal variation of the client's culture, such as a Native American who hears a dead relative's voice while grieving. Some symptom clusters are uniquely associated with certain cultures, such as an *ataque de nervios* (nervous attack) in the Hispanic population (APA, 2000). In clients with depression, biological symptoms (e.g., sleep and appetite disturbances) may tend to be universal, whereas psychological symptoms have been shown to vary by culture. Members of certain ethnic groups may be more likely to present with somatic complaints. Culture-specific rating scales may therefore be helpful in assessing clients from diverse backgrounds (Marsella, 2003).

Culturally competent assessment also requires sensitivity to the process of assessment. The client's comfort level in regard to disclosing private issues with unfamiliar people, having physical closeness with unfamiliar people, involving family in the assessment process, and being addressed by first name varies among age, socioeconomic, and ethnic groups. Because of a history of negative experiences that certain groups such as Native Americans have had with mainstream medicine, members of these groups may be reluctant to participate in the traditional Western assessment or treatment process (Vedantam, 2005). The presence of language barriers must be carefully assessed, because clients who appear to speak English adequately may be more comfortable in their native tongue, especially when discussing emotional issues. Ideally, interpreters are familiar with medical terminology and are not members of the client's own family (to decrease communication problems and protect the client's privacy).

The efficacy of different treatment modalities and beliefs regarding the etiology and treatment of mental illness may also vary among cultures and must be considered when developing a treatment plan. Among some people in certain cultures, mental illness may be viewed as a punishment for past wrongdoing or as a result of a curse; convincing clients with these beliefs that Western medication will treat the illness can be challenging. Enlisting the help of community elders or traditional healers, instead of arguing against the beliefs, may be helpful in this regard (Vedantam, 2005). The role of the extended family and community in assisting with the treatment of the mentally ill also differs among groups, which will also need to be considered when delineating care. In some cultures, the mentally ill tend to be ostracized whereas in others the community takes pride in caring for these individuals. Even the efficacy, dosing, and side effects of psychotropic medication may differ significantly among ethnic groups (Vedantam, 2005).

Although it is important to have a working knowledge of general differences among cultures, it is essential that the nurse avoid stereotyping individual clients on the basis of ethnic, racial, or social group membership. Data supporting that African Americans and whites presenting with comparable symptoms are diagnosed with different mental illnesses (with the African Americans more likely diagnosed with pervasive illnesses such as schizophrenia) point to continued prejudices within our healthcare system (Blow et al., 2004; Neighbors, Trierweiler, Ford, & Muroff, 2003). The first step toward culturally sensitive practice is healthcare workers' examination of their prejudices regarding other cultures and the effect that their own culture has on their work.

The psychiatric nurse must consider the client's culture without stereotyping the client.

Spirituality and Values

Spirituality is an often neglected aspect of assessment, especially in the acute care setting. Nursing as a profession may have overlooked the spiritual aspects of assessment and care as it has struggled to assert itself as a research-based profession (Govier, 2000). However, a client's lack of or sense of spirituality may have a tremendous impact on illness and treatment.

The belief in a divine plan and a benevolent God is comforting to many clients, and spirituality decreases their sense of aloneness and despair. Spirituality and religious beliefs may deter suicide and violence. Conversely, some clients may become angry with God for having caused their suffering and lose faith. Spiritual aspects of treatment, such as the concept of a higher power in the 12-step treatment program for alcohol and drug abuse, may engage spiritually minded clients but deter those who are not religious. A diagnostic category of religious or spiritual problems is included in the ***Diagnostic and Statistical Manual of Mental Disorders*, 4th edition, text revision (DSM-IV-TR)** (APA, 2000).

Religion is a way of expressing spirituality through an organized framework and through rituals. Clients should be asked about religion and whether or not they would like clergy involved in their treatment. Religiosity is correlated with relatively high levels of social support, decreased rates of depression, high levels of cooperation, and high levels of cognitive functioning (Koenig, 2007; Koenig, George, & Titus, 2004). In adolescents, religiosity is correlated with lower levels of drug abuse, violence, and behavioral problems (Barnes, Plotnikoff, Fox, & Pendelton, 2000).

Spirituality is a much broader concept than religion; it includes sources of motivation and strength and finding meaning and connectedness to one's self, others, the environment, and a higher power.

We often equate religion with spirituality; however, spirituality is a much broader concept. Although atheists do not believe in God and agnostics are unsure of God's existence, it cannot be assumed that spirituality is absent in members of these groups. Govier (2000) did an extensive literature search and determined that an exploration of reason, reflection, relationships, and restoration were other important components of spirituality that should be assessed. Reason and reflection refer to the client's sources of motivation and strength and the client's ability to take time to reflect on the meaning of his or her life or situation. Relationships refer to the client's sense of connectedness to others and to the environment. Restoration refers to the ability of the spiritual dimension to positively influence the physical aspect of care. On the other hand, spiritual distress (which can be the outcome of certain adverse life events) can precipitate or aggravate a course of illness.

A client's past coping style may help to identify useful strategies to cope with the present illness.

Nurses who are not in touch with their own spirituality will tend to shy away from including an in-depth spiritual assessment of clients, so self-awareness is the first step toward performing a competent spiritual assessment. Observing for the presence of a Bible, cross, or Star of David may also give clues to the client's spirituality. Being present with the client, using active listening skills, being nonjudgmental, and taking care not to impose one's personal beliefs onto the client are essential skills in addressing a client's spiritual side.

Critical Thinking Question

What kinds of challenges would you expect when working with a client whose cultural or spiritual background differs from yours? What would you do to overcome potential difficulties?

Coping Skills

Coping skills are mechanisms people use to manage internal and external stressors. Coping behaviors can enable an individual to alter a stressful situation by controlling, or at least minimizing, the stress resulting from the situation. Clients with chronic psychiatric or life-threatening medical illness may be unable to alter their condition, but they can attempt to control the stress and minimize its effect on their lives through the use of one or coping behaviors. They may seek more information about the illness and treatment options. They may participate in self-care and reach out to others, including healthcare professionals, family members, and friends. Clients may also attend support groups and express feelings about self-concept, body image, and physical function. They may practice deep breathing relaxation exercises.

Conversely, maladaptive coping mechanisms are behaviors that ultimately interfere with the client's ability to confront the stressor, may be harmful, and usually produce additional stress. Unfortunately, they are tried and true mechanisms; the client has successfully used them in the past to maintain emotional stability in the short term. Consequently, clients tend to rely on these coping mechanisms to deal with future stressors. Such behaviors include alcohol and drug abuse, overeating, inappropriate anger, and social withdrawal.

Discerning the client's characteristic pattern of coping—whether it is adaptive or maladaptive—helps the nurse to predict how the client may react to a future stressor. It is often helpful to spend time uncovering and encouraging the use of the adaptive coping mechanisms that have been successfully used by the client in the past, because clients in current crisis are often feeling overwhelmed and may need prompting to remember the skills in their arsenal.

Ascertaining a client's adaptive coping skills during the assessment process will enable the nurse to more effectively coach the client to calm him- or herself if the client becomes upset or agitated during the course of treatment.

Content of the Psychiatric Nursing Interview: Mental Status Examination

Whereas the biopsychosocial history is a record of the client's entire lifetime, the mental status examination is an evaluation of the client's present state. Behavior and general appearance, **mood** and **affect**, speech, thought process and content, perceptual disturbances, impulse control, cognition, knowledge, **judgment**, and insight are assessed. Although it is termed an examination, this assessment guideline requires little direct questioning beyond what is required for taking a biopsychosocial history; most pertinent information is gleaned from the interview process and content.

The acronym BEST PICK can assist in the recall of the main elements of the mental status examination. It stands for **b**ehavior and general appearance; **emo**tions: mood and affect; **s**peech; **t**hought content and process; **p**erceptual disturbances; **i**mpulse control; **c**ognition and sensorium; and **k**nowledge, insight, and judgment.

Behavior and General Appearance

Note the client's body frame, posture, dress, grooming, and age appropriateness of appearance. Some common adjectives used to describe the client's general appearance include *disheveled, well-groomed, heavily made-up, younger* or *older looking than biologic age, tensely postured, under-* or *overweight*, and *casually dressed.*

In terms of behavior, assess the client's gait, activity level, gestures, mannerisms, and psychomotor activity. Manic clients may be agitated and unable to sit still, whereas clients with schizophrenia may exhibit bizarre postures or psychomotor retardation. Observe for the rare symptoms of echopraxia (a mimicking of the interviewer's behavior), catatonia (statue-like immobility), and waxy flexibility (when limbs can be moved by the interviewer into positions that the client then maintains). Attempt to differentiate between movement disturbances secondary to mental illness and those resulting from medication side effects. Some antipsychotic medications may cause akathisia (motor restlessness), dystonia (sustained muscle spasm), or dyskinesia (involuntary muscle movement).

The psychiatric nurse should always evaluate how the client relates to the interviewer and to the interviewing process. Is the client cooperative or uncooperative, bored, angry, or flirtatious?

Emotions: Mood and Affect

The client's mood is the pervasive subjective emotional state, and the visible expression of this state is termed the affect. Mood is the client's self-assessment; affect is an observed state. Observe the depth, range, and fluctuation of emotional expression during the interview. Ask the client directly about his or her mood if the information is not offered spontaneously. Both mood and affect can be described as euthymic (normal), labile (rapidly changing from one mood state to another), depressed, irritable, anxious, angry, euphoric (excessively happy), frightened, or empty. Variability in the client's affect should be noted, ranging from flat (no variability) to labile (rapid fluctuation in affect). It is important to note congruity or incongruity of mood and affect. For example, some depressed clients look depressed, whereas others who are depressed appear euthymic.

A euthymic mood is a normal mood. A labile mood is one that changes rapidly from one state to another. A euphoric mood is an excessively happy one.

The acronym BEST PICK is a helpful way to remember the composition of the mental status examination:
Behavior and general appearance
Emotions: mood and affect
Speech
Thought content and process
Perceptual disturbances
Impulse control
Cognition and sensorium
Knowledge, insight, and judgment

Speech

The psychiatric nurse must observe the rate, amount, style, and tone of speech the client uses during the interview. Speech may range from pressured to hesitant, loud to inaudible, spontaneous to nonspontaneous, slurred to clear, and monotonous to dramatic. The client may be described as talkative or taciturn, depending upon the quantity of speech. Observe for evidence of dysarthria (physical difficulty in vocalizing), echolalia (the repetition of the interviewer's words), perseveration (the repetition of the same words or themes), aphasia (difficulties in understanding or producing speech), and other disorders or oddities of speech.

Dysarthria is a physical difficulty in vocalizing. Echolalia is the repetition of the interviewer's words. Perseveration is the repetition of the same words or themes. Aphasia includes problems in understanding or producing speech.

Thought Content

The psychiatric nurse should note any abnormalities in the client's thought content. Obsessions are intrusive thoughts or ideas that the client recognizes as crazy but acts in accordance with anyway (e.g., compulsive hand washing from an obsessive fear of germs). Hypochondriasis is an obsession with physical concerns that do not exist in reality.

Referential delusions (ideas of reference) are false beliefs that things in the environment relate to the client or have special meaning for the client.

Delusions are convictions that have no basis in reality. Delusions may be paranoid, grandiose, somatic (involving bodily concerns), erotic, nihilistic (involving death or destruction), guilty, bizarre, or referential (indicating belief that benign, random occurrences relate to or have special meaning for the client). An example would be the belief that a newspaper headline held a special message for the client. Referential beliefs are differentiated as ideas of reference or delusions of reference based on the level of conviction. If the client's belief is fixed and unshakeable, the term *delusion* applies. The degree of congruence between the client's mood and the type of delusion experienced should be noted. Delusional content is occasionally revealed spontaneously during the psychiatric interview. For example, a client may ask the nurse to help him to hide from a Mafia hit man. Conversely, the nurse should be aware that a paranoid client may be guarded in his or her discussion of delusions secondary to pervasive lack of trust. In most cases, clients have little insight that their thoughts are delusional and do not label them as such. The validity of delusions should not be questioned by the interviewer; such questioning is ineffective in changing the client's beliefs and often causes alienation and anger (Sadock et al., 2009).

A detailed account of the client's suicidal and homicidal thoughts must be obtained through direct questioning.

Assessment of suicidal and homicidal thoughts is a priority in all evaluations of thought content. **Suicidal thoughts** are the client's desires to kill or harm him- or herself, and homicidal thoughts are the client's desires to kill or harm others. Contrary to popular belief, discussing these feelings with a client does not increase, and may lower, the likelihood of the client's acting on them. Direct questioning is essential. Questions regarding suicidal and **homicidal thoughts** should elicit information regarding the client's exact plan (including method, extent of lethality of method, availability of the means to carry out the plan), motivation, or desire to carry out the plan, and steps already taken to complete the plan. Risk factors for suicide that may be identified during the assessment process include a history of past suicide attempts, substance abuse, major depression or psychotic illness; past trauma; recent loss; and social isolation. Another recognized risk factor is access to firearms. Risk factors detected in the client's current mental status include depressed mood, impulsivity, psychosis, anxiety, hopelessness, and helplessness. Factors *decreasing* the risk of a suicide attempt include religiosity and a sense of obligation to others (e.g., children, pets) (Hales & Simon, 2006).

It is widely accepted that the utilization of a standardized tool to gauge suicide and violence risk plays an important role in the prevention of self-harm and harm to others in the clinical setting, although there is no clear evidence demonstrating the superiority of one risk assessment tool over the others. The presence of active suicidal or homicidal thoughts constitutes a psychiatric emergency, and immediate action to ensure the safety of the client or the object of the client's anger is necessary. A summary guide for suicide assessment is provided in **Table 4-4**.

Clinical Example

Laura is a 26-year-old female hospitalized with an acute exacerbation of chronic paranoid schizophrenia. After the clients watched a televised news segment about Jerusalem, Laura was overheard discussing with the other clients her need to go on a pilgrimage to Jerusalem. Laura verbalized that one particular newscaster was speaking directly to her during the show, which is how she knew that she needed to go there. After Laura was accidentally bumped into by her hospital roommate later that day, Laura told her nurse that she then realized that the roommate was determined to join her in the pilgrimage. The nurse recognized these interchanges as referential delusions, active symptoms of Laura's schizophrenia.

Thought Process

The thought process is the way in which the client thinks. It is often evinced in the client's speech. Loose associations are marked by an illogical, difficult-to-follow shifting of ideas. Tangential thinking is exhibited when the client wanders from the subject at hand to a related one and is unable to come back to the original topic. Loose associations, tangential thought, word salad (completely nonsensical combination of words), and neologisms (nonsensical string of sounds that are formed into made-up words) often indicate schizophrenic disorders.

Circumstantial thought is demonstrated by clients who get lost in details but eventually return to the relevant topic. Thought blocking occurs when the thinking process stops altogether and the mind goes blank. Flight of ideas, as seen in mania, involves pressured speech with rapid topic changes; the topics may be associated, but in a strange way. For example, "I

Table 4-4 Suicide Assessment Guide

Suicide assessments should be conducted at first contact, following any suicidal behavior, increased ideation, or pertinent clinical change, and, for inpatients, prior to increasing privileges and at discharge.

1. Risk factors	**Current/past psychiatric diagnoses:** Especially mood disorders, psychotic disorders, alcohol/substance abuse, Cluster B personality disorders. Comorbidity and recent onset of illness increase risk. **Key symptoms:** Anhedonia (loss of pleasure in activities previously enjoyed), impulsivity, hopelessness, anxiety/panic, global insomnia, command hallucinations. **Suicidal behavior:** History of prior suicide attempts, aborted suicide attempts or self-injurious behavior. **Family history:** Of suicide, attempts or Axis 1 psychiatric diagnoses requiring hospitalization. **Precipitants/stressors:** triggering events leading to humiliation, shame or despair (i.e., loss of relationship, financial or health status—real or anticipated). Ongoing medical illness (especially central nervous system disorders, pain). History of abuse or neglect. Intoxication. **Access to firearms**
2. Protective factors	Protective factors, even if present, may not counteract significant acute risk. **Internal:** Ability to cope with stress, religious beliefs, frustration tolerance, absence of psychosis. **External:** Responsibility to children or beloved pets, positive therapeutic relationships, social supports.
3. Suicide inquiry	Specific questioning about thoughts, plans, behaviors, intent. **Ideation:** Frequency, intensity, duration—in last 48 hours, past month and worst ever. **Plan:** Timing, location, lethality, availability, preparatory acts. **Behaviors:** Past attempts, aborted attempts, rehearsals (tying noose, loading gun), vs. nonsuicidal, self-injurious actions. **Intent:** Extent to which the patient (1) expects to carry out the plan and (2) believes the plan/act to be lethal vs. self-injurious. Explore ambivalence: reasons to die vs. reasons to live.
4. Homicide inquiry	When indicated, especially postpartum, and in character-disordered or paranoid males dealing with loss or humiliation. Inquire in four areas listed above under "Suicide inquiry."

Source: Education Development Center, Inc., and Screening for Mental Health, Inc. (2007).

can see! The sea is washing away the shells." Confabulation, often indicating dementia, is a fabrication of information to fill in for memory gaps. For example, a client may give an elaborate but untrue story about how he or she spent the day.

A client with a **concrete thought process** as opposed to an abstract thought process is only able to understand conversations literally. For example, a client who is asked what brought him or her to the hospital and responds, "an ambulance," is manifesting concrete thinking. A client's ability to think abstractly may be ascertained by assessing the client's interpretation of a proverb such as "people in glass houses should not throw stones" or the client's ability to describe similarities between objects such as a chair and table. Concrete thought is common in clients with schizophrenic disorders. A concrete thought process is not pathological when exhibited by children, however, who developmentally may not have the capacity for abstract thought until early adolescence (Sadock et al., 2009).

Perceptual Disturbances

Illusions, which are common in delirium, are misinterpretations of true stimuli. An example is when a curtain in a dark room is mistaken for a person. **Hallucinations** are defined as sensations experienced by the client without real external stimuli. A patient may not have intact reality testing, the ability to accept evidence that these perceptions are not real. Clients who appear to be talking to imaginary others or pointing at nonexistent objects during the assessment are probably experiencing hallucinations or illusions. Direct questioning regarding perceptual disturbances is usually required to elicit the specific symptoms. Hallucinations may be auditory, visual, gustatory, olfactory, or tactile; clients may hear, see, taste, smell, or feel things that in reality do not exist. Auditory hallucinations are the most common type; the more unusual visual, gustatory, olfactory, and tactile hallucinations may indicate medical illness or substance intoxication or withdrawal.

Hypnagogic and hypnopompic hallucinations are false sensory perceptions that occur while falling asleep and while awakening from sleep, respectively. Depersonalization is a perceptual difficulty in which the client feels unreal, dead, or mechanical; derealization is the sensation that the outside world is unreal. Hypnagogic and hypnopompic hallucinations, derealization, and depersonalization are considered within the normal range of experience and are not considered pathologic unless they cause undue distress or problems with daily functioning.

Impulse Control

Impulse control is the ability to delay, modulate, or inhibit the expression of behaviors and feelings. Clues to the client's ability to control his or her impulses are found in the content and process of the general interview. A client who describes a recent history of binge drinking and indiscriminate sexual contacts has poor impulse control. A person who storms out of an interview when difficult topics are broached also evinces poor impulse control. Assessing the client's ability to control impulses is an integral part of determining potential for acting on suicidal and violent thoughts.

Cognition and Sensorium

Level of consciousness, orientation, concentration, and memory are especially important to determine when assessing clients with coexisting medical problems or those who reveal symptoms of dementia during the interview. During the psychiatric interview, clients provide many clues to their sensorium. A client with an altered level of consciousness during the interview demonstrates a fluctuating ability to maintain awareness of the environment. Orientation is assessed by simply asking the client additional questions regarding full name, current location, date, and time.

A client's memory and concentration are determined by the ability to answer questions regarding psychiatric history. Concentration may also be assessed by asking the client to count backward from 100 by 7s (100, 93, 86 . . .), and memory is tested by asking the client to remember three objects immediately and to recall them after 5 minutes. Be aware that clients may have impairments in remote, recent past, recent, and immediate memory. The Mini-Mental Status examination (MMSE) efficiently and objectively measures cognition (Folstein, Folstein, & McHugh, 1975). A score of 23 or lower suggests cognitive impairment with some variation based on education and reading levels. The psychiatrist, psychologist, or advanced practice nurse typically performs this examination.

The client's intellectual functioning (below average, average, superior) may be estimated from the interview process as well.

Knowledge, Insight, and Judgment

Knowledge, insight, and judgment are related concepts usually ascertained while taking the client's history and while observing and discussing the client's actions in social situations and in dealing with mental illness. Judgment is the capacity to identify possible courses of action, anticipate their consequences, and choose the appropriate behavior. Insight refers to the extent of the client's awareness of illness and maladaptive behaviors. A client who is admitted to the hospital for the third time because of nonadherence with antipsychotic medication and who states that he stopped taking the medication because he is not really mentally ill lacks knowledge of and insight into his illness and demonstrates poor judgment in regard to treatment. A client's judgment may be assessed by evaluating the answer to a hypothetical question such as: "What would you do if you found a stamped, addressed envelope in the street?"

Critical Thinking Question

What kind of information gathered in the mental status examination would prompt you to take immediate action? Specifically, what action would you take?

The Process of the Psychiatric Nursing Interview

The psychiatric nurse must pay attention to both the content of the client's words and the process of communication. How the client interacts with the nurse and the behaviors the client exhibits during the interview often provide important information concerning the client's symptomatology and ability to relate to others.

The interviewing process varies, ranging from casually talking with clients while, at the same time, assisting them with activities of daily living, to utilizing a standardized rating scale. Different methods may yield different information.

Phases of the Interview

An interview consists of a beginning, middle, and termination phase. In the initial moments of the interview, the nurse should begin to develop a rapport with the client and to engage the client in the meeting. Establishing a good rapport with a client is not simple; the nurse must put the client at ease, empathize with the client's suffering (i.e., understand how the client feels in a particular situation by mentally putting oneself in the client's place), listen compassionately, become the client's ally, and instill the client's trust of the nurse's expertise. The nurse must clarify the purpose of the meeting, which is to gain an understanding of the client's problems and to determine the best way to help. The client should be informed about the healthcare setting and the interviewer's credentials, and the rules of confidentiality should be discussed; these are requisite to making the client feel comfortable enough to share information.

During the middle phase of the interview, data are collected and processed. The nurse obtains information from and gives information to the client. For example, the nurse may assist the client in identifying ways to cope with symptoms.

The termination phase of the interview summarizes what has been accomplished during the meeting. A tentative diagnosis and an initial care plan are formulated and shared with the client. The termination phase is also used to help the client relax from the often emotional interaction.

Interviewing Techniques

One of the most important interviewing skills is the ability to be silent and attentive. Nonverbal communication, such as nodding in understanding and leaning slightly toward the client, demonstrates caring and attentiveness. Encouraging words, such as "I see" or "go on," enable the nurse to gather information without bombarding the client with questions. Allowing the client to discuss the chief complaint during the first few minutes of the interview is often an effective strategy to induce the client to open up. Paraphrasing or summarizing the content and feelings related during the interview demonstrates that the nurse understands what the client has said and helps both the interviewer and the client to process an abundance of information. The nurse may need to ask questions for clarification to avoid jumping to conclusions about nebulous communications. Gentle transition statements such as, "What you are telling me is important; however, there is one more important thing that we still need to discuss," keeps the interview on track without offending the client. Interviewing techniques must be individualized to the client's specific problems and personality. See Chapter 3, Table 3-4 for examples of therapeutic communication techniques.

Self-Disclosure

Revealing personal information about oneself is a controversial technique that requires nursing experience, insight, and sophistication on the part of the interviewer. The nurse should share personal information with a client only if, after careful evaluation, the nurse believes that this sharing would benefit the client and improve treatment. The nurse should never disclose personal information for selfish reasons.

Critical Thinking Question www

What kind of personal information would be appropriate to share with a nonpsychotic client on the first interview? How and in what context would you disclose this information?

Choosing Appropriate Questions

The client's state and the subject being evaluated determine whether to ask open-ended or closed-ended questions. Open-ended questions are vague and may be answered in many different ways. The nurse may say, "Tell me about your problem." Open-ended questions are most helpful in obtaining a broad range of information from clients without thought disorders. Closed-ended questions elicit specific and concise information. Disorganized clients who are unable to tolerate a long interview usually need to be guided by closed-ended questions when giving information. Some topics of discussion, such as suicidal thoughts, lend themselves to direct questioning; clients who are given more freedom to answer may skirt the issue or provide incomplete information. Questions typically become more specific or closed-ended as the interview progresses (Sadock et al., 2009).

The nurse's interviewing skills are based on experience, intuition, critical-thinking ability, personality, and communication style.

Empathy is the ability to put oneself in someone else's place. The nurse who can empathize with a client is able to understand how the client feels in a particular situation.

Certain types of questions should be avoided when evaluating the client, because they may taint the information elicited. Leading questions such as, "You do not abuse street drugs, do you?" steer the client to answer in a certain way. Questions beginning with *why* may make the client become defensive. For example, "Why did you not follow your physician's instructions and take your medication?" is more confrontational than "Tell me more about your decision to stop taking medication." Questions leading to yes or no answers such as, "Do you drink alcohol?" may yield incomplete data, as opposed to an open-ended question, such as, "Describe your alcohol use."

Client-Related Factors Influencing the Interview

A client may provide unreliable or incomplete information during the interview. Symptoms of mental illness such as delusions, disorganized thought, or disorganized speech may interfere with communication and alter the client's sense of reality. The client's lack of insight may also lead to an altered perception of reality. For example, an alcoholic may tell the nurse that he or she only drinks socially. Some clients may purposely distort or provide false information (e.g., an undocumented alien who feigns citizenship or a client with antisocial personality disorder who denies a criminal history). A client who is poorly motivated for treatment (e.g., an involuntary client) often resists giving information, but a client's resistance may also be self-protective.

Resistance refers to the client's defense against the anxiety associated with acknowledging personal troubles and an unwillingness or ambivalence to change. In many cases, reticence increases when the client is confronted directly. During the initial interview, the client genuinely may be too paranoid, disorganized, despondent, or agitated to respond to all the questions. Confronting resistance in these circumstances by asking the client why he or she is not being up front with the interviewer may cause the client to retreat further. Temporarily changing the subject when a client becomes extremely angry or upset may enable the client to continue with the interview. Validating the client's feelings that underlie the resistance often effectively encourages the client to speak. For example, a reluctant client is more likely to self-disclose if the nurse agrees that it must be difficult to trust a virtual stranger with personal information.

Clinician-Related Factors Influencing the Interview

The nurse's level of skill affects the flow of the interview and the information obtained. Interviewing skills are related to the nurse's degree of psychiatric experience, use of intuition or gut feeling, critical thinking abilities, personality, and communication style. The nurse's ability to convey acceptance and **empathy** helps the client to feel comfortable in sharing information that is of a sensitive nature. The nurse's interest and enthusiasm may help the client to overlook small interviewing errors and inexperience (Sadock et al., 2009). The nurse's ability to be genuine is also important, because clients usually sense when others are acting unlike their true personalities. For example, the nurse should not attempt to bond with an inner-city adolescent by using unfamiliar slang.

The nurse's culture, race, age, religion, gender, socioeconomic status, and intellect necessarily affect the interview process. A nurse must not avoid issues that are important to the client but that are difficult for the nurse because of personal background. For example, a nurse for whom spirituality is unimportant must not ignore the client's spirituality.

Interview Duration

The duration of the evaluation interview depends on the purpose of the evaluation, the client's state, and the nurse's availability. The interview should be relatively brief (10 to 15 minutes) if the client is acutely ill and unable to tolerate much contact and exploration. The interview may be spread out over several short interactions, and the nurse may need to sit on the floor or even stand if the client's state requires it. Focused evaluations, such as those evaluating a client for entry into an incest survivor group, are usually shorter than a broad evaluation interview because of the limited content. If an interview is abbreviated as a result of the nurse's workload, the nurse must return at a later time or delegate further interviewing tasks to a colleague.

Environmental Issues

Uncomfortable furniture, air temperature, and interruptions such as a ringing phone or beeper may

impair the flow of an interview. A peaceful and comfortable environment enhances the interviewing process. The interview environment should be private enough so that confidentiality is not compromised. At the same time, the environment in which the interview takes place should also ensure the nurse's safety; leaving the door ajar and positioning oneself near the door of the room will usually conserve privacy while allowing for safe egress should a client become aggressive. Many settings have safety measures such as emergency buzzers and overhead paging systems by which other workers can be called in to assist in a crisis situation.

Collateral History

If a client is deemed an unreliable historian, additional history should be obtained from family, friends, colleagues, and healthcare providers, including mental health professionals who have had previous contact with the client; this **collateral history** may be obtained only with the client's consent, unless it is an emergency. Those accompanying the client to the evaluation interview should be interviewed at that time, if possible. The client may feel more or less comfortable being interviewed simultaneously with a significant other, and the nurse should follow the client's lead. Clients should also be allowed time alone with the interviewer; this gives them privacy to disclose important information they may not be willing to discuss in the presence of others.

Psychological Testing

Psychological testing involves evaluation tools that objectively measure personality, intelligence, or symptomatology of specific mental illnesses. Neuropsychological testing is useful in detecting subtle cognitive defects in clients who are not obviously demented or brain damaged. Psychological and neuropsychological tests are usually performed by experts in the field or specially trained nurses/mental health professionals. At minimum, nurses should be sufficiently familiar with the different tests to be able to glean meaningful information about a client from reading the testing reports. Nurses must know enough to be able to recommend that certain tests be performed.

Increasingly, nurses utilize standardized rating scales such as those used during the assessment process. Rating scales that are administered by trained healthcare professionals provide objective baseline data of a client's symptoms that can be compared to later scores to evaluate the efficacy of treatment. This is important given the current emphasis on quality assessment, cost effectiveness, and managed care. Despite the trend toward using standardized tools for data collection, studies regarding which instruments should be routinely used in practice are equivocal (Montgomery, Rose, & Carter, 2009). The use of standardized scales should supplement, and not replace, the nurse–client interview in terms of assessing clients.

Some rating scales were designed for clients, and not professionals, to complete. Certain self-rating scales such as the Beck Depression Inventory yield reliable and valid data that can assist professionals in the diagnosis of mental illness or to gauge treatment progress. Self-report mental health screening tools such as the Patient Health Questionnaire for Depression (PHQ-9) (**Figure 4-2**) are utilized in general medical settings to screen clients for mental health issues (Leung, French, Chui, & Arthur, 2007). Clients who are being treated in some facilities are asked to complete computerized rating scales upon admission, discharge, and at various intervals in between both for research as well as clinical purposes (Allen, et al., 2009). Other self-rating systems are less precise but are useful for the client's self-monitoring of illness symptoms and coping skills. A nurse and his or her client can even design their own rating scale for the client based on the client's specific illness symptoms, for use in relapse prevention. See **Table 4-5** for commonly performed psychological tests, including rating scales.

With the client's consent, a collateral history may be obtained from family, friends, colleagues, or mental health professionals to ensure an accurate account of the client's history.

Physical Assessment

The term *mental disorder* implies a distinction between mental and physical disorders. In actuality, there is much physical in mental and much mental in physical disorders (APA, 2000). Some clients who present primarily with psychiatric symptoms may be suffering from an underlying medical illness, such as hypothyroidism or acute intermittent porphyria, a familial blood disorder with both physical and mental symptomatology. When a client presents with behavioral symptoms or changes in mental status, a medical workup is indicated to rule out an underlying physical illness. The medical workup also ensures that the client is well enough to tolerate psychopharmacologic and other psychiatric treatments safely.

Standardized rating scales provide objective data to supplement information obtained through the nurse–client interview.

PATIENT HEALTH QUESTIONNAIRE (PHQ-9 Patient Depression Questionnaire)

NAME: ______________________ DATE: ____________

Over the last *2 weeks*, how often have you been bothered by any of the following problems? *(use "✓" to indicate your answer)*

	Not at all	**Several days**	**More than half the days**	**Nearly every day**
1. Little interest or pleasure in doing things	0	1	2	3
2. Feeling down, depressed, or hopeless	0	1	2	3
3. Trouble falling or staying asleep, or sleeping too much	0	1	2	3
4. Feeling tired or having little energy	0	1	2	3
5. Poor appetite or overeating	0	1	2	3
6. Feeling bad about yourself—or that you are a failure or have let yourself or your family down	0	1	2	3
7. Trouble concentrating on things, such as reading the newspaper or watching television	0	1	2	3
8. Moving or speaking so slowly that other people could have noticed. Or the opposite—being so figety or restless that you have been moving around a lot more than usual	0	1	2	3
9. Thoughts that you would be better off dead, or of hurting yourself	0	1	2	3
	Add columns	+	+	

TOTAL:

(Healthcare professional: For interpretation of TOTAL, please refer to accompanying scoring card).

10. If you checked off *any problems*, how *difficult* have these problems made it for you to do your work, take care of things at home, or get along with other people?	Not difficult at all ________ Somewhat difficult ________ Very difficult ________ Extremely difficult ________

A2663B 10-04-2005

PHQ-9 Patient Depression Questionnaire

For initial diagnosis:

1. Patient completes PHQ-9 Quick Depression Assessment.
2. If there are at least 4 ✓s in the shaded section (including Questions #1 and #2), consider a depressive disorder. Add score to determine severity.

Figure 4-2 Patient Health Questionnaire (PHQ-9).

(Continues)

PATIENT HEALTH QUESTIONNAIRE (PHQ-9) *(Continued)*

Consider Major Depressive Disorder

—if there are at least 5 ✓s in the shaded section (one of which corresponds to Question #1 or #2)

Consider Other Depressive Disorder

—if there are 2–4 ✓s in the shaded section (one of which corresponds to Question #1 or #2)

Note: Since the questionnaire relies on patient self-report, all responses should be verified by the clinician, and a definitive diagnosis is made on clinical grounds taking into account how well the patient understood the questionnaire, as well as other relevant information from the patient.

Diagnoses of Major Depressive Disorder or Other Depressive Disorder also require impairment of social, occupational, or other important areas of functioning (Question #10) and ruling out normal bereavement, a history of a Manic Episode (Bipolar Disorder), and a physical disorder, medication, or other drug as the biological cause of the depressive symptoms.

To monitor severity over time for newly diagnosed patients or patients in current treatment for depression:

1. Patients may complete questionnaires at baseline and at regular intervals (eg, every 2 weeks) at home and bring them in at their next appointment for scoring or they may complete the questionnaire during each scheduled appointment.
2. Add up ✓s by column. For every ✓: Several days = 1 More than half the days = 2 Nearly every day = 3
3. Add together column scores to get a TOTAL score.
4. Refer to the accompanying **PHQ-9 Scoring Box** to interpret the TOTAL score.
5. Results may be included in patient files to assist you in setting up a treatment goal, determining degree of response, as well as guiding treatment intervention.

Scoring: add up all checked boxes on PHQ-9

For every ✓ Not at all = 0; Several days = 1;

More than half the days = 2; Nearly every day = 3

Interpretation of Total Score

Total Score	**Depression Severity**
1–4	Minimal depression
5–9	Mild depression
10–14	Moderate depression
15–19	Moderately severe depression
20–27	Severe depression

A2662B 10-04-2005

Figure 4-2 Patient Health Questionnaire (PHQ-9) (*Continued*)

Table 4-5 Commonly Performed Psychological Tests and Rating Scales

Name of Test	Purpose of Test	Description of Test
Wechsler Adult Intelligence Scale	Intelligence test	This test includes six verbal and five performance subtests, yielding a verbal intelligence quotient, a performance intelligence quotient, and a full-scale intelligence quotient. It is the most widely used intelligence quotient test.
Minnesota Multiphasic Personality Inventory	Personality assessment	This is a self-report inventory of over 500 yes or no questions, the results of which are scored on 10 different scales (e.g., depression scale, paranoia scale). The pattern of scores is interpreted by the tester by comparing the scores and subscores against standardized data.
Rorschach test	Projective personality assessment	Clients are shown inkblots and asked to describe what they see. Clients project their needs, fantasies, and thoughts into the inkblots because of their ambiguity. This test is very difficult to analyze.
Substance Abuse Subtle Screening Inventory	To identify people who have a high probability of substance use disorders, even when they are unlikely to admit to the problem outright. There is one version of the test for adults, and another for adolescents.	A 15-minute questionnaire, including face valid items as well as subtle items that do not address substance misuse in a direct or apparent manner.
Abnormal Involuntary Movement Scale	To test for psychomotor side effects of psychotropic medication.	A 12-item inventory performed by trained evaluators who rate the client's involuntary muscular movements on a scale of 0 to 4.
Hamilton Depression Rating Scale	To test for severity of depression in clients already diagnosed with an affective disorder.	A 21- or 17-item inventory performed by trained evaluators who rate physical and psychological symptoms of depression on a scale of 0 to 4.
Beck Depression Inventory	To measure attitude and symptoms that are characteristic of depression.	A 21-item inventory performed either by a trained professional *or* by the client, who rates depressive symptoms and attitudes on a scale of 0 to 3.
Brief Psychiatric Rating Scale	To assess psychopathology in clients with, or suspected of having, schizophrenia or other psychotic illness.	A 16-item inventory of a broad range of psychiatric symptoms, scored by a trained professional using a 7-point Likert scale.
Mini-Mental State Examination	To screen for cognitive impairment caused by dementia.	A nine-item structured clinician-rated interview scale incorporating pencil-and-paper tasks.
Patient Health Questionnaire-9	To screen for depression in primary care settings and nursing homes and gauge client progress in treatment of depression.	A nine-item scale of depressive symptom severity, rated by the client on a scale of 0 to 3.

The medical workup consists of a physical examination, clinical laboratory tests, and specialized diagnostic procedures.

The physical examination is an essential part of the workup and may be performed by the advanced practice nurse. Basic-level nurses assess the client's vital signs, teach the client about the examination, and reassure him or her throughout the examination. Important clinical laboratory tests include serum and urine drug screens; thyroid, liver, and kidney function tests; complete blood counts; and sexually transmitted disease screening. Serum tests are also used to evaluate the levels of psychotropic medications in the client's blood. A low lithium level, for example, may precipitate a manic episode. A number of medical illnesses present with psychiatric symptoms, and specific diagnostic tests are used to detect them (**Table 4-6**).

Table 4-6 **Physical Illnesses Presenting With Psychiatric Symptoms**

Physical Illness	Physical Symptoms	Psychiatric Symptoms	Tests Used to Diagnose Physical Illness
AIDS	Fever, weight loss, ataxia, incontinence, seizures, and opportunistic infections	Progressive dementia, personality changes, and depression	HIV antibody test, CT scan, MRI, lumbar puncture, and blood cultures
Acute intermittent porphyria	Abdominal pain, fever, nausea, vomiting, constipation, peripheral neuropathy, and paralysis	Depression, agitation, paranoia, and visual hallucinations	CBC, pulse, and Δ-aminolevulinic acid and porphobilinogen levels
Brain neoplasm	Headache, vomiting, papilledema, and local finding on neurological examination	Personality changes	Lumbar puncture, skull x-ray, CT scan, and EEG
Hepatic encephalopathy	Hyperreflexia, ecchymosis, liver enlargement, and ataxia	Euphoria, disinhibition, psychosis, depression	LFTs, serum albumin level, and EEG
Huntington's disease	Rigidity and choreoathetoid movements	Depression and euphoria	Genetic testing
Hyperglycemia	Polyuria, anorexia, nausea, vomiting, dehydration, abdominal complaints, acetone on breath, and seizures	Anxiety, agitation, and delirium	Finger stick for blood glucose and urine dipstick for glucose and ketones
Hyperthyroidism	Sweating, diarrhea, weight loss, tachycardia, tremor, palpitations, vomiting, and heat intolerance	Nervousness, irritability, pressured speech, insomnia, and psychosis	TFTs and ECG
Hypoglycemia	Sweating, drowsiness, stupor, coma, tachycardia, tremor, restlessness, and seizures	Anxiety, confusion, and agitation	Pulse rate and finger stick for blood glucose
Hyponatremia	Excessive thirst, polydipsia, stupor, and coma	Confusion, lethargy, and personality changes	Serum electrolytes
Hypothyroidism	Dry skin, cold intolerance, constipation, weight gain, and goiter	Lethargy, depression, personality changes, and psychosis	TFTs and ECG
Multiple sclerosis	Sudden transient motor and sensory disturbances	Anxiety, euphoria, mania, and personality changes	Lumbar puncture and head CT
Seizure disorder	Sensory distortions and aura	Confusion, psychosis, dissociative states, catatonia-like states, violence, and bizarre behavior	EEG
Systemic lupus erythematosus	Fever, photosensitivity, butterfly rash, headache, and joint pain	Depression, mood changes, and psychosis	ANA, lupus erythematosus test, CBC, chest X-ray
Tertiary syphilis	Skin lesions, arthritis, respiratory distress, and progressive cardiovascular disease	Personality changes, decreased performance of activities of daily living, irritability, confusion, and psychosis	VDRL and lumbar puncture
Thiamine deficiency	Neuropathy, cardiomyopathy, nystagmus, and headache	Confusion and confabulation	Thiamine level
Vitamin B12 deficiency	Pallor, dizziness, peripheral neuropathy, and ataxia	Irritability, inattentiveness, and psychosis	Vitamin B12 level, Schilling test, and CBC

Note: HIV = human immunodeficiency virus; CT = computed tomography; MRI = magnetic resonance imaging; CBC = complete blood count; EEG = electroencephalogram; LFTs = liver function tests; TFTs = thyroid function tests; ECG = electrocardiograph; ANA = antinuclear antibody test; VDRL = venereal disease research laboratory test.

All registered nurses are licensed to diagnose and treat human response to actual or potential health problems.

Specialized diagnostic procedures performed on psychiatric clients include an EEG, which discerns if a seizure-like basis for an illness, such as an impulse control disorder, exists. In delirium, as a result of metabolic problems, the EEG generally shows high-voltage, slow-wave activity. Other tests including MRI, computed tomography (CT), and positron emission tomography (PET) identify space-occupying lesions and metabolic brain disorders. While there are no brain scans or blood tests currently available to definitively diagnose particular psychiatric illnesses, certain tests may identify biologic markers of mental illness. Researchers have found evidence of increased brain ventricle size detected by MRI and CT and decreased frontal cortex activity detected by PET in clients with certain forms of schizophrenia (Sadock et al., 2009). Research suggests that biomarkers may someday aid in the diagnosis and treatment of mental illness, but critics warn of negative ethical implications such as the potential for discriminative practices in health insurance coverage (Shaheen, Vieira, & Hamlat, 2010).

Clinical Example 

Kay, a 52-year-old woman, was admitted to the psychiatric unit from the emergency room. She presented primarily with agitation. She seemed to be hallucinating, speaking to people who were not there. On closer examination, Kay was delirious with waxing and waning cognitive abilities. She was disoriented to place and time, and she was tachycardic and diaphoretic. Kay was able to provide a history of hypothyroidism, which had been treated sporadically with thyroid replacement hormone. Her family provided additional history concerning Kay's chronic alcoholism. Kay was transferred to a medical unit where she was placed on chlordiazepoxide (Librium) as part of an alcohol detoxification protocol, and her thyroid level was stabilized. Most of her presenting symptoms resolved.

Organizing Data: Diagnosis

Formulating the client's diagnosis is an integral part of the psychiatric evaluation. During the assessment, the nurse must keep an open mind and avoid settling on a definitive diagnosis early in the interview. All aspects of the holistic assessment must be considered.

Nursing Diagnosis

The American Nurses Association (ANA, 2007) states that nurses diagnose human responses to actual or potential health problems. The practice of nurses diagnosing clients has met with long-standing resistance. Many nurses who graduated prior to the inclusion of the nursing diagnosis in the college curricula feel that making a diagnosis is beyond their scope. Nurses who were exposed to the theoretical aspects of the nursing diagnosis in school often have difficulty translating this knowledge into practice. Other professionals, notably physicians, may fear that boundaries are being crossed when nurses formulate diagnoses. Clients may be wary when nurses take a leadership role in their treatment.

Nursing diagnoses (see Appendix II) were originally categorized by the North American Nursing Diagnosis Association (www.nanda.org) (NANDA) in 1986 and are revised at regular intervals. Nursing diagnoses may relate to actual problems, risks for problems, or wellness issues. Traditionally, a nursing diagnosis includes the diagnostic label/definition, related factors, and defining characteristics. One example of a nursing diagnosis written in this format is "posttrauma syndrome related to physical abuse, as evidenced by flashbacks, nightmares, and hypervigilance."

Formulating nursing diagnoses is difficult because of the array of possible human responses and the causes of these responses. Prioritizing these diagnoses is therefore essential. Without question, safety issues must be of primary concern (e.g., the risk for self-directed violence). Some diagnoses are addressed immediately, and others require long-term intervention. Remember that several diagnoses may be addressed simultaneously and that they will continue to be addressed in the outpatient setting (e.g., with home care, day program, psychotherapy, or psychopharmacology). The client and family should actively participate in prioritizing the nursing diagnoses.

Diagnostic and Statistical Manual of Mental Disorders

The *Diagnostic and Statistical Manual of Mental Disorders* has been the primary resource used throughout the United States for classifying mental disorders since its original publication in 1952. More than 1,000 health professionals analyzed scientific data and performed field trials to test for validity and reliability of diagnostic categories to prepare the *DSM-IV* (APA, 1994). In 2000, the American Psychiatric Association revised parts of the text portion of the *DSM-IV* to include new research information regarding associated features; culture, age, and gender features; prevalence; course; and familial pattern of many of the mental disorders listed. The *DSM-5*, slated for publication in 2013, will likely have more significant modifications than the prior revision (APA, 2010).

Psychiatric nurses must be well versed in the DSM classification system and terminology *in order to communicate effectively with other mental health professionals in the assessment and treatment of mental disorders*, but only the advanced practice registered nurse (APRN) may use the guide to diagnose a mental disorder. The nurse must have appropriate training and experience to make a DSM diagnosis (APA, 2000).

When working with the *DSM*, the nurse must remember that normal reactions to stressful events, such as the death of a loved one, are not considered mental disorders. Additionally, some phenomena, which in the mainstream would indicate a mental disorder, are not symptomatic for a mental disorder if they are culturally appropriate. For example, in certain Hispanic cultures persons may talk to their dead mother's ghost. Socially unacceptable behavior, such as crime, does not necessarily indicate a mental illness. Lastly, the nurse must remember that the person's *diagnosis* is being classified, not the person him- or herself; the client is not just a "schizophrenic," but a multifaceted individual who happens to have schizophrenia (APA, 2000).

Multiaxial *DSM-IV* Diagnosis

Diagnosing mental disorders with the *DSM-IV-TR* is not foolproof; various mental disorders have overlapping symptoms, and individuals with the same disorder may differ significantly. The manual provides text and decision-tree diagrams that assist in establishing the **differential diagnosis.** The *DSM-IV-TR* also provides guidance to diagnose clients with insufficient information or information that does not fit neatly into one category. A diagnosis may be deferred, declared provisional, or delineated as atypical

www Mr. C **CASE STUDIES**

Psychosocial history: Mr. C., a 60-year-old man, was brought to the hospital by ambulance immediately following a suicide attempt by hanging. This hospitalization marked his first contact with the mental healthcare system. Mr. C. arrived combative and in four-point restraints and presented with the chief complaint, "I just wanted to die. . . . I feel hopeless and lost." According to the client, he had been feeling depressed for 2 months preceding the attempt and had experienced diminished appetite, insomnia, anhedonia, hopelessness, helplessness, and worthlessness during the 2 weeks prior to his suicide attempt.

The client identified that his troubles began 1 year prior, when his cardiologist advised Mr. C. to leave a job that he had held for over 30 years because of his compromised physical condition following a coronary bypass operation. Although Mr. C. had not planned an early retirement, he heeded the physician's advice and applied for disability payments. He soon fell into debt, resulting from the lengthy waiting period for disability payments, family weekend gambling excursions to Atlantic City, and accumulating medical bills. Mr. C., who had always been the head of household in his traditional family, felt that he had no choice but to return to work. He also became noncompliant with his heart medications, began to withdraw from social events, had frequent arguments with his wife, and experienced a reemergence of chest pain.

Mr. C. finally terminated his employment a few months later, upon receipt of disability checks. A month prior to the suicide attempt, Mr. C. received notification from the disability office that he was ineligible for the entitlement because he had worked for those few months after having applied and that he owed $4,000 in back pay. It was also around this time that his teenaged grandson was incarcerated for armed robbery.

Mr. C. had no previous psychiatric history. He did not use drugs or alcohol, but has smoked one pack per day for 40 years. His medical history was significant for heart disease. Mr. C. had a family history of hypertension and heart disease. He reported that his mother suffered from postpartum

(Continues)

CASE STUDIES Mr. C. *(Continued)*

depression after the birth of her third child, which resolved without treatment. Mr. C. was the oldest of three children in a middle-class family. Mr. C. met normal developmental milestones. Mr. C.'s father died when he was 14 years of age, after which Mr. C. was forced to drop out of school in order to work to help support his family. Although Mr. C. was close with his siblings in his youth, he fell out of touch with them after their mother passed away. He and his wife had been married for nearly 40 years at the time of the hospitalization. Their two grown children were living out of state. Mr. C. was normally in close contact with his children by telephone. He had several close friendships through his job and from his church, but lately had not been socially involved with anyone besides immediate family.

Although Mr. C. had never earned his high school diploma, he had a successful career with the local utilities company until his recent health problems. Mr. C. verbalized a strong belief that the male in the household should be the primary provider for his family and that the woman should tend to the home. Mr. C. considered himself religious, regularly attended services, and took comfort in his belief in God. When asked about coping skills, Mr. C. reported that in the past he talked about his problems with friends and his priest. He reported that smoking gave him some relief from anxiety.

On the mental status examination, Mr. C. was a well-groomed Caucasian man who appeared older than his years. His posture was poor, and he exhibited psychomotor retardation. He was cooperative with the interview for 20 minutes, after which point he stated that he was too tired to continue. The client's mood was depressed, with a depressed affect that was constricted in range. His speech was slow, soft, and nonspontaneous. Mr. C. evinced no formal thought disorder. Mr. C. denied experiencing hallucinations, and there was no evidence of delusional thought. He expressed ambivalence about having survived his suicide attempt but stated that he had no plan to try again while in the hospital, because he wanted to see if hospital personnel could help him with his problems. Mr. C. stated that perhaps his surviving the attempt was God's way of telling him that other people needed him here on Earth. His impulse control, judgment, and insight were poor to fair, as shown by his gambling, going back to work against his doctor's advice, noncompliance with cardiac medications, impulsive suicide attempt, and ambivalence about his survival. Mr. C. was alert and oriented to person, place, and time. His memory for recent history was intact, and his concentration seemed mildly impaired. His level of intellect was deemed average, and he seemed to be a reliable historian.

Mr. C. rated his depression by using the Beck Depression Inventory, scoring in the range indicative of severe depression. The review of Mr. C.'s activities of daily living was significant for diminished appetite with a 20-pound weight loss as well as initial insomnia over the past year. His laboratory tests were all within normal limits. Mr. C.'s physical examination was significant for hypertension.

See **Table 4-7** for the diagnostic formulation for Mr. C., and "Nursing Care Plan: Depression" for the associated nursing care plan.

Table 4-7 Diagnostic Formulation of Mr. C.

DSM-IV-TR Diagnosis	NANDA-I Diagnosis
Axis I: 296.2 Major depressive disorder, single episode Axis II: 312.31 Provisional diagnosis: pathological gambling 799.9 Diagnosis deferred on Axis II Axis III: Atherosclerotic heart disease, hypertension Axis IV: Adjustment to forced early retirement, medical illness, financial difficulties, family discord Axis V: GAF = 20 (on admission to hospital)	Risk for suicide related to depression and stressful life events, manifested by serious suicide attempt Ineffective health maintenance related to financial difficulties and depression, manifested by noncompliance with cardiac medication Imbalanced nutrition: less than body requirements related to depression, manifested by decreased appetite and weight loss Sleep deprivation related to depression, manifested by insomnia Situational low self-esteem related to medical illness, forced early retirement, and depression; manifested by inability to maintain family finances and marital discord

Note: DSM-IV-TR = Diagnostic and Statistical Manual of Mental Disorders, 4th ed., text revision; NANDA-I = *Nursing Diagnoses: Definitions and Classifications, 2012–2014*; GAF = global assessment of functioning.

Nursing Care Plan **Depression**

Expected Outcomes	Interventions	Evaluations
• Will not make suicidal gestures.	• Monitor client on a 1:1 observation.	• Completing suicide risk assessment tool upon admission and discharge • Evaluating for suicidal thoughts, plan, intent, lethality, and access to means each shift.
	• Ensure the environment is free of objects that could be used for self-harm, each shift	• Assessing the client's reasons to continue living. • Assessing the environment for potential hazards
• Will sleep 6–7 hours a night.	• Teach relaxation techniques.	• Evaluating the client's demonstration of relaxation techniques, evaluating number of hours slept nightly.
• Will improve nutritional intake.	• Assess for likes and dislikes, encouraging small, frequent meals, referring to a nutritionist.	• Monitoring for weight gain on a weekly basis.
• Will learn alternative coping mechanisms.	• Assist the client in identifying coping mechanisms that have worked in the past in similar situations. • Teach new coping skills.	• Evaluating current adaptive coping skills • Observing for increased use of adaptive coping mechanisms.
• Will be compliant with treatment.	• Teach the client about heart disease and treatment.	• Monitoring compliance with cardiac medication. • Monitor blood pressure
• Will have improved sense of self-worth.	• Identify and assist in correcting cognitive distortions.	• Administering Beck Depression Inventory at regular intervals.
• Will establish contact with community resources.	• Discuss possible community resources and support systems.	• Evaluating the client's participation in a heart disease support group.

Visit http://go.jblearning.com/mentalhealth for additional care plans and exercises.

or not otherwise specified (NOS; APA, 2000). The diagnostic categories of the *DSM-IV-TR* often include several subtypes as well as descriptive statements that indicate the severity and course of the illness.

The **multiaxial *DSM-IV-TR* diagnosis** is divided into five categories, or axes.

Axis I

Axis I comprises mostly clinical disorders such as major depression, chronic schizophrenia, and attention deficit disorder. Specific diagnostic criteria, consisting of the signs and symptoms of the illnesses, are provided for each of these disorders. Some of these criteria must be present before a diagnosis is made, and other symptoms may accompany them. The information obtained through the interview and testing is compared with the signs and symptoms found in the descriptions of the *DSM-IV-TR* for specific disorders.

Axis II

Axis II includes personality disorders and mental retardation, along with the related diagnostic signs and symptoms. Axis II diagnoses are deemed secondary to Axis I diagnoses, unless it is clearly stated that the client's primary diagnosis is on Axis II. Axis I and Axis II together contain the entire classification of mental disorders, numbering over 300 illnesses. This list of disorders is large but incomplete because the classification system constantly evolves through research.

Axis III

Axis III denotes the client's physical disorders or medical conditions. A medical illness may be the cause of the mental disorder (e.g., human immunodeficiency virus [HIV] infection on Axis III with dementia secondary to HIV infection on Axis I), the result of the mental disorder (e.g., cirrhosis on Axis III with alcohol dependence on Axis I), or unrelated to the mental disorder.

Axis IV

Axis IV recognizes psychosocial and environmental factors that may precipitate, result from, or affect the treatment of mental illness. Axis IV lists psychosocial and environmental events that would have a strong impact on the average person and that were experienced by the client in the year preceding the evaluation. Events occurring prior to that time should not be included unless they are catastrophic, in which case they may be directly involved in the etiology of the mental disorder (e.g., childhood abuse leading to PTSD). Stressors may include negative events, such as job loss, as well as events ordinarily deemed positive, such as the birth of a child. The *DSM-IV-TR* categorizes these stressors into clusters that the clinician should use as evaluation guidelines. The client's specific problems should be listed under Axis IV.

Axis V

Axis V indicates the client's overall ability to function. Using the **Global Assessment of Functioning (GAF) scale** (**Table 4-8**), the interviewer rates the client's total psychological, social, and occupational or academic well-being on a scale of 1 to 100 (1 being virtually nonfunctional and 100 being asymptomatic with superior function in all realms). Both the severity of psychiatric symptoms and the degree of social, work, or school impairment are considered on the scale, which represents a continuum of mental health and mental illness. A person's GAF score changes over time; thus the clinician must rate the client for the most pertinent time period (e.g., upon admission, upon discharge, highest level in past year) and identify the time frame of the rating. The GAF score is useful when operationalizing a client's progress from admission to discharge. It is also helpful in formulating a prognosis; a high premorbid GAF score portends a good prognosis.

Outcome Identification and Planning of Nursing Care

The initial nursing care plan is based on the comprehensive assessment and attendant nursing diagnoses, with consideration of the medical diagnosis. Initial planning of care marks the final phase of the psychiatric client's evaluation. The care plan consists of the nursing diagnoses or problem list, outcome goals, interventions used to attain these outcomes, and evaluation of the interventions and their efficacy in achieving desired outcomes. Outcome identification

Table 4-8 **Global Assessment of Functioning (GAF) Scale**

Domain	1–10	11–20	21–30	31–40	41–50	51–60	61–70	71–80	81–90	91–100
Symptom Severity	Persistent danger of severely hurting self or others (e.g., recurrent violence) Or Serious suicidal act with clear expectation death.	Some danger of hurting self or others (e.g., suicide attempts without clear expectation of death; frequently violent; manic excitement) Or Gross impairment in communication (e.g., largely incoherent or mute)	Behavior is considerably influenced by delusions or hallucinations Or Serious impairment in communication or judgment (e.g., sometimes incoherent, acts grossly inappropriately, suicidal preoccupation)	Some impairment in reality testing or communication (e.g., speech, is at times illogical, obscure or irrelevant)	Serious symptoms (e.g., suicidal ideation, severe obsessional rituals, frequent shoplifting).	Moderate symptoms (e.g., flat affect and circumstantial speech, occasional panic attacks)	Some mild symptoms (e.g., depressed mood and mild insomnia)	If symptoms are present, they are transient and expectable reactions to psychosocial stressors (e.g., difficulty concentrating after family argument)	Absent or minimal symptoms (e.g., mild anxiety before an exam), Generally satisfied with life. No more than everyday problems or concerns (e.g., an occasional argument with family members).	No symptoms
Level of Functioning	Persistent inability to maintain minimal personal hygiene	Occasionally fails to maintain minimal personal hygiene (e.g., smears feces)	Inability to function in almost all areas (e.g., stays in bed all day, no job, home or friends)	Major impairment in several areas, such as work or school, family relations, judgment, thinking, or mood (e.g., depressed man avoids friends, neglects family, and is unable to work; child frequently beats up younger children, is defiant at home and is failing in school).	Any serious impairment in social, occupational, or school functioning (e.g., no friends, unable to keep a job).	Moderate difficulty in social, occupational, or school functioning (e.g., few friends, conflicts with co-workers).	Some difficulty in social, occupational or school functioning (e.g., occasional truancy, or theft within the household), but generally functioning pretty well, has some meaningful interpersonal relationships.	No more than slight impairment in social, occupational, or school functioning (e.g., temporarily falling behind in school work).	Good functional in all areas, interested and involved in a wide range of activities, socially effective.	Superior functioning in a wide range of activities, life's problems never seem to get out of hand. Is sought out by others because of his or her many positive qualities

is an important part of the nursing process; interventions cannot be delineated without first outlining the goals of the interventions (ANA, 2007).

The outcome measures should be client centered, realistic, observable, measurable, specific, time limited, and mutually agreed upon by client and nurse. Some diagnoses lend themselves to easily operationalized outcome measures, and others present some difficulty as a result of the subjective nature of the probe. For example, outcome measures for altered nutrition are more easily quantified than are measures for self-esteem disturbance.

In early care planning, the goal is to identify and explore urgent problems. Initial care planning should be done in collaboration with the client, family, and other members of the interdisciplinary treatment team. The **therapeutic contract** is the agreement between the nurse and client to work on these mutually identified problems. A contract may be in written form or may be a verbal agreement. Especially in the beginning of treatment, the amount and type of collaboration the client and his or her family offers may be limited; the nurse must then accept the balance of responsibility for treatment. Some clients actively resist collaboration. When this is the case, the nurse's first priority is to engage the client in treatment by setting firm limits, providing positive reinforcement for small steps, and persevering against resistance.

The comprehensive multiaxial *DSM-IV-TR* diagnosis is congruent with nursing's biopsychosocial paradigm.

The nurse–client relationship is collaborative; the nurse and client share responsibility for the client's care. The healthier the client is, the more responsibility he or she is given.

Interventions in the nursing care plan focus on improving the client's ability to function and his or her quality of life. Some examples of interventions available to the psychiatric nurse include counseling, milieu therapy, self-care assistance, medication administration, education, case management, and health promotion. In addition, advanced practice nurses may implement psychotherapy, prescribe pharmacologic agents, and provide consultation.

In many settings, generic or standardized nursing care plans and contracts for specific nursing diagnoses, medical diagnostic groups, or client problems exist. These plans are good guidelines but should be tailored to the individual client's needs.

Summary

Holistic evaluation of the psychiatric client consists of assessing the client's biopsychosocial history and current mental status through the psychiatric nursing interview. The specific content and process of the interview depends upon the nurse, the client, and the context in which the interview takes place. In terms of content, the biopsychosocial history includes the client's chief complaint; HPI; psychiatric history; alcohol and substance use history; medical, family, developmental, social, occupational, or educational histories; culture; spirituality; and coping skills. The mental status examination comprises an evaluation of the client's current behavior and appearance; the emotions mood and affect; speech; thought content and process; perceptual disturbances; impulse control; cognition and sensorium; and knowledge, insight, and judgment. The nurse may remember these components with the acronym *BEST PICK*.

The *DSM-IV-TR* diagnosis is a multiaxial medical diagnosis that considers major mental illness as well as personality, intellectual functioning, medical illness, psychosocial stressors, and global functioning. The assessment data from the psychiatric nursing interview (with consideration of the *DSM-IV-TR* diagnosis, psychological testing results, and medical workup outcome) are used to formulate nursing diagnoses. These diagnoses are prioritized with input from the client, and safety is the primary concern. The nurse collaborates with the client in formulating the initial nursing care plan, which consists of the identified problems (nursing diagnoses), projected treatment outcomes and interventions, and evaluation of the process.

Annotated References

Allen, J. G., Frueh, B. C., Ellis T. E., Latini, D. M., Mahoney, J. S., Oldham, J. M., . . . Walin, L., (2009). Integrating outcomes assessment and research into clinical care in inpatient adult psychiatric treatment. *Bulletin of The Menninger Clinic, 73*(4), 259–295.
This publication outlines the use of computerized self-report rating scales in the department of psychiatry at the Menninger Clinic.

American Nurses Association (ANA). (2007). *Psychiatric-mental health nursing: Scope and standards of practice*. Washington, DC: American Nurses Publishing.
This text outlines the ANA's recommendations for psychiatric nursing practice. It guides the practice of all psychiatric nurses, especially those new to the field. Psychiatric nurses should keep up with current nursing trends by reading the latest version of the ANA's statement.

American Psychiatric Association (APA). (1994). *Diagnostic and statistical manual of mental disorders* (4th ed.). Washington, DC: Author.

This is the fourth edition of the American Psychiatric Association's official nomenclature of psychiatric conditions and disorders.

American Psychiatric Association (APA). (2000). *Diagnostic and statistical manual of mental disorders* (4th ed., text rev.). Washington, DC: Author.

This is the text revision of the fourth edition of the American Psychiatric Association's official nomenclature of psychiatric conditions and disorders. It provides a systematic listing of the official codes and categories, a description of the multiaxial system for diagnosis, and diagnostic criteria for each of the disorders. It is used by psychiatrists, physicians, psychologists, registered nurses, social workers, therapists, and other mental health workers in all clinical settings. The 2000 text revision includes new research information regarding associated features; culture, age, and gender features; prevalence; course; and familial pattern of many of the mental disorders listed.

American Psychiatric Association. (2010). DSM-5: The future of psychiatric diagnosis. Retrieved from www.dsm5.org

Website with information on proposed revisions to the 5th edition of the Diagnostic Statistical Manual.

Barnes, L., Plotnikoff, G., Fox, K., & Pendelton, S. (2000). Spirituality, religion, and pediatrics: Intersecting worlds of healing. *Pediatrics, 106*(4 suppl.), 1–19.

This article covers the clash between spirituality and biomedicine, and the effect of spirituality on children's health and on the provider of health services.

Bloom, S. L. (1999). Those delicate brains and troubled minds. E-mail from America. *The Psychotherapy Review, 1*(1), 8–9.

A letter to the editor outlining this trauma expert's views on the topic.

Blow, F. C., Zeber, J. E., McCarthy, J. F., Valenstein, M., Gillon, L., & Bingham, C. R. (2004). Ethnicity and diagnostic patterns in veterans with psychoses. *Social Psychiatry and Psychiatric Epidemiology, 39*(10), 841–851.

This study used a national database for veterans diagnosed with serious mental illness and confirmed continued ethnic disparities in diagnosing mental illness, with race being the demographic variable most strongly associated with a diagnosis of schizophrenia.

Erikson, E. (1963). *Childhood and society* (2nd ed.). New York, NY: W. W. Norton & Company.

This pioneering work regarding the evolution of personality over one's lifetime is easy to understand and apply to practice. Development is put into historical and sociological perspective, and the role of the child in society is also explored.

Felitti, V. J., Anda, R. F., Nordenberg, D., Williamson, D. F., Spitz, A. M., Edwards, V., . . . Marks, J. S. (1998). Relationship of childhood abuse and household dysfunction to many of the leading causes of death in adults: The adverse childhood experiences (ACE) study. *American Journal of Preventive Medicine, 14*, 245–258.

This article discusses findings from research regarding long-term adverse consequences of childhood trauma.

Folstein, M. F., Folstein, S. E., & McHugh, P. R. (1975). "Mini-mental state," a practical method for grading the cognitive state of patients for the clinician. *Journal of Psychiatric Research, 12*, 189–198.

This article introduced the mini-mental status examination and scoring method.

Govier, I. (2000). Spiritual care in nursing: A systematic approach. *Nursing Standard, 14*(17), 32–36.

This article advocates for taking a systemic approach to assessing clients' spiritual needs. The need for nurses to evaluate personal spirituality before effectively assessing clients' spiritual needs is also discussed.

Gresenz, C. R., Sturm, R., & Tang, L. (2001). Income and mental health: Unraveling community and individual level relationships. *Journal of Mental Health Policy and Economics, 4*(4), 197–203.

A study by the Rand Organization that examined the relationship between mental disorder and socioeconomic status. The findings confirmed earlier studies that showed individual income to be highly correlated with mental health status.

Guy, W. (1976). *ECDEU assessment manual for psychopharmacology*. Washington, DC: U.S. Department of Health, Education and Welfare.

This is the original publication of the Abnormal Involuntary Movement Scale (AIMS).

Hales, R. E., & Simon, R. I. (Eds.) (2006). *Textbook of suicide assessment and management.* Washington, DC: American Psychiatric Publishing.

This text addresses the multivariate issues surrounding suicide risk, guided by recommendations from the APA's practice guideline for the assessment and treatment of clients with suicidal behaviors. Issues specific to assessing and treating clients with different mental illnesses are discussed. Ethical, legal, and therapist-related dimensions of suicide risk assessment and suicide itself are also addressed.

Kessler, R. C., Sonnega, A., Bromet, E., Hughes, M., & Nelson, C. B. (1995). Posttraumatic stress disorder in the National Co-morbidity Survey. *Archives of General Psychiatry, 52,* 1048–1060.

This article includes epidemiological data on all aspects of PTSD: causes, prevalence, comorbidity, duration, and sociodemographic correlates.

Koenig, H. G. (2007). Religion and depression in older medical inpatients. *American Journal of Geriatric Psychiatry, 15*(4), 282–291.

This study examined the relationship between religious characteristics of older medically ill patients with depression and those of medically ill nondepressed patients. Depression was less severe in patients who identified a religious affiliation and formal religious practices.

Koenig, H. G., George, L. K., & Titus, P. (2004). Religion, spirituality, and health in medically ill hospitalized older patients. *Journal of American Geriatrics Society, 52*(4), 554–562.

This nursing research study, based on patient interviews conducted at Duke University, identified measures of religiosity and spirituality. Religiousness and spirituality predicted fewer depressive symptoms, and organized religious activities predicted better physical functioning and less severe illness.

Leung, S. F., French, P., Chui, C., & Arthur, D. (2007). Computerized mental health assessment in integrative health clinics: A cross-sectional study using structured interview. *International Journal of Mental Health Nursing, 16*(6), 441–446.

This study looked at the efficacy of using computerized self-report mental health screening tools in a primary care setting.

Marsella, A. J. (2003). Cultural aspects of depressive experiences and disorders. *Readings in Psychology and Culture,* Unit 9, Chapter 4. International Association for Cross-Cultural Psychology. Available at www.wwu.edu/culture/Marsella.htm

This paper outlines cultural differences in the experience, etiology, and diagnosis of depression.

Montgomery, P., Rose, D., & Carter, L (2009). Patient health outcomes in psychiatric mental health nursing. *Journal of Psychiatric and Mental Health Nursing, 16*(1), 32–45.

This paper reviews 156 articles from 1997 to 2007 for evidence supporting the use of rating scales for routine use in clinical practice.

Nance, J. J. (2008). *Why hospitals should fly: The ultimate flight plan to patient safety and quality care.* Bozeman, MT: Second River Healthcare Press.

National Child Traumatic Stress Network. (2004). *Childhood traumatic grief educational materials.* Los Angeles, CA: National Center for Child Traumatic Stress. Available at www.nctsn.org/nctsn_assets/pdfs/.../parents_package1-15-04.pdf

This is an in-depth general information guide to childhood traumatic grief with information specific to healthcare providers, parents, and school personnel. It includes a useful reference and resource list.

Neighbors, H. W., Trierweiler, S. J., Ford, B. C., & Muroff, J. R. (2003). Racial differences in DSM diagnosis using a semi-structured instrument: The importance of clinical judgment in the diagnosis of African-Americans. *Journal of Health and Social Behavior, 44*(3), 237–256.

This article analyzed data on 665 African Americans and white psychiatric patients and found that, even when a semistructured diagnostic instrument and DSM criteria were used, whites were more likely than African Americans to receive a diagnosis of bipolar disorder and less likely to be diagnosed with schizophrenia.

Sadock, B. J., Sadock V. A., & Ruiz, P. (2009). *Kaplan & Sadock's synopsis of psychiatry: Behavioral sciences, clinical psychiatry* (9th ed.). Baltimore, MD: Williams & Wilkins.

This text targets psychiatrists in training; thus, the authors tend to stress the biologic aspect of assessment (i.e., genetics, brain anatomy and physiology, neurotransmitters). It is an excellent reference for psychiatric nurses.

Shaheen, E. L., Vieira, K., & Hamlat, E. (2010). Biomarkers in psychiatry: Drawbacks and potential for misuse. *International Archives of Medicine, 3*(1) Published online 2010 January 12. doi: 10.1186/1755-7682-3-1

This article outlines the controversy surrounding biomarker research in psychiatry.

Vedantam, S. (2005, June 26). Patients' diversity is often discounted. *The Washington Post*, pp. A01, A10.

This article contains a discussion of how the presentation of mental illness differs across cultures.

Zauszniewski, J. A., Bekhet, A. K., & Suresky, M. J. (2010). Resilience in family members of persons with serious mental illness. *Nursing Clinics of North America, 45*(4), 613–626, vii.

This integrative review summarizes current research on resilience in adult family members who have a relative with a diagnosed mental disorder that is considered serious.

Internet Resources

For a full suite of assignments and additional learning activities, use the access code located in the front of your book to visit this exclusive website: http://go.jblearning.com/mentalhealth. If you do not have an access code, you can obtain one at the site.

Learning Objectives

After reading this chapter, you will be able to:

- Describe the neuroanatomy and neurophysiology of the brain in relation to mental health and illness.
- Explain the basic processes of neurotransmission and the role of neurotransmitters in the major mental disorders.
- Explain the neurobiologic rationale for the pharmacologic treatment of the major mental disorders.

Key Terms

Allostatic load
Amine neurotransmitters
Amygdala
Apraxia
Ataxia
Autonomic nervous system (ANS)
Axons
Basal ganglia
Brain stem
Broca's area
Central nervous system (CNS)
Cerebellum
Cerebrum
Computed tomography (CT)
Dendrites
Depolarization
Diffusion tensor imaging (DTI)
Dopamine hypothesis
Electroencephalography (EEG)
Extrapyramidal pathways
Frontal lobe
Functional imaging
Genes
General adaptation syndrome
Glia
Hippocampus
Hypothalamic-pituitary-adrenal (HPA) axis
Hypothalamus
Kindling
Limbic system
Magnetic resonance imagery (MRI)
Magnetic resonance spectroscopy (MRS)
Medulla
Membrane potential
Midbrain
Myelin
Neurogenesis
Neuroimaging
Neuron
Neuroplasticity
Neurotransmitters
Parasympathetic nervous system
Peripheral nervous system (PNS)
Pons
Positron emission tomography (PET)
Reticular activating system
Sensitization
Somatic motor system
Stress-diathesis model
Stressor
Structural imaging
Sympathetic nervous system
Synapse
Temporal lobe
Thalamus
Wernicke's aphasia

Neurobiologic Considerations in Psychiatric Care

Karan Kverno and Sherry Goertz

http://go.jblearning.com/mentalhealth 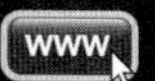

For a full suite of assignments and additional learning activities, use the access code located in the front of your book to visit this exclusive website: http://go.jblearning.com/mentalhealth. If you do not have an access code, you can obtain one at the site.

Introduction

Although the human brain only weighs about 3 pounds, it is composed of approximately 100 billion **neurons** that form intricate communication pathways allowing complex thought, movement, and emotions. It is perhaps not surprising that the neurons, the chemicals that pass between them, and the **genes** that guide them, can at times fail to function properly. Transforming the mental healthcare system into one that is evidence-based requires all health professionals to have an appreciation of the complex biological, psychological and social (biopsychosocial) contributions to mental health and mental illness (Institute of Medicine, 2005). This chapter is intended to provide a basic knowledge of the brain structures and functions, the neurotransmitters and their pathways, and the mechanisms for the development of mental illnesses and disorders and their treatment.

A mnemonic for remembering the 12 pairs of cranial nerves is: "On Old Olympus's Towering Top a Finn and German Viewed Some Hops."

Rapid increases have occurred over the past several decades in the understanding of the neurobiology of mental disorders. New discoveries related to brain physiology, genetic risk factors, and mental illnesses and disorders were reported throughout the 20th century, but especially during the 1990s, a time referred to as the "Decade of the Brain" when the United States Congress provided significant support and funding for brain research. The Surgeon General's Report on Mental Illness (U.S. DHHS, 1999) concluded the decade with a mandate for greater understanding and translation of the neurobiologic underpinnings of mental illness. By 2003, the Human Genome Project (http://genome.gov/HGP/) had mapped the entire sequence of human genes creating databases and improving tools for analyzing the data. With these computerized databases, researchers have been able to study gene sequences and genetic variations associated with psychiatric conditions and behaviors. Vulnerability genes have been identified for most of the mental disorders. The keys to prevention and to new pharmacological and nonpharmacologic treatments for the psychiatric disorders are based upon understanding the interactions between these vulnerability genes and the environment.

The autonomic nervous system (ANS) is responsible for regulation of the organs, glands, and vasculature. The sympathetic and parasympathetic divisions maintain balance, allowing rapid responses to environmental demands, then return to homeostasis.

The Surgeon General's 1999 report at the end of the Decade of the Brain called for more rapid translation of neurobiological research findings into evidence-based treatments for individuals with mental disorders.

The Human Genome Project mapped the entire sequence of human genes by 2003.

Structure and Function of the Nervous System

The central nervous system (CNS) is composed of the brain and spinal cord. The peripheral nervous system (PNS) delivers information to and from the CNS.

The brain and spinal cord make up the **central nervous system (CNS)**. Columns of myelinated **axons** run up and down the spinal cord, delivering information from the periphery to the brain (afferent pathways) and from the brain to the periphery (efferent pathways). The **peripheral nervous system (PNS)** in turn delivers information to and from the spinal cord. **Figure 5-1** shows the divisions of the CNS and PNS. The PNS includes 12 pairs of cranial nerves (with the exception of cranial nerve II, the optic nerve that is part of the CNS; see **Table 5-1** and **Figure 5-2**), 31 pairs of spinal nerves, and two major divisions—the somatic and autonomic nervous systems. The **somatic motor system** is responsible for voluntary control of skeletal muscle. The cell bodies of the neurons that make up the somatic motor system lie within the CNS (in the brain stem or spinal cord), and their axons terminate at neuromuscular junctions. The release of acetylcholine (ACh) triggers contraction of the skeletal muscle. Somatic sensory information from the skin, muscles, and joints enters the spinal cord, and in return, the brain sends commands for voluntary movement.

Traditionally thought of as the involuntary nervous system, the **autonomic nervous system (ANS)** is responsible for the activities of the body that usually take place without conscious guidance—within the internal organs, glands, and vasculature. The two branches of the ANS, the sympathetic and parasympathetic, allow the nervous system to maintain internal balance (homeostasis). In each system, the CNS activates the organs via preganglionic axons that utilize acetylcholine as their neurotransmitter and postganglionic axons that terminate on the effector organs. The postganglionic cell bodies of the ANS lie outside of the CNS either in clusters of cells called ganglia (in the sympathetic nervous system), or on or near the effector organs (in the parasympathetic nervous system). The **parasympathetic nervous system** is responsible for resting functions such as digestion and bowel and bladder function. The vagus nerve (cranial nerve X) provides much of the parasympathetic innervation of the viscera. The remainder comes from the other cranial and sacral spinal nerves. Postganglionic axons in the parasympathetic nervous system also utilize acetylcholine (ACh) as their neurotransmitter. The **sympathetic nervous system** prepares one to fight or flee in an emergency by increasing heart rate and respiratory rate, dilating pupils and bronchi, and stimulating glucose mobilization. Postganglionic axons in the sympathetic nervous system utilize norepinephrine (NE) as their neurotransmitter. Sympathetic activation of the adrenal medulla causes the release

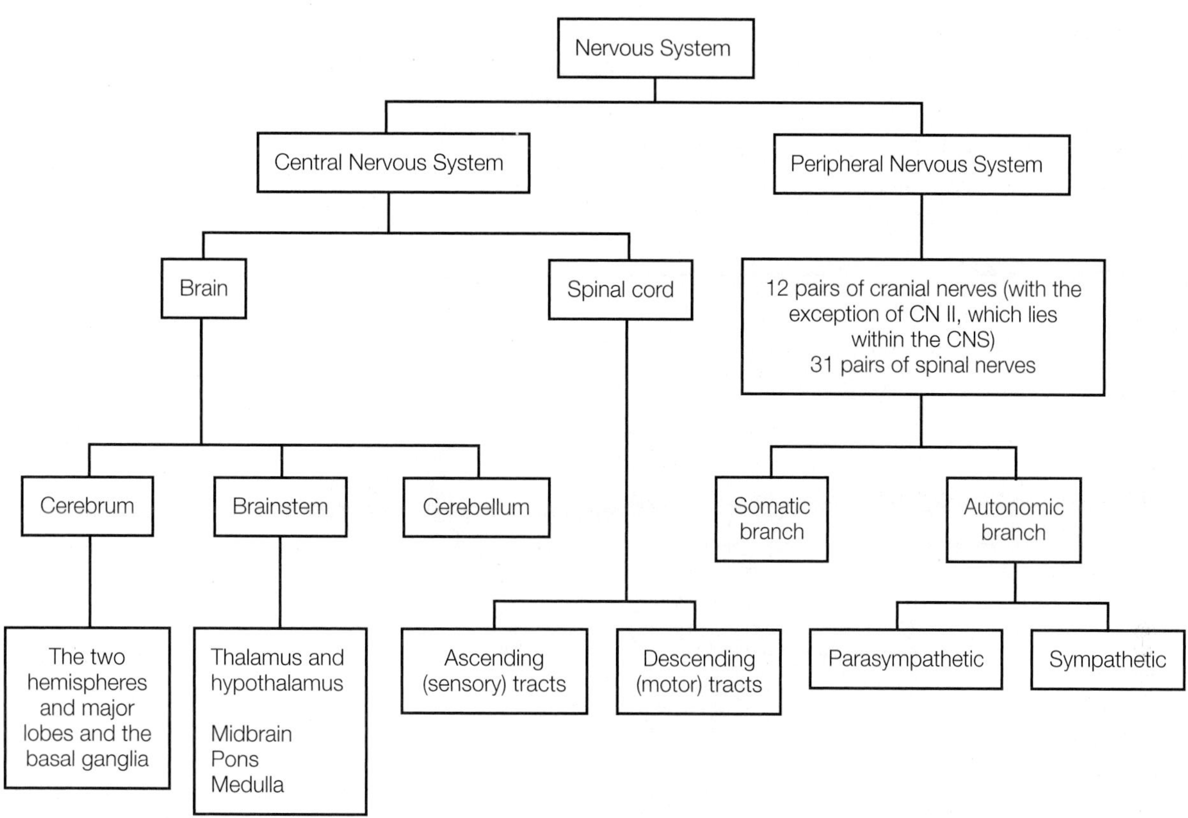

Figure 5-1 Organization of the nervous system.

Table 5-1 The Cranial Nerves

Cranial Nerve	Important Functions
I. Olfactory	Sensation of smell
II. Optic	Sensation of vision
III. Oculomotor	Movements of the eye and eyelid
	Parasympathetic control of pupil size
IV. Trochlear	Movements of the eye
V. Trigeminal	Sensation of touch to the face
	Movements of muscles of mastication
VI. Abducens	Movements of the eye
VII. Facial	Movements of muscles of facial expression
	Sensation of taste in anterior tongue
VIII. Auditory-vestibular	Sensation of hearing and balance
IX. Glossopharyngeal	Movements of muscles in the throat
	Parasympathetic control of the salivary glands
	Sensation of taste in posterior tongue
	Detection of blood pressure changes in the aorta
X. Vagus	Parasympathetic control of the heart, lungs, and abdominal organs
	Sensation of pain associated with viscera
	Movements of muscles in the throat
XI. Spinal accessory	Movements of muscles in the throat and neck
XII. Hypoglossal	Movements of the tongue

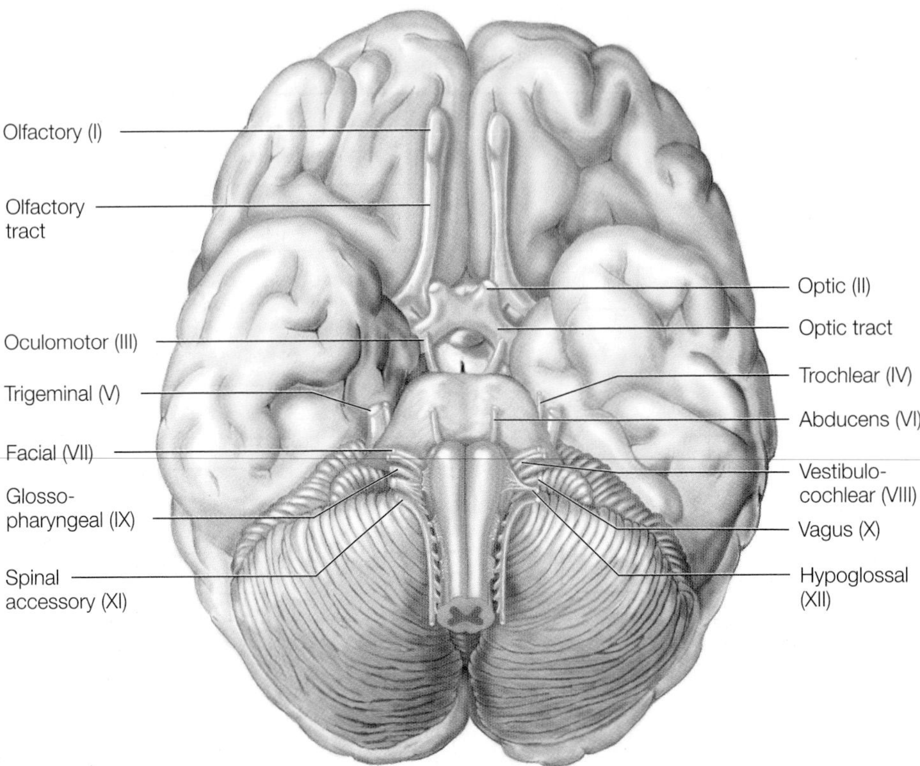

Figure 5-2 The cranial nerves.

of epinephrine (E) (also called adrenaline) into the bloodstream, resulting in a widespread activation. In response to a stressor or threat, the sympathetic nervous system dominates. After the stressor subsides, the parasympathetic system increases in activity and balance is restored. By innervating the same organs, the two opposing systems respond effectively to environmental demands.

In hydrocephalus, CSF builds up, causing the ventricles to enlarge and compress the brain. An increase in ventricular size due to atrophy is not called hydrocephalus.

The CNS is bathed in cerebrospinal fluid (CSF) that flows through the ventricular system and protects the brain from injury. The ventricles of the brain can become enlarged when too much fluid is present (hydrocephalus) or when parts of the brain atrophy, leaving more space for CSF fluid. **Figure 5-3** shows the location of the ventricles of the brain. The CNS can be divided into three major divisions: the cerebrum, the brain stem, and the cerebellum.

Cerebrum

Cerebral Lobes

The **cerebrum** underlies the ability to reason, entertain abstract thoughts, and contemplate concepts like the past and the future, as well as the ability to experience emotions. The cerebrum is the largest portion of the brain and is divided into a left and right hemisphere, each of which contains four major lobes: frontal, temporal, parietal, and occipital (**Figure 5-4**). A fifth area of cortex, called the insula, is less

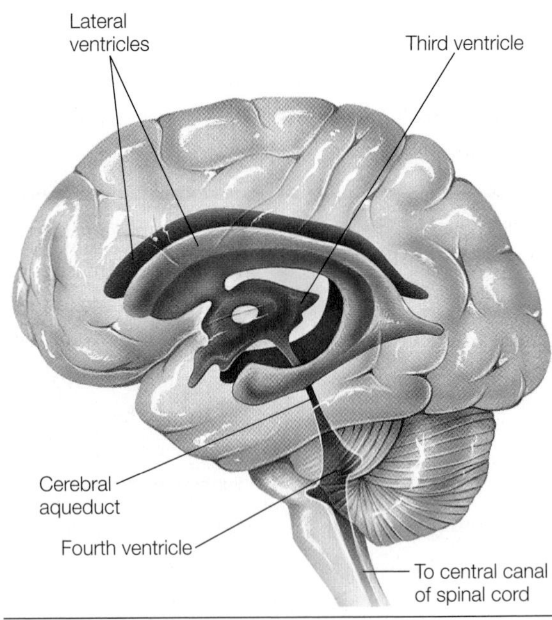

Figure 5-3 The ventricles are filled with cerebrospinal fluid.

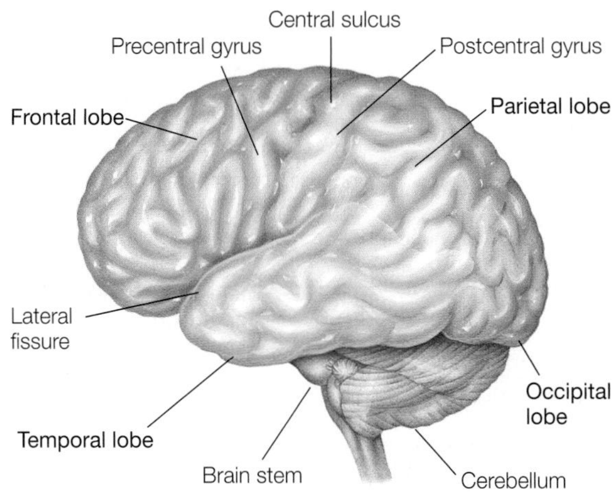

Figure 5-4 The lobes of the human cerebrum. The cortex of the brain is identified by gyri (bumps) and sulci (grooves) or fissures (deep grooves).

well known and understood and is not seen from the outer surface of the brain.

Sitting underneath the lobes are several structures referred to as the **basal ganglia**, which means deep nuclei. Together the cerebral hemispheres and basal ganglia are referred to as the "telencephalon." A band of myelinated axons called the corpus callosum connects the two hemispheres, allowing information to pass between them in a unifying manner. The lobes of the brain serve different functions, and so it follows that injury or illness affecting these structures can result in specific alterations in functioning.

Frontal Lobes

The **frontal lobes** of the brain have evolved to be relatively larger in humans than in other species. In human beings, the frontal aspect of the brain, specifically the prefrontal cortex (anterior to the motor cortex), is responsible for executive functioning—planning, organizing, decision making, and working memory (short-term storage and processing of information). While executive functioning takes place in the lateral and upper (dorsolateral) aspects of the prefrontal cortex, other areas control impulses and regulate mood (orbitofrontal) and are involved in reward processing (ventromedial). Together these prefrontal brain areas work with other structures of the limbic system to regulate impulses, emotions, and behavior. The frontal lobes also contain the primary motor, supplementary motor, and premotor cortex and are involved in the interpretation of incoming motor signals and planning and directing of motor responses. Injury to the frontal lobes can affect motor functioning on the opposite side of the body, executive functioning, and short-term working memory. For the majority of people, language functions are located primarily in the left hemisphere, and injury to **Broca's area** (**Figure 5-5**) can cause expressive aphasia, the inability to express oneself with language. The negative or deficit symptoms that we see with some of the psychiatric illnesses may be a reflection of underactivation or underutilization of the frontal executive functions.

The famous story of Phineas Gage helps us understand other functions of the frontal lobes. Gage was a foreman who worked for the railroad system back in the 1800s. One day an accidental explosion blew a tamping iron right through his skull, obliterating a portion of his frontal lobes. He recovered from the accident, but according to his physician, Dr. John Harlow, his personality changed drastically from one of being hard working and easy going to someone who was unmotivated, fitful, irreverent, and grossly profane.

Critical Thinking Question

Can you think of any psychiatric or behavioral disorders associated with impulsivity? Do individuals with these disorders have additional problems with executive functioning?

Temporal Lobes

The **temporal lobes** are especially important in processing auditory information and consolidating long-term memories. Auditory hallucinations, receptive **Wernicke's aphasia** (the inability to understand spoken speech), and difficulty forming new long-term memories may reflect problems with the temporal lobes.

Critical Thinking Question

Can you think of any psychiatric or behavioral disorders associated with impulsivity? How might impulsivity be a risk factor in substance abuse or dependence? Do individuals with these disorders have additional problems with executive functioning?

Two structures that reside within the temporal lobe are the **hippocampus** and the **amygdala**. The

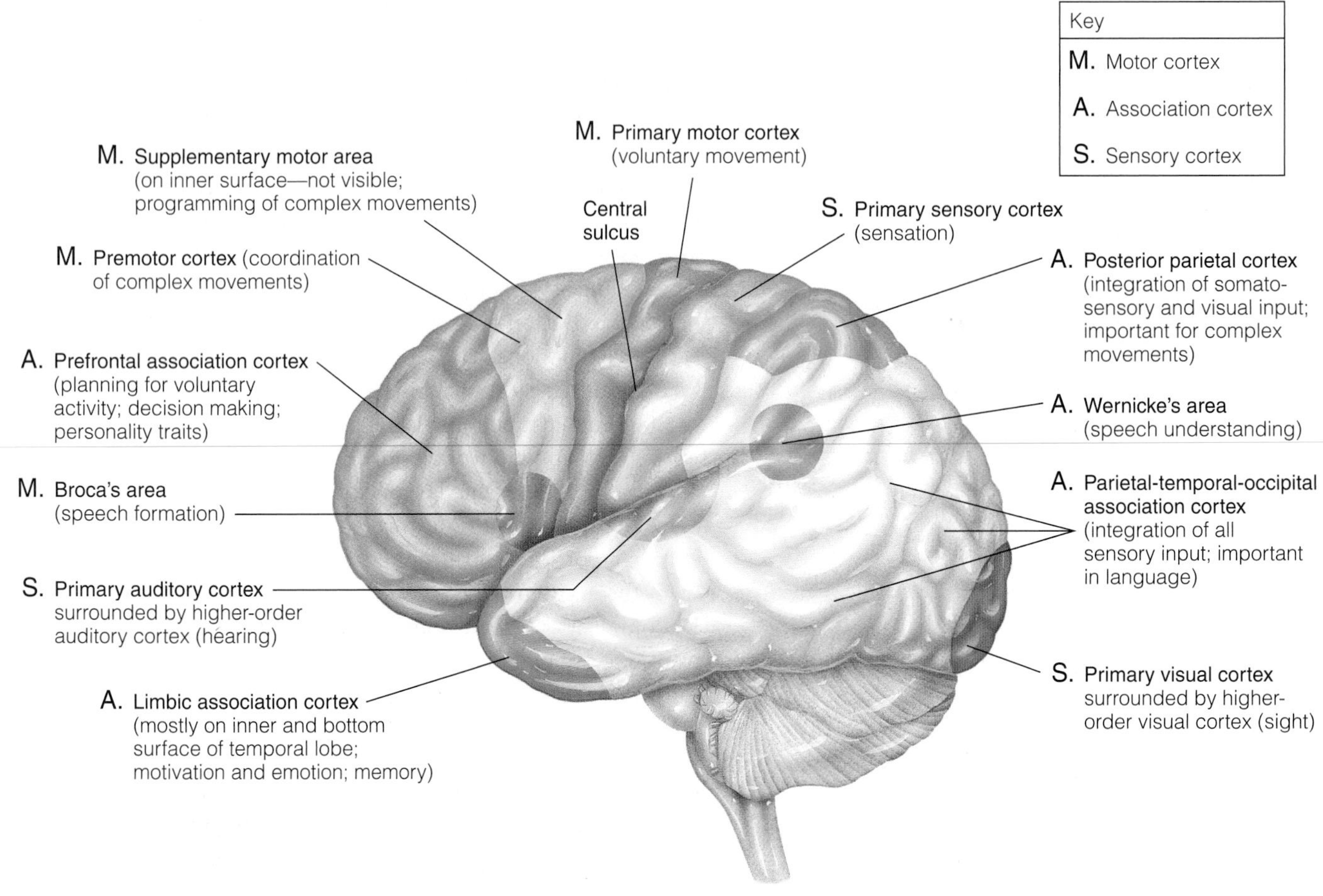

Figure 5-5 **Functional regions of the cortex.** Different functions can be localized to specific areas of the brain. The left hemisphere is dominant for language in the majority of people.

hippocampus, located within the medial temporal lobe, is important in the process of consolidating long-term memories. Without the hippocampus, we would not be capable of storing new information about the facts and events in our lives.

A famous story about a man named Henry Molaison, referred to as "HM," taught us much of what we know today about the functioning of the hippocampal structures. When he was young he had intractable seizures and probably would have died due to complications. In 1953, when he was 23, in an attempt to stop the seizures, surgeons removed both of the anterior portions of his temporal lobes, taking out both hippocampal structures. Following the surgery, HM recovered, and he could recall his life before surgery up to a certain point in time; then his ability to remember just stopped. This type of memory loss is called retrograde amnesia.

The worst problem, however, was that he never again stored or recalled any new facts or events (declarative memories). This type of memory loss is called anterograde amnesia. Dr. Brenda Milner, a researcher at the Montreal Neurological Institute, studied and worked with HM since the 1950s. She introduced herself each time she met him because he had no recollection of ever meeting her. Some types of memory, such as the memory for riding a bike or other skills, are not dependent on the hippocampus. HM improved his skill (procedural memory) at certain activities like table tennis despite not recalling that he had ever played (Milner, 2005). HM died in 2008, but his contributions to neuroscience will live on. Using new methods for three-dimensional digitalized brain modeling, images of HM's brain will soon become available online to neuroscientist researchers worldwide.

The hippocampus is a vulnerable area of the brain. In neurodegenerative illnesses such as Alzheimer's disease, the hippocampus is one of the first areas to show cellular changes and shrinkage. The hippocampus is also vulnerable to chronically elevated levels of circulating cortisol, as might occur in chronic stress-related disorders and depression (Sapolsky, 2003). Unfortunately we cannot avoid stress entirely. The good news is that the hippocampus retains its ability to regenerate neurons throughout life. This process is called **neurogenesis**, and it is facilitated by healthy behaviors such as exercise, good nutrition, and studying for exams!

The amygdala is a small, almond-shaped structure that sits just anterior to the hippocampus in the temporal lobes. The amygdala is very important in relation to stress, serving the function of detecting danger and activating fear and the stress response. Like the hippocampus, the amygdala is important in memory consolidation; however, it specializes in emotional memories and appears to be an essential locus for the storage of fear-related memories (Schafe, Doyere, & LeDoux, 2005). Although it is extremely rare, individuals who do not have either amygdala cannot recognize negative emotion in others. The rare Kluver-Bucy syndrome demonstrates this phenomenon. When the anterior portions of the temporal lobes are removed through disease or injury, individuals display diminished fear and aggression, a tendency to identify objects by oral examination rather than visual inspection and inappropriate sexual behavior.

For most of us, our amygdalas are present bilaterally, yet we all differ in sensitivity. Like a thermostat, some people seem to be able to take quite a lot of threat before triggering the stress or fear response system, whereas others appear to be extremely sensitive and hypervigilant. It is likely that a combination of genes and environmental experiences determines the level of sensitivity. Fortunately, both antidepressants and psychotherapy can reduce the sensitivity and reactivity of the amygdala.

Parietal Lobes

The parietal lobes contain the primary sensory cortex, which receives afferent sensory information about touch, pain, temperature, and proprioception (limb location), and the sensory association cortex where these signals are analyzed and interpreted. When the parietal lobes are injured or lesioned, such as can happen with a cerebrovascular accident, individuals may develop sensory and perceptual problems such as perceptual abnormalities of body image and spatial relationships—even the full neglect of one side of the body. Complex motor movements are coordinated between the frontal lobe (planning and motor) and the parietal lobe (sensory and limb position). A selective inability to perform learned purposeful movements (**apraxia**) or identify objects (agnosia) may suggest parietal injury. Agnosias are defined by their functional deficits; for example, asterognosia refers to the inability to identify objects by touch (e.g., a key in one's pocket), a skill that requires intact sensory perception.

Occipital Lobes

The occipital lobes house the primary and association visual cortices, areas specialized in receiving visual signals and interpreting visual stimuli. Injuries or damage to the occipital cortex can result in vision changes and problems recognizing and interpreting visual information.

Basal Ganglia

The basal ganglia are a collection of neurons deep in the cerebrum. They consist of three major structures that cover the thalamus in each hemisphere: the caudate, putamen, and globus pallidus. Together the caudate and putamen are sometimes referred to as the "striatum." In psychiatric nursing and psychopharmacology, you will hear terms that refer to the basal ganglia. The pyramids refer to the bundles of descending corticospinal motor axons that mostly cross over (decussate) at the level of the medulla. **Extrapyramidal pathways** are motor pathways that are outside of the medullary pyramids. Whereas the pyramidal motor pathways are responsible for voluntary skilled movements, the extrapyramidal system provides support for movement through control of posture and muscle tone and initiation of movement, and it is importantly regulated by the basal ganglia.

When you hear of the extrapyramidal symptoms that include bradykinesia, tremor, and dystonia, what medical condition do you think of? If you thought of Parkinson's disease, you were right. One of the extrapyramidal pathways is a dopamine pathway that travels from the substantia nigra (dopamine producing cells in the midbrain) to the striatum (of the basal ganglia). We refer to that pathway as the nigrostriatal pathway. *Nigro* tells you the origin of the pathway and *striatal* tells you the destination. In Parkinson's disease, the dopamine-producing cells in the substantia nigra degenerate, decreasing the dopamine that is available in the basal ganglia for initiation of movement. Extrapyramidal side effects or EPSs are common in individuals who are taking the first-generation, conventional, antipsychotics that are potent dopamine D2 receptor antagonists. EPSs resemble a Parkinson's-like condition that is reversible once the dopamine receptor antagonism is reduced in the nigrostriatal pathway.

One of the most important functions of the basal ganglia is to facilitate the initiation of willed movements, such as walking or writing.

Brain Stem

The **brain stem** consists of the central structures that sit below and support the cerebrum. The body's vital functions depend on neuron clusters within the brain stem. Also, located within the brain stem is an area called the **reticular activating system** (RAS), whose function seems to be keeping us conscious and awake. Damage to this area of the brain stem can result in a sleeplike state of coma. The brain stem initiates a number of protective, automatic motor behaviors such as maintaining balance, blinking, and head movements.

Thalamus and Hypothalamus

At the superior aspect of the brain stem lie the thalamus and hypothalamus, together referred to as the "diencephalon." Inside the **thalamus** are the major input and output relay nuclei that interact with every portion of the brain. Nerve impulses do not enter or exit the conscious brain without going through the thalamus. The thalamus sorts, amplifies, directs, and integrates sensory information.

The **hypothalamus** lies inferior to (beneath) the thalamus and superior to (above) the pituitary gland, where it helps maintain homeostasis by regulating vital functions, including body temperature, blood glucose level, salt and water balance, and our biologic clock. The hypothalamus is the major control center for the pituitary gland and is central in coordinating the physiological response to detected threats or stress via the **hypothalamic-pituitary-adrenal (HPA) axis**. Axons from the hypothalamic neurons release their neurotransmitters into the portal circulation of the anterior pituitary, influencing the release of pituitary hormones that act on the gonads, thyroid glands, adrenal glands, and mammary glands (**Figure 5-6**).

Midbrain

Clusters of cell bodies that produce monoamine neurotransmitters reside within the **midbrain**, also referred to as the "mesencephalon." The midbrain is the origin of several of the diffuse regulatory pathways of the brain. The cluster of cell bodies that produces norepinephrine is collectively referred to as the "locus coeruleus." The cluster that produces

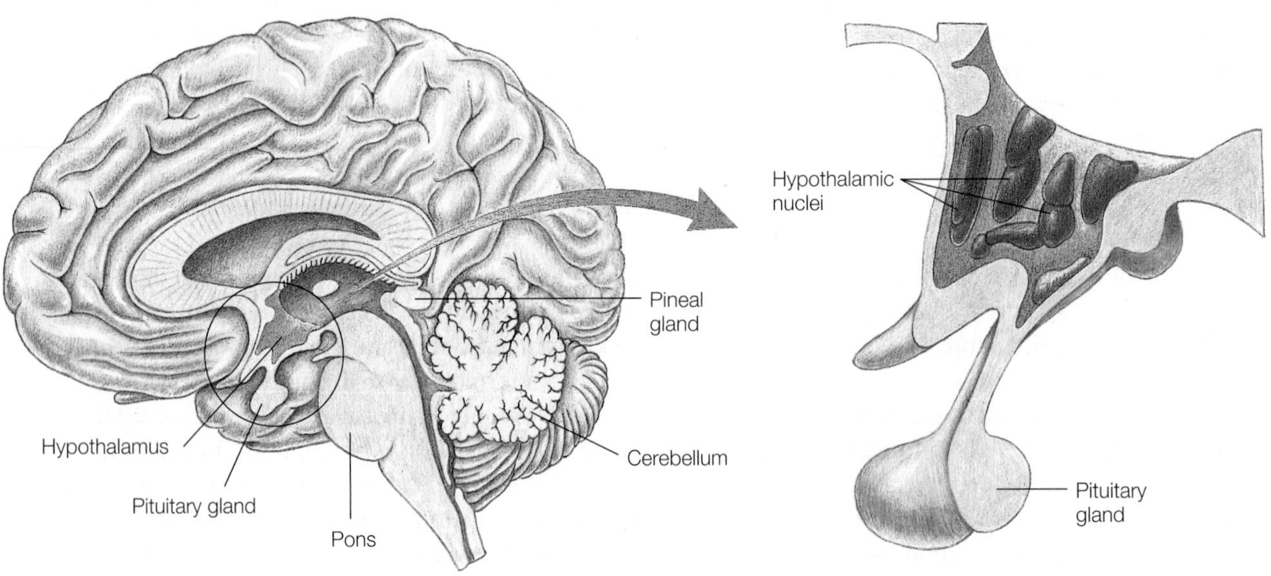

Figure 5-6 The hypothalamus is the master gland of the endocrine system.

dopamine is referred to as the "substantia nigra." The pathways are named by their origin and termination within the brain, so by knowing that *meso* refers to the mesencephalon, you would know that a mesolimbic pathway travels from the midbrain to the limbic structures of the brain.

Critical Thinking Question 

Name the origin and the destination of the following pathways of the brain: (1) corticospinal, (2) spinothalamic, and (3) Nebraska Avenue. Just kidding on number 3. However, sensible naming strategies for pathways make it easier to find your way around the brain than around most cities!

Pons

Not only does the **pons** contain important neurotransmitter-producing cell bodies, but it also is a very important conduit for the ascending and descending pathways that pass between the cerebrum and cerebellum. Scattered groups of cell bodies referred to as the "raphe nuclei" produce serotonin in the midbrain, pons, and medulla.

Medulla

The descending corticospinal tracts cross (decussate) at the level of the **medulla**. This results in the right motor cortex controlling the muscles on the left side of the body and the left motor cortex controlling the muscles on the right side. The crossover accounts for how a cerebrovascular accident in one hemisphere of the brain creates functional difficulty for the other side of the body. The bundles of myelinated axons that course through the medulla are sometimes referred to as the "pyramids." The bundles of axons that lie outside of the pyramids are extrapyramidal pathways.

Cerebellum

Bundles of axons travel between the pons and the **cerebellum**, providing a means for the cerebellum to communicate with the rest of the central and peripheral nervous systems. The cerebellum smoothes out and coordinates the sequence of muscle contractions that are necessary to control movements. Individuals with cerebellar damage will have difficulty touching a finger to their nose or moving an arm to point from one location in space to another. Such an individual might also need to walk with a wide-based gait. The term **ataxia** refers to these uncoordinated and inaccurate movements. Acute and chronic abuse of substances such as alcohol can result in cerebellar dysfunction and ataxia.

Cellular Mechanisms of Communication

The Cells of the Brain

There are two main types of cells in the nervous system: the **glia** and neurons. The most abundant are the glial cells, which provide support and protection to the neurons. Bear, Connors, and Paradiso (2007) use the analogy of a chocolate chip cookie to describe the relationship between neurons and glia. The chips (neurons) are surrounded and supported by the more plentiful dough (glia). In early development, the glial cells also provide the structures upon which the neurons can migrate, with the help of neurotrophic (brain growth) factors, to appropriate sites in the brain. There are five identified types of glial cells. The oligodendroglia form myelin sheaths around the axons in the CNS, just as Schwann cells do in the PNS. The astrocytes provide physical support to the neurons and protect them by regulating extracellular levels of ions and neurotransmitters, such as potassium and glutamate. Microglia are macrophages that play an important role in the brain's immune system. In response to pathogen invasion or tissue damage, they promote an inflammatory response that engages the immune system to initiate tissue repair. The ependymal cells line the fluid-filled ventricles of the brain. Although we tend to think of neurons as being the most important cells in the brain, without glial cells they could not function. Indeed, Einstein's brain was found to have more glial cells relative to neurons in the posterior parietal cortex than a control population (Diamond, Scheibel, Murphy, & Harvey, 1985).

The neuron is the basic functional unit of the brain for information processing. Neurons have three distinct parts—the cell body (soma), **dendrites**, and axon (see **Figure 5-7**). Central to the soma is the nucleus that contains the DNA, the set of genetic instructions that guide development and functioning. The DNA determine the type, production, and distribution of proteins within the neuron and the functioning of the cell. Outside of the nucleus, within the cytoplasm of the soma, are several organelles that

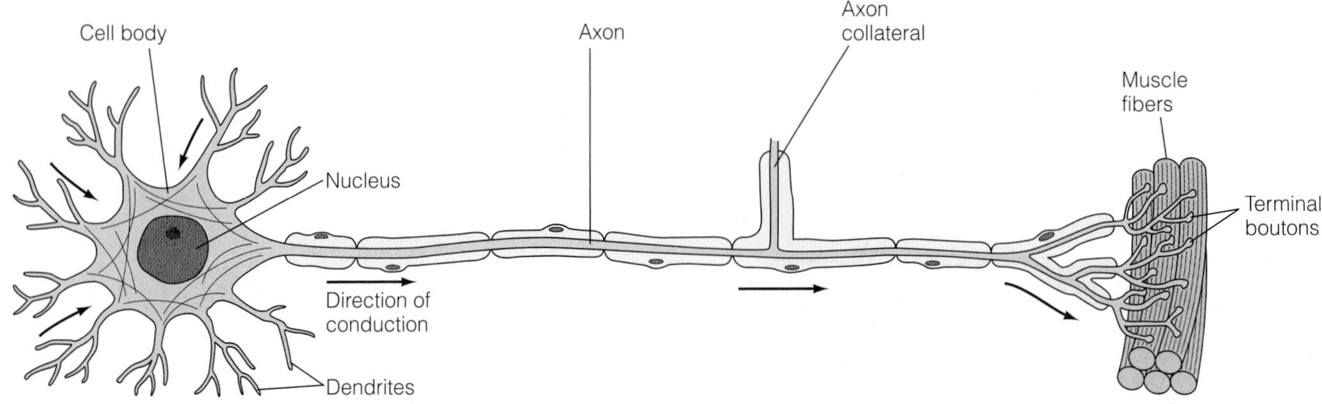

Figure 5-7 A prototypical neuron. Neurons are distinguished from other cells in the body by their dendrites and axons. Their terminals (sometimes called boutons) typically form synapses with the dendrites of other neurons, but may synapse on cell bodies or axons. This figure shows the axon terminating at the neuromuscular junction of skeletal muscle fibers.

serve specific functions in the manufacture of important proteins. Ribosomes are the sites of protein synthesis; Golgi bodies cleave proteins into smaller functional units; and mitochondria produce the energy, adenosine triphosphate (ATP), needed for all cell activity. The proteins produced by neurons are transported to sites within the neuron where they serve as enzymes, receptors, ion channels, transport pumps, peptide neurotransmitters, and membrane and structural proteins.

Dendrites and axons distinguish the neuron from other cells in the body. The dendrites receive chemical signals from other neurons, and the axons conduct electrical signals (action potentials) to their terminals that result in the release of chemical messengers (neurotransmitters), which activate the dendrites and cell bodies of other neurons. A gross inspection of the brain reveals both gray and white matter. The gray matter consists of the cell bodies and other nonmyelinated structures such as glia. The white matter is named for the white appearance of myelinated axons. Axons that are insulated with myelin sheaths are able to conduct the electrical signals more quickly and efficiently, with the axon potential jumping from one break in the **myelin** (also referred to as a "node of Ranvier") to the next (**Figure 5-8A**).

Critical Thinking Question

Multiple sclerosis is a disease characterized by the destruction of myelin. Based on your knowledge of the function of myelin, what symptoms would you expect?

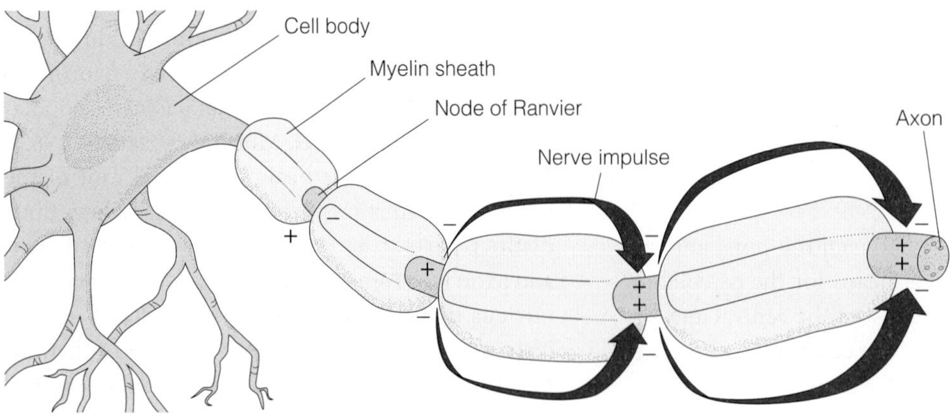

Figure 5-8A Neurotransmission. An electrical signal is conducted down the axon to the terminal.

Neurotransmitters

Large peptide **neurotransmitters** (e.g., beta-endorphins) are produced in the soma and transported to the terminals for release. Smaller amine and amino acid neurotransmitters are produced in the axon terminals and packaged into tiny synaptic vesicles. Neurotransmitters are released into the synapse upon the arrival of electrical signals (action potentials). **Figure 5-8B** depicts the arrival of an action potential at the terminal triggering the release of neurotransmitter from the vesicles. The neurotransmitter diffuses across the synapse and engages the receptors on the postsynaptic membrane. Notice the abundance of mitochondria in the terminal area indicating the great energy needs for the processes of neurotransmission, including reestablishing the membrane potential, transporting neurotransmitters back into the terminal, and repackaging them in vesicles.

Most notable to the etiology and treatment of mental illnesses are the **amine neurotransmitters**: acetylcholine (ACh), serotonin (5HT), dopamine (DA), and norepinephrine (NE). The family of neurotransmitters called catecholamines refers to dopamine, norepinephrine, and epinephrine, all synthesized from a common amino acid precursor called tyrosine. See **Table 5-2** for a list of the common neurotransmitters and their functions. Clusters of cells that produce these neurotransmitters are located in the midbrain, pons, and medulla and send their axons into many areas of the cerebrum. The result is that the neurotransmitter pathways are distributed throughout the brain and have widespread regulatory effects on brain activity. In addition, areas of the brain are connected via circuits for regulation of various functions.

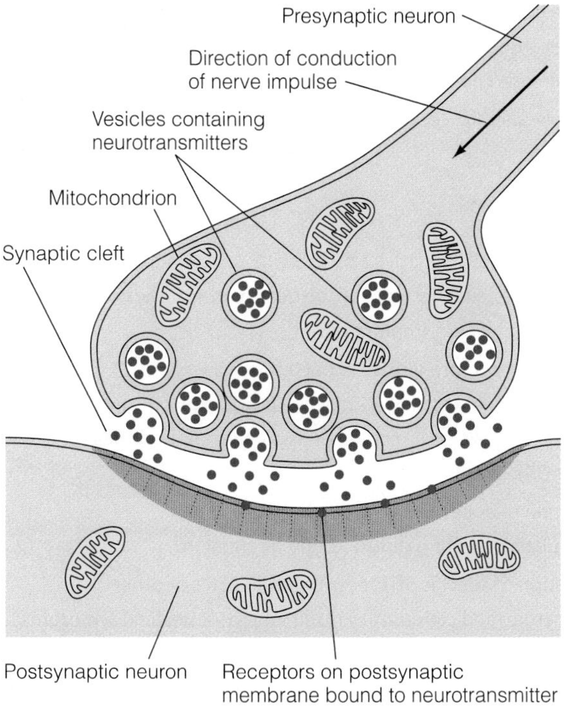

Presynaptic neuron
Direction of conduction of nerve impulse
Vesicles containing neurotransmitters
Mitochondrion
Synaptic cleft
Postsynaptic neuron
Receptors on postsynaptic membrane bound to neurotransmitter

Figure 5-8B A chemical signal is released into the synapse.

Synapses

A synapse is the region of contact between neurons where information is transferred.

Although it might appear that neurons are part of one vast continuous network, they are actually separated from one another by small spaces called **synapses.** Upon the arrival of electrical signals (action potentials), chemical signals (neurotransmitters) diffuse across synapses from presynaptic terminals to postsynaptic receptors. The neurotransmitters do not actually pass into the postsynaptic cells. Instead, like keys, they activate receptors on postsynaptic membranes and then float back into the synapse where they await their fate. Some neurotransmitters float away, others are broken down by enzymes in the synapses, and the rest are pumped back into the terminal. Once in the terminal, the neurotransmitters may be broken down by enzymes (e.g., monoamine oxidase) or repackaged into vesicles for recycling. Note that several familiar psychotropic medications target the pumps (e.g., serotonin reuptake inhibitors) and the enzymes (e.g., monoamine oxidase inhibitors).

Neurotransmitters and their receptors mediate psychiatric disorders and are targets for psychopharmacologic interventions.

Critical Thinking Question

Depression is thought to be related to diminished levels of serotonin and other monoamine neurotransmitters. How would you explain the mechanism of action of fluoxetine (Prozac) to a client?

Each neurotransmitter has several receptor types, and each given receptor type may have multiple subtypes with different actions. Thus, one neurotransmitter can cause multiple actions in different areas of the brain. Neurotransmitters are messengers that activate receptors. Some receptors are actually ion channels that open up rapidly in response to the neurotransmitter, allowing charged ion molecules to flow into or out of the postsynaptic cell. Receptors that open an ion channel are called ligand gated or inotropic. Others use a second messenger on the inside

Neurotransmitters are chemical "messengers" that activate specific receptors.

Table 5-2 Major Neurotransmitters in Mental Health and Illness

Chemical Classification	Neurotransmitter and Receptor Types	Major Pathways and Sites of Action	Normal Functions and Dysfunctional Symptoms in Mental Disorders
Amine	Dopamine (DA) Five major receptor types with multiple subtypes: D1, D2, D3, D4, D5 The term *catecholamine* describes DA, NE, and E. NE is synthesized from DA and E is synthesized from NE.	Mesocortical: ventral tegmental area (VTA) to prefrontal cortex.	Cognition and executive functioning. Deficits: cognitive (negative symptoms), decreased information processing.
		Mesolimbic: VTA to limbic areas of brain.	Emotion regulation: motivation, pleasure, reward. All drugs of abuse increase DA in this pathway. Deficits: reduced motivation, positive affect, joy, interest, pleasure; increased apathy, anhedonia. Excesses: drug craving, positive symptoms of psychosis, increased goal-directed behaviors in mania.
		Nigrostriatal: Substantia nigra to basal ganglia.	Part of the extrapyramidal system that controls movement. Deficits: bradykinesia, tremor, dystonia, akathisia in disorders such as Parkinson's disease, and EPS of dopamine antagonist medications. Excesses: dyskinesias, tics.
		Tuberoinfundibular: Hypothalamus to anterior pituitary.	Inhibits prolactin. Risk of galactorrhea with dopamine receptor antagonist (antipsychotic) therapy.
Amine	Norepinephrine (NE) Two major receptor types with multiple subtypes: alpha and beta NE is converted to epinephrine (E) in the adrenal medulla. E is also known as adrenaline.	Locus coeruleus to prefrontal cortex.	Concentration, working memory, speed of information processing. Deficits: decreased alertness, cognitive dysfunction.
		Locus caeruleus to limbic system, especially the amygdala and its projections.	Mood regulation. Deficits: reduced positive affect, loss of energy, psychomotor retardation. Excesses: anxiety, panic, hypervigilance, psychomotor agitation.
		Postganglionic neurons of the sympathetic nervous system.	Participates in the regulation of the autonomic nervous system. In response to stress, facilitates fight or flight. Excesses: symptoms of activation without corresponding stressor (e.g., increased heart rate, blood pressure, respiratory rate).
		Adrenal medulla releases E into the bloodstream in response to stress.	E is involved in the coordination of the visceral response to stress.
Amine	Serotonin (5HT) At least seven major receptor types with multiple subtypes: 5HT1–5HT7	Raphe nuclei to prefrontal cortex and limbic system.	Mood regulation. Deficits: increased negative affect, depressed mood, guilt, worthlessness, suicidal ideation, disgust, fear, anxiety, hostility, irritability, loneliness, impulsivity.
		Raphe nuclei to basal ganglia.	Deficits: worry, apprehensive expectation, obsessions. Excesses: side effects of SSRIs may include Parkinsonism or akathisia from excess inhibition of dopamine (5HT normally inhibits DA).
		Raphe nuclei to hypothalamus.	Regulation of appetite and eating behavior. Dysregulated in eating disorders and depression.
		Raphe nuclei to brain stem regulatory centers and spinal cord.	Stimulation of specific 5HT receptors with SSRIs or other serotonergic medications may result in gastrointestinal symptoms, nausea, sleep disturbances, and sexual dysfunction.

Table 5-2 **Major Neurotransmitters in Mental Health and Illness *(Continued)***

Chemical Classification	Neurotransmitter and Receptor Types	Major Pathways and Sites of Action	Normal Functions and Dysfunctional Symptoms in Mental Disorders
Amine	Acetylcholine (ACh) Two major receptor types with multiple subtypes: muscarinic and nicotinic	Brain stem nuclei and Meynert's nucleus to hippocampus, amygdala, and throughout the cortex.	Critical role in memory and higher cortical executive functions such as learning, problem solving, and judgment. Deficits resulting in learning and memory problems in cognitive decline, Alzheimer's dementia, and excessive medication-induced anticholinergic states.
		Other sites of cholinergic-producing neurons include all motor neurons in the spinal cord and brain stem.	Causes contraction of skeletal muscle. Deficits result in muscle weakness (e.g., myasthenia gravis).
		ACh is the preganglionic neurotransmitter of sympathetic and parasympathetic neurons and the postganglionic neurotransmitter of parasympathetic neurons.	Effects on cardiac muscle: ACh slows heart rate. Parasympathetic ACh activity facilitates digestion, growth, immune responses, and energy storage. Activity of the parasympathetic nervous system is generally reciprocal to activity in the sympathetic system.
Amino acids	Glutamate Four major receptor types: NMDA, AMPA, kainite, and metabotropic	Synthesized from glucose and other precursors in all cells.	Serves as an excitatory neurotransmitter throughout the brain. Plays a key role in long-term potentiation, memory formation, and synaptogenesis. The NMDA receptor is thought to mediate normal excitatory neurotransmission by opening positively charged calcium ion channels leading to rapid depolarization of postsynaptic cells. Excitotoxicity: too much glutamate lets in too much calcium, which results in excess free radical formation and eventual death of the neuron. This is thought to be a mechanism in neurodegenerative disorders. Less toxic increases in glutamate may be related to other positive symptoms such as anxiety, panic, psychosis, and mania.
	Gamma-aminobutyric acid (GABA) Two major receptor types with several subtypes: GABA A and GABA B	Synthesized from glutamate in neurons that use it as a neurotransmitter. It is not one of the 20 amino acids used to make proteins.	Serves as an inhibitory neurotransmitter by allowing negatively charged chloride to enter, reducing the chances that a neuron will fire. Deficits in GABA inhibitory activity have been linked to anxiety disorders and insomnia. Excessive inhibitory activity can result in sedation, ataxia, and memory disturbance.

Source: Adapted from Stahl (2008).

of the postsynaptic membrane to cause a cascade of chemical changes, eventually even influencing the expression of the genes that guide the cellular functions. The receptors that use a second messenger are called G-protein or metabotropic receptors. G-protein receptors have slower, longer-acting, modulating effects.

Let's look at glutamate as an example. Glutamate has four identified receptors (see Table 5-2). Three of the receptors are linked to ion channels and create rapid changes in the postsynaptic cell: NMDA (N-methyl d-aspartate), AMPA (amino-3-hydroxy-5-methyl-4-isoxazolepropionic acid), and KAR (kainate). The NMDA receptor mediates normal excitatory neurotransmission. Too much glutamate action at NMDA receptors may eventually be excitotoxic to the cells and may be part of the mechanism of neurodegeneration in illnesses such as Alzheimer's disease. The fourth glutamate receptor is a metabotropic receptor that uses a second messenger system. The NMDA is implicated in the creation of lasting changes in synapses, a process called long-term potentiation (LTP), as well as in excitotoxicity (the death of cells due to too much glutamate letting too much calcium into cells). LTP is thought to be a key neuroplastic change in the brain involved in forming long-term memories. Although the complexity of neurotransmitter–receptor actions is enormous, new receptor subtypes are continually being discovered, and as they are, newer drugs can be designed that have more specificity and fewer side effects. Memantine, an NMDA glutamate receptor antagonist medication, holds promise for reducing the excitotoxic effects of excessive glutamate and is being used to decrease the rate of neurodegenerative processes in individuals with Alzheimer's disease.

Neurotransmission

Neuroplasticity describes the dynamic nature of the brain and its functions that permit humans to adapt to environmental changes, learn, and remember.

The membrane potential is the separation of charge between the outside and inside of the neuron.

Neurogenesis is the birth of new neurons.

Due to a combination of diffusion and electrical factors, the inside of resting neurons is more negatively charged than the outside, polarized at about −65 millivolts. The separation of charge between the outside and the inside of the neuron is referred to as the **membrane potential**, and it is largely maintained by the sodium-potassium pump drawing potassium into the neuron and sodium out—both against their concentration gradients. A great deal of cellular energy (adenosine triphosphate or ATP) is required to maintain the difference in potential. Because ATP is manufactured from oxygen and dietary sources of energy, when oxygen is lacking the pumps fail and the neurons can no longer function, resulting in brain damage within four minutes.

When an action potential arrives in the presynaptic terminal, it causes a brief **depolarization** (a shift in the charge towards 0 millivolts and above) of the membrane potential due to a rapid influx of positively charged calcium ions, the calcium in turn triggering the release of neurotransmitter into the synaptic cleft. Following depolarization, the cell quickly repolarizes so that it can be ready to respond to the arrival of the next action potential. So now imagine thousands of axon terminals releasing neurotransmitters into the synaptic clefts of the dendrites or the cell body of a single neuron. The neurotransmitters may be excitatory (like glutamate) or inhibitory (like gamma-aminobutyric acid—GABA). If the neurotransmitter is excitatory, it causes positively charged sodium or calcium to flow into the postsynaptic neuron, depolarizing it and shifting the charge toward the threshold for firing an action potential. If the neurotransmitter is inhibitory, it causes negatively charged chloride to flow into the postsynaptic neuron, resulting in the cell becoming negatively charged (returning the cell toward its resting potential and less likely to fire off another action potential. Small currents build and move along the dendrites toward the cell body. Between the cell body and the axon is an area called the axon hillock, somewhat like a toll booth on a highway. If there is enough currency (depolarization) to pay the fare (shifting the charge from −65 millivolts to a threshold level of about −50 millivolts), then an all-or-none action potential is generated and it travels down the axon. If there is not enough depolarization at the axon hillock, the cell does not fire. The frequency and pattern of action potentials is like a Morse code of the brain, transmitting information to be processed and interpreted.

Neuroplasticity

The ability that we have to adapt to environmental changes, learn, and remember reflects the amazing **neuroplasticity** of the brain. It is difficult to imagine how complex thoughts, feelings, and behaviors emerge from small electrical and chemical signals in the brain. Neuroplasticity describes the dynamic nature of the brain and its functions. We now know that new cells are born (neurogenesis) throughout one's lifetime. A peak number of synapses is present around age 6, followed by a period of extensive pruning and increased efficiency. Long-term potentiation or strengthening of synapses builds our memories. Long-term depression or weakening of synapses helps us forget. Receptors are up regulated or down regulated depending on the availability and need for specific neurotransmitters. When a neurotransmitter is deficient, the receptors up regulate in an attempt to compete for more of the neurotransmitter. Likewise, when a medication increases the levels of a neurotransmitter, the receptors down regulate to decrease the overload. Feedback loops to the nucleus assure that cells are always responding to ever-changing environmental demands. Because the brain has so much plasticity in the early years, children have more capacity than adults to compensate for major brain injuries. Individuals who keep their brains active in later life through physical exercise and cognitive activities show continual neurogenesis and may have more of a buffer against neurodegenerative processes and dementia.

Two important processes involving neuroplasticity have recently been implicated in the development of psychiatric disorders: disturbances in myelination and energy metabolism. Myelination of brain pathways is a developmental process that continues for several decades after birth. Because of this, myelination of brain neurons is thought to be influenced by factors such as levels of environmental enrichment and neuronal activity. Deficits in myelin formation or demyelination may lead to disruptions in functional connectivity between brain regions and impaired cognitive functioning. New research evidence suggests that the impaired cognitive functioning seen in a variety of psychiatric conditions reflects myelin abnormalities (Assaf & Pasternak, 2008; Fields, 2008). Mitochondria, the energy-producing organelles in neurons, have also been found to play important roles in neuroplasticity and cellular resilience, including neurogenesis, the growth of axons and dendrites, and synaptic changes. Disturbances in mitochondrial energy metabolism have been implicated in several neurodegenerative and psychiatric disorders, including Alzheimer's dementia, bipolar disorder, and schizophrenia (Clay, Sillivan, & Konradi, 2010).

The limbic system regulates emotion, learning, and memory.

Regulation of Emotion

The Limbic System

The **limbic system** describes several structures that function as a system to regulate emotion, behavior, memory, and learning. **Figure 5-9** depicts the major structures together with their connections—the frontal cortex, thalamus, hypothalamus, cingulate gyrus, hippocampus, amygdala, and mammillary bodies. The limbic system is crucial to our motivation and important in producing behaviors that are critical to the survival of the species, such as behaviors that foster appropriate social interactions and success in producing offspring. Love and desire arise from this system, as well as fear and paranoia. Memory for the events of our lives and the emotional texture is what helps us make decisions and plan for the present and future. Mental disorders involve dysregulation of the limbic system.

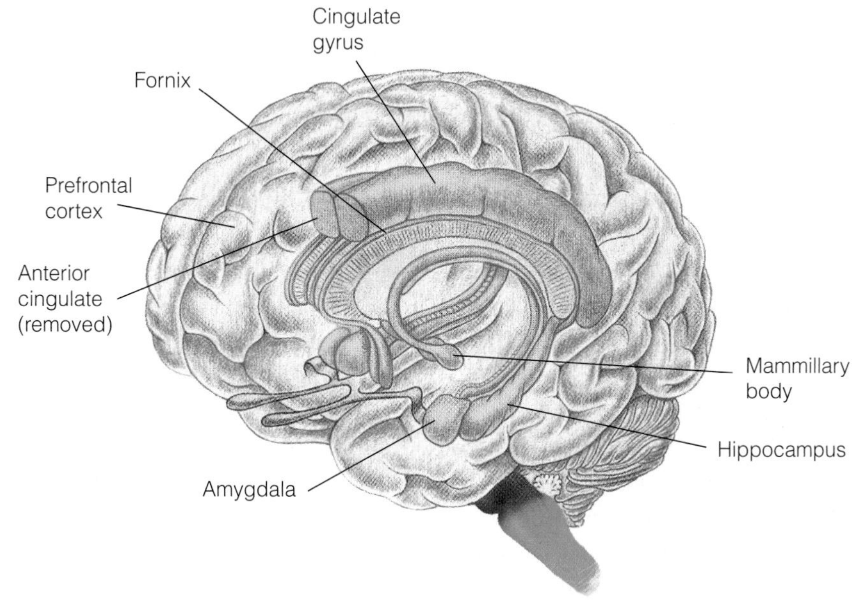

Figure 5-9 **The limbic system.** The limbic structures form a ring around the thalamus and hypothalamus (not shown). The structures and their connecting pathways (e.g., the fornix) are involved in the regulation of emotion and memory.

The Stress Response

The modern-day concept of stress is influenced by the work of Hans Selye and the publication of his theory of **general adaptation syndrome (GAS)**. In his publication, *The Stress of Life* (1956), Selye identified three stages in the human response to stressors. In the first, the alarm stage, an individual becomes aware of the stress or stressor and the sympathetic nervous system springs into a fight-or-flight reaction. In the second stage, resistance, the body attempts to adapt to the stress response, and in many instances adaptation occurs. If homeostasis is not restored, the third stage is that of exhaustion, where the body can no longer respond to the stress and over time may develop illnesses or die. Selye conceived of the response as nonspecific—in other words, the same response regardless of the type of stressor or the individual.

Selye's general adaptation syndrome model did not account for individual differences in stress reactivity. We now know that the stress response is triggered when an individual perceives that the demands of a situation outweigh his or her capacity to adapt. What might be fun to some people (e.g., skydiving) is experienced as frightening and stressful to others. Some people seem more naturally resilient to stressors and demonstrate less reactivity than others. Genetic contributions as well as life experiences probably account for these differences.

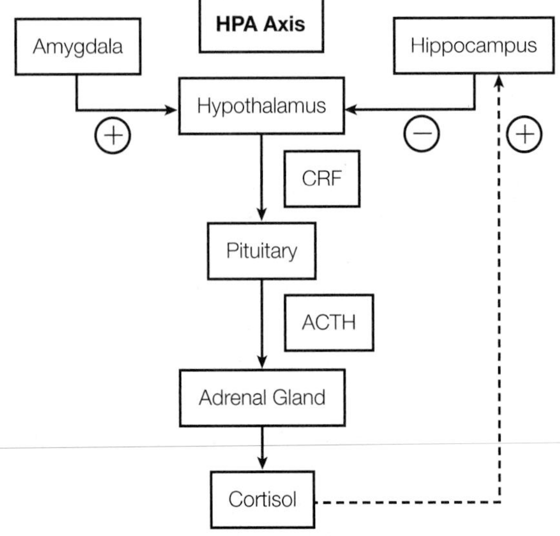

Figure 5-10 **The HPA axis.** In response to stress, neurons in the hypothalamus release a peptide neurotransmitter called corticotrophin-releasing hormone (CRH) into the blood of the pituitary circulation, triggering the release of adrenocorticotrophic hormone (ACTH) into the general circulation. ACTH triggers the release of cortisol from the adrenal cortex. Amygdala activation stimulates the HPA axis and hippocampal activation suppresses it.

Acute Stress

Chronic stress, such as that experienced by individuals living in poverty or with illness, is characterized by elevated levels of cortisol and its physiological correlates.

A stressor (acute or chronic) is anything that threatens the body's homeostasis.

A **stressor** is anything that threatens homeostasis. Potential stressors may be acute physical challenges, such as hunger, cold, restraint, chemicals, shock, surgery, and bodily injuries, or psychological challenges, such as adversity, emotional illness, financial hardships, work issues, social hierarchy conflicts, and neglect. Our bodies are well adapted to dealing with acute stressors. The stress response is characterized by the activation of two major stress pathways: the **hypothalamic-pituitary-adrenal (HPA) axis**, yielding increases in the glucocorticoid called cortisol (**Figure 5-10**), and the sympathetic nervous system (SNS), yielding increases in the catecholamines norepinephrine (NE) and epinephrine (E). Cortisol increases the availability of blood glucose for energy and suppresses the immune system. The catecholamines sharpen the attention and activate the cardiovascular system to increase blood flow to the large muscles (for fighting or fleeing). If acute stress continues, short-term reversible impairments in memory may occur. Once the stressor is avoided or dealt with effectively, homeostasis is restored and digestion, growth, and other resting functions return.

Chronic Stress

Unfortunately, humans have many more things to worry about than being chased by predators and fighting or fleeing. Instead, we are bombarded by constant mild to major stressors. In addition, a large portion of our population suffers from the chronic stress of low socioeconomic status—poverty, hunger, manual labor, sleep deprivation, and low levels of personal control. Others are threatened by neglect or abuse, domestic or community violence, or even war. Persistent activation of the stress response appears to be a risk factor for the development of physical illness as well as depression and anxiety disorders. Although the fight-or-flight response may subside, the HPA axis remains overactive and neurotrophic factors such as brain-derived neurotrophic factor (BDNF) may be reduced. Hippocampal neurons are especially vulnerable to the chronically elevated levels of glucocorticoids and include a metabolic syndrome characterized by elevated blood pressure, increased abdominal fat, and elevated blood sugar (Kyrou, Chrousos, & Tsigos, 2006; Sapolsky, 2005). Whereas elevated levels of glucocorticoids (cortisol) decrease inflammation with acute stress, excessive exposure over prolonged periods has been linked to a deteriorated immune response accompanied by neuroinflammation (Sorrells, Caso, Munhoz, & Sapolsky, 2009). Furthermore, excessive glucocorticoids may lead to reductions in astrocytes and resultant increases in glutamate, leading to excitotoxicity and neuronal damage or death (Rajkowska & Miguel-Hidalgo, 2007). These studies have linked neurodegenerative changes to the effects of chronic stress.

McEwen (2001) refers to the process of maintaining stability or homeostasis through adaptation as "allostasis." **Allostatic load** is the wear and tear produced by the repeated activation of allostatic (adaptive) mechanisms. He identifies four types of allostatic load: (1) repeated challenges/chronic stress, (2) failure to habituate with repeated challenges, (3) failure to shut off the response after the challenge is past, and (4) failure to mount an adequate response. Developmental or environmental determinants of differences in allostatic load can include early stressful life experiences resulting in increased reactivity of the HPA axis function and increased sensitization to later stress exposure (Charney, 2003; Heim, Newport, Mletzko, Miller & Nemeroff, 2008), and stressful adult experiences that cause lasting changes in HPA functioning (Mason et al., 2001).

Stress is relevant to all of the psychiatric disorders, first because of its potential role in their etiology and maintenance, and second because of the chronic stress of living with mental disorders. Stress also contributes to the development, maintenance, and outcome of substance use disorders by increasing drug cravings, altering subjective responses to alcohol, and increasing alcohol consumption. Fortunately the effects of stress can be prevented or reversed through primary (e.g., education) and secondary (screening) prevention efforts.

Mental Disorders

Gene and Environmental Influences

Are mental disorders inherited? The answer is yes, at least partially. Genetic factors provide the vulnerability or risk for mental illness but they do not explain the whole picture. Consider the case of two identical twins (monozygotic) who share the same genes but are discordant for an identified mental disorder. In monozygotic twins, concordance is thought to reflect genetic vulnerability, and discordance is thought to reflect the environmental contribution to mental disorders. All of the mental disorders have been found to show some degree of discordance. Reviews of twin studies indicate that the heritability is highest for schizophrenia (82–85%) (Kendler, 2001), bipolar disorder (85%) (Bienvenu, Davydow, & Kendler (2011), autism spectrum (80%) (Lichtenstein, Carlstrom, Rastam, Gillberg, & Anckarsater, 2010), attention-deficit/hyperactivity disorder (ADHD) (79%) (Lichtenstein et al., 2010), and Alzheimer's dementia (75%) (Bienvenu et al., 2011); it is midlevel for alcoholism (52–58%) (Kendler, 2001) and lowest for the anxiety disorders (28–53%) (Bienvenu et al., 2011; Kendler, 2001) and major depression (29–52%) (Kendler, Gatz, Gardner, & Pedersen, 2006).

Allostasis is the process of maintaining stability or homeostasis through adaptation.

Genome-wide analyses are being used to identify disorders. Genetic researchers are also attempting to identify the epigenetic and environmental risk factors. Epigenetic refers to the study of reversible changes in gene function that occur without a change in the DNA sequence. Environmental factors may influence the epigenetic processes to switch genes on or off. Therefore epigenetic research is also seeking more knowledge on how to reverse the environmental and epigenetic contributions to the development of mental disorders.

The **stress-diathesis model** describes the environmental interaction in mental disorders. Diathesis refers to the genetic predisposition or vulnerability, and stress describes the contribution of environmental factors. Environmental contributions to the development of mental illness may occur in utero, as in the case of one fetus getting more oxygen or more of a virus than the other. They may also stem from childhood experiences. Individuals who have experienced early childhood stress, such as the loss of a parent, neglect, or abuse, are much more vulnerable to depression and anxiety disorders later in life. Stress may also trigger the earlier onset of a mental disorder such as schizophrenia or bipolar disorder. In addition, severe or chronic stress in adulthood is associated with vulnerability to anxiety and mood disorders. Finally, individual differences contribute to the environments in which individuals choose to live, so genes affect the environment and the environ-

The stress-diathesis theory explains the development of psychiatric disorders as a combination of diathesis (genetic predisposition) and environmental stress.

Genetic factors provide the vulnerability or risk factors for an individual to develop a mental illness, but they do not explain the whole process.

ment affects the gene expression, perhaps through changes in epigenetic factors.

The following content discusses the current theories of etiology for a sample of mental disorders. The most recent neurobiological discoveries far outpace the development of new drugs for treatment. For each disorder, the interrelated and overlapping theories of etiology illuminate the complexities of gene–environment interactions and challenge our current diagnostic categories of the mental disorders.

SSRIs inhibit the pumps that transport serotonin back into the presynaptic terminal, resulting in an increase in available serotonin in the synapse.

Mood Disorders

Unipolar Depression

Depression appears to be related to a depletion of monoamine neurotransmitters such as serotonin, norepinephrine, and dopamine.

Sadness and grief are normal responses. Prolonged periods of sadness or anhedonia (lack of pleasure) accompanied by other physiological symptoms such as appetite and weight changes, sleep disruption, fatigue, and psychomotor agitation or retardation are not normal. Persons with these symptoms are experiencing depression, a serious yet common illness. Findings from the Global Burden of Disease Study (World Health Organization, 2008) indicate that depression is the third leading cause of disability worldwide and the first in middle- and high-income countries, creating an enormous burden for society.

The vulnerability to depression is heritable. Children of parents who have had depression have a higher risk for depression than their counterparts, yet early life stressors such as the loss of a parent, neglect, or abuse can predispose a person to the development of depression even without an obvious family history of depression (Gutman & Nemeroff, 2003; Heim et al., 2008). In addition, the illness is not the same for every person. Approximately half of individuals with depression have elevated levels of cortisol, suggesting a prolonged stress response (Lee, Ogle, & Sapolsky, 2002). These individuals may show a prolonged response to the dexamethasone suppression test, demonstrating a weakened ability to shut down cortisol activity in the body. Prolonged elevation of cortisol is toxic to the neurons of the hippocampus, the area of the brain involved in long-term memory consolidation.

Monoamine oxidase inhibitors (MAOIs) block the enzyme MAO from destroying monoamine neurotransmitters, allowing them to accumulate in the presynaptic cell.

Depression appears to be, to some extent, due to a depletion of monoamine neurotransmitters such as serotonin, norepinephrine, and dopamine. The exact mechanism for this is unclear; however, one possibility is that an enzyme that metabolizes monoamines is elevated, leading to lower than normal levels (Meyer et al., 2006). The monoamine reduction hypothesis is supported by the observation that antidepressants effectively reduce depression, and all antidepressants increase the availability of monoamine neurotransmitters. However, individuals differ in their responsiveness to antidepressants. Some individuals with depression respond best to antidepressants that specifically target the serotonin system (e.g., selective serotonin reuptake inhibitors or SSRIs). Others do best with antidepressants that target the serotonin and norepinephrine systems (e.g., serotonin-norepinephrine reuptake inhibitors (SNRIs), tricyclics), and others do best with antidepressants that target the dopamine system (e.g., bupropion). Approximately 30% of depressed patients fail to go into remission with antidepressant treatment (Caraci, Copani, Nicoletti, & Drago 2010).

Finally, late-life (after age 50) depression is a risk factor for the development of Alzheimer's disease. Studies suggest that both disorders are associated with neuroinflammation and impairments in neurotrophic (brain growth factor) signaling. Chronic inflammation may be associated with neurodegenerative changes and the development of dementia (Caraci et al., 2010; Hashioka, McGeer, Monji, & Kanba, 2009). Antidepressants decrease brain inflammation and increase the release of neurotrophic factors, so they are somewhat protective, and researchers are developing new drugs to target these pathways.

Critical Thinking Question

Antidepressants increase the availability of monoamine neurotransmitters almost immediately. Why, then, does it take 3–6 weeks to achieve therapeutic reductions in depression? This is a very difficult question, and no one knows for sure; however, think through some of the neuroplastic changes or brain adjustments that take place over time. For example, consider the up-regulation of monoamine receptors that might occur in depression and the readjustment that might need to take place in recovery.

Bipolar Disorder

Bipolar disorders are characterized by the occurrence of manic (bipolar I) or hypomanic (bipolar II) episodes. Most individuals who have experienced manic episodes will also experience depressive episodes. Dr. Robert Post and his colleagues (Post et al., 2003) at the National Institute of Mental Health (NIMH) have spent years trying to identify the neurobiologic underpinnings of bipolar illness and have come up with two descriptive concepts—sensitization and kindling. **Sensitization** describes the tendency for initial mood episodes to be linked to identified stressors, but later episodes require less of a stressor or none at all. People seem to become sensitized to the episodes themselves, such that the occurrence of mood episodes increases the risk for future episodes. **Kindling** is a term used to describe the lowered threshold for setting off neuronal activity in seizure disorders. Manic episodes are like seizures in that they result from too much neuronal activity, something like a limbic-lobe seizure. Support for this model is gained from the observation that antiseizure drugs are effective in treating and preventing manic episodes. Lithium and the mood stabilizers appear to stabilize the neuronal membrane, making it less sensitive and increasing the threshold for activation. Bipolar depression may be treated with antidepressants; however, mood stabilizers are generally given concurrently to prevent swings from depression into mania.

Specific brain structural changes associated with bipolar disorder are reduced anterior cingulate volume (part of the limbic system that is important in directing attention), early-onset white matter (myelin) abnormalities, and, less consistently, reduced hippocampal volume and enlarged ventricular volume. Behavioral changes that might be accounted for by the structural changes are deficits in attention (anterior cingulate) and deficits in learning and memory (hippocampus). Prefrontal cortex abnormalities are suggested by abnormalities in the reward system of the brain, with a decreased responsiveness during periods of depression and an increased responsiveness during periods of mania. NIMH researchers Hasler, Drevets, Gould, Gottesman, and Manji (2006) suggest that these brain changes may be mediated by interactions among hypercortisolemia, glutamate neurotoxicity, and stress-induced reduction in neurotrophic (brain growth) factors.

Anxiety

Anxiety can be a symptom, a syndrome, or a disorder. As a symptom, anxiety and its stronger variant, fear, constitute the emotional component of a stress response. When the stress response is activated by a perceived threat, the sympathetic fight-or-flight response is accompanied by anxiety or fear. The main neurotransmitters involved in the sympathetic fight-or-flight response are the noradrenergic (NE) and adrenergic transmitters (E). Aside from anxiety, other symptoms of norepinephrine (noradrenergic) and epinephrine (adrenergic) activation include tachycardia, tremor, and sweating.

Anxiety can also be part of a syndrome, associated with other disorders such as substance intoxication or withdrawal or medical problems. The *Diagnostic and Statistical Manual of Mental Disorders*, 4th ed., text revision (*DSM-IV-TR*; APA, 2000) lists anxiety as a part of a syndrome of intoxication for alcohol, amphetamine, caffeine, cannabis, cocaine, hallucinogens, inhalants, and phencyclidine, and of withdrawal for alcohol, cocaine, sedatives, hypnotics, and anxiolytics. In addition, anxiety is a common symptom associated with numerous over-the-counter and prescribed medications, including bronchodilators, corticosteroids, sympathomimetics, and thyroid preparations. All of these conditions and medications have the activation of the CNS in common.

The treatment of choice for anxiety as a symptom or as part of a syndrome is generally a sedative-hypnotic, like a benzodiazepine, which quiets down the CNS by enhancing the inhibitory activity of GABA. Other drugs are also used, depending on the target symptoms. Beta-blockers and other antihypertensives (e.g., clonidine) may be used to decrease the peripheral symptoms of tremor or behavioral activation but are less powerful in blocking the subjective and emotional aspects of anxiety.

Finally, anxiety can be a mental disorder. The *DSM-IV-TR* anxiety disorders include panic disorder, simple phobia, social phobia, obsessive compulsive disorder (OCD), acute stress disorder, posttraumatic stress disorder (PTSD), and in children, separation anxiety disorder. The neurobiologic mechanisms for the anxiety disorders are more complex, and treatment is not simply aimed at decreasing sympathetic activity or increasing inhibitory activity. Two overlapping neurobiologic brain regions and circuits that are implicated in the primary symptoms of anxiety include the amygdala (anxiety or fear), and the cortex-basal ganglia circuit (worry and obsessions) (Stahl, 2008). Many neurotransmitters are involved in regulating these two circuits, and any or all may be involved in anxiety disorders. Potential neurotransmitter abnormalities include excessive cortisol from

Anxiety can be a symptom, a syndrome, or a mental disorder.

dysregulation of the HPA axis, too much excitatory (glutamate) activity, too little inhibitory activity (GABA), or dysregulation of any of the monoamine neurotransmitters. In chronic anxiety, serotonergic dysregulation seems to be an important contributor, because the SSRI antidepressants are the first line of treatment. Consider the following two examples of anxiety OCD and PTSD.

In individuals with OCD, approximately 50% do not respond to the SSRIs alone (Stahl, 2008), implying that serotonin dysregulation cannot be the only explanation. OCD shares similarities with other disorders that involve the dopamine pathways of the basal ganglia: Tourette's disorder and pediatric autoimmune neuropsychiatric disorders associated with streptococci (PANDAS) (Snider & Swedo, 2003). These disorders tend to be associated with movement irregularities or tics involving too much dopamine and OCD symptoms. Treatment with neuroleptics (dopamine antagonists) decreases both the tics of the body and the tics of the mind. Individuals with OCD who do not respond to SSRIs alone are often treated with the addition of a neuroleptic. Taken together, these findings suggest that OCD may be a disorder involving dysregulation of serotonin and dopamine in the basal ganglia and its connections.

Posttraumatic stress disorder (PTSD) is a response to severe environmental stress, such as might be produced by sexual or physical abuse or military combat. PTSD has become a national concern now that 23.7% and 30.5% of active duty and National Guard troops, respectively, meet *DSM-IV-TR* criteria for PTSD at 12 months postdeployment from a war zone, and 7.3% and 11.3% have serious functional impairment (Thomas et al., 2010). The symptoms of PTSD include persistent reexperiencing of a traumatic event, persistent avoidance of stimuli associated with the event, and persistent symptoms of increased arousal. Each of these symptoms may have a different neurobiological mechanism. Persistent intrusive thoughts and reexperiencing may result from an inability of higher cognitive structures to repress negative emotional memories. Avoidance symptoms of PTSD are thought to result from conditioned fearlike encoding of the environment surrounding a traumatic event. Hyperarousal and hypervigilance may result from hyperactivity of the amygdala and noradrenergic signaling. Finally, the HPA axis is also affected; however the evidence suggests that, in contrast to healthy participants and those with major depression, cortisol concentration may be decreased in the plasma of persons with PTSD (Martin, Ressler, Binder, & Nemeroff, 2010).

Schizophrenia involves both neurodevelopmental and neurodegenerative processes.

In summary, an individual's perception of threat and feelings of fear and anxiety are associated with the amygdala and its activation of the stress response pathways (1) from the locus coeruleus to the sympathetic nervous system's release of norepinephrine and epinephrine, and (2) from the hypothalamus to the adrenal gland's (HPA axis) production of cortisol. Under normal conditions, once the stressor is gone, homeostasis is restored. Under chronic stress conditions, however, balance is not restored. Heightened peripheral sympathetic nervous system arousal may persist, especially in panic disorder. The HPA axis may continue unabated, releasing CRH, ACTH, and cortisol, especially during the anticipatory anxiety of a panic disorder and in avoidance of situations associated with phobias (Martin et al., 2010).

Critical Thinking Question 

What stress management techniques do you use to reduce your own stress levels? Do you think that stress management should only be in the treatment plan of individuals with anxiety disorders? If not, why?

Schizophrenia

Schizophrenia, the most common psychotic disorder, generally gets diagnosed as a person reaches one's late teens or early 20s, at a time when the prefrontal portions of the brain are completing their migration, connections, and pruning. The course of schizophrenia can be described by both neurodevelopmental and neurodegenerative changes. Critical gene–environment exposures that may increase the risk for schizophrenia include advanced paternal age, intrauterine adversities such as fetal hypoxia, maternal stress or illness, postnatal brain injuries and illnesses, and severe early life trauma (Perrin, Kleinhaus, Messinger, & Malaspina, 2010). As the normal brain develops after birth, the maximum numbers of synapses are formed by around the age of 6 years, and after that a preprogrammed process of pruning takes place, ultimately making the brain more efficient. In schizophrenia, faulty migration and misalignment of neurons are suggested by early developmental delays in motor, cognitive, and social/

emotional functioning. The brains of children and adolescents with schizophrenia also show enlarged ventricles and decreased gray matter maturation compared to their healthy age-matched peers (Rapoport, Addington, Frangou, & MRC Psych, 2005). This finding suggests that the cortical matter either has not developed as much compared to normal peers or was excessively pruned.

Structural scans of adults with schizophrenia show ventricular enlargement (indicating smaller brains), medial temporal lobe volume reductions (hippocampus), and frontal lobe volume reductions (Ross, Margolis, Reading, Pletnikov, & Coyle, 2006). Dysfunction of the prefrontal cortex is apparent on tasks of working memory and executive functioning.

Psychotic disorders such as schizophrenia are diagnosed by the presence of positive symptoms of hallucinations, delusions, disorganized speech, or disorganized behavior. For over 50 years, the **dopamine hypothesis** of schizophrenia has been a guiding framework in understanding the disease. The hypothesized mechanism for the positive symptoms involves excessive amounts of dopamine in the limbic system. Support for this hypothesis comes from the efficacy of dopamine antagonists in reducing positive symptoms.

Dopamine antagonists do not reduce the negative symptoms (e.g., affective flattening, alogia, and avolition) of schizophrenia. The conventional antipsychotics are especially strong antagonists of one of the dopamine receptors, called the D2 receptor. D2 antagonism in the dopamine pathways that terminate in the prefrontal cortex (involved in executive cognitive functioning) may even worsen negative symptoms. This is because dopamine is an important neurotransmitter in mediating motivation and higher level cognitive functioning. Fortunately, the newer atypical antipsychotics (serotonin-dopamine antagonists) spare dopaminergic functioning in the prefrontal cortex through the relation between serotonin and dopamine. The result is that with atypical antipsychotic treatment, individuals may experience decreases in both the positive and negative symptoms of schizophrenia.

Extrapyramidal Side Effects

EPS can occur as a result of treatment with conventional antipsychotics, and the nurse may be the first healthcare practitioner to identify and treat the symptoms. To understand the potential EPS, it is useful to know that there are four major dopaminergic pathways, named by their origin and terminus, in the brain:

1. The mesocortical pathway goes from the mesencephalon (another name for the midbrain) to the frontal cortex.
2. The mesolimbic pathway travels from the midbrain to the limbic system.
3. The nigrostriatal pathway travels from the substantia nigra in the midbrain to the striatum (the basal ganglia) and is involved in movement.
4. The tuberoinfundibular pathway travels from the hypothalamus to the infundibulum (the stalk) of the anterior pituitary.

We have already discussed the hypothesis that, in schizophrenia, dopamine is elevated in the mesolimbic pathway and deficient in the mesocortical pathway. But what about the other two pathways?

The nigrostriatal dopaminergic pathway is not usually affected by schizophrenia itself; however, when the pathway is blocked by a conventional antipsychotic, movement-related EPS can result. Bradykinesia, tremors, and dystonias are all possible antipsychotic-induced symptoms of Parkinsonism. Akathisia is severe restlessness. Another less common EPS side effect is lactation, which is caused by the antagonism of D2 receptors in the tuberoinfundibular pathway.

It is important for nurses to understand that the EPS are side effects and not changes in the psychotic disorder, and that they can be treated and reversed. The best practice today is to avoid the EPS by using an atypical antipsychotic as a first-line agent. If the conventional agents are used, it may be necessary to add another medication such as an anticholinergic, antihistamine, benzodiazepine, beta blocker, or alpha adrenergic antagonist to reduce the side effects. Abnormal movements should be closely monitored for early intervention and evaluation of outcomes. The Abnormal Involuntary Movement Scale (AIMS; National Institute of Mental Health, 1975) is an excellent tool for that purpose. Treatment compliance is essential to recovery, and nurses are often the first healthcare practitioners to notice and report changes in functioning or condition.

The dopamine hypothesis of schizophrenia cannot explain all of the symptoms, nor can it explain the neurodevelopmental and neurodegenerative aspects of the disorder. Recent theories implicate glutamate, microglia, and myelin. A hypothesis of glutamate hypofunction and impaired glutamate NMDA receptor functioning in the pathophysiology of schizophrenia is supported by the observation that phencyclidine (PCP), an NMDA receptor antagonist, mimics the positive symptoms seen in schizophrenia. Glutamate insufficiency may be especially detrimental to hippocampal functioning and memory consolidation (Tamminga, Stan, & Wagner, 2010). Microglia are part of a neuroinflammatory process in the brain. Prolonged microglia activation may produce proinflammatory cytokines and free radicals, leading to neurodegenerative changes including neuronal death (apoptosis), atrophy, and increased ventricular size (Monji, Kato, Kanba, 2009). A myelin dysfunction hypothesis is supported by volume reductions in white matter and impaired functional connectivity. Impaired cognitive functioning in schizophrenia is probably more detrimental to overall functioning and recovery than the positive symptoms (Fields, 2008).

Dementia

Dementia is the loss of memory and cognitive abilities. The most common cause is Alzheimer's disease.

Dementia is the loss of memory and cognitive abilities. The most common cause of dementia is Alzheimer's disease (AD). In the U.S., approximately 15% of persons over the age of 70 have dementia, 10% due to dementia of the Alzheimer's type (Plassman et al., 2007). Other forms include vascular dementia, frontotemporal dementia, Pick's disease, and Lewy body dementia. Dementia is also common in Parkinson's and Huntington's disease. A score of 25 or below on the Mini-Mental State Evaluation (Folstein, Folstein, & McHugh, 1975), or similar measure, can alert the psychiatric nurse that a patient needs further evaluation for possible dementia.

Alzheimer's Disease

Alzheimer's disease progresses slowly and is often mistaken for normal cognitive changes of aging until later in its course. Although a definitive diagnosis cannot be made without an autopsy, the diagnosis may be given once a person manifests multiple cognitive deficits including memory impairment and cognitive disturbances (e.g., aphasia, apraxia, agnosia, executive deficits). Neuroimaging might reveal enlarged ventricles indicating brain atrophy. Microanatomical changes include accumulation of a protein called beta amyloid in the neurons, and neurofibrillary tangles created by clumps of structural components of the cell called microtubules. Needless to say, neurons that become stuffed with plaques of protein and tangles of microtubules are unable to perform their normal functions and eventually die.

Early on in the progression of the disease, acetylcholinesterase inhibitors can be prescribed to slow the metabolism of acetylcholine, improving its availability for learning and memory. Later on, glutamate antagonists may slow the progressive neurodegenerative processes. But nothing has been found to halt disease progression entirely, and, with or without treatment, it continues to destroy brain function. Fortunately, new research is addressing how we might someday be able to target the beta amyloid gene precursors to prevent amyloid plaques and other cellular changes.

Substance Disorders

The *DSM-IV-TR* (APA, 2000) lists substance-specific diagnostic criteria for 11 classes of substances. The *DSM-IV-TR* does not include the term *addiction*, referring to the loss of control over the use of a substance; rather, it defines substance abuse, dependence, intoxication, and withdrawal patterns. What seems remarkable is that although the substances can have strikingly different acute effects, they share the characteristic of being rewarding to the user, a quality that promotes repeated drug use, and in vulnerable individuals, the loss of control in limiting intake. Over time, behavior can change to compulsive drug seeking, loss of control, and the emergence of negative emotional states that reflect a motivational withdrawal syndrome when access to the drug is prevented. Koob & Volkow (2010) describe drug addiction as a progressively pathological cycle composed of three interacting stages, each with separate brain circuits: binge/intoxication; withdrawal/negative affect; and preoccupation/anticipation (craving). Impulsivity driven by the positive consequences of drug taking dominates at the early stages, and compulsivity, driven by the negative reinforcement of taking away withdrawal symptoms or stress, dominates in the later stages. Successive neuroadaptations are what shift impulsive drug use into compulsive use and eventually a chronic and relapsing condition.

Binge/intoxication stage. Drugs of abuse cause different acute effects. Nicotine activates cholinergic nicotinic receptors. Alcohol and sedatives enhance GABA inhibition. Marijuana and opiates interact with the brain's own cannabinoid and opiate receptors. Amphetamines enhance norepinephrine and dopamine. Hallucinogens enhance serotonin. In the end, through their connections with dopaminergic cells, all drugs of abuse activate the mesolimbic reward system. The dopamine-producing neurons have their cell bodies in the ventral portion of the midbrain, and their axons terminate in a location rich with cell bodies of other neurons, called the nucleus accumbens (NA) located in the basal ganglia. Drugs that rapidly increase brain dopamine are especially rewarding. The reinforcing effects of drugs may also involve other neurotransmitters such as glutamate and brain opioids. The resultant development of drug habits involves the basal ganglia.

Withdrawal/negative affect stage. Koob and Volkow (2010) report that all drugs of abuse are associated with a motivational withdrawal syndrome characterized by negative mood states and sleep disturbances. This is not the same as the physical withdrawal syndrome that differs with each drug. As a consequence of chronic drug use, the brain adapts by down-regulation of dopamine receptors and by decreasing baseline levels of dopamine, having the unfortunate result of decreasing sensitivity to normally rewarding activities like food or sex. Decreased sensitivity to dopamine may result in tolerance as it takes more of the drug to have the same effect. Neural adaptations in other brain circuits occur as well. Chronic drug use appears to activate the amygdala and the HPA axis during withdrawal, resulting in fear, negative mood states, and stress.

Preoccupation/anticipation (craving). In addition, increased sensitivity to drug-related cues (such as seeing the place where drugs were previously purchased or used) and impairment in the executive functioning of the frontal cortex can lead individuals to become less able to inhibit sudden urges and actions related to drug seeking and taking. Enhanced sensitivity to stress, as well as relevant to changes in the HPA axis and cortisol receptors, may increase the tendency to focus on drug-related cues. Glutamate may also contribute to the learning of drug cues (conditioned responses).

Obviously not everyone who uses a drug becomes addicted or dependent. Drug addictions are the result of complex gene-environment interactions. Individual risk factors may include genetic vulnerability, sensitivity to environmental stressors and rewards, drug availability, adolescence, overall impulsivity, and mental illness. The first step towards treating substance disorders is to understand that the complex neuroplastic changes in the brain are long lasting and that recovery takes time and patience. Treatment should include strategies that enhance the salience of natural rewards, strengthen inhibitory control and executive function, decrease drug cues and conditioned responses to them, and improve mood if disrupted (Volkow & Li, 2005).

Neuroimaging

There are many ways to image the brain, but to date none of them provides definitive diagnoses for mental disorders (**Table 5-3**). **Neuroimaging** has played an important role in expanding our knowledge base related to the structure, function, and neurochem-

Table 5-3 Neuroimaging: What it Measures

Structural	Functional	Other
Computed Tomography (CT): Anatomical image	Functional MRI (fMRI): Change in blood flow related to neural activity	Magnetic Resonance Spectroscopy (MRS): Metabolic or chemical concentrations
Magnetic Resonance Imaging (MRI): Anatomical image	Positron Emission Tomography (PET): Cerebral blood flow and cerebral glucose metabolism	Electroencephalogram (EEG): Surface scalp electrical activity
Diffusion Tensor Imaging (DTI): White matter tract orientation	Single-photon Emission Computed Tomography (SPECT): Cerebral blood flow and glucose metabolism	

istry of the CNS. Two categories of brain imaging may be used—structural imaging and functional imaging. **Structural imaging** with **computed tomography (CT)** and **magnetic resonance imaging (MRI)** gathers information regarding the physical constitution of the brain at any one point in time. These techniques are helpful in detecting structural changes that may result from injury or disease of the brain. The results are not dependent on thought, motor activity, or mood. **Functional imaging**, not surprisingly, tells us about the functioning of the brain. The two most common techniques for examining function are **positron emission tomography (PET)** and functional magnetic resonance imaging (fMRI). These methods detect changes in regional blood flow and metabolism during thought, motor activity, or mood changes.

Clinical indications for imaging in clients with psychiatric disorders are listed in **Table 5-4**. Although the neuroimaging of the brain provides important diagnostic clues that may be helpful in formulating a diagnosis, many of the findings are nonspecific, showing only ventricular enlargements or generalized atrophy, and the techniques are expensive to perform. These procedures are not routinely used in clinical practice; however, with the rapid advances in technology, they have been extremely helpful in expanding our understanding of the neurobiology of psychiatric disorders. Psychiatric neuroimaging continues to evolve in methodologies, techniques for analysis, and clinical utilization.

Structural Imaging

In CT, thin slices or tomographic images of the brain are obtained by X-ray, reconstructed, and entered into a computer. With this technology, a variety of views of the brain can be produced, revealing the gross organization of the gray and white matter and the position of the ventricles. CT is superior to MRI for assessing calcification, acute hemorrhage, and bone injury and is also less expensive and more readily available than MRI. CT studies in persons with schizophrenia have shown enlargement of ventricles and structural alterations in prefrontal and medial temporal areas.

MRI uses radio waves and magnets to obtain images. Since both white and gray matter in the brain have different densities of hydrogen ions, they respond differently to perturbations of a strong magnetic field. As a person rests quietly, the MRI scanner passes an electromagnetic wave (radio signal) through the head while it is positioned between the poles of a large magnet. When the magnetic fields are shifted, the movement of the hydrogen ions is detected and a detailed image of the whole brain, both gray and white matter, is obtained. MRI is superior to CT and generally is the preferred modality when assessing for subcortical lesions, demyelination, and lesions near bone. **Figure 5-11** shows how follow-up MRIs have been used to detect schizophrenia-related brain changes over time.

The advantages of MRI over CT for structural imaging are that it does not require x-irradiation, the image is more detailed, and the computer can construct brain slices in any plane desired. The disadvantages are that it is difficult for individuals to lie still for the approximately 20 minutes that it takes to do an MRI, and some individuals feel frightened by the close proximity of the scanner and the loud noises that it emits. Fortunately, many sites now offer open MRIs that are not as confining. With MRIs, measurement of reduced hippocampal volumes has been reported in multiple studies of depression, bipolar disorder, PTSD, and dementia.

Table 5-4 Clinical Indications for Structural Imaging

Acute change in mental status (affect, behavior, or personality) plus one of the following:

- Age greater than 50
- Abnormal neurological examination
- History of significant head trauma
- New onset psychosis
- New onset delirium or dementia of an unknown cause

Source: Dougherty & Rauch (2008). Guidelines for the use of MRI of the brain in psychiatric populations.

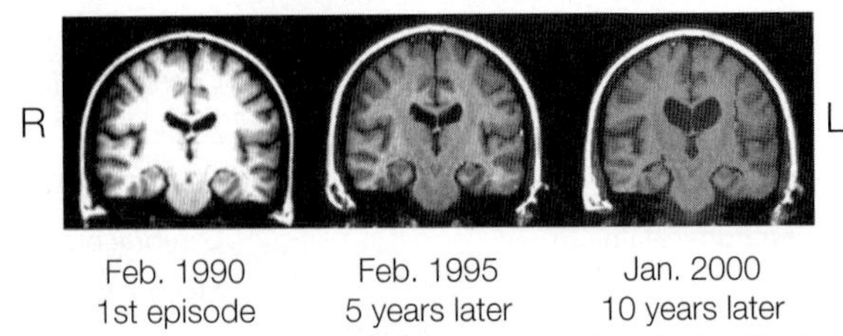

Figure 5-11 An MRI shows progressive atrophy and increased ventricular size in the same female with schizophrenia. She was 34 years-old at the time of the 10 year follow-up.

Magnetic resonance spectroscopy (MRS) relies on the magnetic principals of MRI and is used to detect chemical and metabolic information in certain brain areas. The data are depicted as a spectrum. For example, investigators can detect a chemical that corresponds to neuronal health called NAA. Reductions in NAA can indicate areas of neuronal degeneration. With MRS imaging, comparisons can be made of the concentrations of substances between healthy brains and brains with neuropsychiatric abnormalities. Recent discoveries implicate the use of MRS as a sensitive diagnostic tool that assists with earlier diagnosis of dementia through the measurement of decreases in NAA and increases in another chemical, myoinositol (Mountford, Stanwell, Lin, Ramadan, & Ross, 2010).

Diffusion tensor imaging (DTI), an MRI-based technology that enables visualization and characterization of white matter pathways, has now become one of the most popular neuroimaging methods in brain research. DTI is based upon the observation that the motion or diffusion of water molecules in the brain is faster along white matter fibers than it is perpendicular to them. The difference between the motions (parallel vs. perpendicular), referred to as "anisotropy," is the basis of DTI. Abnormalities in white matter pathways have been identified in all of the psychiatric disorders that are characterized by cognitive deficits, including schizophrenia, Alzheimer's dementia, bipolar disorder, OCD, autism, and attention-deficit/hyperactivity disorder (ADHD). These findings support the hypothesis of functional disconnectivity between brain areas; however, the white matter changes do not identify specific patterns associated with specific psychiatric disorders, so they are not diagnostic (Assaf & Pasternak, 2008; Fields, 2008).

Critical Thinking Question www

What will you teach a client regarding the potential limitations from an MRI related to a diagnosis of mental illness?

Functional Imaging

Functional imaging gives us a sense of what is going on in the thinking, living brain. With functional imaging, we are able to see which areas of the brain are active during certain types of mental tasks and how brain activation and metabolism changes as a result of brain lesions or mental illness. As with other neuroimaging methods, the information is not diagnostic because of the considerable overlap in abnormalities of the limbic structures in mental disorders. Functional imaging has been used extensively in psychiatric research to help further our understanding of functional deficits and pharmacological therapies in clinically defined patient groups. When the brain is active it utilizes more oxygen and glucose (recall that these are needed to make cellular ATP energy) and more blood is sent to the active regions. Both the functional magnetic resonance imaging (fMRI) and the positron emission tomography (PET) scan can detect changes in regional blood flow and metabolism within the brain.

For a PET scan, an individual lies in the scanner, and a radioactive solution is injected intravenously. The emitted radiation is used to recreate a 3D image of the brain. As the individual performs a task such as thinking of a series of numbers, blood flow and metabolism increase in the active areas of the brain. The PET detects the area of the brain that is most active during the task. The disadvantages of PET are the radiation exposure and the relatively slow scanning time that limits the number of areas of the brain that can be studied in any one person at any one time. Although less precise than PET, the single photon emission computed tomography (SPECT) utilizes a radioisotope to measure cerebral blood flow. It can be used to identify areas of hypoperfusion in the brain, such as might be seen in areas of neuronal degeneration in dementia. PET and SPECT can also be used to measure receptor or enzyme binding, although at this point, the technology is not used routinely in clinical practice.

The fMRI has the advantages of coupling structural scanning with images of brain activation, not requiring radiation exposure, and being completely noninvasive. Indirect measures of blood flow and metabolism are made by measuring the ratio of oxyhemoglobin (oxygenated form of hemoglobin) to deoxyhemoglobin (hemoglobin that has donated its oxygen). This technique is called blood oxygen level–dependent contrast. FMRI is the most widely used neuroimaging technique for studying cognitive dysfunction. Examples of how fMRIs have helped us understand more about cognitive dysfunction comes from studies of individuals with schizophrenia and depression. During working memory tasks, individuals with schizophrenia sometimes show hypoactivation of the prefrontal cortex and other times show hyperactivation. The hypoactivation illuminates the difficulties that they have with staying on task, and the hyperactivation illuminates the reduced efficiency of their prefrontal cortex (Weinberger et al., 2001). In depression, hyperactivation of certain prefrontal networks at rest is congruent with rumination and excessive self-focus (Sheline, Price, Yan, & Mintun, 2010). Finally, innovative fMRI approaches include testing the effects of drug administration while persons are engaged in complex cognitive tasks (Pearlson & Calhoun, 2007). These types of findings would not have been possible using structural neuroimaging methods.

Electroencephalography

In electroencephalography (EEG) the pattern of the brain activity on the surface of the brain is visible, but the origin of the activity from within the brain's regions is not.

Electroencephalography (EEG) is the measurement of electrical currents at the scalp that reflect events within the brain. Groups of brain cells that fire synchronously generate electrical potentials that can be measured on the surface of the brain, however, the origin of activity from specific brain regions cannot. Magnetoencephalography (MEG) is a technique that measures magnetic currents at the scalp to detect neural activity deep within the brain. It is noninvasive but is limited to use in research.

Conclusions

Neurobiologic considerations in psychiatric care include clinical expressions of psychiatric illness, genetic contributions, and environmental risk factors. As we gain further knowledge about gene–environment interactions and the reversible epigenetic changes in gene expression, we will have greater ability to identify targets for prevention and intervention. Given what we already know about the deleterious effects of early life stress on the HPA regulation, the brain and metabolic consequences of chronic stress, and the neuroadaptations that occur with drug abuse, psychiatric nurses are positioned to make advances in primary prevention, screening, and treatment.

National reports and initiatives, such as the President's Freedom Commission (2003) and the Institute of Medicine's (2005) report, *Improving the Quality of Health Care for Mental and Substance-Use Conditions*, and the Department of Health and Human Services' Substance Abuse and Mental Health Services Administration's (SAMHSA, 2005) Action Steps for Transforming Mental Health Care, advocate transforming the mental health system to be more evidence-based and consumer driven. This will require nurses to keep up with the changes in our knowledge base regarding the causes and treatments of mental illness and to help translate these findings to patients/clients and their families so that they can make informed decisions regarding their care. Helping clients, families, and the community at large understand the neurobiological considerations will help decrease the stigma and improve the care of individuals with mental illness.

Summary

This chapter has provided a basic knowledge of the brain's structures and their functions, the neurotransmitters and their pathways, and the mechanisms for the development of mental illnesses and disorders and their treatment. There was focused discussion of the structure and function of the nervous system, cellular mechanisms of communication, the role of neurotransmitters in mental illness, neurotransmission and neuroplasticity, the regulation of emotion and the limbic system, stress response (acute and chronic), and genetic factors. Conditions specifically discussed included mood disorders, anxiety, schizophrenia, and dementias. The role of various tests were presented: neuroimaging (CT, MRI, MRS, DTI), functional imaging (fMRI, PET), and electroencephalography (EEGs). The relationship between neurobiology and psychopharmacological treatment was highlighted.

Annotated References

American Psychiatric Association. (2000). *The diagnostic and statistical manual of mental disorders* (4th ed., text revision). Washington, DC: Author.

DSM-IV-TR diagnostic categories describe clusters of symptoms that tend to co-occur, but are not based on neurophysiological etiologies.

Assaf, Y., & Pasternak, O. (2008). Diffusion tensor imaging (DTI)-based white matter mapping in brain research: A review. *Journal of Molecular Neuroscience, 34*, 51–61.

DTI is one of the most popular MRI techniques used in brain research. This review provides a highly readable explanation, complete with color photographs.

Bear, M., Connors, B., & Paradiso, M. (2007). *Neuroscience: Exploring the brain* (3rd ed.). Baltimore, MD: Lippincott, Williams, & Wilkins.
This text was developed for undergraduate students of neuroscience. It is highly readable and highly recommended.

Bienvenu, O. J., Davydow, D. S., & Kendler, K. S. (2011). Psychiatric 'diseases' versus behavioral disorders and degree of genetic influence. *Psychological Medicine*, 41(1), 33–40.
The authors report heritability estimates for psychiatric and substance use disorders.

Caraci, F., Copani, A., Nicoletti, F., & Drago, F. (2010). Depression and Alzheimer's disease: Neurobiological links and common pharmacological targets. *European Journal of Pharmacology, 626*, 64–71.
The authors review the interesting neurobiological similarities between depression and Alzheimer's disease in terms of HPA axis hyperactivation and chronic inflammation.

Charney, D. (2003). Neuroanatomical circuits modulating fear and anxiety disorders. *Acta Psychiatra Scandanavica, 108*(Suppl. 417), 38–50.
Charney reviews the multiple neurotransmitter and structural abnormalities found in the various anxiety disorders and stresses the need to define the circuits related to the specific anxiety disorders as well as factors related to resilience to stress.

Clay, H. B., Sillivan, S., & Konradi, C. (2011). Mitochondrial dysfunction and pathology in bipolar disorder and schizophrenia. *International Journal of Developmental Neuroscience, 29*(3), 311–324.
This is a complicated, but well-organized and thorough review of the potential mechanisms of mitochondria in bipolar disorder and schizophrenia.

Diamond, M., Scheibel, A., Murphy, G., & Harvey, T. (1985). On the brain of a scientist: Albert Einstein. *Experimental Neurology, 88*(1), 198–204.
This article describes the analysis of Einstein's brain and the possible explanations given for his exemplary intellect.

Fields, R. D. (2008). White matter in learning, cognition and psychiatric disorders. *Trends in Neurosciences, 31*, 361–370.
Fields presents the research that suggests that the impaired cognitive ability, disorganized thinking, and hallucinations accompanying psychiatric illness are due to abnormalities in the myelin and functional connectivity between brain areas.

Folstein, M., Folstein, S., & McHugh, P. (1975). "Mini-mental state": A practical method for grading the cognitive state of patients for the clinician. *Journal of Psychiatric Research, 12*, 189.
The authors describe the Mini-Mental State Evaluation and its scoring.

Gutman, D., & Nemeroff, C. (2003). Persistent central nervous system effects of an adverse early environment: Clinical and preclinical studies. *Physiology & Behavior, 79*, 471–478.
This article reviews animal and human studies showing persistent corticotrophin releasing hormone and adrenocorticotropic hormone, and cortisol elevations in response to early childhood physical or sexual abuse.

Hashioka, S., McGeer, P. L., Monji, A., & Kanba, S. (2009). Anti-inflammatory effects of antidepressants: Possibilities for preventives against Alzheimer's disease. *Central Nervous System Agents in Medicinal Chemistry, 9*(1), 12–19.
Based on their review, the authors conclude that the anti-inflammatory effects of antidepressants may help prevent the development of neurodegenerative changes that link late-life depression to dementia.

Hasler, G., Drevets, W., Gould, T., Gottesman, I., & Manji, H. (2006). Toward constructing an endophenotype strategy for bipolar disorders. *Biological Psychiatry, 60*, 93–105.
These NIMH researchers identify genetically relevant aspects of the heterogeneous pathophysiology of the disease.

Heim, C., Newport, D., J., Mletzko, T., Miller, A. H., & Nemeroff, C. B. (2008). The link between childhood trauma and depression: Insights from HPA axis studies in humans. *Psychoneuroendocrinology, 3*, 693–710.

This award-winning paper reviews clinical studies that show the link between childhood trauma and the tendency to develop depression in response to stress.

Institute of Medicine. Committee on *Crossing the Quality Chasm*: Adaptation to Mental Health and Addictive Disorders, Board on Health Care Services. (2005). *Improving the quality of health care for mental and substance-use conditions*. Washington, DC: National Academies Press.
This is a must read for all healthcare professionals. The title is self-explanatory.

Kendler, K. (2001). Twin studies of psychiatric illness. An update. *Archives of General Psychiatry, 58*, 1005–1014.
Kendler reviews heritability estimates for schizophrenia, alcoholism, and major depression from concordance rates in large twin studies.

Kendler, K., Gatz, M., Gardner, C., & Pedersen, N. (2006). A Swedish national twin study of lifetime major depression. *American Journal of Psychiatry, 163*(1), 109–114.
The lifetime prevalence of major depression was assessed in over 15,000 twin pairs.

Koob, G. F., & Volkow, N. D. (2010). Neurocircuitry of addiction. *Neuropsychopharmacology, 35*, 217–238.
This comprehensive, yet easy-to-read, article introduces a theory that describes neuorobiologic circuits that mediate each of three stages of addiction. Dr. Volkow has been the director of the National Institute of Drug Abuse since 2003.

Kyrou, I., Chrousos, G. P., & Tsigos, C. (2006). Stress, visceral obesity, and metabolic complications. *Annals of the New York Academy of Sciences, 1083*, 77–110.
This is a very thorough review of the health effects of chronic stress and the risk for metabolic syndrome.

Lee, A., Ogle, W., & Sapolsky, R. (2002). Stress and depression: Possible links to neuron death in the hippocampus. *Bipolar Disorders, 4*, 117–128.
This article presents a thorough review of the evidence for stress related damage to the hippocampus.

Lichtenstein, P., Carlstrom, E., Rastam, M., Gillberg, C., & Anckarsater, H. (2010). The genetics of autism spectrum disorders and related neuropsychiatric disorders in childhood. *American Journal of Psychiatry, 167*, 1357–1363.
The authors provide an overview of the possible genetic causes of various childhood psychiatric disorders with a focus on the autistic spectrum disorders.

Martin, E. I., Ressler, K. J., Binder, E., & Nemeroff, C. B. (2010). The neurobiology of anxiety disorders: Brain imaging, genetics, and psychoneuroendocrinology. *Clinics in Laboratory Medicine, 30*, 865–891.
This is a very thorough and easy-to-read summary of the genetic, anatomic, neurotransmitter, and neuroendocrine abnormalities associated with the anxiety disorders.

Mason, J., Wang, S., Yehuda, R., Sherry, R., Charney, D., & Soputhwick, S. (2001). Psychogenic lowering of urinary cortisol levels linked to increased emotional numbing and a shame-depressive syndrome in combat-related posttraumatic stress disorder. *Psychosomatic Medicine, 63*(3), 387–401.
The purpose of the study was to search for the intrapsychic correlates of individual differences in cortisol levels in male Vietnam combat veterans with posttraumatic stress disorder.

McEwen, B. (2001). Plasticity of the hippocampus: Adaptation to chronic stress and allostatic load. *Annals of the New York Academy of Sciences, 933*, 265–277.
McEwen reviews research that shows that repeated and long-term elevations in neurochemical, autonomic, and HPA reactivity, as seen in some individuals with recurrent depression or PTSD, might lead to hippocampal atrophy and even permanent damage.

Meyer, J., Ginovart, N., Boovariwala, A., Sagrati, S., Hussey, D., Garcia, A., . . . Houle, S. (2006). Elevated monoamine oxidase A levels in the brain: An explanation for the monoamine imbalance of major depression. *Archives of General Psychiatry, 63*(11), 1209–1216.
This article presents recent evidence from a small comparison study that MAO-A levels may be elevated in individuals with depression.

Milner, B. (2005). The medial temporal-lobe amnesic syndrome. *Psychiatric Clinics of North America, 28*, 599–611.

This is a fascinating review of Dr. Brenda Milner's 40+ year observation of HM, a man who had bilateral medial temporal lobectomies.

Monji, A., Kato, T., & Kanba, S. (2009). Cytokines and schizophrenia: Microglia hypothesis of schizophrenia. *Psychiatry and Clinical Neurosciences, 63*, 257–265.
This review presents a relatively new theory of schizophrenia that focuses on abnormalities in white matter that may account for inflammation and neuronal degeneration.

Mountford, C. E., Stanwell, P., Lin, A., Ramadan, S., & Ross, B. (2010). Neurospectroscopy: The past, present and future. *Chemical Reviews, 110*, 3060–3087.
This article provides a review of the chemical neurospectroscopy research using MRS. Decreases in NAA and increases in myoinositol are sensitive indicators of AD that can be used for early detection and treatment monitoring.

National Institute of Mental Health. (1975). *Development of a dyskinetic movement scale* (Publication No. 4). Rockville, MD: National Institute of Mental Health, Psychopharmacology Research Branch.
This scale became the Abnormal Involuntary Movement Scale and is useful for monitoring and documenting change in movements when patients are taking antipsychotics.

Pearlson, G. D., & Calhoun, V. (2007). Structural and functional magnetic resonance imaging in psychiatric disorders. *Canadian Journal of Psychiatry, 52*, 158–163.
The authors provide a selective review of advances in the use of MRI methods to explore the neurobiology of psychiatric disorders.

Perrin, M., Kleinhaus, K., Messinger, J., & Malaspina, D. (2010). Critical periods and the developmental origins of disease: An epigenetic perspective of schizophrenia. *Annals of the New York Academy of Sciences, 1204*, E8–E13.
This interesting and easy-to-read review examines the contribution of the environment to reversible epigenetic changes in gene expression at critical life periods in the development of schizophrenia.

Plassman, B. L., Langa, K. M., Fisher, G. G., Heeringa, S. G., Weir, D. R., & Ofstedal, M. B. (2007). Prevalence of dementia in the United States: The aging, demographics, and memory study. *Neuro-epidemiology, 29*, 125–132.
The researchers estimated the prevalence of Alzheimer's disease and other dementias in the United States by using a nationally representative sample of 856 individuals over the age of 70.

Post, R., Leverich, G., Altshuler, L., Frye, M., Suppes, T., Keck, P., . . . Walden, J. (2003). An overview of recent findings of the Stanley Foundation Bipolar Network (Part I). *Bipolar Disorders, 5*, 310–319.
The authors describe current understandings of bipolar symptoms and course of illness, including the effects of early environmental adversity on the brain.

Presidents Freedom Commission on Mental Health. (2003). Achieving the promise: Transforming mental health in America. Final report. Rockville, MD: U.S. Dept. of Health and Human Services.
This well-known report challenged health professionals to understand the neurobiological causes of mental illness.

Rajkowska, G., & Miguel-Hidalgo, J. J. (2007). Gliogenesis and glial pathology in depression. *CNS & Neurological disorders—Drug targets, 6*, 219–233.
This review describes the different forms of neuroglia and how stress and excess glucocorticoids may modify glial cell number and affect the physiology of depression.

Rapoport, J., Addington, A., Frangou, S., & MRC Psych. (2005). The neurodevelopmental model of schizophrenia: Update 2005. *Molecular Psychiatry, 10*, 434–449.
These NIMH researchers present a clear update on neurodevelopmental changes in schizophrenia and the gene candidates that are under investigation.

Ross, C., Margolis, R., Reading, S., Pletnikov, M., & Coyle, J. (2006). Neurobiology of schizophrenia. *Neuron, 52*, 139–153.
These researchers review the brain development and neuroplasticity in schizophrenia and examine various susceptibility gene candidates.

Sapolsky, R. (2003). Stress and plasticity in the limbic system. *Neurochemical Research, 28*(11), 1735–1742.
Sapolsky describes how stress affects the limbic system, in particular, the hippocampus.

Sapolsky, R. (2005). Sick of poverty. *Scientific American, 293*(6), 92–99.
This is a very readable summary of the effects of socioeconomic inequalities on physical and mental health.

Schafe, G., Doyere, V., & LeDoux, J. (2005). Tracking the fear engram: The lateral amygdala is an essential locus of fear memory storage. *The Journal of Neuroscience, 25*(43), 10010–10015.
LeDoux and his coworkers are world experts on the amygdala and its functions in mental health and illness. Memories of past threats are stored in the amygdala and influence its function.

Selye, H. (1956). *The stress of life*. New York, NY: McGraw-Hill.
This is a classic book on stress.

Sheline, Y. I., Price, J. L., Yan, Z., & Mintun, M. A. (2010). Resting-state functional MRI in depression unmasks increased connectivity between networks via the dorsal nexus. *Proceeds of the National Academy of Sciences, U.S.A., 107*(24), 11020–11025.
Using fMRIs, the researchers were able to detect resting-state connectivity between brain networks that are thought to be involved in the symptoms of depression, including rumination, excessive self-focus, and emotional dysregulation.

Snider, L., & Swedo, S. (2003). Childhood-onset obsessive-compulsive disorder and tic disorders: Case report and literature review. *Journal of Child and Adolescent Psychopharmacology, 13*(Suppl.1), S81–S88.
The authors review the literature showing a relationship between abrupt onset of tics and OCD and exposure to the *Streptococcus* bacteria. The syndrome is called pediatric autoimmune neuropsychiatric disorder associated with *Streptococcus* or PANDAS.

Sorrells, S. F., Caso, J. R., Munhoz, C. D., & Sapolsky, R. M. (2009). The stressed CNS: When glucocorticoids aggravate inflammation. *Neuron, 64*, 33–39.
This minireview explains how cortisol can have CNS anti-inflammatory properties during acute stress, but increases inflammation during chronic stress.

Stahl, S. (2008). *Essential psychopharmacology. Neuroscientific basis and practical applications* (3rd ed.). New York, NY: Cambridge University Press.
Stahl assists the reader in understanding basic but potentially difficult concepts underlying the pharmacologic treatment of psychiatric disorders. It is easy to read and filled with wonderful cartoon diagrams.

Substance Abuse and Mental Health Services Administration, U.S. Department of Health and Human Services (SAMHSA). (2005). *Transforming mental health care in America. The federal action agenda: First steps.* DHHS

Publication No. SMA-05-4060. Rockville, MD: DHHS.
This essential document outlines specific steps to take in improving mental health care.

Tamminga, C. A., Stan, A. D., & Wagner, A. D. (2010). The hippocampal formation in schizophrenia. *American Journal of Psychiatry, 167*, 1178–1193.
The authors describe a hippocampal glutamate insufficiency model that accounts for the resiliency of positive symptoms in schizophrenia.

Thomas, J. L., Wilk, J. E., Riviere, L. A., McGurk, D., Castro, C. A., & Hoge, C. W. (2010). Prevalence of mental health problems and functional impairment among active component and National Guard soldiers 3 and 12 months following combat in Iraq. *Archives of General Psychiatry, 67*, 614–623.
Persistent psychological and behavioral problems affect up to one third of returning war zone soldiers. This study provides data to guide postdeployment care.

U.S. Department of Health and Human Services. (1999). *Mental health: A report of the surgeon general—executive summary.* Rockville, MD: U.S. Department of Health and Human Services, Substance Abuse and Mental Health Services Administration, Center for Mental Health Services, National Institutes of Health, National Institute of Mental Health.
This important report can be read online at: http://mentalhealth.samhsa.gov/cmhs/surgeongeneral/surgeongeneralrpt.asp

Volkow, N., & Li, T-K. (2005). The neuroscience of addiction. *Nature Neuroscience, 8*(11), 1429–1430.
Volkow and Li present a concise summary of the neurobiologic mechanisms of addiction.

Weinberger, D., Egan, M., Bertolino, A., Callicott, J., Mattay, V., Lipska, B., . . . Goldberg, T. (2001). Prefrontal neurons and the genetics of schizophrenia. *Biological Psychiatry, 50*, 825–844.
This is a wonderful summary by NIMH researchers of cognitive dysfunction in schizophrenia and its possible genetic risk factors.

World Health Organization. (2008). The global burden of disease: 2004 update. Geneva, Switzerland: WHO Press.
This is the final summary of the 2004 WHO Global Burden of Disease study.

Internet Resources

For a full suite of assignments and additional learning activities, use the access code located in the front of your book to visit this exclusive website: http://go.jblearning.com/mentalhealth. If you do not have an access code, you can obtain one at the site.

Learning Objectives

After reading this chapter, you will be able to:

- Name the five major families of psychotropic medications.
- List indications for each family of psychotropic medications.
- Discuss strategies for reducing side effects.
- Describe the management of common side effects of each major family of psychotropic medications.
- Discuss interventions that have been shown to increase client compliance.

Key Terms

Acetylcholine

Agonist

Akathisia

Akinesia

Antagonist

Antianxiety medication

Anticholinergic side effects

Antidepressant

Antidyskinetic

Antipsychotic medications

Benzodiazepine

Compliance

Dopamine

Dystonia

Extrapyramidal

First generation antipsychotics

Hypertensive crisis

Hypnotic

Lag period

Lithium toxicity

Medication adherence

Minor tranquilizers

Monoamine oxidase inhibitor (MAOI)

Mood stabilizer

Negative psychotic symptoms

Neuroleptic malignant syndrome

Neurotransmitter

Norepinephrine

Positive psychotic symptoms

Psychopharmacologist

Psychopharmacology

Psychotropic medications

Second-generation antipsychotics

Sedative

Selective serotonin reuptake inhibitors (SSRIs)

Serotonin

Serotonin syndrome

Side effect

Stimulants

Tardive dyskinesia

Therapeutic effect

Tricyclic antidepressant

Chapter 6

Psychopharmacology

Beth Harris and Patricia G. O'Brien

http://go.jblearning.com/mentalhealth 

For a full suite of assignments and additional learning activities, use the access code located in the front of your book to visit this exclusive website: http://go.jblearning.com/mentalhealth. If you do not have an access code, you can obtain one at the site.

Introduction

Psychopharmacology is the study of medications that affect the *psyche* (the Greek word that refers to a person's spirit or soul). In other words, psychopharmacology is the study of the medications used in psychiatry. These medications often are referred to as **psychotropic medications**, which means medications that "move the spirit" or "move the soul."

There are five major families of medications in psychiatry and an assortment of other smaller families. The five major families are closely related medications that are similar in chemical structure and similar in their physiologic effect on the body. All of the psychotropic medications alter some aspect of brain chemistry. Psychiatric symptoms and illnesses are caused by abnormalities in brain functioning, and the psychotropic medications restore the normal chemical balance of the brain, thus allowing the client to feel healthy and behave normally. For example, psychotic illnesses are thought to be related to overactivity of the chemical neurotransmitters **dopamine** and **serotonin**. Antipsychotic medications reduce the overactivity of one or both of these chemical **neurotransmitters**. Similarly, depression is thought to be related to an underactivity of the neurotransmitters **norepinephrine** and serotonin. Antidepressant medications specifically target these two neurotransmitters, increasing their activity and, by doing so, alleviating the depression. Similarly, each family of psychotropic medications works to restore a normal chemical balance in the brain.

Psychotropic medications do not cure mental illnesses any more than insulin cures diabetes. Like insulin for diabetes, the psychotropic medications treat the symptoms of the underlying illness, allowing the client to feel healthy and function normally.

Critical Thinking Question

If psychotropic medications do not cure mental illness, what are the implications for length of treatment?

The Nurse's Role

Nurses play a pivotal role in psychopharmacology. Most psychiatric nurses administer and monitor psychotropic medications. In advanced practice, psychiatric nurse practitioners prescribe these medications.

The nurse's administration and monitoring role begins with the initial assessment of the client. Because one of the best ways of predicting a medication's effectiveness is to know if it previously worked well for the client or for a close family member (sister, brother, parent, child, grandparent, aunt, uncle, first cousin), the nurse asks about personal and family history of responsiveness to medications. The nurse also collects data about the client's potential vulnerability to **side effects**. For example, it would be inadvisable to give medication with hypotension as a common side effect to a client with a baseline blood pressure of 90/60 mmHg. Finally, the nurse asks about the person's feelings and attitudes about medication and seeks the client's opinion about what medication would be best.

As the client begins to take the medication, the nurse carefully administers each dose, gradually teaching the client about every aspect of the medication: the name of the medication; the exact dose, route, and schedule; and restrictions on certain foods and other medications. Whether the client takes 1 or 10 different psychotropic medications, the client should know the exact purpose of each. As the medication begins to enter the patient's bloodstream, the nurse monitors for the desired effects of the medication. The nurse identifies the target symptoms for the medication, and then regularly and consistently evaluates the presence and strength of each of those symptoms. With this information, the client and prescribing clinician are able to measure the medication's effectiveness in an objective way. Clients don't always recognize when a medication is effective. Therefore, it is important for the nurse to identify improvements in symptoms and behaviors and to verbally point these out to the client. Specifically connecting symptom resolution to the medication will reinforce the value of the medication and increase the likelihood of adherence.

Critical Thinking Question

When identifying target symptoms, why is it important to develop them in collaboration with the client?

The nurse's role in side-effect management is an important one. This is especially true because the patient's response to the medication and its side effects during the first 2 weeks of treatment has proven to be an excellent predictor of their ultimate responsiveness (Kane & Correll, 2010). Psychotropic medications, like all medications, have side effects. For some people they are mild, and for others they are extremely uncomfortable and sometimes dangerous. The nurse teaches the client about the side effects that are most common with the medications being prescribed, so the client can share the task of monitoring for their presence. The client must be informed about side effects that are likely and that may be uncomfortable for the first few weeks or months. The client must be told that it is impossible to predict exactly what side effects will occur or how severe they will be. The nurse reassures the client that they will watch for side effects together and do whatever is necessary to minimize them.

It is extremely important that clients know that most side effects are temporary. Although the side effects begin right away, the desired or **therapeutic effect** may take weeks or months. The **lag period** between the onset of side effects and therapeutic effects may demoralize a patient who has not been informed about it.

Education for Clients and Families

Teaching clients about their medication is one of the most important functions of the psychiatric nurse. Medication teaching is begun as early as medications are discussed (usually at the initial assessment) and is continued throughout the course of treatment. Eventually, if capable, the client is taught to self-administer medication. If it is clear that the medication will be needed long term, even if there will be periodic attempts to reduce the dose, it is important to talk to the client about the course of treatment, because most people find it difficult to accept the long-term use of medications.

The nurse teaches the client and family the name and purpose of the medication, including target symptoms; the dose and exact schedule for taking each dose; the usual course and length of treatment; the importance of taking the medication as prescribed; alternative reminder devices to help remember each dose; the most common side effects and their management; long-term risks; addiction potential; food or medication restrictions; and the importance of informing the prescribing clinician of any problems with the medication.

If long-term risks are associated with taking the medication, clients should know about them so they can help monitor for their occurrence. Of all the psychotropic medications, the only ones that are potentially addictive are the antianxiety medications. Clients must be taught about the addictive potential of the **benzodiazepines** and about the absence of addictive potential for all the other psychotropic medications.

Most psychotropic medications take several weeks to begin working and must be taken consistently as prescribed, dose after dose and day after day, to be maximally effective. For example, many people feel little or no therapeutic effect from antidepressants for as long as 2 months. During this lag period, it is easy for clients to feel discouraged. Most people expect medicines to work right away, similar to the way acetaminophen (Tylenol) helps a headache. They think that the medication either works within a half hour or so, or it does not work at all. The nurse needs to teach clients that taking psychotropic medications is not like taking acetaminophen for a headache. Problems and discomforts that arise during the course of pharmacotherapy need to be discussed by the client and the prescribing clinician, so the medication can be adjusted until the target symptoms are controlled with a minimum of discomfort from side effects. For many people, this is a lengthy process during which a great deal of support is essential.

Because it is so integral to nursing practice, various aspects of client and family education are integrated throughout the chapter.

Most psychotropic medications take several weeks to begin working and must be taken consistently as prescribed, dose after dose and day after day, to be maximally effective.

The nurse's role:
Assess the client's thoughts and attitude about taking medications.
Administer medications safely.
Monitor desired (therapeutic) effects.
Monitor for side effects.
Teach client and family about medication management.

Critical Thinking Question

Can you think of interventions to help a person accept the need for lifelong medications?

Clinical Example

A client with depression started taking an antidepressant. Because she was the mother of young children, she became anxious about her ability to care for her children because of the side effects she was experiencing: sleepiness, tremors, headache, stomach distress, and blurred vision. When taught that these side effects are temporary, usually subsiding within a few weeks, she expressed optimism about continuing to take the antidepressant.

Psychotropic Medications

Major families of psychotropic medications:
- Antipsychotics
- Antidepressants
- Mood stabilizers
- Antianxiety medications
- Stimulants
- Others

Most of the psychotropic medications fall into one of the following five categories: antipsychotic medications, antidepressant medications, mood stabilizers, antianxiety medications, and stimulants. Each of these five families will now be described in detail.

Clinical Example 

A young man with bipolar disorder was stabilized on valproate (Depakote) following his first manic episode. When attending a medication group on the unit, he learned that bipolar disorder is a lifelong condition and must be treated continuously with medication to prevent relapse into active symptoms. He expressed disbelief and anger that he would need to take medication for the rest of his life. Other members of the group who had a longer experience with bipolar disorder shared their own experiences of long periods of wellness stabilized on medication followed by relapse upon stopping their medication. After several such stories, the nurse encouraged the patient to think of his taking valproate as similar to a person with diabetes continuing to take insulin for a lifetime.

Table 6-1 Antipsychotics: Names and Usual Range of Daily Doses for Adults in Acute Therapy

Generic Name	Brand Name	mg/Day
Aripiprazole*	Abilify*	10–30
Asenapine*	Saphris*	10–20
Chlorpromazine	Thorazine	300–1,000
Clozapine*	Clozaril*	200–600
Fluphenazine	Prolixin	6–20
Haloperidol	Haldol	6–20
Loxapine	Loxitane	30–100
Molindone	Moban	30–100
Olanzapine*	Zyprexa*	5–20
Paliperidone*	Invega*	3–12
Perphenazine	Trilafon	30–100
Pimozide	Orap	3–10
Quetiapine*	Seroquel*	150–800
Risperidone*	Risperdal*	4–10
Thioridazine	Mellaril	300–800
Thiothixene	Navane	15–50
Trifluoperazine	Stelazine	15–50
Ziprasidone*	Geodon*	80–160

* Second-generation or atypical antipsychotic.

Antipsychotic Medications

Common indications for antipsychotic medications:
- Schizophrenia
- Schizoaffective disorder
- Bipolar disorder
- Major depression with psychotic symptoms
- Tourette's disorder

Antipsychotic medications (shown in **Table 6-1**) are used to treat psychotic symptoms. Psychotic symptoms are labeled as positive or negative. Positive psychotic symptoms reflect an exaggeration or distortion of normal functioning. Negative symptoms refers to a restriction or loss of normal functioning and expression. Target symptoms of antipsychotic medications are listed next.

Positive Symptoms
- Hallucinations
- Delusions
- Paranoia
- Ideas of reference
- Racing thoughts
- Unclear thoughts
- Agitation
- Uncontrollable hostility
- Inappropriate dress
- Severe impulsiveness

Negative Symptoms
- Slowed or blocked thinking
- Flat affect
- Lack of motivation
- Lack of interest
- Alogia or poverty of speech
- Neglect of personal hygiene
- Social withdrawal or isolation

Neuroleptic malignant syndrome is a rapidly developing syndrome of profound muscle stiffness, fever, and tremor. Medication should be stopped immediately.

Whatever the cause of the psychosis, the symptoms themselves can be effectively treated with antipsychotics. The **negative psychotic symptoms** are often less responsive than the **positive psychotic symptoms.**

There are two groups of antipsychotic medications. The older group, first introduced in the mid-1950s, comprises the **first-generation antipsychotics.** The newer group, the **second-generation antipsychotics** (identified in Table 6-1 by an asterisk), first became available in 1989 when clozapine (Clozaril) was approved by the Food and Drug Administration (FDA). The first-generation antipsychotics, referred to as typical or conventional antipsychotics, work by creating a postsynaptic dopamine blockade in the brain in the subgroup of dopamine receptors called the D_2 receptors. Second generation, or atypical, antipsychotics have a lesser effect on the D_2 receptors and focus on blocking the serotonin postsynaptic receptors and other subtypes of dopamine receptors (e.g., D_1 and D_5). Because of these actions, the typical antipsychotics are effective against positive psychotic symptoms, while the atypical generation are effective against both positive and negative symptoms and are the first line of treatment for schizophrenia.

The atypical antipsychotics have a more favorable side effect profile than the typical antipsychotics. **Anticholinergic side effects**, notably dry mouth, constipation, urinary retention, and blurred vision are more evident in the typical antipsychotics than in the atypical antipsychotics. For many years, the atypical antipsychotics were believed to induce fewer **extrapyramidal** (muscular) side effects, though this has been called into question in recent independent trials (Shirzadi & Ghaemi, 2006)

Agranulocytosis, a failure of the bone marrow to manufacture neutrophils, the most common of the white blood cells, is a rare, but serious, side effect primarily associated with the atypical antipsychotic, clozapine (Clozaril). Agranulocytosis puts clients at risk for overwhelming, life-threatening infections. In order to start clozapine, the client's white blood count (WBC) must be at least 3500 mm^3, and the absolute neutrophil count (ANC) must be at least 2000 mm^3. The WBC and ANC are monitored weekly for 6 months, every 2 weeks for an additional 6 months, and every month thereafter. These blood levels are monitored weekly for 1 month following discontinuation of clozapine.

Agranulocytosis rarely develops in persons who take clozapine, because of the mandatory WBC and ANC testing. When it does occur, agranulocytosis is detected before it becomes full blown, thereby preventing danger, discomfort, and possible death. Clients are instructed to report symptoms of sore throat, fever, or malaise immediately. When agranulocytosis does begin to develop, the clozapine must be stopped and cannot be used again due to the risk of agranulocytosis immediately recurring. In such cases, one of the other atypical antipsychotics is usually substituted.

Other problematic consequences of the atypical antipsychotics are the weight gain, metabolic changes, and diabetes mellitus that sometimes occur as side effects—these are most pronounced with olanzapine (Xyprexa) and clozapine. When these occur, they add greatly to the morbidity associated with the psychotic illness alone. **Table 6-2** lists side effects associated with antipsychotic medications.

Neuroleptic malignant syndrome (NMS) is a rapidly developing syndrome of profound muscle

Table 6-2 **Antipsychotic Side Effects**

Extrapyramidal Symptoms (EPS)
Dystonia (sustained muscle contraction)
Akinesia (slowing or lack of movement)
Tremor
Akathisia (motor restlessness)
Tardive dyskinesia (abnormal, involuntary movements—more common with first-generation antipsychotics)
Finger rubbing or jerking
Twitching or overactivity of the tongue
Changes in posture
Exaggerated blinking
Puckering or chewing movements of the mouth
Ticlike movements of the face
Neuroleptic malignant syndrome (NMS) (Life threatening)
High white blood cell count (WBC), high creatine phosphokinase (CPK)
Muscular rigidity
Increased or labile blood pressure, pulse, and respiration
Fever
Diaphoresis
Drooling
Dysphagia
Sexual Side Effects
Delay in orgasm
Reduced sex drive
Amenorrhea
Anticholinergic Side Effects
Constipation
Blurred vision
Urinary retention or hesitancy
Nasal congestion
Dry mouth
Other Side Effects
Orthostatic hypotension
Temperature dysregulation
Increased appetite with weight gain
Abnormal glucose metabolism (atypical)
Sensitivity to sunburn
Sedation
Agranulocytosis (1% risk with clozapine, very low risk with others)
Increased salivation (aripiprazole, clozapine)
Hypertension
Prolonged QT interval (thioridazine, paliperidone, ziprasidone)
Nausea and vomiting (minimal risk except with clozapine)
Seizures (typical, clozapine)
Urinary incontinence (clozapine only)

Evidence-Based Practice

The Schizophrenia Patient Outcomes Research Team (PORT) Treatment Recommendations (Kreyenbuhl, Buchanan, Dickerson, & Dixon, 2010)

Recommendations for the treatment of schizophrenia based on existing scientific evidence were developed by the Schizophrenia Patient Outcomes Research Team (PORT). Based on exhaustive reviews of the treatment outcomes literature, the treatment recommendations focus on treatments for which there is substantial evidence of efficacy. Their recommendations include the following:

1. In people with treatment-responsive, multiepisode schizophrenia who are experiencing an acute exacerbation of their illness, antipsychotic medications, other than clozapine, should be used as the first-line treatment to reduce positive psychotic symptoms.
2. Antipsychotics, other than clozapine and olanzapine, are recommended as first-line treatment for persons with schizophrenia experiencing their first acute positive symptom episode.
3. People with first-episode schizophrenia exhibit greater treatment responsiveness and a higher sensitivity to adverse effects compared with people with multiepisode schizophrenia. Therefore, antipsychotic treatment should be started with doses lower than those recommended for people with multiepisode schizophrenia.
4. People with treatment-responsive, multiepisode schizophrenia who experience acute and sustained symptom relief with an antipsychotic medication should be offered continued antipsychotic treatment in order to maintain symptom relief and to reduce the risk of relapse or worsening of positive symptoms.
5. Long-acting injectable antipsychotic medication should be offered as an alternative to oral antipsychotic medication for the maintenance treatment of schizophrenia when the long-acting injectable is preferred to oral preparations.
6. Targeted, intermittent antipsychotic maintenance strategies should not be used routinely in lieu of continuous maintenance treatment regimens due to the increased risk of symptom worsening and relapse.
7. Clozapine should be offered to people with schizophrenia who continue to experience persistent and clinically significant positive symptoms after two adequate trials of other antipsychotic agents.
8. In a person treated with clozapine who has failed to demonstrate an adequate response, a clozapine level should be obtained to ascertain whether the clozapine level is above 350 ng/ml.
9. A trial of clozapine should be offered to people with schizophrenia who present with persistent symptoms of hostility and/or display persistent violent behaviors.
10. A trial of clozapine should be considered for people with schizophrenia who exhibit marked and persistent suicidal thoughts or behaviors.
11. In people treated with first-generation antipsychotics, prophylactic use of antiparkinsonian agents to reduce the incidence of extrapyramidal side effects should be determined on a case-by-case basis. The use of prophylactic antiparkinsonian agents in people treated with second-generation antipsychotics is not warranted.
12. An oral or intramuscular antipsychotic medication, alone or in combination with a rapid-acting benzodiazepine, should be used in the pharmacological treatment of acute agitation in people with schizophrenia.

The antipsychotics are not addictive. The major risks include agranulocytosis with clozapine; neuroleptic malignant syndrome, which occurs infrequently with both first- generation and second-generation antipsychotics, but carries a mortality rate of 10%; and **tardive dyskinesia** (TD), potentially irreversible involuntary movements. Each of these risks can be minimized with early detection. Agranulocytosis is prevented by the required regular WBC and ANC counts, neuroleptic malignant syndrome can be detected by rapid clustering of its symptoms, and TD can be diagnosed at an early stage by regular screening using the Abnormal Involuntary Movement Scale (AIMS; **Figure 6-1**; Guy, 1976).

Abnormal Involuntary Movement Scale (AIMS)

Patient's Name (Please print)________________ Patient's ID information ________________

Examiner's Name________________

Current Medications and Total mg/day

Medication #1________ Total mg/day________ Medication #2 ________ Total mg/day________

Instructions: Complete the examination procedure before entering these ratings.

	None, normal	Minimal (may be extreme normal)	Mild	Moderate	Severe
Facial and Oral Movements					
1. Muscles of facial expression, e.g., movements of forehead, eyebrows, periorbital area, cheeks; include frowning, blinking, smiling, grimacing	☐ 0	☐ 1	☐ 2	☐ 3	☐ 4
2. Lips and perioral area, e.g., puckering, pouting, smacking	☐ 0	☐ 1	☐ 2	☐ 3	☐ 4
3. Jaw, e.g., biting, clenching, chewing, mouth opening, lateral movement	☐ 0	☐ 1	☐ 2	☐ 3	☐ 4
4. Tongue Rate only increases in movement both in and out of mouth, NOT inability to sustain movement	☐ 0	☐ 1	☐ 2	☐ 3	☐ 4
Extremity Movements					
5. Upper (arms, wrists, hands, fingers) Include choreic movements (i.e., rapid, objectively purposeless, irregular, spontaneous); athetoid movements (i.e., slow, irregular, complex, serpentine). DO NOT include tremor (i.e., repetitive, regular, rhythmic).	☐ 0	☐ 1	☐ 2	☐ 3	☐ 4
6. Lower (legs, knees, ankles, toes) e.g., lateral knee movement, foot tapping, heel dropping, foot squirming, inversion and eversion of foot	☐ 0	☐ 1	☐ 2	☐ 3	☐ 4
Trunk Movements					
7. Neck, shoulders, hips e.g., rocking, twisting, squirming, pelvic gyrations	☐ 0	☐ 1	☐ 2	☐ 3	☐ 4

SCORING:

- Score the highest amplitude or frequency in a movement on the 0–4 scale, not the average.
- Score activated movements the same way; do not lower those numbers as was proposed at one time.
- A POSITIVE AIMS EXAMINATION IS A SCORE OF 2 IN TWO OR MORE MOVEMENTS or a SCORE OF 3 OR 4 IN A SINGLE MOVEMENT.
- Do not sum the scores: e.g., a patient who has scores 1 in four movements DOES NOT have a positive AIMS score of 4.

Overall Severity					
8. Severity of abnormal movements	☐ 0	☐ 1	☐ 2	☐ 3	☐ 4
9. Incapacitation due to abnormal movements	☐ 0	☐ 1	☐ 2	☐ 3	☐ 4

	No awarness	Aware, no distress	Aware, mild distress	Aware, moderate distress	Aware, severe distress
10. Patient's awareness of abnormal movements (rate only patient's report)	☐ 0	☐ 1	☐ 2	☐ 3	☐ 4

Dental Status	Yes	No
11. Current problems with teeth and/or dentures?	☐	☐
12. Does patient usually wear dentures?	☐	☐

Comments:________________

Examiner's Signature________________ Next Exam Date ________________

Figure 6-1 The Abnormal Involuntary Movement Scale (AIMS).

stiffness, fever, and tremor. Within the space of a few hours, a person can become completely immobile, unable to swallow, to speak, or to move. Neuroleptic malignant syndrome varies in its presentation, and it may have a potentially fatal course or a relatively benign, self-limited course. The most important intervention for this side effect is to immediately stop administering the antipsychotic medication that is causing the problem. To do that, neuroleptic malignant syndrome must be recognized by its characteristic symptoms and laboratory findings (Table 6-2).

Once this syndrome is detected, the client is given supportive care (hydration, exercise, control of fever) for the few days it takes for the syndrome to resolve. Several **antidyskinetic** medications can be helpful in resolving the stiffness, including benztropine (Cogentin) and amantadine (Symmetrel). Other medications that have been effective include bromocriptine (Parlodel) and dantrolene (Dantrium) (**Table 6-3**).

Many clients with a lifelong psychiatric illness (e.g., schizophrenia, schizoaffective disorder, bipolar disorder) need to take antipsychotic medications indefinitely to maintain optimum symptom relief and functioning. The prescriber may make periodic attempts to reduce the dose, but for many people the course of treatment is a lifelong one.

Common indications for antidepressant medications:
- Attention-deficit/hyperactivity disorder
- Bipolar disorder
- Bulimia or anorexia
- Dysthymic disorder
- Major depression
- Obsessive-compulsive disorder
- Panic disorder
- Schizoaffective disorder
- Social phobia

Clinical Example 

A young man with schizoaffective disorder says he stopped taking his medication after discharge because he does not "want to become a junkie." He and his nurse went online to the National Alliance on Mental Illness during their clinic appointment to find information that would reassure the client that his antipsychotic medication is not addictive.

Table 6-3 **Antidyskinetic Medications: Names and Usual Range of Daily Doses for Adults**

Generic Name	Brand Name	mg/Day
Amantadine	Symmetrel	100–400
Benztropine	Cogentin	1–6
Biperiden	Akineton	2–8
Diphenhydramine	Benadryl	25–300
Orphenadrine	Norflex	50–400
Procyclidine	Kemadrin	7.5–20
Trihexyphenidyl	Artane	2–15

Antidepressant Medications

Antidepressant medications (**Table 6-4**) are widely prescribed both in psychiatry and in other specialties where they are used to treat several pain syndromes, ulcers, and insomnia. **Antidepressants** fall into four major classifications, based on either their chemical structure or effect on the brain. **Tricyclic antidepressants** (TCAs) work by blocking the reuptake of norepinephrine and serotonin at the nerve synapse. **Selective serotonin reuptake inhibitors (SSRIs)** selectively block the reuptake of serotonin back into the nerve endings, making more serotonin available in the neuronal synapse. **Monoamine oxidase inhibitors** (MAOIs) act by blocking monoamine oxidase needed to break down norepinephrine, serotonin, and dopamine, thereby increasing the amount of these neurotransmitters. The fourth category of "other antidepressants" includes tetracyclics, serotonin norepinephrine reuptake inhibitors (SNRIs), a serotonin (5-HT_2) **antagonist** and reuptake inhibitor, and a combination noradrenaline transporter/dopamine transporter inhibitor (NAT/DAT).

In psychiatry, antidepressants are the treatment of choice for the common psychiatric disorder, major depression. In addition, they are an excellent treatment for several of the anxiety disorders. The target symptoms of the antidepressants when treating depression are

- Guilt
- Hopelessness and helplessness
- Increased or decreased appetite
- Insomnia or hypersomnia
- Loss of energy or sex drive or pleasure
- Preoccupation with death or suicide
- Psychomotor retardation or agitation
- Sad or anxious mood
- Trouble concentrating

Clinical Example 

A retired lawyer whose bipolar disorder was stabilized with lithium for 30 years decided on retirement that the reduction of stress after giving up his law practice would eliminate the need for lithium. When he and his prescriber gradually decreased the dose, his symptoms that had been in control for many years began to reappear in the form of sleeplessness, pressured speech, and irritability. Rather than continue the dose reduction, the client decided to return indefinitely to the dose of lithium that had kept him well for so long.

Table 6-4 Antidepressants: Names and Usual Range of Daily Doses for Adults

Generic Name	Brand Name	mg/Day	Classification
Amitriptyline	Elavil	75–200	Tricyclic
Amoxapine	Asendin	100–400	Tetracyclic
Bupropion	Wellbutrin	300–400	NAT/DAT inhibitor
Citalopram	Celexa	20–60	SSRI
Clomipramine	Anafranil	75–250	Tricyclic
Desipramine	Norpramin	75–200	Tricyclic
Desvenlafaxine	Pristiq	50–400	SNRI
Doxepin	Sinequan	75–200	Tricyclic
Duloxetine	Cymbalta	40–60	SNRI
Escitalopram	Lexapro	10–20	SSRI
Fluoxetine	Prozac	20–40	SSRI
Fluvoxamine	Luvox	100–300	SSRI
Imipramine	Tofranil	75–200	Tricyclic
Isocarboxazid	Marplan	10–60	MAOI
Maprotiline	Ludiomil	150–200	Tetracyclic
Mirtazapine	Remeron	15–30	Tetracyclic
Nefazodone	Serzone	200–400	SNRI
Nortriptyline	Pamelor	25–100	Tricyclic
Paroxetine	Paxil	20–50	SSRI
Phenelzine	Nardil	15–90	MAOI
Protriptyline	Vivactil	30–40	Tricyclic
Selegiline (transdermal patch)	Emsam	6–12/24 hr	MAOI
Sertraline	Zoloft	50–200	SSRI
Tranylcypromine	Parnate	30–40	MAOI
Trazodone	Desyrel	200–400	5-HT2 antagonist and reuptake inhibitor
Trimipramine	Surmontil	75–200	Tricyclic
Venlafaxine	Effexor	75–300	SNRI

Like the antipsychotics, antidepressants have a lag period during which the side effects appear (**Table 6-5**) but the therapeutic or desired effect is not yet achieved. This can be a difficult and dangerous time for clients who are already depressed and have probably tried everything in their power to recover before resorting to antidepressant medications. After starting antidepressants, they often find themselves continuing to suffer from the symptoms of depression and also suffering from the antidepressant side effects.

Constant support and protection may be needed during this period to help clients survive until the beneficial effects of the medications begin.

A great deal of attention has been paid to a documented increase in suicidal ideation that occurs in children, adolescents, and adults taking antidepressant medications. All antidepressants carry a warning of suicide risk for children, adolescents, and young adults. Although there is a slight increase in deaths from suicide in children and adolescents during the early weeks of antidepressant treatment, most studies show that in adults, there is an increase in suicidal ideation, but no increase in the number of deaths from suicide (Simon, Savarino, Operskalski, & Wanget al, 2006). There is some evidence that one of the SSRIs, sertraline, is less likely to produce suicidal behavior than other antidepressants (Geddes, Barbui, & Cipriani, 2010; Stone et al., 2009). The increase in suicidal ideation in the early weeks of treatment, whether due to the lag period issues noted earlier or to a medication effect, must remain a focus of treatment until a full antidepressant response is seen.

The increase in suicidal ideation in the early weeks of treatment must remain a focus of treatment until a full antidepressant response is seen.

Table 6-5 Antidepressant Side Effects and Management Strategies

Side Effects	Management Strategies
All Antidepressants	
Suicidal ideation and increased depression	Can happen to any client; children, adolescents, young adults. Observe clients of all ages for worsening of symptoms, unusual behavior, or sudden increase in energy. Educate client, family, significant others to report suicidal ideation.
Drowsiness or fatigue	Request prescription for low-sedating medication; take medication at bedtime; avoid driving and operating dangerous equipment if sedated. Sedation may lessen over time.
Dry mouth	Drink sips of water during day; chew sugarless gum; practice good oral hygiene.
Sexual problems with desire or performance	Client should discuss with prescribing clinician; a change in dosing or medication may be indicated.
Anxiety or agitation	May decrease over time; client should discuss with prescribing clinician; a change in dosing or medication may be indicated.
Discontinuation syndrome	Medication needs to be gradually discontinued to avoid unpleasant symptoms, including anxiety, depression, hypomania, cardiac arrhythmias, headache, and nausea.
Tricyclic Antidepressants	
Orthostatic hypotension, lightheadedness, dizziness	Check blood pressure (BP) lying down and standing; check with prescribing clinician if there is a significant drop in BP when standing; instruct client to change positions gradually, drink adequate fluids to avoid dehydration; observe falls precautions.
Constipation	Instruct client to drink fluids, eat high fiber foods, and exercise.
Urinary hesitancy or retention	Instruct client to report difficulty urinating. Men with enlarged prostate are at risk. Consider need to monitor intake and output.
Blurred vision	Advise client that this is usually temporary. Client should not drive until vision clears.
Palpitations or tachycardia	Cardiogram may be indicated prior to initiating tricyclic especially in older clients.
Weight gain	Educate client about risk, and explore calorie reduction; encourage walking and other physical exercise.
Photosensitivity	Wear sunscreen and protective clothing when in the sun.
SSRIs and SNRIs	
Weight loss initially, then weight gain	Monitor calorie intake and weight.
Insomnia	Take medication in the morning, not at bedtime; educate client on sleep hygiene and nonpharmacologic interventions, including relaxation techniques.
Sexual dysfunction	See "Sexual problems with desire or performance" under "All Antidepressants."
Headache	Aspirin or NSAIDs as indicated. Inform prescribing clinician if headache continues.
MAOIs	
Orthostatic hypotension, light-headedness, dizziness	See "Orthostatic hypotension, lightheadedness, dizziness" under "Tricyclic Antidepressants."
Weight gain	See "Weight gain" under "Tricyclic Antidepressants."
Muscle twitching	May lessen after a couple of weeks. Instruct client to discuss with prescribing clinician.
Increased sweating	May lessen after a couple of weeks. Instruct client to discuss with prescribing clinician. Wear clothing made with natural fibers.
Other Antidepressants	
Priapism (trazodone)	Seek emergency treatment if erection lasts longer than 1 hour; notify prescribing clinician immediately of any prolonged erection. Priapism is rare, but may require surgical intervention and can lead to impotence.
Seizures (bupropion)	Assess client for seizure history.
Hepatic failure (nefazodone)	Can cause life-threatening hepatic failure; liver function should be assessed prior to treatment; monitor for jaundice of skin or sclera, loss of appetite, nausea, vomiting, malaise. Educate client to report these signs and symptoms to primary care provider immediately.

Most of the time, the proper dose of antidepressant is determined by the client's clinical response. The prescriber starts with a low dose that is gradually raised until the client feels better, the side effects become too strong, or the dose has reached beyond the therapeutic range (see Table 6-4). For a few of the antidepressants, blood levels can be drawn and used to guide dosage if the clinical response is equivocal or disappointing. The antidepressant that is best guided by blood levels is nortriptyline (Pamelor), which works optimally only when blood levels are between 50 and 150 mg/ml.

The most widely used antidepressants are the selective serotonin reuptake inhibitors (SSRIs) (e.g., fluoxetine [Prozac] and paroxetine [Paxil]). Along with the "other" category of antidepressants, the SSRIs are considered an advance over the older tricyclic family (e.g. imipramine [Tofranil] and amitriptyline [Elavil]) because their side effects are considerably milder and more tolerable and because they are less lethal in overdose. Several of the more sedating antidepressants are often prescribed as sleeping pills, most commonly trazodone (Desyrel) and amitriptyline (Elavil).

There is one subgroup, the monoamine oxidase inhibitor (MAOI) antidepressants (e.g., phenelzine [Nardil], tranylcypromine [Parnate], isocarboxazid [Marplan], and selegiline [Emsam]), that requires some very important food and medication restrictions. This group is not widely used, but, in some instances, it may be the only effective alternative.

Table 6-6 lists the restrictions for people taking an MAOI. The restrictions are vitally important to follow, because eating foods that are high in the amino acid tyramine or taking the restricted medications can cause **hypertensive crisis**, a life-threatening condition. In addition to elevated blood pressure, symptoms of hypertensive crisis include severe headache, palpitations, chest pain, nausea, and vomiting. Symptoms may progress to heart attack, stroke, coma, and death. Immediate medical intervention is indicated.

Another life-threatening complication that can develop in clients who are on antidepressant medi-

Table 6-6 Food and Medication Restrictions With Monoamine Oxidase Inhibitor Antidepressants

Foods To Be Avoided	Medications To Be Avoided
Aged cheese	Codeine
Beer and nonalcoholic beer	General anesthetics
Brewer's yeast	Local or spinal anesthetics containing epinephrine or levonordefrin
Chocolate (more than 1 oz)	Meperidine (Demerol)
Cured, smoked, or dried meats or fish, such as sausage, pepperoni, salami, and corned beef	Morphine
Fava beans	Oxycodone (OxyContin)
Game meats	Hydrocodone
Hydrolyzed protein extracts	Nasal decongestants
Liver	Other non–monoamine oxidase inhibitor antidepressants
Monosodium glutamate	Buspirone (Buspar)
Red wine	Over-the-counter cough, cold, allergy, and sinus medications that contain sympathomimetics, including ephedrine, epinephrine, norepinephrine, oxymetazoline, phenylephrine, pseudoephedrine, or phenylpropanolamine
Pickled foods	Stimulants and amphetamines, methylphenidate (Ritalin), acetaminophen with dextroamphetamine (Adderall), cocaine, and the herbs ginseng and ephedra)
Snow pea pods	
Sauerkraut	
Tofu	
Use with caution:	
Avocado	
Caffeine	
Nuts	
Processed and pasteurized cheese	
Sour cream	
Yogurt	

cations is **serotonin syndrome.** The syndrome is the result of elevated levels of serotonin caused by high doses or combinations of medications that increase serotonin, including antidepressants, lithium, certain pain medications, antimigraine medications, an herbal antidepressant known as St. John's wort, and some drugs of abuse, such as ecstasy and LSD (lysergic acid diethylamide). Symptoms occur within hours and may include confusion, agitation, diarrhea, heavy sweating unrelated to activity, fever, muscle spasms (myoclonus), overreactive reflexes (hyperreflexia), shivering, and tachycardia. Treatment consists of discontinuing the medication and controlling the symptoms. Serotonin antagonists or benzodiazepines may be prescribed to reduce serotonin levels and counter the agitation and muscle rigidity.

Someone with a strong family history of depression, who has had repeated episodes, or who has suffered a profoundly severe or damaging episode of depression may opt for lifetime maintenance with antidepressants. If not, the antidepressant is generally continued for a minimum of 6 to 12 months after recovery (which may, itself, take 6 to 12 months) and then slowly and gradually tapered until it is discontinued.

Some people have one episode of depression and do not become ill again. But about one half of people who have a first episode of major depression go on to have a series of depressions and a lifelong vulnerability to relapse in times of stress. This group of people, once they suffer a second episode, are said to have recurrent major depression. For them, there are strong arguments in favor of their continuing lifelong maintenance treatment with an antidepressant to prevent future relapses. Because antidepressants are not addictive and because there are no long-term risks associated with their use, lifetime maintenance treatment is an excellent alternative for many people.

Clinical Example 

A woman, whose depression responded well to phenelzine (Nardil), took an over-the-counter cold medicine containing both an antihistamine and pseudoephedrine. She was aware that antihistamines were safe to take with her MAOI antidepressant, but did not think to check whether or not pseudoephedrine was contraindicated. Within a half hour, her blood pressure rose precipitously, causing a severe headache that brought her to her local emergency department where her hypertensive crisis was diagnosed and successfully treated.

Mood Stabilizers

Mood stabilizers (**Table 6-7**) are used primarily to treat bipolar disorder (also called manic-depressive illness).

Contrary to intuition, the mood stabilizers both elevate depressed mood and suppress elated mood. It is unusual for a medication to have opposite effects on different people or opposite effects on the same person at different phases of illness, but that is, in fact, what mood stabilizers do. When a person with bipolar disorder is hypomanic or manic, the mood stabilizer brings the mood down to normal. During depression, the mood stabilizer elevates the mood. As a prophylactic medication, a mood stabilizer prevents both mania and depression, although the effect is often less robust in preventing depression. Bipolar disorder is almost always a lifelong condition, so people who take mood stabilizers ordinarily take them for a lifetime. Symptoms of mania targeted by the mood stabilizers include the following:

- Increased social or work activity
- Increased talkativeness
- Rapid or racing thoughts
- Grandiosity
- Decreased need for sleep
- Distractibility
- Involvement in self-destructive activities such as overspending, reckless driving, bad business deals, or hypersexuality

Symptoms of depression targeted by mood stabilizers include the following:

- Undereating or overeating
- Insomnia or oversleeping
- Agitation or general slowing down
- Loss of interest in usual activities
- Lack of energy or fatigue

Table 6-7 Mood Stabilizers: Names and Usual Range of Daily Doses for Adults

Generic Name	Trade Name	mg/Day
Carbamazepine	Tegretol	600–1,000
Gabapentin	Neurontin	900–1,800
Lamotrigine	Lamictal	250–500
Lithium carbonate	Eskalith	300–1,500
Oxcarbazepine	Trileptal	600–2,400
Topiramate	Topamax	100–400
Valproic acid	Depakote	750–5,000

- Feelings of worthlessness or guilt
- Inability to concentrate
- Recurrent thoughts of death or suicide

Mood stabilizers are a relatively recent addition to the psychopharmacologic arsenal. They were not available in the United States until 1970, when lithium was approved by the Food and Drug Administration. Lithium was the first mood stabilizer, and for a number of years it was the only one. Over the past 3 decades, other mood stabilizers have been gradually added. Lithium is used almost exclusively as a mood stabilizer, but all the other mood stabilizers are anticonvulsants that were originally used for treating seizures and were only later discovered to be effective in stabilizing mood. All except lithium are still used for treating other conditions.

The mood stabilizers are unusual among psychotropic medications in that for some of them, their dosages are determined by the blood level of the drug. For clients who take the anticonvulsant carbamazepine (Tegretol), blood levels must be drawn every few months throughout the entire course of treatment. Clients treated with lithium have serum levels evaluated every 3 to 4 days during initial therapy and every 1 or 2 months thereafter, or more frequently if the dosage needs to be adjusted based on symptoms or side effects. Lithium blood testing should be drawn 12 hours after the last dose of lithium.

Therapeutic lithium levels during acute manic episodes range from 1 to 1.5 mEq/L and lower, 0.6 to 1.2 mEq/L, for maintenance treatment. Fine hand tremor, mild nausea, polyuria and mild thirst may occur during initial therapy for the acute manic phase. These side effects frequently subside with continued treatment, but may persist throughout treatment. Lithium has a narrow therapeutic window with toxic levels starting at 1.5 mEq/L. Older adults or persons sensitive to lithium may develop toxicity at even lower levels. Early indications of **lithium toxicity** may include nausea, vomiting, severe diarrhea, and poor coordination. When lithium levels exceed 2 mEq/L, symptoms may include ataxia, tinnitus, blurred vision, giddiness, and a large output of dilute urine. If the medication is not discontinued and levels continue to rise, nystagmus, seizures, coma, and death may ensue. Clients must understand the importance of regular blood tests and be knowledgeable about the signs and symptoms of toxicity. At the first signs of toxicity, the client should not take lithium and should seek immediate medical attention.

Blood levels of lithium are sensitive to sodium and fluid balance and are dependent on adequate renal functioning. To maintain therapeutic levels, clients should be instructed to maintain adequate salt intake, drink 10 to 12 eight ounce glasses of fluid a day, and replace water lost to perspiration, diarrhea, vomiting, or heavy exercise. Lithium should generally not be given to patients with significant renal or cardiovascular disease, severe debilitation or dehydration, or sodium depletion, since the risk of lithium toxicity is very high in such patients. Certain medications, including, diuretics, angiotensin converting enzyme (ACE) inhibitors, and nonsteroidal anti-inflammatory drugs (NSAID) may also increase the risk of lithium toxicity.

Renal, thyroid, and cardiac functioning should be assessed prior to the initiation of lithium therapy and at intervals throughout the duration of therapy. Serum electrolytes, urinalysis, and fluid intake and output are also monitored.

Side effects associated with anticonvulsant medications include drowsiness, vision disturbances, blood dyscrasias, and severe skin rashes. Clients should be educated about the side effects and advised to report double or blurred vision, bruising, rash, or signs of infection, such as fever and sore throat, to the physician immediately. Because these medications can cause hepatotoxicity, clients should be advised to also report any signs of liver damage, such as dark urine or yellowing of the skin or sclera. All anticonvulsants carry a warning from the Federal Drug Administration (FDA) regarding the risk of suicidal thoughts among persons taking anticonvulsant medications. A recent study found that out of 297,620 new episodes of anticonvulsant therapy, there were 26 suicides, 801 suicide attempts, and 41 violent deaths identified (Patorno, Bohn, Wahl, Avorn, Patrick, Liu, & Schneeweiss, 2010). The study included clients being treated for a variety of illnesses and did not focus on persons being treated for psychiatric disorders. The reason for the increased suicidal ideation is not understood, but may be related to undesirable behavioral symptoms, including depressed mood, hyperactivity, and aggression, sometimes experienced by persons taking anticonvulsants. The greatest risk for suicide appeared to be within the first 14 days of starting treatment. Clients need to be cautioned about this risk and advised to report suicidal thoughts to their physicians immediately. Families and clients need to be informed of emergency services in their communities.

None of the mood stabilizers are potentially addictive. Like the other medications discussed previously, mood stabilizers have a lag period of a week or

Common indications for mood stabilizers:
Bipolar disorder
Cyclothymic disorder
Major depression

Lithium blood testing should be drawn 12 hours after the last dose of lithium.

Early indications of lithium toxicity may include nausea, vomiting, severe diarrhea, and poor coordination. When lithium levels exceed 2 mEq/L, symptoms may include ataxia, tinnitus, blurred vision, giddiness, and a large output of dilute urine.

To maintain therapeutic levels, clients should be instructed to maintain adequate salt intake, drink 10 to12 eight ounce glasses of fluid a day, and replace water lost to perspiration, diarrhea, vomiting, or heavy exercise.

Table 6-8 Mood Stabilizer Side Effects

Generic Name	Brand Name	Common Side Effects
Lithium	Eskalith and others	Fine hand tremor Thirst, polydipsia Increased urination Headache Mild nausea Weight gain Worsening of acne or psoriasis Bradycardia or tachycardia Metallic taste in mouth Hypothyroidism Memory loss
Carbamazepine	Tegretol and others	Nausea, vomiting Sedation Dizziness, lightheadedness Rash (can be severe) Blurred vision Dry mouth Urinary retention Temporary double vision Sore tongue Bone marrow suppression
Valproic acid	Depakote, Depakene	Nausea Mild stomach cramps Sedation Weight gain Rash Prolonged bleeding time Elevated liver function tests (hepatotoxicity)
Gabapentin	Neurontin	Fatigue; drowsiness Dizziness Ataxia Blurred vision Nystagmus Tremor Nervousness
Lamotrigine	Lamictal	Rash (can be severe) Dizziness, ataxia Sleepiness Headache Double vision Blurred vision Nausea, vomiting
Oxcarbazepine	Trileptal	Dizziness Headache Nausea, vomiting Ataxia Dyspepsia Double vision Decreased effectiveness of oral contraceptives
Topiramate	Topamax	Numbness Tingling Drowsiness, fatigue Nausea Confusion Dyspepsia

two before they become therapeutically effective. Side effects (**Table 6-8**) can be uncomfortable during the first few weeks while the dose is being adjusted and the body is getting accustomed to the medication.

Antianxiety Medications

Antianxiety medications, also called **minor tranquilizers**, **sedatives**, or **hypnotics**, are the oldest psychotropic medications (**Table 6-9**).

The earliest members of this family, the barbiturates (e.g., secobarbital, phenobarbital) and the nonbarbiturate, nonbenzodiazepine members (e.g., chloral hydrate, meprobamate), have fallen into relative disuse in psychiatry because of their high addiction potential and the danger of overdose from doses only slightly higher than therapeutic doses. The antianxiety medications in widest use today belong to the subgroup known as the benzodiazepines.

The benzodiazepines are used widely both inside and outside of psychiatry. When used to treat anxiety, the target symptoms for these drugs include the following:

- Restlessness or feeling keyed up, overwhelmed, or on edge
- Difficulty concentrating or mind going blank
- Dizziness
- Insomnia
- Irritability
- Being easily fatigued
- Lump in the throat
- Muscle tension
- Nausea or upset stomach
- Palpitations
- Shortness of breath
- Sweating
- Tremors
- Weakness or tingling in the arms or legs

There is a great deal of misunderstanding about the potential for addiction from the benzodiazepines. These medications clearly are capable of producing an addiction with the characteristics of craving, tolerance, and withdrawal. Tolerance refers to the need for increased doses of a medication to achieve the same effect that was previously achieved with lower doses and is a sign of physical dependence. However, for most people who use them for the treatment of anxiety disorders, addiction is not a severe problem, even when benzodiazepines are taken for long-term prophylaxis. Although tolerance soon develops to the sedative properties of these medications, it is unusual to develop tolerance to the antianxiety properties.

Table 6-9 Antianxiety Medications: Names and Usual Range of Daily Doses for Adults

Generic Name	Brand Name	mg/Day
Commonly Used Benzodiazepines		
Alprazolam	Xanax	0.25–5
Chlordiazepoxide	Librium	5–100
Clonazepam	Klonopin	0.5–5
Clorazepate	Tranxene	7.5–60
Diazepam	Valium	2–40
Estazolam	ProSom	0.5–2
Flurazepam	Dalmane	15–30
Lorazepam	Ativan	1–4
Oxazepam	Serax	10–60
Quazepam	Doral	7.5–15
Temazepam	Restoril	15–30
Triazolam	Halcion	0.25–0.5
Other Sedatives That Are Not Benzodiazepines		
Eszopiclone	Lunesta	2–3
Zaleplon	Sonata	5–10
Zolpidem	Ambien	5–20

As a result, the client continues to get good anxiety relief with no loss of effectiveness at exactly the same dose for prolonged periods. If the decision is made to stop the medication, it must be slowly and gradually tapered to prevent severe withdrawal symptoms including grand mal seizures and, potentially, death. Clearly, a physiological addiction occurs with long-term use. However, as long as the client takes the benzodiazepine regularly, as prescribed, and undergoes a careful detoxification procedure when it is time to stop the medication, addiction may be a minor issue.

However, benzodiazepines can be abused or misused. One of the most common misuses is taking a benzodiazepine for a long time as a sleeping pill. As mentioned before, tolerance quickly develops for the sedative properties—usually within a month or two. When that occurs, the benzodiazepine no longer induces sleep unless its dosage is increased. This process repeats every few weeks, and higher and higher doses are required to induce sleep. If the dosage is not gradually raised to keep ahead of tolerance, the benzodiazepine becomes ineffective as a sleeping pill, even as it creates an addiction, necessitating eventual detoxification and causing the rebound insomnia

Common indications for antianxiety medications:
- Agoraphobia
- Akathisia as a side effect of antipsychotics
- Detoxification from alcohol or other sedative-hypnotics
- Generalized anxiety disorder
- Lysergic acid diethylamide (LSD) and phencyclidine (PCP) psychoses
- Panic disorder
- Sedation in mania or psychosis
- Situational or anticipatory anxiety
- Sleep disorders

Table 6-10 Side Effects of Antianxiety Medications (Benzodiazepines)

Ataxia
Light-headedness
Sedation
Dry mouth
Headache
Nausea
Constipation
Paradoxical reaction (insomnia, irritability, nervousness)

Clinical Example 

A client with panic disorder unresponsive to antidepressants or beta blockers found that the only medication that reduced her anxiety enough for her to return to her job as a special education teacher was lorazepam (Ativan) 0.5 mg QID. Following a long discussion with her nurse practitioner about balancing the risk of addiction with the potential damage from being unable to work, she decided to continue the lorazepam for the remainder of the school year. At the end of that time, she and the nurse would reevaluate their plan.

Indications for stimulants:
Attention-deficit disorder
Attention-deficit/hyperactivity disorder
Depression
Narcolepsy

that usually accompanies withdrawal from benzodiazepines. Benzodiazepines work well as short-term treatments for situational anxiety or insomnia. Most **psychopharmacologists** recommend continuing their use only for several days or weeks. For sporadic insomnia, occasional use (2 or 3 nights a week) is recommended if other nonmedication interventions are unsuccessful.

For chronic anxiety disorders, such as panic disorder or agoraphobia, benzodiazepines can be used successfully for long periods (months or years) without loss of effectiveness.

Unlike most of the medications used in psychiatry, there is no lag time before these medications become effective. The antianxiety effect can be felt within the first hour after the first dose. Side effects are usually mild and quite tolerable (**Table 6-10**).

One antianxiety medication, buspirone (BuSpar), is quite different from the benzodiazepines in that it has no addiction potential. Because a full response cannot be expected for 1–2 weeks of regular dosing, buspirone is ineffective as an as-needed medication and often is found to be unsatisfactory by those who previously had the experience of more immediate relief of anxiety with a benzodiazepine.

Stimulants

The **stimulants** (**Table 6-11**) are used primarily in the treatment of attention-deficit disorder (ADD) and attention-deficit/hyperactivity disorder (ADHD).

These conditions initially occur in childhood but often continue into adulthood, although usually without the hyperactivity. For both children and adults, stimulants are the treatment of choice for ADD and ADHD. In people who do not have these conditions, stimulants cause stimulation, as their name suggests, but in ADD and ADHD they have an opposite, almost calming effect. Target symptoms of the stimulants when used for ADD and ADHD include the following:

- Distractibility
- Impulsivity
- Irritability
- Overactivity
- Restlessness
- Short attention span

The side effects of the stimulants (**Table 6-12**) are not usually problematic, but one of them is more noticeable than the others: when a child or adolescent is taking stimulants, growth in height and weight is temporarily slowed.

Table 6-11 Stimulants: Names and Usual Range of Daily Doses for Adults

Generic Name	Trade Name(s)	mg/Day
Amphetamine mixture	Adderall	5–40
Dextroamphetamine	Dexedrine	2.5–60
Lisdexamfetamine	Vyvanse	30–70
Methylphenidate	Ritalin, Concerta, Daytrana	10–60
Modafinil	Provigil	5–100

Table 6-12 **Side Effects of Stimulants**

- Abdominal pain or nausea
- Agitation
- Decreased appetite
- Dizziness
- Headache
- Irritability
- Palpitations
- Psychosis
- Sadness, listlessness, or lethargy
- Temporary slowing of growth in children or adolescents
- Tics
- Tremor
- Trouble falling asleep at night

Often, children and adolescents are directed to take their medication every school day, because the tight structure of a school day is particularly difficult for someone with untreated ADHD or ADD. During school breaks and vacations, including summer vacations, the medication is often stopped. The result for many of these young people is that they remain stable in height and weight during the school year but grow rapidly, catching up with their peers, during summer vacation and to a lesser extent during the longer midyear school breaks. This is because stimulants significantly diminish appetite. During vacation periods without the stimulants, these children often eat voraciously and soon catch up to their peers both in height and weight.

Clinical Example 

A young minister who has had attention-deficit disorder since childhood is functioning well as a congregational minister, husband, and father stabilized on methylphenidate (Concerta). Prior to taking this medication, the minister found that the symptoms of his illness interfered with his ability to function in each of these roles.

Other Medications Used in Psychiatry

Beta Blockers

The beta-adrenergic blockers (**Table 6-13**) have a variety of uses in psychiatry. One of the earliest uses was to treat performance anxiety or stage fright. A single dose taken 30 minutes before a performance reduces the physical manifestations of anxiety, such as tremors, sweating, and palpitations. Beta blockers perform a similar function for people with social phobia who are overwhelmingly anxious in specific, predictable circumstances.

Table 6-13 **Beta Blockers: Names and Usual Range of Daily Doses for Adults**

Generic Name	Trade Name(s)	mg/Day
Atenolol	Tenormin	50–100
Metoprolol	Lopressor	100–200
Nadolol	Corgard	40–80
Pindolol	Visken	15–40
Propranolol	Inderal	40–80

Beta blockers also can be helpful to people who are overwhelmed by angry or violent feelings. They reduce the physiologic arousal associated with anger, thus allowing the person to regain and maintain control. Other uses of beta blockers include treatment of side effects of some of the psychotropic medications, including tremor from antidepressants or lithium, akathisia from antipsychotics, and palpitations or tachycardia from antidepressants or antipsychotics.

Clinical Example 

A concert violinist stabilized on lithium for her bipolar disorder finds her mild tremors tolerable except during performances. At these times, a small dose of atenolol (Tenormin) taken 1 hour before a performance prevents the tremors from interfering with her playing.

Alpha-adrenergic **agonists**, including clonidine (Catapres) and guanfacine (Tenex), are used as adjuncts in detoxifying clients from alcohol or antianxiety medications. They are prescribed during the actual detoxification only (i.e., for a week or slightly less) to reduce discomfort from adrenaline-based symptoms of withdrawal: tremor, anxiety, agitation, tachycardia, or sweating.

Clonidine and guanfacine are sometimes effective in treating the adrenaline-based symptoms of posttraumatic stress disorder (PTSD), including palpitations, tremor, anxiety, sweating, flashbacks, and agitation. When they successfully treat the symptoms of PTSD, they are prescribed as a standing dose over a period of months or years. Both of these medicines are also sometimes used successfully in regular, consistent doses to treat the tics of Tourette's disorder or the hyperactivity of ADHD.

Cholinergic Agonists

There are four cholinergic agonists—donepezil (Aricept), tacrine (Cognex), rivastigmine (Exelon), and galantamine (Reminyl)—that improve cognitive functioning for some people in early-stage Alzheimer's disease. These medications prolong independent functioning by increasing the activity of the neurotransmitter **acetylcholine**. Another medication that is sometimes useful in later stages of Alzheimer's disease is memantine (Namenda), a low to moderate affinity NMDA (N-methyl-D-aspartate (NMDA) receptor antagonist. Memantine selectively blocks the toxic effects associated with abnormal transmission of glutamate thought to be responsible for cell death in Alzheimer's dementia.

Addiction Medications

Addiction medications are used for prevention and/or treatment of substance abuse and dependence. Disulfiram (Antabuse), acamprosate (Campral), and naltrexone (ReVia) are used as adjuncts in the treatment of alcoholism to help prevent relapse. Disulfiram acts as a deterrent to drinking because it induces extreme discomfort in a person who drinks even a small amount of alcohol, including symptoms of flushing, throbbing in the head and neck, headache, nausea, profuse vomiting, difficulty breathing, thirst, chest pain, palpitations, weakness, and blurred vision. Naltrexone works in a different way, blocking the desired effects of alcohol and opiates. Drugs, including alcohol, will not produce intoxication in a person taking naltrexone. Acamprosate lessens the sleeplessness and anxiety associated with alcohol withdrawal. Naltrexone is also useful in preventing a relapse into use of intravenous opioids, as are methadone (Dolophine) and buprenorphine (Subutex, Suboxone).

Naloxone (Narcan) is used in the emergency treatment of opiate overdose or intoxication. It is an opiate antagonist that, given intravenously, immediately cancels the effects of opiates.

Thyroid Medications

Sometimes thyroid medications (**Table 6-14**) are necessary as replacement therapy for people who have developed hypothyroidism as a side effect of lithium. Because thyroid function often returns to normal when lithium is withdrawn, thyroid hormone replacement therapy often only be necessary as long as lithium is prescribed. Occasionally, thyroid hormone is used as a booster or augmenter for antidepressants.

Table 6-14 **Thyroid Medications: Names and Usual Range of Daily Doses for Adults**

Generic Name	Trade Name	mcg/Day
L-triiodothyronine (T_3)	Cytomel	25–50
Levothyroxine (T_4)	Synthroid	75–125

Thyroid medications are also used to augment antidepressant medications, even in cases where thyroid function is normal. The thyroid medications are prescribed for people who have only partially responded to an antidepressant and who wish to have a fuller response. A 2006 study offers hope to clients who have failed to improve on two different antidepressants. This study found that the addition of thyroid medication brought about improvement in a significant number of previous nonresponders (Nierenberg et al., 2006).

Drug Interactions

Many clients take multiple medications, including both psychotropics and nonpsychotropics. Because many medications interact with one another, it's important to consider drug–drug interactions (**Table 6-15**) whenever a new medication is added to an existing regimen. Interactions must be considered among prescribed medications, OTC medications, alcohol and other substances, and herbal preparations. Sometimes adding a new medication will raise the level of other drugs in the blood, and other times the opposite will happen. For example, alcohol will potentiate the sedative effect of antipsychotic, antidepressant, antianxiety and anticonvulsant medications. The effectiveness of oral contraceptives is lessened in clients who take certain anticonvulsant medications for their mood stabilizing effect. Nicotine lessens the effectiveness of psychotropic medications (Desai, Seabolt, & Jann, 2001) and is a concern given that the rate of smoking is higher among persons with psychiatric disorders than the general population (Lawrence, Mitrou, & Zubrick, 2009). It is impossible

Table 6-15 Drug–Drug Interactions

Psychotropic Medication	Other Agent	Result
Antianxiety medications: benzodiazepines	Nicotine	Decreased antianxiety effect
	Alcohol, other sedating medications	Respiratory suppression and increased sedation
	Some SSRI antidepressants, isoniazid, estrogens, disulfiram (Antabuse), and cimetidine (Tagamet)	Increased sedation Raised benzodiazepine levels
Antidepressants, general	Nicotine	Decreased antidepressant effect
	Alcohol	Increased sedation and lowered antidepressant levels
	Other sedating medications	Increased sedation
	Guanethidine (Ismelin), clonidine (Catapres), and reserpine (Serpasil)	Antihypertensive effects are blocked with some antidepressants
	Anticonvulsants, barbiturates, glutethimide (Doriden), chloral hydrate, and oral contraceptives	Additive CNS depression
	Cimetidine (Tagamet), antipsychotics, and stimulants	Raised antidepressant levels
Antidepressants: MAOIs, (e.g., phenelzine [Nardil], tranylcypromine [Parnate])	Amphetamines, methyldopa, levodopa, dopamine, epinephrine, norepinephrine, desipramine, guanethidine, reserpine	Hypertensive crisis
	Bupropion (Wellbutrin)	Delirium, grand mal seizures, and hypertension
	Meperidine (Demerol), carbamazepine (Tegretol)	Hypertension or hypotension, coma, convulsions, death
Antidepressants: SSRIs, (e.g., fluoxetine [Prozac], paroxetine [Paxil], fluvoxamine [Luvox])	Dextromethorphan, pseudoephedrine (Sudafed), MAOIs, triptans, and other serotonergic medications	Serotonin syndrome: hyperthermia, CNS irritability, hypertension, restlessness, myoclonus, hyperreflexia, sweating, shivering, tremor, loss of consciousness, and seizures
Antidepressants: tricyclic (e.g., amitriptyline [Elavil], imipramine [Tofranil])	MAOIs	Hypertension, tachycardia, convulsions
Antipsychotics (e.g., chlorpromazine [Thorazine], haloperidol [Haldol], clozapine [Clozaril], risperidone [Risperdal])	Nicotine	Decreased effectiveness of antipsychotic medication
	Antidepressants, beta blockers, cimetidine (Tagamet), alprazolam (Xanax), chloramphenicol (Chloromycetin), disulfiram (Antabuse), MAOIs, acetaminophen (Tylenol), buspirone (Buspar), and fluoxetine (Prozac)	Raised blood levels of antipsychotic with increased risk of toxicity
	Clozapine (Clozaril) cannot be combined with other medications that suppress bone marrow	Increased bone marrow suppression
	Barbiturates, nicotine, phenytoin (Dilantin), cimetidine (Tagamet), carbamazepine (Tegretol), rifampin (Rifadin), and griseofulvin (Fulvicin)	Lowered antipsychotic levels with less therapeutic effect
	Antacids	Decreased absorption of oral antipsychotics
	Alcohol and other sedating medications	Increased sedation
	Antihypertensives	Increased antihypertensive effects
	Glutethimide (Doriden) and clonidine (Catapres)	Block antihypertensive effect of additional agents

(Continues)

Table 6-15 Drug–Drug and Other Interactions *(Continued)*

Psychotropic Medication	Other Agent	Result
Mood stabilizers: carbamazepine	Erythromycin, verapamil (Calcan), ketoconazole (Nizoral), diltiazem (Cardizem), dextropropoxyphene, propoxyphene (Darvon), isoniazid, and valproate (Depakene)	Raised carbamazepine levels
	Must not be combined with clozapine (Clozaril)	Increased risk of bone marrow suppression and agranulocytosis
	Antipsychotics, methadone, antiasthmatics, warfarin (Coumadin), valproate (Depakene), antidepressants, benzodiazepines, and hormonal contraceptives	Lowered levels and decreased effectiveness of these agents
Mood stabilizers: lithium	Theophylline	Increased excretion of lithium
	Nonsteroidal anti-inflammatory drugs (e.g., naproxen [Naprosyn], indomethacin [Indocin], phenylbutazone [Butazolidin], sulindac [Clinoril], diclofenac [Voltaren], thiazide diuretics, amiloride [Midamor])	Raised lithium levels
Mood stabilizers: topiramate, lamotrigine, oxcarbazepine	Oral contraceptives	Decreased effectiveness of birth control medication
Mood stabilizers: valproate	Chlorpromazine (Thorazine), aspirin, fluoxetine (Prozac), and cimetidine (Tagamet)	Raised valproate levels
	Phenobarbital (Nembutal), benzodiazepines, phenytoin (Dilantin), and some antidepressants	Raised levels of phenobarbital, benzodiazepines, phenytoin, and some antidepressants with increased sedation
	Carbamazepine (Tegretol)	Lowered valproate level
	Warfarin (Coumadin)	Increased risk of bleeding

to know or recall all of the possible drug interactions. The nurse should consult a reliable drug reference to identify drug interactions for the purposes of safe administration and client education.

It is also a good practice to recommend that clients take medications with water. Table 6-16 lists some of the beverages that can alter the blood levels of psychotropic medications. If the blood level is increased,

Table 6-16 Other Interactions

Psychotropic Medication	Substance	Result
Antianxiety medication (Ativan)	Grapefruit juice	Decreased blood levels
Antidepressants, antipsychotics	Alcohol	Severe CNS depression
Liquid risperidone (Risperdal)	Tea or cola	Decreased effectiveness
Calcium channel blockers	Grapefruit juice	Increased blood levels
MAOIs	Food (see Table 6-6)	Hypertensive crisis
Liquid doxepin (Sinequan)	Grape juice	Precipitate forms
Liquid fluoxetine (Prozac)	Orange juice	Precipitate forms
Liquid fluphenazine (Prolixin) or perphenazine (Trilafon)	Caffeine-containing beverages, tea, apple juice	Precipitate forms

there is a risk of toxicity, and if the blood level of the medication is too low, the client will not achieve a therapeutic response. Risperidone oral solution may be taken with low-fat milk, orange juice, or coffee, but not with tea or cola. It is important that the nurse and the client follow the manufacturer's directions to ensure proper absorption of the medications.

Genomics and Personalized Psychopharmacology

One of the great hopes in psychopharmacology (and in general pharmacology) is to find a way to select in advance the most effective drug for each individual patient and to prescribe it in the most effective dose. It has been known for some time that individuals with the same symptoms often respond very differently to the identical medication. It is also well known that some patients require doses that are much lower or higher than average. The reasons for these variations are becoming better known and seem to be due to one or more of the following: ethnicity; comorbid conditions; medication interactions; dietary or environmental factors; and the genetically determined activity level of various enzyme systems involved in metabolizing medications (Chaudhry, Neeam, Duddu, & Husain, 2008; Tang & Helmeste, 2010).

For example, it has been shown that Asian patients generally respond to psychotropic medications at lower doses than Caucasians. When given what are generally considered normal doses, they are more apt to experience side effects. It may also be true that African Americans generally require lower-than-average doses of tricyclic and SSRI antidepressants. These differences are thought to be generally true but do not necessarily apply in every individual case. Furthermore, as the different metabolic pathways of psychotropics are mapped, it is clear that a small but significant number of individuals from different backgrounds metabolize psychotropics far slower or more quickly than average, sometimes leading to either toxicity or nonresponse at what are generally considered normal doses.

These genetic variations, or polymorphisms, hold extreme promise, but they are often complex and multifactorial. Over time they will probably help guide prescribing, but the present state of knowledge suggests only that there are many influences on drug choice and dose, including all the aforementioned factors. In the meantime, the nurse needs to consider the fact that there will be individual patients who for one reason or another require much lower or much higher doses of medications for therapeutic response.

Special Populations

Doses of the psychotropic medications are generally lower for children and the elderly. Adult doses are usually indicated starting at the onset of puberty. Side effect profiles may also differ somewhat by age; side effects are generally more pronounced in the elderly. For many psychotropic medications, there are special considerations in medicating pregnant or breastfeeding women. For these special populations, it is essential to check a reliable source such as a hospital formulary for any warnings or special considerations.

Medication Adherence

Medication adherence refers to the client taking the correct medication, at the correct dose, according to the prescribed schedule and duration. Adherence, as opposed to compliance, implies a client's understanding and acceptance of the treatment protocol. Medications work only when they are taken. Unfortunately, half the people who take medication for any condition—psychiatric or nonpsychiatric—take their medication incorrectly. Sometimes this is accidental or the result of unintended error. Other times clients fail to take their medication correctly or at all because of one or more of the following reasons:

- The medication imposes changes in lifestyle or habits that are unacceptable to the client.
- The medication regimen is complex, involving multiple medications or several doses per day.
- The medication causes uncomfortable side effects, especially side effects related to weight gain and sexual dysfunction.
- The client does not have knowledge of the medical condition and treatment plan.
- The cost of the medication is prohibitive.
- There is a lack of support from family or friends for taking medications.
- The client feels well for a long time and does not understand the need for continuing the medication.
- The client desires a return of symptoms, such as grandiosity or elation.

The nurse must be alert to the variety of factors that influence the client's compliance with medication regimens.

Evidence-Based Practice

The reader is referred to an excellent qualitative study that provides insight into clients' views about ways to improve their participation in treatment (Goodwin & Happel, 2006). Recipients of mental health services were interviewed in depth about what factors are important to them in establishing a working partnership with a nurse. The most important factor was whether the patient felt the nurse was respectful. Other factors important to clients were encouragement from the nurse, a spirit of working collaboratively with the nurse, and the nurse's ability and willingness to assist the client to overcoming barriers in the healthcare system. Nurses can learn from these findings how to strengthen their effectiveness as counselors and teachers. This can be most important in helping clients comply with medication treatments.

- The client fears the independence and responsibility that comes with recovery.
- The client views the medication as harmful (Claxton, Cramer, & Pearce, 2001; Mitchell & Selmes, 2007; Ritsner, Perelroyzen, Ilan, & Gibel, 2004; Sirey et al., 2001).

There are many things the nurse can do to improve adherence. Since communication is essential, the nurse must work to establish a therapeutic, trusting relationship. The nurse can educate the client regarding diagnosis and reinforce the effectiveness of medications by connecting symptom resolution to the medication. Since the client's attitudes about medication may affect compliance, the nurse needs to identify the client's concerns and preferences. Gray, Rofail, Allen, & Newey (2005) found that most patients who had been prescribed antipsychotic medications did not feel involved in their treatment and had not been given any written information about the medications or possible side effects. The nurse can be a source of information and can discuss the management of side effects, including the need to communicate with the prescribing clinician before stopping medication. With the client's consent, family and friends can be included in education meetings so they can encourage and support the client.

A structured discussion prior to discharge from the hospital can provide an opportunity to ascertain whether the client understands the treatment plan. By asking the client to repeat what he or she has been told, the nurse can validate if learning has been successful. Written instructions regarding the medications, how to take them, and expected side effects can also be helpful (Makaryus & Friedman, 2005). Simple aids, such as calendars and daily pill boxes can help clients remember to take medication. At follow-up visits, it is important to ask direct questions about thoughts to discontinue medication, handling of missed doses, and any problems the client may be experiencing (Mitchell & Selmes, 2007).

When the nurse makes the medication regimen simple and comfortable, patients are helped immeasurably in their quest for wellness. To accomplish this goal, the following guidelines are offered for increasing adherence:

- Teach the client and family members about the medications.
- Provide explicit, consistent, written information about the medications.
- Reinforce the importance of medication in relapse prevention.
- Explore specific ways that the medication is helpful.
- Provide contact information for when questions arise about the medication.
- Express optimism about the medication's efficacy.
- Alert the client that unpleasant symptoms return after stopping a medication.
- Research the relationship between stopping medications and relapse in the past.
- Encourage family and friends to support the use of medications.
- Equate taking medications with wellness and taking responsibility for oneself.

The nurse can work with the prescribing clinician to ensure that the medication schedule is simple with as few doses per day as possible.

Summary

A broad range of psychotropic medications is available to manage the symptoms of mental disorders. The role of the nurse includes administration of the medication, evaluation of the client's response to the medication, and education of the client and family regarding all aspects of the medication.

This chapter reviews the usual dosage, actions, and side effects of drugs in each category of psychotropic agents. In addition, food and drug interactions that can alter medication absorption and produce untoward—and even life-threatening—effects are presented. Finally, factors that affect the client's adherence to prescribed medication regimens are discussed.

Annotated References

Chaudhry, I. B., Neeam, K., Duddu, V., & Husain, N. (2008). Ethnicity and psychopharmacology. *Journal of Psychopharmacology, 22*(6), 673–680.
This paper reviews literature on the role of ethnicity and race in psychopharmacology.

Claxton, A. J., Cramer, J., & Pierce, C. (2001). A systematic review of the associations between dose regimens and medication compliance. *Clinical Therapeutics, 23*(8), 1296–1310.
This paper reviews studies in which compliance was measured using an electronic device to determine relationships between dose frequency and compliance.

Desai, H. D., Seabolt, J., & Jann, M. W. (2001). Smoking in patients receiving psychotropic medications: A pharmacokinetic perspective. *CNS Drugs, 15*(6), 469–494.
The authors describe the varied chemical effects of cigarette smoking on antipsychotic, antidepressant, and antianxiety medications.

Geddes, J., Barbui, C., & Cipriani, A. (2010). Electronic letters published: Re. Variation in the risk of suicide by antidepressant agent in adults. *Archives of General Psychiatry*, July 22. Retrieved from http://archpsyc.ama-assn.org/cgi/eletters/67/5/497
The authors wrote an online letter challenging a claim that suicide risk was the same for all antidepressant agents that had been made in a previously published article in the same journal.

Goodwin, V., & Happel, B. (2006). In our own words: Consumers' views on the reality of consumer participation in mental health care. *Contemporary Nurse, 21*(1), 4–13.
This qualitative study provides insight into patients' views about ways to improve their participation in treatment.

Gray, R., Rofail, D., Allen, J., & Newey, T. (2005). A survey of patient satisfaction with and subjective experiences of treatment with antipsychotic medication. *Journal of Advanced Nursing, 52*(1), 31–37.
This is a cross-sectional survey to determine patient satisfaction and subjective experiences of treatment with antipsychotic medications.

Guy, W. (1976). *ECDEU assessment manual for psychopharmacology*. Washington, DC: U.S. Department of Health, Education and Welfare.
This is the original publication of the Abnormal Involuntary Movement Scale (AIMS).

Kane, J. M., & Correll, C. U. (2010). Past and present progress in the pharmacologic treatment of schizophrenia. *Journal of Clinical Psychiatry, 71*(9), 1115–1124.
This article presents an historical overview of pharmacologic advances in the treatment of schizophrenia over the past 50 years, as well as a review of current developments at optimizing treatment outcomes.

Kreyenbuhl, J., Buchanan, R. W., Dickerson, F. B., & Dixon, L. B. (2010). The schizophrenia patient outcomes research team (PORT): Updated treatment recommendations 2009. *Schizophrenia Bulletin, 30*(1), 94–103.
This article presents clinical guidelines based primarily on empirical data, first published In 1998 and revised in 2003. The updated report covers research findings on psychopharmacologic and psychosocial treatments from the previous five years.

Lawrence, D., Mitrou, F., & Zubrick, S. R. (2009). Smoking and mental illness: Results from population surveys in Australia and the United States. *BMC Public Health, 9*, 285. doi: 10.1186/1471-2458-9-285. Available at http://www.biomedcentral.com
This paper reports survey findings on the relationship between mental illness and smoking.

Makaryus, A. N., & Friedman, E. A. (2005). Patients' understanding of their treatment plans and diagnosis at discharge. *Mayo Clinic Proceedings, 80*(8), 991–994.
The authors surveyed patients at time of discharge from a municipal teaching hospital to determine their knowledge of diagnoses, name, purpose, and side effects of medications.

Mitchell, A. J., & Selmes, T. (2007). Why don't patients take their medicine? Reasons and solutions in psychiatry. *Advances in Psychiatric Treatment, 13*, 336–346.
This review examines the predictors of partial adherence and discontinuation in persons taking psychotropic medications.

Nierenberg, A. A., Fave, M., Trivedi, M. H., Wisniewski, S. R., Thase, M. E., McGrath,

P. J., . . . Rush, A. J. (2006). A comparison of lithium treatment and T3 augmentation following two failed medication treatments for depression. *American Journal of Psychiatry, 163*(9), 1519–1530.
This study identifies strategies that increase the effectiveness of antidepressant medications.

Patorno, E., Bohn, R. L., Wahl, P. M., Avorn, J., Patrick, A. R., Liu, J., & Schneeweiss, S. (2010). Anticonvulsant medications and the risk of suicide, attempted suicide, or violent death. *JAMA, 303*(14), 1401–1409.
An exploratory study of the relationship between anticonvulsant medications and the risk of suicidal thoughts and behaviors.

Ritsner, M., Perelroyzen, G., Ilan, H., & Gibel, A. (2004). Subjective response to antipsychotics of schizophrenia patients treated in routine clinical practice: A naturalistic comparative study. *Journal of Clinical Psychopharmacology, 24*(3), 245–254.
This study examined subjective satisfaction and tolerance in patients stabilized receiving antipsychotic medications for schizophrenia.

Shirzadi, A. A., & Ghaemi, S. N. (2006 May-June). Side effects of atypical antipsychotics: Extrapyramidal symptoms and the metabolic syndrome. *Harvard Review of Psychiatry, 14*(3), 152–64.
This article examines the two major classes of side effects with atypical antipsychotics: extrapyramidal symptoms (EPS) and the metabolic syndrome (the triad of diabetes, dyslipidemia, and hypertension, with associated obesity), and concludes that atypical antipsychotics continue to have notable risks of EPS, particularly akathisia, and metabolic syndrome.

Simon, G. E., Savarino, J., Operskalski, B., & Wang, P. S. (2006). Suicide risk during antidepressant treatment. *American Journal of Psychiatry, 163*(1), 41–47.
The authors used population-based data to evaluate the risk of suicide death and serious suicide attempt in relation to the initiation of antidepressant therapy.

Sirey, J. A., Bruce, M. L., Alexopoulos, G. S., Perlick, D. A., Raue, P., Friedman, S. J., & Meyers, B. S. (2001). Perceived stigma as a predictor of treatment discontinuation in young and older outpatients with depression. *American Journal of Psychiatry, 158*(3), 479–481.
The study found that fear of stigma affected discontinuation of treatment in older patients.

Stone, M., Jones, M. L., Levenson, M., Holland, P. C., Hughes, A., Hammad, T. A., . . . Rochester, G. (2009). Risk of suicidality in clinical trials of antidepressants in adults: Analysis of proprietary data submitted to U.S. Food and Drug Administration. *British Medical Journal, 339*, doi: 10.1136/bmj.b2880
This paper reports a meta-analysis of 372 double-blind clinical trials of antidepressants for the purpose of examining the risk of suicide, in which researchers found an increased risk among young adults.

Tang, S. W., & Helmeste, D. (2010). Personalized psychopharmacology for the affective disorders and schizophrenia: Where is the evidence? *Personalized Medicine, 7*(4), 421–426.
The author reports that the current contribution of genetic studies related to individualizing psychopharmacology is limited to selecting the drug with the least side effects for a particular patient.

Additional Resources

Munetz, M. R., & Benjamin, S. (1988). How to examine patients using the Abnormal Involuntary Movement Scale. *Hospital and Community Psychiatry, 39*(11), 1172–1177.
This classic article provides detailed instructions for administering the Abnormal Involuntary Movement Scale.

Schatzberg, A., Cole, J., & DeBattista, D. (2010). *Manual of clinical psychopharmacology* (7th ed.). Washington, DC: American Psychiatric Publishing.
As of 2011, this is the most recent edition of one of the classic texts on psychopharmacology.

Internet Resources

For a full suite of assignments and additional learning activities, use the access code located in the front of your book to visit this exclusive website: http://go.jblearning.com/mentalhealth. If you do not have an access code, you can obtain one at the site.

Learning Objectives

After reading this chapter, you will be able to:

- Identify different variables that may contribute to a crisis or psychiatric emergency.
- Describe techniques of crisis intervention and how they can be used in the nursing process.
- Explain the effects crises, emergencies, and disasters may have upon victims and caregivers.
- Clarify the role of the nurse in dealing with crises, psychiatric emergencies, and disasters.

Key Terms

Acute stress disorder

Adventitious crisis

Bereavement

Burnout

CODE-C

Compassion fatigue

Complicated grief

Crisis

Crisis intervention

Critical incident stress management (CISM)

Debriefing

Defusing

Disaster

Dissociation

Maturational disturbance

Postintervention treatment

Posttraumatic stress disorder (PTSD)

Psychiatric emergency

Situational disturbance

Suicide

Traumatic flashbacks

Triage

Vicarious traumatization

Chapter 7

Crises, Psychiatric Emergencies, and Disasters

Winifred Z. Kennedy

http://go.jblearning.com/mentalhealth 

For a full suite of assignments and additional learning activities, use the access code located in the front of your book to visit this exclusive website: http://go.jblearning.com/mentalhealth. If you do not have an access code, you can obtain one at the site.

Introduction

Psychiatric crises and emergencies are dynamic and unpredictable. The healthcare practitioner may treat a client with an urgent or emergent condition in an emergency room setting, or the client may be seen in his or her home, an ambulatory clinic, a mobile crisis unit, or a general hospital. The nurse may be responsible for **triage**, assessment, monitoring the client's condition or milieu, direct intervention or evaluation, education, mental health services, or referral for appropriate follow-up. Even those who do not consider themselves generalists or specialists in psychiatric care may be on the front line and called on to help.

Urgent or emergent emotional, psychologic, or psychiatric problems are basically critical care problems; just as in a critical care situation, anticipation and preparation for the unexpected are necessary. Safety issues take precedence, regardless of the setting. Everyone is responsible for **suicide** prevention, assessing the potential for violence, and identifying suspected cases of abuse. All staff members are involved in considering the safety of the client, others in the area, and themselves. General assessment skills, people skills, basic knowledge about **crisis intervention** and normal and abnormal behavior, anticipation of and preparation for emergencies and disasters, and various intervention modalities are used to treat acute psychiatric problems. In any situation requiring immediate intervention and treatment, the goal is to stabilize the client as quickly as possible, address and normalize any variables that may be precipitating or sustaining the need for emergent care, and treat any life-threatening symptoms.

Overview

Psychiatric and behavioral health management skills are helpful in a variety of situations. When caring for individuals, families, or groups whose problems vary in urgency, the three main problem areas are times of crisis, emergency, and disaster. During these times, typical coping skills and normal functioning may be impaired, or the situation may be life threatening. Disturbances challenge previously held expectations or responses. Clients attempt to use normally held patterns, but internal and external resources are insufficient to meet these new demands on the system. The risk of regression, withdrawal, or failure exists, as well as the potential for new development or outreach.

An urgent condition requires prompt attention but is not immediately life threatening. An emergent condition requires immediate attention and is life threatening.

There are three types of disturbances. A **maturational disturbance** involves adaptation and transition of normal developmental phases. Some examples are the movement from childhood to adolescence, from high school pupil to college student, and from occupational employment to retirement. A **situational disturbance** involves accidental, planned, or imposed transitions, such as injury in a motor vehicle accident, a geographic relocation, or job insecurity related to layoff, termination, or employee displacement. Maturational and situational disturbances can occur alone or in combination, or several disturbances can occur periodically, sustaining the length of a crisis. An **adventitious crisis** is an accidental catastrophic event or disaster that causes disturbances affecting groups or communities.

Crisis

A **crisis** is usually a self-limited transitional period in which the individual confronts an event or situation perceived to be threatening and potentially dangerous, which precipitates a period of psychologic disequilibrium and functional impairment. Traditionally, the potential for harm or change has been emphasized, as demonstrated by the root Chinese character for the word crisis, which combines the characters for both danger and opportunity. A crisis may be developmental or maturational, situational, adventitious or social, psychosocial or physiologic in nature. The crisis may be related to one significant, potentially hazardous stressor or may be the cumulative result of a series or succession of stressors. Balancing factors include the presence or absence of the client's realistic perception of the event, adequate situational support, and previously learned or selected coping mechanisms. Crisis intervention, brief psychotherapy, cognitive therapy, and referrals to mutual self-help groups are useful interventions during crises. The goal of treatment is the client's return to the same or a higher level of functioning experienced prior to the crisis (Aguilera, 1998; Callahan, 2000).

Psychiatric Emergency

A **psychiatric emergency** is an unforeseen, acute, potentially serious and life-threatening event or situation in which the client is threatened or may represent a danger to him- or herself or others. The psychiatric emergency may be intrapsychic, interpersonal, biologic, or a combination of these factors. The emergency can manifest as a disturbance of affect, behavior, cognition, mood, perceptions, physiologic responses, relationships, or thoughts. Immediate intervention is necessary because of the potential for serious medical problems, self-harm, suicide, and violence toward others. Treatment options may involve stabilizing the client's medical and psychiatric conditions and referring the client for further intervention and outpatient or inpatient treatment on a voluntary, emergency, or involuntary basis (Callahan, 2000; Puskar & Obus, 1989; Zeller, 2010,).

Disaster

A **disaster** is an unpredicted, overpowering, traumatic event that disrupts usual life circumstances and assumptions. It devastates most individuals, overwhelms the usual coping responses and support systems, and impairs normal functioning. Disasters are considered adventitious or accidental crises that are rare, unplanned, and cause extreme stress to everyone involved. The threat to survival in a disaster can involve individual (e.g., hostage, fire victim) or collective trauma (e.g., communities of victims and survivors in the World Trade Center terrorist attacks, school shooting sprees, or hurricanes; **Figure 7-1**). Disasters may include natural and man-made catastrophic events, environmental hazards, armed conflict and civil unrest, and disease epidemics. Victims of disasters include those directly injured physically and emotionally, uninjured survivors, family members and friends of the victims and survivors, and the disaster workers.

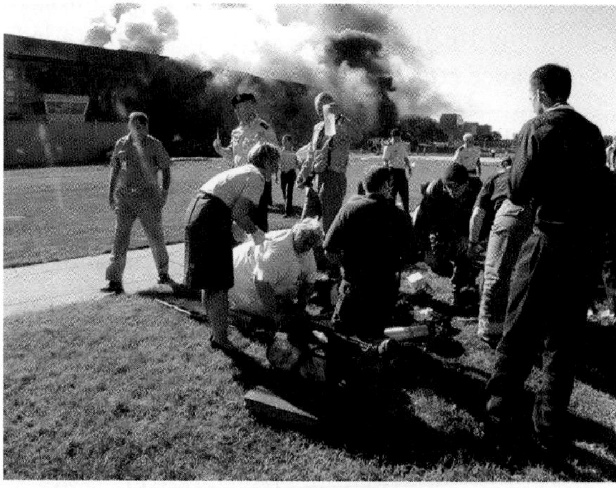

Figure 7-1 **Arlington, Virginia (Sept. 11, 2001)** Medical personnel and volunteers work the first medical triage area set up outside the Pentagon after a hijacked commercial airliner crashed into the southwest corner of the building.

Postintervention treatment involves voluntary psychologic first aid to all those involved directly and indirectly in the disaster in order facilitate coping and to prevent lasting sequelae. The emphasis is upon psychological health, problem solving, and crisis intervention. Focus on building resistance, resiliency—the ability to bounce back—and recovery are the foundations of psychological first aid and the basis of the development of an integrated continuum of care (Everly & Mitchell, 2008). Evidence-based practice for care (also discussed in Chapter 18, "Anxiety and Dissociative Disorders") suggests that the emphasis should be on crisis intervention over time rather than on isolated debriefing and defusing or psychotherapy. Initial postintervention treatment is based upon ensuring safety, comfort, coping skills, and access to supports. Not all individuals involved would be referred for further services such as critical incident stress management or linkage to local mental health services (Hawker, Durkin & Hawker, 2010). Appropriate crisis intervention and triage are the first steps in intervention. Individuals should not be coerced into participation or into reliving traumatic events.

When single or multiple stressors precipitate a crisis, the usual coping mechanisms or supports are inadequate or ineffective, anxiety and tension increase, and maladaptive responses or disorganized behavior result. The goal of crisis intervention is to assist the client to develop an appropriate perception of the crisis, adequate coping mechanisms, and support systems so that the client may return to normal functioning.

After the initial postintervention treatment and triage, some individuals or groups may be offered more formalized intervention programs on a voluntary basis. **Critical incident stress management (CISM)** is a crisis intervention that allows all who are involved in the disaster experience to process what has occurred and begin the recovery process (Charney & Pearlman, 2000; Puskar & Obus, 1989; Raphael, 1986). CISM has been found to be helpful and supportive to those involved in a significant traumatic event and beneficial for preventing development of long-term problems that may interfere with functioning. Participation is voluntary, temporary, usually short term with some longitudinal follow-up or referral, and targeted to individuals or groups who have been involved in the same incident. Steps in emergency trauma work utilize the format of consultation, outreach, debriefing and defusing, education, and crisis counseling (**CODE-C**; Myers & Wee, 2005). Interventions often involve crisis intervention, grief work and death and dying issues, and individual and group psychotherapy. Rescue workers and others who help in crisis intervention and disaster work often experience **vicarious traumatization** as a result of the urgency and camaraderie, physical and

Critical incident stress management (CISM) is a method of individual and group intervention that allows those involved in crisis intervention to share thoughts and experiences, review events, give mutual support, normalize the experience, and provide meaning. This prevents dissociation and decreased functioning.

Vicarious traumatization is a process in which traumatic damage is transferred to helpers or rescuers involved in crisis work by exposure to traumatic experience through their work or through their intense involvement in the experiences of others.

Countertransference is the process in which positive or negative feelings from significant figures and conflicts in the clinician's past are transferred to the client.

A traumatic flashback is a transient, intense, intrusive, repeated reexperience in the present of the thoughts, emotions, and physical sensations surrounding a past disturbance.

Dissociation, an unconscious defense mechanism, involves distancing or numbing oneself to protect against painful emotions or thoughts associated with anxiety, conflict, or trauma. Symptoms may include detachment, depersonalization, derealization, decreased awareness of surroundings, and dissociative amnesia or fugue states.

emotional demands of the disaster situation, intensity of countertransference issues, and close involvement with feelings of grief, hopelessness, and helplessness.

Stress-Related Disorders and *DSM-IV-TR*

The *Diagnostic and Statistical Manual of Mental Disorders*, 4th edition, text revision, lists many problems as conditions rather than as specific disorders, such as abuse or neglect (e.g., physical abuse of a child or adult), relational problems (e.g., parent-child or partner relational problems), and numerous conditions that may be the focus of clinical attention (e.g., bereavement and acculturation problems). Normal **bereavement** is seen as the usual response to loss and grief. The bereavement process may involve a sense of suffering and distress as the individual goes through the stages of grieving. These conditions are coded as "v" codes on Axis I. Psychosocial stressors and environmental problems are also noted on Axis IV. Many of these conditions may appropriately describe the kinds of situational disturbances that crisis intervention targets. In addition, many clients who meet the requirements for specific disorders may present in crisis or as psychiatric emergencies. For example, a client with a history of dysthymic disorder may present after a suicide attempt, or a client with a panic attack may present with hyperventilation syndrome. Adjustment disorder also may be an appropriate diagnosis to describe responses to maturational or situational disturbances. Adjustment disorders may be specified as occurring with depression, anxiety, disturbances of conduct, or mixed (American Psychiatric Association [APA], 2000). Only if the symptoms of grief are prolonged and interfere with normal functioning over time would the individual be evaluated for an adjustment or affective disorder. **Complicated grief** responses are prolonged and interfere with functioning and relationships over time, and clients with complicated grief may have many of the characteristics of major affective disorder or posttraumatic stress disorder.

Acute stress disorder and **posttraumatic stress disorder (PTSD)** are two psychiatric disorders frequently associated with crises and emergencies. An acute stress disorder can occur 2 days to 4 weeks after a threatened or actual traumatic event. It involves combinations of affective, behavioral, cognitive, physiologic, and relational symptoms and dissociative symptoms that typically last from 2 days to 4 weeks. Symptoms are significant enough to impair functioning. PTSD can occur at any point following a threatened or actual traumatic event. It involves combinations of affective, behavioral, cognitive, physiologic, and relational symptoms that last at least 1 month and significantly interfere with normal functioning. The client may experience **traumatic flashbacks** or intensely reexperience the disturbance. The main differences between PTSD and acute stress disorder are the time to onset and duration of symptoms, and the presence or absence of dissociative symptoms and traumatic flashbacks (Aguilera, 1998; APA, 2000). Posttraumatic stress disorder is also discussed in Chapter 18 ("Anxiety and Dissociative Disorders").

Incidence and Prevalence

Some studies estimate that as many as 30% of all emergency room clients require psychiatric intervention (McCaig & Burt, 2004). Suicide attempts are life-threatening emergencies. In the United States, the incidence of suicide is 12.7 deaths per 100,000 people. The estimated prevalence ranges from 1% to 12%. The prevalence increases among those over 75 years of age—the elderly rate of suicide is two to three times higher than that of the rest of the population (Chiles & Strosahl, 1995).

Research suggests that clients with chronic psychiatric conditions account for 7–18% of emergency service visits. The client may repeatedly visit the emergency room because of a gap in available services or providers (e.g., lack of a neighborhood continuing treatment or recovery program), a lack of insurance coverage for other services, no means of obtaining prescriptions, or to change a treatment plan established with another provider or agency (Fisher, 1989).

Stress-related responses often include psychophysiologic reactions. An estimated 75% of victims of catastrophic or traumatic, life-threatening, stressful events experience somatic or physical body symptoms (Hardin, 1996). Clients may present in the emergency room with apparent psychiatric or functional symptoms that later are determined to be related to a medical illness or organic problem. Physical illness is responsible for psychiatric symptoms in approximately 50% of all emergency room visits (Dreyfus, 1987).

Etiology

The etiology of crises and emergencies varies. Internal and external stressors and resources change as people age and affect individual responses. For individuals under stress, planned and unplanned developmental and situational issues or adventitious occurrences may precipitate a crisis. Certain challenges and tasks are present at each maturational or developmental stage. The stages of infancy and childhood, latency and puberty, adolescence, adulthood (early, middle, late), retirement, and old age all require different responses from the individual for each task and life-changing event. Preparation, ability and capabilities, personality style, usual coping mechanisms, social roles, norms, and relationships all influence the response. The physiologic integrity of the system, genetic predisposition, and biologic levels of functioning influence the individual's ability to respond. The uncertainty and vulnerability associated with illness; perceptions of self-esteem and body image, as well as expectations of loss and decreased functioning; and the pain and suffering experienced in acute and chronic illness vary in different situations and periods of development. Some of the issues involving the responses to acute and chronic medical and mental illnesses are covered in Chapters 14 and 16. In the case of an adventitious disaster, the random or chance nature of the event, the risk of injury, and the inherent threat to what is considered normal or usual may leave the survivors without the usual security of shelter or access to support networks.

Some of the underlying problems in psychiatric emergencies are outlined in **Table 7-1**. Many clients have medical problems that must be treated. Some cli-

Underlying problems such as medical conditions, cognitive disorders (dementia, delirium), drug and alcohol use, and history of psychiatric treatment should be identified.

Table 7-1 Underlying Problems

Condition	Symptoms or Issues
Delirium	Sepsis, endocrine disorders, electrolyte imbalance, encephalopathy, toxicity
Dementia	Cognitive impairment, regression, loss of social controls
Physical abuse (perpetrator)	History of violence, aggressive behavior
Physical abuse (victim)	History of unexplained injuries, fearful
Personality disorders	Antisocial, paranoid
Mood disorders	Depression, mania, suicidal ideation
Conduct and impulse disorders	Disorganized behavior, violence, legal problems, episodic loss of control or rage, fire setting, impulsive behavior (gambling, kleptomania, trichotillomania, eating disorders), blackouts, withdrawal, intoxication
Alcohol abuse	Intoxication, dependence, withdrawal, ethanol or methyl alcohol poisoning, toxicity, potentiation of other drugs or pharmaceuticals
Drug abuse	Hydrocarbons (glue, petroleum products, paint thinner), phencyclidine (PCP, angel dust), amphetamines (dextroamphetamine [Dexedrine] and methamphetamines), hallucinogens (LSD, mescaline), cocaine and crack cocaine, opioids, methadone, cannabinoids, designer drugs (such as flunitrazepam [Rohypnol], GHB [gamma-hydroxybutyric acid], MDPV [Methylenedioxprovalerone] and mephedrone, ecstasy [5,6,-Methylenendioxy-*N*-methyl-2-aminoindano MDMA]), caffeine, tobacco, over-the-counter medications, pain medications, herbal preparations and plant based drugs (such as stimulant cathinone found In the African plant khat, peyote [LSA], and betel nut, salvia [Salvinorin-A])
Psychotic disorders	Delusions (paranoia, grandiosity, body dysmorphia or somatic delusions, jealousy, guilt, thought insertion or broadcasting, mind control or reading), hallucinations (auditory, visual, olfactory, or tactile), thought disorders, psychomotor disturbances (e.g., catatonia)
Disturbed perceptions	Illusions, hallucinations

(Continues)

Table 7-1 Underlying Problems *(Continued)*

Condition	Symptoms or Issues
Effects of prescription drugs	Polypharmacy; steroids; anticholinergic agents; cimetidine; sympathomimetic agents; overuse of pain medications; psychotropic medications (e.g.; toxicity); neuroleptic malignant syndrome; serotonin overload; food–drug interactions with monoamine oxidase inhibitors; withdrawal, especially with alcohol; benzodiazepines; and barbiturates; extrapyramidal reactions; akathisia; acute dystonic reactions; tardive dyskinesia
Chronic pain	Loss of hope, polypharmacy, overdose
Disorders of thought or language	Illogical or overly detailed and circumstantial speech, problems in organizing thoughts, derailed or fragmented speech

ents with brain injury, dementia, or delirium may be at higher risk because of an altered level of consciousness and an inability to make their needs known or respond to internal and external stressors. Many behavioral or psychiatric symptoms are directly related to a physical or organic problem. These symptoms may be lessened or reversed by treating the medical problem. Many psychosocial problems or psychiatric disorders accompany or coexist with physical illness. Treatment of these underlying functional or psychiatric problems occasionally helps mitigate the client's physical symptoms or physiologic response to stress. Some of the medical problems associated with mental disorders are discussed in Chapter 13.

Clients who present with psychiatric emergencies can be categorized according to their presentation and priority (Puskar & Obus, 1989; Zeller, 2010). Their problems include depression, anxiety, phobias, disorientation, suicidal threats or attempts, thought disorders, impulse control, alcohol or substance abuse, trauma or brutality, and social problems and homelessness. Alcoholic intoxication, acute schizophrenic reaction, psychotic depression, and acute situational disturbances appear to be the most common problems. Specific psychiatric disorders and special at-risk populations are discussed in other chapters.

Violence or the threat of violence can present as a psychiatric emergency in different ways. The staff may be treating the victim, perpetrator, or both at the same time. Some of the forms of potential and actual violence include:

- Self-inflicted violence (self-destructive behavior, self-mutilation, suicide threat or attempt)
- Intrafamily violence (child, partner or spouse, elder abuse)
- Interpersonal violence (aggressive and violent behaviors, assault, battery, muggings, attempted murder, murder, gang membership, criminal activity)
- Sexual harassment, coercion, assault, and rape
- Stalking
- Workplace violence
- Bullying and cyberbullying

A family history of abuse is an important factor in the etiology of intergenerational exposure to violence and its repetition and recurrence in other situations. Physical, social, emotional, or economic isolation and dependence are factors in abuse and violence. At-risk clients often have a history of multiple unexplained or poorly explained injuries or use different healthcare practitioners to avoid detection.

Suicide

Suicide is a frequent psychiatric emergency; at-risk clients may present in various settings from the emergency room, hospitalized patients, community and ambulatory settings (Joint Commission, 2010). The threat or attempt may be associated with other physical or psychiatric disorders, alcohol or substance abuse, or acute situational disturbances. Clients may feel as if they would be better off dead because of pain, illness, changes in lifestyle or relationships, or a fear of being a burden to others. The client may have recurrent thoughts or fears of dying or may be preoccupied with death. These thoughts may be accompanied by a specific threat or plan. The client's fear of these thoughts, fear of loss of control, or fear of the responses of others with whom these thoughts have been shared can precipitate a crisis. Suicide threats and plans need to be evaluated to determine their potential lethality, how accessible the intended means for suicide is, and the likelihood of the act being carried out. The client's intent to act on the plan may have been demonstrated by recent or past attempts, ongoing suicidal ideation and a specific plan, or the expression of intent to carry out the plan. Clients at greatest risk have impaired impulse control; concomitant psychiatric or medical illnesses; alcohol or substance abuse; feelings of hopelessness, helplessness, and guilt; no resolution of developmental, situational, or relational stressors; and a lack of situational supports.

Suicide Assessment

- Screening for depression or other mental health issues
- History of past suicide attempt or attempts by family members or friends
- Thoughts of suicide and intent to carry through with thought, specific threat, or plans
- Access to means to carry through with plan
- Assessment of potential lethality of plan
- Preparations for death or suicide (saying farewell, giving away belongings, etc.)
- Use of alcohol or drugs
- Use of prescription medications that are associated with increased risk of suicide as side effect
- History of impulsive behavior
- Chronic pain; concurrent medical illness
- Crisis or change of circumstance
- Availability of support systems
- Giving up, hopelessness, or helplessness

Critical Thinking Question 

Identify client information that would be important to include as part of an assessment of suicide risk. What would be important factors to consider in determining immediate risk?

Clients may be unaware of the potential lethality of over-the-counter medications (e.g., acetaminophen [Tylenol] overdose) and combinations of drugs (e.g., acetaminophen [Tylenol] and diphenhydramine [Benadryl], alcohol and a benzodiazepine [Valium]) or may misjudge the time frame in which they can be rescued.

Substance Abuse Problems

Clients with drug and alcohol problems may present with problems associated with abuse such as intoxication, toxicity, dependence, or withdrawal. Clients may use these chemical substances to get high or in-

Clinical Example 

Linda, a 69-year-old homemaker, was brought to the emergency room by her family. They reported that she was not feeling well and appeared to be in pain. The physician who made the initial medical assessment did not find any significant problems and had ruled out a myocardial infarction. The family was distressed because the client seemed no better but was about to be discharged. The staff reported that the client was tearful and that the family stated she had a history of psychiatric problems. A psychiatric consultation was requested. The family told the psychiatric consultation liaison nurse specialist that the client had been hospitalized for depression after the birth of her third child 40 years earlier and again approximately 20 years after that, after the death of her spouse. They stated that she had been tearful on and off for a while and seemed withdrawn, but they were worried because she was acting funny (e.g., not remembering things, especially the recent death of her grandson). Several generations of the family had gathered together for the funeral of the young man, who had a history of lymphoma. They worried that Linda was depressed and unable to function, because she had not taken her usual role of matriarch at that family gathering. As part of the assessment, the nurse interviewed Linda and completed a mental status examination. The client was somewhat withdrawn and tearful during the interview, but her affect was labile and seemed to vary with no relation to the subject matter being discussed. The client reported having problems with her memory. When she was reminded of her grandson's death, she expressed concern and distress briefly. Based on the mental status examination, the nurse suggested that the client be evaluated for possible dementia. A computed tomography scan showed multiple lacunae infarcts as well as a right-sided infarct; an electroencephalogram revealed marked bilateral dysfunction. In addition, the client's thyroid-stimulating hormone level was elevated; she was treated for hypothyroidism.

Linda was facing a combination of maturational (aging and adjustment to decreased functioning) and situational (diagnosis of physical illness) changes. After the initial evaluation, the psychiatric consultation liaison nurse specialist assisted the client and family, helping them to adjust to this new loss and understand Linda's present capacity at a time when they were dealing with another situational disturbance, a death in the family. The client, family, and staff also were told that the client's tearfulness was lability related to a dementia rather than a symptom of depression.

toxicated, pass out, anesthetize pain, or avoid dealing with conflicts or relationships and intolerable emotions or thoughts. In addition, the client may have associated physical and mental disorders, may have made a suicide attempt, undergone trauma, or threatened aggressive behavior. Situational disturbances may alter typical patterns of abuse or have no relation to abuse and dependence. Abuse of sedatives, anxiolytics, and pain medications is often associated with alcohol abuse and dependence.

Medical and Mental Disorders

Burnout is a term used to describe an individual's maladaptive response to a chronically stressful work situation.

Clients often experience emergencies involving the onset of psychiatric disorders or acute exacerbations of known disorders. Sudden, unexpected, or debilitating symptoms of anxiety or panic may require emergency treatment. Acute and chronic grief reactions, sudden life losses or changes, and suicide threats and attempts all may be associated with depression. Deprivation and genetic predisposition may be involved in the development of depressive disorders. Researchers report that various biologic and genetic theories explain the development of psychotic symptoms. Psychosis also is associated with cognitive disorders and drug and alcohol abuse. Emergencies may be precipitated by taking psychiatric medications alone or in combination with other medications or substances of abuse.

Response of Caretakers

Intervention helps provide the support and feedback necessary for caretakers to continue their work. Caretakers with inadequate support risk **compassion fatigue** and **burnout**, which manifest as psychosomatic symptoms, fatigue and exhaustion, disturbed relationships, or acting out behaviors.

With compassion fatigue, the individual worker or volunteer is overwhelmed with the effects of chronic

Clinical Example

Maria, a 42-year-old secretary with no previous medical history, was admitted to the hospital with acute abdominal pain. Exploratory laparotomy revealed metastatic ovarian cancer. A total hysterectomy and oophorectomy were performed. Postsurgery, the client had a myocardial infarction, coded, and was resuscitated three times. She was transferred to the surgical intensive care unit and was treated for septic shock.

A psychiatric consultation was requested for evaluation of anxiety. The client had no memory of her time in the intensive care unit, no problem sleeping in the hospital, and was eating. She had no history of depression or psychiatric follow-up. Maria was tearful and said she was upset about starting chemotherapy. She had been told that she would experience premature menopause, and she was frightened. She wanted to go home to her two young children before anything else went wrong. The spouse and children visited frequently. The client stated she wanted to do anything she could to help herself get better, but she did not want to ask too many questions or bother the staff. She felt they had saved her life and that she might seem ungrateful by worrying about menopause or talking about dying. At the same time, she did not want to add to the distress of her family by talking with them about her concerns.

The clinical impression was of adjustment disorder. In identifying issues and discussing different options with the psychiatric nurse, the client stated she felt better being able to talk about some of the things that were worrying her and learning about what to expect over time. She could ask questions, and the nurse anticipated some of her concerns and reassured her that she was responding in a normal manner. Maria did not know how to discuss the care of the children or her illness with her husband, because all he talked about was how much better she was. The nurse set up meetings with the client and spouse. An understanding of crisis intervention and grief counseling formed the basis of the interventions selected. The married couple's relationship and the stage of their marriage's development as parents of young children, the client's maturational stage and life tasks, and their children's development were important issues. Although Maria was unable to be home mothering the children and directing the household, she still took an active role in some of the tasks she missed. Then the children and both grandmothers, who had acted as caretakers during the client's hospitalization, were included in the discussions. After the client's immediate concerns were met and the psychiatric nurse had demonstrated her helpfulness, Maria became interested in anything that would help her with the chemotherapy and the discomfort she anticipated. Guided imagery was used as adjunctive therapy.

stress. The term *burnout* refers to an unproductive response to overwhelming and chronically stressful work situations. CISM is helpful for individual staff and groups.

The staff are like the members of a Greek chorus, standing witness to the suffering and tragedy around them. Past experiences of loss and childhood trauma can be reexperienced while facing loss, separation, and grief as adults, particularly if the experiences have not been successfully resolved. Research indicates that persons in the helping professions often have greater levels of perceived deprivation in childhood (Raphael, 1986). The shared concerns and experiences of the crisis or disaster, close involvement with loss and grief, and a sense of altruism and empathic involvement all place the individual at risk for emotional exhaustion (**Figure 7-2**). To protect against painful feelings of loss, the individual may attempt to repress or deny these feelings. This can eventually lead to psychic numbing, detachment, and burnout. A sense of unbearable and overwhelming tragedy may be induced by certain normal or routine events in the helping professions, such as the loss of a client who is well known to the staff or someone with whom the staff identify strongly. Conversely, an event may be outside the range of normal experience, such as a suicide on the unit, an accident or assault, or the unexpected death of another staff person. Concern for others demands openness and extending oneself to others. If the staff have lost the capacity to respond, the response may become blocked and mechanical. Treatment focuses on the event and the feelings experienced to break down the sense of isolation or turmoil associated with symptoms of traumatic flashbacks or survivor guilt. This prevents the numbing that leads to the inability to feel or empathize with others (Raphael, 1983; 1986).

Figure 7-2 Emotional exhaustion or burnout can make it difficult to maintain a compassionate attitude.

Postintervention treatment, or psychological first aid in a crisis, focuses on providing voluntary access to short-term, cognitively based, pragmatic services. Hobfoll and colleagues (2007) outline five essential elements to trauma intervention including providing for safety, calming, a sense of self and collective efficacy, connectedness, and hope. The intent is to emphasize that stress is a normal response to abnormal events and to meet basic needs. **Defusing** and **debriefing** are interventions used to deal with staff responses to traumatic events. Defusing is a brief, immediate intervention used with small groups that focuses upon gathering facts (who, what, when, where, and how), exploring thoughts, acknowledging feelings, and providing encouragement and anticipatory guidance. Debriefing focuses on larger scale and time-limited structured groups to provide for screening, supporting, and education.

Postintervention treatment, or psychologic first aid, involves offering access to safety and comfort, problem solving, education, skill building in stress management, to relax and utilize stress reduction skills (such as meditation, self-talk, deep breathing, etc.), social supports, practical assistance, and reframing.

Staff should be offered opportunities for dealing with traumatic stress and grief that focus on assessment, expression of feelings, opportunity for empathy and validation, encouragement of discovery and meaning, provision of didactic information, and time for recreational and self-management and self-care techniques (breathing and movement exercises, meditation and prayer, etc.).

Physiology

The initial response to stress, the fight-or-flight reaction, was identified by Walter Cannon in 1914. Previous studies attempted to show how the activation and arousal of physiologic systems that affected the ability of the individual to defend or to flee a perceived threat were adaptive and useful in the face of danger. The activation of biologic systems affects the system's response, including appropriate levels of alertness, decreased vegetative functions, changes in circulation and respiration, and focused attention to take aggressive action or to escape. In the 1930s, Hans Selye described the phases of alarm, resistance, and exhaustion of general adaptation or stress syndrome. The intensity and duration of the response, the resistance of the system, and the ability of the system to recover from the impact of the stress are all factors in the patterns of response that influence the system's ability to adapt. Activation of the autonomic nervous system is an immediate and normal response, but perseveration and continuation of the response, particularly when there is no immediate danger, leads to physical and psychological problems.

This model has been modified to show how the stress system response involves neurophysiologic and biochemical events associated with successful adaptation or dysregulation. Stress involves adrenergic, noradrenergic, and histaminic arousal responses. Facilitation of the fight-or-flight response is mediated by the behavioral inhibition system. The neurotransmitters epinephrine and norepinephrine are involved in the initial response. The stress system involves the effects of corticotropin-releasing hormone and locus coeruleus-norepinephrine/autonomic release norepinephrine systems and the hypothalamus-pituitary-renal axis. The locus coeruleus activates noradrenergic arousal of the hypothalamus and limbic and central nervous systems. Low serotonin levels increase locus coeruleus activity. The raphe nuclei in the brain stem affect serotonin modulations and pathways.

Researchers have hypothesized that the response is meant to be limited to actual threat and that excessive or chronic strain causes hypersecretion of corticotropin-releasing hormone and influences the development of stress-related disorders (e.g., anxiety, anorexia, and depression) and chronic disease (e.g., immunosuppressive response). Chrousos and Gold (1992) hypothesized a V-shaped response in which hypo- or hyperfunctioning influences response and dysregulation. After initial arousal and preparation for fight or flight, catecholamine is released, norepinephrine levels increase, and cortisol levels decrease. The ratio of norepinephrine to cortisol, with increased norepinephrine from locus coeruleus activation and decreased serotonin levels, is associated with the chronic stress of PTSD (Burgess & Hartman, 1996). The opioid-benzodiazepine system (locus coeruleus, hypothalamus, and amygdala) accounts for hormones that have an analgesic effect to control pain and activate the behavior-inhibiting cycle. Dysregulation may cause the symptoms of numbing or blunting associated with **dissociation** (Burgess & Hartman, 1996).

Clarification of the immediate situation is helpful. The nurse should determine who brought the client to the emergency center or clinic (self-referral, involuntary, possible support systems); what circumstances or problems caused the client to seek help now, especially if the problem has existed for some time; when the problem started; and how similar situations were dealt with in the past (helpful and unhelpful methods, medications).

It is hypothesized that the amygdala is important in communicating anxiety and the hippocampus in encoding memories of trauma. Stimulation of the amygdala induces feelings of fear and anxiety and activates the sympathetic nervous system. The orbitofrontal cortex of the frontal lobe is associated with the defensive experiences of fear and anxiety, and it is the area of the cortex that influences information processing to the limbic system. Neurobiologic theories are discussed in depth in Chapter 5.

Neurobiologic and Genetic Factors

Studies indicate that there are long-term consequences of exposure to chronic, toxic levels of stress. Gestational fetal exposure to biologic and psychologic stress influences fetal development, birth outcome, and neonatal functioning. This has both direct and indirect effects upon emotional development and cognitive, motor, and brain development (Sandman, Davis, Buss, & Glynn, 2011). A protein, FKBP5, of the hypothalamic-pituitary adrenal (HBA) system modulating the glucocorticoid receptors, has been reported to be genetically associated with depressive disorders and suicidal behavior. Genotype studies indicated that single-nucleotide polymorphisms of the FKBP5 stress related-genes correlated with the severity of child abuse and the level of adult symptoms of posttraumatic stress disorder (Binder et al., 2008). The amount of exposure, the cumulative effects, and the multiple risks of substance abuse and adverse events also influence health risk behaviors and mental and medical illness in the adult (Scott et al., 2011). Dysregulation of the hypothalamic-pituitary-adrenal axis and parasympathetic and catecholamine responses have been shown to have long lasting effects upon health (Glaser, 2003). Postmortem studies of brains of suicide victims who had a history of child abuse showed changes in the NC3R1 gene that regulates stress response, the NGF1 transcription factor, and NGF1A (McGowan et al., 2009). In posttraumatic stress disorder, researchers have shown neurologic damage of chronic hyperarousal associated with pituitary adenylate cyclase-activation polypeptide and the PAC1 receptor. Women who have two copies of the CC genotype with two copies ADCYAP1R1 are more likely to develop posttraumatic stress disorder, a relationship that is not found in men with similar single-nucleotide polymorphisms (rs2267735), suggesting the influence of estrogen upon women (Ressler et al., 2011).

Clinical Presentation

The client may exhibit different signs of stress depending upon the situation and his or her personality

www Mrs. P **CASE STUDIES**

Ms. P., an 18-year-old student, was brought to the emergency room by ambulance from her college campus. Her friends stated that she had complained of feeling dizzy and almost collapsed. When they had expressed their concern, the client protested that she was fine. However, her condition came to the attention of an instructor when she appeared dazed and unresponsive during class for a few minutes, and help was summoned. The client had missed 2 days of classes, which was unusual, but she had explained to her friends that she had a virus. Her friends said that she had looked tired and wan and attributed her withdrawn behavior to her recent illness. She admitted that she had not slept for 2 days before coming to the emergency center and had not eaten because she had a lump in her throat and could not hold anything down. She complained that she felt alternately hot and then chilled. When the staff attempted to examine her, Ms. P. began to cry and would not allow the male physician to touch her. She eventually confided to the nurse that she had been raped 2 days earlier.

At first, Ms. P. stated that she did not remember any details of the attack. It seemed unreal to her, like a movie or something that had happened to someone else. Eventually, the story was pieced together. Ms. P. had stayed late in the computer resource room to finish a class project. She went to the restroom before leaving the building. No one appeared to be in the restroom, but a large man approached and quickly overpowered her, although she attempted to push past him. After the assault and rape, she felt degraded, humiliated, and helpless. She ran home and did not report the incident to anyone.

Ms. P. stated that she felt somewhat responsible for what had happened because she knew it was not safe to stay alone late at night. She said she had even felt uncomfortable about going to the restroom alone, but dismissed the feeling. She stated that she felt as if her skin was turned inside out and everything bothered her. For 2 days she had been afraid to leave her room, kept the door closed and the shades down, and had not answered the phone. She said she jumped at every sound and worried that the man would find her again. She was concerned that the man had given her a sexually transmitted disease, and she showered and cleaned herself repeatedly. She felt dirty. She could not concentrate on her school work. All she wanted to do was sleep and forget what had happened, but she was unable to rest and kept thinking about what had happened, what she felt she should have done, and what she would do if ever faced with a similar situation.

The medical protocol for rape involves a physical examination that includes inspection of the bruises or injuries incurred in the attack; inspection of the genitalia, anus, mouth, throat, or other areas violated in the assault; the collection of specimens of hair, semen, or other evidence of the assault; and the treatment of any injuries or sexually transmitted diseases. Many victims shower or douche or delay treatment after an assault, complicating the examination and collection of evidence. Intervention is often needed to facilitate physical examination, the collection of specimens, and reports to legal authorities. Victims may need a supportive person to be with them through the examination and investigative procedures. Many police departments have special rape teams with women officers to help female victims feel comfortable in cooperating with the report and investigation procedures. Female victims may also have concerns about possible pregnancy and/or prevention of pregnancy. Male and female victims need assessment for the presence of alcohol or drugs that could have been used in commission of the assault and follow-up for the possible transmission of hepatitis, syphilis, and HIV.

Ms. P. was experiencing an acute, expressive reaction to the assault, but some victims respond by appearing calm, controlled, and untouched by the experience. The symptoms she experienced also are seen in acute stress disorders; many rape victims show signs of PTSD. Although Ms. P. did not feel she precipitated the attack and did not know her attacker, she felt, unrealistically, that she was partly to blame. Victims rarely precipitate or participate in sexual assault, but their beliefs and feelings about the assault can be complicated, particularly if they know the assailant. Ms. P.'s first impulse, to seclude herself and not tell anyone about the attack, isolated her and eliminated the possibility of getting help. It is difficult to establish information regarding the incidence and prevalence of sexual assault and rape because many victims do not report the crime because of fear, guilt, humiliation, or lack of faith in the criminal justice system.

Crisis intervention with Ms. P. focused on helping her safely explore what had had happened to her, cognitively and emotionally. She needed to recognize the symptoms she was experiencing and to know what she could expect to experience in the immediate future. The psychic numbing she was experiencing had some protective value but also limited her ability to cope with what had happened and to reach out to others for support. Intervention was needed to widen her available support base and to help her utilize the supports already in place. Long-range goals focused on minimizing the impact of rape-trauma syndrome—the emotional and behavioral consequences that affect adjustment and the ability to maintain relationships. Medical follow-up for possible sexually transmitted diseases and pregnancy should also be arranged.

Nursing Care Plan **Sexual Assault**

Nursing Diagnosis 1: Ineffective coping related to impaired functioning related to missing classes and problems concentrating.

Nursing Diagnosis 2: Impaired communication related to related psychic numbing as evidenced by withdrawal and isolation.

Nursing Diagnosis 3: Disturbed sleep pattern related to inability to sleep related to repeated intrusive thoughts of event and fears of falling asleep.

Outcomes	Interventions	Evaluations
• Participates in appropriate self-care.	• Support client during assessment and physical evaluations.	• Demonstrates participation in self-care and tolerated examination and diagnostic procedures.
• Experiences ability to express thoughts about the event.	• Provide safe environment and time for client to recall and retell events.	• Subjective reports of appropriate grieving process and recovery.
• Arranges follow-up care and appropriate support.	• Assist client in identifying personal support sources (family, friends, etc.) and offer referral to therapists, support groups, and community resources.	• Identification of support sources and contact with appropriate referral sources.
• Decrease in stress-related symptoms.	• Teaching and anticipatory guidance appropriate to client's needs.	• Return demonstrations of self-management and self-care techniques.

Visit http://go.jblearning.com/mentalhealth for additional care plans and exercises.

Triage is a classification process developed from battlefield techniques to rapidly assess acuity and attempt to balance needs and available resources. Derived from the French word *trier* (to choose), triage is a way of making certain that the right client, place, time, and care provider are identified and treatment needs are coordinated.

and response repertoire. The client's appearance may vary. He or she may be well groomed or unkempt or show signs of possible abuse or trauma such as bruises, scars, or injury. The mood also may vary, and the client may be angry, anxious, or sad. The client's affect may be intense, labile, blunted, or inappropriate to the situation or topics being discussed. The client may be apathetic, detached, or in a daze. Conversely, she or he may be irritable, restless, or agitated and engaged in frantic overactivity. Visible signs of distress may appear, such as an unsteady voice, flushed face, tearfulness, tremulousness, distractibility, and hypersensitivity or hypervigilance to environmental stimuli. The client may experience some observable or measurable physiologic responses to stress, such as sweating or increased pulse, rapid respirations, elevated blood pressure, and elevated blood glucose levels. The client may describe subjective symptoms such as a feeling of internal restlessness, weakness or fatigue, or impending doom.

Triage

Triage for potential psychiatric emergencies requires the appropriate assessment of the client's needs, assurance of safety, and differentiation between organic and functional problems (Dreyfus, 1987; Rosenzweig, 1992). Immediate concerns include identification of medical and psychiatric problems and assessment of the risk for violence or elopement. Assurance of client and staff safety is established by assessing the client's potential for violence. The nurse should consider any threats of loss of control, aggression, self-harm, suicide, or homicide. Clients who are agitated, confused, intoxicated, manic, paranoid, or psychotic are at risk for losing control. A history of violence, brain injury, or substance abuse indicates the potential for violence. Clients receiving psychiatric treatment may have medical problems associated with their medications, such as a cholinergic response to neuroleptics or tricyclic antidepressants, neuroleptic malignant syndrome from neuroleptics, serotonin overload from serotonin reuptake inhibitors, toxicity from high doses of medications such as lithium or anticonvulsants, food–drug interactions such as hypertensive crisis with monoamine oxidase inhibitors, and withdrawal, particularly from benzodiazepines and barbiturates (see Chapter 5).

Puskar and Obus (1989) divide psychiatric problems that present for triage into the following six groups:

1. Emergent or life-threatening psychiatric emergencies that require immediate attention, including acutely agitated, violent, suicidal, or homicidal clients and clients brought in involuntarily by the police or protective services
2. Urgent or serious psychiatric emergencies that are potentially life threatening, such as manic or psychotic clients; clients with a history of violence, self-harm, or drug abuse; or clients who appear restless, confused, or disoriented
3. Potentially serious psychiatric problems or crisis situations, including most clients in crisis with a psychiatric problem who come in voluntarily and clients who require urgent medical attention or have a history of medical illness associated with behavioral symptoms
4. Crisis situations that present no immediate danger, including clients in nonacute and chronic situations with no situational support and clients with chronic psychiatric problems
5. Situations in which there is no immediate danger, threat, or change in situation or supports, such as a client with a history of psychiatric problems coming in for an unrelated physical complaint, reassurance, or renewal of psychiatric medications
6. Problems resulting from a physical illness, including situations in which a medical problem is identified and no psychiatric problems are present or an underlying psychiatric problem is stable or does not require immediate attention

Clinical Course and Complications

The initial response to crisis is often denial, disorganization, and disruption of normal response patterns. The client may respond with feelings of anxiety and depression. Shock, confusion, lethargy, and heroics also have been noted in response to catastrophic stress (Hardin, 1996). Certain response strategies may be of particular value to an individual or may have been useful in other circumstances. The client may persevere in using the same response or regress to coping mechanisms that were useful in an earlier stage of development.

Many factors affect the clinical course. Some developmental stages, such as adolescence, may be more problematic in certain cultures. The client may not have successfully completed the normal, expected developmental tasks. This may lead to a limited repertoire of coping responses, less flexibility in coping responses, and less skill in learning new responses. Other mediating factors include family history, generational legacies of response patterns and learning skills, lack of supports, chronic physical illness, chronic psychiatric illness, poverty, guilt, hopelessness, helplessness, and alcohol and drug abuse. It is difficult to know why some situations or combinations of stresses are problematic for a particular individual or why two individuals at the same life stage respond very differently to similar sets of experiences, choices, and challenges.

In a psychiatric emergency, usually the client presents with symptoms of agitation or aggression, suicidal or homicidal ideation and behaviors, or with an acute problem such as drug intoxication or withdrawal or a sudden change in mental status. A client may present with a new psychiatric symptom such as psychosis or mania or with an acute exacerbation of a chronic problem such as schizophrenia. The client may present voluntarily, be brought in by family or police, or be an involuntary client who is sent for evaluation or who becomes agitated or threatening while receiving emergency care.

During a disaster, clients may have difficulty dealing with the immediate emotional impact. As in times of crisis, the initial response is most often denial and the second response is disbelief: "This could not happen here!" or "How could this happen to me?" Initial reactions may range from fear, guilt, anger, and sadness to heroic disregard for the client's own needs. Raphael (1986) describes the stages of response as victims face the sudden, unexpected warning or threat. Victims occasionally respond with disbelief and disregard, feelings of loss, or recognition of survival and response to being rescued by others or by their own heroic efforts. The sense of shared adventure, the closeness to others involved in the disaster and its aftermath,

CASE STUDIES Ms. Q

Ms. Q., a 45-year-old woman, was brought by ambulance from the train station to the emergency center. The client stated that she was on her way to work when she began to experience increased shortness of breath, palpitations, tearfulness, and feelings that she was going to die. Once on the train the client felt threatened with so many people around, and she started to breathe rapidly and passed out. Ms. Q. had no history of anxiety disorder, panic attacks, or phobias. The staff requested a psychiatric evaluation.

Upon questioning by the psychiatric nurse, the client said she was not usually a nervous person but had been under stress recently. She was on her way to work for the first time in several weeks. She began to weep as she told of her 16-year-old son's murder approximately 2 months before. After her son died, she had been seen by a counselor from victim's services, who had been helpful. At first she had been overcome with guilt and plagued with repetitive, intrusive thoughts of her son's death. She could not sleep and kept imagining what he must have gone through and how she might have prevented it. After a while, she felt much better and decided to go back to work. She had not known it would be so difficult. She said that people were supportive after the murder, but most had returned to their own lives. Her married daughter, who had stayed with her for several weeks after the funeral, had returned home. The client did not want to burden her daughter. The counselor from victim's services was on vacation.

A few days before her scheduled return to work, Ms. Q. began to reexperience symptoms. She was awakened by thoughts about how her son looked when he left the house that evening and how she had felt when the police told her about his death. She felt partly responsible because he had bought a new jacket with money she had given him. Her son had been killed during an attempted robbery. Ms. Q.

Nursing Care Plan **Survivor of Violence**

Nursing Diagnosis 1: Anxiety related to situational crisis as evidenced by shortness of breath, palpitations, and feelings of impending doom.

Nursing Diagnosis 2: Impaired grieving related to loss of son as evidenced by feelings of guilt and intrusive thoughts.

Nursing Diagnosis 3: Impaired coping related to social isolation as evidenced by inability to access available support systems.

Expected Outcomes	Interventions	Evaluations
• Will experience reduction in anxiety symptoms.	• Provide opportunity for nonjudgmental listening in safe environment.	• Able to relate feelings to anxiety.
	• Teach breathing relaxation techniques.	• Demonstrates breathing relaxation techniques.
• Will facilitate grieving process.	• Identify past and present effective coping mechanisms and reinforce use.	• Subjective reports of appropriate grieving process and recovery.
• Will identify appropriate support systems.	• Assist client in identifying supports that have been helpful to her.	• Decreased reluctance to utilize available supports appropriately.
• Will return to normal level of functioning.	• Involve client in identifying short- and long-term goals.	• Return to home and work activities without interference from psychologic symptoms.

Visit http://go.jblearning.com/mentalhealth for additional care plans and exercises.

was a single mother—perhaps, she thought, if there had been a man in the household, he would have been better able to teach her son how to protect himself. She wondered if her son's murderers were still nearby. She wanted to look for them and see that they were caught. At the same time, she worried that she was a bad person and not true to her faith because she could not find it in her heart to forgive them.

The primary clinical intervention was to allow Ms. Q. to vent her feelings in a safe place and to help her tell her story and not to be overwhelmed by the intensity of her grief. The anxiety symptoms and traumatic flashbacks made Ms. Q. feel as if she were losing control. Ms. Q. was grieving appropriately and understood the extent of her loss. The only disturbances in her perception of the events were lingering feelings of guilt and the thought that she might have been able to change things.

Ms. Q. required assistance to strengthen and maintain her ability to cope during the temporary absence of the support person from victim's services. Often the network of social and community support is decreased by the crisis itself, loss of faith in the system, or the inability of former supports to bear the enormity of the tragedy. Victim's services becomes a valuable support that facilitates recovery and the client's ability to help the police and participate in court follow-up (Masters, 1998). The nurse taught Ms. Q. a self-management technique to help her control the symptoms of hyperventilation, if they recurred. The client was instructed to use deep-breathing techniques to relax and to slow her breathing further by placing her cupped hand or a paper bag over her mouth and nose. Arrangements were made for her to stay with her daughter. The client verbalized recognition of the need for follow-up and planned to return to victim's services for individual and group support.

and learning to cope with a new experience initially may lead to a better level of functioning, followed by a return to previous or lesser levels of coping as the individual begins to deal with the long-term effects of extreme stress.

Persistence and stability may not function for a particular system during times of crisis. Occasionally, resistance must be overcome. The client may need to experiment with different coping methods before finding an adequate method and completing successful adaptation. Existing social support systems may not be used because they are fragile and tenuous, inadequate for the task at hand, involved in crisis themselves, psychologically or geographically distant, or lacking the durability to sustain the client during a particular crisis. The client may need encouragement to develop a new or different network that combines new and old support systems or to utilize the support system in different ways if external resources are inadequate. Formal and informal support systems are facilitated by involvement with professional support systems or mutual self-help groups. The process of reorganization reinforces what has been learned, defines the experience and response, and illustrates what can be anticipated and applied in the future. Many factors impact the individual's ability to participate in social learning.

Bereavement and Complicated Grief

Bereavement, or uncomplicated grief, is a normal and acute response to loss. Just what is considered a normal response in bereavement varies widely between individuals and among cultural groups. The funeral and mourning rites of different communities and religions are formally culturally sanctioned methods for dealing with grief and usually include recognized expressions of support and mourning to help facilitate bereavement. Grief may occur in response to any loss such as a loss of functioning or may be anticipatory when the individual is forewarned of a possible loss such as in response to a terminal diagnosis or for caretakers of clients with chronic illnesses. During periods of bereavement it is not unusual for the client to experience periods of sadness and mourning, problems with appetite, insomnia, or loss of interest in usual activities. Somatic symptoms are also common. The client may be distracted and have problems with concentration or memory. The stages of grieving (denial, anger, bargaining, depression, and acceptance) are discussed in Chapter 17, "Mood Disorders." These stages may vary in intensity and sequence for varied durations after a loss. Anniversary dates, holidays and celebrations, or certain events may exacerbate symptoms of mourning or recall memories of the loss. Some individuals may seek additional support during this time. If the client has not successfully handled previous losses, if he experiences significant distress, or if he has inadequate supports, a crisis may develop. Crisis intervention can be helpful in these situations.

Complicated grief refers to a prolonged period of bereavement and impairment of normal functioning that may have many of the symptoms and characteristics of other mental disorders such as mood disorders or posttraumatic stress disorder. Complicated grief is associated with significant distress and disability (Boelen & van den Bout, 2008). The physical and psychologic symptoms of bereavement are chronic in complicated grief. Individuals with a past history of depression or trauma, a history of substance abuse or dependence, separation anxiety, or untimeliness or lack of preparation for a significant loss, as in the death of a child, may be at greater risk for development of complicated grief response. In complicated grief, there are problems with acceptance of the loss and a sense of hopelessness or loss of a sense of future. Clients with complicated bereavement may have problems with aspects of self-care and often withdraw from others and from social engagements. They may experience recurrent and intrusive thoughts about the loss as well as feelings of guilt for their own survival. Clients with complicated grieving may have a history of chronic depression and experience chronic feelings of loss and significant impairment of their interpersonal relationships and self-care. Complicated grief would be considered a disorder because of the degree of disturbance and the problems in functioning.

Physical or Sexual Abuse

Situations involving physical or sexual abuse can complicate the clinical course. The client may be in a potentially dangerous situation. The risks or threats of remaining in the present situation should be investigated with the client. He or she may not cognitively or emotionally recognize the potential threat and may need help in identifying and avoiding it. Feelings of guilt, shame, anger, or fear may interfere with the client's ability to make choices that are self-protective and protective of others. The client may have difficulty initiating and maintaining healthy relationships. At-risk clients may need assistance in identifying the necessary legal and social support systems available. The client may avoid or delay treatment for injuries or may be unable to cooperate with treatment. The nurse may need to identify the steps in intervention (e.g., reporting abuse, getting an order of protection, arranging for a safe environment such as a shelter or safe house, leaving a relationship) and assist the client in following through with these steps. For long-term problems, the client still may be overwhelmed with feelings of anger, guilt, or fear that interfere with present coping and relationships

Clinical Example

Ms. K. C. is a 60-year-old woman who lived with her parents until their deaths several years ago. She states she was so upset when her father died 6 years ago that she was unable to go to the funeral. Since her mother's death 3 years ago at age 85 years old, Ms. K. C. has been preoccupied with concerns that the doctors did not do everything possible to help her; she continues to call them periodically to question them about the care and what if something else were done. She has intrusive thoughts and images of her mother's last days in the hospital intensive care unit; her mother had a feeding tube, was lethargic, dependent upon a ventilator, and receiving dialysis. Ms. K. C. often finds herself talking to her mother and wishing that she were still present. Ms. K. C. continues to use the smaller of two bedrooms in the apartment and finds herself unable to clear out her mother's belongings or to rearrange the furniture. She feels guilty if she finds herself enjoying an activity because her mother is not there to experience it, so she is reluctant to celebrate holidays or family gatherings. She resents her brother for continuing to hold family celebrations at holidays and describes him as being disrespectful to their parents by focusing on his own family. Ms. K. C. worries that if she moves on as her family and friends encourage her, she will forget her mother.

and impair responses to other developmental and situational crises.

Risk of Suicide

The potential for suicide also complicates the clinical course. The nurse must identify the risk of suicide with direct questions. Thoughts about suicide should be taken seriously, and if the client states that action may follow, these verbalizations also should be taken seriously. The questions should focus on attempting to evaluate the nature of the suicidal ideation and to clarify whether it is accompanied by threats or specific plans. If the client has a plan, the nurse should note whether it is vague or specific and whether the client has access to the means. The client also should be questioned about past attempts and whether treatment or hospitalization followed these attempts. Suicidal gestures (i.e., threats rarely carried out or threats made in the presence of others so intervention is readily available) are not intended to be lethal attempts. A client with a history of high lethality (serious overdose, gunshot wound, jumping from heights) or near lethality (attempt made without notifying others and discovered accidentally) is at high risk for suicide. The presence or absence of available supports is important in determining potential risk. Clients who live alone, have experienced multiple losses, have limited social skills and resources, and have unsatisfactory or no relationships are at high risk for suicide. Alcohol, a depressant that lowers impulse control, is an important risk factor, as are other substances of abuse. Impaired cognitive ability can interfere with the client's competency to make valid, informed decisions.

Substance Abuse

Alcohol and substance abuse impede the client's ability to respond to crises, cloud the sensorium, and may precipitate a psychiatric emergency. Intoxication impairs insight and judgment, and it complicates assessment procedures because an intoxicated client is unable to cooperate with examination or treatment. Diagnostic blood work may indicate anemia or elevated liver enzymes, and physical assessment may indicate other medical problems associated with chronic alcohol use, such as cardiac or liver disease. An increased tolerance is indicated by the client's relatively alert state accompanying intoxication, high blood alcohol levels, and need for differing amounts and duration of intake. The client may experience blackouts or a history of withdrawal syndrome with decreased use.

The nurse identifies the risk of suicide by the use of direct questions to determine the nature of the suicidal ideation, the existence of a plan, and the client's ability to carry out the plan.

Alcohol and drug abuse and dependence must be treated first. Other interventions and treatments may have to wait until treatment is completed. The client with chronic alcohol or substance abuse may have poor support systems or supports that are no longer available for contact. These clients may have lost their job, family, support systems, and housing and may have legal problems. Most clients with a dual diagnosis of mental disorder and substance abuse have multiple problems. Assessment of the potential risk of withdrawal is an important determinant in psychiatric emergencies, as is the possible interaction of alcohol with other substances of abuse and pharmaceuticals.

Alcohol and substance abuse contribute to an increased risk of suicide.

Medical Illness

Problems requiring medical treatment such as injuries from a recent suicide attempt, physical or sexual abuse, or trauma are added stressors that prompt their own psychophysiologic responses. Clients with acute or chronic medical illness are vulnerable to the effects of acute stress reactions, the long-term consequences of adaptation to illness, and the accompanying physical symptoms and distress. The diagnosis and treatment affect clients who also may be responding to the threat of illness or to maturational

Evidence-Based Practice

Cutcliffe, Stevenson, Jackson, and Smith (2006) utilized Glaserian grounded theory (identifying a basic psychosocial process and establishing a credible theory) to study the role of psychiatric nurses in the care of the suicidal person. The core variable centered on reconnecting the person with humanity by reflecting an image of humanity, guiding the individual back to humanity, and learning to live. The authors identified the key processes to move the suicidal person from a death-oriented focus to a life-oriented focus. The nurse–patient relationship was described as copresencing. Further predictive research is indicated to identify specific suicidal behaviors and cognitive assumptions as well as specific nursing interventions involved.

or situational disturbances unrelated to the physical disorder. In addition, the client may have difficulty adhering to diagnostic and treatment regimens as a result of the symptoms of chronic medical or mental illness. Prescription medications, singly or in combination and even at prescribed doses and therapeutic levels, may cause acute or chronic problems. The client with asthma, for example, may benefit from the use of pharmaceuticals while experiencing uncomfortable side effects. The use of steroids may prompt the symptoms of an affective or a delusional disorder. Clients may experience adverse long-term effects from medications that benefit them greatly. Clients who take antiseizure medications and those who take antipsychotics must balance the potential benefits with the potential burdens treatment places on them.

Violence

Threats or actual violence also can complicate the clinical course. Clients with a history of alcohol or other substance abuse may present with uncontrolled aggressive or self-destructive behaviors. Clients with a history of brain injury may experience an impulsive loss of control, changes in their typical personality because of the injury, or delusion syndromes. Many clients with behavioral symptoms of physical or psychiatric illness experience periods of disorganized behavior or diminished capacity for making decisions and controlling volition. Disorganized behavior can present as withdrawal, illogical activity, negativism, excitation, or agitation. Irrational beliefs and magnified or wrongly perceived interactions with others and the environment can prompt abnormal responses. Issues involving intrafamily, interfamily, and workplace violence need to be reported and prevented whenever possible. Clients with a history of legal problems (e.g., recent arrest, past assaults, imprisonment) or gang membership are more likely to continue to be involved in violent acts. Acts of violence against healthcare workers are not unusual and are exacerbated by poor staffing, overcrowded physical environments, prolonged waiting time, and lack of health coverage.

This problem is not limited to the United States. In some places, legislation protects healthcare workers in the same manner as police and emergency workers.

Differential Diagnosis

Although the problem's initial description by the client or others suggests a psychiatric disorder, a careful assessment is necessary. Many organic and physical problems present as apparent functional psychiatric symptoms or behavioral manifestations related to psychiatric disorders. Cognitive, communication, and cultural problems may further complicate identification, assessment, and validation of the nurse's inferences. Past encounters with outside systems and agencies, belief systems concerning how to deal with emotions and medical or psychological problems, and experiences with illness or trauma all influence the client's communication with healthcare providers.

Evidence-Based Practice

Ryan, a 27-year-old man, collapsed at a sheltered workshop during a period of record high summer temperatures and was brought to the emergency department when staff at the workshop noted he seemed to be confused before he collapsed. In the emergency department, Ryan had a temperature of 103.6 degrees, elevated blood pressure, and rapid pulse, and he was oriented to person only. He was dressed in multiple layers of clothing, some of which were the custom of a religious group and some of which seemed to be his own idiosyncratic style. He had been incontinent of urine. The patient had a history of serious persistent mental illness and was taking a combination of several antipsychotic medications and a seizure medication; he also had a history of hypertension, for which he took Vaseretic (enalapril maleate/hydrochlorothiazide). The patient was treated for neuroleptic malignant syndrome.

As Ryan recovered, staff learned that he lived in a single room and did not have a fan or air conditioner. He was in the habit of making sure the window and door to the room were locked, and he usually walked to the workshop rather than accept a ride on the bus. In addition, Ryan stated he did not like to use the water cooler at the workshop because others used it; and he limited his use of fluids at home because he did not like to leave his room to use the bathroom in the residence.

Critical Thinking Question

In developing a comprehensive client assessment, what factors can facilitate or deter a client's ability to communicate with healthcare practitioners? What factors facilitate comprehensive service delivery?

It is important to speak with everyone involved to determine what happened and how the client usually responds to a crisis. The client's history (if available) and others with whom the client interacts can provide valuable information and assist the clinician in making sense of chaotic and disorganized situations. Often, there is no traditional family system to rely on for information. However, neighbors, landlords, service providers such as bartenders or beauticians, clergy, primary healthcare providers, and community agencies may have had previous contacts with and knowledge of the client.

It is important to try to fit all the varied perceptions of the client's history, insight, present behavior, and support systems into a holistic assessment that considers possible stressors, support systems, standards of care, and reasonable expectations for the success or failure of different options. Decision making and treatment selection vary widely based on available information.

People usually respond in familiar, fairly predictable patterns. If a client's response is unusual for him or her, an effort should be made to evaluate the situation and determine what changed and if there are alternative explanations for the change. Do not assume that a client with a history of chronic psychiatric problems has come to the emergency room for treatment of a psychiatric problem. To assess clients with a history of psychiatric problems, information should be recorded about their usual symptoms, treatment, and response and how these match with the presenting problem. For example, a client with an identified psychiatric history may present with confused and disorganized behavior. If previous contacts during psychiatric crises have been confined to times when the client was depressed with mood-congruent psychotic features, alternative explanations for the change in mental status should be identified. Disorientation is more likely related to an underlying medical disorder. Before presuming a psychiatric emergency, consider underlying medical problems; head injury or seizure; exposure to drugs, alcohol, or other toxins; and side effects from prescribed medications.

In some situations, people remain biased against clients with known psychiatric problems. It is im-

Clinical Example

Robert, a 23-year-old man, was brought to the emergency room following a suicide attempt. When interviewed by the psychiatric nurse, Robert was reflective and convincing in describing the suicide attempt as an impulsive, insignificant gesture that he now regretted. He stated that he was sorry that others had mistaken his actions and overreacted. Robert told the nurse that he would call his therapist for a crisis appointment and that he just wanted to take a shower, go home, and apologize to his family for causing problems.

The appearance of a calm client and a resolved situational disturbance is often deceiving. The emergency medical technicians who brought the client to the emergency room reported that the client was locked in his room and that after they forced entry, they found the client with a noose around his neck and a suicide note on the dresser. When contacted, the client's therapist stated that the client had not adhered to outpatient treatment plans, did not take medications as prescribed, and had a history of making nearly successful suicide attempts when he was depressed. The client's family stated that they were afraid to take the client home because he had made several threats in the past week and had been feeling increasingly hopeless because he had been unable to find a job whereas his younger brother had just graduated from college. The parents stated that they were exhausted from taking turns sitting up all night to watch him. In the past, they had been able to support the client but were worried that they could no longer sustain the same level of involvement, because the client's father was scheduled for open-heart surgery the following week. Recognizing the importance of the collateral information and the stressors experienced by the patient and the family, the nurse clinician in the emergency room was able to evaluate the seriousness and potential lethality of the situation.

portant to ensure that all clients receive the same standard of care. The physical complaints of clients with known psychiatric disorders should not be dismissed as somatic delusion or psychiatric symptoms. For example, clients with somatoform disorders (see Chapter 19) should have regular physical evaluations and evaluations of new symptoms so that new or concomitant physical problems are detected.

Clients with a history of medical or psychiatric problems may already take multiple medications, some of which have synergistic or competing effects. During a crisis or psychiatric emergency, clients may be unable to tell the interviewer all the medications they are taking or the reasons that they are taking a particular medication. The clinician should take nothing for granted and assume nothing. Clients may have their own supply of medication, may be taking another person's medication, or may be using additional substances. Clients may have been prescribed medications, but for a multitude of reasons may not be taking them as directed. The client may be seeing multiple healthcare practitioners who are unaware that other prescriptions have been written. Another possibility is that the client may have been prescribed a medication for a purpose unknown to the interviewer or triage. This includes many herbal and nutritional supplements that may have side effects of their own or may interact with prescribed medications.

When assessing a client's potential for violence, be aware of the client's affective, behavioral, and cognitive responses and your responses to the client. Learn to recognize cues of impending violence, such as increasing restlessness (inability to sit still, restlessness, pacing, agitation, kicking walls) and provocative verbal or physical behaviors (angry shouting, threats and cursing, raised fist, menacing posture, closure of territorial boundaries, picking up a weapon).

Management and Treatment

Management of psychiatric crises and emergencies begins with appropriate triage, assessment, and differentiation among functional or psychologic problems, organic or medical problems, and substance abuse problems. Determining the present disturbance includes evaluation of the potential for violence and appropriate intervention. The nurse should ask directly about issues of abuse, suicide, and violence and take the appropriate protective measures or protocols for reporting. Protection of the client, potential victim, and staff is important. The assessment of safety issues is as important with discharge arrangements as it is with the initial triage. Cognitive behavioral therapy is useful in dealing with stress and generalized anxiety. Crisis intervention techniques are useful in many situations. One novel approach to cognitive therapy found that playing Tetris for half an hour, giving clients a sense of control of sensory-perception cues, reduced trauma flashbacks in the following week (Holmes, James, Coode-Bate, & Deeprose, 2009). Hopkins (1994) emphasized the need for nurses to recognize the family's distress, particularly in trauma situations, and to provide them with comfort, information, visits with the client, time to adjust to the impact of change and role shifts, and the opportunity to meet with staff to discuss treatment and expected outcomes.

Occasionally, treatment options are limited by extrinsic factors such as legal constraints, insurance (or lack of insurance and eligibility for government-sponsored entitlements), and limits on disposition planning from lack of space or facilities, demands of managed care contracts, or other personnel and resource limitations. If the problems are not under the clinician's control, the choice of options, limits, and reasons that one option was chosen over another should be documented. Knowledge of internal and external systems and negotiation skills have become increasingly necessary both for survival and for advocacy.

Evidence-Based Practice

A study comparing hospital staff and relatives caring for clients with schizophrenia and depression showed that nearly one fourth of both groups showed a high degree of burnout. Subjects were interviewed using the Maslach Burnout Inventory, which measured emotional exhaustion, depersonalization, and personal accomplishment. A limitation of the groups was that the caregivers with the highest symptoms of burnout were more likely to have already withdrawn from caretaking responsibilities. Another limitation was the use of untrained staff in the hospitals studied. The study suggested that mutual self-help groups, psychoeducation groups, and support programs for partners of the mentally ill might be beneficial. For professional staff members, specific training was suggested (Angermeyer, Bull, Bernert, Dietrich, & Kopf, 2006). The study suggested that better qualified staff would cope better with burnout. Further studies are needed regarding the common factors in professional and family caregivers' burnout in dealing with chronic mental illness and how both groups can be supported.

Nursing Interventions

Nursing interventions identify and address specific problematic symptoms and their commonly associated nursing diagnoses. Skilled interpersonal therapeutic intervention offers emotional support and empathy, an opportunity for catharsis, a model for interpersonal relationships, feedback regarding clients' thoughts and behaviors, and education to facilitate change. If the client is very disorganized or has regressed, the nurse may need to provide specific directives on how to meet basic daily needs. In most crisis and emergency situations, the nurse is concerned with immediate and short-term goals. The client may need physical or emotional attention, medication, and assistance in mobilizing resources, or direction and supervision. Assessment of the client's ability and reliability to follow the treatment plan is essential. The clinician needs to assess to what degree the initial reason for treatment was resolved. Total resolution may not be reasonably expected, but there should be some symptom relief or hope that further treatment will be reasonably successful. The availability and reliability of support systems help determine which treatment and follow-up plans are likely to succeed.

Stress Reduction

Comfort measures, distraction, touch (if tolerated by the client), and the nurse's quiet presence soothe clients who may be feeling vulnerable. Stress-reduction techniques are an important adjunct to other treatment interventions. During a crisis or psychiatric emergency, the client may be too anxious or preoccupied to participate fully in other treatment interventions. The nurse can be involved in offering support and may be a means for the client to become involved in self-management tasks. These stress-reduction techniques are easy to learn and to incorporate into treatment planning. The client may benefit from learning simple relaxation techniques.

The natural impulse in times of stress is to stop breathing or to breathe rapidly. Teaching the client deep-breathing techniques involves him or her in self-care and takes the focus off distressing symptoms and feelings of helplessness. First, have the client take a deep breath and release it. Occasionally, it helps to have the client place his or her hand over the abdomen to feel the difference between shallow and deep breathing. Instruct the client to take a deep breath, hold it, and let it out slowly. This can be done over several minutes, gradually instructing the client to take deeper and longer breaths.

In progressive relaxation, the client is taught to tense and relax various muscle groups alternately for several seconds and then to increase gradually the length of time the muscles are tensed and relaxed. Clients are taught to tense and relax the toes, gradually move up and tense and relax the legs, trunk, upper limbs, and then the face.

Meditation is another relaxation technique. The client selects a word or phrase and slowly repeats the sounds while concentrating on slowing the breathing. In guided imagery, the client is presented with a vivid description of a pleasant or relaxing experience. The therapist uses a calm voice and images of as many sensory experiences as possible. Suggestions for successfully mastering an experience or facing troublesome symptoms can be incorporated.

In the technique of desensitization, the situation that causes stress is broken down into small, tolerable steps. This helps the client focus on manageable steps that can be successfully completed.

Working closely with people in crisis situations is demanding work. To prevent staff burnout, it is important to give the staff the opportunity to express their concerns and frustrations, access to support in dealing with the physical and emotional responses they experience, and ample clinical supervision. Nurses must know when they need help and when to ask for it. Too often, clinicians believe they can help others without taking care of themselves. This response leads to problems for the individual experiencing the stress. It also affects others in the environment in terms of lost productivity and may lead to lateral or horizontal workplace violence directed at coworkers.

The following principles guide the nurse's interaction with clients who present in crisis:
Introduce yourself.
Present a calm, nonthreatening demeanor.
Speak in a low to normal tone.
Attempt to make eye contact.
Respect the client's personal space.
Explain what you are going to do and what is going to happen next.
Avoid competitive situations.

When encouraging a client to verbalize feelings, it may be necessary to monitor and to titrate the client's catharsis (discharge of intense emotion) by pacing the interview and switching from specific to more general topics.

Stress-reduction techniques include:
Progressive relaxation
Deep-breathing exercises
Meditation
Guided imagery

Desensitization uses relaxation induction to help the client cope with increasingly stressful images or situations.

Considerations for Client and Family Education

- Focus on the present and the immediate problem.
- Provide specific directions on what needs to be done first and plan for the next step.
- Investigate options for possible support for the client and for the caretakers.
- Assist in developing perspective of the precipitating stressor and coping style.

Clinical Example 

Everyone acknowledged that Barbara was a model nurse; she was just not the easiest person to work with. She was extremely competent and very career oriented. She volunteered regularly to take on the most difficult assignments and districts, never complained when asked to work overtime, and was inevitably the one who worked alone when the unit was short, letting the other nurses utilize the unlicensed assistive personnel. She occasionally took her breaks, rarely took lunch, and never called in sick. She often commented that it was easier to do things herself rather than ask for help because no one could do things as well as she could. She had little patience for others who did not meet her standard of perfection. She never seemed to have anything positive to say about her coworkers, the administration, or the hospital. Her coworkers were reluctant to ask her for help because she seemed so irritable and hypercritical. Her patients had no complaints, but said they did not want to ask for anything or bother her because she always seemed so busy and so tired. Over time Barbara had isolated herself from other staff and rarely participated in unit social activities or met with friends outside of work. Staff felt that some intervention was needed when Barbara was overheard telling the family of an orientee who she was not involved in precepting that the orientee was incompetent and should not be allowed near patients.

Critical Thinking Question 

Identify some strategies for recognizing signs of burnout in yourself or a colleague. What are some possible sources of support or organizational resources that can be used in dealing with this problem?

Crisis Intervention

Crisis intervention focuses on a particular identified disturbance and is meant to be brief and flexible. The first step in crisis intervention is the assessment of the client's perception of the present event, prior and present coping mechanisms, and available situational supports. Clients are encouraged to tell the stories of their crises and how they experienced them. A problematic crisis results when one or more balancing factors (realistic perception of event, adequate supports, viable coping mechanisms, ability to incorporate new methods of dealing with the situation) are absent or inadequate (**Table 7-2**). Intervention primarily involves, but is not limited to, four goals:

1. Assisting the client in developing intellectual understanding
2. Gaining awareness of present feelings
3. Examining alternate coping mechanisms
4. Reopening the social system to incorporate new people and possibilities

The goal is to restore, replace, *or* revitalize the missing balancing factors to resolve the immediate crisis situation. Reinforcement of learning, successful adaptive coping mechanisms, and anticipatory guidance for future crises are important for resolution (Aguilera, 1998). An assessment includes any predisposing factors, the perception of the precipitating event and any factors perpetuating the crisis (**Figure 7-3**).

Psychiatric Emergencies

The management of psychiatric emergencies focuses on immediate treatment goals. The first step in treatment and in the prevention of violence is the development of a therapeutic relationship or therapeutic alliance with the client using communication and deescalation skills (Zeller, 2010). To provide a safe environment, the nurse must ensure the client's safety as well as the safety of other clients and staff. If a client threatens self-harm or suicide, the client and the environment should be checked to limit access to potentially harmful objects or medications. The nurse may need to separate the client from the family if the client makes threats of elder, child, or spousal abuse. The nurse should take an active role in identifying possible cases of abuse, in client assessment, and in intervention. In abuse cases, the nurse should know the various reporting mechanisms and whether reporting of cases is mandatory. This may vary. For example, the reporting of child abuse and legal protocols for spousal assault may be mandatory, but the reporting of elder abuse may not be.

If the client threatens violence, isolating him or her in an area with minimal environmental stimuli may be necessary—a place with no access to potential weapons, victims, or hostages where the client can be closely observed and, if necessary, contained. If the client has threatened to harm another and violence is a risk, the clinician has the duty to warn the potential victim. This is based on the decision in *Tarasoff*

Table 7-2 Nursing Interventions for Clients with Complicated Grief

Nursing Diagnosis	Nursing Interventions	Rationales
Dysfunctional grieving	Offer presence.	Decrease sense of isolation.
	Provide an opportunity for nonjudgmental listening in a safe environment.	Establish trust and enable sharing of feelings.
	Provide a safe environment and time for the client to recall feelings of loss and retell events.	Explain how feelings are a normal response. Impaired verbal communication increases sense of isolation. Help establish realistic perspective of events. Allow for reality testing and support.
	Screen for other mental health issues and suicide.	The presence of other mental health issues may complicate grieving and increase risk of suicide.
	Screen for ability to engage in self-care activities.	Feelings of guilt, hopelessness, and isolation may place the client at risk.
	Identify past and present effective coping mechanisms and reinforce use.	Feelings of worthlessness, guilt, or depression may cause distress and limit the client's ability to engage in self-care activities. Loss of appetite, weight loss, and sleep dysfunction can accompany depression.
	Assess adequacy and availability of effective coping mechanisms.	Reduce sense of helplessness. Prevent crisis and assist in recovery.
	Discuss alternative coping mechanisms if present coping is ineffective.	Reinforce use of effective coping mechanisms and self-management techniques to reduce feelings of anxiety and inability to deal with loss. Assist in development of new coping skills to meet demands of new situations in order to prevent crisis.
	Assist in identification of supports that have been helpful.	Decrease sense of isolation and reestablish necessary supports and comfort.
	Assess adequacy and availability of support system.	Provide links to additional services if necessary in order to prevent crisis.
	Involve the client in identifying short- and long-term goals.	Encourage client to establish priorities and participation. Planning for the future reduces hopelessness and helplessness.
	Teaching and anticipatory guidance appropriate to the client's needs.	Assist the client in problem-solving skills and feelings of mastery. Assists in decreasing anxiety and sense of helplessness.
	Discuss how others in the family and culture deal with feelings of loss and separation.	Find ways in which client can memorialize feeling regarding loved ones in a culturally sanctioned manner. Participation in rituals or memorial ceremonies can create a sense of closure.
	Identify the positive things about the deceased loved one and the relationship and how these things can be remembered.	Facilitate grief work and validates feelings of loss. Identifies positive aspects of feelings and how these feelings can be expressed and connected to other aspects of life and relationships. Completes the process of letting go and the cycle of life.

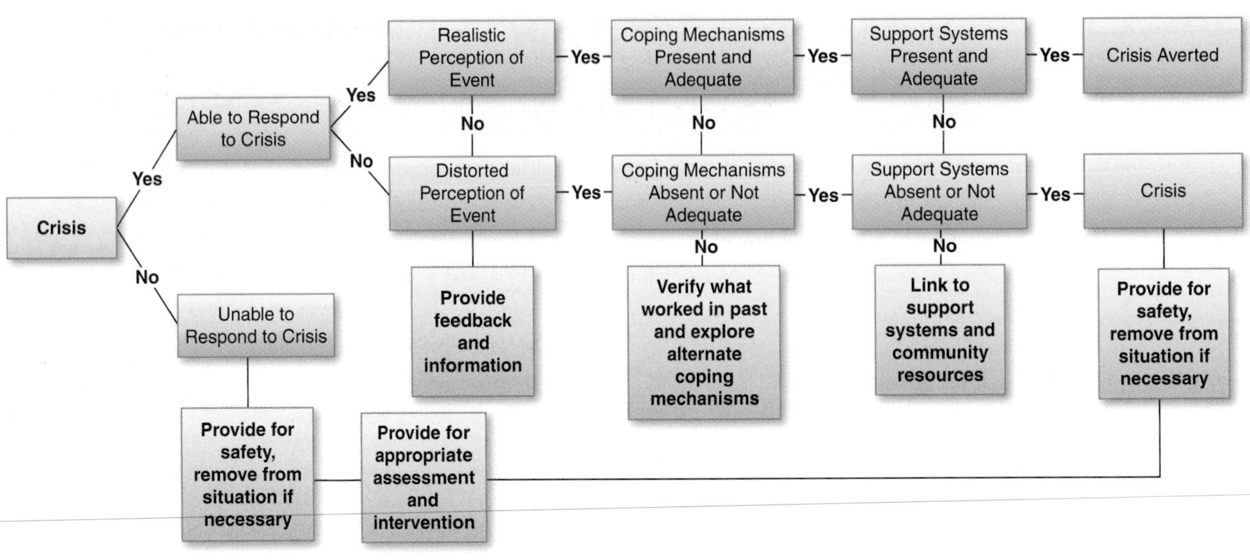

Figure 7-3 Crisis Theory

v. Regents of University of California (1976), which stated that it is the legal duty of the therapist to warn a potential victim of danger. The nurse should be aware of the legal and professional guidelines regarding client restraint and seclusion.

Medication

"A thorough crisis evaluation requires understanding of the client's premorbid personality, support systems, previous episodes of decompensation, past treatments, and the interaction of a precipitant with a particular personality structure." (Mindnich & Hart, 1995, p. 28)

Crisis intervention involves the use of cognitive and short-term psychotherapeutic techniques to help the client gain a realistic perception of events, become aware of feelings, develop active coping skills, and experience social support.

During an emergency, medicating a client may have different implications, depending on whether the client accepts the medication on a voluntary or involuntary basis. This varies among agencies and legal jurisdictions. The nurse should be aware of the possible legal problems when administering medication on an involuntary basis. When administering any medication, the nurse should not assume that the client understands what is going on or that the client is incapable of understanding. Let the client know that a medication has been ordered, what it is, why it was ordered, anticipated action and side effects, and who will administer the medication. In most situations, medication is first offered in oral form (sublingual, concentrate, tablets, or capsules) before intramuscular form. The development of sublingual (Asenapine [Saphris]) and inhaled (loxapine [Loxitane]) medications offer the opportunity for a rapid and less threatening form of medication (Ng, Zeller, & Rhoades, 2010).

In rapid tranquilization, the client is given neuroleptic or sedating medication or both on a regular, frequent basis until the intended effect of control or sedation is achieved. When rapid tranquilization is required, many medications can be administered intravenously. If the nurse believes that administering the medication may cause problems, it is a good idea to alert others and have them available in the area to assist if necessary.

Once a medication is given, it is important to monitor the effects of pharmacotherapy and document the response and any untoward effects. A particular medication is selected based on its action, duration, effects, synergism or interaction with other medications, and the client's past response to a particular medication regimen. Many psychiatric medications come in time-release or long-acting depot forms. The nurse must know what medications have been prescribed and what medications have actually been taken. For example, if a client is taking a depot medication, such as a long-acting form of haloperidol (Haldol) or fluphenazine (Prolixin), the nurse must know when the client received the last injection and when the next injection is scheduled. Taking a medication as prescribed requires the capacity to understand its purpose and benefits and a commitment to adhere to a treatment schedule. Involving the client in treatment planning, having flexible healthcare providers and clients, and providing anticipatory guidance and information regarding medication support groups improve adherence to medication schedules.

If a client's agitation continues to escalate and presents a significant danger to the client or others, the nurse must set appropriate limits in a clear, calm,

Evidence-Based Practice

Murphy (2002) reviewed consensus guidelines for the treatment of potentially assaultive clients. Use of nonphysical interventions such as verbal intervention, voluntary medication, deescalation techniques, or show of force should be tried first. Research indicates that oral medication such as risperidone and a benzodiazepine or derivative or, less commonly, olanzapine or ziprasidone, can be used as an effective alternative to intramuscular Haldol (haloperidol) and may limit side effects. Before restraints are used, the client should be evaluated by the appropriately authorized licensed independent healthcare practitioner (doctor of medicine, PA, nurse practitioner) and, if indicated, the family or healthcare proxy should be notified. Murphy suggests that an appropriate range of responses to potentially violent behavior may lead to a decrease in client and staff injury and patient side effects, an increase in long-term patient treatment compliance, and an improvement in staff–client relationships. Implications for further research include evaluation of guidelines across practice areas and evaluation of various medications in emergency situations.

matter-of-fact manner and avoid competitive or conflicting confrontations with the client. Responses from all the staff involved should be consistent. Methods used to limit physical interventions include assessment, observation, verbal intervention, reduction of environmental stimuli, appropriate medication, awareness of territoriality, and physical space issues. Negotiation and conflict resolution skills are helpful but not always sufficient to deescalate potentially dangerous situations. If the client is about to lose control or has lost control, the staff may need to physically intervene and attempt to restrict the activity of or restrain the client. Preparation involves having an adequate number of experienced, properly trained staff and environmental controls in place. A course in self-protection and the management of violent clients with regular policy reviews and simulation of procedures may be included. The client may initiate a request for restraints, or may have given direction that restraints can be used in certain circumstances, or may have appointed a proxy to make such decisions in an emergency. Restraints are discussed in more detail in the following section.

Evidence-Based Practice

A review of the literature on deescalation (Cowin, 2003) showed that deescalation is an effective method when used by staff in dealing with potentially violent patients. Education in deescalation techniques is particularly effective with new or temporary staff. Implications for further nursing research include investigation of conflict and response of staff and patients as well as studies across different practice areas as to the effectiveness of the techniques for prevention and intervention.

Restraints or Seclusion

Restraint or seclusion use is limited to emergencies where there is a risk that the client may harm him- or herself or others. To control extremely agitated or potentially violent psychiatric clients, as in a medical code management situation, the nurse should establish the person in charge of the team and identify each person's responsibility. An accepted routine should be in place as well as a method of calling upon ancillary support staff, including security guards, to ensure the presence of sufficient personnel to manage an emergency. If the opportunity is available, meet briefly when the team is assembled to plan for problems and review procedures. Initially, a show of force (i.e., having enough people present in the environment ready to intervene if necessary) may be all that is necessary to facilitate the client's cooperation. The nurse may still be able to talk the client down, and verbal intervention should be employed to calm the client, communicate expectations, have the client consider alternatives, and offer acceptable choices and consequences (limit setting, medication, physical restraint, seclusion). The client may withdraw, accept medication, or even voluntarily agree to restraints. However, if a takedown is necessary, having sufficient staff present ensures safety for both the client and staff. At least five people should be present, one person to protect the client's head and one for each limb. Safety restraining nets or other physical barriers such as mattresses can be used. Once the client is safe, he or she may need to be moved to another area, or the staff may utilize physical restraints or seclusion.

Legal restrictions and agency policies regarding ordering, assessment, observation, treatment, documentation, and time of use may vary, and the

The Centers for Medicare and Medicaid Services require training for staff in evaluating treatment approaches. This includes identification of possible staff and patient behaviors or environmental stimuli that might trigger use of restraints and seclusion, the safe application and monitoring of these procedures, alternate treatment techniques, and formal notification of clients and their families to ensure that client rights are protected and safety is ensured. See www.cms.hhs.gov.

nurse should be aware of the legal and professional responsibilities inherent in the use of restraints and seclusion. Joint Commission and Centers for Medicare and Medicaid Services regulations specify who is able to start restraints (a licensed independent practitioner), and times of observation and reevaluation. In an emergency situation, the RN may initiate this intervention, but the client must be evaluated by the person responsible for ordering this procedure within a short period of time, usually 1 hour. The order is time limited, and times for a valid order differ for an adult and for a child. The client should be observed while in restraints. This may vary with the age of the client and the types of restraints used. In addition, the client needs to be released from restraints at regular intervals (e.g., with four-point restraints, one limb at a time can be released if necessary for client and staff safety). The client may have voluntarily requested to be placed in restraints or may have advanced care protocols or a healthcare proxy. As part of the nursing assessment, the client should be asked if he or she has ever been a victim of abuse or has been assaulted. If possible, the client should be asked what helps him or her calm down if he or she is upset or agitated and whether he or she has ever been placed in restraints or seclusion during previous hospitalizations.

Staff need to reassess the use of restraints and discontinue their use as soon as it is appropriate. The order for restraints needs to be renewed periodically, usually every 4 hours for adults, and the person ordering the restraints needs to reevaluate the client periodically, usually every 8 hours. When the client is released from restraints, the nurse can help the client reintegrate into the milieu. Once these interventions are used, their implications should be discussed with the client, allowing him or her to express thoughts, fears, and/or resentment and to explore alternative coping mechanisms.

Trust the feelings and intuitions you and your team members experience. If you feel threatened or frightened, ensure your own safety and the safety of the client and others.

Staff themselves also must have the time to review the event and have support to deal with the effects of any potentially traumatic event. Preparedness and training to deal with emergencies, sufficient staffing and break times, and, if needed, voluntary self-referral to employee assistance programs or counseling services outside the employment setting are helpful. Defusing is an effective method of dealing with these stressors within the regular work shift. If there are other, more longstanding workplace issues or an acute overwhelming trauma, utilization of other postintervention treatment or psychological first aid techniques may be helpful.

Disasters

Disasters may involve an individual, a group of individuals, a family, or larger communities. Many institutions and community agencies (hospitals; police, fire, and emergency medical departments; volunteer rescue teams; ambulance corps; federalized disaster teams; American Red Cross) incorporate planning and preparation for potential disasters into their general operating plans. Part of the planning process includes identifying resources, such as human resources, supplies, and communication networks; coordination of services with other public and private agencies; formation of crisis teams; and training and simulation exercises. The responsibilities of different team members, types of training, and available services may vary. The nurse may be a program administrator, triage nurse, team member or leader, consultant, community activist, or volunteer.

Sharon Stanley RN, PdD, RS, chief nurse of the American Red Cross and Director of Disaster Health and Disaster Mental Health, emphasized the need to have a nurse-led community response model aligned with Institute of Medicines's *The Future of Nursing: Leading Change, Advancing Health* report recommendation to remove scope of practice barriers. She stated "within the chaos that can occur during a disaster, no amount of written material can address every health situation that may arise. The nurse-led disaster health services community response model allows the Red Cross Team to provide the best in care while partnering with community health care systems on the ground to better address disaster client needs" (American Red Cross, 2011). As pointed out by Nancy McKelvey, RN, MSN, former chief nurse of the American Red Cross, "nurses bring a public trust; they bring an ability to translate technical knowledge into lay language; and they bring their whole health background to the table" (Palmer, 2002, p. 68). Preparedness is a key factor in disaster work, and nurses should be knowledgeable about their own role in the disaster plan at their place of employment as well as local, state, and national programs. Coordinating responses of workers and volunteers, maintaining services to the community, and planning for short- and long-term needs are important facets of disaster work. Training in crisis intervention techniques is necessary, as is the rapid mobilization of resources and response capabilities. In discussing the ethical questions of reporting for work in a disaster, Chaffee (2006) examined factors such as the potential for dan-

Clinical Example 

A state trooper had just completed his basic training when he was sent to New York City after September 11, 2001. During a rest period, he was able to discuss his feelings regarding his assignment with a psychiatric nurse who had volunteered to work with rescue workers and survivors. The young trooper explained that this was his first time in New York City and that he had grown up in a rural upstate area. Not only was being in a large urban area a new experience for him, he had experienced a series of worsts. First he thought that seeing the aftermath of the destruction was the worst thing he would ever experience. Then, it was helping survivors and family members search for missing friends and families that seemed to be the worst ever. It was even harder being the one who told people that the person they were searching for had not survived. Still there were more worsts to come—accompanying family members as they tried to identify remains and assignments to help bring remains to the city morgue for identification. The trooper was dealing with a series of situational and maturational crises.

This was an opportunity for the nurse to help the trooper tell his story of the event, verbalize his emotional response to and distress regarding the trauma, and discuss normal adaptive reactions and stress management.

ger, the nurse's relationship to her or his clients and to her or his own family, degree of training, and duty schedules and other work or volunteer obligations.

Critical Thinking Question 

What factors would influence your decision to respond to a disaster situation? Do professionals have an obligation to prepare for disasters and to respond?

In disaster response, basic physical needs take precedence. Immediate treatment concerns include appropriate triage for medical and psychosocial intervention, provisions for safety and shelter, and establishing communication. The primary intervention may be directed at helping victims withstand the initial effects of shock and trauma. It is important to monitor responses to the acute stresses, projected recovery phases, and long-term consequences (Hardin, 1996). Intervention for victims and survivors usually includes referral for appropriate follow-up with clinics, community agencies, or support groups and mutual self-help groups, as well as access to postintervention treatment or psychological first aid and voluntary referral for team members and volunteers.

Pharmacology

During times of acute stress or crisis, medications are sometimes used as an adjunct to other treatments in

Clinical Example 

Suzanne is a 32-year-old woman who relocated to another area after the loss of her home and job in New Orleans due to flooding. After recovering from the devastation, Suzanne felt she was managing well and that she was rebuilding her life. She married her fiancé, who had family in the area, and soon became pregnant. During the second trimester, the client found herself becoming more and more depressed, tearful for no reason, and unable to sleep or eat. The client sought help from her nurse midwife who referred her to a local mental health center. Suzanne told the staff she felt overwhelmed by everything that was happening to her, the changes in her life and in her body. She described how she missed her old friends and neighborhood. There she was surrounded by familiar people and things. She had lost all her family photographs and sentimental artifacts from her mother and grandmother in the flood. In speaking with the nurse at the mental health center, the client remembered that the anniversary of her mother's death a few years before and of Hurricane Katrina took place in the same month.

Active listening was the key nursing intervention. The nurse was able to provide the patient with an opportunity to verbalize painful emotions, recognize how the response to stress was normal, deal with the normal stages of bereavement, and begin to plan for the future.

order to target specific symptoms such as anxiety or disturbances in sleep.

Selective serotonin reuptake inhibitors, such as escitalopram (Lexapro), citalopram (Celexa), paroxetine (Paxil), fluoxetine (Prozac), and sertraline (Zoloft), are considered to be effective in the treatment of anxiety. Less typical medications such as the serotonin-norepinephrine reuptake inhibitor venlafaxine (Effexor) and the anxiolytic pregabalin (Lyrica), a gabapentinoid, are also effective, as is buspirone (BuSpar). Some tricyclic antidepressants and benzodiazepines are used at times but are considered of limited use. Tricyclic antidepressants are noted to have low tolerance due to side effects, and like buspirone (BuSpar), may take up to 2 weeks for effects to be noted; they should not be used along with a monoamine oxidase inhibitor. Use of benzodiazepines has an association with the development of tolerance, a potential for abuse, and the danger of development of withdrawal symptoms with long-term use. Buspirone (BuSpar) should not be used in clients with seizure disorders (Baldwin & Polkinghorn, 2000). Sleep disturbances are covered in Chapter 22.

At times, medications are used in the prevention and treatment of PTSDs. Selective serotonin reuptake inhibitors such as citalopram (Celexa), escitalopram (Lexapro), sertraline (Zoloft), fluoxetine (Prozac), and paroxetine (Paxil) are often the first-line medications used; recommendations for use are that they may be needed for up to 1 year after the significant event. Trials with benzodiazepines have not been considered to be effective. In clients who have been refractory to treatment, studies indicate that a combination of selective serotonin reuptake inhibitors and atypical antipsychotic medications such as olanzapine (Zyprexa), risperidone (Risperdal), and quetiapine (Seroquel) have been used. For treatment of refractory clients with mood symptoms, combinations of selective serotonin reuptake inhibitors and mood stabilizers such as lamotrigine (Lamictal), valproate (Depakene), and carbamazepine (Tegretol) have been effective (Portier, Bakker, van Balkom, & Stein, 2005).

Summary

Clients are extremely vulnerable during times of crisis, emergency, or disaster. Psychiatric emergencies or disaster situations bring rapid changes, and lives may be at risk. Triage and differentiation between urgent and emergent situations and between medical and psychologic problems are important. An acute response to stress and trauma is normal, just as bereavement is a normal grief response and in most cases is self-limiting. Crisis intervention is used to treat maturational, developmental, and situational disturbances and involves an assessment of balancing factors such as the client's perception of the crisis, typical coping mechanisms, and the availability of support systems. In crisis intervention, the goal is to assist the client return to baseline functioning by assisting in learning and problem solving, helping the client develop new coping skills and provide links to possible support from others. As a result of the life-threatening potential of psychiatric emergencies, treatment usually focuses first on the immediate problems of proving safety and protection from harm from self or others. Follow-up for crises and emergencies may include outpatient or inpatient treatment or referral to mutual self-help groups. Crisis intervention is intended to be short term, flexible, and pragmatic. Treatment of victims of disasters involves immediate assessment; psychosocial support for individuals, groups, or communities; and referral for follow-up to stabilize functioning and minimize the risk of chronic stress reactions. Support and postintervention treatment or psychological first aid should be made available to staff to prevent burnout, compassion fatigue, or vicarious traumatization.

Annotated References

Aguilera, D. C. (1998). *Crisis intervention: Theory and methodology* (8th ed.). St. Louis, MO: Mosby-Year Book.

This classic text is an excellent guide for those interested in crisis intervention. Clear situational examples and guidelines are provided for applying crisis theory, problem solving, and short-term therapy techniques. Updated sections on legal implications of crisis work, professional Internet use and abuse, and violence are included.

American Psychiatric Association. (2000). *Diagnostic and statistical manual of mental disorders* (4th ed., text rev.). Washington, DC: Author.

This is the fourth edition, with text revision, of the American Psychiatric Association's official nomenclature of psychiatric conditions and disorders. It provides a systematic listing of the official codes and categories, a description of the multiaxial system for diagnosis, and diagnostic criteria for each of the disorders. It is used by psychiatrists, physicians, psychologists, registered nurses, social workers, therapists, and other mental health workers in all clinical settings.

American Red Cross. (2011) American Red Cross Nurse-led Community Response Model Aligns with Institute of Medicine Recommendations for Future of Nursing. Retrieved from www.redcross.org
Press release for new nurse-led disaster community response model.

Angermeyer, M. C., Bull, N., Bernert, S., Dietrich, S., & Kopf, A. (2006). Burnout of caregivers: A comparison of partners of psychiatric clients and nurses. *Archives of Psychiatric Nursing, 20*(4), 158–165.
This study compared German hospital staff and family caregivers and showed that one quarter of each group scored high on burnout when dealing with clients with chronic mental illness.

Baldwin, D. S., & Polkinghorn, C. (2000). *Evidence-based pharmacotherapy of generalized anxiety disorders in evidence-based psychopharmacology*. Cambridge, UK: Cambridge University Press.
This is a review of treatment of generalized anxiety disorders.

Binder, E. B., Bradley, R. G., Liu, W., Epstein, M. P., Deveau, T. C., Mercer, K. B., . . . Ressler, K. J. (2008). Association of FKBP5 polymorphisms and childhood abuse with risk of posttraumatic stress disorder symptoms in adults. *Journal of the American Medical Association, 299*(11), 1291.
This article reports on a cross-sectional study of genetic and environmental risk factors in clinic patients with significant levels of childhood abuse to determine gene-environment interactions and genetic polymorphisms of FKBP5.

Boelen, P. A., & van den Bout, J. (2008) Complicated grief and uncomplicated grief are distinguishable constructs. *Psychiatry Research, 157*(1–3) 311–314.
This article discusses differentiated symptoms of uncomplicated and complicated grief in a group of 242 mourners who were at least 6 months postloss.

Burgess, A. W., & Hartman, C. R. (1996). Rape trauma and posttraumatic stress disorder. In A. B. McBride & J. K. Austin (Eds.), *Psychiatric-mental health nursing: Integrating the behavioral and biological sciences* (pp. 53–81). Philadelphia, PA: W. B. Saunders.
This chapter identifies the biologic and structural changes that occur when a client has a traumatic experience, and it details the application of various therapeutic models and nursing interventions in case studies of rape and posttraumatic stress disorder.

Callahan, J. (2000). Crisis theory and crisis intervention in emergencies. In P. M. Kleespies (Ed.), *Emergencies in mental health practice: Evaluation and management* (pp. 22–40). New York, NY: Guilford Press.
This chapter discusses the history and current theories of crisis work and applicable frameworks.

Chaffee, M. (2006). Making the decision to report to work in a disaster. *American Journal of Nursing, 106*(9), 54–67.
This article discusses the impact of disaster on the healthcare delivery system and the individual nurse's ethical decision making in terms of relationships to family, community, employer, clients, and companion animals.

Charney, A. E., & Pearlman, L. A. (2000). The ecstasy and the agony: The impact of disaster and trauma work on the self of the clinician. In P. M. Kleespies (Ed.), *Emergencies in mental health practice: Evaluation and management* (pp. 418–435). New York, NY: Guilford Press.
This chapter discusses countertransference concerns and roles of the therapeutic helper in crisis work and provides suggestions for protection from vicarious traumatization.

Chiles, J. A., & Strosahl, K. (1995). *The suicidal client: Principles of assessment, case management*. Washington, DC: American Psychiatric Press.
This guidebook discusses assessment, crisis management, and treatment of suicidal clients. It provides useful hints on how to manage clients with repeated suicidal behaviors and includes a description of the use of therapeutic contracts and crisis cards.

Chrousos, G. P., & Gold, P. W. (1992). The concepts of stress and stress system disorders: Overview of physical and behavioral homeostasis. *Journal of the American Medical Association, 267*(9), 1244–1252.
This article discusses the stress system response as a V-shaped curve of hypo- and hyperfunctioning. It suggests that chronic response can lead to disease, particularly stress-related disorders, and that this would impact diagnosis and treatment of stress-related disorders.

Cowin, L. (2003). De-escalating aggression and violence in the mental health setting. *Inter-*

national Journal of Mental Health Nursing, 12(1), 64–73.
This article reviews the use of deescalation techniques as an intervention to decrease the potential for violence.

Cutcliffe, J. R., Stevenson, C., Jackson, S., & Smith, P. (2006). A modified grounded theory study of how psychiatric nurses work with suicidal people. *International Journal of Nursing Studies, 43*(7), 791–802.
This article is an investigation of the nurse–client relationship and identifies the concept of copresencing.

Dreyfus, J. K. (1987). Nursing assessment of the ED client with psychiatric symptoms: A quick reference. *Journal of Emergency Nursing, 13*(5), 278–282.
This article provides clear, step-by-step guidelines for performing a complete assessment of a client with psychiatric symptoms. The author covers the triage and posttriage phases of assessment, staff and client safety issues, and commonly seen diagnoses in the emergency room. It is very useful for anyone involved in triage or crisis work.

Everly, G. S., Jr., & Mitchel, J. T. (2008). *Integrated crisis intervention and disaster mental health*. Ellicott City, MD: Chevron.
Based on the Johns Hopkins University model, this book gives practical advice regarding roles of crisis intervention and other mental health aspects of disasters.

Fisher, H. L. (1989). Psychiatric crises: Making the most of an emergency room visit. *Journal of Psychosocial Nursing, 27*(11), 4–8.
This article discusses why clients go to the general or psychiatric emergency room. The author covers helpful strategies and the need for clear communication and consistency.

Glaser, D. (2003). Child abuse and neglect and the brain—a review. *Journal of Child Psychology and Psychiatry, 41*(1), 97–116.
This article discusses a study of the neurology of child abuse and neglect.

Hardin, S. B. (1996). Catastrophic stress. In A. B. McBride & J. K. Austin (Eds.), *Psychiatric-mental health nursing: Integrating the behavioral and biological sciences* (pp. 82–106). Philadelphia, PA: W. B. Saunders.
This chapter provides a therapeutic model for viewing responses, reactions, and recovery from catastrophic stress.

Hawker, D. M., Durkin, J., & Hawker, D. S. (2010). To debrief or not to debrief our heroes: That is the question. *Clinical psychology psychotherapy*. doi: 10.1002/cpp.730.
This article discusses questions regarding evidence-based practice and psychological first aid and referral for additional services.

Hobfoll, S., Watson, P., Bell, C., Bryant, R., Brymer, M., Friedman, M. J., . . . Ursano, R. J. (2007). Five essential elements of immediate and mid-term mass trauma intervention: Empirical evidence. *Psychiatry, 70*(4), 283–315.
This article outlines techniques for intervention and gives specific examples for intervention.

Holmes, E. A., James, E. L., Coode-Bate, T., & Deeprose, C. (2009). Can playing the computer game "Tetris" reduce the build-up of flashbacks for trauma? A proposal from cognitive science. *PLoS ONE, 4*(1), e4153. doi: 10.1371/journal.pone0004153.
This article discusses a study that showed that playing Tetris reduced unwanted flashbacks of viewing a traumatic film shown to subjects.

Hopkins, A. G. (1994). The trauma nurse's role with families in crisis. *Critical Care Nurse, 14*(2), 35–43.
This article discusses trauma victims' and their families' responses to injury, potential nursing interventions, and expected outcomes.

Joint Commission. (2010, November 17). A follow-up report on preventing suicide: focus on medical/surgical units and the emergency department. *Sentinel event alert* 46. Retrieved from www.jointcommission.org
This report provides recommendations for screening for suicide across medical/surgical and emergency department settings.

Masters, R. (1998). Death on the doorstep: Helping the families of murder victims rejoin the community. *Family Therapy Networker, 22*(3), 38–44.
Intervention with victims and survivors is essential for their recovery. This article clearly shows the grief and trauma faced by these clients and their caregivers. Rosemary Masters, a lawyer and social worker who worked for Victim's Services in New York City, discusses some of the immediate and long-range forensic and psychosocial problems faced by this population and the wider community.

McCaig, L. F., & Burt, C. W. (2004). *National hospital ambulatory medical care survey: 2002 emergency department summary*. Advance

data from Vital and Health Statistics no. 340. Hyattsville, MD: National Center for Health Statistics.
The National Hospital Ambulatory Medical Care Survey reviewed 53 million mental health–related emergency department visits from 1992 to 2001 by using mental health related International Classification of Disease coded diagnoses. Review of data showed an increase in the number of emergency room visits for mental health conditions in most geographical areas in the United States except for the Midwest.

McGowan, P. O., Sasaki, A., D'Alessio, A. C., Dymov, S., Labonte, B., Szyf, M., . . . Meaney, M. J. (2009). Epigenetic regulation of glucocorticoid receptor in human brain associates with childhood abuse. *Nature Neuroscience, 12*(3), 342–348.
This article reports on a study of changes in DNA regulates of stress in suicide victims with a history of abuse.

Mindnich, D. S., & Hart, B. (1995). Linking hospital and community. *Journal of Psychosocial Nursing, 33*(1), 25–28.
This article describes the role of the psychiatric consultation liaison nurse specialist in an emergency room setting. The psychiatric consultation liaison nurse specialist functions as a bridge or link among the emergency room, psychiatric services, and the community.

Murphy, M. C. (2002). The agitated psychotic client: Guidelines to ensure staff and client safety. *Journal of the American Psychiatric Nurses Association, 8*(4), 2–8.
This article reviews responses to client-perpetrated violence and use of restraints governed by guidelines of the Joint Commission and the Centers for Medicare and Medicaid Services as well as consensus guidelines for medicating agitated psychiatric clients.

Myers, D., & Wee, D. F. (2005). *Disaster mental health services: A primer for practitioners.* New York, NY: Brunner-Routledge.
This book covers various topics dealing with crisis and psychiatric emergencies including CISM and CODE-C models, stress management, and responses to grief, trauma, disasters, terrorism, and weapons of mass destruction. The sections on the potential impact upon caregivers are particularly helpful.

Ng, A. T., Zeller, S. L., & Rhoades, R. W. (2010). Clinical challenges in pharmacological management of agitation. *Primary Psychiatry, 17*(8), 46–52.
This article discusses medications used in emergency settings for the control of agitation.

Palmer, J. (2002). Building on the past, preparing for the future. In Sigma Theata Tau (Eds.), *Disaster, trauma and emergency nursing* (pp. 67–70). Indianapolis, IN: Sigma Theta Tau.
This chapter features a nurse in a nontraditional role as chief nurse of the American Red Cross since 1987. Nancy McKelvey, RN, discusses her role and the roles of nurses who may be in nontraditional roles in their communities as well as opportunities for volunteerism.

Portier, C. B., Bakker, A., van Balkom, A. J. L. M., & Stein, D. (2005). Evidence-based pharmacotherapy in post traumatic stress disorder. In D. Stein, B. Lerer, & S. Stahl (Eds.), *Evidence-based psychopharmacology* (pp. 121–136). Cambridge, UK: Cambridge University Press.
This chapter is an examination of treatment studies evaluating medication usage in PTSD.

Puskar, K., & Obus, N. (1989). Management of the psychiatric emergency. *Nurse Practitioner, 14*(7), 9–18, 23–26.
This article discusses the treatment of psychiatric emergencies and crises.

Raphael, B. (1983). *The anatomy of bereavement.* Northvale, NJ: Jason Aronson.
This book provides an excellent description of loss and bereavement issues across the life span, including normal bereavement and grief response, delayed bereavement, and chronic grief.

Raphael, B. (1986). *When disaster strikes: How individuals and communities cope with catastrophe.* New York, NY: Basic Books.
This text describes the stresses experienced by those involved in disasters. Numerous case studies show the application of crisis theory with victims and survivors.

Ressler, K., Mecer, K. B., Bradley, B., Jovanovic, T., Manan, A., Kerley, K., . . . May, V. (2011). Posttraumatic stress disorder is associated with PACAP and the PAC1 receptor. *Nature, 470*(7335), 492–497.
The authors report on a study of neurologic damage of chronic stress.

Rosenzweig, L. (1992). Psychiatric triage: A cost-effective approach to quality management in mental health. *Journal of Psychosocial Nursing, 30*(6), 5–8.
This article discusses some of the common dispositions of triaged clients, documentation, and placement problems identified by a task force studying problems in a Minnesota medical center. Useful examples of problem solving and

quality improvement that led to the development of a psychiatric triage team are provided.

Sandman, C. A., Davis, E. P., Buss, C., & Glynn, L. M. (2011). Prenatal programming of human neurological function. *International Journal of Peptides.* doi:10.1155/2011/837596.
The article discusses the effects of stress hormones and fetal development.

Scott, K. M., VonKorff, M., Angermeyer, M. C., Benjet, C., Bruffaets, R., DeGiroldama, G., . . . Kessler, R. C. (2011). Association of childhood adversities and early-onset mental disorders and adult-onset chronic physical conditions. *Archives of General Psychiatry, 68*(8), 838–844.
This article describes a cross-sectional study showing a relationship between childhood abuse and trauma and mental and physical disorders.

Tarasoff v. Regents of University of California. (1976). 17 Cal3d 425.551 P2d334, 131 CalRptr14.
These court cases set precedent regarding the therapist's duty to warn potential victims.

Zeller, S. L. (2010). Treatment of psychiatric patients in emergency settings. *Primary Psychiatry, 17*(6), 35–41.

Additional Resources

Atkinson, M. (2008). Resurrection after rape: A guide to transforming from victim to survivor. Oklahoma City, OK: RAR Publishing, Inc.
This is a guide for survivors of rape that includes activities to prepare for the experience of dealing with the trauma, changing self-talk, and reframing beliefs regarding the experience.

Cox, E., & Briggs, S. (2004). Disaster nursing: New frontiers for critical care. *Critical Care Nurse, 24*(3), 16–22.
This article provides some examples of roles fulfilled by nurses in disasters and collaborative efforts of government agencies.

Gebbie, K., & Quershi, K. (2002). Emergency and disaster preparedness: Core competencies for nurses. *American Journal of Nursing, 102*(1), 47–51.
This piece discusses preparedness, response skills, flexibility and knowledge of management plans, lines of communication, and appropriate skills that are needed for appropriate intervention in emergencies and disasters.

Fuimano-Donley, Julie. (2011). Caring under pressure. *American Nurse Today, 6*(9), 69–70.
Hints for dealing with some of the negative emotions that can be involved in compassion fatigue.

Lindemann, E. (1979). *Beyond grief: Studies in crisis intervention.* New York, NY: Jason Aronson.
This classic book is based on the author's experiences helping victims of the Cocoanut Grove nightclub fire as well as clients at Massachusetts General Hospital, who were coping with illness and pain.

Mitani, S., Kuboyama, K., & Kuboyama, K. (2003, October–December). Nursing in sudden-onset disasters: Factors and information that affect participation. *Prehospital and disaster medicine, 18*(4), 359–366.
This article discusses research gleaned from nurses from four hospitals who participated in disaster response to 1995 earthquake relief efforts in Japan. Teams of nurses were involved in the acute and reconstruction phases of this crisis.

National Child Traumatic Stress Network. (2009). *Psychological recovery—field operations guide.* Sacramento, CA: Castle Press.
This piece provides information regarding psychological first aid. Online training in a PDF version is available on the National Child Traumatic Stress Network website (www.nctsn.org) and on the National Center for PTSD site (www.ncptsd.va.gov).

Neimeyer, R. A., Harris, D. L., Winokuer, H. R., & Thornton, G. F. (Eds.). (2011). *Grief and bereavement in contemporary society: Bridging research and practice.* Oxford, UK: Routledge.
This article examines concepts of bereavement and complicated grief in various cultural contexts and therapeutic modalities.

Saakvitne, K. W., & Pearlman, L. A. (1996). *Transforming the pain: A workbook on vicarious traumatization.* New York, NY: W.W. Norton & Company.
This is a workbook on self-care issues for clinicians.

Sigma Theta Tau. (Ed.). (2006). *Disaster trauma and emergency nursing (Nurse Advance Collection).* Indianapolis, IN: Author.
This book contains a collection of evidence-based nursing articles on trauma and emergency nursing.

Stephan, S. (2006). *Emergency department treatment of the psychiatric patient: Policy issues and legal requirements*. New York, NY: Oxford University Press.

This article provides an overview of care of the mental health client's needs and problems seeking care.

World Health Organization. (2003). *Mental health in emergencies: Mental and social aspects of health of populations exposed to extreme stressors.* Geneva, Switzerland: Department of Mental Health and Substance Disorders.

This piece discusses public health aspects of adventitious crisis including recommendations for preparedness, intervention, and collaboration.

Wynd, C. (2006) A proposed model for military disaster nursing. *OJIN: The Online Journal of Issues in Nursing, 11*(3), Manuscript 4.

This article outlines the role of nurses in the various phases of disaster and the models of military nurses who have historically been on the front lines in disasters.

Internet Resources

For a full suite of assignments and additional learning activities, use the access code located in the front of your book to visit this exclusive website: http://go.jblearning.com/mentalhealth. If you do not have an access code, you can obtain one at the site.

Learning Objectives

After reading this chapter, you will be able to:

- Identify legal and ethical issues that guide psychiatric-mental health nursing practice.
- Outline the elements for informed consent.
- Describe the issues related to confidentiality and the mentally ill client.
- Describe the legal issues related to psychopharmacology.
- List the responsibilities of nursing personnel when treating a suicidal client.
- Distinguish among mandatory hospitalization, involuntary outpatient treatment, and the right to refuse treatment.
- List the criteria to guide nursing practice with the use of seclusion and restraint.

Key Terms

Autonomy

Beneficence

Boundaries

Confidentiality

Duty to protect

Duty to warn

Electroconvulsive therapy (ECT)

Extrapyramidal symptoms (EPS)

Informed consent

Justice

Least restrictive environment

Mandatory outpatient treatment (MOT)

Privileged communication

Psychiatric advance directive (PAD)

Restraints

Right to refuse medication

Right to refuse treatment

Right to treatment

Seclusion

Sexual misconduct

Suicide

Tardive dyskinesia (TD)

Violence

Chapter 8

Legal and Ethical Considerations

Amy Wysoker

http://go.jblearning.com/mentalhealth 

For a full suite of assignments and additional learning activities, use the access code located in the front of your book to visit this exclusive website: http://go.jblearning.com/mentalhealth. If you do not have an access code, you can obtain one at the site.

Introduction

Legal and ethical considerations pertaining to psychiatry are extremely pertinent to the psychiatric-mental health nurse and advanced practice psychiatric-mental health nurse (APRN). The goal of treatment is to provide safe, therapeutic care. Knowledge of the various legal and ethical issues can protect the nurse from professional confusion and litigation. Nurse practice acts, codes of ethics, and standards of professional practice guide the practice of psychiatric nursing.

In addition to being in compliance with the state's nurse practice act, professional nurses are required to follow standards of practice and standards of professional performance as established by the profession; accrediting organizations, institutions, and agencies; and the profession's code of ethics.

State Nurse Practice Acts

Nurse practice acts, established by individual states, are the legal basis for all nursing practice.

Licensure is the legal basis for the practice of nursing. State nurse practice acts are the legal documents that govern practice. These documents outline the nurse's legal mandates. The various state nurse practice acts primarily include a definition of nursing, requirements for licensure, exemptions from licensure, and what entails professional misconduct and unprofessional conduct. All nurses must know what is set forth in their particular state's nurse practice act in order to be in legal compliance.

The three primary ethical principles that guide professional psychiatric-mental health nursing practice are autonomy or self-determination, beneficence, and justice.

Ethical Principles

Ethics in nursing refers to how nurses carry out their responsibilities and render care to clients. Three ethical principles guide the care that psychiatric nurses provide. **Autonomy** or self-determination is the underlying principle that allows clients to make their own decisions. Individuals have the right to make decisions that affect their lives, as long as the decision does not infringe on the rights of others. **Beneficence**, the second principle, means to act in the client's welfare by preventing harm and doing no harm. The third principle of **justice** states that people should be treated equally and fairly.

The *Code of Ethics for Nurses* by the American Nurses Association addresses such issues as respect for human dignity; the client's right to privacy; protection of information; protecting the health and safety of the client; acceptance of responsibility and accountability; personal responsibility for competence, consultation, and collaboration; the protection of the rights of human participants in research; responsibility to the public and the profession for standards; maintaining high-quality nursing care; protecting the public from misinformation and misrepresentation; and maintaining a professional relationship with other healthcare disciplines.

Nurse practice acts encompass ethical concerns, and professional associations outline their specific codes of ethics in separate documents. The American Nurses Association (ANA, 2001) document, *Code of Ethics for Nurses with Interpretive Statements*, specifies ethical responsibilities and emphasizes the nurse's role as client advocate. Nurses must be familiar with the components of the *Code of Ethics*. The *Guide to the Code of Ethics for Nurses: Interpretation and Application* (ANA, 2008) provides an in-depth discussion and serves as an excellent resource.

Standards of Professional Practice

Nurses also are judged according to national professional standards. The American Nurses Association and specialty nursing organizations have established standards of practice and standards of professional performance for general nursing practice, as well as for specialty practice. A Louisiana court in 1999 declared that a "legal duty of care or standards of care means a nurse must have and use the knowledge and skill ordinarily possessed and used by nurses actively practicing in the nurse's specialty area" (Guido, 2010, p. 75).

Psychiatric-mental health standards are available for both the general psychiatric nurse and the APRN (ANA, 2007). This resource is a significant document that describes the essentials of psychiatric-mental health nursing, its activities, and its responsibilities at all practice levels and settings. Standards of practice are also outlined in numerous documents including institutional policy and procedure protocols, The Joint Commission (TJC)—formerly the Joint Commission on Accreditation of Healthcare Organizations (JCAHO)—standards and those of other credentialing bodies, nursing textbooks, nursing journals, and government statutes and regulations. ANA's professional standards of practice and performance and the Code of Ethics are the authoritative sources for nursing practice. While they are not legal documents, in a court of law the nurse is judged not only by a state's nurse practice act, but also by these authoritative sources. This chapter addresses the legal and ethical issues that apply to all psychiatric nurses. Topics such as informed consent, the right to receive and to refuse treatment, psychopharmacology, suicide, seclusion and restraints, electroconvulsive therapy (ECT), discharge planning, and sexual misconduct are all discussed.

Critical Thinking Question

How does understanding the legal scope of practice as defined in state nurse practice acts and the profession's code of ethics impact upon the actual practice of a nurse in a clinical situation?

Informed Consent

All clients, including those receiving psychiatric care, have the right to determine their own treatment. This right is based on the principle of autonomy or self-determination. Information must be provided so that clients make informed decisions about the care they are to receive. The doctrine of informed consent requires the practitioner to provide information relevant to making the decision, and the client to voluntarily make the decision and be competent to do so (Grisso & Borum, 2003). Prior to obtaining **informed consent**, it must be determined that the client is competent to understand the necessary information. To be considered competent, the client must be able to comprehend the proposed treatment and the choices available and then be able to verbalize a choice.

It is not usually the nurse's responsibility to obtain informed consent. Primary healthcare providers may legally delegate the responsibility of obtaining informed consent to nurses, but that provider still is accountable. Many health care facilities have established policies preventing this, for it creates an additional liability to the institution (Guido, 2010). However, if a nurse is the authorized practitioner performing a procedure for which informed consent is required, the nurse can obtain that specific consent (see **Figure 8-1**). As client advocates, nurses should monitor the informed consent process. If questions arise concerning the client's ability to comprehend the process, the nurse must discuss them in team conferences and with the physician or other mental health practitioner responsible for the client's care. Informed consent should include the following components (Appelbaum & Grisso, 1988; Grisso & Appelbaum, 1998; Grisso & Borum, 2003):

- Proposed treatment in words the client understands
- Possible risks and side effects of treatment
- Possibility for a successful outcome
- Alternatives to proposed treatment
- Course of the illness if treatment is not instituted.

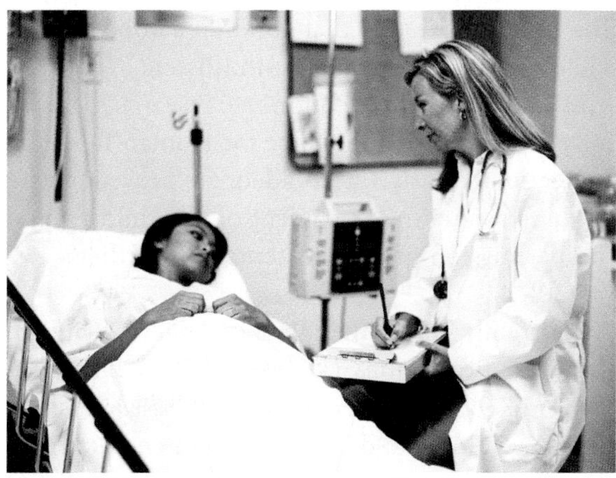

Figure 8-1 Obtaining informed consent.

The psychiatric-mental health advanced practice registered nurse (APRN), either nurse practitioner or clinical nurse specialist, can also be the primary therapist who is responsible for explaining and obtaining informed consent. Psychiatric personnel should view informed consent as a continual process, not a single occurrence, in which the client regularly receives current information. It is important to adhere to the informed consent process and document all discussions in the healthcare record. The MacArthur Competence Assessment Tool-Treatment (MacCAT-T) is utilized by therapists to determine a client's competency and ability to make informed treatment decisions (Grisso, Appelbaum, & Hill-Fotouhi, 1997). Four areas of focus include the client's ability to state a choice, to understand the relevant information, to appreciate the nature of the situation, and to reason (MacArthur Research Network on Mental Health and Law, 2004).

Research indicates that although most clients disclose sensitive information, a significant portion do not (Farber, 2003). Mental health practitioners, functioning as psychotherapists, must also stress self-disclosure in the therapeutic process (Galen, 1993). Nurse therapists must explain to clients the risks of withholding information and how sharing their thoughts and feelings can help them. It must be emphasized that not sharing all pertinent information can adversely affect treatment. The therapist must document that this was discussed. If clients injure themselves later while receiving treatment, the nurse's liability could be reduced because of information that was discussed previously.

Informed consent is the process of sharing information with the client regarding the proposed treatment. The client must be competent to understand the information provided, and consent must be voluntary.

Nurses providing long-term psychotherapy must cover certain criteria during the informed consent process. They should explain the following (Wenning, 1993):

- The recommendation for treatment and the diagnostic model used
- The possible risks and benefits of the proposed treatment
- Other treatment options, including those that are less expensive and of shorter duration

- The reasons for psychotherapy
- Insurance coverage and possible restrictions by the insurance carrier
- The plans for continuous evaluation of the client's status

Saks (2011) provides an excellent review of the statutes, regulations, and cases addressing informed consent in psychotherapy and the accompanying debate regarding informed consent for psychoanalytic psychotherapy.

Research

In 1979, the National Commission for the Protection of Human Subjects of Biomedical and Behavioral Research issued the Belmont Report. This study discussed the relationship of three principles to the ethics of research. Respect for persons allows individuals to be treated as autonomous agents making informed decisions and affords additional protection for individuals with diminished autonomy who are incapable of making decisions. The concept of beneficence in research includes maximizing possible benefits and minimizing or preventing possible harm. The final concept, justice, states that everyone has the right to partake in research and protects those who may be continuous targets of research (National Commission for the Protection of Human Subjects of Biomedical and Behavioral Research, 1979; OHRP, 2009). When participating in research, psychiatric nurses facilitate the informed consent process, advocate for those who cannot make autonomous decisions, monitor the research process, remain alert for possible harm, and protect the rights of the mentally ill. Yanos, Stanley, and Greene (2009) provide a decisional framework to assist in evaluating the category of risk presented in a study. Nurses involved in research with psychiatric clients must be knowledgeable about the literature related to psychiatric research and cognizant of the requirements specified by the federal government (OHRP, 2010; U.S. DHHS, 1991) for informed consent when conducting research:

- A statement that the study involves research
- An explanation of the purpose of the research
- The duration of the subject's participation
- A description of the study procedures
- An explanation of any experimental aspect
- An explanation of foreseeable risks or discomforts that may result
- A description of benefits that may be expected
- A discussion of alternative procedures or treatments available
- A statement that confidentiality will be maintained
- Who can be contacted for information
- Who can be contacted if a research-related injury occurs
- A statement that participation is voluntary
- A statement that one can withdraw at any time without penalty or loss of benefits to which she or he would be entitled without consenting to the research

Nurses who participate in the research process and advocate for the client must ensure adherence to these criteria. This promotes ethical research. When embarking on research, nurses should check state laws for specific regulations in addition to federal requirements. All consent forms must be completed prior to initiating the research project, and a copy needs to be given to the client. Mental Health America's Position Statement 26, *Participant Protections in Psychiatric Research* (MHA, 2007), provides the nurse with additional guidelines as does the American Psychiatric Association's *Task Force Report on Research Ethics* (APA, 2006).

Children and Research

The use of children in mental health studies and medication trials is often hotly debated by clinicians and society. Children are persons who have not attained the legal age for consent to treatments or procedures involved in research, under applicable law of the jurisdiction in which the research will be conducted. Generally the law considers any person under 18 years old to be a child, unless one has been determined to be an emancipated minor. The usual position is that children can be used as subjects in research as long as the dissent of children from and the assent of children to research are carefully safeguarded. The Office for Human Research Protections clearly states "adequate provisions are made for soliciting the assent of the children and the permission of their parents or guardians . . ." (45CPR 46).

Currently, under the DHHS's Office for Human Research Protections (DHHSOHRP, 2000; USDHHR, 2009, n.d.), when a proposed research study involves children and is supported or conducted by the DHHS, the research institution's institutional review board (IRB) must take into consideration the mandated regulatory requirements that provide additional protection for the children involved in research. The IRB must consider the potential benefits, risks, and discomforts of the research to children and assess the justification for their inclusion in the research. In assessing the risks and potential benefits, the IRB should consider the circumstances of the children to be enrolled in the study (e.g., their health status, age, and ability to understand what is involved in the research) as well as the potential benefits to the subjects themselves, other children with the same disease or condition, or society as a whole. Hoop, Smyth, and Roberts (2008) address the issues related to including children in the research process and stress the importance of educating psychiatrists and other clinicians to best communicate to families the importance of participation and be knowledgeable about the necessary components.

For any protocol involving children, the IRB must determine which of the four categories of research apply to that study (45CPR 46; U.S. DHHS, 2000). These categories are

- Research not involving greater than minimal risk to the children
- Research involving greater than minimal risk but presenting the prospect of direct benefit to the individual children involved in the research
- Research involving greater than minimal risk and no prospect of direct benefit to the children involved in the research, but likely to yield generalized knowledge about the specific disorder or condition
- Research that the IRB believes does not meet the regulatory conditions, but that does present a reasonable opportunity to further the understanding, prevention, or alleviation of a serious problem affecting the health or welfare of children

In all circumstances, the research must be conducted in accordance with sound ethical principles and adequate provisions made for soliciting the assent of the children and the permission of their parents or legal guardians.

Critical Thinking Question 

How do the ethical principles of autonomy, beneficence, and justice relate to informed consent?

The Right to Treatment

In 1972, the court ruled in *Wyatt v. Stickney* that all clients with mental illness or mental retardation must be treated in psychologically and physically humane facilities that provide an adequate number of staff, individualized treatment plans, and an active therapeutic setting. The staffing must include therapists from multiple disciplines to provide a wide range of treatment. Individualized treatment plans that meet the client's needs are mandatory. These requirements adhere to nurses' ethical principle to do good. If psychologically and physically humane treatment is not provided, the client's **right to treatment** is being abused. These legal standards must be met for treatment to be provided.

In 1972, the court in *Wyatt v. Stickney* ruled that all persons with mental illness or mental retardation must be treated in psychologically and physically humane facilities.

Unfortunately, many mentally ill people do not seek treatment due to anosognosia, the lack of understanding and awareness of their illness. In 2010, approximately 7.7 million Americans had schizophrenia and bipolar disorder. However, 40% of those with schizophrenia and 51% of people with bipolar do not receive treatment. The Treatment Advocacy Center (n.d.) addresses the serious consequences of untreated mental illness. Some of these consequences include homelessness, victimization, suicide, increased rates of violence and increased costs to the taxpayers. Another consequence of untreated mental illness is incarceration. A survey in 2010 indicated that more mentally ill clients are incarcerated than are in hospitals receiving treatment. Nurses need to be proactive in developing and collaborating with other health professionals to address these issues and to advocate for ways of helping those in need of treatment receive humane treatment rather than fall victim to the consequences of nontreatment.

Emergency room treatment needs to address the needs of the mentally ill client in crisis. For example, at a Brooklyn, New York City, psychiatric emergency room, a client died after being there for over 24 hours without being seen by medical personnel. Conditions in this large city hospital were in question prior to this episode. After investigation and legal action, the following reforms were to be implemented by the facility (ACLU, 2010):

- Ensuring patients in the psychiatric emergency room receive timely assessments and care and prevent overcrowding in the psychiatric emergency room. Stays in the psychiatric emergency room must not exceed the state mandate of 24 hours.

- Preventing the use of restraints on patients except as a last resort when the patient is an immediate threat to himself or others, and reducing the use of emergency psychotropic medications.
- Instituting appropriate discharge planning to place patients into the least restrictive setting possible that provides the support they need. This will prevent patients continually cycling through the hospital.
- Promoting staff accountability, protecting whistleblowers, and facilitating reporting of patient grievances.
- Compiling accurate data on the treatment, flow, and disposition of patients in the psychiatric emergency room and inpatient units, which must be delivered to plaintiffs periodically.

All persons have the right to refuse treatment for a mental disorder or condition unless they represent a danger to themselves or others.

Another ethical issue concerns the closure of psychiatric hospitals in recent years. What is the nurse's role in advocating for many different treatment modalities? Is the community the best place for treatment of all mentally ill clients? A significant portion of the homeless population in the United States is mentally ill. The limited number of treatment facilities may have resulted in more homeless with mental illness. Furthermore, it is reported that public libraries have become unintended shelters. A survey in 2009 based on responses from 124 librarians indicates that libraries have become safe havens for the mentally ill from violence and living in the streets (TAC, 2009). Is this population better cared for in psychiatric hospitals than in community-based programs? Consumer groups have advocated for less hospitalization and more community services. However, it can be argued that the homeless client with mental illness may need inpatient hospitalization to receive adequate treatment.

The Right to the Least Restrictive Environment

All individuals undergoing treatment for mental disorders have the right to the least restrictive environment.

There are many different types of treatment facilities. Clients have the right to the **least restrictive environment**, and this was acknowledged in *Dixon v. Weinberger* in 1975. Least restrictive environment means not to restrict one's civil rights more than needed to protect the individual. Subsequent court cases have reaffirmed this right and made decisions for care accordingly. Clients' care must be decided based on their individual needs (Guido, 2010). When evaluating a facility, consider the type of setting, the institutional procedures for running the setting, client involvement, the consequences of breaking rules, the modes of treatment provided, the level of authority between employees and clients, and the clients' abilities to participate in their care related to their clinical needs (Garriston, 1983). The psychiatric team must evaluate all these areas when deciding which type of setting is appropriate for the client. Addressing these areas helps to define the least restrictive setting. This ensures that the ethical principle of beneficence is met.

The Right to Refuse Treatment, Including Hospitalization

All persons, including the mentally ill, have the right to refuse treatment. The right to refuse treatment includes the right to refuse hospitalization. This is based on clients' right to live as they choose and conduct themselves accordingly, as long as they do not interfere with the rights of others. Mentally ill individuals have the **right to refuse treatment** as long as they are not endangering themselves or others.

Nurses need to be aware of institutional policies regarding the hospitalization of a person against his or her will. False imprisonment pertains to detaining a person without a legal authority to confine the individual. There are many court cases addressing the issue of whether a client should or should not have been hospitalized against his or her will (Guido, 2010). The nurse is also guided by knowledge of specific state laws. In many states and hospitals, two physicians must certify that the client is a danger to himself or herself or others before the client can be hospitalized involuntarily. The staff needs to be careful to avoid violating the rights of clients; the hospital and treatment personnel are liable if violations occur. All psychiatric personnel must document in the medical records the behaviors and reasons leading to their decision to hospitalize a client involuntarily. This decreases liability in the event of litigation.

Clients have the legal right to submit a request for discharge if they disagree with their involuntary hospitalization. During this process, the hospital presents the reasons that involuntary hospitalization is necessary, and the client's legal representation submits reasons for opposing the hospitalization. The treatment staff, including nurses, may be asked to testify and describe the client's condition and needs. A judge then makes the final determination.

Involuntary Outpatient Treatment

Although clients have a right to refuse involuntary hospitalization, laws have been passed in most states that address involuntary outpatient treatment (Treatment Advocacy Center [TAC], 2000, 2011). These laws may be referred to as involuntary outpatient treatment (IOT), assisted outpatient treatment (AOT), or **mandatory outpatient treatment (MOT)**. Many of the laws have also been named after individuals who have lost their lives due to an act of a mentally ill person, such as Kendra's Law in New York State and Laura's Law in California. These types of treatment are court-ordered treatment with specific guidelines and criteria. The Treatment Advocacy Center has a model law to guide the states as they lobby for passage of the legislation. Studies have found that AOT has been successful, and interviews with recipients indicated that after having been committed, they either were neutral about it or agreed with the intervention (TAC, 2011). Also, challenges to the state laws have been upheld by the courts (TAC, n.d.). The American Psychiatric Nurses Association's (APNA's) position paper on mandatory outpatient treatment (2003) outlined the association's position on outpatient treatment. Recommendations included

- Mandatory outpatient treatment should be a last resort that is used to protect the public and provide treatment to those in need of psychiatric treatment.
- Advance psychiatric directives should be incorporated into treatment.
- Services and a comprehensive treatment plan should be made available, and independent panels should provide oversight.
- Therapeutic alliances should be established to promote medication adherence rather than mandatory medication; however, each case should be evaluated individually.
- Laws should not be named after individuals who have lost their lives because this continues to stigmatize the mentally ill.

The **psychiatric advance directive (PAD)** is an important legal document that psychiatric nurses should be educating clients regarding and advocating for its use. It provides a client the opportunity to share, in writing, his or her wishes regarding treatment. If and when the client relapses, the identified wishes can then be honored. A client's preferences for psychotropic medications, electroconvulsive therapy (ECT), in-patient facility, mandatory outpatient treatment (MOT), therapist, psychiatrist, and attorney, as well as any other preference, can be included in the advance directive. The client also has the right to change or revoke the advance directive when he or she is well and not experiencing acute symptoms (APNA, 2003; Geller, 2000; Mental Health Treatment Preference Declaration Act, 1990). PADs provide empowerment to the individual, and many studies have researched issues related to its use. A study by Kim and colleagues (2007) interviewed clients with PADs to learn more about their experience. The findings indicated that clients felt that having a PAD was beneficial, but reported problems with mental health providers understanding its importance and use. Another study (Scheyett, Kim, Swanson, & Swartz, 2007) addressed barriers relating to the PAD, such as difficulties creating the PAD; lack of knowledge and endorsement by mental health providers; and obtaining the PAD during a psychiatric crisis. Another study suggests that clients should appoint a surrogate decision maker to ensure that their wishes are respected in a crisis (Srebnik & Russo, 2007). Nurses as leaders, educators, and advocates can partake in pursuit of resolution of these issues. The psychiatric advance directive can be an important document in assisting the psychiatric community and the courts if MOT needs to be implemented. State-by-state information on PADs is available online at the National Resource Center on Psychiatric Advance Directives website (www.nrc-pad.org).

Laws that mandate involuntary outpatient mental health treatment are referred to as involuntary outpatient treatment, assisted outpatient treatment, or mandatory outpatient treatment.

Although states differ in their wording, some of the criteria needed for involuntary commitment to occur include that the person must suffer from a mental illness; must be deemed unlikely to be safe in the community without oversight, based on clinical recommendations; must have a history of nonadherence that has resulted in hospitalization or incarceration within a specified time frame; must have had one or more acts, attempts, or threats of serious violent behaviors either toward self or others within a specified time frame; must be in need of outpatient treatment in order to prevent relapse as determined from history; must not be freely participating in treatment; and must be someone who would benefit from treatment (TAC, 2000; 2011).

Involuntary outpatient treatment is a controversial issue. Balancing clients' rights and protection of the public is a legislative and nursing concern. The ANA *Code of Ethics* helps psychiatric nurses balance the mentally ill client's right to self-determination and the need to protect the public. The code states

> The nurse recognizes that there are situations in which the right to individual self-determination may be outweighed or limited by the rights, health and welfare of others, particularly in relation to public health considerations. Notwithstanding, the modification of individual rights must always be considered a serious deviation from the standard of care, justified only when there are no less restrictive means available to preserve the rights of others and the demands of justice. (ANA, 2001, p. 9)

Advocating treatment for the mentally ill population and maintaining their rights is a priority of psychiatric nurses: "The need to safeguard patient rights and provide MOT is the challenge brought before the psychiatric community. Both can be done, but not one without the other" (Wysoker, Agrati, Collins, Marcus, & Thelander, 2004, p. 250).

The Right to Refuse Medication

All persons have the right to refuse medication except when, by refusing medication, they may represent a danger to themselves or others. Institutions and agencies should establish policies for the emergency administration of medication.

The **right to refuse medication** has been addressed in the courts. Nurses must be aware of the proper procedure when a client refuses to comply with treatment. The one exception to the right to refuse medication is in an emergency situation where the client is a danger to self or others. Only during such an occurrence can medication be administered against the wishes of the client. Hospital policy should inform the nurse of the protocol to follow for emergency administration. General guidelines include the following:

- Interventions have been attempted prior to the decision to medicate.
- The nurse has explained to the client that he or she is a danger to self or others.
- The procedures to inform the psychiatrist or other responsible treating mental health practitioner of the dangerous situation and the interventions to take have been followed.
- Documentation of these interventions is in the medical or health record.

Psychotropic medication effectively treats many mental illnesses and disorders. The benefits and risks of such treatment must be discussed with an individual before initiating treatment. Clients need to be carefully monitored for both expected and unexpected side effects and adverse reactions.

The nurse gradually educates the client about the reasons for taking medication and how it can be beneficial. Thus, the client steadily gains an understanding of the medication's importance and is able to make an informed decision. If education is unsuccessful and the client continues to refuse medication, a court order needs to be obtained. Everything the nurse has taught the client must be documented in the medical record. The court then examines the client's response to educational intervention. Only court approval can override the client's decision. Nurses must verify in the medical record that court approval was granted, and the judge's order needs to be included with the documentation. It is imperative for the nurse to verify the document's presence prior to administering the medication. The court order should detail, among other specifications, the length of mandated medication therapy. Medication may be administered intramuscularly upon refusal, but only under court order.

Many ethical issues are raised when clients refuse medication. Nurses feel strongly that clients have the right to respect and self-determination. Conversely, the nurse may also strongly believe that the medication is necessary and may form the clinical judgment that administering the medication without a court order will do good or prevent harm. Alternatively, the nurse may believe the client has the right to decide his or her own fate by refusing medication. The nurse may then experience conflict about giving the medication intramuscularly as detailed in the court order. The client may need to be physically held in order for the nurse to administer the medication, thus compromising the client's dignity and respect. Issues of doing good versus doing harm must be explored carefully, and the nurse may need assistance from nursing colleagues and other clinicians in deciding on a course of action.

Critical Thinking Question

What are the ethical issues impacting mandatory outpatient treatment, and how are they different or not different from the ethical issues surrounding mandatory medication administration?

Psychopharmacology

Psychotropic medication has dramatically improved the quality of life of clients with mental illness. However, the accompanying side effects of these medications have raised questions concerning the benefits of treatment versus the risks of incurring serious problems. The prescribing practitioner, psychiatrist, or APRN must weigh the risks and benefits when deciding the course of treatment. Prior to the initiation of therapy, clients must be informed of the benefits and risks and agree to the treatment plan. They must be part of the decision-making process. Crickard, O'Brien, Rapp, and Holmes (2010) are developing a youth shared decision-making model to facilitate successful medication adherence in the mental health population. Having a collaborative approach with clients is part of nurses' professional responsibilities as client advocates.

Nurses need to be aware of medication side effects, such as **extrapyramidal symptoms (EPS)** and **tardive dyskinesia (TD)**. If side effects are observed, they must be reported to the prescribing practitioner, and treatment must be initiated. To decrease side effects, the dose may be changed, a different medication may be prescribed, or an antiparkinsonian drug may be added to the regimen. The interventions taken and the rationale for this course of treatment must be documented in the client's record. Alternative options should also be addressed. The client's understanding of the chosen treatment regimen must be noted as well. Consent forms for the administration of medication are now being used in many institutions. However, many professionals still use the medical record, because consent is an ongoing process and indicates the client's continual involvement. Many states have laws requiring written consent. Nurses should be familiar with state laws and follow them accordingly.

The Abnormal Involuntary Movement Scale (AIMS) measures the presence of tardive dyskinesia (TD). It is recommended for all clients receiving antipsychotic medication. The American Psychiatric Association's task force on TD recommends regular examinations for the presence of TD at least every 6 months, and that informed consent should be documented in a progress note (APA, 1992). The Extrapyramidal Symptom Rating Scale is another tool to assess symptoms of parkinsonism, akathisia, dystonia, and tardive dyskinesia resulting from psychotropic medications to treat the mental disorder (Chouinard & Margolese, 2005).

Nurses must listen to the client and family to determine which treatments have been effective and ineffective in the past. The dosage should be monitored, and appropriate action should be taken if side effects occur. Communication among psychiatric personnel is crucial; it improves the health of clients and minimizes the negative consequences of medication.

Many nurses question the ethics of using medications when the side effects are commonplace. Nurses confronted with these concerns must weigh the benefits of ameliorating the symptoms versus the risks of side effects. Doing good and preventing harm frequently create an ethical dilemma when treating a client with medication.

Critical Thinking Question

Knowing that psychotropic medication is a very important treatment modality for mental illness but can also cause serious side effects, how can the nurse best provide medication education?

Electroconvulsive Therapy

Electroconvulsive therapy (ECT) is a mode of treatment that is used primarily to treat clinical depression. It is generally used for clients whose medical conditions contraindicate the use of antidepressants or antipsychotics, those who have not responded to their medication regimen, and those who are severely ill and need a rapid treatment response. Baghai and Moller (2008) specifically address the various indications for ECT. Mayo, Kaye, Conrad, Baluch, and Frost (2010) provide an update on the important issues related to anesthesia considerations. The following rules for ECT guide the nurse and decrease the liability risk (APA, 1990, 2001):

Electroconvulsive therapy (ECT) is primarily used to treat clinical depression for clients who cannot receive psychotropic medications because of other medical conditions, those who have not responded to a trial of psychotropic medication, or those who are so severely depressed that immediate intervention is needed.

- Informed consent must be obtained.
- A comprehensive medical examination must have been performed.
- Emergency management procedures must be in place and have been followed in the event of an emergency.
- Adequate client supervision must be provided during and after the treatment.

ECT has a long history of effective use, abuse, and misunderstanding. As a result, a stigma has been attached to the therapy by both the public and nurses. It is important for the nurse to understand both the benefits and the side effects of this treatment. There are many resources that describe when ECT should be an option for treatment, as well as the role of the nurse in the procedure and the treatment of accompanying side effects (Fitzsimons, 1995; Kellner, 2010; 2011; Kelly & Zisselman, 2000). The American Psychiatric Nurses Association's position statement on ECT (2011) supports the use of ECT in the treatment of severe depression that has been refractory to medication treatment. A greater understanding of this therapy helps nurses to make informed decisions and prevents them from feeling like they are providing ethically compromised care. When nurses adhere to evidence-based ECT guidelines, they will be ethically and legally meeting standards of practice (Wysoker, 2003a).

Suicide

Suicide is a complex matter that requires an intensive multidisciplinary approach for prevention and protection.

Suicide is a major concern for psychiatric nurses because they are entrusted with the client's care 24 hours a day. If a client successfully commits **suicide**, much blame and guilt are usually placed on nursing personnel. However, the treatment of a suicidal client is a complex matter, and the psychiatric staff needs to work collectively to prevent this occurrence. One of the most frequent reasons for in-patient admission is risk of suicide. The goal of psychiatric admission is to provide a safe environment for the client (Billings, 2003). The therapist must address the issues that are making the client want to end his or her life. The nursing staff needs to provide interventions to help clients balance their negative and positive views of life.

The nurse's first priority and legal duty is to protect the client from immediate harm. *Hooper v. County of Cook* (2006) specified that reasonable care must be exercised by hospital personnel to protect suicidal clients from their own inflicted self-harm. *Reid v. Altieri* (2007) addressed the need to hospitalize a client if he or she has a suicidal plan. Other court cases (*Soderman v. Smith*, 2007; *Kinchen v. Gateway Community Service Board*, 2006) have concluded that if a client does commit suicide, the hospital holds no liability if it is found that hospital personnel followed standards of care. The interventions, not the outcome, was the reasoning. Another court case (In re *Baptist Hospitals of Southeast Texas*, 2006) notes that the person's diagnosis must be taken into consideration. If a client is delusional, his or her denial of suicide intentions could not be relied on (Guido, 2010). The responsibilities of nursing personnel include the following:

- Assessing the client's suicide risk
- Informing other staff of client's suicide risk
- Ensuring a protective environment
- Intervening to protect the client from harm
- Eliminating all dangerous objects that could be used for suicide
- Initiating appropriate observation by the staff, either one-to-one, 15-minute checks, or 30-minute checks
- Documenting actions taken in the medical record as dictated by hospital policy

Self-Reflection About Suicidality

The Ohio Nurses Association provides guidance to nurses regarding their own thoughts and feelings about suicide. Specifically written for the nonpsychiatric nurse, these guidelines can be useful for novice psychiatric nurses as well (Ohio Nurses Association, 2011, p. 1).

Questions to ask yourself:

1. Do I believe suicidal patients are sinful, weak, or shameful?
2. Do suicidal patients arouse high anxiety in me—perhaps making me minimize warning signs or avoid caring for them?
3. Do suicidal patients elicit anger in me?
4. Do I feel the need to rescue suicidal patients?
5. Have I experienced intense guilt or rejection after a patient's suicide or attempt?
6. Do I have personal experience with a family member, friend, coworker, or patient committing suicide?
7. Could my reactions to this event be impacting my care of suicidal patients now?
8. If I have a diagnosed mental illness, does working with suicidal patients worsen my symptoms?

Finally, if you have concerns about working with suicidal patients, please:

1. Speak with your supervisor.
2. Seek personal counseling if needed.

- Documenting the client's status, including all behaviors observed and therapeutic interventions initiated

Following these guidelines helps to decrease the risk of a successful suicide. At the same time, the nursing administration must carefully consider the institution's suicide prevention policies and comply with written policies.

A typical protocol involves assigning one staff member to a one-to-one observation of the client for the entire shift, relieved only during lunch and break periods. One-to-one observation means that one staff member observes one client at all times. However, to implement this type of observation, sufficient staff must be available to carry out the nursing care responsibilities for all of the clients. Sometimes, a staff member is assigned to one-to-one observation, but is given other unit responsibilities as well. This contradicts the definition of one-to-one observation, minimizes the seriousness of the client's condition, and increases the potential for suicidal behavior resulting in death. Nurses must make the administration aware of these conflicting orders to protect the client and avoid placing nursing staff and the treatment facility at greater risk for litigation should suicide occur. Most importantly, these orders prevent clients from being kept safe and receiving the excellent nursing care they deserve (Wysoker, 1997, 2003c).

The common practice of assigning one staff member to watch one suicidal client for the entire shift raises other ethical concerns. Realistically, one staff member cannot effectively watch a suicidal client for an entire shift. It is difficult, if not impossible, to watch someone every minute for seven or more hours. This practice actually provides clients with more opportunities to engage in a dangerous act. A client who is continually observed by the same person may also experience increased anxiety, which negates the benefits of therapy (Wysoker, 1997). Assigning different nursing personnel every 2 hours (at a minimum) increases client interaction with various staff members, allows for better distribution of staff assignments, and prevents administrators from breaching their institution's written policies. This is also a more realistic intervention.

Psychiatric-mental health APRNs in private practice need to be aware of their additional responsibilities when treating a potentially suicidal client. In some instances, managed care organizations by restricting a client's therapy hours and number of visits has hampered the care that practitioners provide. The ethical principle of justice raises the issue of fair distribution of resources in mental health care. Cost-containment efforts often conflict with clinical decisions. Negotiating hospitalization for a suicidal client may be difficult. It is therefore imperative that if the nurse therapist judges hospitalization necessary to protect the client from harm, treatment must be negotiated with the appropriate insurance company. If hospitalization is denied, the practitioner must appeal the decision. The courts have determined that practitioners are liable if the decision is not appealed (*Wilson v. Blue Cross of Southern California*, 1990). Clinical decisions must prevail, and the nurse should advocate on the client's behalf for the right to receive appropriate treatment. Ethically and legally, nurses who overlook these important issues are neglecting their professional responsibilities.

One-to-one observation requires that the client be observed by one member of the nursing or treatment staff at all times. The client must never be out of sight of the staff member for any reason.

Seclusion and Restraints

The use of **seclusion** and **restraints** as therapy is fraught with controversy. General guidelines, however, exist for these interventions. Seclusion and restraints should be used only as a last resort after all other therapeutic interventions have failed. Furthermore, this therapy must only be employed to prevent clients from harming themselves or others.

Seclusion is the process of placing a client in a safe, contained environment separate from other clients. Restraints are mechanical or manual devices used to limit the client's physical mobility. These should never be used as forms of punishment.

In 1999 federal legislation was passed governing the use of seclusion and restraints (42 CFR Part 482 Section 482.13, Condition of Participation: Patients' Rights). The following statements provide guidance to agencies and nursing personnel:

- The patient (client) has the right to be free from any form of restraints that are not deemed medically necessary or are used as coercion, as a form of discipline, convenience, or retaliation by staff.
- The term *restraints* pertains to both physical restraints and drugs that are used as a means to restrain a person (client).
- Physical restraint is any type of manual method, physical or mechanical device, material, or any type of equipment that is attached to one's body and cannot be removed by that person and restrains movement.
- Drugs used as restraints are those that are used to control behavior or to limit movement and are not standard treatment for the person's condition.
- Seclusion is when a person is involuntarily confined in a room or area and is physically not permitted to leave.

- Seclusion or restraints can be used only in emergency situations if necessary to ensure safety, after less restrictive interventions have been ineffective.
- Only a licensed physician or practitioner legally authorized by state law to order restraints and seclusions may do so. The treating physician must be contacted if he or she is not the practitioner who ordered the restraint or seclusion.
- Orders can never be written as standing or prn (if necessary) orders.
- A licensed practitioner, as defined by state law, must see and evaluate the need for restraint or seclusion within 1 hour after the initiation of this intervention.
- Each written order for a physical restraint or seclusion is limited to 4 hours for adults, 2 hours for children and adolescents from 9 to 17 years, and 1 hour for children under 9 years.
- The restraint must be implemented in the least restrictive manner.
- Safe appropriate restraining techniques must be used and ended at the earliest time.
- Restraints and the use of seclusion cannot be used together unless a staff member is continually monitoring the patient (client) face to face or by staff using both video and audio equipment and in close location.
- The patient's (client's) condition must be continually assessed, monitored, and reevaluated.
- Staff must have ongoing education and training in the proper use and safe application of seclusion and restraints and must learn alternative methods for handling behavioral symptoms.
- Hospitals need to report any death when the patient (client) is restrained or in seclusion or death is related to its use.

As a result of a strengthened federal patients' rights rule, since early in 2007, the Centers for Medicare and Medicaid Services have been requiring stricter staff training and documentation requirements for nurses and physicians who place patients (clients) in restraints. The criteria for reporting client deaths was also revised. The new training is aimed at ensuring that the treatment is appropriate and that the individual's rights are not violated. This federal rule is a condition of participation for Medicare and Medicaid healthcare facilities and applies to short-term, psychiatric, rehabilitation, long-term care, pediatric, and substance abuse facilities (Centers for Medicare and Medicaid Services [CMS], n.d., 2006).

Nursing personnel must create an environment in which these treatment methods are required only in emergency situations. If they become necessary, the nurse must follow institutional policy regarding the application of restraints and placement in seclusion. These policies should follow state regulations and laws and must specify the following (Johnson, 1994):

- The types of restraints permissible under state law
- How to initiate and apply these treatments safely
- Who can apply the restraints
- The type of written orders needed and from which level of practitioner
- The length of time that clients may be kept restrained or in seclusion
- The interventions needed to monitor care
- The physical care interventions
- The necessary documentation

In addition to the aforementioned, the American Psychiatric Nurses Association's 2007 *Position Statement on the Use of Seclusion and Restraint* (2007a) and the *Seclusion and Restraints Standards of Practice* (APNA, 2000; revised 2007b) provides the nurse with an understanding of the expected standard of practice. All hospital personnel must also follow guidelines on seclusion and restraints set forth in 2003, revised in 2009 by The Joint Commission.

Nurses are frequently placed in an ethical dilemma when considering the use of restraints. Restraining a client is a treatment of last resort and should be instituted only when clients present a danger to themselves or others. If the decision is made to restrain a client, that individual's right to freedom is removed. Nursing personnel who are responsible for initiating this treatment modality must be prepared to explain the rationale for using this treatment. Nurses are both ethically and legally responsible when implementing this treatment modality.

The nurse needs to be particularly aware of the negative consequences of using restraints on clients with a history of sexual abuse. Clients who have been sexually abused have been placed in positions where they were unable to resist their abuser. Restraints limit free movement and can bring back terrible memories of the past when escape was impossible. Furthermore, the act of tying someone down and positioning his or her legs and arms far apart may intensify the memories of sexual abuse. Seclusion is indicated, rather than restraints, for clients with a history of sexual abuse. Clients may also be asked which calming methods are most helpful and least traumatic for them. A staff and client debriefing session should follow any use of restraints or seclusion to facilitate learning from the situation and to prevent further use.

Critical Thinking Question 

What are the psychological issues related to the use of restraints? With this understanding, how can a nurse best provide treatment if and when it may be necessary to incorporate restraints into treatment?

Discharge Planning

The Mental Health Parity Act (MHPA), a federal law initially enacted in 1996, established legal requirements for insurance companies to offer coverage for mental disorders as with other illnesses. The Mental Health Parity and Addiction Equity Act of 2008 (MHPAEA) extended the requirements to addiction disorders (U.S. DHHS-CMS, 2011). Many states also have their own state laws addressing parity for mental health services. The Patient Protection and Affordable Care Act of 2010 (Public Law 111–148) provides for positive changes in mental health benefits. The psychiatric nurse needs to stay updated as these critical benefits evolve over time. The federal government has a website, http://www.healthcare.gov, to access up-to-date information. However, despite these laws, other issues relating to treatment can be problematic. Legal issues surface when clients are improperly prepared for discharge because of inadequate discharge planning. Psychiatric nurses are instrumental in instructing clients about medication and follow-up appointments. Nurses need to include the client and family in the discharge plan to ensure agreement and compliance. The discharge plan, acceptance by the client and family, and the plan's rationale must be documented in the health record. Discharge summaries should include all the pertinent information needed by the next treatment facility or aftercare center. If necessary information is omitted and legal action results, the referring facility and staff may be held liable for not providing adequate information, especially for suicidal clients.

Another ethical dilemma confronting nurses is that current hospital stays, often as a result of managed care, are of shorter duration than in previous years. Discharged clients who are supposed to receive follow-up outpatient aftercare may find that adequate referral sources are limited. From an ethical standpoint, what should the nurse do when it is apparent that the referral source may not meet the client's needs? Should the nurse follow the discharge plan or advocate for more treatment time until an appropriate referral source can be located? This second course of action may restrict the client to unnecessary inpatient hospitalization no longer warranted by the condition.

Confidentiality

Confidentiality takes on an added dimension in psychiatry because of the stigma related to mental illness. Like all nurses, psychiatric nurses must keep the client's information confidential. It is an ethical and legal responsibility. A frequent breach of confidentiality occurs when nurses and other healthcare practitioners discuss clients in areas where other people may overhear the conversation. In addition, nurses often have the most access to health records. Thus, it is imperative that they prevent anyone not directly related to the client's care from viewing the health record. Client confidentiality also pertains to photographs containing client pictures. In *Cedars Healthcare Group, Ltd, v. Freeman* (2002), the court ruled that even if names were removed, the pictures themselves would be infringing on the right for confidentiality. Additionally, recognizing one's picture may prevent mentally ill clients from seeking treatment (Guido, 2010).

Discharge planning and plans for aftercare treatment should be developed by the multidisciplinary treatment team in collaboration with the client, family, and significant others to ensure the client's agreement and compliance.

Family members are frequently interviewed to obtain information to aid in the assessment. When interviewing family members, the psychiatric nurse must carefully refrain from inadvertently discussing information the client has shared. In this way, the nurse protects the client's confidentiality. In addition, clients have the right to refuse to allow the nurse to speak with others. This request must be honored, even if it prevents the nurse from learning important information. Nurses frequently have difficulty with this concept, because they believe it is in the client's best interest to gather all possible information. It is unethical to do so, and the nurse must address this ethical dilemma.

The Health Insurance Portability and Accountability Act (HIPAA) of 1996 was the first federal law mandating individuals' right to privacy of their personal health information. Under this law, enacted in 2003, healthcare providers do not need to obtain an individual's consent prior to disclosing protected health information for three purposes: to provide treatment to the client, to obtain payment for the treatment, and to carry out healthcare operations (45 C.F.R.164.506; Wysoker, 2003b). Although psychiatric nurses need to understand that HIPAA permits these uses, they still need to use their professional nursing judgment as to what information should be shared and for what specific reasons. A New York State court decision (Thomson Reuters, 2011) ruled that HIPAA superseded New York State's assisted treatment law (Kendra's Law regarding involuntary hospitalization). The courts made it clear they were not undermining Kendra's Law, but rather health records would need to be released based on client consent or court order.

Confidentiality issues concerning discharge planning need to be addressed and must be documented accordingly. For nurses to disclose information to referring parties, the client must understand what, why, with whom, and when this information will be shared. The client must agree to disclosure. Many facilities have begun using consent forms to facilitate this process.

Professional nurses have both an ethical responsibility and a legal obligation to provide nursing care and to protect clients and others from harm.

Another area taken into consideration in HIPAA pertains to incidental disclosures. HIPAA makes adjustments when a client's information may be inadvertently overheard as long as the facility has taken reasonable safeguards to protect this from occurring on a regular basis. Although psychiatric inpatient facilities have always been concerned about confidentiality, psychiatric nurses have not had areas designated where they can privately engage in therapeutic conversations. Psychiatric nurses do not have offices, and many interactions have occurred in treatment rooms and dayrooms where interruptions are a common occurrence. Psychiatric nurses, like other mental healthcare practitioners, should have a private area where they can engage in confidential conversations. Nurses should advocate for their clients' privacy. HIPAA may allow incidental disclosures; however, nurses should advocate for reasonable safeguards for their work with clients (Wysoker, 2003b).

Privileged communication is confidential information provided by a client that is shared with a person in a position of trust, such as a mental health practitioner, who has a legal duty not to disclose the shared information in a court.

Privileged Communication

Privileged communication is a legal term that refers to information shared between certain individuals as protected by law. Communication is privileged between physician and client, attorney and client, priest and parishioner, and husband and wife. These persons are not legally mandated to testify or share confidential information in certain legal proceedings if the other person wishes them not to do so. However, cases of suspected child abuse and clients who present a danger to others are exceptions to privileged communication, and this information needs to be reported to the appropriate authorities (Keglovits, 1992).

Although psychiatric nurses are not listed in the statutes of all states, a United States Supreme Court decision, *Jaffe v. Redmond* (1996), determined that psychotherapist–client confidentiality privileges exist. However, whether psychiatric nurse–client communication is privileged must be further defined by the courts in many states. Psychiatric nurses should assume they are privileged and must not share information unless directed by the courts or legal counsel.

Duty to Warn and Duty to Protect

In *Tarasoff v. Regents of the University of California* (Monahan, 1993), the court ruled that mental health practitioners have a **duty to warn** those endangered by clients. Nurses working in ambulatory settings and APRNs conducting psychotherapy have a duty to warn and protect; they must report information to the proper authorities and/or other parties if there is evidence that a client may inflict danger on himself, herself, or another individual. It is the nurse's ethical responsibility both to provide care for the client and to protect others in the process. Despite the confidential nature of the therapeutic relationship, nurses must take appropriate legal action to protect others from harm. Nurses are also mandated by law to report suspected child abuse and, in some states, elder and spousal abuse. The nurse should be aware of state laws and follow them accordingly.

Felthous (1999, 2001) analyzed the issue of the clinician's duty to warn or protect and has developed an algorithm to help clinicians make decisions as to when to utilize the duty to disclose information to protect others. However, clinical judgment takes precedence. The algorithm is:

1. Is the client a danger to others?
2. Is the danger related to mental illness?
3. Is the danger imminent?
4. Is the danger aimed at a specific person?

Nurses also have a **duty to protect** clients from harm. This results from the client's inability due to illness to distinguish between dangerous situations (Guido, 2010). The *Estate of Hollan v. Brookwood Medical Center* (2007) and the *Department of Mental Health v. Hall* (2006) court decisions held the agencies responsible for failure to protect a client from elopement and subsequent death. *Ball v. Charter Behavioral Health* (2006) determined that if there was no indication that the action would take place, the nurse or facility would not be held responsible (Guido, 2010).

Critical Thinking Question 

A nurse has established a trusting therapeutic relationship with a client. For some time the client has been discussing his relationship with his girlfriend of 8 years. One day he is very anxious and agitated and shared that his girlfriend broke up with him. He angrily shouts that he will never let her leave him. What ethical and legal issues need to be considered, and what interventions should the nurse consider?

Violence

Nursing staff are with clients 24 hours a day and are therefore in the best position to assess for possible **violence**. Nurses are ethically responsible for protecting clients from being harmed by others as well as protecting themselves and other psychiatric personnel. The duty to protect from harm, discussed previously, applies to violence. In addition to the client's psychiatric condition, other factors must be considered to decrease the incidence of violence. Overcrowding, lack of privacy, an unappealing milieu, staff inexperience in dealing with potentially violent individuals, and poor staff attitudes toward clients all contribute to a potentially explosive environment (Davis, 1991). When nursing personnel address these issues, client care improves and violent episodes decrease. Collaboration among personnel and teamwork within the psychiatric unit is critical. Whenever violence erupts and injury results, liability issues place the nurse in a difficult position. Thus, prevention and early intervention are crucial.

Psychiatric nurses need to be very much aware of the legal concepts of assault and battery. Assault is "any action that places another person in apprehension of being touched in a manner that is offensive, insulting, or physically injurious without consent or authority" (Guido, 2010, p. 10). Battery is "a harmful or unwarranted contact. . ." (Guido, 2010, p.11). The difference is that in an assault, touching is not necessary. The mere threat is considered assault if there is a possibility of harm taking place at the time. An example is threatening a client with an injection if he or she does not comply with a request. In battery, actually coming in contact with the client without his or her consent is necessary. Resulting harm is not required. The act of touching without consent is required to qualify as battery (Guido, 2010). Obtaining informed consent for procedures prevents accusations of battery. Restraining clients without following proper guidelines (see "Seclusion and Restraints," previously in this chapter) is an example of battery. Psychiatric nurses need to be careful that they are not placed in situations where assault or battery against a client can inadvertently occur. Nurses' ethical responsibilities prohibit this type of behavior.

Laws are being passed to protect nurses from violent acts committed by clients. Nurses, too, can be recipients of assault and battery. New York State's Violence Against Nurses Law (New York State Nurses Association, 2010) makes it a felony to assault a registered nurse or licensed practical nurse while on duty. It is felt that such laws will have health care administrators consider the safety of the care environment, make changes to promote safe environments, and inform the public that violence against a nurse will lead to criminal prosecution. Nurses are also able to sue in civil courts for injuries resulting from violent acts. The American Nurses Association provides extensive information on workplace violence. It is an excellent resource for nurses and provides the status of various state statutes (ANA, 2011).

Sexual Misconduct

Nursing personnel must constantly be aware of their interactions with clients. The nurse's primary responsibility is to provide appropriate and therapeutic care. The relationship needs to remain professional. **Sexual misconduct** includes the expression of any thoughts, feelings, or gestures that could be construed by the client as romantic or erotic. This inappropriate behavior is deemed unethical and has no place in psychiatric nursing.

Boundaries are limits that permit the client and mental health professional to have a therapeutic relationship based on the needs of the client.

The concept of **boundaries** is important, and nurses must be very careful not to cross the boundaries of acceptable professional behavior. The *Code of Ethics for Nurses With Interpretative Statements* states: "In all encounters, nurses are responsible for retaining their professional boundaries. When those professional boundaries are jeopardized, the nurse should seek assistance from peers or supervisors or take appropriate steps to remove her/himself from the situation" (ANA, 2008, p. 152).

The National Council of State Boards of Nursing (NCSBN) has published a guide for nurses on the importance of appropriate professional boundaries (NCSBN, n.d.). Four concepts are identified:

1. Professional boundaries are the spaces between the nurse's power and the client's vulnerability.
2. Boundary violations can result when there is confusion between the needs of the nurse and those of the client.
3. Boundary crossings are brief excursions across boundaries that may be inadvertent, thoughtless, or even purposeful if done to meet a special therapeutic need.
4. Professional sexual misconduct is an extreme form of a boundary violation and includes any behavior that is seductive, sexually demeaning, harassing, or reasonably interpreted as sexual by the client.

Although not every boundary crossing indicates sexual misconduct, the courts do not look favorably on them. Violations of boundaries (Gabbard, 2009; Gutheil & Gabbard, 1993) include the following:

- Using first names
- Ongoing conversations concerning the nurse's personal life
- Body contact such as pats on the shoulder
- Accepting or giving gifts
- Wearing clothing inappropriate to the professional relationship
- Meeting at inappropriate times and places (e.g., late night meetings outside the office)
- Physical contact that can be misinterpreted (e.g., hugging the client when he or she is distressed)

Some of the actions listed do not indicate sexual misconduct. In fact, frequently crossing one of these boundaries may be harmless as long as sound clinical judgment supplies an appropriate rationale. It is imperative for the nurse to document the rationale in the medical record. In addition, nurses need to be cognizant of the client's perceptions of interventions. What may seem to the nurse an innocent intervention (e.g., a pat on the arm or shoulder; **Figure 8-2**) may be misinterpreted by the client. These misinterpretations should be explored with the client, and the behavior must be omitted to eliminate further confusion.

To prevent boundary violations of a sexual nature, Epstein and Simon (1990) formulated a tool (Exploitation Index) that provides therapists with guidance to help them monitor their behavior and act as a signal that boundary violations may be occurring. Psychiatric-mental health clinical nurse specialists and psychiatric nurse practitioners need to be continually evaluating their professional behaviors. Consultation with peers will assist this evaluation process. Continuing education needs to be available to help nurses stay current on boundary issues and the related ethical and legal concerns (Wysoker, 2000).

Figure 8-2 Although intended innocently, body contact can be misconstrued by clients.

Critical Thinking Question

What should a nurse be aware of when she or he begins to have personal feelings for a client? What ethical and legal principles apply, and how should the nurse proceed?

Summary

Psychiatric nurses are responsible for providing safe, quality care to clients with mental illness. Nursing's *Code of Ethics* requires professional behavior at all times. At the same time, nurses and other clinicians must provide care in a litigious society. As a result, a great deal of pressure is placed on the practitioner to provide quality care while protecting one's professional license. An awareness of the legal and ethical issues accomplishes both goals, without compromising either, and allows the nurse to provide excellent and appropriate psychiatric-mental health nursing care.

Evidence-Based Practice

The legal and ethical considerations associated with psychiatric-mental health nursing are areas where more research studies are definitely needed. A 2002 study assessed and compared patients' and staff members' attitudes about what rights hospitalized psychiatric patients should have. The results indicated that the patients were less likely than staff to express the view that involuntary hospitalization, the use of force or physical restrictions, or the compromise of confidentiality is justified; there were no significant differences in the attitudes of the staff and patients toward patients' rights to obtain information about their illness and treatment and their right to refuse treatment (Roe, Weishut, Jaglom, & Rabinowitz, 2002).

In their study of the factors that influenced the decision-making process around seclusion, Wynaden and colleagues (2002) interviewed seven psychiatric-mental health nurses and one physician within 48 hours after the decision was made to seclude a patient. Findings indicated that seclusion was utilized only after all other interventions that were less restrictive were not successful. The American Psychiatric Nurses Association (2001) document, *Seclusion and Restraint: Position Statement & Standards of Practice*, is an important document that helps psychiatric nurses guide their practice in this treatment choice.

Nurses are often particularly concerned about how to meet the needs of clients who have attempted suicide and what the appropriate follow-up treatment is. In a study conducted by Brown and colleagues (2005), it was found that when cognitive therapy was given to patients who had recently attempted suicide, they were 50% less likely to attempt to take their lives again within 18 months, compared to individuals who did not receive the therapy.

Annotated References

American Civil Liberties Union. (2010, January 8). *Settlement secures major reforms at Brooklyn hospital where patient died on waiting room floor.* Retrieved from American Civil Liberties Union website: http://www.aclu.org/human-rights/settlement

This provides information on the legal settlement that was reached with this hospital where a client death occurred in a hospital's ER waiting room.

American Nurses Association. (2001). *Code of ethics for nurses with interpretative statements.* Washington, DC: Author.

This text discusses the code of ethics for professional nurses and is based on the belief of the independent, autonomous nature of individuals, nursing, health, and society.

American Nurses Association. (2007). *Scope and standards of psychiatric-mental health nursing practice.* Silver Spring, MD: Author.

This book provides definitions and descriptions of basic and advanced psychiatric-mental health clinical nursing practice and the standards of practice and professional performance associated with that practice.

American Nurses Association. (2008). *Guide to the code of ethics for nurses: Interpretation and application.* Silver Spring, MD: NursesBooks.org

This publication provides nurses with an analysis of the components of the ethical provisions of the code and suggestions for their application in practice.

American Nurses Association. (2011). *Workplace violence.* Retrieved from the American Nurses Association website: www.nursingworld.org

This site provides a review of legislation in the states through 2010 related to workplace violence.

American Psychiatric Association. (2006). Ethical principles and practices for research involving human participants with mental illness. *Psychiatric Services 57*, 552–557.

Provides guidance for the psychiatric nurse on ethical issues and practices associated when research involves clients with mental illnesses.

American Psychiatric Association. (1990). *The practice of electroconvulsive therapy: Recommendations for treatment, training and privileging.* Washington, DC: Author.

This source establishes guidelines for using electroconvulsive therapy as a treatment modality in psychiatry.

American Psychiatric Association. (1992). *Tardive dyskinesia: A task force report.* Washington, DC: Author.

This report comprehensively reviews tardive dyskinesia, one of the main side effects associated with psychotropic drugs, and includes recommendations for the psychiatric clinician.

American Psychiatric Association. (2001). *A task force report on the practice of electroconvulsive therapy: Recommendations for treatment, training and privileging* (2nd ed.). Washington, DC: Author.
This source establishes guidelines for using electroconvulsive therapy as a treatment modality in psychiatry.

American Psychiatric Nurses Association. (2001). *Seclusion and restraint: Position statement and standards of practice.* Arlington, VA: Author.
This text provides a position statement and standards of practice for psychiatric nurses regarding seclusion and restraints.

American Psychiatric Nurses Association. (2003). *Position statement on mandatory outpatient treatment.* Arlington, VA: Author.
Provides specific guidelines to be followed when utilizing mandatory outpatient treatment in the care of a psychiatric client.

American Psychiatric Nurses Association. (2011). *Position statement: Electroconvulsive therapy.* Retrieved from American Psychiatric Nurses Association website: http://www.apna.org/i4a/pages/index.cfm?pageid=4448
The official position on ECT is provided by this nursing organization for psychiatric nurses.

Appelbaum, P. S., & Grisso, T. (1988). Assessing patients' capacities to consent to treatment. *New England Journal of Medicine, 319*(25), 1635–1638.
This well-written article discusses specific criteria psychiatric clinicians can use to assess the client's ability to understand and provide informed consent to treatment.

Baghai, T. C. & Moller, H. J. (2008). Electoconvulsive therapy and its different indications. *Dialogues Clinical Neuroscience, 10*(1): 105–117.
The authors provide an overview of ECT and its application in treatment for mental disorders.

Ball v. Charter Behavioral Health. (2006). WL 2422866 (La. App., August 23, 2006).
This is the citation for a legal case that raised the question about the responsibility of a facility and its personnel in the elopement and death of a client.

Billings, C. (2003). Psychiatric in-patient suicide: Assessment strategies. *American Journal of Psychiatric Nursing, 9*(5), 176–178.
This article presents an overview of in-patient suicide and suggests various assessment strategies.

Brown, G. K., Have, T. T., Henriques, G. R., Xie, S. X., Hollander, J. E., & Beck, A. T. (2005). Cognitive therapy for the prevention of suicide attempts: A randomized controlled trial. *Journal of the American Medical Association, 295*, 563–570.
This article explores cognitive therapy as a means of decreasing future suicide attempts in patients who have attempted it.

Centers for Medicare and Medicaid Services. (n.d.). *Homepage.* Retrieved from http://www.cms.hhs.gov
The initial website portal for information on the variety of programs available through the Centers for Medicare and Medicaid services including Medicare, Medicaid, and low-cost health insurance for children (SCHIP).

Chouinard, G., & Margolese, H. C. (2005). Manual for the extrapyramidal symptom rating scale (ESRS). *Schizophrenia Research. 76*(2), 247–265.
This publication provides direction for the clinician who wants to incorporate use of the ESRS into practice.

Crickard, E. L., O'Brien, M. S., Rapp C. A. & Holmes C. L. (2010). Developing a framework to support shared decision making for youth mental health medication treatment. *Community Mental Journal, 46*(5), 474.
A review of the literature and feedback from families and staff at a Midwestern urban community mental health center guided the development of a framework for youth shared decision making regarding medication treatment.

Davis, S. (1991). Violence by psychiatric patients: A review. *Hospital and Community Psychiatry, 44*(6), 125–132.
This article comprehensively reviews the different violent behaviors exhibited by psychiatric clients, risk factors, and suggestions for intervention.

Department of Health and Human Services. (1991). *Regulations for protection of human subjects (45 CFR Section 46.116).*

Washington, DC: Government Printing Office.
This federal document establishes national guidelines for the protection of human subjects in research.

Department of Health and Human Services, Office for Human Research Protections (OHRP). (2000). *Special protections for children as research subjects*. Retrieved from http://www.hhs.gov/ohrp/children-The Department of Health and Human Services, Office for Human Research Protections website provides comprehensive information on conducting research on human subjects in the United States.

Epstein, R. S., & Simon, R. I. (1990). The exploitation index: An early warning indicatory of boundary violations in psychotherapy. *Bulletin of the Menninger Clinic, 54*(4), 450–465.
The authors provide a self-assessment questionnaire (Exploitation Index) for therapists that serves as an early warning indicator of boundary violations.

Estate of Hollan v. Brookwood Medical Center. (2007). 912202 (Ala. Cir. Ct., February 15, 2007).
Legal citation to retrieve the information on this court case.

Farber, B. A. (2003) Patient self-disclosure: A review of the research. *Journal of Clinical Psychology, 59*(5), 589–600.
The author discusses the issues regarding patients' self-disclosure of information. Including that a significant number purposely withhold information that would be helpful to the treatment process.

Felthous, A. R. (1999). The clinician's duty to protect third parties. *Psychiatric Clinics of North America, 22*(1), 49–60.
A discussion on a clinician's duty to protect third parties, including an algorithm to aid mental health practitioners in making critical decisions regarding hospitalization and disclosures to protect others.

Felthous. (2001). Introduction to this issue: The clinician's duty to warn or protect. *Behavioral Sciences & the Law, 19*(3), 321–324.
The author is a national and international authority on forensic psychiatry. In this article he discusses the therapist's responsibility to protect patients and others when information is obtained that harm might occur.

Fitzsimons, L. M., & Mayer, R. L. (1995). Soaring beyond the cuckoo's nest: Health care reform and ECT. *Journal of Psychosocial Nursing and Mental Health Services, 33*(12), 10–13.
A commentary on the need for healthcare reform in the management of ECT services.

Gabbard, O. (2009). *Textbook of Psychotherapeutic Treatments in Psychiatry*. Arlington, VA: American Psychiatric Publishing, Inc.
This is an excellent resource for students and clinicians on the various treatment modalities in psychiatry.

Galen, K. D. (1993). Assessing psychiatric patients' competency to agree to treatment plans. *Hospital & Community Psychiatry, 44*(4), 361–363.
This article provides simple and direct suggestions for psychiatric clinicians to assess appropriately a client's competency and ability to understand and agree to a treatment plan.

Garritson, S. H. (1983). Degrees of restrictiveness in psychosocial nursing. *Journal of Psychosocial Nursing, 21*(12), 9–16.
This article was written when psychiatric-mental health nursing first adopted the concept of least restrictiveness. It explores the premise that least restrictiveness is more than a set of techniques, and involves the adoption and incorporation of certain social and philosophical issues.

Geller, J. (2000). The use of advance directives by persons with serious mental illness for psychiatric treatment. *Psychiatric Quarterly, 71*(1), 1–13.
This article focuses on the use of psychiatric advance directives.

Grisso, T., & Appelbaum, P. S. (1998). *Assessing competence to consent to treatment: A guide for physicians and other health professionals*. New York, NY: Oxford University Press.
This is an excellent practical guide to assess patients' competency to consent to treatment.

Grisso, T., Appelbaum, T. S., & Hill-Fotouhi, C. (November, 1997). The MacCAT-T: A clinical tool to assess patients' capacities to make treatment decisions. *Psychiatric Services, 48*(11), 1415–1419.
This study concluded that the MacCAT-T offers a flexible yet structured method with which caregivers can assess, rate, and report patients' abilities relevant for evaluating competence to consent to treatment.

Grisso, T. & Borum, R. (2003). *Evaluating competencies: forensic assessments and instruments* (2nd ed.). New York, NY: Springer.
This book offers a conceptual model for understanding the nature of legal competencies. The model is interpreted to assist mental health professionals in designing and performing assessments for legal competencies defined in criminal and civil law, and to guide research that will improve the practice of evaluations for legal competencies.

Guido, G. W. (2010) *Legal and Ethical Issues in Nursing* (5th ed.). Upper Saddle River, NJ: Pearson.
This is an excellent reference combining legal and ethical knowledge for both nursing students and practicing nurses.

Gutheil, T., & Gabbard, G. (1993). The concept of boundaries in clinical practice: Theoretical and risk management dimensions. *American Journal of Psychiatry, 150*(2), 188–196.
This article provides an excellent discussion about establishing boundaries in psychiatric practice and the various risk-management considerations.

Hoop, J. G., Smyth, A. C., & Roberts, L. W. (2008). Ethical issues in psychiatric research on children and adolescents. *Child Adolescent Psychiatric Clinics of North America, 17*(1), 127–148.
The authors provide an excellent review of the numerous issues involved when children and adolescents are subjects in research studies.

Hooper v. County of Cook. (2006). WL 1319458 (Ill. App., May 15, 2006).
This is the legal citation for this opinion on protecting suicidal patients from their own self-destructive acts.

In re *Baptist Hospitals of Southeast Texas.* (2006) WL 2506412 (Tex. App., August 31, 2006).
This is the legal citation for this opinion on including knowledge of the patient's diagnosis when determining the potential for harmful acts.

Jaffe v. Redmond, 64 U.S.L. LW 4491 (1996).
This Supreme Court case established the existence of the psychotherapist-client confidentiality privilege.

Johnson, V. P. (1994). Psychiatry. In L. M. Harpsler & M. S. Veach (Eds.), *Risk management handbook for health care facilities* (pp. 165–176). Chicago, IL: American Hospital Association.
This chapter addresses risk-management cases in psychiatry.

Keglovits, J. (1992). Legal issues and clients' rights. In K. S. Wilson & C. R. Kneisel (Eds.) *Psychiatric nursing* (pp. 930–952). Redwood City, CA: Addison-Wesley.
This chapter offers an extensive review of the various constitutional and legal issues and rights of clients.

Kellner, C. (2010). ECT Today: The good it can do. *Psychiatric Times*. Retrieved from Psychiatric Times website: http://www.psychiatrictimes.com/electroconvulsive-therapy/content/article
This article provides a thoughtful discussion of the positive uses and outcomes of ECT in modern psychiatric treatment.

Kellner, C. (2011). Electroconvulsive Therapy: The second most controversial medical procedure. *Psychiatric Times, 28*(1). Retrieved from Psychiatric Times website: http://www.psychiatrictimes.com/display/article
The author continues his defense of the utilization of ECT in psychiatric treatment.

Kelly, K. G., & Zisselman, M. (2000). Update on electroconvulsive therapy (ECT) in older adults. *Journal of the American Geriatrics Society, 48*(5), 560–566.
This article provides an update on the indications for ECT, how it is administered, common complications, its efficacy, and recommendations for management.

Kim, M. M., Van Dorn, R. A., Scheyett, A. M., Elbogen, E. E., Swanson, J. W., Swartz, M. S., McDaniel, L. A. (2007). *Understanding the personal and clinical utility of psychiatric advance directives: A qualitative perspective.* Retrieved from CINAHL Plus with Full Text database.
The authors provide a thoughtful analysis of the positive results for patients with mental illness who utilize a psychiatric advance directive in their treatment plan.

Kinchen v. Gateway Community Service Board. (2006) WL 3803014 (11th Cir., December 28, 2006).
This is the legal citation for this court case that discusses the responsibility of a hospital in protecting a suicidal patient.

MacArthur Research Network on Mental Health and Law. (2004). *The MacArthur Treatment Competence Study, Executive Summary.*

Retrieved from MacArthur Research Network on Mental Health and Law website: http://www.macarthur.virginia.edu/treatment.html
This study was supported by the Research Network on Mental Health and the Law of the John D. and Catherine T. MacArthur Foundation, was designed to provide information to policy makers and clinicians to help them address questions about the decision-making capacities of people who are hospitalized with mental illness.

Mayo, C., Kaye, A.D., Conrad, E., Baluch, A., & Frost, E. (2010). Update on anesthesia considerations for electroconvulsive therapy. *Middle East Journal Anesthesiology, 20*(4), 493–498. Retrieved from PubMed.
The authors discuss the issues associated with anesthesia when administering ECT.

Mental Health America. (2007). Position statement 26: Participant protections in psychiatric research. Retrieved from Mental Health America website: http://www.mentalhealthamerica.net/go/position-statements/26
This position statement discusses measures that MHA believes are essential to protecting the health and rights of research participants, while also facilitating scientific advances.

Mental Health Treatment Preference Declaration Act, Illinois Stat. Public Act 86-1190. (1990).
Illinois law establishing the parameters under which an adult can establish guidelines for what type of mental health treatment the adult would want and under what circumstances.

Monahan, J. (1993). Limiting therapist exposure to Tarasoff liability. *American Psychologist, 48*(3), 242–250.
This article discusses implications of the Tarasoff case for therapists.

National Commission for the Protection of Human Subjects of Biomedical and Behavioral Research. (1979). *The Belmont report: Ethical principles and guidelines for the protection of human subjects of research.* Washington, DC: Department of Health, Education, and Welfare (Publication Nos. OS-78-0013 and OS-78-0014).
This classic document established the current guidelines for using human subjects in clinical research projects.

National Council of State Boards of Nursing (NCSBN). (n.d.). *Professional boundaries.* Chicago, IL: Author. Retrieved from http://www.ncsbn.org/ProfessionalBoundaries.pdf
This is a guide for professional nurses on the importance of appropriate professional boundaries.

New York State Nurses Association. (2010). *Violence Against Nurses law takes effect Nov. 1.* Retrieved from the New York State Nurses Association website: www.nysna.org
This is a newsletter report on the successful passage of law making it a felony to attack a nurse in NYS who is on duty caring for patients.

Ohio Nurses Association. (March, 2011). Screening and Intervening with suicidal patients. Help for the non-psychiatric nurse. *The Official Publication of the Ohio Nurses Foundation for Nurses, 4*(2), 1, 11–14. Retrieved from Ohio Nurses Association website: http://www.ohnurses.org
A list of questions for nurses to ask themselves when caring for suicidal patients.

Patient Protection and Affordable Care Act of 2010. (Public Law 111–148). Retrieved from the U.S. Department of Health & Human Services website: www.HealthCare.gov
The governmental site for retrieving information on the federal law that changed health care in the nation.

Reid v. Altieri. (2007). WL 750596 (Fla. App., March 14, 2007).
The legal citation for a court case on the need to hospitalize a patient who has a plan to commit suicide.

Saks, E.R. (2011) *Informed consent to psychoanalysis: The law, the theory, and the data.* University of Southern California Law School. University of Southern California Legal Studies Working Paper series. Paper 75. Retrieved from bepress legal repository website: http://law.bepress.com/usclwps/lss/art75
A discussion on the use of informed consent when patients are engaged in psychoanalysis.

Scheyett, A., Kim, M., Swanson, J., & Swartz, M. (2007). Psychiatric advance directives: A tool for empowerment and recovery. *Psychiatric Rehabilitation Journal, 31*(1), 70–75.
This article examines arguments for and against PADs and looks optimistically toward their use

as an alternative to more coercive approaches to mental health treatment.

Soderman v. Smith. (2007). WL 2389564 (Super. Ct. Sacramento Co. Cal., July 13, 2007).
This is the legal citation for this court case that discusses the responsibility of a hospital in protecting a suicidal patient.

Srebnik, D. S., & Russo, J. (2007). Consistency of psychiatric crisis care with advance directive instructions. *Psychiatric Services, 58*, 1157–1163.
This article discusses how often psychiatric advance directives are utilized during psychiatric emergencies.

Roe, D., Weishut, D. J., Jaglom, M., & Rabinowitz, J. (2002). Patients' and staff members' attitudes about the rights of hospitalized psychiatric patients. *Psychiatric Services, 53*(1), 87–91.
This is a research study that interviewed both patients and staff members regarding the rights of hospitalized mentally ill patients.

Thomson Reuters News & Insight. (May 10, 2011). *NY's highest court rules HIPAA trumps Kendra's law*. Retrieved from Thomson Reuters News & Insight website: http://newsandinsight.thomsonreuters.com/Legal/News/2011/05_-_May/NY_s_highest_court_rules_HIPAA_trumps_Kendra_s_law
This article provides information on the court ruling on HIPAA having precedence over a state law.

Treatment Advocacy Center. (2000). *Model law for assisted treatment*. Retrieved from http://www.psychlaws.org/LegalResources/ModelLaw.htm
This organization works to eliminate barriers to timely treatment of severe mental illnesses.

Treatment Advocacy Center [TAC]. (n.d.). *Legal Resources. Key opinions*. Retrieved from Treatment Advocacy Center's website: http://www.treatmentadvocacycenter.org
This organization provides information on legal resources available to those with mental illness and their families.

Treatment Advocacy Center [TAC]. (2009). *Public libraries. Unintended shelters. Catalyst*. Retrieved from Treatment Advocacy website. Our reports and studies. http://www.treatmentadvocacycenter.org.
This is a discussion of how the nations homeless shelters are becoming treatment centers for the mentally ill.

United States Department of Health and Human Resources [USDHHR]. (n.d.). *Special Protections for Children as research subjects*. Retrieved from the Office for Human Research Protection website: http://www.hhs.gov/ohrp/
The governmental website for accessing information on the rights of children participating in research.

United States Department of Health & Human Services, Centers for Medicare and Medicaid Services (2011). *The Mental Health Parity and Addiction Equity Act of 2008*. Retrieved from the CMs website: https://www.cms.gov
The governmental website on accessing information on the mental health parity legislation and its impact upon services.

United States Department of Health and Human Resources [USDHHR], U.S. Food and Drug Administration. (2009). CFR Title 21. Subpart B-Informed Consent of Human Subjects.
The governmental website for accessing information on the use of informed consent when individuals are participating in research studies.

Wenning, K. (1993). Long-term psychotherapy and informed consent. Hospital and *Community Psychiatry, 44*(4), 364–366.
This article discusses the problems in determining ongoing informed consent for treatment when the client is engaged in long-term therapy.

Wilson v. Blue Cross of Southern California, 271 Cal.Rptr. 876 (1990); 222 Cal. App. 3 dsp 660 (1990).
This case established a practitioner's responsibility to appeal the decision of a managed care company to deny care if the practitioner thinks that the patient will suffer because care was denied.

Wyatt v. Stickney, 344 Fed. Supp. 373 (1972).
This case established that all clients with mental illness or mental retardation must be treated in psychologically and physically humane facilities.

Wynaden, D., Chapman, R., McGowan, S., Holmes, C., Ash, P., & Boschman, A. (2002). Through the eye of the beholder: To seclude or not to seclude. *International Journal of Psychiatric Nursing, 11*(4), 260.

This article discusses the decision-making process involved in deciding to use seclusion with a patient.

Wysoker, A. (1997). Risk management in psychiatry. In F. Kavaler & A. Speigel (Eds.), *Health care risk management: A strategic approach* (pp. 225–294). Sudbury, MA: Jones and Bartlett.
This chapter provides a more extensive discussion of risk-management issues in psychiatry.

Wysoker, A. (2000). Sexual misconduct. *Journal of the American Psychiatric Nurses Association, 6*, 131–132.
This article reviews sexual misconduct in psychiatric nursing.

Wysoker, A. (2003a). Legal and ethical considerations: Electroconvulsive therapy. *Journal of the American Psychiatric Nurses Association, 9*, 103–105.
This article responds to the stigma associated with ECT and how psychiatric nurses need to speak from an evidence-based background and educate the public.

Wysoker, A. (2003b). Legal and ethical considerations: HIPAA and psychiatric nurses. *Journal of the American Psychiatric Nurses Association, 9*, 173–175.
This article addresses HIPAA's implications for psychiatric nursing.

Wysoker, A. (2003c). Risk management in psychiatry. In F. Kavaler & A. Speigel (Eds.), *Health care risk management: A strategic approach* (pp. 225–294). Sudbury, MA: Jones and Bartlett.
This 2nd edition chapter provides a more extensive and current discussion of risk-management issues in psychiatry.

Wysoker, A., Agrati, G., Collins, J., Marcus, P., & Thelander, B. (2004). Legal and ethical considerations: Mandatory outpatient treatment. *Journal of the American Psychiatric Nurses Association, 10*, 247–253.
This article explains the American Psychiatric Nurses Association position statement on mandatory outpatient treatment.

Yanos, P. T., Stanley, B. S., & Greene, C. S. (2009). Research Risk for Persons With Psychiatric Disorders: A Decisional Framework to Meet the Ethical challenge. *Psychiatric Services*. doi: 10.1176/appi.ps.60.3.374.
The authors reviewed research on vulnerability, risk, and procedures to mitigate risk in studies with this population to help inform evaluation of such research.

Internet Resources

For a full suite of assignments and additional learning activities, use the access code located in the front of your book to visit this exclusive website: http://go.jblearning.com/mentalhealth. If you do not have an access code, you can obtain one at the site.

Learning Objectives

After reading this chapter, you will be able to:

- Describe the types and characteristics of therapy groups, self-help groups, and networks available to clients, practitioners, families, and the community.
- Explain the primary functions of a therapy group, a self-help group, and a network.
- Discuss the stages of therapy group and the different roles of group participants.
- Identify the curative factors of a therapy group.
- Describe the differences between self-help groups and networks and the distinctive benefits they, as community groups or online self-help networks, can provide.
- Describe different ways in which nurses can tap into, develop, and support different types of groups.

Key Terms

12-step approach

Advocacy

Autocratic leader

Democratic leader

Group dynamics

Group therapy

Laissez-faire leader

Latent content

Manifest content

Mental health consumers

Parataxic distortion

Self-help clearinghouses

Self-help groups

Self-help networks

Group Theory and Practice

Winifred Z. Kennedy and Edward J. Madara

http://go.jblearning.com/mentalhealth 

For a full suite of assignments and additional learning activities, use the access code located in the front of your book to visit this exclusive website: http://go.jblearning.com/mentalhealth. If you do not have an access code, you can obtain one at the site.

A self-help group is a nonprofit support group run by and for people who join together on the basis of common experience to help one another. It is not professionally run, although professionals are frequently found in supportive ancillary roles.

Introduction

Humans socialize and interact both as individuals and as members of groups whether in small work groups, families, larger groups, or organizations. Throughout history, group interaction has been utilized to support therapeutic and spiritual needs through the use of such interaction. In different cultures, groups have utilized art, drama, music, movement, religion, and ritual to express different themes including healing. These shared exercises and experiences provide opportunities for interaction, catharsis and learning. The idea of therapy groups is now part of everyday culture. While our views of therapy groups are likely influenced by scenes from movies such as *One Flew Over the Cuckoo's Nest* with Nurse Ratched taking a commanding lead over a group while the members sat in a circle on folding chairs or from reality-based television shows such as *Intervention* in which family and friends confront one member of the group, our daily experiences may be very different. On a daily basis as nurses, we may interact with groups of nurses, groups from different departments or agencies, interdisciplinary staff groups, groups of patients, and family groups. At various times we may be group member, facilitator, consultant, or leader.

Psychotherapy groups address such issues as transference and countertransference; the manifest content, latent content, unconscious meanings, and verbal and non-verbal meanings of communications; and willingness or resistance to deal with issues.

The use of groups organized for psychotherapy developed in the 20th century along with the popularization of psychoanalytic theory. Therapy groups have been used as a mechanism for both intrapsychic and interpersonal change. The significance and meaning of expression and exposure of the individual is seen in terms of the connections and bonds made among group members. The working alliance developed among and between members of the group is considered the basis for such change. In addition, task-oriented groups, while dedicated to specific production, also provide an opportunity for therapeutic use. In milieu therapy, the interaction of all participants is considered essential. Therapeutic communities such as Phoenix House or other group-based social networks developed utilizing the power of group interaction to facilitate change and rehabilitation and utilize group therapy theory. Group theory also underlies support groups and peer groups, although they might not be therapy groups. Self-help groups and social networks are also a large source of support for individuals faced with various shared problems or interests.

An ever-increasing number of community **self-help groups** and of online **self-help networks** help individuals and families to better cope with a wide variety of illnesses, disabilities, addictions, caregiver concerns, bereavement situations, and other stressful life problems and transitions. Although an increasing number of health organizations and professionals do recognize value in groups, another reason for not investing staff time in nurturing linkages is the apparent inability of self-help groups to generate revenue as therapy groups do. Nurses who have worked with self-help groups have found that they are in a better position to understand and meet the needs of clients and the community (Adamsen & Rasmussen, 2003). Whether advising a stroke client and his or her family of the availability of a local stroke group, speaking on stress reduction techniques before an existing Well Spouse Association group, or assisting parents of children with cancer to organize a local chapter of Candlelighters, nurses can both tap into and develop these client care resources to expand the degree, reach, and long-term impact of their nursing care.

A number of healthcare and social trends are contributing to the increased use and relevancy of the groups. The prevalence of chronic illness and disability continues to grow as the percentage of the aged population grows larger. At the same time, continuing medical advancements succeed both in saving lives and extending life expectancy. Yet traditional sources of social support and practical information, formerly found within extended families, neighborhoods, and community organizations, have become less available.

As the move to more efficient and patient-centered health care encourages patients to take more responsibility for their health care and participate in making more informed health decisions, self-help groups in both their traditional community and new online forms remain a valuable but still relatively untapped volunteer-run resource. With attention to continuous quality improvement (CQI) practices in hospitals and healthcare agencies, self-help groups can provide informed customer feedback and serve as potential partners for health service planning, delivery, and evaluation. Finally, with increasing work pressures, self-help groups serve as welcome allies for those nurses who risk burnout because they are expected to be all things to their clients.

Studies continue to indicate the value of self-help groups and reflect how professional interaction with self-help groups is desirable (Law, King, Stewart, & King, 2001).

Critical Thinking Question

In what particular ways might students better educate themselves in understanding the value, variety, and dynamics of therapy and self-help groups?

Evidence-Based Practice

In a study of 125 women with breast cancer, researchers randomly divided the subjects into two groups. One group participated in a psychoeducational group that provided supportive-expressive therapy and information about their illness. The control group was provided with self-directed educational materials and a yearlong membership in a consumer health library. The women in the therapy group experienced significant reduction in mood disorders and trauma symptoms (Classen et al., 2001).

The Beginnings of Therapy Groups

Therapy groups began as an outgrowth of psychoanalytic, interpersonal, and systems theories. First utilized for dealing with the large population of institutionalized patients, the model of group therapy gained popularity after World War II with the experiences of dealing with veterans and other groups who had been exposed to the popularization of psychotherapeutic theories in the 1950s. Deinstitutionalization and the emphasis placed by managed care for minimizing costs also helped popularize treatments that could be provided in outpatient settings and to groups rather than individuals. This is particularly true as mental health treatment became less stigmatized and was utilized by more diverse populations. With continued interest in short-term treatment and the financial implications of care, there is continued interest in utilization of group therapies.

Nurses have always been involved in treatment of individuals, families, and community groups. Hildegard Peplau stressed the importance of the nurse–patient relationship as a therapeutic alliance and the influences that this interpersonal process might have between individuals and among groups. The stages of the nurse–patient relationship (orientation, identification, exploitation, resolution) are similar to the stages of a group relationship and the skills and problem solving used by nurses are similar to cognitive behavioral therapy and client education. The nursing roles of nurse as teacher, leader, resource person, and counselor are all utilized in group situations. Recognizing the important influence of groups for nurse educators and psychiatric nurses, she arranged clinical experiences in group therapy for graduate students, (Calloway 2002).

Critical Thinking Question

Peplau has discussed how the various roles of a nurse, such as teacher, leader, resource person, and counselor are utilized in group work. Describe how a nurse as a therapy group leader can incorporate these different roles to benefit the group and its members.

Evidence-Based Practice

Oppawsky (2010) reported use of a three-session group approach dealing with crisis stabilization in depressed patients with structured topics for discussion. In the first session, clients are asked to introduce themselves and describe their experiences. The group then develops themes from the discussion. In the second session, clients discuss coping strategies for dealing with depression that have been successful and those that have been unsuccessful. The third session focuses on experiences clients have had using the successful coping strategies and changing behavior. Members of the first group named the experience "Depression School." Clients showed an improvement in scores on the Beck Depression Index (BDI); clients with the highest scores before the experience showed the most improvement. Clients were then transitioned to various services such as other therapy groups or self-help groups, individual therapy, or case management.

The Characteristics of Therapy Groups

Group therapy gained initial popularity as a way of dealing with the experiences of WWII veterans and the needs of deinstitutionalized mentally ill individuals.

Group therapy is a psychotherapeutic process in which individuals or members meet at regular intervals or sessions with one or more group leaders for a common purpose and goals. Sessions usually involve discussion, development of relationships and alliances within the group, and development of skills that can be used outside of the group setting. A psychotherapy or therapeutic group differs from most group experiences, including support groups. The purpose of a therapy group is intrapsychic or interpersonal change. The boundaries of therapeutic relationships within the group are defined and limited. The topics discussed in the group are usually circumscribed and dealing with the here and now. In other types of groups, members are not necessarily seen as patients, improvement may not be the ultimate goal, and the boundaries of group members may be more flexible and interchangeable. Psychotherapy groups are usually based upon theoretical frameworks that are, in turn, based upon interpersonal or cognitive behavioral psychology, psychoanalytic therapy, and systems or family therapy. Issues such as transference and countertransference, the meanings of the **manifest content**, or concrete, surface meaning, and the **latent content**, or underlying and often unconscious meanings of what is discussed, may be the focus of the group. Communication is seen as both verbal (spoken) and nonverbal (silences, movement, changes in posture and breathing, expressions, closeness, and distance); and both verbal and nonverbal communication may be the focus of the interaction. The therapist may comment upon or interpret what is happening in the group and attempt to have the individual or group members work with the issues or the resistance to dealing with the issue in the group. The interactions between group members and between the group and its leader may mirror the interactions that members have in other relationships outside the group. Feedback from the leader and other group members provide an opportunity for feedback, support, and reflection. Other therapeutic groups may be considered task oriented or supportive and deal with a variety of issues and group selection itself may be open and heterogeneous. Therapeutic groups may also consider some of the relationship problems or psychodynamic issues of the group interactions.

A psychotherapy (therapeutic) group differs from most group experiences, including support groups, as its purpose is intrapsychic or interpersonal change in the individual.

Groups may be classified as "closed," offering stability, continuity, and a sense of safety, while "open" groups offer the opportunity for many to experience therapy without a long-term commitment.

Therapy Group Size

Group size is a characteristic that may vary according to the type of group. Usually a group is considered a formation of three or more persons. For example, a family therapy group may be confined to a small group such as one family (parents and children) or to multifamily groups (multiple families or generations). The size of the group may limit the type of information that can be discussed or the amount of time and attention that can be given to any individual or issue. This is true of groups outside of therapy as well. If you look at the size of a typical Cub Scout den, for example, the group is usually limited in size and approximately 6–8 members with 12 being the upper limit for optimal interaction, allowing for absences from the group and adequate for the different group tasks and roles to be performed. Support groups or educational groups may be able to incorporate larger memberships. In some ways, the size of a group has a direct influence upon the dynamics or interactions of a group. A group member may have more opportunities to interact in a smaller group. In the same way, more attention, demands, and responsibilities for participation may be placed upon a member in a smaller group. Larger groups offer the potential for more anonymity and less participation.

The ideal size of a therapy group is six to eight members.

Therapy Group Membership

Membership in a group may vary. Groups may be open (allowing members to self-select or to join at different points of the group experience) or closed (allowing only members selected by the leader, meeting certain criteria, or joining at the same time). Closed groups offer stability and continuity that allow members the safety to develop intimate and intense relationships. An open group may offer the opportunity for many to experience therapy and an opportunity to some members who would not be willing to make a long-term commitment (Yalom & Leszcz, 2005). Some of this may be dictated by the focus of a group. For example, inpatient psychotherapy groups may be open to accommodate the regular admission and discharge of patients. Some groups may be time limited and other groups may be ongoing and accommodate a change of membership over time. Group members may be heterogeneous (having the different or varied characteristics as in a group of patients with different medical illnesses or problems) or homogenous (having the same or similar characteristics such as a group composed of persons of the same gender and similar age or clients with the same illness).

Selection of Members for a Therapy Group

Selection of members for the group varies with the type and size of the group as well its purpose, for example, psychotherapy, support, or education. For a psychotherapy group, an understanding of the group members' current interpersonal relationships and level of functioning is helpful. An individual assessment over time is helpful to try to predict how a prospective member might function in the group and to prepare the potential member for what might be expected during the experience of group therapy. Members should be able to interact with others, and to give and receive feedback. There is an expectation that the member will be able to be verbal and to tolerate self-disclosure as well as to make a commitment to the responsibilities to the group, such as attendance, confidentiality, time limitations, rules, and boundaries (Yalom & Leszcz, 2005). For some groups, such as group therapy for hospitalized inpatients, the number of patients for selection and the criterion for exclusion may be limited.

Just as group members may vary, there may be a variation in group leadership style. The most common leadership styles are the autocratic or dominant leader, the democratic or empowering leader, and the laissez-faire, laid-back, or less directive leader. There may be a predominant leadership style or the leader may demonstrate different styles during different phases of a group or according to the type of group. In a group with an **autocratic leader**, the leader will usually take a more authoritative or directive role determining the rules and conduct of the group and controlling the group interactions. Leadership functions center on an autocratic leader and the group looks to the leader for direction. This is a top-down style of leadership. A group with a **democratic leader** will be encouraged to take more responsibility for the group rules and decisions. In a democratic group, the leader will seek to be less authoritative while facilitating the group. Leadership functions are shared in a democratic group, and group members have more of a say and more responsibility for how the group functions. A group with a **laissez-faire leader** may be directionless or disorganized, losing productivity while it tries to determine its rules and decisions. The laissez-faire leader's hands-off approach may cause the group to be less productive as more time is taken to develop its rules and style and may be less likely to form a cohesive team until various group roles are established. When there is no leader to take charge, there is usually more of a power struggle among the group members until leadership is established.

Physical Space and the Group

As in milieu therapy, the physical environment as well as the interaction of those involved is important and plays a role. The group leader is often responsible for ensuring that a regular space is available and suitable for the group. The size of the space should be adequate for the size of the group. Finding a comfortable and inviting space can help minimize members' anxiety regarding participating in the group. There should be adequate seating and space for the size of the group. Issues of territoriality and geography sometimes become a part of the group process. Members may have assigned seats, or, in open seating, change seating. An empty space from a missing member or the alliances formed by members who choose to sit near or apart from each other can become part of the discussion in a therapy group.

The Stages of Therapy Groups

The stages of a group are the initial stage, the conflict stage, the cohesiveness stage and the termination stage. Several intermediary stages have also been suggested such as the preorientation phase before the initial or forming stage of the group and a norming stage where the group begins to define itself before the preforming or working stage of the group.

Groups have various types of leaders: a) autocratic leaders take a directive role with the group looking to the leader for direction; b) democratic leaders share leadership responsibilities with the group members, and c) laissez-faire leaders take a hands-off approach that can result in a less cohesive and productive group.

Initial Stage

The initial stage is the beginning of the group and sets the stage for orientation to the group. It is the role of the leader to orient the group. The rules may be set by the leader or jointly by the leader and the group. Usually these are the ground rules for group interaction and may include setting standards for interaction such as how someone is recognized to speak, confidentiality regarding what is said in the group, and what the relationships are between the leader and group members and among group members. Group members may worry that they don't know what will happen in the group or if they will be accepted or fit in.

Conflict Stage

The conflict stage is the testing stage of the group. At times the leader is tested by a group member who feels more qualified or better able to run the group. If there are coleaders, group members may attempt to split the leaders of the group. Group members may be focused upon their role and place in the group. There may be conflict between group members or subgroups and criticism of the leader for not being effective in controlling this. Judgmental statements regarding group members and the leader are common.

The stages of a therapy group are the initial stage, conflict stage, cohesiveness stage, and termination stage.

Clinical Example 

A study of nursing students who participated in group therapy while transitioning from classroom to practice areas showed examples of the different stages of a therapeutic group. In the initial stage or beginning, group members discussed their feelings of anxiety about being accepted (e.g., *"When I'm anxious, I talk, talk, talk."*). Then the group moved into an orientation phase where they began to develop rules and standards for group participation (*"I think you have the right to put forward a subject as well."*). In the conflict/dominance phase, group members shared their concerns regarding their subjects and teachers as well as conflicts experienced in adapting to their work and the expectations others had of them, their idealizations and frustrations (e.g., *"But the teachers think they don't make mistakes; they protect themselves."*). In the cohesiveness or working phase, they were able to form a team and work together in problem solving (e.g., *"There's no dialogue out there. You're not heard; here you are listening."*). In the termination phase, students shared how they missed it if there were no group session on a particular day and what the group had meant to them. They described the mutual attraction and cohesion that developed and the learning that had taken place (e.g., *"Another good thing that helped to relieve anxiety, in this process we've been through, in this care term, was because we were all in the same boat; we went through the same things and this helped to relieve me a lot. . . . I have to go ahead. In college, I felt great fear and insecurity; I think everyone felt it and knowing this relieved me a lot. I loved group therapy; I loved it because I didn't feel alone."*) (Scherer, Scherer, & Carvalho, 2007).

As a group leader, the nurse becomes concerned that the verbal and nonverbal communication among the group members is not congruent. What types of nonverbal communicaton is the leader observing that may have raised this concern?

Working Stage

In the working or cohesive stage of the group, the members have begun to develop trust and a relationship with others as well as an identity as a group or team. Members begin to look more to each other and to direct communication more to each other than through the leader as intermediary. Acceptance between members is strengthened and bonds develop within the group. The focus may be on the differences between what happens in the group and outside the group as members begin to compare their experiences and relationships. The emphasis in the group is on helping each other achieve their individual and group goals.

Termination Stage

The termination, or adjourning stage, marks the ending of the group or separation of a member or members from the group. There may be a sense of grieving or loss. As in any therapeutic relationship, discussion of possible feelings regarding this ending actually begins in the working phase of the group. The termination stage is marked by a sense of grieving and loss for group members. There is an expectation that learning will be transferred to experiences outside of the group.

The Roles of Therapy Group Members

Participants in a group may fulfill various roles during the experience. Often nurses are called upon to lead therapeutic or educational groups. In the work environment, nurses may be called upon to lead project or work groups of other nurses or interdisciplinary groups. Some advanced practice nurses develop skills in leadership of psychoanalytic or psychotherapeutic groups or in family and systems therapy.

The roles of the group can be described in different ways. One way is to differentiate between the roles of the group leader and group members. Another way is to describe the different roles that group members may take on during the group experience.

The group therapy leader is responsible for the group orientation and development. Depending upon the theoretical background of the leader and the clinical experience of the leader, the tone and nature of the therapy group may vary. The group leader is both a role model and educator, modeling appropriate communication and behavior in the group. The leader is expected to direct the group and to outline the expectations for the group. At times, there may be a decision to have coleaders. A decision to have coleaders may be based upon many factors such as the size of the group, the clinical experience or background of the leaders, or the need for continuity. Differences in the age, gender, style, or theoretical background of the leaders may influence the way they interact with each other and with the group. Just as in a family system, group members may try to split the leaders or imitate the differences in style. Coleaders need to work as a team and part of this is learning each other's styles, establishing their roles in the group, and working on their communication skills as a team. The group leader is responsible for group maintenance and stability and maintaining a culture of acceptance and caring within the group. The leader of a therapy group helps members link feelings and behaviors and explores the reasons behind beliefs and expectations (Clark, 2009).

The role of the group member is to make a commitment to attend the group and to participate. An expectation of most groups is that members are active within the group and attend regularly, actively listen to other participants, share their thoughts and feelings with the group, and treat group members with respect while maintaining confidentiality.

Clinical Example

Puskar and colleagues (2007) describe some of the barriers and benefits of having advanced practice nurses as group leaders in the treatment of alcoholics. The authors describe the development of a model nursing curriculum on substance abuse education for advanced practice nurses designed to build skills in substance-related disorders research and education at New York University as well as the ANA *Scope and Standards of Psychiatric Mental Health Nursing*. Seen as an extension of Peplau's interpersonal theory, the nurse's involvement in care of substance abusers is an extension of the care to specific populations of patients and involvement in assessment, education, and treatment. Also, substance abuse is seen not only as a problem for the individual but as a problem for the family dynamic. The authors describe the role of the nurse as a leader in group therapy as a cost-effective and efficient way to address the problems faced by groups of substance abusers as well as addressing family dynamics.

There are various other roles that have been described. Some differ according to the stage of the group or the tasks of the group. Some of these functional roles may be shared by members of the group. Roles may differ as to whether they help in group maintenance or tasks, such as those of the gate keeper or information seeker. Some roles, such as the harmonizer and the boring member, focus on personal goals or social interaction. Some roles, such as the silent member and the monopolizer, are dysfunctional.

- **Gate keeper**—allows for acceptance of members in the group; reminds group members of tasks at hand; allows for interactions and flow of information
- **Facilitator**—attempts to focus on the ability of the group to actively focus upon and achieve goals; keeps the group on track; encourages participation
- **Tension reliever**—attempts to maintain calm and reduce possible conflict by using humor, refocusing the group on common ground, or putting differences in wider context to diffuse disagreements
- **Observer**—comments on what is happening in the group, but may remain aloof and apart
- **Silent member**—maintains minimal active participation; withdrawn, sometimes overlooked or can be the focus of attention as others try to include her or become angry at lack of participation
- **Harmonizer**—the group peace maker; attempts to find common ground
- **Monopolizer or attention seeker**—actively participates but tends to dominate or refocus the group's attention on himself
- **Boring member**—contributes little other than what the member feels is expected, offers no opinions and shares little with group, thus avoiding conflict; rarely initiates interaction, spontaneity, or tension relief
- **Psychotic member**—usually not selected because of disorganized thinking and behavior; however, if the member has been a long-time member, others in group will usually be supportive during this period of decomposition
- **Member with characterologic difficulty or severe personality disorder**—can be inappropriate for a group depending on the degree of impairment in functioning, ability to accept feedback, and flexibility in trying new styles
- **Special or personal interest member**—has a special agenda or goals that may vary from that of the group, competes for attention but may not reveal her own conflict of interest

Group members can assume a variety of functional roles within the group. These include gatekeeper, information seeker, harmonizer, monopolizer, and the boring or silent member.

Critical Thinking Question

Find an opportunity to observe a therapy group or observe interactions in a group where you are a participant. Observe the patterns of communication within the group. Can you identify the group leader and the style of leadership? Do group members communicate to and through the leader? Do the members communicate to the group as a whole or to individual group members? Can you identify some of the roles within the group? At what stage of development does the group appear to be?

Clinical Example 

In a therapy group of nursing students, group members summarized group norms and their sense of cohesiveness as follows:

> Diane: When you are working in a team you have to learn how to listen, talk, stop a bit to think. I learned that in the group.
>
> Flavia: The group had the goal, reached it and it was time to end, (. . .) it helped me to grow and to accept, but it ended.
>
> Victoria: In the group we had rules, discipline, because we didn't move on without that. That was something we learned: everything has rules, discipline, if not, it becomes a mess. I think it is sad that the group has to end (. . .), but the subject finished, LIGIE finished (the laboratory where the meeting was held). We assumed a commitment, we closed friendships, we liked to be in LIGIE, this moment was ours only. (Scherer et al., 2007, p. 221)

Therapeutic Factors of Groups

The therapeutic or curative factors common to groups include: instillation of hope, universality, self-understanding, identification, catharsis, altruism, corrective recapitulation, socialization techniques, imitative behaviors, existential factors, cohesiveness, guidance, and interpersonal learning.

Yalom and Leszcz (2005) recognized several therapeutic factors common to groups. These are sometimes known as curative factors as they may lead to healing and change. The importance and influence of these various factors may vary according the clinical background of the group leader, the age and diagnosis of the client, the level of functioning of group members, and the function and stage of the group. The factors follow.

- **Instillation of hope**—expectation of future, promise of relief and survival as seen from others in different phases of recovery and wellness.
- **Universality**—establishing connections and common ground; recognizing that others share the same experiences and feelings reduces sense of isolation.
- **Self-understanding**—develop understanding of communication and relationships through feedback and information provided in the group.
- **Identification**—recognizing similarities in traits or experiences shared with others.
- **Catharsis**—relief provided by expression of emotions seen in context of sharing within the group and receiving feedback and recognition.
- **Altruism**—learning by experience of giving and finding meaning in experience of giving to others. Members learn that they can be useful to others and benefit from helping others.
- **Corrective recapitulation of the primary family group**—experience of transference and countertransference of relationships within the group may allow group members to experience new ways of perspectives on relationships that were originally experienced within the family setting. Members receive feedback on how they interact with others and how this affects their relationships with others. Members are challenged to experience relationships in new ways rather to reenact old patterns in the group.
- **Socializing techniques**—practice, development, and feedback of social skills in the group, development of relationships within the group that are nonjudgmental and empathetic.
- **Imitative behavior**—group members may imitate or mirror the behavior, communication style, or interactions of the leader or other members.
- **Existential factors**—acknowledgment of basic themes of the human condition and individual responsibility.
- **Cohesiveness**—the sense of acceptance and belonging to the group experienced as a sense of oneness with others that comes from the experiences of making a commitment to the group, sharing, and developing alliances.
- **Guidance or imparting information**—the sharing of knowledge and experience both by the leader and other group members. Members learn by participating in the group.
- **Interpersonal learning**—relationship and communication skills developed in a group are based upon interpersonal theory. The group is seen as a microcosm of the social environment. Work within the group is focused upon the present—what happens in the here and now.
- **Self-understanding**—an awareness or insight into one's own behavior and interaction with others developed by learning and reflecting upon experiences. Members' experience of

self-understanding may lead to a willingness to develop new skills or to change.

Clinical Concepts and Considerations in Group Process

Group dynamics is the study of what happens in a group including communication and interpersonal relationships. The various forms of therapeutic communication techniques are discussed in Chapter 3 and, at different times, may be important in interactions within the group. Interactions within the group may be directed towards the leader particularly in the beginning stage or orientation phase of the group. One of the goals in group development is to direct group members to begin to communicate to the group as a whole or to respond to individual members rather than to direct all their communications in and through the leader. The group leader may use different communication techniques to encourage participation and interaction as well as to develop a therapeutic alliance. In group therapy, there is a particular focus upon the here and now, the development of group norms, latent and manifest content of communication, and upon the influence of transference and countertransference upon the group.

The focus of an interpersonal therapy group is upon what is happening in the present, or the here and now, in the group. Part of the orientation process is to clearly explain what the group will focus upon and the boundaries of the group. In the beginning stages of the group, the leader may need to refocus the group to stay within the parameters of the group and limit discussion. The focus of the group is what happens within the group and how relationships and behaviors outside the group may affect the present group interactions. In later stages, group members may share the responsibility of maintaining the focus of the group. The leader is responsible for summarizing what happens in the present and commenting upon the interactions or interpreting how they are influencing the group.

Group dynamics is the study of what happens in a group including communication and interpersonal relationships.

The development of group norms is an important function of any group. The leader helps in identification of the purpose of the group, and both the leader and group members are responsible for developing the group norms or group culture. It is typical for a group to value open communication, inclusiveness, mutual aid, and confidentiality as part of the group norms. Development of norms by the group is a shared task that helps develop cohesiveness. Participating in the development of the group norms is the responsibility of the group leader and members.

In discussions within the group, common themes may develop. The group leader is responsible for attributing meaning to the communication process and interactions in the group. One way this is done is by keeping track of what is going on in the group and commenting upon it. Group process is ongoing and takes place on several levels. The latent content is the underlying feeling content of the communication and may be on an unconscious level. The manifest content is the spoken or observable content of the communication and may be seen in the literal or obvious content of the communication. The latent and manifest content may match in meaning and be congruent. If the latent and manifest content do not match and are incongruent, the communication itself may be unclear. The group leader may need to summarize the interaction and provide a structure for the discussion.

Group process is ongoing and takes place on several levels with the latent content being the underlying feeling content and the manifest content being the spoken or observable content of the communication.

Interpersonal theory supposes a **parataxic distortion** or distorted view of most interactions that takes place because our perceptions of how we perceive others and how we think others view us are inaccurate. The process of parataxis was developed as part of Sullivan's interpersonal theory (Yalom and Leszcz, 2005). Transference is the process whereby the members' feelings about an individual are influenced by their feelings regarding someone in their past, and often the group members are not aware of the transference. The group leader may comment on

In a group, transference is the process whereby the member's feelings about an individual are influenced by their feelings regarding someone in their past.

Countertransference is the presence of underlying feelings and thoughts in the therapist towards a client. In a group, the leader needs to be aware of the potential for countertransference and how it impacts a group and its members.

Clinical Example 

The members of a group in its initial stage have finished introducing themselves. The leader comments, "We've done a great deal here today so far. Each of you has shared a great deal about yourself, your pain, and your reasons for seeking help. But I have a hunch that something else is going on, and that you're sizing one another up, each arriving at some impression of the others, each wondering how you'll fit in with the others. I wonder if we could spend some time discussing what each of us has come up with so far" (Yalom and Leszcz, 2005, p. 157). This directive helps refocus the group on the present, the "here and now."

this process as part of the group interaction in order to help the members become aware of this. Countertransference is the presence of these underlying feelings and thoughts in the nurse towards the client. In a group, the group leader should recognize that transference and countertransference are common and a part of the group process. The group leader needs to be aware of her own countertransference and how this influences her interactions as well as to how transference issues are demonstrated by the group members.

Types of therapy groups include psychotherapy, psychoeducational, expressive arts, inpatient, and self-help.

Types of Therapy Groups

- **Psychotherapy groups**—These are therapeutic groups based upon theory such as psychoanalytic, cognitive-behavioral, systems, or interpersonal theory that involve participation in a group and the development of a therapeutic alliance. These groups may be for a long or short term, they may be open or closed, and they usually involve high-functioning members who are able to actively participate in the group. Groups focus on intrapersonal dynamics and interpersonal relationships.
- **Inpatient groups**—These are usually directive and structured groups that take place in an inpatient setting. The function of the group may vary according to the membership of the group. Groups may have high- or low-functioning members or a combination of both. Membership may be open as patients are admitted and discharged from the inpatient group and enter and leave the therapy group. The therapist assists the group and the individual members in setting goals. Inpatient groups often focus on developing specific skills such as communication skills and can be briefer and more frequent than psychotherapy groups. Part of the goal of inpatient groups may be to help orient the client to what happens in a therapeutic group and develop skills that can be used in groups in an outpatient setting.
- **Psychoeducational groups**—These are therapeutic groups that may have a specific agenda in helping members develop life skills or be more directive in developing a specific agenda. The group leader may be more directive in maintaining the focus of the group upon specific tasks. The group may be time limited or open and ongoing with members at different stages of learning. Groups may focus upon giving information about a specific disorder or illness and the development of coping skills. Guidance and skills training may be limited to specific groups of clients and their caretakers or the focus of the problems may affect wider community groups and be open to those who want information and socialization with others who have similar experiences.
- **Expressive arts groups**—These are therapeutic groups such as psychodrama groups, art therapy groups, dance and movement therapy groups, music groups, poetry groups, and play therapy. The focus of the group is upon artistic self-expression as a form of communication and the interactions of the group members with each other and with the group leader in understanding that communication and interpreting the symbolic communication. The level of functioning of group members may vary.

Critical Thinking Question

Think about two different types of groups in which you have been a participant (school, work, community). Describe the leadership style of the group leader, supporting your observation with specific examples of the leader's behaviors and how they were received by group members. What were the types and purposes of the groups? How did they differ?

Clinical Example

Nurses are often responsible for developing and running psychoeducational groups. Since these are not psychotherapy groups, group leaders need not be advanced practice registered nurses. An example of a psychoeducational group is an educational group for aging clients that focuses upon psychosocial adjustment and development of coping strategies (Schenider & Cook, 2005). Topics might include discussion of normal developmental stages, healthy aging, loneliness,and grieving and loss. The role of the group leader is to impart information, facilitate discussion, and provide feedback. Members of the group are encouraged to recognize the impact of the changes of aging in their lives, share experiences and skills, and support each other.

Evidence-Based Practice

Patients in an ambulatory oncology clinic were randomly assigned to one of three groups while they received chemotherapy. Patients assigned to the verbal relaxation group or to the verbally guided relaxation group experienced a significant reduction in anxiety associated with chemotherapy. Patients in the music therapy group and patients with high-state anxiety received the most benefit (Linn, Hsieh, Hsu, Fetzer, & Hsu, 2011).

The Beginnings of Self-Help Groups

The number and variety of member-run self-help groups have multiplied since what is believed to be the very first group, Alcoholics Anonymous, was started in 1935. Approximately 100 different groups have now adapted the **12-step approach** developed by Alcoholics Anonymous to apply to a variety of other specific addictions and problems.

Another early group is Recovery, Inc., a group that was started in 1937 with the help of a psychiatrist, Dr. Abraham A. Low, whose book detailing Recovery, Inc., techniques is still used by members worldwide. Recovery is run by those suffering from various emotional and mental conditions. The Recovery method teaches people how to change the thoughts, reactions, and behaviors that cause their physical and emotional symptoms. The principles are similar to those found in cognitive-behavioral therapy. Recovery groups today continue to be especially open to working in partnership with professionals, as reflected in their willingness to provide demonstrational meetings for professionals and students (Snyder & Weyer, 2000).

If one examines the development of most health associations and movements in the United States, a small self-help support group of clients or families can usually be identified as the initial seed for that growth. For example, Sylvia Lawry, whose brother had multiple sclerosis, placed an ad in a Brooklyn newspaper to bring together others with the disease and their families to form what in 1946 became the Multiple Sclerosis Society. It was a small group of parents of children with developmental disabilities who organized the Association for Retarded Citizens (ARC) in the 1950s. Marjorie Guthrie, the wife of the folksinger Woody Guthrie, pulled families together to form what became the Huntington's disease Society in 1967. She said her one regret was that no professional had encouraged her 10 years earlier to bring together families, when her husband was first diagnosed with Huntington's—for if that had happened, "We would be a decade further down the road in terms of research by now."

In some cases, self-help groups develop well before a particular health problem is recognized by professionals. Years before postpolio syndrome was officially recognized as a disorder by the medical community, groups of polio survivors were banding together in self-help groups to compare the pain and weakness that they were experiencing and to advocate for needed research. It was a self-help group of Vietnam veterans who, having lost a member to suicide, were instrumental in advocating for recognition of what eventually became known as PTSD (posttraumatic stress disorder) by the Veterans Administration (National Public Radio, 2003). Families of Vietnam veterans who were suffering from Agent Orange exposure and subsequently families of Iraqi war veterans with Gulf War syndrome compared notes and advocated for research through their respective early mutual support networks.

Polly Murray, a housewife and consumer advocate with no formal training in medicine, is credited with most of the epidemiologic groundwork that led to the discovery of Lyme disease in the United States and the development of the first support group in her hometown of Lyme, Connecticut. In 1995, ELASTIC (Education for Latex Allergy Support Team Information Coalition) was started by nurses and other medical professionals who were experiencing serious debilitating allergies associated with the protective gloves they wore. Their organization, which grew to have over 50 local self-help groups, advocated for hospital protocols to protect allergy-sensitive staff and clients, as well as for research and changes in the manufacturing of latex gloves.

Nurses who work with self-help groups can learn from the groups and expand the impact of their nursing interventions.

Critical Thinking Question

In what particular ways might students better educate themselves in understanding the value, variety, and dynamics of self-help groups?

The Variety of Self-Help Groups

Many individuals and families who face a disorder, illness, addiction, disability, loss, or other disruptive life event often seek out those who have been in the same boat to learn about the expectations, coping skills, available resources, options, and successes those persons had in facing that same challenge.

There are about 400 self-help groups for specific illnesses and disorders, and more are developing each year. They range from the Aarskog Syndrome Family Support Network to the Xeroderma Pigmentosum Society, and from Arthritis Clubs across the country to the White Lung Association with local groups for asbestos victims and their families. There are many disability groups such as those for amputees or for people who are ventilator dependent. There is the national Phoenix Society for burn victims and even a Lightning Strike and Electric Shock Survivors International organization, whose members work with medical professionals to assess effects on their long-term health. There are also survivor groups for victims of incest, sexual assault, and other crimes.

Mental Health

There are several national self-help groups for persons with depression or bipolar disorder and their families, most notably the national Depression and Bipolar Support Alliance (DBSA), which, like most other national groups, provides interactive message boards and a wide variety of downloadable brochures, posters, and videos for patients, families, and professionals at its website, www.dbsalliance.org. As one example of their efforts to sensitize professionals to the experience of illness and treatment, with funding from SAMHSA, they produced a 19-minute video, *Partners in Recovery: Creating Successful Practitioner-Consumer Alliances*, viewable at www.stopstigma.samhsa.gov/partnersinrecovery.htm. Other groups that address depression and bipolar disorder include Recovery Inc., Depressed Anonymous, GROW, and Emotions Anonymous.

The number of national self-help groups continues to increase as needs are identified.

For those persons with a diagnosis of schizophrenia, the primary group available is Schizophrenics Anonymous, which provides a six-step program that members follow. There are also local self-help groups for persons with phobias, anxiety disorders, obsessive-compulsive disorders, or anorexia and bulimia.

Self-help groups help their members cope with a variety of illnesses, disabilities, and addictions, as well as bereavement, parenting, and many other stressful problems.

NAMI, the National Alliance on Mental Illness, has about 1,200 local self-help groups for families of those with a mental illness, but also now has 185 NAMI-CARE groups for **mental health consumers**. The national Federation of Families for Children's Mental Health has affiliated chapters with local support groups for parents of children and youth with emotional, behavioral, and mental health challenges. The local state parent organizations have also been developing mutual support groups for youth.

The National Institute of Mental Health, and later the Center for Mental Health Services, through the national Community Support Program, first provided federal funding for annual national mental health consumer conferences in 1985. Subsequent funding has been provided for national technical assistance centers, research centers, and state programs that promote a wide variety of consumer-run centers and related services, of which local self-help and advocacy groups for mental health consumers are but one part of their accomplishments. For local self-help group information, visit the website of the National Mental Health Consumers' Self-Help Clearinghouse at www.cdsdirectory.org/programs.html#SupportGroup. For state contacts, which can also advise on local self-help groups, visit the website of the National Empowerment Center at www.power2u.org/consumerrun-statewide.html.

Similar to how the field of alcoholism treatment recognized the special value of employing those who were in recovery to serve as professional counselors, there has been increasing recognition of how consumer/survivor providers (Bluebird, 2004) can provide professional services as peer specialists based upon their firsthand knowledge of mental illness, recovery, and healthcare system shortfalls.

A number of 12-step groups have been developed just for those persons with co-occurring disorders (such as recovering from alcohol/drug abuse and a mental illness). One study of members of 21 Double Trouble in Recovery groups in New York City found that drug/alcohol abstinence among surveyed members increased from 54% at baseline to 72% a year later (Magura et al., 2003). Other groups for co-occurring disorders that have local groups are Dual Recovery Anonymous, Dual Disorders Anonymous, and Dual Diagnosis Anonymous.

Parenting

There are hundreds of different groups for parents, including groups for single parents, adoptive parents, potentially abusive parents, and parents of children with special needs. The last group alone includes the Fetal Alcohol Network, for those caring for children with fetal alcohol syndrome; the Association of Birth Defect Children, for parents of children with defects due to environmental agents; and the National Father's Network, with local groups for fathers of special-needs children. Some groups address prevention, such as Sidelines, where mothers who had complicated pregnancies and premature births help high-risk expectant mothers.

Bereavement

There is a wide variety of groups for adults who have lost a loved one, from young, widowed persons (www.youngwidow.org) to adults who have lost a sibling (www.adultsiblinggrief.com). In many communities, there are unaffiliated local groups open to any adult who has lost a loved one. Groups can be quite specific, such as COPS (Concerns of Police Survivors) for families of police killed in the line of duty, and the national Twinless Twin Support Group for those who have lost a twin. Compassionate Friends and Bereaved Parents of the USA are the two main national groups for parents who have lost a child. SHARE is one national group that helps parents who have experienced a miscarriage, stillborn, or early infant death. Self-help groups now exist just for parents who have lost children to sudden infant death syndrome, miscarriage, heart defects, drunk driving, murder, suicide, or a drug overdose. For those parents who have lost one or more children in multiple births, there are two international support networks; and there is one for parents who have lost an only child or all their children. A number of national groups have been started by parents who lost children to newborn disorders.

Addiction

There are many groups like Alcoholic's Annonymous, Crystal Meth Anonymous, Heroin Anonymous, Marijuana Anonymous, Nicotine Anonymous, Overeaters Anonymous (for compulsive overeating), Cleptomaniacs and Shoplifters Anonymous, and Workaholics Anonymous. There are also national addiction groups that have developed as alternatives to the 12-step approach, such as Secular Organizations for Sobriety and Women for Sobriety. For self-help groups for family and friends of addicts, there are national groups like Al-Anon, Alateen, Nar-Anon, Gam-Anon, Adult Children of Alcoholics, Families Anonymous, and S-Anon (sexual addiction).

Hidden Clients

A large number of groups exist for family members and friends, who are often hidden clients and whose own health can be adversely affected by the stress of an illness or stressful situation. We just reviewed groups dealing with addiction. For others, when family members are often the key caregivers and their well-being and support are crucial to the health outcome of the client, there are groups like the Well Spouse Association, adult children caring for elderly parents, and Siblings for Significant Change (siblings of those with a disability). There are also model groups, like Mothers Supporting Daughters With Breast Cancer in Maryland, that can be replicated in other parts of the country.

Rare Disorders

In addition to the groups for the vast majority of chronic illnesses, there is an ever-increasing number of rare disorder self-help groups. Their growth has been made possible primarily by the Internet and the ease with which one can start an online self-help network. Cardio-Facio-Cutaneous International was started in 1997 by the mother of a child with the very rare genetic disorder who developed an e-mail discussion group, and the group now has almost a hundred families worldwide. But a few rare disorder groups, once organized, seem to attract more members than original estimates had calculated; for example, the founder of the Ehlers-Danlos National Foundation noted how the incidence of E.D. syndrome had gone from 1 per 750,000, to 1 per 5,000 within 10 years. The groups feel their education of both professionals and the public regarding their disorders plays a key role in improved recognition of the disorder.

Disaster Recovery

Following both natural and man-made disasters, survivors have sometimes improvised their own self-help groups to help cope with the postdisaster turmoil and grief they face. In the case of natural disasters, the groups have usually taken the form of local community groups after a tornado, flood, or earthquake. Myers and Wee (2005) describe how self-help groups not only provide emotional support, practical information, and an enhanced sense of community, but also increase members' sense of control, political empowerment, and opportunities to help others. Myers and Wee go on to describe the importance and uniqueness of empathy provided by other survivors, noting the following regarding professionally run support groups:

> Trauma comes with its own unique constellation of suffering that can only really be grasped by oth-

A 12-step approach encourages members to follow a program based on learning and applying 12 steps, which are usually adapted from the 12 steps of Alcoholics Anonymous.

ers who are similarly affected. Regardless of the capacity for empathy of the facilitators, only other survivors know just how they feel. . . . The sense of being understood in this basic and profound way reduces isolation and is an essential ingredient of recovery. (pp. 216–217)

Some tragedies reflect a repeated cycle of survivors' willingness or need to reach out and help survivors of similar future disasters. For example, Betty Polec, who founded the Flight 255 Family Support Group after losing her daughter in the Detroit Airport crash in 1987, reached out to help Pan Am 103 families in late 1988. In turn, Pan Am 103 Families Group aided Heidi Snow, who lost her fiancé in the 1996 TWA Flight 800 disaster, and went on to found the ongoing self-help group ACCESS (AirCraft Casualty Emotional Support Services) for those who lose a loved one in any type of air crash. As traumatologist Charles R. Figley noted,

> Trauma survivors . . . they become thrivers, and they become teachers. They can go back and remember various things, and answer all those questions we have. They have hope, and they have sense, and the ability to care about other people . . . to look into the eyes of others who have gone through the things that they have gone through, and to be at peace with that, and to show that they did it. (Gift from Within, 2001)

Other Stressful Life Situations

Self-help groups have developed to help people with a range of other potential difficulties such as for divorce, job layoffs, career changes, sexual orientation, or being an incest survivor or another type of crime victim. There are also general women's groups and men's groups that examine the concerns that members raise. There are also cultural variations; for example, for stay-at-home mothers of color, there is the national network of groups called Mocha Moms, and for African American breast cancer survivors there is the national Sisters Network.

Self-help groups provide social support, education, and sometimes advocacy. Education consists of the practical information, successful coping techniques, and related experiential knowledge pooled from members' shared experiences.

A self-help network provides mutual help to members through an interactive newsletter, correspondence, telephone, video, or online exchange.

Characteristics of Self-Help Groups

Mutual Help

Self-help groups can be more appropriately described as mutual-help groups, because this is the primary way that members help one another within their self-help group or network. Mutual help is usually provided as members share their experiences, strengths, and hopes in small, face-to-face group meetings. Since the mid-1990s, an increasing number of new types of self-help networks have developed on the Internet. As many national and international self-help groups established an online presence, they started online self-help networks of their own.

Member Run

Groups are run by their members, not professionals, although professional assistance is often provided. In one of the very first books on self-help groups, Katz (1961) used the term *self-organized groups* to describe what later became known as self-help groups. Because self-help groups are member run, they provide a true sense of community and feeling of belonging. In being member run, they are also more sensitive and responsive to their members' needs.

Composed of Peers

Members share the same problem or experience. They know that others in the group understand because they have been there.

Nonprofit

There are no fees and only minimal dues to sustain support costs, if any. The group is nonproprietary. Self-help group members were first referred to as being "prosumers" (Toffler, 1980) in that they develop services for themselves, rather than being only consumers of another's service.

Primary Functions

All self-help groups perform two major functions: support and education. Some groups take on an additional third function: **advocacy**.

Social Support

Clients and their families report finding comfort and relief from isolation when they finally meet with peers in a group. Some describe it as an instant sense of community. They receive stress-buffering support from others who truly understand their problems and emotions. Support is often provided between meetings through buddy systems, phone calls, newsletters, e-mail contacts, social events, and sometimes through home and hospital visitation programs.

Education

Members share the practical coping skills and resource information that they have found helpful in coping on a daily basis with a chronic illness, disability, or other stressful life problem. Members' experiences, coping strategies, and successes provide other members with a range of options for problem solving and help new members realize that they are not helpless.

Members discuss and evaluate professional and social services (e.g., entitlements, housing, health care, legal information, and employment) and learn how to negotiate the systems. Groups are adept at collecting educational and journal articles and at tapping professional knowledge bases. Groups that are open to professional involvement at meetings frequently have professionals as guest speakers to share their insights, perspectives, and engage in discussion and joint learning. Some groups also discover their strength-in-numbers ability to tap professionals for their knowledge by having them as free guest speakers, or by having them contribute to training workshops, group newsletters and websites, and advisory boards. Such interactions can foster additional collaboration in education, treatment, and research development efforts.

Critical Thinking Question 

Consider how experiential knowledge is often first articulated by clients and then used by practitioners to improve the quality of a business, health care, or other service delivery. Can you think of an example?

Advocacy

Many, but not all, groups engage in advocacy to address needs that cannot be met within the group, such as deficiencies that may exist in the healthcare system or the larger society. Advocates work to educate the public or professionals about the lack of awareness of a disorder, lack of treatment or rehabilitation services, or the presence of discrimination. Local groups often support national and international advocacy efforts. For example, self-help groups for persons with disabilities successfully advocated passage of the Americans With Disabilities Act, and Mothers Against Drunk Driving (MADD) has worked for tougher laws to reduce drunk driving. However, 12-step groups do not engage in advocacy efforts because of their tradition of not endorsing or lending their name to outside interests. It was strongly felt that such actions would divert them from their primary purpose and introduce controversial issues that might divide their membership.

How Groups Help

A variety of dynamics common to self-help groups contribute to their vitality, popularity, and effectiveness.

Helper Therapy

The basic concept behind the helper-therapy principle (Riessman, 1965) is that those who help others gain special benefits themselves. In helping others, the helper experiences an increased sense of self-worth and self-esteem, often when it is most needed. The act of helping others also reinforces for the helper the principles, learning points, and/or program that the helper is following. Helpers develop a firmer understanding of their own recovery process and goals when helping others, as expressed in slogans sometimes heard in 12-step groups, such as, "If you help someone up the hill, you get closer to the top yourself." Even new members can experience the helper's high or increased sense of belonging when they listen to others and simply acknowledge with a nod to them that they truly understand what that person is saying. Through helper therapy, most groups turn what society considers a liability (i.e., one's experience as an addict, a widow, or a person with an illness) into an asset (that member's unique ability to provide help to others).

Helping others within the group has been reported as one of the more important benefits that members receive from their participation in the group (Bacon, Condon, & Fernsler, 2000; Knight, 2006). In a study of members of self-help groups for co-occurring disorders, the experience of the helper-therapy process was associated with increases in abstinence from drug and/or alcohol abuse (Magura et al., 2003).

Advocacy promotes a specific educational, political, or social cause or change in the community or society.

Positive Role Models

Experienced or veteran members demonstrate to new members that success, coping, and recovery are possible. They model competence and attest to how the problems that members face can be overcome. Their example and actions often provide needed encouragement and the installation of hope that otherwise is not available, because such role models are rarely found in agency settings or outside the group. The observance of role models by new members encourages them to assume more responsible action and pursue further learning.

Clinical Example

Some self-help groups have developed in response to the need for advocacy. For example, International Nurses Anonymous, now an informal network, was originally founded in 1988 in response to the special needs of nurses in recovery. Nurses were regularly being denied licenses if they simply acknowledged that they were recovering alcoholics. Many state nurses associations and state boards now have programs specifically geared for nurses in recovery and have peer involvement and support. Many other fellowships have developed for health professionals, such as Anesthetists in Recovery, a national support network for recovering nurse anesthetists; International Doctors in AA; and International Pharmacists Anonymous.

Accessibility

Because there are no fees, groups are financially accessible. Many groups are geographically accessible in the community and schedule meeting times that are more convenient than most professional services. They also are psychologically more accessible in several ways. In the many anonymous 12-step groups, last names are not given. Most groups require no registration. One can go to a group simply for education, which is much more affordable both emotionally and financially than having to assume the role of a patient for mental health treatment. Yet these self-help groups often "grease the skids" for needed referrals of individuals to professional treatment services by both destigmatizing problems and explaining the true benefits and processes of professional treatment, as only those who have experienced it can.

Alternatives

As members pool experiences, literature, and problem-solving skills, they are exposed to a range of different coping strategies and options for dealing with their individual situation. This can be especially helpful for new members who come to a meeting feeling helpless and hopeless.

Clinical Example

Lara is a 29-year-old married woman who speaks of feeling depressed over the last few weeks. She has had difficulty sleeping and has experienced a loss of appetite. Except for the delivery of an abnormal stillborn baby a little over a year ago, her medical history was unremarkable. Lara tells the nurse in the clinic she feels as if she has been managing well, and she does not want to burden her family by telling them how she feels. She does not feel as if anyone understands the loss she has experienced. The nurse points out that sometimes people reexperience feelings of loss around the anniversary of the event. In reinforcing how her feelings are normal, the nurse discusses options for referral including referral to a self-help group composed of other women who have experienced a similar loss.

Normalization

For many people, the experience of illness, disability, or trauma results in isolation and alienation. After new members meet with others who have similar

Clinical Example

Miguel is a 35-year-old married man who was admitted to the hospital with a blood alcohol level over 350. While hospitalized and treated for withdrawal symptoms, Miguel told hospital staff that he felt lonely and isolated. Separated from his family, with no legal status in the United States, Miguel has been working long hours in order to send money to his family back home. He was frustrated because of the separation from his family and his inability to speak English. Staff encouraged him to recognize the need to abstain from alcohol, and Miguel expressed a desire to stop drinking. The nurse was able to contact AA/Intergroup and find a meeting for Miguel in his own language and in his own neighborhood.

Clinical Example 

One example of the dedication of group members occurred in the wake of the September 11, 2001, terrorist attack on the World Trade Center. Members of the Oklahoma City bombing Family Support Group, the Victims of Pan Am 103 family group, and the Beirut Connection for families of the marines killed in the terrorist barracks bombing in Lebanon volunteered to travel at their own expense to comfort families who had lost loved ones in the September 11 attack. In several meetings in the months after the tragedy, they consoled the families and assured them, as no one else could, that although the pain of their loss would never go away, it would ease and they would once again be able to experience joy in life.

experiences, they often report feeling normal again. People are comforted by knowing that their experiences and feelings are not unusual. They also can satisfy their human need for basic feedback as to how they are doing in comparison with others.

Prevention Equation

To varying degrees, self-help groups serve a preventive function by enhancing social ties and connections that serve as a buffer to stress and by promoting the ability of people to cope with stress and adversity for many of life's transitions and crises. Silverman (1985) points out that although many stressful life transitions cannot be prevented, the mutual-help group may be one of the more powerful modalities for facilitating the acquisition of coping skills subsequent to stress. Albee's prevention equation (1982) theorizes how groups help prevent or lessen the incidence of psychopathology and stress-related illness by strengthening social support, coping skills, and competence:

$$\text{Incidence of dysfunction} = \frac{\text{stress + constitutional vulnerabilities}}{\text{social support + coping skills + competence}}$$

Empowerment

Seeing how others have taken responsibility for their health and recovery encourages members to take responsibility to educate themselves, become self-reliant, change their lifestyles, gain valuable self-advocacy skills, and support others. This, along with any group advocacy efforts, contributes to an increased sense of personal and collective efficacy.

Source of Altruism and Meaning

Some members remain in self-help groups long after they have been helped, because they find the work in helping others personally satisfying and rewarding. In many groups, including those for persons with terminal illness, members report that the group has helped them to find new meaning, direction, or spirituality in their lives. Frankl (1959, p. 116) noted,

> We must never forget that we may also find meaning in life even when confronted with a hopeless situation, when facing a fate that cannot be changed. For what then matters is to bear witness to the uniquely human potential at its best, which is to transform a personal tragedy into a triumph, to turn one's predicament into a human achievement.

Growth of Online Self-Help Networks

The number of online self-help networks has increased dramatically over the last decade. For example, Yahoo! Groups recently indicated that 34,851 e-mail groups were available under the "Support" heading of their Health & Wellness category (http://groups.yahoo.com). Although the average American can choose from among several dozen different face-to-face self-help groups in his or her local area, Internet access allows that same person to participate in any one of thousands of different online self-help groups. At the same time, a Pew Internet study found that at least half of the American adult population has already turned to the Internet to seek health information, making it the third most popular online activity (Fox & Fallows, 2003). Virtual social networks may offer both the potential for greater access and less privacy. At the same time, there is a potential for noninteractive lurking and obscuring of identity (Demiris, 2006).

Online self-help networks are growing, eliminating many barriers that previously kept people from developing or participating in a community group. They primarily take the form of interactive websites, e-mail discussion groups, newsgroups, and commercial forums or conferences.

Online computer systems are removing many of the barriers that previously prevented people from participating in a community self-help group, including the lack of any local group, an individual's lack of transportation to an existing group, the limitations of disabilities or chronic illnesses that prevent access to community groups, 24-hour-a-day caregiver or parenting responsibilities, and the rarity of an illness or condition that made it previously impossible to draw together enough people to have a local meeting (Bacon, Condon, & Fernsler, 2000).

The three primary ways that people currently participate in online self-help groups are through website message boards or forums, e-mail discussion groups or electronic mailing lists, and live chat room meetings. The most prevalent form of online mutual help is the message threads found on various website message boards. These messages are often displayed as discussion threads, which are similar to self-help group discussions but evolve in slower motion. Unlike real-time group discussions, these responses are usually carefully and thoughtfully prepared offline before being posted. This asynchronous dialogue, available every day around the clock, is often richer than real-time meeting exchanges. One example is the Totally Hip website and discussion board (www.totallyhip.org), developed by a woman who went through two hip replacement surgeries. Second, there are e-mail discussion groups or Listservs that allow subscribing members to send and receive messages using e-mail. Each message and every response is sent to all subscribers as individual e-mails, or as one daily digest that compiles all messages of the previous day into one e-mail message. One good example is the Association of Cancer Oncology Resources (www.ACOR.org), which has over 140 separate e-mail discussion groups dealing with specific cancers and some caregiver situations (such as partners of breast cancer patients, or those facing the death of a loved one). ACOR, which was started by the husband of a cancer patient after he found e-mail discussion groups to be very helpful to him and his wife but not easy to locate, generates over 1.5 million individual e-mail messages shared by members each week. Ferguson (2000) describes how one cancer patient, having been aided by an ACOR e-mail list, developed a very comprehensive website for lung cancer patients, where she works with leading physicians to help promote patient awareness of their work.

Third, there are online chat rooms where groups meet in real time mostly for group discussion or, in fewer cases, for a guest speaker or resource person. Meetings are often scheduled for evenings or weekends. One example is the National Ataxia Foundation (www.ataxia.org), which has been having three real-time group meetings scheduled at the same time each week for several years. The foundation also has a message board or bulletin board for exchanges at other times.

Although online support networks lack some attributes of face-to-face self-help groups (nonverbal communication such as handshakes, hugs, and human presence), they do provide mutual support, information, a sense of belonging, and medical and resource referrals as needed. Lieberman, Golant, Winzelberg, McTavish, & Gustafson (2003–2004) studied differences among several different professionally run and self-directed or self-help online groups for breast cancer patients and determined that groups conducted by professionals expressed significantly more negative emotions, anxiety, hostility, and depression, and fewer positive emotions than self-directed groups. The researchers noted that professionals had encouraged the greater expression of negative emotions in their groups because the open expression of such emotions has been shown to be beneficial, whereas the lay leaders more often responded with support and reassurance to members who expressed painful emotions.

A study of one online support network found that most respondents rated as most helpful the group's ability to help them put cancer in perspective, obtain needed information, lessen their sense of isolation, and permit them to help others (Fernsler & Manchester, 1997). In a study of one online group for parents of children with special needs, "the majority of participants not only obtained what they sought, but found more than expected in terms of insight and people to trust" (Baum, 2004, p. 29).

Clinical Example 

Deanna is a 24-year-old single mother of three who is hospitalized with renal insufficiency. She is newly diagnosed with systemic lupus erythematosus (SLE). She mentions to the staff that because she has three young children it is difficult for her to find time under normal circumstances to leave home without the children and find a babysitter. One thing she enjoys doing is keeping in touch with her family and friends using the computer. Deanna is eager to learn about SLE. As part of patient teaching at discharge, the nurse discusses possible referral to an online support group in addition to other referrals for follow-up care.

Roles for Nurses

Identify and Refer to Groups

Identifying local groups is not always an easy task, but some areas of the country and the world are served by local **self-help clearinghouses** (such as the one at http://www.mentalhelp.net/selfhelp/selfhelp.php?id5859), which provide local group contacts and sometimes online or hard copy directories. If a local clearinghouse is not available, local help lines and mental health associations can sometimes provide group contacts and listings. The American Self-Help Clearinghouse provides a keyword-searchable database of over 1,100 national, international, model, and online self-help groups at its website (http://mentalhelp.net/selfhelp). Once there, one enters a keyword, and then is shown a list of links to national group websites, where access to information on the existing local groups is usually available. Group brochures, publications, newsletters, conference announcements and reports, and videos are increasingly available via download, or they may be ordered online.

Self-help groups are not regulated or credentialed, which has made it possible for groups to be started by lay persons and operate with no fees. Groups both in the community and online are in various stages of development and decline. A group may have difficulty recruiting members or retaining adequate leadership. Therefore, it is appropriate to routinely request client feedback as to whether the local self-help group has proven helpful. If it is not found helpful, determine whether any problem was experienced that may be threatening the group's ability to help its members.

Liaison

If a nurse often works with clients with a certain disorder or problem, he or she can request or order literature from appropriate local groups, post meeting notices, and keep a supply or display of brochures on hand. A nurse can also consider subscribing to the group's newsletter and establishing an ongoing liaison. When nurses provide referrals, local groups sometimes reciprocate by distributing agency materials and providing referrals to the professional health services.

Resource Person

Some local groups invite professionals to speak to their members. Nurses may offer to speak or help to identify speakers. They may help the group meet its needs for professional advisers, consultants, researchers, or special services. It is important to determine group needs that an agency might meet, such as providing meeting space, help with mailings, photocopying, or secretarial help.

Nurses can make clients aware of groups, serve as resource persons to groups in multiple ways, tap groups for various educational efforts, and help develop needed new groups.

Education

Group representatives can be invited to provide an overview of their work and issues at staff meetings or to speak at in-service training sessions, workshops, or conferences. Group members bring real experiences and personal insights to education. Linking groups with other community agencies might be considered. Some groups have a special interest in doing outreach focused on prevention of specific health problems, such as laryngectomy groups speaking on smoking cessation in schools or spinal cord injury groups speaking on pool or driver safety.

Considerations for Client and Family Education

- There are different types of therapy groups, and participation in group therapy can offer the same benefits as individual and other forms of therapy.
- Participation in group therapy usually involves sharing individual and common experiences and feelings as well as discussing what is happening within the group itself.
- Members in a therapy group receive feedback from other members in the group and the group leader.
- Self-help groups can be a valuable resource for mutual support and education.
- Participation in a self-help group can provide an opportunity to develop alternate coping strategies.
- Roles within a self-help group vary and participants can find ways to help and advocate for themselves and others.
- When contact with others with similar problems or access to services is difficult, online self-help groups and support networks are a valuable source of support and information.

Development

Nurses are in a favorable position to identify, encourage, and link people who could join with others to start a local self-help group. Nurses are often the first to recognize common unmet needs among clients.

In terms of productivity, a health professional can help start several self-help groups serving different patient and community health needs in less time than it takes for that same professional to plan and lead just one group by himself or herself for a year. Moreover, those ongoing self-help groups can provide a greater spectrum of empowering and supportive benefits, often to many more members, long after that professional is no longer available.

Summary

Therapy groups, self-help groups, and self-help networks utilize the shared common experiences of members to stimulate participation, interaction, and support. Group therapy is utilized in various inpatient and ambulatory settings and can be utilized during different phases of treatment such as during a crisis situation or during recovery and rehabilitation. There are different types of therapy groups, and groups typically evolve during stages of development from orientation, or forming stages, to termination, or adjourning stages. There are different approaches in group leadership and varied group roles. In group therapy, the emphasis is upon the members' participation in group sessions and focuses upon the interactions within the group. Nurses may be involved in orienting clients to group therapy approaches or, based on their training and interests, by participating in groups as a leader or as a member. Self-help groups continue to grow because they meet needs for support, education, and advocacy for varied populations and interest groups. Better understanding, use, and support of these community and online resources by nurses can help them to better meet their clients' and communities' health needs.

Annotated References

Adamsen, L., & Rasmussen, J. M. (2003). Exploring and encouraging through social interaction: A qualitative study of nurses' participation in self-help groups for cancer patients. *Cancer Nursing, 26*(1), 28–36.
This study explored the experiences oncology nurses had with cancer patients and self-help groups, reflecting how nurses function as social networkers encouraging relationships between patients and the formation of informal self-help groups for patients with cancer.

Albee, G. W. (1982). Preventing psychopathology and promoting human potential. *American Psychologist, 37*, 1043–1050.
Dr. Albee was a leading authority on prevention. Here he reviews various theories, reflecting on their value and potential implementation.

Bacon, E. S., Condon, E. H., & Fernsler, J. I. (2000). Young widows' experience with an Internet self-help group. *Journal of Psychosocial Nursing and Mental Health Services, 38*(7), 24–33.
The authors researched perceptions of members of one online group. They determined that the group was useful in reducing isolation and helping members to cope. The article suggests that nurses can guide their patients to Internet support groups for self-care when traditional groups are not available.

Baum, L. S. (2004). Internet parent support groups for primary caregivers of a child with special health care needs. *Pediatric Nursing, 30*(5), 381–388.
An exploratory study of 114 parents/caregivers who participated in online groups reflected that they had found more than they expected in terms of insight and people to trust. The strongest outcome factor was related to their satisfaction with an improved caregiver-child relationship.

Bluebird, G. (2004). Redefining consumer roles: Changing culture and practice in mental health care settings. *Journal of Psychosocial Nursing and Mental Health Services, 42*(9), 46–53.
This article explains how professionals who have personal experience in recovery from mental illness can uniquely serve as positive role models, instilling hope and empowering patients, while also responding to systemic deficiencies of which they may have firsthand knowledge.

Calloway, B. J. (2002). *Hildegard Peplau: Psychiatric nurse of the century*. New York, NY: Springer Publishing Company, Inc.
This is a biography of Hildegard Peplau. It discusses her innovative and groundbreaking work in nursing including obtaining clinical experiences for graduate students in education and psychiatric nursing to lead group therapy experiences.

Clark, C. C. (2009). *Group leadership skills for nurses and health professionals* (5th ed). New York, NY: Springer Publishing, Inc.

This book provides a description of the role of leader in different types of groups, a description of stages of groups and types of interactions, and a focus upon group process and evaluation.

Classen, C., Butler, L. D., Koopman, C., Miller, E., DiMiceli, S., Giese-Davis, J. J., . . . Spiegel, D. (2001). Supportive-expressive group therapy and distress in patients with metastatic breast cancer: A randomized trial. *Archives of General Psychiatry, 58*(5), 494–501.
This article reports on a randomized study of clients with metastatic breast cancer. Patients with this diagnosis have a high incidence of mood and trauma symptoms. Participation in supportive-expressive group therapy reduced symptoms.

Demiris, G. (2006). The diffusion of virtual communities in healthcare: Concepts and challenges. *Patient Education & Counseling, 62*(10), 78–188.
This article discusses the social structure and potential ethical problems of virtual social communities and their use in healthcare and consumer education.

Fernsler, J. I., & Manchester, L. J. (1997). Evaluation of a computer-based cancer support network. *Cancer Practice, 5*, 46-51.
This article compiles the results of a study conducted by two nurses, one of whom had cancer, and initiated the research of the Compuserve Cancer Forum.

Ferguson, T. (2000). Online patient-helpers and physicians working together: A new partnership for high quality health care. *British Medical Journal, 321*, 1129–1132.
Dr. Ferguson describes the value of an online website for lung cancer, developed by a cancer survivor. The article speaks to the growing demand for online health information, and the benefits to physicians aiding patients in their efforts and working with online patient helpers.

Fox S., & Fallows, D. (2003). *Internet health resources: Health searches and email have become more commonplace, but there is room for improvement in searches and overall Internet access.* Washington, DC: Pew Internet & American Life Project. Retrieved from http://www.pewinternet.org/PPF/r/95/report_display.asp
This article reviews the impact of Internet searches and intervention on health care consumers' behavior and choices. The PEW Internet & American Life Project is one source of search engines that provides reports on the impact and trends of the Internet on daily life including use of peer-to-peer networks, resources to make healthcare decisions, and public opinion.

Frankl, V. E. (1959). *Man's search for meaning.* New York, NY: Beacon Press.
This is an account of a psychiatrist's dehumanizing experiences in Nazi death camps that led to his development of logo therapy, a form of existential analysis.

Gift From Within. (2001). *Recovering from traumatic events: The healing process* (video). Camden, ME: Author.
This video is narrated by members of the International Society for Traumatic Stress Studies, who discuss practical approaches to recovery, with survivors recounting their experiences and recovery. It reflects how survivors can learn to be thrivers and then teachers of the healing process.

Katz, A. H. (1961). *Parents of the handicapped.* Springfield, IL: Charles C Thomas.
This is the first book to describe the earliest self-help groups that evolved into national organizations of parents who have children with specific disabilities.

Knight, E. L. (2006). Self-help and serious mental illness. *Medscape General Medicine, 8*(1), 68. Retrieved from http://www.medscape.com/viewarticle/519009
This article provides a review of various reports and studies that have examined the meaning and value of self-help groups, primarily for persons who have serious mental illnesses.

Law, M., King, S., Stewart, D., & King, G. (2001). The perceived effects of parent-led support groups for parents of children with disabilities. *Physical & Occupational Therapy in Pediatrics, 21*(2/3), 29–48.
A qualitative study of members of nine groups indicated that the effects of belonging to a parent-led parent support group were substantial. Parents reported increased skills in dealing with day-to-day issues, an increased sense of power and support, and a sense of belonging.

Lieberman, M. A., Golant, M., Winzelberg, A., McTavish, F., & Gustafson, D. H. (2003–2004). Comparisons: Professionally-directed and self-directed Internet groups for women with breast cancer. *International Journal of Self Help and Self Care, 2*(3), 219–235.
Researchers compared support group messages from professionally run and self-directed online groups for women with breast cancer and found

professionally run groups expressed significantly more negative emotions and fewer positive emotions than self-directed ones.

Linn, M. F., Hsieh, Y. J., Hsu, Y.Y., Fetzer, S., & Hsu, M.S. (2011). A randomized controlled trial of the effect of music therapy and verbal relaxation on chemotherapy-induced anxiety. *Journal of Clinical Nursing, 7*(8), 988–999.
Discussed study of 98 subjects in three groups demonstrating the effectiveness of expressive therapy to reduce anxiety in cancer patients receiving chemotherapy.

Magura S., Laudet, A. B., Mahmood, D., Rosenblum, A., Vogel, H. S., & Knight, E. L. (2003). Role of self-help processes in achieving abstinence among dually diagnosed persons. *Addictive Behaviors, 28*(3), 399–413.
This study found that drug/alcohol abstinence among members of 21 Double Trouble in Recovery groups increased from 54% at baseline to 72% a year later. Helper-therapy and reciprocal-learning activities within the group were associated with better abstinence outcomes.

Myers, D., & Wee, D. F. (2005). *Disaster mental health services.* New York, NY: Brunner-Routledge.
Chapter 6, "Support Groups in Disaster Mental Health Programs," discusses the use of self-help groups as one form of support group that provides opportunities for emotional support and information sharing, helping others, maintaining personal sense of control, and increasing political involvement.

National Public Radio. (2003, August 19). All things considered: Post-traumatic stress disorder. Retrieved from http://www.npr.org/templates/story/story.php?storyId=1401789
NPR's Alix Spiegel traces the creation of the concept of posttraumatic stress disorder. He interviews Vietnam War veteran Jack Smith regarding his group's action in taking the head of the Veterans Administration hostage for a teach-in. Psychiatrists Robert Jay Lifton and Art Blank, who were invited to the group's meetings, are also interviewed.

Oppawsky, J. (2010). Depression school: A three-session group crisis stabilization intervention. *Annals of the American Psychotherapy Association, 13*(3), 60–64.
This is a report of clients with depression who use a group model of three sessions to stimulate group interaction and support dealing with common themes and coping strategies.

Pusker, K., McClure, E., & McGinnis, K. (2007). Advanced practice nurses' role in alcohol abuse group therapy. *The Australian journal of advanced nursing, 10*(3), 64–69.
Defines the benefits of utilizing advanced practice nurses in treatment of substance abusers and the benefits of nurses as leaders of group therapy for this population.

Riessman, F. (1965). The helper therapy principle. *Social Work, 10*, 26–32.
This article examines the various benefits derived when people with a problem help others with the same problem, as originally reflected in student tutoring programs but especially found in self-help groups.

Scherer, Z. A. P., Scherer, E. A., & Carvalho, A. M. P. (2007). Group therapy with nursing students during the theory-practice transition. *Revista Latino-Americana de Enfermagem, 15*(2), 214–223. Retrieved from www.scielo.br/pdf/rlae/v15n2/v15n2a05.pdf
This article provides a description of student participation in group therapy during their transition to practice areas and description of their interactions.

Schneider, J. K., & Cook, J. H. (2005). Planning psychoeducational groups for older adults. *Journal of Gerotological Nursing, 31*(8), 33–38.
Discusses development of nurse-led group classes to discuss healthy aging and age related changes.

Silverman, P. (1985). Tertiary/secondary prevention-preventive intervention: The case for mutual help groups. In R. K. Conyne (Ed.), *The group workers' handbook* (pp. 237-258). Springfield, IL: Charles C Thomas.
This chapter presents ways in which self-help groups contribute to prevention and reduce the risk of relapse.

Snyder, M. D., & Weyer, M. E. (2000). Collaboration and partnership: Nursing education and self-help groups. *Nursing Connections, 13*(1), 5–12.
This article describes the development of a collaborative partnership between a psychiatric nursing course and Recovery, Inc., which afforded undergraduate students a better appreciation of the role of self-help groups and provided some students with personal insights into the universality of the human experience.

Toffler, A. (1980). *The third wave*. New York, NY: William Morrow.
A futurist analyzes the different forces contributing to a third stage in the development of civilization, following the agricultural and industrial revolutions.

Yalom, I. D., & Leszcz, M. (2005). *Theory and practice of group psychotherapy* (5th ed.). New York, NY: Basic Books.
This book is considered the foundation text for group therapy. It discusses theoretical framework and group dynamics.

Additional Resources

Antai-Otong, D. (2007). *Nurse–client communication: A life span approach*. Sudbury, MA: Jones & Bartlett.
This book is a resource for therapeutic communication techniques including cultural aspects of communication, team building, and negotiations. It identifies roles and responsibilities of the nurse in various settings as group leader or member.

Brown, L. D., & Wituk, S. (2010). *Mental health self-help: Consumer and family initiatives*. New York, NY: Springer.
This book provides an overview of mental health self-help and support groups and information on funding and groups.

Humphreys, K., & Moos, R. H. (2007). Encouraging posttreatment self-help group involvement to reduce demand for continuing care services: Two-year clinical and utilization outcomes. *Alcoholism Clinical and Experimental Research, 31*(1), 64–68.
This study of male substance-dependent patients showed that those referred for aftercare to 12-step-based self-help groups showed a higher rate of drug abstinence after 2 years and a cost savings for care related to less frequent use of outpatient and inpatient mental health services.

White, B. J., & Madara, E. J. (Eds.). (2002). *Self-help group sourcebook* (7th ed.). Denville, NJ: Self Help Clearing House.
This guide contains information on better understanding self-help groups' dynamics and benefits, and it provides descriptions of over a thousand national, international, and model groups. It includes chapters on starting community groups, and summaries of rigorous research outcome studies.

Internet Resources

For a full suite of assignments and additional learning activities, use the access code located in the front of your book to visit this exclusive website: http://go.jblearning.com/mentalhealth. If you do not have an access code, you can obtain one at the site.

Learning Objectives

After reading this chapter, you will be able to:

- Describe various complementary modalities and their application to psychiatric nursing.
- Identify evidence-based applications of complementary therapies.
- Identify the beliefs and philosophy of holistic nursing.
- Discuss the relevance of spirituality to holistic nursing practice.
- Identify the elements of a holistic assessment.

Key Terms

Acupuncture

Alternative therapy

Autogenic training

Biofeedback training

Breathing

Centering

Chamomile

Complementary therapy

Ginkgo (*Ginkgo biloba*)

Grape seed extract (*Vitis vinifera*)

Holistic nursing

Hypnosis

Imagery

Inner reflection

Intention

Journaling

Kava (*Piper methysticum*)

Meditation

Omega-3 fatty acids

Progressive muscle relaxation

Qi gong

Reiki

Relaxation

SAMe (S-adenosyl-L-methionine)

St. John's wort (*Hypericum perforatum*)

Tai chi

Therapeutic touch (TT)

Valerian root (*Valeriana officinalis*)

Yoga

Holistic Nursing and Complementary Modalities

Jeanne Anselmo and Patricia G. O'Brien

http://go.jblearning.com/mentalhealth 

For a full suite of assignments and additional learning activities, use the access code located in the front of your book to visit this exclusive website: http://go.jblearning.com/mentalhealth. If you do not have an access code, you can obtain one at the site.

Introduction

Contemplating the mysteries of life and death, finding meaning in suffering, cultivating hope, finding peace, exploring religion and our beliefs, and dealing with growth, change, loss, chaos, illness, and healing comprise the spiritual or psychospiritual dimensions of nursing. These life experiences touch us deeply and invite us to explore our personal beliefs, our understanding of our place in the universe, our reason for being here, the sacredness of living, and our relationship to a power greater than ourselves.

We touch dimensions of the sacred each day in nursing. Understanding how spirit and our sense of interconnectedness, meaning, and purpose impact our health and life continuously offers us new opportunities for growth, renewal, deepening, and learning. Whether we are new nurses or experienced practitioners, the journey continues to unfold. In this chapter, you will explore holistic nursing practice and be introduced to **complementary therapies**.

Holistic nursing is directed at healing the whole person, and, as defined by the American Holistic Nurses Association (AHNA), is a specialty based on a body of knowledge, evidence-based research, sophisticated skill sets, defined standards of practice, and a philosophy of living and being that is grounded in caring, relationship, and interconnectedness (2006). Complementary therapies are healing measures that clients may choose to use in addition to traditional therapy to treat the symptoms of emotional distress and psychiatric illness. It is important to make the distinction between complementary and **alternative therapies**. Complementary means the use of these therapies *together with* traditional treatment modalities. Alternative refers to the use of these therapies *in place of* conventional treatment. The boundaries between complementary, alternative, and conventional approaches are not absolute. Over time, and based on research, alternative measures may enter the mainstream and become part of conventional standards of care. The therapies presented here are intended as complements to traditional therapy and part of holistic nursing practice.

Complementary Modalities in Holistic Nursing Practice

Over the past 35 to 50 years, our culture has begun to explore ancient healing practices and traditions from cultures around the world, especially the East, such as yoga, meditation, Zen, Buddhism, healing, Hinduism, shamanism, Native American healers, mysticism, Chinese medicine, acupuncture, herbs, Ayurveda, and chanting. People in our culture are just becoming aware of the benefits of these ancient healing practices, many of which have been practiced for more than 5,000 years.

In this section you will explore an overview of some of the most frequently used complementary modalities, with suggestions for use in hospitals, home care, and community health. Holistic and complementary practices are learned first through experience and practice. Practicing these holistic healing arts offers us (1) the direct experience of the therapy; (2) the opportunity to explore its personal impact; (3) the understanding of our own personal path needed to learn this practice; (4) the knowledge of how our beliefs, expectations, and attitudes are impacted by these practices; and (5) the enhancement of our sense of well-being and empowerment.

Self-Healing and Self-Regulation

Your own personal experiences, beliefs, attitudes, expectations, and intentions can impact professional practice. You develop insight into these issues by inner reflection and active exploration of information. This active learning will encourage you to be mindful of your beliefs, reflections, and attitudes. To introduce you to holistic nursing practices, we begin by exploring the arts of **centering**, **inner reflection**, and **journaling**.

Breathing, centering, inner reflection, and journaling are complementary therapies used for self-care, self-healing, and self-awareness and offer insight into the **holistic nursing** process. These practices offer an opportunity to release the tensions of the day, concentrate one's attention, and open oneself to new ideas and greater awareness for one's own healing journey.

Take a moment to quiet your mind and relax your body. Turn off any extraneous noises, lower or turn off your phone ringer, and find a comfortable position on a bed or chair. You can read through this exercise and then try it yourself, invite someone to read it to you slowly, or tape this exercise so you can just relax and listen.

Uncross your arms and legs. Find a comfortable position on a bed or a chair (**Figure 10-1**). If you are sitting, place your feet on the floor. Close your eyes

Figure 10-1 Start your centering exercise in a relaxed position.

or focus on a point, so your attention can turn inward rather than outward. Focus your attention on your **breathing**, taking a long, slow breath. Imagine as you exhale that you are allowing all the tension to be released from your body. As you inhale, imagine you are breathing in quiet and calm. Allow this to happen at your own pace, continuing to focus on your breathing. As you exhale, breathe out any tension. Sometimes it helps to say the words as you breathe, "I am breathing in calm," and as you exhale, "I am letting go of any tension or negativity." Allow yourself to be in the moment. Gently focus your attention on your breath. Then, when you are ready:

- Reflect for a moment on what moved you to enter nursing. Maybe you remember some event or experience that helped you to know that this is what you wanted to do as your life's work. What qualities did you notice or experience in that moment? Pause. Reflect. Breathe.
- Try to remember your first experience of healing. How have you carried this experience into your life and work? How has it helped you in your life? Pause. Reflect. Breathe.

When you are ready, again focus on your breathing and gently scan how you feel in your body, mind, and spirit. Note any changes. There is no right or wrong way to do this. Whatever is happening is okay. Just note and observe it. Breathe and be present. If your mind wanders, gently bring your attention back to your breathing. Write down any reflections, images, ideas, and remembrances in a journal, notebook, or on a piece of paper. Throughout the chapter you will be invited to reflect and record in your journal as part of this experiential learning journey (**Figure 10-2**).

A nurse's own belief system about illness, spirituality, health, and self-healing could impact the client and the plan of care.

Experiential healing practices expand our capacity for intuitive knowing, awareness of subtle cues, insight, and compassion. These practices also support our direct experience of how we can impact our own healing.

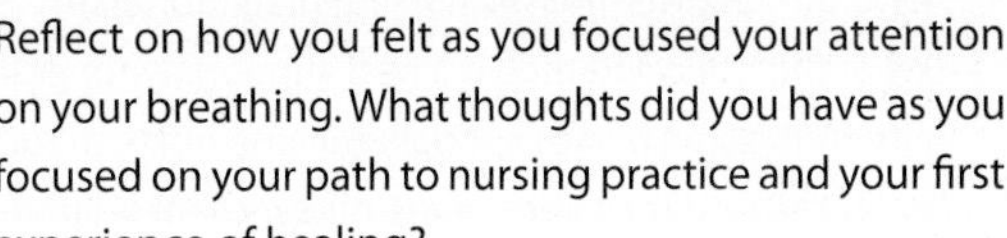

Reflect on how you felt as you focused your attention on your breathing. What thoughts did you have as you focused on your path to nursing practice and your first experience of healing?

During the breathing and centering practice, you may experience a variety of responses from feeling calm, relaxed, quiet, and at ease, to feeling no change or to feeling aware of your stress. Each awareness practice gives you information about yourself that can help you on the path of personal and professional growth. The more we expand our awareness and deepen our appreciation for subtle and intuitive ways of knowing, the greater the potential for growth of our creativity, healing capacities, insight, and understanding. Understanding more about ourselves helps us to understand others. By reflecting on personal and professional themes, we begin to understand some of the challenges our clients face

Figure 10-2 Journaling can help reveal insights into your nursing practice.

Table 10-1 A Nurse's Personal and Professional Self-Assessment

Reflect upon the following:

- Your intention in working with this client.
- Your reason for entering into this profession.
- Your belief about the contribution of nursing to spiritual and psychospiritual care of clients.
- Your philosophy of nursing practice.
- Your experiences that are similar to or different from those of your client.
- Your support network, resources, colleagues, pastoral care, community, and clergy.
- Your beliefs about spirituality, religion, a person's ability to heal, the meaning of illness, and forgiveness, and your comfort in dealing with death and dying issues.
- Your ability to introduce a complementary modality into your plan of care (i.e., breathing, relaxation, prayer, journaling). These are some of the practices most easily introduced by nurses and are usually most familiar to nurses and clients.

Questions to ask:

- What nursing collegial resources can you bring to this client (therapeutic touch practitioners, nurse healers, nurse psychotherapists, holistic nursing practitioners)?
- What theoretical framework best supports your practice perspective? Most nurses practice utilizing a synthesis of theories, although some nurses specialize in one nurse theorist's perspective of care.
- What caring dimensions of the nurse–client relationships are your strengths (building trust, developing safety, caring presence, receptive listening, empathy)?

that we might not otherwise explore until or unless illness or trauma affects us personally. Through inner reflection we contact our personal and professional beliefs that help us to be open, as well as those beliefs that hold us back from being open with our clients. Examine **Table 10-1**.

Exploring these issues helps us to recognize the impact of beliefs, attitudes, expectations, and behaviors on people during crisis and to realize that our belief systems can impact clients emotionally, physically, psychically, and behaviorally. Breathing, centering, reflecting, and journaling offer nurses who are exploring holistic dimensions of nursing practical tools to develop compassion, insight, caring, understanding, and awareness necessary for quality care, professional practice, and personal growth.

Once considered alternative, complementary healthcare practices are now integrated into the Western scientific system of practice.

These practices can be used as therapeutic interventions as you guide clients in self-regulation methods. This is done with the intention that clients learn to use the practices for self-healing and self-care. Biofeedback, relaxation, meditation, and breathing are a few of the self-healing and self-regulating practices.

Critical Thinking Question

How can exercising self-care practices and reflecting on insights help you in your nursing practice? What benefit does this active learning and experiential practice offer you?

Critical Thinking Question

Can you imagine a time when you were going through a difficult challenge or illness? What helped you get through it? What impact or meaning did this event have in your life? What changes did you make as a result of that event? Stop. Breathe. Center. Reflect. Journal.

Clinical Example

A nursing student practices what she has learned in a nursing elective on complementary and alternative modalities. Working, going to school, and being a mother can be stressful. One night when she had a headache and the demands of the children were stressing her out, she remembered a centering exercise from class (**Table 10-2**). The student explains, "I changed some of the words so I could use them at home. It helped me to clear my head. I never realized that, with just slowing down for a moment, I could somehow relax, even for a short time. It made me think more clearly. It made me realize that my daughter was tired and then I became more patient."

Table 10-2 Centering Technique for Health Caring

1. Before you enter a client's room, take a moment to clear your mind of distractions so you can give your full attention to your client in this moment.
2. Take a deep breath.
3. Remind yourself that you are entering your client's personal space, a sacred act.
4. Set the intention that your work is for the "greater good of the client, with harm to none" (Dossey, Keegan, & Guzzetta, 2005, p. 176).
5. Center yourself by using a heart-centered modality such as that used by healing touch and therapeutic touch practitioners. They are taught to "stay in their hearts," which is how they define centering (Dossey, Keegan, & Guzzetta, 2005, p. 194).
6. Remember you are a coparticipant with your client in the creation of a healing environment.
7. Create an affirmation that works for you, such as "I am an instrument of healing," or "I am peaceful and calm, offering my best self."
8. Release expectations of a specific outcome for the interaction.
9. Take another deep breath to still your mind.

Source: Adapted from Dossey, Keegan, & Guzzetta, 2005.

Critical Thinking Question

Can you imagine someone with a life-challenging illness telling you that this was the best thing that ever happened to him or her? How would that impact your life and work? *Breathe. Center. Close your eyes. Stop and journal.*

Critical Thinking Question

What cultural healing practices did/do your family (great-grandparents, grandparents, mother, father, uncles, or aunts) practice? How have you or your family integrated this healing information into your current healthcare beliefs or practices?

Self-regulation practices are very different from those practices that rely on the intervention of a therapist. Self-regulation practices depend deeply on the person's own inner commitment and participation.

Doing the centering and breathing practices on your own are examples of self-regulation exercises that arise from the principle that people can heal themselves. Many cultures and traditions perform self-healing practices the way others perform morning hygiene for self-care and health.

Mind–Body Practices

Relaxation exercises include the dimensions of breathing, awareness, and attending to the body, and have always been part of yoga, Chinese energy practices, and meditation. The ancient healing traditions underscore the importance of deep rest—that is, quieting the mind, body, emotions, and spirit and allowing a peaceful, deep, harmonious rest to arise. Deep rest supports and facilitates the natural ability of our body, mind, and spirit to heal.

Relaxation practices are effective interventions for pre- or postprocedure fear, sleep difficulty, anxiety, restlessness, stress, and pain relief. Some have evidence of inducing physiologic changes, including lowered blood pressure, and psychologic benefits, such as improved mood and a sense of well-being.

Deep Breathing Relaxation

Deep breathing involves slow and deep inhalation through the nose, usually to a count of 10, followed by slow and complete exhalation for a similar count. The process may be repeated 5 to 10 times, several times a day. Deep breathing is a relaxation technique that can lower stress and promote relaxation. Breathing exercises are easy to learn, require no special equipment, and can be done any place or time. Often, people are not aware that they are breathing in an inefficient manner. When people are anxious, they tend to take shallow breaths, but shallow breathing can also induce a subjective state of anxiety. Breathing exercises can break this cycle. Clients are instructed to take slow, deep breaths while observing for a rise in the abdomen. See **Table 10-3** for an example of a deep breathing exercise.

Progressive Muscle Relaxation

Biofeedback relaxation, centering, breathing, and meditation are self-healing and self-regulating practices.

Progressive muscle relaxation, developed by Edmund Jacobson, invites clients to attend to subtle as well as distinctive signals associated with sequentially tensing and relaxing each muscle group. Progressive muscle relaxation is performed with the intention to help clients (1) recognize the difference between

Clinical Example 

Breathing exercises are familiar to nurses who have taught abdominal breathing pre- and postoperatively as well as during natural childbirth. Breathing practices can be used to help a child with asthma who must learn to belly breathe without overusing the trapezius muscles. (People with asthma have a tendency to brace their shoulders and overuse their chest muscles involved in breathing.) Breathing also is a useful exercise to reduce anxiety. It is a simple bedside intervention that can be practiced in the hospital, clinic, or home.

tension and relaxation in the body (this is important, in that many people adapt to levels of tension in the body and consider that normal), and (2) learn how to relax at will. The original practice focused on only tensing and releasing muscle groups without the use of visualization. Since then, most clinicians have devised modified progressive muscle relaxation to include imagery and autogenic phrases that induce sensations of calm and relaxation.

Table 10-3 Deep Breathing Exercise

1. Lie down or sit in a comfortable chair, maintaining good posture. Your body should be as relaxed as possible. Close your eyes. Scan your body for tension.
2. Pay attention to your breathing. Place one hand on the part of your chest or abdomen that seems to rise and fall the most with each breath. If this spot is in your chest, you are not utilizing the lower part of your lungs.
3. Place both hands on your abdomen and follow your breathing, noticing how your abdomen rises and falls.
4. Breathe through your nose.
5. Notice if your chest is moving in harmony with your abdomen.
6. Now place one hand on your abdomen and one on your chest.
7. Inhale deeply and slowly through your nose into your abdomen. You should feel your abdomen rise with this inhalation, and your chest should move only a little.
8. Exhale through your mouth, keeping your mouth, tongue, and jaw relaxed.
9. Relax as you focus on the sound and feeling of long, slow, deep breaths.
10. Practice this exercise for 10 minutes twice a day.

Source: Taken from Davis, M., Eshelman, E. R., and McKay, M. (1982). *The relaxation and stress reduction workbook* (2nd ed.). Oakland, CA: New Harbinger Publications. © Academic Skills Center, Dartmouth College, 2001.

Learning from the inside out arises out of practices such as breathing, quieting, and calming. Experiential learning draws on our personal experience, intuition, and inner knowledge.

A sample progressive muscle relaxation practice follows:

> *Instruct the client to focus attention on a muscle group such as the hand, becoming aware of the area, noticing how it feels, then tensing or clenching the fist. Hold it. Count to 5. Then release and notice the difference in body awareness. Go through all the muscle groups from head to toe, sequentially using the same process, and close with an opportunity for the client to focus on the body's response to the experience.*

Caution should be used when performing progressive muscle relaxation with clients who are experiencing muscle spasms. It is important to be sure that they are able to relax after tensing their muscles during the exercise. Clients who experience pain should not practice progressive relaxation. If clients have a history of injury or pain at a particular area, they can be instructed to not tense that muscle during the exercise.

Autogenic Training

Autogenic training is a popular relaxation technique that focuses on using self-statements suggesting heaviness and warmth (e.g., "My arms are heavy and my hands are warm. Warmth is flowing down my arms and into my hands."). Research has compared the impact of autogenic training with progressive muscle relaxation. Both were found to be effective in treating anxiety and depression by reducing the intensity of symptoms (Dossey, Keegan, & Guzzetta, 2005).

The most important aspect is to learn any relaxation practice from the inside out. Practice on yourself, your family, and your colleagues first to understand the many possible reactions each practice can elicit. When working with clients, monitor signals of their relaxation response through visual cues. Even with their eyes closed, you may note rapid eye movement (REM), increased swallowing, change in skin coloring, vasodilatation of blood vessels in the hands, loosening or relaxing of jaw and shoulders, and deepening and slowing down of respirations. These are all signs of a decrease in sympathetic activity and an increase in parasympathetic activity. Track clients on insulin, hypertensive medications, antianxiety medications, and pain medications as they learn, practice, and improve their self-regulation abilities. You may notice clients reporting less need for medication, and it is helpful to work with prescribing professionals in order to titrate clients' medications appropriately.

You can incorporate breathing, progressive muscle relaxation (tense and then relax), and autogenic phrases ("I am calm; my hands are warm") in a relaxation exercise script or practice. This can be used as an intervention on its own or in conjunction with biofeedback and imagery.

When introducing a client to the practice of relaxation, it is important to create an unhurried environment, conducive to learning the new skill. Start by quieting the environment. Turn off any extraneous noises, and turn down any bright lighting. You may want to play soft, soothing music in the background or just allow silence.

If using a relaxation script, read the phrases or script slowly, allowing time after each statement. A good practice is to do the relaxation technique along with the client. Slow your breathing and allow two or three breaths after each statement as a timing device and as a means to monitor your own level of participation. Gauge how much time you have to spend with your client and leave time for the client to open his or her eyes, return to the moment, and share some experiences with you. Plan to allow approximately 3 to 6 minutes for this waking up and debriefing. You may choose to focus on only one or two areas of the body or to focus on places throughout the body from head to toe. Areas you could include are the scalp, eyes, jaw, neck, shoulders, arms, hands, fingers, chest, breathing, lungs, and heart. ("My stomach is calm. I am allowing vitality and nourishment to flow through my whole body.") The exercise can be ended in one of the following three ways: The first encourages patient self-care, the second supports the client in awareness and awakening, and the third allows the client to continue relaxing quietly and possibly to drift to sleep:

1. This is your time. Your whole body is relaxing at its own pace. The benefits of this practice can continue after this exercise. You have the option of continuing to focus on any of these statements as part of your own practice,

Design the exercise based on the client's needs and available time. Pain clients benefit by focusing on positive, soothing statements and overall well-being.

Experiment with doing the relaxation exercises with friends and ask for feedback. Check how you feel as you practice.

A sample autogenic relaxation script follows:

Start by taking a long, slow, deep breath and releasing it. Allow yourself to follow the rhythm of your breathing. Focus your attention on a specific point or close your eyes. When you are ready, pay attention to your forehead. Begin by telling yourself to breathe, and repeat the word breathe three times after each of the following phrases:

I am allowing my forehead to relax.

I am allowing my forehead to relax.

I am allowing my forehead to relax.

Allow time to observe the sensations in your forehead. Relax and quiet yourself at your own pace. Then focus attention on your jaw. Allow your jaw to loosen slightly by leaving a space between your upper and lower teeth. Then say gently in your mind, "Breathe," and repeat three times after each of the following phrases:

I am allowing my jaw to relax.

I am allowing my jaw to relax.

I am allowing my jaw to relax.

Then continue the exercise by focusing your attention on each part of the body, using similar phases and releasing or loosening each area, such as unclenching the fist, uncurling toes, and allowing the shoulders to release.

whether before sleep or anytime you want to bring more comfort or calm to yourself.

2. Take some deep breaths. Continue to focus on your breathing, while scanning yourself, and see if you notice any difference in how you feel. (Pause.) When you are ready, gradually take a deep breath and open your eyes.
3. Continue to state quietly and calmly to yourself in your mind, "I am allowing myself to be calm, relaxed, quiet, peaceful, and restful." Continue to breathe easily and repeat this sentence on your own, allowing yourself to tune into any sensations of calm and comfort. You can continue on your own just by breathing, and I will remain silent. (Sit for a few moments with the client and then leave quietly.)

Try this with a partner and notice how it feels practicing with your "client." Get feedback on your tone of voice, timing, and presence. Critiquing can help with your comfort level, confidence, and presentation when you do this with a client.

Now reverse and allow yourself to experience the exercise. How did you feel? What benefits did you experience? Note if you felt any changes in respirations, hand and foot temperature, heart rate, muscle tension, and emotional well-being. What would you expect to see happen to blood pressure and oxygen saturation rate after introducing this exercise? Try taking your own blood pressure before and after the exercise, noting any differences.

Biofeedback Training

Biofeedback training uses technology, including electronic thermometers (to measure temperature and peripheral blood flow), electromyography (EMG; to measure muscle activity), electroencephalography (EEG; to measure brain wave activity), heart rate monitors, blood pressure monitors, and electrodermal response (to measure sympathetic nervous system outflow) to feed back information to clients who can learn to regulate or change an imbalance in their systems.

Specialized training and certification are available in biofeedback. Even without extensive study, you can apply simple biofeedback principles in nursing practice in the home, hospital, critical care unit, and ambulatory care center by tracking clients' responses on monitors, if available, and feeding back the information (reading with interpretation) to inform, teach, and empower.

Neurofeedback, formerly known as EEG biofeedback, offers clients a vehicle with which to work with epilepsy, sleep disorders, attention-deficit/hyperactivity disorder (ADHD), and trauma. These areas require specialized education and practice. Many insurance carriers reimburse for biofeedback to treat incontinence as well as generalized feedback for stress-related disorders. Biofeedback clients need to be screened for non–stress-related causes of their symptoms by a nurse practitioner or physician prior to initiating the biofeedback process.

Imagery

Imagery can be used in conjunction with biofeedback monitoring, or it can be practiced on its own. Imagery is the practice of assisting clients to self-heal and self-regulate by bringing them into a state of relaxation (see script for relaxation) and then inviting them to visualize, using any or all of their senses. Images can be felt, sensed, heard, visualized, intuited, tasted, and smelled. Imagery has been helpful in improving immune function, in reducing pain and anxiety, and in working with insight (Dossey, Keegan, & Guzzetta, 2005; Snyder & Lindquist, 2002). A simple imagery practice is to imagine a healing place.

Try this for yourself. Allow yourself to focus on the special qualities of a healing place, the beauty of nature, and the sense of peace and healing that it brings to you. Use all your senses to help bring out the healing qualities this place embodies for you. Use your journal as a place to record your images, dreams, and reflections to track your self-healing from the unconscious to the conscious mind. See **Table 10-4** for a guided imagery exercise.

Meditation

Meditation is an ancient spiritual practice found in traditions around the world. Two popular types

Clinical Example

Biofeedback information from an electromyogram (EMG) can be used to teach a client how to relax or reduce muscle tension and spasm in the shoulder or trapezium muscles. A client also may learn how to regulate blood flow to relieve suffering from a migraine headache by relying on feedback from a thermometer that measures hand temperature.

Table 10-4 Guided Imagery: The Forest

To begin the visualization, sit or lie down in a comfortable position and close your eyes. Take several slow, deep, abdominal breaths. As you begin relaxing, you may be aware of a variety of physical sensations or thoughts. Scan your body for any muscle tension. If you become aware of any tension, tense the muscles for a couple of seconds and relax them. Acknowledge any thoughts without trying to get rid of them. You may imagine thoughts or concerns as puffs of smoke that rise into the air and eventually disappear.

Now imagine that you are walking down a path into a lush forest. As you walk along the path you completely take in the sights, sounds, smells, and feel of the place. All around you are trees, grasses, ground cover, and fragrant flowers. You hear the soothing sounds of birds chirping and the wind as it gently blows through the treetops. You smell the rich dampness of the forest floor, the smells of rotting vegetation and new growth. Through gaps in the treetops, you see the sun high in a cloudless, blue sky. The sun is dispersed through the canopy of the treetops and filters down onto the forest floor, creating intricate patterns of light and shadow. With each breath you take in this place you feel a deep sense of peace and relaxation.

You soon come to a clearing. There are several flat rocks in the clearing surrounded by soft moss. A small stream runs among the rocks. You lie back on one of the rocks or on the cushiony moss and put your feet into the cool water. You feel the warm sun and a gentle, light breeze through your hair and across your skin. The sparkling, clear water rushes around the multicolored rooks, making little whirlpools. You put your hand into the water and lift a handful to your lips. The water is cool and refreshing. You close your eyes listen to the water trickling through the rocks. You bathe in the warm sun and feel as though you are floating ... relaxing deeper and deeper.

You let yourself sink further into relaxation, while continuing to be aware of the sights, smells, sounds, and feel of the forest around you. You allow yourself to let go of any concerns or worries and to feel completely refreshed and rejuvenated in this place.

When you are ready, imagine that you slowly get up and leave the clearing. As you walk back down the path through the forest, fully take in this place and realize that you may return whenever you wish by the same path. Each time you enter this place you will feel relaxed and at peace.

Source: © Chuck Zanone, Ph.D., Georgia Southern University Counseling and Career Development Center

of meditation are transcendental and mindfulness meditation. Although they have some variations in practice, they both involve learning to be present in the moment, focusing attention on one thing (a word or sound, called a mantra, or one's breath), letting go of everyday problems and distractions, and developing a caring, nonjudgmental attitude. Prayer is a form of meditation. Meditation is believed to lead to an increased state of calmness and relaxation. Mindful meditation teaches a person to recognize early signs of muscle tension that can increase pain and discomfort. The person can then use techniques, such as breathing or stretching, to counter the pain.

Mindful walking meditation is a movement practice of awareness of mind, breath, and being with each footstep (**Figure 10-3**). Early studies have shown meditation to be effective in lowering blood pressure and in reducing stress and anxiety-induced illnesses. A recent randomized, controlled study of the effects of transcendental meditation on college students showed a significant improvement on measures of psychological distress, anxiety, depression, anger/hostility, and coping ability, as well as a decrease in blood pressure in students at risk for hypertension (Nidich et al., 2009). Scientists have also related mindfulness meditation to documented structural changes in areas of the brain that affect empathy and

Figure 10-3 Walking a meditation path.

Clinical Example 

A client practicing a relaxation exercise while having blood pressure, heart rate, and oxygen saturation monitored can get feedback about the efficacy of the relaxation practice and compare this to the subjective reaction to the exercise. The nurse might say, "Your blood pressure went down 10 points while doing that breathing exercise. This is very good. If you practice this regularly, you may be able to keep your pressure down. How did it feel to you?"

stress, which may have implications for the treatment of posttraumatic stress disorder (Hölzel et al., 2011).

Hypnosis

Hypnosis is the practice of working with an altered state of consciousness or trance for therapeutic benefit. It is a verbal way to reduce arousal with relaxation, imagery, and concentration (Valente, 2003). The hypnotic trance is the result of focused attention and concentration. The process may be self-guided or guided by a therapist. It is voluntary and reversible. Hypnosis has been effective in treating pain, addiction, anxiety, and posttraumatic stress, and in inducing anesthesia, sleep, and memory (Dossey, Keegan, & Guzzetta, 2005). With education and supervision, psychiatric nurses can use hypnosis to help clients achieve symptom control and improve confidence and self esteem. Through self-hypnosis, clients have reduced pain and anxiety associated with breast biopsy (Lang et al., 2006). Combined with progressive relaxation, hypnosis has evidence, although still at a low level, that it can reduce nightmares associated with PTSD (Amsterdam et al., 2009).

Manipulative and Body-Based Practices

Massage

Massage has a long history as a nursing intervention and in healing. The therapeutic use of hands and touch has been found to be significant in growth and development and has been used with newborns and in neonatal care. Stroking, holding, and massaging offer tactile nurturance, improve circulation, and enhance a feeling of safety, calm, and connection found in the relaxation response (**Figure 10-4**). This benefit

Clinical Example 

Annette was receiving hospice services due to severe chronic obstructive pulmonary disease (COPD). It would sometimes take her 5 minutes to catch her breath after just answering the door. She would sit on the seat on her walker, tethered by her oxygen tubing. Annette had begun to fulfill her dream to paint watercolor flowers, and although this was helping, she was becoming more anxious as it took her longer and longer to still her breathing. The nurse understood her love for color and flowers from earlier discussions, and asked if Annette had ever used imagery to relax. She had not. The nurse asked her to think of a place she could remember or dream of that was beautiful and peaceful for her. Annette said she loved Hawaii. With encouragement, she was able to describe a flower garden she loved there, and closed her eyes when the nurse asked her to imagine the sights, sounds, smells, and climate she experienced there. Annette smiled and agreed she would try this at night to help her relax and when she felt anxious. Over time, and with practice, Annette was able to use all of her senses to experience the flower garden, and within minutes, even seconds at times, a feeling of calmness would come over her and her breathing would ease.

has been demonstrated in people with cancer, hospice clients, institutionalized elders, and those suffering from dementia (Snyder & Lindquist, 2002). A literature review found that most of 22 studies on the effect of massage on relaxation, comfort, and sleep showed either physiologic relaxation or significant anxiety reduction (Richards, Gibson, & Overton-McCoy, 2000).

Massage is generally a practice of working with long strokes running down the muscles of the body, as in Swedish massage; however, there are numerous techniques and styles of practice. Different states have different standards for who can practice massage therapy and the education required.

Back massage has been demonstrated to effect a relaxation response in some clients and sympathetic arousal in others. Overall, massage has been found to promote relaxation, facilitate sleep, lessen pain and fatigue, reduce edema, improve mobility, lessen anxiety and depression, and enhance well-being (Snyder & Lindquist, 2002). This ancient form of healing practice offers a connection between the practitio-

Figure 10-4 Massage can enhance a sense of peacefulness and relaxation.

ner and the client and may be helpful in pinpointing areas of soreness, tenderness, or discomfort.

Reflexology

Reflexology is the practice of massaging the hands and feet with an awareness that the whole body system is mapped onto the hands and feet. By massaging the arch of the foot, one can help the spine to relax. This practice offers easy access to help support, quiet, and calm the client while relieving pain, anxiety, and discomfort.

Yoga

Yoga is a practice that involves gentle exercise combined with physical positions, breathing techniques, and meditation. It originated thousands of years ago in India and is intended to balance the mind, body, and spirit. It is credited with relieving stress, increasing flexibility, and fostering a sense of well-being. Physiological changes, specifically in the levels of the stress-related chemicals cytokine interleukin-6 and C-reactive protein, may be responsible for the calming effect and improved mood associated with meditation (Kiecolt-Glaser et al., 2010).

Energy-Based Practices

Therapeutic Touch

Therapeutic touch (TT) is a form of energy healing, a frequently used intervention in holistic nursing practice. Derived from laying on of hands, TT invites nurses to focus on their **intention** to heal, center, assess, and then treat by directing life energy to the client using their hands. The client takes on and internalizes this energy to facilitate healing and restore balance.

TT has been shown to be of benefit for the relief of pain, anxiety, and discomfort, resulting in an improved sense of well-being, accelerated healing, reduction of blood pressure, reduction of fight-or-flight response, and improved oxygen saturation levels (Snyder & Lindquist, 2002). A patient satisfaction study of 605 clients who had received TT treatments in a general hospital reported that most clients reported a positive result, such as decreased pain and anxiety (Newshan & Schuller-Civitella, 2003).

TT consists of centering, assessment, unruffling, and transmitting energy. The centering that nurses practice is similar to the simple breathing practice at the beginning of this chapter. During this centering, the practitioner's attention is focused on helping, healing, and visualizing the client as a whole. The next phase of practice focuses on assessing the client's energy field by scanning the field with the palms held approximately 2–5 inches above the body, starting at the head and moving gradually to the feet making a mental note of any differences in sensation, temperature, density, activity, or lack of activity along the way. It is of value to assess both the front and back of the client whenever possible.

Unruffling is the use of sweeping hand motions through areas of congestion in the energy field to enhance receptivity to energy. The transfer of energy occurs when the practitioner intentionally and consciously acts as a channel for the universal life force to flow through the practitioner into the client.

Reiki

Reiki is a form of Japanese spiritual healing with roots in Tibetan Buddhism. The aim of Reiki is to promote health, maintain well-being, and reduce anxiety. *Reiki* is derived from two Japanese words: *rei* meaning universal spirit and *ki* meaning life energy. Reiki practitioners believe that human energy flows through meridians (or pathways) in the body that can be sensed by trained practitioners. A disturbance in the flow of this energy may be caused by physical illnesses or negative emotions.

Treatments involve the systematic placing of the hands in 12–15 varying positions. Hand positions are held for approximately 2–5 minutes each. The practitioner's hands may be placed directly on a clothed patient or held 1–2 inches above the skin. The practitioner's hands are positioned palm-side down with the fingers and thumb extended. Reiki practitioners believe that therapeutic effects of this technique are obtained from a universal life energy that provides strength, harmony, and balance to the body and mind. Life energy is thought to be transferred to patients when practitioners place their hands on or directly above treatment areas.

Reiki is similar in many respects to therapeutic touch, described previously. The differences are in underlying philosophy and practitioner training, as well as a possible qualitative distinction attributed to the sensation of energy movement with Reiki therapy (Potter, 2003).

Tai Chi

Tai chi is a noncombative martial art that consists of slow, gentle movements, combined with breathing techniques and meditation, to improve the flow of qi, or life energy, thereby calming the mind and promoting health. The movement routines can be practiced alone or in groups. A metastudy of 40 smaller studies found a direct connection between active participation in tai chi exercises and reduced stress and anxiety, reduced depression, and improved self-esteem (Wang et al., 2010). The strongest, most consistent evidence of health benefits is for bone health, cardiopulmonary fitness, balance, and falls prevention (Jahnke, Larkey, Rogers, Etnier, & Lin, 2010).

Acupuncture

A recent study of systematic reviews of acupuncture question its efficacy and safety.

Acupuncture is one of the ancient arts of traditional Chinese medicine (**Figure 10-5**). Dating back 5,000 years, Chinese practitioners learned how to work with *chi* or universal life force or energy. They activate, balance, and harmonize this energy through the use of breathing, awareness, internal chi kung, tai chi, Chinese herbs, massage, energy transfer (external chi kung), and acupuncture. Acupuncture requires specialized study and is reimbursed by some insurance companies. It is used to relieve pain, stress-related illnesses, asthma, headaches, and muscle pain; to enhance immune system function; and to treat addictions (smoking, eating, drugs). A landmark study established acupuncture as an effective complement to conventional arthritis management. This rigorous study demonstrated that acupuncture reduces pain and functional impairment of osteoarthritis of the knee (Berman et al., 2004). However, doubts about its efficacy and safety remain. A recent critical evaluation of systematic reviews of acupuncture as a treatment of pain reported an absence of convincing evidence that acupuncture relieved pain. Importantly the study also noted serious adverse effects, associated with the use of acupuncture, including pneumothorax and infections (Ernst, Lee, & Choi, 2011).

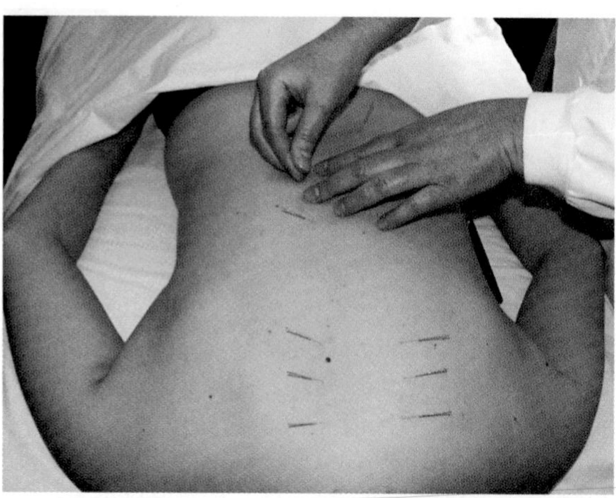

Figure 10-5 Acupuncture is used to relieve many physical and mental problems.

Shiatsu or *acupressure* is acupuncture without needles. Using the same map of the body as in acupuncture, the shiatsu practitioner activates meridian or energy points along the body. Through stretching and variations in pressure, this practice focuses on restoring energy, balance, relaxation, and relief from discomfort and anxiety.

Qi Gong

Qi gong (pronounced "chee gung") is an ancient system of healing and energy medicine from China. It is the art and science of using movement, breathing techniques, and meditation to cleanse and strengthen the circulation of life energy (qi) around the body. Qi gong practice is thought to better health and vitality and a tranquil state of mind. A recent scientific review shows evidence that qi gong, similar to tai chi, increases confidence and promotes bone health and balance (Jahnke et al., 2010).

Critical Thinking Question

WWW

Think of a client for whom you have recently cared. How could you introduce one or more of the practices just discussed into his or her care?

Herbal Therapies

Herbal medicines are easily available and frequently used in the United States (Beaubrun & Gray, 2000). Be sure to include questions about a patient's use of natural remedies, herbal medicines, or over-the-counter medications when inquiring about medication use. Clients may be reluctant to reveal such information or forget to include it, not considering such preparations to be medications. Data obtained on the patient's use of herbals is an important nursing function. As part of patient education, it is important to convey that just because these medicines are natural does not mean they are safe. The research data are not conclusive and are often contradictory about the effectiveness and safety of herbals. In particular, the nurse practitioner with prescriptive privileges needs to be aware and make sure clients are aware of potential interactions between prescribed medications and herbal preparations that the client may be using, and nurses need to include this information as part of patient and family education.

Psychiatric clients might self-medicate with some of the following herbal preparations.

St. John's Wort

St. John's wort (*Hypericum perforatum*) is a plant, and its flowers are used to produce teas, tablets, and capsules containing concentrated extracts. Recognized for medicinal value in ancient Greece, today it is used to by consumers to treat depression, anxiety, and insomnia. Research has been contradictory regarding its effectiveness in treating depression.

A review of 29 randomized, double-blind studies of St. John's wort in the treatment of major depression found that it was more effective than placebo, as effective as standard antidepressant therapy, and had fewer side effects (Linde, Berner, & Kriston, 2008). A review of available evidence by the American Psychiatric Association's (APA's) Task Force on Complementary and Alternative Medicine suggests that St. John's wort is more effective for mild to moderate depression than for a severe depression (Freeman et al., 2010).

Cautions include photosensitivity leading to a rash and possible blisters in fair-skinned people; also, people with a history of affective disorders, mania, or hypomania may find their condition triggered by this remedy (McGovern, Lockhart, Malay, Palatnik, Stiebeling, 2002; Pilkington, Boshnakova, & Richardson, 2006). St. John's wort alters levels of the neurotransmitters serotonin and dopamine. When used with serotonin reuptake inhibitors, serotonin syndrome may result, causing changes in mental status and motor and autonomic function (Ernst, Pittler, Wider, Boddy, 2006). Clients with HIV need to know that the herb can decrease the effectiveness of some protease inhibitors. St. John's wort stimulates a drug-metabolizing enzyme (cytochrome P450 3A4) that metabolizes at least 50% of the drugs on the market. Therefore, it could potentially cause a number of drug interactions that have not yet been reported.

Ginkgo

Ginkgo (*Ginkgo biloba*) is used to treat age-related memory impairment, dementia, and senility. Some studies have shown ginkgo to be effective in delaying clinical deterioration of patients or in bringing about symptomatic improvement (Cass, 2004; Ernst et al., 2006). (See "Evidence-Based Practice" on p. 240 for more information.) Ginkgo potentiates the action of anticoagulants and increases the effects of monoamine oxidase inhibitors (MAOIs), a class of antidepressants (Cuellar, 2006; Ernst et al., 2006; Herbert-Ashton & Clarkson, 2005).

Kava

Kava (*Piper methysticum*) is used for short-term treatment of anxiety or stress. The active ingredients in kava, kava lactones, have significant analgesic and anesthetic properties. However, kava is used most frequently for its antianxiety effect. As with other substances marketed as herbal supplements, kava has not had to undergo the quality requirements of the Food and Drug Administration (FDA). It was reported that one patient developed persistent parkinsonism when being treated with extract of kava for anxiety (Meseguer et al., 2002). Kava potentiates drugs that act on the central nervous system, including alcohol, benzodiazepines, and barbiturates, and it may decrease the effects of levodopa, used to treat Parkinson's disease (Cuellar, 2006; Ernst et al., 2006; Spencer & Jacobs, 2003). In 2002, the FDA issued a consumer advisory that kava containing supplements were associated with potential risk for severe liver damage. Because of the risk of toxicity, kava is contraindicated for patients with liver disease.

Kava containing supplements may be severely toxic to the liver.

If taken with prescribed antidepressant medications, St. John's wort can cause serotonin syndrome.

Valerian

Valerian root (*Valeriana officinalis*) is used for anxiety and insomnia. Valerian is believed to affect the amygdala, an area of the brain responsible for memory and emotions, and also to inhibit the breakdown of GABA, thereby inducing sedation. Research has not established its effectiveness beyond a reasonable doubt, but early evidence indicates it might be useful by itself to promote sleep. In theory, it can potentiate the effects of sedatives or other CNS depressants at high dosages (Ernst et al., 2006). Clients should not drink alcohol, take other CNS depressants, or operate heavy machinery while taking valerian (Herbert-Ashton & Clarkson, 2005).

Chamomile

Chamomile is an herb that has been considered an effective antianxiety agent and, in tea form, is promoted to enhance relaxation and sleep. Until recently, scientific evidence for this has been lacking. Evidence was found by researchers at the University of Pennsylvania, who conducted a randomized, double-blind, placebo-controlled trial to test the effects of chamomile extract capsules in patients diagnosed with mild to moderate generalized anxiety disorder (GAD). Compared with placebo, chamomile was associated with a statistically significant reduction in mean Hamilton Anxiety Scale (HAM-A) scores—the study's primary outcome measure (Amsterdam et al., 2009). These results suggest that chamomile may have modest benefits for some people with mild to moderate GAD and warrants further study.

Nutrient Supplements

Omega-3 Fatty Acids

Omega-3 fatty acids are a group of polyunsaturated fatty acids that are important for a number of functions in the body, including brain development and functioning, blood clotting, and muscle contraction and relaxation. The American diet is low in omega-3 fatty acids. Since the body does not create these essential nutrients, they must be consumed in the diet. Good sources are fish, flaxseed, leafy green vegetables, vegetable oils, and supplements. Studies show that fish oil supplements are effective in reducing several cardiovascular disease risk factors and may help with some aspects of rheumatoid arthritis (National Center for Complementary and Alternative Medicine [NCCAM], 2009). After a review of the evidence, the APA's Task Force on Complementary and Alternative Medicine concluded that omega-3 supplements may be helpful for people with depression or bipolar disorder as a complement to standard care (Freeman et al., 2010). Omega-3 fatty acid supplements are considered safe for most adults in low to moderate doses. In high doses, they can interfere with blood thinners and some antihypertensive medications (NCCAM, 2009).

Grape Seed Extract

Grape seed extract (*Vitis vinifera*) is produced from seeds of grapes obtained from wineries. The grape and its leaves have been used medicinally since ancient Greece. Grape seed extract, in the form of a pill or capsule, has since been shown to be effective in treating venous insufficiency. Small, preliminary studies suggest grape seed extract has antioxidant properties and also may prevent further deterioration in persons with macular degeneration of the eye. In animal studies, grape seed extract was shown to inhibit abnormalities in tau proteins in the brain, a condition that is associated with certain neurodegenerative diseases, including Alzheimer's dementia (Ho, Yamul, Wang, & Pasinetti, 2009). Grape seed extract appears to be well tolerated. Interactions with other medications and supplements have not been well studied.

S-Adenosyl-L-Methionine

SAMe (S-adenosyl-L-methionine) is a chemical that is found naturally in the body. SAMe has been available as a dietary supplement in the United States since 1999, but it has been used as a prescription drug in Italy since 1979, in Spain since 1985, and in Germany since 1989. Researchers discovered the potential usefulness of SAMe for treating osteoarthritis by accident.

Several studies have shown that SAMe can be beneficial and might be as effective as some prescription medications used for depression (tricyclic antidepressants). Based on evidence, the APA's Task Force on Complementary and Alternative Medicine concluded that SAMe might be effective monotherapy for people who don't have a good response to a prescription antidepressant (Freeman et al., 2010).

SAMe increases a brain chemical called serotonin. Some medications, including antidepressants, meperidine (Demerol), over-the-counter cold and cough preparations, and the herbal preparation, St. John's wort, also increase serotonin. Taking SAMe along with these medications can cause serious side effects including heart problems, shivering (serotonin syndrome), and anxiety. SAMe can chemically change levodopa in the body and decrease the effectiveness of levodopa. Taking SAMe along with levodopa might make Parkinson's disease symptoms worse.

SAMe is considered relatively safe. It can sometimes cause gastrointestinal side effects, dry mouth, headache, mild insomnia, anorexia, sweating, dizziness, and nervousness, especially at higher doses. As is true of standard antidepressants, it can make some people with depression feel anxious, and it can cause people with bipolar disorder to convert from depression to mania.

Holistic Nursing Practice

During the past few decades, some nurses have committed their nursing practice to cultivating self-care and self-healing practices for themselves and clients. Their focus has been on seeing human beings as whole and bringing spirituality into nursing practices. Many have chosen to call themselves holistic nurses. Understanding the framework of what we do and the theory and philosophy of why we do it is an important dimension of holistic nursing.

Description of Holistic Nursing

Being a holistic nurse is *who* the nurse is rather than *what* the nurse does. It is the quality of presence and being (i.e., a caring capacity) that in its essence describes holistic nursing. At its best, all nursing is holistic. Calling yourself a holistic nurse could mean that complementary or holistic modalities are incorporated into your practice; it also could mean, for example, that if you work as a nurse in an intensive care unit (ICU) you can offer presence, touch, caring, compassion, counsel, skillfulness, healing, and wisdom, call yourself holistic, and truly be accurate.

Holistic nursing is officially recognized by the American Nurses Association as a nursing specialty with a defined scope and standards of practice (AHNA, 2006). The holistic nurse is an instrument of healing and a facilitator in the healing process. Holistic nurses honor the individual's subjective experience about health, health beliefs, and values. To become therapeutic partners with individuals, families, and communities, holistic nursing practice draws on nursing knowledge, theories, expertise, intuition, and creativity.

Spirituality

Spirituality is a dimension of every human life, whether or not one recognizes or acknowledges it; not everyone practices a religion. Asking clients about experiences of wholeness or experiences in which they feel interconnected, allowing them to experience a sense of timelessness, peace, inner calm, or joy helps clients to understand what spiritual experiences are. Most people, if given the opportunity, can speak of simple ways in which they nourish their spirit, even if they do not practice or believe in a religious tradition. You can ask, "Do you have a faith practice that helps you?"

Nurses can help clients recognize their ability to cope with the natural flow of life. Often clients are so fearful of death, loss, or illness that they cannot live their present life, even when they are not actively ill or dying. Helping clients to connect with what is healing in their lives, with what gives them hope, peace, or joy is a simple yet profound intervention. Weaving these kinds of topics, questions, and issues into interactions with clients helps bring out much more authentic responses than those elicited by just asking direct questions, such as "What religion are you?" Exploring for more authentic responses also helps to foster the nurse–client therapeutic relationship.

Nurses have access to clients in their most vulnerable and intimate moments—the birth of a child, the moment of death, and the traumas, pains, joys, and fears of life. Many times we are the spiritual support that holds the hand, witnesses the first breath or the last breath, and offers solace and understanding.

Helping clients recognize the difference between their religious beliefs and their spiritual beliefs and teaching clients to seek purpose, meaning, wholeness, and understanding of the mysteries of life are important contributions of nursing. Forgiveness, prayer, meditation, reconciliation, and connection to family and community are all vital elements of exploring spiritual and psychospiritual dimensions of nursing care.

The client's support system includes the client's family, friends, and community and, when appropriate, clergy and religious centers. Nurses are resources and advocates to help the client navigate his or her life's challenge within their support system.

Critical Thinking Question

How do you see spirituality and religion? Are they the same? How are they different? How has psychospiritual support been helpful for you or for your clients?

Psychospiritual Assessment

It is important to establish a therapeutic relationship with the client. A psychospiritual assessment can be performed through questions, interviews, and discussions with the client to explore the client's (1) sense of well-being and inner strengths (what brings joy, peace, a sense of wholeness into life), (2) support systems that are currently available (community, family, spiritual or religious support, work-related support), and (3) traditional or cultural rituals appropriate for the client's experience. Explore the client's purpose in life; feelings about suffering and illness; experience with self-healing; sense of hope and faith; capacity for forgiveness; comfort with death and dying; belief in religion, God, or a higher power; and comfort with spiritual practices such as prayer, meditation, healing and holistic practices, relaxation, and imagery. Include how the client connects to nature (gardening, walking in nature), cycles of the seasons, the environment, and the planet and learn which pets, plants, and other living things support the client's well-being each day.

In a wellness model that focuses on self-healing and empowerment, including the client in the planning of care is essential. Levels of participation by the client will vary, depending on the individual's capacity and comfort level. Even clients in crisis, coma, and trauma who are not verbal can be included by involving the client's family, friends, or proxy in this phase of care.

A Practice Model

Holistic nursing practice can occur in a variety of settings: as part of hospital inpatient or outpatient services, as part of a holistic health center, in the client's home, or in the nurse's private office. Holistic nursing utilizes the holistic practices described in this chapter, including biofeedback, relaxation, healthcare teaching and counseling, stress reduction, mindfulness meditation, and imagery, in nurses' work with a variety of clients.

Treatment may focus on relieving stress, anxiety, headaches, hypertension, or pain. It is always important that clients have a full evaluation by a nurse practitioner or physician to rule out non–stress-related physical conditions. Holistic nursing practices can be effective for clients with life-threatening illnesses; for example, guided imagery can be used for cancer as well as biofeedback and relaxation for immune enhancement (Dossey, Keegan, & Guzzetta, 2005; Snyder & Lindquist, 2002).

The holistic nurse supports clients in developing a plan of care, exploring treatment options, developing self-healing practices, exploring the meaning of the crisis and their illness, developing family support, and dealing with bereavement, loss, and death. The nurse can help clients take a proactive, empowered stance with physicians and other healthcare professionals.

One of the authors worked in an urban health center with homeless women recovering from addiction and incorporated general healthcare teaching on wellness, holistic health, safe sex practices, hypertension, headaches, premenstrual syndrome, women's

Evidence-Based Practice

Ginkgo biloba has long been regarded as having the ability to improve cognitive functioning. Several small, preliminary studies found that ginkgo may be as effective as standard cholinesterase inhibitors in the treatment of mild to moderate Alzheimer's dementia, thus lending support to the association between ginkgo and cognition.

However, in 2008, the largest completed randomized, double-blind, placebo-controlled dementia prevention trial to date, the Ginkgo Evaluation of Memory (GEM) study, found that ginkgo was no better than placebo in preventing dementia or Alzheimer's disease.

In the study, 3,069 community-dwelling adults aged 72–96 years received a twice-daily dose of 120-mg extract of ginkgo biloba (n = 1,545) or an identical-appearing placebo (n = 1,524). Change in cognition was assessed by various tests for global functioning and for functioning in the domains of memory, language, attention, visuospatial abilities and executive functions. There was no evidence that ginkgo affected global cognitive functioning or functioning within any of the tested domains (DeKosky et al., 2008). Additional analysis showed that ginkgo did not prevent or delay age-related changes in individuals with normal cognition, nor did it slow the rate of decline in those characterized as having mild cognitive impairment (Snitz et al., 2009).

The study was conducted at six academic medical centers in the United States between 2000 and 2008, with a median follow-up of 6.1 years. The GEM study can be regarded with confidence, given its size, strong design, long duration of follow-up, and breadth of the neuropsychological evaluation, including measurement of multiple cognitive domains.

health issues, anxiety, and depression. The women shared their feelings and experiences by writing or drawing after a meditation or imagery session. Many offered spontaneous poetry and have continued to write in their journals.

Summary

What we are able to implement varies according to our skill level, the client's receptivity, and the culture of our practice setting. Innovation, inclusion of complementary modalities, and multidisciplinary care are rapidly becoming a part of healthcare practice. Exploring possibilities of what is available in individual facilities and communities to offer clients the best possible care is an essential responsibility of nursing practice. There is a joy in nursing that is nourished by these self-care and complementary practices, for both you and the client. These practices afford us a great opportunity to offer empowered quality care to our clients and professional self-development to ourselves. We owe it to ourselves, our clients, our society, and to nursing. Enjoy the journey.

Annotated References

American Holistic Nurses Association. (2006, December 1). Holistic nursing achieves ANA specialty status. Press release. Retrieved from http://www.ahna.org/AboutUs/ANASpecialtyRecognition/tabid/1167

This announcement by the official organization for holistic nurses defines holistic nursing and explains the implications of specialty recognition by the American Nurses Association for the future of holistic nursing.

Amsterdam, J. D., Yimei, L., Soeller, I., Rockwell, K., Mao, J. J., & Shults, J. (2009). A randomized, double-blind, placebo controlled trial of oral *Matrcaria recutita* (chamomile) extract therapy for generalized anxiety disorder. *Journal of Clinical Psychopharmacology, 29*(4), 378–382.

The findings of the first controlled clinical trial of chamomile extract for generalized anxiety disorder (GAD) suggests a modest anxiolytic effect in patients with mild to moderate GAD.

Beaubrun, R., & Gray, G. (2000). Review of herbal medicines for psychiatric disorders. *Psychiatric Services, 51*(9), 1130–1133.

This is a useful article for psychiatric nursing regarding the herbal medicines clients may be using for self-medication.

Berman, B. M., Lao, L., Langenberg, P., Lee, W. L., Gilpin, A. M. K., & Hochberg, M. C. (2004). Effectiveness of acupuncture as adjunctive therapy in osteoarthritis of the knee: A randomized, controlled trial. *Annals of Internal Medicine, 141*, 901–910.

This article describes a randomized, controlled trial that demonstrates the effectiveness of acupuncture to improve function and pain relief as an adjunctive therapy when compared with credible sham acupuncture.

Cass, H. (2004). Herbs for the nervous system: Ginkgo, kava, valerian, passionflower. *Seminars in Integrative Medicine, 2*(2), 82–88.

This article is a useful introduction to these herbals, featuring current research.

Cuellar, N. G. (2006). *Conversations in complementary and alternative medicine: Insights and perspectives from leading practitioners.* Sudbury, MA: Jones and Bartlett.

This book uses interviews to teach information about complementary modalities.

DeKosky, S. T., Williamson, J. D., Fitzpatrick, A. L., Kronmal, R. A., Ives, D. G., Saxton, J. A., . . . Furberg, C. D. Ginkgo Evaluation of Memory (GEM) Study Investigators. (2008). Ginkgo biloba for prevention of dementia: A randomized controlled trial. *JAMA, 300*(19), 2253–2262. Erratum in *JAMA, 300*(23), 2730–2739.

This article reports the findings from the largest completed randomized, double-blind, placebo-controlled dementia prevention trial to date.

Dossey, B. M., Keegan, L., & Guzzetta, C. E. (2005). *Pocket guide for holistic nursing.* Sudbury, MA: Jones and Bartlett.

This pocket guide is a quick reference for the most important concepts from holistic nursing. It is an excellent, readable introduction to holistic nursing practice.

Ernst, E., Pittler, M. H., Wider, B., & Boddy, K. (2006). *The desktop guide to complementary and alternative medicine: An evidence-based approach* (2nd ed.). Philadelphia, PA: Mosby Elsevier.

This is an easy-to-use resource for research on CAMs.

Ernst, E., Lee, M. S., & Choi, T. Y. (2011). Acupuncture: Does it alleviate pain and are there serious risks? A review of reviews. *Pain, 152*(4), 755–764.

This critical evaluation of systematic reviews reports a lack of convincing evidence that acupuncture relieves pain and finds serious risks associated with its use.

Freeman, M. P., Fava, M., Lake, J., Trivedi, M. H., Wisner, K. L., & Mischoulon, D. (2010). Complementary and alternative medicine in major depressive disorder: The American Psychiatric Association Task Force report. *Journal of Clinical Psychiatry, 71*(6), 669–681.
This article is a summary of the task force's review of selected complementary and alternative medicine treatments for the treatment of major depressive disorder.

Herbert-Ashton, M. J., & Clarkson, N. E. (2005). *Quick look nursing: Pharmacology* (2nd ed.). Sudbury, MA: Jones and Bartlett.
This text is a quick reference book, useful for clinical practice.

Ho, L., Yemul, S., Wang, J., & Pasinetti, G. M. (2009). Grape seed polyphenolic extract as a potential novel therapeutic agent in tauopathies. *Journal of Alzheimer's Disease, 16*(2), 433–439.
This study demonstrated the ability of grape seed extract to modify the aggregation of tau peptides that are implicated in certain neurogenerative disorders, including Alzheimer's disease.

Hölzel, B. K., Carmody, J., Vangel, M., Congleton, C., Yerramsetti, S. M., Gard, T., & Lazar, S. W. (2011). Mindfulness practice leads to increases in regional brain gray matter density. *Psychiatry Research: Neuroimaging, 191*, 36–43.
This article reports on research related to use of mindfulness therapy and its effect on the brain as measured by magnetic resonance imaging.

Jahnke, R., Larkey, L., Rogers, C., Etnier, J., & Lin, F. (2010). A comprehensive review of health benefits of qigong and tai chi. *American Journal of Health Promotion, 24*(6), e1–e25.
This paper examines the outcomes from randomized, controlled trials of qi gong and tai chi, practices that are similar in theory, proposed action, and expected benefits.

Kiecolt-Glaser, J. K., Christian, L., Preston, H., Houts, C. R., Malarkey, W. B., Emery, C. F., & Glaser, R. (2010). *Psychosomatic Medicine, 72*(2), 113–121.
This paper reports the effects of yoga on biological measures of stress.

Lang, E. V., Berbaum, K. S., Faintuch, S., Hatsiopoulou, O., Halsey, N., Li, X., . . . Baum, J. (2006). Adjunctive self-hypnotic relaxation for outpatient medical procedures: A prospective randomized trial with women undergoing large core breast biopsy. *Pain, 126*(1–3), 155–164.
The study compared the effects of standard care, structured empathic attention, and self-hypnotic relaxation in managing anxiety and pain related to a medical procedure. Both empathic attention and self-hypnosis decreased pain and anxiety; hypnosis provided more powerful anxiety relief.

Linde, K., Berner, M. M., & Kriston, L. (2008). St. John's wort for major depression. Cochrane Database of Systematic Reviews, Issue 4. Art. No.: CD000448. DOI: 10.1002/14651858.CD000448.pub3
This article summarizes results of a review of 29 studies comparing St. John's wort with placebos or standard antidepressants for the treatment of depression.

McGovern, K., Lockhart, A., Malay, P., Palatnik, A.M., Stiebeling, B. (Eds.). (2002). *Nurse's handbook of alternative and complementary therapies* (2nd ed.). Philadelphia, PA: Lippincott Williams & Wilkins.
This easy-to-read text is a quick reference for an overview of alternative and complementary modalities.

Meseguer, E., Taboada, R., Sanchez, V., Mena, M. A., Campos, V., & De Yebenees, J. G. (2002). Life-threatening parkinsonism induced by kava-kava. *Movement Disorders, 17*(1), 195–196.
This article raises the issue of the safety of kava-kava.

National Center for Complementary and Alternative Medicine (NCCAM). (2009). *Omega-3 supplements: An introduction.* NCCAM publication No. 0436, updated August 2010. Retrieved from nccam.nih.gov/health/omega3/introduction.htm
Information about omega-3 fatty acids: what they are, action, uses, side-effects, interactions, scientific evidence of effectiveness.

Newshan, G., & Schuller-Civitella, D. (2003). Large clinical study shows value of therapeutic touch program. *Holistic Nursing Practice, 17*(4), 189–192.
This article reports findings of the largest published sample size of therapeutic touch outcomes using data from a continuous quality improvement clinical study and a patient satisfaction survey. Although this is not a research study, tools were developed to evaluate a TT program in a hospital.

Nidich, S. I., Rainforth, M. V., Haaga, D. A., Hagelin, J., Salerno, J. W., Travis, F., . . . Schneider, R. H. (2009). A randomized controlled trial on the effects of the transcendental meditation program on blood

pressure, psychological distress, and coping in young adults. *American Journal of Hypertension, 22*(12), 1326–1331.
This is the first randomized controlled trial to demonstrate that a selected mind–body intervention, the transcendental meditation program, decreased blood pressure in young adults at risk for hypertension.

Pilkington, K., Boshnakova, A., & Richardson, J. (2006). St John's wort for depression: Time for a different perspective? *Complementary Therapies in Medicine, 14*(4), 268–281.
This article provides a literature review of meta-analyses, systematic reviews, and qualitative studies of St. John's wort for the treatment of depression.

Potter, P. (2003). What are the distinctions between Reiki and therapeutic touch? *Integrated Care, 7*(1), 89–91.
The author speculates on the differences between these practices and describes personal experience.

Richards, K. C., Gibson R., & Overton-McCoy, A. L. (2000). Effects of massage in acute and critical care. *AACN Clinical Issues, 11*(1), 77–96.
This article discusses the results of a systematic review of 22 articles examining the effects of massage on relaxation, comfort, and sleep.

Snitz, B. E., O'Meara, E. S., Carlson, M. C., Arnold, A. M., Ives, D. G., Rapp, S. R., . . . DeKosky, S. T. Ginkgo Evaluation of Memory (GEM) Study Investigators. (2009). Ginkgo biloba for preventing cognitive decline in older adults: A randomized trial. *Journal of the American Medical Association, 302*(24), 2663–2670.
Findings from the largest completed randomized, double-blind, placebo-controlled dementia prevention trial to date.

Snyder, M., & Lindquist, R. (2002). *Complementary/alternative therapies in nursing* (4th ed.). New York, NY: Springer.
This book encourages nurses to explore the modalities that can be offered without physicians' orders, thereby developing autonomy in professional practice. These modalities include music, therapeutic touch, imagery, relaxation, movement, prayer, humor, advocacy, support groups, and biofeedback.

Spencer, J. W., & Jacobs, J. J. (2003). *Complementary and alternative medicine: An evidence-based approach*. St. Louis, MO: Mosby.
This text is a valuable reference book that emphasizes research, analyzes the effectiveness of each therapy, and provides practical information on how the therapies can be used to treat illness.

U. S. Food and Drug Administration (2002). *Consumer advisory: Kava-containing dietary supplements may be associated with severe liver injury*. Retrieved from U. S. Department of Health and Human Services website: http://www.fda.gov/Food/ResourcesForYou/Consumers/ucm085482.htm

Valente, S. M. (2003). Hypnosis: A useful strategy for symptom relief. *Journal of the American Psychiatric Nurses Association, 9*(5), 163–166.
The author addresses applications for hypnosis in nursing practice, including to control symptoms, improve self-esteem, and increase self-confidence.

Wang, C., Bannuru, R., Ramell, J., Kupelnick, B., Scott, T., & Schmid, C. (2010). Tai chi on psychological well-being: Systematic review and meta-analysis. *BMC Complementary and Alternative Medicine.*
This article discusses the benefits of tai chi as reviewed through a search of databases. The review included randomized and nonrandomized controlled trials and observational studies.

Additional Resources

Krieger, D. (1987). *Living the therapeutic touch: Healing as a lifestyle*. New York, NY: Dodd, Mead.
This personal and scientific volume focuses on therapeutic touch and the autobiographic story of a personal transformation. This is an important volume for nurses interested in healing and holism.

O'Brien, M. E. (2011). *Spirituality in nursing: Standing on holy ground* (4th ed.). Sudbury, MA: Jones and Bartlett.
O'Brien discusses the relationship between spirituality and nursing from more than 20 years of research and includes interventions and a spiritual needs assessment. This edition includes a chapter dedicated to September 11, 2001.

Internet Resources

For a full suite of assignments and additional learning activities, use the access code located in the front of your book to visit this exclusive website: http://go.jblearning.com/mentalhealth. If you do not have an access code, you can obtain one at the site.

Learning Objectives

After reading this chapter, you will be able to:

- Identify what constitutes intimate partner abuse, child abuse, and elder abuse.
- Recognize the prevalence and clinical presentation of various types of family abuse and violence.
- Understand the cycle of abuse and victimization.
- Discuss the various types of family violence and appropriate nursing interventions.

Key Terms

Active neglect
Battered child syndrome
Battered partner syndrome
Batterer
Child abuse
Domestic violence
Empathy
Empowerment
Family violence
Incest
Intimate partner violence
Material exploitation
Neglect
Passive neglect
Victim

Family and Intimate Partner Violence

Claudia Mitzeliotis and Winifred Z. Kennedy

http://go.jblearning.com/mentalhealth 

For a full suite of assignments and additional learning activities, use the access code located in the front of your book to visit this exclusive website: http://go.jblearning.com/mentalhealth. If you do not have an access code, you can obtain one at the site.

Introduction

A victim is any person of any age who is violated by acts of disorderly conduct, harassment, reckless endangerment, entrapment, or assault, including attempted assault.

Family violence is the use or threat of physical, emotional, sexual, or economic abuse to control a family member.

The potential for abuse or violence exists within the home, the community, the workplace, and other institutions. Abuse or violence can occur between individuals, intimate partners, family members, or adults and children within the community. Family violence has become a national issue, and it is one that cannot be taken lightly. Healthy People 2020, the framework for a national prevention agenda, continues to maintain a focus upon maternal child health care disparities, violence, mental health, and substance abuse, which are all factors in domestic and intimate partner violence. The Healthy People 2020 initiative is dedicated to designing national health objectives, identifying the most significant preventable threats to health, and establishing national goals to reduce these threats. Family violence, including child maltreatment and physical abuse and intimate partner assault, is a threat to the safety and well-being of all family members, not only the victim (*Healthy People 2020* Summary of Objectives, 2009). This chapter will focus on three forms of **domestic violence** (also called **family violence**): intimate partner violence, child abuse, and elder abuse. Domestic violence is recognized as a common problem; screening and counseling are included as free, preventive services under the Affordable Care Act (U.S. Department of Health and Human Services, 2011).

The emphasis on safety highlighted by The Joint Commission includes screening all adolescents and adults for intimate partner violence, domestic abuse, child abuse, maltreatment, and exploitation.

General Description

Family can be defined as any group of two or more people who live together and are emotionally involved with each other. Although families are usually considered a refuge from the turbulent outside world, some homes experience a great deal of domestic turmoil. The emotional involvement can be of a loving and caring nature or one of violence. The incidence of family or domestic violence has steadily increased, and many people do not feel safe in their own homes.

Family violence consists of one family member threatening or mistreating another family member or partner as a way to control that individual. Family violence manifests itself in various forms of spousal or intimate partner abuse, child abuse, or elder abuse. These forms of abuse are addressed separately in this chapter.

Family violence is not identified with a particular class or culture. The **victim** may be of either gender. Most victims of **intimate partner violence** are women. The nurse must remember that men also can be victims; however, abused men are usually reluctant to come forward, fearing humiliation. Some clients in same-sex relationships may also fear being stigmatized or misunderstood. Violence is not limited to physical acts; the phrase encompasses a wide variety of behaviors. Victims may be subjected to economic abuse that limits their expenditures or earnings and results in monetary losses. Emotional, sexual, and psychologic abuse are considered forms of family violence. It is important for the nurse to identify the signs of family violence, because the victim's environment may be life threatening. Physical abuse need not be present. Emotional abuse can have an equally life-threatening impact.

Intrafamily violence, intimate partner violence, and child and elder abuse are not classified on Axis I or II in the *Diagnostic and Statistical Manual of Mental Disorders*, fourth edition, text revision (*DSM-IV-TR*; American Psychiatric Association [APA], 2000). Rather, these problems are identified in the section concerning conditions that may be a focus of clinical attention. Included under relational problems are relational problem related to a mental disorder or general medical condition, parent–child relational problem, partner relational problem, and sibling relational problem. Specific coding for domestic violence distinguishes physical or sexual abuse of an adult versus a child and also indicates whether the focus of clinical attention is the victim or perpetrator of the abuse. Included under problems related to abuse and **neglect** are physical abuse of a child, sexual abuse of a child, neglect of a child, physical abuse of an adult, and sexual abuse of an adult. The client may meet an Axis I category related to the abuse such as a mood or anxiety disorder, acute stress disorder, or posttraumatic stress disorder. In addition, the client may meet criteria for an Axis II disorder such as intermittent explosive disorder, impulse-control disorder, or a personality disorder.

There have been many myths and misconceptions associated with family violence. These myths have been ingrained into our society and have deterred interventions, leading to adverse outcomes for clients. There are five well-known myths on this subject, which are shown in **Table 11-1**.

Table 11-1 Myths of Family Violence

1. Myth: The victim caused the violence. The batterer claims, "He (or she) asked for it."
   Fact: The batterer caused the violence. He or she is responsible for his or her actions.
2. Myth: The victim enjoys the abuse or else he or she would have left.
   Fact: No one enjoys being abused or victimized.
3. Myth: If the victim left, the violence would stop.
   Fact: Victims have been found to be in more danger after they left.
4. Myth: Family violence only occurs in low socioeconomic groups.
   Fact: Family violence occurs in all socioeconomic groups.
5. Myth: The assault is an isolated incident and will not occur again.
   Fact: Battering is a complex pattern related to power and control.

Table 11-2 Common Triggers of Family Violence

Critical Crisis	Economic Issues
Alcohol or substance abuse	Unemployment
Serious or injury or one requiring long-term recovery	Change in employment
A death in the family	Retirement
Pregnancy or birth of a child	Partner's employment status
Separation or divorce	Income level
Mental health problems	Caretaking burden
Chronic medical problems	Lack of medical insurance
Cognitive changes in family member	Credit card spending

Note: These are merely stimuli that can provoke an episode, not the actual cause. The causes of domestic violence are more serious underlying issues.

If these myths are seen as truths, the victim is in danger of not getting the help he or she needs. The healthcare worker will perpetuate the abuse by not believing the victim.

Epidemiology of Family Violence

Violence may be associated with crime, gangs, mental health problems, substance abuse, and alcohol problems. Aggression may range from sneering or verbal harassment to bullying, school violence, sexual harassment and assault, and the use of hand guns or assault weapons. Exposure to violence comes in many forms from the media, movies, games, and even music or the reporting of the daily news. The effects of violence are felt by those abused and the abuser as well as upon children who witness violence, other family, friends, coworkers, and other community members. Violence can also be a learned behavior and is often—but not always—associated with lower economic class, poor education, and cultural expectations. It has been hypothesized that there is an intergenerational transmission between aggressors and victims, and the victims then go on to victimize others. Although certain risk factors have been identified, intrafamily violence has been found across varied racial, economic, and educational backgrounds. Some common triggers are seen in **Table 11-2**.

Many theories have been proposed to explain why a victim remains in an abusive relationship, including attachment to the abuser and views about relationships and available options. It is important to remember that this is a phenomenon that is difficult to generalize and theorize. Each victim is an individual, and why he or she chose to stay in an abusive relationship is unclear and cannot be generalized. Many survivors report conflicts regarding financial dependence, feelings of shame or blame, concerns for children or other family members or lack of other support systems, feelings of powerlessness, and fears about how they will manage by themselves or fears of retaliation and further violence.

In overt abusive behavior, the abuser acts openly. The agenda is clearly defined. In covert behavior, the abuser conceals his or her agenda.

In domestic violence, the abuser acts violently toward the intimate partner. Intimate partner violence is not associated with a particular social or economic group.

Clinical Example 

A woman living in a shelter decided to return to her partner. She found that he had not changed. She stated that the emotional abuse does not leave physical scars, but scars were left on her heart. She named emotional abuse, financial abuse, and destruction of property and pets as leaving her scarred. Her return is characteristic of psychological entrapment. She continues to give power to the abuser and her self-esteem is low.

Carnes (1997) theorized that a bonding described as traumatic bonding takes place in relationships that have domestic violence. Two primary characteristics of this theory are (1) that the victim feels dominated by the abuser, setting up an imbalance, and (2) that the abuse is not continuous but rather intermittent.

Other theories that have been associated with family violence include learned helplessness, psychological entrapment, and the Stockholm syndrome. These theories focused on the victim and why she remained in the relationship. For example, in the description of Stockholm syndrome, if captors showed their hostages any degree of kindness, the hostages would have some **empathy** for their captors because they had shared a common experience and survived. This is similar to the abuse victim having empathy for the **batterer** once kindness and remorse are shown.

In a situation of learned helplessness, the victim gives up. In an animal experiment, subjects who were shocked repeatedly eventually gave up trying to escape the shock. In a similar manner, victims of repeated abuse become demoralized and begin to lose motivation to try to escape the abuse. Victims may feel pressured by cultural or community expectations or may be fearful of being involved in the legal system or of being unprotected by the court system.

Patterns of Abuse

Patterns of Abuse
Escalation phase: Tensions build until the abuser loses control. In this phase, a victim might provoke the batterer to strike to get it over with.
Acute phase: Battering and abuse occur, whether physical or verbal. The victim does not fight back; emotional detachment decreases confrontation.
Deescalation phase: The victim seeks a reward for submission. The batterer is loving and promises to care for the victim.

The patterns of abuse escalate slowly, making identification difficult. The abuser appears loving, and the overprotectiveness is seen as caring. The abuser's goal is to completely control the victim. There are three distinct phases of abuse:

1. In the escalation phase, the batterer begins to control and isolate the victim. This subtle stage often masks the abuser's true motives. The batterer often prevents the victim from working full time. This initially isolates the victim and establishes financial control.
2. In the acute phase, the batterer uses threats and force to instill fear and to reinforce control. Physical violence is common.
3. The deescalation phase follows immediately after the acute phase. The batterer becomes apologetic and promises never to harm the victim again, giving the victim false hope for improvement. The apologies tend to work if this is the first offense. Over time, as the pattern continues, the victim lives in constant fear of further attacks.

Clinical Presentation

The following symptoms and psychological complaints may indicate an ongoing abusive situation. The common types of injuries associated with family violence include contusions, lacerations, abrasions, stab wounds, human bites, burns, gunshot wounds, sprains, and fractures. These injuries are usually seen on the head, neck, chest, breasts, abdomen, and genital area. It is important to question the cause of injuries, even minor ones.

The nurse must investigate all medical complaints and findings. A history of repeated falls or chronic injuries should be questioned. The nurse should also look for injuries in different stages of healing. Clients may complain of unexplained medical symptoms of chronic pain, psychogenic pain, or pain-related trauma without visible signs of injuries.

Other common complaints voiced by clients who have been abused include decreased concentration, chronic headache, and sexual dysfunction as well as abdominal, gynecologic, and gastrointestinal complaints. Some clients experience frequent vaginal or urinary tract infections. The clinician should be aware of frequent visits to medical personnel with vague complaints but no physical findings.

Psychiatric symptoms are most prevalent when abuse is present. Clients commonly are isolated. The clinician may note evidence of overt or covert signs of suicide attempts or gestures. Psychiatric symptoms range from anxiety attacks to panic attacks. It is also common for clients to exhibit depression. The nurse should observe for posttraumatic stress disorder. Clients may exhibit sleep and appetite disturbances and may also abuse drugs or alcohol. Statistics show that clients often return to their batterers, making intervention very difficult. Taking photographs will help in monitoring the abuse and can be used later in the judicial system. However, the patient must sign a consent form to be photographed, and a witness must also sign. The consent form becomes part of the patient's records along with the pictures taken.

Intimate Partner Violence

As mentioned earlier, domestic violence is not confined to any particular socioeconomic status, gender, race, ethnic group, age, or employment status. In intimate partner violence, the threat of abuse or intimidation is found between heterosexual or homosexual couples and current or former spouses. Women account for the majority of victims of intimate partner violence—approximately 85% of cases. In most cases the abuse or assaults are never reported. The National Crime Victimization Survey estimates that there are approximately 1 million cases of intimate partner violence each year. This accounts for 6% of all rape and sexual assault cases, 11% of all murders, and 30% of all female murders. The highest rates of intimate partner violence are for women between 20 and 24 years old (U.S. Department of Justice, 2007). Younger women are also at risk. A study of 404 students, with an average age of 12 years both male and female, indicated that they engaged in risky behaviors in beginning relationships online (Dowdell, Burgess & Cavanaugh, 2009). A large percentage of middle school students—both male and female—later met with the contact in person and were sexually assaulted or inappropriately touched. Of the sexual offenders polled, most stated they disguised their identity online, brought up the topic of sex during the first contact and preferred communicating with girls rather than boys (Dowdell, Burgess, & Flores, 2011) Researchers (Bonomi et al., 2007) also found women 65 years of age and older reported more than 25% life time incidence of relationship-related violence in their lifetime and many reported more than 20 episodes of violence as well as rating the events as severe ranging from 30.1% (forced sex or sexual contact) to 70.7% (threats).

Critical Thinking Question

Susan has come to the emergency room four times in the past month with repeated injuries she refers to as falls/accidents. How will you gain her confidence and try to assess whether she is a victim of domestic violence? In examining Susan, you feel it is important to document with photos the markings on her body. It is important to consider Susan's feelings on this, as well as the legal ramifications. What steps are needed before you can take photos of the victim's body demonstrating the degree of abuse?

Special Considerations: Teen Dating/Relationship Abuse

Dating is a time when one begins to explore the concept of trust. In early childhood development, one learns to trust the caregiver; in dating, this concept is once again touched upon. One does not want to believe that the person one chose to date would abuse him or her. However, intimate partner violence and sexual assault are common forms of violence among adolescents and young adults. This can have long-term damaging effects on self-concept, self-esteem, and choosing a partner in the future. As in domestic violence, relationship abuse can be any one of the four methods: sexual abuse, emotional abuse, physical abuse, or psychological abuse. It is difficult to identify relationship abuse because most young people would not discuss this with anyone, and these crimes are often unreported. It is important if you are a school nurse to be aware that this is occurring within the community. Studies indicate that 1 in 10 female high school students report being physically and/or sexually abused while dating (Centers for Disease Control and Prevention, 2006). Surveys of female college students indicate that 1 in 4 had experienced some form of intimate partner violence (U. S. Department of Justice, 2007).

It is the role of the nurse working in high schools, junior high schools, and universities to teach students the characteristics of an abusive relationship. Information regarding date rape is also included in most programs, as well as information regarding behaviors that may place individuals at risk for this and other problems. It is important to implement support groups. The risk of abuse and violence is higher for young women, but both young men and women need to know that they have a right to be treated with dignity and respect. Abuse and violence awareness programs can be designed by nurses to educate young people on the signs of an abuser and safe dating. It is important in these programs to include common characteristics and warning signs of abusers. These programs should be made available to both genders because, as with domestic violence, dating violence is not limited to one gender or to heterosexual relationships. Emergency room nurses and psychiatric

Critical Thinking Question

Tom is living with his wife, who calls him names and humiliates him in front of the children. She tells him to leave and that she hates him and will kill him in his sleep. He is emotionally paralyzed and stays. He tells the nurse he wants a family. He is hoping his wife will change because at times she is nice. He also feels it is his fault. He continues to stay in his marriage being emotionally and verbally abused. What interventions would you use to help Tom?

CASE STUDIES Ms. C.

Ms. C. was taken to the emergency department after ingestion of approximately 30 tablets of acetaminophen for a headache. She told the staff that she had impulsively taken the medication after a fight with her spouse and had not intended to kill herself. She minimized the event, telling everyone how stupid she was. The pain was so bad she just hadn't realized how many pills she had taken. However, when the nurse asked her if she felt safe at home, Ms. C. began to cry and shake. Although there was no reason for his jealousy and rage, her partner often became violent and had beaten her. He had returned to the house drunk and was verbally accusatory. She could never do anything right. No wonder he had to drink. She couldn't keep the house clean, the dog quiet, and the bills from piling up. He was provocative, throwing things around the house and breaking furniture. The last time this had happened he had tried to choke her and she passed out. Ms. C. told the nurse that the only reason she thought she hadn't died that time was that he was too drunk to finish her off. She felt that the only way to get away from the house and from him was to take the medication. She didn't really care if she died; she was desperate to find a way out. She felt so ashamed; she would rather be dead than return home.

nurses need to include questions regarding relationship status and potential assault in their assessments of young people.

The Centers for Disease Control and Prevention (CDC) have developed a special program, the National Youth Violence Prevention Resource Center and website (www.safeyouth.org) to help teens and the people who care about them to understand relationship abuse. This website is helpful and has creative programs that can be implemented to assist in educating young people on relationship abuse.

Studies indicate that drug use is a common factor in most cases of sexual assault. In addition, date rape drugs are used in approximately 5% of the cases involving women (Preidt, 2006). Common date rape drugs such as Rohypnol (flunitrazepam) and GHB (gamma hydroxybutyrate) are tasteless and odorless, making prevention difficult. One group of nursing students utilized the College of Registered Nurses of British Columbia standards for nursing practice highlighting client education and advocacy to work with the police to develop Student Nurses for Clean

Nursing Care Plan **Intimate Partner Violence**

Nursing diagnosis: Risk for injury related to report of abuse as evidenced by history of intimate partner violence.

Nursing diagnosis: Fear related to verbal and physical threats as evidenced by partner's accusations and throwing furniture.

Nursing diagnosis: Disabled family coping related to suicidal and homicidal threats as evidenced by patient's impulsive overdose and her partner's history of violence (beating and attempting to choke her) and alcohol abuse.

Expected Outcomes	Interventions	Evaluations
• Will decrease risk of injury by self or others.	• Assessment of risk for self-harm, assault, suicide, and homicide.	• Client is able to contract for safety and recognizes choices.
• Will evaluate possible history of or presence of intrafamily violence.	• Provision of appropriate assessment and evaluation.	• Documentation of physical status, appropriate photographs, and collection of evidence.
• Will decrease fear and anxiety.	• Development of nurse–client relationship.	• Empowerment to participate in assessment and counseling.
• Will assist client in developing a safety plan.	• Discuss options for referral and follow-up.	• Client verbalizes willingness to take the next step to protect self from abuse and violence.

Visit http://go.jblearning.com/mentalhealth for additional care plans and exercises.

Clinical Example 

Suppose an 18-year-old female comes to the emergency room with bruises on her arms and legs and a black eye. She says she injured herself falling off her bicycle. You accept this and treat her injuries. She returns 2 weeks later with similar bruises. She tells you that she had a fight with her roommate. She doesn't want to report it because she has to share the room with her and doesn't want to make waves. You decide at this point you will have to report this and have her room changed. She stops you and begins to sob, confiding that it is actually her boyfriend on campus who has assaulted her. She insists he does not mean to hurt her; but admits that when he drinks, he loses control. She states that she feels responsible because she did not want to have sex with him. She feels lucky that he is dating her because he usually does not date girls who will not have sex with him.

Drugs, an education project spotlighting the dangers to young people (Priest, 2005).

Clinical Course and Complications

Emotional abuse ranges from name calling to yelling, constantly criticizing, or undermining behavior directed toward the spouse or partner.

The victim becomes isolated, especially if the abuser is jealous. The jealous abuser makes it difficult for the victim to see family or friends. Occasional incidents of public humiliation reinforce that isolation. See **Table 11-3**.

Economic abuse is also considered a type of domestic violence. Perpetrators may deny the victim access to bank accounts and credit cards. They may insist that the victim account for every expenditure. This category also includes preventing a person from getting a job or returning to school. In immigrant families, the abuser may tell the victim that he will be deported or not eligible for legal status if he leaves. Economic control may place restraints on receiving adequate health and dental care and filling prescriptions.

Batterers or abusive individuals share several characteristics. They deny responsibility for their actions, and they are unable to trust people; this is projected in all relationships. Batterers expect immediate gratification from their partners. They are extremely jealous and unwilling to negotiate.

Table 11-3 **Abusive Behavior**

Behavior	Description
Breaking promises	Not following through, not taking responsibility, refusing to help with childcare or household duties.
Emotional withholding	Not expressing how one feels, not being supportive, not giving compliments; disregarding the rights or opinions of others.
Minimizing, denying, and blaming	Making light of the behavior; not taking the concerns or feelings of the victim seriously. Denying the abuse happened; shifting the responsibility. Blaming the victim for upsetting him.
Economic control	Interfering with the victim's work or not allowing the person to work. Refusing to give the victim money.
Self-destructive behavior	Abusing substances, threatening to kill herself.
Isolation	Preventing the victim from seeing or making it difficult to see friends or relatives. Monitoring phone calls, telling the victim where to go.
Harassment	Making uninvited visits or calls, following the victim, checking up on him, refusing to leave, and embarrassing him in public.
Pressure tactic	Using guilt trips to force the victim into making decisions. Manipulating the children, telling them what to do.
Destructive criticism/verbal abuse	This can range from name calling and yelling to swearing and mocking.
Abusing authority	Always claiming to be right, telling the victim what to do.
Disrespect	Interrupting, changing topics, not listening or responding, twisting the person's words or statements, putting the person down in public.

Threats are as damaging as any of the other behaviors. They can leave a victim feeling paralyzed and helpless. Threats vary in degrees ranging from inflicting harm on the person to kidnapping the victim's child. Weapons are often displayed as an additional means of threatening the individual. The victim lives in a state of fear, trying to remain neutral in order to avoid the threats. The abuser uses anger to manipulate the victim.

Physical violence associated with domestic violence includes grabbing, pushing, hitting, kicking, choking, biting, punching, and slapping. The nurse must remember that pregnancy does not protect a woman from physical violence. Pregnant women have been thrown down the stairs or punched in the stomach, resulting in miscarriages. In the clinical setting, clients may present with gynecologic disorders, sexually transmitted diseases, pregnancy difficulties, or orthopedic problems. Also, the potential for violence continues even after the relationship with the abuser has ended.

Differential Diagnosis

To obtain a comprehensive history, it is vital that the nurse maintain a supportive and nonjudgmental atmosphere. Victims need safety and a chance to speak openly. Questioning the victim in the presence of the abuser may lead to more violence because the victim may be unable to communicate openly in this situation. Therefore, it is necessary to interview the victim separately.

Initially, the victim may not have enough trust in the nurse to discuss these issues. It is helpful to use action verbs such as hit, kick, or yell when asking questions. This helps victims verbalize the form of abuse. The nurse should rephrase questions when necessary if the client gives evasive answers. When questioning victims about violence during follow-up visits, the nurse must reassure the victim that his or her safety is a primary concern. Clinicians must also be aware of their own beliefs when interviewing a potential victim. It is important to be nonjudgmental and to remember that domestic violence is not restricted to a certain class or group.

It is helpful to show the client the Domestic Abuse Intervention Project Power and Control Wheel and have her point out which sections on the wheel diagram she identifies with. The Power and Control Wheel diagram was developed from the experiences of abused women and has been used to help during the assessment stage of treatment (The Duluth Project, 1987). It includes descriptions of types of physical abuse ranging from pushing and shoving to using a weapon. Forms of power and control range from isolation and intimidation to economic and sexual abuse. It helps the victim to feel not alone and to identify specific incidents of abuse.

There is also a wheel diagram that was designed during a domestic violence project to demonstrate how the healthcare system can perpetuate the abuse. Categories described in this visual diagram include:

- *Violating confidentiality:* Interviewing in front of family, telling colleagues information discussed in confidence without the patient's permission, calling the police without the patient's consent
- *Trivializing and minimizing the abuse:* Ignoring the complaints and not taking them seriously
- *Blaming the victim:* Asking the victim why she or he did not leave or what she or he did to upset the abuser.
- *Not respecting the victim's autonomy:* Giving suggestions on what the victim should do (e.g., go to a shelter, go to the police)
- *Ignoring her or his need for safety:* Not acknowledging the danger the victim is in
- *Normalizing victimization:* Seeing her or his abuse as normal in the relationship, failure to respond to her or his disclosure of the abuse

Evidence-Based Practice

Biroscat, Smith, Roznowski, Tucker, and Carlson (2006) investigated the Michigan Intimate Partner Violence Against Women (IPVAW) interventions in 23 emergency departments across the state over a 2-year period. Chart review confirmed 2,926 incidents of physical and/or sexual assault, and more than one third of these cases were attributable to intimate partner violence. A considerable percentage of the victims were young women abused by an ex-boyfriend. Further research and a wider sample are needed to determine the extent of relationship abuse.

Management and Treatment of Intimate Partner Violence

Nurses have many roles that they use when delivering quality care to clients. The key component is self-

Table 11-4 Sample Interview Questions

"I have noticed you have a number of marks and bruises on your body. Could you tell me how this happened? Has anyone hurt you?"

"I have heard from patients I treated that a person close to them has hurt them. Has this happened to you?"

"You shared that sometimes your partner loses his temper. Could you describe what happens when he loses his temper? Has he ever hurt you?"

"Do your verbal fights sometimes get physical?"

"Does your partner sometimes try to control your actions?"

reflection. The nurse must first identify his or her own feelings about the subject and concepts of domestic violence. Empathy is one of the key elements needed to assist the victim. An important role the nurse will utilize is the role of advocate. See **Table 11-4** for sample interview questions to determine whether the client is being abused or feels unsafe at home. The following categories are seen as key components of the advocate role:

- *Respect confidentiality:* Interviews should take place in a private area away from family members. This simple tactic will enhance the therapeutic relationship and build a trusting relationship.
- *Respect the victim's autonomy:* Respect the victim's right to make decisions in his or her life in his or her own time frame.
- *Believe and validate the client's experiences:* Listen to her or him and believe her or him. Reassure the victim that he or she is not alone.
- *Acknowledge the injustice:* The violence is not his or her fault. No one deserves to be abused.
- *Help plan for future safety:* Explore what measures were taken in the past and if they were helpful. Is the victim aware of agencies and shelters that can help?
- *Promote access to community services:* Have a list of shelters available to give the client. Provide a hotline number the client can use at any time.

Some clinicians will want to keep a checklist of interventions they can refer to when working with the battered partner. See **Table 11-5** for some interventions for battered partners.

Include intervention goals such as developing independence and promoting love of self and feelings of

Table 11-5 Education for Clients and Families for Intimate Partner Violence

- Recognize that some individuals do not see themselves as being abused.
- Provide a supportive setting.
- Help the client identify alternatives rather than returning to the batterer.
- Provide information on obtaining legal assistance and a court order for protection.
- Identify and treat extreme mental and physical fatigue.
- Reassure the victim that she or he is not alone.
- Identify feelings of guilt and self-blame.
- Recognize that counseling alone has limited effectiveness while the violence continues; counseling works only when the victim is safe and the abuser is in treatment as well.
- Inform the battered partner that she or he may leave and return several times before making a final decision, and that plans for safety should be continued.
- Provide a 24-hour hotline and shelter information.

self-worth to promote assertiveness that can be used to demonstrate components of a healthy relationship. Respect, responsibility, honesty and accountability, economic and social partnership, negotiation, and fairness are key hallmarks of a healthy relationship.

The client should help decide the composition of the treatment plan. This is the first step to empowering the client. Knowledge of the components of a healthy relationship is useful in helping to show the client what is acceptable in a mature relationship and allowing the client to make choices. It is important to allow the client the autonomy to make these decisions. If the nurse makes the decisions she or he is only reinforcing the abuse by reinforcing the client's place in a helpless situation.

It is frightening to leave home when one is financially dependent upon someone else. The client can benefit from joining a domestic violence support group or self-help group. These groups provide resource information and empower the victim. **Empowerment** is the key to successful treatment. The forced isolation experienced by victims may have been responsible for restricting access to family, friends, or community resources with their employ-

Empowerment: Survivors of abuse gain self-esteem and self-confidence to control their environment.

ers and healthcare practitioners. Reestablishing these links to social networks helps decrease the perceived isolation and increase support.

Evidence-Based Practice

In a randomized, controlled study of two prenatal clinics in the Northwest and Midwest, 1,000 women between 13 and 23 weeks' gestation were offered either an abuse video or access to a nurse case manger; participants identified as at risk for abusive relationships received nursing case management throughout their pregnancy. Curry, Durham, Bullock, Bloom, and Davis (2006) concluded that nurses needed to focus on client-identified needs, which may not be the abusive relationship. This study has implications for client teaching and interventions.

Evidence-Based Practice

In a randomized study of two groups, one who received a referral card and another who received a case management protocol, McFarlane, Groff, O'Brien, and Watson (2006) found that women in both groups experienced a significant increase in safety behaviors and a decrease in utilization of costly inpatient and outpatient services. The process of abuse assessment and subsequent disclosure of abuse has the potential to interrupt the cycle of abuse and increase safety. Inclusion of abuse assessment was shown to be an important nursing intervention.

Battered partner syndrome is a term used to describe a victim who is exposed to multiple traumas, is passive and socially isolated, and often finds it difficult to leave the batterer.

Clients should have access to emergency shelters and hotlines to assist them in times of crisis. Many times a client is afraid to even accept information, fearing that his or her partner may find evidence that he or she has spoken with someone outside of the household about the abuse. For this reason, the referral information is often printed on wallet-sized cards or even matchbooks so they may be confidentially and safely carried by the client. The nurse must work with the client to explore the benefits and drawbacks of remaining at home. The client should be assisted to develop a stepwise safety plan. Part of the nursing intervention is helping the client recognize the importance of having a plan and planning to use it. The client can be asked when she or he will feel ready to take the next step. It is important to remember that many times the victim leaves and returns to the batterer. The nurse must always remain objective and supportive.

It is also valuable to consider that once the client makes a decision, a shelter may well be the last and only safe alternative. Many times, survivors escape in the middle of the night with their children and only the clothes on their back. Shelters often are not set up to accept male clients alone or with children, and other resources must be found. These clients are running for their lives and their sanity to a shelter. For these clients, anonymity and refuge are essential.

Once at the shelter, these women will be examined by the nurse and interviewed by caseworkers. Children are placed in the local school and encouraged try to carry on as if all is well. The children tend to be upset and some cry, talking their mom into returning to the batterer. The batterer might not have abused the children, and even when there is **child abuse** also, the children might want to return. The children are frightened and want to return to a familiar setting. Shelters often have time limits and limited financial resources. It is sometimes difficult for the survivor to develop alternate plans for financial support, a job and housing within the time limits and resources available. Some do not stay in the shelter system and return to their home. It is important to remain nonjudgmental. The main thing in caring for these clients is self-reflection. It is important to assess your own feelings and be able to treat these clients objectively.

A diagnosis of **battered partner syndrome** is associated with a battered person who is unable to leave the batterer. In this case an individual develops a set of personality traits initiated by the abuse, making survival in the relationship possible. The victim has become tuned in to the cycle of domestic violence. She or he anticipates the next explosion and may passively comply with the assault in order to go on to the next phase where the batterer will express remorse and vow never to be abusive again. The victim is not fighting back, has become withdrawn, and has given up. The battered partner sees escape as impossible, and depression compounds this entrapment. Assessment and treatment of this syndrome are vital if the victim is to survive. Recidivism is a barrier to treatment.

In conjunction with these patterns, the survivor of intimate partner violence is also faced with the conflicting concepts of love, hope, and fear.

Love: The idea of love for one's partner and the thought that any relationship has its good points and is not all bad

Hope: The hope that things will change (the victim notes that his or her partner was not abusive at the beginning, and hopes the batterer will change)

Fear: The very real fear that the batterer will follow through on threats to kill one or one's family

Child Abuse

Child abuse has existed for centuries and across national boundaries. Nurses are considered mandated reporters for suspected cases of child abuse and neglect. (Additional discussion of child abuse can be found in Chapter 27.)

Incidence and Prevalence

The World Health Organization (WHO, 2006) report on preventing child maltreatment notes that the prevalence of child abuse is higher in societies where there is a tolerance for violence, gender, and social inequality, poor living standards, and child pornography, prostitution, and child labor. The 2002 incidence of deaths related to child abuse was 31,000 deaths per 100,000 cases of reported violence and neglect by parents or close family members. Depending upon the country, from one fourth to one half of all children report experiencing some form of child abuse in their lifetime. Nearly 20% of women and 10% of men report a history of early sexual abuse. It is estimated that in the United States, the cost of child abuse is $94 billion a year, or nearly 1% of the gross national product. Hospital costs related to child abuse are $13 billion a year, mental health costs are $425 million, child welfare costs are $14.4 billion, and costs related to criminal activity are approximately $55.4 billion a year (WHO, 2006).

Epidemiology

Child abuse may be related to a parental history of abuse or sexual assault, a parental history of engaging in substance abuse or criminal activity, medical or mental health problems, or difficulty bonding or physical problems at birth. Isolation, poverty, and lack of self-control and impulse control have also been identified as factors (WHO, 2006).

Child abuse, maltreatment, or neglect, as in other categories of family violence, should not be associated with a particular social class or ethnic group. However, it is possible that incidents of neglect and physical abuse may correlate to higher levels of financial stress.

A child living in a home where domestic violence occurs is considered a victim of abuse. A child in this environment lives in fear and anticipation of losing a parent to violence. Living with domestic violence can also have long-term effects. For example, the child may eventually be diagnosed with an Axis I disorder, be involved in an abusive situation as a victim or batterer, have chronic health problems, or have long-term problems forming relationships.

Child abuse occurs when a temporary or primary caregiver intentionally harms or threatens a child. It is also defined as maltreatment either by physical abuse, sexual abuse, emotional abuse, or neglect. Emotional abuse varies from an emotionally distant parent to one who is overbearing or demeaning. Forms of emotional abuse include name calling and humiliating a child in public. Pressuring children to meet unrealistic expectations can damage them emotionally. Interfering with the child's social and psychological development in any way is also considered emotional abuse. Neglect can be life threatening. In these instances, the caregiver fails to provide the basic requirements of food, shelter, medical care, and supervision. Children have died from this form of abuse.

Child abuse consists of physical injury, emotional abuse, or sexual abuse that occurs when the child is neglected, isolated, or shamed and demeaned.

Physical abuse can also be life threatening. This type of abuse consists of inflicting bodily harm. Forcing children to exercise excessively or to participate in activities against their will is also considered physical abuse.

Sexual abuse ranges from exposing the child inappropriately to sexual acts or materials to using the child for sexual stimulation. It is important to remember that in addition to other types of abuses, sexual abuse of children occurs in all socioeconomic classes.

Incest is a serious form of sexual abuse that is not easily detected. Children often do not report these occurrences. They are filled with fear and confusion, especially if the violator is a parent. Incest is defined as intimate sexual contact between members of the same family; in this case, the family members are closely enough related to be legally prohibited from marrying one another.

Incest involves sexual intercourse or intimate sexual behavior with members of the same family. In the treatment of incest, it is important to remember to collect evidence, because criminal charges may be filed.

Critical Thinking Question

Ms. Smith brought her daughter, age 5, in for her annual physical. Alice used to be a smiling and joking child, but during this appointment, she was quiet and withdrawn. The nurse commented on the change she noticed. Her mom dismissed it and said she was growing up and maturing. The nurse noticed that Alice was uncomfortable with taking off her clothes and being examined. She asked Alice if anything hurt, and Alice said it hurt when she urinated. The nurse asked how long she had been having pain. She said since daddy had been sleeping in her bed at night. Her mother chuckled and dismissed this as her imagination. The nurse was uncomfortable with pursuing her thoughts. She dismissed the child's statements and went on with her nursing tasks.

This case scenario took place 40 years ago. Alice, in therapy at the age of 45, shared the abuse she endured. Her father repeatedly sexually abused her. He penetrated her at age 5, and this went on for almost 5 years until her parents were divorced. Her mother continued to deny that any abuse took place. Alice felt used by both parents—the abuser and her mother who never rescued her or allowed her to be rescued. Today, how would this situation be handled?

Battered child syndrome takes place when a child has multiple traumas and has been beaten repeatedly. Shaken baby syndrome refers to rough handling and shaking of infants that results in brain injury and possible death.

Clinical Presentation

To assess whether maltreatment has occurred, the nurse must be understanding and empathetic. This will encourage the child to disclose events. A concise interview, including a thorough psychosocial and medical history, aids in detecting signs of abuse. Repetitive bruising is an indication of abuse and must be explored, although the child may deny any abusive incidents. If children exhibit overly aggressive behaviors, this also may be a sign of physical abuse. This trait is seen most often in boys, but it can be observed in girls as well.

As mentioned previously, child abuse may be present where domestic violence occurs. If a husband physically abuses his wife, he most likely will also physically abuse the children. Even when the wife leaves the batterer, the perpetrator will use the child or children as a means of control.

Children are afraid to report abuse in the home. It is important to remember that the child is loyal to the family and may initially fear the repercussions of disclosure. As in all cases where abuse is suspected, separate interviews with the victim and suspected perpetrator are advised. Simple interviewing techniques to remember include establishing eye contact and adopting an open body position that shows interest. An interviewer might say, "Do people in your family hit each other when they get mad?" It is important to coordinate interviews by clinicians and state agencies, because multiple interviews can be upsetting and not in the child's best interest.

Multiple lesions or bruises at different stages of healing are considered suspicious and warrant further investigation. **Battered child syndrome** refers to children who exhibit multiple traumas and who appear to have been beaten repeatedly. Battered child syndrome is associated with children 3 years of age and younger. These children are shaken, beaten, or otherwise traumatized brutally, causing severe injuries and even death. Multiple fractures and bruises are associated with this syndrome. Repetitive bruising is an indication to explore these incidents fur-

Clinical Example

Rick was the youngest of three children. The household was chaotic and his father was physically abusive toward his mother. His father was later imprisoned, and his parents separated. When Rick was 3 years old, his mother, who was using drugs, was charged with neglect. He and his older siblings were placed in care with his grandmother. A few years later, Rick was returned to live with his mother. This plan failed when Rick was physically abused by his stepfather; teachers in school noted physical bruising and frequent absences. Rick was placed in foster care. He had some behavioral problems and was moved through several foster homes and group homes. Things seemed to be looking up for Rick when he was 13 years old and he returned to live with his mother and siblings. However, when he was 15 years old, his mother told him that it was her turn for a good life. She told him that she was going to remarry and that he would have to leave the apartment. For several months Rick carried on going to school. Sometimes he stayed with relatives and sometimes he slept over at friends' apartments. Eventually, the nights that he had no place to stay became more frequent. He dropped out of school and began to live on the street.

ther. You may suspect child abuse, but the child may deny it.

The child's development and growth pattern should be assessed. A weight of less than the fifth percentile for the age group may indicate signs of neglect. Complaints of genital or abdominal pain without cause are other indicators of possible abuse. Because incest is a form of sexual abuse, the symptoms are the same: expressions of fear, aggressive behaviors, and sexual behaviors. These symptoms can appear together or as isolated occurrences.

The child should be observed for nightmares or withdrawn behavior. Child victims may exhibit fear when they see perpetrators. Another symptom caused by fear is regression. Symptoms of aggressive behavior are hitting, biting, breaking toys, head banging, and tantrums. These symptoms appear as a result of the intense anger the child is experiencing. The child is angry at the person who has abused him or her and at the parent who was trusted to protect the child. The child who is a victim of incest feels emotionally abandoned by the nonabusive parent if the abuse goes undetected.

Reporting child abuse is mandated by legislation in the United States. Statutory requirements override the client–nurse confidentiality rule. Failure to report can result in penalties. Professional immunity may be granted when reporting suspicions. Nurses should be familiar with the requirements for reporting child abuse in the states where they practice.

Management and Treatment of Child Abuse

It is difficult to single-handedly treat a case of child abuse. The clinician should coordinate treatment with social workers, attorneys, and medical personnel. No consensus has been reached concerning the most effective form of treatment. Foster care offers some respite, but it may also be abusive, causing further trauma when the child is separated from the family. Children who have been sexually abused or who are victims of incest should not be returned to the abuser.

Maintaining the continuity of the family during treatment, however, is also a consideration. The nurse must attempt to involve the family and assess its social, physical, economic, and emotional needs if the child is to remain in the home during treatment. Community resources can provide a sense of security for the family and increase the members' self-esteem and sense of control. See **Table 11-6** for potential interventions for abused children.

Table 11-6 Education for Clients and Families of Abused Children

- Identify the child's fears caused by a violent home environment.
- Teach the abused child to express feelings rather than act them out.
- Allow the child to express feelings of guilt, particularly if the child is angry with the abuser.
- Aid and encourage the parent and child to discuss their fears openly.
- Teach children acceptable ways of expressing their emotions. Denial is used as a protective device. Through play therapy, young children are able to express their feelings openly.
- Focus on helping older children work through emotions of guilt, shame, responsibility, anger, and depression.

The nurse demonstrates empathy when viewing the client's world from his or her internal frame of reference. This involves the nurse's sensitivity to the client's current feelings and the ability to communicate this to the client in a language that can be understood. This technique is most useful in establishing trust and expresses understanding and concern.

It is important to incorporate the abusive parent/parents in your treatment plan. There are a number of interventions that can be used; see **Table 11-7**.

Elder Abuse

The media and healthcare profession have only recently begun to address elder abuse. In the 1990s, the U.S. Department of Health and Human Services created a task force to define and identify preventive measures that would be beneficial to the treatment

Table 11-7 Education for Abusive Parents

- Encourage the abusive parent to express feelings freely.
- Remain nonjudgmental.
- Empathize with the parents' frustrations.
- Provide information on parenting support groups.
- Explore alternative childcare services.
- Help parents identify triggers to abusive behavior.
- Discuss alternate coping mechanisms.
- Identify sources of community and family support.
- Refer for appropriate treatment if indicated.
- Assist the parent during the referral and reporting process.

Elder abuse describes acts of commission or omission resulting in harm or threatened harm to the health or welfare of an older adult. Elder abuse may include physical, emotional, or economic abuse as well as neglect.

Neglect is a condition in which a caregiver fails to provide physical and/or emotional care to a child or elderly person.

Passive neglect is an unintentional failure to deliver caregiving obligations or inflicting distress without willful intent. Active neglect is intentional failure to fulfill the caregiving obligations or inflicting physical or emotional distress.

Material exploitation is an example of economic abuse using resources inappropriate for one's own needs.

of abused elders. In some states, elder abuse is covered under domestic violence laws or laws applying to nursing homes and home healthcare agencies, whereas in others there are specific laws covering mandatory reporting.

The characteristics of elder abuse are similar to other types of abuse and may be intentional and direct or unintentional and indirect; it is often unrecognized and underreported. Because the victim may be frail and in poor health, it is often difficult to determine the source of bruising, fractures, or poor nutritional status. In addition, there may be sensory, language, or cognitive problems contributing to poor communication. The elderly person depends on his or her caregiver for the basic necessities and may be reluctant to provide potentially damaging information. There are four types of elder abuse: physical abuse including sexual abuse, emotional abuse, material exploitation or misappropriation of funds, and neglect (Paris, Meier, Goldstein, Weiss, & Fein, 1995).

Elders are at particular risk for the effects of physical abuse due to the effects of aging and concurrent physical disorders or the side effects of medication. Physical abuse is when an act is carried out with the intent of causing physical pain or bodily harm. Violent actions range from slapping and hitting to occasionally using objects to strike others. One slap may not be considered to be a pattern of abuse, but it can cause injury in a vulnerable and frail adult. Such mistreatment can result in lacerations, bruises, burns, abrasions, and occasionally skeletal fractures. When the client has a history of falls at home, is demented and may accidentally leave the stove on, or is on blood-thinning agents that can cause bruising after minor injuries, it is difficult to assess whether the injuries are due to intentional maltreatment by others. The elder may not be able to communicate or remember what happened. Victims of abuse may be able to file for an order of protection against the abuser.

Psychological or emotional abuse is any threat that causes emotional pain. Threats to abandon or institutionalize the victim increase the elder's sense of insecurity and heighten the emotions of fear and despair. Insulting the elder and humiliating him or her are characteristics of psychological and emotional abuse.

Material exploitation and/or misappropriation of funds are another form of elder abuse. The caregiver might cash the elder's Social Security or pension check and keep the money. Force is often used to coerce the victim into signing over the checks. Caregivers may convince their victims to sign over all their assets and change their wills to benefit the caregiver. At times, the address is changed and statements are sent to another home, or there may be a change in the volume of usual banking activity with suspicious signatures or unusually large withdrawals.

Neglect is difficult to define clearly, because it depends on the caregiver's abilities and the elder's needs and capacity. One caregiver may have a knowledge deficit and be unable to deliver the care needed or provide access to proper medical care (**passive neglect**) whereas another caregiver might deliberately choose not to provide adequate food for the elder (**active neglect**). Therefore, it is important to distinguish between passive and active neglect. Neglect is identified in a person who should be but is not thriving in the community. All aspects of the elder's health and dietary needs, social needs, and safety should be examined when looking for signs of neglect.

An extreme form of neglect would be abandonment. Abandonment is when the person who has assumed care of the elder or is responsible for care deserts the elder or does not provide care. In cases of abandonment, there is refusal to fulfill obligations to an elder by the family or caregiver.

Evidence-Based Practice

Baker and Heitkemper (2005) reported that elders who live independently are at lowest risk for elder abuse, as are those with social support. Those with dementia, particularly those with aggressive or disruptive behaviors, are at highest risk. Caregivers with a history of mental illness, aggressive personality style, dependence on the victim for support, and substance and alcohol abuse are more likely to be abusive. In institutional settings, risk factors for abusers include poor staffing, mandatory overtime, and lack of training and clinical supervision. Roles for nurses in preventing elder abuse include being educators, researchers, and case managers and providing expert consultation on public policy and community service project teams.

Incidence and Prevalence

It is difficult to estimate the prevalence of the elder abuse problem due to differences in definition, reporting mechanisms, and data collection. Reporting of elder abuse is not mandatory in all states. It is estimated that 1 in 14 incidents of elder abuse are

Clinical Example 

Alice was released from the hospital after she broke her ankle and wrist in a fall. The hospital arranged for some part-time assistance at home. Alice was comfortable with home care arrangements and looking forward to going home and regaining her independence. However, over the next few weeks, her friends became more and more concerned. It became increasingly difficult for them to contact Alice directly, and they were told that she was not receiving visitors. When one friend went directly to the home, she was denied access. The friend became anxious and contacted the police. The police found Alice in the company of a woman who identified herself first as Alice's relative and later as a tenant. Alice's residence was unkempt, drug paraphernalia was in view, and there were several adults and children living in the home. When the police insisted on speaking with Alice, they found her dehydrated, confused and disoriented, and lying on a soiled mattress covered in feces. Alice was brought to the hospital. The tenant who had befriended Alice had apparently moved in, stopped the home care follow-up, taken possession of Alice's checkbook, and denied Alice access to contact with her friends and neighbors. Isolated and neglected, denied access to her usual medications and medical care, Alice had become ill and increasingly dependent upon her abuser.

reported and only 1 in 25 cases of material exploitation are reported. The frequency of elder abuse is estimated to range from 2% to 10% depending on the sampling, survey methods, and case definitions of the studies done (National Center on Elder Abuse [NCEA], 2005).

The 1998 National Elder Abuse Incidence Study estimated that approximately 551,000 community-dwelling elders, those living in their own home or with a family member, were abused or neglected. A state-by-state survey in 2000 estimated the number of reports to be 473,813. Under the Long Term Care Ombudsman program, there were 20,673 cases of suspected abuse investigated in nursing home residents (NCEA, 2005). Additional cases of self-neglect have not been estimated.

The incidence of abuse increases with age. It is estimated that the rate of abuse is two to three times higher for those 80 years old and older. The incidence also is higher among elders not physically able to care for themselves (International Council of Nursing, 2006). Accurate estimates are not available for elders living in institutional settings, but these elders are considered to be at highest risk for all types of elder abuse.

Epidemiology

A rapidly growing elder population and a society ill prepared for caretaking responsibilities increase the risk for possible abuse. Underlying abuse in a domestic situation may be a long-standing history of domestic abuse, impaired parent–child relations, criminal or substance abuse problems, and chronic physical and mental health problems. Intergenerational relations, financial and caregiver stress, and the increased dependency of a frail elderly spouse or parent can upset a previously stable but fragile balance. Elders may be isolated in the community and dependent upon strangers or transient caretakers. Institutionalized abuse may be complicated by financial problems, lack of health care, or overcrowded conditions.

Clinical Presentation

Assessing elder abuse can be challenging. Frequent accidents and unexplained bruises should be evaluated thoroughly. The clinician must establish an atmosphere to encourage full disclosure. The victim might not report incidents, fearing institutionalization or separation from the family member. As mentioned earlier, however, reporting elder abuse is mandatory in some but not all states.

The nurse must utilize several resources. Interviewing a number of family members is helpful. As in all types of family violence, all parties involved should be interviewed separately. The nurse may ask the elder how meals are prepared or ask the person to describe a typical day to establish communication. It is also appropriate to ask if violence has occurred in the home or if the victim fears abandonment.

Psychological or emotional abuse is difficult to assess. At times the elder may be isolated from usual contacts and become increasingly dependent upon the abuser. The elderly person must be evaluated for signs of depression. Clients may exhibit signs of withdrawal, express anxiety, have vague health

Table 11-8 Education for Clients and Families for Abused Elders

- Provide a supportive, empathetic, and nonjudgmental atmosphere.
- Interview both parties separately.
- Emphasize the importance of remaining socially active with family and friends.
- Remind the elder that one does not have to live with a violent person.
- Assess whether abuse is intentional or related to a knowledge deficit, and act accordingly.
- Know the state laws regarding reporting.
- Include the elderly person in the treatment plan.
- Contact significant others or a protective service if the elderly person is unable to make decisions.

complaints, or express a desire to die. These covert signs indicate that the individual may be living in an abusive environment. If these symptoms worsen, early intervention can prevent further deterioration.

Education facilitates the diagnosis of elder abuse. Discussing and teaching the client the appropriate quality of life and health expectations prompt more accurate answers to future questions. A checklist is helpful when querying the victim. The following sample questions can help elicit information: Has anyone ever taken something of yours without permission? Are you home alone for long periods? Has anyone ever hit you? Have you ever felt fear of abandonment? Describe a typical day at home. This last entry allows the nurse to assess the patterns of daily living including mealtimes, general hygiene, medical needs, and administration of medications.

Management and Treatment of Elder Abuse

The victim's wishes should be considered when developing the treatment plan. The victim's input often helps to remedy the situation. Caregivers are often overburdened and unaware of available resources. In this case, the situation resolves once caregivers receive aid. Conversely, the elder may be in serious danger and require different living arrangements. See **Table 11-8** for education for clients and families dealing with elder abuse and **Table 11-9** for nursing interventions with abused elderly clients.

Prevention is a key part of treatment of the elderly. Neighbors, friends, or relatives should visit often. Encourage elderly clients to participate in community activities and have them make arrangements to have their Social Security checks or pensions placed by direct deposit into a bank account. Meet with family members to decide who will be available to help if the elderly person becomes incapacitated. The clinician should assist the elder to evaluate a family member's ability to provide home care. Discuss resources available to the elder such as Meals on Wheels, supportive services, assisted living options, or nursing homes if the elder can no longer live at home. If necessary, the client may be referred to Protective Services for Adults or other abuse prevention programs for further evaluation and intervention. Alternate housing for the abuser or for the elder may be suggested.

CASE STUDIES Mr. S.

Mr. S. is an elderly man who recently lost his wife. He has a daughter, Susan, who lives in another state; a son, David, who is busy working and has an active family life; and another son, James, who never married and who lives upstairs. James has a history of intermittent substance abuse and unemployment. David speaks to his father every morning and visits him twice a week. He began to notice in his telephone conversations that his father was getting more distressed and complaining of missing money. At first David thought his dad may have misplaced his money. He noticed, however, that this had been occurring more often, and he began to investigate. He suspected his brother was taking advantage of his father.

Suppose you are interviewing Mr. S. for his annual physical and noticed he is losing weight and forgetful. Suppose further that David shares that his father is misplacing his money, which reinforces your observation of cognitive changes. Mr. S. also begins to complain about his other son and shares with you that he feels he is taking his money. He becomes angry, however, and verbally attacks you when you mention reporting his son James for elder abuse. It is critical that this case be handled with care and respect for Mr. S.

Table 11-9 Nursing Interventions for Clients Coping with Abuse and Family Violence

Nursing Diagnosis	Interventions	Rationales
Posttrauma syndrome	Provide for appropriate screening and for safety and security.	A client who is a survivor of family violence may be at further risk for abuse. Provide a safe area so that the client may feel secure. This also ensures for safety of staff who may be in the area if the abuser becomes violent. If the partner or abuser has accompanied the client, ensure that they are separated so that the client will be able to interact with staff and cooperate with the assessment without fears for safety or retaliation. If the client is accompanied by children or other family members, ensure that they are taken care of so that client may feel comfortable taking care of his or her own needs.
	Offer presence and establish therapeutic alliance.	Establishing a trusting relationship with the client will help the client feel comfortable talking about possible abuse or injuries and cooperating with physical and psychologic assessments and treatment.
	Provide for nursing assessment.	Helps establish what has happened, the client's perception of events, and begins the problem-solving process. Offering the client help with the problem that brought him for assistance or with any practical problems that arise helps the client begin to trust and to recognize that staff may be helpful in other ways. Interview and physical assessment may be needed to document situation or injuries.
	Evaluate usual coping mechanisms and support systems.	If coping mechanisms and support systems are not available or adequate, crisis intervention may be needed.
	Engage the client in treatment planning.	Assisting the client in establishing priorities helps facilitate treatment planning. The client is more likely to follow through if her priorities are met. Encourage the client in following through with the next steps to ensuring safety, whether that is by accepting information, beginning to develop a safety plan, linking with community services, filing charges, or seeking shelter from the abuser.
	Establish follow-up plan and determine if the situation is one in which mandatory reporting is required or if the client wishes legal follow-up or social services.	Some situations may require staff to make a report of injuries or potential abuse/neglect. In other situations, the client will need to agree to file charges or seek an order of protection. If the client or others in household require protection, evaluate possible resources. Ensure appropriate documentation of interventions.

Nursing Care Plan **Elder Abuse**

Nursing diagnosis 1: Impaired memory related to forgetfulness as evidenced by increasing complaints regarding misplaced money, weight loss, and suspected problems with ADL/IADL.

Nursing diagnosis 2: Ineffective coping related to distress and complaints as evidenced by accusations against caretakers and problems with financial management.

Nursing diagnosis 3: Imbalanced nutrition related to possible decreased intake or changes in intake after loss of wife as evidenced by loss of weight.

Expected Outcomes	Interventions	Evaluations
• Will establish trust with the client and family.	• Orient client and family. • Question client and family separately. • Maintain confidentiality. • Identify necessary resources.	• Validate inferences. • Make appropriate referrals to other healthcare providers, social service, and behavioral health.
• Will determine if the patient is a victim of elder abuse or neglect.	• Assess the client's mental status; perform a mini-mental exam. • Assess the client for changes in thought process and mood. • Assess the client's ADL. • Assess the client's nutritional intake.	• Score mini-mental test and evaluate the patient's perception of the test. • Observe the quality of speech and content for paranoid statements. • Observe client's appearance and interview him focusing on his grooming habits and daily activities. • Review with the client his dietary intake. Does he eat alone? Who prepares his meals?
• Will explore alternative coping mechanisms and ways of managing his finances.	• Assist the client in identifying coping mechanisms that have worked in the past in similar situations.	• Review with the client how he monitors his finances.
• Will establish contact with community resources for follow-up care.	• Discuss possible community resources and support systems with the client and appropriate family members.	• Determine if referral for further evaluation of exploitation is needed. • Evaluate the client's participation with follow-up care.

Visit http://go.jblearning.com/mentalhealth for additional care plans and exercises.

Summary

Family violence has become more prevalent. Domestic and intimate partner violence, child abuse, and elder abuse share similar characteristics. The abuser in all incidents attempts to control and isolate the victim. The false sense of power and security fuels further acts of violence. Typically a honeymoon phase follows the abusive act. The abuser apologizes and promises the abuse will never happen again. The victim wants very much to believe this, and therefore stays in the relationship. Elderly and younger people tend to fear abandonment or placement outside the home.

The nurse must remain objective and empathetic and demonstrate concerned interest during the interview. Low self-esteem may prevent the victim from trusting anyone. Thus, the healthcare provider must establish an atmosphere of trust. The parties should be interviewed separately for accuracy of information, confidentiality, and safety. Additionally, it is important to know the laws of the state regarding mandatory reporting.

Documentation must be accurate and concise, quoting the victim clearly without interjecting the nurse's opinion. A diagram should document the location of physical injuries, and, if possible, color pictures of the injuries should be taken. These become part of the victim's permanent health record.

Flexible treatment plans that focus on safety should improve the client's living conditions. Ultimately, clinicians seek to improve the victim's quality of life. The nurse should urge the batterer to seek help by referral to appropriate agencies. Healthcare professionals' responsibilities involve assessing the client's global quality of life, including the home environment.

In all cases, prevention is the best intervention. Parenting classes and support groups can provide much-needed outlets for the frustrations experienced during the parenting years. Teaching the batterer and victim responsibility and mutual respect may be the first step toward resolution. Providing assistance to caregivers decreases stress.

The literature also demonstrates that there are characteristics of the abuser the nurse can be made aware of, and that it is often difficult for the victim to leave the situation or to report the abuse. It is always important not to generalize, and to treat the individual as unique. Evidence-based research can help the nurse understand the phenomenon and explore treatment modalities that have proven to be beneficial.

Annotated References

American Psychiatric Association. (2000). *Diagnostic and statistical manual of mental disorders* (4th ed.). Washington, DC: Author.
This is the fourth edition of the American Psychiatric Association's official nomenclature of psychiatric conditions and disorders. It provides a systematic listing of the official codes and categories, a description of the multiaxial system for diagnosis, and diagnostic criteria for each of the disorders. It is used by psychiatrists, physicians, psychologists, registered nurses, social workers, therapists, and other mental health workers in all clinical settings.

Baker, M. W., & Heitkemper, M. (2005). The roles of nurses on interprofessional teams to combat elder mistreatment. *Nursing Outlook, 53*(3), 253–259.
This article discusses the role of nurses on Elder Abuse Project teams in the Seattle, Washington area to help recognize and manage abuse, including assessment and screening, mandatory reporting, direct care, and investigation of complaints.

Biroscat, B., Smith, P., Roznowski, H., Tucker, J., & Carlson, G. (2006). Intimate partner violence against women: Findings from one state's E.D. surveillance system. *Journal of Emergency Nursing, 32*(1), 12–16.
This study is a 2-year review of 2,926 cases of intimate partner violence cases seen in Wisconsin emergency departments. It found most violence to be directed toward younger women.

Bonomi, A. E., Anderson, M. L., Reid, R. J., Carrell, D., Fishman, P. A., Rivara, F. P., & Thompson, R. S. (2007). Intimate partner violence and older women. *The Gerontologist, 47*(1) 34–41.
A survey of older women and their reports of exposure to violence throughout their lifetime and exposure within the past year highlights the need to include assessment for domestic violence in health assessments of elders.

Carnes, P. (1997). *The betrayal bond: Breaking free of exploitative relationships.* Deerfield Part, FL: Health Communications, Inc.
Traumatic bonding and intimate partner violence is explained.

Centers for Disease Control and Prevention. (2006). Physical dating violence among high school students—U.S., 2003. *Morbidity and Mortality Weekly Report (MMRW), 55*(19), 532–535.
This study reviewed data from a 2003 national survey of students in grades 9–12 who self-reported incidents of physical dating violence in the preceding 12 months.

Curry, M. A., Durham, L., Bullock, L., Bloom, T., & Davis, J. (2006). Nurse case management for pregnant women experiencing or at risk for abuse. *Journal of Obstetrics, Gynecological, and Neonatal Nursing, 35*(2), 181–192.
A multisite study of two groups of pregnant women receiving safety information concluded that the women experienced a significant reduction in stress.

Dowdell, E. B., Burgess, A. W., & Cavanaugh, D. J. (2009). Clustering of internet risk behaviors in middle school student population. *Journal of School Health, 79*(11): 547-53.
This article discusses online risk behaviors of both male and female middle school students.

Dowdell, E. B., Burgess, A. W., & Flores, J. R. (2011). Online social networking patterns among adolescents, young adults, and sexual offenders. *American Journal of Nursing, 111*(7) 28–36, quiz 37–38.

This article discusses research based upon self report surveys of middle school, high school and college students as well as adults who had been convicted of Internet sexual offences and/or hands on sexual offences to find patterns in Internet and social network exchange of sexual information between sexual predators and students.

The Duluth Project. (1987). *Power and control equality wheels*. Duluth, MN: Domestic Abuse Intervention Project, Minnesota Program Development, Inc. Retrieved from http://www.theduluthmodel.org/wheelgallery.php
Information regarding the use of wheel diagrams for power and control, equality, child abuse, nurturing, and the creator. The diagrams can be copied for educational purposes as long as they are credited to the Domestic Abuse Intervention Project. There are visual wheel diagrams available in different languages and a Muslim wheel developed by Dr. Shaufa Alkahteek to use to explain the power relationships in that culture.

International Council of Nursing. (2006). *Fact sheet on elder abuse*. Retrieved from http://www.icn.ch/matters_elder.htm
Information and policy statement on elder abuse and other topics are available from the International Council of Nursing.

McFarlane, J. M., Groff, J. Y., O'Brien, J. A., & Watson, K. (2006). Secondary prevention of intimate partner violence: A randomized control study. *Nursing Research, 55*(1), 52–61.
Women attending urban primary care clinics were offered a referral card or a 20-minute case management protocol. Both groups showed an increase in safety behaviors and a decrease in utilization of community resources.

National Center on Elder Abuse. (2005). *Elder abuse prevalence and incidence. National Center on Elder Abuse fact sheet*. Washington, DC: Author.
This fact sheet provides information on elder abuse.

Paris, C. E. B., Meier, E. D., Goldstein, T., Weiss, M., & Fein, E. D. (1995). Elder abuse and neglect: How to recognize warning signs and intervene. *Geriatrics, 50*(4), 47–52.
This article presents a case study to assist the reader in learning how to recognize and treat cases of elder abuse. The client is first seen in the emergency room. As the clinician assesses the victim, the reader learns how to detect elderly abuse and neglect.

Preidt, R. (2006, May 11). Sexual assaults. *Health Day*. News release. University of Illinois at Chicago.
This news release identified risk factors in sexual assault cases.

Priest, A. (2005, April). Student nurses for clean drinks. *Nursing BC, 37*(2), 7–11.
This article describes nursing students who organized a group for client education and advocacy concerning date rape drugs.

U.S. Department of Health and Human Services. (2011). *Affordable Care Act ensures women receive preventive services at no additional cost*. Retrieved from www.healthcare.gov/news/factsheets/2011/08/womensprevention08012011a.html
Fact sheet on preventive services for women including screening for intimate partner violence.

U.S. Department of Justice, Bureau of Justice Statistics. (2007). *National crime victimization survey*. Retrieved from http://www.bjs.ojp.usdoj.gov/index.cfm?ty=pbdetail&iid=1000
The Bureau of Justice statistics provides data regarding crimes and characteristics of victimization.

World Health Organization (WHO). (2006). *Preventing child maltreatment: A guide to taking action and generating evidence*. Geneva, Switzerland: Author.
This is an extensive report on violence against children.

Additional Resources

Baker, M. W. (2007). Elder mistreatment: Risk, vulnerability, and early mortality. *Journal of the American Psychiatric Nurses Association, 72*(6), 313–321.
Baker reviews the role of nurses in efforts to prevent elder abuse and assesses the relationship of geriatric symptoms and chronic stress.

Bremner, J. D., & Narayan, M. (1998). The effects of stress on memory and the hippocampus throughout the life cycle: Implications for childhood development and aging. *Developmental Psychopathology, 10*, 871–886.

Research on the long-term effects of trauma upon delayed memory recall and traumatic amnesia.

Carretta, C. M. (2008). Domestic violence: A worldwide exploration. *Journal of Psychiatric Nursing, 46*(3), 26–35.
This article reviews cultural aspects and incidence of domestic violence and the role of nurses in ensuring screening, disclosure, identification, and treatment.

Carrion, V. G., Weems, C. F., & Reiss, A. L. (2007). Stress predicts brain changes in children: A pilot longitudinal study on youth stress, post traumatic stress disorder and the hippocampus. *Pediatrics, 119*(3), 509–516.
This article reports on a longitudinal study of children exposed to maltreatment shows association between stress, cortisol levels and hippocampal changes.

Healthy People 2020 Summary of Objectives. (2009). *Healthy People 2020* Summary of Objectives: Intimate Partner Violence, 1–17. Retrieved from www.healthypeople.gov/2020/topicsobjectives2020/pdfs/Injury.pdf

Humphreys, J., & Campbell, J. C. (Eds.). (2010). *Family violence and nursing practice* (2nd ed.). New York, NY: Springer Publishing Company, LLC.
This text provides theoretical frameworks and standards of care for dealing with family, intimate partner, and elder violence, including abuse and danger assessment.

Jordan, C. E., Nietzel, M. T., Walker, R., & Logan, T. K. (2005). *Intimate partner violence: A clinical training guide for mental health professionals.* New York, NY: Springer.
This book is a guide to the assessment of violence and victimization, and interventions with victims and offenders.

LaViolette, A. D., & Barnett, O. W. (2002). *It could happen to anyone: Why battered women stay.* Thousand Oaks, CA: Sage.
This text discusses theories applicable to the subject. The authors use case histories to explain family violence and the cycle of abuse.

Martin, D. (1981). *Battered wives.* Volcano, CA: Volcano Press.
This is one of the earliest pieces of literature that focuses on the subject of domestic violence. It is considered to be a classic among practitioners who work with battered women. One section focuses on legal issues and survival tactics.

Podnieks, E., Kosberg, J. I., & Lowenstein, A. (Eds.). (2005). *Elder abuse: Selected papers from the World Congress on Family Violence.* San Diego, CA: Haworth Maltreatment and Trauma Press.
This book provides information regarding elder abuse and evidence-based research.

Reece, M. R., & Christian, C. (Eds.). (2008). *Child abuse: Medical diagnosis and management* (3rd ed.). Elk Grove, IL: American Academy of Pediatrics.
This book helps medical practitioners identify, evaluate, and treat the medical conditions related to child abuse. One section describes symptoms that can be mistaken as child abuse and sexual abuse. There is also a chapter devoted to documentation, reporting, and testifying in abuse cases.

Ristock, J. L. (Ed.). (2011). *Intimate partner violence in LQBTG lives.* New York, NY: Routledge.
This book surveys patterns in relationship violence.

Schofield, R. B. (2006). Office of Justice programs focusing on studying and preventing elder abuse. *Journal of Forensic Nursing, 2*(3), 150–153.
This article provides information on research on elder abuse, neglect, and exploitation.

Wang, J., Lin, J., & Lee, F. (2005). Psychological abusive behavior by those caring for the elderly in a domestic context. *Geriatric Nursing, 27*(5), 284–291.
This article reports on a study to identify possible risk factors for abusive behavior by caretakers.

Internet Resources

For a full suite of assignments and additional learning activities, use the access code located in the front of your book to visit this exclusive website: http://go.jblearning.com/mentalhealth. If you do not have an access code, you can obtain one at the site.

Part II

Mental Health Disorders and Conditions

Learning Objectives

After reading this chapter, you will be able to:

- Discuss how childhood communication disorders relate to childhood onset of psychiatric or behavioral disorders.
- Describe common child and adolescent behavioral disorders.
- Differentiate the symptoms of mood and affective disorders in children from those disorders in adults.
- Discuss the impact of early childhood trauma on a child's mental health.
- Identify nursing interventions for a child or adolescent with a psychiatric or behavioral disorder.
- Develop teaching plans for children with psychiatric or behavioral disorders and their families.

Key Terms

Attention-deficit/hyperactivity disorder (ADHD)

Bipolar disorder of childhood

Communication disorder

Conduct disorder

Encopresis

Enuresis

Expressive language disorder

Generalized anxiety disorder (GAD)

Individualized Education Program/Plan (IEP)

Learning disorders

Major depressive disorder

Obsessive-compulsive disorder (OCD)

Oppositional defiant disorder (ODD)

Panic attack

Pediatric autoimmune neuropsychiatric disorder associated with group A *Streptococcus* (PANDAS)

Pervasive developmental disorder

Reactive attachment disorder (RAD)

Selective mutism

Separation anxiety

Stuttering

Tourette's disorder (TD)

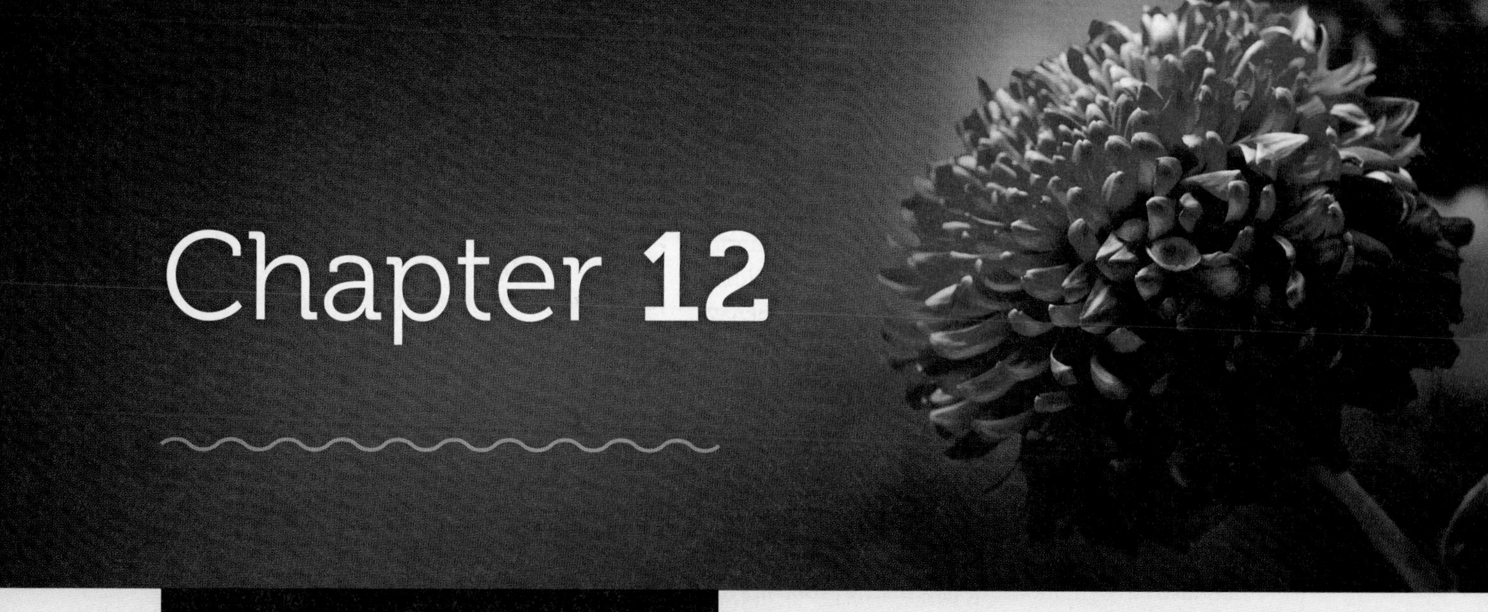

Disorders Diagnosed in Infancy, Childhood, or Adolescence

Bethany A. Murray and Karen A. Ballard

http://go.jblearning.com/mentalhealth 

For a full suite of assignments and additional learning activities, use the access code located in the front of your book to visit this exclusive website: http://go.jblearning.com/mentalhealth. If you do not have an access code, you can obtain one at the site.

Introduction

Infancy is the period from birth to approximately 12 months; childhood refers to the period from 1 year of age to approximately 13 years; and adolescence is the transitional period from puberty to adulthood, usually ending with high school graduation.

The Surgeon General of the United States of America has reported that as many as 20% of U.S. children suffer from a diagnosable mental health or behavior disorder sometime between the ages of 9 and 17 years (U. S. Department of Health and Human Services, 1999). The *Diagnostic and Statistical Manual of Psychiatric Disorders*, fourth edition, text revision (*DSM-IV-TR*; American Psychiatric Association [APA], 2002) has identified a number of disorders that are first seen in childhood. However, children may also have emotional or psychiatric problems that are more frequently diagnosed in adults. Childhood psychiatric illnesses may look similar to adult-onset disorders, or a child may present with significant differences in symptoms based on the child's level of cognitive, emotional, mental, and physical development. Similarly, although it might seem logical to assume that disorders arising first in infancy, childhood, or adolescence will persist into adulthood, there is very little evidence to support this. Problems in development such as mental retardation or autism will almost certainly continue into adulthood, whereas other problems, such as childhood anxiety, may be self-limiting and disappear by adolescence. However, many adults with psychiatric illnesses will report that they have had problems since childhood. Severe disorders such as schizophrenia are commonly recognized as having an average onset in mid to late adolescence (for further discussion of schizophrenia, refer to Chapter 16), although symptoms may begin in school-age children as well. Yung and McGorry (2004) identified three at-risk behaviors or mental states in early childhood that may be associated with adult-onset schizophrenia. These included abnormal social behaviors, cognitive problems, and delayed walking. These risk factors were even more significant when the child had a first-degree relative with a psychotic disorder.

Classification of Disorders

Current *DSM-IV-TR* classification of disorders usually first diagnosed in infancy, childhood, or adolescence include mental retardation (intellectual disabilities), learning disorders, motor skills disorders, communication disorders, pervasive developmental disorders, attention-deficit and disruptive-behavior disorders, feeding and eating disorders, tic disorders, elimination disorders, and other occurring disorders. Generally, childhood disorders are coded on Axis I except for mental retardation (intellectual disabilities), which is coded on Axis II (discussed in Chapter 26). Childhood disorders in this chapter are conceptually grouped into the following categories:

- Disorders related to development (expressive language disorder, phonological disorder, stuttering, Tourette's disorder, enuresis, encopresis)
- Disorders related to behavior (attention-deficit/hyperactivity disorder, oppositional defiant disorder, conduct disorder)
- Disorders related to anxiety (separation anxiety, selective mutism, generalized anxiety disorder, obsessive-compulsive disorder)
- Disorders related to trauma or abuse (reactive attachment disorder)
- Disorders related to mood (major depressive disorder, bipolar disorder)

In the proposed *DSM-5*, the APA is considering an increased focus on the importance of development in mental illness. Four areas of research are of particular significance for childhood disorders: clinical presentation, natural history, developmental psychopathology, and age at onset of the disorder (Pine, Costello, & Dahl, 2010). Some proposed childhood disorders, not currently in the *DSM-IV-TR*, include posttraumatic stress disorder in preschool children, disruptive mood dysregulation disorder, learning disorder, nonsuicidal self-injury, language impairment, late language emergence, social communication disorder, and voice disorder. Reactive attachment disorder will be divided into new childhood disorders and Rett's disorder, and expressive language disorder may be removed. In addition, the diagnostic age criteria for attention-deficit/hyperactivity disorder (ADHD) will be changed from requiring symptoms to be present before 7 years of age to before 12 years with the requirement for the number of presenting symptoms being decreased from 6 to 4 in some of the types of the disorder. Autism and Asperger's syndrome may become a unified autism spectrum disorder with a single set of criteria (APA, 2011).

Disorders Related to Development

Mental retardation, pervasive developmental disorder, autism, and Asperger's syndrome are frequently seen in the child mental healthcare setting and may occur along with psychiatric illnesses such as obsessive-compulsive disorder, anxiety disorders, attention-deficit/disorder, major depressive disorder, and bipolar disorder. The *DSM-IV-TR* provides criteria for differentiating these neurobiological disorders. Consult Chapter 26 of this text for a more thorough discussion of the prevalence, recognition, management, and nursing care of the child with a pervasive developmental disorder.

Learning Disorders

Learning disorders (learning disabilities) that involve reading, writing, or mathematical concepts are frequently encountered in the academic setting and are rarely thought of as a psychiatric problem. However, learning disabilities often present in mental health care as secondary or complicating variables to treatment. A learning disorder is diagnosed when an individual's achievement on a standardized test is substantially below that expected for age, schooling, and level of intelligence. Again, Chapter 26 of this text can be consulted for an in-depth discussion of the numbers and types of learning disorders identified in the *DSM-IV-TR*.

Communication and Language Disorders

Communication disorders that will be discussed here consist of expressive language disorder, phonological disorder, and stuttering. Diagnosis of an **expressive language disorder** requires that the child scores lower than expected on standardized tests that measure language development. While such a child generally understands language that is addressed to him, he does not talk very much. A phonological disorder is a failure to use developmentally expected speech sounds. **Stuttering** differs from phonological problems in that the pronunciation of the letters and words is not impaired, but there is a disturbance in the fluency and time patterning of the speech. Stuttering may be absent when reading aloud, singing, or talking to pets or toys. Environmental factors and regional dialects should be considered when assessing a child's speech (APA, 2002).

Incidence and Prevalence

Language delays, in particular expressive language disorders, are common in children under the age of 3 years (10–15%); however, by school age the prevalence drops to around 3–7% of the population. Phonological development problems are more prominent in males than in females and occur in about 2% of the population. Phonologic disorders in about three quarters of children spontaneously decrease by age 6. Stuttering is three times more common in males than in females and occurs in 1% of children prior to puberty (0.8% postpubescent) (APA, 2002).

Etiology and Physiology

Communication and language disabilities may be associated with other developmental delays (mental retardation, fragile X syndrome), or there may be no identifiable precipitants. Toxic insults such as prenatal drug or alcohol exposure may affect learning. Disorders may also be associated with brain injury (hypoxia, trauma) or poisonings (lead). Phonologic and speech problems are commonly seen in children with hearing loss and deafness (APA, 2002). Laboratory screening tests should be used to rule out underlying physical disorders. Communication and language delays cannot be identified or diagnosed on computerized axial tomography (CAT) scans, magnetic resonance imaging (MRI), positron emission tomography (PET), or X-rays.

Clinical Presentation

When evaluating a child's speech pattern, it is important to consider environmental factors, regional dialects, and hearing.

The child with an expressive language disorder will have difficulty answering questions and may seem to provide information that differs from that requested. In responding, the child may hesitate before speaking and then select words that are not quite accurate or may seem unusual. For example, when asked "Where does your father work?" the response may be "When you go to town, and there's a place there and people park there." Frequently, the child will demonstrate word-finding or vocabulary errors, a limited range of word choices, a limited amount of speech, difficulty acquiring new words, simplified or shortened sentences, use of unusual words or word order, omissions of parts of sentences, and a slow rate of language development that is inconsistent with intellectual capabilities. Phonological disorders are exhibited as errors of pronunciation. Common errors are mispronunciations of letters or substitutions of one sound for another (such as *t* for *k*). Lisping (pronouncing *th* for *s*) is also relatively common.

In stuttering, there may be frequent repetitions or prolongations of sounds, syllables, or words. Blocking (silences between words), broken words (pauses within a word), word substitutions, or other disturbances may be noted. The extent and intensity of the disturbance varies between situations and is often more severe when the individual is feeling under pressure or anxious. Motor movements such as eye blinking or head jerking may accompany stuttering (APA, 2002).

Differential Diagnosis

Expressive language disorders may exist alone or in combination with receptive language problems.

Expressive language disorders may exist alone or in combination with receptive language problems. An in-depth speech and language evaluation, often offered by universities or available through the public school system, will help to make this differentiation. Mental retardation and other **pervasive developmental disorders** may be present and should be assessed. Severe environmental neglect may produce language delays as well.

Clinical Course and Complications

An expressive language disorder is usually recognized by age 3 years. However, an acquired disorder may occur suddenly anytime following a traumatic injury to the brain. The majority of children improve significantly by adulthood; however, some may have symptoms as adults and subtle language difficulties will persist. Children are occasionally perceived as being oppositional, defiant, or inattentive by parents and may present for psychiatric evaluations for these symptoms. Approximately three-fourths of children with mild to moderate phonologic problems show normalization of the disorder by age 6. Stuttering may develop from around age 2–5 years over many months; it tends to be more insidious than other phonological problems and has some waxing and waning of symptoms. Most children (20–80%) recover spontaneously from stuttering before the age of 16 years (APA, 2002).

Communication and language disorders are associated with lowered self-esteem, negative self-image, peer problems (teasing, bullying), academic delays (which may lead to parental conflict), and social withdrawal. These disorders are also correlated with higher rates of attention problems and ADHD, mood disorders, and anxiety (APA, 2002).

Management and Treatment

Treatment of communication and language disabilities consists of a speech and language evaluation, academic (achievement) testing, individualized instruction or tutoring, and an **Individualized Education Program (IEP)**, sometimes referred to as a plan. Medication management is not helpful or appropriate. Speech therapy through the school system may be indicated for phonologic disorders and stuttering. Relaxation counseling can help individuals (children and adults) to live with stuttering.

Tourette's Disorder

Tourette's disorder (TD) or syndrome is a severe neurobiological disorder whose hallmarks are chronic, unpredictable, and unremitting vocal and motor tics (involuntary skeletal muscle spasms). Chronic tic symptoms can be extremely embarrassing to the individual and lead to fears of rejection or humiliation in social situations. Tourette's disorder is often accompanied by other psychiatric, developmental, or behavioral problems, which may include Asperger's syndrome or other social skills deficits, obsessive-compulsive disorder or traits, attention-deficit/hyperactivity disorder, learning disabilities, or mood disorders.

Incidence and Prevalence

Tourette's disorder occurs in approximately 4 percent of every 10,000 children in the United States. The average onset is between 7 and 10 years (National Institute of Neurological Disorders and Stroke [NINDS], 2011). More transient tic disorders occur in 15–20% of school-age children. Tourette's disorder occurs 3–4 times more often in boys than in girls, and it occurs in all ethnic groups (Coffey et al., 2000; NINDS, 2011). While TD can become a lifetime disorder, generally fewer than 20% of children with TD continue to experience a moderate level of the impairment into adulthood. Only fewer than 20% of persons with TD continue to experience a moderate level of impairment of global functioning by the age of 20 years (Bloch, et al., 2006).

Etiology and Physiology

The causes of TD are unclear. The disturbance is not due to the direct physiologic effects of a general medical or substance condition. An inherited susceptibility is suspected; genetic studies have also demonstrated that some forms of ADHD and obsessive-compulsive disorder (OCD) are related to TD (NINDS, 2011). Current research identifies abnormalities in certain brain regions, including the basal ganglia, frontal lobes and cortex, the interconnections among these regions, and the neurotransmitters—dopamine, serotonin, and norepinephrine (NINDS, 2011). Dopamine receptor hypersensitivity has been the primary hypothesis for TD and tic disorders due to the responsiveness of the motor and vocal tics to dopamine antagonists (haloperidol, risperidone, ziprasidone) and agonists (aripiprazole; Coffey, 2002). Tourette's disorder is undetectable on CAT, PET, or MRI scans. There are no laboratory tests to aid in making the diagnosis. The most promising research is in genetic studies (APA, 2002). Individuals with TD may also be at higher risk for other mental disorders such as depression or substance abuse; therefore, genetic counseling should include the potential for hereditary diseases in the family (NINDS, 2011).

Clinical Presentation

Common simple motor symptoms, sudden brief, repetitive movements involving limited number of muscle groups, associated with Tourette's disorder include eye blinking, facial scrunching or grimacing, neck jerking, head turning, tongue protrusion, and licking (**Figure 12-1**). Complex tics, distinct, coordinated patterns of movement involving several muscle groups, may involve stooping, walking, hopping, twirling, or other multistep activities, and sniffing or touching objects. Some motor tics may result in self-harm. Vocal tics may be expressed as grunts, squeaks, squeals, sniffs, snorts, coughs, barks, throat clearing, or whole words or phrases. Coprolalia, a complex vocal tic occurring in fewer than 10% of individuals with Tourette's disorder, involves the spontaneous uttering of obscenities (NINDS, 2011).

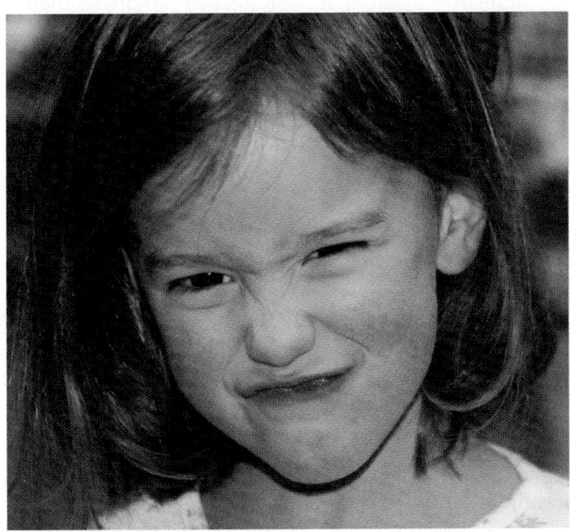

Figure 12-1 Facial tics are commonly associated with Tourette's disorder.

Differential Diagnosis

Tourette's disorder cannot be diagnosed when substances such as stimulant medications have been used or when a medical condition such as Huntington's chorea or viral encephalitis is present. Tourette's disorder symptoms must begin prior to the age of 18 years and the child must have both motor and vocal tics for at least a year (NINDS, 2011).

Tourette's disorder (TD) is a severe neurobiologic disorder consisting of a pattern of chronic motor and vocal tics.

Clinical Course and Complications

Tourette's disorder may be lifelong, or it may spontaneously remit. The severity, frequency, disruptiveness, and variability of the tics can wax and wane over time, and the characteristics of the tics can change without warning. Anxiety and excitement tend to exacerbate tics, making school performance demands difficult for a child with the disorder. TD does not impair the individual's intelligence.

Tourette's disorder has been associated with a number of other psychiatric problems, in particular anxiety disorders (25–40% incidence), attention-deficit/hyperactivity disorder (50–70% incidence), obsessive-compulsive disorder (40% have the disorder, up to 90% have traits), mood disorders such as major depressive disorder (up to 50% incidence), bipolar disorder (16% incidence), and other developmental disorders (20% incidence; Coffey, 2002). While the tic symptoms may abate with age, other disorders (depression, panic attacks, mood swings, and antisocial behaviors) may persist into adulthood (NINDS, 2011).

Coprolalia, a complex vocal tic occurring in less than 10% of individuals with Tourette's disorder, involves the spontaneous uttering of obscenities.

Management and Treatment

Children with TD often present a complicated clinical picture. Therapy is not indicated for the specific treatment of tic disorders or TD. Counseling is extremely useful for the comorbid conditions, especially when self-esteem problems and depression occur. Motor and vocal tics are not harmful and can be left untreated if they are mild and not bothersome to the child. More severe tics or tics that result in social ostracization should be managed with medications.

Medications are very beneficial in reducing the frequency and intensity of tics. Primary medication treatment should be with the alpha-adrenergic agonist medications clonidine (Catapres) and guanfacine

(Tenex), which have norepinephrine activity. Second-line choices include the new-generation atypical antipsychotics, which alter dopamine transmission in the brain. These include risperidone (Risperdal), aripiprazole (Abilify), olanzapine (Zyprexa), quetiapine (Seroquel), and ziprasidone (Geodon). Despite their established effectiveness, none of the alpha-adrenergic medications or new-generation antipsychotics has Food and Drug Administration (FDA) approval for TD. Older medications including pimozide (Orap) and haloperidol (Haldol) are FDA approved and are proven to successfully suppress tics; however, side effects (sedation, weight gain, cognitive dulling) occur often with these drugs. Stimulants (methylphenidate, amphetamine) tend to exacerbate or worsen motor and vocal tics (Coffey, 2002; NINDS, 2011).

Normal children soil their underwear; this is not necessarily a pathologic or psychiatric symptom. Daytime control is usually attained before nighttime control, and bowel control is usually attained before full bladder control.

Enuresis and Encopresis

Two types of elimination disorders, encopresis and enuresis, are identified in the *DSM-IV-TR*. **Encopresis** is the involuntary (or voluntary) passage of feces at inappropriate times or in inappropriate places. In primary encopresis, the child has never obtained bowel control. Primary encopresis may be associated with other developmental delays (mental retardation) or with inadequate toilet training and/or parental neglect. Secondary encopresis occurs when a previously bowel-trained child develops fecal incontinence, usually between the ages of 5 and 8 years. Secondary encopresis is more often related to psychosocial stress such as a parental divorce or birth of a sibling, physical or sexual abuse, or other distressing events. To be diagnosed as a psychiatric or behavioral disturbance, medical causes must first be ruled out. A nursing history should include consideration of issues such as history of toilet training, discipline, family conflict, abuse, or molestation. Encopresis can result in in embarrassment and teasing by other children and therefore be socially devastating to a child (APA, 2002).

Enuresis is the involuntary (or voluntary) passage of urine at inappropriate times or in inappropriate places. Enuresis is subdivided into nocturnal only, diurnal only, and both nocturnal and diurnal subtypes. Enuretic episodes must occur at least twice a week for 3 months or more in a child who is age 5 or older to meet the diagnosis requirements. The amount of impairment associated with enuresis depends on the age of the child, type of wetting, and how the wetting impacts peer and family relationships.

Incidence and Prevalence

Approximately 1% of 5-year-old boys have encopresis, with the disorder being more prevalent in males than

Evidence-Based Practice

Coffey looked at 156 individuals ages 5–20 years diagnosed with Tourette's disorder for correlations between comorbid conditions and psychiatric hospitalizations. They found hospitalization rates of 12% in the study group. Illness morbidity was strongly associated with mood disorder comorbidity (major depressive disorder, bipolar disorder), more so than with the frequency or severity of the motor and vocal tics. The researchers concluded that major depressive disorder and bipolar disorder, in the presence of Tourette's syndrome disorder, were robust predictors of psychiatric hospitalization (Coffey et al., 2000). This information is important to the healthcare practitioner when assessing a client with Tourette's disorder. A thorough history should be obtained, paying particular attention to the possibility of depression, suicidal thoughts or other self-harm behaviors, aggression, severe moodiness, explosive outbursts, or other symptoms of a mood disorder. More intensive services may be needed when this combination of symptoms is present.

The National Institute of Neurological Disorders and Stroke is responsible for supporting and conducting research on the brain and central nervous system. Current knowledge about Tourette's disorder is being obtained from studies on genetics, neuroimaging, neuropathology, clinical trials, and epidemiology and clinical science. There are a number of epidemiologic studies investigating the relationship between TD and autoimmune brain injury associated with group A, beta-hemolytic streptococcal infections. Mell, Davis, and Owens (2005) reported that children with TD, tic disorders, and OCD were more likely than control subjects in the study to have had a prior streptococcal infection in the 3 months before onset of symptoms, with children who had multiple such infections in the 12 months before onset having a significant increased risk for developing TD. Parents need to be counseled about the importance of treating this type of infection for many different health reasons, including the potential for developing a pediatric autoimmune neuropsychiatric disorder associated with a streptococcal infection (PANDAS).

in females. Prevalence rates for enuresis are relatively high; they are 5–10% of children age 5 years, 3–5% of children ages 5–10 years, and around 1% of children ages 15 years or older. Seventy-five percent of all children with primary enuresis have a first-degree biological relative who has had the disorder (APA, 2002).

Etiology and Physiology

Encopresis is often the result of constipation or impaction, which may be due to psychologic stress (anxiety, fear, defiance) or illnesses such as dehydration. Painful stool passage will predispose the child to avoidance behavior, which will in turn increase the withholding and constipation (APA, 2002). Primary encopresis may be associated with gastrointestinal disorders, or it may lead to severe stool retention and impaction. Children will complain of nausea and stomach pain when this occurs.

Enuresis can be the result of a urologic malformation (shortened urethra) or a urinary tract infection. While there appears to be a strong genetic component, for most children with enuresis, a specific etiologic factor cannot be determined. In an epidemiologic study of nocturnal enuresis and urinary incontinence, there were significant associations demonstrated between parental and child nocturnal enuresis and parental and child urinary incontinence; specifically the odds ratio for nocturnal enuresis was 3.28 times higher in maternal and 1.85 higher in paternal nocturnal enuresis (von Gontard, Heron, & Joinson, 2011). Regardless, it is important to assess for urologic, developmental, psychosocial, and sleep-related causes for both conditions (American Academy of Child and Adolescent Psychiatry [AACAP], 2004).

Clinical Presentation

The essential feature of encopresis is the passing of feces (either voluntarily or involuntarily) into inappropriate places (clothing, closets, floor, or toy box). To be diagnosed as encopresis, the behavior must occur at least once a month for 3 months or longer in a child over the age of 4. Children with enuresis will have voiding accidents (either involuntary or intentional) during the day, at night, or both several times a week for 3 months or longer. The child must be over the age of 5 to make this diagnosis.

Differential Diagnosis

Medical causes must always be ruled out for both encopresis and enuresis before psychologic treatment is initiated. Encopresis cannot be diagnosed in the presence of other medical disorders that are associated with constipation, and the disorder cannot be diagnosed when it is due to the direct effects of a substance such as a laxative. Enuresis can be diagnosed when medical disorders are present (e.g., bladder infections, neurogenic bladder) but only if the child was previously continent of urine and developed a secondary incontinence.

Clinical Course and Complications

Encopresis can persist with intermittent exacerbations for years. It can be improved with psychologic counseling (secondary types), parent education, and bowel retraining programs. Enuresis occurs more often in children with attention-deficit/hyperactivity disorder, developmental delays, or sleep disorders (sleepwalking, sleep terrors). Enuresis is less related to psychologic distress than is encopresis, and it often spontaneously remits. Spontaneous remission rates for these conditions are around 5–10% by adolescence (APA, 2002). Both enuresis and encopresis can severely limit a child's social development, can cause negative self-esteem in the child, and can result in parental disapproval, anger, resentment, and rejection.

Management and Treatment

It is imperative to address both the self-esteem of the child and the parents' embarrassment in any management program. Treatment for encopresis involves bowel-retraining programs. The child is usually put on a daily laxative such as mineral oil and may also be given a fiber supplement. Parents should be educated about high-fiber diets that include fruit juices, whole fruits, vegetables, and whole-grain cereals. The parents should toilet the child on a regular basis, usually right after breakfast, asking the child to sit without straining for several minutes (not more than 5 minutes at a time). A set of clean clothes should be kept at school for the child. Alerting the school nurse, classroom teacher, and school aide of the problem may help to diminish some of the social and personal embarrassment associated with encopresis. Prior to beginning the program, parents should be counseled to never ridicule the child for lack of control, threaten to tell peers, or deprive the child of peer, school, social, or family activities because of wetting or soiling.

The essential feature of encopresis is the passing of feces either voluntarily or involuntarily into inappropriate places (clothing, closets, floor, or toy box). Children with enuresis have voiding accidents either involuntary or intentionally during the day (diurnal type), at night (nocturnal type), or both.

Psychological counseling for the child and family, including an assessment for physical or sexual abuse, is helpful in determining what psychosocial stressors

Clinical Example: Disorders of Development

Billy is an 8-year-old boy referred by his pediatrician for the evaluation and management of multiple motor and vocal tics, aggressive behaviors, school failure, poor social skills, and intermittent nocturnal bedwetting. During the assessment, the nurse notes that he gets overly concerned with the rules at school, and he doesn't seem to be able to differentiate between friendly joking by peers and being made fun of. His mother reports that he has attacked peers on the playground several times, and spends more time in the office than in the classroom. Academically, Billy is unable to read words that are longer than three or four letters, but he has already memorized his multiplication tables. He passed the math portion of the fall ISTEP (standardized test) but has failed the language portion. His full-scale IQ was tested at 85, but the tester noted a vast discrepancy between language and performance scores. At home, Billy tells his parents that he is stupid and that no one likes him. He demonstrates a variety of motor tics including eye blinking, head jerking to the right, and sticking out his tongue. He also makes chirping noises and grunts. Billy is diagnosed with Tourette's disorder, reading disorder, enuresis (nocturnal), and is ruled out for childhood depression. He is started on Risperdal (risperidone) 0.25 mg tid to treat both the tics and aggression, and he is given DDAVP 0.1 mg tablets to take at bedtime for the enuresis. Additionally, his family is referred to a Tourette's disorder support group in the community and scheduled with a child and family therapist and advised to advocate for an IEP (Individualized Education Program) at school, which includes a smaller, more self-contained classroom setting to minimize peer conflicts, an individualized reading tutorial, and more predictable routines and structure.

may be present and to help the family to manage the emotions aroused by the toileting accidents. Once medical causes are ruled out, the treatment of enuresis is usually a combination of medications and behavior modification. Medications used include DDAVP (desmopressin), a synthetic antidiuretic hormone; Detrol (tolterodine) or Ditropan (oxybutynin chloride), used to treat adult incontinence; and Tofranil (imipramine), a tricyclic antidepressant. DDAVP is available orally or in a nasal spray (one spray in each nostril). Detrol and Ditropan are also oral preparations and may be given during the day or at bedtime. Imipramine is only available orally and is usually given at bedtime in low doses. Imipramine at doses higher than 20 mg places the child at risk for slowed cardiac conduction, thus an EKG tracing is advised during follow-up visits.

Two types of behavior management are useful for treating enuresis. Parents may purchase a pad that sets off an alarm when it becomes wet, which is designed to wake the child, prompting use of the toilet. Parents can set an alarm clock and check on the child at increasingly earlier hours nightly until they find the point at which the bed becomes wet. On subsequent nights, they wake the child prior to that wetting time and escort the child to the bathroom. Additionally, it is prudent to restrict fluids within an hour of bedtime and to ask the child to urinate before retiring. Pull-up diapers at night may be acceptable in young children, but they can be emotionally traumatic for the older child. Diurnal, or daytime, wetting is best treated by toileting routines of sending the child to the bathroom every 2–3 hours (AACAP, 2004; Bottomley, 2011).

Critical Thinking Question

What are some normal or typical childhood activities that might be more difficult for a child who has a developmental disorder? What modifications might be made so that the child with a developmental disorder can have a more rewarding social experience?

Disorders Related to Behavior

Perhaps the most commonly seen presenting complaint of parents or teachers is behavior problems. Children, more than adults, are likely to act out in a variety of ways when under stress, which may include challenges in the academic setting. A behavior problem can be minor such as repeatedly bothering other kids, talking out in class, or running in the hallways, or it can be quite significant, such as throwing furniture, kicking or hitting others, screaming for long periods, threatening self-harm, or running away. The clinician is charged with examining the behavior and its implications for the child in the home, school, and social settings. A behavior in and of itself does not provide much information as to the cause or diagnosis of the child until it is taken in context with developmental age, family circumstances, and other environmental or medical factors. The most commonly observed behavior disorders in the child/adolescent mental health setting include attention-deficit/hyperactivity disorder, oppositional defiant disorder, and conduct disorder.

Attention-Deficit/Hyperactivity Disorder

Attention-deficit/hyperactivity disorder (ADHD) is the most frequently encountered psychiatric diagnosis in children. ADHD has been described in the literature since the 1930s, although terminology has changed over time. Early diagnoses included minimal brain disease or dysfunction, because it was felt that ADHD symptoms were similar to behaviors seen in individuals with central nervous system injuries. Since that time, ADHD has been called hyperactive child syndrome (1950s), hyperkinetic reaction of childhood (1968), then attention-deficit disorder (ADD) or attention-deficit/hyperactivity disorder (ADHD). In 1984, the *DSM-IV* further defined the diagnosis, stating that there is only one ADHD, but subtypes include with hyperactivity, without hyperactivity, or combined presentation (APA, 2002).

Many ADHD symptoms are developmentally normal at certain ages, which contribute to much of the difficulty in making the diagnosis. For example, very young children are talkative, impulsive, and very active. Tired children are inattentive and have poor concentration. Excited children are distractible. A diagnosis of ADHD can only be made when the symptoms are determined to be at a level that is greater than expected for the average child of the same age and in similar circumstances.

Incidence and Prevalence

According to the Centers for Disease Control and Prevention (CDC) (2011), as of 2007, approximately 9.5% of children (5.4 million) aged 4–17 years in the United States have been diagnosed with ADHD. Boys, at 13.2%, were more likely than girls, at 5.6%, to have ADHD. As of 2007, 66.3% of children (2.7 million) with ADHD (4–17 years) were receiving pharmacologic treatment for the disorder with children 11–17 years more likely than those 4–10 years of age to be taking medication, and boys were 2.8 times more likely than girls to be on medication (CDC, 2011). Using a cost of illness framework and a prevalence rate of 5%, it has been estimated that the annual societal cost of ADHD in children and adolescents is between $36 and $52.4 billion in the United States (Pelham, Foster, & Robb, 2007).

Etiology and Physiology

The cause of ADHD is not known. It has been found to be more common among first-degree biological relatives, and clinicians note that many ADHD children have at least one ADHD parent. Molecular genetic studies point to the involvement of the dopamine receptor and transporter (DATI) genes in this disorder with some genes such as DATI appearing to affect the individual sensitivity to environmental etiologic factors (Millichap, 2008). Overall, the gene–environment interface seems to be particularly involved in ADHD.

In some children, there may be a history of child abuse or neglect, lead or other toxin exposures, brain infections, prenatal drug or alcohol exposure, or mental retardation. Prematurity, low birth weight, and maternal nicotine dependence have been associated with ADHD, though there is no clear research evidence to support these correlations (APA, 2002). There are no laboratory tests or radiologic exams that are used in making the diagnosis of ADHD. PET scans have been used to demonstrate some changes in brain activity in children with ADHD, though no clear information yet exists. ADHD is more likely to occur in children and adolescents who have brain injuries or other psychiatric/behavioral disorders.

Clinical Presentation

The inattentive features of ADHD consist of persistent difficulties in maintaining attention or focus, high distractibility, difficulty in getting organized, forgetfulness, losing things, poor listening skills, and reluctance to engage in any activities that require mental effort, such as homework (**Figure 12-2**). The impulse/hyperactive subtype is characterized by higher than usual levels of impulsivity, hyperactivity, poor judgment, a lack of patience (such as when taking turns), interrupting or intruding on others, talking excessively, restlessness, and running about or climbing excessively (APA, 2002).

Children with ADHD are often described as constant engines. These children have trouble sitting quietly. They are frequently running and often are impulsive, hurtful towards others, quick tempered, disorganized, prone to accidents, unpopular, loners, and poor students.

Features that are not direct symptoms of ADHD but are associated with the disorder include low frustration tolerance, temper outbursts, emotional lability or moodiness, stubbornness, bossiness, demands that needs be met immediately, and significant academic

Figure 12-2 The inattentive features of ADHD can make it difficult to pay attention during school.

impairment in the absence of any other learning disorders. Lost recess time, in-school suspensions, frequent visits to the principal's office, and suspensions and expulsions may be seen, which serve to further interrupt the learning process. Individuals with the predominantly inattentive type have fewer behavior problems, but they tend to be withdrawn, socially passive, poor school performers, and neglected by peers (APA, 2002).

Differential Diagnosis

Physical examinations should be conducted to rule out other causes of hyperactivity (e.g., thyroid disease) or mood lability (e.g., type 1 diabetes mellitus). A parent's history is the best source of diagnostic information because most parents first observe ADHD symptoms when the child is a toddler, although most treatment options begin at age 6. Other psychiatric disorders such as depression or social anxiety may mimic the inattentive components of ADHD.

Clinical Course and Complications

Most parents report increased motor activity when the child is a toddler. The diagnosis is usually made

CASE STUDIES Joey

Joey is a 10-year-old boy who is being treated by his pediatrician for attention-deficit/hyperactivity disorder. He is in the fifth grade but is reading at the third-grade level due to his problems with staying focused and paying attention to what he is reading. He has been taking dextroamphetamine (Adderall XR) 30 mg every morning for about 3 years.

Joey was admitted to the child behavioral unit of the local hospital after he became agitated and aggressive toward his teacher and other children in the school. He started to scream and curse, threw his books across the room, and overturned the desks.

The nurse doing the admission assessment interviewed both Joey and his parents and obtained the following information: Joey has been arguing and defiant at home for several months. His temper ignites quickly, and once angered, he loses all sense of reason and will damage property or attempt to hurt his parents and siblings. It seems to take him hours to calm down. His parents are fed up with his behavior and have been seeing a counselor for marital therapy because they are fighting with one another over how to handle him. There are three younger children at home, and Joey's mother fears for their safety as well. Joey is failing in school because he is in the principal's office nearly every day for acting out. The school is considering expelling him; the parents would have to provide home schooling if this occurs.

The admitting nurse noted that Joey is in the 10th percentile of weight for his age group and is in the 85th percentile for height. His mother noted that Joey is too angry to eat breakfast, and his medication causes him to have a loss of appetite at lunchtime. He eats some dinner with the family, but he prefers junk food and high-sugar-content foods. He throws fits if his parents do not provide what he wants.

The nurse identifies the following problem list:

- Aggressive to others and destructive of property
- Unpredictable and prolonged outbursts
- Poor control of impulses
- Poor attention span, focus, and concentration
- Failing in school
- Problems getting along with parents/siblings/peers
- Not gaining weight as expected due to medication side effects

Some nursing diagnoses that can be utilized in planning for the care of a child with attention-deficit/hyperactivity disorder include impaired nutrition related to medication side effects and poor eating habits, as evidenced by body weight in the 10th percentile for age/height; interrupted family processes related to the child's out-of-control behaviors, as evidenced by the parents' report of marital conflict; and risk for other-directed violence related to poor impulse control, as evidenced by unpredictable and prolonged outbursts.

Nursing Care Plan Attention-Deficit/Hyperactivity Disorder

Nursing Diagnosis 1: Risk for violence (self-directed or other-directed) related to impaired neurologic development as evidenced by history of aggressive behavior

Nursing Diagnosis 2: Impaired social interaction related to disturbed relationship with parents as evidenced by difficulty making friends

Nursing Diagnosis 3: Impaired parenting related to disturbance in parental attachment as evidenced by behavioral disorder

Expected Outcomes	Interventions	Evaluations
• Child will not harm others.	• Assess for triggers that typically induce outbursts in client. Most outbursts are associated with specific triggers, and identifying them may help to prevent problems. • Identify nonverbal behaviors that precede aggression. Increasing anxiety can be seen as pacing, restlessness, fleeting eye contact, or loud voice tone.	• Child does not harm others or destroy property. • Outbursts are reduced to less than once per week.
• Child will talk about how he is feeling to others and will express his anger appropriately.	• Teach child other ways to express feelings (drawing, writing, talking). Children may lack the innate ability to verbalize their feelings and can benefit from being given tools to do so. • Teach child physical means to help displace anger (exercise) as increased stress hormones (e.g., fight-or-flight response) may be alleviated through vigorous physical activity. • Maintain a calm, nonconfrontational approach as responding to anger with more anger or agitation will worsen the behavior.	• Child is writing or drawing pictures in his daily journal. • Child asks to shoot baskets in the gymnasium when he is feeling upset, and identifies riding his bicycle at home as an activity that he can do.
• Parents will identify ways to cope effectively with child's behaviors including community support networks.	• Assess family functioning and the presence of any pathology in family members as parental depression may significantly impact the ability to manage family dynamics. • Educate parents as to child's diagnosis and typical behaviors that they may see as understanding that the child has a brain-based disorder that he cannot control may help to reduce some blaming by the parents. Learning about the disorder will help parents be better able to advocate for their child. • Teach parents how to structure the home environment more predictably as providing external routines and structure reduces anxiety for a child who lacks internal self-control.	• Parents are both fully involved in learning about the child's diagnosis and treatment. • Parents can identify behaviors that will not be tolerated and agree on consequences for these behaviors. • Family maintains a balanced structure of work time, play time, and so on, and schedules meals, bedtime routines, etc.
• Parents will implement behavior management techniques for ADHD children.	• Teach parents how to use reward and consequence-based behavior management techniques as behavior management techniques will act to promote positive, adaptive behaviors and extinguish maladaptive patterns.	• Parents utilize star charts and identify behaviors that will be rewarded.
	• Provide the parents with referral information (e.g., ADHD support group) as families benefit from getting advice and suggestions or making friends with other families having similar problems.	• Parents attend at least one ADHD support group.

(Continues)

Nursing Care Plan **Attention-Deficit/Hyperactivity Disorder *(Continued)***

	• Refer parents and children for family therapy as family therapy can help to restructure the power and control of the family system, and empower the parents to feel that they have taken back management of their family life.	• Parents make and keep an appointment with a family therapist.
• Child will gain weight to at least the 50th percentile for height and age.	• Teach parents to ensure that the child is provided a full breakfast and adequate time to eat it in the morning (this may involve waking him up earlier), pack a nutritious lunch and afternoon snack, and provide the child with a high-calorie, high-nutrition bedtime snack (e.g., peanut butter sandwich with whole milk). • Provide Boost, Pediasure, or other nutritional supplements daily, or mix Carnation Instant Breakfast with whole milk for client daily as supplements will add 240–360 calories daily. • Put the child on a daily multivitamin as a vitamin supplement will help the child to get necessary nutrients that he is missing in his diet.	• Child is eating a wider range of foods. • Child gets a bedtime snack incorporated into his routine every night. • Parents are providing more nutritious meals, snacks, and supplements.
• Parents report the child is making better food choices.	• Teach parents to role-model good eating habits (e.g., family dinners, a variety of fresh fruits and vegetables, and minimal sugary snacks or colas) as the child will feel like a part of the family and will eat more nutritiously if the entire family is eating healthier. • Consult with the prescribing practitioner to determine if medication can be tailored or adjusted to reduce anorexia side effects as other, equally efficacious, ADHD medications may be used that have less appetite suppression as a side effect. • Check weight once a week on the same day of the week to monitor progress as children should gain a pound of body weight or more every month.	• Child returns to at least 50th percentile for body weight.

Visit http://go.jblearning.com/mentalhealth for additional care plans and exercises.
Source: Adapted from Ackley & Ladwig (2010).

once the child enters the school system around age 4 or 5 years. Children with ADHD, predominantly inattentive subtype, may not be identified until later, when teachers note that the child's intelligence and abilities are not consistent with academic performance. The hyperactive and impulsive symptoms of ADHD often change or attenuate through adolescence and young adulthood, although the inattentiveness and poor concentration symptoms tend to remain more constant (APA, 2002). As late as the early 1970s, ADHD was thought to occur only in childhood, but we now know that adult ADHD prevalence rates are around 4.4% of the population (Kessler, Adler, & Barkley, 2005).

Approximately half of the children diagnosed with ADHD will also have oppositional or defiant behaviors, or conduct disorders, and almost one third will have another psychiatric/behavioral disorder. The most common comorbid conditions seen are oppositional defiant disorder, conduct disorder, anxiety disorders, mood disorders (both major depressive disorder and bipolar disorder), learning disorders, tic disorders including Tourette's disorder, and communication disorders (APA, 2002).

Evidence-Based Practice

The National Institutes of Health (NIH) and National Institute of Mental Health (NIMH) supported the Multimodal Treatment Study of Children with ADHD, published as *NIMH Research on Treatment for Attention Deficit Hyperactivity Disorder (ADHD)* in 1999. The study examined 579 children between the ages of 7 and 9.9 years over a 14-month period, all of whom had a diagnosis of attention-deficit/hyperactivity disorder. The study compared and examined four treatment modalities: medication alone (stimulant medications were used), medication plus behavioral therapy, behavioral therapy alone, and community-based (nonpsychiatric) care. The study found that 56% of the children who received medication alone improved significantly, as compared to 60% of the children with medication plus behavioral therapy, 45% of the children with behavioral therapy but no medications, and 36% of the children cared for by primary care providers or in support group programs (community-based care; NIMH, 1999).

The Multimodal Study of ADHD treatment provides good guidelines for evidence-based practice. Well over half of ADHD children improved with medications and only 4% of children on medications did better when behavioral therapy was in place. This seems to suggest that utilizing medications is an integral part of the treatment of ADHD and should not be minimized or ignored by the clinician.

Pressman and colleagues (2006) examined family environmental factors and their relationship to ADHD in a study of 220 families with an ADHD child. They reported strong links between increased functional impairment in children with ADHD and high family conflict, low family overall achievement, and low family organization.

Research such as Pressman's could lead the nurse to hypothesize that chaotic, highly conflicted, and disorganized families may contribute to more dysfunction in ADHD children. Additionally, because there is a high degree of familial ADHD, functioning in families with ADHD parents might be lower than in families without an ADHD parent, a potential area for future research.

Management and Treatment

The treatment of ADHD consists of parent education, teaching the child internal controls and more acceptable behaviors, behavior management and coaching, reinforcing structure (routines) in the child's environment, strengthening peer and family relationships, environmental modifications, academic testing, evaluations for other psychiatric or learning disorders, individualized educational programs or plans (IEPs), and medications.

Medication interventions can significantly reduce ADHD symptoms and lead to a dramatic improvement in functioning. Stimulants are highly effective and are considered the first-line treatment. These drugs work by delaying the release of dopamine from the neurotransmitters in the brain, thus slowing or regulating chemical conduction at the neuron level. Some children tolerate one type of stimulant better than another. Stimulant medications work within 30 minutes, and are completely metabolized and eliminated by the body in the same day. They provide considerable flexibility in dosing; some parents choose to utilize them on school days only. Side effects to stimulant medications (even at therapeutic doses) include jitteriness, stomach upset, decreased appetite, and insomnia. Rarely do seizures occur. Weight and height, blood pressure, and heart rate should be checked at each follow-up appointment. Indications that the medication level is too high include mental dulling, flat emotions, agitation, or moodiness. Overdose can result in hallucinations, psychosis, tachycardia, and cardiac arrhythmias. Occasionally, children develop motor or vocal tics, which may require dose adjustments or additional medications. Laboratory testing is not necessary when utilizing stimulant medications because dosages are determined based on clinical response and side effects. Stimulant medications fall into two groups: methylphenidate based and amphetamine based. **Table 12-1** provides more information on the number and types of stimulant preparations currently available (Spencer, Biederman, & Wilens, 2000).

Children with ADHD and their families need ongoing support to cope with the multiple disorganizing symptoms of the disorder, the medication therapy, and the changing family dynamics.

Strattera (atomoxetine) treats ADHD in a different way. Atomexetine is a norepinephrine-reuptake inhibitor; it slows down the transmission of norepinephrine through the neuronal pathways of the brain. Strattera is highly effective in reducing hyper-

Table 12-1 Stimulant Medications for Attention-Deficit/Hyperactivity Disorder

Methylphenidate-Based	Dosage	Delivery	Duration	Special Comments
Ritalin (methylphenidate hydrochloride)	5–60 mg daily	Oral tablets	3–4 hours	Administered: tid or qid Age: 6 and older
Ritalin SR, Ritalin LA (methylphenidate hydrochloride)	5–60 mg daily	Oral capsules; Extended release	6–8 hours	Administered: qam or bid Age: 6 and older
Metadate ER, Metadate CD (methylphenidate hydrochloride)	5–60 mg daily	Oral capsules; Extended release	6–8 hours	Administered: qam or bid Age: 6 and older
Concerta (methylphenidate hydrochloride)	18, 27, 36, 54 mg tablets	Oral tablets	12 hours	Administered: qam, occasionally repeated at noon Age: 6 and older
Daytrana (methylphenidate)	10, 15, 20, 30 mg	Transdermal skin patch	9 hours	Administered: By application in the morning; removed after 9 hours. Age: 6 and older
Methylin solution (methylphenidate hydrochloride)	5–60 mg daily	Oral liquid syrup	3–4 hours	Administered: tid or qid Age: 6 and older
Focalin (dexmethylphenidate)	2.5–30 mg daily	Oral tablets	3–4 hours	Administered: tid Age: 6 and older
Focalin XR (dexmethylphenidate)	2.5–30 mg daily	Oral capsules; Extended release	6–8 hours	Administered: qam or bid Age: 6 and older
Amphetamine-Based	**Dosage**	**Delivery**	**Duration**	**Special Comments**
Adderall (dextroamphetamine and amphetamine)	5–60 mg daily	Oral tablets	4–6 hours	Administered: bid Age: 3 and older
Adderall XR (dextroamphetamine and amphetamine)	5–60 mg daily	Oral capsules; Extended release	12 hours	Administered: qam Age: 6 and older
Dexedrine (dextroamphetamine)	5–60 mg daily	Oral capsules	4 hours	Administered: tid Age: 3 and older
Dexedrine Spansules (dextroamphetamine)	Up to 60 mg daily	Oral capsules; Extended release	8 hours	Administered: qam or bid Age: 3 and older
Vyvanse (lisdexamfetamine)	30 mg daily in the morning	Oral capsules	8 hours	Administered: qam Age: 6 and older

Source: Information taken from Spencer, T., Biederman, J., & Wilens, T. (2000). Pharmacotherapy of attention deficit hyperactivity disorder. *Psychopharmacology, 9*(1), 77–97; National Institute of Mental Health. (2011). Attention deficit hyperactivity disorder (ADHD): Medications. Retrieved from http://www.nimh.nih.gov/health/publications/attention-deficit-hyperactivity-disorder/; and Drugs.com. (2011). Vyvanse. Retrieved from http://www.drugs.com/pro/vyvanse.html

active-impulsive symptoms, and moderately effective in improving the inattention symptoms. It may also be useful for modulating the moodiness and irritability experienced by some children. Strattera is not immediately effective; it requires a titration over 4–5 days, and then it takes 2–4 weeks to achieve a steady state. Dosing is based on the weight of the child. Common side effects reported include stomach upset and insomnia. Rare side effects associated with Strattera include suicidal thoughts (which requires a Food and Drug Administration black box warning) and liver problems. The norepinephrine activity may precipitate mania in an undiagnosed bipolar client, but is helpful in an ADHD child with comorbid anxiety. Strattera is not associated with the development of motor or vocal tics (Spencer, Biederman, & Wilens, 2000).

Many other medications are also used off-label to treat the symptoms of ADHD. These include the alpha-adrenergic medications, clonidine (Catapres) and guanfacine (Tenex), which act by reducing norepinephrine in the frontal part of the brain; older tricyclic antidepressants, which are potent norepinephrine-reuptake inhibitors; and newer generation antipsychotics, which have dopamine blocking activities. Provigil (modafinil) is under FDA study for ADHD due to its ability to improve wakefulness, attention, and concentration in adults, and its low side effect profile in adults and in early child studies. Clonidine, guanfacine, and modafinil will not induce or contribute to the development of motor or vocal tics, and they are not associated with weight loss or insomnia (Spencer, Biederman, & Wilens, 2000).

Oppositional Defiant Disorder

Oppositional defiant disorder (ODD) is characterized by a recurrent pattern of negative, defiant, and/or hostile behavior toward authority figures and sometimes peers to a degree that is not developmentally appropriate. Parents of children with ODD describe them as having a bad attitude, as being stubborn or unwilling to compromise, or as being very disagreeable and difficult to live with.

Incidence and Prevalence

Rates of oppositional defiant disorder have been reported as low as 2% and as high as 16%, depending on the population sampled and the methodology used. The behavior is more common in males than females before puberty; after puberty, it occurs equally (APA, 2002).

Etiology and Physiology

Oppositional defiant disorder has no clear cause. When it occurs in males, it has been shown to be more prevalent in those who had problematic temperaments or high motor activity in the preschool years. ODD appears to be more common in families in which at least one parent has a history of mood disorder, oppositional defiant disorder, conduct disorder, ADHD, antisocial personality, or a substance-related disorder. ODD is also more common in families with a high degree of marital discord (APA, 2002). There are no specific physiological findings described in the child with an oppositional defiant disorder.

Clinical Presentation

Children with ODD often lose their temper, argue frequently with adults, defy rules or refuse to comply with requests of adults, deliberately annoy others or blame others for their own mistakes, tend to be resentful and angry, and can be spiteful or vindictive. They may even be unhappy about the high degree of conflict in their lives, but seem to be unable to control their behaviors (APA, 2002).

Differential Diagnosis

Oppositionality and defiance may be a result of an atypical episode of a major depressive disorder, particularly in adolescents. Commonly, ODD symptoms can be confused with conduct disorder or bipolar disorder of childhood as well. ODD occurs more often in the presence of ADHD; a careful documentation of the child's symptoms will aid in making an accurate diagnosis.

Parents of children with oppositional defiant disorder (ODD) describe them as having a bad attitude, as being stubborn or unwilling to compromise, or as being very disagreeable and difficult to live with.

Clinical Course and Complications

ODD usually becomes evident in early childhood before the age of 8 years. Onset is typically gradual over months or years. Children with ODD may or may not progress to developing a conduct disorder. Some of the ODD symptoms such as irritability and anger may also be characteristics of childhood depression, and a thorough assessment for depression should be done. ODD is highly present in children with ADHD, with as many as 50% of these children being both inattentive/hyperactive and oppositional-defiant (APA, 2002).

Management and Treatment

Treatment for ODD consists of individual and family therapy and behavior modification (rewards/consequences). Medications are not particularly helpful, although an underlying depressive disorder should be carefully considered, and if such a disorder is found, antidepressants may be found to be helpful.

If antidepressants are started, a selective serotonin reuptake inhibitor (SSRI) is usually prescribed.

Conduct Disorder

Children with conduct disorders appear not to care about anything, have no remorse or feelings of guilt, and generally have very poor self-esteem. Setting fires is a particularly dangerous symptom observed in these children.

The main features of a **conduct disorder** are repetitive and persistent patterns of behavior in which the rights of others or social rules are consistently violated (APA, 2002). Children with this disorder are aggressive, deceptive, and destructive, with these symptoms being the primary reason for psychiatric referral.

Incidence and Prevalence

Prevalence reports vary from 1% to 10% of the child/adolescent population with significantly higher rates among boys (12%) than girls (7.1%) (Nock, Kazdin, Hiripi, & Kessler, 2006). Rates appear to have increased late in the 20th century, and are higher in urban settings than in more rural environments. While males are more likely than females to have a conduct disorder, this is changing over time as more and more girls are committing violent acts (APA, 2002).

Etiology and Physiology

Conduct disorder is influenced by both genetic and environmental factors. The risk for conduct disorder is increased in families in which a sibling has conduct disorder, where one parent has an antisocial personality disorder, or in which there is family discord. It may also be higher in families where one parent has a substance-related disorder, alcohol dependence, mood disorder, or schizophrenia (APA, 2002). There are no medical correlates to conduct disorder. Some studies have suggested lower heart rate and lower skin conductance (of which both measures are used in polygraph or lie detector tests) in individuals with conduct disorder.

Clinical Presentation

Children or adolescents with this disorder often act aggressively toward others, and they display little empathy or concern for the feelings of others. They may feel justified in their behaviors, and feelings of guilt or remorse are often absent. Poor frustration tolerance, recklessness, irritability, and temper outbursts are associated features. Truancy, promiscuity, gang activity, fire setting, drug use, and other criminal actions may exist, and children with conduct disorder are frequently involved with the legal system (APA, 2002).

Differential Diagnosis

Children with a conduct disorder should be evaluated for ADHD, learning or communication disorders, anxiety disorders, mood disorders, and substance-abuse problems. Many children have periods of antisocial behavior that are bothersome and require intervention. This transient behavior does not necessarily constitute a conduct disorder.

Clinical Example: Disorders of Behavior

Sean is a 10-year-old boy presenting for an evaluation due to academic and behavior problems without an apparent learning disability or developmental disorder. His parents report that he has always been all boy. He likes to climb trees, he rode a bike without training wheels by age 4, and he is always on the go. He has trouble staying in his seat throughout a meal, and runs off from his parents when out in public. He is in the fourth grade for the second time (he did not meet academic requirements the previous school term) and he is making *D*s and *F*s in most of his subjects. He tends to rush through his worksheets, and he often says he doesn't have any homework when he does. Many times he will lose his homework before turning it in. In fact, he loses shoes, toys, jackets, and other things frequently. The teacher says he talks out of turn and pesters the other children. When corrected, he argues or refuses to comply with requests. He has trouble completing tasks that require more than two steps, and he is easily distracted by activity in other parts of the room. His parents complain that he back talks and that he has a bad attitude. Sean is physically healthy and well developed. He sleeps well but has trouble winding down to sleep at night. Testing has revealed his IQ to be 76 with equal verbal and performance scores. Sean is diagnosed with attention-deficit/hyperactivity disorder (combined type) and oppositional defiant disorder. His parents are referred to a support group for ADHD and family therapy to work on behavioral management techniques. Sean is started on Concerta (methylphenidate) 18 mg, one tablet every morning. A release of information is signed to the school to coordinate services.

Clinical Course and Complications

The first significant symptoms of conduct disorder usually emerge in middle childhood to early adolescence. Onset is rare after age 16 years. In a majority of individuals, the disorder will abate by adulthood. However, a high proportion of these children will go on to demonstrate adult antisocial personality disorder. The earlier the onset, the worse is the prospect for lifelong legal and substance-abuse problems associated with the disorder.

Management and Treatment

Treatment for conduct disorder consists of individual and family therapy. Such intervention teaches the adults living with the child how to control the unacceptable behavior in an age-appropriate manner for the child and to control their own aggressive and angry responses to the child's behavior. The child needs to be helped to understand internal conflicts and moods. These children often have no understanding of how their feelings relate to their actions. Often the parents are themselves products of a violently disturbed family and may need to learn new, acceptable behaviors through role modeling. Occasionally, the child may require residential treatment that provides a safe environment, defuses an angry family situation, and permits the child and family members to learn new behaviors. Frequently, the child or adolescent is involved with the legal system in the form of probation, deferred prosecution, or even juvenile detention. Medications have not been found to be of benefit for this disorder.

Critical Thinking Question 

Other than medications, what are some ways a parent or a teacher can manage a child with a behavior disorder? How can a child be taught to understand how one's feelings relate to actions and behaviors?

Disorders Related to Anxiety

Anxiety disorders in children and adolescents are not uncommon and can be frightening to both the children and their families. Disorders such as separation anxiety and selective mutism are specifically classified by the *DSM-IV-TR* as childhood-onset disorders, whereas generalized anxiety disorder, obsessive-compulsive disorder, and other anxiety problems may begin at any point in life. For a complete discussion of anxiety and dissociative disorders, see Chapter 18.

Anxiety Disorders

Often parents think that the panic demonstrated by a child when faced with an anxiety-provoking situation is defiance or rebellion, and family stress levels may be quite high as a result. Children and adolescents with anxiety disorders suffer in their schoolwork and their peer relationships as well. Many times frequent and unnecessary visits to the healthcare practitioner's office due to vague physical complaints (headaches, stomach aches, and lethargy) may result, leading to high absenteeism or truancy.

Incidence and Prevalence

The prevalence of **generalized anxiety disorder (GAD)** in children and adolescents is estimated to be around 3%, with females more likely to be overanxious than males (approximately 3:1) (APA, 2002). **Obsessive-compulsive disorder (OCD)** occurs in approximately 1–2.3% of persons, including children, with rates significantly higher when the child has Tourette's disorder (35–50%). OCD is more common in boys than in girls during childhood, which reverses in adults when the disorder becomes more common in women (APA, 2002).

Separation anxiety occurs in approximately 4.1% of the population of children and young adolescents and is not considered an uncommon disorder (Shear, Jin, Ruscio, Walters, & Kessler, 2006). It occurs more frequently in children who have parents with anxiety disorders. In most clinical samples, males are approximately equal to females; however, epidemiological studies suggest that the disorder is more common in females (APA, 2002). **Selective mutism** is highly correlated with other anxiety disorders, but with a prevalence rate of 1%, it is rarely seen alone (APA, 2002).

Etiology

The causes for anxiety disorders in children, as with all mental health or behavioral disorders, are basically unknown. There are no specific physical findings or laboratory tests that aid in making the diagnosis of an anxiety disorder. Individuals with generalized anxiety disorder frequently report symptoms starting very early in life. Obsessive-compulsive disorders have been noted to be strongly associated with disruptions in the brain's neurotransmitters.

One particular type of OCD, **pediatric autoimmune neuropsychiatric disorder associated with group A *Streptococcus* (PANDAS)**, can arise abruptly following an infection with a *Streptococcus* bacterium. PANDAS is associated with both OCD and the rapid onset of tic disorders. In a study of 12 children with PANDAS, the mean age at onset was found to be 7 years with a 4:1 ratio of males to females. All of these children developed a rapid onset of OCD or tic disorder following a *Streptococcal* throat infection; parents could identify the exact day the symptoms began. Prior to this date, there was no evidence of any neuropsychiatric disorders in any of the children. Seventy-five percent of the compulsions were bacteria related, and more than half also had urinary urgency and frequency without infection. The children were treated with broad-spectrum antibiotics for 10 days, and the OCD symptoms resolved in 14 days. Six of the children relapsed and again had positive throat cultures for group A *Streptococcus*. Recommendations of the study were to consider PANDAS in a child with a sudden onset of strange behaviors following a recent sore throat or fever. The child should be placed on a course of antibiotics in addition to any psychiatric interventions. Currently it is not known if PANDAS is predictive of a later onset OCD or tic disorder (Hughes, 2002).

Separation anxiety tends to be more often found in families that are very close to one another. Cultural variations exist in the amount of interdependence sanctioned by families. The disorder may arise following a major life stressor such as the death of a parent or grandparent; it may be characterized by periods of exacerbations and remissions (APA, 2002). Selective mutism is intricately linked with other anxiety disorders including posttraumatic stress disorder and is not related to any known specific causal factor (APA, 2002).

Children having panic attacks often cannot describe what they are feeling and may be perceived as having tantrums; adolescents' panic attacks more closely resemble adult experiences, and they are better able to describe what they are experiencing.

Physiology

When children or adolescents are confronted with an anxiety-provoking event or situation, they may demonstrate symptoms of a panic attack. A **panic attack** is a discrete period of intense fear in the absence of any real danger. Panic attacks have numerous cognitive and physical symptoms including an increase in heart rate and blood pressure (followed by a rapid drop in blood pressure when a vasovagal response occurs), shortness of breath, chest palpitations, sweating, tremors, choking sensations, nausea, dizziness, numbness, extreme fearfulness, a fear of dying, or an overwhelming sense of doom. Children having panic attacks often cannot describe what they are feeling and may be perceived by adults as having tantrums. Panic attacks in adolescents more closely resemble those in adults, and adolescents are better able to describe what they are experiencing than younger children are. Panic attacks are accompanied by a desire to escape or flee. They may last for minutes to an hour or more and can be quite disabling to the child or adolescent (APA, 2002).

Clinical Presentation

An understanding of normal growth and development is essential in the identification and treatment of an anxiety disorder in a child (e.g., a fear of strangers is normative in a 2-year-old but should become less intense as a child ages).

Children with generalized anxiety disorder can have such problems as trembling, feeling shaky inside, muscle aches or soreness, sweating, nausea and diarrhea, and exaggerated startle responses. Children with GAD seek out constant reassurance from others. They may complain of vague stomachaches or headaches or have other physical complaints or they may worry about a variety of adult issues such as paying bills, buying groceries, or keeping appointments. School functioning can be significantly impacted due to the child's preoccupation with home life worries.

Children with obsessive-compulsive disorder have recurrent obsessions (intrusive thoughts) or compulsions (ritualistic behaviors) that cause marked distress to the child, are usually unwanted, and are severe enough to be time consuming. The intrusive thoughts associated with obsessions may seem to arise without reason. Children with OCD may not recognize that their thoughts or actions are excessive or unreasonable. Common obsessions include fears of germ or disease contamination, repeated worry or doubt, or a need to have things in order. Children with obsessions initially attempt to ignore or suppress the thoughts, later often finding behaviors that provide some temporary relief from the anxiety. The compulsive behaviors may have some logical association with the obsession (e.g., washing hands with a germ phobia) or they may not. The most common compulsive behaviors include counting, checking, cleaning or washing, rank ordering, demanding assurances, or repeating actions. Panic attacks are associated with OCD when the child feels unable to carry out the compulsive behavior. Compulsive behaviors can take hours to perform and can be quite disabling for the child and disruptive to family life.

Separation anxiety may be hard to recognize in an older child because the behaviors exhibited may be more indirectly related to the anxiety. Fears of monsters, concerns over the death of loved ones, aggression with authority figures, or an eagerness to please all can be symptoms of the disorder. Separation anxiety is characterized by excessive fear and apprehension when separated from home or from close attachment figures such as parents or the main caregiver. The anxiety experienced must be developmentally excessive and last for at least 4 weeks in order to meet the definition of an anxiety disorder. Symptoms leading to the diagnosis must be present prior to the age of 18 and cause significant impairment in social, academic, or other areas of functioning. Children with separation anxiety often demonstrate extreme homesickness when away from attachment figures and they may ask repeatedly about them or want to telephone them frequently. They fantasize that their loved ones are ill or injured, or that they themselves will be lost. The preoccupation with returning home can overwhelm the child and make it impossible to attend to any other activities. Children with separation anxiety also frequently complain of physical symptoms (upset stomach, headaches, and dizziness), and they may be unable to sleep alone without having nightmares or panic symptoms.

Children with selective mutism persistently refuse to speak in social situations, interfering with peer relations, education, and other important areas of functioning. Children with selective mutism may communicate with gestures, monosyllabic words, or even by using an altered voice (AACAP, 2006; APA, 2002).

Differential Diagnosis

Anxiety disorders are differentiated from one another based on the ability to identify the stressor or anxiety-provoking event. It is critical that medical conditions or their treatments that could be causing the behaviors (e.g., hyperthyroidism, asthma) be ruled out. Selective mutism cannot be diagnosed if the refusal is related to embarrassment over a phonological or communication disorder or when the language is not native to the child.

Clinical Course and Complications

For the most part, anxiety disorders all begin at some point in childhood and may worsen, remit entirely by adolescence, or continue to exacerbate and remit throughout adulthood. Anxiety disorders are highly comorbid with other psychiatric disorders of childhood, and an assessment for anxiety should be done when any mental health problem is suspected in a child or adolescent. Most of the time, separation anxiety and selective mutism symptoms are gone by adulthood. Selective mutism is intricately linked with other anxiety disorders including posttraumatic stress disorder and is not related to any known specific causal factor (APA, 2002).

Management and Treatment

Treatment for generalized anxiety disorder and obsessive-compulsive disorder should include individual therapy with the child. Cognitive-behavioral therapy and exposure therapy are generally the most helpful. Cognitive-behavioral techniques help the child to rehearse the association among thoughts, feelings, and behavioral responses. Exposure therapy gradually exposes the child to the feared object or situation. Children respond very well to relaxation training and guided imagery, which can significantly help in preventing the anxiety from advancing to a panic state (Chard & Gilman, 2005). The treatment of separation anxiety and selective mutism consists of individual and family therapy and incorporating rewards for increasing levels of autonomy. Medications are of limited usefulness in separation anxiety.

Separation anxiety disorder should not be confused with the developmentally normal separation anxiety that occurs in children between 1 and 3 years of age. Nor should it be confused with the tolerance some cultures have for supporting interdependence among children and other family members.

However, medications are very effective in treating generalized anxiety disorder and obsessive-compulsive disorder in children. The most effective medications are selective serotonin reuptake inhibitors (SSRIs) such as sertraline (Zoloft), which is the only FDA-approved SSRI medication for use in childhood. It is approved specifically for OCD down to age 6 years. Other effective medications used include citalopram (Celexa), escitalopram (Lexapro), mirtazapine (Remeron), and fluoxetine (Prozac). Luvox (fluvoxamine) is specifically indicated for OCD and has FDA approval for older children and adolescents, but it is sedating and has several drug interactions. Anafranil (clomipramine), a tricyclic antidepressant, was FDA approved in the 1980s for use in children down to age 10 years; however, it has a significant number of side effects such as weight gain, sedation, cardiac conduction problems, and an increased seizure risk. Other tricyclic antidepressants (imipramine, desipramine, nortriptyline, and amitriptyline) are all also effective for treating anxiety and OCD, but they also have problematic side effects including a risk for cardiac conduction problems that may lead to dangerous cardiac arrhythmias (AACAP, 2006).

Disorders Related to Trauma and Abuse

Posttraumatic Stress Disorder and Acute Stress Disorder

Stressful or traumatic events in early childhood may have long-lasting effects on brain development, affecting neural and endocrine systems that mediate the response to stress and exhibit persistent alterations after the trauma (Gillespie & Nemeroff, 2005). Posttraumatic stress disorder (PTSD) and acute stress disorder (ASD) occur in response to a personal experience of an event where there is actual or threatened death or serious injury, in response to witnessing an event that involves death or serious injury, in response to learning about unexpected or violent death, or in response to childhood abuse or neglect, serious harm, or threat of death or injury to a family member or close friend. The individual responds with feelings of intense fear, helplessness, or horror. Children may express agitated or disorganized behaviors (APA, 2002). For a more detailed discussion of both PTSD and ASD, please refer to Chapter 18; for information on family violence and child abuse, see Chapters 11 and 27.

Reactive attachment disorder (RAD; inhibited or disinhibited) is a failure to develop appropriate social relatedness associated with grossly pathological caretaking.

Two controversial interventions, rebirthing techniques and compression holding therapy, include physically restraining a child to improve attachment, and they can be very dangerous, having resulted in death.

Reactive Attachment Disorder

Reactive attachment disorder (RAD) is a failure to develop appropriate social relatedness associated with grossly pathological caretaking. There are two subtypes: inhibited and disinhibited. Children with this disorder have had severe disruptions in their early bonding and caretaking relationships (AACAP, 2011). The pathological care history may include a persistent disregard for the child's basic physical or emotional needs or repeated changes in caregivers that prevent formulation of stable attachments. This disorder is frequently seen in children with a long history of out-of-home placement (foster homes, residential programs, hospitals, and orphanages) particularly when they have been moved often (APA, 2002; 2011). There are conflicting data on the prevalence of RAD. The *DSM-IV-TR* reports that it appears to be uncommon. However, the practice parameters for RAD published by the American Academy of Child and Adolescent Psychiatry (AACAP) report a likely rate of 1% of the U.S. population of children. Other studies have indicated rates as high as 38–44% in children in orphanages or foster care (AACAP, 2005). The cause of RAD appears to be grossly pathologic care; in fact, severe neglect is required in order to make the diagnosis. Physical examinations of the child with RAD may reveal other evidence of neglect and/or abuse including failure to thrive, growth delays, malnutrition, vitamin deficiencies, bruising, or old fractures on X-rays (APA, 2002). Developmental delays in the absence of neglect cannot be considered a cause for RAD.

In the inhibited type of RAD, the child demonstrates a pattern of hypervigilant, ambivalent, or highly inhibited behaviors toward caregivers. The child may be resistant to comfort measures or appear to be watchful or suspicious of others. In the disinhibited type, the child will show diffuse and nondiscriminatory attachments toward others, with behaviors such as hugging or climbing into the lap of relative strangers. Safety of the child may be a particular concern for the caregivers.

The onset of RAD is usually prior to the age of 5 years, although the diagnosis may not be made until later. The severity and duration varies according to the intensity of the environmental deprivation and/or abuse and the consistency of interventions. Indiscriminate sociability (disinhibited type of RAD) may persist for years. The child or adolescent should be assessed for other signs of trauma including flashbacks, nightmares, hypervigilance, and dissociation, all symptoms of acute or chronic posttraumatic stress disorder. Major depressive disorder should also be considered. There are very few long-term studies of these children and their outcomes (APA, 2002).

Reactive attachment disorder treatment consists of a combination of family therapy, which may involve foster or adoptive parents, and a stable, nurturing, permanent home and caregivers. Medications are useful only if there is a comorbid anxiety or other disorders responsive to medication. Some therapists have used so-called rebirthing techniques or compression holding therapy as treatments. These interventions, which include physically restraining a child to improve attachment, are controversial and can be very dangerous. Withholding or forcing food and water may also be used. At least six documented child fatalities have occurred related to the use of these unproven methods (AACAP, 2005).

Critical Thinking Question 

What effect do you think the extensive television coverage of events such as terrorist attacks, various global wars, and natural disasters (earthquakes, tornadoes, hurricanes, tsunamis) has on children who have been previously traumatized? What factors might serve as protection for a traumatized child?

Disorders in Childhood Related to Mood and Affect

In addition to discussing conditions most often present first in childhood, *The Diagnostic and Statistical Manual of Mental Disorders* discusses variations in disorders based upon developmental stages and includes children in the other *DSM-IV* diagnostic categories when their symptoms meet the criteria for the disorder (e.g., major depressive disorder, bipolar disorder, adjustment disorders, and anxiety disorders; problems related to abuse or neglect). Regardless of the diagnostic category, nurses must recognize symptoms indicating that a child is having problems and intervene appropriately. The following discussion highlights major depressive disorder and bipolar disorder.

Other Disorders Related to Mood and Affect

Mood disorders and anxiety disorders are present in a high percentage of children presenting for treatment in a mental health setting. Although disorders of behavior are often identified and referred for care, disorders of mood and affect are subtler in children and can be easily overlooked, leading to potentially dire consequences including chronic self-esteem and socialization problems, impaired learning, more family conflict, and even self-harm behaviors.

Major Depressive Disorder

Major depressive disorder is characterized by a period of at least 2 weeks during which there is either a loss of interest or pleasure in nearly all activities or a significantly depressed or irritable mood. Children and adolescents tend to present with grouchiness or irritability in addition to, or instead of, overt sadness (APA, 2002). For a complete discussion of this disorder, consult Chapter 17.

An understanding of normal growth and development rates for children and adolescents and the corresponding behaviors is essential in order to assess for and diagnose depression. Five percent of children and up to 8% of adolescents become depressed (Wagner et al., 2003; AACAP, 2008). This number is higher for children with one or more family members with major depressive disorder and for children who have experienced a major loss or trauma, including abuse (APA, 2002). Many medical disorders present an increased risk for major depressive disorder in children, including hypothyroidism and type 1 dia-

Clinical Example: Disorders of Trauma and Abuse 

Missy is a 15-year-old girl who is seen in the office with her group home houseparent. Missy has been in three unsuccessful foster homes since the death of her mother 2 years previously. When younger, Missy was molested by her father, and her mother was found unable to protect her. She was placed with her maternal grandmother from the age of 2 to 13. After her grandmother died, Missy was moved to her mother's home. At 13 she found her mother dead of a drug overdose and she was moved to foster care. While in foster care, Missy became depressed and started self-mutilating. She reported seeing her dead mother's face in her room at night and said she felt numb all over. After a brief hospitalization, she was moved to another foster home. From there, she ran away with an 18-year-old boy she had known for 2 weeks. She was then moved to a third foster home, where she was caught fondling an 8-year-old girl in the home. At this point, she was placed in a group home setting where she remains. Missy is diagnosed with PTSD and a reactive attachment disorder. Individual therapy is recommended along with Zoloft 50 mg every morning.

betes mellitus. Laboratory findings and changes in brain imaging found in depressed adults (elevated glucocorticoid secretion, blunted growth hormone, and thyroid-stimulating hormone and prolactin responses to test agents) are not usually seen in children or young adolescents.

Children and adolescents with major depressive disorder often think that it would be better if they had never been born and exhibit behaviors such as sleep changes, appetite problems, listlessness, apathy, disinterest in social or play activities, trouble concentrating on schoolwork, or preoccupations with themes of death or violence.

Children and adolescents with major depressive disorder may exhibit sleep changes, appetite problems, listlessness, apathy, disinterest in social or play activities, trouble concentrating on schoolwork, or preoccupations with themes of death or violence. They may say that they never really feel happy or that they think the family would be better off if they had never been born. Depressed children and adolescents stop caring about hobbies or activities, including spending time with friends or family, or at school. Common sleep disturbances in a child with depression consist of normal to slightly delayed onset of sleep followed by middle-of-the-night wakening. Sleep is described as not restful, and children may report nightmares or be found wandering about the house. Fatigue and low energy are pronounced during the day. Adolescents who are depressed become self-isolating and disinterested in activities with friends or family. Grades may drop at school and they may exhibit more tardiness, truancy, or other behavior problems including substance experimentation (Wagner et al., 2003).

Concentration problems and behavior problems may lead children to be misdiagnosed as having ADHD or an oppositional defiant disorder. Somatic (physical) complaints are fairly common in depressed children. Anxiety symptoms may present in combination with depression. Depressive symptoms usually develop over several weeks. An untreated episode of major depressive disorder may last 4 months or longer, in children as well as in adults (APA, 2002).

The most critical complication of major depressive disorder for children as well as adults is the very real possibility of suicide. In 2007, suicide was the third leading cause of death for 15–24-year-olds in the United States (NIMH, 2010). The suicide rate for children 10–14 years of age was 0.9 per 100,000, and 6.9 per 100,000 for adolescents aged 15–19 years (NIMH, 2010). Children and adolescents who are contemplating suicide may provide hints such as giving away prized possessions, writing about it in diaries or journals, or making verbal comments such as you won't have to worry about me anymore. The presence of any hallucinations or delusions is also a risk factor for suicide (Wagner et al., 2003). Children are more likely to use firearms, suffocation, and poisoning to commit suicide (NIMH, 2010).

Treatment for major depressive disorder in a child or adolescent generally includes a combination of individual and family therapy. Children may respond to antidepressant medications; selective serotonin reuptake inhibitors (SSRIs) or the dopaminergic medication bupropion (Wellbutrin) are often used. Fluoxetine (Prozac) is approved for use in children down to age 12. Caution should always be taken when giving children and adolescents SSRIs and other antidepressant medications because in 2005, the U.S. Food and Drug Administration began requiring a black box warning for antidepressant use in children due to an increase in suicidal thoughts and behaviors in children on antidepressants (3.6%) as compared to depressed children not taking medications (1%). Theories as to why this occurs include the following: antidepressants may cause a child to act on previously only contemplated thoughts (discussed in the adult literature fairly extensively); antidepressants may precipitate bipolar, manic states in children and adolescents; or the research methodology used did not account for extraneous other variables. Nevertheless, when antidepressants are used, treatment staff must follow the child closely (weekly appointments are recommended), and parents should be well educated on signs of suicidal thoughts or behaviors (Wagner et al., 2003).

Major depressive disorder in the child or adolescent clearly has serious implications that should not be ignored by the healthcare practitioner. Family discord and parental depression may be associated with the development of major depressive disorder and anxiety disorders later in life; substance-related disorders are higher in depressed children and adolescents; and suicide attempts are a real risk. Nurses should obtain thorough family histories when assessing children and adolescents, and they should keep the child's safety in mind as a top priority when developing care plans.

Bipolar Disorder of Childhood

Childhood **bipolar disorder** is a controversial diagnosis that has only been recognized since the mid-1990s as occurring in children and adolescents. Children with this disorder typically are unpredictably explosive, moody, and aggressive toward themselves and others. Traditionally, these children have carried a variety of diagnoses (intermittent explosive, impulse control, mood, and conduct disorders) and have been treated with a combination of medications including lithium, antiepileptics, sedatives, and antipsychotics. Institutionalization may have been recommended by healthcare practitioners in the past to protect the family and the community from the child's unpredictable behaviors. Society has since moved away from large, regional, residential placements and toward an emphasis on deinstitutionalization of the mentally ill, adults as well as children, with the result being that more children are living at home, attending public school, and being treated in an outpatient setting. These children can be very difficult to manage and often require a multidisciplinary team approach to their care. Polypharmacy is common due to the high comorbidity with other psychiatric illnesses. Healthcare practitioners have little data on the safety of many medications used for bipolar disorder in children and adolescents, due in large part to the lack of agreement on diagnostic criteria. Clark (2004) discusses this diagnostic controversy as arising from two basic questions:

1. Does diagnosing bipolar disorder in children require discrete episodes of mania, as in adults, or can it be chronic and unremitting?
2. Must elation of mood and/or grandiosity be present, or can irritability and mood lability suffice?

The classic mania/hypomania episodes seen in adults are rarely seen in a child or younger adolescent (Clark, 2004).

Massat and Victor (2005) found that problems with diagnosing children with bipolar disorder arise from skepticism that the disorder could exist, misdiagnosis due to inconsistent diagnostic criteria, and overlapping symptoms with other psychiatric disorders of children including ADHD. They describe the atypical picture in children as characterized by persistent irritability, violent behaviors, affective storms, and prolonged or aggressive temper outbursts. Symptoms of grandiosity or hypersexuality commonly seen in adults with manic episodes are uncommon or difficult to diagnose in a prepubescent child or young adolescent. Overlapping symptoms with other disorders include overactivity, irritability, distractibility, emotional lability, impulsivity, and racing speech or talkativeness (Massat & Victor, 2005).

There are no laboratory or imaging studies that help to make the diagnosis of bipolar disorder. Meyer and Carlson (2003) discuss the relationship between parents with a known bipolar disorder and their children, noting that children with one or more parents who have been diagnosed as bipolar exhibited more motor restlessness, motor agitation, anxiety, mood lability, inattentiveness, stubbornness, and excitability than did children without bipolar disorder–diagnosed parents. The *DSM-IV-TR* reports that 4–24% of individuals with bipolar disorders have first-degree relatives with either bipolar I disorder or major depressive disorder (APA, 2002).

Children with bipolar disorders almost always have a mixed presentation. Cycling of moods is less clearly differentiated than in adult clients. Mania is frequently characterized less by euphoria and more by agitation, with explosive anger outbursts and violent episodes. These outbursts can be triggered with very little provocation; both the intensity and the abruptness of the outburst may be very frightening for those around the child. Normal temper tantrums in children are usually self-limiting and respond to firm directives. Outbursts seen in a child with a bipolar disorder are much more intense and may involve hitting or kicking adults, biting, destroying property, attacking pets or younger children, or using weapons. The duration of these episodes can last from a few minutes to several hours and they usually do not end until the child is exhausted.

Children with bipolar disorder may exhibit symptoms as early as age 3, with parents often reporting that the child always had a bad temper or was difficult to calm. Early childhood disorders tend to be episodic and chronic. By the late teens, the adolescent may have fewer rage outbursts and the disorder may disappear completely, or the mood swings may become more cyclical in nature, more closely approaching the criteria for a bipolar I disorder (APA, 2002). Bipolar disorder comorbidity with other psychiatric conditions is very high. Wilens and colleagues (2004) reported that in a study of 57 adolescents meeting the criteria for bipolar disorder, 74% had ADHD, 63% had conduct disorder, 93% met the criteria for ODD, 91% had met the criteria for major depressive disorder at some point, psychosis occurred in 28%, multiple anxiety disorders were found in 79%, and 32% had substance abuse disorders, while 21% smoked cigarettes.

Children with bipolar disorder have atypical symptoms including persistent irritability, violent behaviors, affective storms, and prolonged or aggressive temper outbursts, contributing to the difficulty with diagnosing the disorder.

The treatment of bipolar disorder nearly always includes mood-stabilizing medications. To date, lithium, Risperdal (risperidone), and Abilify (aripiprazole) are the only medications approved by the FDA to treat bipolar disorder in young people. There is some evidence that lithium might act as an antidepressant and help prevent suicidal behavior (NIMH, 2010). However, the response rate to lithium is only about 50%, and it is associated with side effects in-

Evidence-Based Practice

Carlson, Potegal, Marguiles, Gutkovich, and Basile (2009) studied children's severe anger outbursts (rages) that have often been associated with many childhood disorders, including bipolar, oppositional defiant, and conduct disorders. A total of 130 hospitalized 5–12-year-olds were evaluated. Rages were operationally defined as "agitated or angry behaviors requiring seclusion or medication"(p. 281) and categorized as they occurred. The study used direct observation to define the children's rages. It was anticipated that the symptom of rages would be the most frequent reason for hospitalization because of prior treatment failure and that the rages would occur less in the hospital, with those children having in-hospital rages being those with the most comorbid conditions and impairments.

The children's behaviors during the rages were evaluated using the Children's Agitation Inventory with the following behaviors being ultimately identified:

> (1) physical aggression which included hitting, kicking, pushing and pulling, biting and scratching, throwing objects, kicking or throwing the time-out chair, and punching the wall; (2) verbal aggression which consisted of cursing, yelling and screaming, making threats, and whining; (3) other behaviors which included biting self, throwing self on the floor, and stamping feet; (4) mood and psychiatric symptoms that identified sad and tearful appearance, looking and sounding fearful and anxious, pacing, being withdrawn and unresponsive, reporting or appearing to be having hallucinations; (5) cooperative behavior that was evidenced by the child's willingness to take a time out, being calm, quiet, and able to process. (Carlson et al., 2009, p. 282)

Of the children who had rages while hospitalized, 33 (75%) had three or more diagnoses compared to 52.3% without rages. ADHD-combined type, either or both ADHD and ODD/CD, and learning and/or language disorders occurred 5 to 8 times more often in children with rages, and anxiety disorders occurred 2.7 times more often in children without rages. A preadmission diagnosis of bipolar disorder occurred three times more often in children with in-hospital rages versus those without rages. However, observation by clinicians during hospitalization confirmed episodes of mania in very few children with or without rages. Only half of the children who had rages prior to hospitalization had them during hospitalization, and these were the younger, more diagnostically complex children with more comorbidities and prior treatment failures (more medications, special education needs, and prior psychiatric hospitalizations). Such serious deficits impair the child's ability to self-regulate behaviors or verbally express frustration and anger.

The researchers concluded that:

> the combination of impulsivity and low frustration tolerance from severe ADHD and the inability to process and express frustration because of learning and language problems initiate and perpetuate rages. Although medications can sometimes dampen the behaviors, they have not yet proven sufficient to eliminate them, at least quickly, in many children. (Carlson et al., 2009, p. 284).

This research can assist healthcare practitioners in understanding and intervening with children who experience rages both in and out of hospitals.

cluding tremors and a narrow therapeutic-to-toxic range. Short-term treatment with risperidone can help reduce symptoms of mania or mixed mania in children ages 10 and up, while aripiprazole is approved to treat these symptoms in children 10–17 years old who have bipolar I (NIMH, 2010). All of the medications used in adults are also utilized in children off-label, or without FDA approval. Many mood stabilizers are also antiepileptics and have FDA approval for the treatment of seizure disorders in children, but they are not approved for bipolar disorder. Mood-stabilizing medications have a variety of side effects. Sedation, appetite increases, and weight gain are common. Newer generation antipsychotics are generally thought to be safer, but they still carry risks for extrapyramidal side effects (EPS) and tardive dyskinesia (Clark, 2004).

Critical Thinking Question

What are the benefits and risks to utilizing antidepressant medications in children and adolescents with major depressive disorder, anxiety disorder, or bipolar disorder? What are some ethical concerns in using non-FDA approved, off-label medications in children and adolescents?

Clinical Example: Disorders Related to Mood and Affect 

Sara is a 13-year-old girl who is brought in for an assessment by her parents because of concerns they have over her moodiness and self-harm thoughts. Sara is physically healthy and experienced menarche 4 months before the appointment. In the past 4 months she has been crying frequently with very little provocation. She feels that none of the girls at school like her, and she has been isolating herself in her room. Her grades have dropped from an honor roll level to a C average. She recently has refused to eat with the family, and her mother believes she may have lost 10 pounds; she is 5′2″ and weighs 95 pounds. She is having trouble staying asleep at night. The evening prior to the assessment, her mother found her making some superficial cuts on her left wrist. When asked, Sara said she wanted to be in heaven with her grandmother and she didn't think anyone would miss her. She was started on fluoxetine 20 mg daily. Six days later, her parents called the emergency services to report that Sara was agitated, screaming at them, stomping through the house, not sleeping, and was tearing apart her room. She was admitted to the hospital's adolescent psychiatric unit and diagnosed with bipolar I disorder. She was taken off of the fluoxetine and started on a titration of lamotrigine (Lamictal) up to 100 mg bid along with individual and group therapy. Her parents were also entered into family therapy and referred to a community support group for family members of individuals with bipolar disorder.

Table 12-2 **Nursing Interventions for Children with Disorders of Infancy, Childhood, and Adolescence**

Nursing Diagnoses	Nursing Interventions	Rationales
Risk for violence: self-directed or other-directed	Remove potentially dangerous items from the child's environment	Safety is a primary concern.
	Place child on a one-to-one level of observation	The child needs external controls of behavior in order to prevent self-destructive acts and aggression/violence towards others.
	Remove the child from excessive environmental stimuli	A calm environment can help reduce the child's aggressive feelings and provide a sense of security and peace.
	If the child appears to be about to lose control, nurses should interrupt the behavior immediately by any appropriate means (time outs, quiet room)	Preventing injury is a primary concern; identify behaviors that the child can use to reduce need for these interventions; only use them for safety, not punishment.
Impaired social interaction	Observe the child for examples of negative behaviors that are interfering with social interactions	When negative behaviors are identified, the child can be helped to substitute more age-appropriate, adaptive behaviors.
	Use therapeutic play, role playing, storytelling, and therapeutic games to increase the child's social skills	Many children have never had positive social skills role modeled in their family situations; role modeling interventions help the child learn new, adaptive ways of interacting with peers and adults.
Impaired parenting	Assess the main caregiver's/family members' knowledge of normal growth and development, children's behaviors, and parenting skills	Before caregiver/family can be helped with learning about the child's behavior, a baseline of knowledge needs must be identified.
	Discuss with family how the child's behavior is impacting the various members	This will assist the nurse in understanding the different aspects of the family situation and the stressors involved with the child's disorder.
	Collaboratively identify and plan with the child and family goals for changes in the child's behavior and family interactions	Mutually agreed-upon goals result in more potential that the changes in behavior and interactions will be achieved.

Evidence-Based Practice

Pilowsky, Wickramaratne, Nomura, and Weissman (2006) looked at the effects of parental depression and family discord on offspring psychopathology. This longitudinal study interviewed 182 subjects in 83 families at age 17 years and again 20 years later. Results indicated that parental depression and family discord are consistent risk factors for the development of major depressive disorder and various anxiety disorders later in adulthood. Wagner and colleagues (2003) reported a literature review of 376 children and adolescents with major depressive disorder. They found frequent hospitalizations, with almost 50% of the subjects attempting suicide at some point. Additionally, up to 25% had experienced some form of substance abuse.

Education for Clients and Families

Historically, mental health treatment has been provided with the individual client in mind; however, children and adolescents rarely live in a vacuum. The impact of a healthy and well-functioning family unit cannot be overemphasized. Nursing has long recognized that the individual exists in a holistic environment where physical, mental, social, emotional, and spiritual needs cannot be separated from the individual. A nurse who would exclude the impact of the family or environment on the child would not be very effective.

Assessment for mental health problems in parents and other family members is an integral part of treating children and adolescents. Many of the disorders discussed in this chapter have familial associations and heritability factors; it is common to find more than one person in a family with a diagnosable psychiatric illness. Gartstein and Sheeber (2004) examined 69 mothers of 3–6-year-old children who had been diagnosed with major depressive disorder, looking at issues of parenting competence, attachment to the child, the child's impact on the family unit, and the child's behavior problems. Findings were that child behavior problems were associated with maternal depression, with a positive relationship among high maternal depression, high family dysfunction, and low maternal self-perception of parenting competence.

CASE STUDIES Sandra

Sandra is a 15-year-old girl whose parents divorced 2 years ago. She chose to live with her mother and finish school, and her father moved to a neighboring state, but she continued to see him over holidays and in the summer. She is an only child. Sandra's father was killed in a motor vehicle accident while driving drunk 6 months ago. It occurred during a weekend that she normally would have visited him, but she wanted to go to a cheerleading camp instead. Since his death, Sandra has been increasingly isolating herself at home. Her mother says she has stopped going to practices, she won't talk to her friends on the phone anymore, and she cries in her room at night. Sandra's grades are worsening and she is more listless and apathetic in her schoolwork. Sandra's mother found a letter in which Sandra says her family would be better off if she were dead, and it's her fault her father died. In the letter, Sandra outlines different ways she could kill herself and which ones would be more likely to be effective. Her letter also alludes to visits from her deceased father at night, and hearing his voice calling her name as if he were beckoning her to join him.

Sandra was admitted to the inpatient adolescent behavioral healthcare unit for major depressive disorder, single episode, with psychotic features, and is started on antidepressant medications. During her admitting assessment, the nurse noted that she had lost about 10 pounds in the past 6 weeks, but she was still within normal height and weight range for her age. Sandra said she couldn't sleep at night—she was tossing and turning, had dreams about her dad, and awoke frequently. Consequently, she felt fatigued and exhausted during the day. She couldn't concentrate at school, and she just wanted this to be over with.

The nurse identified the following problem list:

- Bereavement
- Depressed and guilty mood
- Lack of interest or motivation in activities
- Impaired social interactions (not seeing her friends)
- School performance failure
- Thoughts of suicide
- Vague reports of auditory and visual hallucinations
- Insomnia

In establishing a plan of care, the nurse identified nursing diagnoses related to dysfunctional grieving, self-care deficit (sleep deprivation), and impaired social interaction.

Nursing Care Plan **Major Depressive Disorder**

Nursing Diagnosis 1: Dysfunctional grieving related to the loss of a parent as evidenced by periods of depression and suicidal thoughts

Nursing Diagnosis 2: Self-care deficit related to decreased physiologic conditions as evidenced by persistent insomnia and preoccupation with thoughts of dying

Nursing Diagnosis 3: Impaired social interaction related to self-concept disturbance and self-imposed isolation as evidenced by dysfunctional interaction with peers and families and remaining secluded

Expected Outcomes	Interventions	Evaluations
• The adolescent will be able to freely express her feelings over her father's death without becoming completely overwhelmed or suicidal.	• Assess the adolescent's stage of grieving as having an understanding of where the adolescent is in the grief process to help to guide interventions. • Encourage the adolescent to talk openly about her father and to express her feelings associated with how he died (including feelings of guilt) as the adolescent may have felt that she could not talk about her father without upsetting her mother, or that she needed to be strong. • Encourage the adolescent to cry as crying helps to release pent-up feelings and reduce some of the distress associated with them.	• The adolescent talks about her father's death and her own feelings in individual and group sessions.
	• Encourage adolescent to keep a journal and write in it her thoughts and feelings about her father.	• The adolescent writes about the experience in her personal journal.
	• Assist the adolescent in starting a scrapbook or memory book of memories of her father. Ask her mother to assist her in finding photos, etc., to put in the memory book, as reviewing memories will aid in the grief process.	• The adolescent begins a scrapbook or memory book about her father.
	• Refer the adolescent to community-based grief support group programs, especially those designed specifically for children/adolescents, as adolescents respond well to peer interaction based on their normal developmental tasks, and the adolescent may find a great deal of relief in meeting other children with similar losses.	• The adolescent attends at least one bereavement support group meeting.
	• Refer the adolescent for individual counseling after she leaves the hospital, as a trained therapist can help her to continue to gently challenge false beliefs (i.e., responsibility over her father's death) and let go of her guilt.	• The adolescent agrees to meet privately with a therapist for ongoing counseling and support.
	• Educate the adolescent's mother that the girl will need to feel okay about having good memories of her father (and she may seem to forget conflicts between her parents prior to the divorce) as loved ones may be idealized for a period of time after their death by those left behind, which is a normal process.	

(Continues)

Nursing Care Plan **Major Depressive Disorder *(Continued)***

• The adolescent will be sleeping no fewer than 6 uninterrupted hours per night or 8 hours total. • The adolescent will report feeling better rested and more energetic the next day.	• Assess things that may be preventing adequate rest (e.g., caffeine, leaving the television on at night). • Encourage the adolescent to do quiet, restful activities at bedtime such as taking a warm bath or reading a book, as this will allow her to become gradually drowsy and eventually fall asleep. • Keep the environment around the adolescent quiet at night (turn down telephone ringers, keep staff voices low) as a noisy environment can be disruptive to sleep. • Obtain orders for a prn sleep medication that's safe for use in adolescents.	• The adolescent is reading books before bedtime and is avoiding caffeine or television right before sleep. • The adolescent asks for her prn sleep medication 30 minutes prior to bedtime.
• The adolescent will be able to identify activities that she normally enjoys. • The adolescent will participate in her usual preillness activities again.	• Use active listening skills to establish a therapeutic relationship with the adolescent, as presenting self as actively interested in the girl will promote self-esteem and verbalization. • Encourage the adolescent to list things she enjoys doing with her friends, as this will help the girl to review and remember things that she enjoys in life. • Encourage letters to friends and visitations from friends while in the hospital as doing so will keep the adolescent connected with those who care about her.	• The adolescent is observed talking more about things she wants to do with friends once she leaves the hospital. • The adolescent has a more positive outlook and is future oriented.

Visit http://go.jblearning.com/mentalhealth for additional care plans and exercises.
Source: Adapted from Ackley & Ladwig (2010).

A basic understanding of normal developmental tasks of childhood is essential in managing the child with a mental health disorder. Often families are not well versed in normal developmental stages (e.g., they may perceive normal defiance associated with a 2-year-old and a 14-year-old as pathologic when it is not). Parents should be helped to learn normal and expected developmental behaviors of their child.

Education regarding the specific psychiatric-mental health disorders once they are diagnosed is necessary to help parents understand that the behavior exhibited is not intentional or malicious, nor is the child always in control.

Education of the family is essential for the child psychiatric-mental health nurse. Education regarding the specific psychiatric-mental health disorders once they are diagnosed is necessary to help parents understand that the behavior exhibited is not intentional or malicious, nor is the child always in control. Parents can be directed to a number of resources (library, Internet) that will aid in this process. Many support groups exist (e.g., Children and Adults with Attention Deficit Disorder [CHADD], Tourette's support, autism support programs) where parents have the opportunity to network with other families with children having similar problems.

Medication treatment can be overwhelming and confusing to parents because there is a proliferation of medications being used, and often many medications used in child psychiatry are off-label. Parents should be taught the specific reason the child is receiving a particular medication, its dosage schedule, any dietary limitations, side effects, and adverse effects (especially any requiring an FDA black box warning), and what to do if they are concerned that the child is having a reaction to the medication.

The nurse should not assume that parents have a good grasp of basic parenting or behavior management techniques. Families vary widely in their parenting knowledge, tolerance for routines and structure, or use of rewards and consequences.

Some parents enforce strict bedtimes and expect their children to do chores, while other parents are more laissez-faire and tolerate more casual, or even chaotic, home environments. Parenting classes are excellent means of providing some basic parenting instruction and may be more acceptable to some families that perceive family therapy as an implication of personal deficiencies.

All children in the United States are guaranteed an education. Many times, children with psychiatric or behavioral disorders are a challenge in the classroom. Parents of children who are struggling to learn should be advised that they can request intelligence (IQ) and academic testing, speech and language evaluations, hearing tests, and other necessary evaluations from the school system. The school system is required to make appropriate accommodations for a child who has special learning, developmental, emotional, or mental health needs. Parents should be meeting frequently with their child's teacher and other representatives of the school system to ensure that an individualized education program (IEP) is in place when needed.

Summary

Disorders of infancy, childhood, and adolescence have profound effects on the child and family and often have a lifelong impact on the individual's ability to function in a family and in society. This chapter has presented information on disorders in childhood related to development, behavior, anxiety, trauma or abuse, and mood. See **Table 12-2**.

A basic understanding of normal developmental tasks of childhood is essential in managing the child with a mental health disorder. A childhood disorder that is not treated adequately will cause problems in adulthood. Education regarding the specific psychiatric-mental health disorders is indispensable in helping parents understand that the child's behavior is not intentional or malicious, nor is the child always in control, and to provide the parents and caregivers with necessary information and skills.

Annotated References

Ackley, B. J., & Ladwig, G. B. (2010). *Nursing diagnosis handbook: An evidenced-based guide to planning care* (9th ed.). St. Louis, MO: Mosby/Elsevier.

This handbook helps the nursing student or practicing nurse make diagnoses and plan care utilizing the diagnoses approved by the North American Nursing Diagnosis Association (NANDA). Additionally, nursing outcomes classifications (NOC) and nursing interventions classifications (NIC) are provided.

American Academy of Child and Adolescent Psychiatry. (2004). Practice parameter for the assessment and treatment of children and adolescents with enuresis. *Journal of the American Academy of Child and Adolescent Psychiatry, 43*(12), 1540–1550.

The AACAP has developed standardized criteria expanding on the *DSM-IV-TR* manual looking at the specific etiology, diagnosis, and treatment of child psychiatric disorders. This article presents the practice parameters for enuresis including etiology, assessment, and treatment of the disorder.

American Academy of Child and Adolescent Psychiatry. (2005). Practice parameter for the assessment and treatment of children and adolescents with reactive attachment disorder of infancy and early childhood. *Journal of the American Academy of Child and Adolescent Psychiatry, 44*(11), 1206–1219.

The AACAP has developed standardized criteria expanding on the *DSM-IV-TR* manual looking at the specific etiology, diagnosis, and treatment of child psychiatric disorders. This article presents the practice parameters for reactive attachment disorder including etiology, assessment, and treatment of the disorder.

American Academy of Child and Adolescent Psychiatry. (2006). *Practice parameter for the assessment and treatment of children and adolescents with anxiety disorders*. Retrieved from http://www.aacap.org/galleries/PracticeParameters/JAACAP_Anxiety_2007.pdf

The AACAP has developed standardized criteria expanding on the *DSM-IV-TR* manual looking at the specific etiology, diagnosis, and treatment of child psychiatric disorders. The practice parameter for anxiety disorders was approved June 17, 2006, and published in February 2007. This parameter presents data based on extensive literature reviews of the etiology, assessment, and treatment (both pharmacologic and nonpharmacologic) of anxiety disorders in children and adolescents.

American Academy of Child and Adolescent Psychiatry. (2008). *Facts for families: The*

depressed child. Retrieved from http://aacap.org/cs/root/facts_for_families/the_depressed_child
This is a fact sheet on childhood depression for families.

American Academy of Child and Adolescent Psychiatry. (2011, March). *Facts for families: Reactive attachment disorder*. Retrieved from http://aacap.org/cs/root/facts_for_families/reactive_attachment_disorder
This is a fact sheet on reactive attachment disorder for families.

American Psychiatric Association (APA). (2002). *Diagnostic and statistical manual of mental disorders* (4th ed., text rev.). Washington, DC: Author.
The *DSM-IV-TR* applies a standard nomenclature based on relatively stringent diagnostic criteria to provide the psychiatric clinician with a standardized text for recognizing, differentiating, and diagnosing psychiatric, behavioral, and substance use disorders.

American Psychiatric Association (APA). (2011). Disorders usually diagnosed in infancy, childhood or adolescence. *DSM-5 development*. Retrieved from www.dsm5.org/proposed revisions/pages/infancychildhood adolescence.aspx
This APA website contains information, recommendations, and discussion of the proposed revisions for the DSM-5.

Bloch, M. H., Peterson, B.S., Scahill, L., Otka, J., Katsovich, L., Zhang, H., Leckman, J. F. (2006). Adulthood outcome of tic and obsessive-compulsive symptom severity in children with Tourette syndrome. *Archives of Pediatric Adolescent Medicine, 160*:65–69.
The authors provide a review of the continuance and severity of these types of disorders in children into their adult lives.

Bottomley, G. (2011, June). Treating nocturnal enuresis in children in primary care. *The Practitioner, 255*(1741), 23–26.
The author describes enuresis and medication and alarm methods of treatment.

Carlson, G. A., Potegal, M. P., Marguiles, D., Gutkovich, Z., & Basile, J. (2009, June). Rages—What are they and who has them? *Journal of Child and Adolescent Psychopharmacology, 19*(3), 281–288.
The authors examine rages and systematically define their associated clinical and diagnostic conditions.

Centers for Disease Control and Prevention. (2011). *Attention-deficit/hyperactivity disorder (ADHD)*. Retrieved from http://www.cdc.gov/ncbddd/adhd/
This website provides information on the symptoms, diagnosis, data, statistics, treatment, and research on ADHD.

Chard, K. M., & Gilman, R. (2005). Counseling trauma victims: 4 brief therapies meet the test. *Current Psychiatry, 4*(8), 50–64.
The authors discuss adapting cognitive-behavioral therapy techniques to posttraumatic stress disorder clients, with a discussion of modifications specific for children and adolescents.

Clark, A. (2004). Particular aspects of diagnosis, management, and treatment of bipolar disorders in children and adolescents. *Clinical Approaches in Bipolar Disorders, 3*(2), 49–54.
The author reviews issues related to diagnostic confusion in childhood bipolar disorder including methods of assessment, criteria used, and differential diagnoses and comorbidity. Additionally, the author offers expert opinion on appropriate management and pharmacologic treatment of the disorder.

Coffey, B. (2002, March 16). *Tics and Tourette's disorder*. Paper presented at the Conference on Child and Adolescent Psychopharmacology, Boston, MA.
This paper contains lecture notes from the 2002 Psychopharmacology of Childhood Conference in Boston, Massachusetts, as presented by Dr. Barbara Coffey on the subject of Tourette's disorder.

Coffey, B., Biederman, J., Geller, D., Spencer, T., Kim, G., Bellordre, . . . Magovcevic, M. (2000). Distinguishing illness severity from tic severity in children and adolescents with Tourette's disorder. *Journal of the American Academy of Child and Adolescent Psychiatry, 39*(5), 556–561.
This article examines a study of 156 youth ages 5–20 years who were diagnosed with Tourette's disorder and discusses the comorbidity of other psychiatric disorders found in these children and adolescents.

Gartstein, M., & Sheeber, L. (2004). Child behavior problems and maternal symptoms of depression: A mediational model. *Journal of Child and Adolescent Psychiatric Nursing, 17*(4), 141–150.
The article suggests an association between maternal depression and child behavior problems in a study of 69 mothers of 3–6-year-old

children and examines three variables that may be mediating for the severity of dysfunction in the mother.

Gillespie, C. F., & Nemeroff, C. B. (2005). Early life stress and depression. *Current Psychiatry, 4*(10), 15–30.
This article examines the impact of early life stress as a risk factor for the development of mood and anxiety disorders.

Hughes, D. (2002). Sudden onset of obsessive-compulsive disorder may point to PANDAS. *Neurology Reviews.com, 10*(4). Retrieved from http://www.neurologyreviews.com/apr02/pandas.html
The website Neurology Reviews covers emerging news in neurology and neuroscience and is updated monthly, with a focus on practical approaches to treating neurologic disorders. This report discusses one of the first systematic studies that looked at PANDAS and its relationship to obsessive-compulsive disorder.

Kessler, R. C., Adler, L. A., & Barkley, R. (2005). Patterns and predictors of attention-deficit/hyperactivity disorder persistence into adulthood: Results from the National Comorbidity survey replications. *Biological Psychiatry, 57*, 1442–1451.
The authors replicated the National Comorbidity survey by screening 3,199 individuals ages 19–44 years, finding the prevalence rate of attention-deficit/hyperactivity disorder to be 4.4% in the sample.

Massat, I., & Victor, L. (2005). Early bipolar disorder and ADHD: Differences and similarities in pre-pubertal and early adolescence. *Clinical Approaches in Bipolar Disorder, 4*(1), 20–28.
The article discusses a number of studies, including clinical, cognition, neuroimaging, genetic, and pharmacologic studies that highlight the differences and similarities between childhood bipolar disorder and attention-deficit/hyperactivity disorder.

Mell, K., Davis, R. L., & Owens, D. (2005, July 1). Association between streptococcal infection and obsessive-compulsive disorder, Tourette's syndrome, and tic disorder. *Pediatrics, 116*(1), 56–60.
The authors discuss the epidemiologic evidence that PANDAS may arise as a result of postinfectious autoimmune phenomena induced by childhood streptococcal infection.

Meyer, S. E., & Carlson, G. A. (2003). Bipolar disorder in youth: An update. *Current Psychosis and Therapeutic Reports, 1*(2), 79–84.
The authors highlight findings in childhood bipolar disorder literature regarding definition of the disorder, epidemiology, comorbidity, developmental aspects, family studies, medication responsiveness, and treatment.

Millichap, J. G. (2008, February). Etiologic classification of attention deficit /hyperactivity disorder. *Pediatrics, 121*(2), e358–e365.
The author provides an overview of the environmental factors in the etiology of ADHD.

National Institute of Mental Health (NIMH). (1999). *NIMH research on treatment for attention deficit hyperactivity disorder (ADHD): The Multimodal Treatment Study—questions and answers.* Retrieved from http://www.nimh.nih.gov/trials/practical/mta/the-multimodal-treatment-of-attention-deficit-hyperactivity-disorder-study-mta-questions-and-answers.shtml
The Multimodal Treatment Study of Children with ADHD brought together 18 nationally recognized authorities in ADHD at six different university medical centers and hospitals to evaluate the leading treatments for ADHD, including various forms of behavior therapy and medications. It included nearly 600 elementary school children. The NIMH website reports the results of that study.

National Institute of Mental Health (NIMH). (2010). *Suicide in the U.S.: Statistics and prevention.* Retrieved from http://www.nimh.nih.gov/health/publications/suicide-in-the-us-statistics-and-prevention/index.shtml#children
This is a fact sheet of statistics on suicide with information on treatments and suicide prevention.

National Institute of Neurological Disorders and Stroke. (2011). *Tourette syndrome fact sheet.* Retrieved from http://www.ninds.nih.gov/disorders/tourette/detail_tourette.htm
This NINDS website provides information on the causes, symptoms, clinical course, diagnosis, treatment, genetics, prognosis, and research on Tourette's syndrome.

Nock, M. K., Kazdin, A. E., Hiripi, E., & Kessler, R. C. (2006, May). Prevalence, subtypes, and correlates of DSM-IV conduct disorder in the national comorbidity survey replication. *Psychological Medicine, 35*(5), 699–710.
The authors discuss that conduct disorder (CD) is prevalent and heterogeneous in the U.S. popula-

tion, and more severe subtypes and the presence of active CD are associated with higher risk of comorbid disorders.

Ozonoff, S., Young, G. S., Carter, A., Messinger, D. & Yirmiya, N. (2011). Recurrence risk for autism spectrum disorders: A baby siblings research consortium study. *Pediatrics*, originally published online August 15, 2011; DOI 10/1542/peds. 2010-2825.
A prospective study of the siblings of children with ASD discovered that the sibling reoccurrence rate of ASD is higher than suggested by previous studies.

Pelham, W. E., Foster, E. M. & Robb, J. A. (2007, July). The economic impact of attention-deficit/hyperactivity disorder in children and adolescents. *Journal of Pediatric Psychology, 32*(6), 711–727.
Using a cost of illness (COI) framework, the authors examine the economic impact of ADHD in children and adolescents.

Pilowsky, D., Wickramaratne, P., Nomura, Y., & Weissman, M. (2006). Family discord, parental depression, and psychopathology in offspring: 20-year follow-up. *Journal of the Academy of Child and Adolescent Psychiatry, 45*(4), 452–460.
The authors look at the independent effects of parental depression and family discord on children at high and low risk of depression over a 20-year span.

Pine, D. S., Costello, E. J., & Dahl, R. (2010). Increasing the developmental focus in DSM-V: Broad issues and specific potential applications of anxiety. *Evolution of the DSM-V conceptual framework: Development, dimensions, disability, spectra, and gender/culture*. Arlington, VA: APA.
The authors explore the need for an increase in the role of developmental issues with regard to anxiety in the proposed DSM 5.

Pressman, L., Loo, S., Carpenter, E., Asarnow, J., Lynn, D., McCracken, J., . . . Smalley, S. (2006). Relationship of family environment and parental psychiatric diagnosis to impairment in ADHD. *Journal of the American Academy of Child and Adolescent Psychiatry, 45*(3), 346–354.
The authors examine the links among family environment, parental psychiatric diagnosis, and child impairment in 220 families who had at least two children with the diagnosis of attention-deficit/hyperactivity disorder.

Shear, K., Jin, M. A., Ruscio, A. M., Walters, E. E., & Kessler, R. C. (2006, June). Prevalence and correlates of estimated DSM-IV child and adult separation anxiety disorder in the national comorbidity survey replication (NCS-R). *American Journal of Psychiatry, 163*(6), 1074–1083.
Results of the first epidemiological study of adult separation anxiety disorder (SEPAD) and its relationship to childhood SEPAD are presented in this report.

Spencer, T., Biederman, J., & Wilens, T. (2000). Pharmacotherapy of attention deficit hyperactivity disorder. *Psychopharmacology, 9*(1), 77–97.
This article discusses the current pharmacotherapy models for the treatment of attention-deficit/hyperactivity disorder utilizing recommendations of the American Academy of Child and Adolescent Psychiatry practice parameters.

U.S. Department of Health and Human Services. (1999). *Mental Health: A report of the surgeon general*. Retrieved from http://www.surgeongeneral.gov/library/mentalhealth/home.html
This report is the product of an invigorating collaboration between two Federal agencies (NIMH and SAMHSA) makes evident that the neuroscience of mental health—a term that encompasses studies extending from molecular events to psychological, behavioral, and societal phenomena—has emerged as one of the most exciting arenas of scientific activity and human inquiry.

von Gontard, A., Heron, J., & Joinson, C. (2011, June). Family history of nocturnal enuresis and urinary incontinence: Results from a large epidemiological study. *The Journal of Urology, 185*(6), 2303–2306.
The authors report on the genetic risks between child and parental nocturnal enuresis and urinary incontinence.

Wagner, K., Ambrosini, P., Rynn, M., Wohlberg, C., Yang, R., Greenbaum, M. S, . . . Deas, D. (2003). Efficacy of sertraline in the treatment of children and adolescents with major depressive disorder. *Journal of the American Medical Association, 290*(8), 1033–1041.
Two randomized controlled trials discuss major depressive disorder in children and adolescents and examine the safety and tolerability of selective serotonin reuptake inhibitors in 376 youths ages 6–17 years.

Wilens, T., Biederman, J., Kwon, A., Ditterline, J., Forkner, P., Moore, H., . . . Faraone, A. (2004). Risk of substance use disorders in adolescents with bipolar disorder. *Journal of the American Academy of Child and Adolescent Psychiatry, 43*(11), 1380–1386.
The authors examine the risk of substance use disorder in children with a diagnosis of bipolar disorder (n = 57) and without a diagnosis of bipolar disorder (n = 46).

Yung, A., & McGorry, P. (2004). Precursors of schizophrenia. *Current Psychosis and Therapeutics Reports, 2*(2), 67–72.
The authors attempt to detect a precursor stage for emerging psychosis associated with the onset of schizophrenia by reviewing precursor research and assimilating their findings.

Internet Resources

For a full suite of assignments and additional learning activities, use the access code located in the front of your book to visit this exclusive website: http://go.jblearning.com/mentalhealth. If you do not have an access code, you can obtain one at the site.

Learning Objectives

After reading this chapter, you will be able to:

- Differentiate among delirium, dementia, amnesia, and other cognitive disorders.
- Discuss common etiologic factors associated with dementia and delirium.
- Describe symptoms of common types of dementia and delirium.
- Identify effective nursing interventions for the confused client.

Key Terms

Agnosia
Alzheimer's disease
Amnesia
Anterograde amnesia
Aphasia
Apoptosis
Apraxia
Asterixis
Creutzfeldt-Jakob disease
Delirium
Dementia
Huntington's disease
Korsakoff's syndrome
Lewy body disease
Parkinson's disease
Pick's disease
Prion
Retrograde amnesia
Sundowning
Vascular dementia

vascular accidents (CVAs) will increase globally by the year 2020. This is partly because of declining mortality rates as a result of better prenatal and infectious disease care and the gradual aging of society; the prevalence of these disorders increases greatly in the elderly. The 2006 World Health Report predicted that the number of persons over 65 years of age in developing countries will increase by 200–400% over the next 25 years (Lopez, Mathers, Ezzati, Janison, & Murray, 2006).

Delirium affects an estimated 10–20% of hospitalized clients, making it a disorder frequently seen in the emergency room, particularly in the very young and very old. Delirium is most prevalent in hospitalized clients older than 65 years of age and in clients with an underlying baseline dementia. It is often associated with sepsis, anoxia, polypharmacy, arrhythmia, intoxication, or substance abuse. A sudden deterioration in the client's condition is often linked to an identifiable cause that can be treated and potentially reversed.

Although not a sign of the normal aging process, dementia is more common among individuals 60 years of age and older, and the incidence rises rapidly for clients 80 years of age and older. For example, although less than 2% of the population younger than 60 years of age is diagnosed with Alzheimer's disease, it is estimated that approximately 50% of persons older than 80 years of age have this diagnosis. The 2006 World Health Organization (WHO) report estimated that approximately 22 million individuals worldwide are affected by Alzheimer's disease and vascular dementias and predicted that approximately 80 million people will be affected by the year 2020 (Ferri et al., 2005; Lopez et al., 2006) and 105 million by 2050 (Dartigues, 2009).

Dementia occurs more commonly in developing and developed countries. Alzheimer's disease has been determined to be the fourth leading cause of death in the United States. Cardiovascular disease, the third leading cause of death in the United States, increases the risk for developing arrhythmias, transient ischemic attacks (TIAs), or CVAs that can lead to vascular or multi-infarct dementia. Smoking, alcohol abuse, diabetes, vasculitis, and coagulopathies also increase the risk for vascular dementia. In the United States, the National Stroke Association (NSA) estimates that the risk of stroke is greater for women and for those over 55 years of age; two thirds of all stroke clients are older than 65 years of age. WHO estimates that the incidence of Parkinson's disease is approximately 500 per 100,000 with a prevalence of 0.07%. Huntington's disease is estimated to have a frequency of 4–7%. Creutzfeldt-Jakob disease, a rare disorder in which clients show progressive signs of deterioration similar to clients with Alzheimer's disease, occurs with an incidence of one case per 1 million people each year (Lopez et al., 2006). Some researchers posit an association between Creutzfeldt-Jakob disease and mad cow disease or bovine spongiform encephalopathy (BSE). Although the incidence of both of these diseases is low, Creutzfeldt-Jakob disease has an increased prevalence along with BSE (also known as new-variant Creutzfeldt-Jakob disease) due to improvement of the sensitivity and specificity of diagnostic testing, identification of wider genetic susceptibility, and a possible carrier status, as well as the potential uncertainty regarding the incubation period (Seitz et al., 2007).

Etiology

Cognitive disorders may occur from temporary or permanent changes in the function of the brain as a result of genetic predisposition, infections, toxins, metabolic disorders, or injury. Delirium may be caused by general medical conditions, substance abuse, or multiple causes, or it may have an unknown etiology. Dementia may be caused by **Alzheimer's disease**, a vascular or medical condition, or a substance abuse–induced pathology.

Deliriums are usually considered to be temporary and potentially reversible states. Some physiologic causes of delirium include infections, particularly those affecting the CNS; encephalopathies; toxic metabolic events; acute or chronic exposure to heavy metals or industrial toxins; intoxicants; inhalants and volatile solvents; cannabinoids or hallucinogens; and overdoses of prescription or over-the-counter (OTC) medications. Many prescription medications can, by themselves or in combination with other medications, contribute to the development of delirium. These medications include anesthetics and pain medications, antihistamines, commonly used gastrointestinal medications and hypnotics, steroids, and psychotropic medications. Delirium can be caused by drug intoxication or withdrawal. Malabsorption problems and dietary problems also cause cognitive changes that may be reversible. These include chronic alcohol abuse that can result in a vitamin B_{12} deficiency, pellagra resulting from a niacin deficiency, or an amnesiac syndrome such as **Korsakoff's syndrome** resulting from a thiamine deficiency. In clients with seizure disorders, the frequency and duration of seizures, the prolonged use of medication or overmedication, and the underlying disease or injury can contribute to the development of cognitive disorders. The physiologic changes experienced by a client with grand mal, petit mal, temporal lobe, or psychomotor seizures may present in an acute confusional state as a result of continuous or breakthrough seizure activity, as well as a postictal state.

Deliriums are usually temporary and reversible. Dementias are typically chronic and progressive.

Isolation, sleep deprivation, and immobilization also can contribute to the development of delirium. The most common example of this phenomenon is that of demented clients who experience worsening of confusion and restlessness at night. This is known as **sundowning**. The routine practice of giving hypnotics or antianxiety medications to demented clients who have been isolated in the strange new environment of a hospital room to quiet them down exacerbates this problem. The commonly used term *intensive care unit (ICU) psychosis* usually inaccurately describes the disoriented, disorganized behavior of a client who is delirious. The delirium may be caused by an underlying medical problem or an iatrogenic problem as a result of the use of restraints or medical or surgical interventions.

Clinical Example

Betty is a 67-year-old woman who called the police for assistance and was found in her apartment screaming that her family was trying to poison her and wanted her dead. Her family reported that Betty had no past history of psychiatric problems and no medical problems except for hypertension, which seemed to be controlled with medication. They reported no changes in her health or regular medication. They mentioned that the patient was a little nervous anticipating traveling to visit her daughter in another state. Because she was having some trouble sleeping, the patient had been taking an over-the-counter medication containing diphenhydramine (Benadryl). Using a new prescribed medication or over-the-counter medication can lead to new symptoms usually associated with a psychiatric disorder.

Dementias are usually considered chronic and progressive. Alzheimer's disease is probably the most frequently encountered dementia. As mentioned earlier, a distinction is made between clients who have early-onset dementia and those who have late-onset dementia. Dementia may be accompanied by symptoms of delirium, delusions, depressed mood, hallucinations or other perceptual problems, behavior disorders, or communication problems. Some of the disorders most commonly associated with dementia are as follows:

- *Degenerative dementias:* These include Alzheimer's disease, Lewy body disease, amyotrophic lateral sclerosis (ALS), Pick's disease, Creutzfeldt-Jakob disease, Parkinson's disease, Parkinson's plus (Parkinson-like syndromes with multiple system degeneration), Huntington's disease, and BSE/new-variant Creutzfeldt-Jakob disease.
- *Ventricular disorders:* Ventricular disorders include normal pressure hydrocephalus (NPH) and obstructive and nonobstructive hydrocephalus.
- *Infectious disorders:* These include human immunodeficiency virus type 1 (HIV-1), encephalopathies, and neurosyphilis.
- *Vascular disorders:* The vascular disorders are Binswanger's disease (subcortical arteriosclerotic encephalopathy), subarachnoid and subdural hematomas, vasculitis, small vessel disorders, and CVAs.
- *Immunologic disorders:* These include multiple sclerosis (MS), systemic lupus erythematosus (SLE), and HIV-1.
- *Convulsive disorders:* These may result from injury, epilepsy, stroke, or metabolic disorders.
- *Systemic disorders:* Systemic disorders include brain cancer and metastatic disease, uremia or renal failure, and other metabolic, endocrinologic, or electrolytic imbalances.
- *Traumatic injury:* Examples of trauma include head injury and postanoxic states.

Evidence-Based Practice

Tullman, Mion, Fletcher & Foreman (2008) identified strategies for nursing assessment and supportive nursing care for patients with delirium. Basic assessment is obtaining baseline information, evaluating alertness, attention, and current medical status. Supportive nursing care includes comfort measures, preventing the hazards of immobility, clear communication, and family education. Further research is needed on the standardization of assessment tools and validation of nursing actions.

- *Toxicity:* Toxicity results from exposure to toxins, heavy metals, or alcohol or other drug abuse.

Amnesic disorders include short- and long-term memory problems that can be caused by trauma, brain lesions, strokes, encephalitis, or chronic alcohol abuse. Transient global amnesia, a period of less than 24 hours of memory loss and confusion, is thought to be primarily vascular in origin. Other medical conditions or surgical interventions also may be associated with amnesic disorders (APA, 2000).

Neurobiologic and Genetic Basis

Dementias

Dementias are usually considered chronic, progressive disorders. Some of the most common degenerative disorders are Alzheimer's disease, Lewy body disorders, frontal and frontal-temporal lobe dementias, and Down syndrome.

Alzheimer's disease involves the development of neurofibrils, neurofibrillary tangles, and beta-plated amyloid plaques, first in the cortex and hippocampus and later in the frontal, parietal, and temporal lobes. Additional changes include cortical atrophy, increased ventricular dilation, and decreased levels of acetylcholine, norepinephrine, and other neurotransmitters. Many of the changes are in the basal forebrain, which is the cortex's source of acetylcholine. This process differs from the normal developmental process of **apoptosis**, the naturally occurring cell death that is part of aging, which may involve the development of amyloid plaques. Acetylcholine is believed to play an important role in memory. Twin and family studies have shown a genetic link, G4 allele (apolipoprotein E [APOE]), that may predispose some individuals to Alzheimer's disease. Genes encoding proteins APP (amyloid precursor protein), PS1 (presenilin-1) and PS2 (presenilin-2) influence development of Alzheimer's disease. Chromosomes 21, 14, and 1 have been associated with early onset development and chromosome 19 APOE with susceptibility. The phenotypic profile for the development of Alzheimer's disease and vascular dementia differ, but it is common for most dementias to be mixed Alzheimer's and vascular dementia (Ginzburg & Willard, 2010). Ongoing research studying subjects who are mutation carriers of one of three genes (APP, PSEN1, and PSEN2) have shown decline in cognitive functioning compared with noncarrier siblings and increased levels of tau and phosphorylated tau. The association of age of onset of Alzheimer's disease in relatives appears most obvious in autosomal dominant families and it has been hypothesized that APOE only alters risk for age of onset. Genetic factors appear to be less prominent in late-onset Alzheimer's disease (David, Fleminger, Kopelman, Lovestone, & Melers, 2009). In addition, there is some indication that long-term exposure to pollutants or intoxicants may contribute to the development of the disease in those individuals with a predisposition to Alzheimer's.

Some studies have indicated that persons with relatives who have Parkinson's disease also have cortical symptoms. Gene mutations have been shown to influence both the development of Parkinson's disease and to modify the risk of development of disease in others. Research using MRI neuroimaging has been shown to identify those at risk for Parkinson's disease by identifying compensatory changes in motor activity before there are clinical dopaminergic changes (Ginzburg & Willard, 2010). Exposure to drugs of abuse such as methamphetamine are at an increased risk of developing Parkinson's disease, which is a dopamine deficiency disorder (Callaghan, Cunningham, Sykes, & Kish, 2011). In clients with frontal lobe dementias such as Pick's disease, ALS, and progressive supranuclear palsy, there can be frontal temporal lobe hypometabolism and a progressive, degenerative course similar to Alzheimer's. Lewy body dementias also have the plaques and tangles associated with Alzheimer's disease as well as Lewy bodies in the substantia nigra and the cortex, as in Parkinson's disease. In Lewy body dementia and Parkinson's disease, there are aggregates of synuclein in Lewy bodies and other lesions. Lewy bodies may also be found in Alzheimer's and Parkinson's diseases (David et al., 2009). In clients with Lewy body disease, visual hallucinations and delusions are usually more prominent than would be suspected by the degree of cognitive impairment, and the client may have extrapyramidal symptoms as do clients with Parkinson's disease.

Parkinson's disease and Huntington's disease are primarily subcortical dementias. The predominant features of these diseases tend to be the symptoms of movement disorders, mood disorders such as depression, and changes in personality (regressive behavior). Clients with Parkinson's disease have degeneration of the substantia nigra. Parkinson's disease is caused primarily by a dopamine deficiency in the substantia nigra, caudate, and putamen that results in basal ganglia dysfunction. Lewy bodies are also found mainly in the autonomic nervous system and brain. Extrapyramidal symptoms such as rigid posture, tremors, and bradykinesia (slowed movements) are common. The observation of family clusters of Huntington's disease has led to genetic mapping studies that have identified Huntington's as an autosomal-dominant disease in which the hypermetabolism of glucose and tissue atrophy cause choreic movements (jerking, ticlike involuntary movements) and progressive dementia (David et al., 2009). Huntingtin protein (HTT), which is associated with Huntington's disease, has been identified as changes to chromosome 4, which affects the sequence of three nucleotides CAG [cytosine(C), adenine (A), and guanine (G)], and testing is done by measuring the number of CAG repeats. Individuals with more than 40 repeats of this CAG sequence are diagnosed with Huntington's disease (Ginzburg & Willard, 2010). In Huntington's disease there is usually a gradual onset of symptoms between ages 40 and 50 years. Since Huntington's disease has been determined to be an autosomal dominant disorder, a large percentage of family members elect to have genetic testing to determine their risk.

Prions are almost indestructible particles that accumulate, form plaques, and damage neurons.

In most multi-infarct dementias, encephalopathies, infectious diseases, systemic illnesses, endocrinopathies, and exposure to drugs and toxins, both cortical and subcortical damage occur. There are certain rare vascular disorders that have a strong genetic component, and the risk for vascular disorders usually increases with age. Common risk factors for Alzheimer's disease and cardiac disease such as APOE variation and amyloid deposits in blood vessel walls are found in both and may increase vulnerability. Changes in Alzheimer's disease and cardiac disease can be found 10–15 years before symptoms are significant for diagnosis (David et al., 2009). Disorders that are transmitted, such as Creutzfeldt-Jakob disease and BSE/new-variant Creutzfeldt-Jakob disease, are thought to be caused by **prions** (proteinaceous infectious particles containing deoxyribonucleic acid [DNA]). Prions are almost indestructible particles that self-replicate by connecting to other proteins and accumulate, form plaques, and cause spongiform vacuoles, or spongelike holes that damage neurons.

Taking a complete client history may help to identify the various causes of head injuries. Elderly clients may hurt themselves by falling, epileptics might hurt themselves during seizures, and alcoholics may be injured as a result of abuse of alcohol. Sports injuries and motor vehicle or bicycle accidents also are frequent causes of brain injury.

Immunologic and infectious disorders such as multiple sclerosis (MS), neurosyphilis, and human immunodeficiency virus-1 (HIV-1) also cause symptoms of a cognitive disorder as a result of changes to the CNS. In HIV-1, as the disease progresses, white matter and subcortical structures are often destroyed. However, the damage can be complicated by reduced resistance to other infections including meningitis, toxoplasmosis, cytomegalovirus (CMV), and neoplasms such as lymphoma and Kaposi sarcoma. MS is an autoimmune disease in which extensive periventricular demyelination causes symptoms of dementia with no correlation to the duration of the illness or to other symptoms of disease progression (Mendez & Cummings, 2003).

Cardiac, vascular, and pulmonary problems may cause disturbances in the regulation of cerebral blood flow. This can cause oxidative damage and hypoperfusion in the subcortical white matter of the brain. This damage is shown by changes in microglial cell activation, beta-amyloid processing, and long-term potentiation on glutamate-mediated neurotransmitters. In vascular dementias, ischemic events or emboli as well as vascular changes may affect certain areas in the brain and after a time are seen as ischemic changes to the white matter. Following a TIA, damage may be only temporary or not apparent at all. However, over time, the client may develop lacunae infarcts in which the surface of the brain is pitted from small infarcts. Damage to vital areas may also occur. Damage to certain areas may cause speech and language problems.

An **aphasia** is a speech or language disorder. Left-sided temporal lobe lesions often cause Wernicke's aphasia, a receptive disorder in which there are problems comprehending sensory stimuli. Lower left-sided temporal lobe lesions cause Broca's aphasia, an expressive disorder in which there are problems with speech or speaking. Clients with right-hemisphere lesions often present with an abnormal posture, apathy, an altered perception of body image that causes inattention to or denial of disability, and problems with constructional ability (inability to reproduce figures correctly), recognition (difficulty in identifying objects or faces), and spatial orientation (Pinel, 2010). The client with dementia is usually alert during the day while some may experience a night/day reversal. The client with delirium may have fluctuating levels of consciousness throughout the day.

A client with grand mal, petit mal, temporal lobe, or psychomotor seizures undergoes physiologic changes that may result in either an acute confusional state from continuous or breakthrough seizure activity or a postictal state in which periods of amnesia are experienced. Trauma to the head, such as the repetitive injury and abuse boxers and football players suffer, can cause physiologic and structural changes that produce symptoms of dementia or amnesia. Neurofibrillary tangles and amyloid plaques, which are associated with memory and cognitive functioning, can develop.

Evidence-Based Practice

Mezey and Maslow (2008) reviewed best practices in assessment and recognition of dementia in hospitalized older adults. By using targeted questions regarding memory problems, diagnosis of Alzheimer's disease or dementia, family questionnaire of daily activities and memory, and patient behavior triggers to record symptoms of possible dementia, nurses could increase recognition of dementia. Mezey and Maslow suggest incorporating questions and behavior profiles in the nursing assessment and hospital forms. Basic questions focused on forgetfulness, repetition, problems following directions, and problems managing the household and making decisions, and staff recorded behavioral symptoms usually associated with dementia. A history of dementia is often not listed in the hospital record or used in determination of acuity. Further research is needed regarding whether early identification of dementia and delirium would be beneficial in identifying high-risk patients in the hospital, as well as in reducing problems such as falls, agitated and aggressive behaviors, and functional decline.

Amnesias

The memory disturbances of amnesia are thought to be caused by interruptions to cerebral blood flow, blows to the head, effects of medication, or drug abuse. Damage to the hippocampus in the medial temporal lobe or to the cortex can cause amnesia. Korsakoff's syndrome is associated with chronic alcohol use. Memory loss may be attributable to thiamine deficiency and possibly to lesions in the brain and damage to the mediodorsal nuclei of the mediodorsal thalamus. Wernicke's encephalopathy is caused by acute thiamine deficiency. It is seen in chronically malnourished alcoholics who may have a genetic predisposition that prevents thiamine bonding. Wernicke's encephalopathy is an acute confusional state that usually resolves with treatment. Clients with a persistent or profound memory loss, particularly for recent events, usually have brain lesions and chronic impairment and exhibit the symptoms of dementia or Korsakoff's syndrome (Mendez & Cummings, 2003; Pinel, 2010).

Clinical Presentation

The signs and symptoms of changes in mental status are often the first clues to the presence of cognitive impairment. Other signs include changes in the individual's ability in one or more areas of comprehension, object naming, organizational skills, insight and judgment, spatial and visual abilities, and the ability to perform complex sequences of tasks. The mental status of a client is assessed by examination of appearance, alertness, affect and mood, speech and language, general cognitive functioning, and psychologic state.

The mental status examination often begins by observing the level of consciousness, which is usually defined as part of a continuum of interaction with or sensitivity to environmental stimuli. It includes the level of consciousness and ability to attend and recognize stimuli. The client may exhibit anything from hypervigilance to alertness, lethargy, stupor, obtundation, and coma. An alert client is fully awake and responsive and readily interacts with the examiner. A lethargic client may appear to be sleeping, may respond readily to verbal stimuli but be unable to attend to the interviewer and may soon fall back to sleep if not continuously stimulated. In contrast, a stuporous client may appear to be sleeping soundly. An obtunded client may be only minimally responsive to painful stimuli, and a comatose client may not respond at all. Unless the client is fully alert, it is difficult to involve him or her in an assessment. The client would be unable to focus and to shift attention at will.

Family members and other caretakers can be questioned to determine if the level of consciousness or alertness of the client varies or fluctuates throughout the day, worsens at night, or occurs in response to a specific event or stressor. If a CVA is suspected, it is important to note when the changes occurred and whether the changes were witnessed (e.g., the client was observed having problems speaking) or unwitnessed (e.g., the client was found unresponsive on the floor) and whether they lasted for a particular length of time. Family members or caretakers also can describe the client's usual living arrangements and whether the client functions independently, requires some assistance with household responsibilities, or needs supervision of personal activities of daily living (ADLs). These changes may have occurred so slowly that the client or family may not be aware of the accommodations that have been made for progressive disability. Conversely, abrupt changes in the client's usual level of functioning may also occur.

Observation of the client's appearance, ability to communicate, and behavior is also important. The nurse must check to see if the client is groomed properly and if the clothing is appropriate for the situation and season. The nurse should note if there are bruises or signs of injury. The nurse must also note if the client's features are symmetrical and if posture, gait, mouth, or tongue are impaired. Clients with dementia may exhibit the loss of the ability to perform skilled motor acts, a condition referred to as **apraxia**. The client's speech and language skills can be observed as they interact with others in identifying and recalling objects, responding to questions, and making their needs known.

The mental status examination is an important part of client assessment. Many of the same symptoms can be found in clients with cognitive disorders and functional psychiatric disorders. The mental status examination initially helps the clinician build a foundation for the differential diagnosis.

Also of importance is the client's ability to recall personal identity, to orient to his or her present location, and to give the date and time. The nurse should see if the client can describe his or her living situation and give details such as the names of the primary healthcare provider, family members or caretaker, and usual medications. The nurse can perform a quick assessment of the client's reading and comprehension skills. If the responses are spon-

Clinical Example

Roberto is an employed 63-year-old man who was brought to the emergency department after he was observed by his family to have a period of slurred speech and inability to move his right arm when awakening from a nap at home. The patient had been watching a ballgame on television and had fallen asleep. The family is concerned because Roberto didn't seem to recognize them at first and didn't seem able to communicate with them. Roberto appeared to recover in a few minutes. Now despite some weakness in his right arm, he insists he is fine and wants to go home. His wife recalls that he had a similar episode several weeks before but the symptoms disappeared so quickly that the client said his arm must have fallen asleep.

CASE STUDIES Ms. S

Ms. S. is a 60-year-old woman with no psychiatric or drug abuse history whose son brought her to the psychiatric center. The client was evaluated by the advanced practice nurse. The client's son stated that he had become alarmed during a visit when his father told him that his mother had been acting very strangely and crazy. The client's son and husband attributed these changes to her early retirement 3 years ago. The family stated that the client had been a home attendant and had worked regularly up until then, although the agency for which she worked had been calling her less and less for about a year before her retirement and had eventually stopped calling her. In addition, they said that she formerly had done everything in the house, was very strong and healthy, and took no medications. However, she had been forgetting to pay bills lately, leaving the stove on, burning dinners, and neglecting the housework and her appearance. She had stopped doing many of her usual activities such as going to church, and she previously had been very active in church work. Her husband said that he noticed that she never read the Bible any more, which had been very important to her.

The previous night she had left the house without saying anything to her husband and was gone for hours. He assumed that she was acting strangely again and had gone to her sister's house. However, when she did not return the following morning, and her sister said that she had not visited, her husband went looking for her. He found her walking up and down the block several streets from their home. Ms. S. had wandered from home. She had not found her sister's home or found her way back to her own home. Her only explanation at the time was that the house was wrong. During the interview, the client seemed very embarrassed and apologized to everyone. She was unable to recall objects, do simple arithmetic problems, recite the months of the year backward, or draw a simple figure of an open cross. The initial clinical impression was dementia of the Alzheimer's type with early onset (before age 65) (see **Table 13-1**), and she was referred for a dementia workup, which was to include neurologic examination; diagnostic tests for possible sepsis, anemia, electrolyte imbalances, vitamin B_{12} deficiency, folate deficiency, syphilis (VDRL), and thyroid functioning; computed tomography (CT) scan of the head; electroencephalogram (EEG); toxicology screen; ammonia levels; and liver function tests.

Nursing Care Plan **Dementia**

Nursing Diagnosis 1: Wandering related to impaired way-finding as evidenced by getting lost on way to sister's house and inability to find way home.

Nursing Diagnosis 2: Social isolation related to inability to perform activities independently as evidenced by stopping usual activities such as church going.

Nursing Diagnosis 3: Impaired role performance related to cognitive decline as evidenced by inability to manage household.

Expected Outcomes	Interventions	Evaluations
• Will decrease potential for injury.	• To provide anticipatory guidance to the family regarding the client's disabilities.	• The client has begun to wear a Medical Alert bracelet.
• Will be able to interact with others to maximum of cognitive ability.	• To discuss options for possible referral to an adult daycare program.	• The client participates in an adult care program with activities for demented clients.
• Will experience improved interaction and support with family.	• To refer the family to an Alzheimer's Association family support group.	• Family members verbalize feelings of loss.
• Will be able to accomplish activities of daily living by self or with support of others.	• To educate the client and the client's family regarding the need for memory cues such as clocks, calendars, and lists of routines.	• The family has set up stable household routines.

Visit http://go.jblearning.com/mentalhealth for additional care plans and exercises.

Table 13-1 **Assessment for Dementia**

1. History of cognitive decline (e.g., progressive decline in Alzheimer's-type dementia or more sudden or step-wise decline in vascular-type dementia)
2. Evidence of cognitive impairment (e.g., Mini Mental State score of less than 26/30, aphasia, apraxia, agnosia, history of impairment in higher cortical functioning such as inability to do abstractions or problem solving)
3. Examples of decline from premorbid functioning (e.g., inability to maintain household, inability to drive car)
4. Elimination of possible reversible causes of impairment (e.g., decreased vitamin B_{12}, folate, or niacin, and abnormal thyroid or liver functioning; positive Venereal Disease Research Laboratory test (VDRL); sepsis)
5. Elimination of possible medical disorders that better explain functional problems (e.g., Huntington's disease, Parkinson's disorder, normal pressure hydrocephalus)
6. Elimination of possible mental disorders that better explain functional problems (e.g., depression, psychosis, developmental disorder)
7. Identification of presence or absence of behavioral problems (e.g., severe agitation, wandering) associated with the decline in cognitive functioning

taneous and fluent, a formal cognitive test may not be needed unless a specific problem is suspected or the client's history suggests a problem such as noncompliance with medical treatment (possibly attributable to comprehension or memory problems). The nurse must observe whether the client has trouble concentrating or performing the task at hand. The nurse should look for signs of problems with immediate memory (recalling new ongoing events), recent memory (recalling contemporary events), or remote memory (recalling past events). Often a client will mention having problems with memory or concentration. At this point, a more formal measure of cognition such as the Mini-Mental

State Examination or another brief cognitive rating scale can be introduced as a natural extension of the interviewer's assessment.

Agnosia, or the inability to recognize objects, which cannot be explained by a reduced level of alertness, may suggest a dementia. Any unusual preoccupations such as paranoid beliefs, delusional thinking, or unusual experiences such as hallucinations are important to note, as are assessments for suicidal or homicidal thoughts and the potential for aggressive or violent behavior. The presence of visual hallucinations usually indicates a delirium rather than psychotic features of a functional psychiatric disorder. Visual hallucinations can be prominent in Lewy body dementias and are often not distressing or frightening to the client.

Table 13-2 **Assessment for Delirium**

1. Identification of sudden change in mental status (e.g., changes within a few hours or days) or history of preexisting dementia that may make the person more prone to development of delirium (e.g., previous history of postoperative delirium in a client with known dementia, confusion in a client with known history of stroke who showed behavior changes in the past when diagnosed with a urinary tract infection)
2. Observation of levels of consciousness that show sudden and fluctuating changes (e.g., periods of clarity alternating with lethargy, presence of visual hallucinations or illusions)
3. Development of cognitive changes that may also be sudden and fluctuating (e.g., periods of disorientation, communication problems, memory problems) not better explained by preexisting disorder such as dementia or central nervous system disorders
4. Identification of specific medical disorder or reversible cause for symptoms (e.g., sepsis, exposure to toxins or substances of abuse, or electrolyte imbalance)

CASE STUDIES Ms. T

Ms. T. is a 72-year-old woman who was brought to the emergency room by police after her neighbors called to report that she had been found wandering in the hallway of the apartment building. Neighbors stated that she was screaming about snakes in her room that were coming out of the floor and ceiling. The neighbors stated that Ms. T. was normally a very quiet woman who was very active in the senior center but had not been performing her usual activities for several days. When the client's family was called, they were very upset to see Ms. T. Her daughter stated that she had seen her mother 2 days earlier to help her with shopping and that everything had seemed fine. The client had called her daughter the day before and said that she did not feel well and thought she had a slight cold, so she was going to stay home. Her daughter stated that she would not have recognized her mother, who now appeared unkempt and tremulous. This was an abrupt change from the client's usual well-groomed and confident appearance. The client was described as a very strong and forceful woman who required only minimal assistance with household management. The daughter added that the client was proud that she had never been sick a day in her life, was on no prescription medications, and rarely took any OTC medications other than aspirin. There was no psychiatric history. Now the client appeared frightened and asked her daughter to stay near her because she did not understand why she had been arrested and brought to the police station. The client became more distressed when the curtain was drawn around her bed in the emergency room. She complained that there were worms moving on the striped curtain. The client had a slight cough and elevated temperature, and the staff reported that the initial chest X-ray indicated pneumonia.

The initial clinical impression was of delirium (**Table 13-2**), and diagnostic testing was done to determine if the client was septic. It would be expected that the delirium would resolve as the infection was treated. Because an underlying dementia can sometimes cause a client to be more prone to developing delirium, the client should be evaluated for possible dementia after the delirium resolves. If the delirium is superimposed upon a preexisting dementia, the diagnosis would be dementia with delirium (APA, 2000). Delirium is a symptom of a medical emergency, and the client should be evaluated to determine the cause of the delirium.

Nursing Care Plan **Delirium**

Nursing Diagnosis 1: Disturbed sensory perception related to visual hallucinations as evidenced by seeing worms moving on curtains.

Nursing Diagnosis 2: Acute confusion related to disorientation to place as evidenced by belief that she was in the police station.

Nursing Diagnosis 3: Risk for falls related to decreased independence as evidenced by confusion in new environment and increased dependency on others.

Expected Outcomes	Interventions	Evaluations
• Will be oriented to environment and assisted to maintain orientation when needed.	• To provide reorientation for the client (e.g., introducing self, explaining procedures, having a clock and calendar in the room).	• Observation of increased levels of functioning and orientation with appropriate cueing.
• Will experience decreased anxiety.	• To observe and identify ways in which the client expresses anxiety related to confusion.	• Observation of decreased anxiety.
• Will decrease potential for injury to self or others.	• To review fall precautions and other safety policies with unlicensed assistive personnel involved in care of the client.	• Supervision of fall precautions on the unit.
• Will receive assistance in identifying and coping with symptoms of hallucinations.	• To assess the client's cognitive status and presence of visual hallucinations.	• Involvement of the staff in client assessment and appropriate interventions.

Visit http://go.jblearning.com/mentalhealth for additional care plans and exercises.

Differential Diagnosis

The differential diagnosis of a cognitive disorder as a reflection of abnormal brain functioning is often determined by the onset, progression, and types of symptoms that occur. The onset of delirium is usually sudden and progresses rapidly, but symptoms may appear to fluctuate during the day and worsen at night, or they may fluctuate from day to day. The client's level of consciousness and orientation may be impaired or seem to fluctuate at times. The client may perceive common environmental stimuli incorrectly or have visual as well as other types of hallucinations. Memory problems are common and may affect recall and short- and long-term memory.

Asterixis, known as liver flap, is a condition of motor tremors where the client is unable to maintain a posture or position without moving. For example, the client is unable to hold his or her hands in a flexed position without flapping them. To test for asterixis, clients are asked to extend their arms outward and raise the fingers so that the palms of their hands face outward. The nurse should also be aware of the presence of sepsis, a systemic disorder, substance abuse, exposure to toxins, or structural damage as a result of an accident or stroke, because these are all possible causes of delirium. Asterixis can be found in patients with metabolic encephalopathies, electrolyte imbalance, and drug use.

Taking a complete history of any trauma, medication use, operative and postoperative complications, cardiac disease, and hypertension is important to understand the etiology of the disorder as well as contributing factors that, if treated, could resolve the delirium. Behavioral changes are not always a clear indication of delirium because the client may either be agitated and hyperactive or withdrawn and sedated. Overmedication, drug interactions, and substance abuse may be related to the development of delirium. If related to substance abuse withdrawal, treatment for withdrawal symptoms may be indicated, or the client may need to be tapered slowly from the offending agent to avoid seizures or autonomic instability. Although delirium is considered a tem-

The differential diagnoses of dementia or delirium should include consideration of any underlying psychiatric disorders and drug and alcohol abuse.

Many clients present with a mixed picture of symptoms that may be attributable to several different disorders. For example, a demented client may become delirious, a client with Alzheimer's disease may also have a vascular dementia, or a client with a substance-abuse disorder may have normal pressure hydrocephalus.

porary and potentially reversible problem, recovery time may be prolonged in the elderly or those who are medically compromised.

An important differential is to determine whether the symptoms represent pseudodementia or dementia-like symptoms of poor memory and functioning that are actually caused by a mood disorder—usually depression. Whereas clients with dementia usually attempt to cooperate with cognitive testing or to minimize and hide deficits, clients with pseudodementia have inconsistent responses that make them appear to be worse than they actually are. For example, they may have better immediate and short-term memory than long-term memory and improve in the hospital rather than worsen in the new environment or at night. Treatment of the depression improves the cognitive impairment of a client with pseudodementia. Observations and methods used to differentiate among delirium, dementia, vascular dementia, and pseudodementia are given in **Table 13-3**.

Dementia may be the initial presenting problem or an underlying problem predisposing the development of delirium. Dementia should be distinguished from the normal aging process. Identifying the cause

Evidence-Based Practice

Gaudreau, Gagnon, Harel, Tremblay, and Roy (2005) studied use of a brief, five-item observational scale noting disorientation, inappropriate behavior, disorganized communication, illusions/hallucinations, and psychomotor retardation to identify clients with manifestations of delirium. Interrater reliability was determined between nurses and physicians and between the scale used and the Confusion Assessment Method (CAM), a more widely used scale. Use of the Nursing Delirium Screening Scale (Nu-DESC) was validated and beneficial in helping recognized unidentified cases.

Table 13-3 Comparison of Delirium, Dementia, Vascular Dementia, and Pseudodementia

	Delirium	Dementia	Vascular Dementia	Pseudodementia/ Depression
Onset	Acute	Chronic	Acute or chronic	Chronic
Clinical course	Sudden	Slowly progressive	Sudden, gradual, or stepwise	Acute or chronic
Impairment	Fluctuating	Progressive	Discrete or global problems	Inconsistent
Disorientation	Usually	Progressive	Sometimes	Oriented
Cognitive impairment	Rarely	Progressive	Usually	Patchy
Language	Sometimes	Naming objects	+/– speech problems	None
Perceptual	+/– visual hallucinations; +/– tactile hallucinations	Sometimes	Sometimes	Rarely, +/– auditory hallucinations
Aphasia	Occasionally	Sometimes	+/– speech and language problems	Rarely
Apraxia	Rarely	Progressive	Sometimes	Rarely
Agnosia	Rarely	Progressive	Sometimes	Rarely
Asterixis	+/– asterixis	Rarely	Rarely	Rarely
CT scan	Normal	Atrophy	Abnormal	Normal
EEG	Abnormal	Normal or slowed; slowing increases when advanced	+/– abnormalities	Normal
MRI	+/– changes	Normal or hippocampal atrophy	White matter disease; ischemic changes	Normal

Note: CT = computed tomography; EEG = electroencephalogram; MRI = magnetic resonance imaging.

of dementia assists in treatment and management. A history of falls may be the first sign of Alzheimer's disease or of a Lewy body dementia. Other medical conditions should be eliminated as contributing factors. There may be multiple etiologic factors identified with the dementia. In a vascular dementia, there are usually associated focal neurologic signs. It is common to find combinations of Alzheimer's and vascular dementia.

Clinical Course and Complications

The clinical course in cognitive disorders varies from acute to chronic conditions and may be accompanied by other physical and psychiatric disorders. An outline of the clinical course of delirium, Alzheimer's disease, and other forms of dementia appears in **Table 13-4**.

Delirium is usually associated with an acute medical condition and is potentially reversible. Clients with preexisting dementia may be more prone to developing the symptoms of a delirium when they experience the physiologic changes associated with an electrolyte imbalance, pharmacotherapy, or medical illness (see Chapter 14). It is important to identify and treat the underlying cause of the delirium as well as to avoid anything that may cause or contribute to the delirium. Untreated pain or overmedication with pain medications can contribute to delirium. Screening should include a history of medications, herbals, and supplements the client may be taking as well as a determination of substance use and abuse. The symptoms of delirium may vary during the course of the illness in terms of the level of alertness and orientation and as to the presence or absence of symptoms of agitation, delusions, or hallucinations.

Clients with Alzheimer's disease may experience a gradual progression of symptoms for several years. This may include periods when symptoms occasionally level off or stabilize. The problem typically noted first is delayed recall. As the disease progresses, problems include difficulties in recognizing and naming objects, problems in recognizing people, and socially inappropriate and disinhibited behaviors. At this point, the client requires total care and supervision of ADLs. The onset of vascular dementia may be more

Table 13-4 **Clinical Course of Delirium, Dementia, and Amnesia**

	Onset	Clinical Course	Signs and Symptoms
Delirium	Sudden	Acute, reversible	Confusion and disorientation
Dementia	Varies with disease	Generally irreversible	Varies with disease
Alzheimer's disease	Gradual < age 65	Progressive	Cognitive decline, disorientation, incontinence, wandering, and behavior changes
Vascular dementia	Acute	Stepwise	Cognitive changes, speech problems, and paresis
Parkinson's disease	> age 40	Progressive	Bradykinesia, tremor, and gait and posture problems
Pick's disease	Sudden	Rapid and progressive	Personality changes and cognitive decline
Huntington's disease	Age 35–40	Progressive	Movement disorder, emotional instability, and personality changes
Creutzfeldt-Jakob disease (CJD)	Age 40–60	Progressive	Cognitive disorder and personality changes
BSE (new-variant CJD)	Age varies	Progressive	Similar to CJD
Normal pressure hydrocephalus	Gradual; > age 50	Chronic and possibly reversible	Apathy/depression, gait problems, and incontinence
HIV	Varies	Varies	Increased by presence of other disorders and acute/chronic infection
Substance induced	Drug abuse history	Acute or chronic; +/− withdrawal	Memory problems, cognitive problems, and behavior changes
Amnesia	Sudden; not part of delirium	Depends on cause	Memory problems: anterograde, retrograde, and transient global

Predominant features complicating the clinical course of a dementia may include the presence of delirium delusions, depressed mood, or behavioral disturbances.

Clinical Example

Dennis, a 65-year-old man, has been having increasing problems concentrating since he retired. He worries about problems with his memory and loses track of bills and appointments. He has lost interest in his usual activities and doesn't shower or shave regularly saying, "What's the difference; I'm not going anywhere?" He appears to have lost weight since his last clinic visit. He identifies his biggest problem as fatigue and states he has had trouble falling asleep and staying asleep. During questioning, Dennis answers, "I don't know. I just don't know," to simple questions while appearing to easily answer more difficult questions.

Clients with depression may be indifferent to testing or highlight their inability to answer questions, and some frequently give up and not answer. This is in contrast to clients with dementia who may struggle with the test, ask for frequent feedback on responses, or answer with a near miss.

noticeable and rapid for both client and family. The disease may progress for many years, but symptoms might not be seen until a critical area of the brain is affected or the additive effects to many different areas of the brain are apparent.

Critical Thinking Question

At times, changes in cognition may be so slow and gradual that the client and family accommodate to these changes, making it difficult for them to recognize and acknowledge problems. Problems may not be recognized until the client is in a new environment such as the hospital. How can client and family teaching be used to assist the client and family in recognizing when further assessment or assistance might be needed? Give an example of how these topics could be introduced to the client and family.

In amnesic disorders, the onset may be rapid and is usually associated with trauma or disease. In many cases, memory gradually returns over time. Past events are usually remembered first before more recent memories. However, there may be no memory of a traumatic event itself or the events immediately preceding or following it. With **anterograde amnesia**, the client has problems learning new material. With **retrograde amnesia**, the client has problems recalling past events or learned material but immediate and recent memory is not impaired.

Management and Treatment

Nursing Interventions

Management of cognitive disorders includes reorientation. The nurse should restructure the environment and activities of the client to maximize his or her abilities and minimize distractions and hazards. This restores the individual to an optimum level of functioning.

Remotivating involves the client as much as possible in self-care activities and appropriate social activities and reinforces appropriate coping mechanisms, adaptive skills, and social supports. In addition, clients are encouraged to reminisce and review their lifetime memories as well as developmental stages and tasks. Dysfunctional symptoms are regulated by treating coexisting illnesses and administering the appropriate medications as required.

Disorientation is often a problem; therefore, frequent reorientation may be necessary. Based on an assessment of the client's deficits, the staff frequently will need to incorporate information to help the client reestablish a correct orientation to person, place, and time. Environmental cues such as easily read calendars and wall clocks, appropriate signs and area decorations, color coding of different areas, and access to information and news sources are important. Staff members should be aware of any sensory defi-

Considerations for Client and Family Education

- Develop awareness of changes in levels of confusion and symptoms that may indicate the need for treatment of medical or psychiatric illnesses.
- Assist the client and family to anticipate and prepare for some changes in roles and caretaking responsibilities.
- Recognize the importance of developing support systems for both the client and caretakers.
- Provide guidance in recognizing and dealing with symptoms of stress and fatigue.

cits and memory and language problems when they provide explanations or interact with a disoriented client in any way.

Critical Thinking Question

Identify environmental factors that can contribute to confusion and some strategies and suggestions for dealing with these problems. How can these suggestions be adapted to the home environment?

The client's attention span and ability to concentrate may be impaired, or there may be varying levels of consciousness. There also may be physical disabilities as a result of illness or a movement disorder. Because of these factors, the environment must be physically safe, accessible for those with disabilities, and structured to minimize dangers. At times, having a family member present helps reorient the client. If the client is agitated or wanders, a companion or sitter at the bedside may help. It may be necessary to evaluate whether the use of partial side rails or safety restraints and full side rails on beds is needed. The staff needs to be aware of the problems that may actually be caused by restraint use. Proper lighting during the day and night lights in the evening are helpful. Ensuring that clients have appropriate supervision, assistance with ADLs, and access to their eyeglasses, hearing aids, dentures, and other adaptive aids is important. Clients with memory problems or wandering (a problem occurring in the later stages of some dementias) may need to wear a Medical Alert bracelet or some other form of identification, and their physical environment may need to be changed to ensure safety.

Evidence-Based Practice

Futrell, Melillo, Remington, and Schoenfelder (2010) identified assessment criteria for wandering including identification of the consequences of wandering, travel patterns, wandering behaviors, and risk factor of premorbid lifestyle characteristics. Appropriate environmental modifications such as providing a secure place to wander, providing cueing, and making exits less accessible in addition to providing appropriate therapeutic interventions such as regular structured activities including exercise, music, and social interaction are effective in decreasing wandering. Further studies of effective assessment tools and interventions would be helpful.

Restoring the client to an optimum level of functioning may be difficult as a result of communication or other cognitive problems, isolation, poor nutrition, or inadequate access to health care. The client may not understand instructions or take prescribed medications. It is important to ensure that the client is getting proper nutrition. The nurse must assess whether problems exist with feeding, dentition, and gum disease, as well as whether there are mechanical problems with chewing or swallowing. Fatigue, limited mobility or movement disorders, incontinence, and alterations in sleep patterns may require changes in a client's routine and physical environment. In addition to the assessment and treatment of their medical problems, clients should be evaluated for the necessity of speech, physical, and occupational therapies.

Critical Thinking Question

With progressive symptoms of dementia, the client may eventually be unable to take food orally. How can dysphagia be evaluated? What quality of life and ethical factors might the client or family consider in deciding on the option for tube or percutaneous endoscopic gastrostomy PEG feedings?

Clients may have low self-esteem and an altered body image. Feelings of hopelessness, helplessness, and isolation may require the staff to become involved in remotivating the client. Social interaction, group support, and activities should be geared to the client's abilities. Art, music, and movement therapies are useful adjuncts, as is appropriate involvement in exercise groups. The staff should provide access to familiar religious and cultural activities as well as to

Evidence-Based Practice

Hendry and Douglas (2003) focused on identification of a multidimensional approach to meet the needs of clients diagnosed with dementia using stage-specific communication and recreational interventions as well as adjunctive therapies and the therapeutic interactive process. They concluded that this interaction best meets the cognitive, functional, and developmental needs of the client and improves quality of life. Further research is indicated as to the specific staging and interventions used.

the person's usual religious or spiritual advisor. Hospital chaplain services also should be provided. The staff should assess whether the client is able to make decisions. Once that determination is made, the staff should encourage the client's participation in choosing care, planning activities, and problem solving.

Evidence-Based Practice

Gerder (2010) investigated the use of individualized music selections in the management of agitation in confused elderly. Structured monitoring of the use of individualized patient-preferred music to reduce agitation and combativeness, medication use, and physical restraints showed that this can be an effective intervention. Further research across settings, the involvement of family members in selecting music, and the correlation of the music selected and the degree of significance to the individual would be useful.

Remember the six Rs:
*R*eorient the client.
*R*estructure the environment.
*R*estore normal functioning and health.
*R*emotivate the client and involve him or her in
*R*eminiscence.
*R*egulate dysfunctional psychiatric symptoms.

The nurse must identify the strengths of clients, instruct them thoroughly, and modify their behavior and environment. This will reinforce appropriate coping and adaptive skills. Family members may require respite services or advice regarding guardianship laws. The client or family may require referral to legal or social services as well as to community and self-help organizations.

Clients should reminisce and review their lives; this is an important developmental task. It helps them reflect upon their life experiences and relationships and maximizes the use of remote memory, which is usually the last to deteriorate. Reminiscing increases feelings of mastery and self-esteem. Family photographs, oral or video recordings, and familiar objects or artifacts from home can be used to stimulate memories and social interaction and to encourage clients to relate their personal histories and to express their feelings regarding the purpose and worth of their lives and relationships.

Regulating the problematic symptoms of coexisting psychiatric disorders, such as anxiety, depression, and behavioral problems, allows the client to remain involved and active. Relaxation therapies to treat anxiety and supportive-expressive and cognitive therapies to treat depression have been helpful. Physical and movement therapies as well as ambulation can help reduce restlessness or agitation. Paranoia or delusional thinking, hallucinations, and depressive disorders all may be present in clients with dementia or delirium and require treatment. Behavioral problems such as restlessness, agitation, aggressiveness, or socially inappropriate behavior should be monitored and exposure to possible stimuli limited. Sample nursing interventions and rationale for clients with general medical conditions are included in **Table 13-5.**

Pharmacology

The causes of acute delirious states can usually be identified and treated. The treatment of Alzheimer's disease, particularly in the early stages, focuses on attempts to slow memory loss and cognitive decline.

Table 13-5 **Nursing Interventions for Clients with Dementia**

Nursing Diagnosis	Nursing Interventions	Rationales
Disturbed sensory perception	Evaluate environment and select needed interventions such as providing for safety features to prevent injury or falls such as eliminating clutter, providing proper lighting and night light at night, ensuring that carpets and throw rugs are secure, installing hand and safety rails if needed, obtaining safety monitors or life alert systems. Provide environmental cues such as clocks, calendars, medication boxes, etc.	Establishing safe environment will help reduce the danger of falls and environmental modifications will allow client to maintain independent functioning.
	Provide opportunities for social contact such as structured and informal groups such as reminiscence groups, hand massage and therapeutic touch, and recreational groups.	Reduce isolation and loneliness. Reduce risk of emotional disorders.
	Assess abilities and simplify multistep activities if necessary or break into manageable steps.	Assist in maintaining problem solving skills and promote independence.
	Provide multisensory experiences such as expressive arts therapies and sensory integration.	Stimulate interaction with environment and maximize cognitive functioning.

In early stages of mild or moderate dementia, a 3-month trial with a cholinesterase inhibitor (ChEI) is suggested because this may mitigate some of the effects of the disease process. By blocking cholinesterase enzymes, it is expected that the levels and action of acetylcholine will increase in the synapses, facilitating cholinergic neurotransmission. The most common medications used are donepezil (Aricept), galantamine (Reminyl), and rivastigmine (Exelon), and there are some differences in their dosage schedules and reported side effects. Tacrine (Cognex), one of the first ChEIs, is only rarely used because it may cause nausea and liver damage. Titration of beginning doses and gradual increases in the doses of donepezil, galantamine, and rivastigmine are recommended. Adverse effects are common and should be monitored. When it is suspected that a drug may no longer be helpful, a drug holiday or trial discontinuation for a short period is recommended. There is evidence that memantine (Namenda), a low-affinity NMDA (*N*-methyl-D-aspartate), may be effective in clients with Alzheimer's vascular and mixed dementias (Evans, Wilcock, & Birks, 2005). Exelon (rivastigmine transdermal) is thought to minimize side effects in its patch form and may benefit clients who have problems swallowing.

Many clients find the use of vitamin E supplements, Ginkgo biloba, statins, folate, and estrogen supplements to be helpful. Curcumin, found in the herb turmeric, has been found helpful in reducing amyloid plaques in dementia and for its anti-inflammatory response (Mishra & Palanievelu, 2008). Research is continuing to determine the usefulness of these products to treat the symptoms of dementia. Selegiline, an MAO-B inhibitor that does not require tyramine dietary modifications, has been used elsewhere as an adjunct to treatment for Parkinson's disease and to slow neuronal damage in Alzheimer's disease; however, research continues to determine its clinical effectiveness and long-term value (Evans et al., 2005).

The treatment of vascular dementia may include aspirin or other anticoagulants, ticlopidine (Ticlid), a clot-dissolving agent such as streptokinase (Streptase), exercise, and antioxidants coupled with medications for accompanying conditions such as hypertension, hyperlipidemia, diabetes, smoking, and vasculitis. Limited studies have been completed regarding the effectiveness of medications such as pentoxifylline (Trental) and ergoloid mesylates (Hydergine) to increase blood flow. Further study is indicated regarding neural protective medications such as nimodipine (Nimotop), propentofylline, and posatirelin.

Research on the relationship between Alzheimer's disease and seizure activity have observed elevated hippocampal activation in clients. Clinical trials indicate that treatment with an anticonvulsant, levetiracetam (Keppra) appears to slow the cognitive impairment associated with Alzheimer's disease and may prove helpful as an early intervention (Lowry 2011).

Behavioral and Psychological Symptoms

Due to the possibility of side effects, polypharmacy, risk of adverse effects, and studies showing limited efficacy of using antipsychotic medications with patients with dementia, nonpharmacologic interventions should be utilized first. Clients with dementia should be evaluated for pain, and a standardized protocol for pain management may reduce the behavioral disturbances without the use of antipsychotic medications (Husebo, Ballard, Sandvik, Nilsen, & Aarsland, 2011). There may be times when there are no potentially reversible underlying causes or when behavioral or environmental controls are ineffective. If the symptoms are potentially dangerous or significantly distressing to the client and family, the client may be evaluated for medications. Concerns for polypharmacy, drug interactions, potentiation of anticholinergic side effects, falls, sedation, or increased confusion should be considered when prescribing or administering medications.

The Food and Drug Administration has issued warnings regarding use of typical and atypical antipsychotic medications in dementia. However, if a client who displays agitation or aggressive behavior needs to be evaluated for medication, a sedating serotonergic agent such as trazodone (Desyrel) or mirtazapine (Remeron) may be used if psychotic symptoms are not present. Antipsychotic medications are used with caution in the elderly due to the risk of extrapyramidal symptoms. Many sedating agents have been associated with lowered blood pressure and raised heart rate. Orthostatic hypotension is a particular problem with the risk of falls. Atypical antipsychotic medications such as olanzapine (Zyprexa), risperidone (Risperdal), and quetiapine (Seroquel) have been used in low doses; however, there is some evidence to suggest that these medications may not be effective with clients with dementia. Onor,

Saina, Trevisiol, Cristante, and Auglia (2006) found that low doses of risperidone (Risperdal) appear to be well tolerated by clients with Alzheimer's disease and appeared effective in reducing behavioral and psychotic symptoms. At times, low doses of haloperidol (Haldol), sometimes given in combination with low doses of lorazepam (Ativan), is used to control symptoms of severe agitation, hallucinations, or delusions. Benzodiazepines are used cautiously due to the risk of oversedation, confusion, and falls. In a double-blind study, Holmes and colleagues (2004) studied the efficacy of donepezil (Aricept) for treatment of behavioral and psychologic symptoms in dementia. Significant reduction in behavioral symptoms was found over a 12-week period, as well as a reduction in distress experienced by caretakers for these patients. The possible cognitive benefits of donepezil (Aricept) were found to be reduced by concomitant use of antipsychotic medications. Antiseizure medications such as carbamazepine (Tegretol), divalproex sodium (Depakote), and gabapentin (Neurontin) are sometimes used as mood stabilizers in clients with restlessness and agitation. Elderly persons or those with additional medical problems must be kept under observation, as any of the medications have cumulative effects and potential side effects, which can be more of a burden than the benefit of the medications.

Depression

Clients who exhibit symptoms of depression are usually treated with nonsedating selective serotonin reuptake inhibitors (SSRIs) such as escitalopram (Lexapro), citalopram (Celexa), fluoxetine (Prozac), paroxetine (Paxil), sertraline (Zoloft), and venlafaxine (Effexor). Clients with depressive disorders with agitation and other severe symptoms may benefit from an evaluation to determine if a small dose of a tricyclic antidepressant such as desipramine (Norpramin), nortriptyline (Aventyl), doxepin (Sinequan), or amitriptyline (Elavil) should be used. In medically ill clients plagued by fatigue and depression as well as dementia, psychostimulants such as methylphenidate (Ritalin) or pemoline (Cylert) are occasionally used. A research study of nursing home patients indicated that the risk of falls greatly increased in clients with new prescriptions for non-SSRI antidepressants or increased dose of these medications within 2 days of the change (Berry et al., 2011).

Buspirone (BuSpar) or short-acting antianxiety medications such as alprazolam (Xanax), lorazepam (Ativan), or oxazepam (Serax) treat the symptoms of anxiety as well as panic disorders. As with other medications, an elderly client may require a reduction of the normal dose.

Summary

Cognitive disorders encompass a number of problems that produce changes in the function of the brain. Deliriums and dementias are differentiated in that deliriums are felt to be temporary and potentially reversible and dementias are chronic and irreversible. It is important to identify and treat any underlying or concomitant disorders for both syndromes. Treatment consists of avoiding infections, trauma, or agents that may cause brain dysfunction and minimize any problematic symptoms. Treating the causes of the delirium will hopefully return the client to baseline functioning without sequelae. The treatment of dementia focuses on stabilizing the client's abilities and delaying disease progression for as long as possible. When treating clients with amnesia, the symptoms must be explained well, and reassurance should be given. Reorientation and rehabilitation are priorities. Restraints, whether chemical or mechanical, should be used cautiously and only for client safety, not for staff convenience, because restraints and restrictions can exacerbate confusion and agitation. Treatment of coexisting behavioral disorders or psychiatric symptoms involves a combination of environmental and behavioral modifications and pharmacologic intervention that minimize sedative, anticholinergic, and extrapyramidal side effects. For the pseudodementia of depression, treatment of the underlying depressive disorder with antidepressants is indicated. Any coexisting medical illnesses also are treated, and considerable effort is made to minimize the anticholinergic and sedative side effects of the medications.

Annotated References

American Psychiatric Association. (2000). *Diagnostic and statistical manual of mental disorders* (4th ed., text rev.). Washington, DC: Author.
This is the fourth edition, text revision, of the American Psychiatric Association's official nomenclature of psychiatric conditions and disorders. It provides a systematic listing of the official codes and categories, a description of the multiaxial system for diagnosis, and diagnostic criteria for each of the disorders. It is used by

psychiatrists, physicians, psychologists, registered nurses, social workers, therapists, and other mental health workers in all clinical settings.

Berry, S. D., Zhang, Y., Lipsitz, L. A., Mittleman, M. A., Solomon, D. H., & Kiel, D. P. (2011). Anti-depressant prescriptions: An acute window for falls in the nursing home. *The Journal of Gerontology*. doi:10.1093/gerona/glr113

This study indicated risk of falls for seniors in a nursing home within 2 days of receiving a new prescription or increased dose of non-SSRI antidepressant.

Boden, C. (2004). *Who will I be when I die?* Pymble NSW, Australia: HarperCollins Publishers PTY Ltd.

This is an autobiography of a woman diagnosed with Alzheimer's disease.

Callaghan, R. C., Cunningham, J. K., Sykes, J., & Kish, S. J. (2011). Increased risk of Parkinson's disease in individuals hospitalized with conditions related to use of methamphetamine or other amphetamine-type drugs. *Drug and Alcohol Dependence* doi:10.1016/jdrugalcdep.2011.06.013

Dependence or abuse of methamphetamine increases risk of developing Parkinson's disease by 76% according to research studying individuals hospitalized for abuse of methamphetamine and related drugs.

Cassels, C. (2011). Has the silver tsunami begun? Retrieved from http://www.medscape.com/viewarticle/743338

This is a report of studies presented at the 2011 American Psychiatric Association annual meeting indicating an increase in the number of elderly expected to require psychiatric care due to cognitive and behavioral problems.

Dartigues, J. F. (2009) Alzheimer's disease: Global challenge for the 21st century. *Lancet Neurology, 8*(12), 1082–1082.

This article discusses predicted increases in incidence and prevalence of Alzheimer's disease in the future.

David, A. S., Fleminger, S., Kopelman, M. D., Lovestone, S., & Melers, J. D. C. (Eds.). (2009). *Lishman's organic psychiatry: A textbook of neuropsychiatry* (4th ed.). Hoboken, NJ: Wiley-Blackman.

This text covers basic concepts in neuropsychology and relationship to psychiatry including information on dementia.

Evans, J. G., Wilcock, G., & Birks, J. (2005). Evidence-based pharmacotherapy of Alzheimer's disease. In D. Stein, B. Lerer, & S. Stahl (Eds.), *Evidence-based psychopharmacotherapy* (pp. 290–319). Cambridge, UK: Cambridge University Press.

This chapter is a review of medications used to treat Alzheimer's disease.

Ferri, C. P., Prince, M., Brayne, C., Brodaty, H., Fratiglioni, L., Ganguli, M., . . . Alzheimer's Disease International. (2005) Global prevalence of dementia: A Delphi consensus study. *Lancet, 36*(9503) 2112–2117.

Due to changes in underdeveloped countries, an aging worldwide population, and changes in mortality, estimates in prevalence of dementia are important in future needs and costs in health care.

Futrell, M., Melillo, K. D., Remington R., & Schoenfelder, D. P. (2010). Evidence-based protocol: Wandering. *Journal of Gerontological Nursing, 36*(2), 6–16.

This article discusses guidelines for the identification of type of wandering, consequences, and behaviors and development of environmental modifications and interventions.

Gaudreau, J. D., Gagnon, P., Harel, F., Tremblay, A., & Roy, M. A. (2005). Fast, systematic, and continuous delirium assessment in hospitalized clients: The nursing delirium screening scale. *Journal of Pain and Symptom Management, 29*(4), 368–375.

Discusses the use of a five-item scale, the Nursing Delirium Screening Scale (Nu-DESC) to standardize observation for signs of delirium in hospitalized clients.

Gerder, L. (2010). Evidence-based protocol: Individualized music for elders with disorientation. *Journal of Gerontological Nursing, 36*(6), 7–15.

The author studied using music that has some meaning to the client in order to reduce restlessness and agitation in confused clients.

Ginzburg, G. S., & Willard, H. E. (2010). *Essentials of genomic and personalized medicine*. San Diego, CA: Elsevier, Inc.

This text covers research in genomics and the influence upon susceptibility and determinants of disease and response to pharmacotherapy.

Hendry, K. C., & Douglas, D. H. (2003). Promoting quality of life for clients diagnosed with dementia. *Journal of the*

American Psychiatric Association, 9(3), 96–102.

This article focuses on the need for a multidimensional approach focusing on client strengths, developmental needs, and stage of dementia to improve quality of life rather than focusing on behavioral disturbances.

Holmes, C., Wilkinson, D., Dean, C., Vethanayagam, S., Olivieri, S., Langley, A., . . . Damms, J. (2004). The efficacy of donepezil in the treatment of neuropsychiatric symptoms in Alzheimer disease. *Neurology, 63*(2), 214–219.

This article reports on a randomized study of patients with dementia and neuropsychiatric symptoms who received donepezil. The study results showed that donepezil had significant efficacy in the treatment of patients with mild to moderate Alzheimer's disease.

Husebo, B. S., Ballard, C., Sandvik, R., Nilsen, O. B., & Aarsland, D. (2011) Efficacy in treating pain to reduce behavioral disturbances in residents in nursing homes with dementia: Clustered randomized clinical trials. *British Medical Journal.* doi:343d.4065 1–10

A study in England and Norway recommended assessment for pain and a standardized protocol for pain management ranging from no pain medication or use of acetaminophen to use of buprenorphine and then pregabalin. This was found to better control behavioral disturbances and reduce the routine use of antipsychotic medication.

Lopez, A. D., Mathers, C. D., Ezzati, M., Janison, D. T., & Murray, C. J. L. (Eds.). (2006). *Global burden of disease and risk factors.* New York, NY: World Bank Publications.

This is a good source of public health data and information regarding the global impact of disease and disability.

Lowry, F. (2011). *Levetiracetam may slow progression to Alzheimer's.* Retrieved from http://www.medscape.com/viewarticle/747019

Discusses ongoing research by Dr. Michela Gallagher on the clinical efficacy of low dose levetiracetamfor hippocampal hyperactivity in amnestic mild cognitive impairment; also reported in *The JHU Gazette* on July 20, 2011. It posits that NIMH clinical trials show use of low-dose levetiracetam may aid in early intervention to slow cognitive decline in Alzheimer's disease.

Mendez, M., & Cummings, J. L. (2003). *Dementia: A clinical approach.* Boston, MA: Butterworth-Heinemann.

This is a serious text for the industrious student who wants an in-depth discussion of dementia and delirium or for the researcher who needs information on a specific topic or disorder. This book contains everything you need to know about dementia-related topics from AIDS to Wernicke-Korsakoff syndrome.

Mezey, M., & Maslow, K. (2008). Recognition of dementia in hospitalized older adults. *Try this: Best practices in nursing care for hospitalized older adults, 1*(D5). New York, NY: The Hartford Institute for Geriatric Nursing, Division of Nursing, New York University.

This text is a study of best practices in identifying at-risk hospitalized older adults.

Mishra, S., & Palanievelu, K. (2008). The effect of curcumin (turmeric) on Alzheimer's disease: An overview. *Annals of Indian Academy of Neurology, 11*(1), 13–19.

This article discusses the use of curcumin as a food and for medicinal purposes in the prevention of Alzheimer's disease.

Onor, M. L., Saina, M., Trevisiol, M., Cristante, T., & Auglia, E. (2006). Clinical experience with risperidone in the treatment of behavioral and psychological symptoms of dementia. *Progress in Neuropsychopharmacology and Biological Psychiatry, 31*(1), 205–209.

The authors studied efficacy and tolerability of use of risperidone to treat behavioral and psychological symptoms in clients with dementia.

Pinel, J. P. J. (2010). *Biopsychology* (8th ed.). Upper Saddle River, NJ: Prentice Hall.

This is a user-friendly text and CD for those interested in a biologic and psychologic approach to learn more about the anatomic, physiologic, psychologic, and behavioral characteristics and learned and inherited features of cognition, memory, and amnesia. The text describes different problems that can affect cognitive functioning, including organic brain syndromes and disorders.

Reeve, C. (1996). Democratic National Convention Floor Speech. Retrieved from http://www.chrisreevehomepage.com/sp-dnc1996.html

This is a transcript of a speech from the 1996 Democratic National Convention in Chicago, Illinois. It is also available on video from American Rhetoric, Product ID 101704, on www.learnoutloud.com

Seitz, R., von Auer, F., Blumel, J., Burger, R., Buschmann, A., Dietz, K., . . . Zerr, I. (2007). Impact of vCJD on blood supply. *Biologicals, 35*(2), 79–97.
This is a review of possible transmission and risk assessment for BSE and variant Creutzfeldt-Jacob disease vCJD as well as screening methods and precautionary measures.

Tullman, D. E., Mion, L. C., Fletcher, K., & Foreman, M. D. (2008). *Nursing standard protocol. Delirium: Prevention, early recognition, and treatment.* New York, NY: Hartford Institute for Geriatric Nursing.
This text provides guidelines for the rapid assessment and nursing interventions for clients with delirium.

Additional Resources

Curry, S. M., & Drosel, C. (2011). *Treating dementia in context: A step by step guide to working with individuals and families.* Washington, DC: American Psychological Association.
Provides helpful evidence based information on the relationship and experiences of caregiver and dementia clients as well as suggestions for caregiving and maintaining quality of life.

Mace, N. L., & Rabins, P. V. (2006). *The 36-hour day: A family guide to caring for persons with Alzheimer's disease, related dementing illnesses, and memory loss in later life* (4th ed.). Baltimore, MD: The Johns Hopkins University Press.
This text describes the often unending demands on families and caretakers in meeting the overwhelming needs of clients with dementia. The tremendous toll upon family life, the concerns and ambivalence of caretakers, and descriptions of the stages of disability are discussed.

Sendelbach, S., & Guthrie, P. F. (2009). *Acute confusion/delirium.* Iowa City, IA: University of Iowa Gerontological Nursing Interventions Research Center, Research Translation and Dissemination Core.
This text provides guidelines for assessment and intervention in prevention and treatment of delirium.

Snyder, L. (2010). *Living your best with early stage Alzheimer's: An essential guide.* North Branch, MN: Sunrise River Press.
This article provides useful tips to be used with clients, caretakers, and families for dealing with Alzheimer's.

Waszyniski, C. M., & Petroviek, K. (2008). Nurses' evaluation of the Confusion Assessment method: A pilot study.
The authors report on a study of nurses' use of the Confusion Assessment method (CAM) for assessment of the presence or absence of delirium.

Internet Resources

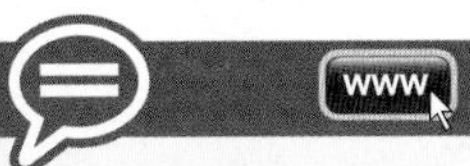

For a full suite of assignments and additional learning activities, use the access code located in the front of your book to visit this exclusive website: http://go.jblearning.com/mentalhealth. If you do not have an access code, you can obtain one at the site.

Learning Objectives

After reading this chapter, you will be able to:

- Identify indications a mental disorder may be due to a medical condition.
- Describe the most common medical disorders that may cause psychiatric symptoms.
- Discuss the nurse's responsibility in assessing clients for mental disorders due to a general medical condition.

Key Terms

www

Mental disorder

Personality disorder

Mental Disorders Due to General Medical Conditions

Joan C. Masters

http://go.jblearning.com/mentalhealth 

For a full suite of assignments and additional learning activities, use the access code located in the front of your book to visit this exclusive website: http://go.jblearning.com/mentalhealth. If you do not have an access code, you can obtain one at the site.

Introduction

A psychiatric disorder may be a direct physiologic consequence of the medical condition. Client history, including history of present illness, physical examination, and laboratory tests and other diagnostic findings, support this relationship.

This chapter discusses **mental disorders** caused by the direct physiologic effects of a medical condition. It is important to note, however, that mental disorders and medical conditions can be related to each other through several mechanisms. The cause and effect of the condition are not always readily discernible; thus, it is often difficult to determine which appeared first. The clinician must remember that a mental disorder is not an expected or normal response to a particular event such as the death of a loved one. Independent of the original cause, the disorder must be considered a manifestation of a behavioral, psychologic, or biologic dysfunction (American Psychiatric Association [APA], 2000).

Medical conditions can affect mental health and well-being whether the observed behavior results from physiologic or nonphysiologic processes. This is termed a *secondary mental disorder*. Conversely, a medical condition may exacerbate a primary mental disorder. A primary mental disorder is caused by a medical condition and is not substance induced from the effect of drugs such as alcohol, side effects from prescribed medications, or toxins.

Regardless of the clinical setting, nurses have traditionally used a combined psychologic, biologic, cultural, and spiritual approach to assess clients. Florence Nightingale expressed concern about the body's effect on the mind, writing, "The sick suffer to excess from mental as well as bodily pain" (Nightingale, 1946, p. 34). The *Diagnostic and Statistical Manual of Mental Disorders*, fourth edition, text revision (*DSM-IV-TR*) distinguishes mental disorders due to medical conditions, but this does not mean that fundamental differences exist between mental disorders and medical conditions. Nor does it mean that mental disorders are unrelated to physiologic or biologic factors or that medical conditions are unrelated to behavioral or psychosocial factors or processes. Mental disorders and medical conditions are distinguished to encourage thorough evaluations and to enhance communication among healthcare providers (APA, 2000). A comprehensive assessment of the client helps the entire healthcare team to be aware of alternative or differential diagnoses.

Signs and symptoms of psychoactive drug withdrawal or toxic exposure are not considered disorders due to a general medical condition but are substance-induced disorders.

General Description

Medical conditions that can cause mental disorders were originally categorized as organic mental syndromes and disorders by the *Diagnostic and Statistical Manual of Mental Disorders*, third edition, revised (*DSM-III-R*). Delirium, dementia, and psychoactive substance-induced mental disorders were included in this category (see Chapter 13). The authors of the *DSM-IV-TR* used the term *general medical condition* to categorize medical conditions not listed under mental and behavioral disorders in the International Classification of Diseases (ICD). *General* represents several medical conditions in which the physiologic effects manifest as mental disorders (**Table 14-1**).

Table 14-1 General Medical Conditions

- Infectious and parasitic diseases
- Neoplasms
- Endocrine, nutritional, and metabolic diseases and immunity disorders
- Diseases of the blood and blood-forming organs
- Diseases of the nervous system and sense organs
- Diseases of the circulatory system
- Diseases of the respiratory system
- Diseases of the digestive system
- Diseases of the genitourinary system
- Complications of pregnancy, childbirth, and puerperium
- Diseases of the skin and subcutaneous tissue
- Congenital anomalies
- Certain conditions originating in the perinatal period
- Symptoms, signs, and ill-defined conditions

Excluding substance-induced mental disorders, a mental disorder that is a direct physiologic consequence of a medical condition is diagnosed as a mental disorder due to a general medical condition (**Table 14-2**). Medical and mental conditions are coded using the *DSM-IV-TR*'s multiaxial assessment (see Chapter 4). The mental disorder is noted on Axis I along with the associated medical condition. The medical condition, along with its ICD-9-CM code, is noted on Axis III. For example, a mood disorder resulting from hypothyroidism with depressive features is coded on Axis I, whereas hypothyroidism is coded on Axis III.

Physical illnesses are common among psychiatric clients, and in some cases these physical illnesses worsen or even cause psychiatric problems. The *DSM-IV-TR* classifies disorders that present with psychiatric signs and symptoms but that are medical in origin as "mental disorders due to a general

Table 14-2 Major Mental Disorders Due to a General Medical Condition

- Delirium
- Dementia
- Amnestic disorder
- Psychotic disorders
- Mood disorders
- Anxiety disorders
- Sleep disorders
- Sexual dysfunction
- Acute brain syndrome that develops rapidly (within hours or days) and is characterized by cognitive impairment not induced by a preexisting or evolving dementia. Signs and symptoms fluctuate daily and include clouding of consciousness, disorientation, memory impairment, and decreased ability to focus, shift, or sustain attention.
- Diffuse brain dysfunction characterized by a gradual, progressive, and chronic deterioration of intellectual function. Judgment, memory, affect, cognition, and attention span are affected.
- Memory disturbance resulting in impaired ability to learn new information or recall previously learned information or past events.
- Mental disorder characterized by impaired thought, communication, and interpretation of reality.
- Disorder of mood characterized by depression, mania, and hypomania.
- Disorder characterized by excessive worry, uncertainty, and uneasiness about events or activities. The anxiety must occur more often than not for at least 6 months to be classed as a disorder.
- Disorder characterized by abnormalities in sleep–wake generating or timing mechanisms.
- Disturbance in sexual desire and the psychologic and physiologic changes that characterize the sexual response cycles.

medical condition" (APA, 2000, p. 181). This group of disorders is grouped with delirium, dementias, and amnestic disorders but is distinguished from them in an important way. Delirium, dementias, and amnestic disorders are characterized primarily by cognitive impairment; that is, deficiencies in attention, language, and memory. People who have a mental disorder due to a general medical condition may have some cognitive impairment, but cognitive impairment is not the predominant problem; instead they present with other psychiatric symptoms such as psychosis, mood disorder, or personality and behavioral changes. It is important with all clients to consider whether a medical illness may be contributing to what initially appears to be a psychiatric issue (Sadock & Sadock, 2007).

Nurses may see these clients in psychiatric settings either because the medical basis for their apparent psychiatric problems are not recognized or because their behavior is so disruptive they cannot be cared for on a medical unit. These clients are frequently seen in the emergency department (ED); approximately one third of clients with a psychosis seen in the ED have an underlying medical condition causing the psychotic symptoms (Koran et al., 2002; Larkin, Classen, Edmond, Pelletier, & Camargo, 2005; Saliou, Fichele, McLaughlin, Thauin, & Lejeux, 2005).

It is important nurses understand that psychiatric symptoms can originate from medical conditions, so clients can be correctly treated. Misdiagnoses can lead to delayed treatment or no treatment, resulting in a client suffering or potentially even dying, and at the very least resulting in increased healthcare costs. It can be difficult to accurately diagnose clients with changes in behavior and/or thinking whose problems suggest a primary psychiatric illness but whose illness is medical in origin.

Critical Thinking Question 

What factors might contribute to missed medical diagnoses in clients with psychiatric disorders?

Incidence and Prevalence

The extent of the problem of mental disorders due to a general medical condition is not clear because

Evidence-Based Practice

A group of researchers interested in the extent and severity of medical illnesses in psychiatric patients assessed 289 patients who were admitted to an inpatient psychiatric unit over a 6-month period. The patients were given a routine physical exam and laboratory tests (complete blood count, blood chemistry, thyroid function, vitamin B_{12}, folate levels, and urine analysis). The patients also completed a 10-item medical symptom questionnaire. The patients were referred for a medical consultation if the physical exam, laboratory tests, or questionnaire indicated an active or serious medical disorder. The majority of patients were diagnosed with schizophrenia (62%) and mood disorder (24%). The remainder were diagnosed with adjustment disorders (9%) or dementia and other disorders (4%). Of the 289 patients in the study, 29% (84) had active and serious medical disorders. Of the 119 disorders detected (some patients had more than one disorder), 20% (24) were undiagnosed before the study.

In only one case was a disorder—hypothyroidism—that was considered to have caused psychiatric symptoms detected. In two other patients with schizophrenia, their worsening psychosis was attributed to hypothyroidism. For 14 other patients, physical problems caused or worsened psychiatric symptoms. These included drug withdrawal, epileptic psychosis, postconcussion syndrome, hyperthyroidism with hypoparathyroidism, myocardial infarction, quadriplegia with anemia, dementia comorbid with schizophrenia, and cerebral degeneration comorbid with major depression.

A number of medical disorders were diagnosed in the study, which, while not an immediate threat to the patients' mental health, had the potential to cause psychiatric symptoms if not treated. These included syphilis (two patients), anemia (six patients), diabetes, alcoholic cirrhosis (three patients), thalassemia, vitamin B_{12} deficiency, hepatitis, chronic obstructive pulmonary disease, urinary tract infections, cellulitis, and proteinuria (Koran et al., 2002).

by their nature these disorders are thought to be frequently misdiagnosed or overlooked. However, there are indications from some research studies that physical health problems are common among psychiatric clients, and that these problems may cause or worsen a client's psychiatric illness.

Etiology

General medical conditions may be linked to mental disorders in several ways (**Table 14-3**). The clinician must distinguish whether the medical condition is causing or exacerbating the mental symptoms.

Mental disorders unrelated to a medical condition are coded separately on the multiaxial assessment. Mental disorders that are reactions to a medical condition are termed adjustment disorders. These disorders occur within 6 months of the event and are coded as follows: A client who develops an adjustment disorder with depressed mood, reacting to a diagnosis of breast cancer, is coded on Axis I. Breast cancer is coded on Axis III.

Additionally, certain medical conditions, not directly related to the mental disorder, have important prognostic and treatment implications. One example is the choice of an antidepressant for the client who takes cardiac medications such as antiarrhythmics. Another example is insulin monitoring for the diabetic client who is also schizophrenic.

Physiology

Along with the client's history, physical examination, and laboratory results, the chronologic relationship between the physiologic and mental disorder should be determined.

Medical Conditions

The clinician must determine when onset, exacerbation, and remission of both the medical condition and the mental disorder occurred. Did the mental disorder resolve after initiating specific medical treatment? For example, following surgical excision of parathyroid tissue, which restores normal calcium levels, the client's anxiety resolves.

The symptoms of a mental disorder may be seen before the underlying pathology of systemic or cerebral disease is detected. The depression that precedes choreiform movements in Huntington's disease exemplifies this. Conversely, treating the general medical condition may not resolve the mental disorder, such as failing to improve depressed mood despite administering thyroid hormone replacement for hypothyroidism. Treating the mental disorder and medical condition concurrently often symptomatically relieves both conditions. Treatment that targets the medical condition, however, provides stronger etiologic evidence.

Table 14-3 **Etiology of Mental Disorders Due to Medical Condition**

Mental Disorder	Medical Condition
Delirium	Hypoxia, hypercarbia, hypoglycemia, fluid or electrolyte imbalances, hepatic or renal disease, thiamine deficiency, postanesthesia states, emergence delirium, hypertensive encephalopathy, focal lesions of right parietal lobe, and inferomedial surface of the occipital lobe
Dementia	Pick's disease; normal pressure hydrocephalus; Parkinson's disease; Huntington's disease; traumatic brain injury; anoxia; human immunodeficiency virus (HIV); syphilis; hypothyroidism; hypercalcemia; hypoglycemia; thiamine, niacin, and B12 deficiency; systemic lupus erythematosus (SLE); hepatic conditions; metabolic disorders; multiple sclerosis
Amnestic disorder	Cerebrovascular disease; metabolic conditions; seizures; closed head trauma; damage to medial, diencephalic, and temporal lobe brain structures (penetrating wounds, surgical intervention, hypoxia); infarction of posterior cerebral artery; herpes simplex encephalitis
Psychotic disorder	Neoplasms, cerebrovascular disease, Huntington's disease, epilepsy, auditory nerve damage, hypo/hyperglycemia, hypo/hyperthyroidism, fluid or electrolyte imbalances, hepatic or renal disease, autoimmune disease (e.g., SLE)
Mood disorder	Parkinson's disease, Huntington's disease, cerebrovascular disease (stroke), B_{12} deficiency, hypo/hyperthyroidism, hypoadrenocorticism, autoimmune disease (e.g., SLE), hepatitis, mononucleosis, HIV, cancer of pancreas
Anxiety disorder	Vitamin B12 deficiency, porphyria, hypo/hyperthyroidism, hypoglycemia, pheochromocytoma, congestive heart failure, pulmonary embolism, arrhythmia, chronic obstructive pulmonary disease, pneumonia, hyperventilation, neoplasms, vestibular dysfunction, encephalitis
Sleep disorder	Parkinson's disease, Huntington's disease, cerebrovascular disease (upper brainstem vascular lesions), hypo/hyperthyroidism, viral encephalitis producing insomnia, insomnia caused by pain or cough from pulmonary disease
Sexual dysfunction	MS, spinal cord lesion, neuropathy, temporal lobe lesion, diabetes mellitus, hypo/hyperadrenocorticism, pituitary dysfunction, vascular conditions, genitourinary conditions

Atypical features of a primary mental disorder include the following:

- The onset of schizophrenia-like symptoms of delusions, hallucinations, disorganized speech, and grossly disorganized behavior at 75 years of age, when the typical age of onset is late teens to early 30s
- Significant weight loss with only mild depressive symptoms
- Disproportionate cognitive deficits
- Detection and location of a brain lesion or known pathophysiologic mechanism likely to affect brain function

Critical Thinking Question

What barriers to receiving medical treatment might exist for clients with chronic mental illness?

Catatonia

A central nervous system (CNS) motor disturbance characterizes catatonia due to a general medical condition (**Table 14-4**). This motor disturbance is a direct physiologic effect of the medical condition. Client history, physical examination, and laboratory findings exclude the following neurologic conditions and metabolic disorders: malignant brain neoplasm and other neoplasms, head trauma, cerebrovascular accident, encephalitis, hypercalcemia, hepatic encephalopathy, homocystinuria, and diabetic ketoacidosis.

Critical Thinking Question

Identify some of the range of symptoms that might be seen in catatonia that might also be seen in a client with a psychotic disorder or schizophrenia.

Diagnostic tests are valuable therapeutic tools for evaluating direct physiologic effects.

Clients with cognitive changes generally ignore or minimize perceived behavioral changes; therefore, it is necessary to interview family members because they are often the first to notice these changes and can provide vital information.

Table 14-4 Signs and Symptoms of Catatonia

Signs and Symptoms	Features
Motor immobilization	Fully conscious but unresponsive and mute
Motor excitability	Uncontrolled, aimless motor activity
Negativism	Refusal to cooperate with simple requests for no apparent reason
Stereotypical	Repeated but non–goal-oriented movements (e.g., rocking)
Peculiarities of voluntary movement	Bizarre or uncomfortable postures (e.g., squatting) for long periods
Echopraxia	Mimicking the gestures of another person
Echolalia	Parrot-like repetitions of another person's words or phrases

Personality Changes

Personality changes from a general medical condition's direct physiologic effects involve a pathologic disturbance in functioning brain systems. These systems mediate language, perception, memory, attention, and other cognitive systems. Normal behavior is assessed as a by-product of these functional systems. Thus, compromised function alters behavior. Knowledge of particular brain system functions is vital in recognizing corresponding behavioral changes. A fundamental review of these systems and their functions is presented in **Table 14-5**.

Personality changes can result from many neurologic and medical conditions. The most common causes include closed head injury (symptoms occurring years after the injury), traumatic lesions of the frontal and temporal lobe, and tumors and strokes affecting the frontal lobe. Other causes include Huntington's disease, Wilson's disease, epilepsy, infectious diseases with CNS involvement, endocrine conditions, and systemic lupus erythematosus.

As the personality changes progress, behavior becomes grossly inappropriate. The client is at risk of injuring him- or herself or others and may require hospitalization.

Personality changes resulting from a general medical condition may present as a predominant symptom associated with the affected brain system. Common manifestations include affective instability, poor impulse control, outbursts of aggression or rage

Table 14-5 How Systems of the Brain Affect Human Behavior

Systems	Functions
Prefrontal	Social judgment Volition Integration of new information Ability to plan and make decisions Ability to generate new thoughts and ideas Mediation of attention and perceptions, affect, and emotions
Limbic system and hypothalamus	Emotional stability Adherence to social and sexual mores and norms
Basal ganglia	Regulation of emotion and cognition

disproportionate to the precipitating stressor, apathy, suspiciousness, and paranoid ideation. The *DSM-IV-TR* categorizes particular personality changes by the predominant symptom (**Table 14-6**).

Clinical Presentation

There are certain characteristics of medical disorders that present with psychiatric symptoms:

- *An atypical presentation:* The psychiatric symptoms seen in disorders with a medical origin are not classic psychiatric symptoms (Chuang & Forman, 2006).
- *An early or late onset (before age 12 or after age 40) of psychiatric symptoms:* Except for the dementias, psychiatric disorders tend to develop early in life. Psychiatric disorders occurring later in life suggest a possibly physical origin (Reeves et al., 2010).
- *A rapid onset of symptoms:* New symptoms, particularly vague somatic complaints, or symptoms of confusion and disorganization may be preclinical or prediagnostic manifestations of underlying medical disorders (Chuang & Forman, 2006).
- *A lack of response or an atypical response to treatment for psychiatric symptoms:* If a client is treated for what is assumed to be a psychiatric condition but which is actually a medical condition, he may react in an unexpected way; for

Table 14-6 Personality Changes Due to a General Medical Condition (Categorized by the Predominant Symptom)

Type	Predominant Symptom
Labile	Affective lability
Disinhibited	Poor impulse control, sexual indiscretion
Aggressive	Violent and aggressive behavior
Apathetic	Marked indifference and apathy
Paranoid	Suspiciousness, hypervigilance, paranoid ideation
Other	May be associated with a seizure disorder
Combined	One or more predominant features
Unspecified	Absence of a predominant feature

example, he may not improve or may get worse instead of better (Chuang & Forman, 2006).

- *Visual or tactile hallucinations:* Auditory hallucinations are characteristic of psychiatric, not medical, disorders (Reeves et al., 2010).
- *Altered level of consciousness or disorientation:* Clients with psychiatric disorders may demonstrate odd behavior and speech but they are usually awake and alert and not disoriented (Reeves et al., 2010).
- *Unusual physical signs:* Unusual findings will be present on the physical exam (Reeves et al., 2010).
- *Suggestions of toxin ingestion or exposure:* The client or a collateral informant may report that the client has taken an overdose of medication or some other substance, a urine and serum blood screen is positive for illicit substances, or the client may have evidence of product on her, for example, traces of paint on her face and hair (Reeves et al., 2010).
- *A history of a medical illness:* If a person has a new onset of psychiatric symptoms and is known to have a medical illness, the medical illness should be investigated at the beginning of the assessment as the source of the person's problems. Clients should also be asked about their use of prescribed and over-the-counter medications (Chuang & Forman, 2006).
- *Abnormal vital signs:* Psychiatric disorders do not usually alter vital signs (Chuang & Forman, 2006; Reeves et al., 2010).
- *No history of psychiatric illnesses in the client or family:* The index of suspicion of a possible medical illness is higher if there is no preexisting history of similar psychiatric symptoms in the client or no family history of psychiatric illness (Chuang & Forman, 2006).

Differential Diagnosis

One makes a differential diagnosis to determine whether the mental disorder is caused by a direct physiologic mechanism, which distinguishes the disorder from a primary mental disorder. The following questions also aid the clinician:

- *Does the medical condition precipitate or exacerbate a mental disorder without a known physiologic link?* For example, there is no known physiologic link between osteoarthritis and depression. People with arthritis may experience an adjustment disorder with depressive features, but this is not physiologically based.
- *Is there evidence of recent substance abuse?* This includes prescribed medications with psychoactive effects as well as herbals, nutritional supplements, and over-the-counter medications and substances commonly abused.
- *Is there evidence of withdrawal from a substance? Has the client been exposed to a toxin?* Urine and blood toxicology screens as well as other laboratory data help establish this diagnosis.
- *Does the clinical presentation represent the combined effects of a general medical condition and substance abuse, including medications?* These presentations may include delirium, dementia, psychotic disorder, anxiety disorder, sleep disorder, and sexual dysfunction (see Table 14-2 earlier in the chapter). Both mental disorders due to a general medical condition and substance-induced mental disorders apply in these cases.
- *Does the disturbance occur only during periods of delirium?* For example, psychosis, mood disorder, and anxiety occurring only during periods of delirium are considered associated features of delirium and do not require a separate diagnosis. Should these signs and symptoms occur other than during a delirium, a mental disorder due to a general medical condition may be diagnosed, such as depression from hypothyroidism.

Signs and symptoms of a mental disorder occurring during a delirium are considered associated features of the delirium. Signs and symptoms occurring other than during a delirium suggest a primary mental disorder.

- *Does a mix of different symptoms complicate assigning the condition to one category?* If yes, a subcategory is used based on the predominant clinical features. Finally, if it is impossible to determine whether the mental symptoms are primary, substance induced, or resulting from a general medical condition, use the not otherwise specified (NOS) category (see Tables 14-1, 14-2, and 14-3 earlier in the chapter).

Clinical Course and Complications

In a review of the medical records of clients who had been admitted to the Veteran's Administration hospital from 2001 to 2007 with changes in mental status, a group of researchers found a variety of unrecognized medical conditions (Reeves et al., 2010). Clients had been inappropriately referred from the emergency department to the psychiatric service with such serious and potentially life-threatening conditions as severe alcohol or drug intoxication, alcohol or drug withdrawal, and overdose of a prescription medication. A variety of other diagnoses were also overlooked including hypoglycemia, diabetic ketoacidosis, lithium toxicity, anticonvulsant toxicity, neuroleptic malignant syndrome, pneumonia, urinary tract infection, sepsis, cerebrovascular accident, heart failure, neurosyphilis, subdural hematoma, hyperthyroidism, hepatic encephalopathy, and uremic encephalopathy. Instead of being diagnosed with a medical illness, the clients were incorrectly admitted with diagnoses of schizophrenia, psychotic disorder not otherwise specified, depression, and bipolar disorder. In reviewing the client records, the researchers found that in many of the clients, the only part of the mental status exam done was assessment of orientation. Not one of the clients had received a comprehensive mental status exam, and physical exams were omitted or incomplete in some of the clients. Indicated laboratory tests and radiological exams were overlooked in about a third of the cases. Other errors included failure to obtain an available history, ignoring abnormal vital signs, and failure to obtain indicated neuroimaging; some errors occurred more than once in some clients.

The researchers concluded that ED staff were too quick to diagnose that altered mental status and behavioral problems were due to a psychiatric condition and therefore did not carry out a detailed workup. Even a brief mental status exam would have picked up most problems of the clients. A majority of the clients (85.5%) had a previous psychiatric diagnosis, and this may have biased the examiners toward a psychiatric diagnosis. However, a psychiatric history does not preclude having a medical illness (Reeves et al., 2010). According to the *DSM-IV-TR*, mental conditions due to a general medical disorder can only be diagnosed when there is a direct physiological link between signs and symptoms and the medical disorder. (This is in contrast to primary psychiatric disorders, in which the link is more tenuous.)

Mental conditions due to a general medical disorder are organized by symptoms in the *DSM-IV-TR*. For example, disorders characterized by problems in mood would be found with the mood disorders, but also with mood disorders due to a general medical condition in the mental disorders due to a general medical condition section. The major categories of mental disorders due to a general medical condition are as follows:

- Mood disorder due to a general medical condition
- Psychotic disorders due to a general medical condition
- Anxiety disorders due to a general medical condition
- Sleep disorders due to a general medical condition
- Sexual dysfunction disorders due to a general medical condition
- Mental disorders due to a general medical condition not elsewhere classified (This category includes the following three types of disorders: catatonia due to a general medical condition, personality change due to a general medical condition, and mental disorder not otherwise specified due to a general medical condition; Sadock & Sadock, 2003)

Critical Thinking Question

How might the experiences of a client with a history of chronic mental illness influence or shape the client's explanation of medical symptoms? How might these experiences influence their ability to recognize medical symptoms or their willingness to seek medical treatment?

Mood Disorders Due to a General Medical Condition

People with mood disorders due to a general medical condition (also known as secondary mood disorders) experience depression or mania (an elevated or expansive mood) directly related to a physical condition. These disorders have not been widely studied and the number of people affected is not known. However, mild and major depression are frequently seen in people experiencing neurological disorders such as Parkinson's disease, Huntington's disease, stroke, multiple sclerosis (MS), and infections such as HIV and syphilis. Mania is less common than depression as a secondary mood disorder. The goal in treatment is to address the underlying medical disorder. Clients may also benefit from treatment with antidepressants or electroconvulsive therapy (ECT) (Sadock & Sadock, 2007).

Other medical conditions are also known to present with depressive symptoms. For example, pancreatic cancer is notorious for presenting as depression. Pancreatic cancer should always be suspected in middle-aged adults who have a new onset of depression; depression may precede physical symptoms of cancer by as much as 6 months. Other medical causes of depression include hypothyroidism, Addison's disease, Cushing's syndrome, lupus, hypoparathyroidism, hyperparathyroidism, hepatic encephalopathy, acute intermittent porphyria, Wilson's disease (an autosomal recessive disorder of copper metabolism), and AIDS. Like MS, Huntington's disease may also cause depression or euphoria (Sadock & Sadock, 2007).

Multiple Sclerosis

Multiple sclerosis (MS) is a disorder in which mood is frequently affected. People with MS can have both cognitive and psychiatric symptoms. Although depression is common, about 25% of people with MS develop euphoria that is unrelated to anything going on in their lives. Clients may spontaneously cry or

Ms. S. CASE STUDIES

Ms. S. is a 33-year-old teacher admitted to the hospital with complaints of weakness, blurred vision, and ataxia. While on the unit, her family told the staff they were worried that she was depressed and needed a psychiatric evaluation. They reported she was tearful at times and crying for no reason. In the months prior to admission, she seemed to have become a different person (e.g., irritable at times, suspicious of others, and easily distracted). During the preceding summer, she had become less active, giving up her usual interests in jogging and tennis, and had become more isolated. Her memory was poor. She had not been sleeping regularly, although she frequently complained of being fatigued. Since she was hospitalized, her family was worried that she may not be able to cope with a possible medical diagnosis.

When the psychiatric consultation liaison nurse specialist spoke with Ms. S., Ms. S. said she could understand why her family was worried about her. She denied being depressed, but was very worried that she was going crazy. Ms. S. stated that she does not know whether she should be upset because she is undergoing diagnostic testing for multiple sclerosis or relieved that she would finally find out what has been going on. Ms. S. reported that she felt as if she were losing her mind. During the summer, she had felt as if she were out of control (i.e., one day feeling like herself and another day feeling as if she couldn't do anything or remember anything). One day she would have muscle cramps and blurred vision, and then those symptoms would go away. Another day she would feel giddy, and she would feel as if she were going to faint. She thought the symptoms she was having were not real and were all in her mind. She had always been healthy and felt as if she were becoming a hypochondriac.

Once the school year restarted, she was concerned that she could not fulfill her job responsibilities. She was afraid to tell anyone and tried to pretend that there was nothing wrong. Once she was in the hospital, she felt that if the doctors knew what was wrong with her, she would be able to get some help. Ms. S. told the nurse that she recalled that Shirley Temple had multiple sclerosis, and that Shirley Temple had been able to do a great many things in her life. Ms. S hoped that she would still be able to do many things in her life.

Ms. S. told the nurse that she was interested in learning everything she could about multiple sclerosis. She was worried about being a burden for her family and was reluctant to talk to them about her concerns. She didn't want to worry them, although they have always been very supportive to her. Ms. S. states she dreads the idea that she might not be able to continue to teach, and didn't know how she would cope if the doctors told her she could not go back to work.

Nursing Care Plan **Multiple Sclerosis**

Nursing Diagnosis 1: Risk for situational low self-esteem related to decreased functioning as evidenced by loss of sense of control, feelings of isolation, and inability to care for self.

Nursing Diagnosis 2: Readiness for enhanced hope related to sense of loss as evidenced by concerns for future and worries that she will be a burden for her family.

Nursing Diagnosis 3: Interrupted family processes related to diagnosis of illness in a family member as evidenced by changes in personality, role performance, and family relationships.

Expected Outcomes	Interventions	Evaluations
• Client and family will be involved in learning about illness and treatment.	• To involve the client and family in assessment, education, and treatment planning. • To discuss options for treatment and follow-up with client and family.	• Client and family discuss potential problems and needs.
• Client and family will understand that personality and mood symptoms are related to the medical problem. • Client will recognize possible symptoms related to stress, physical fatigue, or medications.	• To refer client and family to client education groups and MS center. • To involve client and family in discussions and problem solving. • To discuss mechanisms for coping with stress.	• Client verbalizes recognition of need for continued medical follow-up. • Client's involvement in group activities helps maintain sense of control and mastery. • Client is able to avoid situations and activities that increase stress and fatigue.
• Client will experience hopeful sense of future.	• To assist the client in evaluating personal goals and a sense of future with regard to adaptation and serviceable sense of denial.	• Client is able to adapt interests to present abilities and choose activities to help maintain a healthy lifestyle. • Client is able to identify activities that are pleasurable and increase positive perception of self-esteem and sense of personal well-being.

Visit http://go.jblearning.com/mentalhealth for additional care plans and exercises.

laugh but do not understand this emotional lability and can become very distressed.

About 350,000 people in the United States have MS; it is the most common chronic neurological disease in young adults. Depression is the most common psychiatric diagnosis in people with MS, with a lifetime risk of 40–60%. The etiology of depression in MS is complex but is thought to be related to focal demyelination in areas of the brain involved in regulating mood, immune dysfunction, adverse effects of treatment with interferon B, the psychosocial stress of disability, decreased social support, and unemployment (Wallin, Wilken, Turner, Williams, & Kane, 2006). Depressed clients also have been shown to have an increased immune response, and MS is a chronic inflammatory disease with immune dysfunction.

People with MS should be routinely screened for depression. It is important to keep in mind that many vegetative symptoms of depression, such as disturbed sleep and fatigue, are common in people with MS who are not depressed, so a careful distinction needs to be made so as not to overinterpret physical symptoms.

There is an increased risk of suicide in people with MS. It is estimated that suicide is the cause of death in approximately 15% of clinic clients with multiple sclerosis (Wallin et al., 2006; Goldman Consensus Group 2005).

Psychotic Disorders Due to a General Medical Condition

The extent of secondary psychotic disorders is unknown, but these disorders may be seen in any condition that affects brain function. Clients should first be evaluated for dementia; it is unusual but possible for people who have a degenerative brain disorder such as Alzheimer's disease or Huntington's disease to first present with psychotic symptoms such as hallucinations and delusions before showing the more common cognitive impairments (disorientation, memory loss) associated with these disorders. People experiencing a delirium may also experience psychotic symptoms, but they will have a fluctuating level of consciousness. In comparison, the person who has a psychosis due to a psychiatric condition such as schizophrenia will be awake and alert. As with all mental disorders due to a general medical condition, the prognosis depends on the effectiveness of treatment for the underlying disorder. Medical conditions that may cause a psychosis include seizure disorders, lupus, hepatic encephalopathy, vitamin B_{12} deficiency, Cushing's syndrome, Addison's disease, hyperthyroidism, AIDS, and neurosyphilis (Sadock & Sadock, 2007).

Neurosyphilis

Syphilis is a sexually transmitted disease caused by the bacterium *Treponema pallidum*. Before the widespread availability of penicillin in the 1940s, one in five admissions to psychiatric hospitals was due to neurosyphilis (tertiary syphilis). As of 2009, about 1% of psychiatric admissions are due to neurosyphilis (Friedrich, Geusau, Greisenegger, Ossege, & Aigner, 2009). In 1941, there were 100,000 cases of syphilis reported in the United States; this number declined to 10,000 in 1951 but increased to 32,000 in 2002 and has increased approximately 12% in 2005–2006 (Centers for Disease Control and Prevention [CDC], 2010). However, syphilis may be underdiagnosed. Even though effective treatment is available for syphilis, the incidence of neurosyphilis is increasing because of the increase in HIV, overall increase in syphilis, and undertreatment of syphilis. Infection does not convey immunity, and people may become repeatedly infected. People also may be asymptomatic or have symptoms but not realize what is wrong with them and not seek treatment (Sanchez & Zisselman, 2007).

Syphilis has been called "the great imitator" because the signs and symptoms mimic many other diseases (CDC, 2010). Psychiatric symptoms can develop at any stage of the illness, but are more common later in the illness. Psychiatric symptoms are variable but include psychosis, mania, depression, irritability, paranoia, violent or other aberrant behavior, personality changes, memory loss, slowed thinking, and the inability to learn new material. Grandiose delusions undistinguishable from those seen in delirious mania are common. Neurologic symptoms include tremors, handwriting difficulties, stroke, and slowed speech. As the disease progresses, the dementia is very much like dementias from other disorders (Friedrich et al., 2009; Sanchez & Zisselman, 2007). Neurosyphilis can also worsen a concurrent psychiatric illness, for example, precipitating relapse and making medications less effective in remission. About one third of people with untreated late latent syphilis will develop tertiary syphilis. It used to take as long as 20 years for neurosyphilis to develop, but HIV-associated immunosuppression has shortened that time for many people (Sanchez & Zisselman, 2007).

The usual screening test for syphilis is the RPR (rapid plasma reagin), but neurosyphilis is difficult to diagnosis on the basis of one test, and a negative RPR does not mean a client does not have neurosyphilis. There should be a high suspicion of neurosyphilis in people who have new psychiatric or neurologic symptoms. This is particularly true for those who are at high risk of a sexually transmitted disease, especially if they have another STD, or HIV or AIDS. Psychiatric clients with schizophrenia, bipolar disorder, and substance abuse are especially vulnerable to these disorders because of impaired judgment and insight and impulsivity.

Anxiety Disorders Due to a General Medical Condition

Medical disorders where anxiety may be the most important presenting symptom include hyperthyroidism, hypoglycemia, hyperglycemia, hypoparathyroidism, MS, pheochromocytosis and systemic lupus erythematosus. In all of these conditions, the client would have behavioral problems and abnormal laboratory and physical examination findings.

Other Disorders Due to a General Medical Condition

In rare circumstances, medical conditions cause sleep disorders, sexual disorders, catatonia, personality changes, and mental disorders not otherwise specified (Sadock & Sadock, 2007).

Pellagra

Pellagra presents with the four *D*s of dermatitis, dementia, diarrhea, and death. Pellagra is a potentially fatal disease brought on by a deficiency of the vitamin niacin (nicotinic acid). It was once a common cause of dementia in the American South and was associated with an acorn-based diet. Adding vitamin supplements to the food supply has made pellagra almost entirely disappear from the United States, but its rarity may also mean that it is overlooked as the etiology for neuropsychiatric symptoms (Kertesz, 2001). The three systems involved in pellagra are the skin (rash, hyperpigmentation), gastrointestinal system (nausea, vomiting, diarrhea, discomfort after meals, and glossitis), and neuropsychiatric system (memory loss and other cognitive dysfunction, anxiety, depression, psychosis, seizures, and ataxia). The first signs are reddened skin, like sunburn, on areas of the body exposed to the sun.

Catatonia Due to a General Medical Condition

A central nervous system (CNS) motor disturbance characterizes catatonia due to a general medical condition (see Table 14-4 earlier in the chapter). This motor disturbance is a direct physiologic effect of the medical condition. Client history, physical examination, and laboratory findings exclude the following neurologic conditions and metabolic disorders: malignant brain neoplasm and other neoplasms, head trauma, cerebrovascular accident, encephalitis, hypercalcemia, hepatic encephalopathy, homocystinuria, and diabetic ketoacidosis.

The *DSM-IV-TR* helps to interpret information gathered from the client's mental and physical assessment and presents other criteria that aid in making a differential diagnosis of catatonia. For example, the *DSM-IV-TR* states that the disturbance is not better accounted for by another mental disorder such as a manic episode, or that the disturbance does not occur exclusively during the course of the delirium (APA, 2000).

Clinical Example 

Gerald, an 81-year-old man who lived by himself, was brought to the hospital via ambulance after his neighbors called stating that he was becoming increasingly anxious at home and unable to manage. The neighbors reported that he had been having more trouble caring for himself and appeared to be losing weight. Gerald appeared visibly shaken and told staff that he felt panicky all the time and just knew that something terrible was going to happen. He could not explain why he was frightened or what was making him nervous. Gerald told staff he had food at home and was eating normally but was losing weight. Gerald had no psychiatric history. Staff in the emergency department noted that he appeared jaundiced and his liver function tests were elevated. He was admitted to the hospital and was found to have pancreatic cancer.

Behavioral disturbances represent changes from the client's previous personality patterns.

Personality changes that are associated features of a general medical condition are not coded as personality change due to a general medical condition.

Other conditions to rule out include medication-induced movement disorders. Abnormal positioning may result from neuroleptic-induced acute dystonia. Catatonic-type schizophrenia also must be ruled out. This is distinguished both by the absence of a general medical condition related etiologically to the catatonia and by the presence of characteristic signs of schizophrenia such as delusions, hallucinations, and disorganized speech.

Clinical Example 

A 58-year-old homeless man was admitted to the hospital with complaints of chest pain, fever, cough, 10-pound weight loss, night sweats, nausea, vomiting, watery diarrhea, a burning sensation on discolored skin, and a labile mood. The patient had been diagnosed with bipolar disorder in the past, but although he was labile when he was admitted, he was neither manic nor depressed. The patient received an extensive physical examination and laboratory tests, all of which were negative, including those for tuberculosis and HIV, or they were only mildly abnormal. The patient's nutritional history was then assessed. The patient reported that he did not eat at shelters and had lived mostly on alcoholic beverages and corn chips for 4 months. The patient was started on 100 milligrams of niacin twice a day and began to eat meals at a shelter. Within 2 weeks all of his symptoms, including his irritable mood, subsided (Kertesz, 2001).

The third condition to exclude is mood disorder with catatonic features. This is also distinguished by the absence of a general medical condition and the presence of symptoms that meet the criteria for a major manic or major depressive episode.

Personality Changes Due to a General Medical Condition

Clients sometimes experience personality changes due to a general medical condition because of brain lesions due to trauma, tumors, strokes, seizures, hyperthyroidism, and hypocortisolism, although any medical condition may cause a personality change (Sadock & Sadock, 2007). The type of symptoms a person experiences is related to the location of damage. People with a traumatic brain injury are more likely to have persistent problems with personality. Personality changes due to general medical conditions must be differentiated from personality disor-

Table 14-7 Nursing Intervention for Clients with Mental Disorders Due to General Medical Conditions

Nursing Diagnosis	Nursing Interventions	Rationales
Ineffective coping	Assess client and family understanding of illness.	Establish preconceptions and knowledge of client's and family's understanding of illness. By not making assumptions and establishing baseline, the nurse can make an informed assessment and validate inferences.
	Identify how illness has changed things.	Help establish how the client's roles and relationships have changed due to illness. The nurse needs to assess coping skills and adequacy of support systems.
	Establish client and family priorities in seeking help.	Assisting client and family with problems that they identify ensures the development of trust and establishes the basis for a future relationship among client, caretakers, and nursing.
	Assess level of problem-solving skills.	Identify ways in which the client and family have handled things successfully and unsuccessfully in the past in order to build upon problem-solving skills.
	Involve client and family in education regarding symptoms and illness.	Promote understanding and involvement.

der, the primary mental disorder that involves certain stable behaviors and patterns. Personality changes resulting from a general medical condition can only be diagnosed if a direct physiologic mechanism that has caused or maintained changes is established. The presence of chronic medical conditions associated with personality changes also facilitates the differential diagnosis. Conditions that cause pain and disability are often responsible for personality changes and thus should be excluded. In addition, if the criteria for dementia are met, a separate diagnosis of **personality disorder** caused by a general medical condition is not warranted. Similarly, personality changes occurring only during the delirium are not caused by a medical condition; they are considered associated features of the delirium. Personality changes may be caused by another mental disorder due to a general medical condition. Examples include mood disorder due to a brain tumor with depressive features, personality changes due to substance abuse, and personality changes due to other mental disorders. The absence of both a specific general medical condition and evidence of its direct physiologic effect strongly suggests a primary mental disorder. (See Table 14-6 earlier in the chapter.)

Management and Treatment

Management and treatment focus on the careful assessment and identification of the primary medical disorder. Proper treatment of the primary medical disorder can mitigate or reverse the psychiatric symptoms at times. However, other symptoms, such as personality changes or affective symptoms related to steroids, can develop or increase even if the client's medical problems are being adequately managed and the client has had no problems in the past with the same regimen. If the psychiatric symptoms are disturbing to the client or interfere with functioning, the client should be evaluated to determine whether the symptoms can be managed with medication, changes in environment or medication, or psychotherapeutic intervention. Sample nursing interventions and rationales for clients with general medical conditions are included in **Table 14-7**.

Although the term *personality* is commonly linked to both changes and disorders, personality changes due to a general medical condition are coded on Axis I, whereas personality disorders are coded on Axis II.

Considerations for Client and Family Education

- Clients or family members should be aware that when new or atypical psychiatric symptoms are present, even in a client with a previously identified mental disorder, careful assessment and evaluation are needed to determine if the symptoms are due to a medical disorder.
- Some psychiatric symptoms related to a medical disorder can be treated or reversed when the general medical disorder is treated.

Critical Thinking Question

Give examples of how you might help and support client's efforts to deal with a new diagnosis of a medical problem that might have symptoms that could be found in a psychiatric disorder.

Summary

Clients who present with psychiatric symptoms may be medically ill. It is essential for nurses to be intellectually curious and question psychiatric diagnoses in clients whose signs and symptoms are atypical and who do not respond well to psychiatric treatment. Nurses then need to be client advocates and work with other caregivers to be sure clients receive comprehensive assessments including physical exams, family and client history, laboratory and neuroimaging studies, and mental status evaluations. Mental disorders due to a general medical condition can have serious and even catastrophic consequences for people, and they deserve competent nursing care.

To diagnose a mental disorder due to a general medical condition, the etiology of the psychiatric disorder must be the result of the physiologic condition. Delirium, dementia, amnesia, psychosis, sexual dysfunction, and mood, anxiety, or sleep disorders may all be directly caused by medical conditions. To manage mental disorders due to a general medical condition, the underlying pathophysiology or etiology must be identified. Some general medical conditions are frequently associated with mental disorders. These are typical considerations in differential diagnoses. Examples of this type of commonly encountered association would be that between hypothyroidism and mood disorders or between hypoxemia and delirium. Once established, treatment targets the medical condition. Occasionally it is necessary to treat both conditions concurrently or to continue treating the mental disorder after the medical condition stabilizes. It is essential for medical and psychiatric practitioners to collaborate.

Annotated References

American Psychiatric Association. (2000). *Diagnostic and statistical manual of mental disorders* (4th ed., text rev.). Washington, DC: Author.
This is the fourth edition, with text revision, of the American Psychiatric Association's official nomenclature of psychiatric conditions and descriptions. It provides a systematic listing of the official codes and categories, a description of the multiaxial system for diagnosis, and diagnostic criteria for each of the disorders. It is used by psychiatrists, physicians, psychologists, registered nurses, social workers, therapists, and other mental health workers in all clinical settings.

Centers for Disease Control and Prevention (CDC). (2010). Sexually transmitted diseases. Syphilis—CDC fact sheet. Retrieved from http://www.cdc.gov/std/Syphilis/STDFact-Syphilis.htm
This fact sheet provides statistical data on syphilis.

Chuang, L., & Forman, N. (2006). Mental disorders secondary to general medical conditions. *Emedicine*. Retrieved from www.emedicine.com/med/topic3447.htm
This article lists criteria for distinguishing medical and psychiatric origins of psychiatric symptoms.

Friedrich, F., Geusau, A., Greisenegger, S., Ossege, M., & Aigner, M. (2009). Manifest psychosis in neurosyphilis. *General Hospital Psychiatry, 31*(4), 379–381.
This article discusses psychosis as a presenting symptom in syphilis and need for continued routine screening for syphilis.

Goldman Consensus Group. (2005). The Goldman consensus statement on depression in multiple sclerosis. *11*(3), 328–337.
This piece reviews the impact of depression upon clients with multiple sclerosis.

Kertesz, S. G. (2001). Pellagra in 2 homeless men. *Mayo Clinic Proceedings, 76*, 315–318.
This article is a discussion of case reports for clients with pellagra.

Koran, L. M., Sheline, Y., Imai, K., Kelsey, T. G., Freedland, K. E., Matthews, J., & Moore, M. (2002). Medical disorders among clients admitted to a public sector psychiatric inpatient unit. *Psychiatric Services, 53*(12), 1623–1625.
The authors conducted a research study on the extent of medical problems in psychiatric clients and found that a large percentage of patients had newly diagnosed medical problems, and some had physical disorders that may have increased symptoms of a mental disorder.

Larkin, G. L., Classen, C. A., Edmond, J. A., Pelletier, A. J., & Camargo, C. A. (2005). Trends in U.S. emergency department visits for mental health conditions, 1992–2001. *Psychiatric Services, 56*(6), 671–677.
This report studied trends in mental health related visits to emergency departments.

Nightingale, F. (1946). *Notes on nursing. What it is and what it is not*. Philadelphia, PA: J.P. Lippincott.

This book presents Florence Nightingale's observations on nursing. It was first published in 1859.

Reeves, R. R., Parker, J. D., & Burke, R. S. (2010). Unrecognized physical illness prompting psychiatric admission. *Annals of Clinical Psychiatry, 22*(3), 180–185.

The case records of over 1,000 clients with unrecognized medical conditions who were inappropriately admitted to psychiatric units were reviewed. The most common missed diagnoses were alcohol or drug intoxication, alcohol or drug withdrawal or delirium tremens, or prescription medication overdose. The most common incorrect diagnoses was schizophrenia followed by psychosis NOS, depression, and bipolar disorder. Except for assessing orientation, mental status exams had not been done and few clients had a physical exam or indicated lab and diagnostic studies or X-rays. The article discusses the problem of unrecognized medical problems in psychiatric clients.

Sadock, B. J., & Sadock, V. A. (2007). *Kaplan and Sadock's synopsis of psychiatry* (10th ed.). Philadelphia, PA: Lippincott Williams & Wilkins.

This is a comprehensive textbook of psychiatry.

Saliou, V., Fichele, A., McLoughlin, M., Thauin, T., & Lejeux, M. L. (2005). Psychiatric disorders among patients admitted to a French emergency service. *General Hospital Psychiatry, 27*(4), 263–268.

This study of admissions to a French emergency service found that 29% of the patients had medical problems.

Sanchez, F. M., & Zisselman, M. H. (2007) Treatment of psychiatric symptoms associated with neurosyphilis. *Psychosomatics, 48*(5), 440–445.

This article discusses psychiatric symptoms associated with neurosyphilis, including cognitive problems, mood disorder, and behavioral problems.

Wallin, M. T., Wilkin, J. A., Turner, A. P., Williams, R. M., & Kane, R. (2006). Depression and multiple sclerosis: Review of a lethal combination. *Journal of Rehabilitation Research & Development, 43*(1), 45–62.

This article reviews the association of depression with multiple sclerosis due to the psychosocial effects of disability, effects of lesions and interferon on brain structures, and immune dysfunctions. The need for assessment, screening, and treatment is discussed along with the risk factors for suicide.

Additional Resources

Foster, R., Olajide, D., & Everall, L. P. (2003). Antiretroviral therapy-induced psychosis: Case report and brief report of the literature. *HIV Medicine, 4*, 139–144.

One month after starting combination antiretroviral therapy, a client developed persecutory delusions, mutism, and catatonia. After discontinuing abacavir (ABC) and starting a low dose of an antipsychotic, the client's psychosis resolved.

Govoni, M., Castellino, G., Padovan, M., & Trotta, F. (2004). Recent advances and future perspective in neuroimaging in neuropsychiatric systemic lupus erythematosus. *Lupus, 13*, 149–158.

Neuropsychiatric symptoms occur in 14–75% of clients with SLE, but remain difficult to diagnose.

Lubkin, I. M. (2006). *Chronic illness: Impact and intervention* (6th ed.). Sudbury, MA: Jones and Bartlett.

This text describes the impact of chronic illness upon the client and family members.

Madhusoodanan, S., Danan, D., & Moise, D. (2007). Psychiatric manifestations of brain tumors: Diagnostic implications. *Expert Review of Neurotherapeutics, 7*(4), 343–349.

This article is a discussion of psychiatric and mood symptoms that may appear in the presence of medical problems such as a brain tumor.

Mohr, D. C., Hart, S. L., Fonareva, I., & Tasch, E. S. (2006). Treatment of depression for clients with multiple sclerosis in neurology clinics. *Multiple Sclerosis, 12*, 204–208.

This article is a discussion of treatment issues of depression in people with MS.

Morgante, L. (2000). Hope in multiple sclerosis: A nursing perspective. *International Journal of MS Care, 2*(2), 1–8.

This article discusses hope as a nursing concept and psychosocial issues in caring for medically ill clients.

Wells, S. M. (2000). *A delicate balance: Living successfully with chronic illness*. Cambridge, MA: Perseus.

This is a helpful book for clients and families dealing with adjustment to chronic illness, including information on typical behavior patterns.

Internet Resources

For a full suite of assignments and additional learning activities, use the access code located in the front of your book to visit this exclusive website: http://go.jblearning.com/mentalhealth. If you do not have an access code, you can obtain one at the site.

Learning Objectives

After reading this chapter, you will be able to:

- Define substance abuse, substance dependence, tolerance, intoxication, withdrawal, and dual diagnosis.
- Assess clients for signs and symptoms of substance-related disorders.
- Identify the nursing diagnoses and interventions relevant to the management and treatment of substance-related disorders, and use these to develop individualized nursing care plans.
- List at least five areas for client and family education related to substance use.
- Describe treatment modalities effective in the treatment of substance-related disorders.
- Identify special needs of clients with a dual diagnosis.

Key Terms

12-step programs

Blackouts

Codependence

Cross-tolerance

Denial

Detoxification

Dual diagnosis

Fetal alcohol syndrome (FAS)

Intoxication

Korsakoff's syndrome

Motivational interviewing

Substance abuse

Substance dependence

Substance-induced disorders

Tolerance

Wernicke's encephalopathy

Withdrawal

Withdrawal delirium

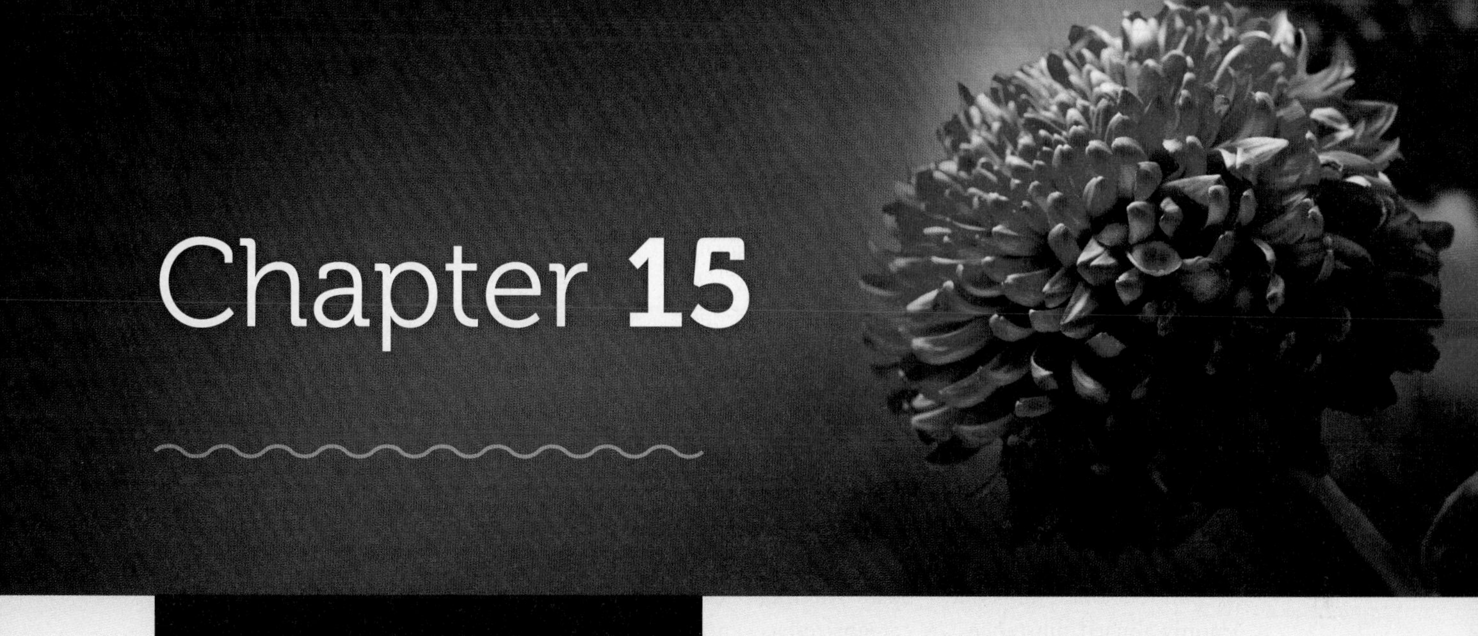

Substance-Related Disorders

Patricia G. O'Brien

http://go.jblearning.com/mentalhealth 

For a full suite of assignments and additional learning activities, use the access code located in the front of your book to visit this exclusive website: http://go.jblearning.com/mentalhealth. If you do not have an access code, you can obtain one at the site.

Introduction

The *Diagnostic and Statistical Manual of Mental Disorders*, fourth edition, text revision (*DSM-IV-TR*) distinguishes between substance-induced disorders and substance-use disorders (American Psychiatric Association [APA], 2000). **Substance-induced disorders** refer to intoxication and withdrawal as well as to other disorders induced by substances, including delirium, dementia, amnesia, paranoia, depression, anxiety, sexual dysfunction, and sleep disorders. *Substance-use disorders* refer to substance dependence and substance abuse. The most commonly abused substances are categorized as central nervous system (CNS) depressants, CNS stimulants, opiates, hallucinogens, cannabinoids, phencyclidine (PCP), inhalants, and nicotine. This chapter discusses intoxication, withdrawal, substance abuse, and substance dependence and presents the principles of diagnosis, treatment, and prevention.

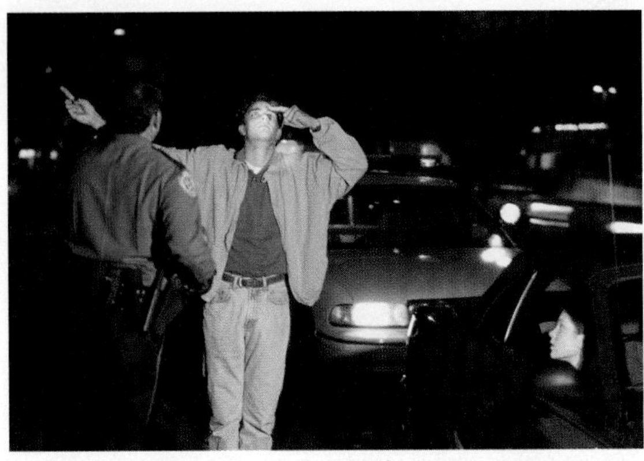

Figure 15-1 Repeatedly driving under the influence is a sign of substance abuse.

Substance-Induced Disorders

Substance **intoxication** is a substance-specific syndrome that results from recent ingestion or exposure to a substance (APA, 2000). The cognitive and behavioral changes that occur are related to the effects the substance has on the CNS and vary depending on the person and the substance. Common responses include belligerence, labile mood, impaired judgment, and loss of motor coordination. The first substance disorder a person is most likely to experience is intoxication.

Substance **withdrawal** is a substance-specific response as well. It occurs when a person stops or decreases use after heavy, prolonged consumption. Signs and symptoms vary depending on the substance, dose, duration of use, and health of the person. The morning-after hangover with the accompanying symptoms of headache, dry mouth, and fine hand tremors is indicative of mild alcohol withdrawal.

Substance-Use Disorders

The *DSM-IV-TR* distinguishes between the two substance-use disorders: substance abuse and substance dependence.

The essential feature of **substance abuse** is a maladaptive pattern of substance use manifested by recurrent and significant adverse consequences related to the substance use (APA, 2000). According to *DSM-IV-TR* criteria, substance abuse can be diagnosed if one of the following criteria is met within a 12-month period, *and if the criteria for substance dependence are not met*:

- The substance abuse interferes with the person's major responsibilities at work, home, or school.
- Repeated use occurs in hazardous situations, such as driving when impaired (**Figure 15-1**).
- The person is experiencing recurrent substance-related legal problems.
- The person has recurring social or interpersonal problems related to substance use.

Examples of behaviors that should be considered in making this diagnosis include frequent absences from work, arrests for driving while intoxicated (DWI), involvement in physical or verbal altercations, and missing significant family events. Substance abuse can include excessive use of substances over brief periods of time, or it may occur as a chronic problem. However, there is an absence of physical or psychologic dependence.

Critical Thinking Question

Which criteria can you find in the clinical example about Tom to support the diagnosis of substance abuse?

A diagnosis of **substance dependence** is made based on evidence of tolerance, withdrawal, or a pattern of compulsive behavior related to the substance. According to *DSM-IV-TR* criteria (APA, 2000), substance dependence requires the presence of three or

Clinical Example

Tom is a 28-year-old, single stockbroker who has developed a pattern of weekend drug abuse. Every Friday, he joins coworkers after work for a few drinks. The other guys generally have a couple of beers before heading home, but Tom drinks faster than the others and averages four or five beers before the group breaks up. Tom drives home and usually stops to pick up a sandwich or a burger and a couple of six-packs of beer. He has a couple of beers with the sandwich before showering and dressing for the club scene. At the club, he mixes shots of vodka with beer, and mellows out with marijuana. It is not unusual for Tom and his friends to get into verbal and even physical altercations during these nights out. After sleeping late on Saturday, the partying continues with alcohol, marijuana, and sometimes the stimulant ecstasy, which Tom uses to enhance his casual sexual encounters. Over the past couple of years, Tom has fallen into the same pattern every weekend. He stops all drinking and drug use early Sunday, noting that he has to sober up so he can be alert for work on Monday morning. However, twice this past month Tom did continue partying into Sunday, and was unable to work on Monday. Tom had a girlfriend for 3 months but she broke up with him because of her concern over his drug use.

more of the following at any time during a 12-month period:

- Tolerance
- Withdrawal
- Greater use of the substance than intended
- Inability to stop or control the substance use
- Preoccupation with obtaining, using, or recovering from the substance
- Giving up important activities in order to use the substance
- Continued use of the substance even when confronted with the risks

Tolerance refers to the person's need for increasing amounts of the substance to achieve the desired effects. Tolerance develops as a result of the body adapting to the presence of the substance. A decrease in the amount or effectiveness of the substance leads to withdrawal. **Cross-tolerance** refers to the increased tolerance that develops for drugs in the same category. A person with tolerance for alcohol will have a tolerance for all sedative-hypnotic and anxiolytic medications. Cross-tolerance has implications for pain medication. If a client has a history of heroin or other opiate abuse, it is likely that higher than usual doses of narcotic medications will be needed to achieve pain relief.

Withdrawal represents a physiologic dependence on a substance, and it occurs when a person stops using a substance after a period of prolonged use. Withdrawal symptoms are not observed with all substances, and not all persons dependent on substances develop a physiologic dependence.

The additional diagnostic criteria for substance dependence are behaviors aimed at protecting and maintaining the substance use. The person uses greater amounts of the substance for longer periods than intended. He or she repeatedly plans to curtail or regulate substance use. The person spends a great deal of time using, obtaining, and recovering from the substance. Important social, work-related, or recreational activities are given up or reduced. Finally, the person continues to use the substance despite the knowledge that it is causing a psychologic or physical problem.

Chemical dependency comes first. Physical, social, and psychologic consequences are caused by the dependency.

Critical Thinking Question

Which criteria can you find in the clinical example about Marcie (p. 344) to support the diagnosis of substance dependence?

Among the revisions proposed for the DSM-5 is the collapse of the current separate diagnoses of abuse and dependence into a single diagnosis of "addiction" and the elimination of the criterion related to legal issues. The rationale for combining the abuse and dependency diagnoses is that clients with significant problems and impaired functioning often did not meet the criteria for alcohol abuse under the DSM IV (APA, 2011). The proposed change has met with some opposition. In addition to abuse and dependence requiring very different treatment approaches, another objection is a concern over the possible stigma associated with the label of addict. It is noted that behaviors currently characterized as abuse may be temporary and may never develop into a physical or psychological dependence. However, clients would be diagnosed as having an addiction, with possible consequences for future employment, insurance, and legal status (Frances, 2010). The Substance-Related Disorders Work Group has also recommended that gambling disorder be moved into

Clinical Example 

Marcie is a 40-year-old, recently divorced, currently unemployed mother with a 10-year-old daughter, Tanya. Marcie was let go from her job as a bank teller due to frequent absences, which she attributed to chronic back pain. Doctors did not find a specific cause for the back pain, but Marcie had prescriptions for benzodiazepine medications, Valium (diazepam), and Klonopin (clonazepam) to help her cope with the pain. Marcie also uses these medications when she has difficulty sleeping. In the past month, Marcie has noted that she needs to take double the dose of these medications in order to fall asleep. She has been experiencing increasing difficulty managing her responsibilities with her daughter, and her ex-husband is threatening to seek custody. Last month, she failed to pick Tanya up after school, and the principal, unable to reach Marcie, had called Tanya's father, who found Marcie at home, passed out on the couch with an empty bottle of wine on the table. Fearing losing custody of her daughter, Marcie promised to stop drinking, but instead has managed to restrict her drinking to after Tanya goes to bed at night. She starts each night planning to have one glass of wine, but always has more, and usually loses count. This past week, Marcie has begun taking a diazepam in the morning to steady her hands.

Nearly 40 states have passed laws that limit the sale of cold medicines containing the decongestants pseudoephedrine and ephedrine, which illegal labs use to make methamphetamine.

Alcohol-related accidents and disorders account for 30% of all emergency room visits and 40% of all general hospital admissions.

this category and the diagnostic category be renamed Addiction and Related Disorders (APA, 2011). The proposed changes will undergo further review before any final decisions are made.

Incidence and Prevalence of Substance-Related Disorders

In the United States alone, more than 100,000 people per year receive inpatient treatment for alcohol and other mind-altering drugs. Substance abuse occurs across all racial, socioeconomic, and ethnic lines. The incidence of alcoholism is higher in cultures that proscribe childhood use but encourage and accept heavy use in adulthood. In recent years, the medical community has become increasingly aware of substance abuse among women and the elderly. Persons between 18 and 24 years of age use the greatest amount of all substances, but there is concern about adolescent use as well. The use of marijuana and alcohol in high school has become common. The average age of first marijuana use is 14; alcohol use often starts before age 12 (American Academy of Child and Adolescent Psychiatry, 2011).

The popularity of certain drugs varies over time and depends to some extent on their availability and how easy they are to use. Marijuana and cocaine are the most commonly used illicit drugs. Among young people in particular, certain drugs have come to be known as club drugs, referring to the dance clubs, bars, and parties (such as raves) where they are commonly available and used. These drugs include ecstasy and methamphetamine.

Prescription drugs, primarily benzodiazepines, can lead to dependence and abuse that is often difficult to detect, because the withdrawal symptoms are similar to the anxiety or insomnia the drugs were originally prescribed to treat. Oxycodone is another prescribed medication that is frequently abused. Primarily because of their availability, over-the-counter (OTC) medications can also be drugs of abuse. In high doses, OTC cough and cold preparations can produce effects similar to PCP. The common decongestants, pseudoephedrine and ephedrine, have been used illegally to manufacture methamphetamine. Most states now restrict the sale of OTC medications with these ingredients.

Alcohol is still the most widely used and abused psychoactive substance in the United States and has been associated with 100,000 to 200,000 deaths each year. Some alcohol-related deaths include accidental or intentional overdoses, drug interactions, traffic or other accidents, injuries sustained in falls, and medically related illnesses.

Etiology

Substance abuse does not have just one cause. Rather, the etiology is a combination of neurobiologic, genetic, social, and psychologic factors. Classic studies conducted with children of alcoholics have established a genetic predisposition, but because the rate of alcoholism never reaches 100% for identical twins, other variables must be involved. Children of parents with substance-abuse disorders are considered at increased risk for developing these disorders. Parents' attitudes and the examples they set may contribute to this risk. Although there is no recognized addictive personality disorder, depression, low self-esteem, loneliness, stress, and behaviors such as pain avoidance and pleasure seeking all may contribute to a reliance on psychoactive substances. However, this situation is not simply one of cause and effect, because depression, low self-esteem, and loneliness may very well be consequences of the addiction. More research is required to discern the etiology of this complex disorder.

Physiology

All abused psychoactive drugs directly affect the brain and CNS, altering the neurotransmitters essential for intercellular communication. This action results in changes in feelings, thoughts, and behaviors. All drugs of abuse are thought to increase brain dopamine in the pathways that drive motivation and reward. Chronic use of alcohol or other drugs may alter the brain chemistry in a way that helps maintain the addiction. Specific neurotransmitter alterations depend on the substance, the route of administration, the amount of the dose, the presence of other drugs, and the general health of the individual. Drugs are commonly classified by the type of effect they exert on the CNS. The psychopharmacologic properties of the major classes of drugs that produce physical dependency are shown in **Table 15-1** (APA, 2000; Deglin, Vallerand, & Sanoski, 2011; Galanter & Kleber, 2008; Perkinson, 2012).

Table 15-1 Drug Categories That Produce Physical Dependency

Drug Category	Symptoms of Intoxication	Time to Onset of Withdrawal	Symptoms of Withdrawal	Detoxification
CNS depressants (alcohol, barbiturates, benzodiazepines)	Inappropriate sexual or aggressive behavior, labile mood, impaired functioning and judgment, slurred speech, unsteady gait, nystagmus, impaired memory, perceptual disturbances, stupor, coma	From last use: 4–6 hours, peaking at 24 hours for alcohol; 12 hours to 3 days for barbiturates, depending on half-life; 7–10 days for diazepam (Valium)	Diaphoresis, elevated pulse and blood pressure, tremors, nausea, vomiting, insomnia, agitation, auditory and visual hallucinations, and seizures	Doses of CNS depressants are tapered. Sample alcohol detoxification: chlordiazepoxide (Librium) 25 mg orally every 4 hours for 24 hours, then 20 mg every 4 hours for 24 hours, so that on the 5th and final day, the dose is 5 mg every 4 hours. Phenobarbital (Luminal Sodium), diazepam (Valium), and lorazepam (Ativan) are also used for detoxification. Detoxification can be extended up to 2 weeks or longer when the drug of addiction is long acting.
CNS stimulants (cocaine, amphetamines)	Hypervigilance, anxiety, confusion, paranoia, dilated pupils, increased or decreased heart rate, chest pain, arrhythmia, respiratory distress, hallucinations, seizures, coma	Wide variations in onset from a few hours to several days	Dysphoric mood, agitation, suicidal ideation, fatigue, insomnia, vivid dreams, extended sleep, hunger, and drug craving	Stabilize vital signs; control behavior. Chlordiazepoxide (Librium), haloperidol (Haldol), and antihypertensives are usually effective.
Caffeine (stimulant)	Restlessness, nervousness, insomnia, tachycardia, arrhythmia, nausea, vomiting, perceptual disturbances	Hours to days	Anxiety, fatigue, drowsiness, dysphoria, irritability, difficulty concentrating	

(Continues)

Table 15-1 Drug Categories That Produce Physical Dependency *(Continued)*

Drug Category	Symptoms of Intoxication	Time to Onset of Withdrawal	Symptoms of Withdrawal	Detoxification
Opiates (heroin, morphine, codeine, meperidine, methadone)	Constricted pupils, slurred speech, impaired judgment and functioning, nausea and vomiting, euphoria followed by apathy, drowsiness	Onset within minutes, hours or days after use; symptoms last 7–10 days	Chills, sweating, dilated pupils, increased pulse and blood pressure, muscle aches, abdominal cramps, drug craving, rhinorrhea, yawning, drowsiness, and coma	Methadone is administered orally in decreasing doses over a period of about 10 days; clonidine (Catapres) 0.3–1.2 mg/day, decreased by 50%/day for 3 days, then discontinued.
Cannabinoids (marijuana, hashish)	Impaired coordination and judgment, euphoria, suspiciousness, anxiety, injected conjunctiva, tachycardia, hallucinations	Mild physical dependence associated with chronic use of high doses	Restlessness, irritability, insomnia, nausea, vomiting, and sweating	No treatment required.
Nicotine (cigarettes, cigars, pipe and chewing tobacco)		Symptoms develop within 24 hours of tapering or not using drug	Irritability, nicotine craving, decreased heart rate, headache, increased appetite, difficulty concentrating, and insomnia	Nicotine is substituted in the form of gum or a patch, which is tapered and eventually discontinued.

Pregnancy and Substance Abuse

Women with substance abuse disorders have an increased risk for complications such as spontaneous abortion, preeclampsia, abruptio placentae, and early and prolonged labor. Nicotine, opioids, cocaine, and alcohol directly affect fetal development, particularly during the third trimester. Substance abuse places the fetus at higher than average risk for birth defects, low birth weight, cardiovascular problems, prematurity, and stillbirth. After birth, the infant may experience substance withdrawal. Intervention early in pregnancy can make a difference. For example, if a woman quits smoking before the third trimester, her risk of having a low-birth-weight baby is no greater than that of a nonsmoker (APA, 2006).

Fetal alcohol spectrum disorders (FASD) are a group of conditions that can occur in a person whose mother drank alcohol during pregnancy. These effects can include physical problems and problems with behavior and learning. **Fetal alcohol syndrome (FAS)** represents the severe end of the FASD spectrum. Fetal death is the most extreme outcome from drinking alcohol during pregnancy. People with FAS might have abnormal facial features, growth problems, and central nervous system (CNS) problems. People with FAS can have problems with learning, memory, attention span, communication, vision, or hearing.

Substances of Abuse

CNS Depressants

Examples of CNS depressants include alcohol, benzodiazepines, minor tranquilizers, barbiturates, chloral hydrate, meprobamate, and methaqualone. Depressants affect the brain stem and respiratory centers. Mechanisms vary but are most likely related to altered concentrations of one or a combination of neurotransmitters. The effects of CNS depressants include the relaxation of muscles, sedation, and decreased anxiety. *Intoxication* from CNS depressants is characterized by slurred speech, ataxia, impaired judgment, agitation, and depression. Severe intoxication can result in paranoia, seizures, stupor, coma, apnea, and even death. Alcohol abuse has been associated with **blackouts** or periods of amnesia during which the person appears to function normally but later does not recall the events that transpired. Following a night of heavy drinking, a person may have no recollection of getting home. In more extreme examples, people report waking up in strange cities with no idea how they got there. An alcohol tolerance usually leads to cross-tolerance with barbiturates and other sedative hypnotics. Combining these drugs with alcohol potentiates the effects of intoxication, particularly respiratory depression.

Withdrawal Symptoms

The onset of withdrawal from CNS depressants occurs within hours or days after stopping or reducing drug use. Withdrawal may occur during prolonged use if the person's high tolerance has decreased the drug's effect. Because alcohol affects the body for only a short time, withdrawal symptoms are usually observed within 4 to 6 hours after drinking ceases. Conversely, diazepam withdrawal may not be evident for 7–10 days. The time to onset of barbiturate withdrawal ranges from 12 hours to 3 days, depending on the half-life of the drug abused.

Symptoms of withdrawal include diaphoresis, elevated pulse and blood pressure, tremulousness (noted in the hand and extended tongue), nausea, vomiting, auditory and visual hallucinations, ataxia, agitation, and a subjective state of restlessness or anxiety. The risk of seizures is greatest in persons with a history of withdrawal seizures. The risk is highest 24–72 hours after the substance was last used. **Withdrawal delirium**, or delirium tremens (DTs), is a life-threatening complication of alcohol withdrawal and has a mortality rate of 15%. It is characterized by agitation, delusions, disorientation, visual hallucinations, elevated temperature, and cardiac arrhythmias.

Detoxification

Alcohol withdrawal is usually treated with progressively decreasing doses of chlordiazepoxide (Librium) at 4-hour intervals for a period of 5 days. Additional doses may be needed based on the presence of withdrawal symptoms and are given as needed. Elderly clients may require lower doses of medication during withdrawal. Withdrawal from CNS depressants is usually accomplished with benzodiazepines or barbiturates. Long-acting drugs such as diazepam and chlordiazepoxide provide a smoother **detoxification**, but some practitioners prefer short-acting drugs to prevent a cumulative effect. Short-acting drugs are indicated for clients whose physical or mental status is unclear, such as when laboratory tests are pending or a head injury is suspected. Short-acting drugs such as lorazepam (Ativan) are used to treat withdrawal in the presence of impaired liver function. Intravenous diazepam is usually administered to treat withdrawal delirium. Anticonvulsants are occasionally prescribed prophylactically for clients with a history of withdrawal seizures.

Chlordiazepoxide (Librium) is contraindicated in the presence of impaired liver functioning. The liver's inability to metabolize chlordiazepoxide leads to accumulation of the drug and causes increased lethargy and coma.

CNS Stimulants

Examples of CNS stimulants are caffeine, cocaine, amphetamines, and methylphenidate (Ritalin). Crack, a less expensive and more readily available form of cocaine, is highly addictive and is characterized by a quick high and a sudden crash, accompanied by profound depression. Methamphetamine, another popular drug of abuse, is also less expensive than cocaine, produces a longer high, and, like crack, results in an intense crash. Methamphetamine and amphetamines can be consumed by smoking, inhalation, or injection. Smoked methamphetamine is often referred to as "ice" or "crystal meth." Ecstasy, also known as MDMA (3,4-methylenedioxymethamphetamine), is a synthetic drug with amphetamine-like effects.

These drugs stimulate the CNS by enhancing the actions of the neurotransmitters dopamine and norepinephrine. CNS stimulants have the following effects: alertness, euphoria, decreased appetite, and an enhanced sexual response. *Intoxication* from CNS stimulants is characterized by anxiety, confusion, paranoia, irritability, grandiosity, rhinitis, insomnia, tactile hallucinations, increased or decreased heart rate, chest pain, cardiac arrhythmias, dilated pupils, and respiratory distress. Seizures can result from cocaine intoxication. Alcohol can counter the undesirable effects of stimulants such as anxiety. The combination of stimulants and alcohol, however, is unpredictable.

CNS stimulants dilate the pupils.

The onset of withdrawal is more rapid, and symptoms do not last as long with drugs that affect the body quickly and only for a short time, such as alcohol. The onset of withdrawal is delayed, and withdrawal symptoms last longer, with drugs such as diazepam that affect the body for a longer period of time.

The delirium experienced during withdrawal can be a life-threatening symptom.

Withdrawal Symptoms

Dysphoric mood, agitation, suicidal ideation, fatigue, insomnia, vivid dreams, extended sleep, hunger, and drug craving are all symptoms of withdrawal from CNS stimulants. Symptoms vary from person to person, and the onset can occur anywhere from a few hours to several days after ceasing or reducing drug use.

Detoxification

Detoxification includes stabilizing the client's vital signs and managing his or her behavior. This requires a combination of supportive therapy and medication with chlordiazepoxide (Librium) or haloperidol (Haldol). Intravenous antihypertensives may be necessary, and diazepam may be used to control seizures. Clients who use an intravenous combination of cocaine and heroin, commonly referred to as "speedball," are detoxified with methadone.

Opiates

Opiates constrict the pupils.

Persons who use hallucinogens can experience flashbacks, or recurrent drug experiences, for months after the last drug use.

Opioid dependency is associated with a death rate as high as 2% a year. Deaths are related to overdose, accidents, injuries, AIDS, and general medical complications.

Examples of opiates include heroin, morphine, codeine, opium, meperidine (Demerol), and methadone. These drugs stimulate opiate receptors in the brain, mimicking the action of natural endorphins. Opiates produce an intense pleasure referred to as a "rush." Other effects of opiates include analgesia and decreased gastrointestinal motility. *Intoxication* from opiates is characterized by respiratory depression, slurred speech, constricted pupils, impaired judgment and functioning, nausea, and vomiting. Clients taking phenothiazines or antidepressants are at greater risk for respiratory depression. An overdose of opiates is indicated by severe respiratory depression, pinpoint pupils, and coma. Intravenous naloxone (Narcan) is administered during acute intoxication to reverse opioid-induced respiratory depression. The effects of opiates are potentiated by all CNS depressants, including alcohol.

Withdrawal Symptoms

Symptoms of opiate withdrawal include chills, sweating, increased pulse and blood pressure, muscle aches, abdominal cramps, drug craving, rhinorrhea, yawning, drowsiness, and coma. These symptoms begin hours to days after drug use ceases and usually subside in 7–14 days. The duration of withdrawal is shorter for heroin, a short-acting drug, and longer for methadone, a longer-acting drug. Methadone detoxification may be extended over several months.

Detoxification

Methadone is administered orally in decreasing doses to detoxify clients. Methadone administered as a maintenance treatment is another option. Women who are pregnant will be maintained on methadone until after delivery because of the risks that withdrawal poses for the fetus. It is safer to withdraw the baby after delivery. If the client is also withdrawing from a CNS depressant, phenobarbital is administered until opiate detoxification is complete. Once detoxification is finished, the phenobarbital is tapered and finally discontinued. Clonidine (Catapres), an alternative drug, manages the symptoms of opiate withdrawal, and, when combined with naltrexone, an opioid antagonist, can significantly shorten the length of time for complete withdrawal. Vital signs must be monitored before each dose of clonidine because of the associated side effects of sedation and hypotension. Nonsteroidal anti-inflammatory medications and antinausea agents are used to manage muscle aches and nausea during withdrawal.

Hallucinogens

Examples of hallucinogens include lysergic acid diethylamide (LSD), mescaline, psilocybin, ketamine, and the synthetic amphetamine-like designer drug, ecstasy. Hallucinogens have a sympathomimetic effect, but the exact mechanism of action has not been determined. These drugs alter the client's sensory perception; taste, smell, and touch are highly intensified; the sense of time and space is distorted; and the client experiences visual illusions and emotional lability. *Intoxication* with hallucinogens is characterized by tachycardia, hypertension, and dilated pupils. It has not been determined whether hallucinogens interact with alcohol.

Withdrawal Symptoms

No physical dependence develops with hallucinogen use; therefore, there are no withdrawal symptoms. However, adverse reactions can include a panic response or bad trip, delirium manifested by hallucinations, paranoia, and agitation. These symptoms usually end within 24 hours, but psychotic symptoms occasionally persist and require treatment with antipsychotic medications.

Detoxification

There is no need for detoxification. The effects of hallucinogens usually subside within 12 hours.

Cannabinoids

Two examples of cannabinoids are marijuana and hashish. These drugs depress the higher organizational centers in the brain. Cannabinoids produce the effects of euphoria and altered perceptions, and *intoxication* is characterized by anxiety, suspiciousness, impaired coordination and judgment, hallucinations, tachycardia, and red, injected conjunctiva (bloodshot eyes). Cannabinoids potentiate the effects of CNS depressants, including alcohol.

Withdrawal Symptoms

Symptoms of withdrawal include restlessness, irritability, insomnia, sweating, nausea, and vomiting. Persons may also experience bad trips, delirium, or flashbacks, but these are not as common with cannabinoids as with hallucinogens.

Detoxification

No treatment is indicated for detoxification from cannabinoids.

Phencyclidine

Phencyclidine (PCP; angel dust) produces peripheral sympathetic and anticholinergic effects as well as central psychotomimetic, anticholinergic, and adrenergic effects. The drug is stored in the brain and adipose tissue, so the serum half-life can be extended for up to 3 days. Depending on the dose, PCP can act as an analgesic, depressant, or stimulant. *Intoxication* results in impaired judgment, nystagmus, elevated heart rate and blood pressure, muscle rigidity, ataxia, seizures, and delirium. Persons with PCP intoxication may become paranoid and exhibit unpredictable, violent behavior. It is not known whether PCP interacts with alcohol.

Withdrawal Symptoms

No withdrawal syndrome is associated with PCP, but clients may experience lethargy, depression, and drug craving.

Detoxification

No detoxification is required.

Inhalants

Inhalants cause diffuse impairment of brain function. Types of inhalants include glue, paint, paint solvents, aerosol sprays, cleaning fluids, gasoline, typewriter correction fluids, nitrous oxide, and amyl nitrite (**Figure 15-2**). These substances produce euphoria, or what is termed a "high," along with altered perceptions. *Intoxication*, which occurs during or shortly after use, is characterized by slurred speech, ataxia, impaired judgment, dizziness, tremors, and attacks on others. An interaction with alcohol has not been established.

On physical examination, persons who abuse inhalants may have a rash around the nose and mouth.

Withdrawal Symptoms

Symptoms include irritability, dysphoria, sleep disturbance, headache, dry mouth, and lacrimation beginning within 24 hours of abstinence and lasting for several days. Psychologic dependence also forms from the use of inhalants.

Inhalant use can result in sudden death, most likely due to acute arrhythmia, hypoxia, or electrolyte abnormalities.

Detoxification

There is no definitive treatment for inhalant withdrawal, although benzodiazepines have been proposed for this purpose.

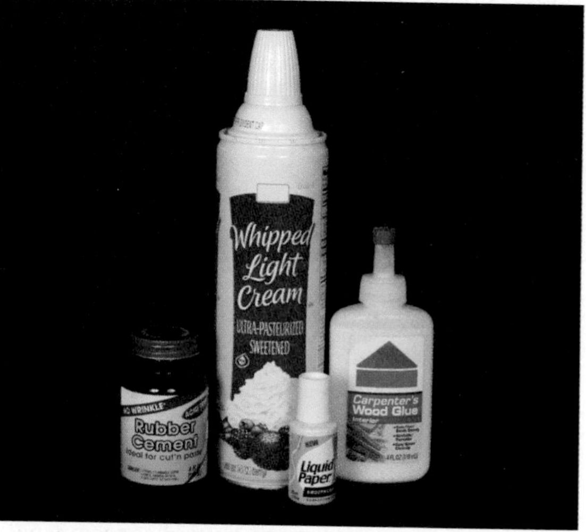

Figure 15-2 Many common household products are used as inhalants.

Over-the-counter drugs such as cough syrups that contain dextromethorphan, a synthetic derivative of morphine, can produce effects similar to those of PCP.

Nicotine

Nicotine dependence has a familial pattern similar to that of alcohol dependence. Twin and adoption studies indicate genetic factors contribute to the onset and continuation of smoking.

Nicotine exerts an agonist effect on nicotine receptors in the central and peripheral nervous systems to initiate drug actions. Cigarettes, cigars, and pipe and chewing tobacco all contain varying amounts of nicotine. Nicotine produces the dual effects of relaxation and stimulation, but it has no recognized intoxication. Nicotine combined with alcohol increases irritation to the oral mucosa, throat, and esophagus.

Withdrawal Symptoms

Symptoms develop within 24 hours of tapering or stopping nicotine use. These include irritability, nicotine craving, decreased heart rate, tremors, headache, difficulty concentrating, and insomnia.

Detoxification

Nicotine patches and chewing gum are effective in relieving withdrawal symptoms, and their use is gradually tapered and discontinued.

Assessment of Clients With Substance-Related Disorders

An intoxicated client may not be a reliable informant.

If the client is intoxicated at the time of the assessment, it may be difficult to obtain accurate information. When possible, the nurse should obtain a complete history from both the client and another person who knows the client and his or her circumstances prior to the assessment. See **Table 15-2** for an outline of the nursing assessment. The information that is obtained should consist of medical, psychiatric, alcohol, and drug histories. The American Nurses Association has established the *Scope and Standards of Addictions Nursing Practice* (2004).

Table 15-2 Substance-Related Disorders: Nursing Assessment

- Physical assessment:
  - VS, neurologic checks, lab values
- Acute medical conditions , e.g.
  - Hypoglycemia
  - Subdural hematoma
  - Pancreatitis
  - Esophageal varices
  - Dementia
  - Hepatitis, cirrhosis
- Psychiatric assessment
  - History of psychiatric symptoms, treatment, hospitalizations
  - Be aware of possibility of dual diagnoses
- Alcohol and drug history
  - Type and amount of substances used
  - Method of use
  - Frequency of use and *time last used* to anticipate withdrawal onset
  - History of detoxification, withdrawal, treatment
- Assess for denial—client minimizes amount of substance use and consequences
  - Two drinks a day could be two 8-ounce drinks
- Assess for loss of control
  - Failed efforts to stop or reduce use
  - Use more than planned for longer time
- History of sobriety
  - How achieved
  - Motivation
  - Quality of life at time sober
  - Situation or events surrounding relapse (if applicable)

Physical Assessment

The nurse needs to consider all possible physiologic causes of the sensory changes associated with substance abuse and intoxication. For example, even in the presence of acute withdrawal, a client can experience acute hypoglycemia or, as the result of a fall, a subdural hematoma. Performing a neurologic examination, including pupil check, level of consciousness, and vital signs are therefore of great importance.

Alcohol abuse can lead to a variety of medical problems, including pancreatitis, esophagitis, esophageal varices, gastritis, hepatitis, cirrhosis of the liver, hepatic encephalopathy, cardiomyopathy, dementia, and peripheral neuropathy. Another serious complication of alcohol abuse is **Wernicke's encephalopathy**, characterized by confusion, ataxia, and eye movement disorders. Wernicke's encephalopathy is due to thiamine deficiency. Early treatment with intravenous or intramuscular thiamine can reverse brain damage and prevent the development of **Korsakoff's syndrome**, characterized by short-term memory loss and confabulation. Korsakoff's syndrome may improve over time with thiamine treatment, but it is often persistent and incapacitating.

Hepatitis, endocarditis, and the human immunodeficiency virus (HIV) are complications of in-

Clinical Example 

Jack W. was admitted to a medical detoxification unit of a large urban hospital. He had been found passed out on the street, obviously intoxicated, with alcohol on his breath. Jack, 70 years old, regained consciousness in the emergency room and admitted to being homeless and to drinking a fifth of whiskey a day. His last drink was reportedly that morning, approximately 5 hours before admission. Jack was already noted to have hand tremors, mild diaphoresis, and an elevated BP and pulse. He was started on 50 mg chlordiazepoxide by mouth every 4 hours with orders for decreasing doses over the next 5 days. On the second day of detoxification, the nurse went to check Jack's vital signs and found him difficult to arouse. When he did wake up, he appeared confused. This change in sensorium alerted the nurse to check Jack's pupils. The left pupil was sluggish. Additional tests confirmed that Jack had a subdural hematoma, a collection of blood in the subdural space of the brain as a result of a ruptured blood vessel. It may have been easy to attribute the confusion and drowsiness to withdrawal, but the nurse knew that patients with substance abuse are often poor historians and may suffer injuries that they either dismiss or do not recall. The nurse's good judgment and knowledge may well have saved Jack's life.

travenous drug use. Pulmonary edema can result from opiate toxicity, and pulmonary, renal, and liver complications, cerebral atrophy, cerebellar degeneration, and an increased risk for acute myelocytic leukemia are associated with abuse of inhalants. Physical examination and relevant laboratory tests including blood chemistries, complete blood count with differential, liver function tests, and prothrombin time can aid in diagnosing potentially life-threatening illnesses. Screening for tuberculosis by skin testing or chest X-ray may also be indicated.

Psychiatric Assessment and Dual Diagnosis

Assessment should include a history of psychiatric symptoms, treatment, and hospitalizations. The hallucinations, paranoia, depression, and agitation that are frequently associated with substance abuse and intoxication may be induced by the substances or may be symptoms of an underlying psychiatric illness such as schizophrenia or a mood disorder. The clinician may find it easier to evaluate and diagnose clients after withdrawal and a period of sobriety. However, even after sobriety is achieved, the diagnosis may not be straightforward. Clients will often report using substances to control psychotic or behavioral symptoms. It may be difficult to determine which came first, the substance abuse or the psychiatric disorder.

The term **dual diagnosis** refers to the simultaneous existence of one or more substance-use disorders and a primary mental disorder. Primary mental disorder refers to a mental disorder that precedes substance use or persists more than 4 weeks after the cessation of acute intoxication or withdrawal. *Dual diagnosis* is used interchangeably with the terms *mentally ill chemical abuse (MICA)* and the more current *co-occurring disorders*. The combination of disorders may vary greatly, and there is no typical dual-diagnosed client. The substance-use disorder may refer to a dependence on or abuse of alcohol, sedatives, amphetamines, cocaine, heroin, marijuana, or phencyclidine. The mental disorder may be a mood disorder, such as depression or bipolar disorder; schizophrenia; an anxiety disorder, including panic attacks, phobias, and posttraumatic stress disorder; an eating disorder; a conduct disorder; an attention deficit disorder; or a personality disorder, most commonly antisocial or borderline personality disorders.

The nurse can expect to encounter dual-diagnosed clients in all areas of practice. According to a study recently published by the Agency for Healthcare Research and Quality (AHRQ, 2007), in 2004, over 1 million adult hospital stays, or 3% of admissions to acute care hospitals, were related to a dual diagnosis—both a substance-related and a mental health disorder. Adolescents have a high prevalence of substance-use disorders associated with psychiatric disorders (Deas, 2006). The geriatric population also is vulnerable, due to a high incidence of depression compounded by significant life changes and loss. Substance abuse can be a way of dealing with feelings of anger, grief, and abandonment, common in this age group.

Researchers hypothesize that serotonin deficits from alcohol abuse, endorphin deficits from opioid dependence, and dopamine depletion that occurs with cocaine dependence predispose one to the development of depression and can actually increase the positive symptoms of schizophrenia, such as hallucinations and paranoia (Addington & Addington, 2001). There is evidence that marijuana use increases the risk of developing schizophrenia among

Clients with substance abuse are at increased risk for suicide.

vulnerable or psychosis-prone adolescents, with the vulnerability partially attributed to a gene that regulates the effects of cannabis (Large, Swapnil, Compton, Slade, & Olav, 2011; Rey, 2007).

Alcohol and Drug History

Most psychoactive substances can be detected in the blood and urine for up to 48 hours after use.

Information that is obtained should include the type of substance or substances used, the length of time the substance was used, the amount of substance used, the method of administration, the history and frequency of use, and patterns of past intoxications and withdrawals, including seizures and delirium. It is very important to determine when the client last used the substance, which is information that can predict when to anticipate the onset of withdrawal symptoms. Toxicology screenings of urine and blood are informative, because most psychoactive substances are detectable for up to 48 hours (and some even longer) after use.

Denial is a psychologic defense that is prominent among alcoholics and leads them to underestimate the amount of alcohol used.

Given the high incidence of substance abuse among hospitalized clients, it is reasonable to include an alcohol and drug history as part of every assessment. It is not uncommon to have a patient go into withdrawal while recovering from orthopedic or other surgery. Hospitalization for any reason may be the first time that a client passes a few days without using alcohol or other drugs, and he or she may develop agitation, anxiety, tremors, and other withdrawal symptoms.

A matter-of-fact, nonjudgmental approach maximizes the likelihood of obtaining accurate information from the client. Understanding the progressive nature of dependence and the subtle process of **denial** that may bias the client's responses is helpful. For example, the client may have started drinking in a socially appropriate way but, because of a high tolerance, gradually increased the amount and frequency of drinking to achieve the desired effect. Progression may include sneaking drinks, hiding alcohol to keep it available, missing social functions, resolving to reduce consumption, experiencing blackouts, and bingeing. Binge drinking is a pattern of drinking that results in a blood alcohol concentration (BAC) of 0.08% or above. This typically happens when men consume more than four drinks and women consume more than three drinks in 2 hours (National Institute of Alcohol Abuse and Alcoholism, 2004). In most states, the legal BAC limit for drivers is 0.10%. However, many states are considering lowering that to 0.08%.

Clinical Example

At family gatherings Carl always volunteers to be the bartender. He prepares the drinks in the kitchen, and this allows him to sneak extra shots out of the sight of his wife and guests.

A group of coworkers agree to buy season tickets for the local baseball team. When Sam learns that the seats are in a no-drinking area, he declines to purchase the tickets.

Alcoholics may state that they have only two drinks per day. However, when questioned, they may acknowledge that the liquor is not measured in a shot glass but freely poured into a glass the size of a tumbler. Clients who abuse alcohol often understate their use, while clients who abuse benzodiazepines and heroin tend to exaggerate their use. Clients may report using five bags a day of heroin, or 15 bags, or more. It is good to ask how many bags the client needs to get straight, or to ease the symptoms of withdrawal. This may be as little as two bags. This information will guide the nurse practitioner or other prescribing clinician to evaluate the initial dose of methadone to use for detoxification.

Frequently, clients' patterns of substance use reflect a loss of control over the amount and frequency of use and preoccupations with planning for the use or attainment of a substance. These behaviors, when pointed out to the client, can help break down denial and help the client to recognize the extent of the substance-abuse problem.

A more thorough assessment will yield information that can be utilized to motivate the client to pursue treatment. This includes which substances, including prescription and over-the-counter medications, the client uses. It is helpful to know the frequency of use as well as the circumstances under which the substances are used. Adverse effects of the substance use, including withdrawal, seizures, and medical, social, or legal consequences, can be important in helping the client confront the extent of the substance abuse or dependence. Knowing if the person has had any past periods of sobriety can help identify interventions that the client found helpful. See **Figure 15-3** for a concept map related to assessment and possible nursing diagnoses for clients with substance-related disorders.

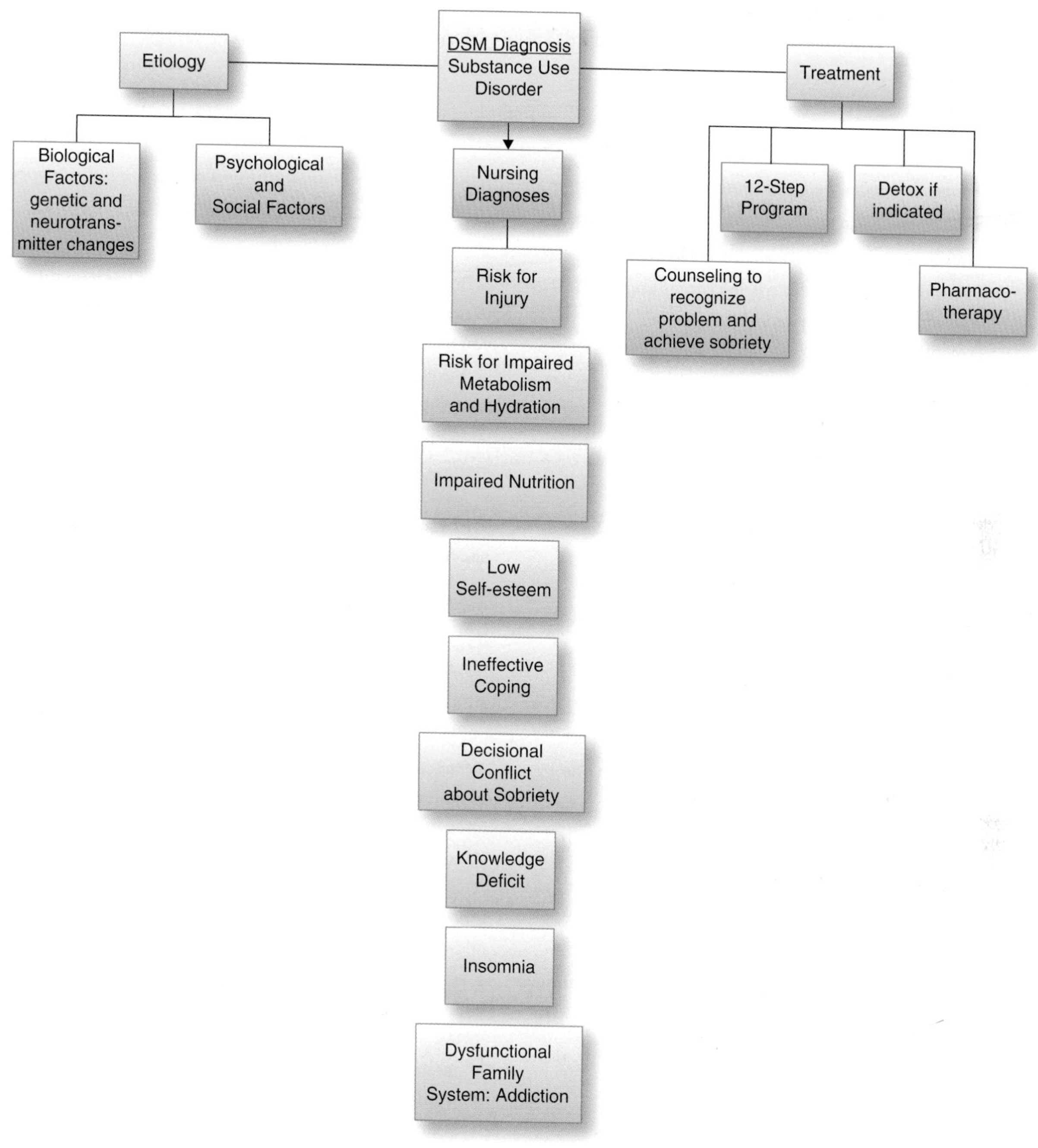

Figure 15-3 Nursing diagnoses concept map for substance-related disorders.

Assessment Tools

A widely used tool to assess for substance abuse is the CAGE test (Mayfield, McCleod, & Hall, 1974), which asks four questions that were originally directed at assessing alcohol abuse but can be adapted for use with other substances, as indicated:

- Have you ever felt you ought to cut down on your drinking or drug use?
- Have people annoyed you by criticizing your drinking or drug use?
- Have you ever felt bad or guilty about your drinking or drug use?
- Have you ever had a drink or used drugs first thing in the morning to steady your nerves or get rid of a hangover (have you ever had a drink or drugs as an eye-opener)?

Two or more positive answers are considered clinically significant, but even one positive response deserves follow-up.

Another assessment tool, Alcohol Use Disorders Identification Test (AUDIT) (**Table 15-3**), like the CAGE, is useful in a variety of settings and with a

Table 15-3 The AUDIT Test

Points associated with each answer are listed below. Keep track of your points as you take this assessment.

1. How often do you have a drink containing alcohol?

(0) Never (Skip to Questions 9–10)
(1) Monthly or less
(2) 2 to 4 times a month
(3) 2 to 3 times a week
(4) 4 or more times a week

2. How many drinks containing alcohol do you have on a typical day when you are drinking?

(0) 1 or 2
(1) 3 or 4
(2) 5 or 6
(3) 7, 8, or 9
(4) 10 or more

3. How often do you have six or more drinks on one occasion?

(0) Never
(1) Less than monthly
(2) Monthly
(3) Weekly
(4) Daily or almost daily

4. How often during the last year have you found that you were not able to stop drinking once you had started?

(0) Never
(1) Less than monthly
(2) Monthly
(3) Weekly
(4) Daily or almost daily

5. How often during the last year have you failed to do what was normally expected from you because of drinking?

(0) Never
(1) Less than monthly
(2) Monthly
(3) Weekly
(4) Daily or almost daily

6. How often during the last year have you been unable to remember what happened the night before because you had been drinking?

(0) Never
(1) Less than monthly
(2) Monthly
(3) Weekly
(4) Daily or almost daily

7. How often during the last year have you needed an alcoholic drink first thing in the morning to get yourself going after a night of heavy drinking?

(0) Never
(1) Less than monthly
(2) Monthly
(3) Weekly
(4) Daily or almost daily

8. How often during the last year have you had a feeling of guilt or remorse after drinking?

(0) Never
(1) Less than monthly
(2) Monthly
(3) Weekly
(4) Daily or almost daily

9. Have you or someone else been injured as a result of your drinking?

(0) No
(2) Yes, but not in the last year
(4) Yes, during the last year

10. Has a relative, friend, doctor, or another health professional expressed concern about your drinking or suggested you cut down?

(0) No
(2) Yes, but not in the last year
(4) Yes, during the last year

Add up the points associated with your answers above. A total score of 8 or more indicates harmful drinking behavior. See your doctor.

Source: © World Health Organization

range of target populations (Babor, Biddle-Higgins, Saunders, & Monteiro, 2001; Bradley et al., 2007).

Management and Treatment

Detoxification

If the client is experiencing symptoms of physiologic withdrawal, initial interventions are directed at safely detoxifying the client and observing for and treating complications (**Table 15-4**). Outpatient management is appropriate for patients with mild to moderate withdrawal symptoms, if they have no important coexisting conditions and have a support person willing to monitor their progress. However, patients with severe withdrawal symptoms, a history of complications, or coexisting medical or psychiatric disorders may require supervised inpatient treatment.

During this stage, the client's mental status and vital signs, including temperature and pupils, should be checked frequently. Vital signs and other objective symptoms of withdrawal such as tremors are used to determine whether the client needs additional medication to control symptoms and maintain comfort. The client should be awakened, if necessary, to check for withdrawal symptoms. The nurse must remember that adequate medication can prevent life-threatening complications and that the detoxification process involves tapering and eventually discontinuing the drugs. This knowledge helps the nurse to avoid a power struggle with clients that can lead to withholding medication.

Table 15-4 Nursing Care During the Detoxification Stage of Treatment

- Check mental status, vital signs, and temperature frequently
- Observe for withdrawal symptoms
- Administer adequate medication
- Maintain adequate nutrition and hydration
- Encourage behavioral interventions for insomnia
- Provide for the safety of clients with impaired judgment, ataxia, confusion, or suicidal ideation
- Anticipate memory deficits, and keep instructions simple and repeat important information
- Develop a supportive relationship

During detoxification, nutrition, especially hydration, often requires supervision. The client's intake and output should be monitored closely during the initial days of the detoxification phase of treatment. Clients may benefit from nutritional supplements. The administration of thiamine can reverse Wernicke's encephalopathy and prevent the development of Korsakoff's syndrome. The twitching of muscles may indicate a need for magnesium, which is thought to exert a protective effect on the heart. During withdrawal and often for months afterward, clients may experience difficulty sleeping. Because benzodiazepines, and even nonbenzodiazepine hypnotics, can be addictive, behavioral interventions and other pharmacologic agents should be considered first. Behavioral interventions include maintaining a regular schedule for sleeping and waking, a relaxing bedtime routine before retiring, avoiding heavy meals, alcohol, nicotine, or caffeine close to bedtime, and exercising regularly but not too close to bedtime. If these do not help, sedating antidepressants such as trazodone may be prescribed.

Nurses must provide for the safety of clients with impaired judgment, ataxia, confusion, or suicidal ideation. Memory deficits indicate the need for repetitive instructions and simple directions. Clients in this condition cannot be expected to remember scheduled times for meetings, meals, or medications. Failures to comply with requests must be understood as the result of the client's mental state and not a volitional act of defiance or control.

Nurse-Client Relationship

Developing a supportive relationship may be the only intervention available to treat some of the symptoms of intoxication and withdrawal. A positive relationship that has been established during the period of acute discomfort may be instrumental in motivating the client to pursue long-term treatment and sobriety. Guilt-ridden, embarrassed, and experiencing low self-esteem, the client may be sensitive to even the slightest indication of rejection. Directing angry outbursts at the staff is one way clients attempt to extricate themselves from both the treatment setting and the uncertainty associated with giving up the substance to which they have become dependent.

The nurse identifies opportunities to improve the client's self-esteem (see **Table 15-5**). He or she recognizes the client's strengths and accomplish-

Table 15-5 Enhancing Self-Esteem Within the Nurse–Client Relationship

- Identify the client's strengths and accomplishments
- Validate the client's feelings and experiences
- Give positive feedback when indicated
- Set realistic goals and acknowledge progress
- Create opportunities for the client to contribute in groups or on the unit
- Maintain respectful communication style

ments, validates the discomfort the client is experiencing, gives positive feedback when indicated, and creates opportunities for the client to contribute to the unit or to assist other clients. Most important, the nurse must show respect for the client as a person. This requires that the nurse examine his or her use of substances and also have a self-awareness of any personal prejudices regarding drug users and alcoholics.

See **Table 15-6** for nursing diagnoses common for clients with substance-use disorders with examples of nursing interventions and rationales.

Table 15-6 Nursing Interventions for Clients with Substance-Use Disorders

Nursing Diagnoses	Nursing Interventions	Rationales
Risk for injury	Monitor mental status, temperature, vital signs, and physiologic functions	Assessment of client's status will guide the treatment plan.
	Assess for suicidal ideation and observe as indicated	Alcohol and substance abuse is associated with increased risk of suicide.
	Provide safe environment: remove alcohol-based products, matches, and cigarettes; supervise ambulation as indicated; provide repeated reminders to ask for assistance.	Alcohol products are temptations to sobriety; judgment, balance, and memory may be impaired.
	Medicate for withdrawal symptoms as prescribed.	This can prevent complications of withdrawal; avoid power struggles since detox is time limited.
Risk for impaired metabolism and hydration	Assess mental status, pain, temperature, lab values for indications of infection, liver or renal disease, gastrointestinal (GI) bleeding, low blood sugar, encephalopathy, dehydration, and other physical complications.	Substance abuse can result in many physical disorders. Early detection and intervention can prevent life-threatening complications.
	Ensure adequate fluid intake.	Dehydration is common.
Impaired nutrition: less than required	Monitor intake and output, observe meal intake, and consider dietary consultation.	Clients often neglect diet while abusing substances.
	Provide small, frequent feedings with foods low in acidity.	This can help if client is experiencing nausea, vomiting, or gastrointestinal distress.
	Provide vitamin supplements as ordered.	Vitamin deficiency, especially in B vitamins, is associated with neuropathies and Wernicke's encephalopathy.
Low self-esteem	Address client with respect and nonjudgmental attitude.	This is an essential component of building trust and a sense of self-worth.
	Assist with grooming as needed.	Appearance contributes to self-esteem.
	Help client identify strengths.	The client may blame himself or herself for the addiction and have difficulty recognizing accomplishments.
	Engage client in problem solving and decision making.	This reaffirms the client's worth and ability to recover.
Ineffective denial	Help identify negative consequences of substance abuse in client's life.	This is essential in reducing denial.

Table 15-6 Substance-Use Disorders: Nursing Interventions *(Continued)*

Nursing Diagnoses	Nursing Interventions	Rationales
	Confront in a gentle way the client's efforts to rationalize or minimize substance abuse.	In the context of a trusting relationship, the client can be helped to examine behavior and accept need for treatment.
	Use motivational interviewing to challenge denial.	Seeking the client's input reduces likelihood of the client becoming defensive.
	Encourage participation in group therapy.	Peers are often effective in recognizing and confronting behaviors.
Ineffective coping	Encourage client to identify and verbalize feelings and thoughts.	This may help the client recognize how feelings and thoughts relate to substance abuse.
	Teach assertive communication skills.	Being able to express oneself effectively increases control and reduces frustration.
	Explore new ways to cope with feelings: physical exercise, meditation, and relaxation exercises.	Part of recovery involves replacing the use of substances with new ways of coping.
	Reinforce activities that promote coping: attending groups, problem solving, communication of feelings, etc.	Praise will encourage the client to pursue the skills needed to form new relationships in recovery.
	Introduce 12-step program for support and socialization.	These programs support sobriety and provide a circle of sober social contacts.
Decisional conflict about sobriety	Apply motivational interviewing process with client.	Active participation in care maximizes success.
	Allow client to talk about fears and expectations associated with sobriety.	Problem solving can be directed at the client's concerns.
	Explore past periods of sobriety to assess what worked and what was problematic for the client.	This information can help develop a plan for sustained recovery.
	Encourage verbalization of feelings in individual and group counseling.	Talking about feelings and fears can make them less formidable and more manageable.
	Reinforce decision to take a day at a time.	It can be less overwhelming to set short-term goals. This builds in success.
Knowledge deficit	Use a variety of methods to educate the client about the biologic and genetic basis of addiction.	Understanding addiction can reduce self-blame. A variety of methods enhances learning.
	Relate substance abuse to physical and mental health issues.	This may increase motivation to change.
	Provide information about cross addiction.	The client will understand the rationale for avoiding medications and substances that can trigger addiction.
	Have the client tell you what was learned.	This validates learning and evaluates the need for further teaching.
Insomnia	Encourage nonpharmacologic approaches to promote sleep.	Many sleep medications have addictive potential.
	Show understanding and support.	Caring and empathy contribute to a trusting relationship.
Dysfunctional family system	Provide education on substance abuse to family.	Understanding of addictions may increase acceptance of the client and decrease anger and blame.
	Reinforce the need for the client to take responsibility for addiction.	Family may enable addiction, thinking it is helpful to the client.
	Encourage self-help groups for family members (Al-Anon, Alateen).	Twelve-step programs for significant others and adolescent children of alcoholics provide support.
	Explore interest in family therapy.	Recovery can be an opportunity to examine family dynamics and improve communication.

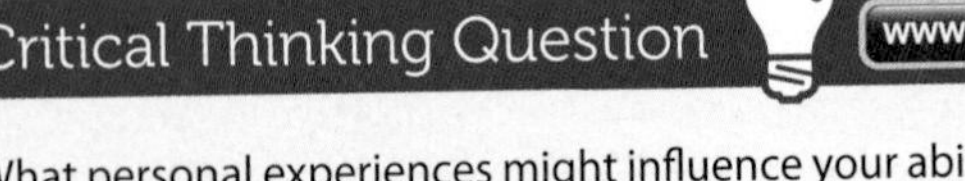

Critical Thinking Question

What personal experiences might influence your ability to work effectively with a substance-dependent client?

Clinical Example

Carrie, a 30-year-old nurse nearing completion of an inpatient detoxification from diazepam and alcohol, had been working closely with one of the nurses to understand her substance dependence. One evening she became uncharacteristically hostile and argumentative with this nurse. Rather than respond defensively, or focus on the negative behavior, the nurse considered what feelings might be behind this behavior. The nurse knew that the client was struggling with a decision to transfer to an inpatient rehabilitation treatment center. Recognizing Carrie's anxiety regarding this huge step, the nurse praised her for the honesty and hard work she had exhibited up to this point in treatment. The compliment surprised Carrie, who became tearful. Carrie's nurse was thus able to change the interaction and help Carrie talk about her fear of failing in her efforts to become sober.

Counseling

Within the context of the therapeutic relationship, the nurse learns about the client's personal history of alcohol and/or drug abuse. The circumstances surrounding his or her drug use and the effect of the addiction on the client's life are revealed. Past efforts at attaining sobriety are explored for information that can be helpful in the present. Therapy may include individual, group, and family work. Responsibility rests on the client not for the illness, but for participating in recovery. The nurse should reinforce the client's pursuit of treatment.

The nurse can be instrumental in motivating the client to accept treatment.

Motivational interviewing (Miller & Rollnick, 2002) delivers interventions in a neutral and empathetic way, actively eliciting the client to identify the pros and cons of sobriety. Also referred to as motivational enhancement therapy, this type of counseling offers specific strategies that have proven successful in helping persons with addictions recognize and accept the need for change. This less defensive, more proactive approach is an alternative to the confrontational style of therapy traditionally used to shake the substance abuser's denial. Motivational therapy has six components summarized in the mnemonic, *FRAMES*:

F = Feedback on personal impairment
R = Emphasis on personal responsibility
A = Clear advice to change
M = Menu of alternative options or choices
E = Empathy as a counseling style
S = Self-efficacy or removal of barriers to achieving goals

Motivational interviewing strategies include:

- Ask open-ended questions.
- Ask the client to present the pros and cons of quitting.
- Demonstrate listening by reflecting the client's thoughts: "You are saying that drinking helps you manage stress."
- Summarize the client's thoughts: "What I hear you saying is that you enjoy smoking, but, on the other hand, it is a source of friction with your spouse, and you are fearful of developing lung cancer."
- Help the client identify and build on past successful attempts to quit.
- Show empathy: "You sound worried about how you would cope without alcohol."
- Ask permission to provide information: "Would you like to hear about . . .?"
- Ask the client to identify strategies for quitting.
- Recognize the client's right to accept or reject change and offer to help when the client is ready for change.

Motivational interviewing can help patients progress toward change. With this technique, clients set the agenda, and the therapist acts as a partner in dialogue rather than an authority. Sometimes clients are not ready to accept abstinence as a goal, and demanding abstinence may drive a person away from treatment. It may be better to accept an interest in controlled drinking as a desire for change and work with the client to achieve moderation. Research into moderate or controlled drinking has shown that this strategy can be successful for some clients, depending primarily on their level of substance dependence. If the client is unsuccessful at achieving this goal, the client may be motivated to try to abstain. Motivational interviewing has been effective in reducing substance use among both older adults (Finfgeld-Connett, 2004) and adolescents (Simkin, 2002).

Cognitive-behavioral approaches have been used to help clients achieve and maintain sobriety. The main goal of cognitive behavior therapy (CBT) is to educate the alcohol or drug-dependent person to change the way he thinks about his substance abuse and to learn new ways to cope with the situations and circumstances that led to his drinking or drug use in the past.

12-Step Programs

Alcoholics Anonymous (AA), Narcotics Anonymous (NA), and other **12-step programs** have a demonstrated success record in helping persons achieve abstinence and improve the quality of their lives in recovery. Twelve-step programs are self-help groups that are based on a set of spiritual guidelines and the fellowship of others who share an addiction for the purpose of supporting each other in the process of recovery. The 12 steps refer to the original principles that guide personal recovery in the AA program. Since then, the steps have been adapted to a variety of self-help programs. Special support groups exist for almost every addiction, as well as for special populations. An example is the double trouble groups for persons who have both a mental disorder and an addiction. Dual diagnosed clients may require assistance in learning the social skills necessary to participate at meetings and to establish a support network. This preparation may require searching, through trial and error, for a group with which the client feels comfortable. Because many of the 12-step meetings are open to persons not in recovery, the nurse can accompany the client to meetings. Closed meetings are designated in the meeting schedule books available from each sponsoring organization and may be attended only by persons who have the addiction being addressed by the group. Beginners' groups are usually a good way to introduce the client to the 12-step program.

Related support groups, such as Al-Anon Family Groups and Adult Children of Alcoholics, are available to help family members share experiences, express feelings, discuss difficulties, and learn ways to cope with problems. Alateen is part of Al-Anon Family Groups. Alateen is a fellowship of young Al-Anon members, usually teenagers, whose lives have been affected by someone else's drinking. The focus in these family support groups is on the family member, not on the person with the addiction.

Pharmacologic Treatment

Pharmacologic agents are also used to aid clients in attaining sobriety. The drug disulfiram (Antabuse), classified as an alcohol deterrent, exerts an adverse effect when combined with alcohol and is used to manage alcohol dependence in selected, highly motivated patients. It is recommended for use in conjunction with supportive and psychotherapeutic treatment. Disulfiram interferes with the metabolism of alcohol, resulting in elevated levels of the toxic chemical, acetaldehyde. The abnormally high levels of acetaldehyde, when combined with alcohol, will cause a severe reaction. During a disulfiram reaction, flushing, sweating, headache, chest pain, nausea, and vomiting occur. It should be used with caution in clients with hepatic or renal disease or with a cardiac or psychiatric history.

The nurse should instruct the client to not take disulfiram for at least 12 hours after ingesting alcohol and to abstain for at least 2 weeks after stopping disulfiram therapy in order to avoid a disulfiram reaction. The client must be cautioned not to use any product containing alcohol, such as cough syrup, cold medicines, mouthwashes, or colognes, while taking disulfiram, since these can also cause a reaction. In case of a medical emergency, it is recommended that the client carry identification that will alert medical personnel that she is on disulfiram.

Naltrexone (ReVia) is in a class of medications called opiate antagonists and works by decreasing the craving for alcohol and blocking the effects of opioid medications. Unlike disulfiram, naltrexone does not cause an adverse reaction if the client uses alcohol or opiates. However, it may prolong withdrawal symptoms and coma and death can result from excessive doses of opiates. Therefore, clients are instructed not to use opiates at all during treatment with naltrexone. Naltrexone is used in the treatment of alcoholism to support abstinence, prevent relapse, and decrease alcohol consumption. Effectiveness is dependent on medication adherence, usually a daily dose. It may cause liver disease if taken beyond the recommended dose, is contraindicated in persons with acute hepatitis or liver failure, and should be used with caution in the presence of any liver disease.

AA has open meetings that nonalcoholics can attend. Anonymity should be respected at all times.

Persons taking naltrexone may not benefit from opioid-containing medicines, such as cough and cold preparations, antidiarrheal preparations, and opioid analgesics. In an emergency situation when opioid analgesia must be administered to a patient receiving naltrexone, the amount of opioid required may be greater than usual, and the resulting respiratory depression may be deeper. Clients should be instructed to carry identification to alert medical personnel to the fact that they are taking naltrexone.

Acamprosate (Campral) is approved to assist alcohol-dependent clients who are already abstinent maintain sobriety in the context of a comprehensive management program that includes psychosocial support. Acamprosate is thought to restore the chemical balance between the neurotransmitters glutamate and gamma-aminobutyric acid (GABA) that was disrupted by chronic alcohol use. The medication can be continued even if the client relapses. It is contraindicated in severe renal insufficiency, and clients and family should be alert for possible suicidal ideation. Studies comparing acamprosate to naltrexone had mixed results, but acamprosate was never found to be more effective than naltrexone (Kennedy et al., 2010).

Methadone maintenance therapy in the form of daily doses is a long-standing treatment of opioid dependence.

Buprenorphine, an opiod partial agonist, is the newest opiod addiction therapy. Like methadone, buprenorphine, either as monotherapy (Subutex) or combined with naloxone (Suboxone), is prescribed for withdrawal or, on a daily basis, for maintenance therapy.

Clonidine (Catapres) is a central alpha-adrenergic agonist hypotensive agent that is also used to treat the symptoms of alcohol, opiate, and nicotine withdrawal, including watery eyes and nose, diarrhea, irritability, and nicotine craving.

Naloxone injection (Narcan), an opioid antagonist, is used to prevent or reverse the effects of narcotic pain relievers. It can instantly reverse the respiratory depression and hypotension related to overdoses of heroin, morphine, oxycodone, and

CASE STUDIES Mr. T

Mr. T. is a 38-year-old divorced male, employed as a sergeant with the local sheriff's office. He is currently on disability for back and neck injuries sustained in an on-the-job auto accident 15 months earlier. He has been attending physical therapy twice a week. Mr. T. was brought to the hospital emergency room at 10 p.m. by a male friend, who is also a police officer, who went to Mr. T.'s home, at the request of his girlfriend and found Mr. T. in a stuporous state, with slurred speech. He had told his girlfriend, in a phone conversation earlier in the day, that he had no reason to live. His girlfriend and his coworker were concerned, given that Mr. T. had access to a gun.

In the emergency room, Mr. T. was cooperative. He was described as average height, overweight, appearing older than his age. A mental status exam noted he was alert but lethargic, with slurred, slowed speech. He was oriented to person and place, but unable to give the date, although he did know the month. He had difficulty with the cognitive task of serial subtraction but had good memory, insight, and judgment, and was assessed to be of average intelligence. He described his mood as depressed and admitted passive suicidal ideation, but denied any plan. He denied homicidal ideation and denied hallucinations or delusions. He admitted to frequent paranoia where he would think that groups of people on the street were talking about him.

On physical exam, Mr. T. was noted to have fine tremors of the hands and tongue and slurred speech. His temperature was 98.8°F, blood pressure was 160/100, pulse 120, respirations 24. He reported using prescribed pain medication and benzodiazepines in daily doses that well exceeded the prescribed doses. This use had been a pattern for close to 1 year. What was new the day of admission was that the patient consumed nearly a quart of alcohol precipitated by the news from his physician that he was not cleared to return to work. Prior to that, he described his drinking as occasional until the past 3 months. At that time, he began drinking two to four drinks a day. This was in the context of keeping his girlfriend company at the bar where she had recently taken a job as bartender.

Mr. T. was divorced 4 years ago after 6 years of marriage. He shares custody of two sons, ages 9 and 7, with his ex-wife. Mr. T. takes the boys every other weekend, 2 weeks during the summer, and some major holidays. He lives alone and has been in a relationship with his girlfriend for 2 years. As noted, Mr. T. was injured a year ago in an auto accident while on duty with the sheriff's office and is on long-term disability. This leaves Mr. T. with much free time. He has two close friends from work and three male friends he has known since childhood who live in the area.

Mr. T.'s parents are both deceased. His mother died from complications of open-heart surgery when Mr. T. was 15 years old. His father, a retired fireman, died from cirrhosis of the liver at age 70.

His father had a history of alcoholism and, at the time of his death, had been sober with the help of AA for 5 years.

other opiate drugs. Naloxone is also available as a nasal spray.

Medications, combined with behavioral changes, can contribute to smoking cessation. In addition to nicotine-replacement therapy, a combination of a longer acting medication—such as the nicotine patch or the drug bupropion (Zyban, Wellbutrin) or varenicline (Chantix)—with a short-acting nicotine replacement product, such as nicotine gum, lozenge, nasal spray, or inhaler, may maximize success. The antidepressant bupropion increases levels of dopamine and norepinephrine, brain chemicals that are also boosted by nicotine. Bupropion helps reduce weight gain associated with stopping smoking, but it also increases the risk of seizures and is contraindicated for clients with a known seizure disorder. Varenicline acts on the brain's nicotine receptors, decreasing withdrawal symptoms and reducing the feelings of pleasure associated with smoking. The selective serotonin reuptake inhibitor (SSRI) antidepressants have been used to reduce drinking or promote abstinence. The SSRIs may reduce symptoms of anxiety and depression that may influence drinking behavior.

Treatment for the Client With a Dual Diagnosis

Integrated Treatment Approach

The Substance Abuse Mental Health Services Administration's (SAMHSA) Co-Occurring Center for Excellence (COCE), a leading national resource for the

Mr. T. is the youngest of four children. His three sisters have with no known history of alcohol or drug abuse. They and their families all live out of state, the closest being 2 hours away. They do not see each other often.

Mr. T.'s medical history is positive for gastroesophageal reflux disease (GERD), for which he takes lansoprazole (Prevacid). He has no history of psychiatric treatment. Mr. T. first used alcohol and marijuana at age 16 with friends. He reported getting drunk the first time he drank alcohol and every time after, until he stopped drinking at age 21. He began inhaling cocaine at age 17 and continued, using 2–3 times a week, also until age 21. He stopped all alcohol and drug use at that time because he did not want to jeopardize his application for a job in law enforcement. He reported that about 10 years ago, he resumed drinking alcohol, mostly beer or whiskey, on an occasional basis, with dinner or with friends on the weekend, but rarely got drunk. As noted previously, his drinking increased to 2–4 drinks a day over the past 3 months. He reported that this past year he started taking painkillers and sleeping medications after suffering back and neck injuries, and gradually began increasing the doses. At the time of admission, he was taking eight hydrocodone and acetaminophen (Vicodin) tablets a day, rather than the three prescribed, and two 20-mg diazepam tablets most nights to sleep. Mr. T. purposely saw two physicians, a physiatrist and an internist, so he would be able to get additional prescriptions. He was careful to fill the prescriptions at different pharmacies.

When in the emergency room, Mr. T. told the nurse practitioner that he had taken two hydrocodone and acetaminophen tablets that morning before going to his doctor's appointment, which was at 10 a.m. From 11 a.m. to 4 p.m. he consumed the fifth of whiskey, and talked to his girlfriend sometime in the afternoon. He then passed out on the couch and woke when his friend came by a little before 10 p.m.

Mr. T. denied any negative consequences related to his escalated drug and alcohol use, but his friend reported that Mr. T. was stopped once last month for driving while impaired, but the officer had let him off without a ticket and drove him home. Mr. T. admits being concerned about his drug and alcohol use, but he denied making any efforts to stop or reduce use of these substances. He had two positive responses on the CAGE assessment inventory: he admitted becoming annoyed when his girlfriend and one of his friends in the sheriff's office spoke to him about his use of pills and alcohol.

Based on history and physical assessment, a diagnosis of alcohol, opioid, and sedative-hypnotic dependence with physiologic withdrawal was made, and Mr. T. was admitted to the hospital for detoxification. An initial nursing care plan was developed at that time.

A week later, when Mr. T. moved to an outpatient substance abuse program, another nursing care plan was developed to reflect revised goals and outcomes.

Nursing Care Plan **Substance Withdrawal**

Nursing Diagnosis: Risk for injury, impaired hydration, and ineffective denial related to substance withdrawal evidenced by withdrawal symptoms, dehydration, depressed mood, and inability to admit impact of disease.

Expected Outcomes	Interventions	Evaluations
• Will not exhibit withdrawal complications and will have minimal discomfort.	• Frequent assessment by observation and evaluation of vital signs and temperature; administer medication as prescribed and prn; ensure adequate fluids and nutrition; reassure that discomfort is temporary.	• Able to taper and discontinue medications over several days; no further signs of withdrawal.
• Will be safe.	• Observation; ongoing mood evaluation for suicidal ideation and plans; encourage verbalization of feelings; remove sharp and dangerous objects.	• Absence of suicidal ideation.
• Will accept ongoing treatment for substance dependence.	• Motivational therapy to increase responsibility and active involvement in recognizing and accepting treatment options; education on cross-tolerance of benzodiazepines, pain medications, and alcohol	• Client makes appointment for outpatient substance abuse treatment and agrees to attend AA meetings.

Visit http://go.jblearning.com/mental health for additional care plans and exercises.

Nursing Care Plan **Substance Dependence**

Nursing Diagnosis: Low self-esteem related to ineffective coping, genetic vulnerability, and knowledge deficit evidenced by substance dependence.

Expected Outcomes	Interventions	Evaluations
• Will achieve abstinence.	• Supportive individual and group therapy; identify antecedents to alcohol/drug use; AA; avoids bars; pharmacologic support with disulfiram.	• Client attends outpatient sessions; gets a sponsor in AA; expresses satisfaction with life.
• Will learn new coping skills.	• Meditation and relaxation training for stress and back pain; encourage swimming for exercise and pain management; learn skills related to antecedents to alcohol/drug use (anger management, boredom, insomnia).	• No longer takes pain or sleep medications; uses natural approaches to reduce insomnia.
• Will experience improved mood and self-esteem.	• Help client to find meaningful activity as a substitute for work (explore creative outlets, volunteer work); ongoing mental status evaluations; antidepressant medications if indicated.	• Absence of depressive symptoms; engages in pleasurable activities.
• Will relate substance abuse to current life problems.	• Confront in a gentle way the client's efforts to rationalize or minimize substance abuse; educate client about addiction; help relate substance abuse to physical and mental health issues.	• Client accepts responsibility for addiction and behavior and commits to long-term treatment.

Visit http://go.jblearning.com/mental health for additional care plans and exercises.

field of co-occurring mental health and substance-use disorders, advocates for an integrated treatment approach. According to COCE, a truly integrated system promotes the seamless delivery of mental health and substance abuse treatment services from therapists who are cross-trained in both specialties and are able to provide integrated screening, assessment, and treatment (Center for Substance Abuse Treatment, 2006). The client would learn to manage both disorders as well as to understand the relationship between the disorders.

Detoxification

When a client with a mental disorder requires detoxification for substance dependence, complications can occur related to interactions or effects of the substances of abuse and medications the client may be taking to treat the mental disorder. The nurse must monitor the client carefully and be aware of the following facts:

- Alcohol and sedative-hypnotic medications may decrease the efficacy of neuroleptic medications, making them less effective in controlling the psychotic symptoms, depression, or seizures for which they were prescribed.
- Clients who abuse alcohol, sedatives, and cocaine and are also taking phenothiazines, a class of neuroleptics, are at increased risk for respiratory depression.
- Because neuroleptic medications lower the seizure threshold, clients taking them are at increased risk for withdrawal seizures.
- The mood-stabilizing drug lithium (Eskalith), usually prescribed for bipolar disorder, is particularly sensitive to changes in fluid and electrolyte balance. Vomiting and diarrhea associated with withdrawal can result in lithium toxicity. Lithium levels must be evaluated if the client is in withdrawal, and lithium should be withheld and the prescribing physician or nurse practitioner notified if the client shows signs of toxicity. Signs of lithium toxicity include vomiting, diarrhea, slurred speech, drowsiness, muscle weakness or twitching, and decreased coordination.

Pharmacologic Treatment

Integrated treatment programs can be supportive to the client who requires pharmacologic intervention to control the symptoms of a psychiatric disorder. Therapists and counselors who have knowledge of both disorders will understand and support the need for these medications. It is helpful if the nurse partners with the prescribing nurse practitioner or other clinician to ensure that medications are appropriate for the client with a dual diagnosis. Some guiding principles are as follows:

- When treating mental illness in the presence of a substance-use disorder, the clinician avoids prescribing medications with a high potential for abuse.
- The potential for overdose with the prescription medication, either alone or in combination with substances of abuse, must also be considered. The SSRIs have a low potential for lethality in overdose.
- Because relapse is possible, the clinician should consider the interactions that may occur between the prescribed medication and the substance of abuse.
- To adhere to the prescribed dose, the side effects must be tolerable; the client should not need to use alcohol or other drugs to counter unpleasant side effects.
- The benzodiazepines, such as lorazepam (Ativan), alprazolam (Xanax), and diazepam, are highly addictive, mood-altering medications that are contraindicated for the dual-diagnosed client after the completion of detoxification. The beta-blocker, propranolol (Inderal), and buspirone (BuSpar) selectively diminish multiple symptoms of generalized and performance anxiety without the acute mood alteration, sedation, and addictive potential of the benzodiazepines. The SSRI antidepressants can also be used to treat anxiety disorders.

Medication for the psychiatric disorder is essential for the client to benefit from or even participate in the process of recovery from a substance-use disorder.

Clients who are being treated with antipsychotic medications and are attempting withdrawal from alcohol or cocaine are at a high risk of developing seizures.

Mr. J. is admitted to the general hospital and is scheduled for elective surgery for a hernia repair the next morning. The nurse brings Mr. J. his prescribed medications, including diazepam, 20 mg, at 10 p.m. for sleep. Mr. J. asks the nurse if he must take the pill, since he is in recovery from addictions and has been clean and sober for 2 years. He explains to the nurse that he avoids all mood-altering medications. How should the nurse respond to the client's concern? What actions might the nurse take?

Critical Thinking Question

Does it affect your ability to care for a patient if you perceive the patient's illness to be the result of a lifestyle choice, such as drinking, intravenous drug use, unsafe sexual practices, smoking, or obesity?

Education for Clients and Family

Education is a large component of treatment. It is through education that the client can begin to understand the nature of addictions. Information must be kept simple, and the major points should be repeated to maximize learning in the presence of cognitive deficits. Families and significant others can be a wonderful source of support and encouragement. Of course, the client needs to consent to have family members involved in treatment. Family members and significant others can also benefit from 12-step programs specifically for them. Important teaching points are as follows:

- Addiction is a chronic illness, and the causes are complex and not fully understood. The client is not responsible for the substance abuse or dependence but is responsible for accepting treatment.
- Clients and families need to learn about the specific actions and effects of the substances involved. They need to understand the concept of cross-tolerance for drugs in the same category. A person with a tolerance for alcohol will have a tolerance for all sedative-hypnotic drugs. Clients are advised to avoid all mood-altering drugs.
- Insomnia can be particularly challenging, since most sleep medications are sedative hypnotics with addictive potential. Clients are encouraged to try nonpharmacologic approaches to induce sleep, including relaxation, warm milk, establishing a bedtime routine, avoiding exercise before bedtime, and reducing caffeine intake. However, insomnia has been linked to relapse, so it is important that the client discuss this issue with the prescribing clinician. Medications with low addictive properties, such as the serotonin modulator, trazodone (Desyrel), an antidepressant with a sedating effect, may be prescribed. A newer sleep medication, ramelteon (Rozerem) is in a class of medications called melatonin receptor agonists. It works similarly to melatonin, a natural substance in the brain that is needed for sleep, and is thought to be nonaddictive.
- The best success has been with an abstinence model. Recovery often requires changes in the recovering person's lifestyle, including new friends and activities. Self-help groups, such as AA and NA, are excellent sources of support in this process and have a proven record of success in maintaining sobriety.
- New coping skills, such as social skills, assertive communication, and relaxation techniques, can be taught in order to assist the recovering person to deal with stress and anger, ask for help, set limits, and express feelings appropriately. Often the client will have relied on drugs or alcohol to cope with these feelings or situations.
- Clients need to learn to take care of themselves by getting adequate nutrition, sleep, and recreation. The importance of a balanced lifestyle as a defense against relapse needs to be understood.
- Positive self-esteem is critical to staying sober, and clients should be advised to avoid people and situations that leave them feeling bad about themselves. Family members and significant others need to relate to the recovering person in a way that reinforces strengths and self-esteem. It is important that goals be realistic in order to maximize successful experiences.
- Relationships and roles change when someone becomes sober. Frequently family members and significant others may not have been aware of how their behaviors actually supported or enabled the drinking or drug use, creating a **codependence**. The client, family members, and significant others need to be prepared to learn new roles and ways of relating. This can be a very difficult process for all involved, and families and significant others can benefit from existing support groups, such as Al-Anon and Alateen.
- In cases where the substance dependence or abuse is ongoing, the family and significant others need education on how to assist the client. Providing a nonjudgmental, factual description of the behavior is most effective (e.g., "You didn't come by to take the children to the baseball game last night."). Family members and significant others need to be

Evidence-Based Practice

Among persons with mental illness, the prevalence of smoking is twice that of the general public, and in addition, mental illness is associated higher levels of smoking among smokers (Lawrence, Mitrou, & Zubrick, 2009). Smoking may well contribute to the significantly shortened life expectancy among persons with mental illness. Given the serious health consequences associated with smoking, the American Psychiatric Nurses Association (APNA) has taken the position that failure by nurses to act on tobacco dependence equals harm (2008). The standard of care is that nurses assess and offer tobacco dependence treatment to all consumers and document the approach and outcome (APNA, 2010).

The U.S. Public Health Service provides evidence-based approaches for use by health professionals to assist clients with smoking cessation, including those with psychiatric and substance abuse disorders (Fiore, Jaén, Baker, Bailey, Benowitz, Curry, et al., 2009). Strategies include asking all clients about tobacco use, assessing readiness to learn, educating smokers and nonsmokers about the dangers of tobacco use, assisting with quit efforts, and referring for further treatment.

Findings from systematic reviews and original research were examined using strength of evidence and, consistent with previous studies, showed that (a) school-based prevention interventions have short-term (but not long-term) effects on adolescents; (b) multicomponent approaches, including telephone counseling, increase the number of users who attempt to quit; (c) self-help strategies alone are ineffective, but counseling and pharmacotherapy used either alone or in combination can improve success rates of quit attempts (Ranney, Melvin, Lux, McClain, & Lohr, 2006). Using effective smoking treatments was strongly encouraged for all populations, especially those with high and heavy rates of smoking, such as psychiatric and substance abuse populations. Furthermore, research shows that, when offered the usual interventions of education, counseling and pharmacotherapy, the quit rates of patients with psychiatric disorders were similar to those of the general population (el-Guebaly, Cathcart, Currie, Brown, & Gloster, 2002).

There is little evidence to support the concern that smoking cessation may worsen a psychiatric condition (APNA, 2010). There is evidence that the smoking history of nurses may be a barrier to the delivery of tobacco education and treatment. According to a recent study, nurses who themselves are smokers are less likely to promote smoking cessation among patients (Sarna, Bialous, Wells, & Kotlerman, 2009). A survey of 100 psychiatric nurses showed that the large majority always or usually asked (87%), advised (70%), and assessed (74%) tobacco use. Only 49% assisted with efforts to quit, and 21% arranged for follow-up. Among the 100 nurses, 56% were former smokers and 20% were smokers at the time of the survey. These groups were less likely to ask clients about tobacco use than those who never smoked.

While this small study shows that the majority of nurses were actively assessing clients, the findings are quite different from those of a 2008 survey of 1,288 members of the APNA. That study showed that only 30% of respondents provide tobacco dependence treatment in line with national best practice guidelines and another 33% rated tobacco dependence as a low priority in their work (APNA, 2008).

While further research is needed to explore the treatment of tobacco dependence among patients with psychiatric and substance abuse disorders, current evidence supports the following:

1. Assessment, education, intervention, and referral for smoking cessation are standards of care for nurses with all clients. Not doing so constitutes patient harm.
2. Evidence-based strategies have been identified and research shows they can be effective with clients who have psychiatric and substance abuse disorders.
3. A positive smoking history may be a barrier to the nurse intervening with tobacco-dependent clients.

cautioned against making excuses that cover up for the substance-abusing or dependent person. This behavior, known as enabling, protects the abuser from facing the consequences of the illness. It is important to reinforce with family and significant others the importance of persons with addictions taking responsibility their own behaviors and helping themselves. Examples of enabling behaviors are lying or covering up, such as calling in sick to work; avoiding talking to the person about the addiction for fear of the response; paying the client's bills; taking care of him when he is intoxicated; and threatening to leave, but not following through.

- Health teaching is an important component of nursing care for clients with addictions. In particular, the nurse can educate the client about hepatitis, sexually transmitted diseases, and HIV, with a focus on prevention. Because of impaired judgment, clients with substance abuse disorders may place themselves at risk for these illnesses. Commonly used medications, such as acetominophen (Tylenol), may be contraindicated in clients with impaired liver functioning.

Education Related to Dual Diagnosis

The nurse can play a pivotal role in motivating and engaging the client in treatment for a dual disorder through client and family education. The following are significant teaching points:

- The neurobiology of the mental disorder and the addiction provides the foundation to help the client and family or significant other understand the relationship between the two disorders.
- The role of prescribed medication must be carefully explained, as well as the importance of not stopping the medication or adjusting the dosage. Compliance with the prescribed schedule and dosage of medications is a predictor of recovery, and failure to comply is a predictor of relapse.
- The nurse should inform the client of possible side effects of psychotropic medications and teach simple strategies to lessen discomfort. Clients have been known to resort to alcohol or other drugs in an attempt to find relief from the side effects of prescribed medication.
- The nurse needs to educate the client about the interaction between prescribed medications and possible substances of abuse so that the client understands the increased risks these substances present. The anticholinergic effects (dry mouth, dry eyes, blurred vision, constipation, difficulty urinating) of some psychotropic medications are enhanced by marijuana. The effectiveness of neuroleptics is decreased if the client uses alcohol, sedatives, or nicotine. Monoamine oxidase inhibitors (MAOIs) may cause a hypertensive crisis if combined with certain forms of alcohol or stimulant drugs.
- Families and clients need to be informed of the warning signs of relapse, and families need to recognize early signs of noncompliance with medications or substance use.

Summary

Substance-use disorders include dependence and substance abuse. A person who is abusing a substance continues to use it despite serious problems that are clearly related to that use. Withdrawal symptoms indicate a physical dependence on the substance. Substances that can be abused fall into many drug classifications, and symptoms of intoxication and withdrawal vary by classification. Withdrawal from alcohol can be life threatening. Treatment includes managing the concomitant physical and psychiatric disorders, detoxifying the client if indicated, and establishing a therapeutic relationship to support the client in the decision to seek help for his or her addiction. With the assistance of a 12-step program, sobriety is the ultimate goal. The nurse can play a critical role in motivating the client to pursue treatment.

It is important that both the client and the nurse accept the fact that addiction is a chronic illness, and, therefore, the patient may experience a relapse. This should not be regarded as a failure. Rather, the nurse should help the client learn from the experience, make necessary changes in the treatment plan, and make a renewed commitment to recovery. Medication adherence and response rates have been found to be similar for drug dependence, type 2 diabetes mellitus, hypertension, and asthma (McLellan, Lewis, O'Brien, & Kleber, 2000). As with all chronic illnesses, relapses should be expected in clients with substance abuse disorders, and they are not a reflection of moral failure or character weakness.

Annotated References

Addington, J., & Addington, D. (2001). Impact of an early psychosis program on substance use. *Psychiatric Rehabilitation Journal, 25*(1), 60–67.

This article highlights the relationship between psychoses and substance-related disorders and the treatment implications.

Agency for Healthcare Research and Quality (AHRQ). (2007). *Care of adults with mental health and substance abuse disorders in U.S.*

community hospitals. Washington, DC: Healthcare Utilization Project.
This is a fact book with demographic and diagnostic data related to clients with mental health and substance-use disorders hospitalized in short-term, nonfederal, public, and private hospitals across the United States. The survey did not include facilities specializing in the treatment of these disorders.

American Academy of Child and Adolescent Psychiatry. (2011). Teens: Alcohol and other drugs. *Facts for Families, 3*, updated March 2011. Retrieved from http://www.aacap.org/cs/root/facts_for_families/teens_alcohol_and_other_drugs
Facts for Families is an AACAP publication intended to provide concise and up-to-date information on issues that affect children, teenagers, and their families.

American Nurses Association. (2004). *Scope and standards of addictions nursing practice*. Washington, DC: Author.
This document establishes a scope of practice and standards of professional performance for the nurse specializing in addiction nursing.

American Psychiatric Association. (2000). *Diagnostic and statistical manual of mental disorders* (4th ed., text rev.). Washington, DC: Author.
This is the American Psychiatric Association's official nomenclature of psychiatric conditions and disorders. It provides a systematic listing of the official codes and categories, a description of the multiaxial system for diagnosis, and diagnostic criteria for each of the disorders. It is used by psychiatrists, physicians, psychologists, registered nurses, social workers, therapists, and other mental health workers in all clinical settings.

American Psychiatric Association. (2006). *Practice guideline: Treatment of patients with substance use disorders, 2nd ed.* doi:10.1176/appi.books.9780890423363.141077
This article provides parameters of practice developed by practicing psychiatrists and researchers.

American Psychiatric Association. (2011). DSM 5 development, proposed revisions, substance-related disorders. Arlington, VA: Author. Retrieved from http://www.dsm5.org/ProposedRevisions/Pages/Substance-RelatedDisorders.aspx
DSM5.org is the APA's official website for updates on proposed revisions to the DSM

American Psychiatric Nurses Association (APNA). (2008). *Psychiatric nurses as champions for smoking cessation*. Arlington, VA: Author. Retrieved from www.apna.org
In this position paper the association advocates for the role of psychiatric nurses in the treatment of tobacco dependence and states clearly that a failure to act Is equal to harm.

American Psychiatric Nurses Association (APNA). (2010). Breaking barriers and implementing changes. Treating tobacco dependence in persons with mental illness: Identifying challenges and opportunities. *Psychiatric Nurse Counseling Points, 1*(3), 4–12.
This is the final installment of a three-part series on tobacco cessation for persons with mental illness and substance abuse addictions.

Babor, T. F., Biddle-Higgins, J. C., Saunders, J. B., & Monteiro, M. G. (2001). *AUDIT: The alcohol use disorders identification test; Guidelines for use in primary health care*. Geneva, Switzerland: World Health Organization.
This is a description and guide for the use of an alcohol assessment tool.

Bradley, K. A., DeBenedetti, A. F., Volk, R. J., Williams, E. C., Frank, D., & Kivlahan, D. R. (2007). AUDIT-C as a brief screen for alcohol misuse in primary care. *Alcoholism: Clinical and Experimental Research, 31*(7), 1208–1217.
This cross-sectional validation study compared screening questionnaires with standardized interviews in 392 male and 927 female adult outpatients at an academic family practice clinic from 1993 to 1994.

Center for Substance Abuse Treatment. (2006). *Overarching principles to address the needs of persons with co-occurring disorders*. COCE overview paper 3, DHHS Publication No. (SMA) 06-4165. Rockville, MD: Substance Abuse and Mental Health Services Administration.
This is a concise introduction to the topic of co-occurring disorders, intended for administrators, policy makers, and providers.

Deas, D. (2006). Adolescent substance abuse and psychiatric comorbidities. *Journal of Clinical Psychiatry, 67*(Suppl. 7), 18–23.
This article presents information on adolescents at risk for developing dual diagnoses.

Deglin, J. H., Vallerand, A. H., & Sanoski, C. A. (2011). *Davis's drug guide for nurses* (12th ed.). Philadelphia, PA: F. A. Davis.
Coauthored by a nurse and two pharmacists, this book is an excellent resource for medication information such as use, interactions, side effects, and client education needs.

el-Guebaly, N., Cathcart, J., Currie, S., Brown, D., & Gloster, S. (2002). Smoking cessation approaches for persons with mental illness or addictive disorders. *Psychiatric Services, 53*, 1166–1170.
This critical review of the literature identifies 24 empirical studies of outcomes of smoking cessation approaches used with samples of persons with mental disorders.

Finfgeld-Connett, D. L. (2004). Treatment of substance misuse in older women: Using a brief intervention model. *Journal of Gerontological Nursing, 30*(8), 30–37.
This article discusses the barriers to diagnosing and treating alcohol and benzodiazepine misuse among older women, and it recommends brief interventions for use with this population.

Fiore, M. S., Jaén, R. C., Baker, T. B., Bailey, W. C., Benowitz, N., Curry, S. J., . . . Wewers, M. E. (2009, April). *Treating tobacco use and dependence: 2008 update. Quick reference guide for clinicians.* Rockville, MD: U.S. Department of Health and Human Services, Public Health Service.
This guide to delivery of care for tobacco dependence is based on systematic review and analysis of scientific literature.

Frances, A. (2010). DSM5 "Addiction" Swallows Substance Abuse. The case for preserving substance abuse as a separate category. *DSM5 in Distress* (Blog), *Psychology Today*, March 25, 2010. Retrieved from http://my.psychologytoday.com/blog/dsm5-in-distress/201003/dsm5-addiction-swallows-substance-abuse
An article by a psychiatrist who was chair of the task force on substance-related disorders for the current DSM-IV.

Galanter, M., & Kleber, H. D. (2008). *Textbook of substance abuse treatment* (4th ed.). Arlington, VA: American Psychiatric Publishing, Inc.
This comprehensive text identifies treatment issues specific to each classification of drugs. It addresses individual, group, and family therapy and special programs including inpatient and adolescent programs, employee assistance programs, community-based treatment, and therapeutic communities.

Kennedy, W. K., Leloux, M., Kutscher, E. C., Price, P. L., Morstad, A. E., & Carnahan, R. M. (2010). Acamprosate. *Expert Opinion on Drug Metabolism and Toxicity, 6*(3), 363–380.
A review the published acamprosate literature focusing on major and recent comparative clinical trials and meta-analyses, focusing on effectiveness.

Large, M., Swapnil, S., Compton, M. T., Slade, T., & Olav, N. (2011). Cannabis use and earlier onset of psychosis, a systematic meta-analysis. *Archives of General Psychiatry, 68*(6), 555–561.
A meta-analysis of peer-reviewed articles to determine the extent to which use of cannabis, alcohol, and other psychoactive substances affects the age at onset of psychosis.

Lawrence, D., Mitrou, F., & Zubrick, S. R. (2009). Smoking and mental illness: Results from population surveys in Australia and the United States. *BMC Public Health, 9*, 285. doi:10.1186/1471-2458-9-285
This article provides survey data from the United States, and Australian sources were used to investigate the relationship between current smoking, ICD-10 mental disorders, and nonspecific psychologic distress.

Mayfield, D. G., McCleod, G., & Hall, D. (1974). The C.A.G.E. questionnaire. *American Journal of Psychiatry, 131*, 1121–1123.
This article introduces a brief tool to assess alcohol abuse.

McLellan, A. T., Lewis, D. C., O'Brien, C. P., & Kleber, H. D. (2000). Drug dependence, a chronic medical illness: Implications for treatment, insurance, and outcomes evaluation. *Journal of the American Medical Association, 284*(13), 1689–1695.
This article is a literature review comparing the diagnoses, etiology, pathophysiology, and response to treatments of drug dependence to type 2 diabetes mellitus, hypertension, and asthma.

Miller, W. R., & Rollnick, S. (2002). *Motivational interviewing, preparing people for change* (2nd ed.). New York, NY: Guilford Press.
This work reviews the conceptual and research background supporting motivational interviewing, outlines specific strategies for building motivation and overcoming ambivalence to change, and provides clinical examples.

National Institute of Alcohol Abuse and Alcoholism. (2004). NIAAA council approves definition of binge drinking. *NIAAA Newsletter, 3*, 3.
This article describes the NIAAA National Advisory Council's approved statement on the definition of binge drinking.

Perkinson, R. R. (2012). *Chemical dependency counseling: A practical guide* (4th ed.). Thousand Oaks, CA: Sage Publications, Inc.
A comprehensive guide for counselors and front-line professionals who work with the chemically dependent in a variety of settings.

Ranney, L., Melvin, C., Lux, L., McClain, E., & Lohr, K. (2006). Systematic review: Smoking cessation intervention strategies for adults and adults in special populations. *Annals of Internal Medicine, 145*(11), 845–856.
Findings from systematic reviews and original research were examined using strength of evidence to evaluate effectiveness of interventions to cease smoking.

Rey, J. M. (2007). Can marijuana lead to psychotic illness? *Current Psychiatry, 6*(2), 36–41, 46.
This article reviews evidence that marijuana use can cause acute psychosis, precipitate schizophrenia, and worsen the prognosis of persons with psychotic disorders.

Sarna, L., Bialous, S. A., Wells, M. J., Kotlerman, J. (2009). Smoking among psychiatric nurses: Does it hinder tobacco dependence treatment? *Journal of the American Psychiatric Nurses Association, 15*(1), 59–67.
This paper reports the results of a survey of 100 psychiatric nurses regarding tobacco interventions.

Simkin, D. R. (2002). Adolescent substance use disorders and comorbidity. *Pediatric Clinics of North America, 49*(2), 463–477.
This article discusses the importance of identifying risk factors associated with specific developmental stages, so that interventions can be made to reduce risk for future substance-use disorders. It stresses the importance of primary care physicians using instruments to assess for mental disorders in children and adolescents.

Additional Resources

AA World Services. (1975). *Living sober*. New York, NY: Author.
This book provides strategies to help maintain sobriety. It is prepared by Alcoholics Anonymous but is applicable to other substance addictions. The text addresses practical concerns such as dealing with drinking friends and situations, managing loneliness and insomnia, and keeping liquor in the house.

AA World Services. (1978). *Twelve steps and twelve traditions*. New York, NY: Author.
This text explains the 12-step program of Alcoholics Anonymous. Available online at http://www.aa.org/twelveandtwelve/en_tableofcnt.cfm

Botelko, R. J., & Skinner, H. (1995). Motivating change in health behavior: Implications for health promotion and disease prevention. *Primary Care, 22*(4), 565–589.
This is a classic article presenting a generic approach for helping practitioners motivate patients to change, introduce the principles of motivational interviewing as a way to help people recognize and do something about their problems, and make a distinction between traditional advice giving and patient-centered advice giving. A practical and thought-provoking guide to working with client resistance.

Internet Resources

For a full suite of assignments and additional learning activities, use the access code located in the front of your book to visit this exclusive website: http://go.jblearning.com/mentalhealth. If you do not have an access code, you can obtain one at the site.

Learning Objectives

After reading this chapter, you will be able to:

- Differentiate among schizophrenia, schizophreniform disorder, schizoaffective disorder, delusional disorder, brief psychotic and shared psychotic disorders, psychotic disorder due to a general medical condition, and substance-induced psychotic disorder.
- Identify positive and negative symptoms of schizophrenia.
- Discuss the clinical course and complications of schizophrenia.
- Develop a nursing care plan for management of a client with hallucinations, delusions, communication problems, and social withdrawal or isolation.

Key Terms

Affective flattening

Alogia

Anhedonia

Assertive community treatment (ACT)

Avolition

Catalepsy

Catatonia

Delusion

Echolalia

Echopraxia

Hallucination

Negative symptoms

Neuroleptic malignant syndrome

Oculogyric crisis

Opisthotonus

Polydipsia

Positive symptoms

Psychosis

Recovery model

Tardive dyskinesia

Thought disorder

Schizophrenia and Other Psychotic Disorders

Winifred Z. Kennedy and Claudia Mitzeliotis

http://go.jblearning.com/mentalhealth 

For a full suite of assignments and additional learning activities, use the access code located in the front of your book to visit this exclusive website: http://go.jblearning.com/mentalhealth. If you do not have an access code, you can obtain one at the site.

Introduction

Schizophrenia is a psychiatric disorder characterized by significant disorganization of thinking manifested by problems with communication and cognition; impaired perceptions of reality manifested by hallucinations and delusions; and sometimes significant decreases in functioning. Symptoms are usually first seen in adolescence or young adulthood and are often chronic and persistent.

In describing her experiences with a psychotic disorder, a young woman wrote,

> Schizophrenia is not just an illness, it is a way of life, and it is a life constantly disrupted by symptoms. I have dealt with a totally delusional world in which I was God—The Creator and The Sufferer—and the trees held magical power, while a great wall and glass dome cut me off from the rest of humanity. More recently, I have gone through excruciating periods of thought-interference and feelings that I did not exist, experiencing my body as a machine that I could see and feel but which I could not perceive as being in the world. The most frightening part for me is how quickly I can be taken by force and projected into another "state" in which all my perceptions are altered, and the world becomes a bizarre place. Sometimes there is confusion about which is the true reality—the objective world or the psychotic world. (Anonymous, 1986, p. C3)

Psychotic disorders are characterized by distortions of reality, speech, thought, behavior, and affect.

The main diagnostic features of schizophrenia are the length of illness presentation—greater than 6 months—and the presence of psychotic symptoms and impaired functioning.

General Description

Descriptions of schizophrenia and other psychotic disorders have been recorded throughout human history and across cultures. Bark (1988) noted descriptions of persecutory delusions and auditory hallucinations in the second millennium BC, Mesopotamian–Old Babylonian period, and Indian Ayurvedic writings from 600 BC that describe endogenous insanity, impaired intellect, incoherent speech, noises in the ears, and feeling of a void in the head that are remarkably similar to contemporary writings. Descriptions and occurrences of bizarre behaviors are similar across Western and non-Western cultures.

In the late 19th and early 20th centuries, Kraepelin used the term *dementia praecox* to emphasize that symptoms began at an early age and were chronic and debilitating. Eugene Bleuler used the term *schizophrenia* to describe the "split mindedness" or the separations between affect, cognition, and emotions. At one time, clinicians utilized Bleuler's 4 As—associative looseness (difficulties in understanding client's verbiage), apathy (avolition), autistic thinking (self-inferential rather than objective), and ambivalence (inability to make decisions)—as the fundamental symptoms of schizophrenia. **Delusions** and **hallucinations** were considered accessory symptoms. Schneider later theorized first-rank symptoms (control of behavior through auditory hallucinations, thoughts spoken aloud, thought control, thought broadcasting, experiences of influence and control) and second-rank symptoms (other hallucinations, affectual blunting, mood disorders, perplexity (Ho, Black, & Andreasen, 2003). Contemporary descriptions of the disorder consider clusters of positive, negative, cognitive, and mood symptoms. The **negative symptoms** of **affective flattening**, **anhedonia** (loss of feeling pleasure), **avolition**, and attentional impairment and the **positive symptoms** of hallucinations, delusions, and **thought disorder** are similar to classic descriptions of schizophrenia.

Psychosis describes significant impairment in functioning, ego boundaries, and reality testing. Impairments in affect, behavior, communication, cognition, perception, and social functioning may be present. Insight, judgment, and impulse control may be impaired. Psychotic symptoms can be present in many different psychiatric disorders including cognitive and mood disorders and schizophrenia.

The *Diagnostic and Statistical Manual of Mental Disorders*, fourth edition, text revision (*DSM-IV-TR*) identifies schizophrenia, schizophreniform disorder, schizoaffective disorder, delusional disorder, brief psychotic disorder, shared psychotic disorder, psychotic disorder due to a general medical condition, and substance-induced psychotic disorders as psychiatric disorders that manifest psychotic features of delusions, hallucinations, and disorganized speech and behavior singly or in combination (American Psychiatric Association [APA], 2000). Hallucinations are false sensory perceptions that exist without objective sensory stimuli. Thought disorders describe cognitive symptoms that may be demonstrated by problems in forming or organizing thoughts or communicating with others. Disorganized behaviors may be demonstrated by isolated, withdrawn, regressed, uncontrolled, or inappropriate, bizarre activity.

The *DSM-IV-TR* identifies delusional disorder, shared delusional disorder, brief psychotic disorder, psychotic disorder due to a general medical condition, and substance-induced psychotic disorder as dis-

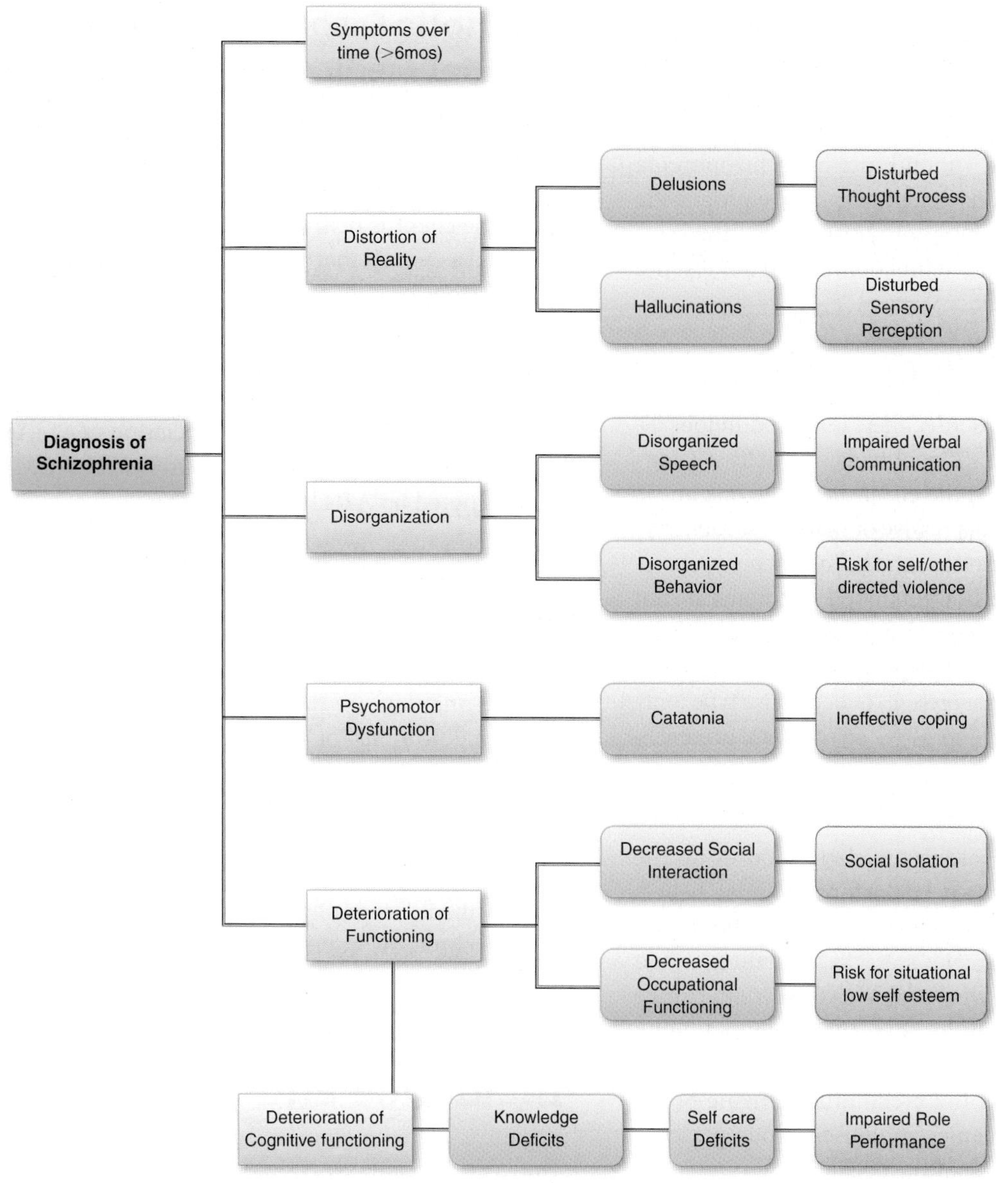

Figure 16–1 Nursing diagnoses concept map for schizophrenia.

orders in which the client exhibits some prominent psychotic features but does not meet the criteria for schizophrenia, schizophreniform, or schizoaffective disorders because of the types of symptoms present or the duration of the symptoms. Delusional disorder and brief psychotic disorder do not generally result from a medical condition or substance abuse (APA, 2000).

Schizophrenia

The main criterion for schizophrenia is that the client has characteristic psychotic symptoms, more or less continuously, for at least 6 months, not related to a medical condition or substance use, and serious enough to impair social and occupational functioning. Figure 16-1 shows common symptoms of schizophrenia and related nursing diagnoses. The main types of schizophrenia are paranoid, disorganized, catatonic, undifferentiated, and residual. Schizophrenia may be further specified as single episode, episodic, continuous, in full or partial remission, with prominent negative symptoms, or with another or unspecified pattern of symptoms or course.

Schizophreniform Disorder

In schizophreniform disorder, symptoms are present for less than 6 months.

The main criterion for diagnosing schizophreniform disorder is that the symptoms of the psychotic disorder have been present for at least 1 month but less than 6 months. This differs from the diagnostic criteria for schizophrenia in that significant impairment in functioning is not required for diagnosis. Within the 6-month period when symptoms first appear, the diagnosis is considered provisional; if symptoms persist beyond the 6-month period, schizophrenia would be diagnosed. Generally, positive prognostic features for schizophreniform disorder are the presence of good premorbid functioning and the absence of impaired affect.

Shared psychotic disorder is relatively rare. The diagnostic criteria are broader than for historical descriptions of folie à deux, a shared delusional disorder.

Schizoaffective Disorder

In schizoaffective disorder, there is the continuous diagnostic criteria for schizophrenia with at least 1 concurrent period when the client meets the diagnostic criteria for a major depressive or manic disorder. Psychotic features of delusions and hallucinations are present for at least 2 weeks when mood symptoms are not prominent. The main types of schizoaffective disorder are bipolar type (major depressive, manic, or mixed episode symptoms are present) or depressive type (only symptoms of major depressive episodes are present).

The main diagnostic features of schizoaffective disorder are symptoms of schizophrenia and an affective or mood disorder.

Delusional Disorder

In a delusional disorder, the client focuses on the presence of a delusion (delusions are false beliefs that exist without objective evidence), and the criteria for schizophrenia are not met. Hallucinations, mood symptoms, or behavior problems, if present, can be explained by the delusion; other areas of functioning are not impaired. Delusional disorders can be further specified, based on the predominant theme of the delusion, as erotomanic, grandiose, jealous, persecutory, somatic, mixed, or unspecified.

Brief Psychotic and Shared Psychotic Disorders

A brief psychotic disorder is one in which the psychotic symptoms (delusions, hallucinations, disorganized speech or behaviors) are present for at least 1 day but less than 1 month. The disturbance may be related to specific stressors that would be disturbing to anyone with a similar cultural background. Symptoms are not related to a mood disorder, medical illness, or substance abuse and do not meet the criteria for schizophrenia or schizoaffective disorder. The diagnosis may be specified with or without marked stressors or with onset within 4 weeks postpartum. In shared psychotic disorder, the client has a close relationship, usually dependent, with someone who has a delusional disorder.

Psychotic Disorder Due to a General Medical Condition

Psychotic disorder due to a general medical condition is associated with a medical illness in which hallucinations or delusions are present at times other than when the client is delirious. The disorder is further specified as to whether the predominant symptoms are delusions or hallucinations. The associated general medical condition is indicated on Axis I (e.g., psychotic disorder due to Huntington's disease), and the medical condition, Huntington's disease, along with the American Medical Association's (AMA) *International Classification of Diseases* (*ICD-9-CM*) code, is noted on Axis III (AMA, 2006).

Substance-Induced Psychotic Disorder

In a substance-induced psychotic disorder, delusions or hallucinations are the direct result of substance abuse, medications, or toxins and are present only when the client is delirious. Symptoms exceed what might normally be expected during periods of intoxication or withdrawal. The drug of abuse and the predominant symptom, delusions or hallucinations, are specified. Drugs of abuse commonly associated with psychotic disorders are alcohol, amphetamines, anxiolytics, cannabis, hallucinogens, hypnotics, inhalants, opioids, phencyclidine, and sedatives.

Incidence and Prevalence

The World Health Organization (WHO) estimates incidence rates for schizophrenia of 13.37 per 100,000 men and 12.94 per 100,000 women. The highest rate occurs in the group 20–64 years of age. The overall prevalence rate for men and women is 0.4% (Ustun & Sartorius, 2001). The estimated lifetime prevalence rate is 0.05–1% (APA, 2000). Schizophrenia is the most common disorder with psychotic symptoms and ranks in the top 10 for disease burden. The average life span of a patient with schizophrenia is reduced by 10 years (Lopez, Mathers, Ezzati, & Murray, 2006).

Progressive decline in functioning, particularly in economic potential (downward drift), occurs in most clients diagnosed with schizophrenia (APA, 2000). While clients with schizophrenia accounted for approximately 40% of inpatient admissions in 1993, this had decreased to approximately 20% in 2004 (Lay, Nordt, & Rossler, 2007). It is estimated that approximately 25–50% of clients with schizophrenia will attempt suicide and from 4–13% will die from a suicide attempt (Meltzer, 2001).

Etiology

The complex syndrome of symptoms in schizophrenia has prompted a broad range of theories regarding its etiology. More than one area of the brain, one neurotransmitter, one gene, and one environmental factor appear to be involved. In addition, some structural abnormalities, endocrine and viral disorders, as well as hallucinogenic drugs or exposure to toxins have been known to simulate psychotic features similar to schizophrenia. Longitudinal phases of premorbid evolution (from conception to symptom development), psychotic decompensation, and long-term evolution (chronicity, residuals, remissions) suggest the interaction of genetic and environmental variables (Walker, Ketler, Bollini, & Hochman, 2004).

Most studies indicate a genetic link and familial pattern. The closer the degree of kinship to someone with schizophrenia, the greater one's genetic risk for schizophrenia. The risk is greatest for monozygotic twins and decreases steadily for dizygotic twins, siblings, those with two affected parents, those with one affected parent, and cousins. Certain ethnic groups such as the Irish in Ireland, southwestern Croatians, Scandinavians in the United States, and West Indians in England show consistently higher rates, consistent with studies that indicate immigrants and migrating populations have a greater risk of schizophrenia than native populations. Other cross-cultural and environmental variables such as obstetrical complications, number of winter births, possible exposure to viruses, and neurodevelopmental disorders have to be considered as possibly responsible for increased rates in certain populations. Research suggests that genes, brain development (particularly areas involved in language processing and cognitive functioning), timing of development, and environmental stressors are involved (McGrath, Saha, Chant, & Welham, 2008)

The neurodevelopment hypothesis in the development of schizophrenia is based upon the observation of schizophrenia in infants exposed to viral infections in the second trimester as well as neurologic soft signs found in evaluating patients with schizophrenia. Developmental, neurostructural, biochemical, and environmental factors influence an individual's ability to process information. Problems in focusing attention, assessing stimuli, and assigning affectual meaning to experiences impair cognition and the ability to interact successfully with the environment. Neurostructural and biochemical factors influence how the individual experiences and perceives the world. As the individual develops and interactions become increasingly complex, the problems in processing information increase because development has been inadequate to meet demands or develop a repertoire necessary to meet new challenges. Impairments in information processing continue as the inability to modulate biologic and psychosocial stressors. Deficiencies in automaticity, the ability to recreate and retrieve past experiences to deal with a present situation, further impair the client's ability to deal with new situations (Fatemi & Folsom, 2009).

Reduced frontal lobe activity in schizophrenics is thought to be associated with reductions in glutamatergic activity and with negative symptoms and cognitive deficits. Increased mesolimbic dopamine activity is hypothesized to be related to schizophrenia. The dopamine hypothesis for the development of schizophrenia is associated with the dopamine-blocking properties of antipsychotic medications and their effects on various neurotransmitter systems.

Research into the family's role in schizophrenia involves differentiation in families using a construct of expressed emotion (EE). High-EE families are seen as being critical and overinvolved. Schizophrenic clients living in households with high EE have a higher rate of relapse. Further research suggests that there are higher levels of arousal in schizophrenic clients living in high-EE households. Social skills training and education for both the family and the client help reduce the levels of arousal and rate of relapse (Turkington, Dudley, Warman, & Beck, 2004).

Psychologic theories hypothesize that a deficit in ego development and functioning leads to a failure of the ego to interpret reality correctly or to modulate id drives. Impaired functioning leads to ego decompensation and a return to more primitive functioning. Problems functioning and relating to others create anxiety. Ineffective coping causes further anxiety and impairment in functioning. Regression helps defend against anxiety but impairs the ego's ability to determine reality. The development of psychotic symptoms signals the individual's inability to differentiate between thoughts and reality; that is, subjective experience is misinterpreted as objective experience. Hallucinations and delusions are the ego's attempt to deal with the anxiety, and the symptoms hold symbolic meaning for the individual.

Critical Thinking Question

What are some concerns a family might have regarding a relative's new diagnosis of schizophrenia? Discuss some strategies that could be used to help the family deal with this diagnosis.

Neurobiologic and Genetic Basis

Neurobiologic theories of schizophrenia are discussed in Chapter 5. Schizophrenia has been defined as a neurodevelopmental disorder in which parts of the brain have not developed properly or function inadequately. The severity of the symptoms depends upon the extent of structural abnormalities and biochemical functioning. The vast diversity of symptoms indicates that more than one area of the brain is involved. Some clients show soft signs of neurologic problems—that is, the presence of primitive reflexes; grimacing; grunting; snuffling; mirroring; mild choreiform and ticlike movements; impaired motor skills, tone, or both; and coordination problems. Neurologic deficits may include impairments in attention, problem solving, memory, and comprehension. Some clients experience problems in concept formation and overall intellectual functioning. Research suggests that clients with schizophrenia are likely to have structural neuropathy. Computerized axial tomography (CAT scan), magnetic resonance imaging (MRI), and positron emission tomography (PET) studies have identified variations in structures that may influence functioning. Structural problems in the frontal cortex may influence negative symptoms, and structural problems in the limbic system may influence positive symptoms. Decreased brain volume and thalamic size, increased ventricular size, and prominent cortical sulci have been identified with schizophrenia. Enlarged ventricles suggest problems in development or loss of brain tissue. Reduced tissue mass has been found in the amygdala, hippocampus, parahippocampal gyrus, substantia nigra, internal globus pallidus, and frontal areas of the brain in clients with schizophrenia. Studies of the epidemiology of schizophrenia emphasize the interaction between infectious agents and genetic predisposition. Some of the diseases that have been implicated are influenza, rubella, polio, herpes simplex, cytomegalovirus, and toxoplasmosis (Yolken & Torrey, 2006).

Dual-risk vulnerability, or genetic diathesis, to schizophrenia suggests that both genetic and other epigenetic factors such as neurodevelopmental defects and gene–environment interaction such as phenotypic variations from the effects of medication are responsible for the development of schizophrenia in some individuals.

Excess dopamine and defects in metabolism of serotonin may also be involved in schizophrenia. Problems in dopamine and other neurotransmitter pathways, or dysregulation, may cause abnormal transmission in the brain and influence the behaviors seen in schizophrenia. Based upon the actions of typical neuroleptics on D_2 dopamine receptor sites, hyperactivity of dopamine (a neurotransmitter associated with limbic and motor nuclei functioning) may be responsible for symptoms in schizophrenia. Studies of other neurotransmitters and receptor sites indicate that norepinephrine is increased or released in schizophrenia, and gamma-aminobutyric acid (GABA) activity increases dopaminergic activity. Atypical neuroleptics affect D_3 and D_4 blockers of dopamine and D_2 activity to a lesser degree, as well as affecting serotonin receptors. Hyperactivity of 5HT2, a serotonin receptor, may influence dopamine receptors and decrease monoamine oxidase (MAO). Serotonin is a neurotransmitter associated with calmness, pleasure, and the reduction of pain. Dysfunction of 5HT2 and hypersensitivity of postsynaptic receptors are associated with negative symptoms of schizophrenia.

Genetic studies suggest that multiple gene variations lead to the development of schizophrenia and that the greater the number of these variants, the greater the risk. Researchers have found a high incidence of schizophrenia in families, particularly among first-degree relatives. Twin studies show a high correlation between identical twins. However, not all first-degree relatives eventually develop symptoms of schizophrenia, suggesting that multiple genes or genetic modifiers and environmental influences are also involved. Relatives may have deficits in one or more endotypes and not develop schizophrenia. Approximately 50–80% of risk is due to genetic factors and the remaining vulnerabilities are due to other factors such as neonatal damage or other environmental factors. Researchers have also found some overlap in the development of schizophrenia and autism, schizophrenia and bipolar disorder, and schizophrenia and Parkinson's disease. These disorders may share genes or share overlapping neural dysfunction and other clinical features (Braff, Freedman, Schork, & Gottesman, 2007). An example of the effect of the interplay between genetic variation and environment is seen in the effects of marijuana upon persons with a defect in the gene COMT (catechol-O-methyl transference), the Val/Val genotype, which increase the risk of development of psychosis by a factor of 10 (Henquet,

DiForti, Morrison, Kuepper, & Murray, 2008). This is an example of genetic diathesis. Clients with high genetic risk for schizophrenia who use marijuana as teenagers may place themselves at higher risk for developing psychosis than their peers who also use marijuana as teenagers.

Clinical Presentation

Clients with schizophrenia and related disorders may present with a mixture of signs and symptoms. Symptom presentation may have been chronic and progressive. Symptoms usually begin to appear when the client is young, usually in adolescence, and rarely after middle age. MRI studies of adolescents and young adults diagnosed with schizophrenia have shown the presence of gray matter brain changes at the time of their first psychotic episode and progressive atrophy during the first 2–3 years of illness (Whitford et al., 2006). Clients may have functioned at a high level before symptoms began and never be able to fulfill their expected level of functioning after symptoms progress. Figure 16-2 is an example of a concept map for clients with schizophrenia who have symptoms related to a diagnosis of social isolation.

Positive Symptoms

Positive symptoms such as hallucinations and delusions reflect disorganized brain function. Clients may misperceive their perceptions or experiences.

Disorganized Thought and Behavior

Cognitive symptoms are seen in the way clients' thoughts are expressed in their speech and use of language and in demonstrations of intellectual functioning. Thought disorder describes disorganized thinking and impaired communication. Clients may be unable to answer questions, frequently change topics, give irrelevant (non sequitur) responses, or speak nonsense. The term **echolalia** describes mimicking the words and phrases of another person. Cognitive problems may also manifest as disorganized behavior. Disorganized behavior can range from childlike and regressed to agitated and aggressive. At times, the disorganization can be seen in the stereotypic ticlike repetition of activities. The client may perseverate words or phrases, thoughts or associations, or mannerisms and actions. **Echopraxia** is the mimicking or repetition of the actions of another person. Schizophrenic clients may exhibit disorganized grooming, sometimes wearing layers of clothing and appearing disheveled or idiosyncratic in their dress. Clients may have problems organizing activities and performing ordinary tasks of daily living.

Catatonia

Behavior may be catatonic. **Catatonia** is characterized by decreased reactivity to one's surroundings. At times, clients may be completely unaware of their surroundings. Mutism, lack of movement, and unresponsiveness characterize catatonic stupor. **Catalepsy** is used to describe the ability to remain in postures. Clients may exhibit rigid posturing and resist being moved or they may have waxy flexibility and assume various postures when moved. In addition to rigidity or limited movement, clients may exhibit excited, unprovoked, and excessive motor activity. Catatonic negativism is the resistance to movement.

Catatonia describes behaviors that include agitation, immobility, and posturing.

Hallucinations

Clients with hallucinations demonstrate altered perception. Although hallucinations can occur in any of the sensory modalities—auditory, visual, olfactory, gustatory, kinetic, tactile—auditory hallucinations occur more frequently with schizophrenia. (Visual and tactile hallucinations are more frequently associated with delirium.) The client with auditory hallucinations usually reports hearing voices (male or female) that are distinct in nature and sometimes speak in full sentences or commands. Humming and ringing in the ears are not characteristic of schizophrenia. Clients with visual hallucinations may complain that there are scorpions crawling on the walls or people stalking them. Hallucinations experienced in schizophrenia are different from the hypnagogic hallucinations that may occur during sleep–wake transitions. Visual, olfactory, and tactile hallucinations usually result from a medical illness or substance abuse rather than schizophrenia. Olfactory and gustatory hallucinations are often experienced together and are associated with a medical disorder, such as a brain tumor.

Hallucinations—sensory perceptions related to internal stimuli—can affect the auditory, visual, tactile, gustatory, olfactory, and kinetic senses. Hallucinations reflect memories of sensory experiences.

Positive symptoms include delusions, hallucinations, and thought disorders.

Word salad is the term used to describe speech consisting of word sequences without connections or meaning.

Delusions

A distorted or exaggerated thinking process may create delusions (false beliefs). The content of a delusion ranges from persecutory to grandiose. Clients frequently experience persecutory delusions and feel as if they are being followed, tormented, ridiculed, or spied on. Clients may also experience referential delusions and state that songs or news broadcasts refer to them and their situations. Bizarre delusions are especially associated with schizophrenia. A client may

Delusions are unrealistic beliefs that are false, inconsistent with reality, and not generally accepted by others with the same cultural background. The content of delusions is usually an exaggerated, common, personal experience. In schizophrenia, the content of delusions tends to be bizarre.

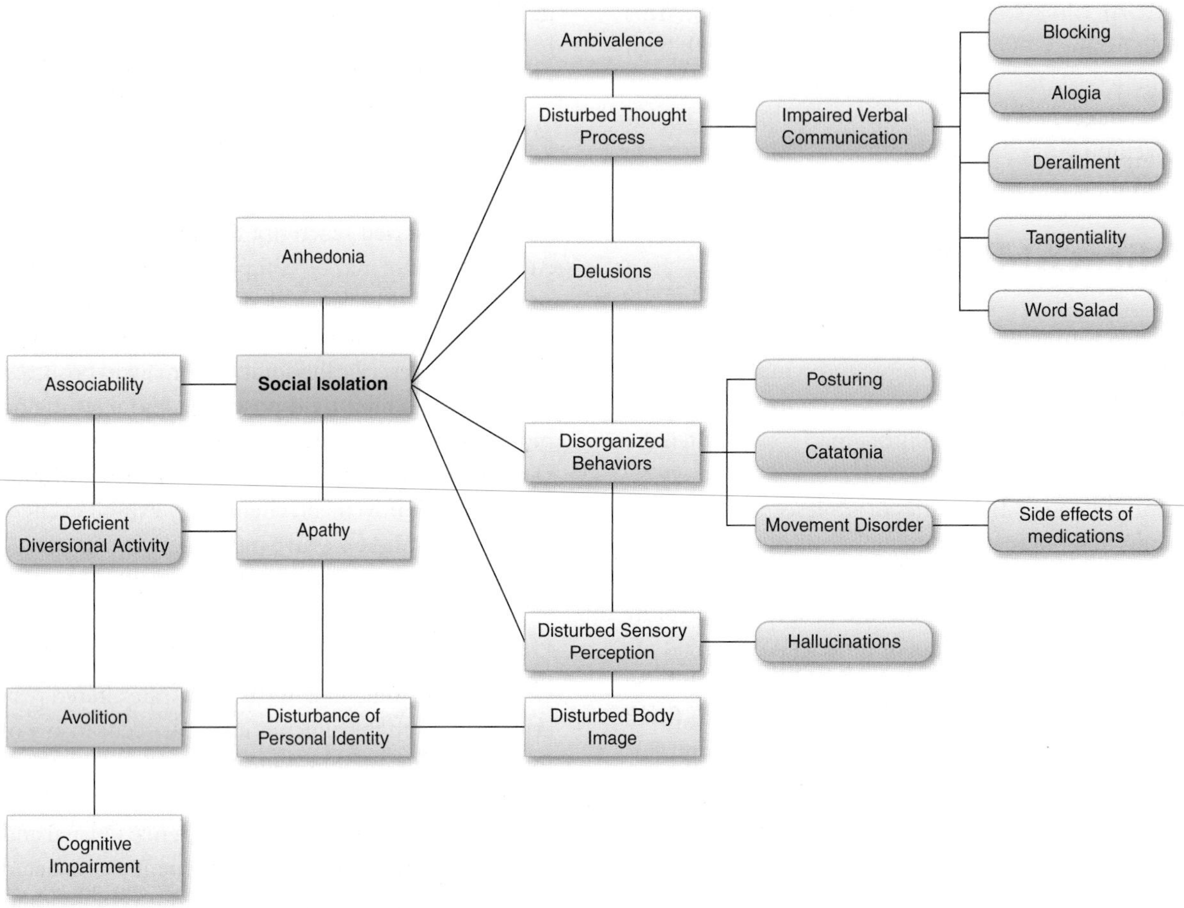

Figure 16–2 Symptom concept map for schizophrenia.

believe that he is a powerful person, such as Jesus Christ. Another client may believe that an alien has taken over her body and is controlling her through electrical waves or thoughts. The theme of the delusion is probably culturally dependent. Historical descriptions of delusions note people believing they were Atlas or Hitler (Bark, 1988). Clients in present-day society are more likely to select a powerful figure known to them. Validation of sociocultural and religious experiences is important. The greater degree of hypervigilance and hypersensitivity in paranoid thinking may be functional or healthy vigilance when seen to a lesser degree in certain environments. For example, there is protective value in suspiciousness and guardedness when dealing with political terrorism, racism, or criminal activity.

Clients with delusion disorders and brief psychotic disorders usually have better premorbid functioning than clients with schizophrenia and may exhibit fewer stigmata of chronic illness. These clients do not have the same impairments in functioning as clients with schizophrenia. They may be better able to maintain their grooming and normal activities and show fewer signs of disorganized thinking and behavior. Clients with delusional disorders may have had symptoms, limited to delusions, for many years. The content of the delusion is usually less bizarre than that seen in clients with schizophrenia and is more likely to be an exaggeration of common experiences such as being jealous or being treated badly by others. Onset of a brief psychotic disorder is likely to be sudden, and the duration of symptoms often is less than 1 month and associated with known stressors.

Negative Symptoms
Affective flattening: Blunted or constricted facial expression
Anhedonia: Inability to experience pleasure
Avolition: Inability to initiate activity
Alogia: Decreased thought content and use of language
Attentional problems: Inability to organize goal-directed activities, process information, and filter stimuli

Negative Symptoms

Negative symptoms are responsible for the amount of morbidity present. The predominant negative symptoms are affective flattening, alogia, avolition, anhedonia, and attentional problems. Clients with affective flattening have facial expressions that appear immobile, masklike, and unresponsive, and they may maintain poor eye contact. Clients with **alogia** respond briefly, and their spontaneous speech is limited; thought content, reflected in the insufficient fluency and use of language, is decreased. Clients with avolition are unable to initiate and pursue goal-directed activities and may have problems engaging in activities and completing tasks. They may sit in one area and demonstrate little interest in their surroundings. Families may report that clients seem aloof from family conversations and activities. Clients with anhedonia experience an inability to find joy or satisfaction in usually enjoyable activities.

The effects of negative symptoms on client functioning are often a major concern of families. Most critical comments in EE families are made in response to negative symptoms. Clients are viewed as lazy or unmotivated.

Critical Thinking Question 

Do you think it would be easier to identify and deal with positive or negative symptoms? Suggest some nursing interventions that would be useful in dealing with both positive and negative symptoms.

Differential Diagnosis

Schizophrenia can be identified in terms of symptoms and duration and major types. It can be further specified as to its phases and prognostic features. Some other psychotic disorders have similar symptoms but may be related to a medical condition or substance disorder, to a cognitive disorder such as dementia, or to a mood disorder with psychotic features. In schizoid personality disorder and schizotypal personality disorder, there can be marked social and interpersonal impairment, cognitive distortions, and underachievement or behavior problems, but not the same persistence of psychotic symptoms that is found in schizophrenia. Clients with a paranoid disorder or a delusional disorder may have certain psychotic symptoms but not the syndrome of symptoms associated with schizophrenia.

Schizophrenia

Schizophrenia differs from the other psychotic disorders in the types and number of symptoms present and the duration of the illness. In a brief psychotic disorder, symptoms are present 1–30 days, and the onset of symptoms may be sudden. In schizophreniform disorder, symptoms last 1–6 months, and significant impairment of functioning is not required for diagnosis. In schizoaffective disorder, symptoms of a major depressive or bipolar disorder are concurrent with symptoms of schizophrenia such as delusions or hallucinations, withdrawal, and impairment of functioning. In delusional disorders, symptoms of false beliefs or delusions are prominent. In schizophrenia, positive and negative symptoms are present for at least 6 months.

Persecutory delusions involve beliefs of being harassed, spied on, or plotted against by an individual or group.

The major types of schizophrenia are paranoid, disorganized, catatonic, undifferentiated, and residual. The types are diagnosed based upon symptomatology during the evaluation phase and the predominant theme of the symptoms. A catatonic type is diagnosed when catatonic symptoms are present regardless of the presence of other symptoms. A disorganized type is diagnosed whenever disorganized speech and behavior and inappropriate affect are prominent. If the client is preoccupied with persecutory delusions, is overly suspicious and hypervigilant, or has hallucinations with a persecutory theme, a paranoid type is diagnosed. In an undifferentiated type, symptoms are not predominantly catatonic, paranoid, residual, or disorganized in nature. In residual type, the client has been diagnosed with schizophrenia but has no positive symptoms at the time of diagnosis. Clients may have negative symptoms and episodes of acute exacerbations interspersed with residual periods.

Paranoid Type

The onset of paranoid schizophrenia occurs later in life, and the prognosis is somewhat better than for other types. Clients usually remain independent and some are able to work. In an acute phase, delusions and hallucinations may be prominent. The delusions are usually persecutory, grandiose, or both, and they tend to be organized around a theme. Hallucinations usually complement the delusion. The client may be anxious, angry, aloof, and argumentative and may project a sense of superiority and intense or highly stylized emotions. The client may appear guarded and suspicious of others. The nurse needs to assess the delusional process, especially if the theme is one of persecution, which can lead to suicidal behaviors.

Table 16-1 Nursing Interventions for Clients with Impaired Social Interaction

Nursing Diagnosis	Nursing Interventions	Rationales
Impaired social interaction	Offer presence.	Aids in development of therapeutic relationship and development of trust. Shows acceptance of client.
	Provide opportunity for frequent, brief interactions.	Avoid overwhelming client. Decrease social isolation and withdrawal. Models social behaviors.
	Observe for situations that may increase client anxiety or agitation.	Identifying potentially problematic situations helps reduce situations that might cause the client to remove himself from the situation or to increase stress and cause decompensation. Developing stress management skills is important in client recovery and helping to prevent crisis.
	Identify coping skills and support systems.	Knowing what helps the client and maximizes self mastery is useful in treatment planning. Alternate coping mechanisms and links to services can be provided in skills and systems that are not adequate.
	Orient client to expectations for behavior and interaction.	Normalize routine and minimize eccentric behaviors or communication styles that can limit the client's acceptance by others. Provide feedback on interactions with others.
	Encourage participation in group activities as tolerated.	Involvement of client in nonthreatening structured activities will help develop positive perception of self-esteem and feelings of mastery. Skills in one area can be transferred to other situations. Provides opportunity for using social skills in nonthreatening settings.
	Model communication skills.	Teaches communication skills. Commenting on links between feelings and behavior and providing feedback to the client helps facilitate learning. Identifying both verbal and nonverbal communication skills assists in learning.
	Role play communication techniques.	Reduce anxiety by allowing practice of new skills or using skills in different situations. Gives the client an opportunity to rehearse social skills. Reinforces both verbal and nonverbal communication skills.
	Give positive reinforcement for appropriate interactions with others.	Positive feedback reinforces learning. Encourages participation in formal and informal social situations.

Clinical Example 

Peter was a 29-year-old man who had studied to be an accountant. After college, his family noticed that he became isolated and argumentative. He stopped going out with his friends and stopped maintaining personal hygiene. After working for 2 years, he suddenly quit his job because he felt that everyone was picking on him and talking about him. He then was unable to hold any job for more than a few months because he had problems functioning, and eventually he stopped looking for work. He spent most of his time alone in his room at home and rarely participated in family activities. The client reported hearing three distinct voices that he was unable to identify. The voices kept telling him that he was no good and a loser and warned him that his food was being poisoned. The client was guarded and hypervigilant and would not eat food brought to him by others. He was suspicious of the hospital food and would eat only apples and oranges. This client demonstrated symptoms of thoughts of persecution, guarded behavior, hallucinations, and delusions.

Disorganized Type

The disorganized type is characterized by an early age of onset, usually around puberty, and more disintegration of personality. The essential features include incoherence, loose associations, and gross disorganization in behavior. The client's affect appears blunted or labile. This type has also been termed *hebephrenic*.

Clinical Example 

Carly is a 20-year-old woman whose family has noticed a steady decline in functioning over the past 2 years. The client was hospitalized briefly 2 years previously for a brief episode of hallucinations, quickly improved on medication, and seemed to be doing well. In the previous year she had taken classes part time in a community college. Her family noted that she was very quiet and seemed to be a loner. However, in the past month, she had become even more withdrawn and sat for long periods without doing anything and seemed oblivious to everything that was going on. The family became increasingly concerned when Carly stopped eating and became so withdrawn that she stopped talking. She seemed uncharacteristically stubborn to them because she refused to follow suggestions or directions. They had tried to get Carly to change her position by moving her chair, but Carly just positioned herself in her usual spot and sat for hours, resisting the family's attempts to move her. Carly had symptoms of withdrawal, mutism, negativism, and posturing.

Catatonic Type

Behavior swings of extreme withdrawal and extreme excitement are often seen in the catatonic type. In the withdrawal stage, the client exhibits stupor, muscular rigidity, mutism, blocking, negativism, and catalepsy. If the client exhibits rigid posturing, attempts to move him or her are met with resistance. The nurse must assess the client for malnutrition and exhaus-

Clinical Example 

Dan, a 17-year-old student, was brought to the emergency center by his family. The family reported that the client began to have problems after starting high school. At first he seemed to make a good adjustment, was popular, and received good grades, but then his appearance and behavior started to change. At first, the family thought he had gotten involved with the wrong crowd, but when they checked with the school counselor, they were told that their son was a loner and that his behavior was disruptive; Dan laughed and talked inappropriately in class. The counselor advised a psychiatric referral. The family was frustrated that no one, not even school authorities, was able to make Dan shape up. The family stated that Dan had become more eccentric in his dress and mannerisms and, over the last few months, had stopped going to school. When he began to neglect his personal hygiene and act more bizarre, they thought he was using drugs. However, no evidence of drug use was ever found, and Dan rarely left his room. His younger siblings were ashamed to bring friends home because Dan acted strangely, used bad language, masturbated in public, and talked about receiving messages from the television set. Neighbors called the police when they saw Dan acting suspiciously and walking up and down the driveway. The client was found picking through garbage cans and storing items in his clothing. His speech consisted of a string of unrelated words. He seemed to be speaking nonsense. This client exhibited grossly disorganized and bizarre behavior.

tion, because catalepsy can last for long periods. In the excitement stage, the client exhibits purposeless and impulsive behaviors that may range from mild agitation or erratic behavior to violence. The client also may exhibit echolalia (mimicking speech pattern or sounds) or echopraxia (mimicking the movements of others).

Delusional Disorder

In delusional disorder, delusion is the prominent symptom. The symptom is not the result of medical problems or substance abuse. The various types of delusional disorder describe the major theme of the delusions. Symptoms of a mood disturbance reflect a response to the delusions and are not related to a mood disorder.

Grandiose delusions involve an exaggerated false belief of self-worth in terms of power, fame, wealth, or influence.

Somatic delusions involve false or distorted impressions of the body image or physical functioning.

Jealous delusions involve false beliefs of betrayal or infidelity by a spouse or lover.

Grandiose Type

In the grandiose type of delusional disorder, clients believe that they have great insight or superior talent. Some clients believe they have made an important discovery or invention. Others may brag about a special relationship with an important person or about having special influence or powers. Some grandiose delusions have a religious aspect. Clients who believe that they have a special connection to a higher power become agitated when this is not recognized. It is important to determine if these beliefs are unusual or considered bizarre by others from the same background and culture.

Clinical Example 

Gary, a 35-year-old man, believes that he is Jesus Christ. He becomes irate when others do not recognize this. His family reports that this belief is not consistent with their religious beliefs. In fact, they report that neither they nor Gary were ever particularly religious or spiritual in their interests or pursuits. Gary feels that his family has a problem because they refuse to recognize him. He feels that his only problem is that he is too human at times. Gary has no symptoms of a mood disorder. Until recently, when he began to talk of quitting his job in order to focus on his mission, he had been functioning normally at work, confining his preaching to a chat room on the Internet and to his family. Gary meets the criteria for delusional disorder, grandiose type.

Clinical Example 

Jeffrey, a 36-year-old husband, accused his wife of cheating on him. There was no evidence that she was cheating. The accusatory behaviors had been present episodically throughout the course of their 10-year marriage. He recently became more suspicious when she lost weight after pregnancy. His wife reported that he was cold and withheld affection when he accused her of betraying him. Psychotic symptoms associated with schizophrenia were not present. Jeffrey did not exhibit symptoms of a mood disorder, and there were no indications of drug or alcohol abuse. There was no history of physical spousal abuse. Jeffrey met the criteria for delusional disorder, jealous type.

Persecutory Type

Clients with delusions of persecution believe that they are being persecuted by a person or group, and may even believe that someone is trying to poison or kill them. Some clients report being followed or harassed. Clients often respond to the persecutory delusions by harming themselves or others in order to protect themselves from the threat. The potential for self-harm or harm to others must be evaluated. Fear of being poisoned can cause clients to reject food and fluids, and their nutritional status should be monitored.

Medical Problems and Substance Abuse

Careful assessment is necessary to determine if the psychotic symptoms are the result of a medical illness, substance abuse, prescription drugs, drug interactions, or exposure to chemicals or toxins. Some medical problems associated with psychotic symptoms are anoxia, autoimmune diseases, encephalopathies, electrolyte imbalances, Huntington's disease, Parkinson's disease, neoplasms, porphyria, vasculitis, certain viral syndromes, and brain injuries. Substances of abuse (e.g., alcohol, amphetamines, cannabinoids, cocaine, hallucinogens, inhalants) and certain medications (e.g., anticholinergic agents, corticosteroids, digitalis, dopamine agonists) have been associated with psychosis.

Other Psychiatric Disorders

The clinician must determine if the behaviors can be better explained or understood as symptoms of a psychiatric disorder other than schizophrenia or a brief psychotic disorder. For example, clients with major depressive disorder or bipolar disorder may exhibit psychotic features. In certain instances, clients with borderline, paranoid, schizoid, or schizotypal personality disorder may display some psychotic symptoms. Some clients with factitious disorders feign psychiatric symptoms, although this is rare.

Clinical Example

Paula, a 50-year-old woman, called the police because she believed that someone was waiting outside to harm her. She had stayed up all night waiting to catch someone trying to break into her apartment, but each time she went to the door she found no one there. She reported that her landlord worked for the Federal Bureau of Investigation (FBI) and was monitoring her behaviors—together with the FBI, the landlord had arranged for new windows with special glass to be installed in the building. She resisted the landlord's attempts to install the new windows in her apartment. Because of this, she felt the landlord had enlisted the other tenants in a plot to trick her into leaving her apartment so the new "security" windows could be installed. Paula had no history of medical or psychiatric illness or drug or alcohol abuse. She met the criteria for delusional disorder, persecutory type.

Clinical Course and Complications

Since the onset of schizophrenia is usually at a young age, clients are faced with a lifetime of dealing with a chronic illness. The clinical course and client functioning may vary during the prodromal, acute, and residual phases of illness. There may be periods of acute exacerbations, maintenance, or remission. Clients with schizophrenia may have problems with symptoms, making a commitment to taking their medications, or dealing with side effects associated with their medications or medical problems.

Phases of Schizophrenia

The clinical course for schizophrenia may include prodromal, acute, and residual phases (APA, 2000). The prodromal phase may last for several months or years. In this period, functioning begins to deteriorate, and, usually, some negative signs of schizophrenia such as increasing social withdrawal and decline in usual activities begin to appear. Diagnostic criteria for schizophrenia require that substance abuse and mood disorder be excluded as causes of the changes in functioning. Symptoms may include decline in social interaction, role functioning, grooming, initiative, and interest in activity, as well as the presence of bizarre beliefs inconsistent with the client's cultural norms, blunted affect, mood problems, perceptual problems, and language problems. Problems with language and communication may include alogia and disorganized and irrelevant speech.

Schizophrenia is associated with prodromal, active, and residual phases. Not all clients experience all phases, and the phases can vary in duration and sequence.

Evidence-Based Practice

With a decrease in the emphasis on inpatient psychiatric hospitalization, particularly on the long-term hospitalization or institutionalization of clients with schizophrenia, along with advances in treatment of schizophrenia, research has shifted to consideration of the variables that influence psychopathology and disability and upon rehabilitation and quality of life. The presence of psychiatric symptoms and decreased social functioning have a major impact upon quality-of-life measures (Galuppi, Turola, Nanni, Mazzoni, & Grossi, 2010). A review of literature indicates that the presence of positive and negative symptoms significantly influences negative perception of quality of life in outpatient settings and the presence of general psychopathology symptoms influences negative perception of quality of life across all settings. Objective indications of neurocognitive deficits such as verbal ability, working memory, processing speed, and executive functioning impair functioning in the community. Improving neurocognitive functioning could improve general functioning in the community (Eack & Newhill, 2007). Studies also indicate that clients with chronic mental illness in supportive employment are more successful in consistently working and wage earning if the program includes cognitive training (McGurk, Mueserk, Feldman, Wolfe, & Ascars, 2007).

CASE STUDIES Mr. D.

Mr. D. is a 42-year-old man brought to the emergency department after he caused a disturbance at a local fast-food restaurant, verbally threatening other patrons and accusing the restaurant staff of poisoning his food. He told the ED staff that his corpus was illegally manslaughtered and that the staff at the restaurant had planted radioactive computer transmitters in his liver in order to watch him and track his movements. He resisted physical examination in the ED because he said his religion prohibited animal testing and that his right for freedom of assemblies was being violated. Mr. D. reported auditory hallucinations telling him to escape or to die that were disturbing and frightening to him.

Mr. D.'s family reported that he had not been taking his medication for several weeks and that his behavior had begun to change over that time period. He seemed depressed, began spending less time at home, had not been eating or sleeping regularly, and had missed several outpatient appointments. During that period he seemed to be more agitated and disorganized, talking to himself and behaving in an erratic manner. He had stopped going to a volunteer job he had visiting animals at a local animal clinic and to a day program he usually attended 3 days a week. They reported Mr. D. had a history of several inpatient psychiatric hospitalizations since his early 20s. He had functioned well until then, graduated college as a science major and began veterinary studies. He had always been quiet and studious, but had become more withdrawn and accusatory towards his family and teachers, isolating himself from others because he believed there was a plot to take over his mind and insert thoughts into his head. After leaving school, he had several brief periods of employment as a veterinary assistant and later as a dog groomer, but he had difficulty getting along with others. He began to feel that animals and people were communicating to him through the radio and television. His family reported that Mr. D. had appointed a healthcare proxy to be notified if he is evaluated for the use of restraints and that, at times in the past, he has voluntarily asked to be placed in restraints. They report that he has had several suicide attempts in the past, usually in response to the voices, or when frightened and threatened.

Mr. D. has a history of serious persistent mental illness beginning in his early 20s with a downward drift, a decrease in his social and occupational functioning that shows he is not functioning at a level that would be expected of a college graduate. He has a history of both positive and negative symptoms and appears to have an acute exacerbation of chronic paranoid schizophrenia. It would be important to validate Mr. D.'s current medication regimen with his primary provider and family if Mr. D. were not able to give this information, as well as to find out which medications have worked in the past and which have not. Mr. D. does not have an advance healthcare directive regarding restraints, but has indicated that his healthcare proxy should be called if he needs to be placed in restraints if he has not voluntarily requested this intervention.

The client may be easily agitated, assaultive, or violent if delusions or command-type hallucinations are acted upon and may be a danger to himself and others in the environment. There is a history of suicide attempts, indicating risk factors for loss of control, violence, and suicide. The patient's impulse control and judgment are impaired; responses are based on the impaired perceptions and distorted reality of the paranoid thoughts and hallucinations he is experiencing. The client may request to be placed in restraints or have an advance healthcare directive that has been discussed with staff. The client's healthcare proxy or other identified significant other should be notified as requested. In any case, patient safety is a priority, especially in emergency situations, and may be initiated by staff in certain circumstances. Mechanical or chemical restraints may be used if the client is unable to respond to environmental controls of milieu therapy and verbal communication and deescalation techniques initiated by staff or a show of force by staff.

If mechanical restraints are used, it is important to be aware of the Joint Commission's and the hospital's policies and procedures. The client needs to be evaluated by an independent licensed practitioner (this may vary from state to state and includes doctors and nurse practitioners) and monitored while in restraints. The client should be observed on a regular basis, removed from restraints on a regular basis, and, as agitation and risk for violence decrease, evaluated for removal from restraints. Careful documentation of restraint and seclusion use is required. The client also needs to be carefully evaluated for medications because medications are considered chemical restraints.

Nursing Care Plan **Schizophrenia**

Nursing Diagnosis 1: Threat of violence to self or others related to inaccurate interpretation of environment as evidenced by thoughts he is being poisoned, accusations towards others, verbal threats, and disturbed behavior.

Nursing Diagnosis 2: Disturbed thought process related to fixed false beliefs, problems thinking and expressing ideas clearly as evidenced by distorted verbal communication and concerns regarding poisoning of food, computer transmitters, and auditory hallucinations telling him to "escape or die."

Nursing Diagnosis 3: Social isolation related to unaccepted social behavior as evidenced by hostility, agitation, disruptive behavior, poor communication skills, and decreased level of social and occupational functioning.

Expected Outcomes	Interventions	Evaluations
• Will be safe.	• Monitor environment and patient behavior for signs of restlessness or agitation, verbal statements regarding suicidal ideation or threats to others, or disturbed sensory perception.	• Absence of threats to safety of self and others.
• Will be compliant with medications.	• Administer medications as prescribed and monitor patient response to medications as well as possible side effects.	• Takes medication as prescribed, verbalizes recognition of need for medication, and becomes involved in medication group on unit.
• Will reduce restless, agitated behavior.	• Maintain structured environment, reduce environmental stimuli as needed, provide regular contact and access to staff, and encourage patient to approach staff, especially when feeling threatened or disturbed.	• Demonstrates an ability to interact appropriately with others in environment; shows appropriate verbal communication and coping skills.
• Will decrease hallucinations.	• Provide opportunity for reality testing and identification of situations that are perceived as threatening, focus on present here and now, and teach self-management techniques such as distraction and cognitive-behavioral skills.	• Increased ability to participate in unit activities and therapeutic groups. Reality testing encourages client to modify assumptions regarding the hallucinations and change responses.

Visit http://go.jblearning.com/mentalhealth for additional care plans and exercises.

In the active phase of the disorder, the client experiences psychotic symptoms for at least 1 month (less if the client has undergone active treatment that has affected symptoms). Catatonic behavior, delusions, and hallucinations are present.

The residual phase follows the active phase and resembles the prodromal stage in that symptoms may be present but to a lesser degree than in the active phase. At least a year after the active phase, the course of the illness may be further specified. The course of illness may include acute exacerbations of active-phase symptoms along with episodes of residual symptoms, or there may be episodes of acute illness without episodes of residual symptoms. The course of illness may be continuous with prominent positive symptoms throughout; negative symptoms may or may not be present. A course of illness may include prominent negative symptoms during the residual period.

All clients with psychotic symptoms should be assessed for risk of suicide. Suicide attempts by clients with schizophrenia have a high rate of mortality.

Complications

Suicide

Because of the severity of the symptoms and the chronicity associated with schizophrenia, the debilitating effects of the disorder and decline in functioning are probably the main complications. In addition, specific symptoms such as hallucinations and delusions or associated features of a mood disorder can increase the client's risk for suicide. The incidence of suicide is higher in clients with schizophrenia than in the general population and higher still when combined with rates for accidental or non-suicide poisonings. It is estimated that the life time risk is up to 40% when reviewing suicide and unnatural deaths. Risk is greater for clients with other illness factors such as depression, active psychiatric symptoms, a history of suicide, or comorbid medical problems (Bushe, Taylor & Haukka 2010). Clients who describe command-type hallucinations directing them to kill themselves or engage in risky activities and clients with guilt feelings or symptoms of a mood disorder are at greatest risk for acting on suicidal ideation.

Critical Thinking Question

Loss of control can be frightening for the client and to other people in the environment. How can staff assist clients to deal with these feelings and explain what steps will be taken to help them remain in control?

Chronic Fluid Imbalance

Polydipsia can lead to confusion, restlessness, nausea, vomiting, and psychosis. The term *psychogenic polydipsia* emphasizes possible psychologic factors, but regulatory imbalances and physiologic effects are prominent in chronic fluid imbalance.

Clients with chronic symptoms of schizophrenia also have a higher incidence, approximately 10%, of fluid dysregulation, known as water intoxication or chronic fluid imbalance. Psychogenic **polydipsia** should be considered if the client has a history of water intoxication or has seizures or hyponatremia-induced confusion. Any assessment should include an evaluation for any common medical causes for fluid imbalance such as diabetes, electrolyte imbalance, thyroid disorder, Cushing's syndrome, shock and CHF, or use of alcohol or certain drugs. Heavy tobacco use in schizophrenics may also be related to development of hyponatremia. Use of other medications such as carbamazepine and SSRIs can also induce hyponatremia and should be stopped. Fluid dysregulation develops in a three-stage process: (1) episodic polydipsia associated with polyuria; (2) water intoxication associated with daytime polydipsia, afternoon hyponatremia, and nocturnal diuresis; and (3) a long-term stage of physiologic complications of hyponatremia (osteoporosis, cardiac failure, brain damage). Clients with fluid dysregulation exhibit repetitive, sometimes compulsive, fluid-seeking behaviors. An estimated 70–80% of clients with this syndrome are chronic schizophrenics. Behavioral techniques, environmental controls, and psychoeducation have been helpful. Demeclocycline (Declomycin) and clozapine (Clozaril) have also been used (Valente & Fisher, 2011).

Evidence-Based Practice

Reynolds, Schmid, & Broome (2004) examined the use of a screening tool in identifying patients at risk for hyponatremia and fluid imbalance. The screening tool ranks clients as to risk—none, low, moderate, or high—based on certain symptoms or behaviors such as smoking, carrying large cups of fluids, drinking from unconventional places (e.g., a toilet bowl), incontinence, hypothermia, and increased sweating. The initial research validated use of the screening tool and predictive value. Further research is needed to determine its effectiveness in multiple settings and the benefits of staff training in screening techniques.

Management and Treatment

Goals of psychiatric case management include assessing the client's strengths and symptoms; establishing a trusting relationship with the client; monitoring symptoms; intervening early; educating the client, family, and community; engaging the client in treatment planning; facilitating client adherence to the treatment regimen; coordinating medical and psychiatric follow-up; minimizing inpatient hospitalization; and maximizing the client's functioning and positive perception of quality of life. Emphasis upon a **recovery model** of treatment includes a focus upon the client's perceptions, goals and self-direction; strengths based with an emphasis upon self-care, mutual respect, and responsibility; peer support; consumer empowerment; respect and social acceptance; and the instillation of hope. For a client, recovery involves the ability "to live a meaningful life in communities of his or her choice while striving to achieve full human potential or 'personhood'" (Bellack, 2006).

Management and treatment of psychotic disorders involves identification and treatment of problematic symptoms and helping the client and the client's family deal with the illness, symptoms, and treatments. The various diagnoses may overlap, so treatment focuses on problematic symptoms. Chronic problems can be managed in partial hospitalization programs, continuing day treatment, rehabilitation programs, and ambulatory settings. Research indicates that a therapeutic relationship can influence improvement in the client's overall functioning (Lysaker, Davis, Buck, Outcalt, & Ringer, 2011). Clients with serious, persistent mental illness may benefit from ongoing psychiatric case management and community support services.

Clients, family members, and others in the client's environment can be taught to identify symptoms and to recognize when intervention is needed. In addition, family support is often needed to assist or supervise the client in order to maintain involvement in self-care activities such as hygiene and health maintenance, social activities with the family or in the community, and adherence with medication regimens. Clients with schizophrenia, as with other chronic syndromes, are often susceptible to relapse if their medications are discontinued abruptly or without supervision. Studies indicate that an alliance between the healthcare professional, the client, and the family or caregiver is important in facilitating adherence to a medication regimen. Factors identified in supporting medication adherence behaviors were the availability of support, information, and involvement, the efficacy of medication, positive medication attitudes and expectations, and minimization of the social aspects of extrapyramidal and other side effects (Kikkert et al., 2006).

Stressful life events can be particularly difficult to navigate with a limited social network without family support. Family members can help facilitate the client's communication with members of the treatment team or act as healthcare proxy when the client is unable to communicate. Family involvement and willingness to participate in psychoeducation programs, opportunities for development of problem solving and communication techniques, and the need for support for family members should be included in assessment and treatment planning (Dixon, Adams, & Luksted, 2000).

Hospitalization may be necessary during an acute phase or when the client presents a danger to self or others. At the time of initial admission or during an acute phase, the client needs a complete medical and psychiatric workup. This helps diagnosis and treatment, particularly if the psychotic symptoms are related to a medical problem or to substance abuse. It is important that the nurse carefully obtain a history, document any subjective complaints or objective findings, and assess the client's potential for self-harm and aggressive behaviors, particularly during the acute phase. Assessing and documenting the effects of pharmacotherapy assist the prescribing healthcare provider in deciding to change, increase, or decrease medications and facilitate client compliance with a more successful treatment regimen. Family and friends can help validate the client's experiences or identify stressors or problems. They can often provide vital information on how the client usually deals with stress or conflicts and what is helpful for the client to maintain control.

In an inpatient unit, the nurse is responsible for maintaining a therapeutic milieu and identifying when the environment or social interactions become overstimulating or overdemanding. Limit setting may be necessary if the client's behaviors become disruptive, provocative, or threatening to others. Eventually, the clients are helped to identify potential stressors and to modify their reactions to stressful situations. Inclusion of the client in treatment planning, learning about medication and self-management techniques, and identification of support systems and coping skills are important parts of rehabilitation that may begin in the inpatient setting but continue on an outpatient basis. The prevention of relapse is one part of rehabilitation. The client's sense of recovery also includes the ongoing development of a sense of purpose and restoration of one's life, establishment of goals, and progress in accomplishing activities and social relationships and interactions (Mueserk & Gingerich, 2006). Nurses are also involved in outpatient treatment settings, recovery and rehabilitation programs, and community treatment teams. The PORT (Patient Outcome Research Team) studies emphasize the need for education regarding illness, crisis, support, and employment for both clients and families.

Clients with severe, persistent mental illness who have had difficulty adhering to treatment plans or who have had a history of frequent decompensations or hospitalizations may be referred to **assertive community treatment (ACT)** teams or intensive case management services that are able to provide local follow-up by a multidisciplinary team. The purpose of the ACT team is to provide individualized and intense follow-up for client education, medication management, goal setting, and development of family and community support systems. The aim of the ACT team is to support the development of independence and recovery in dealing with chronic illness. Research suggests that a combination of this

Considerations for Client and Family Education

- Assist client and family in identifying possible stressors and signs of decompensation.
- Teach problem solving and stress-management skills.
- Identify client strengths and appropriate strategies for managing symptoms.
- Provide information regarding medications and possible side effects.
- Reinforce the need for ongoing support in dealing with a chronic illness.
- Assist client and family in developing a crisis plan to deal with periods of decompensation.
- Involve client, family, and caretakers in treatment planning and goal setting.

intensive case management approach, along with a recovery-based focus (Salvers & Tsemberis, 2007), or having a consumer provider on the ACT team (Wright-Berryman, McGuire, & Sayers, 2011) might be the most effective way to engage clients and provide a recovery-oriented approach.

Evidence-Based Practice

VanMeijel, van der Gaag, Kahn, & Grypdonck (2003) described a randomized trial of an interventional protocol based on review of the literature and consensus guidelines that utilized nurses and the clients' social network to prevent rehospitalization. Clients with chronic schizophrenia and delusional disorders were monitored on a regular basis for signs of decompensation. An action plan that provided 24-hour availability of professional assistance, medication, and stress reduction techniques was instituted. The program was deemed to be successful in providing psychoeducation for the client and the social network and in preventing rehospitalization. Further research is needed to monitor the interventional trajectory and determine the application within nursing practice.

Evidence-Based Practice

Dearing (2004) identified aspects of the nurse–client relationship that influence compliance including establishing rapport, exploring skill development, setting and achieving goals, planning strategies and instilling hope, and approving and reinforcing changes. By providing validation for the nursing process and nurse–client relationship, this study shows it is an important factor in improving treatment compliance. Further study is needed regarding the effects of the nursing assessment and therapeutic relationship and their impact on healthcare delivery and outcomes.

Managing Clients With Hallucinations

The nurse must observe for signs that the client may be responding to the internal stimuli of hallucinations. Is the client talking to him- or herself or laughing? Does the client appear preoccupied during social interactions and unable to attend to the demands of the external environment? The nurse should investigate the underlying experience of the hallucination and help the client verbalize his or her anxiety. Early intervention is important to prevent aggressive outbursts or harm to self or others that may be the response to command hallucinations. The clinician should avoid touching the client and allow sufficient personal space and distance so that the client does not misinterpret the clinician's approach; the client may be paranoid and extremely sensitive to perceived threats and environmental stimuli.

The nurse must express acceptance and remain nonjudgmental. This allows the client to establish trust and to share the experience of the hallucination. As the client begins to talk about what is internally experienced, the nurse can assess the possibility of danger and injury to self and others. It is important not to reinforce the hallucination, and the nurse should refer to the hallucination as "voices" rather than as "he," "she," or "they." For example, the nurse may say, "The voices seem real to you, but I do not hear the same voices," rather than, "They told you to kill the president, but they are wrong." The nurse should reassure the client that, although the voices are frightening, they are not real. The client may begin to realize that the voices are not real and begin to identify the experience of the hallucination and distinguish it from reality. The nurse should try to distract the client from the hallucination by involving him or her in interpersonal activities and by using clear directives and explanations.

Many clients experience hallucinations when they are anxious. Decreasing environmental stimuli and helping the client associate how and when hallucinations are experienced and controlled allows the client to develop mastery over the symptoms. The nurse should help clients identify those situations in which the experience of hallucinations is triggered (e.g., when they are under stress or withdrawn) and teach techniques that reduce the likelihood of experiencing a hallucination, such as getting involved in activities or social interactions.

Managing Clients With Communication Problems

Communication problems can affect the client's ability to engage in social activities or maintain occupational functioning. The nurse can help the client with some of these problems. Validation is one technique often used. Using this technique, the nurse can ask the client for feedback to determine if his or her inferences are correct. For example, "When you say [this], do you mean [that]?" The client may use language in an idiosyncratic or in a symbolic or metaphorical manner. The nurse can give feedback on the communication process. For example, the nurse may say, "I do not understand what that means." This helps the client understand how he or she is being perceived and makes it clear that he or she is not understood. This technique helps the client to feel in control and encourages the client to help the nurse better understand what is being communicated.

Often, a client's disorganized or disruptive behavior is frightening. It is helpful to approach the client in a nonthreatening manner and explain how the behavior is perceived. The client may be unaware that the behavior is alienating others. It is important that the nurse conveys empathy when helping the client manage problematic behaviors. Statements such as, "That must be frightening," "That must have been confusing," or, "Could there be another explanation?" demonstrate concern and encourage interaction and explanation.

Managing Clients With Delusions

When treating clients with delusions, the nurse must remember that the content of the delusion relates to an underlying anxiety or fear. Many clients experience the world as unsafe and distrust their own experiences and others. The nurse needs to reassure clients that they are in a safe place. Overwhelmed by anxiety, a client may develop a false belief to explain what is experienced or to cope with what he or she is feeling. These beliefs function as a defense mechanism to protect the client from painful unconscious or subconscious feelings. The outward expression is usually the opposite of the internal experience. For example, a client frightened by paranoid thoughts may be seen as angry and aggressive by others. If the delusion is the result of an organic problem, the client can be reassured that the cognitive problems are related to a medical condition, medication, or substance abuse and that the problems in the thinking process are temporary and caused by biochemical changes.

The client's interactions with others or with the environment may be impaired because of the false beliefs. For example, if the client believes the food is poisoned, the nurse may have to arrange for food to be provided in individual, closed containers so that the client can maintain adequate nutrition. Careful observation may be necessary to determine if routines need to be changed or if the client is able to make valid, informed decisions regarding self-care activities.

It is not uncommon for the client to ask if the nurse believes what the client is saying. The nurse may respond by saying, "I believe these beliefs seem real to you and explain how you see things." Arguing about the belief provokes anger or defensiveness, and putting forth logical or rational explanations is not helpful. Avoid competitive situations. If the dynamic of the delusion is understood, the nurse can attempt to validate the client's experience and provide reality-based explanations while focusing on the emotions identified with these thoughts. If the underlying feelings are identified and the level of anxiety surrounding the situation is reduced, the client may begin to focus less on the content of the delusion. Some clients find stress reduction and relaxation techniques helpful. Behavioral and cognitive interventions help the client refocus thoughts or practice thought-stopping or thought-switching techniques. Distraction can also help the client refocus on another experience and thoughts.

Psychoeducation and Psychotherapy

The content of a delusion relates to an underlying anxiety or fear.

Psychoeducation and cognitive therapy have been helpful in assisting clients to gain mastery over problematic behaviors. Cognitive skills development begins in the inpatient unit and is continued during the various phases of outpatient rehabilitation, as tolerated by the client. Integrated psychologic therapy and social skills training (e.g., the Social and Independent Living Skills Series by the UCLA Clinical Research Center for Schizophrenia and Psychiatric Rehabilitation) have been identified as effective methods of helping clients deal with communication and social problems. In these structured programs, various exercises in social skills, role playing, problem solving, and task assignments are used to develop the practical skills clients need to facilitate independent functioning. Long-term follow-up indicates that skills in conversation and listening, medication, symptom management, and recreation can be generalized to other areas of psychosocial functioning. Social skills training includes opportunities for repetition, replication, and reinforcement of skills. Attention to information-processing deficits facilitates learning.

Research indicates that clients who participate in either psychoeducation or social skills training groups function better, and their relapse rates are greatly reduced (Lieberman, Derisi, & Mueser, 2001). Skills training and rehabilitation programs focusing upon wellness and recovery improve skills for independent living and increase positive perception of quality of life. Many clients with serious persistent mental illness have problems with forming and sustaining social interactions. Recovery programs emphasize development of social networks with peers, families, and community systems. Opportunities for learning about illness management, developing skills in verbal and nonverbal communication, formal and informal opportunities for socialization, and strategies for increasing support systems are part of the recovery process. Supportive vocational programs and employment opportunities are also important in developing skills (Mueserk & Gingerich, 2006). Social skills training and social competence are important in dealing with social withdrawal as well as the client's coping and communication skills. Improvement in coping skills helps the client manage stress and improve assertiveness and deescalation skills. Improvement in problem-solving skills and social-competence skills is important in decreasing social isolation and managing independent living and employment (Kopelowicz, Liberman, & Zarate, 2006).

Pharmacotherapy is the foundation for treatment of problematic symptoms in schizophrenia. Oral antipsychotic medications or neuroleptics, depot medications, and atypical antipsychotic medications are used to control symptoms of psychosis. Mood stabilizers and antidepressants may be used for specific affective symptoms.

Pharmacology

Pharmacotherapy plays a major role in treating and managing the symptoms of psychotic disorders. Medications have made a dramatic difference in the treatment of schizophrenia; they are particularly important in the acute phase. Because long-term use of some medications caused significant problems in the past, the client or the client's family may resist using medication to treat the disorder; however, the benefits of medications can outweigh any problems the client may experience in adhering to a medication regimen. The National Institute of Mental Health- (NIMH-) funded longitudinal study, CATIE (Clinical Antipsychotic Trials of Interventional Effectiveness), has provided information regarding drug efficacy, effectiveness, side effects, and discontinuation rates. Increased knowledge about drug dosage and side effects as well as new medications with decreased side effects have changed the ways in which medications are prescribed. Studies have also provided information regarding the high number of clients with symptoms of metabolic syndrome at baseline, indicating the need to emphasize the importance of monitoring clients for side effects. The high number of clients who discontinue medication (74%) highlights the importance of interventions to increase adherence to medication schedules (Lieberman et al., 2005).

Studies conducted as part of CUtLASS (Commentary on Cost Utility of the Latest Antipsychotic Drugs in Schizophrenia Study) suggest that the more recently developed atypical antipsychotic medications may be no more effective than the traditional antipsychotics medications in treatment of schizophrenia (Lieberman, 2006). Treatment needs to be individualized to recognize differences among clients who may be treatment resistant, susceptible to side effects, or have problems adhering to a particular medication regimen, particularly with long-term use.

Client education and medication groups can reinforce adherence. Medication groups are task-oriented groups that provide peer support, educate clients regarding medication use and side effects, and identify benefits and possible problems with adherence to treatment plans. Medication management is a module of the Social and Independent Living Skills Series (Bellack, Mueser, Gingerich, & Agresta, 2004; Liberman, Derisi, & Mueser, 2001).

Medications

Two main groups of medications—typical and atypical—are used to treat these disorders. Typical agents are the high-potency neuroleptics such as fluphenazine, haloperidol (Haldol), thiothixene (Navane), and trifluoperazine (Stelazine); moderate-potency neuroleptics such as molindone (Moban) and loxapine (Loxitane); and low-potency neuroleptics such as chlorpromazine (Thorazine) and thioridazine (Mellaril). These agents effectively block the dopamine reaction at the receptor site. The typical agents have been considered important in managing positive symptoms.

Atypical agents are the serotonergic-dopamine antagonists (SDAs). These agents, including risperidone (Risperdal), olanzapine (Zyprexa), quetiapine (Seroquel), and ziprasidone (Geodon), block specific serotonin and dopamine receptor sites. Because they are metabolized in the liver and excreted from the kidneys, careful monitoring of liver and renal functioning is important. Clozapine (Clozaril) and quetiapine showed the lowest reports of extrapyramidal symptoms (EPS). Olanzapine is available in oral and injectable form, but treated patients showed more weight gain and glucose intolerance. Of all the atypical antipsychotics medications, clozapine is the most effective in treatment-resistant patients, but also is the most associated with side effects. Atypical agents are used to treat both positive and negative symptoms. Some research has indicated that olanzapine may help manage mood symptoms associated with psychotic disorders. Aripiprazole (Abilify) is an atypical antipsychotic medication, available as an injectable and as an oral medication, that is a dual dopamine autoreceptor agonist and postsynaptic D_2 receptor antagonist used to control agitation and psychotic symptoms in schizophrenia. Paliperidone (Invega), an atypical antipsychotic that delivers an active agent in risperidone, is available as an extended-release tablet. Patients taking this medication, which passes slowly through the digestive tract, should be informed that they may see the capsules in their feces. An advantage to the extended-release tablet is that it need only be taken once a day and may minimize side effects.

Clozapine is not considered a first-line treatment. It may lower seizure threshold and, because it may cause agranulocytosis, it requires regular blood test monitoring. Dosage monitoring is required, particularly if treatment is stopped and restarted. Research indicates it can be effective for refractory treatment-resistant schizophrenia and is well tolerated in the sense that there is minimal association with EPS and akathisia. Clients whose positive symptoms or aggressive/violent symptoms do not respond to other medications should be evaluated for a trial with clozapine (Buchanan et al., 2010). Risperidone, olanzapine, quetiapine, and haloperidol have also been used in treatment-resistant schizophrenia. Quetiapine has the advantage of not being associated with EPS or increases in prolactin secretion. Hyperprolactinemia is associated with menstrual disturbances and galactorrhea in women and sexual dysfunction and hypergonadism in men.

Evidence-Based Practice

Mahone (2004) studied medication decision making in clients with serious mental illness. Utilizing the Interaction Model of Client Health Behavior (IMCHB) that emphasizes nurse-client interaction, Mahone identified motivational enhancement, behavioral tailoring, and social skills training as nursing interventions that facilitate medication decision making and management. This study has implications for practice, client teaching, and nursing education. Suggested areas for further research include investigation of medication adherence themes, client empowerment, and interventions to address comorbidities at different developmental levels.

Review of current research indicates that atypical antipsychotic medications may be beneficial as first-line treatment because they are effective in the treatment of positive symptoms as well as negative and affective symptoms. Side effects are a large problem, particularly in long-term treatment and adherence to treatment regimens, and atypical antipsychotic medications are less associated with side effects. Atypical antipsychotic medication such as risperidone is available in a long-acting injection, making it a viable treatment alternative for patients requiring a depot medication. Aripiprazole has been found effective with positive and negative symptoms and mood disorders (Emsley & Oosthuizen, 2005). PORT (Patient Outcomes Research Team) studies discussed in Chapter 5, "Neurobiologic Considerations in Psychiatric Care," have shown in longitudinal studies that both first- and second-generation antipsychotic medications have been helpful in dealing with positive symptoms. Clozapine (Clozaril) and olanzapine should still not be considered first-line treatment because of the associated risks of metabolic syndrome and other side effects. The study also suggested that there be further studies of the combination of antipsychotic medications and SSRIs for the treatment of schizophrenia (Buchanan et al., 2010).

Anticonvulsant medications such as carbamazepine (Tegretol), lamotrigine (Lamictal), and valproic acid (Depakote, Depakene) sometimes are used to stabilize behavior and mood symptoms. Drug levels and possible drug interactions should be monitored. Lithium is also a mood stabilizer, but it has been associated with renal dysfunction; thyroid and renal functioning and possible weight gain need to be monitored with lithium usage.

Selection of a medication is based on its type, action, duration, potential side effects, and the client's past experiences and preferences. For example, typical high-potency neuroleptics such as haloperidol (Haldol) may be selected for agitated clients because intramuscular injections begin to work within 60 minutes, and small doses can be given at frequent intervals to allow for dosage monitoring and titration; low-potency medications may require 3 to 4 hours to take effect. Studies of injectable atypical antipsychotic medications show they are somewhat as effective as typical neuroleptics, and patients reported fewer side effects, particularly EPS. Ziprasidone (Geodon) is available in injection form and has been effective when used in situations when rapid tranquilization is required and EPS and prolactin levels are a concern. Some of these medications are available in depot (haloperidol, fluphenazine, risperidone [Risperdal]) or sustained-action form, allowing the client to receive an injection every few weeks rather than receiving daily parenteral doses. Extended-release tablets such as paliperidone allow for once-a-day dosing and are helpful in maintaining a steady state distribution of medication and minimizing side effects. These types are particularly useful with clients who have problems adhering to medication schedules.

Pharmacokinetics can be influenced by a client's gender, age, medical illness, and use of tobacco, as well as by drug interactions. Changes in drug clearance vary according to tobacco use; tobacco causes increased clearance rates and faster elimination rates. Levels of thiothixene, fluphenazine (Prolixin), haloperidol, and olanzapine are influenced by tobacco use. Also, metabolism rates vary in the elderly, in different ethnic groups, and in clients who abuse alcohol. Studies indicate smoking and caffeine use are much higher among schizophrenics than among the general population, and there is strong interdependence for chronic use of both by chronic schizophrenics. Smoking and caffeine can affect CYP1A2 metabolism of psychotropic medications such as clozapine and olanzapine, and blood levels of the drugs may be reduced (Strassnig, Brar, & Ganguli, 2006).

Side Effects

Common side effects associated with neuroleptic medications are anticholinergic effects; autonomic instability including orthostatic hypotension and temperature dysregulation; blood dyscrasias; drug-induced Parkinson's disease; extrapyramidal effects; movement disorders such as acute dystonias, akathisia, and **tardive dyskinesia**; **neuroleptic malignant syndrome**; photosensitivity; sedative effects; and interactions with other medications. Some side effects that are common with typical antipsychotic medications include hyperprolactinemia, neuroleptic malignant syndrome, photosensitivity, QTc interval prolongation, temperature dysregulation, and weight gain. Other side effects such as abnormal glucose metabolism are more common with atypical antipsychotic medications. Agranulocytosis, myocarditis, seizures, and weight gain have been seen with clozapine.

Abnormal Glucose Metabolism

Abnormal glucose metabolism is a risk factor associated most commonly with atypical antipsychotic medications. Patients should be assessed for risk factors associated with diabetes such as family history, age, weight, hypertension, and hypertriglyceridemia. In addition, patients should be monitored for fasting blood glucose and lipid profile levels on a regular basis. Some medications such as olanzapine and clozapine are more associated with risk for metabolic problems than others.

Anticholinergic Side Effects

Anticholinergic side effects include dry mouth, constipation, and blurred vision. Clozapine has been associated with anticholinergic side effects. High-potency drugs such as haloperidol and fluphenazine have fewer anticholinergic side effects. Risperidone is not associated with anticholinergic side effects. Water, sugar-free candy, and alcohol-free and hydrating mouthwashes are sometimes helpful in dealing with dry mouth. Increased fluids and fiber help relieve constipation.

Blood Dyscrasias

Blood dyscrasias such as agranulocytosis, granulocytopenia, and leukopenia have been found in some clients taking antipsychotic medications. Clients taking clozapine in particular must have baseline and periodic blood and granulocyte counts.

Extrapyramidal Effects

Extrapyramidal effects have been associated more with antipsychotic and antiparkinsonian drugs. These include dystonias (**oculogyric crisis**, torticollis, **opisthotonus**), in which the client experiences muscle spasms, pseudoparkinsonism (shuffling gait, masklike faces, drooling, tremor, rigidity), akathisia (motor restlessness), and akinesia (weakness, fatigue, lack of movement). An acute dystonic reaction can be seen within hours of medication administration. Akathisia, an intense sensation of motor restlessness that can appear to be anxiety or agitation, is most associated with typical antipsychotic medications and can be seen within days of starting medication. It can be treated with anticholinergic agents, benzodiazepines, or sometimes beta-blockers such as propranolol (Inderal).

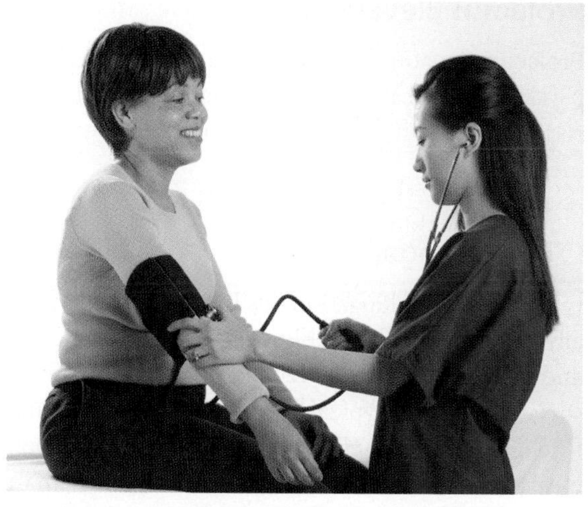

Figure 16-3 Differential blood pressure readings can help diagnose orthostatic hypotension.

Oculogyric crisis, a dystonia involving the eyes, results in an involuntary upward, lateral gaze.

Parkinsonian Symptoms

Drug-induced parkinsonian symptoms associated with typical antipsychotic medications, often seen weeks or months after starting medication, are characterized by muscle spasms and cramping of the neck, face, tongue, or back. Benztropine (Cogentin) or diphenhydramine (Benadryl) is used to reverse acute symptoms. To minimize risk of symptoms, benztropine is sometimes given prophylactically or continued on a regular basis if an acute episode has occurred. High-potency drugs such as haloperidol and fluphenazine are associated with extrapyramidal symptoms. Risperidone may be more associated with EPS than other atypical antipsychotic medications. However, low doses can often be well tolerated, and even atypical antipsychotic medications such as risperidone can be associated with dose-dependent EPS. Clozapine and quetiapine are considered to be less likely to cause EPS. Antiparkinsonian drugs such as trihexyphenidyl HCL (Artane) and benztropine mesylate (Cogentin) are commonly used to relieve EPS by blocking the action of acetylcholine. Antihistamines such as diphenhydramine are also used for EPS to suppress cholinergic activity. Tardive dyskinesia (involuntary ticlike movements, particularly of the tongue, lips, and jaw; dystonia; jerky movements of limbs) often begins after long-term use of typical neuroleptics and is considered irreversible.

Neuroleptic Malignant Syndrome

Neuroleptic malignant syndrome (NMS) is a life-threatening emergency. Symptoms include elevated creatinine phosphokinase levels, fever, diaphoresis, muscle rigidity (often called "lead pipe rigidity"), and autonomic instability. Management focuses on stopping the neuroleptic medication and treating symptoms through cooling, hydration, and prevention of emboli. Treatment with dantrolene (Dantrium) and bromocriptine (Parlodel) has been helpful. Benzodiazepines also have been used to treat symptoms. Some clients tolerate treatment with clozapine or risperidone; however, NMS has also been found with the use of these drugs and can manifest without the symptom of muscle rigidity.

Most movement disorders in schizophrenia are drug induced. Those disorders that start with new medication or dosage changes are often related to the dose or type of medication and are treatable. However, tardive dyskinesia, associated with chronic use of neuroleptics, is irreversible.

Orthostatic Hypotension

Orthostatic hypotension is a common side effect of some neuroleptics that block alpha-adrenergic receptors. Monitor blood pressure when the client is seated and after the client changes to a standing position (**Figure 16-3**). If symptoms are mild, the client can be instructed to change positions slowly, and fall precautions may be instituted. If the symptoms are severe, the client may need intravenous fluids for hypovolemia or treatment with an alpha-adrenergic agonist such as norepinephrine (Levophed) or metaraminol (Aramine).

Photosensitivity

Photosensitivity is a relatively common side effect of typical antipsychotic medications. Sunblock should be available, and clients should be taught to avoid prolonged exposure to strong sunlight.

Neuroleptic malignant syndrome is a life-threatening emergency.

Prolactin Elevations

Prolactin elevations are associated with typical antipsychotic medications and are more common with risperidone than with other atypical antipsychotic medications.

QTc Prolongation

QTc interval prolongation has been a concern usually associated with other known cardiac risk factors and is sometimes dose dependent. This risk is associated with the typical antipsychotic thioridazine (Mellaril). Some research indicates that ziprasidone may be more associated with this side effect than other neuroleptics are, and it is contraindicated in patients with known QTc prolongation (Emsley & Oosthuizen, 2005). Paliperidone should not be used by clients with congenital long QT syndrome or those taking other drugs known to prolong QTc.

Thermal Regulation

Thermal regulation is another problem of autonomic system instability. Clients may experience fever and decreased sweating, and they may collapse. Environmental conditions should be monitored. This is especially important in hospital units where windows cannot be opened or individual controls of heating and cooling are not available in the rooms. Fluids should be made available and clients warned of the symptoms of heat stroke. Active, restless, and agitated clients may not be aware of the need to cool down.

Weight Gain

Weight gain is associated with typical antipsychotic medications as well as atypical antipsychotic medications such as clozapine, olanzapine, quetiapine, and risperidone. Baseline and periodic measures of weight, waist circumference (35 inches in women and 40 inches in men), blood triglycerides, cholesterol and glucose levels, and blood pressure are monitored to establish risk for development of metabolic syndrome.

Summary

Schizophrenia, schizophreniform disorder, schizoaffective disorder, delusional disorder, brief psychotic episodes, and shared psychotic episodes are all syndromes with psychotic symptoms. Psychotic symptoms also may result from medical disorders such as neurologic, viral, and autoimmune diseases or exposures to toxins or may be directly related to substance abuse (e.g., the visual and tactile hallucinations associated with alcohol withdrawal). Psychotic symptoms include hallucinations, disorganized speech and behaviors, delusions, and social and occupational impairment. Positive symptoms include disorganized or bizarre behavior, delusions, hallucinations, and thought and language problems. Negative symptoms include blunted or flattened affect, alogia, avolition, anhedonia, and attention problems that decrease intellectual functioning and the ability to filter out stimuli.

Management of the psychotic client has progressed from isolation and imprisonment, insulin shock, and ice baths to rehabilitation and case management. Treatment of schizophrenia and other psychotic disorders focuses on management of problematic symptoms such as hallucinations, delusions, disorganized thinking, disruptive behaviors, depression, or anxiety. Clients with these disorders are at great risk for self-harm and suicide; clients who experience command-type hallucinations telling them to harm themselves or others are at greatest risk. Psychotherapy, psychoeducation, cognitive and behavioral therapies, social skills training, and rehabilitation have helped clients deal with these symptoms. Emphasis upon a recovery model recognizes the need for collaboration, mutual goal setting, and a recognition that the perspectives of the client, the healthcare providers, and the client's family or caretakers may differ but are not mutually exclusive.

Pharmacotherapy is often an essential part of treatment. In the past, negative symptoms often left the client unable to socialize or participate in activities. New medications that effectively treat negative symptoms have changed the outlook and lives of many clients. Some of the more common symptoms of schizophrenia such as catatonia are rarely seen now because of good pharmacologic management, but side effects of medication are still one of the main reasons for noncompliance.

The chronic course of many psychotic disorders with recurring symptoms, exacerbations of existing symptoms, and progressive decline in functioning is discouraging for the client and the client's family. Often, the client, family, and staff are very anxious when confronted with the symptoms experienced by the client. Clients and their families can learn to identify the prodromal symptoms of anxiety and depression and the psychotic symptoms that indicate decompensation or relapse. Early intervention and problem solving are helpful in dealing with chronic disorders. Due to the chronicity of schizophrenia, family support is essential for better treatment outcomes. Assistance and, when indicated, supervision by family members assists with the client's ability to adhere to treatment and medication regimens. As those closest to the client, family members are vital members of the treatment team.

Working with this population is well worth the challenge. One psychiatric nurse case manager working in the community with clients who had chronic schizophrenia stated that she admired her clients and was moved by their struggles as they sought in very noble ways to deal with difficult and debilitating disorders. Nurses must keep up with the rapid changes in theory and practice to ensure that quality care is being given.

Annotated References

American Medical Association. (2006). *International classification of diseases* (9th rev. ed.; Vols. 1, 2). Dover, DE: Author.
This is the code book for specifying diagnoses.

American Psychiatric Association. (2000). *Diagnostic and statistical manual of mental disorders* (4th ed., text rev.). Washington, DC: Author.
This is the fourth edition, text revision, of the American Psychiatric Association's official nomenclature of psychiatric conditions and disorders. It provides a systematic listing of the official codes and categories, a description of the multiaxial system for diagnosis, and diagnostic criteria for each of the disorders. It is used by psychiatrists, physicians, psychologists, registered nurses, social workers, therapists, and other mental health workers in all clinical settings.

Anonymous. (1986, March 18). "I feel I am trapped inside my head, banging against its walls, trying desperately to escape." *The New York Times*, p. C3.
A young woman with schizophrenia eloquently describes her personal experiences with schizophrenia in this article.

Bark, N. M. (1988). On the history of schizophrenia: Evidence of its existence before 1800. *New York State Journal of Medicine, 88*(7), 374–383.
This article discusses historical writings on mental illness that describe schizophrenia and related disorders.

Bellack, A. S. (2006). Scientific and consumer models of recovery in schizophrenia: Concordance, contrasts and implications. *Schizophrenia Bulletin, 32*(3), 432–442.
Changes in treatment of schizophrenia and the impact of consumer involvement have influenced the models for recovery in schizophrenia, ensuring that treatment is recovery oriented and that clients, families, and consumers are included in treatment planning.

Bellack, A. S., Mueser, K. T., Gingerich, S., & Agresta, J. (2004). *Social skills training for schizophrenia: A step-by-step guidebook* (2nd ed.). New York, NY: Guilford Press.
This book provides guidelines for social skills training.

Braff, D. L., Freedman, R., Schork, N. J., & Gottesman, I. I. (2007). Deconstructing schizophrenia: An overview of the use of endophenotypes in order to understand a complex disorder. *Schizophrenia Bulletin, 31*(1), 21–32.
This article is a discussion of approaches to genetic research in schizophrenia.

Buchanan R. W., Kreyenbuhl, J., Kelly, D. L., Boggs, D. L., Fischer, B. A., Himelhoch, S., . . . Keller, W. (2010). The 2009 Schizophrenia PORT psychopharmacology treatment recommendations & summary statements. *Schizophrenia Bulletin, 36*(1), 71–93.
This article is a review of the updated PORT study recommendations for medications.

Bushe, C. J., Taylor, M., & Haukka, J. (2010) Mortality in schizophrenia—a measurable clinical endpoint. *Journal of Psychopharmacology, 24*(11), (Suppl. 4), 17–25.
Review of 51 studies of mortality rates in schizophrenia indicate that clients with schizophrenia are at higher risk for suicide than the general population but rates for mortality may have begun to plateau due to improvements in medication.

Dearing, K. S. (2004). Getting it, together: How the nurse patient relationship influences compliance for patients with schizophrenia. *Archives of Psychiatric Nursing, 5*(8), 155–163.

In the days of doing more with less, this article reviews the basics of the therapeutic nurse–patient relationship and its relationship with patient compliance with treatment plans.

Dixon, L., Adams, C., & Lucksted, A. (2000). Update on family psychoeducation for schizophrenia. *Schizophrenia Bulletin, 26*(1), 5–20.
This article is a review of family intervention studies to determine evidence-based practice guidelines for family and client education.

Eack, S. M., & Newhill, C. E. (2007). Psychiatric symptoms and quality of life in schizophrenia: A meta-analysis. *Schizophrenia Bulletin, 33*(5), 1225–1237.
This article is a review of studies of schizophrenia and perceived quality of life.

Emsley, R., & Oosthuizen, P. (2005). Evidence-based pharmacotherapy of schizophrenia. In D. Stein, B. Lerer, & S. Stahl (Eds.), *Evidence-based psychopharmacology* (pp. 56–87). Cambridge, UK: Cambridge University Press.
This book reviews studies of pharmacotherapy in the treatment of schizophrenia.

Fatemi, S. E., & Folsom, T. D. (2009). The neurodevelopmental hypothesis of schizophrenia, revisited. *Schizophrenia Bulletin, 35*(3) 528–548.
Review of neurodevelopmental model of schizophrenia, genetics, congentital abnormalities, and environmental factors.

Galuppi, A., Turola, M. C., Nanni, M. G., Mazzoni, P., & Grossi, L. (2010). Schizophrenia and quality of life: How important are symptoms and functioning. *International Journal of Mental Health Systems, 4*(1), 31–39.
The authors surveyed outpatients with schizophrenia regarding perception of quality of life and level of functioning.

Henquet, C., DiForti, M., Morrison, P., Kuepper, R., & Murray, R. M. (2008). Gene-environment interplay between cannabis and psychosis. *Schizophrenia Bulletin, 34*(6), 1111–1121.
Discussion of use of marijuana and development of psychosis.

Ho, B., Black, D. W., & Andreasen, N. C. (2003). Schizophrenia and other psychotic disorders. In R. E. Hales, S. C. Yudofsky, & J. E. Talbot (Eds.), *The American Psychiatric Press Textbook of Psychiatry* (4th ed., pp. 379–438). Arlington, VA: American Psychiatric Press.
This chapter discusses schizophrenia and other psychotic disorders.

Kikkert, J. J., Schene, A. H., Koeter, J. W. J., Robson, D., Born, A., Helm, H., . . . Gray, R. J. (2006). Medication adherence in schizophrenia: Exploring patients, careers, and professionals' views. *Schizophrenia Bulletin, 32*(4), 786–794.
Problems with adherence behaviors to medication in patients with schizophrenia can be positively influenced by development of a therapeutic relationship among providers, clients, and their families or caregivers.

Kopelowicz, A., Liberman, R. P., & Zarate, R. (2006). Recent advances in social skills training for schizophrenia. *Schizophrenia Bulletin, 32*(1), (Suppl. 1), S12–S23.
This article discuses importance of social skills training in schizophrenia.

Lay, B., Nordt, C., & Rossler, W. (2007) Trends in psychiatric hospitalization of people with schizophrenia: a register-based investigation over the last three decades. *Schizophrenia Research, 97*(1), 68–78.
Study of trends in inpatient admission rates for clients with schizophrenia show a decrease in the proportion of clients with schizophrenia in in-patient settings over time related to changes in treatment and treatment settings.

Lieberman, J. A. (2006). Comparative effectiveness of antipsychotic drugs: A commentary on cost utility of the latest antipsychotic drugs in schizophrenia study (CUtLASS 1) and clinical antipsychotic trials of intervention effectiveness (CATIE). *Archives of General Psychiatry, 63*(10), 1069–1072.
This article discusses the cost and effectiveness of antipsychotic medications.

Liberman, R. P., Derisi, W., & Mueser, K. T. (2001). *Social and independent living skills: Social skills training for psychiatric patients (psychology practice guidelines)*. Boston, MA: Allyn & Bacon.
This is a manual for social skills training geared for client education.

Lieberman, J. L., Stroup, T. S., McEvoy, J. P., Swartz, M. S., Rosenheck, R. A., . . . Hsiao, J. K. (2005). Effectiveness of antipsychotic drugs in patients with chronic schizophrenia. *New England Journal of Medicine, 353*, 1209–1223.

This article discusses the effectiveness of various neuroleptics and atypical antipsychotic medications in phase I of the CATIE.

Lopez, A. D., Mathers, C. D., Ezzati, D. T., & Murray, C. J. L. (2006). *Global burden of disease and risk factors*. New York, NY: Oxford University Press.

This book provides an assessment of trends and risks for disability and mortality by demographics for many diseases.

Lysaker, P., Davis, L., Buck, K., Outcalt, S., & Ringer, J. (2011). Negative symptoms and poor insight as predictors of similarity between client and therapist ratings of therapeutic alliance in cognitive behavior therapy for patients with schizophrenia. *The Journal of Nervous and Mental Disorders, 199*(3), 191–195.

This study discusses client and therapist ratings of therapeutic alliance. Development of a good working relationship is the basis for the therapeutic relationship and those clients with a stronger alliance have better outcomes.

Mahone, I. H. (2004). Medication decision-making by persons with serious mental illness. *Archives of Psychiatric Nursing, 18*(4), 126–143.

This article provides an examination of client motivation as it relates to participation in the nurse–patient interaction and its relation to medication adherence and patient satisfaction.

McGrath, J., Saha, S., Chant, D., & Welham J. (2008). Schizophrenia: A concise overview of incidence, prevalence and mortality. *Epidemiologic Reviews, 30*(1), 67–76.

An overview of reviews of epidemiologic studies of schizophrenia shows an increase risk based upon gender, migratory and economic status, and conditions surrounding birth and health.

McGurk, S. R., Mueserk, T., Feldman, K., Wolfe, R., & Ascars, A. (2007). Cognitive training for supportive employment: 2–3 year outcomes of a randomized control trial. *American Journal of Psychiatry, 164*(3), 434–441.

A study of clients in a supportive employment program showed that combining cognitive training with supportive employment increased client ability to be more successful in working and wage earning.

Meltzer, H. Y. (2001). Treatment of suicidality in schizophrenia. *Annals of the New York Academy of Science, 932*(1), 44–60.

This article reviews some of the risk factors for suicidality in schizophrenia, such as a history of past suicide attempts, depression and hopelessness, substance abuse and male gender, as well as the effects of insight and the degree of cognitive impairment.

Mueserk, T., & Gingerich, S. (2006). *The complete family guide to schizophrenia*. New York, NY: Guilford Press.

This book is an information guide for families. It includes information on illness education, crises management, relapse prevention, and stress management.

Reynolds, S. A., Schmid, M. W., & Broome, M. E. (2004). Polydipsia screening tool. *Archives of Psychiatric Nursing, 18*(2), 49–59.

The authors developed a 17-item screening tool for polydipsia and attempted to verify internal consistency, validity, and predictive value of the instrument.

Salvers, M. D., & Tsemberis, S. (2007). ACT and recovery: Integrating evidence-based practice and recovery orientation on assertive community treatment teams. *Community Mental Health Journal, 43*(6), 619–641.

A comparison of ACT teams with high and low recovery orientation found that teams with high recovery orientation were more effective.

Strassnig, M., Brar, J. S., & Ganguli, R. (2006). Increased caffeine and nicotine consumption in community-dwelling patients with schizophrenia. *Schizophrenia Research, 86*(1–3), 269–275.

The authors sampled outpatients to assess dietary habits, food choices, and use of caffeine and nicotine in schizophrenics in order to determine the need for patient education regarding lifestyle choices.

Turkington, D., Dudley, R., Warman, D.M. & Beck, A.T. (2004) Cognitive behavioral therapy for schizophrenia: A review. *Journal of Psychiatric Practice, 10*(1), 5–16.

Reviews use of social skills training, cognitive remediation and family interventions for clients with schizophrenia.

Ustun, T. B., & Sartorius, N. (2001). *Mental illness in general health care*. London, England: John Wiley.

Written in collaboration with the World Health Organization, these authors studied the impact of major mental illness on the public health and the economy and projected their impact across the globe. The information is useful for studies of statistical prevalence and the impact of mental disability.

Valente, S. & Fisher, D. (2010) Recognizing and managing psychogenic polydipsia in mental health. *The Journal for Nurse Practitioners, 6*(7), 546–550.
Reviews evidence-based screening, assessment, and management of polydipsia in clients with psychiatric disorders.

VanMeijel, B., van der Gaag, M., Kahn, R. S., & Grypdonck, M. H. F. (2003). Relapse prevention in patients with schizophrenia: The application of an intervention protocol in nursing practice. *Archives of Psychiatric Nursing, 4*(8), 165–172.
The authors studied psychiatric nurses using an interventional protocol aimed at preventing rehospitalization of chronic psychiatric patients.

Whitford, T. J., Grieve, S. M., Farrow, F. D., Gomes, L., Brennan, J., Harris, A.W., . . . Williams, L.M. (2006). Progressive grey matter atrophy over the first 2–3 years of illness in first-episode schizophrenia: A tensor-based morphometry study. *NeuroImage, 32*(2), 511–519.
This study found progressive gray matter abnormalities present at time of diagnosis of the first psychotic symptoms and over the first few years of illness when comparing young schizophrenics and a control group. There are indications of the predictive value of MRI studies in identifying clients at risk for developing schizophrenia.

Wright-Berryman, J. L., McGuire, A. B., & Sayers, M. P. (2011). A review of consumer-provided services on assertive community treatment and intensive case management teams: Implications for future research and practice. *Journal of American Psychiatric Nurses Association, 17*(1), 37–44.
This article reports on a review of the literature regarding the use of consumer providers on an ACT team and the need for research to investigate integrating services.

Yolken, R. H., & Torrey, E. F. (2006). Infectious agents and gene–environmental interactions in the etiopathogenesis of schizophrenia. *Clinical Neuroscience Research, 6*(1–2), 97–109.
These authors attempted to show the role of infections and other environmental factors as well as genetic predisposition and the importance of susceptibility for development of schizophrenia.

Additional Resources

Bora, E., Yucel, M., & Pantelis, C. (2010). Cognitive impairment in schizophrenia and affective psychosis: Implications for DSM-V criteria and beyond. *Schizophrenia Bulletin, 36*(1), 36–42.
This article is a review of diagnostic criteria of schizophrenia and suggestions for inclusion of cognitive impairment as a criterion.

Canadian Psychiatric Association. (2005, November). Clinical practical guidelines: Treatment of schizophrenia. *The Canadian Journal of Psychiatry, 50*(13, Suppl. 1), 1–59.
This article provides treatment guidelines for assessment, treatment at different stages of illness, and psychosocial interventions.

De Leon, J., Diaz, F. J., Afuilar, M. C., Jurado, D., & Gurpegui, M. (2006). Does smoking reduce akathisia? Testing a narrow version of the self-medication hypothesis. *Schizophrenia Research, 86*(1–3), 256–268.
This study attempted to find a relationship between self-medication with smoking and schizophrenia because many patients describe smoking as relaxing and calming. Further study is needed to establish a linkage.

DeLisi, L. E. (2011). *100 questions & answers about schizophrenia: Painful minds.* Sudbury, MA: Jones & Bartlett Learning.
This book provides information for providers, families, and patients about schizophrenia and its treatment.

Kingdon, D. G., & Turkington, D. (2005). *Cognitive therapy of schizophrenia: Guides to individualized evidence-based treatment.* New York, NY: The Guilford Press.
This book describes treatment techniques suitable for schizophrenia and other psychotic disorders.

Levinson, D. F., Mahtani, M., Nancarrow, D. J., Brown, D. M., Kruglyak, L., Kirby, A., . . . Mowy, B. (1998). Genome scan of schizophrenia. *The American Journal of Psychiatry, 155*(6), 741–750.
This article discusses the possible genetic etiology for schizophrenia. A genome-wide map of different markers found five significant regions but no single gene responsible for schizophrenia.

Substance Abuse and Mental Health Services Administration. (2009). *Illness management and recovery: How to use the evidence-based practices kits*. HHS Pub. No. SMA-09-4462. Rockville, MD: Center for Mental Health Services, Substance Abuse and Mental Health Services Administration, U.S. Department of Health and Human Services.
This publication provides a description of the recovery model and substance abuse. The model can be used for schizophrenia, and almost half of the patients with a diagnosis of schizophrenia have problems with alcohol or substance abuse.

Substance Abuse and Mental Health Services Administration. (2010). *Family psychoeducation evidence-based practices (EBP) kit*. HHS Pub. No. SMA09-4423. Rockville, MD: Center for Mental Health Services, Substance Abuse and Mental Health Services Administration, U.S. Department of Health and Human Services.
This publication provides useful information on the utilization of family psychoeducation.

Tamminga, C. A., & Sirovatap, J. (2010). *Deconstructing psychosis: Refining the research agenda for DSM-V*. Arlington, VA: American Psychiatric Association.
This article is a review of the literature on different aspects of psychotic symptoms and psychotic disorders.

Torrey, E. F. (2006). *Surviving schizophrenia: A manual for families, consumers and providers*. New York, NY: Collins.
This book provides a description of schizophrenia and its impact and information on coping with its effects.

Williams, C. L. (2008). *Therapeutic interactions in nursing* (2nd ed.). Sudbury, MA: Jones and Bartlett.
This book describes the therapeutic use of self and the nurse–patient relationship, giving examples of communication techniques.

Internet Resources

For a full suite of assignments and additional learning activities, use the access code located in the front of your book to visit this exclusive website: http://go.jblearning.com/mentalhealth. If you do not have an access code, you can obtain one at the site.

Learning Objectives

After reading this chapter, you will be able to:

- Describe the diagnostic criteria for mood disorders (unipolar and bipolar).
- Discuss the influence of mood disorders on a client's daily functioning.
- Identify nursing interventions to assist clients experiencing mood disorders.
- Review the major psychopharmacologic agents available to treat clients with mood disorders.
- Identify measures for suicide prevention and assessment of risk.
- Discuss the teaching issues for clients and their families and the available peer support services and referral resources.

Key Terms

Affect
Anhedonia
Bipolar
Cognitive behavioral therapy
Cyclothymic disorder
Deep brain stimulation (DBS)
Dysthymic disorder
Electroconvulsive therapy (ECT)
Euphoria
Euthymia
Flight of ideas
Hypersomnia
Hypomania
Insomnia
Melancholia
Mood
Postpartum depression
Rapid cycling
Repetitive transcranial magnetic stimulation (rTMS)
Ruminations
Serotonin syndrome
Treatment-resistant depression (TRD)
Unipolar
Vagus nerve stimulation (VNS)

Mood Disorders

Valerie N. Markley

http://go.jblearning.com/mentalhealth 

For a full suite of assignments and additional learning activities, use the access code located in the front of your book to visit this exclusive website: http://go.jblearning.com/mentalhealth. If you do not have an access code, you can obtain one at the site.

Introduction

This chapter focuses on both **unipolar** (major depressive) and **bipolar** disorders; discusses the diagnosis, treatment, and appropriate nursing interventions for each; and presents the assessment of risk and measures for the prevention of suicide associated with these disorders. Mood disorders include disorders ranging from major depression to bipolar disorder (see **Table 17-1**). These are separate and differ from the depression, sadness, and euphoria that are normal reactions to losses, disappointments, and joys experienced regularly in one's life. A term used to describe a normal **mood** experience is **euthymia.** It is distinct from dysthymia (a depressed mood) or euphoria (extreme happiness).

The severity of symptoms and length of time separate normal blues from diagnosable depression.

Table 17-1 Range of Mood Disorders

Bipolar disorders:
Bipolar I
Bipolar II
Cyclothymic disorder
Mood disorder due to general medical condition (manic features)
Substance-induced mood disorder (manic features)
Hypomanic disorders
Euthymic disorders:
Major depressive disorder
Dysthymic disorder
Mood disorder due to general medical condition (depressive features)
Substance-induced mood disorder (depressive features)
Unipolar disorders
Specifiers:
Describing the severity:
Mild
Moderate
Severe
With psychotic features
In remission
Describing features:
Chronic
Catatonic
Melancholic
Atypical
Postpartum onset
Describing course:
Seasonal pattern
Rapid cycling

Source: Adapted from the American Psychiatric Association. (2000). *Diagnostic and statistical manual of mental disorders* (4th ed., text rev.). Washington, DC: Author.

Even in ancient times there are recordings of people suffering from depression. The Old Testament speaks of King Saul's struggles with depression. He had David play the harp to soothe his troubled soul. Well-known figures from the worlds of politics, entertainment, the arts, and sports have acknowledged dealing with depression (e.g., Abraham Lincoln, Virginia Woolf, F. Scott Fitzgerald, Patty Duke, Vincent Van Gogh, Jane Pauley, Representative Patrick Kennedy, and Catherine Zeta-Jones; see **Figure 17-1**).

Mood disorders are categorized and coded on Axis I by the *Diagnostic and Statistical Manual of Mental Disorders*, fourth edition, text revision (*DSM-IV-TR*), as conditions in which the major feature is a disturbance in mood (American Psychiatric Association [APA], 2000). Mood disorders are separated into the depressive disorders (often termed *unipolar depression*), the bipolar disorders, and two disorders based on etiology—mood disorder due to a general medical condition and substance-induced mood disorder (APA, 2000). In addition, there are specifiers that denote the severity of the disorders (mild, moderate, severe, with psychotic features, in remission), describe features that add more specificity (chronic, catatonic, melancholic, atypical, postpar-

Figure 17-1 Well-known celebrities such as Catherine Zeta-Jones have had to deal with depression.

tum onset), and connote the course of the disorder (seasonal pattern, rapid cycling; see Table 17-1). In the proposed new structure for the DSM-5, it is proposed that mood disorders will become depressive disorders and the bipolar disorders will become a separate grouping. The disorders are being recognized as neurobiologicly dissimilar from each other, responding differently to certain types of medications (Gever, 2011).

Healthy, well-adjusted individuals in positive life circumstances can experience sad, difficult situations and losses of varying significance and are usually able to get through such situations. The severity of mood variations and the length of time they are experienced mark the major differences between what is generally considered normal sadness (blues) or depression and an actual mood disorder.

Loss, Grieving, and Depression

Grieving is an issue that can be considered either normal sadness or a mood disorder. Certainly with a significant loss, individuals may have symptoms similar to those that occur with major depressive disorder, but they should not have a marked impairment to their social or occupational functioning that continues beyond the fairly immediate time of the loss or experience active suicidal ideation. The *DSM-IV-TR* notes a period of 2 months for normal bereavement (APA, 2000). Many authorities refer to longer time periods, and some cultures mark the entire first year after a family member's or close significant other's death as an official time of mourning. Elisabeth Kübler-Ross (1997), one of the most noted authorities on the subject of death and dying, delineated five stages that the dying person and those close to that person can experience: (1) denial and isolation, (2) anger, (3) bargaining, (4) depression, and (5) acceptance. She emphasized that the time period spent in any stage varies with the individual, and that family members are likely to go through them at different times and in varying ways, often moving back and forth among the stages until the grieving is resolved.

People who have endured a significant loss need to be encouraged to talk about what has happened. They may repeat details over and over again. This is therapeutic and helps them to work through the normal process of grieving. Empathetic listening is one of the most therapeutic measures a nurse can utilize. It is beneficial to assist the person to go through this normal process, but no one can force an individual to move faster or to transition from one stage to another. While depression is not a willful choice, sometimes it can seem easier to remain in a state of depression rather than come to grips with the pain and agony of loss that is part of the work of grieving. Encouraging people to share what they have lost and what they are experiencing helps them to engage in the grief process and to accept that what is happening to them is normal under the circumstances. Most individuals can get through this time without the need for psychiatric assistance or antidepressants. Individuals who experience grieving that extends beyond this description may benefit from mental health services. Some individuals have a delayed grieving time, which is usually more difficult. Some get stuck in the depression stage and seem unable to progress further. When symptoms are severe, the period of grieving continues unabated, or social and occupational functioning are seriously affected, intervention is strongly indicated.

Feelings of sadness and depression are an integral part of grief, yet grief itself is not considered a disorder. The *DSM-IV-TR* considers the depression associated with bereavement a normal reaction to loss, provided it is does not last too long. Depression that lingers beyond what is expected could be a sign that the stress of grieving has triggered an episode of major depression. Studies have shown that the extreme stress associated with grief can trigger both medical illnesses, such as heart disease, cancer, and the common cold, and psychiatric disorders like depression and anxiety. There is no way to define a normal length of bereavement since it varies from person to person and culture to culture. According to the *DSM-IV-TR*, a diagnosis of major depressive disorder is generally not given unless symptoms have lasted beyond 2 months.

Distinguishing Grief From Major Depression

Grief has several symptoms in common with major depressive disorder, including sadness, insomnia, poor appetite, and weight loss. Where they differ is that grief tends to be trigger related. In other words, the grieving person may feel relatively better in certain situations, such as when friends and family and are around to provide support. But triggers, like anniversary dates or special holidays, can cause the feelings to resurface more strongly. Major depression, on the other hand, tends to be more pervasive, with the person rarely getting any relief from his or her

Some symptoms that are common in both grief and major depressive disorder include sadness, insomnia, poor appetite, and weight loss.

symptoms. An exception to this would be atypical depression, in which positive events can bring about an improvement in mood. A person with atypical depression, however, tends to exhibit symptoms that are the opposite of those commonly experienced with grief, such as sleeping excessively, eating more, and gaining weight.

The estimated cost of depression in the United States is more than $80 billion a year.

Major depressive disorder is the main cause of disability in the United States and leads to more days of disability than many other medical illnesses. It is a major public health problem and is costly to the client, families, communities, and employers.

WHO's Global Burden of Disease Report projects major depressive disorder will be the No. 1 cause of disability worldwide by 2020.

Stigma associated with mental illness is one of the major barriers to access of mental health services.

Other clues that one may be experiencing major depressive disorder include:

- Feelings of guilt not related to a loved one's death
- Thoughts of death other than feelings one would be better off dead or should have died with a deceased loved one
- Morbid preoccupation with worthlessness, and disturbed self-esteem which are hallmarks of depression and distinguish it from grief
- Sluggishness or hesitant and confused speech
- Prolonged and marked difficulty in carrying out the activities of day-to-day living
- Hallucinations other than thinking one hears the voice of or sees a deceased loved one

While grief can be extremely painful, there is generally no medical indication to treat it. Some exceptions, however, are:

- If grief-related anxiety is so severe that it interferes with daily life, antianxiety medication may be helpful.
- If the person is experiencing sleep problems, short-term use of prescription sleep aids may be helpful.
- If symptoms last longer than 2 months after the loss and the diagnostic criteria are met, the person may be suffering from major depressive disorder. In this case, antidepressants would be an appropriate therapy.

Intervening with persons experiencing normal grief involves extending oneself, listening intently, and helping the person to recognize and accept resources that are available. Encouraging people to share what they have lost and what they are experiencing helps them to engage in the grief process and to accept that what is happening to them is normal under the circumstances. For those who have had a family member involved in hospice care, there is organized help. Hospice workers make themselves available to assist close family and significant others as needed for a year or longer. When a person is identified as having indications of major depressive disorder, referral needs to be made for adequate mental health care. It can be highly beneficial if the nurse or healthcare provider can partner with a family member or someone close to the depressed individual to increase the likelihood of follow-up.

Major Depressive Disorder

Depression has a significant impact on our national prosperity and well-being (Depression and Bipolar Support Alliance [DBSA], 2006). The estimated cost of depression in the United States is more than $80 billion a year (Greenberg et al., 2003). Major depressive disorder is the main cause of disability in the United States and leads to more days of disability and lost days of work than many other medical illnesses (Druss, Rosenheck, & Sledge, 2000). "Unipolar major depression is the No.1 cause of disability in the Americas, and is projected to be the single leading cause of disability worldwide by 2020, according to WHO's Global Burden of Disease (GBD) report" (National Alliance for Research on Schizophrenia and Depression [NARSAD], 2002, p. 25). "Stigma surrounding mental illness is one of the major barriers to access of mental health services" (DBSA, 2006, p. 4). This problem is also compounded by the fact that many clients do not receive sustained relief following initial treatment and need encouragement to continue treatment for lasting success.

The nursing assessment should begin with a physical examination and thorough history. The client should be questioned about current mood, feelings, thoughts, and level of functioning. Changes in eating and sleep patterns must be noted. A weight gain or loss may be significant. Psychomotor retardation or agitation should be observed, not based solely on the subjective report. The nurse considers the length of the current depressive state and reports of similar episodes in the past. The presence of suicidal thoughts must be assessed and dealt with seriously. Observed behavior should be recorded as well. Family members and significant others may provide additional information that should be documented carefully.

Incidence and Prevalence

Major depressive disorder may occur at any time during the life cycle, but the average age of onset is in the mid-20s. The disorder is "1.5–2 times more common among first-degree biological relatives of persons with this disorder than among the general population" (APA, 2000, p. 373). The occurrence of unipolar disorder, a term used to describe depressive episodes with no occurrence of mania, is higher in women than in men. The lifetime risk for major depressive disorder as noted in the *DSM-IV-TR* varies from 10% to 25% for women and from 5% to 12% for men (APA, 2000). This gender differential becomes significant around the time of puberty. Kessler, Chiu, Demler, Merikanqas, and Walters (2005) reported that 9.5 percent of the U.S. population, 18 years and older in a given year, has a mood disorder.

Critical Thinking Question

What are some possible reasons why the incidence of depression is equal in genders before puberty, but higher in females after puberty?

Mood disorders tend to be cyclical and naturally remitting. The *DSM-IV-TR* (APA, 2000) identifies individuals with a major depressive disorder as having a 60% chance of experiencing a second episode. After a second episode, the risk for a third episode increases to 70%. Those who have had three episodes carry a 90% risk of having a fourth episode. This is strong impetus to support continuing with treatment. The severity of the initial episode appears to indicate the disorder's persistence. The presence of chronic medical illnesses also tends to be a risk factor for more persistent episodes (APA). The suicide rate is dangerously high for individuals with mood disorders. According to the *DSM-IV-TR*, the suicide rate for those with major depressive disorder is up to 15%.

Culture can affect the experience of depression and the way in which the symptoms are communicated or the seriousness of the symptoms is judged (APA, 2000). Some examples of cultural differences are:

- Latinos less often utilize mental health services and frequently present to practitioners with complaints of physical symptoms than mental health issues.
- African Americans more often depend on family and social support systems, church, and folk remedies for help with mental health concerns.
- Asians may delay seeking psychiatric help until symptoms are severe due to concern about stigmatization (Snyder & Matsuno, 2001).

Age and gender may also affect the ways in which depressive symptoms present. Children more often show somatic complaints, irritability, and social withdrawal, yet they are less likely to have delusions, excessive sleeping, and psychomotor retardation than are adolescents and adults. Before puberty and during adolescence, depressive symptoms are more likely to occur along with other mental disorders, including disruptive behavior disorders, attention-deficit disorders (ADD), and anxiety disorders. Adolescents may also experience depressive symptoms along with substance-related disorders and eating disorders. In older adults, cognitive features such as memory loss, disorientation, and distractibility may be particularly apparent, and the death rates are four times higher for individuals over 55 who have major depressive disorder (APA, 2000). Women are significantly more likely than men to experience depression sometime in their lives.

Culture can affect one's expression of the symptoms associated with mood disorders and one's receptivity to intervention and treatment.

Morbidity is higher for clients with severe mental illness than for those in the general population. Individuals with diabetes, myocardial infarction, cancer, and stroke have a 20–25% risk for developing major depression (APA, 2000; Forrester et al., 1992). Nurses can be instrumental with these clients in working to help them in their struggles with conditions such as obesity and hypertension and to "address lifestyle issues of poor nutrition, lack of exercise, and smoking" (Kennedy, Salsberry, Nickel, Hunt, & Chipps, 2005, p. 50). Integrated health care could greatly improve both the mental and physical health of these clients.

For poststroke clients, depression compounds the negative impact on functional recovery and involvement in social activities. In addition, depression increases the morbidity and mortality rates for these clients. Depression is often not recognized or diagnosed in these clients, so they often go without treatment. This lack of treatment adversely affects clients' ability to participate in rehabilitation, which diminishes the rehabilitation outcome (De Man-van Ginkel et al., 2010). Nurses have the knowledge and skills to assess and identify signs and symptoms of depression in these clients and to work with their healthcare team members to address the depression. In more severe cases, referral should be made to mental health professionals. In fact, symptoms of depression can be detected in clients in any population group. Therapeutic listening and the implementation of purposeful referrals are basic skills for all nurses in every healthcare setting, and it is incumbent upon nurses to recognize and intervene when they identify depression.

Genetic, biologic, and environmental factors play a significant role in the cause of depression.

Neurotransmission and neurogenesis both have an impact on the pathophysiology of mood disorders.

Etiology and Physiology

The causes of major depression have not been clearly determined. Research demonstrates that both biologic and psychosocial factors play a significant role, with a combination of factors (multiple causality) being likely. The vulnerability to depression seems to be inherited; both research and clinicians confirm significant family histories of depression. Causation may also be linked to elevated cortisol levels or to a depletion of monoamine neurotransmitters such as serotonin, norepinephrine, and dopamine. (See Chapter 5).

Every October in the United States, in order to identify individuals who are dealing with undiagnosed depression, a national screening day is held to educate and assess for depression. A screening tool is supplied by Mental Health America and has been expanded to include screening for manic depression or bipolar disorder. This is only a screening tool; it is not diagnostic. Depending upon how high an individual scores on the test, he or she should be referred to a mental health practitioner for further evaluation (www.depression-screening.org).

Neurobiologic and Genetic Theories

The pathophysiology of a major depressive episode involves a dysregulation of a number of neurotransmitter systems, including the serotonin, norepinephrine, dopamine, acetylcholine, and gamma-aminobutyric acid systems.

Even with the evolution of the Human Genome Project (Garlow & Nemeroff, 2005), scientists have not been able to identify specific genes or chromosomes that are responsible for vulnerability to the range of mood disorders. Two areas of focus have been the effects of neurotransmitters and their action in the nerve synapse, and neurogenesis, the development of new neuronal tissue. Garlow and Nemeroff have stated "despite 40 years of concerted research, the primary neurochemical pathology of major depression has not been identified" (p. 454). More information is steadily emerging on the interrelationship of the physical and emotional components of depression. According to Goldstein and Potter, "the neuroendocrine effects of stress and the neurotransmitter effects of depression are now recognized to interact in a tightly linked system that offers a homeostatic mechanism for responding to stress" (2004, pp. 21–22). Neurotransmitters play an important role in depression. However, it is important to guard against a one-dimensional interpretation of the part they play. (See Chapter 5.) No laboratory findings have been identified to be diagnostic for major depression (APA, 2000). Sleep electroencephalogram (EEG) abnormalities may occur in as high as 90% of clients hospitalized with major depression (APA, 2000). According to the APA,

Significant loss and major stress play a supporting role in the first episode of depression. Individuals with a major depressive disorder run a 60% chance of experiencing a second episode; after three episodes the risk increases to 90%.

> the pathophysiology of a major depressive episode may involve a dysregulation of a number of neurotransmitter systems, including the serotonin, norepinephrine, dopamine, acetylcholine, and gamma-aminobutyric acid systems. There is also evidence of alterations of several neuropeptides, including corticotrophin-releasing hormone. Functional brain imaging studies document alterations in cerebral blood flow and metabolism in some individuals, including increased blood flow in limbic and paralimbic regions and decreased blood flow in the lateral prefrontal cortex (2000, p. 353).

Clients with depression regularly experience disruptions in their circadian rhythms, including "a reduction in the circadian rhythm of serotonin, norepinephrine, thyroid-stimulating hormone (TSH), and melatonin" (Glod, 1998, p. 351). Changes in circadian rhythms can increase the risk for the onset of depression. These rhythms are responsible for the daily regulation of sleep–wake cycles (Keltner, Bostrom, & McGuinness, 2011) and affect body functions, including temperature, heart rate, and the secretion of hormones.

It has been noted that "family, twin, and to a lesser extent adoption studies all point towards a genetic influence on depressive disorder" (van Praag et al., p. 72). In addition to genes, chronic stress may be able to disturb monoaminergic functioning in the brain, producing a similar appearance to the way the brain looks in depression. There seems to be a strong interplay between genes and the environment in the causation of depression.

Psychosocial and Environmental Theories

Psychosocial and environmental theories attempt to explain how an individual's internal mental life, relationships with others, and life events contribute to depression. Interpersonal theory considers the ways in which a depressed person experiences and perceives loss. Psychodynamic theory addresses how individuals deal with developmental tasks and cope with stress. Important losses, such as the loss of a parent at a very young age, have been noted to increase one's risk for depression. Inadequate nurturing, extreme poverty, any significant change in health or life status, and other adverse conditions can also play a role and increase the risk for depression or another mood disorder.

Adverse life events, significant loss, or other major stressors often can be found to have occurred in the year prior to the onset of depression (van Praag, de Kloet, & van Os, 2004). This relationship seems to be more apparent in the first episode of depression and decreases to some extent with following relapses. It is sometimes hard to tell whether the event or the depression came first. Chronic stress is often cited as a risk factor for major depression. These events may not be sufficient to cause the depression but add to other risk factors, such as biologic ones. Some risk factors for depression include family history, a serious medical condition, a chronic disability, the lack of a support system, a history of abuse, trauma and/or stressful life events, early loss of a significant other, poverty, loss of employment or significant change in status, and medications or chemicals.

Critical Thinking Question 

What is the impact of life circumstances on the onset of mood disorders? What are the implications of those circumstances for someone living with a mood disorder?

Clinical Presentation

The essential characteristic of a major depressive episode is a period of at least 2 weeks of depressed mood or loss of interest in almost everything with no history of manic episodes. In children and adolescents, the mood may present as irritable instead of sad. The symptoms must be accompanied by clinically significant impairment in social and occupational functioning (APA, 2000).

Some individuals report aches and pains and other somatic complaints, show increased irritability and persistent feelings or expression of anger, or experience an almost total loss of interest or pleasure in everything. Most individuals with depression have a greatly reduced appetite with a weight loss of more than 5% in a month, although some instead gain weight. In depressed clients, the most common sleep disturbance is **insomnia** (**Figure 17-2**). Less common is the occurrence of **hypersomnia** or excessive sleeping, usually without any deep, restful sleep. There may be psychomotor agitation or retardation, a noticeable speeding up or slowing down of activity; a greatly reduced energy level with complaints of tiredness and fatigue without the output of physical efforts; or an overwhelming sense of worthlessness or guilt and negative views of self often accompanied by ruminations over past failures. There is often a sense of self-blame for being sick or depressed and failing to fulfill one's responsibilities. A pervasive inability to experience pleasure, called **anhedonia**, takes over the person.

Figure 17-2 Insomnia is a common symptom of depression.

Impairment may occur in the ability to think, concentrate, and process decisions with complaints of memory problems. Children may show a drop in school performance due to poor concentration. Adults may be unable to perform their jobs or home tasks. In older adults, the primary complaint may be memory problems, which are often mistaken for the beginning signs of dementia. Of course, it is also true that a major depressive episode can occur at the onset of dementia when the individuals often realize they are having cognitive difficulty.

The depressed person may feel that others would be better off if he or she were gone. There are frequently thoughts or wishes for death and suicidal ideation or attempts of suicide. Certainly depressed persons represent a very high-risk group, yet "many studies have shown that it is not possible to predict accurately whether or when a particular individual with depression will attempt suicide" (APA, 2000, p. 351). Many depressed persons are tormented by **ruminations** or obsessive patterns of thinking in which unwanted thoughts are repetitively forced into their conscious awareness. These ruminations add to the misery of living with depression.

Chronic, catatonic, melancholic, atypical, and *postpartum onset* are terms used to further describe mood disorders.

Five features (chronic, catatonic, melancholic, atypical, and postpartum onset) are used as further descriptors of mood disorders. It is chronic when the disorder has continued for at least 2 years. The description *catatonic feature* is used when there is marked psychomotor disturbance involving motor immobility, extreme motor activity, excessive negativism, mutism, or other peculiarities of movement or speech. Melancholic features occur more commonly in middle aged or older depressed persons and are more likely to occur in a severe rather than mild form. With **melancholia**, there is a loss of interest in almost everything and no sense of pleasure. The individual does not even feel better if something good happens. Along with this is the distinct element of depression that is routinely worse in the morning and often with early morning awakening. Other characteristics are psychomotor retardation, significant weight loss or anorexia, and excessive guilt (APA, 2000). A diagnosis of atypical features is added when mood reactivity is present, meaning that the individual's mood improves when something positive happens. The client may gain weight or have an increased appetite and may sleep too much. There may be a feeling of heaviness in the arms and legs. In addition, there is often a long history of feeling interpersonal rejection with significant resulting impairment in social or occupational functioning (APA).

Dysthymic disorder is less severe than a major depressive disorder, but symptoms extend over 2 years for an adult and 1 year for children and adolescents.

Symptoms that are observed in postpartum onset are mood fluctuations and preoccupation with the well-being of the infant. According to the *DSM-IV-TR* (APA, 2000) the onset occurs within 4 weeks of delivery. However, many practitioners say the problem can occur anytime within the baby's first year. **Postpartum depression** can occur with or without psychotic features. The risk of danger to the infant is generally much greater with postpartum psychotic episodes. For a woman who has had a postpartum psychotic episode, there is a 30–50% chance of recurrence with every future delivery. With postpartum depression, the mother may experience a lack of interest, be afraid to be alone with the baby, or be overly zealous to the point of interfering with the infant's rest. It is very important to separate postpartum depression from "baby blues", which occur in as many as 70% of women during the first 10 days after delivery. These feelings are different in that they are transient and do not interfere with the mother's level of functioning (APA, 2000). However, a cross-sectional study conducted at the University of California at San Francisco found that the risk for postpartum depression was 40% higher among females exposed to domestic violence (Garabedian, 2009). It is imperative for nurses to reach out to this vulnerable population with strong support and with written information on resources available in their community for assistance.

A substance-induced mood disorder is differentiated from major depressive disorder in that a substance such as a medication, drug of abuse, or toxin is judged to be the cause of the symptoms.

Critical Thinking Question

What are some somatic behaviors that might be experienced by a college student who is experiencing the onset of a mood disorder?

Differential Diagnosis

Dysthymic disorder and major depressive disorder differ in terms of severity and chronicity. With dysthymic disorder the symptoms are less severe than in major depressive disorder, but the symptoms are ongoing for at least a 2-year period for adults and for a 1-year period in children and adolescents (APA, 2000). In adults, dysthymic disorder occurs two to three times more often in women than in men. Personality issues or a diagnosable personality disorder are often present. Dysthymic disorder in children occurs equally in boys and girls until puberty, when the incidence increases for females. Reduced school performance and poor social interaction often result. Low self-esteem, poor social skills, and a pessimistic outlook tend to accompany this chronic disorder even in children (APA, 2000).

Mood disorder due to general medical condition is diagnosed when the alteration in mood is assessed to be a direct physiological result of the individual's general medical condition (APA, 2000). The medical condition could be any illness that a person can have. Certain medical conditions, such as cancers, spinal cord and brain injuries, end stage renal disease and HIV/AIDS, that are chronic, incurable, or involve great pain or disability place the individual at a high risk for suicide (APA, 2000).

A substance-induced mood disorder is differentiated from major depressive disorder in that a substance (i.e., a medication, drug of abuse, or toxin) is judged to be the cause of the symptoms (APA, 2000). With individuals so affected, hopefully the symptoms will clear once the effects of the substance are no longer present. There is also a very strong comorbidity between mood disorders and substance abuse, with many individuals stating they use substances to self-medicate against the depression.

Management and Treatment

Clients with a mood disorder should be screened for the possibility of other medical problems that could be producing symptoms of mood problems or compounding them. This review should include a complete history and physical, screening for substance abuse and a thorough mental status exam, an ECG (electrocardiogram), and a complete blood count with differentials, serum electrolytes, cholesterol test, and liver, thyroid, and renal function tests (Lehne, 2010). It is important to establish a baseline prior to starting a medication regimen because it provides vital information for tracking changes.

The cooperative efforts of the interdisciplinary team are vital in the treatment of clients with mood disorders. Having the expertise of a group of professionals and support staff is of great benefit to clients and family members. It is to everyone's advantage for the team members to work together in a spirit of respect and collaboration with the client's best interest always as the central goal. In acute care settings and in all levels of community-based programs, healthcare practitioners from many disciplines are needed. It is vital to keep the focus of treatment on complete recovery and a meaningful role in one's community, not just symptom relief (DBSA, 2006).

Psychotherapeutic care including counseling, pharmacotherapy, and psychoeducation, and psychosocial care including environmental manipulation, as well as peer support, are important to consider in the treatment of those with mood disorders. With mild depression, psychotherapy alone is often an effective treatment. With more severe depression, better results are usually gained with a combination of treatment with antidepressants and psychotherapy.

All antidepressants have an equal opportunity to be effective, with results being on an individual response basis with each client. If an individual or a close relative has responded positively to a certain medication in the past, the same medication is likely to help the client (Glod, 1998). "About 40% of those given antidepressants achieve full remission; another 20% to 30% achieve at least 50% reduction in symptom severity" (Lehne, 2010, p. 336).

The four major groups of antidepressants are selective serotonin reuptake inhibitors (SSRIs), atypical or novel antidepressants, tricyclic antidepressants (TCAs), and monoamine oxidase inhibitors (MAOIs; see **Table 17-2**). Initial therapeutic response with all antidepressants has a lag time of 1–3 weeks, and maximum effectiveness takes 1–2 months to occur. All too frequently, clients stop taking their antidepressants once they start feeling better. They need to be carefully informed about the negative impact of stopping the medication because it is very likely that it is the antidepressant that is making them feel better, and quitting it will likely result in a return of symptoms. It is recommended for antidepressant therapy to continue for 6 months to 1 year after symptoms have improved. If repeated episodes of depression occur, longer term therapy is strongly indicated. When treatment is first initiated, clients may feel the activating or increased energy that accompanies many of the agents before the mood benefits occur. This may give them the energy to act on any suicidal thoughts. Therefore, clients and their family members or caregivers need to be carefully instructed about this possibility, and clients must be closely monitored. Another serious precaution in the use of antidepressants is the possibility of precipitating mania in individuals with a predisposition for bipolar disorder.

The selective serotonin reuptake inhibitors (SSRIs), including Prozac (fluoxetine), Zoloft (sertraline), Paxil (paroxetine), Celexa (citalopram), and Lexapro (escitalopram), along with the atypical antidepressants, are the first line of medication treatment for depression. The SSRIs selectively block the reuptake of serotonin back into the nerve endings, making more serotonin available in the neuronal synapse. Lehne has observed "over time, this induces adaptive cellular responses that are ultimately responsible for relieving depression" (2010, p. 354). The SSRIs present two major advantages over TCAs and MAOIs in that they have fewer side effects and are less lethal if used by a client in an intentional overdose. In a study of over 400 older subjects, the research results indicated decreased effectiveness of SSRIs with age for those diagnosed with the melancholic subtype of depression, whereas the effectiveness of TCAs did not appear to be influenced by age or depressive subtype (Parker, 2002). "The most common side effects are sexual dysfunction (70%), nausea (21%), headache (20%), and manifestations of CNS stimulation, including nervousness (15%), and anxiety

The four major groups of antidepressants are selective serotonin reuptake inhibitors (SSRIs), atypical or novel antidepressants, tricyclic antidepressants (TCAs), and monoamine oxidase inhibitors (MAOIs).

Table 17-2 Common Antidepressant Medications

Subgroup Categories	Daily Adult Dosage Range (mg)
Selective Serotonin Reuptake Inhibitors (SSRIs)	
Prozac (fluoxetine)	10–80 mg
Prozac (fluoxetine) weekly	90 mg per week
Zoloft (sertraline)	25–200 mg
Paxil (paroxetine)	10–50 mg
Paxil (paroxetine) CR	12.5–75 mg
Celexa (citalopram)	10–60 mg
Lexapro (escitalopram)	10–20 mg
Luvox (fluvoxamine)	50–300 mg
Atypical (novel) Antidepressants	
Wellbutrin (bupropion)	200–450 mg
Wellbutrin (bupropion) SR/XL	150–450 mg
Nefazodone (formerly available as Serzone, now generic only)	200–600 mg
Remeron (mirtazapine)	15–60 mg
Asendin (amoxapine)	50–400 mg
Desyrel (trazodone) (used primarily as a sleep aid)	150–600 mg
Atypical Antidepressants (Serotonin Norepinephrine Reuptake Inhibitors—SNRIs)	
Effexor (venlafaxine)	75–225 mg
Effexor (venlafaxine) XR	75–225 mg
Cymbalta (duloxetine)	40–60 mg
Pristiq (desvenlafaxine)	50–100 mg
Savella (milnacipran); an SNRI with FDA approval only for fibromyalgia	100 mg
Tricyclic Antidepressants (TCAs)	
Tofranil (imipramine)	75–300 mg
Elavil (amitriptyline)	50–300 mg
Norpramin (desipramine)	75–300 mg
Pamelor, Aventyl (nortriptyline)	50–150 mg
Anafranil (clomipramine)	75–250 mg
Monoamine Oxidase Inhibitors (MAOIs)	
Marplan (isocarboxazid)	20–60 mg
Nardil (phenelzine)	15–90 mg
Parnate (tranylcypromine)	30–60 mg
Emsam (selegiline) transdermal patch	6, 9, or 12 mg/24 hr

Note: CR = controlled release; SR = sustained release; XL = extended release.
Sources: Adapted from Lehne, R. A. (2010). Pharmacology for nursing care (7th ed.). Toronto, Canada, Elsevier; Crutchfield, D. B. (2006). *Review of psychotropic drugs*. Wilmington, DE: Astra Zeneca Pharmaceuticals; Keltner, N. L., & Folks, D. G. (2005). *Psychotropic drugs*. St. Louis, MO: Mosby; and Townsend, M. C. (2009). *Psychiatric mental health nursing* (6th ed.). Philadelphia, PA: F. A. Davis Co.

(10%). Weight gain can also occur" (Lehne, 2010, p. 344). Sexual dysfunctions can include impotence and decreased libido and anorgasmia in both males and females. Keltner et al. (2011) suggests several treatment ideas to address this very significant problem, including decreasing the dosage, switching to another antidepressant, and augmenting with other drugs. Drugs that Keltner mentioned include amantadine to inhibit prolactin; amphetamines to increase dopamine; bupropion to increase dopamine; buspirone and methylphenidate as a stimulant; and/or an erection-enhancing agent such as sildenafil (Viagra) (p. 184). In addition, drug holidays are sometimes suggested. "Switching to an antidepressant that causes less sexual dysfunction (e.g., bupropion, nefazodone, mirtazapine)" (Lehne, 2010, p. 357) is another possible approach.

Atypical or novel antidepressants include a group of antidepressants that do not all have a similar pattern of neurotransmitter action. Wellbutrin (bupropion) has a chemical structure that is similar to amphetamine (Lehne, 2010). Remeron (mirtazapine) appears to work by increasing the release of serotonin and norepinephrine; it also blocks histamine receptors. Effexor (venlafaxine) and Cymbalta (duloxetine), also called serotonin norepinephrine reuptake inhibitors, seem to combine the best benefits of the TCAs and the SSRIs. Effexor tends to have fewer drug interactions than other antidepressants, and it does not increase the effects of alcohol (Keltner, 2007). Cymbalta helps to reduce depressive symptoms and may reduce some of the physical pain that often accompanies depression.

The tricyclic antidepressants, including Tofranil (imipramine), Elavil (amitriptyline), and Norpramin (desipramine), were the first class of antidepressants available for the treatment of depression. They work by blocking the reuptake of norepinephrine and serotonin at the nerve synapse. The most frequent adverse reactions are sedation, orthostatic hypotension, and anticholinergic effects, including dry mouth and constipation. Cardiotoxicity is the side effect of greatest concern because it can be lethal (Lehne, 2010). To reduce the risk of suicide, severely depressed clients should be given no more than a week's supply at one time. The combination of TCAs and MAOIs is contraindicated because the two together can precipitate a hypertensive crisis.

The monoamine oxidase inhibitors (MAOIs) are able to increase the amounts of norepinephrine, serotonin, and dopamine in the neuronal synapse by blocking monoamine oxidase, which is a main enzyme needed for the breakdown of these neurotransmitters. Although the MAOIs are as effective as other antidepressants, they are seldom used due to their serious side effects and the life-threatening increase in blood pressure that can occur when MAOIs are used in combination with certain foods and drugs (**Table 17-3**).

In 2006, the Food and Drug Administration (FDA) approved Emsam (selegiline), which is the first transdermal skin patch on the market for the treatment of depression. The drug is delivered via a once-per-day patch that supplies the selegiline, a monoamine oxidase inhibitor, through the skin directly into the bloodstream. According to the FDA,

Table 17-3 Foods, Products, and Medications to Be Avoided by Clients Taking MAOIs

Foods	Products	Medications
Aged cheeses, most cheeses	Yeast extracts	All sympathomimetic agents
Sour cream	Ginseng	Methylphenidate (Ritalin)
Yogurt	Meat tenderizer	Amphetamines
Fermented meats (smoked/aged/spoiled)	Soy sauce	Cocaine
Salami, pepperoni, bologna		Cold remedies
Aged fish (cured/dried/smoked/pickled)		Nasal decongestants
Caviar		Asthma medications
Figs, bananas, avocados, especially if overripe		Meperidine (Demerol)
Fava beans		Tricyclic antidepressants
Sauerkraut		SSRI antidepressants
Soybean paste, fermented bean curd		Antiparkinsonian agents
Imported beers and wines, especially Chianti and other red wines		
Caffeinated coffee, soft drinks, tea (in large amounts)		
Chocolate		
Licorice		

"at its lowest strength, Emsam can be used without the dietary restrictions that are needed for all oral MAO inhibitors that are approved for treating major depression" (U.S. FDA, 2006, p. 1). Clients using patches with higher dosages are instructed to follow the dietary and drug restrictions that are necessary for those taking oral MAOIs.

Antidepressant medications must be taken for several weeks before they become effective. Side effects associated with antidepressant medications are divided into the following categories: central nervous system (CNS), anticholinergic, hypotensive, and cardiovascular effects.

Drowsiness is the most common CNS effect. CNS stimulation occurs occasionally and may include tremors, insomnia, psychomotor excitement, and agitation. Rapid eye movement (REM) sleep may be disturbed. The most common anticholinergic effects include dry mouth, blurred vision, tachycardia, constipation, urinary retention, and palpitations. The degree of distress varies. Dizziness and orthostatic hypotension are serious hypotensive effects that may require dosage or medication changes.

The side effects that are most likely to cause noncompliance with antidepressant medication regimens are weight gain, impotence, and decreased libido.

Numerous cardiovascular effects are caused by antidepressants. Tachycardia, bradycardia, ventricular extrasystole, congestive heart failure, myocardial infarction, atrioventricular block, and bundle branch block have been seen in clients taking tricyclic antidepressants. An electrocardiogram (ECG) should be performed before medications are administered so that clients with cardiovascular problems do not receive the medications.

Antidepressant medications should be chosen based on the symptoms and distress associated with the depression and the severity of the side effects. For example, a client who is sensitive to the sedative effects of certain medications should be prescribed a nonsedating drug, whereas a client in an agitated depression may benefit from a sedative. Side effects such as weight gain, impotence, and decreased libido frequently cause clients to discontinue their medication. Clients are often reluctant to discuss these side effects.

St. John's wort is one of the top-selling herbal preparations in the United States. It is widely touted as beneficial in the treatment of mild to moderate depression. It may decrease the uptake of serotonin, norepinephrine, and dopamine. Various studies have compared St. John's wort to TCAs and to the SSRIs. There is some evidence that the herb is beneficial for individuals with mild to moderate depression. The main side effects reported are dry mouth, dizziness, insomnia, confusion, constipation, GI irritation, and photosensitivity. The herb has the potential risk for serotonin syndrome, especially if combined with other antidepressants. Practitioners, especially prescribers, need to ask clients if they are using herbs and teach them about the possible risks involved in double dosing. This herb also has the potential for inducing mania. A major concern with the use of St. John's wort is that the ingredients in the product may vary with different vendors and dosage equivalency cannot be guaranteed.

The Mayo Clinic is utilizing genotyping for CY2P2D6 and CYP2C19 variations as a tool to help guide its mental health professionals in prescribing medications for its patients. With this method, blood samples are taken to determine the required drugs and dosages that are metabolized by the two enzymes for a specific individual (Pestka, Hale, Johnson, Lee, & Poppe, 2007). Although promising, this method is not widely used.

Special Drug Alerts

Certain medications have a heightened risk of causing significant harm to clients (risk of suicide and serotonin syndrome). Psychiatric mental health nurses need to be aware of the potential for these adverse effects and monitor the client appropriately with directed psychoeducation for the client and family.

Suicide Warning

Mood disorders already carry a high rate of suicide for the client. Antidepressants are the primary medications used to treat these disorders. Nevertheless, symptom relief, especially the lifting of mood, takes 1–3 weeks for initial onset and 1–2 months for maximum effectiveness. However, the elevation in energy level begins early in treatment before the mood benefit. The severely depressed, suicidal client may then have the energy to act on this suicidal ideation. The FDA now requires that all antidepressants use a "black box warning" that the taking of antidepressants can increase the risk of suicide in children, adolescents, and those who are 18–24 years of age. To address this issue, it is imperative for the client, family members, and significant others to be advised of the necessity to be vigilant in observing and reporting any signs of suicidality, especially during this lag time before the therapeutic effects of the medication begin. Instruct family and any care providers to ask the client regularly (at least daily), "Are you thinking of hurting yourself?" "Are you having thoughts of suicide?" Give the client written numbers to call in an emergency. Consider having the client call the clinic or service agency on a daily basis to report a safety status until the mood elevation begins. Let the client and family know that you are invested in a collaborative bond with them to work for improvement.

Serotonin Syndrome

Serotonin syndrome is a potentially fatal syndrome that is caused by too much serotonin in the neuronal synapses in the brain stem and spinal cord and can begin as early as 2 hours after the beginning of treatment with antidepressants or other serotonergic drugs, such as SSRIs or TCAs with MAOIs, SSRIs with St. John's wort, or SSRIs in combination with alcohol, or certain street drugs or diet pills. The symptoms of serotonin syndrome are very apparent with mental status changes that may include agitation, confusion, disorientation, poor concentration, anxiety, and possible hallucinations, along with fever, diaphoresis, diarrhea, tachycardia, incoordination, myoclonus, and hyperreflexia.

Carefully assessing the client and reviewing all medications and chemicals ingested to quickly identify the offending agent are the first steps in treating a client with serotonin syndrome. Withholding any further serotonergic agents is essential, after which the syndrome usually resolves spontaneously. If symptoms are severe, the client may need to be hospitalized for monitoring and administration of intravenous fluids and antipyretic agents.

The risk of serotonin syndrome can be readily reduced by avoiding the use of multiple serotonergic drugs at the same time (Keltner, Bostrom, & McGuinness, 2011; Lehne, 2010).

Psychoeducation

Adhering to a medication regimen is very difficult and requires daily discipline and routine. This is not easy even for clients who believe in the value of their treatment protocol and are committed to adhering to what has been prescribed. The nurse performs an extremely significant role in establishing a positive therapeutic relationship and utilizing this bond in the teaching process. Clients need to understand the purpose of the medications they are taking and the primary side effects that may occur. Teaching them the essential points for managing their own regimen can greatly improve their rate of adherence. It is always useful to begin by asking what clients already know as there is a vast difference in the knowledge base between a person just beginning antidepressant medication and one who has been taking such medication for years. Use the Patient Education for All Antidepressants (**Table 17-4**) in helping clients to adhere to their prescribed therapy. Giving clients a printed list of these instructions can serve as a very useful resource.

Critical Thinking Question www

What are the indications and reasons for someone with a mood disorder to stay on medication during long periods of stability?

Brain Stimulation Therapies

"Brain stimulation therapies involve activating or touching the brain directly with electricity, magnets, or implants to treat depression and other disorders" (NIMH, 2009, p.1). These therapies include electroconvulsive therapy (ECT), vagus nerve stimulation (VNS), repetitive transcranial magnetic stimulation (rTMS), and deep brain stimulation (DBS). Even if clients do not use any of these somatic or nonpharmacologic treatments, clients suffering from unrelenting depression appreciate knowing that there are still other forms of treatment that might offer them some degree of relief. Finances and proximity to available treatment can be limiting factors. Nevertheless, psychiatric mental health nurses need to stay informed about new treatment options and be prepared to find information for clients who want to know about these therapies.

Types of brain stimulation therapies include electroconvulsive therapy, vagus nerve stimulation, repetitive transcranial magnetic stimulation, and deep brain stimulation.

Electroconvulsive Therapy

Electroconvulsive therapy (ECT), the oldest stimulation therapy, was developed in 1938 and has the longest history of use. It has received negative publicity mainly from people who have no real knowledge about the procedure and its therapeutic use. ECT can be a highly effective treatment especially indicated for severe, unrelenting depression. It is mainly used when antidepressant medications have failed to bring relief or when quick response is needed due to the severe threat of suicide. It is effective for about 50% of the clients who do not respond to medications; it can be especially useful for severe depression with

ECT is a highly effective treatment, especially for severe, unrelenting depression. It is mainly used when antidepressant medications have failed to bring improvement or when there is a purposeful threat of suicide.

Table 17-4 **Patient Education for Antidepressants**
Review basic actions and main side effect concerns.
Emphasize lag time of 1–3 weeks for initial therapeutic response.
Stopping medication will likely bring return of symptoms
Stress need for close supervision to monitor for suicidal ideation.
Note lag time of 1–2 months for maximum therapeutic effectiveness.
Point out that side effects may occur prior to therapeutic results.
Instruct client to take medication as ordered.
Instruct client to consult with prescriber before stopping medication.
Instruct client to consult with prescriber or pharmacist before self-medicating.
Instruct client not to stop medication abruptly.
Advise client to take medication with food.
Suggest taking medication in the morning if activating.
Suggest taking medication at bedtime if sedating.
Stress avoidance of alcohol and other CNS depressants.
Instruct client to report side effects or special concerns to prescriber.
Instruct client to report any unwanted changes in intimate/sexual relations.
Monitor the client's diet to avoid weight gain.
Instruct the client to avoid the medication during pregnancy and breastfeeding unless deemed absolutely necessary by prescriber and client.
Additional Teaching Points for TCAs (include previous points)
Make a safety plan for reducing risk of suicidal overdose.
Encourage frequent sips of water and sugarless gum for dry mouth.
Stress the need for high-fiber diet and 8–12 glasses of water to counteract constipation and drying effects.
Inform the client that blurred vision is usually transient.
Caution the client that safety adjustments must be made regarding sedation: no driving or operating of machinery until stable.
Advise the client to rise gradually from sitting/lying position to compensate for drop in blood pressure.
Monitor the client's vital signs.
Point out contraindication of TCAs for clients with cardiac problems, glaucoma, and prostatic hypertrophy.
Additional Teaching Points for MAOIs (include previous points)
Teach precautions concerning food–drug interactions.
Give the client and family a list of items to avoid, and carefully explain the list.
Emphasize the necessity to inform all prescribers of MAOI regimen.
Stress the avoidance of all drugs not approved by the prescriber.
Monitor blood pressure.
Instruct the client to not take MAOIs with SSRIs or other serotonergic drugs.
Instruct the client to observe the wait time before and after MAOIs before using other serotonergic drugs to reduce the possibility of serotonin syndrome.

psychotic features and, sometimes, for severe mania and catatonia.

With ECT, a low-energy electrical current is passed through the brain to cause a brain seizure lasting about 1 minute. During the procedure, the seizure activity in the brain is monitored by an electroencephalogram (EEG). The therapeutic mechanism of action is not fully understood, but ECT is thought to alter the flow of neurotransmitters in the brain. The treatments are usually given 2–3 times per week in a series of 6–12 treatments, the number of which is sometimes extended. The major contraindications for the procedure are brain tumors or increased intracranial pressure. Clients are typically given atropine prior to the procedure to dry secretions and reduce the risk of aspiration, Anectine (succinylcholine) as a neuromuscular blockade, and a short-acting general anesthetic agent, such as Brevital (methohexital) (Keltner, Bostrom, & McGuinness, 2011).

Today, ECT is given after carefully conducted medical screening and in a very controlled environment with an anesthesiologist present. The main risks are those associated with brief anesthesia. Short-term memory loss, especially for the time period surrounding the treatment, may occur. More significant memory loss is rare with the modern application of this treatment. ECT is considered safer than medication for some older adults and for pregnant women after the first trimester, because anesthesia is considered an undesirable risk during the first trimester (Glod, 1998), and positive treatment response occurs more quickly than with medication. It may have to be repeated, and sometimes maintenance treatments about once a month are indicated. A deterrent to the use of ECT is the high cost of the treatments and the lack of wide availability of facilities offering the treatment. Nevertheless, approximately 100,000 clients per year receive ECT for the treatment of depression (DBSA, 2006).

Since ECT is given in limited settings, many healthcare practitioners no longer have observational experiences of the procedure during their educational programs. The nurse's role in educating and supporting the client is vital, with careful monitoring during and following ECT being essential. The client is mechanically assisted to breathe by the anesthesiologist or nurse anesthetist during the procedure. The vital signs are closely monitored, and the client must be assessed for return of the gag reflex. After the treatment, the nurse must continue to carefully monitor until the client is completely revived and reoriented.

Vagus Nerve Stimulation

The FDA approved **vagus nerve stimulation (VNS)** in 2005 for the long-term therapy of clients with **treatment-resistant depression (TRD)**. TRD is defined as a major depressive disorder that is severe, has lasted for at least 2 years, and has failed to respond to at least four different antidepressants. VNS works through a device implanted under the skin that sends electrical pulses through the left vagus nerve. The treatment was first utilized to treat drug-resistant epilepsy, during which some clients demonstrated an elevation in mood. Subsequently, a clinical trial was conducted with clients with TRD. Although the results from the study trials were not clearly supportive, the device won FDA approval anyway. VNS remains a controversial treatment for depression because results of the studies testing its effectiveness have been so mixed.

The actual mechanism of action is unknown for VNS, and the total cost for surgical implantation is about $25,000 (Lehne, 2010). It is also difficult to get insurance coverage for the procedure. There may be complications such as infection from the implant surgery, or the device may come loose, move around, or malfunction, which may require additional surgery. Long-term adverse effects are unknown. The main side effects are hoarseness, voice alteration, cough, dyspnea, neck pain, and difficulty swallowing, all of which tend to decrease over time.

Repetitive Transcranial Magnetic Stimulation

Developed in 1985 and studied since the mid-1990s, **repetitive transcranial magnetic stimulation (rTMS)** is a noninvasive, painless method to stimulate the cerebral cortex with the goal of treating depression, psychosis, and other disorders. In spite of less-than-robust research findings, in October 2008, the FDA approved rTMS for the treatment of major depressive disorder in clients who have not responded to at least one antidepressant medication. The NIMH is currently conducting a large trial to determine the most effective and safe use of rTMS.

A benefit of rTMS is that it can be directly targeted to a specific brain site, which scientists believe reduces the possibility for the kind of adverse effects that are associated with ECT. For rTMS, no anesthesia is needed, and an average session lasts about 30–60 minutes. The treatment is thought to act in a manner similar to anticonvulsant medications. The stimulation of the prefrontal cortex in the brain may work in much the same way as ECT to relieve depression without producing the same side effects. During the procedure, an electromagnetic coil is held against the forehead where short electromagnetic pulses are

Treatment resistant depression (TRD) is a major depressive disorder that is severe, has lasted for at least two years, and has failed to respond to at least four different antidepressants.

administered via the coil. Small electric currents are thought to stimulate nerve cells in the targeted region of the brain. The strength of the magnetic field is similar to that of magnetic resonance imaging (MRI) scans. The client will feel a slight tapping or knocking sensation on the head. Mild headaches or temporary lightheadedness may be experienced after treatments. Long-term side effects are not known as the treatment is relatively new. A critical issue is the lack of consensus on picking the best spot for the focus of treatment and, therefore, more research is needed (NIMH, 2009).

Deep Brain Stimulation

Deep brain stimulation (DBS) was originally developed as a treatment for Parkinson's disease to reduce uncontrollable movements. "In DBS, a pair of electrodes is implanted in the brain and controlled by a generator that is implanted in the chest. Stimulation is continuous and its frequency and level is customized to the individual" (NIMH, 2009). It is only recently that DBS has been studied as a treatment for depression and obsessive compulsive disorder, and at this time such treatment is only available on an experimental basis. DBS involves brain surgery to implant electrodes on each side of a specific part of the brain.

> The electrodes are then attached to wires that are run inside the body from the head down to the chest, where a pair of battery-operated generators are implanted. From here, electrical pulses are continuously delivered over the wires to the electrodes in the brain. Although it is unclear exactly how the device works to reduce depression or OCD, scientists believe that the pulses help to "reset" the area of the brain that is malfunctioning so that it works normally again. (NIMH, 2009, p.1)

Phototherapy

In light or phototherapy, broad-spectrum light exposure provides artificial lighting, which is brighter than usual indoor lighting, to the environment of an individual with seasonal affective disorder (SAD). Light therapy is based on biologic rhythms. Some practitioners use the term *bright light therapy* (BLT), which exposes the client to intense light on a daily basis. Several studies and reports from clients indicate that environmental factors play a definite role in mood disorders. Morning administration seems to be most beneficial. Improvements from BLT are apparent in just a few days, although the exact mechanism of action is not clear. The therapeutic effect is considered to be received through the eyes, not the skin. Many clients claim positive results for nonseasonal depression as well. "Because phototherapy produces few if any adverse effects (e.g., nausea, eye irritation) the risk–benefit ratio favors its use. Contraindications include glaucoma, cataracts, and use of photosensitizing medications" (Keltner, Bostrom, & McGuinness, 2011, p. 420).

Nonpharmacologic Alternative Treatments

Clients with mood disorders can benefit from nonpharmacologic treatment modalities that assist in stabilizing the client, promote recovery, and prevent relapse. Research indicates a higher improvement rate with a combination of psychotherapy and antidepressants. Supportive psychotherapy, cognitive behavioral therapy, family therapy, group therapy, psychoeducational therapy, and interpersonal therapy are various modalities that can be made available to clients. They can be effective alone or in combination (Wieseke, Bantz, & May, 2011).

Critical Thinking Question

When obtaining a medication history, why is it important to obtain information on medications for mood disorders, other medical conditions, and over-the-counter medications that a client may be taking?

Nursing Interventions

Two primary concerns for clients with mood disorders are safety (suicidal potential) and self-esteem. Short-term goals include meeting the client's physical needs resulting from the symptoms the client is experiencing. After baseline data are collected and a physical assessment is completed, the nurse develops nursing diagnoses, interventions and a plan of care (**Table 17-5**) to address the client's physical and mental health needs. Clients who are very depressed may neglect both their health and safety. A maxim to promote for people who are depressed is, "You can't wait until you feel better to do things. You have to do things to feel better!"

Table 17-5 Nursing Interventions for Clients with Mood Disorders

Nursing Diagnoses	Nursing Interventions	Rationales
Risk for suicide	Determine the severity of the risk for suicidal acts and the level of suicide precautions needed.	A client at high risk for self-directed violence (suicide) needs a carefully completed assessment, constant supervision, and a safe environment.
Disturbed thought processes	Use simple, concrete words. Identify the client's previous level of cognitive functioning. Permit the client time to think and frame responses.	A client with a thought disturbance will have slowed thinking and difficulty concentrating. Establishing a baseline of previous functioning allows for evaluation of the client's progress. When a client has slowed thinking, time will be needed to formulate a response.
Impaired social interaction	Provide an environment with less stimulation. Involve the client in one-to-one activities. Gradually increase the client's contact with others.	Minimal distractions promote the ability to focus. Permits the client to focus and increases the potential for successful interactions. Distracts the client from self and such socialization decreases the client's feelings of isolation.
Self-care deficit	Monitor intake, output, and vital signs. Encourage rest periods during the day and after activities.	This will ensure adequate fluid and calorie intake, minimizing weight loss, dehydration, constipation, and cardiac collapse. Lack of sleep can lead to increased feelings of depression, exhaustion, and death.

Nurses may need to provide basic care for clients who lack the energy or interest for self-care. Basic activities of daily living (ADLs) such as bathing, grooming, choosing clothes, and dressing may require assistance. Nurses must promote adequate nutrition and fluid intake for clients who have not been eating or drinking. Nutrition and fluid intake must be monitored and documented carefully. Restoring sleep patterns will provide adequate rest at night and wakefulness during the day, benefiting the client both physically and mentally. Because of the anticholinergic side effects of drug therapy, nurses must encourage good dental hygiene. Sipping water during the day and chewing sugarless gum can help to relieve dry mouth.

Women with mood disorders need special attention during pregnancy and the postpartum period. The nurse needs to talk with the mother and ask for her description of her mood and behavior. Mood changes during this time are too often overlooked. When these changes are discovered, they are treated very much like depression or mania in the general population except for the concern about medication. Although it is generally the best policy to avoid medications and unnecessary chemical intake during pregnancy or breastfeeding, nontreatment may put the mother and child at greater risk. Reaching out to these women can have enormous benefits for them, their children, and others close to them. They need a strong support system, adequate rest, and some time for themselves away from caretaking responsibilities.

A primary nursing goal for a client with a mood disorder is to keep the client safe and prevent self-injury.

Physical activity is very important and should be encouraged even if the client resists. If achievable, the nurse must encourage the client to take part in activities that were enjoyed previously. The client can begin with solitary activities before mixing with others. Physical activity both releases pent-up energy and increases feelings of well-being, accomplishment, and control. Bowel, bladder, and menstrual functions should be monitored, and the nurse should intervene as indicated for constipation, urinary retention, or lack of self-care.

Some helpful statements the nurse can say to someone who is depressed include:

- I know you have a real illness and that's what causes you to feel depressed.
- I can't understand exactly how you feel, but I want to understand and help you.
- Tell me what I can do right now to help you.

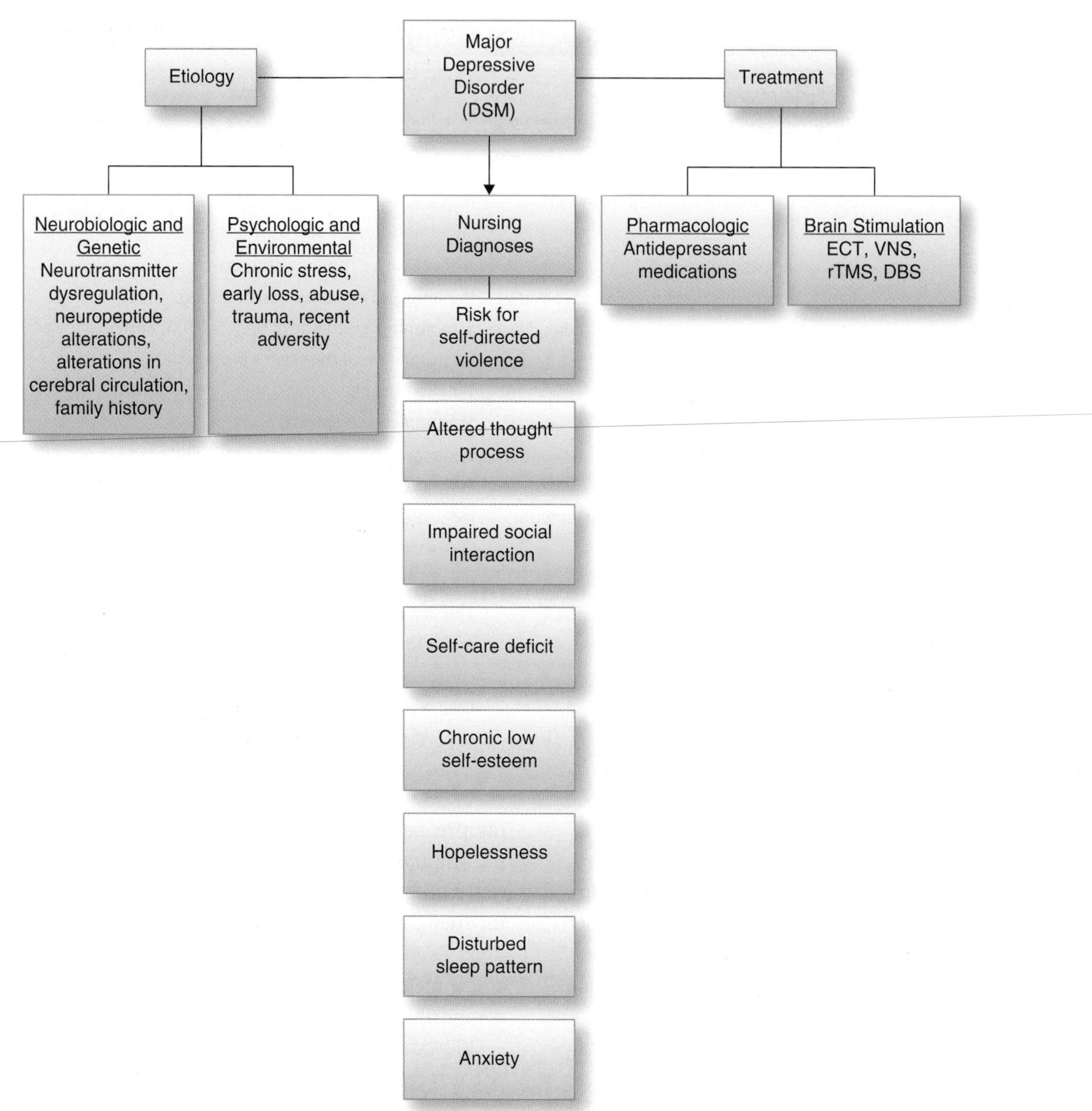

Nursing Diagnoses Concept Map: Major Depressive Disorder.

- You may not believe it, but the way you are feeling now will change.
- Talk to me; I am listening. (DBSA, 2005)

Nurses can provide positive reinforcement by acknowledging the client's accomplishments and validating progress. The nurse can promote the client's existing strengths and resources as well as help the client identify activities or plans that are reminders of past pleasures or future anticipations. In interactions with a client who is depressed, the nurse needs to be mindful of one's own **affect**. A pleasant but neutral affect is usually best. Too much cheerfulness can be almost painful for the client and may cause the client to withdraw and be unable to connect with the nurse. The client's low self-esteem and hopelessness often require the nurse to direct the client's actions. A conscious effort should be made to provide continuous and much-needed encouragement, support, and reinforcement.

Some nursing diagnoses that can be utilized in care planning for clients with a mood disorder such as a major depressive disorder include:

- Risk for violence directed towards self or others
- Impaired social interactions
- Chronic low self-esteem
- Hopelessness
- Powerlessness
- Self-care deficit
- Altered thought processes
- Interrupted family processes
- Altered nutrition
- Disturbed sleep pattern
- Anxiety
- Risk for suicide (North American Nursing Diagnosis Association [NANDA], 2012)

See Appendix II for additional NANDA diagnoses.

Education for Clients and Families

Client education is significant today with shortened hospital stays and reduced funding for community mental health services. Nurses must provide information about the specific mood disorder, its typical symptoms and problems, the clinical course, treatment issues, and the medications used. It is essential to build a therapeutic nurse–client relationship based on trust. Family members and significant others should be involved in the educational process from the beginning of treatment. This creates a support system for the client that can be useful throughout the course of therapy for episodes of depression and to assist in recognizing signs of impending problems. In many instances family members are the primary daily care providers. Clients should be taught to identify the early signs of depression and to seek help when needed to avoid or limit recurrences. Clients should be counseled to continue taking medications even when they start to feel better. They also need to understand the synergistic relationship between some antidepressants (e.g., MAOIs and TCAs) and certain foods and other drugs. Clients also need to be informed that they are at greater risk for tooth and periodontal disease, as the anticholinergic drying qualities of many of the psychotropic medications reduce the natural protective properties of saliva, and, therefore, they should be attentive to their dental regimen and follow-up care (McDermott, 2005).

Bipolar Disorder

Like with unipolar disorders, bipolar disorders occur in a range of severity levels. Bipolar I disorder, formerly known as manic-depressive disorder, is the most classic of these disorders and can be the most severe. Persons with bipolar I disorder experience one or more manic episodes or mixed episodes. Frequently individuals may have had one or more major depressive episodes prior to experiencing mania (APA, 2000). Bipolar II disorder is characterized by at least one hypomanic episode and one or more major

A shift in polarity describes the client's experience with mood cycles changing from highs to lows over a period of time.

CASE STUDIES Mrs. S.

Mrs. S., a 29-year-old married female with an attractive appearance, though somewhat unkempt and profoundly sad, was accompanied by her husband upon admission. She was a homemaker and had two sons, ages 4 years and 13 months. Mrs. S. was admitted to the hospital because she was unable to function at home and care for her children, was having great difficulty sleeping, and began expressing some suicidal ideation. She was crying almost continuously for the previous month, had lost 15 pounds, seemed withdrawn, and said she had no energy or interest to do anything. She had experienced some postpartum blues after the birth of her first child, but did not seek help. Mrs. S. reported that she had more difficulty after the birth of her second child and was treated for postpartum depression by her family doctor. She had been prescribed escitalopram (Lexapro) 20 mg daily. She reported that the medication helped her, but she did not want to be a druggie and quit taking the medication about 2 months previously, when she started to feel better. She had been troubled by recurrent yearnings for death and feelings that her family would be better off without her. Mrs. S. talked about feeling anxious and not wanting to be a poor mother to her children like her own mother who had several hospitalizations for psychotic depression during Mrs. S.'s childhood. Mr. S. was with her on admission and seemed supportive and concerned. He was caring but expressed difficulty understanding what went wrong.

Mrs. S. was diagnosed with major depressive disorder with postpartum onset based on the *DSM-IV-TR*, Axis I. Some nursing diagnoses that apply to this client are identified in the following nursing care plan.

Nursing Care Plan **Major Depressive Disorder**

Nursing Diagnosis 1: Risk for self-directed violence related to depressed mood, as evidenced by appearance, self-reporting, and yearning for death

Nursing Diagnosis 2: Self-care deficit related to lack of energy and interest in caring for oneself or family, as evidenced by unkempt appearance, lack of attention to self, and loss of weight

Nursing Diagnosis 3: Low self-esteem related to perceived role inadequacy, as evidenced by stated guilt regarding inability to care for children, home, or self

Expected Outcomes Short term:	Nursing Interventions	Evaluations
• Will take medication as prescribed.	• Administer prescribed medications such as escitalopram 20 mg, one every morning, and trazodone 50 mg, 1 hour after bedtime if unable to sleep. • Regularly review medication regimen and repeat medication education from the beginning of hospital stay.	• The client is able to correctly repeat information about taking her medication, is compliant with regimen, and can report changes in symptoms.
• Will remain free of self-harm.	• Demonstrate an empathetic, caring relationship with client, letting her know your concern for her safety and gentle optimism for her future progression. • Regularly assess the client for suicidal ideation/intent.	• The client states she no longer wishes to be dead. "I want to be the mother for my boys." • She also states that her spiritual beliefs strongly encourage her to value her life as a special gift.
• Will follow unit schedule and attend therapies.	• Monitor the client's activities and remind her of the unit schedule.	• The client follows the unit's scheduled routines and activities.
• Will bathe and groom daily.	• In a matter-of-fact manner, acknowledge the client's accomplishments. (e.g., "You washed your hair today.") Encourage the client to interact with other clients, both sharing and listening.	• The client bathes, grooms, and dresses neatly on her own.
• Will eat food, selected by her, that is served.	• Have the dietician meet with the client to discuss her preferences. Assist the client in making daily specific goals that she can meet and thereby gradually boost her self-esteem.	• The client eats meals with other clients in the dining room.
• Will make specific daily goals that she can reasonably accomplish.	• Offer the client the opportunity to talk about caring for her children and other concerns that she wants to discuss. • Teach the client relaxation techniques and practice individually and in a group.	• The client asks for one-to-one time with her nurse to discuss her goals and concerns. • The client acknowledges encouragement from others. • The client uses deep-breathing relaxation exercises in the evening in her room.
• Will commit to plans for follow-up care at the psychiatric and counseling center.	• Encourage the client to attend the family night group meeting with her husband. • Review her discharge plan as it is developed. • Involve the client's husband in a review of her discharge plan.	• The client attends family group meetings with her husband. • The client asks her husband to join her for the review of her discharge plan.

Nursing Care Plan **Major Depressive Disorder *(Continued)***

Expected Outcomes Long term:	Nursing Interventions	Evaluations
	• Engage the client in discussion about the impact of follow-up care on maintaining emotional balance after hospitalization.	
• Will participate in family psychoeducation classes with her husband.	• Involve the client's husband in planning post discharge activities. • Give the client's husband information about NAMI's Family to Family classes that help to educate family members about mental health issues	• Schedules her initial, postdischarge appointment with the psychiatric and counseling center.
• Will attend the Depression and Bipolar Support Alliance (DBSA) biweekly groups for mothers of young children.	• Discuss with her and give her a brochure with information about the Depression and Bipolar Support Alliance (DBSA) group meetings with location, meeting times, and contact phone number. • Give the client a card with the phone number for the national 24-hour Suicide Prevention Hotline: 1-800-273-TALK or 1-800-273-8255	• Attends meetings of the local Depression and Bipolar Support Alliance (DBSA) and utilizes community-based support services.

Visit http://go.jblearning.com/mentalhealth for additional care plans and exercises.

depressive episodes. With this disorder, the hypomanic episodes may not result in significant harm. However, the major depressive episodes tend to bring about considerable distress in relationships and occupational functioning. With bipolar disorder, the person's mood vacillates in cycles from high to low over time. The *DSM-IV-TR* refers to this happening as "a shift in polarity" (APA, 2000, p. 382). **Cyclothymic disorder** is a mild form of bipolar disorder. The client with this disorder experiences mood swings for 2 or more years with periods of mild depression and excitement.

With bipolar disorders, four different types of mood episodes can occur: manic episode, hypomanic episode, major depressive episode, and mixed episode. The most expansive type is the manic episode or mania, which often begins with an elevated sense of heightened energy, creativity, and a pleasurable social engagement. These feelings rapidly escalate to a high state of **euphoria** or severe irritability. Individuals with mania or in a manic episode typically lack insight into their situation. They remain in denial that anything is wrong and resist efforts to help. They tend to be very harsh toward anyone who suggests they are ill. In order for the episode to be labeled as manic, the symptoms must be present for at least 1 week or be severe enough to result in hospitalization. In addition to the extreme euphoric or irritable mood, the individual must meet three to four of the following criteria: having an inflated self-esteem or feeling of power and greatness; requiring little sleep yet having a high degree of energy; talking so fast that others cannot keep up; racing thoughts or flight of ideas; being easily distracted; increasing goal-directed activity at work, socially, or sexually; and engaging excessively in pleasurable activities without concern for potential negative consequences, such as extreme spending, indiscreet sexual behavior, or foolish business endeavors. With a manic episode there is severe impairment in social or occupational functioning. The person may have to be hospitalized to prevent harm to self or others, and in extreme cases, psychotic symptoms may occur (APA, 2000).

With bipolar disorders there are four different types of mood episodes: manic, hypomanic, major depressive, and mixed.

The hypomanic episode or **hypomania** is a less severe degree of mania with a distinct period of elevation or mania that must last at least 4 days. The symptoms are similar to mania but less severe and do not cause marked impairment in social and occupational functioning or have psychotic features. Many individuals like the experience of these episodes. They feel better and can be more productive. As a result, clients with bipolar disorder often quit taking their medication in an effort to extend this period of hypomania. These periods rarely last indefinitely, and it has been postulated that "5–15% of individuals with hypomania will ultimately develop a Manic Episode" (APA, 2000, p. 367).

Depression is the downside of bipolar disorder. The symptoms that occur with this phase are the same as those already discussed in the section about major depressive disorder. As with unipolar depression, psychotic features can be present in the depressed period of bipolar disorder. With a mixed episode, symptoms of both mania and depression occur at the same time or alternating, frequently nearly every day for at least a week. Individuals feel elevated or irritable like in the manic state, but are also depressed or agitated. Both the depressed and the mixed episodes cause marked impairment in social or occupational functioning (APA, 2000). Mixed episodes are difficult to endure and to treat. As a result of the high energy and the depression in combination, there is an especially high risk of suicide in clients with mixed episodes.

In bipolar disorder, rapid cycling is the occurrence of four or more mood episodes in a 1-year period. It is more common in women than in men.

In older adults (age 50+) with no previous history or risk factors, baseline screening is especially vital to rule out other causes such as an undiagnosed neurologic or other general medical condition or the effects of using alcohol, drugs, or prescribed medication.

Incidence and Prevalence

The *DSM-IV-TR* notes that the lifetime risk for bipolar disorder varies from 0.4% to 1.6% (APA, 2000). Some sources quote data indicating higher rates for bipolar disorder. At the Sixth International Conference on Bipolar Disorder (2005), new figures were presented indicating that the incidence of bipolar disorder is considerably more prevalent than previously noted.

Bipolar I disorder is characterized by periods of both manic episodes and major depressive episodes, and it occurs equally in both sexes. There is no evidence of variation in the incidence of bipolar disorder in different racial and ethnic groups, but some practitioners are concerned that the disorder is underdiagnosed in certain groups. The typical individual with bipolar disorder will experience four episodes during the first 10 years after diagnosis (Kahn, Ross, Printz, & Sachs, 2000). A number of years can pass between the first two or three manic or depressive episodes, but without treatment, most individuals tend to experience an increase in episodes. For some, moods occur in a seasonal pattern with an onset and remission at certain times of the year, especially the fall and the spring.

> The presence of winter-type seasonal pattern appears to vary with latitude, age, and sex. Prevalence increases with higher latitudes. Age is also a strong predictor of seasonality, with younger persons at a higher risk for winter depressive episodes and with women comprising 60%–90% of persons with seasonal pattern. (APA, 2000, p. 426)

Men are more likely to begin with a manic episode and women with a major depressive episode. With men the episodes of mania usually equal or exceed the number of depressions, but with women the depressive episodes are predominant. The specifier of **rapid cycling** is also more common in women. Rapid cycling is the occurrence of four or more mood episodes in a 1-year period. About 10–20% of those with bipolar disorder experience rapid cycling. Those with a rapid cycling course tend to have a more guarded long-term prognosis (APA, 2000, p. 428).

According to the *DSM-IV-TR*, a person's first manic episode typically occurs in his or her early 20s, but it can begin in adolescence or even after age 50 (APA, 2000). There are also some cases that happen in early childhood. There is a 10–20% risk for the development of bipolar I disorder in adolescents with repeated major depressive episodes. When the first manic episode occurs after age 50 with no previous history of such symptoms, the practitioner should be alert to the possibility of an undiagnosed neurologic or other general medical condition or the effects of using alcohol, drugs, or prescribed medication.

Women with bipolar I disorder have a greater risk for having an episode during their postpartum period. In addition, women with major depressive, manic, mixed, or hypomanic episodes may experience more difficult symptoms during their premenstrual period (APA, 2000). Bipolar II occurs more often in women than in men, and the time period between episodes tends to get shorter with age. Nevertheless, about 85% of clients with this disorder experience quite functional times between episodes. Major changes in their sleep cycle or loss of sleep may trigger an episode (APA, 2000).

Critical Thinking Question

What are some of the concerns for treating women with bipolar disorder during their childbearing years, and what type of counseling is required if a woman is considering becoming pregnant?

Clinical Example

Fifty-eight-year-old Pearl has been living with bipolar I disorder since her mid-teens. Every few months she experiences significant mood fluctuations—periods of euphoria, increased energy, and greatly reduced sleep. She has been known to bake hundreds of cookies for local workers such as the police, firefighters, and postal workers, showing up at odd times of the day or night to distribute her baked goods. On her last admission to the crisis unit, Pearl took off all of her clothes and marched down the hallway singing, "Let Me Love You" while approaching other clients and staff in an overtly sexual manner.

Etiology and Physiology

Bipolar disorder appears to run in families. Many research studies have identified a number of different genes and specific brain structural changes that may be linked to the illness. Different studies indicate different results. The mode of inheritance in bipolar disorder is very complex. Only a fraction of those with the genetic risk actually get the disorder as "first degree biological relatives of individuals with Bipolar I Disorder have elevated rates of Bipolar I Disorder (4%–24%), Bipolar II Disorder (1%–5%), and Major Depressive Disorder (4%–24%)" (APA, 2000, p. 386). It also has been noted that clients with mood disorders in their first-degree biologic relatives are more likely to have an earlier age at onset; extensive twin and adoption studies indicate strong evidence of a genetic influence for bipolar I disorder (APA, 2000, p. 386). Funded in part by the NIMH, the Bipolar Disorder Phenome Database is attempting to link visible signs of the disorder with the genes that may influence them. So far, scientists have determined that certain traits seem to run in families. These include (NIMH, 2011)

- history of psychiatric hospitalization
- co-occurring obsessive compulsive disorder
- age at time of first manic episode
- number and frequency of manic episodes

No laboratory findings have yet been determined to be diagnostic for bipolar I or bipolar II disorder. The diagnosis is based on history, observation, interview, and client report. When compared with clients with major depressive disorder or individuals without any mood disorders, imaging studies "tend to show increased rates of right-hemispheric lesions, or bilateral subcortical or peri-ventricular lesions in those with Bipolar I Disorder" (APA, 2000, p. 385). Hypothyroidism may be associated with rapid cycling. On the other end, "hyperthyroidism may precipitate or worsen manic symptoms in individuals with a preexisting Mood Disorder" (APA, 2000, p. 385). Regardless of the exact biochemical nature of bipolar disorder, it is apparent that individuals with the disorder have an increased vulnerability to emotional and physical stressors (See Chapter 5).

Clinical Presentation

Clients experiencing a manic episode have symptoms that can be observed by the nurse as changes in behavior, cognition, and emotions. Some of the signs that can be recognized in these three categories are discussed in the following sections.

Bipolar disorder appears to run in families, occurs equally in both sexes, and is often underdiagnosed in some racial and ethnic groups.

Behavioral Signs

Clients in a manic episode wake up full of energy after little sleep, do not tire easily, do not need much sleep, and may have insomnia. They show extreme motor activity and an increased or a decreased appetite and pay no attention to hygiene, grooming, or health. Individuals may exhibit uncharacteristic sexual activity or sexual behavior. These clients often dress flamboyantly, have exaggerated mannerisms, wear too much makeup, behave impulsively, and are often intrusive, demanding, domineering, and physically threatening. Family and friends may describe wild shopping sprees, excessive work hours, or elaborate schemes to acquire wealth or fame. Clients experiencing a manic episode are angered at any attempts to set limits; thus, personal interactions are strained. The client may disappear without explanation.

Cognitive Signs

Clients may report that their thoughts are racing, or they have shown poor judgment. They may be hypervigilant, easily distracted, or have impractical ideas. Their speech is pressured, rapid, loud, and even incoherent, with **flight of ideas**, which is pressured speech with rapid topic changes. Clients may have delusions of persecution, grandiosity, or religiosity or may experience hallucinations. They lack insight into their condition.

The three primary categories of medications used to treat bipolar disorder are mood stabilizers, antipsychotic agent, and antidepressants. When antidepressants are used, they should be combined with a mood stabilizer to avoid pushing the client with bipolar disorder toward mania.

Emotional Signs

Clients may have a labile mood that changes rapidly from elation or euphoria to irritability, anger, or rage. Affect may shift from happy to depressed, negative, or hostile. The client typically appears excited and overconfident, feeling like he or she can accomplish anything. Clients may report feeling on top of the world.

Differential Diagnosis

It can be difficult to distinguish between bipolar disorder and various other conditions, including anxiety disorders, schizophrenia, schizoaffective disorder, and sometimes substance disorders. Anxiety, psychotic symptoms, and acting out behavior can occur in all of these disorders. It is also true that many clients with bipolar disorder have a co-occurring alcohol or other substance abuse disorder, especially those with an earlier onset of the bipolar disorder. Other comorbid mental conditions include anorexia, bulimia, ADHD, panic disorder, and social phobia (APA, 2000, p. 384). The *DSM-IV-TR* also states that, "Child abuse, spouse abuse, or other violent behavior may occur during severe Manic Episodes or during those with psychotic features. Other associated problems include school truancy, school failure, occupational failure, divorce, or episodic antisocial behavior" (APA, p. 384). In adolescents who experience recurrent major depressive episodes, about 10–15% will later develop bipolar I disorder.

Lithium is used for clients with bipolar I who have the more euphoric mania and experience less depression with the elevated state. It also can be useful for depression and is often added with other medications; it is less effective in treating mixed manic states and rapid-cycling bipolar disorder.

Management and Treatment

A combination of psychotherapy and medication is usually the most effective approach in treating bipolar disorders. A carefully acquired baseline health assessment is also imperative. It is essential that this include evaluation of cardiac status with EKG, blood pressure, and heart rate; complete blood counts with differential; serum electrolytes; renal function; and complete thyroid function studies (Lehne, 2010).

Psychopharmacology

The three primary categories of medications used to treat bipolar disorder are mood stabilizers, antipsychotic agents, and antidepressants. Benzodiazepines may also be prescribed to help alleviate insomnia, anxiety, or restlessness, especially in the lag time before any of the three main groups of drugs begin to work. The most often prescribed mood stabilizers are lithium and antiepileptic drugs. The antipsychotic medications are used to help control agitation, anxiety, and insomnia during severe manic episodes even if no psychotic symptoms are present. The atypical antipsychotic medications have been found to have mood stabilizing properties and are now preferred over the traditional antipsychotic agents. Clients may also need antidepressant therapy. However, antidepressants must always be combined with a mood stabilizer when treating clients with bipolar disorder to avoid pushing them toward mania. Wellbutrin (bupropion), Effexor (venlafaxine), and the SSRIs are usually the preferred choices of antidepressants. The tricyclic agents have more serious side effects and have a greater tendency to cause a manic episode (Kahn et al., 2000; Lehne, 2010).

Lithium

The usefulness of lithium was first reported in Australia in 1949, but lithium was not approved for use in the United States until 1970 (Lehne, 2010). Lithium appears to be more effective for clients with bipolar I who have the more euphoric mania and experience less depression with the elevated state. However, lithium can also be useful for depression and is often added with other medications. Lithium tends to be less effective in treating mixed manic states and rapid-cycling bipolar disorder (Kahn et al., 2000; Lehne, 2010).

The exact mechanism of action by which lithium (lithium carbonate, Lithobid) stabilizes the mood is not known. However, the evidence suggests that lithium works by altering the distribution of calcium, sodium, and magnesium ions, which are vital to nerve function. It also affects the synthesis and release of norepinephrine, serotonin, and dopamine.

Although the leveling of manic effects begins 5–7 days after treatment begins, maximum benefits may take 2–3 weeks.

The adverse effects of lithium (**Table 17-6**) are closely associated with serum levels. The range of therapeutic serum levels for lithium is 0.6–1.2 mEq/L. The side effects increase as the level of lithium in the blood increases toward the toxic level. Some of these adverse effects occur at therapeutic lithium levels, below 1.5 mEq/L. These milder effects include fine hand tremor, mild stomach irritation, abdominal bloating, mild thirst, polyuria, muscle weakness, tiredness, headache, and weight gain. Many of these mild effects subside, or at least decrease, with time. Clients should continue their lithium as ordered. As beginning toxic levels (1.5–2.0 mEq/L) are reached, the adverse effects increase dramatically. Severe and persistent gastrointestinal symptoms, coarse hand tremors, uncoordination, sedation, and EKG changes occur. Lithium should be withheld and lithium blood levels should be drawn. When severe levels of toxicity are reached (2.0–2.5 mEq/L), clients experience tinnitus, high output of dilute urine, serious EKG changes, severe hypotension, stupor, and seizures. As the level of lithium in the blood rises above 2.5 mEq/L, urine output ceases and cardiac arrhythmia occurs along with peripheral circulatory collapse. Coma and even death can occur (Lehne, 2010). The most frequent cause of severe toxicity is intentional overdose.

The most important way to minimize adverse effects is to sustain a steady state of lithium level and fluid and electrolyte balance. Clients need to maintain a normal salt or sodium intake and replace water lost due to perspiration, diarrhea, or heavy exercise by routinely drinking 8–12 glasses of liquids every day. They should avoid diuretics and nonsteroidal anti-inflammatory drugs (NSAIDs) such as ibuprofen and naproxen. NSAIDs, but not aspirin, can increase renal absorption of lithium and thus cause lithium levels to rise. Lithium should always be taken with food or milk to avoid stomach upset. Lithium can cause birth defects, especially malformations of the heart, and should not be taken during pregnancy, especially during the first trimester or when breastfeeding (Lehne, 2010).

The adverse effects of lithium are closely associated with serum levels. Some of these adverse effects occur at therapeutic lithium levels, below 1.5 mEq/L. The toxic level occurs at 1.5–2.0 mEq/L, and monitoring blood lithium levels is critical.

Monitoring of lithium levels in the blood is essential. There is a small margin between therapeutic and toxic serum levels. Maintaining an adequate fluid level in the body significantly affects the lithium level in the blood. At the onset of treatment, frequent blood samples, every 2–3 days, are required until therapeutic concentration is attained. After stabilization, blood levels should be taken every 1–3 months regularly. For proper evaluation, the blood should be drawn in the morning, 12 hours after the evening dose (Lehne, 2010). (See **Table 17-7**.)

Antiepileptic Drugs

Many of the medications used for the treatment of epilepsy are also used to treat bipolar disorder. These drugs are used to suppress mania and stabilize the mood of clients with the disorder (**Table 17-8**). According to Lehne (2010), lithium and Depakote (divalproex) are the preferred mood stabilizers for

Table 17-6 **Recognizing Levels of Lithium Toxicity by Side Effects**

Blood Level of 1.5 mEq/L	Blood Level of 1.5–2.5 mEq/L	Blood Level of 2.5 mEq/L or Greater
Vomiting	Ataxia	Unconsciousness
Weakness	Diarrhea	Hypotension
Drowsiness	Persistent nausea and vomiting	Increased temperature
Lethargy	Loss of coordination	Dysrhythmias
Muscle twitching	Blurred vision	Grand mal seizures
Mild ataxia	Stupor	Renal failure
Slight tremor	Clonic limb movements	Hallucinations
Dizziness	Syncope	Deep tendon hyperreflexia
Slurred speech	Delirium	Coma or death
Vomiting	EKG and/or EEG changes	
Abdominal pain	Nystagmus	

Note: EEG = electro-encephalogram; EKG = electrocardiogram

Table 17-7 Teaching Points for Clients Taking Lithium

Advise clients to take with food or milk to reduce gastric irritation.

Inform clients to expect fine hand tremors, increase in urination, thirst, mild nausea (these symptoms may decrease with time), and possible weight gain.

Stress side effects that require immediate notification of prescriber (vomiting, diarrhea, severe tremor, muscle weakness, uncoordination, mental confusion) and stopping of medication.

Teach clients to maintain normal sodium (salt) intake.

Encourage clients to drink 10–12 glasses of liquid per day and to maintain normal fluid/sodium balance.

Teach clients to avoid excessive perspiration and to replace any water and sodium lost.

Advise clients to check with prescriber or pharmacist before self-medicating.

Instruct clients to elevate feet often during day to relieve any edema.

Counsel female clients to avoid pregnancy while on lithium due to possible birth defects.

Teach clients the necessity of having regular blood tests for dosage monitoring.

the treatment of bipolar disorder. Anticonvulsants are also used, including Tegretol (carbamazepine), Neurontin (gabapentin), Lamictal (lamotrigine), Trileptal (oxcarbazepine), and Topamax (topiramate). "Lithium alters intracellular conductance; the anticonvulsants act on the GABA system and sodium and calcium voltage-gated channels" (Keltner, Bostrom, & McGuinness, 2011, p. 201).

The effectiveness of the anticonvulsants for mood stabilization is most likely related to the drugs inhibition of kindling activitiy in the brain. The mechanisms of action work to normalize and stabilize neuronal activity which "increases the threshold of stimulation needed for cell firing" (Keltner, Bostrom, & McGuinness, 2011, p. 199). In addition to lithium, the therapeutic serum levels of divalproex, carbamazepine, and oxcarbazepine need to be closely monitored. (See **Table 17-9**.)

An advantage of divalproex is that it has a rapid onset of action, whereas lithium has a lag time of 7–10 days for therapeutic response.

Atypical Antipsychotic Medications

The traditional or typical antipsychotic medications are still used in the treatment of bipolar disorder.

Table 17-8 Antiepileptic Drugs (AEDs) Used for Mood Stabilization

Trade Name	Generic	Advantages	Some Disadvantages
Depakote	Divalproex sodium	Antimanic; particularly effective for treating acute mania; faster and safer than lithium (greater range between therapeutic and toxic levels); also useful for rapid cycling and mixed manic bipolar episodes	Weight gain, sedation, nausea, weak antidepressant properties, rare cases of liver and pancreas toxicity and thrombocytopenia; possible fertility issues for females; hair loss; teratogenic and should not be used during pregnancy
Lamictal	Lamotrigine	Reduces cycle frequency; strong antidepressant effect; no significant weight gain	Stevens-Johnson rash, nausea, headache, blurred vision, dizziness; slow titration to full dose
Tegretol	Carbamazepine	Antimanic	Agranulocytosis; liver toxicity; reduced effectiveness for birth control pills; nausea
Neurontin	Gabapentin	Adjunctive versus monotherapy; reduces anxiety	Fatigue, muscle aches, blurred vision
Trileptal	Oxcarbazepine	Antimanic properties; fewer side effects than carbamazepine.	GI upsets; sedation; can reduce effectiveness of birth control pills
Topamax	Topiramate	May prompt modest weight loss	Cognitive dulling; may reduce effectiveness of birth control pills; possible glaucoma; kidney stones

Table 17-9 Drug Therapeutic Levels

Antimanic Drug	Therapeutic Serum Level
Lithium	0.6–1.2 mEq/L
Depakote (divalproex)	50–115 mcg/mL
Tegretol (carbamazepine)	4–12mcg/mL
Trileptal (oxcarbazepine)	15–35 mcg/mL

Source: Keltner, Bostrom, & McGuinness (2011, p. 195).

However, due to their higher rate of extrapyramidal side effects, including tardive dyskinesia, they are now prescribed less often than the atypical antipsychotic medications. All of the atypical antipsychotic medications, except Clozaril (clozapine), Fanapt (iloperidone), and Latuda (lurasidone) are FDA approved to treat acute mania in bipolar disorder because of their mood-stabilizing effects (**Table 17-10**). Zyprexa (olanzapine) is approved for long-term use to prevent the recurrence of more mood episodes, and Seroquel (quetiapine) is indicated for the treatment of depressive episodes in bipolar disorder, in addition to acute mania. Risperdal (risperidone) and Seroquel (quetiapine) are associated with a more moderate level of weight gain than olanzapine. Geodon (ziprasidone) and Abilify (aripiprazole) contribute less to weight gain, and ziprasidone is considered weight neutral.

There are now three newer atypical antipsychotic medications. Saphris (asenapine) has the advantage of sublingual administration and does have FDA approval for treating bipolar disorder. Iloperidone only has FDA approval for the treatment of schizophrenia, but it is included here due to its off label usage for bipolar disorder. Lurasidone has the advantage of once-daily dosage and for being weight neutral. It has FDA approval for the treatment of schizophrenia and is currently pending approval for the treatment of bipolar disorder. The atypical antipsychotic agents can be used as monotherapy or in combination with lithium or one of the AEDs for the treatment of bipolar disorder (Keltner, 2007; Lehne, 2010).

Although the atypical antipsychotic agents have greater efficacy and fewer antiparkinsonian side effects than the typical or traditional antipsychotic agents, they are not without adverse side effects. Most of these drugs (see **Table 17-11**) increase the appetite and can contribute to significant weight gain. They also have been found to increase the incidence of metabolic disorder including glycemia (glucose in the blood) and dyslipidemia or excess levels of blood lipids such as cholesterol, lipoproteins, and triglyceride (American Diabetes Association, American Psychiatric Association, American Association of Clinical Endocrinologists, & North American Association for the Study of Obesity, (2004). (See **Tables 17-12** and **17-13**.) The incidence of type 2 diabetes has increased significantly for clients taking these medications. Therefore it is imperative for nurses to be vigilant in assessing these clients initially for risk fac-

Table 17-10 Atypical Antipsychotics as Mood Stabilizers

Trade Name	Generic	Advantages	Some Disadvantages
Risperdal	Risperidone	Antimanic; antipsychotic; may reduce cycling	Weight gain; increased prolactin levels
Zyprexa	Olanzapine	Antimanic; antipsychotic; may reduce cycling	Weight gain (significant)
Seroquel	Quetiapine	Antimanic; antipsychotic; may reduce cycling	Sedation; some weight gain; cognitive dulling
Geodon	Ziprasidone	Antimanic; antipsychotic; may reduce cycling; weight neutral	Sedation; potential heart rhythm changes
Abilify	Aripiprazole	Antimanic; antipsychotic; may reduce cycling; little weight gain	Insomnia or sedation; restlessness
Saphris	Asenapine	Approved for acute bipolar I, manic and mixed episodes; sublingual tablet	Market competition
Fanapt	Iloperidone	Off-label option only	Lack of FDA approval for bipolar disorder
Latuda	Lurasidone	Once-daily dosage; weight neutral	Current FDA approval only for schizophrenia; pending FDA approval for tx of bipolar disorder

Table 17-11 Antipsychotic Drugs, Obesity, and Diabetes

Drug	Weight Gain	Diabetes Risk	Dyslipidemia
Clozaril (clozapine)	+++	+	+
Zyprexa (olanzapine)	+++	+	+
Risperdal (risperidone)	++	D	D
Seroquel (quetiapine)	++	D	D
Abilify (aripiprazole)*	+/–	–	–
Geodon (ziprasidone)*	+/–	–	–

+ = increased effect, – = no effect, D = discrepant results
*Newer drugs with limited long-term data.
Note: Dyslipidemia is a disorder of protein metabolism; it is manifested by an elevation of the total cholesterol, the bad low-density lipoprotein (LDL) cholesterol, and the triglyceride concentrations; and a decrease in the good high-density lipoprotein (HDL) cholesterol concentration in the blood.

Source: American Diabetes Association, American Psychiatric Association, American Association of Clinical Endocrinologists, & North American Association for the Study of Obesity.(2004). Consensus development conference on antipsychotic drugs and obesity and diabetes, *Diabetes Care*, 27, 596–601.

Table 17-12 ADA Recommendations on Responding to Antipsychotic-Associated Metabolic Changes

If weight gain is > 5% of body weight, consider interventions, including switching to another second-generation antipsychotic medication.
If glycemia or dyslipidemia worsen, consider switching to a second-generation antipsychotic medication not associated with significant weight gain or diabetes.
Gradually discontinue or cross-titrate the medication.
Closely monitor psychiatric symptoms during periods of changing medications.

Note: Glycemia is the presence of glucose in the blood, and dyslipidemia is excess levels of blood lipids such as cholesterol, high-density lipoproteins, and triglycerides.
Source: American Diabetes Association. (2004). Consensus development conference on antipsychotic drugs and obesity and diabetes. *Diabetes Care, 27*, 596–601.

Table 17-13 Protocol for Monitoring Clients on Second-Generation (Atypical) Antipsychotic (SGA) Medications

Obtain an accurate personal and family history of obesity, diabetes, dyslipidemia, hypertension, and cardiovascular disease.
Closely monitor the client's weight and height so that BMI can be calculated.
Closely monitor changes in the client's waist circumference (at the level of the umbilicus).
Check the client's blood pressure regularly.
Obtain the client's fasting plasma glucose levels and a fasting lipid profile regularly.

Source: American Diabetes Association, American Psychiatric Association, American Association of Clinical Endocrinologists, & North American Association for the Study of Obesity. (2004). Consensus development conference on antipsychotic drugs and obesity and diabetes, *Diabetes Care, 27*, 596–601.

tors, to teach them carefully from the initiation of treatment, and to monitor their course carefully with documentation. Before treatment is begun, clients must be weighed, body mass index (BMI) and waist circumference calculated, and fasting blood glucose and lipid profile tested. With every subsequent visit, clients must be weighed and blood pressure taken. Blood tests also need to be repeated at intervals. If a client gains more than 5% of body weight during the first month on one of these medications, strong consideration should be given for switching to another medication option (ADA, 2004) (See Table 17-12).

Mood stabilizers may take a few weeks to establish a maximum response, so other medications may be used initially to provide more immediate relief from the agitation, nervousness, and insomnia that often accompany a manic episode. The antipsychotic agents mentioned previously may have some calming effect before they help with mood stabilizing. They are also beneficial when psychotic symptoms are present. The benzodiazepines, such as Ativan (lorazepam) or Klonopin (clonazepam), are sometimes used, preferably only on a short-term basis (Kahn et al., 2000; Lehne, 2010). These anxiolytics are schedule

IV controlled substances and may lead to physical dependency with long-term dosing. Their use requires close supervision, and extended use should be avoided for clients with a history of alcohol or drug abuse.

Many clients with bipolar disorder need to have regular adjustments in their medication regimen. Life circumstances and global seasonal environments are constantly in a state of flux, which can have a definite impact on internal body chemistry. It is very helpful for clients to keep descriptive records of their moods. Reporting any mood alterations to their prescribers can greatly facilitate any need for medication adjustment.

Other Medications

Clients who do not respond or who have unacceptable side effects with the medications already discussed may be prescribed other agents such as Calan (verapamil), a calcium channel blocker; Catapres (clonidine), an alpha$_2$-adrenergic agonist; or Inderal (propranolol), a beta-adrenergic receptor blocker (Keltner, Bostrom, & McGuinness, 2011).

Critical Thinking Question

Does taking antidepressants cause bipolar disorder? Support your answer with examples.

Nursing Interventions

Nurses should provide a quiet, stimulus-free environment for clients who are experiencing acute mania. Staff members must discourage clients from acting out in an attempt to entertain the staff with their behavior. A quiet room or time out should be used as needed. Seclusion or restraints are a last resort for clients with safety issues. Medications should be administered as needed.

Although a therapeutic relationship is difficult to establish initially, the client must be emotionally supported and encouraged to inform staff members when feelings of hostility or anger increase. The nurse should not confront clients or argue with them; it is best to maintain a quiet, calm approach and to have brief but frequent contact. The nurse–client therapeutic relationship involves teaching the client and family about the disorder and the need to monitor signs and symptoms carefully to recognize and handle impending recurrences at an early stage.

During an acute manic phase, the nurse must help the client maintain adequate nutrition, sleep, and cleanliness (personal hygiene). Because the client has increased motor activity, the nurse may need to provide finger foods and beverages in small containers that can be consumed on the run. Documentation of intake and output is important. Clients often need assistance with hygiene, grooming, and dress. Medication may be administered to help clients get necessary and adequate rest. (See **Table 17-14.**)

Table 17-14 **Guidelines for Working With Clients With Mood Disorders**

Monitor for safety—always!
Utilize the therapeutic nurse–client relationship.
Demonstrate that you are interested.
Modulate your own mood.
Listen actively to the client and accept the client's feelings and expressions of apathy, hopelessness, gloom, and self-degradation.
Give objective feedback on accomplishments rather than compliments that the client may reject or disown.
Take advantage of teaching moments from the very first contact with the client and at each subsequent contact.
Promote with the client establishment of short- and long-term goals.
Emphasize the value and importance of adherence to treatment.
Direct the client's short-term behavior, when needed, and actively assist in making necessary decisions when the client is unable to self-direct.
Encourage independent self-care practices.
Monitor sleep patterns.
Check nutrition and hydration.
Conduct medication teaching as a continuous process.
Teach relaxation techniques.
Encourage independent self-care practices.
Include family and friends in the client's support network and in teaching.
Connect the client with peer support options and other resources for assistance.
Discuss with the client and family measures for protecting financial safeguards.
Help the client compose a plan for action to take in an emergency.
Supply the client with a list of provider and resource numbers to call.
Give the client a printed card with the number for the National 24-Hour Suicide Prevention Hotline: 1-(800) 273-TALK or 1-(800)-273-8255.

When clients are experiencing acute mania, the nurse should not confront clients or argue with them. The nurse should maintain a quiet, calm approach; have brief but frequent contact; and provide a quiet, stimulus-free environment when clients are experiencing acute mania.

Education for Clients and Families

The nurse must fully explain to the client and family members or significant others why the manic and depressive episodes recur. The nurse can increase the family's understanding and support by explaining that the disorder is an illness that can be treated effectively. Clients also must learn the effectiveness of each treatment and how to minimize side effects. The client should be able to recognize the early signs of mania, accept that treatment is necessary, and seek help as needed. (See **Table 17-15**.)

Clients with bipolar disorder must be warned that the antidepressants they take for depressive episodes may induce manic episodes if taken without a mood stabilizer. This knowledge allows the client and others to differentiate between lifting depression and impending mania. Clients who are receiving lithium should be advised to take food or milk to reduce gastric irritation, expect fine hand tremors and an increase in urination and thirst as well as weight gain, maintain appropriate salt intake, avoid excess perspiration, drink 10–12 glasses of water a day, suck on sugarless candies, elevate their feet for any edema, avoid pregnancy while on the drug, comply with having regular blood tests, and check with their prescribing practitioner before self-medicating for any condition.

Nurses must emphasize repeatedly the importance of taking medication as ordered, that effects will not be felt immediately, and that medication

Table 17-15 **Pointers for People Living With Mood Disorders**
Be your own best advocate.
Educate yourself thoroughly on your disorder and the treatment.
Learn the actions and potential side effects of your medications.
Collaborate with and be honest with your providers.
Follow your treatment regimen.
Take prescribed medication as ordered.
Keep all therapy appointments.
Keep a list of questions for your health care practitioner visits to maximize use of time.
Keep a record of all your medications, dosages, and any side effects.
Maintain a regular sleep schedule.
Maintain a regular schedule of activities.
Keep a journal of your moods and feelings.
Eat a healthy diet and drink adequate healthy liquids.
Avoid alcohol and substances.
Engage in regular exercise.
Attend a self-help, peer support group.
Read books, materials, and website information to expand your understanding.
Reach out to supportive family and friends.
Make a plan for what to do in an emergency.
Have a list of provider and personal numbers to call.
Practice relaxation techniques.
Nourish your own spirituality.
Maintain good dental hygiene.
Take part in positive activities with others.
Plan recreation and fun activities.
Have music you love available.
Be realistic in your expectations of yourself and others.
Be generous with forgiveness for others and self.
Keep a list of your accomplishments in plain view.
In order to help yourself, you have to help others.
Kindness and small acts of thoughtfulness can help one connect with the world, expand emotionally, and improve others' lives and one's own.

CASE STUDIES Mr. M.

Mr. M. is a 31-year-old professor of Italian at a major university. He is single, lives alone, and his family lives out of state. He became depressed during the past year while he was applying for tenure. The psychiatrist he saw treated him with sertraline (Zoloft). The medication was very effective in relieving his depression, but after about 8 months, he became hypomanic with increasing disturbances in his behavior. Prior to this he had not experienced any signs of mental illness. He had received an award as an outstanding professor with an impressive list of publications to his credit.

Mr. M. was brought to the ER by his girlfriend and admitted to the crisis unit. His girlfriend noted that his behavior had been escalating for several weeks. She reported the following behaviors:

- He had slept only a few hours in the past week, experiencing high energy levels with no desire to rest.
- His behavior had become uncontrolled and potentially dangerous, including drinking much more than usual and driving recklessly.
- He had recently been reported for being too friendly with several female students and assistant instructors, with two women filing sexual harassment charges against him.
- He stood up in class that day and declared that he was receiving an important message from God and that he had a plan for bringing peace to the world.
- He had also been spending money furiously, buying venture stocks with some inheritance money, and using his credit cards to buy Italian wines by the case to stock his wine cellar.
- He was calling old friends and colleagues on the phone at all hours of the night.

On the night he was brought to the ER, he was loud and intrusive to other patrons in a restaurant and demanded to be given the special attention deserved by someone of his notoriety. After only two drinks he started singing loudly and swinging around a decorative column. Four staff members struggled to get him out the front door. It was all his girlfriend could do to get him to the car. Against his wishes, she drove him straight to the hospital, yet upon arrival he did agree to sign for a voluntary admission.

The girlfriend told the staff before leaving that she was concerned for Mr. M., especially since he just learned that week that his tenure had been denied, but she was really getting weary of struggling with their relationship. Mr. M. appeared unshaven, with very wrinkled clothes, yet bursting with energy and unable to sit down for his intake interview.

Mr. M. had a *DSM-IV-TR*, Axis I diagnosis of bipolar I, most recent episode manic. Some nursing diagnoses that apply to this client are identified in the following nursing care plan.

must not be discontinued just because the client feels better. Clients must be taught about nutrition because diet and fluid intake can greatly affect the action of the medication. Clients and family members should know when and how to seek help from crisis intervention services and their ongoing support system. The psychiatric nurse is often the practitioner who brings together the client and the needed community resources.

Critical Thinking Question

Should a client tell an employer that she or he has a bipolar disorder? How can such a decision impact the client's work situation?

Suicide and Mood Disorders

Suicide takes the lives of over 30,000 Americans a year—nearly twice the number of homicides—and worldwide, suicide is the leading cause of violent death, outnumbering homicide and war-related deaths. It is the 11th leading cause of death of all Americans; the 8th leading cause of death for all U.S. men, and the 3rd leading cause of death among young people 15–24 years of age. More than four times as many men as women die by suicide, although women attempt suicide three times as often as men. Native American youth are 3–4 times more likely to die by suicide than white or black youth. There are 25 attempts for every completed suicide, with approxi-

Nursing Care Plan **Bipolar I Disorder, Manic Episode**

Nursing Diagnosis 1: Risk for injury related to mania and delusional thinking, as evidenced by believing one is receiving messages from God, intrusive behavior in public, and high energy level.

Nursing Diagnosis 2: Disturbed sleep pattern related to the symptoms of mania, as evidenced by sleeping only a few hours in a week without feeling tired.

Nursing Diagnosis 3: Risk for situational low self-esteem related to change in expected job progression, as evidenced by denial of tenure in academic position and potential loss of significant other

Nursing Diagnosis 4: Ineffective coping related to manic state, as evidenced by drinking more than usual, driving recklessly, making unwelcome sexual advances, and spending money excessively

Expected Outcomes **Short term:**	Nursing Interventions	Evaluations
• Will contract not to harm self or others during hospital stay. Will follow unit rules.	• Develop caring rapport with client. • Regularly assess client for safety. • Review unit rules with client and give him any necessary reminders to help him display acceptable behavior.	• Client remains free of injury during inpatient hospital stay. • Client follows the unit's rules with minimal difficulty.
• Will experience a decrease in or cessation of psychotic ideation.	• Observe client for changes in psychotic ideation.	• Client displays a calming energy level and his thoughts gradually return to a reality base within 72 hours. • Interacts coherently with staff and peers.
• Will not engage in substance abuse/misuse.	• Assess client for substance abuse/misuse.	• Client has no signs of substance abuse, with a normal blood alcohol level and drug screen.
• Will sleep at least 6 hours per night.	• Monitor sleep and promote positive sleep hygiene.	• Client is sleeping for at least 6 continuous hours during the night.
• Will achieve adequate food and fluid intake. • Will bathe and groom daily. • Will participate in unit activity schedule.	• Monitor food and fluid intake for adequacy. • Discuss plans for future career options.	• Client has appropriate food and fluid intake and, is appropriately engaging in self-care, and is groomed. Client is beginning to talk about his job situation and is expressing appropriate feelings of sadness and anger related to his loss and alteration in status. • Client is demonstrating appropriate behavior with staff and peers on the unit and is beginning to discuss his need for follow-up care for his bipolar disorder and excessive substance use.
• Will make appointment for follow-up care with psychiatric and counseling center before discharge.	• Discuss the importance of ongoing follow-up care in the prevention of relapse.	• Makes appointment for two days after planned discharge date.

In addition to maintaining safety and preventing self-injury, nurses must plan for the depressive or manic episodes that clients with mood disorders experience. The nurse may implement a formal agreement (no-suicide contract) specifying that clients will refrain from harming themselves and will notify the nurse or other staff of strong suicidal thoughts or urges. Clients with mood disorders must be regularly assessed for suicidality. Ask, "Are you thinking of hurting yourself?" If the answer is yes, it is imperative to ask, "Do you have a plan in mind?" If this answer is also yes, established suicide precautions must be taken. Psychiatric nurses should be aware of the factors that have been identified as having the potential to protect a client from acting on suicidal ideation, which include involvement in clinical treatment for mental, physical and substance abuse disorders, access to community-based agencies and resources, restricted access to means of suicide, family and community support systems, ability to problem solve and handle stressors, and cultural and religious belief systems that discourage self-destructive behaviors such as suicide (AAS, 2008). These factors can be utilized to help the client with a mood disorder to be able to safely cope with suicidal thoughts.

Critical Thinking Question

Is it ever appropriate to not be concerned if a client reports having ideas about wanting to be dead?

Clinical Example

Michael, who was in his mid-40s, was admitted to the psychiatric unit accompanied by his wife, who reported that in the previous 3 weeks, he was constantly crying, had stopped going to work, was rarely sleeping, and had lost over 20 pounds. During the night of admission, Michael went into the bathroom, and while the door was briefly shut, separating him from observation, he stuffed a sock securely down his throat, lost consciousness, and collapsed to the floor, where his body blocked the door. After several attempts, staff pulled him from the stall, removed the sock from his trachea and attempted resuscitation. It was unsuccessful, and Michael died.

Summary

All individuals experience ups and downs of emotions in daily life, and these can be more marked in times of great loss or grieving. The mood disorders are separated into the depressive or unipolar disorders (major depressive disorder and dysthymic disorder) and bipolar disorders (bipolar I, bipolar II, and cyclothymic disorder). Additionally, mood disorders can be related to general medical conditions or can be substance-induced disorders, and they can occur seasonally or after delivery of an infant.

All of the mood disorders have a neurologic basis, and genetics play a role because the disorders occur in families with psychosocial factors impacting the development and presentation of the disorders. Mood disorders are highly recurrent, with every episode increasing the likelihood of additional episodes. Women are twice as likely as men to experience depression and have a higher incidence rate of bipolar II disorder; bipolar I disorder with classic mania occurs about equally in both sexes.

The selective serotonin reuptake inhibitors, atypical antidepressants, tricyclic antidepressants, and monoamine oxidase inhibitors can all be equally effective in treating the depressive disorders. Lithium remains an effective treatment for clients with bipolar I disorder with classic mania. The antiepileptic drugs also are effective in treating bipolar disorders. Antidepressants should never be given to a client with bipolar disorder without a concurrent mood stabilizer due to the concern of precipitating a manic episode. The goal of medication treatment is to fit the medication to the symptoms of the individual client with consideration for the particular drug actions, advantages, and side effects.

Research indicates a higher improvement rate in the treatment of depression with a combination of psychotherapy and antidepressants. Supportive psychotherapy, cognitive behavioral therapy, and interpersonal therapy are various modalities.

Clients with mood disorders should be regularly monitored for suicidal ideation because the suicide rate for this client population is 10–15%. Teaching clients and family members about their disorders, medications, and other available treatments is important. Nurses should refer clients and their families to peer support networks and other self-help resources.

The possibility of suicide must always be considered when caring for clients with a mood disorder; they should be asked whether they currently have or have had suicidal thoughts or plans.

A no-suicide contract is a formal agreement specifying that clients will refrain from harming themselves and will notify the nurse or other staff of strong suicidal thoughts or urges.

Studies indicate that clients with serious mental illness as well as physical health problems bear a greater burden of disease as they attempt to cope with their various conditions.

Annotated References

American Association of Suicidology (AAS). (2007). Retrieved from http://www.suicidology.org/c/document_library/get_file?folderId=232&name=DLFE-244.pdf
This organization's website provides fact sheets, statistics, references, links of interest, and publications for professionals and interested individuals.

American Diabetes Association, American Psychiatric Association, American Association of Clinical Endocrinologists, & North American Association for the Study of Obesity. (2004). Consensus development conference on antipsychotic drugs and obesity and diabetes, *Diabetes Care, 27,* 596–601.
This article explores the relationship between obesity, diabetes, and dyslipidemia and cardiovascular disease (CVD) when clients are receiving second-generation antipsychotic medications.

American Psychiatric Association. (2000). *Diagnostic and statistical manual of mental disorders* (4th ed., text rev.). Washington, DC: Author.
This is the official nomenclature used by psychiatrists, other physicians, psychologists, registered professional nurses, social workers, occupational and recreational therapists, counselors, and other health and mental health professionals across all settings—inpatient, outpatient, partial hospital, consultation–liaison, clinic, private practice, and primary care, and with community populations.

Crutchfield, D. B. (2006). *Review of psychotropic drugs.* Wilmington, DE: Astra Zeneca Pharmaceuticals.
This book includes a review of current psychotropic drugs including their actions, side effects, adverse effects, and dosages.

De Man-van Ginkel, J. M., Gooskens, F., Schuumans, M. J., Lindemann, E., Hafsteinsdottir, T. B., & Rehabilitation Guideline Stroke Working Group (2010). A systematic review of therapeutic interventions for poststroke depression and the role of nurses. *Journal of Clinical Nursing, 19*(23–24), 3274–3290.
Depression after stroke is an important problem with adverse effects on the patient's ability to participate in rehabilitation and on outcomes. These findings enable nurses to intervene effectively to reduce the occurrence and severity of depression in patients after a stroke.

Depression and Bipolar Support Alliance (DBSA). (2005). *What helps and what hurts.* Chicago, IL: Author.
This brochure from a national advocacy group provides suggestions to help family members communicate with clients who are dealing with symptoms of depression or bipolar disorder.

Depression and Bipolar Support Alliance (DBSA). (2006). *The state of depression in America report.* Chicago, IL: Author.
This report examines the economic, social, and individual burdens of this illness and explores opportunities to improve the availability and quality of care while working toward recovery and better lives for all Americans.

Druss, B. G., Rosenheck, R. A., & Sledge, W. H. (2000). Health and disability costs of depressive illness in a major U.S. corporation. *American Journal of Psychiatry, 157*(8), 1274–1278.
This article explores the cost of depression to a major employer. It concludes that the cost in lost workdays is as great as or greater than the cost of many other common medical illnesses, and the combination of depressive and other common illnesses is particularly costly. The strong association between depressive illness and sick days in younger workers suggests that the impact of depression may increase as these workers age.

Forrester, A. W., Lipsey, J. R., Teitelbaum, M. L., DePaulo, J. R., Andrzejewski, P. L., & Robinson, R. G. (1992). Depression following myocardial infarction. *International Journal of Psychiatry and Medicine, 22,* 33–46.
This study concluded that major depression is common in the acute postmyocardial infarction period and identified that major depressive syndromes were present in 19% (n = 25) of the patients and were associated with prior history of mood disorder, large infarctions, and functional physical impairment.

Garabedian, M. (2009). *Intimate partner violence and postpartum depression.* Society for Maternal-Fetal Medicine: Abstract 194. Retrieved from http://www.goodsearch.com/search.aspx?keywords=garabedian+University+of+California+at+San+Francsisco+postpartum+depression+
This cross-sectional study indicates that female victims of domestic violence have a 40% increased risk of developing postpartum depression.

Garlow, S. J., & Nemeroff, C. B. (2005). The neurochemistry of depressive disorders:

Clinical studies. In D. S. Charney & E. J. Nestler (Eds.), *Neurobiology of mental illness* (pp. 440–460). New York, NY: Oxford University Press.
This chapter describes the state of knowledge of neurochemical mechanisms underlying psychiatric disorders and the implications for diagnosis and treatment.

Gever, J. (2011, May 4). New structure proposed for DSM-5. *Medpage Today*. Retrieved from www.Medpagetoday.com/Psychiatry/DSM-5/26275
This article provides the highlights of the changes being proposed for the DSM-5.

Glod, C. A. (1998). *Contemporary psychiatric-mental health nursing: The brain-behavior connection*. Philadelphia, PA: F. A. Davis.
This is a textbook for nursing students that discusses the theories that are the foundation for linking brain and behavior; it also explores healthy psychological development.

Goldstein, D. J., & Potter, W. Z. (2004). Biological theories of depression and implications for current and new treatments. In D. A. Ciraulo & R. I. Shader (Eds.), *Pharmacotherapy of depression* (pp. 1–32). Totowa, NJ: Humana Press.
This chapter provides an orientation to the biological causes of depression as a basis for the safe and effective use of antidepressants.

Greenberg, P. E., Kessler, R. C., Birnbaum, H. G., Leong, S. A., Lowe, S. W., Bergland, P. A., & Corey-Lisle, P. K. (2003). The economic burden of depression in the United States: How did it change between 1990 and 2000? *Journal of Clinical Psychiatry, 64*(12), 1465–1476.
Using a human capital approach, the authors developed prevalence based estimates of three major cost categories: (1) direct costs, (2) mortality costs arising from depression-related suicides, and (3) costs associated with depression in the workplace. The results revealed that the economic burden of depression remained relatively stable between 1990 and 2000, despite a dramatic increase in the number of individuals who received treatment.

Hagerty, B. M., & Williams, R. A. (1999). The effects of sense of belonging, social support, conflict, and loneliness on depression. *Nursing Research, 48*(4), 215–219.
The study findings emphasize the importance of relationship-oriented experiences as part of assessment and intervention strategies for individuals with depression.

Kahn, D. A., Ross, R., Printz, D. J., & Sachs, G. S. (2000, April). Treatment of bipolar disorder: A guide for patients and families. In G. S. Sachs, D. J. Printz, D. A. Kahn, D. Carpenter, & J. P. Docherty (Eds.), *The expert consensus guideline series: Medication treatment of bipolar disorder 2000: Postgraduate Medicine Special Report*, pp. 97–104. Cincinnati, OH: American Brands.
This guide is part of a consensus report on medication treatment of bipolar disorder. It is intended to answer some of the most commonly asked questions about bipolar disorder.

Keltner, N. L. (2007). Antidepressant drugs. In N. L. Keltner, L. H. Schwecke, & C. E. Bostrom (Eds.), *Psychiatric nursing* (5th ed., pp. 232–251). St. Louis, MO: Mosby.
This is the chapter on antidepressant medications in a textbook that takes a practical, clinical approach to nursing by integrating clinical realities with the theory taught in nursing schools, emphasizing those actions for which nurses are primarily responsible.

Keltner, N. L., & Folks, D. G. (2005). *Psychotropic drugs*. St. Louis, MO: Mosby.
This book is a comprehensive discussion of the biologic basis of psychotropic drugs used for specific disorders; it includes disorder-specific narrative chapters and drug profiles.

Keltner, N. L., Bostrom. C. E. & McGuinness, T. (2011). (Eds.) *Psychiatric nursing* (6th ed.). St. Louis, MO: Mosby.
The authors provide a discussion of the impact of sleep-wake cycles on mood and depression.

Kennedy, C., Salsberry, P., Nickel, J., Hunt, C., & Chipps, E. (2005). The burden of disease in those with serious mental and physical illnesses. *Journal of the American Psychiatric Nurses Association, 11*(1), 45–51.
This book provides a review of the effects of both mental and physical conditions and illnesses on patients and the need for skilled nursing care.

Kessler, R.C., Chiu, W. T., Demler, O., Merikanqas, K. R., & Walters, E. E. (2005). Prevalence, severity, and comorbidity of 12-month DSM-IV disorders in the National Comorbidity Survey Replication. *Archives of General Psychiatry, 62*(6), 617–627.
This article presents the WHO data on prevalence, comobidity, and severity of data from the

World Mental Health survey conducted in the United States.

Kübler-Ross, E. (1997). *On death and dying.* New York, NY: Touchstone.
This is one of the most important books of the 20th century on death and dying. It introduced clinicians, patients, and their families to the grieving process and how one transitions from life.

Lehne, R. A. (2010). *Pharmacology for nursing care* (7th ed.) St. Louis, MO: Saunders.
In a student-friendly manner and with clinical precision and a clear focus on understanding drug prototypes, this book presents pharmacology in the context of nursing care.

McDermott, W. (Ed.). (2005, Winter). Antidepressants can lead to tooth, gum disease. *Schizophrenia Digest, 3*(1), 25.
The author discusses how antidepressants can cause tooth and gum disease and the need for good dental regimens and routine dental care for those taking these medications.

National Alliance for Research on Schizophrenia and Depression (NARSAD). (2002). Brain disorders top list of major cases of disability worldwide. *National Alliance for Research on Schizophrenia and Depression Research Newsletter, 14*(2), 25.
The World Health Organization in 2002 reported that brain disorders were the leading cause of disability from noncommunicable diseases, and their impact was on the rise.

National Institute of Mental Health (NIMH). (2003). *Suicide in the U.S.: Statistics and Prevention.* Retrieved from www.nimh.nih.gov/publicat/harmsway.cfm
Suicide is a major, preventable public health problem. This NIMH report presents a discussion of the statistics, the complexity of the behavior, and some of the risk factors (age, gender, or ethnic group) that may occur in combination or change over time.

National Institute of Mental Health (NIMH). (2009). *Brain stimulation therapies.* Retrieved from http://www.nimh.nih.gov/health/topics/brain-stimulation-therapies/brain-stimulation-therapies.shtml
This is a review of the various brain stimulation therapies that involve activating or touching the brain with electricity, magnets, or implants in the treatment of depression or other disorders.

National Institute of Mental Health (NIMH). (2011). *Bipolar disorder.* Retrieved from http://www.nimh.nih.gov/health/topics/bipolar-disorder/index.shtml
This is a government booklet that describes bipolar disorder symptoms, causes, and treatments, with information on getting help and coping with the disorder.

North American Nursing Diagnosis Association (NANDA). (2012). *Nursing diagnoses: Definitions and classifications—2012–2014.* Philadelphia, PA: Author.
The official compilation of nursing diagnoses from the North American Nursing Diagnosis Association.

Osterweil, N. (2007, May 25). APA: Simple screen improves suicide risk assessment. *Psychiatric Times.* Retrieved from www.psychiatrictimes.com/display/article/10168/58341?pageNumber=2
The author reports on a new, simplified method for screening clients for suicide risk.

Pampallona, S., Bollini, P., Tibaldi, G., Kupelnick, B., & Munizza, C. (2004). Combined pharmacotherapy and psychological treatment for depression: A systematic review. *Archives of General Psychiatry, 61*(7), 714–719.
The authors concluded that psychologic treatment combined with antidepressant therapy is associated with a higher improvement rate than drug treatment alone and, in longer therapies, the addition of psychotherapy helps keep patients in treatment.

Parker, G. (2002). Differential effectiveness of newer and older antidepressants appears mediated by an age effect on the phenotypic expression of depression. *Acta Psychiatrica Scandinavica, 106*(3), 168–170.
The author discusses why the broader based tricyclic antidepressants may be more effective than SSRIs in implicating age and depressive subtype influences.

Pestka, E. L., Hale, A. M., Johnson, B. L., Lee, J. L., & Poppe, K. A. (2007). Cytochrome P450 testing for better psychiatric care. *Journal of Psychosocial Nursing and Mental Health Services, 45*(10): 15–18.
As patient advocates, nurses should understand how to identify patients most likely to benefit from CYP2D6 and CYP2C19 testing, how to ensure informed consent for such testing, and how to educate patients about testing and test results.

Simon, G. F., Ludman, E. J., Tutty, S., Operskalski, B., & Von Korff, M. (2004).

Telephone psychotherapy and telephone care management for primary care patients starting antidepressant therapy. *Journal of the American Medical Association, 292*(8), 935–942.

The authors discovered that for primary care patients beginning antidepressant treatment, a telephone program integrating care management and structured cognitive-behavioral psychotherapy significantly improved satisfaction and clinical outcomes, suggesting a new public health model of psychotherapy for depression.

Snyder, A., & Matsuno, J. (2001). *Psychopharmacology handbook for nurses.* Provo, UT: Utah State Hospital.

This book provides an extensive review of drug therapies utilized in the treatment of mental illness.

Townsend, M. C. (2009). *Psychiatric mental health nursing* (6th ed.). Philadelphia, PA: F. A. Davis Co.

A textbook of essential information for nursing students about psychiatric nursing. It includes highlighted patient education boxes.

U.S. Food and Drug Administration. (2006, February 28). *FDA approves Emsam (selegiline) as first drug patch for depression.* Retrieved from http://www.fda.gov/bbs/topics/News/2006/New01326.html

This is a link to the FDA's press release announcing its approval of Emsam (selegiline) as the first drug patch for depression, including its ability to be used at its lowest dose without the restrictions required of MAOI-class depression drugs.

van Praag, H. M., de Kloet, E. R., & van Os, J. (2004). *Stress, the brain, and depression.* Cambridge, UK: Cambridge University Press.

The authors examine the potential for traumatic life events causing depression. They examine three major themes: the pathophysiologic role of stress in depression, whether or not a subtype of depression that is particularly stress inducible exists, and finally, how best to diagnose and treat depression in relation to its biologic basis.

Wieseke, A., Bantz, D., & May, D. (2011, July). What you need to know about bipolar disorder. *American Nurse Today, 6*(7), 8–12.

The authors review myths, causes, sign and symptoms, pharmacologic and nonpharmacologic treatment, and nursing management of clients with bipolar disorder.

Additional References

Earley, P. (2006). *Crazy—A father's search through America's mental health madness.* New York, NY: G. P. Putnam.

In this book, Earley, a noted journalist, applies the term *crazy* to the broken system the mentally ill face when trying to seek mental health care. He writes about his son's traumatic experiences when he became ill with bipolar disorder. He describes the mental health system, the hospital, outpatient care, the legal system, and the jails, which now house more mentally ill people than the hospitals. Earley also makes suggestions for ways to correct the system and emphasizes the necessity for legal reform and a properly trained crisis intervention team.

Jackson, J. (2004). *The handbook for survivors of suicide.* Washington, DC: American Association of Suicidology.

This book is written as a quick-reference guide for survivors of suicide by a survivor who lost his young wife to suicide. Jackson describes his own journey to recovery and also gives information on how to find support groups in one's area.

Jamison, K. R. (1995). *An unquiet mind.* New York, NY: Vintage.

Dr. Jamison is a noted psychologist and a professor of psychiatry at Johns Hopkins University School of Medicine. This is an autobiography in which Jamison describes her own long-time struggles with the extreme highs and lows of bipolar disorder, including suicidal ideation and even suicidal behavior.

Sherman, M. D., & Sherman, D. M. (2006). *I'm not alone: A teen's guide to living with a parent who has a mental illness.* Minneapolis, MN: Seeds of Hope Books.

This book was written by a clinical psychologist and her mother for teenagers who are living with a parent with serious mental illness. The authors attempt to normalize the teen's wide range of emotions. They also give suggestions for positive coping strategies.

Internet Resources

For a full suite of assignments and additional learning activities, use the access code located in the front of your book to visit this exclusive website: http://go.jblearning.com/mentalhealth. If you do not have an access code, you can obtain one at the site.

Learning Objectives

After reading this chapter, you will be able to:

- Identify the signs and symptoms of the anxiety disorders.
- Recognize the difference between normal and pathological anxiety.
- Identify modalities used in the treatment of anxiety disorders.
- Apply the nursing process to the care of clients with anxiety disorders.
- Define educational objectives for clients with anxiety disorders and their families.
- Identify signs and symptoms of dissociative disorders.
- Identify nursing interventions for clients with dissociative disorders.

Key Terms

Agoraphobia
Anxiety
Behavior therapy
Cognitive therapy
Compulsion
Depersonalization
Derealization
Dissociation
Exposure
Flooding
Obsession
Panic attack
Phobia
Ritualistic behavior
Serotonin
Systematic desensitization

Anxiety and Dissociative Disorders

Patricia G. O'Brien and Loraine Fleming

http://go.jblearning.com/mentalhealth 

For a full suite of assignments and additional learning activities, use the access code located in the front of your book to visit this exclusive website: http://go.jblearning.com/mentalhealth. If you do not have an access code, you can obtain one at the site.

Introduction

This chapter presents a discussion of both anxiety and dissociative disorders. Although they are two distinct disorders, some anxiety disorders are characterized by dissociative behaviors, and the dissociative disorders, like the anxiety disorders, are rooted in a prior traumatic or stressful event. Revisions in the classification of the anxiety disorders is under consideration for the *Diagnostic and Statistical Manual of Mental Disorders*, fifth edition (DSM-5). Obsessive-compulsive disorders (OCD) may remain within the anxiety disorders chapter or be classified separately along with other obsessive-compulsive spectrum disorders, such as skin-picking disorder and hair-pulling disorder. Testing is being done on whether hoarding will be considered as a separate disorder or as a symptom of OCD. The criteria for posttraumatic stress disorder (PTSD), acute stress disorder, and dissociative disorders are also being reviewed and may be classified separately from the anxiety disorders. The content presented here is consistent with the disorders and diagnostic criteria in the *Diagnostic and Statistical Manual of Mental Disorders*, fourth edition, text revision (*DSM-IV-TR*).

Anxiety Disorders

Anxiety is a universally experienced feeling. It is a response to stress that generally has an adaptive function that alerts us to real danger and motivates us to prepare for and succeed in various situations. However, when feelings of anxiety are excessive and interfere significantly with a person's functioning, they are considered pathologic and are diagnosed as an anxiety disorder (American Psychiatric Association [APA], 2000).

Agoraphobia is a disabling complication of panic disorder, characterized by phobic avoidance.

The *DSM-IV-TR*, codes anxiety disorders on Axis I. According to the APA, panic attacks and agoraphobia are not coded disorders; rather, they are considered components of the recognized disorders.

Panic attacks usually start after an illness, an accident, the break-up of a relationship, or the birth of a child.

A **panic attack** is defined as the sudden onset of intense fear, in which the client experiences at least four of the following symptoms: sweating, palpitations, trembling, shortness of breath, choking sensation, chest pain, nausea or abdominal discomfort, lightheadedness or dizziness, derealization (feeling of unreality) or depersonalization (feeling as though one is outside one's body, observing), fear of losing control (sometimes described as going crazy), fear of dying, paresthesia (numbness or tingling sensation), and chills or hot flashes (see **Table 18-1**). The attack may be in response to a specific situation, such as being chased by a dog, or occur out of the blue. The attack generally lasts 5–30 minutes. Panic attacks can be a component of panic disorder, social phobia, specific phobic disorder, or major depressive disorder, or a panic attack may occur as an isolated episode (National Institute of Mental Health [NIMH], 2010).

Table 18-1 Symptoms of a Panic Attack

- Sweating
- Palpitations
- Trembling
- Shortness of breath
- Choking sensation
- Chest pain
- Nausea or abdominal discomfort
- Lightheadedness or dizziness
- Derealization (feeling of unreality) or depersonalization (feeling as though one is outside one's body, observing)
- Fear of losing control (sometimes described as going crazy)
- Fear of dying
- Paresthesia (numbness or tingling sensation)
- Chills or hot flashes

It is not unusual for clients to seek treatment in an emergency room for the symptoms of a first panic attack, which is often attributed to nervousness.

The essential feature of **agoraphobia** is anxiety about being in places or situations from which escape may be difficult or in which help may not be available should a panic attack occur. This leads to the avoidance of situations such as leaving home, being in a crowd, or flying in an airplane. In agoraphobia, the fear is not of the specific situation; the fear is of having a panic attack, losing control, and being helpless. Agoraphobia can interfere with the performance of routine activities such as grocery shopping, traveling to work, and enjoying social functions.

Essential Features of Anxiety Disorders

Although anxiety disorders may be manifested in a number of ways, there are essential features that distinguish the various disorders. Each of the anxiety disorders centers around an experience of irrational and disproportionate fear or dread. Whether the symptoms are physiologic (e.g., palpitations, excessive sweating) or psychologic (e.g., the experience of intrusive, disturbing thoughts), the underlying precipitant is fear. **Figure 18-1** summarizes the *DSM-IV-TR* anxiety disorders. It is not uncommon for people to be diagnosed with more than one anxiety disorder.

Panic Disorder

Panic disorder is characterized by recurrent, unexpected panic attacks followed by at least 1 month of persistent concern about having another panic attack. The panic attack is not due to a general medical condition or the effects of an ingested substance. Attacks can occur with moderate frequency, perhaps once a week, for months at a time, or be more concentrated, such as daily for a shorter period of perhaps 1 week. It is not unusual for weeks or even months to go by with no attacks only for them to resume again. Agoraphobia may or may not be associated with panic disorder. There is a high incidence of major depressive disorder as well as other anxiety disorders associated with panic disorder.

Agoraphobia Without History of Panic Disorder

In agoraphobia without panic disorder, the client has never experienced unexpected recurrent panic attacks, yet fears the occurrence of incapacitating or extremely embarrassing panic-like symptoms or may experience limited-symptom attacks rather than full panic attacks (APA, 2000). In a limited-symptom panic attack, the client experiences fewer than 4 of the 13 symptoms of a panic attack (Table 18-1). For example, the client may feel short of breath and light-headed and have a fear of losing control.

Specific Phobia

The essential feature of a specific **phobia** is a marked and persistent fear of a particular object, place, or situation referred to as a "phobic stimulus." Exposure to the phobic stimulus provokes an immediate anxiety response. As with all anxiety disorders, the diagnosis is appropriate only if avoidance or fear of the stimulus interferes significantly with the client's daily routine, occupational functioning, or social life or causes marked personal distress and is disproportionate to any real danger (APA, 2000). If recurrent panic attacks are always related to a specific stimulus, the diagnosis is specific phobia rather than panic dis-

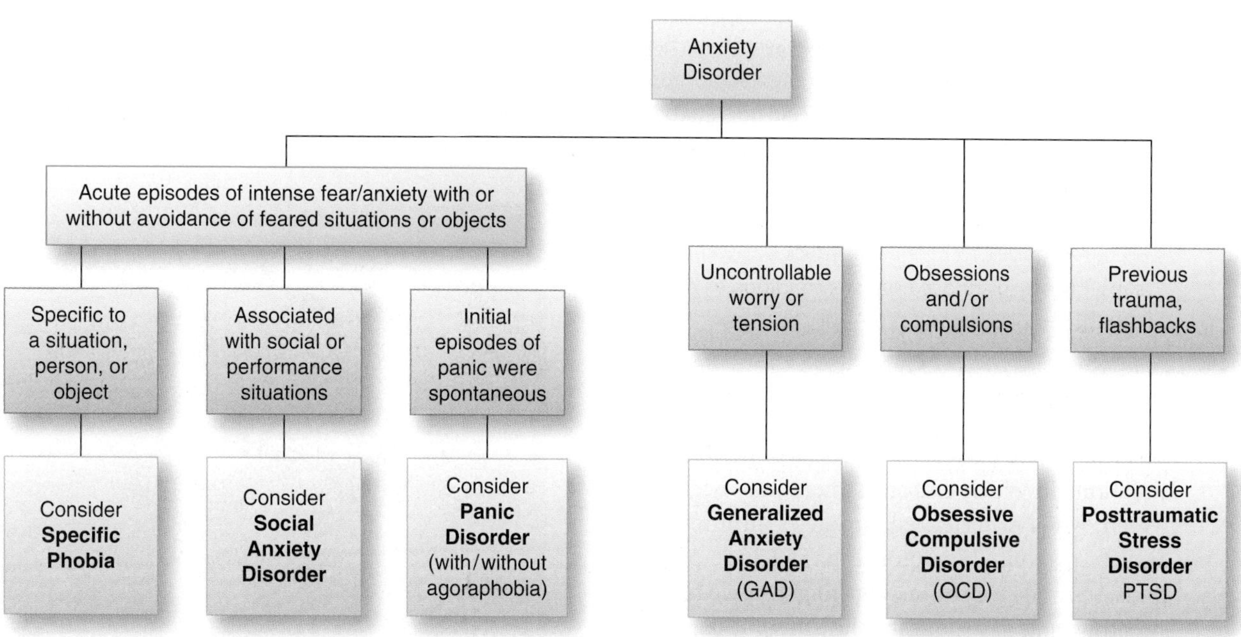

Figure 18-1 Concept Map for DSM Anxiety Disorders
Source: Western Australian Therapeutics Advisory Group. (2008). Anxiety Disorders Drug Treatment Guidelines

Social phobia is potentially debilitating. The impairment caused by the disorder may be extensive, affecting educational attainment, career advancement, and family and social relationships.

Social phobias include fears of eating, drinking, speaking, and writing in front of others and avoidance of public restrooms, restaurants, public transportation, banks, stores, and other public places.

Obsessions are unwanted, recurrent ideas or urges. Compulsions are repetitive behaviors done in response to obsessions. For example, fear of illness from germs is an obsession; frequent hand washing is a related compulsion.

OCD is a pervasive and potentially disabling anxiety disorder.

order. A client with a specific fear of dogs may be able to go about his or her activities and only occasionally encounter a dog. In this example, the person's specific phobia is not considered a psychiatric disorder.

Critical Thinking Question

In the clinical example, how do Nancy's symptoms satisfy the criteria for specific phobia? In this example, is the phobic stimulus the elevator or the office?

Clinical Example

Nancy has lived with a fear of elevators ever since a childhood experience when she was trapped in one for several hours. Nancy had successfully coordinated her life to avoid the need to use elevators. Now 37 years old, Nancy has been employed at the same publishing company for 15 years. The company just recently announced that it would be relocating from a second-floor office suite to the 32nd floor of a new high-rise building.

Shortly after receiving this news, Nancy experienced heart palpitations, shortness of breath, ringing in her ears, nausea, and a feeling she described as "being far away." She told her supervisor she was feeling sick and went home. The symptoms subsided but returned the next day after she arrived at work. Nancy called her doctor, who advised her to go to the nearest ER. By the time Nancy arrived at the ER, her symptoms had subsided. She was evaluated and no physiologic cause was found for her symptoms. Nancy did not return to work that day, but the next day at work she again experienced the symptoms. Nancy went to see her primary physician, and upon further evaluation, her symptoms were recognized to be a panic attack. A psychiatrist subsequently diagnosed Nancy's condition as a specific phobic disorder.

Social Phobia

Social phobia refers to a fear of social or performance situations in which embarrassment may occur and which, when experienced, produces an immediate anxiety response. Symptoms may include palpitations, tremors, confusion, blushing, muscle tension, sweating, and gastrointestinal distress. It is not unusual to experience some of these symptoms when asked to perform or speak in front of a large audience; therefore, diagnosis of the disorder depends on the degree of discomfort and incapacitation that results from the anxiety. Social phobias are self-reinforcing; that is, the fear of performing leads to anxiety, which interferes with performance, causes embarrassment, and increases or reinforces the fear of performing. Persons with social phobias frequently lack social skills and experience severe social and work impairment.

Obsessive-Compulsive Disorder

Obsessive-compulsive disorder (OCD) is characterized by **obsessions** (repetitive, intrusive thoughts that make little sense) and by **compulsions** (repetitive, **ritualistic behaviors** that strive to neutralize the anxiety associated with the obsessions). The obsession may take the form of a persistent worry or an unreasonable belief, such as an exaggerated fear of contracting an illness from the germs acquired by touching a doorknob. Obsessions may include a need to be perfect, can be violent in nature, and may involve a fear of hurting someone. The thoughts cause anxiety, which is partly relieved by compulsive, ritualistic behavior.

For example, frequent hand washing may reduce the anxiety associated with the fear of illness resulting from touching the doorknob (**Figure 18-2**). Other compulsive behaviors are counting rituals, checking and rechecking, and precise arranging of objects in a particular order. To be defined as compulsive behaviors, the rituals must take more than 10 minutes a day (often much more time consuming than that) and must distress the client. Healthy people may also engage in rituals, such as checking several times to assure that they have unplugged the coffee maker before leaving for work. If the checking does not inter-

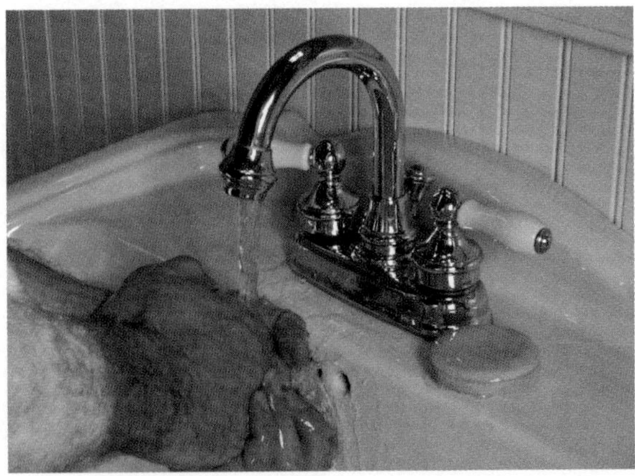

Figure 18-2 Overly frequent hand washing can be a compulsive behavior.

CASE STUDIES Mrs. S.

Ms. M. had a history of being shy and reclusive, and she recalls being uncomfortable at social events all her life. She was even aware of this at childhood birthday parties, and the feelings of anxiety associated with social events led her to avoid socializing in high school and college. Ms. M. could be comfortable at a structured activity, such as a school football game, but once the structured event was over, Ms. M. would become uncomfortable and would usually retreat to her room or the library.

Ms. M. did well academically and attained an excellent position in the computer field after college graduation. Her coworkers are also young, and there is an expected office culture of socialization after work. The times that Ms. M. accompanied her colleagues, she felt like an outsider. She felt very tense and experienced noticeable hand tremors, extreme nervousness, and profuse sweating and was unable to engage in any conversation. Ms. M. was concerned that her inability to socialize would have an impact on her ability to succeed at work. She also genuinely liked her coworkers and wanted to welcome friends in her life.

Nursing Care Plan **Social Phobia**

Nursing Diagnosis: Anxiety related to fear of being judged evidenced by marked discomfort in and avoidance of unstructured social situations.

Expected Outcome	Interventions	Evaluations
• Ms. M. will be more comfortable in social situations.	• Cognitive restructuring: Help Ms. M. identify the thoughts that inhibit social interaction (e.g., people will not like me; I won't know what to say; I will make a fool of myself). • Help Ms. M. challenge the reality of these thoughts and the consequences. • Social skills training: Review basic social skills, including conversation starters, and listening skills. • Role-play social interactions. • Refer Ms. M. to self-help books. • Develop a hierarchy of social activities: Ms. M. may initiate telephone calls to a colleague at work, have an in-office lunch with a colleague, attend an after-hours get-together for a specific short period of time, or invite a colleague to a structured social event (e.g., a movie or a baseball game). Gradually increase activities and duration as comfort and skills increase.	• Ms. M. is able to counter her negative thoughts with positive statements (e.g., is there any evidence that some people or all people do not like you? If people have different tastes, isn't it okay that some people do not like you? Even if this is true, are there some behaviors you can do despite this? If a friend had this same thought what would you suggest?). • Ms. M. appears more confident during role-playing. • Ms. M. identifies strategies she will use in real-life encounters to increase her comfort level. • Ms. M. recognizes positive responses from persons with whom she interacts. • She reports decreased symptoms of anxiety before and during social events. • Ms. M. begins to attend more social functions. • Ms. M. reports increased ease at social events and has made friends.

Visit http://go.jblearning.com/mentalhealth for additional care plans and exercises.

fere with the person's daily life or cause undue stress, this activity would not be considered pathological.

Posttraumatic Stress Disorder

A traumatic event that involved an actual or threatened death or physical injury that was personally directed at the client, witnessed by the client, or experienced by someone else and learned about by the client may be followed by posttraumatic stress disorder (PTSD). The presenting symptoms of PTSD vary and may include those associated with depression, anxiety, sleep disorder, sexual disorder, or even psychosis. Intense reexperiencing through traumatic memories is most common and can involve flashbacks or hallucinations. **Figure 18-3** shows the relationship among symptoms associated with a DSM diagnosis of PTSD.

Examples of traumatic events include the following:

- *Personally experienced events:* Military combat, assault (rape, mugging), kidnapping, being a prisoner of war, internment in a concentration camp, natural disasters (tornado, flood), severe auto accident, or being diagnosed with a life-threatening illness
- *Witnessed events:* Injury or unnatural death of another person from a violent assault, war, accident, or disaster; unexpectedly witnessing a dead body or body parts
- *Learning about events experienced by others:* Assault, serious injury, or accident experienced by a family member or close friend; learning that one's child has a life-threatening disease

Prior psychiatric history and poor social support increase a person's vulnerability to PTSD.

Clinical Example 

"I couldn't do anything without rituals. They invaded every aspect of my life. Counting really bogged me down. I would wash my hair three times as opposed to once because three was a good luck number and one wasn't. It took me longer to read because I'd count the lines in a paragraph. When I set my alarm at night, I had to set it to a number that wouldn't add up to a 'bad' number."

"I knew the rituals didn't make sense, and I was deeply ashamed of them, but I couldn't seem to overcome them until I had therapy."

"Getting dressed in the morning was tough, because I had a routine, and if I didn't follow the routine, I'd get anxious and would have to get dressed again. I always worried that if I didn't do something, my parents were going to die. I'd have these terrible thoughts of harming my parents. That was completely irrational, but the thoughts triggered more anxiety and more senseless behavior. Because of the time I spent on rituals, I was unable to do a lot of things that were important to me" (NIMH, 2010, p. 5).

The response to the traumatic event involves a fear of helplessness and a sense of horror that is reexperienced in recurring thoughts or dreams. An event that resembles the original trauma can produce the same intense emotional and physiological response, including palpitations, shortness of breath, and other symptoms of anxiety. Persons may go to great lengths

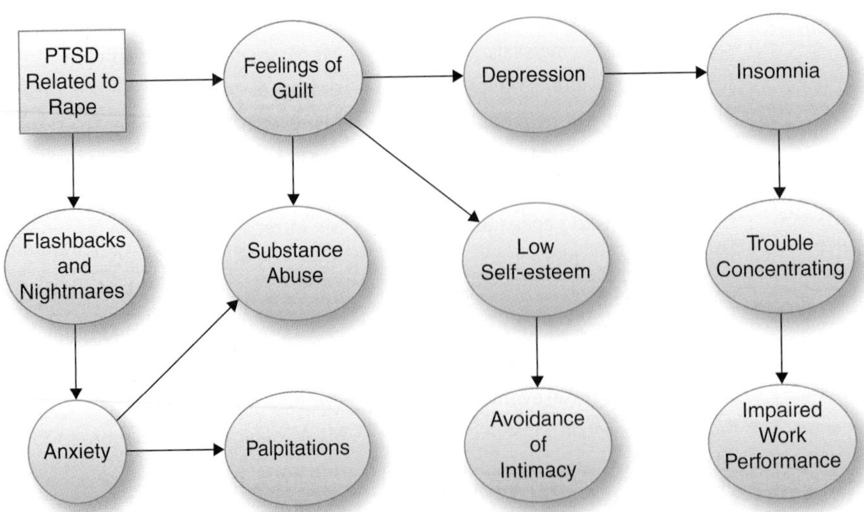

Figure 18-3 Symptom Concept Map for PTSD

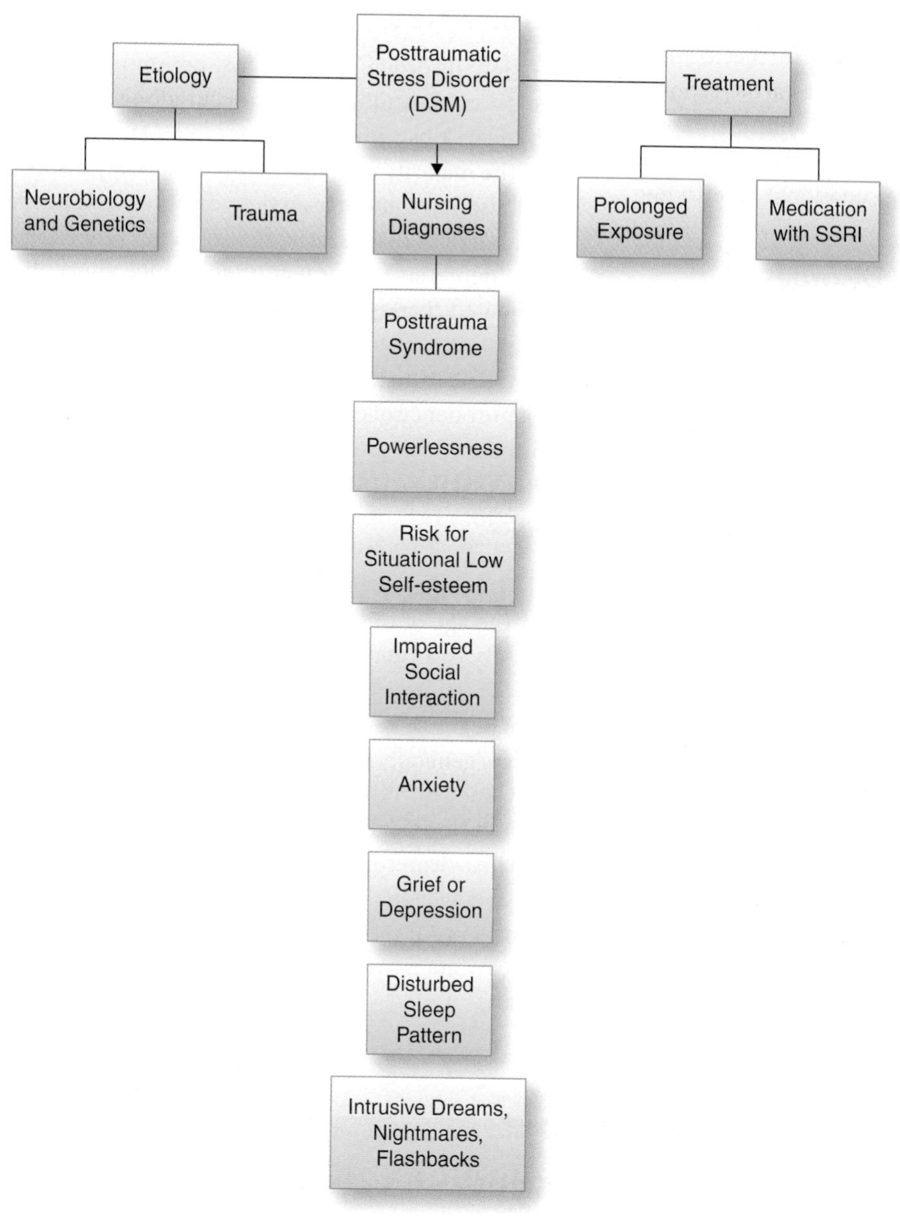

Figure 18-4 Nursing Diagnoses Concept Map: PTSD

The presenting symptoms of PTSD vary and may include those associated with depression, anxiety, sleep disorder, sexual disorder, or even psychosis.

to avoid anything that reminds them of the trauma. The disorder is considered acute if symptoms last less than 3 months, and chronic if they last more than 3 months (APA, 2000). **Figure 18-4** identifies nursing diagnoses that are frequently applicable to clients with PTSD.

Acute Stress Disorder

Acute stress disorder occurs with the development of anxiety, as well as dissociative and other symptoms within 1 month after exposure to an extremely traumatic stressor of the kind that can precipitate PTSD.

In acute stress disorder, the response involves dissociation, which is defined as a disruption in the usually integrated functions of consciousness, memory, identity, or perception of the environment (APA, 2000). Dissociative symptoms include emotional numbing or detachment, derealization, amnesia, and depersonalization. Acute stress disorder, by definition, lasts at least 2 days, but no more than 1 month.

Dissociative symptoms are accompanied by symptoms of anxiety. The client typically expends much energy to avoid situations or people that might trigger recollection of the trauma. As with PTSD, the event and the emotional response are

Complications of PTSD may include violent and aggressive behavior, alcohol and substance abuse, and poor impulse control.

persistently reexperienced and lead to hypervigilant behavior directed at avoiding further trauma. The client may have an exaggerated startle response, difficulty sleeping, and a decreased ability to experience pleasure. The disturbance results in significant impairment in social and occupational functioning.

The elderly are prone to developing anxiety symptoms because of medical illness and polypharmacy.

The primary difference between generalized anxiety disorder and the other anxiety disorders is the frequent absence of a focal symptom or trigger.

OCD and specific phobia are anxiety disorders that may have a childhood onset.

Generalized Anxiety Disorder

The essential feature of generalized anxiety disorder (GAD) is excessive anxiety and worry for most days over a period of at least 6 months in response to several events or activities. The person is unable to control the worry and experiences at least three of the following symptoms: restlessness, fatigue, difficulty concentrating, irritability, difficulty sleeping, and muscle tension.

Substance-Induced Anxiety Disorder

A diagnosis of substance-induced anxiety disorder is made when prominent anxiety symptoms result from the direct, physiologic effects of a substance, which could be a drug of abuse, a prescribed or over-the-counter medication, or a toxin. Substance-induced anxiety disorder arises only in association with intoxication or withdrawal states. The predominant symptoms may be those of GAD, panic attacks, OCD, or phobic disorder.

Incidence and Prevalence

Anxiety disorders are the most common psychiatric disorders and frequently occur along with other physical or psychiatric illnesses (NIMH, 2010).

The majority of people with one anxiety disorder will also have another anxiety disorder, and people with anxiety disorders will also frequently experience depressive disorders or substance abuse. It is estimated that approximately 40 million American adults, ages 18 and older, or 18% of the population, experience an anxiety disorder in a given year, with the prevalence of each disorder estimated to be 2.7% (6 million) for panic disorder, 1% (2.2 million) for OCD, 3.5% (7.7 million) for PTSD, 3.1% (6.8 million) for GAD, 6.8% (15 million) for social phobia, and 8.7% (19.2 million) for specific phobia (Kessler, Chiu, Demler, & Walters, 2005).

The age of onset varies according to the type of anxiety disorder experienced. Specific phobia and OCD may begin in childhood, while social phobia may begin in early adolescence. Other anxiety disorders generally begin in early adulthood.

Genetics and gender also seem to be factors in the development of anxiety disorders, with women and first-degree relatives of clients with anxiety disorders being at higher risk for experiencing an anxiety disorder (APA, 2005). Panic disorders are known to affect women twice as often as they affect men (APA, 2000).

CASE STUDIES Mr. JW.

Mr. JW is a 23-year-old married male. He enlisted in the military after high school and was planning a long-term career in the army. Mr. JW has been deployed to the Middle East three times. During his last deployment, while on patrol with a good friend and fellow soldier, the friend accidentally detonated a roadside improvised explosive device (IED) and was killed instantly. Mr. JW sustained serious injuries and was taken to a military hospital in Germany. After being stabilized at the hospital in Germany, a period that lasted almost 3 months, Mr. JW was returned to his home base in Hawaii for further rehabilitation. After Mr. JW returned home, Mrs. JW noticed that Mr. JW began drinking alcohol excessively. He was frequently hostile and irritable, and would spend most of his time alone. He did not want to discuss his concerns with his wife. He was participating in a weekly physical rehabilitation program on base since his mobility was compromised due to his multiple injuries, but otherwise he did not leave the house. He would not speak with his family members or friends when they called and refused to sleep in bed at night, preferring to sleep on the couch in the living room. On occasion, Mrs. JW would awaken to screams coming from the living room, to find her husband thrashing in his sleep, obviously experiencing terrible nightmares. She became so upset and concerned with her husband's condition and his refusal to discuss the issues that she threatened to leave him. It was at this point that Mr. JW agreed to go for a psychiatric evaluation. During the assessment, Mr. JW acknowledged feeling guilty that he had survived, while his friend had died. He also admitted to having intermittent suicidal thoughts, although he denied a specific plan to hurt himself. Mr. JW was admitted to the inpatient psychiatric unit for further evaluation and treatment.

Nursing Care Plan **Posttraumatic Stress Disorder**

Nursing Diagnosis: Posttrauma syndrome related to direct exposure to a major traumatic event evidenced by guilt, suicidal ideation, difficulty sleeping, nightmares, excessive drinking, irritability, and social isolation.

Expected Outcomes	Interventions	Evaluations
• Mr. JW will be safe from self-injury.	• Evaluate suicidal ideation and provide observation and supervision as indicated.	• Mr. JW does not act on suicidal thoughts and the thoughts decrease over time.
• Mr. JW and his wife will have an understanding of normal responses to stress and will be hopeful that improvement is possible.	• Provide information on neurobiologic and cognitive theories of anxiety so they can understand the cause and treatment; inform the client that symptoms can subside with treatment.	• Mr. and Mrs. JW engage in treatment and verbalize expectation of improvement.
• Mr. JW will begin to resolve feelings of guilt regarding the death of his friend.	• Establish trust: Spend time with Mr. JW; validate that the traumatic event was very stressful; provide consistent staff. • Encourage Mr. JW to express his feelings and to grieve the loss of his friend. • Provide empathy and support. • Assist Mr. JW to recognize sources of support, such as his wife, family, and clergy. • Provide opportunities for Mr. JW to talk about the traumatic event, but do not force this. (There is no evidence that debriefing is of value.)	• Feelings of responsibility and guilt diminish as Mr. JW begins the grieving process.
• Mr. JW will manage anxiety in ways that are not destructive.	• Educate Mr. JW on the use of relaxation techniques, distraction, and physical exercise as ways to decrease anxiety. Use cognitive therapy, including thought stoppage, to control intrusive thoughts and images. • Monitor the use of alcohol to cope with stress. Refer for evaluation if indicated.	• Nightmares, irritability, and drinking decrease as Mr. JW learns to express feelings verbally. • Mr. JW utilizes new coping skills when he feels stressed and experiences a decrease in drinking and other symptoms.
• Mr. JW will establish regular sleep patterns.	• Educate the client on sleep hygiene (see Chapter 22). Refer for sleep medication if insomnia persists. • Reinforce relaxation techniques and other nonpharmacologic methods to assist with sleep.	• Mr. JW sleeps in his bed after discharge.
• Mr. JW will socialize with his wife, family, and friends.	• Provide social skills training. • Explore hobbies, interests, and leisure activities.	• Mr. JW will be more communicative with his wife and allow visits from family and friends. • After discharge, Mr. JW will engage in activities outside the home (shopping, library, walks).

Visit http://go.jblearning.com/mentalhealth for additional care plans and exercises.

Etiology

The development of anxiety disorders can be attributed to a combination of neurobiologic, genetic, and environmental factors. Influences on the development of anxiety disorders may vary depending on the specific disorder.

Neurobiologic and Genetic Basis

Complex interactions of various neurotransmitters and alterations in brain structures appear to contribute to the development of anxiety disorders. One theory is that the amygdala, the portion of the brain that regulates fear, is overactive and the cerebral cortex, the part of the brain that controls fear, is underactive.

Panic disorders and PTSD have been linked to cortisol dysregulation, a physiological response to life stressors. Cortisol, a major stress hormone, is secreted as an adaptive response to an environmental stressor. Under acutely stressful situations, cortisol release is beneficial, but chronic secretion of stress hormones such as cortisol may lead to cell destruction in the brain's hippocampus, which regulates mood, heart rate, and memory. Trauma and, possibly, abuse may affect brain structure and functioning, leading to neurobiologic dysfunction and resulting in dissociation, mood instability, and profound memory lapses (Glod & McEnany, 1995). Receptors for gamma-aminobutyric acid (GABA) are concentrated in the limbic area of the brain and are linked to anticipatory anxiety. Scientists postulate that excessive anticipatory anxiety may trigger a panic attack.

According to the cognitive model, anxiety is the result of the client's interpretation of an event.

Serotonin modulation has long been recognized as a factor in the pathophysiology of OCD, but the exact nature of the relationship is still unclear. Magnetic resonance imaging studies have documented white matter abnormalities in brains of persons with OCD, as well as in first-degree relatives (Fei et al., 2011; Menzies et al., 2008).

GAD has been attributed to excessive noradrenergic activity in the locus caeruleus, a small area of the brain stem. Benzodiazepines are known to facilitate or enhance the inhibitory action of GABA. The efficacy of benzodiazepines and antidepressants in the treatment of anxiety disorders lends support to the neurobiologic theory. The higher incidence of anxiety disorders among first-degree relatives suggests a genetic basis for anxiety disorders. Panic disorder, generalized anxiety disorder, phobias, and OCD all have significant familial occurrence (Hettema, Neale, & Kendler, 2001). Panic disorder is eight times more likely to occur in first-degree biological relatives of people who have the disorder (APA, 2000). Genetic epidemiologic studies have documented that panic and phobic disorders are moderately heritable, but further research is needed to identify specific susceptibility variants (Schumacher et al., 2011; Smoller, Gardner-Schuster, & Covino, 2008). Twin studies, though small in size, provide evidence of a genetic contribution to posttraumatic stress disorder (Gilbertson et al., 2006; Kremen et al., 2007). Studies related to the genetics of OCD have focused on genes that produce a protein known as the serotonin transporter, in part, because the selective serotonin reuptake inhibitor antidepressant medications have been effective in treating OCD in some people (Schruers et al., 2011; Stewart & Pauls, 2010; Wendland et al., 2008). Studies suggest that flaws in the serotonin system are part of the pathology that leads to the disorder. Future research could help identify how combinations of gene variations impact the risk for OCD. Genetics alone is not likely to explain the development of anxiety disorders. Studies indicate that variances in susceptibility are also related to environmental factors (Hettema et al., 2001). Neurobiologic and genetic theories hold promise for the development of effective medications to target specific anxiety symptoms.

Cognitive-Behavioral Theory

Whereas an initial panic attack may be the result of genetic or biologic vulnerabilities or increased stress, the cognitive-behavioral model proposes that recurrent attacks and anticipatory fear are the result of a learned response and distortions in thinking. Initial panic attacks are interpreted as catastrophic, causing the affected person to become sensitized and focused on the body's arousal signals. This causes the person to misinterpret or overreact to normal sensations in a way that makes them seem dangerous. For example, heart palpitations, thought to signal an impending heart attack, further increase the anxiety, which intensifies the sensations and the desire to escape. Agoraphobia is the result of this avoidance conditioning. The individual learns to avoid situations that may lead to the feared sensations.

In OCD, the ritualistic behaviors reduce or neutralize the anxiety associated with obsessive thoughts, thereby reinforcing the compulsive rituals. This, in turn, reinforces the belief that the original obsessive thoughts were dangerous. The client thus learns that other experiences of anxiety may be reduced by compulsive rituals, and the compulsive behavior becomes more extensive.

Clinical Course and Complications

Anxiety disorders can cause major impairment in the level of functioning with a negative effect on the quality of life. They can be accompanied by substance abuse, depression, and suicide attempts. Although most clients with anxiety disorders improve with treatment, relapse is frequent, and maintenance pharmacotherapy is often required.

Nursing Assessment

Guidelines for the nursing assessment of clients with anxiety disorders are summarized in **Table 18-2**. When conducting a client interview, the nurse should observe for signs of anxiety. Clients may have trouble sitting still, tap their fingers, swing their legs, and pace. The mental status examination may reveal difficulty concentrating, poor memory, and distortions in thinking or hearing. The nurse may need to repeat questions to determine if an inappropriate response is the result of inattention or an altered perception of reality. The nurse theorist, Hildegard Peplau (1991), described four levels of anxiety—mild, moderate,

Table 18-2 Guidelines for Nursing Assessment of Clients With Anxiety Disorders

Guidelines	Rationales
The interview should be conducted without interruption in a private, quiet area.	This is intended to limit stimulation and decrease anxiety.
The nurse should present a calm, nonjudgmental, nonthreatening demeanor.	This will promote a trusting relationship.
The nurse may need to repeat questions.	This will help determine if an inappropriate response is the result of inattention or an altered perception of reality.
Mental status examination is part of the assessment.	The examination may reveal difficulty concentrating, poor memory, and distortions in thinking or hearing. Observe for signs of anxiety (trouble sitting still, tapping fingers, swinging foot, pacing).
Ask the client to state the problem.	This helps establish the client as an active participant in the treatment process, which increases his or her sense of personal control, contributes to self-esteem, and does not foster dependency.
Is there a particular event that triggered the symptoms? How long has the client experienced anxiety? Has the client had this experience before, or is it something new? Is there a history of anxiety disorders in the client or family?	These questions help to reveal the nature and history of the client's anxiety symptoms.
How has the anxiety interfered with the client's life? Why is the client seeking help at this particular time?	This information will enlighten the nurse as to the client's level of distress and motivation to engage in treatment.
What is the client's underlying fear? Is there a fear of having a panic attack, or is there a fear of being embarrassed, helpless, or losing control?	The nature of the underlying fear experienced by the client is helpful in determining appropriate interventions.
What coping strategies has the client used to reduce anxiety?	This can help the client recognize strengths, contribute to self-esteem, and begin to engage in a problem-solving approach.
What is the client's understanding of the illness?	This will help identify educational needs.
Ask for permission to meet with family members.	An understanding of the client's disorder may help the family to relate more effectively with the client.
Take a psychiatric and medical history and a history of medication and substance use.	Another primary disorder, medications, or substance use may precipitate or worsen symptoms of anxiety.

Table 18-3 **Levels of Anxiety**

Levels of Anxiety	Client Experiences	Nursing Interventions	Rationales
Mild	Increased focus and improved attention.	None required; client's performance may be enhanced.	Mild anxiety may be beneficial to the client's ability to perform a task.
Moderate	The area of focus narrows and the client has difficulty maintaining attention.	Encourage the client to verbalize feelings. Teach coping skills, including relaxation and problem solving. Distraction may be effective. Assist the client with developing coping skills to manage anxiety in the future.	Moderate anxiety may begin to interfere with a client's ability to appreciate context and therefore problem solve effectively. Therefore, reducing anxiety is important.
Severe	Client experiences extreme discomfort and has pronounced difficulty functioning. The client experiences uncomfortable physiologic response that may include palpitations, nausea, and diaphoresis.	Be direct in working with the client. Remain with the client. Project a calm and reassuring attitude. Reduce environmental stimuli. Provide clear and simple directions. Assist the client to focus on breathing or other relaxation exercises. If able, the client may benefit from walking or other large-muscle exercise. Administer anxiolytic medications as ordered.	As anxiety increases, the client will become more fearful and less able to problem solve. Behavior may be impulsive and unpredictable. Safety is a priority. The client will also begin to experience physiologic symptoms that will reinforce the client's anxiety.
Panic	Client is dysfunctional and experiences a sense of terror. Psychotic symptoms, including hallucinations or delusions may be present.	Stay with the client at all times and maintain a calm, non-threatening manner. Reassure the client that you will stay to ensure safety. Provide care as described for the client with severe anxiety.	Safety is a priority. The experience of panic induces feelings of terror and precludes the client's ability to think rationally and resolve issues. The client requires supervision and specific direction and assistance during this period.

severe, and so extreme that is transcends to a panic state. In the mild stage of anxiety, the anxious person is able to comprehend information and interact in a meaningful way. Mild anxiety, as with mild stress, can actually help a person concentrate, focus, and improve attention. As the levels progress, however, the afflicted person becomes less able to comprehend information and interact and function. Severe anxiety may create such distress for the person experiencing it that he or she begins to disorganize and is unable to make decisions or solve problems. When a person is experiencing panic, he or she may not comprehend information and require very simple directives. He or she loses the ability to process complex information. This is an important area for nursing assessment, since nursing interventions will vary depending on the client's level of anxiety (**Table 18-3**). The interview should be conducted without interruption in a private, quiet area. By limiting the amount of stimuli, the nurse can help contain the client's anxiety.

It is important to determine why the client is seeking help at this particular time. This information will enlighten the nurse as to the client's level of distress and motivation to engage in treatment. Asking the client to state the problem helps establish the client as an active participant in the treatment process, which increases his or her sense of personal control, contributes to self-esteem, and does not foster dependency.

Some questions the nurse may ask to learn the nature and history of the client's anxiety symptoms are: Is there a particular event that triggered the symptoms? How long has the client experienced anxiety? Has the client had this experience before, or is it something new? Is there a history of anxiety disorders in the client or family?

It is important to identify the nature of the underlying fear experienced by the client. Is there a fear of having a panic attack, or is there a fear of being embarrassed, helpless, or losing control? The client may not have thought about the anxiety objectively, and the nurse can provide a supportive relationship in which the client feels safe to consider the meaning of the anxiety.

The client should be helped to be as specific as possible about how the anxiety has interfered with his or her life. It is not unusual for clients to have developed intricate ways of avoiding fears that provoke anxiety, including limiting family, work, and social relationships to control these fears. The nurse must determine the coping strategies employed by the client to reduce anxiety and help the client recognize strengths and resources that will support treatment. This can be caring family or friends, community supports, personal accomplishments, or crises or difficulties that have been successfully handled. When clients are depressed over their current situation, they need help seeing these strengths. Through this discussion, the nurse helps counter the client's negative personal view and sense of hopelessness and contributes to the client's self-esteem.

The client's understanding of the illness will help identify educational needs. Typically, clients with anxiety disorders recognize that their behaviors or fears are exaggerated and irrational, but sometimes clients with OCD, out of shame and guilt, try to hide their behaviors or make them appear rational.

The nurse should ask for permission to meet with family members. They usually benefit from learning the nature of the client's illness and can then relate more effectively with the client.

Differential Diagnosis

The assessment is not complete without a medical history and a history of medication and substance use. Clients with anxiety symptoms should be assessed for depression, given the high comorbidity. Some medical conditions that can cause symptoms of anxiety include endocrine disorders, both hyperthyroidism and hypothyroidism; hypoglycemia; cardiovascular disease; respiratory problems, including hyperventilation; and neurologic conditions, including neoplasms and encephalitis. Substance intoxication and withdrawal also are associated with anxiety. A physical examination and laboratory and clinical tests should be conducted based on the client's presentation.

Treatment

Psychotherapy, primarily cognitive-behavioral therapy (CBT), and pharmacotherapy are the most frequently used modalities in the treatment of anxiety disorders. It is important to realize that each client is unique, and treatments must be individualized and modified according to a client's response.

Clients with OCD are often successful in concealing their obsessive-compulsive symptoms from friends and coworkers before they become severe and time consuming.

Cognitive-Behavioral Therapy

Psychotherapeutic treatment of anxiety disorders combines elements of **cognitive therapy**, **behavior therapy**, and support. The application of these approaches is specific for the type of disorder. Cognitive-behavioral therapy (CBT) focuses on the interplay of maladaptive behavioral, emotional, and cognitive responses that characterize and perpetuate mental disorders (Matthews, Rayburn, & Otto, 2004).

Client education in treatment of panic disorder includes an overview of the fear cycle so that the client understands the rationale for treatment.

Family members may show their anger and resentment, which often results in increased anxiety in the client.

An important initial step in therapy is educating the client on the role that the client's thoughts and beliefs play in activating anxiety. According to the cognitive model, anxiety is the result of distorted thinking. This can take the form of thinking the worst or "catastrophizing," focusing on negative outcomes, perceiving threats where none exist, and generalization, to name a few symptoms. Anxiety disorders are based on fear—fear of looking foolish (social phobia), fear of having a panic attack (simple phobia or panic disorder), or fear of some dire outcome if compulsions are not acted on (OCD). In addition, there is an assumption by the client that he or she lacks the resources to manage these perceived dangers or threats, and this further fuels the client's anxiety.

The cognitive model of panic disorder views the client's greatest fear as the fear of having a panic attack. Anticipatory anxiety and avoidance associated with panic attacks can be reduced if the client recognizes what causes and exacerbates the panic, as well as ways to reduce it. For clients who are medically cleared, purposeful hyperventilation will produce the panic symptoms and running in place or breathing into cupped hands will restore the carbon dioxide balance and eliminate the panic symptoms. This exercise educates the client about the nature of panic symptoms, demystifies the panic response, and gives the client increased control over the symptoms.

Cognitive restructuring helps the client to examine and challenge the thoughts that contribute to the ex-

Table 18-4 **Relationship of Thoughts to Anxiety: Social Phobia**

Antecedent Thought	Behavior	Consequences
If I approach someone to speak with him, he will reject me and I will feel foolish.	I feel anxious and nervous and do not initiate social contact.	My anxiety lessens but I do not achieve my goal and I remain alone.

perience of anxiety by examining the ABCs: antecedents, behavior, and the consequences of one's thoughts (**Table 18-4**). The goal of therapy is to interrupt this process by challenging the antecedent thoughts.

Cognitive restructuring involves asking the client questions to help him or her evaluate negative automatic thoughts and substitute more realistic thoughts.

These may include catastrophic thoughts such as, "I will die" or "I am having a heart attack," personalizing thoughts such as, "I am responsible for whatever happens," or assumptions regarding approval and perfectionism. Agoraphobic and social phobic clients often believe that others can see their anxiety and will reject them because of it. Challenges to the person's automatic thoughts may include the following questions:

- What are the advantages and disadvantages of this thought?
- What is the evidence for and against this thought?
- Is the evidence convincing?
- What if the thought is true? Why would that bother you?
- If someone else had this problem, what advice would you give him?
- If someone else had this problem, would you judge him negatively, as you judge yourself? Why or why not?
- If the thought is true, are there some things you can do to improve the situation? (Leahy, 1996)

Critical Thinking Question 

How would you apply the challenges listed previously to the example shown in Table 18-4?

Cognitive and behavioral therapy are modalities aimed at helping people understand their thinking and the behavioral responses to their thoughts. Once clients have an understanding of their patterns of response they can learn to overcome irrational and erroneous fears and change their behavior. The client can be assisted to identify rational responses to frequently occurring anxious thoughts.

Exposure is a CBT technique that introduces repeated experience or contact with the stress-provoking situation with the goal of extinguishing the emotional response. Assigning time to worry, for example, 15 to 30 minutes a day, exposes the client to the fears but with some control—a specific time, place, and by choice. This practice helps the client learn to accept and tolerate some level of anxiety. Other forms of exposure therapy include systematic desensitization and flooding.

Systematic desensitization involves the pairing of relaxation with imagined scenes depicting situations that cause the client to feel anxious. The rationale is that if the client learns to associate relaxation with imagined stressful situations, the real-life situations will become more manageable. The client identifies an increasing hierarchy of stress-provoking stimuli. A client with a simple phobia of public speaking may be helped by creating a hierarchy of situations that would provoke anxiety, from the least stressful to the most stressful. The low end of the hierarchy may be standing in front of an empty auditorium; the high end may be presenting a marketing plan to the board of directors for a company. The client applies relaxation techniques while imagining being in the stressful situation. The client may also utilize cognitive strategies to identify a level of fear and negative thoughts (e.g., I will faint; I will blush; everyone will know I am nervous; I will forget what to say) during the imagined exposure. The process is repeated for each step in the hierarchy, progressing from least stressful to most stressful, until the anxiety is reduced.

Flooding is a more extreme form of exposure, where the client is confronted with the stress-provoking stimulus while preventing behaviors that would extinguish the anxiety. A person with a specific phobia, say to elevators, would agree to enter an elevator with the therapist and ride to the top floor of a building and back to the ground floor. After a number of exposures in which the avoidance response is prevented, the stimulus no longer elicits anxiety.

The cognitive therapy approach to OCD also utilizes this approach of exposure without a neutralizing response. The client is asked to tolerate the obsessive thought without engaging in the usual ritualistic behaviors that neutralize or reduce the anxiety. A compulsive hand washer would resist washing in spite of an obsession about germs. Tolerance can be introduced in time increments, such as not washing hands for 5 minutes, and gradually increasing exposure to the obsessive thoughts. This process requires that the client understand the rationale and is willing to tolerate the resulting anxiety.

The anxiety lessens with each exposure, *as long as it is not interrupted*. For this reason, during the exposure phase, the client should not use relaxation exercises or try to stop the thoughts as a way of reducing anxiety associated with obsessive thoughts. If the goal is to extinguish the obsessive-compulsive behavior, the client must experience and tolerate the thoughts without taking action to reduce the anxiety, neither carrying out the compulsive behavior nor inducing a state of relaxation. Neutralizing the anxiety would reinforce or strengthen the belief that the thought is indeed dangerous and has to be neutralized (Harvey & Rapee, 1995; Leahy, 1996).

Prolonged exposure (PE) utilizes flooding in the treatment of posttraumatic stress disorder. PE has three components: education about common reactions to trauma, repeated recall of the traumatic event, and real-life (in vivo) exposure to situations or objects that have been avoided because they are reminders of the trauma. Prolonged exposure to the traumatic memories has been most effective and has shown a 65% reduction in symptoms (Foa, Keane, & Friedman, 2000; Schnurr et al., 2007). In fact, there is good evidence that brief cognitive therapy with a focus on trauma exposure can prevent the development of PTSD in persons with acute stress disorder (Shalev, 2009; U.S. Department of Veterans Affairs, U.S. Department of Defense, 2010).

Exposure therapy is a very specialized area of CBT, and the techniques should only be applied by clinicians who have received education and supervision in the field. However, it is important for the nurse to understand these concepts when caring for clients who are engaged in exposure therapy for the treatment of an anxiety disorder. For example, a client hospitalized for OCD may be carrying out this exposure exercise in an inpatient setting. The nurse would need to be supportive without undermining the goal of increasing the client's tolerance for the anxiety.

CBT interventions can be applied, not just in the psychiatric setting, but in any situation where clients are experiencing stress. For example, distracting a child with a video game or talk of sports can reduce the anxiety associated with a traumatic medical procedure, like sutures or a doctor's visit. Music

Knowledge that thoughts or behaviors are irrational or exaggerated is not sufficient to accomplish change. The client must experience anxiety as part of the treatment. There is a fine line between having enough anxiety to motivate treatment and having so much anxiety that one runs from therapeutic situations that temporarily increase discomfort.

Evidence-Based Practice

Value of Meditation

A recent controlled study has documented brain changes after just 8 weeks of meditation. These changes may explain subjective feelings of relaxation and cognitive and psychological improvement reported by those who meditate (Hölzel et al., 2011). The study, out of the Massachusetts General Hospital Psychiatric Neuroimaging Research Program, compared magnetic resonance (MR) images of the brains of 16 participants before and after they took part in the 8-week Mindfulness-Based Stress Reduction (MBSR) Program at the University of Massachusetts Center for Mindfulness. In addition to weekly meetings that included practice of mindfulness meditation—which focuses on nonjudgmental awareness of sensations, feelings, and state of mind—participants, who had no prior experience using meditation, received audio recordings for guided meditation practice at home. Participants practiced an average of 27 minutes a day. MR brain images were also taken of a control group of nonmeditators over a similar time interval. Participants completed a mindfulness questionnaire.

On preintervention and postintervention comparisons, those who meditated showed significant improvement in scores on the mindfulness questionnaire. Postintervention brain images of the meditation group showed increased density in the hippocampus, an area associated with learning and memory, as well as in structures that relate to self-awareness, empathy, and introspection. Of particular interest, lower stress levels correlated with decreased gray-matter density in the amygdala, which plays a role in anxiety and stress. These changes were not observed in the control group.

The findings support the value of meditation in the management of anxiety. Meditation may have a particular role in the treatment of PTSD, where an enlarged amygdala and small hippocampus have been implicated.

is frequently used to promote relaxation in clients receiving chemotherapy. Although the short-term, symptom-focused cognitive therapy model has been demonstrated to be effective in the treatment of anxiety disorders, it requires that the client be ready and willing to actively participate in his or her treatment.

For some clients, this form of treatment is not comfortable, and traditional psychotherapy may be better suited to their needs. The focus of the therapy may include reducing vulnerability to stress, bolstering self-confidence, and improving interpersonal relationships.

Pharmacotherapy

Medication can be used alone or in combination with psychotherapy. As already described, some cognitive therapy approaches require that the client experience anxiety, so the use of medications in conjunction with cognitive therapy is controversial. Some clients benefit from time-limited medication to reduce anxiety enough to engage in treatment and initiate some of the behavior exercises.

Knowledge about the neurobiology of anxiety disorders has developed based on the effectiveness of various pharmacologic agents in treating the related symptoms. The selective serotonin reuptake inhibitors (SSRIs), a class of antidepressants that includes fluoxetine (Prozac) and sertraline (Zoloft), are the first line of pharmacologic therapy for the anxiety disorders and are effective across the range of anxiety disorders (WATAG, 2008), although these medications often achieve only partial response in clients with PTSD (Shalev, 2009). Clomipramine (Anafranil), a tricyclic antidepressant (TCA) that is also an SSRI, is the most consistently effective tricyclic in treating OCD, as well as panic and phobic disorders. The symptoms of OCD often return when medication is stopped.

Benzodiazepines can sedate, induce memory impairment, and increase the intoxicating potency of alcohol and may lead to abuse and dependence after long-term use. Treatment with benzodiazepines should be time limited to prevent the complications of tolerance and dependence.

Propranolol (Inderal) and other beta-adrenergic blockers may be used to alleviate anxiety and improve functioning in persons with phobic disorders and are prescribed most often for performance phobia. Benzodiazepines act quickly and have fewer side effects than the TCAs or the monoamine oxidase inhibitors (MAOIs) and are frequently used to treat the symptoms of anxiety. Regular use of benzodiazepines, however, carries a risk of dependence and abuse. They can be helpful for persons with severe phobias who need time-limited, immediate relief, such as a person with a specific fear of airplane travel who has to fly for a family emergency or a business trip. Buspirone (BuSpar), a nonbenzodiazepine anxiolytic, can be effective for long-term treatment of general anxiety disorder. It has few side effects, making it a good choice for the elderly. It takes 2 to 4 weeks to reach maximum therapeutic response.

Anxiolytics, including the benzodiazepines, and beta blockers are also effective in treating acute symptoms of PTSD. Chronic symptoms are better treated with the SSRIs (fluoxetine [Prozac] and sertraline [Zoloft] or paroxetine [Paxil]) or with the serotonin-norepinephrine reuptake inhibitors (SNRIs); venlafaxine (Effexor). Trazodone or doxepin may be used to treat the insomnia frequently associated with PTSD.

Not all clients react the same to a medication, and in the absence of a therapeutic response, it is reasonable that the client be given a trial with another antidepressant. In can take up to 12 weeks for antidepressants to reduce anxiety symptoms effectively. As with all pharmacotherapy, the nurse must educate the client regarding the expected action and possible side effects of the medication. Some side effects decrease over time. The support of the nurse can be essential to client compliance.

Nursing Interventions

Working with clients who have anxiety disorders requires great patience on the part of the nurse. The initial contact with the client is a time for the nurse to communicate understanding and concern. This can be done by allowing the client to talk about stressful and traumatic experiences. The nurse can help the client identify thoughts and fears and how they relate to the anxiety. This increased awareness can demystify the experience of anxiety and give the client a sense of control. The client should not be forced to talk about traumatic experiences. This is especially important after a traumatic event. Historically, psychologic debriefing for individuals or groups who had survived a traumatic event, like an airplane crash, was considered a way to prevent PTSD. Systematic reviews and meta-analyses have failed to show the efficacy of such debriefings, especially in the absence of acute symptoms, and there is evidence that they may have adverse effects over the long term (Shalev, 2009). Based on the evidence, the value of debriefings is questionable.

It is important that the nurse not appear impatient with the client's behavior. This can be especially difficult with clients who have OCD. In the beginning of treatment, it is important to allow time for the client's rituals. It may be necessary to conduct the nursing assessment in segments to accommodate the client's behavior. The time that the client spends on rituals will be limited over time, consistent with the treatment plan.

Efforts should be made to reduce environmental stimuli. Choose a quiet place to meet with the client and avoid interruptions. Anxiety may interfere with the client's ability to hear things correctly. The client may distort or misinterpret what the nurse says, so it is essential that the nurse asks questions to validate the client's responses. Simple sentences reduce the chance of misunderstanding.

The mental status examination may have reflected memory impairment, another frequent manifestation of anxiety. The anxious client may need reminders and should not be expected to recall appointment times or medication times. The client may find it helpful to write things down. This is an example of how the nurse can help the client identify ways to cope with the anxiety and its effect on functioning.

Critical Thinking Question 

In what ways might the nurse decrease or limit stimulation for a hospitalized patient with an anxiety disorder?

Skills training is tailored to the client's needs. Nurses can use behavioral interventions, such as relaxation, deep breathing, meditation, and distraction to assist clients to manage anxiety more effectively. Relaxation training can be helpful for the client with GAD, whereas social skills training may be indicated for the client with a social phobia. Problem solving is a cognitive skill that is of benefit to most clients; it can increase the client's sense of control over the anxiety and can transfer to other situations.

The nurse should involve the client in setting goals for care. Safety is a primary concern, and the client needs to know how and from whom to request help. Special attention should be paid to the client's nutritional status. Snacks and frequent small meals may work better for clients than regularly scheduled meals. The nurse should convey acceptance and support but must be aware that clients experiencing anxiety may perceive any form of touch as a personal threat. **Table 18-5** summarizes nursing interventions for nursing diagnoses that are commonly associated with anxiety disorders.

Client and Family Education

Initially, the focus of client and family education is on explaining the nature of the disorder. The clinician should discuss the symptoms the client may be experiencing and help both the client and family identify signs of exacerbation of the illness. The clinician should validate both the client and the family's understanding through their ability to describe the disorder in their own words. Once there is a basic understanding of the condition, the clinician can begin to educate the client and family regarding treatment options and the participation that is necessary for success.

Client education includes an understanding of the relationship among thoughts, fears, and anxiety. The nurse can use some of the questioning techniques from the cognitive therapy model to help the client achieve this understanding and to learn new coping behaviors.

The teaching of new skills is a major focus of helping the client handle and control the symptoms of anxiety and is an important nursing intervention. Skills training may include relaxation techniques, meditation, social skills, and problem solving. It is important that the nurse recognizes the client's efforts and progress by verbal acknowledgment, a smile, or some other means, because this reinforcement helps the client sustain positive changes. A person with a social phobia, for example, should be acknowledged for initiating a social contact or for participating in a group session. Family members can be taught to also utilize positive reinforcement to support the client's treatment.

If medications are part of the treatment protocol, the nurse assesses the client's response to medication and ensures that clients and families are given information and are able to articulate an understanding of side effects, drug or food interactions (including alcohol), proper administration, management of missed doses, and possible adverse reactions. Side effects and risks associated with the antianxiety medications are summarized in **Table 18-6**. The nurse needs to be aware of prescribed or over-the-counter medications that the client may be taking for other medical conditions to assess for potentially harmful drug interactions. It is important that the nurse educates the client regarding the potential risk of alcohol and drug abuse in persons with anxiety. This requires an open discussion, including an assessment of current use as well as information to increase the client's awareness of signs of escalated use or abuse.

Table 18-5 Nursing Interventions for Clients with Anxiety Disorders

Nursing Diagnoses	Nursing Interventions	Rationales
Anxiety	Assess level of anxiety. Safety is a priority. Stay with the client, if indicated, and inform the client how to call for help. Maintain a calm, nonthreatening demeanor. Reduce environmental stimuli. Keep communication clear and simple. Use touch carefully. Compensate for memory impairment with reminders and written information.	As the client's anxiety level increases, safety becomes a greater concern. Anxiety is contagious, and the nurse's anxiety or stimuli in the environment will increase the client's anxiety. This may increase cooperation. As anxiety increases, the client has trouble processing and retaining information and making decisions. The client may misinterpret touch and feel threatened.
	Encourage the client to talk about anxious feelings and help the client identify situations that provoke anxiety. Offer medication as prescribed and monitor its effect.	Provides an opportunity to assist the client to examine situations realistically. Learning the connection between thoughts or events and anxious feelings helps the client gain a measure of control. Medication may calm the client and improve functioning.
Ineffective coping	Help the client identify precipitants of anxiety, including thoughts and fears. Involve the client in setting treatment goals. Provide skills training: relaxation, problem solving, social skills. Assist the client to practice new skills when not anxious and then in anxious situations.	This can help the client understand anxiety and gain control over feelings. Skills training will help prepare the client to manage anxiety. Skills must be learned through practice so the client will be able to use the new skills effectively when experiencing anxiety.
Posttrauma syndrome	Validate that the traumatic experience was stressful. Provide opportunities for client to talk about the traumatic experience, but allow the client to set the pace. Help the client clarify thoughts and feelings about the traumatic event. Teach relaxation, thought stoppage, and other coping skills.	Communicates empathy and helps establish trust. It also helps the client accept anxiety as a legitimate illness. Avoidance of the traumatic memory may contribute to flashbacks, nightmares, and other symptoms. Relaxation and other coping skills can reduce autonomic sympathetic nervous system response and can result in decreased anxiety and flashbacks.
Anxiety evidenced by rituals	At the beginning of treatment, allow time for completion of rituals. Be accepting and nonjudgmental. With the client, explore the precipitants of obsessive thoughts and compulsions. Explore how behaviors relate to emotions and anxiety. Provide positive reinforcement as the client begins to limit time spent on rituals.	The client's anxiety level will increase if rituals are prevented or interrupted. This helps establish trust. This can identify underlying issues that contribute to the obsessive-compulsive behavior. The client can learn other, more effective ways to express these emotions, thus lessening the need for rituals. The client will need encouragement to set limits on performing compulsive behaviors.
Fear evidenced by social isolation	Convey respect and acceptance of the client's fear. Teach the client to recognize signs of anxiety and utilize cognitive-behavioral strategies at early signs of anxiety. Offer support for social interactions and group activities; role-play social interactions. Offer positive reinforcement for social interactions.	This communicates trust and helps build the client's self-esteem. The earlier coping skills are introduced, the better chance of countering anxiety response. Behavior rehearsal will increase client confidence and maximize success in real-life social interactions. Positive reinforcement increases the desired behavior.

Table 18-6 Potential Side Effects & Risks with Antianxiety Medication

Medications	Side Effects & Risks
SSRIs/SNRIs • 1st line of treatment • Start at low doses and titrate up • 4–12 weeks for full therapeutic effect	• Anxiety may initially worsen • Sexual dysfunction and insomnia • Discontinuation syndrome • Monitor for suicidal ideation • Paroxetine not recommended during pregnancy
Tricyclic/atypical antidepressants • Start at low doses • Slow onset of action	• Poor tolerance of side effects • Risk of falls • Orthostatic hypotension • Anticholinergic side effects • Cardiotoxicity • Lethality in overdose • Monitor for suicidal ideation
Benzodiazepines	• Drowsiness and confusion • Risk of falls • Risk of withdrawal and rebound anxiety when discontinued • Abuse potential

It is a good idea to make clients and families aware of the costs of medication to be sure that they are able to afford the prescribed drug regimen. Based on financial need, some pharmaceutical companies offer medications at reduced rates. If this is not possible, and if other sources of financial aid are not available, the nurse practitioner or other prescribing clinician may need to consider alternative medications.

As noted previously, the client's safety is a primary concern. Education should include the risk of depression and suicidal thoughts, as well as information about ways to access help and resources in emergency situations.

Dissociative Disorders

Dissociation is a disruption of the usually integrated functions of consciousness, memory, identity, or perception of the environment. The *DSM-IV-TR* identifies five dissociative disorders, discussed in the following sections, and there is considerable overlap in both presentation and symptoms among the disorders. Dissociative disorders are conceptualized as posttraumatic stress syndromes. The dissociative symptoms of emotional numbing (detachment), **derealization**, amnesia, and **depersonalization** are often accompanied by symptoms of anxiety (APA, 2000).

Essential Features

The *DSM-IV-TR* identifies five dissociative disorders. As with the anxiety disorders, the dissociative disorders share common elements but are manifested in different ways.

Dissociative Amnesia

Dissociative amnesia is characterized by selective or generalized recall of repressed memories. This manifests as an inability to recall important personal information, usually of a traumatic or stressful nature, that is too extensive to be regarded as ordinary forgetfulness.

Dissociative Fugue

In dissociative fugue, clients experience sudden, unexpected travel away from either home or place of work accompanied by an inability to recall the past, or even their own names. This can result in the assumption of a new identity.

Dissociative Identity Disorder

Formerly referred to as multiple personality disorder, dissociative identity disorder refers to the presence of two or more distinct identities or personality states that reappear and take control of the individual's

Evidence-Based Practice

In 2008, the Western Australian Therapeutics Advisory Group (WATAG), an independent expert advisory committee funded by the Western Australian Department of Health, published *Anxiety Disorders Drug Treatment Guidelines*. The report summarized the available information on the pharmacologic therapy of anxiety disorders based on current evidence and best practice:

The SSRIs are recommended as first-line pharmacotherapy based on evidence of effectiveness for a wide range of the anxiety disorders, and an acceptable tolerance level. A low risk of morbidity if overdosed and their antidepressant effect are added benefits. To be recommended as first-line treatment, a drug needs to have at least level II evidence, that is evidence obtained from at least one properly designed randomized controlled trial.

The following evidenced based recommendations were made for the use of SSRIs:

- It is recommended to start clients on low doses and gradually titrate to a therapeutic dose.
- Clients need to be monitored for worsening of symptoms and for suicidal ideation.
- Allow up to 12 weeks of treatment to assess client's response to medication.
- Clients need to be informed about side effects of initial jitteriness or anxiety, sexual dysfunction, and discontinuation symptoms if the medication is stopped.
- When starting an SSRI, consider supplemental short-term treatment with a benzodiazepine to reduce anxiety and aid sleep.
- Long-term psychotherapy can be effective alone or with medication and may decrease the risk of relapse.
- Treatment for GAD should be continued for 12 months.

Recommendations regarding medications other than the SSRIs include the following:

- Clomipramine (Anafranil) is most effective in treating OCD, but caution should be exercised with the elderly due to cardiac and CNS toxicity.
- Buspirone (BuSpar) has good evidence of effectiveness in treating GAD, but is not recommended for panic disorder, social anxiety disorder, or OCD.
- Tricyclic antidepressants, MAOIs, benzodiazepines, and the SSRI fluoxetine (Prozac) should not be used in the elderly due to side effects and increased risk of falls.

Recommendations for special populations include the following:

- For children and adolescents, psychologic interventions should be tried before any medications. Most medications are not indicated. A limited number of SSRIs can be used, starting at lower doses.
- If clinically indicated, antidepressants may be prescribed during pregnancy and lactation, but risks and benefits must be discussed with the client. MAOIs, paroxetine (Paxil), high-dose benzodiazepines, and anticonvulsants are to be avoided during pregnancy due to evidence of adverse effects to the fetus. Doxepin (Sinequan), fluoxetine (Prozac), and long-acting benzodiazepines are to be avoided during lactation due to evidence of adverse effects on the infant.

The full report is available online at http://www.watag.org.au

behavior. This disorder also includes amnesia for personal information that extends beyond ordinary forgetfulness.

Depersonalization Disorder

Depersonalization disorder involves a persistent or recurrent feeling of being detached from one's mental processes or body. Persons with this disorder may describe feeling as though they are in a dream state or that they are outside observers of their lives. Depersonalization is also a symptom of some anxiety disorders and schizophrenia. The experience is actually fairly common and must cause considerable distress to warrant a diagnosis. In depersonalization disorder, the client knows that this is a feeling, not reality.

Dissociative Disorder Not Otherwise Specified

The predominant feature in this disorder is a dissociative symptom—a disturbance in the usually integrated functions of memory, identity, consciousness, and perception of the environment that does not meet the criteria for a specific dissociative disorder. This could include trancelike states or a coma not explained by a medical condition.

Incidence and Prevalence

There is little data on the prevalence of the dissociative disorders, although the rate is thought to be 1% or less of the population. Although dissociative disorders appear in both men and women, there are gender differences. Women are more likely to experience dissociative identity disorder, and men more likely to experience dissociative fugue. Dissociative identity disorder is generally diagnosed when the client is in his or her 30s or 40s, and it is known to be more common in first-degree relatives of people with the disorder.

Etiology

The dissociative disorders are viewed as a response to a trauma, often one that occurred in childhood. The traumatic event may have involved physical or sexual abuse. The disorder is more common among family members than in the general population. It is hypothesized that at extreme stress levels associated with traumatic events, the hippocampus-based system basically shuts down while the amygdala-based system is enhanced. This change can lead to an abnormal encoding of the space-time context of memories (Gleaves & Williams, 2005).

Clinical Course and Complications

People with dissociative amnesia generally respond well to treatment and make a full recovery. This is true also for persons with fugue states that are of a short duration. Dissociative identity disorder usually requires long-term psychotherapy. Depersonalization disorder does not respond well to treatment and is often complicated by depression and anxiety.

Critical Thinking Question www

What is the underlying precipitant thought to be common to all dissociative disorders?

Nursing Assessment

Nursing assessment includes a mental status examination, psychiatric and medical history, and information on medication and substance use. The nurse may request permission to question a relative, depending on the client's state of memory. Memory is a major focus of assessment, as well as any history of trauma. The nurse should determine how much understanding the client has about the disorder, as well as the way the disorder has affected the client's day-to-day functioning. It is always useful to learn what coping mechanisms the client has utilized and whether they have been effective in dealing with stress.

Differential Diagnosis

An organic basis, such as a brain tumor or seizure disorder, for dissociative symptoms must be ruled out. Other mental disorders, including factitious disorders and malingering, must also be considered, as well as depression, psychosis, and substance abuse.

Treatment

The primary approaches to treating the dissociative disorders are psychotherapy and medication.

Psychotherapy

The focus of psychotherapy is on the client's response to a traumatic event. If years have passed since the traumatic event occurred, it may be difficult for the client to achieve recall. The accuracy of the memory cannot be certain when the client remembers a long-ago traumatic event. Treatment is directed at obtaining relief for the client through the recovery of lost memories. A recovered memory, even under hypnosis or with the assistance of amobarbital- (Amytal-) induced sedation, is likely to be altered to fit the needs and expectations of the client (Reid, 1997). Clinicians should remain open and nonjudgmental in their approach, neither confirming nor denying the accuracy of reported memories (Gleaves & Williams, 2005).

The process of integrating alter personality states can be very frightening for the client.

In dissociative identity disorder, the goal of treatment is the integration of the parts of the client's personality, referred to as "alters." Integration of an alter personality state implies that it no longer exists by itself.

Pharmacotherapy

The symptoms of dissociative disorders respond to treatment with antidepressants; SSRIs are the medication of choice. Pharmacotherapy is most effective in clients with dissociative disorders when it is combined with psychotherapy.

Nursing Interventions

The nurse's role with clients who have dissociative disorders is largely supportive. The client may be very concerned regarding the loss of memory. The nurse can facilitate the client's exploration of the past and expression of feelings. Safety of the client is a primary concern, especially if the client is depressed or suicidal. The nurse can assist the client to identify and practice healthy coping skills to respond to anxiety and stress.

Summary

Anxiety is a universal phenomenon that allows the nurse to identify with the client's experience and discomfort. However, clients who present for the treatment of anxiety or dissociative disorders have often developed extreme, ineffective patterns of coping with stress. As a result, they usually suffer great personal discomfort combined with psychosocial problems. The client may be experiencing severe impairments in interpersonal functioning that affect his or her ability to enjoy life.

Etiology appears related to a combination of neurotransmitter disturbances, primarily serotonin and gamma-aminobutyric acid, and genetic factors. Treatment requires the client to discover and learn new ways to cope more effectively with the symptoms of anxiety. Peplau referred to this process as "real learning."

> Real learning, . . . trains us to deal with anxiety. In the learning process, we are forced to endure uncertainty while we observe, describe, analyze and formulate the meaning of experience. In the learning process, we gain not only the knowledge needed to deal with new situations, but also we are conditioned to withstand anxiety. (Peplau, 1964, p. 43)

The nurse's role is to help the client with the process of real learning. Anxiety can never be eliminated. However, by recognizing the signs of anxiety and learning more effective coping skills, the client can better manage anxiety and, thereby, improve the quality of life. Evidence supports cognitive behavioral interventions and SSRI medications as effective in the treatment of anxiety disorders.

Annotated References

American Psychiatric Association (APA). (2000). *Diagnostic and statistical manual of mental disorders* (4th ed., text rev.). Washington, DC: Author.
This is the revised fourth edition of the American Psychiatric Association's official nomenclature of psychiatric conditions and disorders. It provides a systematic listing of the official codes and categories, a description of the multiaxial system for diagnosis, and diagnostic criteria for each of the disorders. It is used by psychiatrists, physicians, psychologists, registered nurses, social workers, therapists, and other mental health workers in all clinical settings.

American Psychiatric Association (APA). (2005). *Let's talk facts about anxiety disorders.* Washington, DC: Author.
This brochure contains concise information regarding anxiety disorders, including definitions, symptoms, and available treatments.

Fei, L., Huang, X., Yang, Y., Li, B., Wu, Q., Zhang, T., . . . Gong, Q. (2011, July). Microstructural brain abnormalities in patients with obsessive-compulsive disorder: Diffusion-tensor MR imaging study at 3.0 T. *Radiology, 260*, 216–223.
The authors report findings on a study that used advanced MR imaging to detect brain abnormalities in persons with OCD.

Foa, E. B., Keane, T. C., & Friedman, M. (Eds.). (2000). *Effective treatments for PTSD: Practice guidelines from the International Society for Traumatic Stress Studies.* New York, NY: Guilford Press.
This book is a definitive guide for evidence-based treatment of PTSD.

Gilbertson, M. W., Paulus, L. A., Williston, S. K., Gurvits, T. V., Lasko, N. B., Pitman, R. K., & Orr, S. P. (2006). Neurocognitive function in monozygotic twins discordant for combat exposure: Relationship to posttraumatic stress disorder. *Journal of Abnormal Psychology, 115*(3), 484–495.

The authors evaluated cognitive performance in monozygotic twins to determine if differences were preexisting characteristics that contribute to PTSD or the result of trauma exposure.

Gleaves, D., & Williams, T. (2005). Critical questions: Trauma, memory, and dissociation. *Psychiatric Annals, 35*(8), 649–654.

This article presents a clear and concise review of dissociative disorders and their relation to trauma.

Glod, C. A., & McEnany, G. (1995). The neurobiology of posttraumatic stress disorder. *Journal of the American Psychiatric Association, 1*(6), 196–199.

This article thoroughly discusses the neurobiologic and neurodevelopmental effects of trauma and identifies the implications for nursing practice, education, and research.

Harvey, A. G., & Rapee, R. M. (1995). Cognitive-behavior therapy for generalized anxiety disorder. *Psychiatric Clinics of North America, 18*(4), 859–870.

This article offers a model for treating GAD that combines cognitive and behavioral therapeutic techniques. The authors present a summary of research findings that support the effectiveness of the model.

Hettema, J. M., Neale, M. C., & Kendler, K. S. (2001). A review and meta-analysis of the genetic epidemiology of anxiety disorders. *American Journal of Psychiatry, 158*, 1568–1578.

The authors conducted meta-analyses of data from family and twin studies of select anxiety disorders to explore the role of genetic and environmental factors in their etiology.

Hölzel, B. K., Carmody, J., Vangel, M., Congleton, C., Yerramsetti, S. M., Gard, T., & Lazar, S. W. (2011). Mindfulness practice leads to increases in regional brain gray matter density. *Psychiatry Research, 191*(1), 36–43.

This article reports on research related to use of mindfulness therapy and its effect on the brain as measured by magnetic resonance imaging.

Kessler, R. C., Chiu, W. T., Demler, O., & Walters, E. E. (2005). Prevalence, severity and co-morbidity of twelve-month DSM-IV disorders in the National Comorbidity Survey Replication. *Archives of General Psychiatry, 62*, 617–627.

The article is a report on the face-to-face survey of 9,282 English-speaking adults, conducted between February 2001 and April 2003, reporting on the prevalence, severity, and comorbidity of certain psychiatric disorders.

Kremen, W. S., Koenen, K. C., Boake, C., Purcell, S., Eisen, S. A., Franz, C. E., . . . Lyons, M. J. (2007). Pretrauma cognitive ability and risk for posttraumatic stress disorder. *Archives of General Psychiatry, 64*(3), 361–368.

This article reports on a co-twin control study to determine if pretrauma cognitive ability is associated with risk for PTSD and whether that risk is genetically mediated.

Leahy, R. (1996). *Cognitive therapy: Basic principles and applications.* Northvale, NJ: Jason Aronson.

This very readable book examines the underlying assumptions and models of cognitive therapy. The specific applications, case presentations, and therapist–client dialogues are extremely instructive.

Matthews, J., Rayburn, N. R., & Otto, M. W. (2004). Cognitive-behavioral therapy. In T. A. Stern & J. B. Herman (Eds.), *Massachusetts General Hospital psychiatry update and board preparation* (2nd ed., pp. 457–465). New York, NY: McGraw-Hill.

This chapter provides an overview of the basic principles of cognitive-behavioral therapy and their application to the treatment of specific mental disorders.

Menzies, L., Williams, G. B., Chamberlain, S. R., Ooi, C., Fineberg, M. B., Suckling, J., . . . Bullmore, E. T. (2008, June 2). White matter abnormalities in patients with obsessive-compulsive disorder and their first degree relatives. *AJP in Advance*, 1–8. doi: 10.1176/appi.ajp.2008.07101677

The authors report findings from magnetic resonance imaging studies that found white matter abnormalities in brains of persons with OCD and their first-degree relatives.

National Institute of Mental Health. (2010). *Anxiety disorders.* Washington, DC: Author.

This is a detailed booklet that describes the symptoms, causes, and treatments of the major anxiety disorders, with information on getting help and coping.

Peplau, H. E. (1964). *Basic principles of patient counseling* (2nd ed.). Philadelphia, PA: Smith Kline & French Laboratories.

This is a brief but very rich presentation of the principles of short-term counseling. It reviews basic principles of the nurse–client relationship and has an excellent nurse–teacher question-and-answer section that is very instructive. It is a classic work by one of the foremost leaders in psychiatric nursing.

Reid, W. H. (1997). Anxiety disorders. In W. H. Reid, G. U. Balis, & B. J. Sutton (Eds.), *The treatment of psychiatric disorders* (3rd ed., pp. 239-262). Bristol, PA: Bunner/Mazel.
This comprehensive psychiatric textbook is useful to all mental health professionals. It follows the *DSM-IV* taxonomy and focuses onthe treatment of each disorder.

Peplau, H. E. (1991). *Interpersonal relations in nursing: A conceptual frame of reference for psychodynamic nursing.* New York, NY: Springer Publishing Company.
This highly regarded nurse theorist describes her theory of nursing as an interpersonal process and examines the phases of the process and the varied roles demanded of the nurse.

Schnurr, P. P., Friedman, M. J., Engel, C. C., Foa, E. B., Shea, M. T., Chow, B. K., . . . Bernardy, N. (2007). Cognitive behavior therapy for posttraumatic stress disorder in women: A randomized controlled trial. *Journal of the American Medical Association, 297*(8), 820–830.
This study compared prolonged exposure therapy with supportive therapy for the treatment of PTSD in women and found a significant reduction of symptoms among the women who received prolonged exposure therapy.

Schruers, K., Esquivel, G., van Duinen, M., Wichers, M., Kenis, G., Colasanti, A., . . . Griez, E. (2011). Genetic moderation of CO2-induced fear by 5-HTTLPR genotype. *Journal of Psychopharmacology, 25*(1), 37–42.
This study examined the relationship between the 5-HTTLPR genotype and the affective response of healthy volunteers to inhaled CO_2. Findings suggest that the fear reaction to CO_2 is moderated by a polymorphism in the 5-HT transporter gene.

Schumacher, J., Kristensen, A. S., Wendland, J. R., Nothen, M. N., Mors, O., & McMahon, F. J. (2011). The genetics of panic disorder. *Journal of Medical Genetics, 48*(6), 361–368.
The authors summarize the latest genetics findings about panic disorder and give an overview of anticipated future developments.

Shalev, A. Y. (2009). Posttraumatic stress disorder (PTSD) and stress related disorders. *Psychiatric Clinics of North America, 32*(3), 687–704. doi:10.1016/j.psc.2009.06.001
This paper reviews the empirical evidence on the treatment of acute and chronic PTSD.

Smoller, J. W., Gardner-Schuster, E., & Covino, J. (2008). The genetic basis of panic and phobic anxiety disorders. *American Journal of Medical Genetics C Seminar Medical Genetics, 148C*(2), 118–126.
This article reports findings from family and genetic studies on the etiology of panic and phobic anxiety disorders.

Stewart, S. E., & Pauls, D. L. (2010). The genetics of obsessive-compulsive disorder. *Focus, 8*, 350–357.
This article reviews OCD genetic studies to date.

U.S. Department of Veterans Affairs, Department of Defense. (2010). *VA/DOD clinical practice guideline for management of posttraumatic stress.* Washington, DC: Author.
This publication provides guidelines based on best information available on the treatment of PTSD designed to provide information and assist in decision making.

Wendland, J. R., Moya, P. R., Kruse, M. R., Ren-Patterson, R. F., Jensen, C. L., Cromer, K. R., & Murphy, D. L. (2008). A novel, putative gain-of-function haplotype at SLC6A4 associates with obsessive-compulsive disorder. *Human Molecular Genetics, 17*(5), 717–723.
This study examines the relationship between the serotonin transporter gene and OCD.

Western Australian Therapeutics Advisory Group (WATAG). (2008). *Anxiety Disorders Drug Treatment Guidelines.* Western Australian Department of Health. Retrieved from www.watag.org.au
The report summarizes the available information on the pharmacologic therapy of anxiety disorders based on current evidence and best practice.

Additional Resources

Kelly, V. C., & Saveanu, R. (2005). Performance anxiety: How to ease stage fright. *Current Psychiatry, 4*(6), 25–34.

This is a clear and concise article about performance anxiety and effective interventions currently used in treatment.

Marx, R. F., & Didziulis, V. (2009, March 1). A life interrupted. *The New York Times* (New York edition), p. CY1.
This article presents the story of a young New York City school teacher who experienced dissociative fugue.

Mason, L. E. (1997, August 4). Divided she stands. *New York Magazine*, 44–49.
Writing under a pseudonym, the author relates her personal experience of dissociative identity disorder. It conveys better than any text the complications of everyday functioning caused by this disorder and describes the treatment conflicts.

McDermott, S. P. (2004). Treating anxiety disorders using cognitive therapy techniques. *Psychiatric Annals, 34*(11), 858–872.
A thorough review of cognitive therapy techniques used in the treatment of anxiety, complete with many clinical examples.

Internet Resources

For a full suite of assignments and additional learning activities, use the access code located in the front of your book to visit this exclusive website: http://go.jblearning.com/mentalhealth. If you do not have an access code, you can obtain one at the site.

Learning Objectives

After reading this chapter, you will be able to:

- Describe key characteristics of somatoform disorders.
- Differentiate among somatization disorders, hypochondriasis, factitious disorders, malingering, and pain disorders.
- Identify factors important in differentiating psychiatric disorders with physical symptoms and medical illnesses.
- Formulate nursing interventions for clients with somatoform disorders, factitious disorders, and malingering.

Key Terms

Body dysmorphic disorder

Briquet's syndrome

Conversion disorder

Dissociative

Factitious disorder

Hypochondriasis

La belle indifference

Malingering

Munchausen syndrome

Pain disorder

Psychosomatic

Referred pain

Reframing

Self-management training

Somatization

Somatoform disorder

Somatoform Disorders, Factitious Disorders, and Malingering

Winifred Z. Kennedy

http://go.jblearning.com/mentalhealth 

For a full suite of assignments and additional learning activities, use the access code located in the front of your book to visit this exclusive website: http://go.jblearning.com/mentalhealth. If you do not have an access code, you can obtain one at the site.

Introduction

Soma comes from the Greek word meaning body. **Psychosomatic** refers to symptoms of physical illness that have a mental or emotional origin. *Mental Health: A Report of the Surgeon General* (U.S. Department of Health and Human Services, 2000) emphasizes the need to look at symptoms of medical and psychiatric illnesses as points on a continuum. It suggests that a more viable distinction than mind and body might be to discuss mental and somatic health because this is a neutral distinction acknowledging that the brain, mental functioning, and behavior are interconnected.

In somatoform disorders, physiologic changes or illness are characterized by physical symptoms originating from emotional or mental sources. Somatoform disorders may be acute or chronic, involve physical or psychologic symptoms or both, and may be exaggerated or fabricated. A client in distress seeks relief for the problem and cares little whether the symptoms arise from the mind or the body, even though this distinction may seem to be important to the healthcare provider and insurance company or may eventually influence treatment decisions. Somatoform disorders are considered psychosomatic; they affect the mind and body and usually are not considered organic or primarily physiologic in origin. An organic disorder has an identifiable, objective, physiologic basis that can be demonstrated by examining established structural and functional changes and by diagnostic testing. In functional disorders, the signs and symptoms do not have a physiologic basis, and the diagnosis depends more upon subjective findings or connections to psychic origins.

The client may have learned that presentation of a physical complaint is a recognizable and socially sanctioned method of obtaining attention, affection, assistance, or alliances with others.

Physical disorders may appear more legitimate, tangible, and less of the client's volition than psychologic disorders. Treating a visible wound or casting a wrist fracture may seem more concrete than treating a stress-related illness perceived as imaginary or exaggerated. This psychologic manifestation of physiologic distress without a demonstrated objective causal link does not mean that there are no underlying physical findings or pathology (Reif & Barsky, 2005). However, a dichotomy has been present since Descartes attempted to distinguish between the mind and the body, and this has continued through to today's distinction between traditional mainstream medicine and mental health. This is seen in both the client's willingness to seek help and society's willingness to pay for it.

Within our society, illness is often an acceptable excuse for nonperformance, and a physical illness does not have the same stigma attached to it as an admission of emotional illness. The individual's psychologic and biologic responses to the stress of a perceived illness or a diagnosed disease are similar, whether or not a clear organic or functional basis is present.

Clients with somatoform disorders experience physical symptoms without a known organic or physical cause in response to psychologic stressors or disorders. The production of symptoms is not considered to be under conscious or voluntary control. Somatoform disorders include somatization disorder, hypochondriasis, conversion disorder, body dysmorphic disorder, and pain disorder.

Factitious disorders and malingering are associated because of their link to illness symptoms and behaviors. The production of symptoms is considered to be more under conscious or voluntary control. The nature of the client's reported symptoms may be based upon problems or uncertainties in validating subjective sensory experiences (Rowe, 2010). An organic or physiologic basis is usually not found for the symptoms. Over time, when a physical basis has been found for the symptoms, clients usually respond to treatment, while distressing symptoms remain for those with medically unexplained symptoms (Jackson & Kroenke, 2008). Factitious disorders and malingering also may be associated with the exaggeration of an actual disorder or the intentional production of signs and symptoms of a known medical disorder. For example, a diabetic client might cover a wound with feces or self-administer an overdose of insulin.

Critical Thinking Question

Does including somatoform disorders in the *Diagnostic and Statistical Manual of Mental Disorders*, fourth edition, text revision (*DSM-IV-TR*) reinforce a mind–body duality or does it emphasize how these barriers are blurred?

General Description of Disorders

The *Diagnostic and Statistical Manual of Mental Disorders*, fourth edition, text revision (*DSM-IV-TR*)

Figure 19-1 Getting a headache prior to a stressful event is common.

divides the classification of the various somatoform disorders by the presentation of physical symptoms (American Psychiatric Association [APA], 2000). *Somatizing* is the process of expressing psychologic conflict through physical complaints or symptoms. "Butterflies" in the stomach prior to public presentations, a headache prior to tax season, or the pain of a broken heart are all common ways to express distress (see **Figure 19-1**). This process is universally experienced, particularly during periods of stress. Proposed changes to fifth editon of DSM include grouping somatization disorder, hypochondriasis, undifferentiated somatization disorder, and pain disorder under complex somatic symptom disorder.

Somatoform Disorders

A **somatoform disorder** is a mental disorder in which physical symptoms or preoccupations that may present as a physical disorder are considered primarily psychologic in origin. Typically, clients present with multiple, vague physical complaints without a recognized or demonstrated organic cause. Somatoform disorders are diagnosed on Axis 1.

Somatization Disorder

A **somatization** disorder is a psychiatric disorder that begins before 30 years of age. Clients with this disorder have long-term, recurring, unexplained physical complaints and frequently utilize medical physicians and surgeons. Clients with **hypochondriasis** have persistent, unrealistic fears of having a medical disorder unrelated to an affective or anxiety disorder and not relieved by medical examination and explanation. A diagnosis of hypochondriasis may be further specified by adding that the client has poor insight, if this is a valid descriptor predominant in the current episode. Clients with **conversion disorder** have physical symptoms, often associated with motor or sensory deficits or seizures caused by unconscious psychologic conflicts. Conversion disorders can be further differentiated by presenting symptoms as conversion disorder with motor symptoms or deficits, with sensory symptoms or deficits, with seizures or convulsions, or with mixed presentation if symptoms from one or more different categories are present. **Body dysmorphic disorder** is a mental disorder in which the client believes his or her body is deformed in some manner that is not readily observed by others. The diagnosis of body dysmorphic disorder is not used if symptoms can be better explained by another disorder such as anorexia or major depressive disorder. Likewise, another diagnosis can be used, such as delusion disorder, somatic type, if the symptoms of body dysmorphia disorder have a delusional quality and intensity.

Clinical Example 

Marc is a 42-year-old sales clerk who experiences painful back spasms. Neurologic and orthopedic workups indicate that his symptoms seem to be excessive compared to the physical problems shown on physical examination and repeated MRIs and X-rays. Despite physical therapy and follow-up in a pain management clinic, his pain seems to be getting worse over the past 6 months. Although he initially seemed to get better after treatment, he now is walking with a cane and asks if he can be prescribed a back brace. He states he wishes his life would just get back to normal, but things haven't been the same since his wife was diagnosed with cancer.

Pain Disorders

Pain disorders that are influenced primarily by psychologic factors and cause significant impairment are included under somatoform disorders in the *DSM-IV-TR*. Pain disorders are specified according

Nursing Interventions for Clients with Somatoform Disorders

Nursing Diagnosis	Interventions	Rationales
Risk prone behavior	Provide regular care provider and opportunities for contact at regular intervals.	Develop trust and help reduce anxiety regarding symptoms. Opportunity to validate inferences and evaluate treatment planning.
	Develop collaborative relationship in treatment planning	Need to engage client and provide basis for long term follow-up and support. Clients often have a track record of frequently changing providers or not receiving appropriate follow-up.
	Active listening	Clients will often present with complicated description of symptoms. Hints in history may help differentiate between physical illness that may present with psychiatric symptoms and psychiatric illness that may present with physical symptoms. Changes in symptom presentation may need to be evaluated as possible new development or illness to be investigated.
	Client and family education regarding possible options for diagnostic testing and interventions	Psychoeducation can be helpful in outlining possible benefits and burdens of treatment. Helps client understand rationale for choosing options to minimize possible risk and unnecessary procedures. Family members are often as anxious as the client and may be the client's chief supports.
	Referral for cognitive behavioral therapy as adjunct for symptom relief if appropriate.	Cognitive behavioral therapy has been shown to be an effective treatment method to identify dysfunctional coping mechanisms which can increase medically unexplained symptoms or perceptions of pain and to discuss alternate coping mechanisms.

to whether they are acute (of less than 6-month duration) or chronic (of more than 6-month duration). In addition, the *DSM-IV-TR* further differentiates between those associated primarily with psychosocial factors and those associated primarily with a general medical condition. In pain disorders associated with a general medical condition, the general medical condition or site of the pain is identified on Axis III. For example, a pain disorder is coded on Axis I, and the medical disorder, cervical radiculopathy, is specified on Axis III and identified by its proper clinical modification as coded in the *International Classification of Diseases*, 9th revision (*ICD-9-CM*; American Medical Association [AMA], 2006).

Somatic signs and symptoms found in somatoform disorders may be predominant in other disorders. If the symptoms have a known organic cause, a diagnosis of a mental disorder resulting from a general medical condition (Chapter 14), an eating disorder (Chapter 21), or a sleep disorder (Chapter 22) may be more appropriate. The clinician must differentiate between the multiple somatic symptoms found in a somatoform disorder and similar symptoms better explained by another disorder, such as the mood-congruent symptoms of a depressive disorder (Chapter 17). As noted in the *DSM-IV-TR*, what appears to be hypochondriasis in the elderly is more likely the result of an affective disorder (APA, 2000). Somatoform disorders and substance-related disorders (Chapter 15) must be differentiated from schizophrenia, other psychotic disorders, and dissociative disorders (Chapter 16).

Factitious Disorders

In a **factitious disorder**, signs and symptoms are predominantly associated with psychologic disorders, physical disorders, or combined psychologic and physical disorders. Clients appear to produce or feign symptoms intentionally by fabricating symptoms, self-inflicting signs and symptoms, or exaggerating existing symptoms. Unlike the unconscious motivation of somatization disorders, factitious disorders are associated with a more conscious manipulation. However, the client is not consciously aware of the needs underlying such behavior or the impetus to continue them. Often the client has had some connection with hospitals or healthcare professions in the past and may have a pattern of switching providers when confronted. A pattern of hospitalizations or help-seeking behaviors for various unfounded disorders is seen. In addition, no obvious secondary gain or external force is observed that would explain the behavior. Factitious disorder is usually diagnosed on Axis I and is typically associated with an underlying personality disorder. Thus, the associated personality disorder (e.g., antisocial personality disorder) is specified on Axis II.

Clinical Example 

Amanda is well known to the staff because of the frequent admissions of her 4-year-old daughter who has had a history of multiple allergies, frequent infections, and seizures. She is a concerned parent, well informed and helpful to everyone, patiently explaining the baffling array of symptoms to new staff members and taking on many of the caretaking responsibilities herself. Amanda jokes that she is better at some things such as obtaining specimens and taking temperatures than some of the staff and has learned enough to graduate from medical school herself. However, she hasn't had the time because the child's illness has been such a strain and the family has had to move several times. During one prolonged admission, the staff observes that the patient seems to get dramatically worse at times that are associated with the mother's visits. They begin a systematic investigation and careful observation to rule out factitious disorder by proxy.

Malingering

Malingering consists of intentional or exaggerated symptoms clearly associated with external forces such as the need to avoid work or jail. It is an understandable, obvious manipulation by the client to obtain a specific result. Malingering is classified as a *v* code in the *DSM-IV-TR* because it is a condition rather than a mental disorder. It is specified on Axis I. If malingering is associated with a personality disorder, the personality disorder is specified on Axis II. For example, if malingering is coded on Axis I, the associated avoidant personality disorder is coded on Axis II (APA, 2000).

Incidence and Prevalence

Unexplained physical symptoms are often reported in general medical practices (Feder et al., 2001; Jackson, George, & Hinchey, 2009) and hospital settings (Fink, Hansen, & Oxhoj, 2004). In neurology clinics, it is estimated that approximately 30% of clients met the criterion for diagnosis of a somatoform disorder (Fink, Hansen, & Sondergaard, 2005). A cross-national study of somatization (Gureje, 2004) noted that there was some variability in prevalence and incidence across nations but that the most important factor appeared to be that multiple somatic complaints were more common among clients who did not have an ongoing relationship with their health-care providers. Symptoms are found more often in older clients, women, and those who express greater functional impairment (Feder et al., 2001). Except for factitious disorders and malingering, somatoform disorders are found more often in women. Often others in the same family have similar problems; the disorder is more prevalent in individuals with histories of family and social problems or substance, sexual, or physical abuse (Braun, Greenberg, Smith, & Cassem, 2010).

Factitious disorders are often associated with **Munchausen syndrome,** a disorder in which clients deliberately manipulate symptoms to obtain hospitalization, medical treatment, or surgical intervention. Baron Hieronymus Münchausen lived in the 18th century and was known for the wild, fantastic stories of his adventures that later became fictionalized as *The Adventures of Baron Münchausen*.

Although the World Health Organization has limited data on the incidence of somatoform disorders, in 1995 an estimated 14 of 1,000 men and 26 of 1,000 women between 5 and 64 years of age were considered disabled by somatoform disorders. The prevalence is higher among women and occurs in approximately 1% of psychiatric disorders. The disorder is more prevalent in the least-developed areas and in economies that are in transition. The global prevalence of somatoform disorders is estimated to be 2.7% (Ustun & Sartorius, 1995). It estimated that unexplained physical symptoms are present in approximately 29% of cases presenting as part of mental health problems (Gureje, 2004).

Clinical Example 

Vanessa is a 27-year-old woman who was brought to the emergency department by the police. After her arrest for shoplifting, Vanessa was observed to be breathing rapidly and complained of chest pain. Vanessa had no past history of medical or psychiatric problems and her diagnostic workup in the emergency room, including EKG and cardiac enzymes, was negative.

One study reviewed 33,531 records and, based upon inconsistent or improbable symptoms, estimated that there was an aspect of malingering in approximately 29% of personal injury cases, 30% of disability cases, 19% of criminal cases, and 8% of medical cases studied. Unexplained somatic complaints were present in 39% of cases involving mild head injury, 35% of fibromyalgia/chronic fatigue cases, 31% of chronic pain cases, 27% of neurologic cases, and 22% of cases involving electrical injuries (Mittenberg, Patton, Canyock, & Condit, 2002).

Etiology

It has been suggested that "calamity, conflict, constitution ... [and] compensation ... [all] impinge on human consciousness and have a bearing on causality" (Trimble, 2004, p. 240) and can be predisposing factors for the potential development of somatoform disorders. There has often been a history of stress or trauma, underlying conflict or ambivalence, predisposition to interpreting physical or psychologic symptoms in a particular matter, and some primary or secondary gains involved in the development and maintenance of illness behaviors.

These disorders are diagnosed in adulthood but often begin in adolescence and may have roots in childhood trauma or abuse. The symptoms are associated with stress or a specific event or consequence (Huang & McCarron, 2011). Cultural factors often influence how physical sensations are interpreted as well as how symptoms are described and presented. Certain culture-bound somatic syndromes, such as *koro* or *suo-yang* (a man's fear that his genitals are retracting into his abdomen) and "brain-fag" or *ode ori* (a sensation of noises or something walking around inside one's head), are usually of short duration, do not interfere with functioning, and are meaningful to others with similar cultural experience (Mezzich, Kleinman, Fabrega, & Parron, 1996). There are also cultural differences in the description of illness and treatment planning. For example, Yeung and Deguang (2002) report that in traditional Chinese medicine, there has been no model of medically unexplained symptoms.

Pierre Briquet, an 18th-century physician, described numerous cases of patients (most of whom were female) who appeared to have multiple physical symptoms attributed to hysteria. Briquet's syndrome, a psychologic disorder, formed the basis for the present diagnostic category termed *somatization disorder.*

In today's health-conscious society where illness remedies and hygiene items are advertised and available nearly everywhere, it is almost inappropriate not to have an ache or pain that can be presented in social situations. More people may be willing to seek help because of the services and more sophisticated tests available to identify subtle changes in body structure or functioning. This may result in overutilization of healthcare systems. Concentrating on somatic complaints without a recognizable physical cause may become a problem if it interferes with social or occupational demands or becomes the sole focus of functioning and interaction.

Social learning, family systems, and change theories may be applied to somatization disorders. Cognitive behavioral theories form the basis for behavioral interventions such as relaxation techniques and biofeedback, in which clients are taught to recognize physiologic cues and manipulate biologic responses to change their response to stimuli (Abbass, Kinsley, & Kroenke, 2009). The client may have had a model for symptom presentation, such as another family member who had a real or imagined illness and received attention or support, or one who had a previous experience of illness where considerable secondary gain or attention was received (Huang & McCarron, 2011). Symptoms may be unwittingly reinforced by cultural or social factors. Symptoms occasionally establish a balance in an unstable relationship or family system and are reinforced by this balance. The client may be the symptom bearer or someone who, through the illness, distracts others from problems in the family system or relationship. Issues of dependency and independence among members of the system may allow the client to remain in the dependent role of the sick person and reinforce illness behaviors through secondary gain.

In social learning or adaptation, a response is modified by a new experience or input. Stress may interfere with this learning process. The client may not be able to respond to a new situation in a positive way because of an overload of new input; he or she may respond by giving up. Conversely, if there is cognitive dissonance (a situation in which the inputs are perceived as incongruous), the client may respond by not accepting or denying the new input. *Locus of control* refers to the extent to which an individual feels that he or she has control over a situation; an individual with an external locus of control feels that events are determined by outside forces such as luck or fate. Research posits an inverse relationship between the sense of personal control and somatization (the report of physical symptoms). The sense of personal control is analyzed by identifying measures of behavioral, cognitive, and decision-making control (Abbass et al., 2009). The effects of cognitive dissonance and locus of control on learning are mitigated by other variables such as the amount of control or influence an individual has upon a situation and past experiences.

The symptoms of somatoform disorders are similar to but more specific than those for **Briquet's**

syndrome, which typically occurs in women with a history of multiple somatic complaints without valid physical cause. The syndrome begins before 30 years of age and recurs frequently. Briquet's syndrome includes symptoms of overdramatization, exhibitionism, and seductiveness that previously had been associated with hysteria. The descriptors of somatoform disorder focus on the multiplicity of symptoms, their duration, and the lack of a demonstrated cause.

Pain is identified according to a taxonomy proposed by the International Association for the Study of Pain. It is categorized according to anatomic region, organ system, temporal characteristics and patterns, description of intensity and time since onset, and etiology (APA, 2000). Pain may be a response to stress or can be exacerbated by it. The meanings associated with pain differ according to personality style, cultural background, environmental cues, and the presence or absence of available supports. The same physiologic pain associated with a demonstrated cause (i.e., childbirth) may be assigned different meanings by the same person in different contexts, such as in the client's experience of normal childbirth following a history of fetal demise. The physiologic pathways of pain, unless altered by disease, are similar in all people; however, the cognitive, emotional, and physical responses to pain may vary greatly in the same individual at different times and between individuals in similar circumstances.

Critical Thinking Question

Emily Dickinson wrote:

Pain has an element of blank;
It cannot recollect
When it began, or if there was
A time when, it was not.

What do you think about her characterization of pain? How would you describe the effects of pain?

Physiology

Clients with somatization disorders usually present with physical symptoms that either do not have a physiologic basis or are in excess of any demonstrated or recognized cause. Diagnostic and laboratory tests usually do not show the expected pattern for the degree of symptoms described. Conversely, if a basis for the symptoms is found, the degree of impairment or discomfort exceeds normal expectations or the experiences of others in the same situation. Individuals with somatoform disorder may be more sensitive in identifying physiologic symptoms. In some cultures, more attention is paid to slight changes in body functioning, and there is more of a tendency to attribute changes or variations to a perceived norm as problematic. For example, it is not unusual for overburdened nursing students to worry that they are suffering from the exotic ailments they are studying and to experience relief from the terrible symptoms suffered during examination periods as soon as spring break arrives. Conversely, a student on a football scholarship may underestimate the pain experienced in training or deny pain to teammates and coaches. The athlete whose scholarship is dependent upon the ability to play may be able to admit to the pain only when exposed to the noncompetitive environment of home during school break.

In all cases it is important to rule out physiologic causes for the symptoms. The range of symptoms required to meet diagnostic criteria are unusual in most physical illnesses. An individual with a somatization disorder is expected to have multiple symptoms of pain, gastrointestinal problems, sexual dysfunction, and vague neurologic or **dissociative** (that which is a distancing and disruption of usual functioning in response to psychologic conflict or trauma) complaints. The symptoms should have been problematic enough for the individual to have sought treatment or to have caused significant functional impairment. In addition, the symptoms do not follow the usual patterns for most common illnesses or syndromes and cannot be substantiated by clinical findings or diagnostic tests. Rather than focusing on one symptom or problem, the client usually presents a collection of signs and symptoms often preceded by a history of diagnostic puzzles and problematic treatments. Traditionally, this includes autonomic nervous symptoms such as rapid pulse and rapid breathing, sweating, pressure in the chest, pounding heart or palpitations, muscular tension, flushing, and cold hands and feet.

Pain is associated with psychologic experiences related to early warnings and learned experiences of danger, punishment, aggression and power, loss, and sexual feelings (Engel, 1959).

In somatization disorder, multiple symptoms, such as those that follow, are identified in more than one system (APA, 2000).

Gastrointestinal symptoms: Symptoms include hyperactive bowel, digestive upset, nausea, bloating, and food intolerance.

Pseudoneurologic symptoms: Symptoms include weakness or tingling, loss of sensation, atypical seizures, ataxia, problems swallowing, and loss of consciousness other than fainting.

Sexual dysfunction: Symptoms include painful menses, painful sexual intercourse, lack of sexual response, and ejaculatory or erectile problems.

Pain symptoms: Pain is generalized or specific, unchanging, and unremitting (i.e., nothing helps) and affects at least four areas of functioning (such as painful headache, backache, muscle cramping, and painful sexual intercourse).

Somatization is a response to stress.

Somatization is a psychophysiologic process through which the client's response to stress is expressed. Adaptive responses such as learning, regulation of arousal, and maintenance of an organized conceptual system are regulatory coping responses. Impediments to learning, problems in regulating arousal states, and cognitive dissonance cause maladaptive coping responses and system dysregulation. Examples of this mind–body interface are found in the neural mediation of immunocompetence, cortical functioning, and sympathetic-parasympathetic imbalance; endorphins and pain responses; and autonomic nervous system arousal and anxiety. **Self-management training** aids in stress reduction by decreasing physiologic activation of autonomic nervous system, catecholamines, and endocrine responses (Rief & Barsky, 2005).

Pain is a sensory, physical, and emotional response to actual or potential tissue damage. Increased physiologic and cognitive arousal induces greater physical discomfort, muscle tension, and mental distress. Suffering is primarily an affective and cognitive response associated with the interpretation of pain. Pain may result from direct stimulation of the body or may be a response to structural or chemical changes. The number of pain receptors activated is not as important as the response to the stimulus. Pain activation involves the ratio of small-diameter and large-diameter afferent nerve fibers that trigger neurons up spinal pathways to pain centers in the thalamus or cerebral cortex and down pathways to influence the experience of pain. Small A-delta and C fibers transmit impulses to the spinal cord via the neospinothalamic tract or the paleospinothalamic tract. Ascending pathways are responsible for the sensory-discriminative component of pain. Descending pathways are responsible for inhibitory modulation or control. Interpretation of nociceptive impulses in the cerebral cortex influences the perceptual experience of pain. The endorphin, noradrenergic, and serotoninergic systems also influence the response to pain. Prolonged or excessive pain changes the nervous system and its responses. Alpha-adrenergic transmitters released during stress and negative emotional states activate C fibers termed *unmyelinated nociceptors*. Throughout the nervous system, damage results from excitation of nociceptors from cell contents such as potassium, histamine, acetylcholine, serotonin, and adenosine triphosphate; inflammatory mediators such as prostaglandins and leukotrienes; and nociceptor-releasing substances such as substance P and calcitonin gene-related peptide. Sensitization of nociceptors is known as wind-up. When damaged cells release bradykinin, nociceptors are activated. Transmission mechanisms of acute and chronic pain differ. **Referred pain** is pain that originates in one area of the body and is referred or experienced in another part that is not receiving the noxious stimuli directly.

Clinical Presentation

The client's perception of his or her body image and the nonverbal clues given in the presentation are important in assessment and treatment but are not diagnostic of a somatoform disorder. Historically, clients have been described as having either a highly dramatic presentation or ***la belle indifference***, a calm and somewhat cheerful indifference to the catastrophes presented. Actual clients are not as predictable and may present their complaints in a hysterical or an extremely sincere and convincing manner. A matter-of-fact presentation, a limited range of affect, or even a histrionic (intense and dramatic) presentation may be more indicative of the client's characteristic style than of an underlying problem or psychologic disorder. Chronic, long-standing symptoms, such as those associated with somatization disorder, have been reinforced in the past, and the client has an interest in making his or her distress known to and recognized by others.

The client may relate a history of being more sickly or prone to accidents or disasters than would normally be expected, and the courses of treatment have been more heroic or demanding than the symptoms seemed to require. The symptoms may mimic the beginning stages of physical disorders such as multiple sclerosis, but the actual course of the somatizer's illness and the symptoms themselves may vary dramatically over time. The client's description of his or her history may be overly detailed and circumstan-

Evidence-Based Practice

As part of a nursing assessment, nursing students were asked to involve their patients with chronic illnesses in developing a symbolic representation of their experiences of illness in art, poetry, music, and the like (Michael, Candela, & Mitchell, 2002). Further research is needed to examine what kinds of information can be gleaned from these kinds of experiences and how this can be used as part of the nursing assessment. Another area of research would be in determining how such interactions affect the development of the nurse–client relationship. It would also be interesting to find the implications for use during the assessment process and perhaps as an initiation of complementary therapies.

Research would be needed to determine if using an aesthetic representation rather than a verbal report would allow for an understanding of illness behavior across different cultures.

tial. The client may have had multiple caretakers and treatments, as well as reassurance from many sources that the problem is not as bad as the client thinks or does not exist at all. The client with hypochondriasis focuses on the unrealistic dread of a life-threatening illness, despite reassurance and adequate and appropriate medical follow-up. This focused anxiety persists over time and is the predominant feature of the disorder. Clients with body dysmorphia also may have a chronic history of problems and anxieties, but the focus is usually on one predominant symptom. Clients with body dysmorphic disorder feel that they are deformed by distorted physical characteristics, body or breath odor, or a dermatologic problem such as a rash or infestation that makes them unacceptable to others or the focus of unwanted attention by distinguishing them from others. Usually repeated investigations have not found the problem's source, and others do not perceive the client as deformed or unacceptable.

The acute presentation of symptoms in conversion disorder is often more clearly tied to a specific stressor or event. A conversion disorder often involves a single, isolated presentation of a dramatic symptom such as blindness or hemiplegia. Conversion disorders are changes in body functioning with a known organic cause. The presentation is often dramatic and the precipitating factors apparent and symbolic, such as the man whose hand becomes paralyzed after he raises it to strike his partner. Relief of the symptoms is often as dramatic as the symptom's onset, if the client has confidence in the healthcare provider and is open to suggestions for improvement and treatment.

Clients' descriptions of pain symptoms differ because of many variables, and symptoms are occasionally so intertwined with feelings of suffering that interpretation is difficult. Differences in personality between the client and the healthcare provider should not cause the provider to label the client's pain as imaginary or hysterical. The healthcare provider is only an observer who can help elicit the client's description and subjective experience of pain. Even when the etiology of the pain is psychologic, the clinician's role is to help alleviate the pain and associated suffering the client may be experiencing. The physiologic pathways of pain are clearly established. The descriptions and identified source of the pain may be inconsistent with physical findings and known anatomic pathways. Those pain disorders associated with more than an expected degree of impairment and associated psychologic factors are classified as somatoform disorders to emphasize the need for a holistic treatment approach (Nejad & Alpay, 2010).

Factitious disorders concern client behaviors associated with symptoms of psychologic or physical disorders. Intentional symptom production is not seen as lying but as an attempt to express ambiguous subjective sensory experiences, psychologic conflicts, and anxiety. Clients with factitious disorders may have a poorly differentiated sense of self and a poorly defined sense of reality. Their attempts to seek help for psychologic or physical disorders are intended to stimulate psychiatric, medical, or surgical

Clinical Example 

Kara is a 20-year-old woman admitted to the hospital with severe abdominal pain and cramping. Medical workup has been negative. During the nursing assessment, Kara mentions that her boyfriend has been accepted into medical school and is moving to another state. He has asked her to move in with him. She says that she has been too sick to make any plans. She says she feels frustrated because she can't move out of state to be with her boyfriend. However, she acknowledges that the timing of the move is not the best because if she leaves school she would have no medical insurance or means of support. She now lives with her parents and has not told them that she has been thinking of moving in with her boyfriend.

Evidence-Based Practice

In a random telephone study of 5,584 hospitalized patients, Whelan, Jin, and Meltzer (2004) found that pain and dissatisfaction with pain management were common and that each individual patient should be considered at risk for pain. No group was identified as being at low risk for pain. Patients with higher diagnostic-related group (DRG) weight tended to express greater satisfaction with pain management, suggesting that patients with more serious illnesses received more attention during hospitalizations. Further study is indicated as to the factors influencing prediction of pain and its treatment; interventional studies regarding treatment protocols also would be useful.

The client with somatoform disorder presents a unique challenge to the treating staff: avoid undertreating a real medical condition versus providing unnecessary treatment.

interventions and relationships with caregivers. The client role and the associated relationships with others are meant to provide an externalized framework to validate their internalized experiences and sense of self (Kihlstrom & Cantor Kihlstrom, 2001). The client may use the Internet to research information about a disease and treatment options and obtain recognition and sympathy from others (Feldman, 2000).

Clinical Course and Complications

For many clients with somatoform disorders, presenting their complaints to healthcare providers has been a frustrating process, resulting in no adequate solution to their problems. Many healthcare providers view clients with somatization disorders as worried but well or difficult. Because there is no easy cure, the client may be dissatisfied despite the best efforts of the healthcare provider. The client may be seen merely as a complainer who should be avoided because of the time and attention he or she demands.

CASE STUDIES Ms. X.

Ms. X. is a 46-year-old woman who was brought to the emergency room with increased shortness of breath, palpitations, and chest pain. She told the emergency room staff of her history of treatment for pulmonary emboli and was started on anticoagulants. Although tests for pulmonary emboli were inconclusive, she was admitted to the hospital because she developed a hematoma at the intravenous site, weakness and tingling in her arm, and hematuria that required additional testing. Staff members on the unit requested a psychiatric consultation to evaluate the client for depression. The client had told the staff that she had had many hardships and illnesses in her life and was not certain how she could continue to manage with the terrible pain she was having due to the hematoma. The staff reported that the client was very brave and refused all pain medication because she had multiple allergies. Because of this, she could not participate in physical therapy and required much staff assistance with self-care.

The client told the nurse consultant that she felt overwhelmed with her situation, and could barely feed or dress herself because of the weakness in her arm, but was trying to emulate an aunt who had died at a young age as a result of rheumatic heart disease. The aunt had impressed the client with her courage and cheerfulness in dealing with chronic illness, and everyone loved to visit and bring flowers and keep the aunt company. The sickroom was the brightest room in her grandmother's house.

The client did not think of herself as a sickly child but had become ill in her early 20s. During the first year of her marriage, she had a miscarriage at approximately 6 weeks, before even knowing about the pregnancy. The client said she had had excruciating pain, nearly bled to death, and had terrible reactions to a blood transfusion. Afterward, she always felt that she had gotten the wrong blood, although it was never proved, and had terrible pain afterward during intercourse due to stretching during the miscarriage. She had found her husband unsympathetic and unresponsive to her medical problems, a little rough, wanting sex all the time, but not abusive. Their relationship deteriorated in the next few years partly from the client's frequent hospitalizations for urinary tract infections and diagnostic procedures that eventually excluded endometriosis. Some of the infections caused high fevers, and she had had terrible side effects from almost every antibiotic given. The client stated that her past medical records were all over the place because she had moved frequently since her divorce but that she had consulted many physicians in an effort to find out just what was draining the life out of her. She was proud of her skills as a secretary but had been unable to work full time for years because of her frequent illnesses. She found it increasingly difficult to manage her part-time work because she found she was allergic to many office supplies. The initial clinical impression was somatization disorder (see **Table 19-1**).

Table 19-1 Somatoform and Factitious Disorders

Disorder	Symptoms	Clinical Course	Differential
Somatoform disorder	Pain, gastrointestinal, sexual, pseudoneurologic symptoms in more than one area	Begins when client is < 30 years of age	No physical cause or exaggeration of symptoms
Conversion disorder	Voluntary motor, sensory	Limited, reversible	Unconscious motivation, no delusional symptoms
Hypochondriasis	Fear of illness, preoccupation with illness, misinterpretation of symptoms	Transient or chronic	Not restricted to appearance, no delusional symptoms, duration > 6 months, depression
Body dysmorphia	Preoccupation with imagined defect, usually appearance	Persistent	Delusional disorders, depression
Pain disorder	Pain in more than one area; psychologic factors more likely, greater than expected disability	Acute or chronic	Not intentionally feigned, depression
Factitious disorder	Mimics physical disorder; mimics psychologic disorder	Chronic, persistent	May or may not be conscious, no recognizable benefit
Malingering	Exaggerated, prolonged	Situational, limited	Recognizable goal

These frustrations are complicated by symptoms that present, disappear, and reappear over time. The manner in which the client normally describes symptoms may camouflage an actual physical problem that needs treatment, baffling even the most determined detective. The actual course of the disorder may be complicated by the presence or history of child or sexual abuse, substance disorders, mood disorders,

Nursing Care Plan Somatization Disorder

Nursing Diagnosis 1: Risk-prone health behavior related to frequent presentation of medically unexplained treatment as evidenced by side effects from treatment.

Nursing Diagnosis 2: Defensive coping related to learned illness behaviors as evidenced by model of family member's response to illness.

Nursing Diagnosis 3: Ineffective health maintenance related to lack of consistent medical care as evidenced by multiple providers and frequent changes in healthcare providers.

Expected Outcomes	Interventions	Evaluations
• Will minimize the potential for iatrogenic injury and self-harm.	• Evaluating, with team members, the need for diagnostic testing and medical or surgical procedures.	• Determining the extent to which the client's requests for diagnostic testing and medical or surgical intervention decrease.
• Will identify and select a primary healthcare provider.	• Demonstrating the need for clear communication and continuity of care.	• Selecting and using a single primary healthcare provider to improve communication.
• Will form realistic goals.	• Involving the client in decision making and providing feedback regarding her choices.	• Observing for improvement in decision-making skills.
• Will participate in psychotherapy.	• Encouraging the verbalization of feelings regarding the illness and hospitalization.	• Determining the use of appropriate therapeutic interventions.

Visit http://go.jblearning.com/mentalhealth for additional care plans and exercises.

and personality disorders. Clients with chronic pain need to be identified early to facilitate treatment and avoid prolonged or unnecessary treatment that could delay rehabilitation. Accurate and comprehensive assessment of pain is necessary, because both undertreating and overtreating pain can cause problems. Occasionally, treatment for pain is complicated by the healthcare provider's bias toward particular standardized protocols that are supposed to work for all clients or fears of being manipulated or fooled by an addicted client.

Clients with factitious disorders and clients with malingering may have a history of frequent help-seeking behaviors. These contacts with healthcare providers can be frustrating for both parties, because clients need to prove that their symptoms are valid and in need of attention and treatment. The primary problems affecting the clinical course include maintaining a therapeutic relationship and avoiding unnecessary and intrusive treatments that may harm the client. Confrontations by the provider or a competitive escalation of symptoms by the client to prove the illness and need for treatment are nonproductive and occasionally lead to termination of the therapeutic relationship. An angry client may feel provoked to engage in self-harm, destructive behavior, or flight (Braun et al., 2010).

Differential Diagnosis

Many clients seek medical or surgical treatment for somatoform disorders. Clearly the most important factor is to help the client avoid undertreatment for a medical condition or unnecessary treatment of an illness. Many clients complicate their care unnecessarily by seeking multiple opinions for the same complaints or enlisting multiple healthcare providers for discrete individual complaints, allowing no one to recognize the real problem. It is essential to exclude underlying medical conditions. When faced with multiple and occasionally conflicting signs and symptoms, the nurse should ask what organic disorders could cause these symptoms and whether the

CASE STUDIES Ms. Y.

Ms. Y., a 21-year-old woman, came to her routine postpartum visit complaining of severe, constant headaches over the previous week, with pain in the top and back of her head radiating to the neck. She told staff that she was worried she was going to have a stroke, because the headaches made her arms so weak she could hardly pick up the baby. When she had the headaches, she felt as if the only thing that she could do was lie down. She was concerned that she might have a headache when there was no one around to help her. She asked, "Who would take care of the baby? My older child might harm the baby or get into trouble if there were no one watching. I don't know how I would manage." She said she was eating and sleeping well and was able to enjoy her usual activities. The initial medical and neurologic findings were negative, and the client was referred to the headache clinic and eventually to mental health for evaluation. The client stated that she had not had problems during the pregnancy other than a little fatigue and that the pregnancy had been planned. She and her husband were pleased that their family now consisted of a little boy and a little girl just as they had imagined. Both sets of in-laws and other family members were happy for them and active in welcoming the new family member. This was in contrast to her first pregnancy, which was unplanned and for which she had felt unprepared, as she stated, "I was such a baby myself then." She found it very stressful and had felt sick most of the pregnancy. She stated she had felt depressed and anxious during her first pregnancy but did not feel that way now. She said things were going well with her marriage and that the two children were the best things that had ever happened to her. The client told the nurse that her sister had helped her initially after the baby's birth but now was returning to college after summer break. The client said she did not think she could have survived without her sister's help after the birth. She did not want to be a burden to her sister and was worried because her sister did not want to leave her when she was so sick. The client stated she did not know how she would manage without her sister because the toddler was so active and the baby was so demanding.

She had been seen by a psychiatrist on an outpatient basis during her first pregnancy and years earlier when she was 14 years of age. At 14 years of age, she had been referred to the ambulatory health center by the school nurse after she had suddenly started missing school because of the onset of severe stomach pains. She eventually confided to staff that she had been molested by a male neighbor. During both of those times, she had found behavioral health counseling helpful in dealing with her feelings of anxiety and sadness. The initial clinical impression was conversion disorder (see Table 19-1).

Nursing Care Plan **Conversion Disorder**

Nursing Diagnosis 1: Stress overload related to multiple stressors as evidenced by need to care for self, new baby, and older child, and threatened loss of assistance in caretaking.

Nursing Diagnosis 2: Anxiety related to child care responsibilities as evidenced by feelings of inadequacy and inability to manage.

Nursing Diagnosis 3: Ineffective denial related to development of medically unexplained symptoms as evidenced by headaches.

Expected Outcomes	Interventions	Evaluations
• Will identify possible stressors.	• Assessing the client and family systems.	• Validating the selections and application of appropriate therapeutic techniques.
• Will minimize feelings of anxiety.	• Teaching relaxation techniques.	• Evaluating the client's demonstration of relaxation techniques.
• Will explore alternative coping mechanisms.	• Assisting the client in identifying coping mechanisms that have worked in the past in similar situations.	• Observing for increased use of appropriate coping mechanisms.
• Will establish contact with community resources for follow-up care.	• Discussing possible community resources and support systems.	• Reviewing the client's participation in a parenting support group.

Visit http://go.jblearning.com/mentalhealth for additional care plans and exercises.

symptoms, especially pain symptoms, follow established physiologic and pathologic patterns (Nejad & Alpay, 2010).

Often a diagnosis of exclusion is made after everything else has been considered and ruled out. Many chronic illnesses begin with clients presenting a confusing or transient array of symptoms. Clients with anxiety, depressive, or psychotic disorders may exhibit somatic preoccupations or delusions. Clients with real medical problems, such as a seizure disorder, also may have an overlay of symptoms that are precipitated by psychologic stressors as well as a somatoform disorder related to nonepileptic seizures or pseudoseizures.

The index of suspicion for somatization disorder is high for clients with a long history of an unusually large number of inexplicable symptoms affecting multiple body systems. Such a client may be a hypochondriac, one who is often convinced that he or she has a specific illness and is going to die despite evidence to the contrary. A specific temporal or psychologic link with a specific stimulus may exist in a client with a conversion disorder; the physical symptom may be associated with a specific event or model but is not intentionally or consciously produced. Clients who repeatedly seek treatment for unrealistic concerns about their appearance or odor may have body dysmorphic disorder. These clients' symptoms seem to focus on pain more than would be expected for the type of disorder they have. Conversely, those whose lives are affected more than normally expected in similar circumstances may have a pain disorder with predominant psychologic factors.

Clients with panic or other anxiety disorders or phobias (see Chapter 18) may present with multiple somatic complaints such as paresthesias (neurologic weaknesses) and gastrointestinal symptoms, similar to clients with somatoform disorder. However, in anxiety disorders, the symptoms are usually chronic, may be generalized, and may have differing intensities. In panic disorders, physical symptoms of anxiety (e.g., rapid pulse, pounding heartbeat) are usually confined to periods of panic or situations that exacerbate anxiety.

Clients with somatization disorders, in addition to autonomic nervous system complaints similar to those of clients with anxiety, have symptoms that affect several body parts and complain of pain and sexual dysfunction not confined to specific periods. Clients with somatization disorders are likely to seek medical intervention for their symptoms on a regular basis. Researchers believe that clients with panic or anxiety disorders are likely to seek attention for their problematic symptoms and to accept alternative explanations for their problems as well as psychologic counseling. Some clients with underlying depression or a psychotic disorder also may appear preoccupied with pain or somatic complaints or focused on some aspect of their physical appearance or bodily functioning. Although it may be difficult to differentiate, clients with somatoform disorder present with a multiplicity and range of symptoms and the absence of another clearly identified disorder that would explain their problems. Clients with hypochondriasis may also have underlying psychiatric disorders. If the underlying depressive or anxiety disorder is treated, hypochondriacal symptoms decrease (Braun et al., 2010).

Clients with histories of sexual abuse or trauma may present with chronic abdominal pain or problems with sexual functioning. An underlying history of substance abuse may be causing multiple symptoms. Clients with a history of substance abuse may attribute their symptoms caused by abuse to other causes to minimize or hide their abuse or dependence or to disguise drug-seeking behaviors. Some of the symptoms of body dysmorphic disorder may lead a clinician to suspect substance abuse or withdrawal, even though the usual signs are not present and the diagnosis is not confirmed by history or toxicology screening.

In addition, specific environmental or lifestyle factors that could contribute to malingering (stimulation of a voluntary manipulation of symptoms to escape a noxious response or end) or to a factitious disorder (consciously and intentionally stimulated medical or psychiatric symptoms to obtain treatment) should be excluded. Malingering and factitious disorders are difficult to treat, because the relief of symptoms may produce an unwanted response in which the client must face negative or noxious consequences, such as the loss of disability benefits or a return to jail. Both malingering and factitious disorder are considered only after medical and psychiatric workups have identified no other possible explanations for the symptoms. Clients with malingering have an obvious associated cause for the illness behavior. For example, the client may be involved in a compensation case or be threatened with the loss of other entitlement benefits. However, no similar, readily understandable explanation for the symptoms associated with a factitious disorder exists. For example, in our society, because of the stigma attached to psychiatric disorders, most people would not believe it worthwhile to feign psychiatric symptoms.

For clients with pain disorders, it is important to establish a clear history of the onset and duration of the pain; a description of symptoms, treatments, and responses to treatment; past experiences with illness and pain; past psychiatric and substance abuse history; usual coping mechanisms; variables that increase or decrease symptoms; and past and present levels of social, psychologic, and occupational functioning.

Evidence-Based Practice

Lewandowski (2004) reviewed then-current literature dealing with chronic pain and identified factors associated with pain-related beliefs (sense of personal control over pain, cognitive distortion, fear avoidance), history of traumatic events (history of child or sexual abuse and PTSD), and styles of coping in an attempt to identify factors involved in the experience of chronic pain. The review found that nursing interventions depend upon accurate assessment including identification of underlying depression, history of abuse or trauma, pain beliefs, and coping styles in order to ensure appropriate treatment planning and referral for treatment of other disorders (e.g., depression or PTSD). Cognitive therapy was identified as a treatment approach to decrease excess disability and encourage alternate coping mechanisms and pain relief activities.

Often, the pain is associated with periods of developmental or accidental crisis. Records of past treatment and diagnostic tests are helpful to review. Pain scales and pain logs are often helpful in pinpointing possible problems. New onset of pain or dramatic changes in presentation should be investigated to determine if there is a demonstrated basis for the pain, if it is a new medical disorder that should be treated, or if new psychosocial stressors are affecting symptom presentation.

Critical Thinking Question

How do family and culture influence the development of attitudes towards pain and the expression of pain?

Management and Treatment

Teamwork and cooperation between healthcare providers and the client are important when treating any illness, but are essential when treating clients with somatoform disorders, factitious disorders, and malingering. Important points include problematic symptoms and methods of coping with them. The client needs to be assured that his or her concerns are being considered and that treatment will be helpful. Goals include relieving physiologic and psychosocial symptoms and minimizing interference with normal lifestyle requirements.

During the assessment process, the client should be encouraged to describe the symptoms as well as the context in which they appear or abate. It is helpful to identify the problems these symptoms have caused in the past and what therapies have been tried or found helpful. The identification of specific stressors or trigger factors often helps. Active listening during the assessment process can help differentiate among clients who focus on psychosocial problems, on medical symptoms, or upon the need for medical intervention and testing and how this fits with the client's model for understanding illness (Huang & McCarron, 2011). Focusing attention on the assessment process, treatment planning, and evaluation avoids reinforcing the symptoms while providing the client with the attention necessary to maintain positive self-esteem. This focus also reassures the client of the interest and concern of the healthcare providers.

The clinician should help the client identify personal strengths and social supports. While recognizing that the symptoms are real, present, and problematic, the client should be assisted in managing the symptoms so that normal day-to-day activities and health are not compromised. Clients are taught problem-solving techniques and assisted in setting appropriate goals. The client and family are taught to shift their focus away from the physical symptoms to the more practical and functional management issues. Clients gain control over their symptoms and have a growing awareness of the body's responses. Exercise and physical and occupational therapies assist the client in developing a more positive and sophisticated perception of body image. These task assignments provide measurable goals, such as a gradual increase in the duration of a daily walk, doing one daily social activity with family or a group, or practicing relaxation techniques at regular intervals.

Evidence-Based Practice

The Veterans Administration's (2001) consensus guidelines for treatment of medically unexplained symptoms and chronic pain focus on building a therapeutic alliance; coordinating treatment, client education, and collaboration; self-management; and follow-up to monitor treatment as well as revisit and reassess symptom severity, reinforce goals, and assess for emerging conditions. Further research is needed across varied healthcare systems to evaluate the use of consultative and interdisciplinary services and the use of adjunctive and complementary therapies.

Understanding family dynamics and the client's present relationships often helps in identifying causative factors and possible supports. Changes in the client's behavior or symptom presentation may affect the balance of several relationships. Knowledge of these alliances and connections is useful both in facilitating change and in anticipating problems. In addition, active family involvement in treatment helps sustain the client's involvement. Stress-reduction and behavior-modification techniques actively involve the client in treatment. Self-management training includes assessment of the client's beliefs and behaviors, coping repertoire, problematic symptoms, and physiologic cues; instruction in physiologic control techniques such as biofeedback, relaxation, and self-monitoring techniques; and utilization of behavioral and cognitive therapies. Self-management training focuses on bodily processes that are under voluntary

Treatment of symptoms, stressors, and family systems is important in dealing with somatoform disorders.

The mental health professional who treats clients with somatoform disorders must focus on engaging both the primary healthcare providers and the symptomatic client in active participation in healthcare planning and symptom management.

Considerations for Client and Family Education

- Include the client and family in communications and treatment planning in order to provide for use of collateral information in assessment, provide for clear communication, and maintain support systems.
- Build upon client strengths and help the client develop new coping skills.
- Assist the client to avoid unnecessary tests or procedures and recognize the need to prioritize treatment.
- Reinforce the need to recognize possible precipitants or concomitant factors associated with somatic complaints. By monitoring feelings and stressful situations and the association with somatic symptoms, the relationship between feelings, thoughts, and somatic symptoms can be identified.

Support, suggestions, self-management training, and strengthening coping and social systems are important parts of treatment.

control. For example, cognitive-neural-physiologic responses are assessed to develop a training program that helps the client focus on breathing to control a stress-related symptom such as hyperventilation (Ryan, 2009).

In somatoform disorders, medication is usually not recommended but may be indicated for the temporary treatment of problematic symptoms. Treatment of underlying psychologic disorders such as anxiety or depression may be helpful. Body dysmorphia disorders are treated with serotonin reuptake inhibitors (SRIs), clomipramine, and electroconvulsive therapy (ECT) (Braun et al., 2010).

Analgesics, alone or in combination, are used in treatment of pain disorders, particularly those associated with a general medical condition. Various approaches are used, such as increasing the dosage strength or decreasing the dosage intervals. The drug's effect and the anticipated time to onset and duration of action should be considered. For example, a centrally acting pain medication is often combined with a peripherally acting medication, or a long-acting medication is combined with a short-acting medication to provide adequate pain relief. The presence of breakthrough pain or of different types of pain should be considered in selecting medications and dosage schedules. The client's reported history of use and experiences with the medication is helpful in determining the medication regimen and in eliciting the client's cooperation. Properly and adequately treated pain does not lead to addiction. If addiction or manipulation of drug use is suspected, other underlying, contributing factors are usually found. Undertreatment or insufficient treatment of pain is more likely to lead to chronic pain syndromes than adequately treated pain. Studies also show that nurses' knowledge and attitudes can influence pain assessment and intervention and that this can be minimized by ensuring education and clinical competencies as well as by ensuring that pain management assessment and management are prioritized by institutional practices (Al-Shaer, Hill, & Anderson, 2011).

Peripherally acting pain medications such as acetaminophen (Tylenol), salicylates (aspirin), and nonsteroidal anti-inflammatory drugs (NSAIDs) such as ibuprofen (Advil, Motrin), ketoprofen (Orudis), and naproxen (Naprosyn) or ketorolac tromethamine (Toradol) are commonly used. Some types of pain respond to centrally acting opioid analgesics such as products containing codeine sulfate (Tylenol 3, Tylenol 4), hydrocodone (Vicodin), or oxycodone (Roxicodone). Morphine sulfate (Roxanol) and hydromorphone (Dilaudid) are relatively short acting but are available in sustained-release form (Roxanol-SR). Methadone (Dolophine), a long-acting analgesic, has a half-life that increases with prolonged use. The opioid agonists include morphine (Roxanol), codeine, hydromorphone, hydrocodone (Vicodin), levorphanol (Levo-Dromoran), methadone, oxycodone (Roxicodone), and oxymorphone (Numorphan). Opioid agonist-antagonist and partial agonists include methadone, butorphanol (Stadol), nalbuphine (Nubain), buprenorphine (Buprenex), and pentazocine (Talwin). There are also medications that combine opioids and nonopioids such as oxycodone/acetaminophen (Percocet) and hydrocodone and ibuprofen (Vicoprofen). Medication side effects and interactions, tolerance, dependence, and withdrawal are important considerations when narcotics and opioids are used. Pregnancy, alcohol or other substance abuse history, and noncompliance or self-medication are important contraindications. Many clients prefer to use client-controlled analgesia (PCA) pumps or epidermal patch administration for more individualized pain control schedules.

In clients with pain disorders, a tricyclic antidepressant such as amitriptyline (Elavil), imipramine (Tofranil), or doxepin (Sinequan) is occasionally used in combination with pain medication, because tricyclic antidepressants affect the descending pain pathways, potentiate the action of most pain medications so that smaller doses can be used, and have a somewhat sedative effect along with producing skeletal muscle relaxation. Benzodiazepines and anticonvulsants are sometimes used for paroxysmal pain. These medications are thought to decrease the timing of afferent neurons and antagonize hyperexcitability. Cytokine blockers are used for arthritic pain. The goal in pain management may be to decrease the frequency or dosage of medication rather than to eliminate it entirely. The use of placebos is never indicated, because response to a placebo does not necessarily indicate that the pain is not real.

The emphasis is not on questioning the reliability of the client's report of pain but rather on increasing the client's repertoire of coping mechanisms to manage the pain. For example, massage, guided imagery, relaxation techniques, and behavior modification techniques are helpful when used alone or with other therapies. Acupuncture, cryoanalgesia, local anesthetics, regional block analgesics or surgical blockades, trigger point injections, transcutaneous electrical nerve stimulation (TENS), and electromagnetic stimulation therapy (TheraStim) are considered useful adjuncts for some types of chronic pain. A client with chronic pain may be referred to a pain clinic for consultation. A multidisciplinary, individualized approach is particularly helpful (Schatman & Campbell, 2007). Referral is suggested if there is a history of self-medication, abnormal pain behaviors, complex problems, or history of inadequate treatment (Nejad & Alpay, 2010).

Clinicians can put clients in charge by encouraging them to keep a log of symptom relief using simple pain scales (intensity rating scales of 0–10, from no pain to the worst pain ever). The pain's location (site or area), descriptors (dull, pressing, throbbing, burning, sharp, stabbing), and duration (constant, intermittent, periodic, with diurnal variations) are important in assessment. The pain log alerts healthcare providers to changes in symptoms, the effectiveness of the current drug regimen, and concomitant stressors or environmental changes. The pain log also demonstrates acute changes or shows changes over time that may not be readily observed.

Critical Thinking Question 

What are some pharmacologic and nonpharmacologic methods of pain relief, and what are their potential side effects?

Intentional symptom production to receive attention or to avoid noxious consequences should be identified. Changes in the environment to address the triggers for symptom production should be considered. Along with the client, family members should be instructed regarding somatoform disorders, factitious disorders, malingering, and the need for a holistic approach not totally dependent upon medical or surgical intervention. Similarly, a holistic approach to pain disorders is not totally dependent upon pharmacotherapy. The symptoms may serve to protect the individual client as well as the family system, and the system may need to be changed before the client can accept alternative responses. If the environment cannot be changed, the clinician should attempt to alter the client's response to the environment. **Reframing** is a process of facilitating change by developing alternative options and interpretations.

Critical Thinking Question 

What are some possible staff reactions to a client's behavior when staff feel they have been manipulated or purposively deceived? Discuss some ways staff can minimize these reactions when they are aware of the underlying feelings.

Summary

The five main somatoform disorders are somatization disorder, hypochondriasis, conversion disorder, body dysmorphic disorder, and pain disorders. Somatoform disorders are often frustrating both for the client who feels that her or his complaints are not receiving the proper attention and for the caretakers who feel that the client does not recognize that medical or surgical care is not needed. While unexplained physical symptoms are a common phenomenon, the client with a somatoform disorder experiences multiple symptoms affecting multiple systems and often has a history of trauma or stress, psychological symptoms, and association of illness behaviors with primary and secondary gain.

It is important that the client feels supported. The healthcare provider should suggest ways to make the client more comfortable, involve him or her in treatment, and strengthen and maintain adequate coping mechanisms. Reassuring the client, recognizing changes and strengths, and reinforcing health choices allow the professional to engage the client in managing the symptoms rather than having the symptoms control the client's life. Analgesics and various therapeutic adjuncts are used in combination to treat pain disorders. Individualized treatment strategies based upon carefully conducted client assessments are most effective.

Factitious disorders are chronic mental disorders in which the symptoms of a psychologic or physical disorder are intentionally presented to obtain medical treatment. The goal behind symptom presentation is not readily recognizable. Clients with the disorder of malingering present the symptoms of a psychologic or physical disorder for a readily recognizable goal such as avoiding school or work responsibilities. Because of the primary gain involved in a factitious disorder and the secondary gain involved in malingering, it is difficult to treat these clients. Treatment of underlying or associated personality disorders is helpful. As with somatoform disorders, treatment planning aims at preventing medical or therapeutic interventions that may be more harmful and burdensome than the physical or psychologic symptoms themselves.

Annotated References

Al-Shaer, D., Hill, P. D., & Anderson, M. A. (2011). Nurses' knowledge and attitudes regarding pain assessment and intervention. *MEDSURG Nursing, 20*(1), 7–11.
This article discusses difficulties in assessment of the subjective experience of pain, cultural and social implications, and the effects of nursing education and experience of pain management.

Abbass, A., Kisley, S., & Kroenke, K. (2009). Short term psychodynamic psychotherapy for somatoform disorders: Systematic review & meta-analysis of clinical trials. *Psychotherapy and psychosomatics, 78*(5), 265–274.

American Medical Association. (2006). *International classification of diseases* (9th rev. ed., Vols. 1, 2). Dover, DE: Author.
This is the code book for specifying diagnoses.

American Psychiatric Association. (2000). *Diagnostic and statistical manual of mental disorders* (4th ed., text rev.). Washington, DC: Author.
This is the fourth edition, text revision, of the American Psychiatric Association's official nomenclature of psychiatric conditions and disorders. It provides a systematic listing of the official codes and categories, a description of the multiaxial system for diagnosis, and diagnostic criteria for each of the disorders. It is used by psychiatrists, physicians, psychologists, registered nurses, social workers, therapists, and other mental health workers in all clinical settings.

Braun, I. M., Greenberg, D. B., Smith, F. A., & Cassem, N. H. (2010). Functional somatic symptoms, deception symptoms, and somatoform disorders. In T. A. Stern, G. L. Fricchione, N. H. Cassem, M. S. Jellinek, & J. F. Rosenbaum (Eds.), *Massachusetts General Hospital handbook of general hospital psychiatry* (6th ed., pp.173–188.). Philadelphia, PA: Saunders.
Typical clinical cases of somatoform disorders in hospital and general care settings are described here, including hints on diagnosis and treatment. This handbook provides practical approaches to the more common problems healthcare providers are likely to encounter.

Engel, G. L. (1959). "Psychogenic" pain and the pain-prone client. *American Journal of Medicine, 26*(6), 899–918.
This classic article provides a framework for understanding the experience of pain.

Feder, A., Olfson, M., Gameroff, M., Fuenes, M., Shea, S., Lantigua, R. A. & Weissman, M. M. (2001). Medically unexplained symptoms in an urban general medical practice. *Psychosomatics, 42*(3), 261–268.
This study of patients in an urban general medical practice showed that medically unexplained symptoms were common.

Feldman, M. (2000). Munchasen by Internet: Detecting factitious illness and illness on the Internet. *Southern Medical Journal, 93*(7) 669–669.
This article discusses how individuals have used the internet to obtain information about illness and disease and the utilize postings to deceive others and obtain sympathy.

Fink, P., Hansen, M. S., & Oxhoj, M-L. (2004). The prevalence of somatoform disorders among internal medical inpatients. *Journal of Psychosomatic Research, 56*(4), 412–418.
Study of hospitalized medical patients showed that 38.7% also had a psychiatric diagnosis and 17.6% had a somatoform disorder.

Fink, P., Hansen, M. S., & Sondergaard, L. (2005). Somatoform disorders among first time referrals to a neurology service. *Psychosomatics, 46*(6), 540–548.
New patients presenting to inpatient and outpatient neurology department showed a high prevalence of medically unexplained symptoms and met the criterion for diagnosis with a somatoform disorder.

Gureje, O. (2004). What can we learn from a cross-national study of somatic distress? *Journal of Psychosomatic Research, 56*(4), 409–412.
Report of WHO study in 14 countries of variations in somatoform disorder using similar diagnostic standards that showed the client–doctor relationship was an important factor in client reports of multiple somatic symptoms.

Huang, H., & McCarron, R. M. (2011). Medically unexplained physical symptoms: Evidence-based interventions. *Current Psychiatry, 10*(7), 17–31.
Evaluation of medically unexplained symptoms and reluctance of some clients to discuss their

models for illness and description of interventions including need for support.

Jackson, J. L., George, S., & Hinchey, S. (2009). Medically unexplained symptoms. *Journal of General Internal Medicine, 24*(4), 540–542.
Clients presenting with medically unexplained symptoms are common in medical practice and present challenges in assessment and treatment.

Jackson, J. L., & Kroenke, K. (2008). Prevalence, impact and prognosis of multisomatoform disorder in primary care: A 5-year followup study. *Psychosomatic Medicine, 70*(4), 430–434.
Clients presenting with medically unexplained symptoms are less likely to experience relief of symptoms over time.

Kihlstrom, J. & Canter Kihlstrom L. (2001). Somatization as illness behavior. *Advances in Mind-Body Medicine, 17*(4), 240–243, discussion 270–276.
This article discusses how individuals may use somatization and illness behaviors as an expression of self.

Lewandowski, W. (2004). Psychological factors in chronic pain: A worthwhile undertaking for nursing? *Archives of Psychiatric Nursing, 18*(3), 97–105.
This article discusses implications of research evaluating the role of depression, personality factors, pain-related beliefs, trauma, and coping style in the experience of chronic pain.

Mezzich, J. E., Kleinman, A., Fabrega, H., & Parron, D. L. (Eds.). (1996). *Culture and psychiatric diagnosis: A DSM-IV perspective.* Washington, DC: American Psychiatric Press.
This collection of articles from the Conference on Culture and Psychiatric Diagnosis includes discussions of culture and somatoform disorders, with phenomenologic descriptions of various culture-bound syndromes and the problems of describing culturally diverse experiences in diagnostic terms.

Michael, S. R., Candela, L., & Mitchell, S. (2002). Aesthetic knowing: Understanding the experience of chronic illness. *Nurse Educator, 27*(1), 25–27.
This article discusses being involved with a client's artistic expression as part of a nursing assessment by nursing students.

Mittenberg, W., Patton, C., Canyock, E. M., & Condit, D. C. (2002). Base rates of malingering and symptom exaggeration. *Journal of Clinical and Experimental Neuropsychology, 24*(8), 1094–1102.
This is an examination of 33,531 cases to determine illness behaviors and unexplained symptoms indicating evidence of malingering and symptom exaggeration. Symptom fabrication is likely to be more evident in medicolegal and forensic than clinical contexts.

Nejad, S. H., & Alpay, M. (2010). Pain patients. In T. A. Stern, G. L. Fricchione, N. H. Cassem, M. S. Jellinek, & J. Rosenbaum (Eds.), *Massachusetts General Hospital handbook of general hospital psychiatry* (6th ed., pp. 211–236). Philadelphia, PA: Saunders.
This article discusses evaluation and treatment of pain disorders.

Rief, W. & Barsky, A. J. (2005). Psychobiological perspectives on somatoform disorders. *Psychoneuroendocrinology, 30*(10), 996–1002.
This article reviews some of the influences of physiologic activation including endocrine and immune systems, amino acids and neurotransmitters as well as the interaction of psychobiologic components and cognition, behavior and perception in somatoform disorders.

Rowe, J. B. (2010). Conversion disorder: Understanding the pathogenic links between emotion and motor synthesis in the brain. *Brain, 133*(5), 1295–1297.
This article discusses research in possible effects of increased autonomic arousal and muscle tension and differences in motor performance and sensory feedback in conversion disorders.

Ryan, P. (2009). Integrated theory of health behavior change: Background and intervention development. *Clinical Nurse Specialist: The Journal of Advanced Nursing Practice, 23*(3), 161–170.
This article discusses the importance of nursing assessment of client needs to facilitate change in health related behaviors and application and evaluation of various interventions and techniques. Self-regulatory skills can be an important part in preventive health behaviors.

Schatman, M. E., Campbell, A. (Eds.). (2007). *Chronic pain management: Guidelines for multidisciplinary program development.* New York, NY: Informa Healthcare USA, Inc.

This is an informative text on dealing with pain management issues and impact of interdisciplinary assessment and treatment.

Trimble, M. (2004). *Somatization disorders: A medicolegal guide*. Cambridge, UK: Cambridge University Press.
This book discusses the factors common to the etiology and description of somatization disorders.

U.S. Department of Health and Human Services, SAMHSA Mental Health Information Center. (2000). *Mental health: A report of the surgeon general*. Washington, DC: Substance Abuse & Mental Health Services Administration.
This was the first surgeon general's report on mental health issues.

Ustun, T. B., & Sartorius, N. (1995). *Mental illness in general healthcare*. London, England: John Wiley.
In collaboration with the World Health Organization, this book attempts to study the public health and economic impact of the major mental illnesses and project their impact across the globe. It is useful for studies of statistical prevalence and impact of disability.

Veterans Administration Guidelines Committee. (2001). *VHA/DoD clinical practice guideline for the management of medically unexplained symptoms: Chronic pain and fatigue*. Washington, DC: Veterans Health Administration, Department of Defense, Office of Quality Improvement.
These are consensus guidelines from an interdisciplinary team providing a treatment algorithm for medically unexplained symptoms.

Whelan, C. T., Jin, L., & Meltzer, D. (2004). Pain and satisfaction with pain control in hospitalized medical clients. *Archives of Internal Medicine, 164*, 173–180.
This survey of general medical clients regarding their perception of pain and their satisfaction with pain control during their hospitalization supported JCAHO (currently known as The Joint Commission) recommendations for a systematic approach to pain management that is individualized to the needs of each client.

Yeung, A., & Deguang, H. (2002). Case based reviews: Somatoform disorders. *Western Journal of Medicine, 176*(4), 253–256.
This article provides case examples and treatment suggestions for Asian clients experiencing somatization. It discusses traditional Chinese medicine and the concept of energy flow.

Additional Resources

American Society of Anesthesiologists Task Force. (2010). Practice guidelines for chronic pain management: An updated report by the American Society of Anesthesiologists Task Force on chronic pain management and the American Society of Regional Anesthesia and Pain Management. *Anesthesiology, 112*(4), 810 833.
These guidelines cover conceptualizing and treating chronic pain including use of complementary therapies.

Feldman, M. D. (2004). *Playing sick? Untangling the web of Münchausen syndrome, Münchausen by proxy, malingering, and factitious disorder*. New York, NY: Routledge.
This text discusses factitious disorders and includes case studies, treatment options, and information on cyberdeception—use of the Internet to gather information or sympathy.

Feldman, M. D., & Ford, C. V. (1994). *Client or pretender: The strange world of factitious disorders*. New York, NY: John Wiley.
This text emphasizes the relationship between clients and providers and teaches clinicians how to approach these disorders. A helpful guide to understanding a difficult disorder, this text explains the conflicts and ambivalence surrounding healthcare providers' relationships with these clients.

Ford, C. V. (1984). *The somatizing disorders: Illness as a way of life*. New York, NY: Elsevier Biomedical.
This text discusses somatizing as part of the body's physiologic and psychologic defenses to variations in stress and social support. It includes case studies of common somatizing responses such as medical student illness in which a little knowledge, stress, and vulnerability lead to the misperception of a disease state, and "painmanship," in which psychologic responses to pain are discussed. This classic book is out of print.

Kazanowski, M., & Laccetti, M. S. (2008). *Quick look nursing: Pain management*. Sudbury, MA: Jones and Bartlett.
This book provides guidelines and case studies for assessment and treatment of pain at different developmental stages.

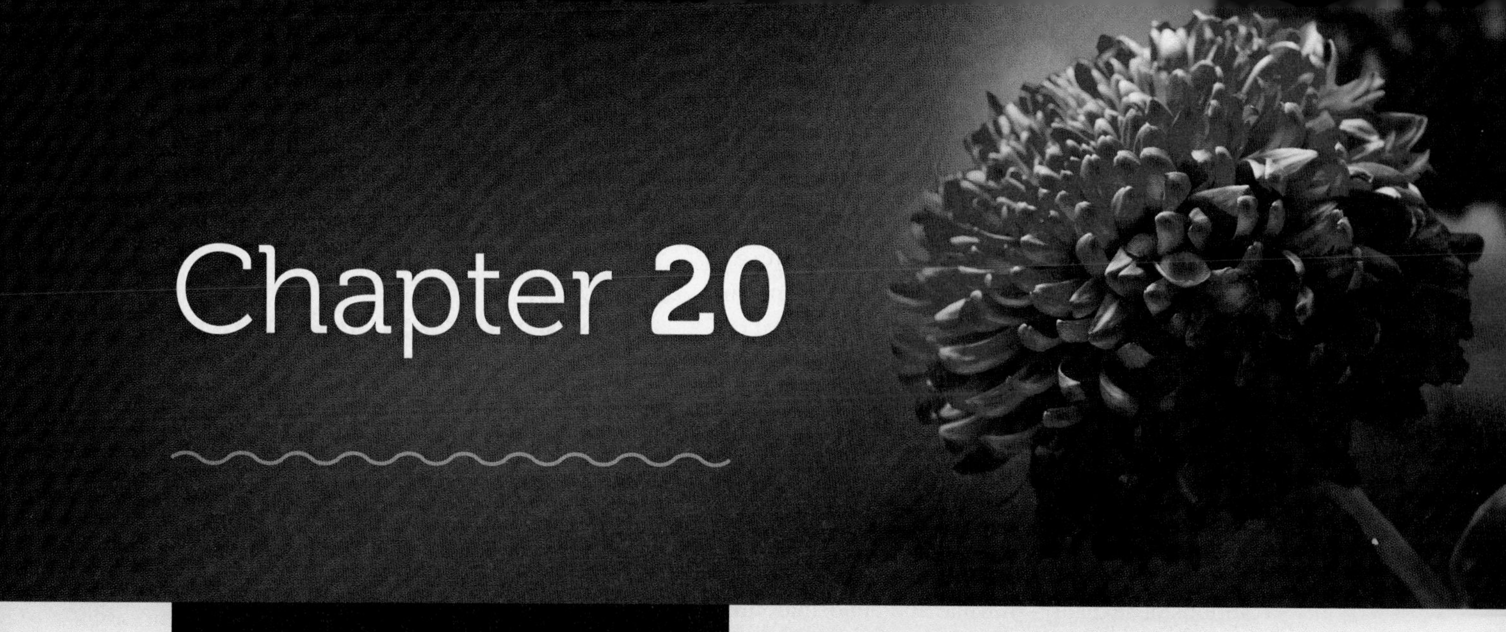

Sexual Disorders and Gender Identity Disorder

Blaine R. Beemer and Patricia G. O'Brien

http://go.jblearning.com/mentalhealth 

For a full suite of assignments and additional learning activities, use the access code located in the front of your book to visit this exclusive website: http://go.jblearning.com/mentalhealth. If you do not have an access code, you can obtain one at the site.

Introduction

This chapter will present strategies for the nurse to follow when assessing clients' sexual health concerns. It will also identify the main features of sexual disorders and gender identity disorders as defined by the American Psychiatric Association (2000). Common treatment approaches for each disorder will be discussed briefly.

Sexual Health

Notions of sexuality—normal and abnormal, functional and dysfunctional—are inevitably changeable and culturally based. Changes in society's view of sexuality have influenced how these issues are addressed in the field of mental health. For instance, a common view among psychiatrists as late as the 1970s was that engaging in sexual activity actually caused or contributed to major psychiatric disorders. Now, sexual expression is broadly considered an aspect of healthy living. Another example of changing views in mental health can be found in the clinical approach to homosexuality. Homosexuality was classified as a mental disorder in the *Diagnostic and Statistical Manual of Mental Disorders* (*DSM*) until 1973 and in the *International Classification of Diseases* until 1992. Its inclusion in previous editions of diagnostic manuals was likely due to a combination of factors, including prevailing popular attitudes toward homosexuality and a dominant psychoanalytic stance that treated same-sex attraction as a failure in psychosexual development.

Early definitions of sexual health tended to concentrate on sexual functioning and the fulfillment of the sexual response cycle of excitement, plateau, orgasm, and resolution identified by Masters and Johnson (1966). Today, the World Health Organization (WHO) uses a broader definition that recognizes the varieties of healthy sexual expression, the role of emotional intimacy, the impediments caused by sexual coercion and violence, and the need for accurate information on sexuality:

> Sexual health is a state of physical, emotional, mental and social well being in relation to sexuality; it is not merely the absence of disease, dysfunction or infirmity. Sexual health requires a positive and respectful approach to sexuality and sexual relationships, as well as the possibility of having pleasurable and safe sexual experiences, free of coercion, discrimination and violence. For sexual health to be attained and maintained, the sexual rights of all persons must be respected, protected and fulfilled. (2010, p. 10)

Biology of Sexual Function

The brain mechanisms of human sexual response are exceedingly complex. The pattern of brain activity associated with sexual activity appears to be extremely diverse and variable, with dominant activity at different times associated with the thalamus, the amygdala, the hippocampus, and frontal cortical structures.

Testosterone clearly acts as the central neurotransmitter for sexual libido. Testosterone reliably produces stereotypic male sexual behavior in laboratory animals, and its absence or blockade extinguishes those effects. Precipitous drops in testosterone in both males and females due to surgical intervention often cause noticeable reductions in libido and sexual functioning; however, gradual, natural reductions due to changes in the life cycle, even when testosterone levels are vastly reduced, do not inevitably lead to elimination of libido or sexual satisfaction. In fact, naturally aging men, with significantly lowered testosterone in their later years, and women, whose testosterone levels in their later years can be almost immeasurable, generally still report high levels of sexual activity and high satisfaction with their sexual lives, even if activity levels decrease.

Types of Sexual and Gender Identity Disorders

The *DSM-IV-TR* (American Psychiatric Association [APA], 2000) recognizes four categories of sexual and gender identity disorders (**Table 20-1**):

1. *Sexual dysfunctions:* Problems with sexual response such as sexual desire, erection, ejaculation, or orgasm; also, sexual pain.
2. *Paraphilias:* Intense urges or sexual activities "that involve unusual objects, activities, or situations and cause clinically significant distress or impairment" (APA, 2000, p. 535). These include problems such as fetishes, exhibitionism, pedophilia, and sexual masochism.
3. *Gender identity disorders:* Intense cross-gender identification and "persistent discomfort with one's assigned sex" (APA, 2000, p. 535).
1. *Sexual and gender disorders not otherwise specified:* These include **intersex conditions** (congenital problems with sex-organ anatomy and sex hormones with accompanying gender

Table 20-1 Sexual and Gender Identity Disorders

- Sexual dysfunctions
  - Sexual desire disorders
  - Sexual arousal disorders
  - Orgasmic disorders
  - Sexual pain disorders
- Paraphilias
- Gender identity disorders
  - Sexual and gender disorders not otherwise specified

identity issues) and "transient, stress related cross-dressing behavior" (APA, 2000, p. 582).

The *DSM-IV-TR* also notes that "notions of deviance, standards of sexual performance, and concepts of appropriate gender role can vary from culture to culture" (APA, 2000, p. 535).

Axis I and III Subtypes in Diagnosis of Sexual Disorders

A variety of subtypes, reflecting differences in onset and causality, are coded on Axis I. They include:

- *Lifelong versus acquired type:* If the condition has occurred since the beginning of sexual activity and has persisted, the condition is classified as lifelong.
- *Generalized versus situational type:* If the disorder or dysfunction occurs only in some instances (e.g., with one partner but not another), the condition is classified as situational.
- *Due to psychologic factors versus due to combined factors:* If a general medical condition or substance abuse is thought to contribute to the disorder or dysfunction but is not deemed to be the main cause, a subtype of due to combined factors is used.

If a general medical condition is thought to primarily account for the sexual disorder, the subtype due to a general medical condition is used. For example, this subtype would be used for erectile dysfunction caused by diabetes. The disorder is still coded on Axis I, but the existence of the general medical condition is stated on Axis III. Substance-induced sexual dysfunction is diagnosed if the direct effects or withdrawal from an illegal drug, medication, or toxin is thought to be the primary causal agent of the condition; it is coded on Axis I.

The Nurse's Role

Nursing Assessment

The topic of sexuality often induces more anxiety for the nurse conducting the interview than for the client. This needs to be overcome in the service of holistic care. Failure to ask relevant questions about sexuality could arise for many reasons. One cause can be that the topics are seen as too private to be held between strangers, even for therapeutic purposes. Some nurses would never even consider asking sexual questions of their clients for this reason. Another source of anxiety is that sexual questions directed at the client may bring up difficult issues for the nurse. Issues such as sexual dysfunction, **sexual orientation**, or marital conflict may resonate strongly with the caregiver and create a hidden no-go zone that reflects the clinician's sensitivities more than the client's. In other instances, nurses may sense that sexual questions are important, but feel they lack the knowledge to question intelligently or to follow up once a response is elicited.

One study among physicians uncovered impediments to the use of sexuality-related questions (Maurice, 2000). Those impediments were:

- Unclear what to do with the answers (uncertainty about the next question; lack of familiarity with treatment approaches)
- Fear of offending clients
- Lack of obvious justification
- Generational obstacles
- Fear of sexual misconduct charge
- Sometimes perceived as irrelevant
- Lack of familiarity with some sexual practices (p. 21)

Critical Thinking Question

Do you think that any of the listed factors might inhibit you from asking a client sexually related questions? If so, what can you do to counter this?

Most patients with sexual concerns hope that health-care professionals initiate the discussion.

Nurses cannot confidently assume that clinicians from other disciplines will assess for sexual concerns. It is up to nurses to raise the issue with their clients because clients are unlikely to raise the subject on their own. Most importantly, clients expect and want healthcare providers to ask about sexual concerns. The best time to begin this discussion is in the initial assessment phase; leaving sexual questions until the end may convey the impression that it is a taboo subject. It is important that sexual health be viewed as an important but unexceptional element of a holistic health assessment. To communicate this, the nurse must be accepting and nonjudgmental when interacting with the client.

Nurses cannot rely on the patient to initiate a discussion about sexual concerns or on other healthcare professionals to assess for the presence of sexual concerns.

Mahan (2003) provides the following examples of direct questions that will facilitate the discovery of sexual problems:

1. Do you have any questions or concerns about your sex life?
2. Are you currently sexually active?
3. Have you recently had less interest in sex?
4. Do you have a problem with vaginal dryness/erection?
5. Are you able to have an orgasm (or to ejaculate)? (p. 90)

Nursing Interventions

Nurses can initiate a discussion of sexual concerns at a depth consistent with their knowledge base. Nurses do not have to be able to solve sexual problems in order to identify patients' sexual concerns.

Once identified, dealing with clients' sexual concerns can appear to be a daunting task. It is impractical for nurses in most general mental health settings to provide sophisticated sexual health interventions. Nurses can, however, provide holistic care by assessing and intervening to the level of their understanding. Nurses can initiate a discussion of sexual concerns at a depth consistent with their knowledge base. Nurses do not have to be able to solve sexual problems in order to identify clients' sexual concerns.

A number of sexuality clinical care models have developed in nursing. Irwin (2002) identifies a range of potential nursing interventions, from general information, to helping clients anticipate potential sexual consequences of a medical or surgical procedure, to detailed problem-solving around sexual difficulties. The last category is clearly the realm of highly trained nurses with specialized skills.

The PLISSIT model (Annon, 1976) (**Figure 20-1**) remains the most prominent sexual intervention model, largely due to its multidisciplinary appeal, its broad applicability to different healthcare settings, and its simplicity. It asks the clinician, in this case the nurse, to identify at which of the four levels it is most appropriate for the nurse to intervene:

P = Permission. *At this most basic level, PLISSIT involves the nurse giving permission for the client to acknowledge his or her existence as a sexual being and to have a right to concern about the sexual consequences of life events, including psychiatric conditions and treatment. This level of intervention is appropriate for practically any nurse in any setting.*

LI = Limited Information. *At the level of LI, the nurse in mental health knows that there are common consequences to a person's sexuality that are associated with psychiatric conditions and their treatment. This knowledge is broadly available in psychiatric textbooks, articles, and reputable websites. Communicating this information to the client can alleviate much anxiety and may promote compliance with treatment. It is reasonable to expect nurses in mental health to be able to provide LI to all their clients, appropriate to each person's mental status.*

The remaining two steps require advanced knowledge and clinical expertise that is not in the domain of the general nurse, but may be acquired by advanced practice nurses.

SS = Specific Suggestions. *At this level, the nurse has thoroughly assessed the sexual health of the individual or couple, is aware of a range of evidence-based interventions, and can confidently offer options for the individual or couple that may improve their sexual satisfaction without compromising their overall treatment. In addition to requiring knowledge, successful SSs require sensitivity to the therapeutic moment of readiness when the clients can take in these suggestions.*

IT = Intensive Therapy. *At this level, the clinician has made a thorough assessment of the individu-*

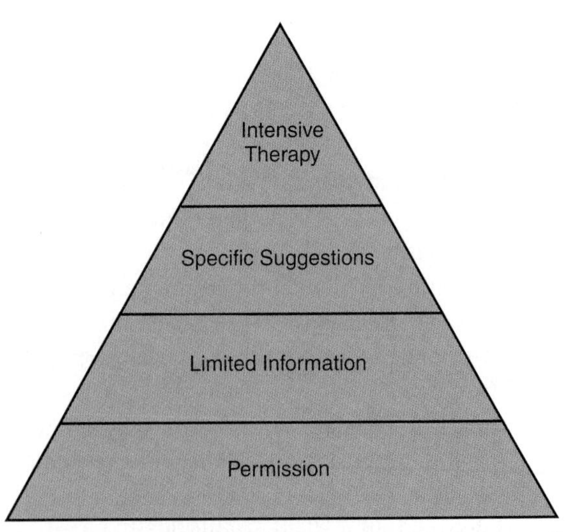

Figure 20-1 The PLISSIT model.

Table 20-2 Nursing Interventions for Clients with Sexual Dysfunctions

Nursing Diagnosis	Nursing Interventions	Rationales
Sexual dysfunction, evidenced by: Decreased libido	Take a sexual history and ask about the client's perception.	This will assist in setting appropriate goals.
Inability to achieve orgasm	Inquire about possible events that may contribute to the symptom.	Medication side effects, medical diagnoses, recent stressors, or life events may relate to the onset of the symptom.
Impotence	Determine if the client has sought treatment in the past and, if so, the client's response.	This may suggest an approach to the current situation.
Premature ejaculation	Educate the client about availability of treatment.	The client may not know that the symptom can be treated.
Pain on intercourse	Ask if the client wants referral to a specialist.	The decision for treatment must come from the client.

al's/couple's sexual health, can offer proven interventions personalized to the condition and the clients, and can problem solve the outcomes of those interventions, generally through multiple visits. The nurse clinician providing IT may be collaborating with other healthcare providers in medicine, social work, occupational therapy, and rehabilitation science, among others, to optimize outcomes.

Critical Thinking Question

What are some ways that the nurse gives the client permission to speak about sexual concerns? How would you determine that a source of sexual information is reliable and valid?

A large part of the nurse's role is education for clients, sexual partners, and family, as indicated. **Table 20-2** identifies nursing interventions for clients experiencing the sexual dysfunctions discussed in the following sections. Considerations for client and family education are addressed later in this chapter.

Essential Features of the Sexual and Gender Identity Disorders

The sexual and gender identity disorders include sexual dysfunctions, which relate to a disturbance in the sexual response pattern; paraphilias, which are intense, disturbing sexual fantasies, urges, or behaviors; and gender identity disorders or transsexualism.

Sexual Dysfunctions

The sexual dysfunctions (**Table 20-3**) correspond with the four phases of the **sexual response cycle**: desire, excitement, orgasm, and resolution.

Sexual Desire Disorders

The *DSM-IV* identifies two sexual desire disorders: one related to a lack of desire, the other to an aversion to sexual activity.

- *Hypoactive sexual desire disorder (HSDD):* This is defined as a persistent or recurrent deficiency or absence of sexual fantasies and

Table 20-3 Sexual Dysfunctions

Sexual Desire Disorders	Sexual Arousal Disorders	Orgasmic Disorders	Sexual Pain Disorders
Hypoactive sexual desire disorder	Female sexual arousal disorder	Female orgasmic disorder Male orgasmic disorder	Dyspareunia Vaginismus
Sexual aversion disorder	Male erectile disorder	Premature ejaculation	

desire for sexual activity (APA, 2000). Sexual desire (and frequency of activity) varies naturally over the course of a romantic relationship, and there is no objective level at which a lack of sexual desire is normal, problematic, or pathologic. However, a lack of desire can have dramatic effects on the individual and the couple. Although couples may stabilize at a level of sexual activity in the long term, a noticeable reduction in desire by either partner may create friction and hard feelings in the relationship. Individuals who experience a drop in desire often mourn the loss. The partner often infers that they have somehow become less desirable or attractive, which has further consequences for the relationship as well as the client's individual self-esteem.

- *Sexual aversion disorder:* Whereas HSDD describes a lack of sexual desire, sexual aversion disorder is notable by "the aversion to and active avoidance of genital sexual contact with a partner" (APA, 2000, p. 541). This aversion may be specific to certain situations or sexual acts or may be global. The aversion must cause distress or difficulties in functioning. Diagnostically, it may be difficult to distinguish between lack of sexual desire, disinterest, discomfort with the experience of arousal, and outright aversion. However, persons with sexual aversion may experience disgust at the thought of sex, and panic when sexual activity is initiated.

Incidence and Prevalence of Desire Disorders. A loss of sexual desire is likely the most common sexual complaint of women; increasingly, however, men present to healthcare professionals with this complaint as well. Prevalence rates of female HSDD in different studies range from 10% to 40% (Dennerstein & Hayes, 2005). Studies of male desire problems are less common, but a prevalence of 6% has been cited (Simons & Carey, 2001). Sexual aversion disorder occurs in both men and women, but exact incidence is unknown (Shafer, 2004).

Etiology of Desire Disorders. Sexual desire problems are perhaps the most complex of sexual dysfunctions in terms of etiology. Desire is a subtle flux of love, biologic drive, motivation, feelings of trust and intimacy, and self-image, especially in long-term relationships. Due to complexities in sexual response, attempts to engage in sexual activity when it is not desired through disinterest, negative emotions, or pain can turn lack of desire into outright aversion.

Some common psychosocial causes of reduced sexual desire are:

- Distractions and fatigue, especially when child rearing
- Depression and anxiety disorders
- Relational conflict and anger at partner
- Fear of sexually transmitted infections or pregnancy
- Body image issues related to age, health status, surgery, or weight
- Lack of an available partner
- Previous unsatisfying, traumatic, or physically painful sexual experiences

Biologic changes such as hormonal deficiencies sometimes play a primary role in desire disorders. The sudden drop in hormones produced by genital surgery or radiation can have a profound effect. Loss of libido can be the result of a medical condition, such as hypothyroidism, diabetes mellitus, some neurological disorders, or local genital disease (Shafer, 2004). Substance abuse, depression, and prescribed medications can also contribute to a loss of sexual desire. A not uncommon cause of sudden loss of libido in younger women is due to side effects from oral contraceptives. Some loss of libido is common in aging, but many individuals maintain libido into their 8th and 9th decades.

Treatment of Sexual Desire Disorders. Once physical and psychiatric causes have been ruled out (especially depression), individual or couples counseling with an experienced therapist can produce benefits. Few, if any, medications or compounds have been found to reliably enhance sexual desire in healthy humans. Some street drugs or medications such as alcohol and benzodiazepines may be disinhibiting, which users may perceive as prosexual. (Of course, disinhibition can interfere with sexual decision making.)

Testosterone treatment is an option for the treatment of HSDD, but its use is controversial. Although some studies suggest that testosterone replacement has some short-term effects on libido in cases where loss of testosterone has been sudden, few long-term studies exist.

Sexual Arousal Disorders

There are also two sexual arousal disorders—female sexual arousal disorder and male erectile disorder (ED).

- *Female sexual arousal disorder (FSAD):* Women with FSAD may attempt to engage in sexual activity but do not become physically aroused. As a consequence, sexual activity becomes unpleasant or impossible. Without physiological arousal, women may experience a lack of vaginal lubrication, leading to painful intercourse. As a consequence, they may experience frustration and anxiety, and may avoid sexual activity altogether.

- *Male erectile disorder (ED):* This disorder, referred to as **erectile dysfunction**, is experienced as a persistent or recurrent inability to attain or maintain an adequate erection until completion of the sexual activity and which causes marked distress or interpersonal difficulty (APA, 2000). Lack of erection, especially with a new partner, can be emotionally demoralizing for a man. He may doubt his ability to satisfy his partner, may doubt his own masculinity, and may fear loss of his relationship. Men may avoid intimacy altogether because of the problem. Fertility issues may arise if the problem is persistent.

Incidence and Prevalence of Sexual Arousal Disorders. Female sexual arousal disorder has a lifetime prevalence of 60% and is linked to problems with sexual desire (Shafer, 2004). Periodic erectile difficulties occur in every age group. Persistent erectile dysfunction, including the complete absence of erection, is far more common in older age groups. In a large study of men 40–70 years of age, over half experienced some form of erectile dysfunction (Feldman, Goldstein, & Hatzichristou, 1994).

Etiology of Female Sexual Arousal Disorder. Physical causes of FSAD are common when a fairly sudden loss of physical arousal is noted. Illness, surgery, radiation therapy, or medications can play a part. Fatigue or anxiety with a new partner can inhibit arousal, and then anticipatory anxiety can produce a chronic condition. Often, FSAD is associated with other sexual problems, such as low desire, sexual aversion, or orgasmic difficulties; FSAD may be a cause or a consequence of these other conditions.

Etiology of Male Erectile Disorder. Between 50% and 85% of all cases of ED have an organic basis (Shafer, 2004). Diabetes and cardiovascular disease are common causes of ED due to both autonomic diabetic neuropathy and penile endothelial changes. Men who smoke have a higher rate of ED, especially in younger age groups, and the effect appears to be dose dependent. Additionally, there is a complex relationship among obesity, metabolic syndrome, hypogonadism, and reduced circulating testosterone, which has many negative general health consequences. Some categories of medications, including cardiovascular, anticonvulsant, and psychotropic agents, may also be factors.

There are also nonmedical reasons for not getting an erection, including fatigue, not being in the mood for sexual activity, alcohol or drug use, partner issues, and insufficient sexual stimulation.

Treatment of Female Sexual Arousal Disorder. Treatment is directed at reducing anxiety and introducing behavioral exercises that focus on providing and deriving sexual pleasure, initially without the goal of intercourse or orgasm. This technique, known as sensate focus, is intended to reduce the anxiety associated with fear of failing to achieve an orgasm. As the couple becomes better able to experience sexual pleasure through mutual touching, they progress to genital touching and eventual orgasm. Although the phosphodiesterase type 5 (PDE-5) inhibitors, such as sildenafil citrate (Viagra), may have a positive effect on a small subset of women who experience psychological arousal but no physiological arousal, these medications have little effect on most women with female sexual arousal disorder (FSAD).

Treatment of Erectile Dysfunction. Prior to the introduction of the PDE-5 inhibitors, erection enhancement involved inhibiting venous outflow using vacuum pumps and restrictor rings; intracavernosal injection (ICI) with combinations of vasoactive agents such as phentolamine, yohimbine, papaverine, and prostaglandin E_1; and surgical options such as implantation of penile prostheses or surgery on penile outflow veins. Most of these treatments leave much to be desired, because they are often complicated, uncomfortable, and expensive. In most clinical contexts, oral agents are now the first-line treatment irrespective of the presumed organic cause of erectile difficulty, with ICI being the second-line treatment.

The three available PDE-5 inhibitors, sildenafil (Viagra), vardenafil (Levitra), and tadalafil (Cialis), are similar in action and efficacy with some differences. Tadalafil is approved for once daily use for men who anticipate sexual activity twice a week or more frequently. The daily regimen is not recommended for men with severe renal or hepatic failure (Ellsworth & Kirshenbaum, 2008). Clients who develop chest pain cannot take nitroglycerin for more than

24 hours after taking a short-acting PDE-5 inhibitor (sildenafil and vardenafil) or 48 hours after taking a long-acting PDE-5 inhibitor (tadalafil). Hearing and vision loss, including nonarteritic ischemic optic neuropathy (NAION), have been associated with the use of PDE-5 inhibitors, although a causal relationship has not been established (Ellsworth & Kirshenbaum, 2008). NAION can result in permanent vision loss. Clients should be advised to stop the medication and seek medical attention if hearing or vision loss is experienced.

Sexual problems in relationships in time often affect both partners. Seeing the patient as part of a relational system is an effective approach.

If the client is in a relationship, treatment of ED may involve couples therapy. Couples may benefit from coaching to optimize the use of medications and to explore sexual activities that do not involve intercourse, especially because these practices generally lead to greater sexual satisfaction for the partner.

Critical Thinking Question

Imagine how a couple's sexual relationship might be affected by the need to introduce external devices, such as vacuum pumps or penile implants. What concerns might both partners have?

Orgasmic Disorders

Orgasm can be described as a sudden, subjective experience of intense pleasure usually accompanied by rhythmic contractions in the pelvic area. Orgasmic capacity varies significantly between males and females, within different individuals of the same sex, from situation to situation, and across the phase of the life cycle. Generally, males first experience orgasm at a younger age, usually through masturbation. Women who find it difficult to orgasm in their teens or 20s may find that their orgasmic capacity increases later in life, whereas men often find that orgasm becomes delayed as they age.

- *Female orgasmic disorder:* Women with orgasmic disorder (also known informally as **anorgasmia**) experience "a persistent or recurrent delay in, or absence of, orgasm following a normal sexual excitement phase" (APA, 2000, p. 547) that causes distress or interpersonal conflict. As with many other sexual dysfunctions, it can be a lifelong problem or occur at any time (acquired type); it can occur in all situations (generalized type) or only in some contexts (situational type). The dysfunction can occur in the absence of any known physical cause.

  Orgasm is a learned reflex, which is why anorgasmia (lack of orgasm) is more common in young women. Once learned, it is unusual for women to lose orgasmic capacity completely, although episodic orgasmic difficulties are not uncommon.

  Most women do not experience orgasm with intercourse alone; they require manual stimulation during intercourse. If a woman can achieve orgasm on her own but not with a partner, she in most cases does not meet the criteria for an orgasmic disorder.
- *Male orgasmic disorder.* The most frequent orgasmic disorder is the situational type wherein the man can have orgasm with masturbation and with manual or oral stimulation by a partner, but not with intercourse. Males commonly experience a longer and longer ejaculatory latency as they age, and, with increased age, they often notice that they need more intense direct stimulation to have an orgasm. Some men lose orgasmic capability at some time in their lives, or have a lifelong problem with orgasm, although either of these conditions is rarer than female orgasmic disorder.
- *Premature ejaculation:* **Premature ejaculation** (PE) is a condition wherein the male ejaculates very quickly. Although a number of formal definitions have arisen for research purposes, the key factor in PE is ejaculation prior to the wishes of the man or his partner. Premature ejaculation can be extremely severe. Some sufferers have a lifelong problem; they ejaculate before they remove their clothes prior to sexual activity, or with the slightest sexual touch, or

Clinical Example

Paul, a 23-year-old male, begins a new relationship after a 2-year romance with a prior partner. However, when he and his new partner attempt to become intimate, he ejaculates as soon as petting begins. The PE was a problem in the early stages of his previous relationship, but went away after a few months. Now, his embarrassment prevents him from discussing this with his new partner, so his anxiety now begins to increase as soon as the kissing starts. As a consequence, he feels forced to ignore the invitations of sexual interest from his partner. Soon, the partner starts to feel rejected and the relationship is endangered—though not directly because of the PE.

while attempting to put on a condom. This can cause embarrassment, shame, enormous self-esteem issues, and relationship strain.

Incidence and Prevalence of Orgasmic Disorders. Studies vary significantly regarding the extent of female orgasmic disorder. One study found that 24% of women had experienced inability to orgasm for at least several months in the past year (Laumann, Gagnon, Michael, & Michaels, 1994). Lifetime prevalence has been estimated at 35% (Shafer, 2004).

Male orgasmic disorder is infrequent, with a lifetime prevalence of 2%, and occurs in men who are usually under the age of 35 years and who are sexually inexperienced (Shafer, 2004).

Studies place the range of prevalence of premature ejaculation at 25–40% of the male population (Carson & Gunn, 2006).

Etiology of Female Orgasmic Disorder. It is unclear why some women experience periodic or lifelong anorgasmia. Sociological factors such as age, education, or socioeconomic status have not been found to be consistent predictors of orgasmic disorder. Anxiety appears to play only a minor role in anorgasmia in many instances. Personality correlates of anorgasmia have yielded inconsistent results.

Female orgasmic disorder is often found with other female sexual disorders of desire or arousal; it may be difficult to determine which of these disorders might be causal or consequential to the others.

Etiology of Male Orgasmic Disorder. A variety of causes are implicated, including drugs, neurologic degeneration due to disease, and surgery. Male orgasmic disorders are often associated with other sexual disorders such as ED and low libido.

Etiology of Premature Ejaculation. Premature ejaculation has a number of causes. Most young men ejaculate more quickly than they expect or want with a partner, even if they have some ejaculatory control on their own. Most notice an increase in ejaculation latency by their late 20s.

For episodic PE, situational and emotional factors explain the experience. Many men experience quicker ejaculation when with a new partner due to the excitement of the situation. Some sexual positions may increase friction and the tendency to ejaculate; some situations, such as fear of discovery, may do the same. On the other hand, lifelong PE may represent a neurobiologic condition with a genetic basis.

Treatment of Female Orgasmic Disorder. No pharmacologic agents have proven consistently effective in treating female orgasmic disorder. Psychoeducation and communication skills, together with physical exercises, appear to produce improvement. Various forms of directed masturbation as part of an overall cognitive behavioral therapy program have produced beneficial results.

Treatment approaches hinge on the natural history and specific circumstances of the orgasmic problem. If orgasm is possible except with a partner, clients may benefit from counseling that focuses on issues of trust and intimacy and improving the sexual atmosphere of the relationship plus coaching of both partners to ensure that sufficient sexual stimulation is present.

Treatment of Male Orgasmic Disorder. Treatment with medications such as amantadine or bupropion has been attempted; further research is needed. Relationship issues can play a role, although lack of sufficient stimulation is likely the most common factor.

Treatment of Premature Ejaculation. Treatment depends on the perceived causes and background to the problem. Occasional PE, especially with a new partner or in stressful circumstances, is treated with reassurance and education. Moderate PE is usually treated with the squeeze or stop-start behavioral technique, a form of systematic desensitization that teaches men and couples how to feel the physical changes prior to ejaculation. However, data on the long-term efficacy of these behavioral methods is lacking.

Lifelong PE responds poorly to reassurance or behavioral techniques alone. The use of the selective serotonin reuptake inhibitors (SSRIs) in the past decade or so has somewhat revolutionized treatment, with paroxetine being one of the most common agents used for the associated side effect of delaying ejaculation. These novel antidepressants are often used in conjunction with the PDE-5 inhibitors such as sildenafil in order to maintain erectile ability even after premature ejaculation.

Most men will ejaculate more rapidly in adolescence and early adulthood, and in a new relationship.

For all of the orgasmic disorders, couples therapy is valuable, with a focus on communication and behavioral approaches.

Sexual Pain Disorders

There are two sexual pain disorders—dyspareunia and vaginismus.

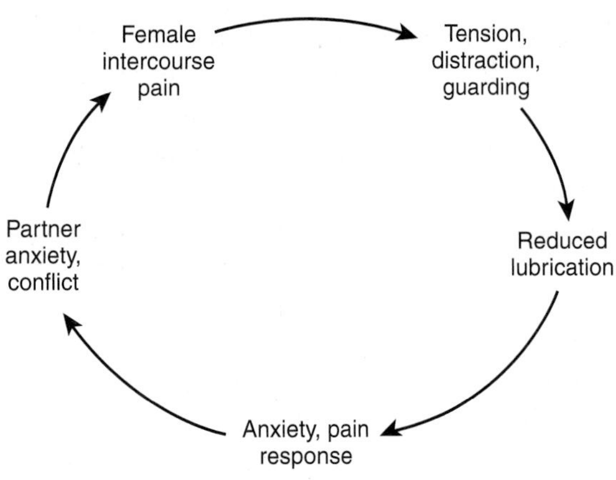

Figure 20-2 Circular pattern: Female sexual pain

1. *Dyspareunia:* **Dyspareunia** is recurrent or persistent genital pain associated with sexual intercourse in either men or women. Technically, dyspareunia is distinguished from painful intercourse caused by any other medical condition, lack of lubrication, or substance abuse, and is therefore something of a psychiatric diagnosis by exclusion. Although occasional pain may be due to lack of sufficient arousal, fatigue, or illness, more than very occasional sexual pain can become ingrained in the entire sexual experience and requires medical attention.
2. *Vaginismus:* **Vaginismus** is an involuntary contraction of the muscle around the vagina that prevents penile insertion. It is often related to the existence or prior existence of a sexual pain disorder. Often, any stimulation around the introitus causes powerful contractions. Use of a tampon or performance of a specular exam may prove impossible. Vaginismus triggers a cycle of responses that then further exacerbates the disorder (**Figure 20-2**). Painful sexual episodes can lead to guarding and reflexive muscle contraction, making intercourse difficult or impossible and sometimes interfering with fertility.

Incidence and Prevalence of Sexual Pain Disorders. Rates of dyspareunia vary significantly from study to study, as do diagnostic criteria and study methods. One large population-based study found a lifetime incidence of 16% (Harlow & Stewart, 2003). The incidence is three times greater among women than men. The frequency of vaginismus is thought to account for less than 10% of female sexual disorders (Shafer, 2004).

Etiology of Sexual Pain Disorders. Although psychological factors may play a role, especially in the chronicity of some of these disorders, the complex physical causes that initiate and sustain these conditions have become much better identified and understood since the early 1990s. A high incidence of pelvic pathology is associated with vaginismus (Shafer, 2004). A broad consensus is emerging that efforts to distinguish between biologic and psychologic causes are not clinically productive.

Treatment of Dyspareunia. Treatment ideally involves addressing any possible physical causes

Evidence-Based Practice

Research is needed to better understand the relationship between androgen activity and sexual function. In the future, pharmacologic treatment of sexual dysfunctions may be possible using estrogen and androgen receptor modulators to enhance the sexual effects of estrogens and androgens (Basson, 2007). However, clinical experts have recommended against the generalized use of testosterone in women until issues of efficacy and long-term safety are established (Wierman et al., 2006). Although the FDA is unlikely to approve a testosterone product for women until long-term safety is addressed, double-blind placebo-controlled studies have demonstrated the effectiveness of a transdermal testosterone patch in the treatment of hypoactive sexual desire disorder (HSDD) (Krapf & Simon, 2009). Data continues to be collected and analyzed in an effort to uncover long-term risks.

There is also interest in developing reliable assessment tools to better diagnose and evaluate treatment of HSDD. Clayton and his colleagues have developed instruments to screen for HSDD and to measure the severity of symptoms. These are respectively, the Decreased Sexual Desire Screener and the Sexual Interest and Desire Inventory-Female (SIDI-F) (Clayton et al., 2009, 2010). Currently, many women with sexual dysfunction go undiagnosed because of a lack of access to expert clinicians. These instruments are designed to facilitate diagnosis and assessment by clinicians who are not trained or specialized in female sexual dysfunction, thus increasing the likelihood of appropriate treatment and referral.

such as inflammatory and infectious processes, pain medications and relaxation techniques, and counseling around the psychologic issues that preexisted the condition. Successful treatment of underlying organic conditions may not relieve the symptoms. A cascade of neurovascular, immune, and muscle tone responses can arise to sustain the initial condition, creating a complex neuropathic pain syndrome requiring multimodal management (Grazziottin & Brotto, 2004).

Treatment of Vaginismus. Treatment involves treating the underlying gynecologic problems if identified, chronic pain management, hypnotherapy, and individual and couples therapy if indicated. Systematic desensitization, sometimes using successively larger vaginal dilators, is a common treatment approach.

Paraphilias

Paraphilias are recurrent, intense, sexually arousing fantasies, sexual urges, or behaviors generally involving nonhuman objects, the suffering of or humiliation of oneself or one's partner, or children or other nonconsenting persons, that occur over a period of at least 6 months (APA, 2000). For some conditions, such as pedophilia and sexual sadism, acting on the urge is sufficient to merit the diagnosis; in others, marked distress is necessary to meet the terms of the diagnosis.

A variety of paraphilias occur. In some cases, inanimate objects such as fur, leather, or female clothing become an erotic obsession; intense attraction to women's clothing (transvestic fetishism) is a common variant. Some individuals are only aroused by experiencing pain (masochism) or providing pain (sadism). Some people find themselves attracted to persons or situations such as prepubescent children (pedophilia) or animals (bestiality). Yet others find themselves preoccupied by specific situations, such as exposing themselves to others (exhibitionism) or secretly viewing others (voyeurism).

In some cases, the paraphilic object becomes the dominant or sole sexual focus. Individuals may be unable to be aroused in the absence of the paraphilic object or situation. Many individuals maintain their paraphilia as a secret activity or fantasy; in couples, the partner may find him- or herself alienated without explanation, as sexual energy is channeled into the paraphilia and not the relationship. Discovery of the paraphilia often creates intense conflict in the dyad, sometimes leading to separation and/or presentation for therapy. Acting on other paraphilias constitutes sexual offenses, and in some cases the courts mandate treatment as a condition of probation or parole.

One of the most common paraphilias is transvestic fetishism. Cross-dressing appears to be a not-uncommon behavior in males and was documented in the early Western sex therapy literature. Cross-dressers describe a whole range of motivations for cross-dressing, ranging from simple fun and burlesque, to "a holiday" from everyday pressures, to expression of a feminine portion of the personality.

Incidence and Prevalence of the Paraphilias

The paraphilias almost always occur in males and have a strong association with attention-deficit/hyperactivity disorder in childhood and with depression, substance abuse, and phobic disorders in adults (Shafer, 2004). Varieties of definitions of what constitutes a pathologic condition and the understandable reluctance for individuals to admit to behavior that may be illegal complicate studies of the epidemiology of the paraphilias.

Etiology of the Paraphilias

The underlying cause of the paraphilias is not well understood. Biologic factors, including temporal lobe abnormalities and disturbances in the hormones that affect sexual arousal, abnormal psychosexual development, and learned experiences, have been implicated as possible causes.

Treatment of the Paraphilias

Individual therapies sometimes employ a relapse-prevention approach similar to those used in addictions treatment. In sex offender settings dealing with males, medications used include antiandrogens such as cyproterone (not approved by the Food and Drug Administration), spironolactone, or gonadotropin hormone-releasing agonists to effect a chemical castration. The SSRIs including fluvoxamine and paroxetine are often used for their antiobsessional properties and also for their effect of reducing libido.

Transvestic fetishism (TF) is the compulsive form of cross-dressing. Identification with the opposite gender, or gender dysphoria, may manifest to varying degrees in persons with TF.

Gender Identity Disorder

Gender identity is based on which gender role feels right, that of a man or a woman. Gender identity disorder (GID), commonly referred to as transsexualism, is a complex condition in which a person feels that his or her inner nature is more like that of the opposite gender. Some feel this difference between their bodies and what they see as their inner nature and experience great suffering (**gender dysphoria**).

The most intense and pervasive forms of adult gender identity disorder usually manifest in childhood. Children with gender identity disorder often assert that they are actually the opposite gender, or that they are destined to grow up to be the opposite gender. They usually show intense aversion to wearing clothes of their natal gender and may insist on using the opposite pronoun to describe themselves. They show an interest in games of the opposite sex and prefer playmates of the opposite sex. Although strong cross-gender identification, that is, the desire to be of the other sex, and a persistent discomfort with one's assigned sex may continue into adulthood, empirical evidence indicates that GID in childhood does not necessarily persist into adulthood (Shechner, 2010).

Anticipated Changes to the *DSM*

Sexual orientation and gender identity are different phenomena. Sexual orientation may change after gender transition but often does not.

The APA has proposed changes to the diagnosis of GID for the 5th edition of the *DSM*, currently planned for publication in May 2013 (APA, 2011). The term gender identity disorder may be replaced with gender dysphoria. This diagnostic terminology would recognize persons who are distressed by their physical sex characteristics or gender role and in need of medical treatment to support transition, but would not label as mentally ill all persons who choose to express gender variance or diversity (GID Reform Advocates, 2011). The diagnosis of gender dysphoria would not apply after successful transition. The proposed revisions also would remove sexual orientation from the diagnostic criteria. This is consistent with current understanding that **transsexual** individuals, like genetic individuals, can be heterosexual, homosexual, or bisexual (Polly & Nicole, 2011).

Critical Thinking Question

Do you know anyone who is transsexual? What are your beliefs about this? Will these beliefs aid or impede your interactions with such clients?

Incidence and Prevalence of Gender Identity Disorder

It is difficult to obtain reliable data on the rate of GID. One study out of the Netherlands, which has an integrated reporting system and a fairly accepting social attitude to gender transition, places the incidence at 1:11,900 for persons with male to female GID (MTFs) and 1:30,400 for persons with female to male GID (FTMs) (van Kesteren, Gooren, & Megens, 1996). Similar ratios were found in a survey of patients undergoing sex reassignment surgery in Belgium (De Cuypere et al., 2007). These numbers are significantly lower than the prevalence rates set by the APA (2000). The 3:1 preponderance of MTFs over FTMs is consistent with the experience of most gender identity clinics. Worldwide, the age at which individuals present for treatment appears to be dropping, which might reflect increased public awareness of the condition and treatment options.

Clinical Example

A 47-year-old client presents to the emergency department (ED) for shoulder pain after a car accident. All current personal identification lists the person as female, but old charts reveal that the client underwent sex reassignment surgery several years before, transitioning from male to female. How should this be handled?

Plan: The client is legally or at least socially female, and unless the client instructs otherwise, the feminine pronoun is the only appropriate one to use. Inquiries about gender transition are relevant to ask only if strictly pertinent to other medical/surgical issues related to the condition at hand. As with other matters of personal privacy, it is intrusive and unprofessional to ask about biographical details merely out of curiosity.

Etiology of Gender Identity Disorder

There is no clearly identified cause for GID. Neuroanatomical differences have been noted in clients with GID, specifically in the size of the central subdivision of the bed nucleus of the stria terminalis, an area of the brain responsible for sexual behavior (Zhou, Hofman, Gooren, & Swaab, 1995). Recent findings suggest that changes in the interstitial nucleus of the anterior hypothalamus in transsexual people may be at least a partial marker of an early atypical sexual differentiation of the brain (Garcia-Falgueras & Swaab,

2008). Advances in magnetic resonance imaging have shown differences in distribution patterns of gray and white matter in the brains of transsexuals compared with nontranssexuals (Luders et al., 2009; Rametti et al., 2011). While not definitive, these studies move researchers closer to a neurobiological understanding of gender identity.

Treatment of Gender Identity Disorder

Treatment may involve psychotherapy, hormones, and sexual reassignment surgery. As noted earlier, most cases of childhood GID abate in adolescence. Adults with GID may choose to live nontraditional or cross-gendered lifestyles without seeking to physically change their bodies, or they may choose to receive hormone therapy and surgery. Clients typically follow three steps in the transition process described as triadic therapy—real-life experience, hormonal replacement therapy, and surgical procedures (Polly & Nicole, 2011).

The approval process for hormonal treatment usually takes several months of visits, then physical assessments to verify their medical safety. Approval for surgery generally takes one or more years and involves a supervised experience of the person living full-time in the desired gender, referred to as the real life experience. The real life experience is designed to provide the full range of experiences in the preferred gender.

After surgery, clients usually describe a sense of relief and a wish to simply get on with their lives in their chosen gender. Most express increasing confidence in their new lives and start ventures or relationships that they had put on hold prior to transition. However, some individuals report that they had expectations prior to surgery that remain unfulfilled in their new gender identity and need help to adjust to this major life change.

Sexual and Gender Identity Disorders Not Otherwise Specified

The *DSM-IV* applies the term *not otherwise specified (NOS)* to a disorder or disturbance that does not meet the criteria for the specific disorders already discussed. This may include marked feelings of sexual inadequacy, transient cross-dressing that is experienced as stressful to the client, or persistent distress about sexual orientation. Also included in this diag-

Individuals with GID may be quite socially and sexually conservative.

www **Mr. L.** **CASE STUDIES**

Mr. L. is an 18-year-old biologic male who presented to a general outpatient mental health clinic in a large urban area with episodes of low mood and anxiety. He had made a suicide attempt 3 years before. Mr. L. was brought to the clinic by his mother.

Mr. L. says that his upbringing was very difficult; he hated the rough-and-tumble of his male classmates. In school, he was embarrassed to change into gym clothes with his male friends, and retreated to the toilet stall to change, and to sit to urinate. Mr. L. preferred to play fantasy games with the girls, often taking the role of the mother or other female figure. He was teased and roughed up frequently by his male classmates for this.

For as long as he could remember, he fantasized about living life as a girl. He recalled going to bed at night as a young child hoping that he would wake up transformed into a girl. He developed a crush on a male teacher, fantasizing about marrying him one day, but did not disclose this to anyone until his mother brought him to the clinic.

By age 10, he began wearing female clothing when his family was out. In his teen years, he began venturing outside cross-dressed, using clothes borrowed from his female friends. He found going out like this exciting, partially due to the fear of being discovered. Mr. L. was known in some circles as a female—or at least as someone who seemed more female than male. Mr. L. reported that he was a virgin, and was uncomfortable touching his genitals.

Mr. L.'s mother stated that Mr. L. had always seemed feminine, and despite being a fairly traditional family, they used the client's gender-neutral middle name since around age 8, when the client insisted on it. After years of consternation, the family implicitly accepted the female gender identity of their child, though they did not understand it.

Mr. L. and his mother presented with a request for information on treatment options for Mr. L.

With Mr. L., it was important for the nurse to include an assessment for psychiatric disorders, especially given a history of depression and a past suicide attempt. A study of 31 clients with GID found that over 70% had Axis I psychiatric disorders, primarily mood and anxiety disorders (Hepp, Kraemer, Schnyder, Miller, & Delsignore, 2005).

Nursing Care Plan **Male-to-Female Gender Identity Disorder**

Nursing Diagnosis: Low self-esteem, related to disturbed personal identity, evidenced by depressed mood and social isolation.

Expected Outcomes	Interventions	Evaluations
• Will be safe and will receive treatment for any concurrent mental disorders.	• Determine if anxiety, depression, and/or suicidal ideation are present. • Conduct mental status examination and suicide assessment.	• Identify depression; client accepts antidepressant therapy.
• Will verbalize feelings and attitude regarding sexual reassignment.	• Establish and maintain therapeutic rapport. • Use the client's preferred name and pronoun.	• Client displays open posture, and uses nondefensive language; discusses sexual issues with nurse.
• Will be informed on GID and treatment options.	• Provide client and family education and reading materials; refer to Internet resources and community agencies; set up follow-up appointment.	• Client accepts information, contacts referral resources, returns for follow-up appointment, asks questions, and engages in discussion.
• Will increase socialization.	• Help identify client's interests; assist with social skills; connect with transgendered-friendly environments in community; educate regarding risk of experiencing violence; discuss safe and potentially unsafe environments for client while cross-dressed.	• Client reports increased comfort in social situations and increased social contacts; expresses awareness of potential societal risks.
• Will establish connections to specialized treatment services.	• Provide referral to local clinicians familiar with assessment and treatment of GID, and provide URL of a website to assist in that search.	• Client has information to secure appointment with qualified specialist.

Visit http://go.jblearning.com/mentalhealth for additional care plans and exercises.

nostic category are clients who present with compulsive sexual behaviors commonly referred to as sexual addiction. A new diagnostic category, hypersexual disorder, is proposed for the *DSM-5* to recognize and diagnose a distinct group of men and women who are already receiving mental health treatment in the form of individual psychotherapy, 12-step group support, pharmacotherapy, and residential treatment (APA, 2010).

In communicating with transgendered clients, the following principles apply:

- Use the name and masculine or feminine pronoun preferred by the individual.
- Provide privacy for the client.
- Avoid gossip about the client's transgender condition or sexual orientation.
- Do not expect the client to educate staff on transgender issues.

Education for Clients and Families

Education is an important component of the nurse's role with all clients. The nurse needs to be knowledgeable regarding the basics of sexual health and needs to be comfortable providing information to clients. This is true for clients who present with a specific sexual disorder as well as for clients being treated for other psychiatric or medical disorders. The rate of sexual dysfunctions in mental health patients is extremely high, approaching 50% even in nonacute general psychiatric outpatient services (Kockott & Pfeiffer, 1996). Evidence suggests that psychiatric clients have unmet educational needs around sexuality and relationships, and they express particular interest in the effects of mental illness and medication on sexual functioning and how to maintain long-term relationships.

Managing Medication Side Effects

Sexual dysfunctions occur in approximately one third of clients treated with antidepressants (Norris, Cassem, Huffman, & Stern, 2004). Although clinicians are primarily concerned with the extrapyramidal side effects of conventional neuroleptics, sexual side effects may be the most distressing for the client. Sexual dysfunction is a major reason that clients discontinue their antipsychotic medications. Because medication noncompliance is a key cause of relapse in schizophrenia, addressing sexual concerns of clients would appear to be an important healthcare intervention for nurses. Clients with certain medical conditions, including hypertension and diabetes, as well as clients being treated with commonly prescribed cardiovascular, anticonvulsant, and gastrointestinal medications may also experience sexual dysfunctions. Other elements are the acute and chronic adverse effects on the sexual life of the client's partner. Partners can benefit by understanding some of the common sexual and relationship consequences of mental health illness and treatment.

It is important, then, that the nurse be knowledgeable about the relationship between psychiatric and medical conditions and sexual functioning and impart this information to the client.

It may take time to determine if the sexual effects experienced by the client are due to the disorder or are a side effect of medication. If the nurse is comfortable discussing this with the client, it can promote treatment adherence. The nurse can assist the client in working with the prescribing nurse practitioner or other clinician to change or adjust medications if this is indicated.

Critical Thinking Question

What questions might you ask a client to determine whether sexual side effects are related to nonadherence with medications for the client's schizophrenia?

Information and Resources

Many clients with sexual dysfunctions will have knowledge deficits. By providing information, the nurse can help the client understand his or her experience, which, in turn, can decrease a sense of isolation and encourage mastery of the situation. This information should be appropriate to the skill level of the nurse and may focus on the disorder itself, treatment alternatives, Internet and community resources, or referrals to expert clinicians. Of course, teaching about safe-sex practices is fundamental to promoting sexual health.

Most medications used to treat psychiatric disorders can cause problems with sexual functioning.

Behavioral Approaches

The nurse need not be an expert, but he or she should have an awareness of the behavioral approaches that are part of the treatment for sexual dysfunctions. There are many self-help books available for clients to assist in increasing sexual comfort, achieving orgasm, maintaining an erection, and reducing performance anxiety. Reduced focus on intercourse and simultaneous orgasm (which is exceedingly rare in any couple) will tend to increase sexual satisfaction, especially for the female partner. Female partners also need to know that most women do not experience orgasm most times if intercourse is engaged in exclusively. Reducing the expectations to realistic levels often has a beneficial effect on the sexual relationship. Again, clients can be referred to expert clinicians for specialized therapy.

Communication Skills

An often underestimated aspect of client education is the teaching of communication skills. The nurse has the opportunity to model open and sensitive communication. This can be a key factor in promoting improved sexual satisfaction for clients. The communication skills learned in the relationship with the nurse can be transferred to the relationship with a sexual partner. Comfort and openness in expressing feelings and needs are important components to achieving sexual satisfaction.

Summary

Sexuality is a matter that touches every client and family. Persons with psychiatric disorders are especially vulnerable to decreases in their sexual quality of life due to elements of the disorder itself, its pharmacological treatment, and the stigma that accompanies mental illness.

A variety of sexual disorders and dysfunctions, as well as gender identity issues, can affect anyone. It is important that nurses have a basic understanding of these conditions and feel comfortable opening up a dialogue about sexual concerns with their clients. Incorporating sexuality into nursing care is a further step towards holistic nursing practice.

Annotated References

American Psychiatric Association (APA). (2000). *Diagnostic and statistical manual of mental disorders* (4th ed., text rev.). Washington, DC: Author.
This compendium of mental health conditions is the major diagnostic manual that guides research and clinical decision making.

American Psychiatric Association (APA). (2010). Retrieved from http://www.dsm5.org/proposedrevision/Pages/SexualDysfunctions.aspx
This is an APA website created to provide updates and rationales on proposed revisions to the *DSM-5*.

American Psychiatric Association (APA). (2011). Retrieved from www.dsm5.org/proposedrevision/pages/genderdysphoria.aspix
This is an APA website created to provide updates and rationales on proposed revisions to the *DSM-5*.

Annon, J. S. (1976). *Behavioral treatment of sexual problems*. New York, NY: Harper & Row.
This early work thoroughly outlines a multidisciplinary framework for assessment and care of sexual problems.

Basson, R. (2007). Hormones and sexuality: Current complexities and future directions. *Maturitas, 57*(1), 66–70.
This article discusses the complexities associated with studying the relationship of estrogen and androgen deficiencies to sexual dysfunction in women.

Carson, C., & Gunn, K. (2006). Premature ejaculation: Definition and prevalence [Review]. *International Journal of Impotence Research, 18*(Suppl. 1), 5–13.
This review article documents the history of PE and the changing approaches to treatment.

Clayton, A. H., Goldfischer, E. R., Derogatis, L., Lewis-D'Agostino, D. J., & Pyke, R. (2009). Validation of the decreased sexual desire screener (DSDS): A brief diagnostic instrument for generalized acquired female hypoactive sexual desire disorder (HSDD). *Journal of Sexual Medicine, 6*(3), 730–738.
The brief 5-item screening instrument was compared with a standard diagnostic interview by an expert clinician and concluded that the DSDS was a sensitive and specific diagnostic instrument for generalized acquired HSDD in women.

Clayton, A. H., Goldmeier, D., Nappi, R. E., Wunderlich, G., Lewis-D'Agostino, D. J., & Pyke, R. (2010). Validation of the sexual interest and desire inventory-female in hypoactive sexual desire disorder. *The Journal of Sexual Medicine, 7*(12), 3918–3928.
The article reports findings that support reliability and validity for this 13-item clinician-administered tool to measure the severity of primary hypoactive sexual desire disorder in women aged 18–65 years.

De Cuypere, G., Van Hemelrijck, M., Michel, A., Carael, B., Heylens, G., Rubens, R., … Monstrey, S. (2007). Prevalence and demography of transsexualism in Belgium. *European Psychiatry, 22*(3), 137–141.
This prevalence and demographic study analyzes data on all Belgian individuals who have undergone sex reassignment surgery since 1985.

Dennerstein, L., & Hayes, R. (2005). Confronting the challenges: Epidemiological study of female sexual dysfunction and the menopause. *Journal of Sexual Medicine, 2*(Suppl. 3), 118–132.
This article specifically focuses on the relationship between female sexual dysfunctions and menopause.

Ellsworth, P., & Kirshenbaum, E. M. (2008). Current concepts in the evaluation and management of erectile dysfunction. *Urologic Nursing, 28*(5), 357–369.
The article presents the American Urological Association Erectile Dysfunction Guidelines, the second Princeton Consensus Panel Guidelines, and updates regarding oral PDE-5 inhibitors.

Feldman, H. A., Goldstein, I., & Hatzichristou, D. (1994). Impotence and its medical psychosocial correlates: Results of the Massachusetts Male Aging Study. *Journal of Urology, 151*, 54–61.
The MMALES study was one of the first major population-based studies of sexual problems in men.

Garcia-Falgueras, A., & Swaab, D. F. (2008). A sex difference in the hypothalamic uncinate

nucleus: Relationship to gender identity. *Brain, 131*(Pt 12), 3132–3146.
The article reports on postmortem examination of specific areas of the anterior hypothalamus from 42 subjects, including male and female control groups as well as transsexual subjects, and nontranssexual subjects who were castrated for treatment of prostate cancer.

GID Reform Advocates. (2011). A fifth edition—opportunity for change? Retrieved from www.gidreform.org/dsm5.html
This text provides information on the proposed *DSM-V* posted on a website for GID Reform Advocates, who are self-described as medical professionals, caregivers, scholars, researchers, students, human rights advocates, and members of the transgender, bisexual, lesbian, and gay communities and their allies who advocate reform of the psychiatric classification of gender diversity as mental disorder.

Grazziottin, A., & Brotto, L. (2004). Vulvar vestibulitis syndrome: A clinical approach. *Journal of Sex and Marital Therapy, 30*, 125–139.
Grazziottin and Brotto review the complexities of women's sexual pain conditions.

Harlow, B. L., & Stewart, E. G. (2003). A population-based assessment of chronic unexplained vulvar pain: Have we underestimated the prevalence of vulvodynia? *American Medical Women's Association Journal, 58*(2), 82–88.
Harlow and Stewart survey a large sample in an attempt to determine the extent of female sexual pain in the community.

Hepp, U., Kraemer, B., Schnyder, U., Miller, N., & Delsignore, A. (2005). Psychiatric comorbidity in gender identity disorder. *Journal of Psychosomatic Research, 58*(3), 259–261.
This small study shows a high rate of psychiatric disorders among clients with GID.

Irwin, R. (2002). *Psychosexual nursing*. Philadelphia, PA: Whurr.
This book is a thorough account of assessment and nursing care of sexual problems, especially to help anticipate sexual consequences of medical care.

Kockott, G., & Pfeiffer, W. (1996). Sexual disorders in nonacute psychiatric outpatients. *Comprehensive Psychiatry, 37*(1), 56–61.
This study identifies the pervasive nature of sexual problems in psychiatric populations.

Krapf, J. M., & Simon, J. A. (2009). The role of testosterone in the management of hypoactive sexual desire disorder in postmenopausal women. *Maturitas, 63*(3), 213–219.
The article reviews research related to the hormonal treatment of hypoactive sexual desire disorder in women over age 50.

Laumann, E. O., Gagnon, J. H., Michael, R. T., & Michaels, S. (1994). *The social organization of sexuality: Sexual practices in the United States*. Chicago, IL: University of Chicago Press.
The first of two large studies that attempted to establish the prevalence and incidence of sexual dysfunctions in the general population.

Luders, E., Sanchez, F., Gaser, C., Toga, A., Narr, K., Hamilton, L., & Vilain, E. (2009). Regional gray matter variation in male-to-female transsexualism. *NeuroImage, 46*(4), 904–907.
This MRI study compared the brains of 30 genetic males and 30 genetic females with the brains of 24 transwomen and found that transwomen had increased gray matter in a specific area of the brain that was not present in genetic men.

Mahan, V. (2003). Assessing and treating sexual dysfunction. *Journal of the American Psychiatric Nurses Association, 9*(3), 90–95.
The article presents an overview of the causes and treatment of sexual dysfunctions.

Masters, W., & Johnson, V. (1966). *Human sexual response*. New York, NY: Little, Brown.
This classic work published the first large-scale studies of sexual response in a laboratory setting and established the dominant physiologic model of its time.

Maurice, W. L. (2000). *Sexual medicine in primary care: A selection of chapters taken from the best-selling book by the same name*. London, England: Mosby-Wolfe.
This short guide contains excerpts of Dr. Maurice's larger manual designed to help primary-care doctors treat sexual problems.

Norris, E. R., Cassem, N. H., Huffman, J. C., & Stern, T. A. (2004). Cardiovascular and other side effects of psychotropic medications. In T. A. Stern & J. B. Herman (Eds.), *Massachusetts General Hospital psychiatry and board update* (2nd ed., pp. 385–393). New York, NY: McGraw-Hill.
This chapter is an excellent resource on medication side effects.

Polly, R., & Nicole, J. (2011). Understanding the transsexual patient, culturally sensitive care in emergency nursing practice. *Advanced Emergency Nursing Journal, 33*(1), 55–84.

This article addresses challenges faced by transsexual individuals in healthcare access and treatment, and provides recommendations for the culturally sensitive care of transsexual patients.

Rametti, G., Carrillo, B., Gómez-Gil, E., Junque, C., Segovia, S., Gomez, Á., & Guillamon, A. (2011). White matter microstructure in female to male transsexuals before cross-sex hormonal treatment. A diffusion tensor imaging study. *Journal of Psychiatric Research, 45*(2), 199–204.

A study, using an advanced MRI technique, showed that white matter microstructure pattern in untreated female to male transsexuals is closer to biologic males than biologic females.

Shafer, L. (2004). Sexual disorders and sexual dysfunction. In T. A. Stern & J. B. Herman (Eds.), *Massachusetts General Hospital psychiatry and board update* (2nd ed., pp. 155–164). New York, NY: McGraw-Hill.

This chapter provides a succinct overview of the sexual disorders.

Shechner, T. (2010). Gender identity disorder: A literature review from a developmental perspective. *Israeli Journal of Psychiatry and Related Sciences, 47*(2), 42–48.

This paper reviews the theoretical and empirical literature on children and adolescents with gender variant behaviors.

Simons, J. S., & Carey, M. P. (2001). Prevalence of sexual dysfunctions: Results from a decade of research. *Journal of Sexual Behavior, 30*(2), 177–220.

This large meta-study surveyed numerous research studies to examine the epidemiology of sexual dysfunctions.

van Kesteren, P. J., Gooren, L. J., & Megens, J. A. (1996). An epidemiological and demographic study of transsexuals in the

Netherlands. *Archives of Sexual Behavior, 25*(6), 589–600.

This is a study of the incidence of GID in a small European company with national record keeping.

Wierman, M. E., Basson, R., Davis, S. R., Khosla, S., Miller, K. K., Rosner, W., & Santoro, N. (2006). Androgen therapy in women: An Endocrine Society clinical practice guideline. *Journal of Clinical Endocrinology and Metabolism, 91*(10), 3697–3710.

A task force established by the Clinical Guidelines Subcommittee of the Endocrine Society developed recommendations for androgen therapy based on a systematic review of available evidence.

World Health Organization, UNFPA. (2010). *Measuring sexual health: Conceptual and practical considerations and related indicators.* World Health Organization: Geneva, Switzerland. Available only online at http://www.who.int/reproductivehealth/publications/monitoring/who_rhr_10.12/en/index.html

This publication by the WHO and the United Nations Population Fund summarizes the recommendations of a task force that studied indicators on sexual health and healthy sexuality, sexual violence and female genital mutilation.

Zhou, J. N., Hofman, M. A., Gooren, L. J., & Swaab, D. F. (1995). A sex difference in the human brain and its relation to transsexuality. *Nature, 378*(6552), 68–70.

This article identified organic differences in persons with GID.

Internet Resources

For a full suite of assignments and additional learning activities, use the access code located in the front of your book to visit this exclusive website: http://go.jblearning.com/mentalhealth. If you do not have an access code, you can obtain one at the site.

Learning Objectives

After reading this chapter, you will be able to:

- Identify factors important in the assessment of eating disorders.
- Define anorexia nervosa, bulimia nervosa, binge eating disorder, and obesity.
- Describe the diagnostic criteria for eating disorders.
- Distinguish anorexia nervosa restricting type from anorexia nervosa binge eating/purging type.
- Distinguish anorexia nervosa binge eating/purging type from bulimia nervosa.
- Delineate treatment modalities for the different types of eating disorders.
- Identify nursing interventions to assist clients experiencing eating disorders.
- Discuss the educational needs of clients and their families.

Key Terms

Anorexia nervosa

Anorexia nervosa, binge eating/purging type

Anorexia nervosa, restricting type

Bariatric surgical procedures

Binge eating disorder

Bulimia nervosa

Maudsley approach

Nonpurging

Obesity

Purging

Refeeding syndrome

Chapter 21

Eating Disorders

Amy Wysoker

http://go.jblearning.com/mentalhealth 

For a full suite of assignments and additional learning activities, use the access code located in the front of your book to visit this exclusive website: http://go.jblearning.com/mentalhealth. If you do not have an access code, you can obtain one at the site.

Introduction

Eating disorders present a treatment challenge to healthcare practitioners. Persons with eating disorders are excessively preoccupied with food, their weight, and the shape of their bodies. Eating disorders affect both psychologic and physiologic development. Studies indicate that in today's society, adolescent girls generally express concerns about weight issues and dieting is commonplace. However, the majority of these adolescents do not develop eating disorders (Rosen, 2010). When there is an overconcern about weight, coupled with inappropriate dieting or weight loss, healthcare practitioners need to take notice (Haines & Neumark-Sztainer, 2006; Rosen, 2010). Additionally, eating disorders previously occurring most often in adolescents and young adult women ages 12–35 are now increasingly occurring in males and minority populations in the United States (APA, 2000; Domine, Bervhtold, Akre, Michaud, & Suris, 2009; Rosen, 2010). The National Institute of Mental Health (NIMH, 2007) reports that approximately 5–15 % of men and boys have either anorexia or bulimia and that 35% have **binge eating disorder**. Researchers have studied the behavioral symptoms in both genders and have found women and men differ in the behaviors exhibited (Striegel-Moore et al., 2008). Another concerning issue is the prevalence of eating disorders in young populations, with statistics from 1999 through 2006 showing hospitalizations increased 119% under the age of 12 and 48% for clients ages 45–64 (Zhao & Encinosa, 2009). The Youth Risk Behavior Surveillance System (YRBSS) noted that 14.3 % of adolescents engaged in some type of disordered eating patterns to control their weight (HealthyPeople.gov, n.d.). A recent analysis indicates approximately 3% of the adolescent population in the United States are affected by an eating disorder (Swanson, Crow, Le Grange, Swendsen, & Merikangas, 2011). The American Psychiatric Association provides practice guidelines for treating patients with eating disorders (Yager et al., 2006). Nurses are often involved in both medical and psychiatric nursing interventions in the treatment of these disorders.

Purging is an attempt to alleviate the perceived negative effects of binge eating on body shape and weight.

This chapter explains **anorexia nervosa** and **bulimia nervosa**, the most common eating disorders classified in the *Diagnostic and Statistical Manual of Mental Disorders*, 4th edition, text revision (*DSM-IV-TR*) (APA, 2000) and are coded as Axis I disorders. Both of these disorders can cause severe medical problems, even death. An additional category, "eating disorder not otherwise specified" (EDNOS), is used for any eating disorder that does not meet the full criteria for either anorexia nervosa or bulimia nervosa. Binge eating disorder is currently one such example of EDNOS, and it will also be reviewed in this chapter.

All eating disorders result in severe psychologic consequences. Despite the criteria set forth by the *DSM-IV-TR*, most persons entering treatment for an eating disorder do not clearly meet the criteria for anorexia nervosa or bulimia nervosa, and, therefore, the diagnosis of EDNOS is frequently used (Annenberg Foundation Trust, 2005; Yager, 2008). It is important to note that a major revision of the APA's *Diagnostic and Statistical Manual of Mental Disorders* will be published in 2013 (APA, 2010d) and will be referred to as *DSM-5*. The Eating Disorders Work Group is responsible for review and recommendations for revisions on disorders included in this chapter (APA, 2010d). Generally, it appears that binge eating disorder will be recognized as a freestanding diagnosis, and the eating disorders category will be renamed *feeding and eating disorders* to reflect the proposal for inclusion of feeding disorders associated with infancy and childhood in this diagnostic category. This chapter will also address some of these recommendations, relating them to the respective disorders.

Although not classified as an eating disorder, **obesity** is addressed in this chapter. The *DSM-IV-TR* does not—nor will the *DSM-5*—consider an excess of body weight a mental disorder, but rather a general medical condition. There is discussion in the psychiatric-mental health field regarding the relationship between obesity and eating disorders, especially in relationship to binge eating disorder (Annenberg Foundation Trust, 2005). This chapter will address this concern and discuss other issues related to obesity.

Anorexia Nervosa

Anorexia nervosa is the extreme pursuit of a thin body accompanied by a profoundly disturbed body image. People with anorexia nervosa have a morbid fear of gaining weight, which causes them to obsessively fear losing control of the amount of food they consume. They view themselves as fat because of their disturbed body image, even though they are actually often emaciated.

In addition to the previously mentioned characteristics, the *DSM-IV-TR* (APA, 2000) identifies the following criterion for establishing a diagnosis of anorexia nervosa: the individual exhibits a persistent refusal to maintain his or her body weight at or above the minimum expected weight. Thus, if a person loses weight, resulting in a weight of less than 85% of the expected weight, the *DSM-IV-TR* criteria are met. Conversely, if during a period of growth the individual fails to gain the expected weight, resulting in a body weight of less than 85% of expected weight, the criteria are also met. Another criterion listed in the *DSM-IV-TR* for anorexia nervosa is the absence of at least three consecutive menstrual cycles.

There is controversy in the field questioning the criteria as set forth by the *DSM-IV-TR*. One debate has been over the word *refusal*. Refusal implies a voluntary decision to refrain from eating; however, clients with anorexia have an obsessive quality and thus have difficulty controlling the behavior that leads to low body weight. It has been suggested that *inability* is a better word to describe the criterion (Annenberg Foundation Trust, 2005). The National Institute of Mental Health (NIMH) uses the word *resistive* to describe this same criterion (APA, 2010d).

The APA's Eating Disorders Work Group has been reviewing these issues. The work group now believes that one's behaviors should be the focus. Thus "restriction of energy intake relative to requirements leading to a significantly low body weight in the context of age, sex, developmental trajectory, and physical health" (APA, 2010a, p. 1) more accurately reflects the problem than *refusal*. This statement also does not provide numerical guidelines for the clinician, which is seen as restrictive and confusing. Likewise, many clients do not verbalize a fear of weight gain and actually deny having a fear of weight gain. As such, the recommendation is to retain this criterion while adding, "or persistent behavior that interferes with weight gain, even though at a significantly low weight" (APA, 2010a, p. 1). Another change reflects the *DSM-IV* criteria relating to amenorrhea. Since many patients have all the other symptoms of anorexia nervosa and still menstruate, or for various reasons do not meet the criteria to have menses, the work group plans to omit this requirement (APA, 2010a).

Binge Eating/Purging Type

It is important to distinguish between the two categories of anorexia nervosa. One is termed **anorexia nervosa, binge eating/purging type**. During a period of binge eating, the person perceives that he or she is out of control. Such an individual cannot resist the temptation to eat specific foods or cannot stop eating until someone interrupts him, the food is no longer available, or his physical condition prevents further intake. Typically, a large amount of food is consumed rapidly during a binge episode. Consensus has not been reached as to how many calories define a binge; the perception of being out of control is more important. Persons with binge eating/purging type anorexia nervosa usually consume several hundred calories during an episode. Self-induced vomiting and laxatives, diuretics, and enema abuse are purging activities (APA, 2000).

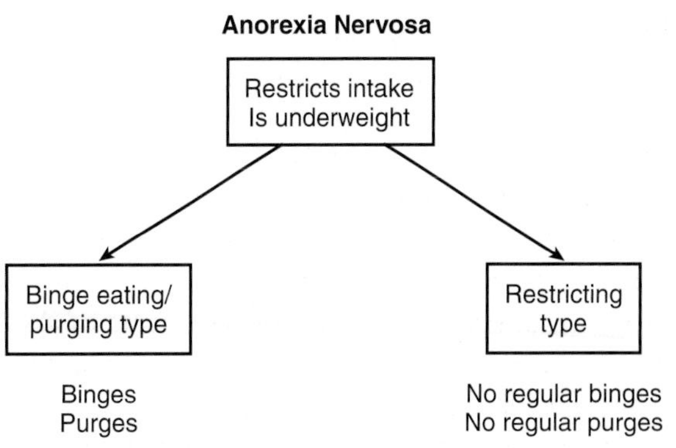

Figure 21-1 Anorexia Nervosa

Restricting Type

The second category of anorexia nervosa is termed **anorexia nervosa, restricting type**. During their illness, persons with this type of anorexia restrict their intake but do not regularly engage in binge eating or **purging** (**Figure 21-1**). The *DSM-IV-TR* specifies a type by what behavior is present during the current episode. Since it is difficult to determine a specific type, proposed changes for *DSM-5* include placing a 3-month time requirement for either type, rather than requiring occurrence during a current episode (APA, 2010b).

What is the difference in the behaviors of clients with the binge eating/purging type of anorexia nervosa and the restricting type?

Incidence and Prevalence

Statistics vary as to the prevalence of anorexia nervosa. It is estimated that in the United States, approximately 0.5% of adolescent girls have the illness (APA, 2000). The American Psychiatric Association's Eating Disorders Work Group reports 0.5–3.7% of females experience anorexia nervosa (APA, 2000). Research has consistently shown that females are more likely than males to develop an eating disorder (APA, 2000; Hoek, 2002; NIMH, 2007). However, more recent data indicate that one in four preadolescent boys has the disorder (NIMH, 2007). Recent data indicate a growing global problem. Studies have been conducted in England, Denmark, and the Netherlands, reflecting highest rates for females occurring between 15 and 19 years old (Herpertz-Dahlmann, 2008).

The mortality rate is estimated to be approximately 0.56% per year, 12 times greater than the annual death rate for females, 15–24 years, from all other causes of death (Sullivan, 1995). NIMH reports that in over 15 years of follow-up, mortality rates were found to be high as 20%. Recent data indicate that those with the illness are 10 times more likely to die compared to people not suffering from an eating disorder (NIMH, 2007). Suicide has been reported to be 50 times more likely in those diagnosed with anorexia and is the highest cause of death in this population (Birmingham et al., 2005; Keel et al., 2003; Rosen, 2010).

Figure 21-2 Exercise and thinness are valued heavily in U.S. society.

Etiology and Physiology

Many social, physical, and psychological factors may be responsible for causing anorexia nervosa. However, there is increasing debate among professionals and researchers regarding the various causes. U.S. society greatly emphasizes the importance of exercise and thinness (see **Figure 21-2**). The pressures and demands placed on adolescents and young adults to be thin may significantly promote the development of this illness. Stice, Spanler, and Agras (2002) found that after exposure to the culture of thinness, such as fashion magazines where thinness is promoted, study subjects reported greater body dissatisfaction and pressure to be thin. Another study conducted in Fiji found that the influence of Western media increased rates of negative body image and body disturbances (Becker, Burwell, Gilman, Herzog, & Hamburg, 2002).

Adolescents with anorexia nervosa are trying to maintain their childhood and avoid sexual development.

Psychological factors are also involved in the development of anorexia nervosa. Adolescents with anorexia nervosa seem to fear the normal developmental tasks of increased independence and increased social and sexual functioning. Their preoccupation with eating and weight gain thus allows them to avoid these normal but difficult developmental tasks. By starving themselves, these adolescents can maintain their childhood roles and avoid sexual development. Young adults with anorexia nervosa often have low self-esteem and feelings of inadequacy.

Additional psychological factors involve issues of control. The adolescent with anorexia who experiences feelings of anxiety and loss of control may counteract these feelings by using food as a source of control. Young adults with anorexia nervosa may have close but conflicting relationships with their parents. When treating these clients, therapists often find unresolved issues of individualization and separation from the mother (Bruch, 1978).

Neurobiologic and hormonal studies of anorexia nervosa have revealed a possible dysfunction of the

Clinical Example 

Casey is a 16-year-old female brought to the hospital by her parents after they found her passed out in her bedroom. Casey was extremely emaciated and according to her parents, weighed 70 pounds. The family reported that Casey consistently refused to eat, claiming she was not hungry, and when she did eat she would vigorously exercise immediately afterwards. Her parents were very concerned. However, their daughter refused to seek treatment because she did not see herself as too thin. The only way they were able to bring her to the hospital was because she passed out and was too weak to refuse.

hypothalamus as well as hormonal changes during adolescence. Researchers are studying the neurotransmitters that regulate appetite, fat distribution, and body size, because these are likely related to this illness (APA, 2000). The hormone leptin, produced in adipose tissue, is believed to have a role in anorexia (Hebebrand, Muller, Holtkamp, & Herpertz-Dahlmann, 2007; Rosen, 2010).

Genetic factors are also being explored by the scientific community. There is increased evidence that genetics contributes to the eating disorders; however, no specific gene has been linked to either anorexia nervosa or bulimia nervosa (Annenberg Foundation Trust, 2005). There has been discussion regarding genetic predisposition, but not necessarily related to eating and hunger, rather towards various trait disturbances including perfectionism and behavioral rigidity (Mazzeo & Bulik, 2009; Rosen, 2010). Genetics and the environment are showing more of a relationship than genetics singularly.

The severely reduced intake of nutrients and calories places the client with anorexia nervosa in a state of starvation. The body devours itself to get the necessary nutrients to survive. The result is a breakdown of the body's systems, often evidenced by cardiac symptoms, abnormal EKGs, and electrolyte imbalances. Anorexia can result in amenorrhea and digestive and gastrointestinal disorders; those who engage in vomiting and diuretic use can develop hypokalemic alkalosis.

Clinical Presentation

The individual with anorexia nervosa typically is a high achiever, seeking perfection and frequently involved in athletic activities such as ballet, gymnastics, or cheerleading. These individuals also have competitive personalities and often present with obsessive features. The individual frequently has low self-esteem and seeks control over life by controlling food (AACAP, 2011). Frequently, the diagnosis is initially made during a medical visit prompted by the symptoms of lack of energy, physical weakness, and poor school performance. Clients with anorexia, binge eating/purging type have stronger impulsive behaviors, which can present as self-mutilation, alcohol or substance abuse, and suicidal attempts (Annenberg Foundation Trust, 2005; Casper, 1990; Garfinkel, Moldofsky, & Garner, 1980). Morgan, Reid, and Lacy (1999) developed the SCOFF questionnaire, which provides a simple tool to assess the possibility of an eating disorder. The following five questions are asked, providing the acronym SCOFF:

1. Do you make yourself **S**ick because you feel uncomfortably full?
2. Do you worry that you have lost **C**ontrol over how much you eat?
3. Have you recently lost more than 14 pounds (**O**ne stone, British weight) in a 3-month period?
4. Do you believe yourself to be **F**at when others say that you are too thin?
5. Would you say that **F**ood dominates your life?

Other researchers have shown the questionnaire's effectiveness in primary care (Luck et al., 2002) and the American Academy of Pediatrics recommends its use (Rosen, 2010).

Behavioral Features

Clients with anorexia present primarily with an emaciated appearance. They often wear multiple layers of loose clothing to hide their physical appearance and refuse to eat with their families or in public places. These clients are always thinking of food; they often collect recipes or prepare elaborate meals for others. Clients with anorexia exercise excessively and avoid being weighed. They often exhibit unusual behavior patterns, such as carrying large amounts of candy in their pockets, hiding food in their napkins or pockets when eating, rearranging food on their plates, and cutting food into small pieces. Up to 50% of these clients have eating binges (APA, 2000). These occur secretly, often at night. Self-induced vomiting follows a binge if the client has binge eating/purging type anorexia. These clients commonly abuse laxatives and diuretics.

Clients who are experiencing binge eating/purging type anorexia commonly abuse laxatives and diuretics.

Clinical Features

Clients with anorexia present with many clinical features, including electrolyte disturbances and dehydration, hypothermia, and dependent edema. These clients often exhibit cardiac symptoms such as bradycardia, hypotension, cachexia (wasting), lanugo (fine downy hair on arms and torso), and metabolic changes. The most serious medical complications result from malnutrition and cardiac arrhythmias (Annenberg Foundation Trust, 2005). Clients with anorexia, restricting type have fewer medical problems compared to the subgroup with binging/purging behaviors (Annenberg Foundation Trust, 2005).

Differential Diagnosis

Because the client is unable to recognize or acknowledge her symptoms or behaviors, it is a most difficult task to diagnose anorexia nervosa. Many problems arise when attempting to obtain an accurate history and perform an adequate assessment. Other conditions must be considered; for example, extreme weight loss may be caused by many serious medical illnesses such as gastrointestinal disorders, endocrine disorders, central nervous system disorders, as well as certain cancers (NIMH, 2007; Rosen, 2010). In addition, weight loss can be symptomatic of many mental health illnesses. Psychiatric comorbidity in clients with anorexia nervosa is approximately 80% (Halmi et al., 1991). Major depressive disorder is the psychiatric illness most often associated with anorexia nervosa, with 50–68% of anorexic clients being so diagnosed (Herzog, Nussbaum, & Marmor, 1996). Clients with depressive disorders may present with extreme weight loss. However, these clients report a decreased appetite, whereas anorexic clients report a normal appetite and feelings of hunger. A lack of appetite exists only in the late stages of anorexia nervosa. A preoccupation with food is not evident in depressive disorders as it is in anorexia nervosa, and depressed clients do not have an intense fear of obesity (Kaplan, Sadock, & Grebb, 1994). Other psychiatric disorders including obsessive-compulsive, anxiety, and substance abuse disorders should also be considered in the differential diagnoses (Herpertz-Dahlmann, 2008; Rosen, 2010). Anorexia nervosa must be differentiated from bulimia nervosa, which is discussed later in this chapter. Clients with anorexia nervosa may have binge eating patterns similar to those with bulimia nervosa; however, clients with bulimia nervosa maintain their weight within the normal range.

Unlike the client with anorexia nervosa, who is dangerously underweight, the client with bulimia nervosa maintains normal weight.

Clinical Course and Complications

Statistics indicate that approximately 50–70% of adolescents suffering from anorexia nervosa actually recover; 20% do improve but continue to experience some symptoms, and 10–20% have a chronic condition (Annenberg Foundation Trust, 2005; Herpertz-

CASE STUDIES Samantha G.

Samantha G. is a 14-year-old girl who was involved in numerous athletic activities at school. She would frequently come home from practice and tell her mom that she wasn't hungry because she ate before her sporting events. Her mother would insist she sit with the family during dinner, which included her parents and two brothers. Her parents would repeatedly question why she would not eat; because it had been many hours since she last ate. Samantha would give various reasons, such as that she didn't get hungry after sports and was tired. When she felt pressured to eat and gave in, she would move food around her plate and play with her food, eating only small amounts. At times, Samantha would eat larger quantities and then excuse herself quickly from the table.

After many weeks of this pattern and noticeable weight loss, her parents realized that Samantha would excuse herself to go to the bathroom and would not return for some time. One evening her mother went to get something upstairs and heard her daughter retching in the bathroom. She demanded that her daughter open the door and noticed that there was vomit in the toilet and that Samantha's fingers were dirtied with vomit. There was also an open laxative bottle.

Mrs. G. pleaded with her daughter to stop this behavior and continuously told her that she was not fat and was too thin. Mother and daughter would get into arguments, and over time nothing changed. Mrs. G. felt frustrated but did not know how to change her daughter's thinking and behaviors. She did speak to a colleague at work who encouraged seeking treatment; however, Samantha refused.

As time progressed, Samantha's health became further compromised. Despite her coach telling her that her weight status was unhealthy and that she would not be allowed to continue in organized sports, she was not able to make changes. Samantha dropped out of organized sports, which upset her terribly. However, she still did not change her behaviors and would continue to excessively exercise at home. Her parents were in extreme conflict because their daughter adamantly refused help, claiming nothing was wrong with her.

One day a teacher found her on the bathroom floor too weak to stand. The nurse called 911. In the emergency department, Samantha was immediately placed on intravenous therapy and monitored for cardiac problems. She was admitted to the hospital and transferred to the eating disorder clinic for comprehensive treatment.

Nursing Care Plan **Anorexia Nervosa**

Nursing Diagnosis 1: Imbalanced nutrition; less than body requirements related to excessive fear of weight gain as evidenced by weight loss, 15% or more under ideal body weight.

Nursing Diagnosis 2: Disturbed body image related to morbid fear of obesity as evidenced by self-destructive behaviors (refusal to eat, vomiting, and abuse of laxatives).

Nursing Diagnosis 3: Ineffective coping related to inadequate coping mechanisms to deal with anxiety and stress as evidenced by denial of feelings, illness, or problems.

Expected Outcomes	Interventions	Evaluations
• Will gain sufficient weight. • Will learn what it is to experience "feeling hungry."	• Treat malnutrition and accompanying medical problems; provide nutritional consultation. • Record intake and output and weight	• Gradual weight gain. • Reports being hungry and eats with others during mealtimes.
• Will cease purging and binging behaviors.	• Observe for vomiting and binging behaviors. • Promote a steady weight gain of no more than 2 pounds a week.	• Overall health status is stabilized.
• Will have improved self-esteem and body image.	• Foster the development of trusting relationships; encourage various types of supportive activities.	• Able to talk about body image and exhibits a gradual improvement in self-esteem.
• Will demonstrate less denial regarding illness and physical appearance	• Involve client in decision making to allow for personal control. • Provide a safe environment where the client can express feelings and thoughts.	• Begins to accept illness; does not refuse to eat, vomit, or use laxatives
• Will commit to long-term remission/rehabilitation/recovery.	• Identify community self-help resources. • Refer for after-care treatment.	• Commits to continuation of treatment post-hospitalization.

Visit http://go.jblearning.com/mentalhealth for additional care plans and exercises.

Dahlmann, 2008; Herpertz-Dahlmann et al., 2001; Steinhausen, 2002; Steinhausen, Winkler, & Meier, 1997). The clinical course varies. Clients may recover, then relapse, or even die from the complications of starvation. Females with anorexia nervosa are 12 times more likely to die than women of a similar age who do not have anorexia nervosa. Suicide is also another cause of death, with a rate 57 times greater than women of similar age (Keel et al., 2003) without the condition. Treatment is difficult because nonrecognition and acknowledgement of the problem is so strong. Even clients who have regained weight remain preoccupied with food and their weight. Positive outcome measures include regaining sufficient weight, reporting hunger, improved self-esteem, and greater acceptance of disorder.

Management and Treatment

A comprehensive treatment approach is necessary for clients with anorexia nervosa. The first and most difficult task involves getting the client to accept treatment. Three phases of treatment are recommended: (1) restoring weight; (2) treating the psychological issues, such as distorted body image and low self-esteem; and (3) establishing long-term remission and rehabilitation or full recovery by decreasing or eliminating the behaviors or thoughts that led to the illness. Preventing relapse is a treatment priority (NIMH, 2001; 2007).

Medical complications and the prospect of impending medical problems from anorexia nervosa warrant hospitalization of the client.

When complications from malnutrition are evident, hospitalization should be mandatory (even if committal is necessary). In addition, if clients exhibit serious psychiatric symptoms such as severe depression, suicidal tendencies, psychosis, and self-mutilation, they should be admitted to a psychiatric hospital.

During medical hospitalization, a structured approach is implemented as a result of the serious nature of the malnutrition-related medical problems. These problems must be addressed before any psychotherapeutic benefits can be expected. Thus, therapy focuses to an extent on the eating behaviors but only because of the client's serious condition. Once the client's condition has stabilized, the practitioner must focus on the underlying causes based on the psychodynamics of anorexia nervosa. Throughout the client's hospitalization, the nurse and healthcare team must treat him or her accordingly. The nurse's goal is to promote in the client a steady weight gain of no more than 2 pounds per week. Rapid weight gain can cause cardiac complications. Clients must be weighed daily to monitor their progress, and malnutrition and accompanying medical problems must be treated. The nurse should record intake and output and observe for vomiting. If noted, strategies must be implemented to prevent vomiting. During any nutritional rehabilitation regimen for anorexia, the nurse must be aware of the potential for **refeeding syndrome**, a major life-threatening risk, characterized by cardiac, hematologic, and neurologic complications, including sudden unexpected death. Refeeding syndrome is most often seen in the severely malnourished client in both mental and physical illnesses (such as anorexia, bulimia, and cancer) and can be avoided by a slow feeding program and monitoring of body weight, heart rate and rhythm, and serum electrolytes on a regular basis (Golden & Meyer, 2004).

Treatment should include both family and individual therapies. Behavioral, cognitive, or interpersonal therapy can be used; all offer different approaches to treatment. Whatever treatment modality is chosen, the therapist must not attempt to change the client's eating behavior, because this both frustrates the practitioner and alienates the client. Clients with anorexia are invested in their symptoms; they believe the symptoms provide them with a form of control. The nurse develops a trusting relationship with the client in counseling sessions. A secure environment where clients can feel safe sharing their feelings and thoughts should be provided. It is crucial for the client to feel in control during therapy and to focus on related issues rather than eating behaviors. After progress is made in therapy, the possibility of changing eating behaviors can be addressed.

Cognitive behavioral therapy (CBT) has been shown to decrease relapse rates following weight gain; however, it has not been shown to be effective prior to weight gain. Studies have indicated that family psychotherapy (conjoint and separated) have been equally effective in the treatment of anorexia nervosa. There have been limited studies on psychotherapy, and healthcare providers need to explore the current information as they decide on treatment (Duvvuri & Kaye, 2009; Yager et al., 2006).

Controversy exists regarding the role of the family, specifically parents, as a cause of anorexia nervosa, resulting in differences of opinion on including the family in treatment. The Academy for Eating Disorders (AED) articulates a position that although family factors may play a role, they are not the primary cause that underlies the risk for developing anorexia. The AED is opposed to any etiologic model of eating that places family factors as the major cause and is adamant that families not be blamed for a member's illness (leGrange, Lock, Loeb, & Nicholls, 2010). It recommends family involvement, specifically with young children, unless contradicted for clinical reasons.

A specific type of family therapy showing success is the **Maudsley approach**. This modality trains parents to regain control of their adolescent's eating behavior. At least one parent or family member is present whenever the adolescent is eating, and if the child suffers from bulimia, must stay with the child for 1 hour after food is ingested. Ongoing research on this approach is necessary as this therapeutic modality becomes more utilized (Duvvuri & Kaye, 2009; Rosen, 2010).

Another management strategy is based on an alternative approach. Andersen (2009) believes that anorexia nervosa and other eating disorders should be viewed along McHigh and Slavney's four perspectives (disease, dimensional, behavior and life-story perspectives) with specific emphasis on the behavioral perspective. In anorexia, the abnormal behavior is self-starvation, thus treatment should address this behavior, and then other perspectives may be utilized. The choice of perspective depends on the individual issues affecting the person.

Medication for the treatment of anorexia is contentious. At the present time, the effectiveness of using medication to treat anorexia nervosa is questionable. Limited research is available to support its

Table 21-1 **Nursing Interventions for Clients with Eating Disorders**

Nursing Diagnoses	Nursing Interventions	Rationales
Readiness for enhanced self-concept	Reserve judgment and convey respect and acceptance of client's feelings about self, body image, and eating behaviors.	Communicates trust and helps improve client's self-esteem. Establishing rapport is essential to the nurse–client relationship.
Disturbed body image	Provide a safe, accepting environment. Encourage the client to verbalize body image concerns, including feelings and thoughts associated with eating behaviors. Help identify strengths and accomplishments unrelated to appearance.	The client needs to feel safe for change to occur. Without exploring the underlying issues, long-term changes will not be successful; helps identify emotional needs that fuel the eating disorder. Helps strengthen self-esteem by recognizing positive self-image not only related to body image.
Imbalanced nutrition: less/more than body requirements.	Provide factual information on the diagnosis, treatment, and program. Involve the client in recording food intake and establishing the goals for the treatment plan to encourage a return to normal eating behaviors. Observe nutritional status and ensure adequate intake; monitor electrolytes; weigh daily after voiding and before eating. Supervise during and after meals to prevent vomiting and/or hiding of food. Monitor elimination pattern to observe use of laxatives or diuretics. Promote a steady weight, with a loss or gain of no more than a set number of pounds a week (approximately 2 lbs.) Set a time limit for meals and encourage a relaxed atmosphere. Reward compliance with treatment and achievement of weight goals.	Serves as a foundation for the client to understand the disorder. When the client participates in making decisions regarding treatment goals and implementation of the plan, the client can begin to recognize the disorder and feels in control. Malnutrition can become a medical emergency leading to life-threatening physical changes. Interventions related to intake and output are necessary in order to stabilize the client's health status. The client may need intervention for constipation. This will help set realistic expectations and reduce stress and anxiety associated with mealtime. Positive reinforcement will encourage and support continued compliance.
Ineffective coping	Explore with the client past and present ways of dealing with life situations. Arrange for situations that encourage the client's autonomy and control in areas other than food.	By identifying past and present coping skills, the client will gain insight into ineffective coping skills and develop new ones. Enhances the client's sense of control and self-esteem.

use. Atypical antipsychotic agents might be helpful. Olanzapine has been studied, but controlled, randomized clinical trials are unavailable (Rosen, 2010). Some selective serotonin reuptake inhibitors (SSRIs) have helped promote weight maintenance and do treat the related psychiatric symptoms (mood and anxiety symptoms) related to anorexia nervosa. However, these medications should be prescribed only if indicated after weight gain has occurred and with extreme caution (NIMH, 2001; 2007).

Bulimia Nervosa

Clients with bulimia nervosa often engage in compensatory behavior (e.g., self-induced vomiting, purging with laxatives and diuretics, fasting, and excessive exercise).

Persons with bulimia nervosa experience recurrent, rapid episodes of eating large amounts of food (binging) while feeling out of control. The binge eating usually terminates with abdominal pain or nausea or with an interruption during the episode. Feelings of extreme guilt, self-disgust, and depression usually follow. To compensate for their fear of weight gain, these persons may self-induce vomiting or repeatedly use laxatives or diuretics (purging). Fasting and excessive exercise (**nonpurging**) are other compensatory behaviors (Agras, 1994).

To meet the *DSM-IV-TR* diagnostic criteria for bulimia nervosa, a person must eat large amounts of food in a discrete period of time, feel a sense of lack of control, and exhibit binge eating and compensatory behaviors at least twice a week for 3 months. In addition to a sense of lack of control, self-evaluation must be based on body shape and weight; these concerns dominate the client's thinking. The symptoms do not occur solely during episodes of anorexia nervosa (APA, 2000).

As previously discussed with anorexia nervosa, there is debate regarding the wording of the *DSM-IV-TR* criteria. For example, the *DSM-IV-TR* defines *amount* to mean "larger than most people would eat" (APA, 2000). Many persons with bulimia nervosa report eating large amounts that are no different than what most people eat. They also consider that the feeling of loss of control is more concerning than the amount eaten. Another concern is what constitutes excessive exercise (Annenberg Foundation Trust, 2005). Proposed changes for *DSM-5* (APA, 2010c) explored this later concern. There was discussion about the inclusion or exclusion of the words *fasting or excessive exercise* due to the difficulty defining these terms. However, it is believed that despite the difficulty defining these terms, the behaviors are evident enough to remain as criterion. The notion of two subtypes (purging and nonpurging) is also in question. Some clinicians believe that clients exhibiting nonpurging behaviors may actually have a binge eating disorder rather than bulimia nervosa. A recommendation for the DSM-5 is for changing the frequency of binge eating and inappropriate compensatory behaviors to at least once a week rather than twice a week as presently defined in *DSM-IV*. Nurses should be aware of these issues and concerns when assessing and treating individuals for the two types of bulimia nervosa (purging and nonpurging).

Purging Type

Individuals with the purging type of bulimia regularly engage in purging activities such as self-induced vomiting or laxative or diuretic abuse after a binge episode.

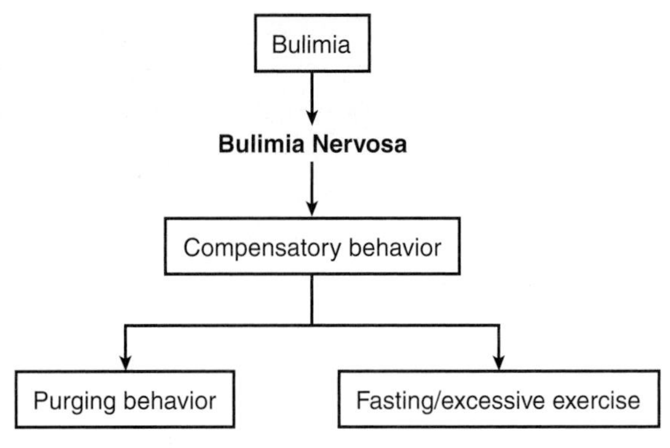

Figure 21-3 Bulimia Nervosa

Nonpurging Type

In the nonpurging type of bulimia nervosa, the individual does not purge but does exhibit other inappropriate compensatory behaviors such as fasting and excessive exercise (**Figure 21-3**).

Incidence and Prevalence

Approximately 1–2% of adolescent girls in the United States have been diagnosed with bulimia nervosa (Herpertz-Dahlmann, 2008; Rosen, 2010). Recent research indicates a decrease in the diagnosis of bulimia; however, it cautions that the reporting of the disease may be less than in the past. It is estimated that the ratio of men to women having bulimia is 1:15 to 1:20 (Currin, Schmidt, Treasure, & Jick, 2005; Herpertz-Dahlmann, 2008; Keel, Heatherton, Dorer, Joiner, & Zalta, 2006). Typically, women of normal weight have this disorder; however, it has also been observed in those with a history of obesity (APA, 2000; Herpertz-Dahlmann, 2008; McGilley & Pryor, 1998; NIMH, 2001; 2007).

Etiology

Many different factors have been related to the causes of bulimia nervosa. Genetic, environmental, psychological, physiologic, and neurobiologic factors all have been associated with the disorder. Current research focuses on the involvement of neurotransmitters in bulimia nervosa. The success of antidepressant medications in the treatment of this disorder implicates the role of serotonin and norepinephrine (Osterhout, Scher, Hilty, & Yager, 2010).

Similar to those with anorexia, individuals with bulimia nervosa are, in part, responding to a society that emphasizes and values women who are thin. This expectation places enormous pressure on developing girls to meet unreasonable standards. The nurse must be aware of the role that social and family dynamics play in this disorder.

Physiology

The repeated vomiting in bulimia may result in gastroesophageal reflux disorder. Additionally, the use of diuretics can cause kidney problems and frequent laxative use can create irritations resulting in gastrointestinal problems. Those who purge by laxatives or diuretics experience abdominal pain, diarrhea, and hypokalemia. Dehydration from loss of fluids is a serious physiological complication resulting in electrolyte imbalances (APA, 2005).

Clinical Presentation

Adolescents with bulimia have been identified as being high achievers. Perfectionism has also been postulated as a risk factor for bulimia; however, research has not demonstrated a direct linkage (Annenberg Foundation Trust, 2005). Many adolescents feel they must match society's norms. Additionally, clients with bulimia nervosa have a history of obesity and dieting due to the pressures of a society that promotes thinness in women (Walsh & Devlin, 1998). Clients with bulimia may have normal weight or fluctuate between being slightly overweight and maintaining normal weight. Many clients have a consistent fear of gaining weight or wanting to lose weight. These individuals are very dissatisfied with their bodies (NIMH, 2007).

Behavioral Features

Clients with bulimia nervosa appear normal and free of problems to those outside the family. These clients are occasionally impulsive or histrionic. They may act out in anger or attempt suicide. In addition to uncontrolled eating impulses, many clients lack impulse control in areas of substance dependence and self-destructive sexual relationships; however, research does not support these clinical observations (Annenberg Foundation Trust, 2005). They visit the bathroom regularly after meals and may eat normally or sparingly in the presence of others. Clients with bulimia may binge in private, usually resulting in feelings of shame or disgust (NIMH, 2007). They then purge with or without fasting and excessive exercise.

Clinical Features

Clients with bulimia nervosa present with several clinical features. Those who binge experience abdominal pain, malaise, and fluctuating blood sugar levels. Clients who purge by vomiting experience chronic hoarseness, hypokalemia, gastric and esophageal tears (these are rare), and cardiac symptoms such as palpitations and chest pain. Oral and tooth-related problems, such as erosion of dental enamel; thermal hypersensitivity; salivary gland enlargement; dryness of the mouth, and decreased salivary flow, can occur (NIMH, 2007).

Critical Thinking Question www

What are some of the behavioral features of bulimia nervosa that nurses need to assess? Are some more critical than others?

Differential Diagnosis

Clients with anorexia nervosa and bulimia nervosa exhibit common behaviors and symptoms. Therefore, it is important to distinguish between the binge eating and purging behaviors that occur during episodes of anorexia nervosa and those that occur during bulimia. Approximately 83% of individuals with bulimia nervosa also report a history of a psychiatric disorder (Fichter & Quadfleig, 1999). Anxiety disorders and substance abuse are also reported (NIMH, 2007). Fifty percent of clients have a lifetime history of a mood disorder, with major depressive disorder being the most common (Herzog, Keller, Sacks, Yeh, & Lavori, 1992; NIMH, 2007).

Clinical Course and Complications

Bulimia nervosa is a chronic disorder with a fluctuating course. Recovery rates range from 35% to 75% after 5 years (Annenberg Foundation Trust, 2005; Fairburn, Cooper, Doll, Norman, & O'Connor, 2000). Approximately one third relapse (Keel & Mitchell, 1997). Clients may not be symptom free after periods of improvement. Some may have a significant period of remission, while others remain disabled by their condition. The prognosis depends on the severity of the purging behavior. If the client's body has been medically compromised as a result of self-induced vomiting or abuse of laxatives and diuretics, the prognosis is less positive. Medical interventions and hospitalization become increasingly necessary. Mortality rates are very low—approximately 0.5%—in bulimia nervosa (Keel, Mitchell, Miller, Davis, & Crow, 1999).

Clinical Example 

Carole was very concerned about her stepdaughter, Alice, who would spend extended amounts of time in the bathroom. Carole also noticed that Alice would have numerous empty junk food bags in her bedroom, and that when Carole returned home from work, a significant amount of recently purchased groceries would be gone. All of Carole's three stepdaughters were very much involved in looking attractive and stylish. Their own mother was preoccupied with being thin and encouraged them to be thin. Carole intervened and asked Alice what she was doing in the bathroom for long periods of time and why there were so many empty food bags in her room. The stepdaughter denied any purging behaviors, although Carole questioned if this was the case. Alice did admit to having concerns about being fat and felt pressure to be thin. She agreed to speak to a counselor and entered treatment.

Management and Treatment

The more serious the purging behaviors, the more destructive they are to the body's system, necessitating appropriate medical interventions. Hospitalization is indicated in cases where purging results in electrolyte imbalances and metabolic disturbances.

Both types of bulimia nervosa must be treated psychologically, with cognitive behavioral therapy (CBT) the method of choice. This type of therapy, which addresses the thoughts and feelings that occur prior to a binge episode, is helpful in recognizing the disturbed patterns that lead to destructive coping mechanisms (Agras & Apple, 1997; Agras et al., 2000; Annenberg Foundation Trust, 2005). CBT utilizes structured approaches to change the binge eating and purging behaviors and provide insight into the thought and emotions that accompany the behaviors. Within this approach maladaptive thoughts regarding weight, one's shape and weight status are explored. In bulimia treatment, the goal of CBT for the client is to gain insight into the illness, establish self-control, and improve body image and self-esteem (Osterhout et al., 2010). The nurse can then help the client make the appropriate behavior changes. Psychodynamic, interpersonal, and family therapies are also frequently used and helpful (Annenberg Foundation Trust, 2005; NIMH, 2001).

Table 21-2 Issues for Medication Management

Medication	Side Effects and Clinical Issues
SSRIs	No medications have been demonstrated to be particularly effective in treating eating disorders. May help with clients who are depressed or highly obsessional. Anxiety may initially worsen. Sexual dysfunction may occur. Monitor for suicidal ideation.
Fluoxetine	The only FDA-approved medication for the treatment of bulimia, especially with the binge-purge cycle Rashes Arthralgias Edema Proteinuria Respiratory distress Observe for serotonin syndrome. Monitor for suicidal ideation. Contraindicated to be used with MAOIs, pimozide and thioridazine

Antidepressant medication, primarily SSRIs such as fluvoxamine and citalopram, has successfully been used in the treatment of clients with bulimia and may also help prevent relapses (Annenberg Foundation Trust, 2005; NIMH, 2001; Osterhout et al., 2010). However, fluoxetine is the only approved medication by the Food and Drug Administration for the treatment of bulimia. See **Table 21-2**.

Binge Eating Disorder

Binge eating disorder differs from bulimia nervosa in that individuals with the disorder are usually overweight rather than normal weight, and, although individuals with either disorder exhibit binging behaviors, clients with binge eating disorder do not involve themselves in the purging behaviors. Binge eating disorder is the most common eating disorder (Yager, 2008; Hudson, Hiripi, Pope, & Kessler,

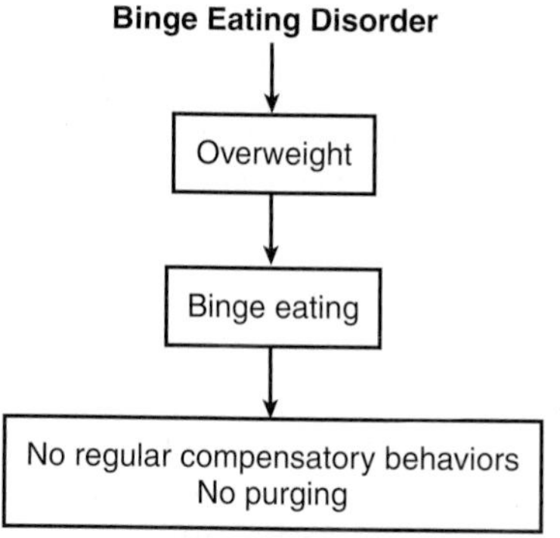

Figure 21-4 Binge eating disorder

2007). Individuals with binge eating disorders were once referred to as compulsive overeaters or obese bingers before being classified with binge eating disorder. This classification should aid in studying and treating the disorder (**Figure 21-4**).

It has been proposed by the APA's Eating Disorders Work Group to establish binge eating disorder as a separate disorder in the *DSM-5*. The proposed criteria are as follows (APA, 2010b):

- Eating, in a discrete period of time more than what most people would eat in that same time period
- Feeling a lack of control as if one cannot stop or control how much and what is being eaten
- The person needs to exhibit at least three of the following during the binge-eating episodes: eating faster than usual, eating until feeling uncomfortably full; eating large amounts when not hungry; eating alone since he or she is embarrassed by his or her eating behavior; feeling depressed, disgusted, or guilty after the binge; extreme distress regarding binge eating; occurs at least once a week for 3 months, and the binge eating is not associated with compensatory behaviors. Additionally, the binge eating is not related to criteria for anorexia, bulimia, or the proposed new disorder of avoidant/restrictive food intake disorder.

It is estimated that approximately 2–5% of Americans have had a binge-eating disorder during a given 6-month time period (Bruce & Agras, 1992; NIMH, 2001; Spitzer et al., 1993). More recent statistics indicate 3.5% of women and 2.0% men in the community have experienced binge eating disorder (Hudson, Hiripi, Pope, & Kessler, 2007; Yager, 2008). Because they do not self-induce vomiting or abuse laxatives and diuretics, there is far less risk of medical complications related to purging. Individuals suffering from binge eating disorders are treated with various psychologic treatments as in bulimia for the binging behavior. CBT has been effective for the binging behavior. Other interventions, such as interpersonal therapy and dialectical behavior therapy, have shown promising results (Yager, 2008; APA, 2005). However, physical problems from binging are still prevalent and must be addressed. Many clients go on to struggle with weight gain and then resort to diets. Research has shown a relationship between binge eating disorder and obesity, and in one study approximately 8% of the overweight population met the criteria for binge eating disorder (Bruce & Agras, 1992). Striegel-Moore and colleagues (2008) found 65% of patients with binge eating disorders were obese. Interventions are usually required after weight gain and the medical problems resulting from episodes of weight cycling. Medications have been prescribed for weight loss (Yager, 2008). However, the safety of these drugs has been questioned with resultant drug recalls. The nurse should be concerned with the cardiovascular problems associated with gaining and losing weight repeatedly (Agras, 1994; NIMH, 2001; 2007). Nurses can be instrumental in weight loss and weight control interventions. Psychiatric mental health clinical nurse specialists and nurse practitioners may also take the lead in providing evidence-based psychotherapeutic interventions.

Binge eating disorder is distinguished by the presence of binge eating and by an absence of purging behaviors, and clients are usually overweight.

Critical Thinking Question

What is the difference in weight status between clients diagnosed with bulimia nervosa and those with binge eating disorder? Why is this distinction important?

Obesity

Although not classified as an eating disorder in the *DSM-IV-TR* or the proposed *DSM-5*, obesity is considered a major health problem in the United States. Statistics (CDC, 2010) indicate that 72.5 million adults are obese and that healthcare costs have reached $147 billion dollars. The individual states vary as to their percentage of obese adults. In 2009, 30% of adults were obese in nine states, significantly higher than in 2000. Moreover, no state reached the Healthy People 2010 objective to reduce obesity by 15% (CDC, 2010).

Childhood obesity has tripled in the last 30 years. Data indicates that from 1980 to 2008, the rate of obesity for 6–11-year-olds increased from 6.5% to 19.6%. Similarly for 12–19-year-olds, the increase was from 5.0% to 18.1% (CDC, National Center for Chronic Disease Prevention and Health Promotion, 2010; Ogden, Carroll, Curtin, Lamb, & Flegal, 2010). Approximately one in three children is either overweight or obese, and in African American and Hispanic communities, the rate is significantly higher at 40% (CDC, National Center for Chronic Disease Prevention and Health Promotion, 2010). In 2010, President Barack Obama convened the first White House Task Force on Childhood Obesity, and, along with First Lady Michelle Obama's Let's Move initiative, many creative approaches to increasing awareness of the problem and decreasing its prevalence have been established (CDC, National Center for Chronic Disease Prevention and Health Promotion, 2010)

The body mass index (BMI) is used to determine weight classification. Adults with a body mass index between 25 and 29.9 are considered overweight; those with a BMI of 30 or greater are considered obese, and morbid obesity begins at a score of 40.

The body mass index (BMI) is used to determine weight classification. Adults with a body mass index between 25 and 29.9 are considered overweight; those with a BMI of 30 or greater are considered obese (CDC, 2006d). In children and teens, BMI is age and sex specific and referred to as BMI-for-age. It is calculated based on percentiles for size and growth patterns (CDC, 2006a). It is the consensus among experts in the field of obesity that anyone with a BMI of greater than 30 could improve his or her health by losing weight. Those with BMIs between 25 and 29.9 and who have two of the following risk factors are also advised to lose weight: (1) family history of certain chronic illnesses (e.g., heart disease, diabetes); (2) preexisting medical conditions (e.g., high cholesterol levels, high blood glucose), and (3) large waist circumference (for women, greater than 35 inches; for men, greater than 40 inches) (NHLBI, n.d.).

Nutrition and physical activity determine one's weight status. An energy imbalance between how many calories are consumed and the amount of exercise performed results in obesity. There are many factors that affect how one eats and one's amount of exercise. An individual's personal characteristics, culture, finances, and environment are all contributing factors. In addition to the behavioral factors mentioned, genetics is a contributing factor as to how one's body burns calories to use for energy and how fat is stored. Researchers from the National Institute on Aging report that individuals who are impulsive, aggressive, or risk takers are more likely to weigh more than conscientious people. The conscientious people are thinner, and their weight does not trigger changes in personality during adulthood (Sutin, Ferrucci, Zonderman, & Terracciano, 2011). Considerable research is being conducted regarding the relationship between heredity and weight (CDC, 2006c).

Obesity is related to numerous illnesses, such as type 2 diabetes, hypertension, heart disease, certain cancers, stroke, osteoarthritis, and other conditions (CDC, 2006b). Clients who are obese often have resorted to various methods of dieting to lose weight. Many experience weight cycling, losing and regaining weight repeatedly. The majority of persons who are either overweight or obese and have lost weight from dieting regain the lost weight within 5 years (Fabricatore & Wadden, 2003; Institute of Medicine, 1995). Mood and anxiety disorders are present in one of four obese individuals (Simon et al., 2006).

Treatment may consist of dieting, increased physical activity, behavior modification, and medication—in cases of morbid obesity (BMI greater than 40), it may include surgical interventions. Surgical interventions have been a recent choice for severely obese persons. According to the American Society for Metabolic and Bariatric Surgery (2011), approximately 220,000 individuals in the United States had **bariatric surgical procedures** in 2008. The three most commonly performed surgical interventions are the vertical banded gastroplasty, sleeve gastrectomy, and the Roux-en-Y gastric bypass. There have been many studies looking at the effects of surgery on the comorbid medical conditions experienced by the morbidly obese; however, few studies have looked at the psychologic and behavior adjustments necessary after surgery. Wysoker (2005) conducted a phenomenological study exploring the experiences of choosing bariatric surgery to lose weight. Four themes were identified: bariatric surgery was a last resort; surgery provides structure; reality sets in; and the client was positive about the decision to have the surgery. These findings provide guidance for psychiatric nurses when treating clients who are considering or have had bariatric surgery.

Obesity treatment must be individually designed. Nurses can be instrumental in assisting clients to determine what they believe is in their best interest and help them toward meeting their goals (Wysoker, 2002). Zitkus (2011) studied nurses who had bariatric surgery and found the lower the BMI, the more successful they were at losing weight. Findings also indicated that those successful losing the weight did not use a specified diet plan. Balkon, Balkon, and Zitkus (2011) discuss the pharmacotherapeutic issues that need to be considered with this treatment modality. These issues include clinicians' reluctance to add pharmaceuticals for weight loss until after other interventions (diet, exercise) have been tried for 6 months and the potential risks/benefits of introducing medications with side effects. Losing and maintaining weight loss is a lifelong commitment, and nurses are in a prime position to address the psychologic, emotional, and behavioral components of weight loss. Nurses need to provide a holistic approach to the care of the obese person.

Considerations for Client and Family Education

The public needs to be educated by nurses regarding the warning signs of eating disorders. The following is adapted from the Annenberg Foundation Trust (2005) and Anorexia Nervosa and Related Eating Disorders (ANRED) Inc. (2006).

A client with an eating disorder:

- Withdraws socially and isolates him- or herself from activities that involve food and/or eating
- Skips meals
- Eats small portions
- Does not eat in front of others
- Has ritualistic eating patterns
- Mixes strange food combinations
- Chews food but then removes it from his or her mouth and does not swallow
- Always has an excuse to avoid eating, such as not feeling well, just ate with friends, or is just not hungry
- Eats only certain foods that he or she believes are safe
- Refrains from meat; eats vegetarian foods but does not eat the necessary foods that provide nutrients
- Drinks diet soda excessively
- Eliminates fat from his or her diet
- Constantly reads food labels
- Has a self-imposed rigid discipline about eating
- Tries to control what the family eats
- Engages in purging behaviors for the purpose of losing weight
- Will go into the bathroom to vomit when he or she deviates from this rigidity
- Will, on the other hand, gorge food, usually alone, and then vomit after the binge
- May leave evidence, possibly indicating desire to be discovered
- Empties food packages
- Has a bathroom that smells of vomit
- Overuses mouthwash and mints
- Uses laxatives, water pills, diet pills, and natural products in health food stores that promote weight loss
- Uses alcohol and street drugs to decrease appetite and omit emotional pain
- Has constant and strong concerns about his or her weight or shape
- Has an extreme fear of gaining weight and being obese
- Is obsessive about clothing size
- Wears baggy clothes or a layer of clothes to hide what he or she thinks is fat
- Has an abnormally low weight or significant fluctuation in weight without medical reasons
- Does not like him- or herself unless he or she is thin
- Complains about being fat despite abnormally low weight
- Spends lots of time looking in the mirror
- Always finds something to criticize
- Dislikes specific body parts and constantly focuses on those parts (e.g., belly)
- Excessively and compulsively exercises
- Denies there is a problem
- Wants to be special, strives to be the best, which includes being thin
- Obsesses about food and has trouble concentrating
- Is unable to talk about his or her feelings
- Says everything is fine
- Is moody and irritable
- Throws tantrums
- Avoids people
- May engage in self-harm
- Socially tries to please everyone
- May avoid sexual activity or become involved in casual sex

Encourage patients and family members to seek treatment. The sooner the eating disorder is discovered, the better the prognosis.

Clinical Example 

Beth reported numerous diets were successful in helping her lose weight, but then she would gain whatever she lost back and some more. She was morbidly obese and was tired of dieting and no longer could motivate herself to go on a diet. Her experience of losing and gaining weight continuously was frustrating, and she knew her health was at extreme risk. Beth reported being desperate and spoke to the nurse about bariatric surgery. The nurse counseled her about the risks and benefits, and Beth chose to have the surgery. Following the surgery, Beth lost weight rapidly, but then realized that if she wanted to keep the weight off she would need to make significant lifestyle changes.

Summary

Eating disorders are caused by numerous, often interrelated, factors. Until nurses and other clinicians more completely understand these developmental, psychologic, societal, neurobiologic, hormonal, and genetic factors, the progress of treatment may be limited. Knowledge of the incidence and prevalence, etiology, behavioral, and clinical features of anorexia nervosa and bulimia nervosa prepares the nurse for confronting the life-threatening nature of these illnesses. Understanding the complexities of making a differential diagnosis, the clinical course of the diseases and their related complications, along with their management and treatment, permits the nurse to offer expert nursing care to clients with these complex diseases. Binge eating disorder and how it differs from bulimia nervosa also has been addressed. Although obesity is not classified as an eating disorder, it was also addressed in this chapter because it is considered a major health problem and involves significant medical complications. The nurse as a clinician, prevention specialist, and client advocate is instrumental in treating and preventing eating disorders and obesity.

Annotated References

Agras, W. S. (1994). Disorders of eating: Anorexia nervosa, bulimia nervosa, and binge-eating disorder. In R. Shader (Ed.), *Manual of psychiatric therapeutics* (2nd ed., pp. 59–67). Boston, MA: Little Brown.
This text provides a review of eating disorders with an emphasis on treatment approaches.

Agras, W. S., & Apple, R. F. (1997). *Overcoming eating disorders: A cognitive-behavioral treatment for bulimia nervosa and binge eating disorder—Therapist guide.*

Evidence-Based Practice

Lock, LeGrange, Agras, and Dare (2001) have formulated a family-based treatment approach to manage anorexia nervosa. The treatment is called the Maudsley approach, and further research has supported its use with bulimia nervosa as well. It is a short-term approach that promotes parent and sibling involvement in treatment. It is used with clients under the age of 18 who live with their family. Research has shown that the benefits of the treatment have been sustained for 5 years posttreatment.

Murphy, Straebler, Cooper, and Fairburn (2010) agree with other clinicians that it is increasingly evident how much in common the eating disorders have, rather than having differences. The disorders share a core psychopathology, the overvaluation of the importance of shape and weight, with longitudinal studies demonstrating that many clients migrate among the diagnoses over time. Accordingly, these researchers believe that an enhanced version of cognitive behavioral therapy (CBT), which is the leading evidence-based treatment for bulimia nervosa, may be applicable to clients with all of the eating disorders.

Wysoker's (2002) study, titled "A Conceptual Model of Weight Loss and Weight Regain: An Intervention for Change," provides a model for intervention in obesity. The model provides three important ways of viewing weight loss and weight regain. Additionally, Daniels's (2006) study, "Women's Descriptions of a Successful Weight-Loss Experience: A Qualitative Study," provides further information to assist nurses and nurse practitioners in helping dieters make lifestyle changes. Another study by Wysoker (2005), titled, "The Lived Experience of Choosing Bariatric Surgery to Lose Weight," elicited the four themes previously mentioned in the text that provide helpful information for nurses and other health professionals when treating the morbidly obese person.

San Antonio, TX: The Psychological Corporation.
This is a guide to using a cognitive-behavioral treatment approach in eating disorders.

Agras, W. S., Crow, S. J., Halmi, K. A., Mitchell, J. E., Wilson, G. T., & Kraemer, H. C. (2000). Outcome predictors for the cognitive-behavioral treatment of bulimia nervosa: Data from a multisite study. *American Journal of Psychiatry, 157*, 1302–1308.
The aim of this study was to discover clinically useful predictors of attrition and outcome in the treatment of bulimia nervosa with cognitive behavior therapy.

American Academy of Child and Adolescent Psychiatry. (2011). Fact for families: Teenagers with eating disorders. Retrieved from http://www.aacap.org/cs/root/facts_for_families/teenagers_with_eating_disorders
This fact sheet provides families with the symptoms and warning signs that adolescents with eating disorders may display.

American Psychiatric Association. (2000). *Diagnostic and statistical manual of mental disorders* (4th ed., text rev.). Washington, DC: Author.
This is the fourth edition of the APA's official nomenclature of psychiatric conditions and disorders that is used by mental health professionals in their work with clients with mental disorders and conditions.

American Psychiatric Association. (2005). Let's talk facts about eating disorders. *Psychiatric News, 40*(10), 2.
This is part of the APA's popular "Let's Talk Facts" pamphlet series that educates the public about mental illnesses and mental health concerns.

American Psychiatric Association. (2010a). *Anorexia nervosa*. Report of the *DSM-5* Eating Disorders Work Group. Retrieved from http://www.dsm5.org/ProposedRevisions/Pages/proposedrevision.aspx?rid=24
This website provides access to the recommendations on the various mental illnesses and disorders for the development of the *DSM-5*.

American Psychiatric Association. (2010b). *Binge eating disorder*. Report of the *DSM-5* Eating Disorders Work Group. Retrieved from http://www.dsm5.org/ProposedRevisions/Pages/proposedrevision.aspx?rid=372
This website provides access to the recommendations on the various mental illnesses and disorders for the development of the *DSM-5*.

American Psychiatric Association. (2010c). *Bulimia nervosa*. Report of the *DSM-5* Eating Disorders Work Group. Retrieved from http://www.dsm5.org/ProposedRevisions/Pages/proposedrevision.aspx?rid=25
This website provides access to the recommendations on the various mental illnesses and disorders for the development of the *DSM-5*.

American Psychiatric Association. (2010d). *Eating disorders*. Report of the *DSM-5* Eating Disorders Work Group. Retrieved from http://www.dsm5.org/ProposedRevisions/Pages/EatingDisorders.aspx
This website provides access to the recommendations on the various mental illnesses and disorders for the development of the *DSM-5*.

American Society for Metabolic and Bariatric Surgery. (2011). *Benefits of bariatric surgery*. Retrieved from http://asmbs.org/benefits-of-bariatric-surgery/
This website article reviews the reasons for and benefits of bariatric surgery.

Andersen, A. W. (2009, March/April). Applying the four perspectives to anorexia nervosa. *Eating Disorder Review, 20*(2), 1–2.
This article provides information on an alternative treatment approach utilizing the disease, dimensional, behavior, and life story perspectives.

Annenberg Foundation Trust (Sunnylands), Adolescent Mental Health Initiative. (2005). *Treating and preventing adolescent mental health disorder: What we know and what we don't know*. New York, NY: Oxford University Press.
This book addresses the current state of knowledge about various mental health disorders in the teenage years and is the first to record the findings of this particular initiative.

Anorexia Nervosa and Related Eating Disorders, Inc. (2006, February). Eating disorders warning signs. Retrieved from http://www.anred.com/warn.html
This fact sheet discusses the early warning signs of eating disorders.

Balkon, N., Balkon, C., & Zitkus, B. S. (2011). Overweight and obesity:

Pharmacotherapeutic considerations. *Journal of the American Academy of Nurse Practitioners, 23*, 61–66.
This article reviews current trends for using pharmacotherapy in combination with other weight loss modalities and offers points for consideration by clinicians in practice.

Becker, A. E., Burwell, R. A., Gilman, S. E., Herzog, D. B., & Hamburg, P. (2002). Eating behaviours and attitudes following prolonged exposure to television among ethnic Fijian adolescent girls. *The British Journal of Psychiatry, 180*, 509–514.
This is a report on a naturalistic experiment that suggests a negative impact of television upon disordered eating attitudes and behaviors in a media-naïve population in Fiji.

Birmingham, C. L., Su, J., Hynsky, J. A., Goldner, E. M., & Gao, M. (2005). The mortality rate from anorexia nervosa. *International Journal of Eating Disorders, 38*(2), 143–146.
This article provides a review of the mortality rates associated with anorexia nervosa and the life-threatening complications of the disorder.

Bruce, B., & Agras, W. S. (1992). Binge eating in females: A population-based investigation. *International Journal of Eating Disorders, 12*(4), 365–373.
This article reports on a study of the characteristics of binge eating in an identified population of women.

Bruch, H. (1978). *The golden cage: The enigma of anorexia nervosa*. Cambridge, MA: Harvard University Press.
This is a classic text on anorexia nervosa and is still applicable today.

Casper, R. (1990). Personality features of women with good outcomes from restricting anorexia nervosa. *Psychosomatic Medicine, 52*, 156–170.
This article examines the personality characteristics of women who had physically and psychologically recovered from restricting anorexia nervosa at an 8- to 10-year follow-up.

Centers for Disease Control and Prevention. (2006a). BMI—body mass index: About BMI for children and teens. Retrieved from http://www.cdc.gov/nccdphp/dnpa/bmi/childrens_BMI/about_childrens_BMI.htm
After BMI is calculated for children and teens, the BMI number is plotted on the CDC BMI-for-age growth charts (for either girls or boys) to obtain a percentile ranking. Percentiles are the most commonly used indicator to assess the size and growth patterns of individual children in the United States.

Centers for Disease Control and Prevention. (2006b). Overweight and obesity. Retrieved from http://www.cdc.gov/nccdphp/dnpa/obesity/index.htm
Data from two surveys show that since the mid-1970s, the prevalence of overweight and obesity has increased sharply for both adults and children.

Centers for Disease Control and Prevention. (2006c). Overweight and obesity: Contributing factors. Retrieved from http://www.cdc.gov/nccdphp/dnpa/obesity/contributing_factors.htm
Obesity and overweight are chronic conditions. A variety of factors play a role in obesity. This section addresses how behavior, environment, and genetic factors may have an effect in causing people to be overweight and obese.

Centers for Disease Control and Prevention. (2006d). Overweight and obesity: Defining overweight and obesity. Retrieved from http://www.cdc.gov/nccdphp/dnpa/obesity/defining.htm
Overweight and obesity are both labels for ranges of weight that are greater than what is generally considered healthy for a given height. The terms also identify ranges of weight that have been shown to increase the likelihood of certain diseases and other health problems.

Centers for Disease Control and Prevention. (2010). Vital signs: State-specific obesity prevalence among adults—United States, 2009. *Morbidity and Mortality Weekly Report [MMWR]*. Retrieved from http://www.cdc.gov/mmwr/preview/mmwrhtml/mm59e0803a1.htm
This article provides access to state-specific information on obesity rates.

Centers for Disease Control and Prevention [CDC], National Center for Chronic Disease Prevention and Health Promotion, Division of Adolescent and School Health. (2010). Let's Move. Retrieved from http://www.letsmove.gov/learn-facts/epidemic-childhood-obesity
This is an introduction to this national movement to get the nation, especially children, increasing their physical activity to decrease the numbers of overweight individuals and improve health outcomes.

Currin, L., Schmidt, U., Treasure, J., & Jick, H. (2005). Time trends in eating disorder

incidence. *British Journal of Psychiatry, 186*, 132–135.
This article is a discussion of the differing aspects of eating disorders across different time frames.

Daniels, J. (2006). Women's descriptions of a successful weight-loss experience: A qualitative study. *The American Journal for Nurse Practitioners, 10*(10), 67–74.
The author provides insight into women's experiences with weight loss and maintenance.

Domine, F., Bervhtold, A., Akre, C., Michaud, P. A., & Suris, J. C. (2009). Disordered eating behaviors: What about boys? *Journal of Adolescent Health, 44*(2), 99–100.
Eating disorders are usually associated with girls and women. The authors provide insight into eating problems in boys and the contributing and differing factors.

Duvvuri, V., & Kaye, W. H. (2009). Clinical synthesis: Anorexia nervosa. *Focus, 7*, 455–462.
This article provides a thoughtful overview of this disorder—its manifestations, types, and treatment.

Fabricatore, A. N., & Wadden, T. S. (2003). Psychological functioning of obese individuals. *Diabetes Spectrum, 16*, 245–252.
This review found that obese individuals in the general population have essentially normal psychological functioning. Obese women, however, are at greater risk than obese men of depression and related complications. Binge eating and extreme obesity further increase the likelihood of patients reporting emotional complications.

Fairburn, C. G., Cooper, Z., Doll, H. A., Norman, P., & O'Connor, M. (2000). The natural course of bulimia nervosa and binge eating disorder in young women. *Archives of General Psychiatry, 57*(7), 659–665.
This article suggests that, among young women in the study, bulimia nervosa and binge eating disorder have a different course and outcome. While the prognosis of those with bulimia nervosa was relatively poor, the great majority of those with binge eating disorder recovered.

Fichter, M., & Quadflieg, N. (1999). Six-year course of bulimia nervosa. *International Journal of Eating Disorders, 22*, 361–384.
In comparison to study samples with bulimia nervosa or binge eating disorder, the 6-year course of anorexia nervosa was less favorable.

Garfinkel, P. E., Moldofsky, H., & Garner, D. (1980). The heterogeneity of anorexia nervosa: Bulimia as a distinct group. *Archives of General Psychiatry, 9*, 1036–1140.
The bulimic group in this study displayed a variety of impulsive behaviors, including use of alcohol and street drugs, stealing, suicide attempts, and self-mutilation. With regard to family history, the high frequency of obesity in the mothers of bulimic patients was noteworthy.

Golden, N. H., & Meyer, W. (2004, April–June). Nutritional rehabilitation of anorexia nervosa: Goals and dangers. *International Journal of Adolescent Mental Health, 16*(2), 131–144.
This is a thoughtful discussion of the challenges of establishing a nutritional rehabilitation regimen for adolescents dealing with anorexia and the dangers associated with refeeding.

Haines, J., & Neumark-Sztainer, D. (2006). Prevention of obesity and eating disorders: A consideration of shared risk factors. *Health Education Research, 21*(6), 770–782.
The authors discuss different issues associated with obesity including dieting, media influences, body dissatisfaction, binging, physical activity, and weight-related teasing.

Halmi, K. A., Eckert, E., Marchi, P., Sampugnaro, V., Apple, R., & Cohen, J. (1991). Comorbidity of psychiatric diagnoses in anorexia nervosa. *Archives of General Psychiatry, 48*, 712–718.
The comorbidity of psychiatric diagnoses was examined with the diagnostic interview schedule in 62 women who participated in a 10-year follow-up study of anorexia nervosa.

Healthypeople.gov. (n.d.). MHMD-3. Reduce the proportion of adolescents who engage in disordered eating behaviors in an attempt to control their weight. Retrieved from http://www.healthypeople.gov/2020/topicsobjectives2020/objectiveslist.aspx?topicid=28
Healthy People, a government-sponsored initiative, provides science-based, 10-year national objectives for improving the health of all Americans. For 3 decades, Healthy People has established benchmarks and monitored progress over time.

Hebebrand, J., Muller, T. D., Holtkamp, K., & Herpertz-Dahlmann, B. (2007). The role of leptin in anorexia nervosa: Clinical implications. *Molecular Psychiatry, 12*, 23–35.
The authors review findings on leptin secretion in anorexia nervosa, focusing on implications, particularly for the hypothalamus-pituitary-gonadal axis, bone mineral density, and physical hyperactivity.

Herpertz-Dahlmann, B. (2008). Adolescent eating disorders: Definitions, symptomatology, epidemiology, and comorbidity. *Child Adolescent Psychiatric Clinics of North America, 18*(1), 31–47.
This article provides an overview of the major issues associated with this disorder.

Herpertz-Dahlmann, B., Muller, B., Herpertz, S., Heussen, N., Hebebrand, J., & Remschmidt, H. (2001). Prospective 10-year follow-up in adolescent anorexia nervosa: Course, outcome, psychiatric comorbidity, and psychosocial adaptation. *Journal of Child Psychology and Psychiatry and Allied Disciplines, 42*, 603–612.
The study concluded that in most patients, adolescent anorexia nervosa takes a prolonged course, although it seems to be more favorable than in adult-onset forms. Those who achieve complete recovery from the eating disorder have a good chance of overcoming other psychiatric disorders and adapting to social requirements.

Herzog, D. B., Keller, M. B., Sacks, N. R., Yeh, C. J., & Lavori, P. W. (1992). Psychiatric comorbidity in treatment-seeking anorexics and bulimics. *Journal of the American Academy of Child and Adolescent Psychiatry, 31*, 810–818.
High levels of comorbidity were noted across the eating disorder samples. Mixed disorder subjects manifested the most comorbid psychopathology and especially warrant further study.

Herzog, D. B., Nusbaum, K. M., & Marmor, A. K. (1996). Comorbidity and outcome in eating disorders. *Psychiatric Clinics of North America, 19*, 843–859.
This article reviews the data on comorbidity, course, and outcome in anorexia nervosa and bulimia nervosa. Recovery, relapse, the process of recovery, and predictors of outcome are reviewed.

Hoek, H. W. (2002). Distribution of eating disorders. In C. G. Fairburn & K. D. Brownell (Eds.), *Eating disorders and obesity: A comprehensive handbook* (pp. 233–237). New York, NY: Guilford Press.
This unique handbook clearly discusses both the traditional eating disorders and obesity.

Hudson, J. I., Hiripi, E., Pope, H. G. & Kessler, R. C. (2007). The prevalence and correlates of eating disorders in the National Comorbidity Survey Replication. *Biological Psychiatry, 61*(3):348–58.
This article discusses eating disorders as a public health concern because they are frequently associated with other psychopathology and role impairment, and are frequently under-treated.

Institute of Medicine. (1995). *Weighing the options: Criteria for evaluating weight-management programs*. Washington, DC: National Academy Press.
Despite widespread public concern about weight, few studies have examined the long-term results of weight-loss programs. This report presents criteria for evaluating treatment programs for obesity and explores what these criteria mean to healthcare providers, program designers, researchers, and even overweight people seeking help.

Kaplan, H., Sadock, B., & Grebb, J. (Eds.). (1994). *Kaplan and Sadock's synopsis of psychiatry* (7th ed.). Baltimore, MD: Williams & Wilkins.
Includes the definitions and classifications of mental illness as contained in the ICD-10.

Keel, P. K., Dorer, D. J., Eddy, K. T., Franko, D., Charatan, D. L., & Herzog, D. B. (2003). Predictors of mortality in eating disorders. *Archives of General Psychiatry, 60*, 179–183.
The study concluded that clinicians treating patients with anorexia nervosa should carefully assess patterns of alcohol use during the course of care because one third of women who had alcoholism and died had no history of an alcohol use disorder at time of intake.

Keel, P. K., Heatherton, T. F., Dorer, D. J., Joiner, T. E., & Zalta, A. (2006). Point prevalence of bulimia nervosa in 1982, 1992, and 2002. *Psychological Medicine, 36*, 119–128.
This article provides a review of the prevalence rates of bulimia in the population over a 20-year period.

Keel, P. K., & Mitchell, J. E. (1997). Outcome in bulimia nervosa. *American Journal of Psychiatry, 154*, 313–321.
This study concluded that treatment interventions may speed eventual recovery but do not appear to alter outcome more than 5 years following presentation. Long-term outcome for women diagnosed with bulimia nervosa remains unclear.

Keel, P. K., Mitchell, J. E., Miller, K. B., Davis, T. L., & Crow, S. J. (1999). Long-term outcome of bulimia nervosa. *Archives of General Psychiatry, 56*, 63–69.
The findings suggest that the number of women who continue to meet full criteria for bulimia

nervosa declines as the duration of follow-up increases.

leGrange, D., Lock, J., Loeb, K., & Nicholls, D. (2010). Academy for Eating Disorders position paper: The role of the family in eating disorders. *International Journal of Eating Disorders, 43*(1), 1–5.
This article is a review of the indicators and pros and cons of involving family members, especially parents, in the treatment of individuals with eating disorders.

Lock, J., LeGrange, D., Agras, W. S., & Dare, C. (2001). *Treatment manual for anorexia nervosa: A family-based approach.* New York, NY: The Guilford Press.
This text provides a detailed and authoritative guide to the Maudsley approach for the treatment of adolescents with anorexia nervosa and their families.

Luck, A. J., Morgan, J. F., Reid, F., O'Brien, A., Brunton, J., Price, C., . . . Lacey, J. H. (2002). The SCOFF questionnaire and clinical interview for eating disorders in general practice: Comparative study. *British Medical Journal, 325*, 755.
This article provides information on the utilization of the SCOFF questionnaire in practice and a discussion of its usefulness.

Mazzeo, S. E., & Bulik, C. M. (2009). Environmental and genetic risk factors for eating disorders: What the clinician needs to know? *Child and Adolescent Psychiatric Clinics of North America, 18*, 67–82.
While there is no single cause of eating disorders in children and adolescents, increasingly, the impact of both environmental influences and genetics is being considered by clinicians.

McGilley, B. M., & Pryor, T. L. (1998). Assessment and treatment of bulimia nervosa. *American Family Physician, 57*, 11.
Bulimia nervosa is characterized by binge eating and inappropriate compensatory behaviors, such as vomiting, fasting, excessive exercise, and the misuse of diuretics, laxatives, or enemas. Although the etiology of this disorder is unknown, genetic and neurochemical factors have been implicated.

Morgan, J. F., Reid, F., & Lacey, J. H. (1999). The SCOFF questionnaire: Assessment of a new screening tool for eating disorders. *British Medical Journal, 319*,1467–1468.
This is an introduction to this tool for assessing clients with eating disorders.

Murphy, R., Straebler, S., Cooper, Z., & Fairburn, C. (2010, September). Cognitive behavior therapy for eating disorders. *Psychiatric Clinics of North America, 33*(3), 611–627.
This article reviews the shared psychopathology of the eating disorders and evidence supporting the use of an enhanced form of CBT in the treatment of not just bulimia nervosa, but all of the eating disorders.

National Heart, Lung, and Blood Institute (NHLBI). (n.d.). *Clinical guidelines on the identification, evaluation, and treatment of overweight and obesity in adults—Guidelines on overweight and obesity.* Electronic textbook. Retrieved from http://www.nhlbi.nih.gov/guidelines/obesity/ob_home.htm
The National Heart, Lung, and Blood Institute, in cooperation with the National Institute of Diabetes and Digestive and Kidney Diseases, released the first federal guidelines on the identification, evaluation, and treatment of overweight and obesity.

National Institute of Mental Health. (2001). *Eating disorders. Facts about eating disorders and the search for solutions* (NIH 01-4901). Bethesda, MD: National Institute of Mental Health, National Institutes of Health, U.S. Department of Health and Human Services. Retrieved from http://www.nimh.nih.gov/publicat/eatingdisorders.cfm
This is a detailed booklet that describes symptoms, causes, and treatments, with information on getting help and coping with eating disorders.

National Institute of Mental Health. (2007). *Eating disorders* (NIH Publication No 07-4901). Bethesda, MD: National Institute of Mental Health, National Institutes of Health, US Department of Health and Human Services.
This brochure provides information on the symptoms, causes and treatments of eating disorders for practitioners and consumers.

Ogden, C. L., Carroll, M. D., Curtin, L. R., Lamb, M. M., & Flegal, K. M. (2010). Prevalence of high body mass index in U.S. children and adolescents, 2007–2008. *Journal of the American Medical Association, 303*(3), 242–249. doi:10.1001/jama.2009.2012
The authors provide an in-depth discussion of the different prevalence rates of BMI rates in the nation's children and adolescents.

Osterhout, C. I., Scher, L. M., Hilty, D. M., & Yager, J. (2010). Bulimia nervosa. Retrieved from http://emedicine.medscape.com/article/286485-treatment#
This site provides a discussion of the need for an interdisciplinary approach to treatment for bulimia.

Rosen, D. S. (2010). Clinical report—Identification and management of eating disorders in children and adolescents. *Pediatrics, 126*, 1240–1253.
The author provides information on the need for identification of the disorders and various treatment and management interventions.

Simon, G. E., von Korff, M., Saunders, K., Miglioretti, D. L., Crane, P. K., van Belle, G., & Kessler, R. C. (2006). Association between obesity and psychiatric disorders in the U.S. adult population. *Archives of General Psychiatry, 63*, 824–830.
An evaluation of the relationship between obesity and a range of mood, anxiety, and substance use disorders in the U.S. general population.

Spitzer, R. L., Yanovski, S., Wadden, T., Wing, R., Marcus, M. D., Stunkard, A., . . . Horne, R.L. (1993). Binge eating disorder: Its further validation in a multisite study. *International Journal of Eating Disorders, 13*(2), 137–153.
This is a study of binge eating disorder and the large number of individuals who suffer from recurrent binge eating, but who do not regularly engage in the compensatory behaviors to avoid weight gain seen in bulimia nervosa.

Steinhausen, H. C. (2002). The outcome of anorexia nervosa in the 20th century. *American Journal of Eating Disorders, 22*, 147–151.
This review addresses the outcomes of anorexia nervosa and whether they changed over the second half of the 20th century.

Steinhausen, H. C., Winkler, C., & Meier, M. (1997). Eating disorders in adolescence in a Swiss epidemiological study. *International Journal of Eating Disorders, 22*, 147–151.
This study concludes that the full clinical syndromes of anorexia nervosa and bulimia nervosa in adolescents are by far less frequent than individual symptoms of eating disorders.

Stice, E., Spangler, D. L., & Agras, W. S. (2002). Exposure to media-portrayed thin-ideal images adversely affects vulnerable girls: A longitudinal experiment. *Journal of Social and Clinical Psychology, 20*, 271–289.
This article reports on a study that concluded exposure to the thin-ideal image resulted in an increase in body dissatisfaction but not negative affect or heart rate.

Striegel-Moore, R. H., Rosselli, F., Perrin, N., DeBar, L., Wilson G. T., May, M. A., & Kraemer, H. C. (2008). Gender difference in the prevalence of eating disorder symptoms. *International Journal of Eating Disorders, 42*(5), 471–474.
The authors discuss the difference in the prevalence and symptoms of eating disorders in girls and boys.

Sullivan, P. F. (1995). Mortality in anorexia nervosa. *American Journal of Psychiatry, 152*(7), 1073–1074.
The study indicated that the aggregate estimated mortality rate for subjects with anorexia nervosa is substantially greater than that reported for female psychiatric inpatients and for the general population.

Sutin, A., Ferrucci, L., Zonderman, A. B. & Terracciano, A. (2011) Personality and obesity across the adult life span. *Journal of Personality and Social Psychology, 101*(3), 579–92 doi:10.1037/a0024286.
The authors explore data from a longitudinal study to examine how personality traits are associated with multiple measures of adiposity and with fluctuations in body mass index (BMI).

Swanson, S. A., Crow, S. J., Le Grange, D., Swendsen, J., & Merikangas, K. R. (2011). Prevalence and correlates of eating disorders in adolescents: Results from the National Comorbidity Survey Replication Adolescent Supplement. *Archives of General Psychiatry*. doi: 10.1001
The authors review the prevalence rates and correlates of eating disorders in adolescents in the United States.

Walsh, B. T., & Devlin, M. J. (1998). Eating disorders: Progress and problems. *Science, 280*, 1387–1390.
This article reviews current thinking on the etiology and treatment of the two major eating disorders and a related syndrome—binge eating disorder.

Wysoker, A. (2002). A conceptual model of weight loss and weight regain. An interven-

tion for change. *Journal of the American Psychiatric Nurses Association, 8*, 168–173.
The model offers a framework for treatment and includes the following three different approaches: (1) one can lose weight and keep it off; (2) it may be impossible to lose weight and keep it off; and (3) women will continue to try to lose weight, despite the long history of losing weight and regaining the lost weight.

Wysoker, A. (2005). The lived experience of choosing bariatric surgery to lose weight. *Journal of the American Psychiatric Nurses Association, 11*, 26–34.
The purpose of this research was to explore issues related to having a surgical procedure performed to lose weight.

Yager, J. (2008). Binge eating disorder: The search for better treatments. *American Journal of Psychiatry, 165*(1), 4–6.
The author discusses the need for and progress in identifying better treatment modalities for clients with binge eating disorder.

Yager, J., Devlin, M. J., Halmi, K. A., Herzog, D. B., Mitchell, J. E., Powers, P., & Zerbe, K. J. (2006). *Practice guidelines: Treatment of patients with eating disorders* (3rd ed.). Arlington, VA: APA Work Group on Eating Disorders.
This publication contains the official guidelines from the American Psychiatric Association on treating eating disorders.

Zhao, Y., & Encinosa, W. (2009, April). *Hospitalizations for eating disorders from 1999 to 2006* (HCUP Statistical Brief No. 70). Rockville, MD: Agency for Healthcare Research and Quality. Retrieved from http://www.hcup-us.ahrq.gov/reports/statbriefs/sb70.pdf
This publication provides a review of the statistics compiled by the agency on hospitalizations for eating disorders over a 7-year period.

Zitkus, B. (2011). The relationship among registered nurses' weight status, weight loss regimens, and successful or unsuccessful weight loss. *Journal of the American Academy of Nurse Practitioners, 23*(2), 110–116.
The author studied and reports on the relationship of BMI and weight loss programs as factors in losing weight.

Internet Resources

For a full suite of assignments and additional learning activities, use the access code located in the front of your book to visit this exclusive website: http://go.jblearning.com/mentalhealth. If you do not have an access code, you can obtain one at the site.

Learning Objectives

After reading this chapter, you will be able to:

- Define dyssomnias and parasomnias and give examples of each.
- Differentiate normal and abnormal sleep patterns.
- Identify factors important in the assessment of sleep disorders.
- Describe appropriate interventions for various sleep disorders.

Key Terms

Breathing-related sleep disorders

Cataplexy

Circadian rhythm

Dyssomnia

Hypersomnia

Insomnia

Multiple sleep latency test (MSLT)

Narcolepsy

Nightmare

Nonrapid eye movement (NREM)

Parasomnia

Periodic limb movements (PLM)

Polysomnography

Rapid eye movement (REM)

Restless leg syndrome (RLS)

Sleep architecture

Sleep terror disorder

Sleepwalking

Sleep Disorders

Winifred Z. Kennedy

http://go.jblearning.com/mentalhealth 

For a full suite of assignments and additional learning activities, use the access code located in the front of your book to visit this exclusive website: http://go.jblearning.com/mentalhealth. If you do not have an access code, you can obtain one at the site.

Introduction

Sleep problems are a common experience caused by variations in environment; developmental stages and psychosocial stressors; work, school, and travel schedules; use of medicines or substance abuse; and physical and mental health. Stephen King's novel, *Insomnia*, captures the exquisite nature of the problems encountered by an insomniac and uses them as the basis for a fantastic horror story. In the beginning of the novel, the main character begins a search for the solution to his sleeping troubles, following a rather common course of seeking advice from friends and physicians, information from popular and medical sources, treatments from folk remedies and pharmacotherapy, and trials of complementary therapies including hypnosis and acupuncture. Others with sleep problems can understand the character's discomfort, search for a cure, and accompanying physical and mental changes experienced as the sleeplessness continues. Sleep problems begin to pervade every aspect of the insomniac's life. The character in *Insomnia* eventually experiences perceptual disturbances and an altered sense of reality with continued sleep deprivation.

It is occasionally difficult to differentiate between normal, temporary variations in sleep patterns and sleep disorders. The amount of time spent sleeping normally varies and decreases with age. Most Americans report sleeping 6.8 hours on weekdays, which is below the average number of hours of sleep considered to be necessary for most people. Short sleepers, people who normally require a shortened or briefer period of sleep or less time than average, and long sleepers, or people who normally require a greater period of sleep or more time sleeping than average, are within normal variations. Rest and activity patterns vary among people who normally function better in the morning (larks) and those who do better at night (owls). Problematic symptoms such as sleepwalking or night terrors may occur during particular periods (such as in childhood). These are temporary conditions rather than sleep disorders because they are of limited duration and interference with general functioning.

General Description of Sleep Disorders

Four main divisions of sleep disorders exist: primary sleep disorder, sleep disorder related to another mental disorder, sleep disorder caused by a general medical condition, and substance-induced sleep disorder. The *Diagnostic and Statistical Manual of Mental Disorders*, fourth edition, text revision (*DSM-IV-TR*), identifies these disorders according to etiology and the disturbance in the amount, quality, and timing of sleep and associated physiologic and behavioral problems (American Psychiatric Association [APA], 2000).

Primary Sleep Disorders

Primary sleep disorders include **dyssomnias** (sleep disorders involving impaired amount, quality, and timing of sleep) and **parasomnias** (sleep disorders involving abnormal physiologic and behavioral events associated with sleep). Dyssomnias include primary **insomnia**, primary **hypersomnia**, **narcolepsy**, **breathing-related sleep disorder**, **circadian rhythm** sleep disorder, and nonspecific dyssomnias (dyssomnia not otherwise specified [NOS]). Parasomnias include **nightmare** disorder, **rapid eye movement (REM)** sleep behavior disorder, **sleep terror disorder**, **sleepwalking** disorder, and nonspecific parasomnias (parasomnia NOS). These disorders are generally coded on Axis I. Breathing-related sleep disorders also may be coded on Axis III. Some of the disorders, such as primary hypersomnia, may be further specified as recurrent if they occur repeatedly. Circadian rhythm sleep disorder also may be further specified according to type (delayed sleep phase, jet lag, shift work, or unspecified).

Sleep Disorders Related to Another Mental Disorder

Sleep disorders related to another mental disorder include insomnia related to another mental disorder and hypersomnia related to another mental disorder. These disorders are generally coded on Axis I, and the associated (Axis I or II) mental disorder is named along with the type of sleep disturbance. In addition, the associated mental disorder is appropriately coded on Axis I or II. For example, insomnia related to a major depressive disorder is coded on Axis I, and the associated mood disorder, major depressive disorder, should be coded on Axis I. Conversely, hypersomnia related to avoidant personality disorder is coded on Axis I, and the associated personality disorder, avoidant personality disorder, should be coded on Axis II.

Sleep Disorder Caused by a General Medical Condition

Sleep disorders caused by a general medical condition may be specified according to several subtypes such as insomnia, hypersomnia, parasomnia, or mixed. The diagnosis of sleep disorder caused by a general medical condition is named along with the subtype of sleep disorder and the associated general medical condition. The diagnosis is coded on Axis I. In addition, the associated general medical condition and its *International Classification of Disorders* (*ICD-9-CM*) code should be noted on Axis III. For example, sleep disorder caused by Parkinson's disease, insomnia type, is coded on Axis I, and Parkinson's disease with its *ICD-9-CM* code should be coded on Axis III.

Substance-Induced Sleep Disorder

Substance-induced sleep disorder is identified according to several subtypes (insomnia, hypersomnia, parasomnia, or mixed) and further specified as either with onset during intoxication or with onset during withdrawal. The specific disorder and type is named along with the suspected causative substance. An example is amphetamine-induced sleep disorder, insomnia type, with onset during intoxication, or amphetamine-induced sleep disorder, hypersomnia type, with onset during withdrawal. If more than one substance is suspected, each should be listed separately; if the substance is unknown, unknown substance-induced sleep disorder may be used. The disorder is generally coded on Axis I. In addition, some sleep disorders may be associated with medication prescribed in therapeutic amounts for a specific general medical condition.

Incidence and Prevalence

An estimated 40% of women and 30% of men report sleep problems. More than 50% of women and men older than 65 years of age report sleep difficulties. Approximately 15–25% of clients seen in sleep disorder clinics for complaints of chronic insomnia are diagnosed with primary insomnia; 5–10% of those with complaints of excessive sleepiness are diagnosed with primary hypersomnia, 0.02–0.16% with narcolepsy, and 1–10% with breathing-related sleep disorders (APA, 2000). Approximately 20–60% of all shift workers report chronic sleep problems (APA, 2000). Clients with concomitant mental and medical disorders have a higher prevalence of sleep disorders. Mental disorders were associated with a diagnosis of primary insomnia in approximately two thirds of cases, and, of those, approximately half were secondary to mood disorders. Insomnia secondary to psychiatric disorders was the most frequent diagnosis of clients presenting to sleep centers (Szelenberger & Soldatos, 2005).

Although everyone at some point may complain about the quality or quantity of their sleep, most people eventually do sleep. Clients with fatal familial insomnia, a rare prion disorder found in family clusters, are the exception. This disorder causes symptoms similar to thalamic dementia such as Creutzfeldt-Jakob disease.

The 2011 Sleep in America Poll by the National Sleep Foundation (2011) revealed that 43% of all respondents between the ages of 13 and 64 years old felt they had a problem with sleep, and 60% reported that they had a problem sleeping almost every night. About 20% reported it took them more than 30 minutes to fall asleep. Insomnia was experienced once a week by 75% of respondents, and 46% experienced excessive daytime sleepiness. Driving while drowsy was experienced by 60% of automobile drivers. In previous studies, of those who reported sleep problems, approximately 27% percent stated they used medications to sleep (10% used prescription medications, 16% used over-the-counter [OTC] medications, and 1% used both prescription and OTC medications), and approximately 11% of respondents used alcohol. The symptom of snoring loud enough to be heard through a door, which indicates a breathing-related sleep disorder, was reported by 16% of respondents. Approximately 3% of respondents reported that a physician had diagnosed them with **restless leg syndrome (RLS)**, uncomfortable pulling or crawling sensations of lower limbs that occur at times of rest or sleep, or **periodic limb movements (PLM)**, twitching or uncontrolled movements of the upper or lower limbs that occur at times of rest or sleep, or both. Among elderly clients with probable dyssomnias, PLMs were most common, affecting approximately 25–44%, followed by breathing-related sleep disorders that affected 24–42%, and RLS, affecting 29% of those over 50 years of age and 44% of those over 65 years of age (Institute of Medicine, 2006; Montplaisir, Allen, Walters, & Ferini-Strambi, 2010).

Etiology

Sleep disorders can be related to disturbances caused by internal or external stimuli, physiologic changes and medical disorders, or pharmacokinetics and pharmacodynamics. Our ability to sleep can be affected by our habits, mood, or degree of fatigue. Sleep may vary at different developmental levels.

Environment

Hospital environments may be an extrinsic source of sleep problems. This strange environment with its machines, treatments, 24-hour operating schedule, roommates, and absence of individualized control over temperature, noise, and lighting contributes to disturbances in circadian rhythms, comfort levels, and psychologic and physiologic regulatory mechanisms.

An environment that is free from distractions and an established bedtime routine can be conducive to a good night's sleep.

Many sleep disorders are caused by environmental problems and poor sleep hygiene. Ambience is important for sleep, as is establishing a basic routine. In preparing infants and young children for sleep, usually a great deal of attention is given to the surrounding comfort measures and routine. The young are fed and cleaned. The sleep space is made inviting with clean, soft bedding. Reduced environmental stimuli (dimmed lighting, decreased attractions) and perhaps soft music or a lullaby are part of the routine, as are forms of relaxation such as touch or massage, prayers or guided imagery, and reading. In contrast, in the average adult's contemporary bedroom, the bed shares space with multiple distractions such as the radio, television, telephone, and computers (see **Figure 22-1**). The person must contend with the conflicting demands of multiple roles, relationships, and occupations. Overtired, under- or overfed, and overstimulated, the adult uses the bed as a battleground rather than a retreat from extrinsic stimuli.

Figure 22-1 Children and adults often sleep in rooms with very different atmospheres.

Rhythm-Disrupting Stressors

Rhythm-disrupting stressors are factors in many sleep problems. Changes in routine, such as finishing a project or studying for an examination, traveling across time zones, working overtime during the week and oversleeping on weekends, and shift work or shift rotation can temporarily or chronically disrupt sleep patterns. Women often are exposed to the common rhythm-disrupting stressors of pregnancy and childbirth, menopause, child care and other caretaking roles, and juggling multiple roles throughout their lives (Attarian, 2006). Individuals with medical, surgical, and psychiatric problems may experience rhythm-disrupting stressors related to anticipated or actual pain, treatments, pharmacotherapy, and hospitalization. Clients with mental disorders such as mood, somatoform, anxiety, and panic disorders; substance-use disorders; and posttraumatic stress disorder also may experience disruptions of sleep–wake cycles.

Critical Thinking Question

How does a hospital environment contribute to sleep disturbances? Suggest some ways these factors can be mitigated.

Poorly Modulated Regulatory Function

Poorly modulated regulatory function is another cause of sleep disorders. Sleep patterns change with normal aging, and many elderly clients have a greater amount of subjective complaints concerning the amount and quality of their sleep. Some age-related changes include an increased time spent in bed, an increased proportion of stage 1 or light sleep, an increase in the number of abnormal breathing events and leg movements, a decrease in the proportion of slow-wave sleep or deep sleep, and rapid eye movement (REM) sleep latency (Bloom et al., 2009). Many medical and psychiatric disorders are associated with sleep disturbances. Clients with cognitive disorders may experience fluctuations in states of consciousness in delirium or sleep–wake cycle variations in dementia including night–day reversal. Other neurologic disorders such as brain stem lesions, Parkinson's disease, Huntington's disease, cerebral vascular disorders, and multiple sclerosis are often associated with sleep disorders. In rapid eye movement behavior disorder, there can be abnormal REM sleep without atonia and observed vocalizations or active motor behaviors, which can be distressing to the client or others with whom they sleep and may cause injury to the client or others. REM sleep disorder has been associated with use of antidepressant medications and can be an early behavioral manifestation of Parkinson's disease, Lewy body dementia, and Alzheimer's disease.

Physical and Mental Disorders

Clients with breathing problems such as bronchitis, chronic obstructive pulmonary disease, or restrictive lung diseases generally experience sleep disorders. Clients with chronic pain problems such as arthritis and fibromyalgia and those with medical, metabolic, and endocrine disorders such as cancer, diabetes, gastric reflux, prostatitis, and thyroid problems also experience sleep disorders. In addition, many clients with schizophrenia or manic-depressive disorder experience sleep problems related to impaired regulatory functioning. For example, a manic client may experience periods of hyperactivity, restlessness, and extreme motor agitation with continual movement and pacing that lead to complete exhaustion.

Critical Thinking Question

What are some nursing interventions that could be used to reduce internal and external stimuli?

Pharmaceuticals and Other Substances

Many pharmaceuticals cause or worsen sleep disorders. Some medications and substances that may cause problems include alcohol, amphetamines, antidepressants, anesthetics, anxiolytics, antihistamines, antihypertensive agents, barbiturates, bromides, bronchodilators, caffeine, corticosteroids, decongestants, hallucinogens, levodopa, opioids, and tranquilizers. Even hypnotics and sedatives specifically intended to treat clients with sleep disorders occasionally worsen the problems.

Critical Thinking Question

What are some of the possible etiological factors that should be assessed in a sleep disorder?

Physiology

Normal sleep is an essential state of consciousness that is periodic, cyclical, and reversible. Its restorative function manifests as alterations in the individual's physiologic and behavioral patterns of interaction. Metabolic and neural activity continue with some variations during sleep as they do during the waking state. During sleep, neural activity is redistributed or reorganized, changes occur in muscle tone and sensory responsiveness, and, usually, the amount and type of activity and interaction with the environment are decreased. **Sleep architecture** is the amount (total sleep time and length of sleep stages) and distribution of sleep stages (cyclical alterations in sleep states).

Sleep Stages

Sleep stages include alternating states of REM sleep and **nonrapid eye movement (NREM)**, or slow-wave sleep. The five sleep stages of normal sleep architecture are:

- *Stage 1:* NREM and low voltage characterize this stage. This is the transition from wakefulness to sleep characterized by drowsiness. Stage 1 normally lasts a few minutes, 2–5% of total sleep time.
- *Stage 2:* This stage is characterized by NREM and sleep complexes on the electroencephalogram (EEG). In stage 2, muscle tone and cerebral activity decrease. This stage accounts for 50% of total sleep time.
- *Stage 3:* This stage is characterized by NREM, delta waves, and slow-wave sleep. This is the transition to stage 4. Stage 3 lasts one third to one half of the night, 10–20% of total sleep time.
- *Stage 4:* This stage is characterized by NREM, deepest sleep, continued slow-wave sleep, and delta waves. The metabolic rate and temperature decrease. Stage 4 is characterized by the lowest level of body functioning. It lasts for one third to one half of the night, 10–20% of total sleep time.
- *Stage 5:* The REM dream state alternates with NREM sleep. Long periods of desynchronized activity alternate with periods of activity similar to alertness. The vital signs are irregular, atonia occurs, and the person has increased fre-

Dreaming, the experience of emotions, images, and thoughts during sleep, occurs during REM sleep.

quency of dreaming as morning approaches. Stage 5 accounts for 25% of total sleep time.

Biologic rhythms can have an almost clocklike rhythm. Ultradian rhythm (e.g., periods of time such as seconds, minutes, hours) is less than 20–24-hour periodicity (e.g., NREM and REM sleep stages). Circadian rhythm (about 1 day) is approximately 24-hour periodicity (e.g., sleep–wake cycles are approximately 23–26 hours). Infradian rhythm (e.g., periods of days, weeks, years) is more than 24-hour periodicity (e.g., menstrual cycle).

Clinical Example 

Danielle is a 32-year-old woman brought to the emergency department by police after her family reported she was loud and angry as well as verbally and physically threatening them. The family reported that Danielle has been unable to sleep for the past week and had not been eating or bathing. In the ED, Danielle was talking nonstop, singing at times, and pacing. Her family stated she had stopped wearing shoes, and her feet were swollen and covered with superficial abrasions. She told staff that she was writing a book about her life experiences as a priestess and that she had to leave immediately because she had a dinner appointment with the pope and Madonna.

Clinical Example 

Saul, an 84-year-old man with a history of progressive dementia and multiple medical problems, is brought to the clinic for a routine evaluation. His daughter, who is the primary caregiver, reports that he is up all night and is very disruptive to the household. During the day, both she and the patient are exhausted so she lets him sleep as much as possible and doesn't disturb him unless he awakens. She feels he needs medications to calm him down and an increase in his sleeping medications.

Sleep architecture refers to the five stages of the normal sleep cycle. An average NREM–REM cycle lasts approximately 90 minutes.

The sleep cycle usually begins in the NREM state, and NREM sleep predominates in the first third of the cycle, while REM sleep predominates in the last third. The cycle alternates between NREM and REM sleep, with an average NREM–REM cycle lasting approximately 90 minutes with rare, brief periods of wakefulness. Variations in sleep cycles are determined by measuring the electrical potential difference between two points on the scalp with an EEG. An EEG records the frequency and amplitude of neuron activity and behavior changes during various states of consciousness and stages of sleep such as alertness, drowsiness, slow-wave NREM sleep, and paradoxical REM sleep. In the waking state, the EEG records alpha waves and mixed-frequency, low-voltage activity. In the sleeping state, this alpha-wave activity decreases, and the cyclical pattern of the five sleep stages begins.

Neurobiologic and Genetic Factors

Different parts of the brain, such as the cortex, hypothalamic system, and reticular system are important for wakefulness and an alert state. Neural systems affecting arousal and sleep are influenced by different parts of the brain's reticular formation. Descending, local, and ascending neural pathways converge on the reticular formation in the core of the brain stem and project from the reticular formation to the brain stem and cerebellum, spinal cord, and higher areas of the cerebellum such as the cerebral cortex, basal ganglia, and limbic system. Aside from the reticular system and noradrenergic and serotonergic nuclei, the cortex influences slow-wave NREM sleep; stimulation of the pontine reticular formation containing cholingergic nuclei influences REM sleep. The locus caeruleus contains norepinephrine-releasing neurons active during slow-wave NREM sleep, and the raphe nuclei contain serotonergic nuclei active during slow-wave NREM sleep. Circadian rhythms are internal rhythms that affect the sleep stages. Light energy in the visual cortex and suprachiasmatic nucleus of the hypothalamus direct circadian rhythm and influence neuroendocrine changes that can affect mood. REM sleep, in particular, is associated with a circadian distribution. Environmental cues and light–dark variations affect the synchronization of sleep cycles. Other rhythmic physiologic variations may affect thermoregulation; endocrine, renal, and hepatic functions; cardiovascular, immune, and respiratory systems; and pharmacokinetics. Neurotransmitters such as acetylcholine, adenosine, 5-hydroxytryptamine, dopamine, norepinephrine, and serotonin influence the initiation and maintenance of sleep–wake cycles. Neurotransmitters influence various patterns of activation, different phases of alertness and arousal, and slow-wave NREM and REM sleep.

Abnormal Sleep

Abnormal sleep is associated with disturbances in slow-wave NREM and REM sleep stages, insufficient sleep, arousals with awakenings or partial awakenings, or hypersomnia with prolonged sleep or unplanned daytime sleeping. Disruptions of normal sleep architecture, sleep efficiency (percentage of time spent asleep compared with time spent in bed), and sleep continuity (balance of sleep to wakefulness during normal sleep cycle) contribute to complaints of abnormal sleep. The National Sleep

Foundation considers 7–9 hours of sleep to be the normal daily requirement. Many complaints regarding abnormal sleep consist of the perception of an inadequate amount of sleep (less than 7 hours). Clients with sleep deprivation (prolonged episodes of sleep loss over time) generally show disturbances of REM sleep and disruption of normal sleep cycles. Clients with sleep fragmentation (frequent interruptions of normal sleep cycles) show disturbances in daytime alertness. New parents frequently complain of this, as do hospitalized clients who are awakened for treatments and clients with RLS, PLM, and breathing-related sleep disorders. RLS and PLM are affected by circadian rhythms and are usually worse in the evening and night than in the day. Regarding excessive amounts of sleep (hypersomnia), clients generally complain of long periods (8–12 hours) of undisrupted sleep at night and problems awakening and staying awake in the day. Sleep of more than 9 hours daily has been associated with cardiovascular disease. In hypersomnia, the REM and NREM sleep stages are normal. Clients with narcolepsy (a less common sleep disorder) also sleep excessive amounts and experience multiple sleep-onset REM periods, sleep attacks, sleep paralysis, and hallucinations. Circadian rhythm sleep disorders may be caused by delayed sleep phases, chronic sleep deprivation, travel-induced jet lag disturbances crossing time zones, and shift work or shift rotation. Jet lag disturbances and shift work cause a mismatch between the client's internal rhythm and need for sleep and the external rhythms of a different time zone or the environmental demands of shift work. Clients with these rhythm disruptions generally have decreased stage 2 and REM sleep. Parasomnias such as nightmare disorder, sleep terror disorder, and sleepwalking disorder are associated with REM sleep disorders and behavioral and motor manifestations of disturbed sleep and sleep–wake transitions. Studies of overtime and extended working hours show relationships with poor general health and illness, job injuries and errors, premature births, weight gain, and increased alcohol and smoking (Caruso, Hitchcock, Dick, Russo, & Schmit, 2004). Researchers studying the transition from wakefulness to sleep have found that repeated firings of neurons in circuits that have been most active during the day while awake cause the release of adenosine triphosphate (ATP) that accumulates and bonds to neurons and glial cells, allowing those cells to absorb other chemicals such as tumor necrosis factor and interleukin 1, which influence sleep (Krueger et al., 2010).

Many sleep studies have suggested genetic components of some sleep disorders. Proteins associated with neural processing, GAP-43 and SNAP25b, suggest that an important function of sleep may be synaptic restoration. The differences between short sleepers and long sleepers have been suggested by identification of DEC2, a mutation of hDEC2-P385R for short sleepers. Identification of the circadian core clock genes Clock, Bmal1, Per1, Per2, Cry1, Cry2 and npas2 have shown an interaction between homeostatic influences on sleep and circadian modulation affecting sleep time, effects of light and dark and sleep recovery, identifying some of the differences between larks and owls. Persons who identify themselves with a perception of greater fatigue and requiring more sleep are associated with the human leukocyte antigen (HLA) DQB*0602. Almost 90% of individuals with narcolepsy-cataplexy have the (HLA) DR15 (DR2). Research indicates that the risk for narcolepsy has been associated with the HLA narcolepsy-associated halotype, as a simple autosomal excessive trait, and a neurotransmitter system using hypocretin peptides (O'Hara et al., 2007). Risk is further increased for narcolepsy in individuals with genetic susceptibility who have a history of strep infections and exposure before age 21 years to smokers in the household.

Clinical Presentation

A sleep disorder may be the primary or secondary complaint presented by the client. Sleep-disordered clients frequently present with fatigue, the symptom of overwhelming and persistent tiredness, or inertia. Common sleep disturbances reported by elderly clients include spending more time in bed but sleeping less, having problems falling asleep, waking frequently during the night, and early morning awakening (Bloom et al., 2009). The presentation of symptoms is often the most important factor in the differential diagnosis. Many medical and mental disorders are associated with feelings of fatigue and are often the underlying cause for the problem. Clients with a related mental disorder may report problems getting restful sleep, problems falling asleep, problems staying asleep, and early morning awakening (Szelenberger & Soldatos, 2005). Sleep disturbances and disorders may be associated with pain, physical illness, and hospitalization or other environmental changes. The sleep disorder may be the primary subjective complaint of clients with stress-related physi-

CASE STUDIES Mr. T.

Mr. T., a 55-year-old man, came to the clinic complaining of fatigue. He stated that he found it difficult to get through a day of normal activity without feeling tired, and he just did not feel like himself at all. He stated that he felt as if he had a virus, but that he had no symptoms other than tiredness and listlessness. Mr. T.'s family medical doctor suggested that the cause might be depression after the client reported he was having problems managing at work and home. He had no history of medical problems, other than occasional sinus problems and headaches, and was taking no medications when he presented at the clinic. He had no history of psychiatric problems or drug or alcohol abuse. Mr. T. stated that he felt he was under a great deal of stress at work and was having more problems concentrating on the tasks at hand. He stated that his job was very demanding and required long hours. Although Mr. T. reported that he felt sad and irritable at times, and was less interested in activities at home and work, he said he did not feel particularly depressed. He had an increased appetite and had gained weight. He often felt drowsy at work, found himself nodding off, and would sometimes fall asleep sitting and watching television at night. He said that even with the daytime sleeping and napping, he just never felt rested.

Mr. T.'s wife stated she also felt that his problem was too much sleep and that he would be better off if he would just get up and do something. In contrast, Mrs. T. said she was the one who had problems sleeping, because Mr. T.'s loud snoring kept her awake. He often awakened her with what seemed to be gasping or choking noises or by sitting up in bed, but then he would quiet down again, lie down, and fall back asleep without seeming to awaken. She said he had always been a noisy and restless sleeper, but things had gotten worse as he had grown older. It had gotten to the point where she felt that separate beds or even a separate bedroom might be a good idea.

The initial clinical impression was a breathing-related sleep disorder. Asking the client's partner about sleeping habits gives valuable information. Questions regarding weight gain and increased collar size, other medical conditions or medication use could have been included in the nursing assessment. The client was referred for further medical evaluation and to a sleep disorder clinic. **Polysomnography**, diagnostic studies involving recordings of oximetry (oxygen saturation), breathing efforts and airflow, EEG, electromyography (EMG), electrooculogram (measurement of extraocular eye movements), and a combination of continuous positive airway pressure (CPAP) and non-CPAP trials would have aided in the differential diagnosis. Treatment of a possible obstructive sleep apnea syndrome involves evaluation, medical or surgical treatment of the breathing problem, CPAP, and weight loss.

Nursing Care Plan **Breathing-Related Sleep Disorder**

Nursing Diagnosis 1: Ineffective breathing pattern related to breathing-related obstructive sleep disorder as evidenced by snoring, disruption of sleep with episodes of apnea and frequent awakenings, weight gain, and excessive daytime sleepiness.

Nursing Diagnosis 2: Readiness for enhanced sleep related to sleep disorder as evidenced by complaints of not feeling rested.

Expected Outcomes	Interventions	Evaluations
• Will be able to demonstrate proper use of CPAP. • Will experience decreased snoring.	• Educate the client and partner on the proper use of CPAP. • Confirm with significant others their perception of the quality of the client's sleep.	• Observing for return demonstration in CPAP use. • Validating the adaptation to and ongoing use of CPAP at continued intervals.
• Will experience decreased daytime sleepiness. • Will begin participation in weight reduction program.	• Assess exercise and activity patterns. • Reinforce client participation in the weight reduction program.	• Taking reports of involvement in exercise program. • Monitoring involvement over time in a weight reduction program and maintenance of weight loss.

Visit http://go.jblearning.com/mentalhealth for additional care plans and exercises.

Mr. M. **CASE STUDIES**

Mr. M., a 55-year-old high school principal, was receiving short-term disability after knee surgery. He came to the emergency room complaining of an inability to sleep for 2 days. The problem had started approximately 2 months previously but was getting progressively worse. He was evaluated by the psychiatric clinical nurse specialist. Mr. M. stated that he had injured his knee playing tennis just before the start of the fall term and had been very nervous about the idea of surgery. At first, he thought the sleeping problems were a result of the pain he experienced and the surgery. However, the various sleep medications he used were unable to help him resume a normal sleep pattern. The client stated that he had been increasingly anxious and depressed since he had knee surgery. He said he felt as if his world were falling apart and that he was losing control of everything. Mr. M. stated that he did not know what was happening to him or how to stop it. He only knew that he felt humiliated by his inability to do anything about how he was feeling and that he was worried about everything. His worst fear, that he would never be normal again after surgery and would be permanently disabled, appeared to be coming true. He said he was particularly frightened by thoughts that his life was not worthwhile, that he had accomplished nothing, and that he would be better off dead. His wife reported that he had been increasingly dependent, had a decreased appetite with a 20-pound weight loss, and had experienced mood swings.

The client had been on various sleep medications for different periods and at different dosages over the previous 2 months, including lorazepam (Ativan), alprazolam (Xanax), buspirone (Buspar), clonazepam (Klonopin), and trifluoperazine (Stelazine). These were prescribed initially by his orthopedist, then by his family doctor, and later by a third doctor who was recommended by his managed care company. At the time he went to the emergency room, he was taking sertraline (Zoloft) and thioridazine (Mellaril) prescribed by a psychiatrist he had consulted as an outpatient 1 week before and oxazepam (Serax) prescribed by yet another physician to whom he was referred by his managed care company. His wife reported that for the previous week, with medications, Mr. M. had continued to have problems falling asleep. He would sleep approximately 2 hours after taking the medications and then sleep restlessly, often awakening in a panic-like state in which he would be agitated and ruminating on financial problems and unrealistic fears of losing his job. She described him as an independent, high-functioning man who never had a spare moment before the accident that led to his knee surgery but who since then seemed unable to do anything for himself. He had no history of psychiatric problems or drug or alcohol abuse.

The initial clinical impression is sleep disorder caused by a mental disorder (depression) that was complicated by polypharmacy. The nursing assessment can include information regarding medical and psychiatric history and validation of medication changes and actual use.

Nursing Care Plan **Insomnia Caused by Mental Disorder**

Nursing Diagnosis 1: Ineffective therapeutic regimen management related to polypharmacy as evidenced by multiple prescription medications.

Nursing Diagnosis 2: Disturbed sleep pattern related to depression as related to problems falling asleep and staying asleep.

Expected Outcomes	Interventions	Evaluations
• Will resume normal sleep patterns.	• Foster a safe environment conducive to sleep.	• Subjective reports of decreased fears surrounding falling asleep and staying asleep.
• Will decrease fears of falling asleep and staying asleep.	• Assess and observe sleep patterns.	• Development of normal sleep patterns.
• Will select and use appropriate sleep medications.	• Monitor pharmacotherapy.	• Decreased use of sleep medications/short-term use of medications.
• Will be able to fulfill normal occupational and social roles without impairment.	• Assist client in developing short- and long-term goals.	• Return to work without impaired functioning from insomnia.

Visit http://go.jblearning.com/mentalhealth for additional care plans and exercises.

Hypnagogic hallucinations are intense, dreamlike illusions that occur at the transition from wakefulness to sleep, just before falling asleep. Hypnopompic hallucinations are intense, dreamlike illusions that occur at the transition between sleep and awakening, just before awakening.

ologic changes or psychiatric disorders and may be the result of an affective or behavioral disorder, or of substance abuse, or a side effect of pharmacotherapy.

The nurse should determine if the client is getting too little or too much sleep. In addition, clients often complain of problems just before, during, or just after sleep, such as during preparation for sleep or the periods of time while just asleep or awakening. Environmental problems, situational disturbances, and recent changes in schedule or time, including travel, should be determined. Some clients' descriptions of difficulties focus on problems while sleeping (i.e., they may be aware of disturbances caused by sleep apnea, nightmares, or RLS). Family members may present additional clues by describing their observations of the client's sleeping patterns and domestic habits.

Clinical Course and Complications

Some people complain that they sleep too little and others that they sleep too much. The clinical course can vary according to the type of sleep disorder, the pattern of sleeping and wakefulness, and the individual's response to normal variations in sleep. Some complications are related to things outside our control such as familial tendencies or medical disorders and others to factors more within our control such as work and travel schedules.

Insomnia

Insomnia is characterized by difficulty initiating, maintaining, or experiencing restorative sleep. It is associated with increased arousal at night, anxiety, impaired daytime performance, and negative sleep conditioning (APA, 2000).

Insomnia may be temporary (associated with a rhythm-disrupting stress such as normal bereavement) or chronic. It may be related to a mental disorder, a general medical condition, or substance abuse. Chronic insomnia presents similarly to learned or psychophysiologic insomnia in that attempting to sleep becomes a struggle associated with excessive time spent in bed or trying to compensate for missed sleep (Bloom et al., 2009). Chronic insomnia may be complicated by the negative conditioning associated with psychophysiologic insomnia (APA, 2000). The medications used for insomnia occasionally cause or worsen insomnia.

Hypersomnia

Hypersomnia is characterized by excessive sleepiness at night or daily daytime sleep episodes, usually greater than 9 hours a day and often described as nonrestful or impairing daytime functioning. Hypersomnia is usually a chronic problem, but there are recurrent forms that last at least 3 days and occur several times a year for at least 2 years. Examples of recurrent forms of hypersomnia include problems of regulatory functioning such as Kleine-Levin syndrome, where the client may experience excessive sleep greater than 11 hours a day, and menstrual cycle–related symptoms of excessive sleep (APA, 2000). Complications of hypersomnia include sleep drunkenness (a state of confusion in which the client experiences a prolonged impaired state of alertness upon awakening) and automatic activity (a cognitive state in which the client engages in repetitive or stereotypic behaviors requiring little conscious thought) such as overeating.

Narcolepsy

Narcolepsy is characterized by hypocretin deficiency and repeated sleep attacks (irresistible, periodic, unintended urges to sleep that are temporarily relieved by sleep periods of 10–20 minutes but return approximately 2–6 times per day), **cataplexy** (sudden periods of loss of muscle tone lasting from seconds to minutes), and recurrent episodes of REM sleep at times of sleep–wake transitions demonstrated by hypnopompic or hypnagogic hallucinations or sleep paralysis (temporary inability to move or speak). Chronic daytime sleepiness is a symptom and complication of narcolepsy. Episodes of cataplexy are triggered by strong emotions and increased by sleep deprivation. Sleep attacks and cataplexy impair social and occupational functioning and can cause traumatic injury.

Breathing-Related Sleep Disorders

Breathing-related sleep disorders are characterized by the disruption of normal sleep cycles as a result of ventilation abnormalities leading to insomnia or, more frequently, hypersomnia. Daytime sleepiness, memory problems, and irritability are frequent complications. The disorder's frequency increases with age. The development of these disorders is usually chronic, progressive, and potentially life threatening.

Obstructive sleep apnea syndrome, central sleep apnea syndrome, and central alveolar hypoventilation syndrome are breathing problems identified as sleep-related breathing conditions. Obstructive sleep apnea hypopnea syndrome is associated with upper-airway structural abnormalities and obstructed respirations characterized by periods of loud snoring, gasps, silence, and body movements. It is more common among, but not limited to, heavy or overweight clients. Apneic periods resulting from airway obstruction usually last a few seconds. Central sleep apnea syndrome is characterized by periods of nonventilation or periods of Cheyne-Stokes respirations related to cardiac or neurologic problems without associated obstruction and loud snoring. Central alveolar hypoventilation is frequently seen in morbidly obese clients. It is associated with impaired ventilation with periods of decreased respirations lasting a few minutes, low arterial oxygen levels, increased carbon dioxide levels, and frequent arousals from sleep with breathing disturbances or bradytachycardia.

Circadian Rhythm Sleep Disorders

Circadian rhythm sleep disorders include disrupted sleep patterns related to alterations of typical circadian patterns, in contrast to external and environmental demands that lead to impaired cognitive, social, or vocational functioning. The client may have problems falling asleep or staying awake at appropriate times, and the disorder may be associated with acute or chronic disruptions. Circadian rhythm sleep disorders are most commonly associated with travel across time zones (**Figure 22-2**). In addition, most people who work odd shifts or who have to rotate shifts never fully adjust to these rhythm changes. Fatigue, decreased vigilance, and poor work/school performance can be related to circadian rhythm sleep disorders.

Figure 22-2 Airline travel can cause circadian sleep rhythm disorders.

Critical Thinking Question

What are some ways in which nursing organizations, professional nurses, and employers have dealt with the ethical responsibilities of guarding against fatigue in the workplace related to shift work and voluntary or mandated extended work hours?

Clinical Example

Dylan is a 20-year-old man with no known medical problems who was brought to the emergency department after being involved in a motor vehicle accident, apparently after having fallen asleep while driving. Although the toxicology screen in the emergency department was negative, staff reported that the patient had acted strangely and acted as if he were unable to move or speak. Staff on the medical unit reported the patient complained of hallucinations early the next morning when he was getting up. His family reported that he always seemed to fall asleep during the day and had recently lost a job because of this, although he seemed to get enough sleep at night. They described him as very clumsy and said he had a history of falls. Because of this he was very shy and avoided activities where he might be embarrassed because this only seemed to make things worse. A recent medical exam and neurologic workup for seizures were negative.

The term *pickwickian syndrome* came from a character (not Mr. Pickwick) in Charles Dickens's *The Pickwick Papers* who was repeatedly falling asleep. The term was used to describe obesity related to hypoventilation and hypersomnia (Burwell, Robin, Whaley, & Bikelman, 1956).

Parasomnias

Parasomnias, or disorders of arousal, are characterized by abnormal motor or physiologic behaviors that manifest during sleep. In confusional arousals, there can be repeated episodes of incomplete awakening without terror or ambulation. Nightmares and sleep terrors are usually accompanied by partial or complete awakenings. Nightmares are frequently associated with intense, frightening dreams during REM sleep that can be recalled by the client, who is easily awakened, and the nightmares are not usually associated with substance abuse, delirium, or other medical disorder or from posttraumatic stress disorder. Sleep

Nightmares are frightening dreams that can be recalled by the client. In sleep terror disorder the client experiences amnesia, and has little or no dream recall.

terror disorder is associated with a high degree of autonomic arousal, unresponsiveness to others, no clear dream recall, and amnesia for the episode of sleep terror. Sleepwalking disorder is characterized by arousal, usually during NREM sleep, and complex motor activities such as walking or attempting other tasks. The event is followed by amnesia. Parasomnias are disturbing for the client and others in the same environment and interfere with sleep and daytime functioning.

A multiple sleep latency test is used to differentiate narcolepsy from hypersomnia.

Differential Diagnosis

Many variations of normal and abnormal sleep exist among individuals of different health status, developmental stage, and environmental situation. A complete physical examination and mental status evaluation are essential for accurate differential diagnosis. Often the client's initial description of the complaint is incomplete or inaccurate, and it is helpful to obtain descriptions of the client's usual sleep habits and behaviors from others. A sleep history, a description of sleep behaviors over time, should be obtained. Sleep diaries or sleep logs also help differentiate the quality, quantity, and timing of sleep. In addition, psychophysiologic insomnia, the sleeplessness related to negative conditioning and learned sleep behaviors related to poor sleep hygiene, is common. Many clients with psychophysiologic insomnia report that their sleep improves when they are away from home (e.g., on vacation, in the sleep laboratory).

Many medical and mental disorders are associated with various sleep disorders, and identifying these factors is important in the differential diagnosis. These should be excluded before other sleep disorders are considered. Substances of abuse, therapeutic doses of pharmaceuticals, and exposure to toxins can contribute to sleep disorders. Carefully assess commonly associated problems before performing specific diagnostic tests for sleep disorders. For example, a client with a history of insomnia and travel across time zones probably has circadian rhythm disorder, whereas a client with a history of insomnia and depressive symptoms may have sleep problems resulting from a mood disorder rather than a primary sleep disorder.

Clients with medical problems such as diabetes, cardiovascular disease, gastric reflux, and prostate disease may also experience frequent nighttime arousals. Often medications, such as diuretics, or medication schedules that require nighttime awakenings or administration early in the day to avoid stimulating the client are the problem. If possible, symptoms should be controlled and medications evaluated to control for nighttime disturbances.

The diagnosis of RLS is often made based on the client's subjective experience of uncomfortable leg sensations that are particularly noted at bedtime and often relieved by movement. Clients often complain that these uncomfortable sensations prevent them from getting rest. Clients may experience problems falling asleep or experience arousals from sleep. Conversely, PLM disorder often does not wake the client; the suspected diagnosis is based on reports from others or is identified during polysomnography. The client may complain of muscle soreness or fatigue (Bloom et al., 2009; Smith & Tolson, 2008).

The multiple, simultaneous diagnostic tests taken during the client's normal sleeping period are termed *polysomnography*. Usually done in a sleep laboratory, the tests help differentiate sleep disorders. Differences in brain activity at varying sleep stages are determined by EEG to exclude various disorders and confirm the diagnosis. The client is monitored outside of the sleep laboratory or hospital setting using wrist actigraphy, an assessment tool (Bloom et al., 2009). Polysomnography helps confirm whether apnea is present. Physical examination is also important in differentiating breathing-related sleep disorders. For example, identification of excessive soft tissue obstructing the upper airway is symptomatic of obstructive sleep apnea syndrome. A **multiple sleep latency test (MSLT)** confirms the duration of sleep latency periods. MSLT is a diagnostic sleep test in which the client is encouraged to take multiple daytime naps, usually at 2-hour intervals, to determine average sleep latency and REM episodes. Daytime MSLT with shortened sleep latency periods or the appearance of REM sleep during repeated MSLT indicates narcolepsy and helps differentiate narcolepsy from the excessive daytime sleepiness of hypersomnia. Wrist actigraphy allows the client to ambulate and may be used outside of a sleep laboratory. It may also be used for differential diagnosis.

Management and Treatment

Anticipatory guidance, client education, and appropriate interventions are important to manage and treat sleep disorders. Psychophysiological or learned sleep disorders in particular are treated with behavioral therapies and changes in the sleep environment. Nonpharmacologic interventions such as cognitive and behavioral therapies should be used first. Information regarding normal sleep hygiene allays the client's fears and encourages active involvement in treatment planning (Townsend-Roccichelli, Sanford, & VandeWaa, 2010).

Critical Thinking Question

Describe several normal variations in sleep patterns that can have their basis in situational or maturational differences. Can you think of any cultural factors that may influence sleep habits?

Extrinsic and Intrinsic Factors

Modifying extrinsic factors, such as ventilation, lighting, and noise level in the sleep environment, or altering bedding or supports are the easiest changes to make. Changing individual routines by altering rest and activity patterns, decreasing the use of the bedroom and bed for activities other than sleep, changing the times of going to bed and awakening, and avoiding alcohol, caffeine, and other substances may be effective. Many clients find that a regular routine, perhaps including a light snack of turkey or milk which contain tryptophan and a warm, relaxing bath before bed, is helpful. Although strenuous exercise should be avoided because it is too stimulating, many clients, particularly those with RLS or PLM, find that some exercise or stretching routines are helpful prior to bedtime.

Intrinsic factors such as perceived stress or the inability to relax occasionally are relieved using complementary therapies such as aromatherapy, deep-breathing exercises, guided meditation, or progressive relaxation exercises to aid in relaxation. Clients also may be encouraged to get out of bed rather than struggle to sleep and to engage briefly in another activity such as reading or light housekeeping until they feel tired.

Normalizing Circadian Rhythm

Circadian rhythm sleep disorder (jet lag or time zone changes, shift work) is relieved when clients attempt to normalize their routine and expectations to fit the schedule and to adapt to the new time zone or shift time. Exposure to sunlight is desirable, especially upon awakening rather than prior to bedtime, and can be helpful in adjusting to different time zones. Full-spectrum lighting and melatonin also may be helpful in circadian rhythm disorders. Most studies suggest that shift rotation should be minimized. Many people do not adjust to shift work, and provisions for adequate rest periods both on and off the job occasionally help. Although parents and teachers may be frustrated by adolescents who go to bed late and want to sleep later in the day, studies indicate that teens have a normal but delayed sleep cycle and may benefit from changes in scheduling.

For most clients with sleep disorders, maintenance of a regular sleep routine and proper sleep hygiene is the first line of treatment. The evaluation and treatment of associated mental and medical disorders is secondary. All clients should avoid alcohol, drugs of abuse, and medications that can cause sleep disturbances. Pharmacologic interventions should be carefully evaluated and individualized.

Evidence-Based Practice

Clients given audio tapes with educational material on sleep and relaxation reported significantly fewer sleep problems when compared to the control group subjects (Williams & Schreiber, 2005). The tapes proved to be an effective educational tool, and the use of the diaries were helpful in self-monitoring behaviors. This study has implications for client education and nursing interventions.

Considerations for Client and Family Education

- Variations in sleep patterns are normal across the life span and often are temporary.
- Sleep medications are not the primary means of treating sleep problems and are meant to be used as prescribed, usually on a temporary basis.
- Examination of sleep habits, sleep hygiene, and change of patterns of behavior often provide long-term relief of sleep problems.
- Explain the benefits of avoiding caffeine, nicotine, alcohol, and large meals prior to going to bed.
- The administration of sleeping medications should be timed to avoid problems associated with participating in certain activities, such as use of machinery or driving.

Evidence-Based Practice

A study of hospital nurses indicated that suffering from sleep disorders, having night duties, and duration of natural light exposure were predictors of work stress; exposure to daylight for at least 3 hours a day was found to be a mitigating factor (Akunigkymu & Donmez, 2005). Although the authors suggest a larger and more cross-sectional sample size would be helpful, there are implications to nursing research for shift workers, prevention of burnout in nurses, and nurse retention.

Treating Underlying Disorders

Sleep disorders associated with medical or psychiatric disorders such as menopause, prostate problems, cancer, gastric reflux, fibrositis, breathing disorders, hypomanic states, depression, psychosis, and anxiety are helped by treating the underlying problems and disorders. For example, clients with a breathing-related sleep disorder such as obstructive sleep apnea find relief through surgery to relieve the obstructive airway or with CPAP. Laser surgery occasionally is used to cut away the soft tissue that may partially block air passages. Somnoplasty, in which an electrode is implanted in the soft palate and radio-frequency waves are used to heat tissue, causing it to shrink and tighten, is used as well. Treatment with CPAP by nose mask with low-pressure oxygen provides a pneumatic splint that prevents upper-airway collapse during inspiration and keeps the upper airway open. With CPAP, the nurse is often involved in teaching the client and monitoring home use in the early stages, in providing back-up services, in fitting the mask and assessing dentition and pressure levels, and in encouraging consistent use over time. Only distilled water should be used in machines requiring water. If the client with medical problems or psychiatric disorders is hospitalized, the nurse assesses the client; provides comfort measures such as promoting hygiene, providing back rubs, turning and positioning the client, and changing bed linens; maintains a therapeutic milieu; and sets limits by ensuring client safety, reducing stimuli, and ensuring adequate rest periods.

Pharmacology

Pharmacotherapy is often used alone or in combination with other management techniques to treat sleep disorders. Underlying medical and/or psychiatric disorders should be evaluated. Often clients report subjective improvement after the first night of good sleep. Many different types of medications are available (**Table 22-1**), and selection depends on whether they are used for short or long periods. Most medications have a similar time to onset but differ in duration of action. Sleep medications should only be taken before going to bed, and the client should be asked about the use of other medications, alcohol, and tobacco as well as possible pregnancy. Some medications, such as ramelteon (Rozerem), can be affected by grapefruit juice. One of the most commonly used medications for insomnia is zolpidem tartrate (Ambien, 5–10 mg), which is taken approximately 30 minutes before bedtime.

Evidence-Based Practice

An algorithm developed for use with sleep disorders in long-term care settings advised initiating an evaluation of medical problems and medications and a sleep history. It starts with nonpharmacologic aids and treatment of underlying problems, goes on to use sleep medications in conjunction with nonpharmacologic aids if the initial methods did not work, and finally monitors response (American Medical Directors Association, 2006). It would be useful to determine if this algorithm is effective across different settings.

Since most benzodiazepines and benzodiazepine derivatives differ in duration and pharmacokinetics, they are prescribed cautiously for clients with liver disease; long-term use is discouraged because they are associated with serious withdrawal effects and psychologic and physical dependence. Eszopiclone (Lunesta), a nonbenzodiazepine, is being studied for possible longer term use. Ramelteon, a melatonin receptor agonist that aids in sleep onset, has been approved for longer term use. Ramelteon should not be taken after a high-fat meal or with other CYPaA2, CYP2C, and CYP3A4 metabolizing drugs, for example fluvoxamine (Luvox), rifanpin (Rifadin), donepezil (Aricept), and azole antifungals such as ketoconazole (Nizoral), and fluconazole (Diflucan).

Older varieties of hypnotic medications such as chloral hydrate and barbiturates such as secobarbital and phenobarbital are rarely used because of the potential for misuse and addiction. Long-acting medications can accumulate with multiple doses and

Table 22-1 Common Sleep Medications

Drug Class	Medication	Selection Criteria
Melatonin receptor agonist	Ramelteon (Rozerem)	Approved for long-term use
Nonbenzodiazepine	Eszopiclone (Lunesta)	Approved for long-term use
Imidazopyridine	Zolpidem (Ambien)	High efficacy, low risk tolerance
Benzodiazepine	Temazepam (Restoril)	Short-term use, tolerance
	Flurazepam (Dalmane)	
Pyrazolopyrimidine	Zaleplon (Sonata)	Nonbenzodiazepine, low risk tolerance
Triazolopyridine	Trazodone	Low risk tolerance, moderate efficacy
Alprazolam	Xanax	See benzodiazepine
Salicylate	Aspirin	Pain relief, possible soporific effect
Alternative Medications		
5–hydroxytryptophan (5-HTP)	Tryptophan metabolite	Unpredictable, serotonin
Melatonin	Synthetic melatonin	Unpredictable response
Valerian	Valerian root	Unpredictable response, false-positive drug test
Other Medications		
Many antidepressants, particularly SSRIs, are used for sleep.		
Antidepressant	Amitriptyline (Elavil)	Anticholinergic side effects, low risk tolerance, helpful for neuropathy, pain
	Doxepin (Sinequan)	Low risk tolerance, helpful for neuropathy, pain
	Nortriptyline (Pamelor)	
Tetracyclic	Mirtazapine (Remeron)	Strongly antihistaminic, increased weight
Antihistamines are readily available and most are somewhat sedative.		
Antihistamine	Diphenhydramine (Benadryl)	Anticholinergic side effects, unpredictable, cause confusion
	Hydroxyzine (Atarax, Vistaril)	
Antianxiety medications are used for sleep.		
Anxiolytic (benzodiazepine and derivatives)	Clonazepam (Klonopin) Diazepam (Valium) Flurazepam (Dalmane) Lorazepam (Ativan) Oxazepam (Serax) Temazepam (Restoril)	Short-term use, high hypnotic efficacy, high risk tolerance, increase confusion
Antipsychotic medications are used for sedation.		
Antipsychotic	Chlorpromazine (Thorazine)	Anticholinergic side effects, low risk tolerance
Barbiturates are rarely used now because of the high risk of dependency.		
Barbiturate	Pentobarbital (Nembutal)	High hypnotic efficacy, high risk tolerance Potential for misuse and addiction
	Phenobarbital (Liminal)	As above
Nonbarbiturate	Chloral hydrate (Noctec)	High hypnotic efficacy, drug hangover
	Paraldehyde (Paral)	

Table 22-2 Nursing Interventions for Clients with Sleep Disorders

Nursing Diagnosis	Interventions	Rationales
Readiness for enhanced sleep	Assess for medical disorders that may interfere with sleep.	Many medical disorders including obstructive pulmonary disorders and sleep apnea can interfere with restful sleep. Patient may need to be referred for assessment of physical and pharmacologic causes of sleep disorder. If client uses CPAP or Bi-PAP, ensure that appliances and proper masks are available.
	Assess for pain and discomfort.	Pain and discomfort can interfere with restful sleep. Evaluation of pain and effects of pain medication can promote comfort and sleep.
	Assess medications and drug interactions.	Certain prescribed and over-the-counter medications can interfere with sleep.
	Assess client use of caffeine-containing substances.	Use of stimulants including caffeine can interfere with restful sleep.
	Assess client use of alcoholic beverages or substances of abuse.	Alcohol is used by many people to promote sleep as it is a depressant, but use of alcohol before sleep can promote sleep fragmentation. Commonly abused substances can interfere with sleep, as can intoxication and withdrawal.
	Prepare environment for sleep.	Comfortable bed, ambient temperature, and reduction in background noise and stimuli have been found to help promote sleep. Limit visiting during normal rest periods.
	Decrease environmental stimuli.	Light, noise, and activity have been found to affect sleep. Quiet time hours based upon normal circadian rhythms have been found to help promote restful sleep in hospitalized clients. If possible, reduce interruptions and awakening client for assessments and diagnostics during periods of rest.
	Discuss fundamentals of sleep hygiene with client.	Establishment of routine and preparation for sleeping has been found to promote sleep.
	Assess for concomitant mental disorders.	Problems with sleep are associated with many mental disorders particularly depression. Client may need referral for further evaluation and treatment.
	Teach use of self-mastery and relaxation techniques.	Deep breathing, relaxation techniques and guided meditation including use of prepared tapes and CDs can be helpful. Music can be used for relaxation and to block background noise.
	Encourage client to verbalize concerns regarding falling asleep and sleep.	Verbalization of feelings can help reduce anxiety. Feedback and cognitive control can be as effective as pharmacologic interventions.

Table 22-2 Nursing Interventions for Clients with Sleep Disorders *(Continued)*

Nursing Diagnosis	Interventions	Rationales
	Assess and evaluate use of sleep medications.	Sleep medications can be effective, particularly on a short-term basis.
	Evaluate for use of fall precautions.	Clients taking sleep medications can be at increased risk for falls.
	Observe patterns of sleep and discourage excessive napping.	Excessive daytime sleeping can interfere with ability to fall asleep at night.

may cause confusion, particularly in elderly clients with impaired ability to metabolize medications. Using antihistamines for sleep also may be problematic because of their anticholinergic properties and unpredictable results.

Some antidepressants are prescribed for administration at night because of side effects that may make the client sleepy. Mirtazapine (Remeron), a tetracyclic antidepressant, is usually taken at night and may be helpful for clients experiencing sleep difficulties by decreasing the amount of time it takes for them to fall asleep and increasing total sleep time. Tricyclic antidepressants occasionally are used. For example, low-dose doxepin (Sinequan) is sedating and good for neuropathic pain. However, these medications also have anticholinergic properties.

Symptoms of excessive daytime sleepiness and narcolepsy have been treated with modafinil (Provigil; Mitler, Hash, Hirshkowitz, & Guilleminault, 2000; Schwartz, Feldman, Fry, & Hash, 2002). An advantage is the low potential for abuse. This medication has also been approved for use in symptoms related to shift work and in clients being actively treated for sleep apnea. Psychostimulants that have been used for these symptoms include dextroamphetamine (Dexedrine), dextroamphetamine and amphetamine (Adderall), and methylphenidate (Ritalin, Ritalin SR). These medications have a high potential for abuse. Cataplexy has been treated with venlafaxine (Effexor) and, less often, with atomoxetine (Strattera). Atomoxetine should not be given with albuterol or with CYP2D6 inhibitors. Another medication used for cataplexy to promote deep sleep and limit frequent awakenings is sodium oxybate (Xyrem). This medication is related to GHB (gamma hydroxybutyrate) and has a potential for abuse. Sleepwalking has also been reported by some clients who have used sodium oxybate.

Treatment for PLM may involve L-dopa (Dopar), carbidopa (Lodosyn), clonazepam (Klonopin), or trazodone (Desyrel). Opioids, benzodiazepines and derivatives, dopaminergic agents, and antiepileptic agents have been used for RLS. Ropinirole (Requip) has been approved for treatment of RLS. Ropinirole has sedative side effects and can potentiate side effects of L-dopa and exacerbate dyskinesia. Dosage of ropinirole may need to be adjusted if used with other medications that affect CYP1A2 metabolism. Treatment for RLS may also include dietary iron or iron supplements and magnesium supplements or clonazepam (Smith & Tolson, 2008). Recommendations for over-the-counter quinine supplements have not been found to be effective, and off-label use for quinine sulfate was withdrawn by the FDA due to the possibilities of adverse hemolytic reactions and side effects from the use of quinine (FDA, 2009).

Many clients try herbal supplements. There has been some research regarding the effectiveness of melatonin and tryptophan for sleep. There is limited evidence that other popular herbal remedies such as valerian root, kava kava, and St. John's wort are effective for sleep problems. With all medications, whether over the counter (OTC) or herbal remedies or controlled or noncontrolled prescription medications, there is always the possibility of side effects and/or drug interactions.

Critical Thinking Question

What are some of the considerations regarding the use of prescription or OTC medications for sleep?

Summary

Sleep disorders are chronic disturbances in normal sleep patterns or behaviors that affect the amount, quality, timing, and stages or transitions of sleep and interfere with normal cognitive, physical, and psychosocial functioning. Sleep disorders include primary sleep disorders, sleep disorders related to another mental disorder, sleep disorders caused by a general medical condition, and substance-induced sleep disorder.

Primary sleep disorders include dyssomnias and parasomnias. Dyssomnias are disorders in initiating and maintaining sleep as well as problems associated with inadequate sleep (insomnia) and excessive sleep (hypersomnia). Narcolepsy is an example of dyssomnia. Parasomnias include disorders associated with sleep and sleep–wake cycles and transitions involving physical and behavioral manifestations. An example of parasomnia is sleepwalking disorder. Sleep disorders related to another mental disorder include sleep disorders attributed to a mental disorder such as anxiety (e.g., panic disorders), cognitive (e.g., dementia or delirium or both), mood (e.g., depression or mania or both), and psychotic (e.g., schizophrenia) disorders. An example is insomnia related to bipolar disorder, manic type. Sleep disorders caused by a general medical condition are those sleep disorders directly resulting from the physiologic effects of a known general medical condition (e.g., cancer, chronic obstructive pulmonary disease). An example is sleep disorder caused by Huntington's chorea, insomnia type. Substance-induced sleep disorder is related to drug use, intoxication, abuse, dependence, or withdrawal. Substances commonly associated with sleep disorders include alcohol, amphetamines, anxiolytics, caffeine, cocaine, hypnotics, opioids, and sedatives.

Management and treatment depend on a comprehensive assessment of the client's health status and sleep habits (**Table 22-2**). The nurse should ask about concomitant medical and psychiatric problems and any prescribed or OTC medications or supplements. Cognitive and behavioral therapies, environmental manipulations and supportive care measures, pharmacotherapy, and other complementary therapies, alone or in combination, are helpful in the treatment of common sleep disorders. When selecting the appropriate pharmacologic agent for intermittent, short- or long-term use, the clinician must consider its action, onset, duration, possible drug interactions, and side effects. The potential for abuse, tolerance, and psychologic or physiologic dependence also must be considered.

Annotated References

Akunigkymu, M. K., & Donmez, L. (2005). Daylight exposure and the predictors of burnout among nurses in a university hospital. *International Journal of Nursing Studies, 42*(5), 549–555.

The authors studied the effects of daylight exposure on sleep and burnout among hospital nurses.

American Medical Directors Association. (2006). *Sleep disorders*. Columbia, MD: Author.

The authors reviewed the evidence base for dealing with sleep disorders and developed an algorithm for dealing with sleep disorders in long-term care settings. Based upon expert consensus, the committee was composed of an interdisciplinary team including nursing input.

American Psychiatric Association. (2000). *Diagnostic and statistical manual of mental disorders* (4th ed., text rev.). Chicago, IL: Author.

This is the American Psychiatric Association's official nomenclature of psychiatric conditions and disorders. It provides a systematic listing of the official codes and categories, a description of the multiaxial system for diagnosis, and diagnostic criteria for each of the disorders. It is used by psychiatrists, physicians, psychologists, registered nurses, social workers, therapists, and other mental health workers in all clinical settings.

Attarian, H. P. (Ed.) (2006). *Sleep disorders in women from menarche through pregnancy to menopause: A guide for practical management*. Totowa, NJ: Humana Press.

This book reviews sleep problems in women and problems of gender in sleep research and treatment

Bloom, H. G., Ahmed, I., Alessie, C. A., Ancoli-Israel, S., Buysse, D. J., Kryger, M. H., … Zee, P. C. (2009). Evidence-based recommendations in the assessment and management of sleep disorders in older persons. *Journal of the American Geriatrics Society, 57*(5), 761–789.

This article discusses normal age-related sleep problems and disturbances and common sleep disorders. It provides a comprehensive overview of assessment and treatment problems. The article includes an excellent summary of complaints among elderly clients, underlying pathology, suggestions for assessment, and possible interventions.

Burwell, C. S., Robin, E. D., Whaley, R. D., & Bikelman, A. G. (1956). Extreme obesity associated with alveolar hypoventilation—a pickwickian syndrome. *American Journal of Medicine, 21*(11), 811–818.
This article discusses obesity as a factor in hypersomnia. Pickwickian syndrome, named for Mr. Wardle's boy, Joe, "a fat red-faced boy" who was a character in Charles Dickens's *The Pickwick Papers*, is another name for hypoventilation syndrome.

Caruso, C. C., Hitchcock, E. M, Dick, R. B., Russo, J. M., & Schmit, J. M. (2004). *Recent findings on illnesses, injuries and health behaviors.* (DHHS [NIOSH] Publication No. 204-143). Washington, DC: U.S. Department of Health & Human Services.
This publication reviews and summarizes 52 research studies on health behaviors and work performance.

Food and Drug Administration (FDA). (2009). Quinine sulfate (marketed as Qualaquin) off-label (not approved by FDA) use of quinine. *Post Market Reviews, 2*(2). Washington, DC: U.S. Food and Drug Administration.
Use of quinine is not recommended for restless leg syndrome due to potential side effects.

Institute of Medicine. (2006). *Sleep disorders and sleep deprivation: An unmet public health problem.* Washington, DC: The National Academies Press.
This publication discusses problems of sleep disorders and implications and recommendations for long-term goals for treatment.

Krueger J. M., Taishi P., De, A., Davis, C. J., Winters B. D., Clinton, J., … Zielinski, M. R. (2010, November). ATP and the purine type 2 X7 receptor affect sleep. *Journal of Applied Physiology, 109*(5), 1318.
This article reports on a study of ATP's role as a chemical trigger for the transition from wakefulness and sleep.

Mitler, M. M., Hash, J., Hirshkowitz, M., & Guilleminault, C. (2000). Long-term efficacy and safety of modafinil (Provigil) for the treatment of excessive daytime sleepiness associated with narcolepsy. *Sleep Medicine, 1*(3), 231–243.
Follow-up over 40 weeks of clients with narcolepsy who were treated with modafinil.

Montplaisir, J., Allen, R. P., Walters, A. S., & Ferini-Strambi, L. (2010). Restless legs syndrome and periodic limb movements during sleep. In M. H. Kryger, T. Roth, & W. C. Dement (Eds.), *Principles and practice of sleep medicine* (5th ed., pp. 1026–1037). Philadelphia, PA: W. B. Saunders.
This article discusses restless leg syndrome (RLS), which is often associated with neuropathies and periodic limb movement (PLM). Most clients with RLS will have PLM, but not all clients with PLM have RLS.

National Sleep Foundation. (2011). *2011 sleep in America poll: Communication technology in the bedroom.* Retrieved from http://www.sleepfoundation.org/publications
National poll of sleep habits and problems focused on the use of technology and its effect upon sleep.

O'Hara, B. F., Ding, J., Bernat, R. L., & Franken, P. (2007). Genomic and proteomic approaches towards an understanding of sleep. *CNS & Neurological Disorders-Drug Targets, 6*(1), 71–81.
The authors discuss research in roles of genes and protein control of sleep–wake states and their potential use in development of medications.

Schwartz, J. R. L., Feldman, N. T., Fry, J. M., & Hash, J. (2002). Efficacy and safety of modafinil in improving daytime wakefulness in clients previously treated with psychostimulants. *Sleep Medicine, 4*(1), 43.
Comparison of clients treated with modafinil showed efficacy and low potential for abuse or side effects.

Smith, J. E., & Tolson, J. M. (2008). Recognition, diagnosis, and treatment of restless leg syndrome. *Journal of the American Academy of Nurse Practitioners, 20*(8), 396–401.
This article reviews the assessment for restless leg syndrome and of pharmacologic and nonpharmacologic treatment options, including

stretching exercises and use of pneumatic leg compression devices.

Szelenberg, W., & Soldatos, C. (2005). Sleep disorders in psychiatric practice. *World psychiatry, 4*(3), 186–190.
The authors review incidence and prevalence of sleep disorders in clients with psychiatric illness and their presentation to sleep center and recommendations for research.

Townsend-Roccichelli, J., Sanford, J. T., & VandeWaa, E. (2010). Managing sleep disorders in the elderly. *Nurse Practitioner, 35*(5), 30–37, quiz 37–38.
The authors review sleep disorders and present the review in CEU format.

Williams, S. A., & Schreiber, A. M. (2005). The role of education in managing fatigue, anxiety and sleep disorders in women undergoing chemotherapy for breast cancer. *Applied Nursing Research, 18*, 138–147.
Subjects in an experimental group who were given an audio tape with information on sleep and relaxation had improved self-report and logs of sleep compared to a control group.

Additional Resources

Chokroverty, S. (2008). 100 questions and answers about sleep and sleep disorders. Sudbury, MA: Jones and Bartlett.
This text provides answers to common questions about sleep and is helpful for education for clients and families.

Kryger, M. H., Roth, T., & Dement, W. C. (Eds.). (2010). *Principles and practice of sleep medicine*. Philadelphia, PA: W. B. Saunders.

This comprehensive review of normal and abnormal sleep includes common sleep disorders and interventions.

Lee, K. A., & Ward, T. M. (2005). Sleep assessment guide. *Issues in Mental Health Nursing, 26*(7), 739–750.

This article provides a format for nursing assessment of sleep disorders that can be used with children or adults.

McKay, M., & Fannng, P. (2008). *Progressive relaxation and breathing* [Audio CD]. Oakland, CA: New Harbinger Publications, Inc.

This commercially prepared CD is an excellent example of the types of materials available for client education and treatment. The CD includes instruction in progressive relaxation techniques and autogenic exercises. Other CDs in the series include guided imagery, meditation and visualization, and relaxation techniques to help drift off to sleep.

Pandi-Permual, S. R., Ruoti, R., & Kramer, M. (2007). *Sleep and psychosomatic medicine*. London, England: Informa Healthcare.

This comprehensive text describes physiologic changes, medical conditions, and psychologic responses and behaviors associated with sleep and sleep disorders.

Internet Resources

For a full suite of assignments and additional learning activities, use the access code located in the front of your book to visit this exclusive website: http://go.jblearning.com/mentalhealth. If you do not have an access code, you can obtain one at the site.

Learning Objectives

After reading this chapter, you will be able to:

- Define impulse-control disorders.
- Describe the specific behaviors associated with these disorders.
- Discuss treatment modalities for these disorders.
- Identify nursing diagnoses and nursing interventions to assist clients with these disorders.
- Identify the teaching needs of clients and their families including available support and resource services.

Key Terms

Impulse-control disorders

Intermittent explosive disorder (IED)

Kleptomania

Pathological gambling

Pyromania

Trichophagia

Trichotillomania

Impulse-Control Disorders

Karen A. Ballard

http://go.jblearning.com/mentalhealth 

For a full suite of assignments and additional learning activities, use the access code located in the front of your book to visit this exclusive website: http://go.jblearning.com/mentalhealth. If you do not have an access code, you can obtain one at the site.

Introduction

Impulse-control disorders are categorized by the presence of uncontrollable and irresistible urges to engage in behavior that is potentially harmful or self-destructive to the client or others. The client continues the behavior despite the adverse outcomes and experiences extreme pleasure during the performance of the behavior (American Psychiatric Association [APA], 2000). These disorders include intermittent explosive disorder, kleptomania, pyromania, pathologic gambling, and trichotillomania (hair-pulling disorder). All of these disorders are coded on Axis I in the APA's *Diagnostic and Statistical Manual of Mental Disorders*, fourth edition, text revision (*DSM-IV-TR*) (2000).

The diagnostic criteria and classification of these disorders are being reconsidered by an expert panel involved in the preparation of the DSM-5. Pathological gambling may be grouped with the addictive disorders, and hair-pulling disorder may be classified as a type of obsessive-compulsive disorder. The proposed changes are based on improved understanding of the nature of these disorders. These disorders affect a significant number of adolescents and adults and result in serious life problems, including an increased risk of suicide. This chapter will present the characteristics and treatment of the impulse disorders, as well as nursing interventions appropriate to the care of clients with the disorders.

Impulse-Control Disorders

Five main impulse disorders:
Intermittent explosive disorder
Kleptomania
Pyromania
Pathological gambling
Trichotillomania (hair-pulling disorder)

There are five types of generally accepted impulse-control disorders, which are intermittent explosive disorder, kleptomania, pyromania, pathological gambling, and trichotillomania. Although these conditions appear dissimilar on the surface, they all are characterized by an experience or stimulus that is perceived by an individual as a challenge, threat, or potentially harmful.

According to the American Psychiatric Association (2000, p. 609), **intermittent explosive disorder (IED)** is characterized by "discrete episodes of failure to resist aggressive impulses resulting in serious assaults or destruction of property" that are expressed as unwarranted episodes of anger; **kleptomania** is characterized by "the recurrent failure to resist impulses to steal objects not needed for personal or monetary value"; **pyromania** is characterized by "a pattern of fire-setting for pleasure, gratification, or relief of tension"; **pathological gambling** is characterized by "recurrent and persistent maladaptive gambling behavior"; and **trichotillomania** is characterized by "recurrent pulling out of one's hair for pleasure, gratification, or relief of tension that results in noticeable hair loss." These disorders are generally underdiagnosed, and they can cause clients considerable emotional problems while negatively impacting family relationships, friendships, and the ability to function at work and school.

Critical Thinking Question

Impulse-control disorders are characterized by urges. What are the different types of urges associated with the five distinct disorders?

Incidence and Prevalence

The incidence and prevalence rates for the impulse-control disorders differ and in some conditions are not reliably known. Intermittent explosive disorder, absent of any other mental disorders or physical conditions, is generally considered to be fairly rare, occurring mostly in young males with low frustration tolerances. However, a study funded by the National Institute of Mental Health (NIMH) found, depending upon how broadly it is defined, intermittent explosive disorder may affect as many as 7.3% of adults (11.5–16 million Americans) in their lifetimes (Kessler et al., 2006). Kleptomania is also fairly rare, occurring in fewer than 5% of the individuals arrested for shoplifting, about 6 instances per 1,000 thefts, and is more common in females (Black & Andreasen, 2011). Because kleptomania results in an illegal act, it is probably underreported to practitioners by the client who is ashamed of the behavior. True pyromania is quite rare compared to single episodes of fire setting, which is observed in some children and adolescents in different developmental stages, or deliberate fire setting by an arsonist. Pyromania occurs more often in males with poor social skills and learning disabilities.

According to the National Gambling Impact Study Commission Final Report (1999), in any given year in the United States, there are between 1.8 and 2.5 million adult pathologic gamblers. Both the incidence and prevalence rates for pathological gambling may be as high as 3% of the adult population, and they are growing as gambling is legalized across the nation. In states where gambling has been legal for fewer than 10 years, 0.5% of the adult population has been classified as probable pathologic gamblers; in states where gambling has been legal for more than 20 years, 1.5% of the adults have been classified as pathologic gamblers, with women and minorities at greatest risk for acquiring the disorder (APA, 2000). Approximately one third of pathologic gamblers are women (Schreiber, Odlaug, & Grant, 2011), yet they are underrepresented in treatment programs. While the mean age for onset of pathological gambling is 30 (Grant & Kim, 2001), the behavior may begin in adolescence and has many characteristics of addiction, with individuals either displaying patterns of addiction from the beginning or having a long history of progressive addiction. See **Table 23-1** for behaviors that indicate a problem with gambling.

Trichotillomania (impulsively pulling out one's hair) is thought to affect 1% to 2% of the population (Odlaug & Grant, 2010). It is found equally in male and female children but persists into adulthood in more women than men. Most afflicted clients report a childhood onset (APA, 2000; Black & Andreasen, 2011).

Table 23-1 **Gambling Assessment**

If one answers "yes" to any of the following statements, one should seek professional help:

- You have often gambled longer than you had planned.
- You have often gambled until your last dollar was gone.
- Thoughts of gambling have caused you to lose sleep.
- You have used your income or savings to gamble while letting bills go unpaid.
- You have made repeated, unsuccessful attempts to stop gambling.
- You have broken the law or considered breaking the law to finance your gambling.
- You have borrowed money to finance your gambling.
- You have felt depressed or suicidal because of your gambling losses.
- You have been remorseful after gambling.
- You have gambled to get money to meet your financial obligations.

Source: National Council on Problem Gambling (2007).

Etiology

There are few studies on the etiology of impulse-control disorders. In the past, these disorders were thought to result from psychodynamic conflicts. More recently, however, the focus is on understanding the neurobiology of these disorders. The neurobiologic etiology for the impulse disorders is not well understood, but certain brain structures—including the limbic system, which is linked to emotions and memory, and the frontal lobe, the part of the brain's cortex linked to planning functions and controlling impulses, are thought to affect the disorder. Specific biologic changes have been identified in persons with the disorders. Electroencephalogram (EEG) changes, abnormal serotonin metabolism in cerebrospinal fluid, and abnormal findings in neurologic and psychologic screenings (reversal of letters, mirror movements, poor coordination) have been associated with intermittent explosive disorder. Research suggests a relationship between pathologic gambling and abnormalities of the noradrenergic system, particularly the dopamine system. This is supported by the evidence that dopamine replacement therapy for the treatment of Parkinson's disease can cause pathologic gambling and other impulse-control disorders (Reiff & Jost, 2011).

Impulse disorders are underdiagnosed; they can cause clients considerable emotional problems and negatively impact family relationships, friendships, and the ability to function at work or school.

Individuals with trichotillomania do not have any known underlying dermatologic disorders; however, skin biopsies have shown short and broken hair shafts, with damaged or deeply pigmented hair follicles. Clients experience a tingling sensation in the scalp, but the skin usually shows no signs of significant inflammation or disease (APA, 2000; Black & Andreasen, 2011).

The high incidence of comorbidity between the impulse-control disorders and other Axis I mental disorders, primarily mood disorders, substance abuse, and anxiety disorders, lends further support to a neurobiologic basis for impulse disorders (Schreiber et al., 2011; Spitzer, Gibbon, Skodol, Williams, & First, 2002). In addition, it is not unusual that first-degree family members share the impulse disorder or a diagnosis of one of the comorbid mental disorders associated with the impulse disorders.

Clients with intermittent explosive disorder describe these episodes as spells or attacks and report a period of tension prior to the aggressive explosion, followed by a sense of relief and remorse.

Clinical Presentation

Intermittent Explosive Disorder

Individuals with intermittent explosive disorder report having spells or attacks of explosive, aggressive behavior. The explosive episode is usually preceded by a period of tension or arousal, and after the explosion the client reports a sense of relief coupled with remorse, regret, and embarrassment. The aggressive event is usually disproportionate to the precipitating cause, and the episodes recur (Lion, 1992; Spitzer et al., 2002). Some episodes of road rage, throwing and breaking objects during angry outbursts, and domestic violence may indeed be caused by this disorder.

Kleptomania

Clients with kleptomania know that their behavior is wrong. They usually steal items that they do not need and often can afford and then discard the stolen items.

Clients who admit to kleptomania are aware that the behavior is wrong. They often steal items that they do not need or could easily afford to buy, frequently giving or throwing them away after the event. The client experiences a period of increasing tension prior to the stealing episode and feels pleasure, gratification, and relief during the episode. Kleptomania is a solitary event. Individuals with kleptomania do not purposely put themselves into a stealing episode that will likely result in arrest. Stealing as a result of kleptomania is not done in anger, for revenge, or in response to hallucinations or delusions. In some respects, kleptomania is similar to obsessive-compulsive disorder; both disorders involve irresistible, uncontrollable urges, and the stealing episode frequently appears to have a ritualistic pattern (McElroy, Pope, Hudson, Keck, & White, 1991; Spitzer et al., 2002).

Clinical Example

Amy has been taking objects from stores on and off for almost 10 years without being discovered. One day on a visit to Chicago, she finds herself in an exclusive women's accessory store. While there Amy becomes increasingly tense and finds herself repeatedly returning to a display of brightly colored scarves. Finally, she can no longer stand the tension and she grabs a handful of scarves and stuffs them into her handbag. Amy almost immediately experiences relief from the tension and leaves the store. Store security arrests her outside the store. She is embarrassed and unable to explain why she took the scarves. Since there is no previous criminal record, Amy is placed on probation and required to attend counseling and a 12-step program.

The euphoria associated with pathological gambling is similar to a substance-induced high.

Individuals with trichotillomania usually pull the hair out of their scalps. Other areas for pathologic hair pulling are eyebrows, eyelashes, axilla, and the pubic and perirectal areas.

Clients with pyromania are often fascinated with fire houses, fire-fighting equipment, and uniforms. They may even become fire fighters.

Pyromania

Clients with pyromania report multiple episodes of fire setting. This is different from the young child whose fascination with fire results in a single, albeit potentially dangerous, fire-setting episode. These individuals report tension prior to setting the fire, an almost uncontrollable attraction to remaining near the fire, perhaps participating in putting out the fire or assisting in rescue attempts. In pyromania, fire setting is not done for money, in defense of any particular ideology, as a result of impaired judgment, or in response to hallucinations or delusions. Clients with pyromania are usually fascinated with fire houses, fire-fighting equipment, and uniforms and may even become fire fighters. Arsonists set fires for monetary gain and do not fit into this category of impulse-control disorder (Soltys, 1992; Williams, 2002).

Clinical Example

Evan's mother has asked for an appointment with the school psychologist to discuss his obsession with fires. She shares that after his recent 12th birthday party, she found him setting fire to the party favors and throwing them up into the air. Apparently, Evan has been caught by his family playing with matches or lighters several times since he was about 6 years old. His mother reports that his most prized possession is a volunteer firefighter's badge that his uncle gave him. When the psychologist interviews Evan, he finds that he gleefully talks about fires that he has set or times that he has played with matches in the home without being caught. He brags that he is good at putting fires out. Not surprisingly, Evan wants to be a firefighter when he is older. The psychologist recommends both individual and family therapy.

Pathological Gambling

Pathologic gamblers report an ever-increasing loss of control over their behavior. The course of this disorder very closely resembles addictions such as alcoholism. Clients report preoccupation with thoughts about gambling such as what the last bet felt like and planning for the next gambling opportunity. They report that they are after the action more than the money, and that it takes larger and larger bets to produce the euphoria associated with the gambling event (very similar to the addict's substance-induced high) (Spitzer et al., 2002; Volberg, 1994).

Trichotillomania

Clients with trichotillomania pull hair out of any part of the body (scalp, eyebrows, eyelashes, axilla, and

Clinical Example 

David is a successful, middle-aged lawyer who was recently caught diverting funds from a client's trust fund. It turns out that he has been increasingly gambling, with losses over $100,000. David borrowed $50,000 from a loan shark and desperately needed cash to meet this debt because he was being threatened. He is embarrassed and readily admits to his wrongdoing, stating that he cannot control himself. His mother mortgaged her house to allow him to return the lender's money. David is placed on probation by the court, given community service, told to attend Gamblers Anonymous meetings, and reported to the bar association for unethical behavior.

the pubic and perirectal areas). The most common area is the scalp. The actual act of hair pulling can last seconds or hours. Clients report that stress can precipitate hair-pulling episodes and that they also pull out their hair when relaxed and watching television, at a movie, or involved in a pleasurable activity. Some individuals experience tension just before pulling out the hair and others as they seek to resist pulling the hair. All report feelings of relief, gratification, and pleasure during the hair-pulling episode. Clients usually are not completely bald but have discrete bald spots or patches and may be missing all or some of their eyebrows and eyelashes (Christenson, Mackenzie, & Mitchell, 1991; Woods et al., 2006). In a study of 1,697 individuals with this disorder, 34.6% with severe hair pulling reported daily interference with occupational tasks, and 48.7% reported avoiding social situations, such as dating or participating in group activities (Woods et al., 2006). Clients with trichotillomania often report feelings of low self-esteem.

Differential Diagnosis

In intermittent explosive disorder, it is imperative to determine that the episodes are not related to underlying physical conditions such as brain tumors or to neurologic problems secondary to trauma such as an automobile accident. This disorder is excluded for individuals whose explosive, aggressive episodes are related to delirium, dementia, alcohol or substance abuse, conduct disorder, personality disorder, manic episode, or schizophrenia.

Kleptomania is not ordinary thievery or shoplifting, which are deliberate acts of taking something that belongs to someone else. Kleptomania is rare, whereas thievery and shoplifting are common and annually cost the economy millions of dollars. Kleptomania needs to be distinguished from obsessive-compulsive disorder, antisocial personality disorder, and conduct disorder.

Arson or intentional fire setting for profit, protest, terrorism, or to attract attention is not pyromania. Fire-setting episodes that occur secondary to conduct disorder, manic episode, antisocial personality disorder, or in response to a delusion or hallucination also are not pyromania and should not be so classified.

Arson is intentional fire setting for monetary gain or revenge; it is not pyromania.

Individuals can engage in social gambling with friends and in professional gambling as an occupation and not be pathologic gamblers. Gambling episodes occurring in relationship to manic episodes or by individuals with antisocial personality disorder are not classified in this category.

Hair pulling associated with delusions, hallucinations, stereotypic movement disorder, and factitious disorder is not trichotillomania. Physical causes of alopecia (hair loss) should be excluded (alopecia areata, male pattern baldness, and lupus erythematosus). Some children engage in a time-limited developmental phase of twisting, tugging, and pulling at their hair. This time-limited behavior should be treated as a temporary habit, not as trichotillomania.

Clinical Course and Complications

For most individuals, the course of an impulse-control disorder requires a lifetime of attention to controlling the abnormal behavior. Some of these disorders, such as intermittent explosive disorder and pyromania, have the potential for significantly injuring others; therefore, maintaining the safety of others and of the client is a primary concern for the psychiatric nurse and other practitioners. When hospitalized, these individuals need to be monitored carefully to prevent aggressive outbursts or fire-setting episodes that may harm other clients or staff. Many individuals with impulse-control disorders find themselves alienated from their families, in difficulty with the legal system, even incarcerated, and not tolerated at work or in school and social situations. Individuals with intermittent explosive disorder have a high rate of hospitalization secondary to unsafe behaviors such as reckless driving and violent physical fights. Some individuals with trichotillomania eat their hair (**trichophagia**) and develop hair balls, nausea and

Some clients with impulse disorders have the potential to significantly injure others, so maintaining the safety of the client and others is a primary concern for the psychiatric nurse.

vomiting, abdominal pain, and bowel perforation (Christenson, Mackenzie, & Mitchell, 1991; Lion, 1992; Soltys, 1992; Woods et al., 2006).

Critical Thinking Question

What types of behavior should alert a nurse that a client with an impulse-control disorder might harm him- or herself or others? What would be an appropriate nursing intervention?

Management and Treatment

Intermittent Explosive Disorder

The plan of care for clients with intermittent explosive disorder can include maintaining a journal, meditation, imagery, using time-outs, developing treatment contracts, exercise programs, teaching conflict management, and the use of medication.

For individuals with intermittent explosive disorder, safety for self and others is an important treatment goal. Clients should be taught to recognize when they are feeling angry and explosive and to identify the stress that produces these feelings. The next step is to help them identify ways of controlling these impulses and the concurrent angry feelings and behaviors. Individual and group therapy can assist the client in understanding these behaviors and developing personal strategies for coping and maintaining control. Since this type of behavior has probably alienated family members, family therapy sessions focused on improving the functioning of the family unit are probably essential to reintegrating the client into the family unit. Clients in outpatient care should be monitored carefully for failure to comply with the treatment plan and for return of violent behaviors.

Short-term drug therapy with mood stabilizers, SSRI antidepressants, or beta blockers is sometimes prescribed to help in alleviating some of the tensions or aggressive impulses associated with intermittent explosive disorder. There is not enough research to conclusively recommend any one pharmacotherapeutic treatment approach for intermittent explosive disorder (Schreiber et al., 2011).

Pyromania in adults is treated with individual psychotherapy focusing on the underlying anger, revenge, or sexual stimuli of the irresistible urges and learning alternative and adaptive behaviors for coping with the stress.

In covert sensitization, a behavioral approach to the treatment of kleptomania, the client is guided in associating images of nausea and vomiting with the desire to steal.

Kleptomania

There is little in the literature describing successful interventions and management of kleptomania. The client's shame and guilt associated with the behavior often keep it hidden from the practitioner. Individual psychotherapy is recommended to assist the client in dealing with the underlying guilt and need for punishment, and in maintaining control over destructive aggression and addressing behavior changes (Reid, Balis, & Sutton, 1997; Williams, 2002). Some behavior therapists recommend covert sensitization, a process in which the client is guided to associate images of nausea and vomiting with the desire to steal, or establishing a contract with the client in which the client agrees to be accompanied by others during all shopping activities. There has been some recent interest in using antidepressants such as fluoxetine (Prozac) to provide relief for these overwhelming urges (Black & Andreasen, 2011). Self-help recovery groups can be successful in supporting the individual to resist the urge (Shulman, 2005). Evidence indicates that the opioid antagonist, naltrexone (ReVia), should be the first line of treatment for kleptomania (Schreiber et al., 2011).

Pyromania

True pyromania in adults is treated with individual psychotherapy with a focus on understanding the underlying anger, revenge, or sexual stimulus of the urges and learning alternative and adaptive behaviors to cope with the resulting stress. All fire-setting behaviors must be treated seriously because the potential for harm to others is so grave. In children and adolescents, a variety of strategies are used to interrupt the maladaptive fire-setting behavior. The practitioner usually treats this as a family problem and works with the parents to deal with any family issues that might have led to the fire-setting episode and to discuss nonpunitive methods of discipline. In addition, the child or adolescent and the family can be engaged in a mastery program that teaches cause and effect as well as how to restrain the uncontrollable "internal fire."

Local fire departments frequently have programs that teach families and children how to ignite and extinguish actual fires properly. Children are assisted in repeatedly starting and extinguishing fires, with adult supervision, in appropriate places such as barbecues and fireplaces. Some programs link fire setters with firefighters in a type of Big Brother program; others bring children and adolescents to burn units to see the effects of fire on people's bodies (Reid et al., 1997; Williams, 2002). The rate of success of treatment is higher in children than in adults.

Pathological Gambling

Treatment of pathologic gambling is usually multifaceted, including individual psychotherapy, family therapy, aversive conditioning, and a 12-step program. Individual psychotherapy appears to be more successful with this impulse control disorder than with any of the others. Therapy focuses on helping the gambler understand the reasons for gambling and dealing with the feelings of helplessness, depression, and guilt. It is important for the client to identify the psychosocial factors or stressors that trigger gambling behaviors and learn how to either avoid them or deal with them more appropriately. Twelve-step programs help the gambler establish a new life without the addictive behavior of gambling being in control. Many clients describe the high that gambling brings them and report having the same sensation with drug and alcohol use; indeed, some clients experience withdrawal symptoms when faced with mandatory abstinence as part of the therapy (Meintz & Larson, 1994; Williams, 2002). Family therapy is particularly important because the lying, cheating, abuse, mistrust, and financial problems created by the behaviors of the pathologic gambler have alienated the family. For real recovery to take place, the family must learn to trust the client again, heal the emotional hurts, and learn to use more effective communication skills with each other and more appropriate coping behaviors.

Research on the effectiveness of the SSRI antidepressants for the treatment of pathological gambling suggests they might be useful for clients who have a subtype of the disorder that is related to obsessive-compulsive disorder, but not for clients with an addictive type of gambling (Iancu, Lowengrub, Dembinsky, Kotler, & Dannon, 2008). One study of the mood stabilizer lithium carbonate (Eskalith, Lithobid) showed promising results (Hollander, Pallanti, Allen, Sood, & Rossie, 2005). The opioid antagonist, naltrexone (ReVia), has had more positive than negative results and may be effective for clients who have a family history of substance abuse (Grant, Kim, & Hartman, 2008).

Pathological gambling affects the individual, similar to how alcohol and substance abuse affects an addict, with rushes, highs, withdrawal symptoms, and the need to abstain to control the disorder.

Trichotillomania

The most common type of treatment for trichotillomania is behavior therapy that focuses on hair pulling as a bad habit. Simple behavioral techniques such as positive feedback for more adaptive behavior and mild aversive conditioning (e.g., snapping a rubber band on one's wrist instead of hair pulling) have good results. Individual psychotherapy addresses the cli-

CASE STUDIES

www

Ms. C.

Ms. C., a 26-year-old graduate student, came to the college clinic in the middle of the spring semester. She was tearful and hesitant, unable to communicate the true nature of her problem to the nurse practitioner. She stated, "I need help with my head." In response to gentle questioning by the nurse, Ms. C. elaborated that she did not know how she was going to interview for jobs after graduation with her head looking like it did. The nurse practitioner noticed that Ms. C. had a pretty scarf wound around her head. With encouragement, Ms. C. removed it, and the nurse practitioner observed multiple circular patches of missing hair that created a polka-dot effect. In addition, Ms. C. had no eyebrows and very sparse eyelashes. She told the nurse practitioner that she had seen many physicians over the years but that no one had been able to cure her problem. After a thoroughly obtained history and assessment, the nurse practitioner was satisfied that there was no underlying physical condition causing the hair loss.

With support and encouragement, Ms. C. eventually agreed to be evaluated at a local mental health clinic. During her evaluation, Ms. C. spoke glowingly of her family and how they had often urged her to seek help for her bad habit. She recounted that her parents had taken her to dermatologists, but none of the prescribed treatments had worked. She could not remember exactly when she started pulling her hair out, but said that she remembered always playing with it and that at some point in her early teens, the playful tugging became actual pulling. She said her worst time in high school was when some of the boys started to tease her and call her "Dottie"; that was when she started wearing hats and scarves that coordinated with her outfits.

Ms. C. agreed to try a course of medication and to attend twice-weekly therapy sessions until the end of the semester. After 3 weeks, she reported feeling better and was not pulling at her hair as often but felt that she could not stop the behavior. Her therapy focused on improving self-esteem so that she would be successful in her job-hunting process and on encouraging her to seek ongoing therapy when she returned to her hometown. Ms. C. understood that her problem was long-standing and that there was no quick fix. With her parents' assistance, a psychotherapist near her home was identified and contacted.

Nursing Care Plan **Trichotillomania (Hair-Pulling Disorder)**

Nursing Diagnosis: Ineffective coping related to persistent urges, stress, and anxiety evidenced by hair pulling as well as hair loss.

Expected Outcomes	Nursing Interventions	Evaluations
• The client will understand the relationship of specific stressors to feelings and actions.	• Assess the client and family for all types of impulse-control disorders or obsessive-compulsive disorder. • Ask the client to recall situations that trigger the behavior.	• Shares with treatment staff that as a child she thought that her behavior was normal because her older brother also had bald spots as a result of hair pulling, and he outgrew it.
• The client will experience a reduction in level of anxiety and episodes of hair pulling.	• Listen empathetically to the client's thoughts regarding her feelings and what she experiences before, during, and after a hair-pulling episode.	• Discusses how angry she has been with her parents for forcing her to attend college and to get steady work when all she has ever wanted to do was to be a landscaper and to work outside making the environment beautiful.
• The client will utilize alternative coping behaviors.	• Teach relaxation techniques. • Provide positive feedback when client uses more adaptive coping behaviors. • Encourage the use of mild aversive conditioning techniques (band snapping) when the urge to pull hair occurs.	• Successfully uses some of the suggested relaxation techniques. • Reports fewer symptoms such as abdominal pain. • Increasingly uses more appropriate coping behaviors. • Learns self-hypnosis to control the hair-pulling episodes.
• The client will participate in individual and group psychotherapy.	• Discuss the importance of participating in therapy sessions.	• Attends all scheduled sessions as an inpatient.
• The client will follow a medication regimen.	• Review the medication regimen and associated education with the client on a daily basis.	• Takes medication as prescribed and can successfully repeat information about the medication schedule and the specific drug information.
• The client will understand the need for ongoing therapy after discharge from the inpatient unit.	• Discuss the importance of continuing therapy as an outpatient.	• Signs a discharge treatment plan to continue treatment modalities as an outpatient. • Accepts information about self-help support groups.

Visit http://go.jblearning.com/mentalhealth for additional care plans and exercises.

Evidence-Based Practice

Studies into the understanding of such forces as motivation, reward, and addiction have provided new insight into the causation and pathophysiology of substance and behavioral disorders. There appears to be a strong neurobiological link between substance abuse disorders and such behavioral addictions as pathologic gambling, kleptomania, pyromania, compulsive buying, and compulsive sexual behavior. Improved understanding of the relationship of these disorders and their frequent co-occurrence can assist practitioners in improving treatment strategies for intervening with these clients (Grant, Brewer, & Potenza, 2006).

Considerations for Client and Family Education

Nurses should encourage clients with impulse-control disorders to recognize the feelings, tensions, and stressors that produce the particular behaviors. Clients can be helped to recognize those controls within themselves, in their family relationships, and in the community that help them manage the impulse-control behavior. Nurses should discuss with the client the importance of continuing therapy (psychotherapy, family therapy, complementary therapies, 12-step programs, and medications) even when the specific symptom appears controlled. The client must recognize that control is linked directly to the therapy, and noncompliance with therapy can easily cause a relapse. Families and significant others should be advised how to intervene and whom to call if the behaviors become self-destructive or potentially harmful to others. Nurses can discuss complementary therapies such as massage, relaxation, meditation, imagery, exercise, and aversive conditioning with clients. Clients and families should be assisted in recognizing that controlling these behaviors is often a lifelong challenge.

ent's low self-esteem, family relationships, and correction of false beliefs (e.g., no one likes the client because of the hair loss) (Black & Andreasen, 2011). Some success in helping the client substitute behaviors, and self-hypnosis can be taught to the client for support between therapy sessions (Reid et al., 1997). The medication most successful in treating this disorder has been the tricyclic clomipramine (Anafranil). Studies of escitalopram (Lexapro), a selective serotonin uptake inhibitor, found it was no more effective than a placebo (Schreiber et al., 2011). Unfortunately, recurrence of this disorder is common and can be precipitated by a variety of physical and emotional stressors.

Nursing Interventions for Clients With Impulse-Control Disorders

The following are some activities that the psychiatric nurse and other practitioners can consider:

- Encouraging the client to keep a journal to help identify specific people, times, or events that act as triggers for the behavior
- Teaching relaxation techniques, such as meditation and imagery to establish control, and how to use personal time-outs as a means of escaping stress or gaining control (**Figure 23-1**)
- Developing treatment contracts focusing on the expectations for and consequences of certain behaviors
- Encouraging participation in regular exercise programs
- Teaching the client how to manage conflict

An individual with an impulse-control disorder responds best to a combination of these suggested interventions. **Table 23-2** presents nursing interventions and rationales for nursing diagnoses that might apply to clients with impulse-control disorders.

Critical Thinking Question

Why are 12-step programs often helpful in treating patients with impulse-control disorders?

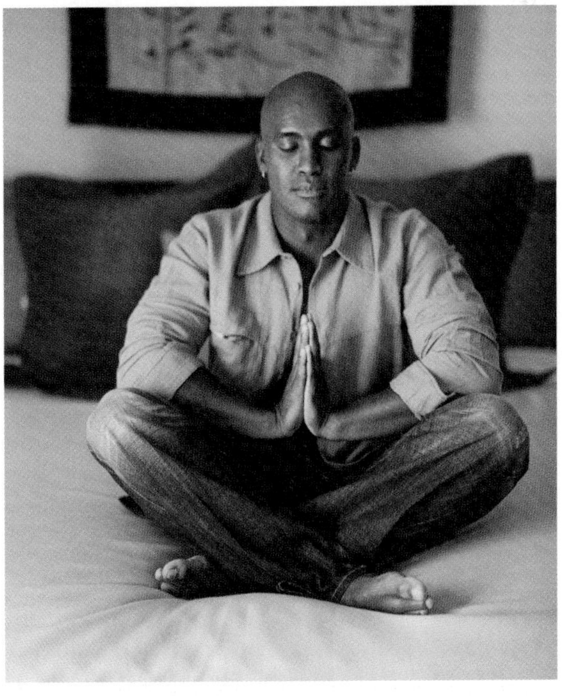

Figure 23-1 **Meditation is one technique for controlling intermittent explosive disorder.**

Table 23-2 Nursing Interventions for Clients with Impulse Control Disorders

Nursing Diagnoses	Nursing Interventions	Rationales
Risk for self-injury and other directed violence	Inform the client on admission that harm to self, others, or property is unacceptable. Tell the client that staff members are willing to assist through multiple means to help the client gain control (medication, time-outs, quiet areas). Remove potentially dangerous items. Remove the client from excessive environmental stimuli.	Clear limit setting and rules can reassure the client of safety. Establishes the nurse and staff as allies; provides support for what seems daunting to the client; frames interventions as therapeutic and helpful, not punitive. Safety is a primary concern. A calm environment can help reduce aggressive feelings.
	If the client appears to be about to lose control, nurses should interrupt the behavior immediately by any appropriate means (seclusion, restraint)	Preventing injury is a primary concern; discuss possible use of restraint or seclusion in advance; identify behaviors that can help reduce the need for these interventions; only use them for safety, not punishment.
Ineffective coping	Assist the client to recognize feelings or events that precipitate behaviors; keeping a diary or log. Reinforce all efforts made by clients to exert appropriate internal controls over behavior. Assist clients to identify how maladaptive impulsive behavior is not in their best interest. Provide alternative channels for expression of feelings such as exercise, journaling, meditation. Establish a standardized, consistent staff response plan for any client's impulsive behavior.	Increases self-awareness and is the initial step to introducing alternative behaviors. Reinforcement (praise and recognition) increases the appropriate behaviors. The client's recognition of problems will increase motivation to change; it is more effective than being told what the problems are by someone else. New behaviors can interrupt the impulse to carry out problem behavior. To successfully limit problem behavior, all staff must know which behaviors are unacceptable and give a consistent response.
Chronic low self-esteem	Approach the client with an accepting, nonjudgmental attitude. Address the client by name in the manner preferred by the client. Spend time with the client. Assist the client to identify strengths and accomplishments. Involve the client in decisions and strategies to change behavior.	Communicates respect and helps build trust and confirms client's worth. A client with low self-esteem may not be able to recognize or value his or her own strengths; this challenges negative self-assessment. The client can then take credit for changes and increases his or her likelihood of success.

Summary

Although each of the impulse-control disorders has unique behavioral characteristics, they share the presence of uncontrollable urges to perform potentially harmful or self-destructive behaviors. These disorders are generally underdiagnosed. Clients with impulse-control disorders have considerable emotional problems and behaviors that negatively impact on family relationships, friendships, and the ability to function at work or school. Treatment consists of a combination of behavioral, supportive and pharmacologic therapies. Nursing interventions focus on building trust, communicating acceptance, identifying precipitants to urges and behaviors, recognizing underlying feelings, setting limits in a clear and consistent manner, teaching alternative methods of coping, and reinforcing reduction in the problem behaviors and the use of more effective coping strategies.

Annotated References

American Psychiatric Association. (2000). *Diagnostic and statistical manual of mental disorders* (4th ed., text rev.). Washington, DC: Author.

This is the fourth edition of the American Psychiatric Association's official nomenclature of psychiatric conditions and disorders. It provides a systematic listing of the official codes and categories, a description of the multiaxial system for diagnosis, and diagnostic criteria for each of the disorders. It is used by psychiatrists, physicians, psychologists, registered nurses, social workers, therapists, and other mental health workers in all clinical settings.

Black, D. W., & Andreasen, N. C. (2011). *Introductory textbook of psychiatry* (5th ed.). Washington, DC: American Psychiatric Press.

This is a basic psychiatric medical textbook. It is simple, clear, and factual and can be used by students of medicine, nursing, psychology, social work, and other counselors and therapists.

Christenson, G., Mackenzie, T., & Mitchell, J. (1991). Characteristics of sixty adult chronic hair pullers. *American Journal of Psychiatry, 148*, 365–370.

This article carefully reviews the characteristics and histories of 60 individuals with prolonged experiences of hair pulling.

Grant, J. E., Brewer, J. A., & Potenza, M. N. (2006). The neurobiology of substance and behavioral addictions. *CNS Spectrums, 11*(12), 924–930.

This article discusses the biochemical, functional neuroimaging, genetic studies, and treatment research that suggest a strong neurobiologic link between behavioral addictions and substance use disorders.

Grant J. E., & Kim S. W. (2001). Demographic and clinical features of 131 adult pathological gamblers. *Journal of Clinical Psychiatry, 62*(12), 957–962.

One hundred thirty-one subjects with *DSM-IV* pathologic gambling were interviewed to elicit demographic data and information on the phenomenology, age at onset, course, associated features, treatment history, and response to treatment of the disorder.

Grant, J. E., Kim, S. W., & Hartman, B. (2008). A double-blind, placebo-controlled study of the opiate antagonist naltrexone in the treatment of pathological gambling urges. *Journal of Clinical Psychiatry, 69*(5), 783–739.

This study examined the efficacy and tolerability of the opioid antagonist naltrexone in adults who have urges to gamble.

Hollander, E., Pallanti, S., Allen, A., Sood, E., & Rossi, N. (2005). Does sustained-release lithium reduce impulsive gambling and affective instability versus placebo in pathological gamblers with bipolar spectrum disorders? *American Journal of Psychiatry, 162*(1), 137–145.

The first placebo-controlled treatment study in pathological gamblers with bipolar spectrum disorders, the study compares sustained-release lithium carbonate to placebo.

Iancu, I., Lowengrub, K., Dembinsky, Y., Kotler, M., & Dannon, P. N. (2008). Pathological gambling: An update on neuropathophysiology and pharmacotherapy. *CNS Drugs, 22*(2), 123–138.

This paper presents theories of the neuropathology of pathologic gambling and a literature review of current pharmacologic treatment strategies for pathologic gambling.

Kessler, R. C., Coccaro, E. F., Fava, M., Jaeger, S., Jin, R., & Walters, E. (2006). The prevalence and correlates of DSM-IV intermittent explosive disorder in the National

Comorbidity Survey Replication. *Archives of General Psychiatry, 63*(6), 669–678.
This article reports that intermittent explosive disorder is a much more common condition than previously recognized. It also states that the early age at onset of IED behaviors, the significant associations with comorbid mental disorders, and the current low proportion of cases in treatment all make IED a promising disorder for early detection, outreach, and treatment.

Lion, J. R. (1992). The intermittent explosive disorder. *Psychiatric Annals, 22*, 64–66.
This article extensively explores the specific characteristics and treatments associated with uncontrolled outbursts of aggressive behavior.

McElroy, S., Pope, H., Hudson, J., Keck, P., & White, K. (1991). Kleptomania: A report of twenty cases. *American Journal of Psychiatry, 148*, 652–657.
This article provides unique insight into the behaviors and characteristics of individuals with this rarely studied disorder. It focuses on demographics, phenomenology, psychopathology, and family and treatment histories.

Meintz, S., & Larson, C. (1994). Can you spot this kind of addiction? *RN, 75*(7) 42–45.
This article discusses the increase in pathologic gambling behaviors nationally and how nurses can easily monitor for the development of this problem and intervene in the early stages.

National Council on Problem Gambling. (2007). 10 questions about gambling behavior. Retrieved from http://www.ncpgambling.org/i4a/pages/Index.cfm?pageID53439
This is a listing of 10 questions that can be answered by "yes" or "no" to assess whether gambling is a problem for an individual.

National Gambling Impact Study Commission Final Report. (1999). Retrieved from http://govinfo.library.unt.edu/ngisc/reports/fullrpt.html
This is a report to Congress on the status of gambling in the United States by a presidential commission. It reviews the expansion of gambling in the nation, types of gambling, the regulation of gambling, the problems with gambling and pathologic gambling, the impact of gambling on people and places, and recommendations for future research.

Odlaug, B. L., & Grant, J. E. (2010). Impulse-control disorders in a college sample: Results from the self-administered Minnesota Impulse Disorders Interview (MIDI). *Primary Care Companion to the Journal of Clinical Psychiatry, 12*(2), p. ii: PCC.09m00842
This study sought to examine the prevalence rates of and gender differences among impulse-control disorders in a college sample.

Reid, W. H., Balis, G. D., & Sutton, B. J. (1997). *The treatment of psychiatric disorders* (3rd ed.). Bristol, PA: Brunner/Mazel.
This psychiatric textbook specifically addresses mental disorders as classified in the APA's manual. There is a particular emphasis on neuropsychiatric disorders, substance-related disorders, and disorders of childhood and adolescence.

Reiff, J., & Jost, W. H. (2011). Drug-induced impulse control disorders in Parkinson's disease. *Journal of Neurology, 258*(Suppl 2), S323–S327.
This paper reports on findings that excessive or aberrant dopamine receptor stimulation causes impulse-control disorders in persons being treated for Parkinson's disease.

Schreiber, L., Odlaug, B. L., & Grant, J. E. (2011, February 21). Impulse control disorders: Updated review of clinical characteristics and pharmacological management. *Frontiers in Psychiatry, 2*(1). doi:10.3389/fpsyt.2011.00001
This article presents a brief overview about the clinical characteristics of ICDs and pharmacologic treatment options for individuals with ICDs.

Shulman, T. (2005). *Something for nothing: Shoplifting addiction and recovery.* Haverford, PA: Infinity Publishing Company.
This book presents shoplifting or kleptomania as an addiction rather than an impulse disorder and focuses on shoplifting recovery groups as the primary intervention in the behavior.

Soltys, S. (1992). Pyromania and firesetting behavior. *Psychiatric Annals, 22*, 79–83.
This article seeks to explain the motivation and behaviors of individuals who set fires.

Spitzer, R., Gibbon, M., Skodol, A. E., Williams, J. B. W., & First, M. B. (2002). *DSM-IV-TR Casebook: A learning companion to the Diagnostic and Statistical Manual of Mental Disorders* (4th ed.). Arlington, VA: American Psychiatric Publishing, Inc.
This book presents real-life case vignettes illustrating presentations of the diagnoses in *DSM-IV-TR.*

Volberg, R. (1994). The prevalence and demographics of pathological gamblers: Implications for public health. *American Journal of Public Health, 84*(2), 237–241.
This article explores the potential impact of continued legalized gambling on the overall rate of gambling problems in the general population and in specific at-risk groups.

Williams, J. (2002). *Pyromania, kleptomania, and other impulse-control disorders.* Berkeley Heights, NJ: Enslow Publishers.
This book describes the characteristics of impulse-control disorders, the possible genetic, developmental, and chemical causes and methods of treatment.

Woods, D. W., Flessner, C. A., Franklin, M. E., Keuthen, N. J., Goodwin, R. A., Stein, D. J., . . . Trichotillomania Learning Center-Scientific Advisory Board. (2006). The Trichotillomania Impact Project (TIP): Exploring phenomenology, functional impairment and treatment utilization. *Journal of Clinical Psychology, 67*(12), 1877–1888.
This is an article on the results of an Internet-based survey of self-selecting individuals who met the *DSM-IV-TR* criteria for trichotillomania.

Internet Resources

For a full suite of assignments and additional learning activities, use the access code located in the front of your book to visit this exclusive website: http://go.jblearning.com/mentalhealth. If you do not have an access code, you can obtain one at the site.

Learning Objectives

After reading this chapter, you will be able to:

- Differentiate between personality traits and personality disorders.
- Name the types of personality disorders.
- Identify the traits and behaviors associated with each personality disorder.
- Describe therapeutic nursing interventions to assist clients who have personality disorders.
- Develop a nursing care plan for a client with a personality disorder.

Key Terms

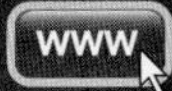

Antisocial personality disorder

Avoidant personality disorder

Borderline personality disorder

Cognitive restructuring

Dependent personality disorder

Dialectical behavior therapy (DBT)

Histrionic personality disorder

Narcissistic personality disorder

Object constancy

Obsessive-compulsive personality disorder

Paranoid personality disorder

Personality disorder

Personality traits

Schizoid personality disorder

Schizotypal personality disorder

Separation-individuation process

Splitting

Chapter 24

Personality Disorders

Patricia G. O'Brien

http://go.jblearning.com/mentalhealth 

For a full suite of assignments and additional learning activities, use the access code located in the front of your book to visit this exclusive website: http://go.jblearning.com/mentalhealth. If you do not have an access code, you can obtain one at the site.

Introduction

Dominant behavioral patterns or personality traits that become pervasive and problematic may meet the diagnostic criteria for a personality disorder. In the American Psychiatric Association's *Diagnostic and Statistical Manual of Mental Disorders*, fourth edition, text revision (*DSM-IV-TR*), personality disorders are classified on Axis II and are distinguished from the major mental disorders classified on Axis I (APA, 2000).

Personality traits differ from personality disorders. Personality traits are enduring patterns of perceiving, relating to, and thinking about oneself and one's environment that are exhibited in a range of social and personal contexts. Only personality traits that are inflexible and maladaptive and cause significant functional impairment or personal distress constitute personality disorders. A **personality disorder** is an enduring pattern of inner experience and behavior that deviates markedly from the expectations of the individual's culture, is pervasive and inflexible, has an onset in adolescence or early adulthood, is stable over time, and leads to distress in important areas of functioning (APA, 2000, p. 686).

Everyone at one time or another exhibits behaviors that characterize the various personality disorders. A person must have functional impairment as a result of the behaviors to actually be diagnosed with a personality disorder.

A personality change that appears suddenly in response to a life situation is not diagnosed as a personality disorder. This holds true even though the change may be problematic, such as increased dependency after the death of a spouse. A personality disorder can coexist with an Axis I diagnosis, but the major features of some mental disorders, such as schizophrenia and anxiety disorders, are more properly associated with the primary diagnosis rather than a personality disorder.

Types of Personality Disorders

The *DSM-IV-TR* identifies 10 specific personality disorders and 1 additional category for a personality disorder not otherwise specified. The personality disorders are organized into 3 clusters that define the predominant characteristics of the disorders. A pattern of behaviors is associated with each of the personality disorders (APA, 2000).

Cluster A

Cluster A includes odd or eccentric behavior. A person with **paranoid personality disorder** is distrustful and suspicious and tends to interpret others' motives as malevolent. Those with **schizoid personality disorder** are detached from social relationships and have a restricted range of emotions. Persons with **schizotypal personality disorder** experience acute discomfort in close relationships, have cognitive or perceptual distortions, and demonstrate eccentric behavior.

Cluster B

Cluster B includes dramatic, emotional behavior. People with **antisocial personality disorder** disregard and violate the rights of others. A person with **borderline personality disorder** has unstable interpersonal relationships, self-image, and affect, as well as marked impulsivity. Those with **histrionic personality disorder** have excessive emotions and are attention seekers. Clients with **narcissistic personality disorder** are grandiose, need admiration, and lack empathy.

Cluster C

Cluster C consists of anxious, fearful behavior. People with **avoidant personality disorder** have social inhibition, feelings of inadequacy, and hypersensitivity to negative evaluation. Clients with **dependent personality disorder** are submissive, and their clinging behavior is related to an excessive need to be cared for. Those diagnosed with **obsessive-compulsive personality disorder** are preoccupied with orderliness, perfectionism, and control.

Not Otherwise Specified

Personality disorder not otherwise specified does not meet the full criteria for any one personality disorder. Rather, it has the features of more than one personality disorder that causes significant impairment in functioning.

Significant reformulations of the assessment and diagnosis of personality disorders have been proposed for the APA's *DSM-5*, anticipated for publication in 2013. The proposal would limit the number of personality disorders to six: antisocial, avoidant, borderline, narcissistic, obsessive-compulsive, and schizotypal. According to the current recommendation, the criteria for personality disorders will be based on three assessments: personality functioning related to self and interpersonal disturbances, type of personality disorder, and the degree that behaviors match one or more dimensions of personality traits. It is anticipated that the changes will allow for more specific diagnoses and thereby contribute to both treatment and research (APA, 2011).

Incidence and Prevalence

The prevalence of personality disorders is difficult to determine because the diagnosis of personality disorder varies with cultural norms, because people may display symptoms of more than one personality disorder, and because not all people who meet the diagnostic criteria for a personality disorder enter the treatment system. It is estimated that 9–16% of the general population meets the criteria for one or more personality disorders (Black & Andreasen, 2011). The percentage is significantly higher among psychiatric populations, especially those in inpatient settings. Persons with obsessive compulsive disorder have a very high incidence of personality disorders, especially the cluster C anxious type disorders. The incidence of antisocial personality disorder among psychiatric inpatients ranges from 3% to 30%; the highest frequency is seen among clients diagnosed with substance abuse disorder.

Borderline personality disorder accounts for 30–50% of all people diagnosed with personality disorder (Smallwood, 2004). Paranoid personality disorder is found in 1–30% of psychiatric inpatients, and dependent personality disorder is most prevalent among clients followed in mental health clinics.

The impression that borderline personality disorder is more prevalent in women than in men and antisocial personality disorder more prevalent in men may be attributed to a gender bias in diagnosing the disorders. No actual gender differences have been identified for the personality disorders (Reichborn-Kjennerud, 2010), and, specifically, there is no evidence that borderline personality disorder is more common in women (Leichsenring, Liebing, Kruse, New, & Leweke, 2011).

Personality disorders are usually diagnosed in adolescents and young adults. Although traits suggestive of some personality disorders, including paranoid, schizoid, and schizotypal types, may be seen in children, these traits may change as the child progresses to adulthood. Therefore, children are rarely diagnosed with personality disorders. The diagnosis of antisocial personality disorder is made only if the client is at least 18 years of age.

Nurses are likely to encounter clients with personality disorders in all healthcare settings and clinical specialties.

Etiology

Developmental Factors

A variety of conceptual frameworks for understanding personality development were introduced in Chapter 1, including Sullivan's interpersonal theory, Erikson's psychosocial theory, and Freud's psychoanalytic theory. An interruption in the normal course of psychologic and emotional development or a failure to achieve the defined tasks associated with individuation are thought to contribute to the development of personality disorders. Mahler, Pine, and Bergman (1975) described the individuation process as a series of phases through which the individual progresses during the first 3 years of life. Each phase is associated with a primary task (**Table 24-1**).

The child must successfully complete the **separation-individuation process** to develop effective relationships with significant others. A disruption in any of the tasks may predispose one to the development of a personality disorder. The separation-individuation process is based on object relations theory,

Although developmental stages are usually presented in a stepwise, orderly fashion, the phases actually overlap because individuals mature at different rates.

Table 24-1 Phases of Individuation

Age	Phase	Task
Birth–1 month	Autistic phase	Waking–sleeping
1–5 months	Symbiotic phase	Fusion with mother
5–10 months	Differentiation phase	Awareness of separateness between self and mother
10–16 months	Practicing phase	Increased independence and exploration of the environment
16–24 months	Rapprochement phase	Becomes fearful of separation from mother and seeks closeness
24–36 months	Object constancy phase	Completes the individuation process

Source: Adapted from Mahler, Pine, & Bergman, 1975.

Splitting is a hallmark of borderline personality disorder.

an offshoot of psychoanalytic theory. The theory is concerned with interpersonal relationships, and *object* refers primarily to another person. Relationships are experienced as positive or negative. The goal of development is to eventually integrate the positive and negative associations and develop the capacity to recognize and tolerate both loving and hostile feelings toward the same object or person. This is referred to as **object constancy**. According to object-relations theory, borderline personality disorder is due to a failure to master the rapprochement phase, leading to a fear of abandonment evidenced by clinging, dependent behavior, and an inability to achieve object constancy (Kernberg, 1976). This manifests as a tendency to view others as all good or all bad. This phenomenon, referred to as **splitting**, is considered a hallmark of borderline personality disorder. Splitting behaviors can be challenging and nursing approaches are discussed later in this chapter.

Freud theorized that specific personality disorders can be matched with a fixation at a particular stage of ego development. Fixation at the oral stage was thought to result in dependent personality disorder. Fixation at the anal stage was associated with OCD, and fixation at the phallic stage was matched with histrionic personality disorder. However, there is little evidence that fixation at a particular stage of development leads to a specific personality disorder.

With an increased understanding of neuroscience and genetics, research on the etiology of personality disorders has shifted the focus from developmental theories toward neurobiologic factors.

Environmental Factors

The events and sequences that result in personality pathologies are complex and difficult to unravel.

The inadequate achievement of early developmental tasks has been attributed to environmental factors such as emotional deprivation or inconsistent parenting. The relationship between the environment and the development of personality disorders is not clearly understood, and we are becoming better informed about the role of neurobiology in the etiology of personality disorders. Thus, it is essential to avoid harshly judging or blaming the parents of clients with personality disorders. Many consumer and mental health advocacy groups, including families of clients with personality disorders, are working with professionals to understand better what influences the development of these disorders.

The relationship between early prolonged, severe trauma and the development of borderline personality disorder remains unclear and is an area of continuing research (Goodman, New, & Siever, 2004). While sexual abuse has been identified as a contributing factor in borderline personality disorder, a sizable minority (20–45%) of individuals diagnosed with the disorder report no history of sexual abuse, and most people (80%) with a history of sexual abuse do not demonstrate personality disorders (Foti et al., 2011). Humiliation and emotional trauma also have been related to paranoid personality disorder. Exposure to trauma may interfere with the development of trust and intimacy and result in an inability to modulate emotions.

Biogenetic Factors

Genetic epidemiologic studies indicate that all 10 personality disorders are modestly to moderately heritable, with the genetic factors being related to negative emotions, impulsivity, and introversion (Reichborn-Kjennerud, 2010). Familial links between some of the personality disorders and the Axis I mental disorders are further evidence of a genetic basis. An increased incidence of schizotypal personality disorder is seen among the relatives of persons with schizophrenia, and a familial link exists between paranoid personality disorder and paranoid schizophrenia. Persons with borderline personality disorder have a high incidence of comorbidity with major depressive disorder.

The emotional deficits and traits, including impulsiveness, avoidance, and aggression, that are associated with personality disorders may be the result of genetically mediated alterations in the neurotransmitter pathways, especially the serotonergic and dopaminergic systems. The impulsive aggression associated with borderline personality disorder has been attributed to deficits in the neurotransmitter serotonin, as well as to changes in the prefrontal cortex and reduced volume of the hippocampus and amygdala (Leichsenring et al., 2011; Sala et al., 2011; Siever, 2009). There is evidence that difficulties in interpersonal negotiation and cooperation in persons with borderline personality disorder may be biologically based, specifically related to decreased neural activity in the anterior insula, an area of the brain known to respond to violations in social norms (King-Casas et al., 2008). There is also evidence that impaired social understanding in persons with antisocial personality disorder is genetically based (Langley, Heron, O'Donovan, Owen, & Thapar, 2010).

The neurobiologic study of personality disorders is still in its infancy and has the potential to influence knowledge, diagnosis, and treatment of these disorders.

Clinical Presentation

The APA (2000) offers broad criteria to identify personality disorders as well as criteria specific to the individual personality disorders.

Diagnostic Criteria

The general diagnostic criteria for personality disorder aid in distinguishing a personality disorder from personality traits, an Axis I mental disorder, or an organically based personality change (**Table 24-2**).

Additional Criteria

The *DSM-IV-TR* provides additional criteria that establish the diagnosis of each of the recognized personality disorders (APA, 2000). These criteria focus on behaviors that characterize the disorder and help inform the nurse's assessment. Behaviors associated with each personality disorder are identified in the following sections, as are the likely functional areas in which the client may be experiencing distress.

Table 24-2 **Diagnostic Criteria for a Personality Disorder**

1. A pattern of behavior that includes at least two of the following:
    - Thought disturbances, including how one perceives and interprets him- or herself, others, and events
    - Mood disturbances, including the range, intensity, lability, and appropriateness of one's emotions
    - Troublesome interpersonal relationships
    - Impulsive behavior
2. These behaviors
    - Have their onset in adolescence or early adulthood
    - Deviate from expected cultural behavior
    - Are enduring, inflexible, and extend across a range of personal, social, and occupational situations
    - Cause significant distress
    - Are not a manifestation of another mental disorder
    - Are not due to a medical condition, a medication, or other substance

Source: Adapted from American Psychiatric Association, 2000.

Paranoid Personality Disorder

Clients with paranoid personality disorder are often difficult to get along with because of their argumentative, sarcastic, and often hostile manner of relating to others. Not surprisingly, their behavior elicits a negative response in others that only serves to justify their actions to themselves. Clients with paranoid personality disorder have a fundamentally suspicious view of the world that makes them view the simple mistakes of others as deliberate intentions to cause personal harm. These people usually have problems establishing and maintaining close relationships and often are guarded during interviews, making it difficult for the nurse to obtain a personal history.

Paranoid personality disorder begins in early adulthood.

Few people with personality disorders display the traits of only the one disorder with which they have been diagnosed. Typically, people exhibit traits belonging to several of the defined personality disorders.

Schizoid Personality Disorder

Clients with schizoid personality disorder have a profound inability to form personal relationships, even with members of their immediate family. Even as children or teenagers, these clients were viewed as different by their peers, perhaps teased by others, and often described as underachievers. As adults they seem indifferent to others, lack close friends, and show little interest in sexual relationships or marriage. However, not all loners have schizoid personality disorder. According to the general criteria, the diagnosis requires that the traits be inflexible and maladaptive, causing significant impairment or subjective distress. These clients may be referred for treatment resulting from difficulties in an occupational setting.

Schizotypal Personality Disorder

Clients with schizotypal personality disorder also have paranoid features and are socially isolated but can be distinguished from clients with paranoid and schizoid personality disorder by the presence of cognitive and perceptual distortions. These distortions may take the form of magical rituals, excessive superstitions, and their belief that they can influence events through their thoughts. They are frequently described by others as odd or eccentric and may have inappropriate emotional responses in social situations. Clients with this disorder exhibit no desire for relationships and typically describe a severe social anxiety that worsens rather than abates over time. The assessment must exclude a concurrent major depressive disorder that is commonly seen with this personality disorder.

Antisocial Personality Disorder

In order to be diagnosed with antisocial personality disorder, clients must be at least 18 years of age and have displayed some evidence of a conduct disorder before 15 years of age. Early symptoms include a display of aggression toward people or animals, destruction of property, deceitfulness or theft, and a violation of rules. This pattern of behavior continues into adulthood and is characterized as guiltless, exploitative, and irresponsible. These clients show little regard for others and make use of a superficial charm to deceive and manipulate others for personal gain (e.g., power, money, sex). The assessment may reveal clues to this disorder, such as a dishonorable military discharge, a criminal record, serial or multiple sexual relationships, frequent physical altercations, and an inability to support oneself. A family history is not uncommon, nor is the coexistence of major depression or substance abuse.

People with antisocial personality disorder may enter treatment through the forensic system.

Borderline Personality Disorder

Borderline personality disorder behavior is unstable, and hospitalization is often precipitated by self-inflicted injury or a suicide attempt.

Clients with borderline personality disorder (see **Table 24-3**) have a fear of abandonment that results in unstable and intense interpersonal relationships. These clients often sabotage close relationships or even pending successes, fearing their inability to meet the demands of the situation. Sudden anger is a way of avoiding another person's rejection. Mood instability and intense anger characterize this disorder. The history often reveals that these clients have seen multiple therapists because they cannot tolerate risking the rejection that accompanies a close interpersonal relationship. These clients describe feeling empty and have a history of self-mutilating and suicidal behavior. Borderline personality disorder also has a familial pattern and is associated with an increased incidence of depression and substance abuse. **Figure 24-1** displays the relationship among the various symptoms and behaviors associated with borderline personality disorder.

Although persons with borderline personality disorder can improve over time, often the improvement is noted in some symptoms, while other symptoms persist. Comparisons between younger and older persons being treated for borderline personality disorder found that older clients were less likely to experience problems related to impulsivity and suicidal behavior, but symptoms related to emotional distress (depression, anxiety, anger) were more consistent across age groups. Studies of the personality disorder in later life could yield information about the impact of the disorder on health, social relations, marital adjustment, the handling of life events and transitions, and longevity (Oltmanns & Balsis, 2011).

Table 24-3 **Diagnostic Criteria for Borderline Personality Disorder**

A pervasive, enduring pattern of behavior beginning by early adulthood and present in a variety of contexts, as indicated by five or more of the following:

1. Frantic efforts to avoid abandonment
2. Unstable and intense interpersonal relationships characterized by alternating between extremes of idealization and devaluation
3. Unstable self-image or sense of self
4. Impulsiveness in at least two areas that are potentially self-damaging (e.g., spending, sex, substance abuse, reckless driving, binge eating)
5. Recurrent suicidal acts, gestures, or threats or self-mutilating behavior
6. Marked mood swings (e.g., intense episodic dysphoria, irritability, or anxiety)
7. Chronic feelings of emptiness
8. Inappropriate, intense anger
9. Transient paranoid ideation or dissociative symptoms

Source: Adapted from American Psychiatric Association, 2000.

Histrionic Personality Disorder

Clients with histrionic personality disorder express their emotions very theatrically and dramatically. Their need for attention often interferes with establishing significant relationships. A superficial quality characterizes their approach to both people and projects. Initial enthusiasm is rapidly replaced with boredom, making a commitment to long-term goals difficult. They have an inordinate need to impress others with their appearance and engage in attention-seeking behaviors, including seductiveness and somatization.

Narcissistic Personality Disorder

Clients with narcissistic personality disorder convey a grandiose sense of self-importance and feel entitled to preferential treatment. They talk about themselves at length, neglecting the feelings of others. Interpersonal relationships and work performance may be impaired by an extreme need for admiration and an

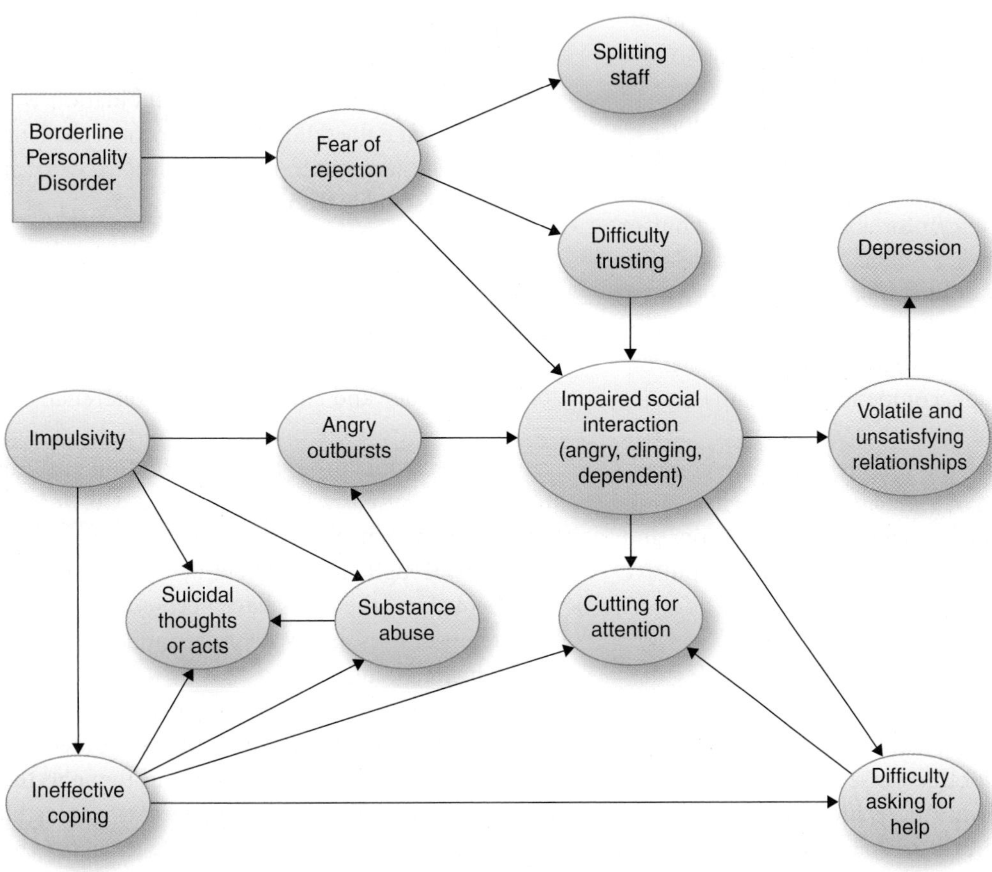

Figure 24-1 Symptom Concept Map for Borderline Personality Disorder

intolerance for criticism. These clients often overreact to criticism or defeat with deep humiliation. The clinical assessment should consider the concurrent existence of substance abuse or anorexia nervosa.

Avoidant Personality Disorder

Clients with avoidant personality disorder are sensitive to rejection in social situations because they are inhibited, anxious, and have low self-esteem. They may describe themselves as shy or timid. The absence of social skills, extreme self-consciousness, and fear of embarrassment can interfere with the development of interpersonal relationships and with job performance or advancement.

Dependent Personality Disorder

Dependent personality disorder is characterized by an excessive reliance on others, typically a parent or spouse, for emotional support. The client lacks confidence in the ability to be self-reliant, is generally uncomfortable being alone, is incapable of making independent decisions, and is fearful of separation. The client is particularly vulnerable when the dependent relationship is threatened by events such as death or divorce. The client often immediately seeks a replacement relationship. Avoidance of responsibility as a result of intrinsic self-doubt may impair interpersonal and occupational performance. Dependent personality disorder does not apply to cultural and situation-appropriate circumstances, such as a person with a disability.

The person with dependent personality disorder may act in a way that is anticipated to earn the nurse's approval.

Obsessive-Compulsive Personality Disorder

Persons with obsessive-compulsive personality disorder are preoccupied with orderliness and perfection. Paying strict attention to rules, details, procedures, lists, and schedules is their way of achieving control. They tend to save everything in case it has future importance. These clients are workaholics who almost never take vacations. Even leisure activities are structured in the form of a game or sport to be conquered. Work and structured activities allow the client to avoid situations with family or friends that may call for the expression of emotions, something that makes them uncomfortable. The perfectionism may result in missed deadlines, difficulty in delegating responsibility, and trouble adjusting to change. Depending on the nature of the client's occupation, these behaviors may be detrimental to their performance. The ambition, competitiveness, and hostility associated with this personality disorder also are risk factors for cardiac disease. Unlike obsessive-compulsive disorder, the Axis I anxiety disorder with a similar name, there is an absence of true obsessions and compulsions in clients with obsessive-compulsive personality disorder.

Assessment

When taking the history, the nurse should be alert for patterns of behavior that cause the client distress. In establishing the client's motivation for treatment, the nurse must consider the reason the client presents for help at that particular time. The clinician who elicits a history consistent with one or more personality disorders must consider the duration of the symptoms, including the age at onset, and determine that the symptoms are pervasive across a range of situations and are related to impaired functioning.

The client may not be aware of how a behavioral pattern has affected interpersonal, social, or work relationships. A person with antisocial personality disorder may not readily provide information about arrests or other aberrant behaviors. When establishing a diagnosis, it is helpful to obtain the client's consent to corroborate information with relatives, former therapists, friends, and significant others. The nurse may learn much from the client's interactions during the assessment process, but persons who have known the client for a long time can provide information from extended observation.

Organic causes, including dementia, head injury, or brain tumor, must be considered if the personality changes had a sudden onset. Substances of abuse as well as prescribed medications can alter behavior; taking a thorough drug history is essential. Other mental disorders must be excluded before establishing the diagnosis of personality disorder. A mental status examination and family medical and psychiatric histories are helpful in determining the diagnosis.

Treatment

Some form of psychotherapy, in combination with medication, and the skillful management of challenging behaviors are common approaches to the treatment of personality disorders.

Psychotherapy

Psychotherapeutic approaches to the treatment of personality disorders vary depending on the nature of the disorder and the therapist's preference and training. Regression therapy attempts to change current behavior through the exploration and understanding of early life experiences. Conversely, supportive psychotherapy avoids the past and focuses on strengthening current defenses. Cognitive and behavioral therapies have been adapted to the treatment of personality disorders and include the following techniques:

- *Cognitive restructuring:* **Cognitive restructuring** is a process in which the client identifies common negative or catastrophic thoughts that interfere with functioning. Negative thoughts are replaced with constructive thoughts that assist the client in changing feelings and behaviors.
- *Systematic desensitization:* Systematic desensitization gradually reduces the client's anxiety and fear related to situations through real or imagined exposure.
- *Dialectical behavior therapy:* **Dialectical behavior therapy (DBT)** is a cognitive-behavioral treatment for clients with borderline personality disorder (Linehan, 1993). Individual therapy utilizes validation and problem-solving strategies, emphasizes the client's strengths, and applies the principles of positive reinforcement to motivate behavioral changes. Coping skills are taught in group sessions and focus on identifying and correcting skill deficits in all aspects of the client's life. Treatment goals include reducing suicidal gestures, preventing attrition from therapy, regulating emotions, and tolerating distress (Hampton, 1997).

Psychotherapy is conducted either individually or in groups. Groups may be particularly effective for clients who have little insight into their behavior and relationships with others. The group members are helpful in pointing these out to the client. Whereas group therapy may be appropriate to counter a client's social anxiety, some clients with schizoid per-

Clinical Example: Cognitive Restructuring 

A person with avoidant personality disorder who is tempted to cancel a job interview may be thinking, "If I go on this interview, I will be very nervous and will not know what to say. I will make a fool of myself. I have no chance of getting this job anyway." The cognitive therapist helps the client challenge the validity of these statements and gradually replace them with realistic thoughts that the client can accept. These may consist of, "I am nervous, but most people are nervous on interviews. I can prepare some things to say about myself and my experience. I may not get the job, but it is good experience. I may be less nervous the next time. At least I will have a chance at the job."

sonality disorder may find a group too threatening, at least in the beginning of treatment. The therapist's skills are essential in controlling attention-seeking behaviors without communicating rejection. Paranoid personality disorder can result in distortions of what is said or done in a group and requires monitoring by the therapist.

Regardless of the psychotherapeutic approach, the therapist's attitude is the critical factor. The therapist must be alert to countertransference—that is, the feelings experienced by the therapist in relationship to the client. It is important for the therapist to acknowledge the client's feelings, thus validating his or her experiences and worth, and to relate to clients in a direct, open, and honest style that communicates respect and support.

Pharmacotherapy

Medication has a limited role in the treatment of most personality disorders. The second-generation antipsychotic medications, aripiprazole (Abilify) and olanzapine (Zyprexa), should be the first line of treatment for the cognitive and perceptual distortions that can be present with schizotypal or borderline personality disorders. Aripiprazole is also effective for the treatment of overall impulsivity. Olanzapine, however, was found, in the majority of random clinical trials, to not be effective in reducing self-mutilating and suicidal behaviors (Lieb, Völlm, Rucker, Timmer, & Stoffers, 2010). The risk of metabolic disorders and weight gain associated with the second-generation antipsychotics must be weighed against potential benefit.

Placebo controlled trials have shown selective serotonin reuptake inhibitors (SSRIs) to have only a small to moderate effect on reducing anger and impulsivity associated with borderline personality disorder (Bates, 2009; Leichsenring et al., 2011; Lieb et al., 2010). The major value of SSRIs may be in the treatment of co-morbid major depressive disorder and personality disorders. Mood stabilizers, second-generation antipsychotics, and haloperidol (Haldol), a first-generation antipsychotic, are recommended for the affective dysregulation, or difficulty controlling one's mood, that is often present in borderline personality disorder (Lieb et al., 2010). In treating clients with borderline personality disorder, consideration is given to a medication's potential for lethal overdose and dependence. This limits the usefulness of tricyclic antidepressants and benzodiazepines.

Pharmacotherapy has limited applications to other personality disorders. Lithium carbonate (Eskalith), carbamazepine (Tegretol), and propranolol (Inderal) have been used to decrease physical aggression in clients with antisocial personality disorder, borderline personality disorder, and other disorders. The SSRIs, including fluoxetine (Prozac), can effectively treat phobic symptoms in clients with avoidant personality disorder.

Clinical Example: Systematic Desensitization 

The therapist guides the client to relax while imagining a stressful situation such as a job interview. The client is instructed to imagine increasingly stressful events leading up to the interview, such as calling to schedule an appointment, then reviewing a resume, then calling to confirm the appointment, then dressing for the interview, traveling to the interview, and finally, imagining the actual interview. At each step, the client uses relaxation techniques and views his or her performance as going well. This gradual imagined exposure to increasingly challenging tasks when combined with social skills and assertiveness training helps to decrease anxiety and improve performance in the real situation.

Patients with personality disorders are prescribed psychotropic medications with greater frequency than almost any other diagnostic group, often based on anecdotal evidence rather than rigorous data (Ripoli et al., 2011). An increased understanding of the neurobiology of personality disorders may lead to more rational pharmacotherapy for this population.

Nursing Diagnoses and Interventions

Nursing interventions for clients diagnosed with personality disorders are directed at validating the client's experience, ensuring client safety, and teaching effective coping strategies. The interventions target the client's behavior. Borderline personality disorder is the personality disorder encountered most frequently on both psychiatric and medical inpatient units. **Figure 24-2** identifies nursing diagnoses commonly associated with borderline personality disorder. The psychiatric clinical nurse specialist on the consultation-liaison service for a general hospital is called upon frequently to assist the nursing staff with persons whose personality disorders interfere with efforts to deliver care. Even in the absence of a personality disorder, behavioral traits can interfere with the client's recovery or disrupt the clinical setting. Applying specific principles and approaches to behaviors that these clients commonly display (**Table 24-4**) can increase the nurse's sense of competence and decrease frustration. As noted earlier, countertransference impairs the ability to provide effective treatment. The following sections discuss nursing interventions for client behaviors that may be challenging to nursing staff.

Manipulative Behavior

A behavior is labeled manipulative if the other person feels he or she has been taken advantage of, used, or exploited. The client's behavior is likely to be termed manipulative if it challenges the nurse's control of a situation or if the client achieves some outcome the nurse did not intend. To provide effective therapy, the nurse needs to recognize the behavior as a symptom

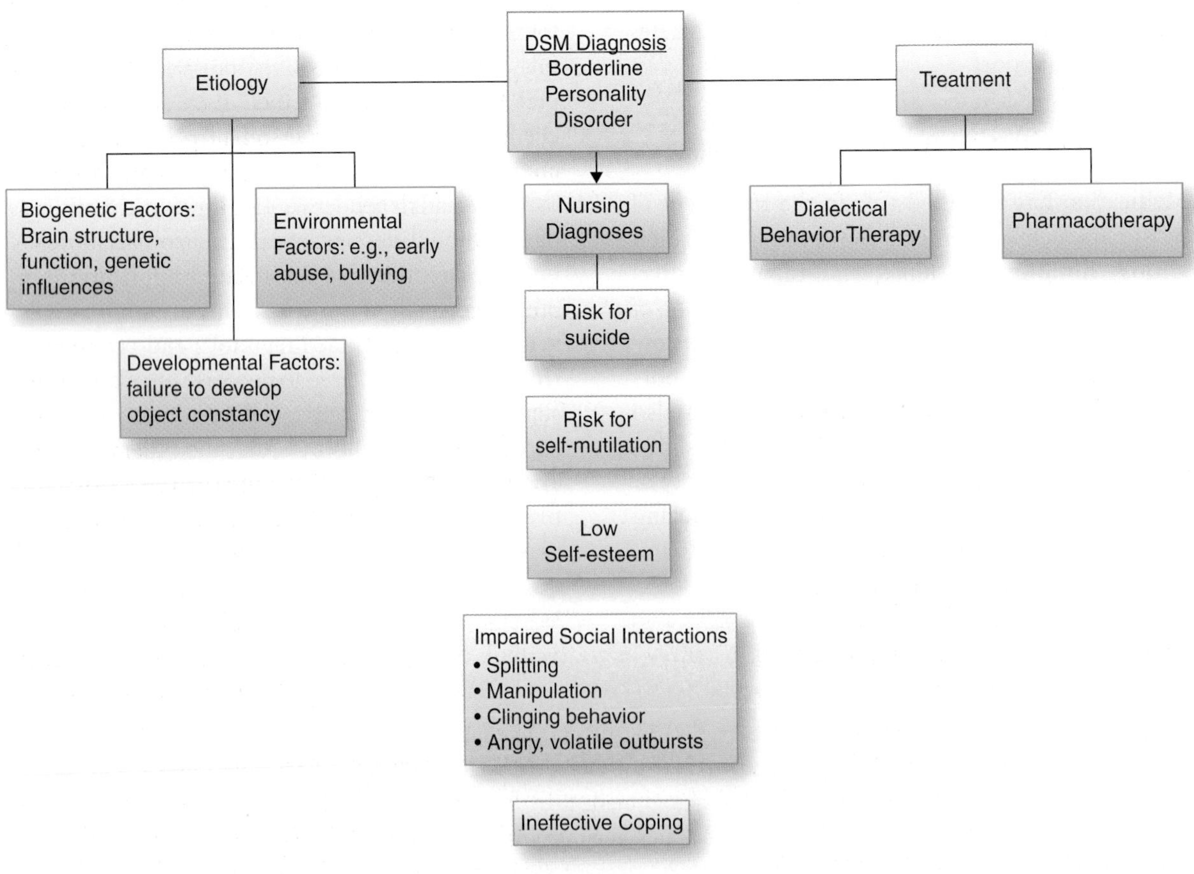

Figure 24-2 Nursing Diagnoses Concept Map: Borderline Personality Disorder

Table 24-4 Client Behaviors Associated With Personality Disorders

Behavior	Description
Manipulation	Client attempts to communicate important need; staff may feel exploited or taken advantage of
Suicidal and self-mutilating behavior	Often precipitated by threats of rejection or separation or increased responsibility
Splitting	Client is unable to integrate positive and negative feelings; related to fear of abandonment
Impulsivity	Client acts without thought about consequences; often an expression of aggression; may be a response to perceived loss or rejection

of the client's illness. The appropriate nursing interventions should be based on what the client is trying to accomplish.

To apply behavioral interventions, it is reasonable to start from the premise that all behavior has meaning. The client with borderline personality disorder who throws a tantrum or self-mutilates is indirectly communicating an unmet need. The client is not always able to identify what the need is, and thus the nurse may have to assess the unstated goal of the client's behavior. The nurse accomplishes this by carefully observing the client's behavior, paying attention to the antecedents and consequences of the behavior.

> Manipulative behavior can be viewed as a patient's unique attempt to communicate an important need. If the staff does not respond to that need, either because of a lack of understanding, or because of negative feelings towards the patient, it may be analogous to staff withdrawal. ... The patient, unsuccessful in meeting some need, can be expected to become more manipulative. (O'Brien, 1988, p. 239)

The therapeutic intervention the nurse chooses to use with a client is based on the individual client's need at that time. In the next Clinical Example, for instance, the initial intervention may involve imposing a brief time-out in an effort to limit the temper tantrum behavior. The therapist then spends time with the client and discusses the avoided therapy or visitor. If the nurse feels manipulated, the accompanying frustration and anger may lead to an extended period of isolation for the client, withdrawal of privileges, or other punitive and nontherapeutic actions. If the client's need for attention is unmet, the client may see a need to up the ante. If the client is trying to avoid therapy or avoid seeing a particular visitor and is successful, then the tantrum behavior is reinforced. The nurse must determine what purpose the behavior serves for the client and then help the client meet that need in an acceptable way.

Suicidal and Self-Mutilating Behavior

Among clients with borderline personality disorder, 70–80% engage in suicidal behavior, with a suicide rate of up to 9% (Linehan et al., 2006). No suicide attempt or threat should be treated casually. A half-hearted first attempt does not mean that the risk of suicide is low. People who use suicidal gestures to gain attention may, in desperation or through miscalculation, actually kill themselves.

The nurse should ask the client directly about the presence of suicidal thoughts. The risk of suicide is greater in clients who have a plausible plan and the means to carry it out. For example, a client who describes a plan to take a drug overdose and has a supply of potentially lethal medication poses a serious suicide risk. Contrary to popular opinion, inquiring about suicidal thoughts does not plant the suggestion in the mind of a client who was not already suicidal.

Asking about suicide does *not* cause the client to consider suicide.

Parasuicide is a term used to refer to self-injurious behavior that is not intended to be suicidal. Self-mutilation may be an effort to gain attention in a person who lacks the skill to ask for help in a more effective way. Persons with borderline personality disorder have described self-mutilation as a way to relieve stress and anxiety, or to confirm their existence, in response to feelings of emptiness or not feeling real. Examples of self-injurious behaviors include cutting, biting, excessive piercings, scratching, head banging, and hair pulling.

Control is the central issue for manipulative clients. They are always aware of who has power in personal interactions and seldom see themselves as that person.

Client safety may dictate the search for and removal of potentially harmful objects. This search should be conducted whenever possible in the client's presence and always with the client's knowledge. The purpose should be clearly stated as an effort to protect the client from dangerous impulses and in a context of concern. The client may agree to speak to the nurse when suicidal feelings occur. This type of contract begins to identify an alternative approach to acting on suicidal feelings. An appropriate level of observation and client contact needs to be maintained. With help from the nurse, the client may begin to identify the feelings or events that trigger suicidal thoughts. Limiting the time spent discussing suicidal thoughts and extending the time spent discussing other issues or in recreational activities may reinforce nonsuicidal thoughts.

Clinical Example

A tantrum that occurs after a delay in responding to a client's question or in the presence of another client interacting with staff may be the client's way of communicating a need for attention. A tantrum thrown at the beginning of a therapy session or immediately prior to visiting hours may be a way of avoiding therapy or spending time with an expected visitor.

Splitting

Splitting, a phenomenon that characterizes borderline personality disorder, can be particularly disruptive on inpatient units. As a result of early developmental failure to achieve separation-individuation, the client lacks object constancy and is, therefore, unable to integrate positive and negative feelings. Such a client tends to view people and situations as all good or all bad. The behavior is a primitive defense against an overwhelming fear of abandonment. The client typically idealizes some staff members and rejects others, and countertransference splits the staff's approach to the nursing care plan. The resulting inconsistencies in the staff's treatment of the client's behavior contribute to an escalation of maladaptive behavior. The staff members occasionally resort to assigning the same people to care for the client to minimize the splitting. If the staff members recognize what is happening and maintain excellent communication among themselves, they can employ an alternative approach of assigning a variety of people to care for the client. This avoids the development of dependency on particular staff members and helps diminish the underlying fear of abandonment.

Impulsivity

Impulsivity is characterized by a need for immediate gratification. It is a feature of borderline and antisocial personality disorders and is also evident, to some extent, in the other cluster B personality disorders. The person with impulse control issues has a tendency to act quickly without giving thought to possible consequences. Impulsive behavior is often a response to an emotional event involving the expression of anger or aggression. Impulsive behaviors may include excessive spending, sexual promiscuity, displays of temper, threatening behavior, or physical altercations. In clients with borderline personality disorder, the impulsive behavior is often a reaction to loss or separation that triggers feelings of rejection. The aggressive impulses of the person with antisocial personality disorder may be associated with a disregard for rules and laws, accounting for why this disorder is common among the forensic population. On an inpatient unit, impulsivity can place the client at risk for self-mutilation, self- or other-directed violence, promiscuous sexual behavior, and verbal and physical altercations.

Critical Thinking Question

Imagine arriving to work on an inpatient psychiatric unit, and one patient greets you, saying in a loud voice, "Oh, don't tell me you're in charge today. Everything is so much better when you're not here." How might you feel? How might you react?

Clinical Example

David, who is 8 years old, follows the nurse everywhere she goes on the unit, and his constant presence is making it difficult for the nurse to do her work. The nurse assesses this behavior to represent David's need for attention. Rather than send David away or tell him that he cannot follow her, the nurse explains why this behavior is problematic. The nurse suggests some other interim activity for David to do (write her a letter, draw a picture) and agrees that if David does this, the nurse will spend time with him at a later agreed-upon time.

In this example, the nurse's explanation educates David about appropriate behavior, helps him identify alternative behaviors, and, at the same time, meets David's need for attention. The attention becomes a reward that David earns.

Clinical Example 

The concerns for patient safety on inpatient psychiatric units require particular vigilance regarding the presence of contraband, such as drugs or other restricted items. Some clients will challenge the staff by attempting to sneak items on the unit or taunting the staff with verbal reminders that they can do this. The implication is that the staff is not so smart, and the client is smarter.

Staff can respond by imposing further restrictions on the client, including limiting or prohibiting visitors. An alternative approach would be to acknowledge that, despite the staff's efforts, the client could probably find a way to outsmart the staff. Admitting this to the client avoids a power struggle and allows the nurse to focus on the client's need to challenge authority and his or her difficulty committing to the treatment goals.

Of course, the staff continue to conduct searches and visitor inspections and carry out whatever procedures are in place to secure the unit. However, by choosing to not engage in the power struggle, the nurse opens the door for more meaningful dialogue with the client.

In the first response, the staff get caught up in establishing their authority, and the relationship becomes defined in those terms. The alternative approach indicates an understanding that this power struggle has meaning for the client. In this case, the behavior may have served the purpose of helping the client avoid a therapeutic relationship.

Setting Limits

Depending on the particular personality disorder, part of the treatment plan may include limiting certain behaviors, such as angry outbursts, excessive clinging, dependent behavior, or drug-seeking activities. Effective limit setting must be clear, firm, and consistent, and it must be accompanied by the reinforcement of appropriate behavior. Rewarding

Considerations for Client and Family Education

Behavioral theory states that maladaptive behaviors are to a large extent acquired through learning and represent an attempt to cope with an immediate need (O'Brien, 1997). The nursing goals are to help the client identify how the current behavior interferes with achieving satisfactory interpersonal relationships and to teach the client ways to communicate his or her needs more effectively.

An important aspect of nursing care for clients with personality disorders involves engaging the client in the process of learning new skills and adaptive behaviors. The nurse often has the advantage of observing a client's behavior over time. This provides the nurse with an understanding of the client's ineffective behaviors and the situations in which clients have the most difficulty. Certain skills and their applications have been discussed previously. The nurse can employ social skills training and role playing. This provides clients with tools to lessen their social isolation. Assertiveness training, especially learning to ask for help, aids clients who resort to self-inflicted injury or other extreme behaviors when in need of support. Problem-solving skills reduce helplessness and dependency. Clients with dependent personality disorder can utilize this approach to build confidence and experience in decision making. Groups that focus on problem solving efficiently meet the needs of a variety of clients and concurrently provide an opportunity to practice communication skills. Relaxation training teaches clients methods to reduce anger, anxiety, and impulsivity.

Family members can benefit from learning the principles of limit setting, including the importance of rewarding desired behaviors and strategies for avoiding power struggles. It is critical that family members know to take threats of suicide seriously and to seek immediate assistance in a crisis.

Compliance with medication is enhanced if the client and family understand the purpose of the medication and if the client is actively involved in evaluating the medication's effectiveness on targeted symptoms. Low initial doses of medication help to achieve an effective level with minimum side effects. The nurse is significantly involved in monitoring the effects of medication and in educating the client and family.

Evidence-Based Practice

Most of the research and published reviews on personality disorders is related to etiology, diagnosis, comorbidity, and treatment approaches. While these finding have some implications for nursing practice, the research finding most relevant for nursing practice is the qualitative study by Langley & Klopper (2005).

This study offers evidence for the importance of the nurse–client relationship in influencing client outcomes. The authors, interested in developing a practice model for the psychiatric community nurse, conducted individual and group interviews with clients diagnosed with borderline personality disorder and with mental health clinicians experienced in treating the disorder. Themes were then extrapolated from the interviews, and trust was identified as the foundation for therapeutic intervention. Both clients and therapists recognized trust as essential for the establishment and maintenance of a therapeutic alliance, stressing that without trust any intervention was unlikely to succeed.

For clients, this trust or belief in the other person was linked to the concept of hope. Once trust was established, the client began to believe that the clinician might help him or her, and this provided the basis for the therapeutic relationship. Therapists indicated that a trusting relationship was necessary before implementing any therapeutic interpretations of client behavior.

Clients identified conditions that contributed to the development of trust: the clinician was perceived as available, trying to understand by listening, caring in a way that made the client feel emotionally and physically safe, and honest in all interactions. Also important were maintaining confidentiality, relating to the client as an adult, rather than as an expert, and remaining calm during discussions with the client. It was acknowledged that trust takes time to develop, and clients were likely to test the therapist, and, if the client perceived the therapist as wanting, it was difficult to continue in the relationship.

In the interest of establishing trust, clinicians spoke of the importance of knowing the client—a full history, knowledge of the client's strengths, patterns of coping, and support system. In addition, they stressed the importance of empathy, understanding, and acknowledging that, even if the client's coping was ineffective at times, the clinician recognized that the client was doing the best he or she could do.

This research supports the importance of the nurse taking time through respect, the use of confirming communication techniques, and other interventions to develop a trusting collaboration between the nurse and client. This sense of trust was what allowed the client to hope that help was possible. The findings are a testament to the significant impact the nurse can have on the outcome of care.

CASE STUDIES Ms. C.

Ms. C., a 23-year-old, was admitted to a psychiatric inpatient unit after cutting herself superficially on both wrists in a self-described suicide attempt. She was brought to the emergency room (ER) by her boyfriend, Mr. M., who had found Ms. C. at her apartment passed out on her couch, with a small amount of bleeding from her wrists and an empty quart-size bottle of vodka nearby. He had come to the apartment after finding a message on his voice mail from Ms. C., stating that she was going to kill herself. In the ER, Ms. C. explained the precipitant for her suicide attempt was Mr. M.'s decision 2 weeks earlier to delay their plans to become engaged.

Ms. C. had one prior psychiatric admission 3 years ago when she was in college. The admission was related to an overdose of over-the-counter sleeping medications and alcohol, and it was also precipitated by a breakup with a boyfriend.

Ms. C.'s family, her mother and two younger sisters, lived in another city, approximately a 3-hour drive away. Her closest support was her roommate, Ms. G., but she had not spoken to Ms. G. in a reasonable way for the past 2 weeks because she was convinced that Ms. G. was responsible for Mr M.'s decision to delay their engagement.

On mental status examination, Ms. C. described feeling empty, with periods of tearfulness, insomnia, and irritability over the prior 2 weeks. She relates having had angry outbursts in recent weeks with Mr. M., Ms. G., her mother, and coworkers. Her diagnosis was borderline personality disorder with suicide attempt and alcohol intoxication.

Nursing Care Plan **Borderline Personality Disorder**

Nursing Diagnosis 1: Risk for self-injury related to feelings of emptiness evidenced by cutting and self-destructive behaviors.

Nursing Diagnosis 2: Impaired social interaction related to fear of abandonment evidenced by splitting and angry outbursts.

Nursing Diagnosis 3: Ineffective coping related to inadequate coping skills evidenced by anger, impulsivity, and alcohol use when stressed.

Expected Outcomes	Interventions	Evaluations
• The client will not hurt herself or engage in self-destructive behaviors.	• Assess for suicidal ideation. • Place on special observation status. • Encourage verbalization of feelings. • Remove dangerous objects. • Limit flirtatious behaviors with copatients and staff.	• The client reports absence of suicidal ideation. • The client talks with staff rather than mutilating herself. • The client engages in therapeutic activities with staff. • The client avoids impulsive sexual encounters.
• The client will develop a therapeutic relationship with the nurse and interact in acceptable ways with staff and peers.	• Establish a trusting relationship. • Be aware of countertransference, if anger is displaced on the nurse. • Identify strengths: achievements, friends, family, work. • Use confirming communication—this conveys respect and interest. The client is sensitive to rejection, so be sure to keep agreements. • Teach and reinforce appropriate behaviors and communication techniques. Try to respond immediately to appropriate requests. • Set limits with angry, clingy, or splitting behaviors. Staff on all shifts must share information and be firm, clear, and consistent with the client. • Help the client connect thoughts and feelings to behavior. • Rotate staff to decrease dependence on one person and reduce splitting.	• The client expresses beginning understanding of her behavior and effect on self/others. • The client demonstrates fewer angry outbursts. • The client engages in verbal therapy. • The client interacts appropriately with several staff members and peers.

• The client will learn alternative coping skills.	• Reward efforts to behave appropriately.
	• Talk about the source of feelings of anger/rejection.
	• Provide skills training:
	  • Assertiveness training: ask for help; express disappointment and anger; communicate feelings.
	  • Stress management: encourage physical exercise and relaxation as a substitute for alcohol; this may help with anger control.
	  • Problem-solving skills
	  • Acknowledge the client's use of new skills.
		• The client practices new skills.
		• The client reports the new skills are helpful in meeting needs.

Visit http://go.jblearning.com/mentalhealth for additional care plans and exercises.

appropriate behavior is likely to be more effective than imposing punishment when striving for behavioral changes.

When setting limits, the expected behaviors must be stated clearly in a firm, nonpunitive manner.

In setting limits, the nurse must be careful to avoid creating a power struggle. Clients, especially those with personality disorders, are often sensitive to reminders that the nurse is in charge. Acknowledging the client's feelings and concerns communicates respect and can be effective in disarming the client who anticipates that the nurse will be punitive and controlling. The nurse needs to have realistic goals and to be alert to the danger of using limit-setting activities as a way to act out anger toward the client.

The Nurse–Client Relationship

Nursing interventions often involve personal interactions in which nurses use their skills and training, as well as their unique personalities, to effect growth and change. The nurse models appropriate communication styles and is a safe person on whom the client can try out new skills and behaviors. The nurse must communicate acceptance and respect to help this process. Clients with low self-esteem are particularly sensitive to rejection, a symptom of several personality disorders.

The nurse's manner of relating to the client is either confirming or nonconfirming. Confirming communication includes listening to the client, validating the client's feelings, maintaining appropriate eye contact, asking the client's opinion, and engaging the client in problem-solving activities. Examples of nonconfirming communication include talking over the client, interrupting, not looking at the client, engaging in another activity while talking to the client, and offering solutions without considering the client's opinion.

Critical Thinking Question

What types of people and what behaviors are likely to make you angry? Why is that?

Table 24-5 Nursing Interventions for Clients With Borderline and Antisocial Personality Disorders

Nursing Diagnoses	Nursing Interventions	Rationales
Risk of suicide	Conduct a suicide assessment • Ask direct questions. • Assess the nature and frequency of the thoughts. • Inquire if the client has a plan. • Determine if the client has the means to carry out the plan. • Establish if there is a history of suicide attempts, gestures, or self-mutilation. • Identify supports. • Evaluate the client's ability to resist urges and seek help from staff (contract for safety).	Client's safety is a priority; frequent thoughts and past attempts may indicate increased risk; client's willingness to contract for safety, while not a guarantee, does reinforce the client's control and responsibility for behavior. Seeking help from staff supports the communication skill of asking for help and provides an alternative to acting on suicidal impulses.
Risk for other-directed violence	• Be honest, direct, and respectful in communication with the client.	Helps establish trust and improves self-esteem.
	• Remove objects that can be dangerous.	Helps maintain a safe environment.
	• Observe the client for anger and impulsiveness.	Anger and impulsiveness can contribute to sudden violence.
	• Be clear and consistent about rules and expected behavior.	This can limit the client's efforts to challenge the rules and manipulate staff.
	• Use a calm manner and reduce stimulation in the environment.	These can decrease agitation and aggression.

Table 24-5 **Nursing Interventions for Clients With Borderline and Antisocial Personality Disorders *(Continued)***

Nursing Diagnoses	Nursing Interventions	Rationales
Risk for self-mutilation	• Place the client on special observation status. • Provide for direct supervision. • Protect from sexual encounters. • Remove dangerous objects.	Observation allows for early intervention to prevent self-destructive acting out. When possible, observation should be unobtrusive to avoid inadvertent reinforcement of negative behaviors through increased attention from staff.
	• Encourage verbalization of feelings.	Expressing feelings in words may diminish the need to act out feelings in self-destructive ways.
	• If the client cuts him- or herself, care for wounds in matter-of-fact manner. Do not discuss the event until after wound care is complete.	By limiting verbalization while tending to self-inflicted wounds, the nurse minimizes reinforcement of this negative behavior.
Low self-esteem	• Establish a therapeutic relationship • Maintain a respectful, nonjudgmental approach • Identify the client's strengths. • Use confirming communication. • Start from the premise that all behavior has meaning. • Attempt to meet the client's needs in an acceptable way. • Reward positive behavior.	Promotes trust and self-esteem; reinforcement increases positive behaviors; the therapeutic process helps identify the client's feelings
Impaired social interactions • Splitting • Manipulation • Angry, hostile behavior • Clinging behaviors • Intimidating behaviors	• Meet with the client. • Encourage verbal expression of feelings. • Help relate the client's behavior to an underlying fear of rejection and other feelings. • Role play appropriate expression of anger. • Give recognition for appropriate behaviors.	Helps develop insight, motivate change, and reinforce new behaviors.
	• Give timely feedback in a direct, matter-of-fact manner for inappropriate behaviors.	Calm but direct approach reduces the likelihood of reinforcing maladaptive behavior.
	• Rotate staff.	Rotating staff allows the client to learn to trust and relate to more than one person, decreasing dependency.
	• Set clear personal boundaries.	Revealing personal information to the client is not consistent with a professional relationship. The client may experience this as rejection, so the nurse should explain this in the context of the nurse–client relationship.
	• Avoid physically touching the client.	Comforting the client by touch can be misinterpreted by the client.

(Continues)

Table 24-5 Nursing Interventions for Clients With Borderline and Antisocial Personality Disorders *(Continued)*

Nursing Diagnoses	Nursing Interventions	Rationales
	• Engage the client in the process of identifying and reducing self-defeating behaviors (angry outbursts, clinging/dependent behavior).	Engaging the client enhances motivation and supports the collaborative nature of the nurse–client relationship.
	• Teach the client alternative behaviors and reward positive changes.	The client can only replace negative behaviors when new ones have been learned.
	• Be clear, firm, and consistent when setting limits.	Consistency and recognition are important to reinforce appropriate behavior and to extinguish undesirable behaviors.
	• Focus on the client's goals and issues whenever the client attempts to split staff. • Avoid discussing staff with the client or criticizing staff.	By being neither flattered nor defensive when the client makes comments about the nurse or other staff, the nurse interrupts the client's destructive pattern and allows for more appropriate interactions.
Ineffective coping	• Provide skills training specific to the client's needs. • Social skills • Assertive communication • Relaxation training • Anger management • Problem-solving skills	These skills can increase or lead to supportive relationships, control over one's environment; and the ability to ask for help, express feelings, and reduce stress. This can reduce reliance on ineffective measures, such as self-mutilation or suicidal acts.

Critical Thinking Question

Can you think of a time when you were speaking with someone and you realized that the person was not really interested in what you were saying? What behaviors on the part of the other person made you think that?

Confirming communication validates the client's importance and promotes a trusting relationship.

Confirming communication validates the client's importance and promotes a trusting relationship. In a study of effective treatment for clients with borderline personality disorder, trust was the concept identified by both clients and clinicians as crucial for the establishment of the therapeutic alliance and the foundation of treatment (Langley & Klopper, 2005).

To assist in developing a nursing care plan for the client with a personality disorder, refer to **Table 24-5** for a list of nursing interventions and rationales.

Summary

Clients with personality disorders present a broad spectrum of behavioral symptoms and often require lifelong therapeutic intervention. The advanced practice nurse may be either the primary psychotherapist for these clients or the consultant to other caregivers who need direction in establishing a therapeutic relationship. The nurse who is not at the advanced level of practice is likely to encounter these clients in all clinical (medical-surgical and psychiatric) settings. These clients are most challenging, but nurses who recognize the clients' behaviors as symptoms of an illness and an expression of limited coping skills can convey an accepting and hopeful attitude to the client. The nurse's belief that the client is capable of change may be the most important part of working with those who have personality disorders.

Annotated References

American Psychiatric Association (APA). (2000). *Diagnostic and statistical manual of mental disorders* (4th ed., text rev.). Washington, DC: Author.

This is the American Psychiatric Association's official nomenclature of psychiatric conditions and disorders. It provides a systematic listing of the official codes and categories, a description of the multiaxial system for diagnosis, and diagnostic criteria for each of the disorders. It is used by psychiatrists, physicians, psychologists, registered nurses, social workers, therapists, and other mental health workers in all settings.

American Psychiatric Association (APA). (2011). *DSM-5 development, personality disorders*. Retrieved from www.dsm5.org/proposedrevision
This is a website maintained by APA to provide information and receive comments on proposed revisions to the *DSM*.

Black, D. W., & Andreasen, N. C. (2011). *Introductory textbook of psychiatry* (5th ed.). Washington, DC: American Psychiatric Press.
This text provides a succinct summary of the personality disorders with some clinical vignettes.

Bates, B. (2009). Practical psychopharmacology, borderline personality disorder: Go easy on SSRIs. *Clinical Psychiatry News, 37*(10), 56.
This paper summarizes research data related to the psychopharmacotherapy of borderline personality disorder.

Foti, M. E., Geller, J., Guy, L. S., Gunderson, J. G., Palmer, B. A., & Smith, L. M. (2011). Borderline personality disorder: Considerations for inclusion in the Massachusetts parity list of "biologically-based" disorders. *Psychiatric Quarterly, 82*(2), 95–112.
This review considers borderline personality disorder (BPD) parity, using the Massachusetts mental health parity statute as a model.

Goodman, M., New, A., & Siever, L. (2004). Trauma, genes, and the neurobiology of personality disorders. *Annals of the New York Academy of Science*, December, *1032*, 104–116.
This review article examines the current state and limitations of neurobiologic theories of personality disorders.

Hampton, N. D. (1997). Dialectical behavior therapy in the treatment of persons with borderlinepersonality disorder. *Archives of Psychiatric Nursing, XI*(2), 96–101.
This article describes dialectical behavior therapy, a form of cognitive-behavioral therapy that has been effective in reducing hospital stays, suicide attempts, and therapy attrition.

Kernberg, O. E. (1976). *Object-relations theory and clinical psychoanalysis*. New York, NY: Aronson.
This is the classic presentation of Kernberg's psychoanalytic ego psychology and object-relations theory. The underlying ego structure is viewed as the essence of the pathology of borderline personality disorder and is the target of expressive therapy.

King-Casas, B., Sharp, C., Lomax-Bream, L., Lohrenz, T., Fonagy, P., & Montague, P. R. (2008). The rupture and repair of cooperation in borderline personality disorder. *Science, 321*(5890), 806–810.
Fifty-five persons with borderline personality disorder played a multiround economic exchange game and were tested on a measure of cooperation. They were found to have a profound incapacity for cooperation.

Langley, K., Heron, J., O'Donovan, M. C., Owen, M. J., & Thapar, A. (2010). Genotype link with extreme antisocial behavior: The contribution of cognitive pathways. *Archives of General Psychiatry, 67*(12), 1317–1323.
The study replicated the association between the COMT genotype and antisocial behavior in persons with attention-deficit/hyperactivity disorder and tested whether impaired social interaction and executive control act as intermediate phenotypes for this association.

Langley, G. C., & Klopper, H. (2005). Trust as a foundation for the therapeutic intervention for patients with borderline personality disorder. *Journal of Psychiatric Mental Health Nursing, 12*(1), 23–32.
This article reports on a qualitative research study that supports the importance of establishing trust between client and clinician for the effective treatment of borderline personality disorder.

Leichsenring, F., Liebing, E., Kruse, J., New, A. S., & Leweke, F. (2011). Borderline personality disorder. *Lancet, 377*(9759), 74–84.
This paper provides a comprehensive overview of borderline personality disorder: characteristics, etiology, and treatment, including pharmacotherapy and psychotherapy.

Lieb, K., Völlm, B., Rucker, G., Timmer, A., & Stoffers, J. M. (2010). Pharmacotherapy for borderline personality disorder: Cochrane systematic review of randomised trials. *British Journal of Psychiatry, 196*(1), 4–12.
This article reports on a Cochrane Collaboration systematic review and meta-analysis of randomized comparisons of drug vs. placebo, drug vs. drug, or single drug vs. combined drug treatment in adult patients with borderline personality disorder.

Linehan, M. M. (1993). *Cognitive-behavioral treatment of borderline personality disorder.* New York, NY: Guilford Press.

This text presents a comprehensive therapeutic strategy for the treatment of borderline personality disorder that focuses on coping, not curing. The core of the treatment is the balance of acceptance and change strategies, and specific strategies are provided for contingency management, exposure, cognitive modification, and skills training.

Linehan, M. M. (2006). *Understanding borderline personality disorder: The dialectical approach.* A Dawkins production [DVD or VHS manual (37 min., color)]. Available from Guilford Press, 72 Spring Street, New York, NY 10012; 800-365-7006; 212-966-6708 (fax).

This video presents fundamental information about borderline personality disorder and how it can be effectively treated with DBT.

Linehan, M. M., Comtois, K. A., Murray, A. M., Brown, M. Z., Gallop, R. J., Heard, H. L., … Lindenboim, N. (2006). Two-year randomized controlled trial and follow-up of dialectical behavior therapy vs therapy by experts for suicidal behaviors and borderline personality disorder. *Archives of General Psychiatry, 63*, 757–766.

The paper reports the findings of a 1-year randomized control trial, plus 1 year of post-treatment follow-up, comparing effects of two treatment approaches on suicidal behaviors.

Mahler, M. S., Pine, E., & Bergman, A. (1975). *The psychological birth of the human infant: Symbiosis and individuation.* New York, NY: Basic Books.

This book describes the separation-individuation process that occurs between birth and 3 years of age in which the child develops a sense of self, a permanent sense of significant others, and an integration of both good and bad as a component of self-concept.

O'Brien, P. G. (1988). Manipulation: A behavioral conceptualization. In M. J. Krebs & K. H. Larson (Eds.), *Applied psychiatric-mental health nursing standards in clinical practice* (pp. 225–247). New York, NY: John Wiley & Sons.

This book is a comprehensive presentation of therapeutic nursing interventions for clients who exhibit manipulative behavior. It offers clinical examples and guidelines for analyzing staff's feelings in relation to patients' behaviors.

O'Brien, P. G. (1997). The manipulative patient: A behavioral conceptualization. *The American Journal for Nurse Practitioners, 1*(1), 13–15, 29.

This article focuses on the need to understand the meaning behind client behavior and identifies nursing approaches for setting limits and teaching new behaviors.

Oltmanns, T. F., & Balsis, S. (2011). Studying personality disorders in later life: Questions about the measurement, course, and impact of disorders. *Annual Review of Clinical Psychology, 7*, 321–349.

This review explores the benefits of considering older adults in the study of personality disorders to examine links between personality pathology and consequential outcomes in people's lives.

Reichborn-Kjennerud, T. (2010). The genetic epidemiology of personality disorders. *Dialogues in Clinical Neuroscience, 12*(1), 103–114.

This paper summarizes current knowledge of personality disorders based on genetic epidemiologic studies and addresses many areas, including comorbidity between the personality disorders, comorbidity between personality and other mental disorders, and genetic and environmental risk factors.

Ripoli, L. H., Triebwasser, J., Siever, L. J. (2011). Evidence-based pharmacotherapy for personality disorders. *International Journal of Neuropsychopharmacology*. doi:10.1017/S1461145711000071

This is a summary of the best available evidence regarding medication treatment of personality disorders, with most evidence relating to borderline and schizotypal personality disorders.

Sala, M., Caverzasi, E., Lazzaretti, M., Morandotti, N., Marraffini, E., Gambini, F., ... Brambilla, P. (2011). Dorsolateral prefrontal cortex and hippocampus sustain impulsivity and aggressiveness in borderline personality disorder. *Journal of Affective Disorders, 131*(1–3), 417–421.

This study investigated whether hippocampus and DLPFC anatomy sustains impulsive and aggressive behaviors in BPD.

Siever, L. J. (2009). The neurobiology of personality disorders: Implications for psychoanalysis. *Journal of the American Psychoanalytic Association, 57*(2), 361–398.

This is an interesting presentation of the role psychoanalysis may play in modulating genetic biological effects on the internalized representation of the self in persons with personality disorders.

Smallwood, P. (2004). Personality disorders. In T. A. Stern & J. B. Herman (Eds.), *Massachusetts General Hospital psychiatry update and board preparation* (2nd ed., pp. 187–194.) New York, NY: McGraw-Hill.

This is a succinct presentation of the personality disorders.

Additional Resources

Berman, C. W. (2009). *Personality disorders: A practical guide.* Philadelphia, PA: Wolters Kluwer Health/Lippincott Williams & Wilkins.

This publication provides a comprehensive overview of the personality disorders, including clinical examples.

Internet Resources

For a full suite of assignments and additional learning activities, use the access code located in the front of your book to visit this exclusive website: http://go.jblearning.com/mentalhealth. If you do not have an access code, you can obtain one at the site.

Part III

Nursing Management of Special Populations

Learning Objectives

After reading this chapter, you will be able to:

- Discuss the different theoretical frameworks for understanding chronic illness.
- Describe the parameters of chronic mental illness in a client.
- Identify the challenges to clients and families coping with chronic mental illness.
- Identify the various therapies that assist clients in coping with chronic mental illness.
- Identify nursing interventions in assisting clients and their families to cope with chronic mental illness.

Key Terms

Chronic illness
Chronic mental illness
Grief
Homelessness
Loss
Persistent mental illness
Psychiatric rehabilitation
Psychoeducation
Psychosocial typology
Severe mental illness
Trajectory model

Clients With Chronic Mental Illness

Karen A. Ballard

http://go.jblearning.com/mentalhealth 

For a full suite of assignments and additional learning activities, use the access code located in the front of your book to visit this exclusive website: http://go.jblearning.com/mentalhealth. If you do not have an access code, you can obtain one at the site.

Introduction

Chronic mental illness presents a considerable challenge to clients and their families or significant others because it occurs over a long period, with accompanying and varying stages of **grief** and **loss**. Nurses who practice in this specialty area of psychiatric-mental health nursing utilize their interpersonal skills to form and maintain a therapeutic relationship with clients and their families, who often have been coping with mental illness for prolonged periods. Clients with chronic mental illness, like individuals with chronic physical illness, have to deal with the condition indefinitely, often for their entire lives.

Chronic illness, mental and physical, includes all diseases or disorders that remain with the individual for the rest of the client's lifetime once the condition has been diagnosed.

Chronic illness, mental and physical, includes all diseases or disorders that remain with the individual for the rest of the client's lifetime once the condition has been diagnosed. Chronic illness encompasses

> all impairments or deviations from the normal which have one or more of the following characteristics: are permanent; leave residual disability; are caused by nonreversible pathologic alteration; require special training of the patient for rehabilitation, or may be expected to require a long period of supervision, observation, or care. (National Commission on Chronic Illness, 1957, p. 4)

Rolland's theoretical model postulates that there are three time phases of chronic illness—crisis phase, chronic phase, and terminal phase.

Chronic mental illness is synonymous with both persistent mental illness and severe mental illness.

Chronic mental illness is synonymous with both **persistent mental illness** and **severe mental illness**. The terms *chronic*, *persistent*, and *severe* identify the gravity of the diagnosis. Chronic mental illness tends to last for a long time, if not a lifetime, and may be characterized by periods of relapse or reoccurrence. All psychiatric disorders have the potential to persist and become chronic. However, schizophrenia, major depressive disorder, and bipolar disorder are the most prevalent major psychiatric disorders shown to develop a chronic course.

Theoretical Frameworks of Chronic Illness

Some prominent theorists and mental health practitioners have developed theories to understand chronic illness. The conceptual frameworks of Rolland, Corbin, Strauss, Lubkin, and Larsen are presented in this section.

John Rolland

John Rolland (1984, 1987, 1988a, 1988b, 1990) postulated that chronic illness is an impediment to health with the potential to completely consume an individual's life and the lives of those close to the person. Rolland's model has three dimensions: the **psychosocial typology** of the illness, the time phase of the illness, and the illness-specific components of family. According to Rolland's model, chronic illness affects every dimension of a person, and to understand chronic disease it is crucial to consider the psychosocial typology. Analysis of the psychosocial typology reveals the concepts of onset, course, outcome, and degree of incapacitation. The onset of the illness is classified as either acute or gradual. The course of the illness is progressive, constant, or relapsing/episodic. The outcome of the illness is its ability to cause death or limit the life span. The degree of incapacitation is the proportion of disability or impairment caused by the chronic illness (Rolland, 1984).

Rolland's model postulates three time phases of chronic illness. The initial phase is the *crisis phase*. This involves the time period prior to the diagnosis of the disease through the initial adaptation to the disease. The second phase is the *chronic phase*, involving the period after initial adaptation to the illness until issues of death and terminal illness predominate. The third phase is the *terminal phase*, which surrounds death, and includes a pretrial phase where the thought of death becomes prominent (1990).

Rolland's model also addresses family attributes that impact on chronic illness, including the family's illness belief system; the transgenerational history of illness, loss, and crisis; and the interface of the illness, the individual, and family life cycles (Rolland, 1990). He further hypothesizes that the individual's and family's values, culture, religion, belief system, worldview, and family paradigm are integral components of the illness belief system (1988b). Rolland believes that how people have dealt with past stress-

Critical Thinking Question 

What are some common, shared behaviors that a nurse can expect to identify in clients with chronic illness, be it a physical or mental condition?

Critical Thinking Question 

How do different family attributes impact how an individual with a chronic illness will be able to cope with the lifelong challenge of the disease?

ors and the evolution of that adaptation over time are important aspects when examining the client's history of coping with illness, loss, and crisis.

For individual and family development, Rolland (1987) emphasizes the need to examine the life cycle or course of development of the individual, family, and illness and the structure of the underlying pattern of one's own or the family's life at any point in the cycle. There are two styles within the individual's and family's life cycle—centripetal (closeness) and centrifugal (disengagement). In the centripetal style, a person is involved with family life and works on its development rather than on the external world. In the centrifugal style, the person's and family's focus shifts outside themselves to the environment.

There are two styles within the individual's and family's life cycle—centripetal (closeness) and centrifugal (disengagement).

Juliet Corbin and Anselm Strauss

Corbin (2003), a nurse theorist, and Strauss (Corbin & Strauss, 1992) developed a conceptual model to help nurses address chronic illness. Strauss and colleagues (1984) state that to treat a chronically ill individual adequately, the person must be given ample medical, psychological, and social knowledge including, but not limited to, how to deal with and manage the illness and how the illness, its management, and its symptoms affect the life of the client and the client's family and significant others.

Strauss and coauthors (1984) characterize chronic diseases differently from other pathologies. Chronic illnesses are multiple and long-term diseases, have an uncertain nature, are disproportionately intrusive, and are expensive. They require much greater efforts at palliation and a wide variety of ancillary services.

Corbin and Strauss's **trajectory model** identifies the course of the chronic illness as having an uncertain trajectory or course that requires those with the illness, their family members, and their healthcare practitioners to work together to shape the illness (Corbin & Strauss, 1991).

In their conceptual model, Corbin and Strauss describe a person's need to establish a new biography that is a reshaping of identity, away from who the person was before the diagnosis and toward who the person becomes. This biography of self includes all experiences with the disease itself and with the healthcare system, and the person's new ways of relating to friends, colleagues, family, and even strangers (Corbin & Strauss, 1992).

They also postulate that illness is experienced in eight stages or phases (**Table 25-1**).

Table 25-1 Corbin and Strauss's Eight Phases of Illness (Trajectory Model)

Onset: The diagnosis has been made and the disease begins.

Stable: The person maintains everyday activities—work, school, family, and fun.

Unstable: The person is unable to keep symptoms under control and life is disrupted while the person works to regain stability.

Acute: Severe and unrelieved symptoms, and/or the development of complications necessitate hospitalization or bed rest to bring the illness under control.

Crisis: A life-threatening episode occurs and emergency services are necessary.

Comeback: The person, by working hard, gradually returns from periods of instability, acute episodes, and crisis to an acceptable way of life.

Downward: Gradual physical decline is accompanied by increasing disability and continuous alterations in everyday life activities.

Dying: The person relinquishes everyday life interests and activities, brings closure to his or her biography, lets go, and dies peacefully.

Source: Corbin & Strauss (1992).

Corbin and Strauss, in their conceptual model, recognize that illness is experienced in eight stages or phases: onset, stable, unstable, acute, crisis, comeback, downward, and dying.

The client with a chronic illness moves back and forth among these stages until there are no longer any resources that can mitigate the condition's increasingly downward spiral.

Rolland, as well as Corbin and Strauss, recognizes how varied chronic illnesses are. Both models also address the unpredictability of chronic disease. This unpredictability adds to the stress of managing the illness. According to these models, chronic illness is very different from acute illness. Chronic physical and mental illness cause a great deal of continual stress and loss; mental illness also involves significant loss, grieving, and diminished self-worth and self-esteem.

Chronic physical and mental illness cause a great deal of continual stress and loss; mental illness also involves significant loss, grieving, and diminished self-worth and self-esteem.

Critical Thinking Question

How might a client with a chronic mental illness experience coping with the condition in a trajectory model and move among at least three stages or phases?

Corbin and Strauss's trajectory model identifies the course of the chronic illness as having an uncertain trajectory or course that requires those with the illness, their family members, and their healthcare practitioners to work together to shape the illness.

Irene Morof Lubkin and Pamala Larsen

Lubkin and Larsen define chronic illness as the irreversible presence, accumulation, or latency of disease states or impairments that involve the total human environment for supportive care and self-care, maintenance of function, and prevention of further disability.

Nurse theorists have utilized the models of Rolland and of Corbin and Strauss to address various health concerns. Lubkin and Larsen (2006) challenge the nursing profession to recognize that the current acute care system is grossly inadequate and that the needs of a growing elderly population (the aging baby boomers) and others with chronic illness do not fit within the current paradigm of health care. Curtin and Lubkin offer as a definition of chronic illness, "the irreversible presence, accumulation, or latency of disease states or impairments that involve the total human environment for supportive care and self-care, maintenance of function, and prevention of further disability" (1995, pp. 6–7). When the client experiences a physical or a mental chronic illness, such factors as the trajectory of the illness, stigma, chronic pain, social isolation, altered mobility, fatigue, body image, quality of life, family impact, caregiver stress, and powerlessness can impact the client. Larsen provides this insight into chronicity of illness: "Chronic illness, by its very nature, is never completely cured" (2006, pg. 6).

The mental disorders mostly likely to result in chronic disease are schizophrenia, bipolar disorder, and major depression.

Incidence and Prevalence

Chronic illness is the most important health problem in the United States, with an estimated 133 million persons currently living with one chronic illness. In addition, approximately 157 million individuals are expected to have a chronic illness by 2020.

Chronic disease, whether physical or mental in origin, is occurring throughout the United States with increasing prevalence every year. It is the most important health problem in America. The Partnership for Solutions (2004) estimated that, in the United States, 133 million persons are living with one chronic illness and that approximately 157 million individuals will have a chronic illness by 2020.

Chronic mental illness affects people of all ages, races, socioeconomic levels, and walks of life and can occur at any stage of the life cycle. The study funded by the National Institute of Mental Health (NIMH), known as the National Comorbidity Survey Replication (2005) used modern psychiatric standards to estimate the prevalence of mental disorders in a nationally representative sample. Although the survey reports that 26% of the general population reported symptoms consistent with a diagnosis of a mental disorder, the prevalence rates probably were underestimated because the survey did not include the homeless or institutionalized populations in its data collection.

The study spotlighted its finding that mental disorders are the chronic disorders of young people in the United States (National Institute of Mental Health, 2005). The study also noted:

- Mental illness begins very early in life; half of all lifetime mental disorders begin by age 14 and three quarters by age 24.
- Unlike physical conditions, young people with mental illness suffer disability when they are in the prime of their lives and when they should be most productive.
- Prevalence rates increase from the 18–29-year-old age group to the next oldest age group of 30–44-year olds, and then decline.
- Females have a higher rate of mood and anxiety disorders; men have a higher rate of substance use disorders and impulse-control disorders.

The mental disorders most likely to result in chronic disease are schizophrenia, major depressive

Clinical Example 

Ron (33 years old) has been diagnosed since adolescence with schizophrenia, evolving into undifferentiated chronic schizophrenia with acute exacerbations. Ron has had many losses. He lost his father at a young age, and he lost his childhood by assuming his father's responsibilities. College became impossible due to exacerbations of his illness, and he lost his dream of becoming an architect by dropping out of school. Ron lost his dyadic relationship with his wife when his daughter was born, and he lost his job and income as a result of both a physical illness and untoward side effects from his medication. Ron's successful treatment ended when his clozapine (Clozaril) had to be discontinued. His level of functioning deteriorated with each exacerbation and his poor response to other drug therapy. Ron lost his family life when he was moved into a group home, and his wife decided to leave him, taking their daughter. He refused to take medications or participate in treatment groups when he heard about losing his job and family, resulting in a rehospitalization.

Ron's recent life has changed with the exacerbation of his schizophrenic symptoms, and he is not functioning adequately in his roles of husband, father, and employee. The illness's overwhelming impact on his past, current, and future life is evident.

disorder, and bipolar disorder. These are the most prevalent chronic psychiatric disorders.

Schizophrenia is a heterogeneous brain disease. The course of the disorder varies, and symptoms include hallucinations, delusions, and disordered thought. Clients with schizophrenia are unable to experience pleasure, have a diminished emotional range, experience difficulty making choices, and have an ego breakdown with boundary disruption. See Chapter 16.

The serious mood disorders of major depressive disorder and bipolar disorder alter affect, mood, behavior, and thought. Major depressive disorder is accompanied by restricted mood, negative affect, and diminished level of functioning that is often seen with fatigue; feelings of worthlessness, hopelessness, and helplessness; weight change (usually a loss); sleep change (usually insomnia); suicidal ideas, gestures, or both; loss of interest or pleasure; psychomotor slowing; and bodily aches and concerns. Bipolar disorder is another mood disorder in which the individual experiences cyclical changes between extreme highs (mania) and extreme lows (depression). The same individual exhibits symptoms of both mania and depression, depending on where the illness is on its cycle. See Chapter 17.

Clinical Course and Complications

One specific clinical course for all chronic mental illnesses does not exist. All chronic mental illnesses impact both the client and those closest to him or her. The illness affects others around the client, such as family members, classmates, coworkers, peers, and neighbors. Chronic mental illness is long term, with relapses consisting of periods of relative stability and adequate functioning to periods of more acute symptomatology. There are additional consequences, including complications of the primary illness; pharmacotherapy reactions, including mediocre effectiveness of medication or positive effectiveness of medication with intolerable or life-threatening side or toxic effects; changes in life circumstances, such as altered income, lifestyle, and roles; and even unforeseen events, such as encounters with police, the judicial system, and incarceration.

Clients with mental illness and their families go through stages of adjustment to the illness, often at widely varying times or levels of understanding. Families experience different losses; for example, when the client is absent from family activities when hospitalized, incarcerated, or unable to participate because of disease symptomatology.

Critical Thinking Question

What types of challenges do you think that a 20-year-old, who has been coping with a mental illness since late childhood, might experience in a workplace or in college?

Clinical Example

Matthew (58 years old) is a recently remarried businessman who is brought into the psychiatric emergency room by the local police. He is dirty, unkempt, unshaven, and profoundly sad looking. When the staff calls his home, Matthew's wife reports that he has not been home or at work for 3 days, but he did call to say that he was all right. He refused to talk about what was bothering him, but would cry for prolonged periods on the call. In the ER, he turns away from the psychiatrist, refuses to make eye contact, crouches in a corner, and rocks back and forth crying and wringing his hands. According to his healthcare record, Matthew was previously hospitalized for depression in both his 20s and 30s.

Matthew is admitted to the inpatient unit for observation, individual therapy, and medication management. For the first 2 days, he continues to cry, refuses to care for himself, is sleeping erratically, and only picks at his food. He tries to cut himself with a plastic knife and to hang himself with a string of paper clips and tells staff that he is such a failure, "I can't even kill myself." Matthew shares with his nurse that he had been demoted at work because "the bosses don't like me, they think that I am a jerk;" according to Matthew's wife, it was because of cutbacks in the company and that he was retained because of his skills. While he accepts his medication, he frequently tells staff that he is afraid of becoming a druggie and that the medication will make him less of a man to his bride. Matthew is diagnosed as having a major depressive disorder.

Chronic mental illness is long term, with relapses consisting of periods of relative stability and adequate functioning to periods of more acute symptomatology.

In another type of loss, the client cannot participate appropriately in family interactions. Permanent family disruption can occur by the client either abandoning the family or committing suicide. The individual also often experiences family-related losses, lowered economic status because of job loss, loss of a place to live because of eviction, diminished mental functioning when the illness is exacerbated, an inability or difficulty returning to premorbid functioning after the psychosis has stabilized, loss of involvement with significant others when relationships are strained consistently, an increased probability of additional psychopathology resulting from the use of substances or alcohol to cope, and impairment in physiologic functioning as a result of adverse reactions to psychopharmacologic agents.

Classic grief reactions are exhibited both by the individual with the mental illness and by family members as they experience the stages of denial, anger, bargaining, depression, acceptance, modification, and resolution.

Classic grief reactions are exhibited both by the individual with the chronic mental illness and by family members—they grieve for what might have been or what has been lost. Unresolved grief can lead to suicide, substance abuse, self-destructive acts, criminality, and disintegration of the family as a unit and support system. They experience the stages of denial, anger, bargaining, depression, acceptance, modification, and resolution. Some individuals, including the client with the mental illness as well as significant others, may not progress beyond the stage of grieving. These individuals are unable to reach acceptance and resolution until they receive extensive support and **psychoeducation** based on the psychiatric rehabilitation model.

Management and Treatment

Clients with mental disorders need assistance in dealing with the stigma attached to mental illness. It can become a significant barrier to recovery as it impacts the client's ability to find jobs and housing and to make friends. Community education is essential to assist the public in understanding mental illness; accepting individuals and agencies into the community; reducing the stigma of mental illness; and curbing resistance and discrimination against those who live with a chronic mental illness. This is especially essential to ensure the availability in communities of supportive housing, a key component in reducing rates of homelessness and reoccurrences of symptomatology.

Empowering clients allows them to be "pilots" of their own mental health care. The nurse's role is that of an advocate, not a rescuer. Using empowering techniques allows the person and the family or significant others to control the decision making process and assists in maintaining the client's hopefulness. Empowerment helps clients gain control over their lives, which leads to increased self-esteem, greater feelings of self-worth, improved self-concept, and an improved self-image.

Grief and loss counseling is critical because the family and the individual incur multiple losses (relationships and family support systems, life as it existed prior to the illness, employment, finances, deaths of significant others) as a result of the chronic mental illness. If both the client and family can work through their losses, this assists them in accepting and managing the disorder.

Self-esteem, self-efficacy, life skills, and social support need to be fortified, and stressors need to be reduced for the client to benefit from treatment. The key to successful mental health treatment for the chronically mentally ill is that it should be sustained, ongoing, and executed patiently. There are multiple areas that need to be considered in treatment planning (see **Table 25-2**). This allows the client and significant others to carefully institute realistic behavioral and other life changes. The various agencies must collaborate in treatment and include the client in the care planning. The client, family, school, social services department, drug abuse treatment program, health department, housing agencies, criminal justice system, and multidisciplinary team of mental health practitioners (psychiatrists; psychiatric nurses, including psychiatric-mental health clinical nurse specialists and nurse practitioners; social workers; psychologists; medical physicians; occupational, recreational, and other activity therapists; dieticians; spiritual leaders; employment counselors; and other specialists as necessary) need to be involved collectively, providing integrated, holistic mental health care.

Table 25-2 **Treatment Concerns for the Client With a Chronic Mental Illness**

Activities of daily living	Conflicts
Anger management	Legal concerns
Chemical dependency	Social anxiety
Family conflicts	Social skills deficits
Finances	Parenting
Intimate relationships	Self-determination deficits
Sexuality concerns	Concerns related to specific disorders

Source: Adapted from Jongsma, Berghuis, & Bruce (2008).

Figure 25-1 Happy life events, such as weddings, may be stressful to someone who has a chronic mental illness.

Stress management helps clients and their families to cope with the stressors associated with chronic mental illness. Many stressors exist for clients with chronic mental illness, and the clients' coping mechanisms are usually significantly impaired. Happy life events such as weddings, holiday dinners, birthday parties, and vacations that are pleasurable to most people may be overly stressful to someone living with a chronic mental illness such as schizophrenia, bipolar disorder, or major depressive disorder (**Figure 25-1**). The nurse needs to incorporate stress management techniques into the planned nursing interventions. An exercise program for clients can be an important adjunctive therapy in reducing stress and preventing weight gain and metabolic problems in clients (Weber, 2010). Cognitive behavior therapy has been demonstrated to assist families and clients in addressing the wide range of stressors associated with recovery and maintaining a productive life in the community (Hofmann & Tompson, 2004).

Social support groups also benefit those with chronic mental illness and their family members by helping them cope. Participation in support groups promotes self-confidence, exposure to adequate coping behaviors, increased problem-solving ability, and a sense of identity and belonging. Nurses should encourage clients to participate in appropriate psychotherapeutic and social support groups. Clients can be encouraged to include assertiveness programs in the treatment plan to help them make decisions regarding their health care, work, and living arrangements.

In community-based care, the psychiatric-mental health nurse delivers care "in partnership with patients in their homes, work sites, mental health clinics and programs, health maintenance organizations, shelters and clinics for the homeless, crisis centers, senior centers, group homes, and other community settings" (ANA, 2007, p. 25). One method is the Assertive Community Treatment (ACT) model which is "an interdisciplinary team approach to the care of people with severe mental illness. It provides services in the individual's natural setting, including homeless shelters" (ANA, 2007, p. 25). See Chapter 2.

Psychiatric rehabilitation, when utilized within the community, benefits this population. Such an approach allows for the active involvement by the client. The client is taught assertiveness and appropriate decision-making skills to function adequately in the least restrictive treatment environment. **Psychiatric rehabilitation** encompasses relearning skills and competencies needed for successful interpersonal, social, and vocational functioning. It is an essential modality in hospital, residential, and community mental healthcare settings and in home care to prevent those with chronic mental illness from becoming further debilitated. See Chapter 2.

Crisis intervention is utilized to address critical issues such as **homelessness**, incarceration, job loss, family issues, and recurring psychiatric symptomatology. Providing crisis intervention to assist clients during exacerbations of their illness is essential, because it reassures them that the nurse and other members of the multidisciplinary team are available to help them cope.

Crisis intervention assists clients during exacerbations of their illness and reassures them that the nurse and other members of the multidisciplinary team are available.

Clients with chronic mental and physical disorders improve more rapidly with specific, well-planned nursing interventions. Nurses should adopt caring, nonthreatening, nonjudgmental, accepting, and long-term approaches to care for all individuals with chronic mental illness. Nurses orchestrate links between services so that the client does not slip through any part of the system, especially when the client needs ongoing care to prevent reoccurrence.

Clients with chronic mental illness who are homeless must have their housing needs met, and those who are incarcerated must receive adequate mental health services within the correctional facility.

Ongoing nursing case management is necessary to reduce psychiatric symptoms, the impairments associated with the illness, and the disruptions in living caused by the chronic mental illness. In psychiatric-mental health nursing, case management involves

> population-specific nursing knowledge coupled with research, knowledge of the social and legal systems related to mental health and expertise to engage a wide range of services for the patient, regardless of setting ... [these] activities may be with a single client or with a designated population such as the seriously and persistent mentally ill. (ANA, 2007, p. 23)

Ongoing integrated nursing case management can reduce the client's psychiatric symptoms, the impairments associated with the illness, and the disruptions in living caused by the chronic mental illness.

Support groups for clients with chronic mental illness promote self-confidence, exposure to adequate coping behaviors, increased problem-solving ability, and a sense of identity and belonging.

Nursing management should be comprehensive and integrated with the entire multidisciplinary treatment team, social system, and community. Integrated care benefits clients by following them through the healthcare system and anticipating or eliminating problems.

Nursing management for those with chronic mental illness, whether they are in the hospital, a long-term care facility, residential setting, or the community, must incorporate several elements to prevent the individual from becoming totally disabled. The nurse should address both personal and environmental safety to assist the client and family in addressing their anxiety and anger. This is paramount in both the hospital and community settings so that the clients, their families and significant others, and society are free from harm.

Advanced practice registered nurses (clinical nurse specialists and nurse practitioners) functioning as psychotherapists can effectively provide individual, group, and family psychotherapy.

The nurse needs to employ an individualized and integrated approach when working with the client and family to make sure their specific and various needs are met. The nursing plan needs to be individualized, integrated with the care provided by other members of the psychiatric team, and realistic. When family members and the client are actively involved in planning, it helps in the development of realistic goals that meet and satisfy the client's and family's needs. Individual, group, and family psychotherapy can benefit the client and significant others. Advanced practice registered nurses (APRNs) functioning as psychotherapists can effectively provide these therapies as well as psychopharmacologic management.

The psychopharmacologic medications used in the treatment of chronic mental illness are primarily the conventional antipsychotic medications, antidepressants, and mood stabilizers. Nurses need to know the clinical indications for these medications, adverse and toxic reactions, and therapeutic dose information, as well as related nursing implications. The nurse must share medication information with the client and the family and stress the importance of compliance with the prescribed regimen. See Chapter 6.

The nurse also endeavors to provide to clients psychoeducation, basic cognitive and academic skills training, group work, social skills training, vocational training, interpersonal skill building, behavior modification (making small life and behavioral changes at a time), and medication management.

Critical Thinking Question

Why would a happy life event become a negative stressor for a client with chronic mental illness?

Clinical Example

Bonnie (42 years old) was initially diagnosed with bipolar disorder in her senior year in high school. During college, she had frequent and major fluctuations in her mood, resulting in her changing roommates three times in her freshman year, twice in her sophomore year, and finally choosing to live alone off-campus in her last 2 years. In her senior year, she painted the apartment in combinations of dark red and black, resulting in angry altercations with her landlord.

Bonnie is artistically talented, but her ability to focus on her painting and sculpture is related to how controlled her bipolar symptoms are. In her mid-30s, she destroyed a dozen paintings the night before a gallery-sponsored exhibit because of a depressive episode. The exhibit was cancelled and never rescheduled. During the same time period, she was married and divorced twice. After the second divorce, she entered individual psychotherapy, was placed on medication, and joined a support group. After a year, Bonnie reported feeling much better and opened an arts and crafts store with a member of her support group.

In the last few months she has been experiencing significant and ever-increasing mood fluctuations—periods of euphoria, increased energy, hypersexuality, greatly reduced sleep patterns, and even sometimes depression. Two weeks ago, in a 48-hour period, Bonnie baked 200 cupcakes for a church bake sale. She became angry, throwing cupcakes against the wall when the bake sale organizers questioned why she did so much baking. Her store partner called Bonnie's therapist, who suggested that she be brought into the clinic. After a lengthy session, in which she admitted to stopping her medication because she felt really "much better and in control," Bonnie agreed with her therapist to a voluntary inpatient admission. Afterwards, Bonnie's store partner expressed her frustration that Bonnie had precipitated her relapse and worried that such behavior was jeopardizing both their business and personal relationships.

Considerations for Client and Family Education

Psychoeducation involves teaching clients, their families, and significant others about the disease or condition (i.e., the specific chronic mental illness), types of psychotherapy, medication management, complementary therapies, compliance with different treatment modalities, rehabilitation, signs of relapse, and community resources. By improving the client's and family's knowledge base and understanding, there is a greater potential for ongoing control of the client's condition. Clients should also be taught skills to successfully modify their lifestyles, enhance their therapies, and live productive lives.

Psychoeducation also involves teaching coping strategies to the clients' families, significant others, and caregivers in order to help them deal more effectively with the client. It can help reduce stress and anxiety within the family and community. The family is assisted in understanding the prolonged course of the chronic mental illness and its impact on family dynamics and functioning.

Summary

Individuals with chronic mental illnesses and their families need care from motivated, realistic, and informed nurses. Nurses need to employ effective approaches to properly assist individuals in living and coping with chronic illness on a daily basis. Such approaches include the following:

- Using concrete and simple goals to allow individuals the opportunity for successful attainment
- Teaching stress management and coping strategies
- Understanding the trajectory nature of chronic illness
- Being realistic

Nurses need to be vigilant and active advocates in the healthcare, social service, and political arenas to ensure that the necessary services for clients with chronic mental illness are accessible, coordinated, and provided.

Annotated References

American Nurses Association. (2007). *Psychiatric-mental health nursing: Scope and standards of practice*. Silver Spring, MD: Author.

Corbin, J. M. (2003). The body in health and illness. *Qualitative Health Research, 13*(2), 256–267.

Evidence-Based Practice

Since the early 1970s, practitioners caring for those with chronic mental illness have sought to reduce the rehospitalization experiences of their clients. Husted and Jorgens (2000) proposed that therapies or procedures that work in one geographic locale might have very different results in another. They determined that mental health practitioners need to take into account where the client lives. The usual practice of placing rural clients with chronic mental illness in areas of greater population density may actually lead to more cognitive and perceptual disruptions in the clients. Therefore, decisions regarding placement of clients who might be more comfortable and functional in a rural setting should be considered in working toward developing a milieu that minimizes the risk of rehospitalization for these clients.

Hayes and coauthors (2006) studied the effectiveness of using cognitive therapy in the treatment of clients with chronic mental illness. In a study that examined the added benefits of cognitive versus supportive therapy to the treatment milieu, the authors determined that the clients who participated in the cognitive groups were more motivated and active than those in the supportive group.

Mohr analyzed three studies where cognitive behavioral therapy (CBT) was used in treating clients with schizophrenia. The results of the three studies included evidence that a majority of clients reported fewer hallucinations and cognitive problems and a better quality of life; a group of clients receiving CBT as opposed to a nonspecific supportive intervention continued to improve in their recovery as opposed to clients in a different group who did not receive CBT; and a third group receiving CBT in another study showed an improvement in positive symptoms (Melynk & Fineout-Overholt, 2005).

This is a discussion of the body in the context of chronic illness compared with that of health. The author provides insight into chronic illness with respect to time, space, morality, aesthetics, morality, technology, information, and interpersonal relationships.

Corbin, J. M., & Strauss, A. (1991). A nursing model for chronic illness management based on the trajectory framework. *Scholarly Inquiry for Nursing Practice, 5*, 155–174.
This article presents Corbin and Strauss's conceptual model for nursing practice.

Corbin, J. M., & Strauss, A. (1992). A nursing model for chronic illness management based on the trajectory framework. In P. Woog (Ed.), *The chronic illness trajectory framework: The Corbin and Strauss nursing model* (pp. 9–28). New York, NY: Springer.
In this chapter, the authors present their conceptual model, a chronic illness trajectory. They further discuss implications for nursing practice, teaching, research, and policy making.

Curtin, M., & Lubkin, I. (1995). What is chronicity? In I. Lubkin (Ed.), *Chronic illness: Impact and interventions* (3rd ed., pp. 6–7). Sudbury, MA: Jones and Bartlett.
This textbook illustrates how healthcare professionals can effectively assist the chronically ill in better managing the course of their illness and their lives.

Hayes, S. A., Hope, D. A., Terryberry-Spohr, L. S., Spaulding, W. D., Vandyke, M., Elting, D. T., … Sullivan, M. (2006). Discriminating between cognitive and supportive group therapies for chronic mental illness. *Journal of Nervous and Mental Disorders, 194*(8), 603–609.
This study examined the growing evidence that cognitive therapy is effective in the treatment of clients with chronic mental illness.

Hofmann, S. G., & Tompson, M. C. (2004). *Treating chronic and severe mental disorders: A handbook of empirically supported interventions*. New York, NY: The Guilford Press.
The authors provide evidence-based approaches to treating schizophrenia, mood disorders, substance abuse problems, and severe personality disorders.

Husted, J., & Jorgens, A. (2000). Best practice: Population density as a factor in the rehospitalization of persons with serious and persistent mental illness. *Psychiatric Services, 51*(5), 603–605.
This article considers the implications of placing clients with chronic mental illness in areas of greater population density and the impact on rehospitalization.

Jongsma, A. E., Berghuis, D. J., & Bruce, T. J. (2008). *The severe and persistent mental illness treatment planner (practice planners)* (2nd ed.). Hoboken, NJ: Wiley.
This guide is organized around 31 behavioral issues ranging from employment problems and family conflicts, to financial needs and homelessness, to intimate relationships and social anxiety.

Lubkin, I. M., & Larsen, P. D. (Eds.). (2006). *Chronic illness: Impact and interventions* (6th ed.). Sudbury, MA: Jones and Bartlett.
This textbook presents the various aspects of chronic illness that influence both patients and their families.

National Commission on Chronic Illness. (1957). *Chronic illness in the United States* (Vol. I). Cambridge, MA: Harvard University Press.
This publication gives an overview of chronic illness in the United States, including an operational definition, prevalence, incidence, prevention, and summary of information on chronic disorders.

National Institute of Mental Health. (2005). *NIMH-funded national comorbidity survey replication study (NCS-R)*. Retrieved from http://www.nimh.nih.gov/health/topics/statistics/ncsr-study/index.shtml
The landmark study is described in four papers that document the prevalence and severity of specific mental disorders. The papers provide significant new data—such as days lost from work—caused by specific disorders, including mood, anxiety, and substance abuse disorders.

Partnership for Solutions. (2004). *Chronic conditions: Making the case for ongoing care*. Retrieved from http://www.partnershipforsolutions.org/statistics/prevalence.html
The partnership, led by Johns Hopkins University and the Robert Wood Johnson Foundation, is an initiative to improve the care and quality of life for the more than 125 million Americans with chronic health conditions.

Rolland, J. S. (1984). Toward a psychosocial typology of chronic and life-threatening illness. *Family Systems Medicine, 2*, 245–263.
This article addresses Rolland's conceptual model for chronic and life-threatening illnesses.

Rolland, J. S. (1987). Family illness paradigms: Evolution and significance. *Family Systems Medicine, 5*, 482–503.
In this article, Rolland clarifies important variables of family-illness paradigms and describes how beliefs shape the manner in which families adapt to chronic and life-threatening illnesses.

Rolland, J. S. (1988a). Chronic illness and the family life cycle. In B. Carter & M. McGoldrick (Eds.), *The changing family life cycle: A framework for family therapy* (2nd ed., pp. 433–456). New York, NY: Gardner Press.
In this chapter, Rolland explains chronic illness as an evolutionary thread that intertwines with the individual's and family's life cycles.

Rolland, J. S. (1988b). A conceptual model of chronic and life-threatening illness and its impact on families. In C. S. Chilman, E. W. Nunnally, & F. N. Cox (Eds.), *Chronic illness and disability* (pp. 17–68). Beverly Hills, CA: Sage.
In this chapter, Rolland discusses his conceptual model in relation to chronic illnesses within families.

Rolland, J. S. (1990). The impact of illness on the family. In R. E. Rakel (Ed.), *Textbook of family practice* (4th ed., pp. 80–100). Philadelphia, PA: W. B. Saunders.
In this chapter, Rolland presents his three-dimensional conceptual model and how chronic disease affects the life cycles of the person and his or her family.

Strauss, A. L., Corbin, J., Fagerhaugh, S., Glaser, B. G., Maines, D., Suczek, B., & Weiner, C. (1984). *Chronic illness and the quality of life* (2nd ed.). St. Louis, MO: C. V. Mosby.
These authors give a comprehensive picture of the problems of living with chronic illness, patient hospital experiences, and the healthcare system and chronic illness.

Weber, M. (2010). The importance of exercise for individuals with chronic mental illness. *Journal of Psychosocial and Mental Health Services, 48*(10), 35–40.
The author identifies the current state of the science for the use of an exercise program as a psychiatric nursing intervention.

Internet Resources

For a full suite of assignments and additional learning activities, use the access code located in the front of your book to visit this exclusive website: http://go.jblearning.com/mentalhealth. If you do not have an access code, you can obtain one at the site.

Learning Objectives

After reading this chapter, you will be able to:

- Define *mental retardation, intellectual disability* and *developmental disability* in accordance with criteria established by the Developmental Disabilities Assistance and Bill of Rights Act, American Psychiatric Association, and American Association of Mental Retardation.
- Distinguish among mental retardation, pervasive developmental disorders, and other intellectual and developmental disabilities.
- Identify general guidelines and considerations for working with clients with intellectual and developmental disabilities.
- Identify nursing interventions in assisting clients and their families to cope with intellectual and developmental disabilities.
- Describe important components in teaching clients and their families about these disorders.

Key Terms

Adaptive functioning

Anticipatory molding

Applied behavior analysis (ABA)

Asperger's disorder

Autistic disorder

Childhood disintegrative disorder

Classifications of mental retardation

Developmental disability

Down syndrome

Dyslexia

Echolalia

Habilitation

Inclusion

Intellectual disability

Intelligence quotient (IQ)

Interdependence

Learning disorder

Mental retardation

Pervasive developmental disorder

Rett's disorder

Transdisciplinary team

Clients With Intellectual and Developmental Disabilities

Donna R. Falvo and Karen A. Ballard

http://go.jblearning.com/mentalhealth 

For a full suite of assignments and additional learning activities, use the access code located in the front of your book to visit this exclusive website: http://go.jblearning.com/mentalhealth. If you do not have an access code, you can obtain one at the site.

Introduction

Developmental disability encompasses a wide and varied number of conditions that occur in childhood, are lifelong, affect intellectual and/or physical functioning, and require ongoing special services and support. The definitions, categorization, and classification of these conditions have changed significantly since the term *developmental disability* was first coined in the Developmental Disability Act of 1978. Continued effort has been directed to develop definitions and diagnostic categories that will best describe and accurately reflect characteristics of specific conditions without the negative connotations that have existed in the past.

Definitions and classifications have evolved as knowledge and attitudes regarding these conditions have changed and as there has been increasing realization that there is a need for more positive and less stigmatizing definitions.

Defining any disability has positive and negative aspects. It can provide guidance for assessment, treatment, or management of specific conditions and can be used to determine eligibility for services. Unfortunately, defining disability can also be a basis for labeling, stereotyping, discrimination, and segregation. In an attempt to avoid such pitfalls, the Developmental Disabilities Assistance and Bill of Rights Act of 1990 emphasized functional capacity rather than categorizations and stressed empowerment of individuals with disabilities (McLaughlin & Wehman, 1996).

Habilitation is the process of developing new skills and abilities. The habilitation process can be very complex for an individual who is mentally retarded or developmentally disabled.

The Developmental Disabilities Assistance and Bill of Rights Act defines developmental disability as:

> a severe chronic disability of an individual that:
>
> a) is attributable to mental or physical impairment or combination of mental and physical impairment;
>
> b) is manifested before the individual attains the age of 22;
>
> c) is likely to continue indefinitely;
>
> d) results in substantial functional limitations in three or more of the following areas of major life activity: self-care, receptive and expressive language, learning, mobility, self direction, capacity for independent living, and economic self sufficiency;
>
> e) reflects the individual's need for a combination and sequence of special, interdisciplinary or generic services; individualized support; or other forms of assistance that are of lifelong or extended duration and are individually planned and coordinated. (Developmental Disabilities Assistance and Bill of Rights Act of 2000)

The Children's Health Act of 2000 established the National Center on Birth Defects and Developmental Disabilities (NCBDDD) at the Centers for Disease Control and Prevention (CDC). The center includes three divisions—the Division of Birth Defects and Developmental Disabilities, the Division of Human Development and Disability, and the Division of Blood Disorders. Its mission is to promote the health of babies, children, and adults and enhance the potential for full, productive living (CDC, 2011).

All nurses need to recognize that the healthcare needs and concerns of persons with developmental disabilities are the same as those in the general population. Orem's self-care deficit nursing theory (Hartweg, 1991) is especially useful when developing a plan of care for a client with a developmental disability. The specialty of developmental disabilities nursing recognizes the full scope of healthcare needs of persons with developmental disabilities (Developmental Disabilities Nurses Association [DDNA], 1995). The origins of developmental disabilities nursing include maternal-child health nursing, psychiatric nursing, and community health nursing. ANA's *Intellectual and Developmental Disabilities Nursing: Scope and Standards of Practice* has identified phenomena of concern related to individuals, family, and communities for nurses who specialize in this area of practice (2004).

In working with clients with developmental disabilities, it is important for the nurse to remember that no matter how severe the condition, individuals have the capacity to learn, grow, and develop throughout life. When working with clients with many conditions or disabilities, the focus may be on rehabilitation (relearning previously learned skills) or in addressing intellectual and developmental disabilities, or **habilitation** (learning new skills). The nurse is the organizer of services in response to the client's health needs. The role of the nurse is to promote health and well-being, to develop strategies that minimize the degree of handicap clients may experience, and to provide necessary supports to enhance the client's ability to function to his or her maximum capacity. The nurse must also consider the individual within the context of the unique needs and concerns of the family as a unit.

Although causes and characteristics of specific developmental disabilities vary, a common feature of such disabilities is a significant developmental delay in one or more areas of function including language, attention, cognition, social behavior, motor skills, and affect. Developmental disability encompasses a wide range of intellectual as well as physical disabilities. This chapter focuses on those intellectual and psychiatric developmental disabilities that may be more commonly encountered in healthcare settings, and are therefore of special interest to the psychiatric nurse. These include those conditions that are classified in the American Psychiatric Association's (APA, 2000) *Diagnostic and Statistical Manual of Mental Disorders*, fourth edition, text revision (*DSM-IV-TR*), such as mental retardation, pervasive developmental disorders including autistic disorder, Asperger's disorder, Rett's disorder, childhood disintegrative disorder, atypical autism, and learning disorders.

For the *DSM-5*, the APA (2010) is proposing a new category of learning disabilities with subcategories for dyslexia (reading) and dyscalculia (mathematics) and a single diagnostic category of *autism spectrum disorder* for the current diagnostic categories of autistic disorder, Asperger's disorder, childhood disintegrative disorder, and pervasive developmental disorder. The APA's Neurodevelopmental Work Group is recommending changing *mental retardation* to *intellectual disability* and that there be only a single diagnostic category for intellectual disabilities with the focus being on impairments in adaptive functioning, not intelligence level (IQ) (APA, 2010).

Critical Thinking Question 

What are the positive and potential negative consequences of identifying intellectual and psychiatric developmental disabilities in an individual?

Mental Retardation (Intellectual Disability)

Mental retardation is a developmental disability that is defined in terms of both cognitive (**intelligence quotient [IQ]** below 70) and adaptive function and is a condition that occurs prior to the age of 18. The American Psychiatric Association's *DSM-IV-TR* places mental retardation on Axis II. The CDC (2005) describes **intellectual disability** as being

> characterized both by a significantly below-average score on a test of mental ability or intelligence and by limitations in the ability to function in areas of daily life, such as communication, self-care, and getting along in social situations and school activities. Intellectual disability is sometimes referred to as a cognitive disability or mental retardation. (p. 1)

Intellectual disability or mental retardation is a complex disorder. Early intervention is essential if each affected child is to receive the services required to foster the attainment of full potential. Nurses and other practitioners need to consider all physical, environmental, and social factors and expeditiously facilitate appropriate interventions.

Incidence and Prevalence

Mental retardation occurs in about 2–3% of the population (Daily, Ardinger, & Holmes, 2000). Approximately 90% of individuals with mental retardation are classified in the mild mental retardation range (Volkmar, Klin, & Paul, 2004).

Etiology and Physiology

The causes of mental retardation or intellectual disability are numerous and can include genetic and/or environmental factors. Studies indicate that a substantial number of cases for this condition are due to genetic abnormalities, such as fragile X syndrome or trisomy 21 (Down syndrome) (Boyd, 2009). The most common cause in the United States is **Down syndrome** (**Figure 26-1**; Yang, Rasmussen, & Friedman, 2002).

Mental retardation or intellectual disability can be congenital or acquired. Congenital causes include brain malformations and chromosomal abnormalities. Prenatal causes include exposures to infection in utero such as rubella or herpes, exposure to toxic substances such as drugs or alcohol, and poor oxygenation of the fetal brain. Mental retardation or intellectual disability can be caused by brain injury either at birth or in childhood due to accident or abuse, infections such as meningitis, exposure to tox-

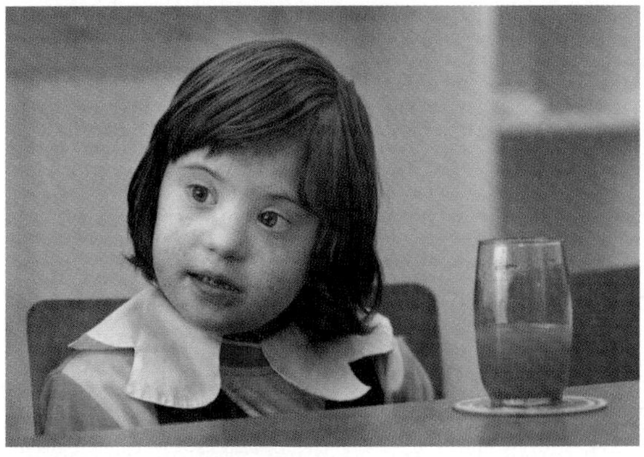

Figure 26-1 Down syndrome is the most common cause of mental retardation in the United States.

ic substances such as lead, metabolic disorders such as phenylketonuria (PKU) or hypothyroidism, malnutrition, and social deprivation. In some instances the specific cause of mental retardation or intellectual disability cannot be determined.

There is no single physiologic process involved. The specific brain malfunction depends on the cause, which may be known and understood or unknown. Some disorders have recognizable physical signs. For example, an individual with Down syndrome has a set of characteristic physical features (short stature; epicanthic fold of the eyelids; flat nose; short, broad hands; small ears; sloping forehead) that manifest the disorder. Some disorders have known associated laboratory findings such as high blood phenylalanine in phenylketonuria (PKU) and trisomy of chromosome 21 in Down syndrome.

Clinical Example

Molly and Teddy, 16-year-old fraternal twins who are moderately retarded, have been followed in the Pediatric Developmental Clinic since early childhood. Both twins were late to walk and speak. With speech therapy and physical rehabilitation, they are able to communicate their needs, engage in activities of daily living, and have a small group of friends with whom they attend special education and social functions. They are functioning at a second-grade level, are sometimes disruptive in large groups, and need extra supervision in times of stress such as when their paternal grandmother died in a car accident. Their parents, who are in their late 50s, are working with the transdisciplinary team on preparing the twins to explore some vocational training that might permit them to participate in the job market or a sheltered workshop, as well as the possibility of a group home as they enter adulthood.

There is not always a direct correlation between the *DSM-IV-TR* and the AAMR classifications, but the relationship is close enough to permit clinical presentation material to be discussed simultaneously for the similar classifications. The *DSM-IV-TR* classifications are mild, moderate, severe, and profound. The AAMR classifications are intermittent, limited, extensive, and profound.

Parents usually present children with intellectual and developmental disabilities for evaluation when they are concerned about the child's level of adaptive functioning—that is, their ability to meet common life demands and to be personally independent.

Clinical Presentation

Individuals with mental retardation or intellectual disability have below average general intellectual functioning for their stage of development as well as limitations in adaptive functioning. **Adaptive functioning** is defined as those skills needed to manage age-appropriate tasks and demands of everyday life such as communication, conceptualization, self-care, self-direction, self-sufficiency, and safety. Because both intellectual and adaptive function are considered essential features in mental retardation, substandard performance on standardized intelligence tests alone is not sufficient for a diagnosis. Impairments in both cognitive and adaptive function must be present prior to the age of 18 in order for a child or adult to be considered as having mental retardation or intellectual disability.

Subaverage intelligence is defined as an intelligence quotient (IQ) of 70 or below as determined through standardized intelligence testing. Interpretation of test results as well as measurement of cognitive function and results should always be made in the context of the person's cultural, language, environmental, and individual factors. For example, individuals who interpret questions or responses differently due to cultural interpretation or who are being given a test not in their native language may obtain scores that are not reflective of their actual intellectual capacity. Likewise, physical discomfort or medical conditions may also affect an individual's ability to perform to maximum capacity during testing.

Degrees of severity of mental retardation as reflected by one's IQ are categorized in the *DSM-IV-TR* as mild, moderate, severe, or profound. The IQ levels for each of these categories are mild retardation IQ: 55–70; moderate retardation IQ: 40–54; severe retardation IQ: 25–39; and profound retardation IQ: below 25.

When individuals 18 years of age or younger demonstrate an intellectual capacity that is below average (below 70) and when they demonstrate functional impairment in at least two or more areas of adaptive functioning, a diagnosis of mental retardation is made (American Psychiatric Association [APA], 2000). Adaptive function is determined by the person's ability to learn and problem solve as well as by assessing the individual's ability to manage age-appropriate tasks and demands of everyday life. Assessment of adaptive function should always include observations of the person in his or her natural environment and should be based on a history of behavior, which has been obtained from persons who know the individual well. Age, cultural, and individual differences should also be considered.

Because mental retardation cannot be defined by cognitive ability alone, the American Association of Mental Retardation (AAMR) defines mental retardation in terms of the types of supports individuals need in order to function on a day-to-day basis. The AAMR **classifications of mental retardation** are:

- *Intermittent:* Supports required periodically, or on a short-term basis during times of transition or crisis; when supports are needed they may be either high or low intensity.

- *Limited:* Low-intensity, time-limited supports needed for specific needs, such as job training or school transition.
- *Extensive:* Ongoing, regular supports needed on a low-intensity basis in order to maintain adequate function in home or work environment.
- *Pervasive:* Extensive ongoing high-intensity support required for safety and well-being (American Association of Mental Retardation, 1992; Luckasson et al., 2002).

Critical Thinking Question

How could the differences and/or similarities between the American Association of Mental Retardation's (AAMR) definition of mental retardation and the categories of mental retardation as specified in the *DSM-IV-TR* influence a nurse's understanding of this condition?

Differential Diagnosis

The diagnostic criteria for mental retardation include subaverage intellectual function of 70 or below as well as deficits in adaptive functioning (e.g., self-care, self-direction, ability to work). In order to meet the qualifications for diagnosis, deficits in intellectual and adaptive function must occur prior to the age of 18. Mental retardation is coded on Axis II. Diagnostic tests that are utilized include the Weschsler Intelligence Scales for Children, Stanford-Binet, Kaufman Assessment Battery for Children, Vineland Adaptive Behavior Scales, and AAMR Adaptive Behavior Scale.

The diagnosis of mental retardation or intellectual disability in young children is often overlooked because of misconceptions about the presentation of the condition or the belief that young children cannot be tested (Daily et al., 2000). The most important aspect of identifying this condition in young children is a complete child and family history, including information about the pregnancy. Resources such as early intervention programs or rehabilitation services can enable the child to reach a maximum level of functional capacity.

Management and Treatment

Mental retardation or intellectual disability, although diagnosed in childhood, is not only a childhood disability. Individuals with the condition live into adulthood, and increasingly are living into older age, which may mean an increasing prevalence of chronic disease (Noble, 2001) and multiple and complex health problems that change over the life span (Prater & Zylstra, 2006). Clients with intellectual disabilities who also develop hypertension, diabetes, or other chronic medical conditions present challenges in management. They may also develop psychiatric diagnoses, which compound existing management problems. The overall goal is to help the person attain and maintain an optimal level of health and function throughout the life span within the range of their capacity.

The greater the severity of mental retardation or intellectual disability, the more likely it is that the client has a coexisting medical condition.

Currently there are glaring health disparities regarding availability of adequate health care for individuals with mental retardation or intellectual disability as compared to that available to the general population (National Institute of Child Health and Human Development, 2001). The *Standards of Developmental Disabilities Nursing Practice* states: "The nurse intervenes as guided by the nursing care plan to implement nursing actions that promote, maintain, or restore wellness, prevent illness, and effect habilitation" (DDNA, 1995, p. 8). **Inclusion** refers to the integration of all persons, regardless of special needs and disabilities or the environment (e.g., school, community), with typical peers in the least restrictive

Considerations for Client and Family Education

When mental retardation or intellectual disability is associated with a specific condition, such as Down syndrome, the nurse should help parents understand the condition. Helping parents know how to respond to questions they may encounter from family members, friends, or casual observers can help decrease any anxiety parents may have in social situations with their child. Parents should be taught what to expect in terms of specific behaviors or issues their child may experience in the future and to understand that children with this condition will also experience many of the same developmental issues as other children. Important teaching issues that the nurse should address on an ongoing basis with parents include the importance of providing structure and discipline, as appropriate; helping their children develop social skills in accordance with their abilities; and understanding the child's sexuality and need for socialization.

Figure 26-2 The transdisciplinary team is a care model based on free-flowing communication, and the transfer of knowledge and skills across discipline boundaries in the service of a common, client-centered goal.

Common characteristics of dyslexia include difficulty with the manipulation of sounds (phonologic processing) and/or rapid visual-verbal responding.

setting. Innovative programs geared to the person's strengths and capabilities must be provided (American Nurses Association, 2004). The concept of inclusion (being a part of the whole) rather than being in the community is essential to understanding the expectations of individuals with mental retardation. **Interdependence** (mutual dependence) is a method to accomplish inclusion. Nurses and other clinicians are involved in both discipline-specific and transdisciplinary team evaluation processes that should be ongoing and continuous to ensure best outcomes. The **transdisciplinary team** is a care model based on free-flowing communication and the transfer of knowledge and skills across discipline boundaries in the service of a common, client-centered goal (**Figure 26-2**).

Learning Disorders

Learning disorders are classified as reading disorders, mathematics disorders, and disorders of written expression.

Learning disorders, formerly called academic skills disorders, are conditions in which the level of achievement in either verbal or nonverbal areas is less than what would normally be expected for one's age and intellectual ability. Learning disorders include conditions associated with reading, mathematics, and written expression. They have a significant negative impact on academic achievement or activities of daily living (ADLs) such as using money, reading instructions, or completing applications or forms (APA, 2000). Learning disorders are often not identified early. Therefore, the individual's symptoms may be attributed to lack of interest, not trying, or lack of cognitive ability.

Incidence and Prevalence

Learning disorders are present in approximately 2–5% of the population in the Western world (Gillberg & Soderstrom, 2003). **Dyslexia**, a specific reading disorder that impairs one's ability to read words, affects approximately 5% of all school-aged children (Boyd, 2009).

Evidence-Based Practice

When researchers (Ailey, Miller, Heller, & Smith, 2006) utilized the Interpersonal Model of Depression (IMD) tool to evaluate the level of depression among 100 adults with Down syndrome, 32% had elevated depression scores, and 40% reported feeling lonely. The relationship among depression, perceived social support, loneliness, and life satisfaction was statistically significant. Utilization of such a framework in monitoring depression in individuals with Down syndrome across their life spans could be an asset in early intervention and treatment.

In 2004, Strand, Benzein, and Saveman reported on the results of a questionnaire that was sent to 164 staff members in 17 different care settings for adults with intellectual and developmental disabilities in Sweden. Because many individuals with intellectual and psychiatric developmental disabilities are being cared for by others in either their own homes or residential settings (assisted-living or group homes), there is concern for the level of violence, abuse, and neglect that might be occurring. Seventy-four percent of respondents reported being involved in or witnessing violent incidents towards clients and 14% admitted to being the perpetrator of the violent act. Most of the violence occurred on a daily basis; it was both physical and psychologic, and it tended to occur in close caretaking situations. This study indicates the importance of supportive supervision, education, and outlets for staff and increasing the training in communication skills for clients with intellectual and psychiatric developmental disabilities.

Etiology and Physiology

No specific cause for learning disorders has been identified. Clients with coexisting neurologic disorders, perinatal injury, or genetic predisposition may also exhibit a learning disorder. However, many

www Mr. J. **CASE STUDIES**

Mr. J., a 28-year-old man with moderate mental retardation, has recently moved from his parents' home to a group home in the community. His parents have been overly protective, and consequently Mr. J. has had little opportunity to develop relationship skills or to explore his own sexuality. Since moving to the group home, Mr. J. has appeared enthusiastic about interacting with other group members socially, often interrupting others with his own stories of his family. Mr. J. has participated in community meetings, is part of the housekeeping team, and, most recently, volunteered to help with gardening. Staff has had to remind him to remember to bathe, brush his teeth, and change into clean clothes. Mr. J. has had the most difficulty with his two roommates as he is not used to sharing a room. He has been very interested in interacting with females, and has, on occasion, frightened several young women visiting the home by grabbing them and touching them inappropriately. Mr. J. has had two fights with other male clients over female clients that he calls his girlfriends.

Nursing Care Plan **Client With Mental Retardation or Intellectual Disability**

Nursing Diagnosis 1: Impaired social interaction related to impaired neurologic development as evidenced by lack of interest or ability to get along with others

Nursing Diagnosis 2: Chronic low self-esteem related to disturbances in development of self-concept as evidenced by overt eagerness to be accepted within the group home

Nursing Diagnosis 3: Self-care deficit related to perceptual or cognitive impairment as evidenced by inability to eat, bathe, toilet, and dress or groom self independently.

Expected Outcomes	Interventions	Evaluations
• The client will develop a positive self-concept and an understanding of his own sexuality without feeling embarrassed or fearful.	• Assess the client's comprehension of his own sexuality. • Provide opportunities for the client to discuss his sexual feelings and to ask questions. • Structure opportunities to explain bodily changes, sexual functions, and issues of intimacy to the client.	• The client asks questions about bodily functions as need arises. • The client talks freely with staff and family about sexual concerns. • The client refrains from inappropriate sexual behaviors and demonstrates ability to avoid inappropriate contact.
• The client will behave in socially appropriate ways.	• Provide the client with information about boundaries and opportunities to distinguish between appropriate and inappropriate social behaviors.	• The client is more comfortable in social situations (one-on-one and group) and develops an appropriate social network.
• The client will develop socially appropriate relationships.	• Provide opportunities for the client to engage in role-playing activities to learn to distinguish between acceptable and unacceptable social behaviors in a variety of simulated social settings.	• The client gets along better with roommates and is spending more time interacting with them. • The client appears more comfortable around female clients and visitors.
• The client will wear appropriate attire.	• Discuss with the client possible choices of clothing depending upon the day's activities.	• The client will make appropriate clothing choices and will feel more comfortable when engaging in activities.

Visit http://go.jblearning.com/mentalhealth for additional care plans and exercises.

clients with learning disorders have no specific identifiable condition to which the learning disorder can be attributed. There are no known physiologic processes associated with learning disorders.

Clinical Presentation

Learning disorders are classified as either verbal or nonverbal. Verbal learning disorder typically refers to deficits in reading and spelling, whereas nonverbal learning disorders refer to mathematics. Learning disorders in children are usually identified in the school. In adults, learning disorders are often observed by nurses and other healthcare practitioners when the adult fails to understand written instructions, complete health forms, take medications on schedule, or remember appointments.

Differential Diagnosis

Diagnosis of a learning disorder is usually made through administration of standardized tests by a clinician (e.g., a psychologist or nurse practitioner) trained to administer and interpret standardized tests. An undiagnosed learning disorder may also be identified in adulthood. Other factors such as inadequate educational opportunities (e.g., deficient teaching, high rate of absenteeism) or sensory impairment (e.g., impaired vision or hearing) may also affect a person's ability to learn or to gain specific skills, so a diagnosis of a specific learning disorder should not be made until these other factors are eliminated as being present or causing the problem.

Autistic disorder is also known as autism and as early infantile autism.

Management and Treatment

Treatment of learning disorders consists of special educational programs to assist children and adults to learn alternative ways of processing information as well as providing special accommodations that enable the client to adapt to deficits he or she is experiencing. The underpinning of effective treatment is tailoring interventions to best meet each individual's specific needs (Dudley-Marling, 2004).

Pervasive Developmental Disorders

Pervasive developmental disorders is the official diagnostic term used in the *DSM-IV-TR* (APA, 2000) to describe a broad range of developmental disorders that are characterized by impairments in multiple areas of development and that vary in subtype and severity. The major conditions included in this diagnostic category are autistic disorder, Asperger's disorder, Rett's disorder, childhood disintegrative disorder, and other pervasive developmental disorders not otherwise specified, including atypical autism. Childhood disintegrative disorder has also been called Heller's syndrome and dementia infantilis and is a category used to describe conditions in which there is severe impairment in social and communication development in addition to stereotyped behavioral features generally observed in autistic disorder. However, criteria for the other pervasive developmental disorders, such as autism or Asperger's disorder, are not met. All of these conditions, absent the presence of other diagnoses or disorders, are coded on Axis I.

The term *autism spectrum disorders* (ASD) is often used as a synonym for pervasive developmental disorders (Simpson et al., 2005). ASD is used to describe a broad range of subtypes and levels of severity of conditions included in the spectrum of autism and pervasive developmental disorders (autistic disorder, Rett's disorder, childhood disintegrative disorder, and Asperger's disorder).

Autistic Disorder

Autistic disorder or autism is the best known of the autism spectrum disorders (ASDs). Symptoms usually appear prior to the age of 3. The condition is characterized by behavioral patterns that show impairment in a range of areas of development, but

Clinical Example

Chuck is a cheerful and engaging second grader who has been having temper tantrums, refusing to do homework, and is increasingly sitting alone in the classroom. During a parent-teacher conference, these behaviors are discussed, and his increasing school problems with recognizing letters and simple words, spelling, and now writing are of concern. The teacher notes and his parents have observed that Chuck's speaking vocabulary is more sophisticated than his written vocabulary and he can easily follow oral directions, but he becomes frustrated and struggles with written assignments. It is agreed that he will receive a physical to rule out any medical condition, and he is referred to the local developmental and learning center.

Considerations for Client and Family Education

Nurses should be aware of the client's deficits when considering the client's and family's specific teaching needs. Approaches to teaching and assistive devices or materials that best accommodate the individual's learning needs should be utilized. Using visual aids, materials written in simple phrases, or auditory rather than visual learning modes can all help individuals learn material in accordance with their own needs. Clients with learning disorders may experience loss of self-esteem or shame if they are unable to perform learning tasks that others take for granted. Teaching clients about their condition, helping family members determine appropriate expectations, and identifying and coordinating specific support systems and educational interventions are important aspects of education for clients with a learning disorder. Multitiered academic and behavioral interventions may be of benefit (Reschly, 2005). Providing specific instructional aids, helping clients identify and acknowledge specific learning needs, and acquiring appropriate supports and resources to meet those needs are examples of interventions that may be instituted.

most commonly include impairments in communication and social interaction.

Kanner was the first to describe autistic children as "having an inability to relate themselves in an ordinary way to people and situations from the beginning of life" (1972, p. 242). Autistic children also have been referred to as "empty fortresses" (Bettelheim, 1967, p. 2). More recently, persons with ASD have been able to share their thoughts on living with such disorders. Dr. Temple Grandin has stated, "All minds of the autism spectrum are detail-oriented, but how they specialize varies. By questioning many people both on and off the spectrum, I have learned that there are three different types of specialized thinking: visual thinking (thinking in pictures, like mine); music and math thinking, and verbal logic thinking" (2011). Daniel Tammet (2007), an autistic savant, who experiences the world through numbers as visual shapes, colors, textures, and motions (synesthesia), shares that "Numbers are my friends, and they are always around me. Each one is unique and has its own personality. The number 11 is friendly and the number 5 is loud, whereas 4 is both shy and quiet—it's my favorite number, perhaps because it reminds me of myself ... To me every number is special" (p. 2).

Incidence and Prevalence

Autistic disorder is the third most common developmental disability (Goolsby & Blackwell, 2001), and it is four times more prevalent in males than females (Bartley, 2006). Per 1,000 children, about 5.8 will be affected by an autistic spectrum disorder (Hirtz et al., 2007; Laider, 2005). Those reports, which show an increased trend in incidence, may be influenced by the increasing awareness of parents and health practitioners as well as by varying methods used by different groups in order to arrive at estimates (Baird et al., 2000). In 2002, information from the Autism Developmental Disabilities Monitoring Network's study of rates of autism spectrum disorder in children from multiple communities in the United States indicated that approximately 1 in 150 children in these communities had a form of ASD—a rate consistent with the upper end of earlier estimated prevalence rates (Centers for Disease Control and Prevention, 2007). Strikingly, a surveillance study from 2002 to 2006 from the same network (2009) reported a 57% average increase in the number of autism diagnoses in the same regions, and it estimated the current prevalence to be 1 in 110 children. This increase can be attributed to multiple factors, including changes in the diagnostic criteria, increased awareness of the disorder, availability of diagnostic testing, and earlier interventions.

Etiology and Physiology

Years ago, autism was attributed to poor parenting skills and the belief that parents who were emotionally unavailable to their children contributed to the development of the disorder. This belief has now been discredited, and parenting skills are no longer thought to be responsible for the development of autism.

Although no definitive cause of autism has yet been found, it is now thought that autism results from a brain function abnormality that is biologically based and arises from a combination of genetic vulnerability and environmental triggers (Blackwell & Niederhauser, 2003). Sibling and twin studies have provided strong evidence that there is a genetic heritability for autism. Researchers have found chromosomal abnormalities in about 3–5% of children with autistic disorders and that about 10% of autism diagnoses can be attributed to genetic abnormalities (Johnson, Gaitanis, & Morrow, 2011).

The cause of autistic disorder is not known, and the treatment is intensive, often required throughout the individual's life span. The disorder can become the focus of family interactions.

If autistic disorder accompanies another condition such as encephalitis, phenylketonuria (PKU), fragile X syndrome, or tuberous sclerosis, corresponding neurologic and medical symptoms are present. Seizures have been noted in up to 25% of all children with autism, especially adolescents, and EEG abnormalities are common even without seizures (APA, 2000; Walz, 2002). When this disorder is diagnosed in conjunction with other medical conditions, the disorders are coded on Axis III.

There has been considerable concern that there is a link between thimerosal, a mercury-based preservative used in vaccines, and autism. Until 1999, vaccines against such diseases as diphtheria, tetanus, pertussis, *Haemophilus influenzae* b (Hib), and hepatitis B contained thimerosal as a preservative. The measles, mumps, and rubella (MMR); varicella (chickenpox); inactivated polio virus (IPV); and pneumococcal conjugate vaccines have never contained thimerosal. Currently, with the exception of some influenza vaccines, none of the vaccines used in the United States to protect children contain thimerosal as a preservative (Food and Drug Administration [FDA], 2009). Both the American Academy of Pediatrics and the Institute of Medicine (IOM) have studied this issue and agree that no vaccine or component of any vaccine is responsible for the number of children who are currently being diagnosed with autism. They conclude that the benefits of vaccines outweigh the potential risks. However, some parents continue to fear vaccinating their children.

Clinical Presentation

Autistic disorder is generally identified and diagnosed in the first 3 years of life. Although symptoms and severity can vary widely, parents often first notice delays in language development or in their child's ability to relate to others or engage in social interaction. Their child may appear aloof, not responding to social cues such as smiles. The child may avoid eye contact or, when looking at another person, may seem to stare through them. Children with autism may not seek and may actually avoid close physical contact such as hugging or cuddling. They prefer solitary behavior, preferring to be left alone rather than engaging in explorative behaviors or other social interaction. They often lack the ability to engage in spontaneous or imaginative play and may show strong attachment to inanimate objects rather than people.

Activity levels may range from overactive to very passive. Some children display repetitive or stereotypic body movements or behaviors, such as body rocking, finger flicking, or staring at their hands at close range. In some instances, children may engage in repetitive, self-injurious behavior such as head banging or biting and exhibit exaggerated and/or aggressive responses to people or objects. Rituals and the insistence on sameness or resistance to change are common in clients with autistic disorder. Changes in their environment or routine may be very difficult.

Clients with autistic disorder often demonstrate hypersensitivity or disproportional response to sensory stimuli, including touch or sound; however, in some instances they may show a decreased response to pain. Often communication deficits in verbal or nonverbal behavior exist and may include the inability to comprehend verbal communication or decipher nonverbal cues.

They may demonstrate difficulty expressing ideas or needs verbally, or conversely, they may be highly verbal; they may engage in **echolalia**, in which a word or phrase is repeated numerous times; and they may have difficulty integrating cognitive functions. Some individuals with autism have normal or above normal intelligence; however, nearly 80% will have IQ scores falling into the range of mental retardation (Yeargin-Allsoff et al., 2003).

Differential Diagnosis

Autistic disorder is distinguished from other pervasive developmental disorders, childhood schizophrenia, blindness, deafness, selective mutism, and other language disorders by its characteristics and pattern of developmental deficits. Diagnostic criteria as outlined in the *DSM-IV-TR* (APA, 2000) include abnormal behaviors in the following categories: deficit in social interaction, deficit in communication, and demonstration of restricted repetitive patterns of behavior, interest, or activities. These deficits must occur before the age of 3 and must be deficits that are not accounted for by another pervasive developmental disorder. Various screening tools including the Childhood Autism Rating Scale (CARS) are used to diagnose autistic disorder (Matson & Minshawi, 2006).

Clinical Course and Complications

Usually parents report that the child, almost since birth, has been perceived as different. During infancy, the child did not enjoy being cuddled, lacked **anticipatory molding**, seldom smiled, and did not respond to games such as peek-a-boo. These children have problems throughout childhood, with either an improvement in or an exacerbation of behavior in adolescence. As adults, they generally need to live in protected environments and require differing levels of supervision.

Management and Treatment

Autistic disorder is a lifelong condition. One of the most important aspects in the management is early identification. In spite of increasing awareness of the prevalence of the disorder, delays in diagnosis frequently occur due to lack of standardized screening for developmental delays during well-child visits (Filipek et al., 2000). Developmental profiles should focus on speech and language, verbal and nonverbal communication, and cognitive and motor function. In addition, audiologic screening and lead screening should be conducted to rule out other causes of developmental delay.

The nurse should understand that communication problems are prevalent in autistic disorder and should ascertain how the individual best communicates (Cade & Tidwell, 2001). During the assessment process, the nurse should incorporate the individual's social, communication, and behavioral strengths as well as limitations. Because there are frequently verbal as well as nonverbal impairments in communication, augmentative systems may be needed (such as signing or use of a communication board) to facilitate communication. Knowledge of behavioral protocols, such as tokens, which have been used successfully, may facilitate interaction.

Establishment of any treatment plan should always include parents or family members as partners in order to develop a plan that is best suited for the child and the particular circumstances. Treatment planning often involves a multidisciplinary approach, including audiologic exam, speech and language evaluation, occupational therapy evaluation, psychiatric observation and interview, and a neurological exam. Each area of function should be measured against standardized norms, and the results should be used to determine the child's special needs.

Referral to an early intervention program, which evaluates needs and assists children with developmental disability, is crucial. Early intervention programs involve the whole family and assist in identifying innovative solutions to behavioral as well as medical problems.

Although no specific medications are considered standard in treating autistic disorder, a number of medications are used for treating related problems and behaviors. Risperidone (Risperdal) has been used with moderate success to reduce aggression and self-injury in children with autism (Research Units on Pediatric Psychopharmacology [RUPP] Autism Network, 2002). Methylphenidate (Ritalin) has also been used to reduce symptoms of hyperactivity and impulsivity (Handen, Johnson, & Lubetsky, 2000). Careful monitoring for side effects should also be part of the general protocol. In instances where other medical conditions, such as seizure disorder, coexist with the disorder, specific medications for treatment of those conditions may be added. When other medications are added to the medication protocol, the nurse should be aware of the potential for drug interaction, and subsequent synergistic untoward effects should also be considered.

Considerations for Client and Family Education

Although it is now known that lack of parenting skills is not responsible for development of autistic disorder, often myths and stereotypes and thus parental guilt linger. The nurse should help parents understand what is currently known about the genetic and environmental basis of the disorder and allay fears that the cause of their child's condition was poor parenting. Helping families learn special techniques that can be used to minimize specific symptoms, such as identifying triggers that induce aggressive behaviors and how to avoid them, or developing skills for redirecting the child's behaviors, can help parents better manage the child in his or her own environment. Parents should be made aware of the role of medication and should be helped to recognize medication side effects and which side effects should be reported. Teaching parents about specific community resources and supports as well as helping them develop their own coping skills are also important aspects of education. Nurses need to work with parents to recognize and meet their own personal, marital, and family needs as well as the individual needs of other family members such as siblings and grandparents. See **Table 26-1**.

Table 26-1 Questions That Parents Can Ask About Interventional Programs

- How successful has the program been for other children?
- How many children have gone on to placement in a regular school, and how have they performed?
- Do staff members have training and experience in working with children and adolescents with autism?
- How are activities planned and organized?
- Are there predictable daily schedules and routines?
- How much individual attention will my child receive?
- How is progress measured? Will my child's behavior be closely observed and recorded?
- Will my child be given tasks and rewards that are personally motivating?
- Is the environment designed to minimize distractions?
- Will the program prepare me to continue the therapy at home?
- What is the cost, time commitment, and location of the program?

Source: National Institute of Mental Health. (2009). *Autism spectrum disorders (pervasive developmental disorders).* Retrieved from http://www.nimh.nih.gov/health/publications/autism/treatment-options.shtml

Applied behavior analysis involves arranging for the child or adult with autistic disorder to experience multiple, repeated opportunities to learn and practice skills throughout every day, accompanied by consistent and abundant positive reinforcement.

Applied behavior analysis (ABA) has been used extensively in treatment of specific autistic behaviors. The goal of ABA is to assist individuals to approach normal functioning as closely as possible and to assist them to gain increasing independence. In order to be most effective, applied behavior analysis must be used consistently over time. Many parents find this requires significant time commitment, stamina, and dedication to maintain the intervention.

Asperger's Disorder

Asperger's disorder or syndrome was identified in 1944 by a German physician, Hans Asperger, who studied a group of high-functioning children with symptoms similar to those experienced in autism (Volkmar & Klin, 2000). In 1987, the American Psychiatric Association (APA) included behaviors characteristic of Asperger's disorder under the classification of pervasive developmental disorder, not otherwise specified. Not until 1994 did the APA include Asperger's disorder as a diagnostic category in the *Diagnostic and Statistical Manual of Mental Disorders*. There has been some controversy as to whether Asperger's disorder should be a separate category or rather defined as high-functioning autism (Klin & Volkmar, 2003). Although some symptoms are common to both conditions, individuals with Asperger's disorder show no significant delay in language or cognitive development, and often are able to function at relatively high levels, establishing careers and living independently (Eisenmajar et al., 1996; Walz, 2002). The APA is recommending for the *DSM-5* that this category be eliminated and subsumed into autistic spectrum disorder with differing levels of severity.

Incidence and Prevalence

Because the definition of Asperger's disorder has varied since it was first defined, and because the diagnostic criteria have changed, the prevalence of the disorder is difficult to determine. It appears to be more common in males and it is estimated that the

CASE STUDIES Katie

Katie appeared to be a physically healthy child. Her parents noted that she was a good baby, rarely crying as an infant. When her speech and language development were delayed, her parents did not attach much significance to it, and they were reassured by their pediatrician that all children develop at different levels, and that Katie's language abilities would develop in time. As time passed, Katie continued not to communicate verbally, and by the age of 4 had a vocabulary of only 20 words. In addition, Katie avoided most eye contact, failed to respond to acts of affection, and often appeared withdrawn. She was unable to attend nursery school because her explosive outbursts, shrill screams, and impulsive hitting of others was scaring the children and generally disruptive. Her parents were referred to an early intervention program and for diagnostic testing at a child study center. Although the parents were told that Katie has autism, they appeared to have limited understanding of what the condition entails and believe that with good nutritional supplements, the condition can be cured.

Nursing Care Plan **Child With Autistic Disorder**

Nursing Diagnosis 1: Impaired parenting related to autistic spectrum disorder as evidenced by unrealistic expectations of themselves or their child.

Nursing Diagnosis 2: Impaired social interaction related to disturbance in attachment with the parent as evidenced by lack of affectional ties to parental figures.

Expected Outcomes	Interventions	Evaluations
• The parents will communicate their concerns, fears, and understanding of their child's disorder.	• Provide parents with a safe place apart from their child to talk with each other and staff about their child's disorder. • Meet regularly with the parents to establish trust and credibility.	• The parents freely communicate and express positive and negative thoughts and concerns about their child and the diagnosis.
• The parents will demonstrate interest in learning more about their child's condition.	• Provide information about autism spectrum disorders and resources for families with children with autism.	• The parents acknowledge their child's disorder and more actively discuss the disorder, clinical management, and interventions. • The parents participate in a parental support group.
• The child will be able to remain in the playroom or classroom with peers.	• Set up a play situation for the child with another peer on a regular, time-limited basis. • Plan with the teacher for classroom activities.	• The child participates in limited periods of play with other children, a first step in socialization. • The child is able to follow specific tasks assigned by the teacher as schooling is the work of childhood and needs to be supported during hospitalization.

Visit http://go.jblearning.com/mentalhealth for additional care plans and exercises.

incidence is in the range of 1 to 3 per 10,000 (Boyd, 2009). The mean age of diagnosis has been reported as 8 years of age (Eisenmajer et al., 1996).

Etiology and Physiology

No clear cause of Asperger's disorder has been established. Because the condition appears to occur in families, a genetic predisposition for the condition has been suggested. However, no clear genetic marker has been established (Volkmar, Klin, Schultz, Rubin, & Bronen, 2000; Kutscher, Wolff & Atwood, 2007). It is currently thought to be neurologically based (Zaretsky, Richter, & Eisenberg, 2005). There are no significant physiologic data associated with Asperger's disorder. However, the high incidence of increased hyperactivity, overstimulation, and inattention seen in this disorder is often frequently misidentified as attention-deficit/hyperactivity disorder (ADHD) (APA, 2000).

Clinical Presentation

Children with Asperger's disorder demonstrate impairments in social interactions and may show repetitive behavior patterns as well as resistance to change, similar to those with autistic disorder. Intellectual and communication function are not usually impaired. Often impairments in social interaction, communication, and imagination are subtle, and therefore difficult to diagnose (Portway & Johnson, 2005). Diagnosis of Asperger's disorder may not be made until children are school age and difficulties with social interaction become apparent. Children as well as adults. with Asperger's disorder are unable to recognize social cues such as body language or other forms of nonverbal behavior, or they may be unable to recognize cues that indicate that their behavior is inappropriate (Kutscher, Wolff & Atwood, 2007; Safran, 2002). They do not adhere to social conventions such as respecting others' personal space, or

Both children and adults with Asperger's disorder have significant difficulty interpreting social cues and, as a result, they may appear to be tactless or rude.

they may talk loudly, relentlessly pursuing a subject of interest to them, even though other children or adults show no interest or are unresponsive. These children and adults may demonstrate an abnormal need to adhere to strict routines, becoming upset and agitated if change is necessary. They also demonstrate poor gross motor function, appear clumsy, or use repetitive behaviors such as ritualistic walking patterns and obsessive-compulsive routines.

Differential Diagnosis

Distinguishing Asperger's disorder from high-functioning autism remains an unresolved issue in the mind of many practitioners (Rourke & Tsatsanis, 2000). The *DSM-IV-TR* (APA, 2000) lists diagnostic criteria as impairment in social interaction, restricted repetitive and stereotyped patterns of behavior, and significant impairment in social, occupational, or other areas of function, with no delay in language acquisition or in cognitive development as well as not meeting criteria for any other pervasive developmental disorder, ADHD, or schizophrenia.

Clinical Course and Complications

This is a lifelong disorder, with one's social abilities waxing and waning or significantly improving into adulthood. Adolescents and adults with Asperger's disorder often learn to use areas of strength such as rote verbal skills or savant-like mathematical skills to compensate for other areas of weakness. As they age, these individuals may experience victimization from peers, social isolation, anxiety, and depression. The overall prognosis is better than for those with autistic disorder (APA, 2000).

Management and Treatment

Even though the *DSM-IV-TR* specifies diagnostic criteria for Asperger's disorder, there are many subtleties of the disorder and diagnostic boundaries that are not always clear (Wing, 2000); the disorder often is misdiagnosed or overlooked, so interventions appropriate to the diagnosis may not be forthcoming. When assessing individuals, symptoms may not be immediately apparent in a one-on-one setting. Obtaining a full history and determining how the individual interacts with other people can be an important diagnostic tool. Because Asperger's disorder is a condition in which there is social disability, the nurse can help by providing referrals and resources for socially based communication and language intervention and social skills development, including helping one learn how to recognize social cues (Landa, 2000). Because coping with change is difficult, the nurse should also attempt to maintain comfortable routines; when change is necessary, it should be introduced gradually.

Those with Asperger's disorder may experience stress due to social deficit and may also experience depression, so medications such as antidepressants may be prescribed for associated symptoms (Martin, Patzer, & Volkmar, 2000).

Critical Thinking Question

How would you expect a child diagnosed with autistic disorder, Asperger's disorder, or a normal developmental delay to behave differently or similarly to developmentally normal children or children with one of the other aforementioned disorders?

Considerations for Client and Family Education

Teaching individuals with Asperger's disorder and their families about the symptoms of the condition can prevent misunderstanding regarding behavior that others may consider socially inappropriate. Families should also be cautioned not to focus on any savant-like behaviors to the detriment of encouraging age-appropriate skills and behaviors. Because the condition involves social skill deficits, the nurse can provide encouragement and feedback, helping the child, adolescent or adult to recognize social cues and ways in which socially appropriate behavior can be integrated into social interactions (Cole Marshall, 2002). Individuals with Asperger's disorder may experience significant stress and anxiety, so teaching them about outlets for stress and anxiety are also important. If medications have been prescribed for symptoms, the nurse should teach clients and families about the specific medication, what to expect, and what types of side effects should be reported. See Chapter 6.

Examples of Other Pervasive Developmental Disorders

Rett's disorder is another condition included under the category of pervasive developmental disorders, but it occurs more rarely than autism or Asperger's disorder. It occurs mainly in females at a rate of 1 in 10,000 to 1 in 23,000 females worldwide (Armstrong, 2005). Rett's disorder is often associated with severe or profound mental retardation. In most cases, Rett's disorder is thought to be due to a genetic mutation on the X chromosome (Armstrong, 2005; Glaze, 2005).

Developmental regression in Rett's disorder typically appears prior to the age of 4. After a period of normal psychomotor development, children with Rett's disorder experience progressive loss of acquired motor, cognitive, and language skills and also experience lack of coordination of movement and decrease in purposeful hand movement (Nomura & Segawa, 2005). There is impairment in expressive and receptive language function, a decreased interest in social engagement, and mental retardation and seizures may also be present.

There are no specific diagnostic tools or laboratory tests used for diagnosing Rett's disorder. Diagnosis is based on the disintegration of psychomotor skills after a previous period of normal development, including lack of coordination in trunk and gait movement, and impaired expressive and receptive language function. Deceleration of head growth has also been observed.

Clinical Example

The Walker family was overjoyed at the birth last year of a baby girl, Sally, and her three older brothers love their baby sister. In the past 2 months, her mother noticed that Sally seems to have trouble breathing and sometimes has shaking movements of her limbs that she is afraid are seizures. At 11 months old, Sally is barely crawling and shows no interest in pulling herself up. She no longer makes cooing sounds and has stopped smiling. Both parents are tearful and not surprised when the staff at the pediatric development clinic, after a battery of medical tests to rule out underlying medical conditions, suggests that Sally has a rare, chromosomal-linked, pervasive developmental disorder known as Rett's disorder.

There is no specific treatment of Rett's disorder other than supportive care. Clients may need assistance with feeding and other activities of daily living. Physical therapy may help prevent contractures. If a seizure disorder is present, precautions to prevent injury during seizures should be taken and medication to treat the seizure disorder may be instituted. Helping parents adjust to their child's debilitation after a period in which they were unaware that a disability existed is a major task in working with families who have a child with Rett's disorder. The nurse should inform parents of resources such as support groups and teach them the necessary skills to care for their child's physical needs as well as helping them learn how to communicate with their child. Most parents experience a grieving that is associated with the loss of the child they knew prior to onset of symptoms.

Rett's disorder is a rare, pervasive developmental disorder that is thought to be caused by a genetic mutation on the X-chromosome characterized by profound developmental regression in behaviors.

Another pervasive developmental disorder is **childhood disintegrative disorder**, a condition characterized by deterioration of previously attained social, language, and play skills after the age of 2 and prior to the age of 10. It is also a rare condition, which appears to be more prevalent in males than females. The rate of childhood disintegrative disorder has been estimated as 0.11 to 0.64 per 10,000 (Mouridsen, 2003). After an apparent period of normal development, children with the disorder show signs of deterioration of expressive or receptive language, social skills, bowel or bladder control, and play skills. Deterioration of motor skills may or may not be present. Loss of previously acquired skills usually occurs between 3 and 4 years of age, but must occur prior to the age of 10 in order to qualify for the diagnosis.

Childhood disintegrative disorder is a condition characterized by severe deterioration of previously attained social, language, and play skills.

Because there are no specific tools currently available for the definitive diagnosis of childhood disintegrative disorder, diagnosis is based on clinical presentation. There are no specific guidelines for treatment of the disorder. In most instances, management of the condition requires a multidisciplinary approach. Supportive care and support groups are important interventions. Special education, which helps the child learn adaptive skills, is also useful. As with other intellectual and developmental disabilities, the nurse should help parents of children with these other types of pervasive developmental disorders learn about the condition and the resources and supports that are available, how to assist their child in coping with life's challenges, and how to deal with the sadness, grief, and anger associated with having their child diagnosed with such a debilitating disorder.

Nursing Interventions for Clients With Intellectual and Developmental Disabilities

Clients with intellectual and developmental disabilities, whether their diagnosis is mental retardation, a learning disorder, a pervasive developmental disorder, or a combination of these disorders, are represented in every age, ethnic, racial, and socioeconomic group. Their healthcare needs and concerns are as diverse as those of the general population. As individuals with intellectual and developmental disabilities enter into mainstream society and survive in increasing numbers, nurses and other mental health practitioners have more contact with them in healthcare settings. For many, the relationship between mental health and intellectual and developmental disabilities is complicated and sometimes confusing.

Communication problems are common in children and adults with intellectual and developmental disabilities, making it difficult for them to cover changes in their physical or emotional well-being.

Although many disorders that are categorized as intellectual and developmental disabilities are found in the *DSM-IV-TR*, a person who is mentally retarded or has a developmental disability does not necessarily require psychiatric mental health interventions. A client with a developmental disability may develop any of the other current *DSM-IV-TR* diagnoses. Within this specialty, there is a subspecialty concerned with the provision of mental health services for children and adults with developmental disabilities. A person with an intellectual or developmental disability who also has a second, classified disorder is considered to have a dual diagnosis—for example, an individual who is mentally retarded and has a diagnosis of depression has a dual diagnosis. Not many nurses and other mental health practitioners have extensive experience in both psychiatric-mental health disorders and intellectual and developmental disabilities. Therefore, the client with a dual diagnosis is at risk for not having the different disorders recognized and appropriately treated. The National Association for the Dually Diagnosed (NADD) is devoted solely to addressing this area of care, and the *Habilitative Mental Healthcare Newsletter* provides nurses and other clinicians with a broad range of pertinent information.

Family violence and abuse is also associated with individuals with intellectual and developmental disabilities and should not be discounted as a potential cause for changes in behaviors.

The nurse is often the central point of contact for children or adults with intellectual and developmental disabilities and their families. Although the role and extent of involvement of the nurse may vary with the type of disability the client experiences and across the different healthcare settings, central principles can be applied that ensure individuals receive care and support most appropriate to their disorder. Knowledge of the specific condition will enable the nurse to provide the most effective and least obtrusive support for clients and their families as they go about meeting the challenges in their everyday lives. Understanding the characteristics of specific disorders enables the nurse to promote independence and self-determination to the extent that is feasible for individuals in accordance with their ability.

Communication problems are common in clients with intellectual and developmental disabilities. For individuals who are unable to communicate adequately, change in behavior or exhibition of challenging behaviors may be the first sign of a medical or psychiatric problem. Assessing the meaning of the behavior as well as the cause, rather than jumping to conclusions about the cause and what treatment should be instituted, is an important step in appropriate case management. Medications should be used only when needed to treat an underlying medical condition, not to control behaviors. Unrecognized medical conditions, psychiatric disorders, or environmental changes can all cause changes or exacerbation of behaviors. Family violence and abuse is also associated with individuals with intellectual and developmental disabilities and should not be discounted as a potential cause for behaviors exhibited by the person (Strickler, 2001).

In the past, clients with intellectual and developmental disabilities have been labeled as being incapable of determining their own best interests or negotiating in order to meet their needs. This myth is slowly being dispelled, as there is increased recognition that each person with an intellectual or developmental disability has individual strengths that can be utilized to meet life's challenges. Clients with these disabilities want the same things that most people want in life, including living in a home environment, having the opportunity for friendship and social interaction, having a romantic and sexual relationship, having the opportunity to fulfill educational and vocational goals to the level of their ability, and perhaps, having a family of their own. Identifying intellectual and developmental disabilities as early as possible and implementing appropriate interventions as soon as possible are important to helping meet these goals (Pinto-Martin, Dunkle, Earls, Fliedner, & Landes, 2005).

Throughout their life spans, persons with intellectual and developmental disabilities encounter some of the same challenges that most people encounter. By the nature of their disability, these children and adults are often more vulnerable to a variety of life's challenges. They should be educated about the inappropriate use of illicit drugs and alcohol, the development of inappropriate relationships, sexuality, sexual abuse, pregnancy prevention, and prevention of sexually transmitted disease (American Academy of Pediatrics, 1996). Psychosocial and environmental problems can be a major concern for many intellectually and developmentally disabled persons. These can be related to the following issues:

- Primary support group (e.g., removal from the home, physical or sexual abuse, parental overprotection)
- Social environment (e.g., difficulty with acculturation, discrimination, death or loss of a friend)
- Educational environment (e.g., conflict with teachers or peers, academic problems)
- Work (e.g., unemployment, difficult work conditions)
- Housing (e.g., inadequate housing, conflict with neighbors or landlord)
- Money (e.g., inadequate finances, inadequate welfare support)
- Health care (e.g., unavailable transportation to facilities, inadequate insurance)
- Legal and justice systems (e.g., victimization, arrest)
- Availability of support services (e.g., conflict with nonfamily caregivers; APA, 1994)

An individual with an intellectual or developmental disability is likely to experience at least one problem in each of these areas by adulthood.

The role of the nurse working with clients with such disabilities is to assist them and their families to identify and eliminate barriers and challenges so that individuals can reach the highest quality of life within the range of their ability. This means the nurse must respect and support the lives of clients with intellectual and developmental disabilities and their families.

Just as advances in medical knowledge and technology have increased life expectancy for the general population, they have also increased life expectancy for individuals with intellectual and developmental disabilities (Horwitz, Kerker, Owens, & Zigler, 2000). Clients with these disabilities are now living longer and confronting the same chronic illnesses that others encounter in later life, frequently compounding existing impairments (Noble, 2001). In addition, the prevalence of mental health disorders, including dementia, is increased in a number of intellectual and developmental disabilities, such as Down syndrome (Cooper, 1998; Fisher, 2004).

Many individuals with these disabilities continue to live with their families into adulthood. In most families, there is a time in which children move out of the parental home to go to school, go to work, or begin their own families. In families in which a family member has an intellectual or developmental disability, this stage of the family life cycle may be postponed or never achieved (Krauss, Seltzer, & Jacobson, 2005). In most instances, whether due to illness or death of the primary family caretaker, decisions about moving the client to another setting are made. Such decisions impact upon the client as well as other family members. The nurse should be aware of the extent of conflict such decisions can cause families and be an available source of support for families involved in making this type of alternative, residential care decision.

Although the client's needs are often based on diagnosis, symptoms, test results, and other resources, the affirmation that each person is an individual with unique circumstances helps the nurse establish a plan that is most appropriate for the individual. Working with the client's strengths, interests, and abilities in creative ways produces better outcomes than trying to treat all clients with the same diagnosis in the same way (Olney, 2000). By thoroughly assessing clients in the context of their circumstances and preferences, the nurse is able to obtain adequate information, which can be used to make appropriate referrals or to establish plans and interventions to help the clients meet their goals to the best of their ability. Strengths, as well as the limitations of the client, serve as a framework. Services and supports are identified in conjunction with mutually identified (client, family, transdisciplinary healthcare team) goals and objectives (see **Table 26-2**).

Critical Thinking Question

What types of challenges will confront a client with mental retardation or intellectual and developmental disabilities who is aging either at home or in another residence?

Evidence-Based Practice

Little and Clark (2006) used an exploratory study of the written responses of 103 matched couples parenting a child with Asperger's syndrome and a nonverbal learning disorder to identify their worries and joys. The parents reported that in the joy category, they counted the child's personality traits, observing the child being happy, and watching the child grow, mature, and succeed. In the worry category, parents focused on the child's future and adulthood. The findings of this study can inform the care provided by nurses in a variety of healthcare settings by suggesting that nurses assess parents for their particular joys and worries and provide reinforcing support and access to services as needed.

Parents of children who are diagnosed with any autistic spectrum disorder experience a personal and family situational crisis. In a randomized trial study, researchers sought to refine a nursing intervention specifically to be used with parents of children with Asperger's disorder and to use this information for a future, more extensive study (Giarelli, Souders, Pinto-Martin, Bloch, & Levy, 2005). The study tested the effects of a specific postdiagnosis nursing intervention on parents' reports of stress, the impact of the event, and the use of support services after the child is newly diagnosed. The researchers recommended a more extensive study of expanded nursing interventions with a larger group of parents. Parents of children with autistic spectrum disorders have education, information, and counseling needs that can be addressed by informed nurses.

Table 26-2 **Nursing Interventions for Children with Intellectual and Developmental Disabilities**

Nursing Diagnoses	Nursing Interventions	Rationales
Risk for violence: self-directed or other-directed	Remove potentially dangerous items from the child's environment. Remove the child from excessive environmental stimuli. If the child appears to be about to lose control, nurses should interrupt the behavior immediately by any appropriate means (time-outs, quiet room).	Safety is a primary concern. A calm environment can help reduce the child's aggressive feelings and provide a sense of security and peace. Preventing injury is the primary concern; identify behaviors that the child can use to reduce the need for these interventions; only use for safety, not punishment.
Impaired social interaction	Observe the child for examples of negative behaviors that are interfering with social interactions. Establish a reward system for interactions (play, attendance at school) with peers.	When negative behaviors are identified, the child can be helped to substitute more age-appropriate, adaptive behaviors. Behaviors that receive positive reinforcement (rewards) are more likely to be repeated.
Impaired verbal communication	Plan one-on-one time with the child on a regular basis throughout the day. Engage the child in both nonverbal and simple verbal play. Encourage vocalizations through positive reactions such as a hug, a treat or a star chart, establishing a goal of certain sounds within a specific time frame.	This can serve as the basis for establishing trust with the child; predictability is important. Children experience their world through play and will feel safe. Behaviors that receive positive reinforcement will most likely be repeated.

Summary

This chapter has presented a discussion of variety of intellectual and developmental disabilities that encompass a wide and varied number of conditions that start in childhood; are lifelong, extending into adulthood; affect intellectual and/or physical functioning; and require ongoing special services and support from a transdisciplinary team. Included were those conditions that are classified in the *DSM-IV-TR*, such as mental retardation, and pervasive developmental disorders including autistic disorder, Asperger's disorder, Rett's disorder, childhood disintegrative disorder, atypical autism, and learning disorders. Including the parents and/or other caregivers in the treatment plan for those affected with any of these disorders is critical. The interventions include identifying the client's strengths and weaknesses; teaching appropriate behaviors, communication skills, social responsiveness, and limit setting; and planning for lifelong opportunities and challenges.

Annotated References

Ailey, S. H., Miller, A. M., Heller, T., & Smith, E. V., Jr. (2006). Evaluating an interpersonal model of depression among adults with Down syndrome. *Research and Theory for Nursing Practice, 20*(3), 229–246.
The IMD provides a framework for assessing depression in adults with Down syndrome. One hundred individuals with Down syndrome were tested, revealing elevated depression scores and feelings of loneliness.

American Academy of Pediatrics. (1996). Sexuality education of children and adolescents with developmental disabilities. *Pediatrics, 97*, 275–278.
This article discusses the importance of addressing sexuality as well as pregnancy prevention, sexual abuse, and illicit drugs with children and adults with developmental disabilities.

American Association of Mental Retardation. (1992). *Definition, classification, and systems of support* (9th ed.). Washington, DC: Author.
This is a report and recommendations by the American Association of Mental Retardation.

American Nurses Association. (2004). *Intellectual and developmental disabilities nursing: Scope and standards of practice.* Washington, DC: Author.
This is the definitive professional statement on the scope and standards for the specialty of intellectual and developmental disabilities nursing.

American Psychiatric Association. (1994). *Diagnostic and statistical manual of mental disorders* (4th ed.). Washington, DC: Author.
This is an early version of the reference manual that provides classification of mental disorders and diagnostic categories, providing structure for consistency in nomenclature, definitions, and classifications for diagnosis of and research with psychiatric disability.

American Psychiatric Association. (2000). *Diagnostic and statistical manual of mental disorders* (4th ed., text rev.). Washington, DC: Author.
As of the publication of this textbook, the *DSM-IV-TR* is the most recent updated and revised edition of this excellent resource book for mental health practitioners; it is used extensively throughout this textbook.

American Psychiatric Association. (2010). *DSM-5 development*. Retrieved from http://www.dsm5.org/ProposedRevisions/
The APA is providing web-based, ongoing information on the proposed recommendations for its new publication, the *DSM-5*, to be published in 2013.

Armstrong, D. D. (2005). Neuropathology of Rett's syndrome. *Journal of Child Neurology, 20*(9), 747–753.
This article reviews the fundamental genetic basis of Rett's syndrome. It describes the complex phenotype of this disorder and its neurobiologic basis.

Autism and Developmental Disabilities Monitoring Network Surveillance Year 2006 Principal Investigators; Centers for Disease Control and Prevention (CDC). (2009, December 18). Prevalence of autism spectrum disorders. *MMWR Surveillance Summary, 58*(10), 1–20.
This is the most recent report from the CDC on the findings from the first and largest summary of prevalence data from multiple communities participating in an ASD surveillance project.

Baird, G., Charman, T., Baron-Cohen, S., Cox, A., Swettenham, J., Wheelwright, S., & Drew, A. (2000). A screening instrument for autism at 18 months of age: A 6-year follow-up study. *Journal of the American Academy of Child and Adolescent Psychiatry, 39*, 694–702.

This article discusses research that assessed the sensitivity, specificity, and positive predictive value of the Checklist for Autism in Toddlers (CHAT) to identify childhood autism.

Bartley, J. J. (2006). An update on autism: Science, gender and the law. *Gender Medicine, 3*(2), 73–78.
This article discusses autism, which is the fastest-growing developmental disability. Research is focusing on genetic implications and early intervention. There is concern about the impact of autism on the legal system as access to services is often litigated, and autistic individuals can have confrontations with the law.

Bettelheim, B. (1967). *The empty fortress: Infantile autism and the birth of self*. New York, NY: Free Press.
This is an early classic text that describes the work of controversial psychiatrist Bruno Bettelheim. Although his methods of study have since been questioned, his skill in describing the autistic child remains noteworthy.

Blackwell, J., & Niederhauser, C. (2003). Diagnosis and management of autistic children. *The Nurse Practitioner, 28*(6), 36–43.
This article profiles autism and addresses issues such as delays in diagnosis, screening and diagnosis, treatment, behavioral technology and social skills training, habilitative services, and alternative therapies.

Boyd, M. A. (2009). *Psychiatric nursing: Contemporary practice*. Philadelphia, PA: Lippincott Williams & Wilkins.
This is a comprehensive text covering a variety of psychiatric conditions as well as nursing relevance.

Cade, M., & Tidwell, S. (2001). Autism and the school nurse. *Journal of School Health, 71*(3), 96–100.
This article reviews diagnostic criteria, biological basis, and communication and behavior of individuals with autism and includes implications for school nurses, including communication and physical needs, medications, and support and education.

Centers for Disease Control and Prevention. (2005). Intellectual disability fact sheet (also known as mental retardation). Retrieved from http://www.cdc.gov/ncbddd/actearly/pdf/parents_pdfs/IntellectualDisability.pdf
Provides information in English and Spanish onlearning the signs of intellectual disability and the need to act early.

Centers for Disease Control and Prevention. (2007, February 9). New data on autism spectrum disorders (ASDs) from multiple communities in the U.S. *Morbidity and Mortality Weekly Report, 56*(SS-1). Retrieved from http://www.cdc.gov/ncbddd/autism/documents/AutismCommunityReport.pdf
This is a report from the CDC on the findings from the first and largest summary of prevalence data from multiple communities participating in an ASD surveillance project.

Centers for Disease Control and Prevention (CDC). (2011). National Center on Birth Defects and Developmental Disabilities. Retrieved from http://www.cdc.gov/ncbddd/AboutUs/index.html
This is the main informational website for the CDC's National Center on Birth Defects and Developmental Disabilities (NCBDDD) is to promote the health of babies, children and adults and enhance the potential for full, productive living.

Cole Marshall, M. (2002). Asperger's syndrome: Implications for nursing practice. *Issues in Mental Health Nursing, 23*, 606–615.
This article stresses the need for attention to and knowledge of Asperger's syndrome in order to differentiate it from closely related disorders. Emphasis is placed on the need for nurses to have more knowledge about Asperger's syndrome and be proactive in defining their role to help children with the disorder in schools and the community.

Cooper, S. (1998). Clinical study of the effects of age on the physical health of adults with mental retardation. *American Journal on Mental Retardation, 102*, 582–589.
This article reviews the physical disorders and pharmacotherapy of a cohort of 134 English subjects 65 years of age and over with mental retardation. Results showed an enhanced incidence of major clinical problems in an older group vs. a younger group. Results suggest that older people with mental retardation have significant physical health needs.

Daily, D. K., Ardinger, H. H., & Holmes, G. E. (2000). Identification and evaluation of mental retardation. *American Family Physician, 61*(4), 1059–1067.
This article emphasizes the importance of a comprehensive personal and family medical history, complete physical exam, and careful developmental assessment of children with mental

retardation in order to guide appropriate evaluations and referrals to provide genetic counseling, resources for the family, and early intervention programs for the child.

Developmental Disabilities Assistance and Bill of Rights Act of 1990 (104 STAT. 1191, Public Law 101-496, October 31, 1990) Title 2, U.S.C. 6000–6083. *U.S. Statutes at Large*, 104, 1191–1204.
This is the federal legislation that established a bill of rights for the developmentally disabled, providing guidelines for them to access critical services.

Developmental Disabilities Nurses Association (DDNA). (1995). *Standards of developmental disabilities nursing practice*. Eugene, OR: Author.
This manual outlines standards of practice for developmental disability nursing.

Dudley-Marling, C. (2004). The social construction of learning disabilities. *Journal of Learning Disabilities, 37*(6), 482–489.
This article challenges the view that learning disabilities are a pathology that resides in the individual. The article critiques the ideology of individualism, offering an alternative perspective of social constructivism that locates learning and problems with learning in the context of human relations and activity. Included is a proposal for instructional implications of a social constructivist perspective.

Eisenmajar, R., Prior, M., Leekam, S., Wing, L., Gould, J., Wenham, M., & Ong, B. (1996). Comparison of clinical symptoms in autism and Asperger's disorder. *Journal of the American Academy of Child and Adolescent Psychiatry, 35*, 1523–1531.
This article compares criteria in the clinical differentiation between Asperger's disorder and autistic disorder. Conclusions are that diagnosing of Asperger's disorder and autistic disorder is being accomplished on the basis of published research and case study accounts. The authors question the extent to which *DSM-IV* and ICD-10 criteria adequately describe the individual with Asperger's disorder, particularly in the communication domain.

Filipek, P. A., Accardo, P. J., Ashwal, S., Barbanek, G. T., Cook, E. H. Jr., Dawson, G., … Volkmar, F. R. (2000). Practice parameter: Screening and diagnosis of autism. *Neurology, 55*(4), 468–479.
This review of available empirical evidence proposes that appropriate tools for routine developmental screening, especially for autism, have not been developed. It advocates for earlier intervention that leads to earlier diagnosis and consequently better prognosis for autistic children.

Fisher, K. (2004). Nursing care of special populations: Issues in caring for elderly people with mental retardation. *Nursing Forum, 39*(1), 28–31.
This article outlines issues associated with health care of an aging population of individuals with mental retardation. It specifies the need for nurses to be educated and have increased exposure to the clinical challenges of caring for individuals with mental retardation.

Food and Drug Administration. (2009). Thimerosal in vaccines. Retrieved from http://www.fda.gov/BiologicsBloodVaccines/Vaccines/QuestionsaboutVaccines/UCM070430
The link in this reference is to an FAQ on thimerosal in vaccines, covering such topics as why exposure to mercury is a concern; what thimerosal is; why it is used in vaccines; what the difference is between thimerosal-free and thimerosal-reduced, and what the government is doing to make vaccines safer.

Giarelli, E., Souders, M., Pinto-Martin, J., Bloch, J., & Levy, S. E. (2005). Intervention pilot for parents of children with autistic spectrum disorder. *Pediatric Nursing, 31*(5), 389–399.
This paper describes a randomized trial to refine a nursing intervention in working with parents of children with Asperger's disorder.

Gillberg, C., & Soderstrom, H. (2003). Learning disability. *The Lancet, 362*(9386), 811–821.
This article provides a comprehensive review of learning disability (which is defined in the article as mental retardation); it includes causes and pathogenesis, associated conditions, psychosocial issues, treatment, and intervention.

Glaze, D. G. (2005). Neurophysiology of Rett's syndrome. *Journal of Child Neurology, 20*(9), 740–746.
This article reviews Rett's syndrome as a neurodevelopment disorder based on a specific mutation and its effects on the central nervous system. It provides specifics on the neurophysiological, electrocardiographic, and electroencephalogic aspects of Rett's syndrome.

Goolsby, M. J., & Blackwell, J. (2001). Clinical practice guideline: Screening and diagnosing autism. *Clinical Practice Guidelines, 13*(12), 534–536.

This article reviews the clinical practice guideline concerning screening and diagnosis of autism, which is developed to help primary care providers of children, including pediatric nurse practitioners and family nurse practitioners, facilitate early identification of children with autism.

Grandin, T. (2011). *Autism: The way I see it.* Retrieved from http://templegrandin.com/templegrandinart.html
Dr. Grandin shares her thoughts and observations about living with ASD and answers questions from readers on her website.

Handen, B. L., Johnson, C. R., & Lubetsky, M. (2000). Efficacy of methylphenidate among children with autism and symptoms of attention-deficit hyperactivity disorder. *Journal of Autism and Developmental Disorders, 30*, 245–255.
This article reviews the effects of methylphenidate on young children with autism and symptoms of attention-deficit/hyperactivity disorder. The study concludes that methylphenidate can be beneficial for children with autism and ADHD; however, some unwelcome side effects may also be experienced.

Hartweg, D. L. (1991). *Dorothea Orem: Self-care deficit theory*. Newbury, CA: Sage.
This book provides an excellent overview of Orem's theory, including unique examples as illustrations for practice.

Hirtz, D., Thurman, D. J., Gwinn-Hardy, K., Mohamed, M., Chaudhuri, A. R., & Zalutsky, R. (2007). How common are the "common" neurologic disorders? *Neurology, 68*(5), 322–323.
This article provides an estimate of the current incidence and prevalence in the United States of 12 neurologic disorders.

Horwitz, S. M., Kerker, B. D., Owens, P. L., & Zigler, E. (2000). *The health status and needs of individuals with mental retardation.* New Haven, CT: Yale University Press.
This book provides an overview of the health status/needs of individuals with mental retardation and service gaps in supporting such needs. It proposes specific recommendations to address the unmet healthcare needs of individuals with mental retardation.

Johnson, H. M., Gaitanis, J., & Morrow, E. M. (2011, May). Genetics in autism diagnosis: Adding molecular subtypes to neurobehavioral diagnoses. *Medicine and Health, Rhode Island, 94*(5), 124–126.
This article focuses on recent progress in genetic studies relevant to autism diagnosis.

Kanner, L. (1972). *Child psychiatry* (4th ed.). Springfield, IL: Charles C. Thomas.
This classic text describes childhood psychoses, focusing specifically on infantile autism.

Klin, A., & Volkmar, F. R. (2003). Asperger's syndrome: Diagnosis and external validity. *Child and Adolescent Psychiatric Clinics of North America, 12*(1), 1–13.
This article is an overview of the history and clinical features of Asperger's syndrome. It describes guidelines for the assessment and treatment of this syndrome. It also discusses severe social disabilities associated with the condition and the need for extensive treatment.

Krauss, M. W., Seltzer, M. M., & Jacobson, H. T. (2005). Adults with autism living at home or in non-family settings: Positive and negative aspects of residential status. *Journal of Intellectual Disability Research, 49*(2), 111–124.
This study investigated residential status as appraised by mothers who were caretakers of adults with autism and the impact on individuals with autism, their families, and their caregivers.

Kutscher, M. L., Wolff, R. R., & Atwood, T. (2007). *Kids in the syndrome mix of ADHD, LD, Asperger's, Tourette's, bipolar and more! The one stop guide for parents, teachers and other professionals*. Philadelphia, PA: Jessica Kingsley Publishers.
The authors have produced a concise and readable reference for parents who have children with learning and pervasive developmental disorders.

Laider, J. R. (2005). U.S. Department of Education data on "autism" are not reliable for tracking autism prevalence. *Pediatrics, 116*(1 Suppl.), e120–e124.
This article demonstrates discrepancies in reporting that lead to different perspectives on the prevalence of autism in the United States.

Landa, R. (2000). Social language use in Asperger syndrome and high functioning autism. In A. Klin, F. R. Volkmar, & S. S. Sparrow (Eds.), *Asperger syndrome* (pp. 125–155). New York, NY: Guilford Press.
This chapter discusses how individuals with Asperger's syndrome and high-functioning

autism utilize and develop language skills in the social environment.

Little, L., & Clark, R. R. (2006). Wonders and worries of parenting a child with Asperger syndrome and nonverbal learning disorder. *American Journal of Maternal Child Nursing, 31*(1), 39–44.
This study describes the joys and pressing concerns of the parents of children with Asperger's syndrome and nonverbal learning disorder.

Luckasson, R., Borthwick-Duffy, S., Buntinx, W. H. E., Coulter, D. L., Craig, E. M., Reeve, A., … Yaeger, M. A. (2002). *Mental retardation: Definition, classification, and system of support*. Washington, DC: American Association of Mental Retardation.
This publication is a report and recommendations regarding mental retardation.

Martin, A., Patzer, D. K., & Volkmar, F. R. (2000). Psychopharmacologic treatment of higher functioning pervasive developmental disorders. In A. Klin, F. R. Volkmar, & S. S. Sparrow (Eds.), *Asperger syndrome* (pp. 210–228). New York, NY: Guilford Press.
This chapter discusses the aspects of medication therapy in individuals with pervasive developmental disorders.

Matson, J. L., & Minshawi, N. F. (2006). *Early intervention for autism spectrum disorders* (Vol. I). Oxford: Elsevier Science.
This book presents an overview on the assessment, management, and treatment of children with mental health disorders and developmental disabilities.

McLaughlin, P. J., & Wehman, P. (Eds.). (1996). *Mental retardation and developmental disabilities* (2nd ed.). Austin, TX: Pro-ed.
This edition expands information on a variety of developmental disabilities. The book reflects a life-span perspective and includes information on service delivery, school issues, and transition from secondary school to adulthood. Also included is information on case management, community-based vocational training, supported employment, supported living, and social security.

Mouridsen, S. E. (2003). Childhood disintegrative disorder. *Brain and Development, 25*(4), 225–228.
This article describes reviews of recent case studies of childhood disintegrative disorder. It also reports on the use of common diagnostic systems and how they relate to treatment and outcome.

National Institute of Child Health and Human Development. (2001). *Closing the gap: A national blueprint for improving the health of persons with mental retardation*. Report of the Surgeon General's Conference on Health Disparities and Mental Retardation. Washington, DC: National Institutes of Health.
This is a report outlining health disparities in people with mental retardation and suggestions for remedying the problem.

Noble, J. (2001). *Textbook of primary care medicine* (3rd ed.). St. Louis, MO: Mosby.
A comprehensive medical text discussing a wide variety of medical conditions and their diagnosis, treatment, and prognosis.

Nomura, Y., & Segawa, M. (2005). Natural history of Rett's syndrome. *Journal of Child Neurology, 20*(9), 764–768.
This article describes the early onset of Rett's syndrome and outlines locomotor dysfunction and language disability as a progression of brain dysfunction.

Olney, M. F. (2000). Working with autism and other social communication disorders. *Journal of Applied Rehabilitation Counseling, 66*(4), 51–56.
This article addresses the special challenges to professionals working with individuals with autism and related developmental disabilities. The article reviews the literature on autism from medical, behavioral, social, and personal perspectives. An analysis of first-hand accounts of people with autism is included.

Pinto-Martin, J. A., Dunkle, M., Earls, M., Fliedner, D., & Landes, C. (2005). Developmental stages of developmental screening: Steps to implementation of a successful program. *American Journal of Public Health, 95*(11), 1928–1932.
This article discusses the challenges of instituting universal developmental screening as part of pediatric care. Two models of existing or planned programs of early screening for autism in the community-based setting and in the pediatric setting are presented, along with the pros and cons of the different strategies.

Portway, S. M., & Johnson, B. (2005). Do you know I have Asperger's syndrome? Risks of a non-obvious disability. *Health, Risk & Society, 7*(1), 73–83.

This paper discusses risks of having an invisible disability such as Asperger's syndrome. Positive and negative issues regarding controversy over the diagnostic label as well as theoretical implications of applying a diagnosis are discussed.

Prater, C. D., & Zylstra, R. G. (2006). Medical care of adults with mental retardation. *American Family Physician, 73*(12), 2175–2180.

This article notes specific medical and behavioral features occurring in adults with mental retardation as well as some of the commonly overlooked health concerns such as sexuality, sexually transmitted diseases, and end-of-life decisions.

Reschly, D. J. (2005). Learning disabilities identification: Primary intervention, secondary intervention, and then what? *Journal of Learning Disabilities, 38*(6), 510–515.

This article discusses early interventions for children to improve overall reading competencies but questions the degree to which these programs actually prevent specific learning disabilities. It discusses issues regarding what should be done about specific learning disability identification after primary and secondary interventions are shown to be inadequate for individual children.

Research Units on Pediatric Psychopharmacology (RUPP) Autism Network. (2002). Risperidone in children with autism and serious behavioral problems. *New England Journal of Medicine, 347*, 314–321.

This article describes the use of risperidone in children with autistic disorder who have serious behavioral disturbances. The article concludes that although these drugs may be beneficial, their safety and efficacy in children is not well understood.

Rourke, B. P., & Tsatsanis, K. D. (2000). Nonverbal learning disabilities and Asperger syndrome. In A. Klin, F. Volkmar, & S. Sparrow (Eds.), *Asperger syndrome* (pp. 231–253). New York, NY: Guilford Press.

This text discusses specific types of learning disabilities observed in Asperger's syndrome.

Safran, J. S. (2002). Supporting students with Asperger's syndrome in general education. *Teaching Exceptional Children, 34*, 60–66.

This article provides educators with strategies that will help children with Asperger's syndrome to practice and learn classroom and life rules that many students naturally acquire. It also discusses communication issues and a review of strategies that represent good teaching practices.

Simpson, R. L., de Boer-Ott, S. R., Griswold, D. E., Smith Myles, B., Byrd, S. E., Ganz, J. B., … Adams, L.G. (2005). *Autism spectrum disorders: Interventions and treatments for children and youth*. Thousand Oaks, CA: Corwin Press.

This comprehensive resource briefly evaluates over 40 commonly used interventions and treatments for individuals with autism spectrum disorders and provides detailed evaluations of their utility and efficiency. The book serves as a resource for school professionals and families who face difficulties in selecting and applying appropriate, effective interventions and treatments for children with autism spectrum disorders.

Strand, M., Benzein, E., & Saveman, B. I. (2004). Violence in the care of adult persons with intellectual disabilities. *Journal of Clinical Nursing, 13*(4), 506–514.

This article is a report on violence towards adults with intellectual disabilities and towards caregiver staff, with recommendations for supportive interventions in both instances.

Strickler, H. L. (2001). Interaction between family violence and mental retardation. *Mental Retardation, 39*, 461–471.

This article investigates the relationship between family violence and mental retardation. The study outlines characteristics that make certain individuals with mental retardation more vulnerable to various types of family violence and its psychologic effects.

Tammet, D. (2007). *Born on a blue day: Inside the extraordinary mind of an autistic savant.* New York, NY: Free Press.

The author provides a unique insight into what it is like to live independently in the world as an autistic savant and the challenges he has had to overcome on a daily basis.

Volkmar, F. R., & Klin, A. (2000). Diagnostic issues in Asperger syndrome. In A. Klin, F. R. Volkmar, & S. S. Sparrow (Eds.), *Asperger syndrome* (pp. 25–71). New York, NY: Guilford Press.

This book discusses specific issues related to making an accurate diagnosis in Asperger's syndrome.

Volkmar, F. R., Klin, A., & Paul, R. (2004). *Handbook of autism and pervasive developmental disorders* (3rd ed.). New York, NY: Wiley.

This book is a comprehensive text with an overview of specific issues related to autism and pervasive developmental disorder.

Volkmar, F. R., Klin, A., Schultz, R. T., Rubin, E., & Bronen, R. (2000). Asperger's disorder. *American Journal of Psychiatry, 157*(2), 262–267.
This article describes a patient with classic presentation of Asperger's disorder. The case presentation is followed by a summary of current controversies in diagnosis, the validity of the diagnostic concept, implications for treatment, and current research.

Walz, M. (2002). *Autistic spectrum disorders: Understanding the diagnosis and getting help*. Cambridge, UK: O'Reilly.
This is a general book for the lay audience. It offers information and guidance for dealing with autistic spectrum disorders.

Wing, L. (2000). Past and future of research on Asperger syndrome. In A. Klin, F. R. Volkmar, & S. S. Sparrow (Eds.), *Asperger syndrome* (pp. 418–432). New York, NY: Guilford Press.
This chapter provides a review of research that has been conducted on Asperger's syndrome and suggestions for research to be conducted in the future.

Yang, Q., Rasmussen, S. A., & Friedman, J. M. (2002). Mortality associated with Down syndrome in the USA from 1983–1997: A population-based study. *Lancet, 359*(9331), 1019–1025.
This study identifies factors responsible for racial differences (e.g., earlier death in certain racial groups), which may aid further improvement in survival of people with Down syndrome. This study describes the incidence of various medical problems in individuals with Down syndrome.

Yeargin-Allsopp, M., Rice, C., Karapurkar, T., Doernberg, N., Boyle, C., & Murphy, C. (2003). Prevalence of autism in a U.S. metropolitan area. *Journal of the American Medical Association, 289*, 49–55.
This article evaluates the concern that there is a possible increase in the prevalence of autism in the United States. The conclusion is that the rate of autism found was higher than the rates from studies conducted during the 1980s and early 1990s, but it was consistent with those of more recent studies.

Zaretsky, H. H., Richter, E. F., & Eisenberg, M. G. (Eds.). (2005). *Medical aspects of disability* (3rd ed.). New York, NY: Springer.
In this book, an overview of themes and principles of rehabilitation is complemented by a discussion of disabling conditions and disorders.

Internet Resources

For a full suite of assignments and additional learning activities, use the access code located in the front of your book to visit this exclusive website: http://go.jblearning.com/mentalhealth. If you do not have an access code, you can obtain one at the site.

Learning Objectives

After reading this chapter, you will be able to:

- Identify four factors that can contribute to a child developing emotional problems or mental disorders.
- Name two types of aberrant behavior in a child.
- List five components of a child's mental status examination.
- Contrast four theoretical models of childhood behaviors.
- Identify nursing interventions to assist children and their families with coping with emotional problems or mental disorders.
- Describe four important components in teaching children about hospitalization, medications, diagnostic tests, and treatments.

Key Terms

Attachment

Attachment model

Behavior modification model

Bonding

Child abuse

Child psychiatry

Child's Bill of Rights

Cognitive model

Developmental history

Discipline

Extended family

Family of orientation

Family of procreation

Intrusive procedure

Maternal deprivation

Mental status examination

Nuclear family

Parenting education

Play stages

Play therapy

Play types

Psychosocial developmental model

Self-concept

Sense of self model

Sibling rivalry

System of care

Temper tantrums

Therapeutic milieu

TRIADS

VIPP teaching

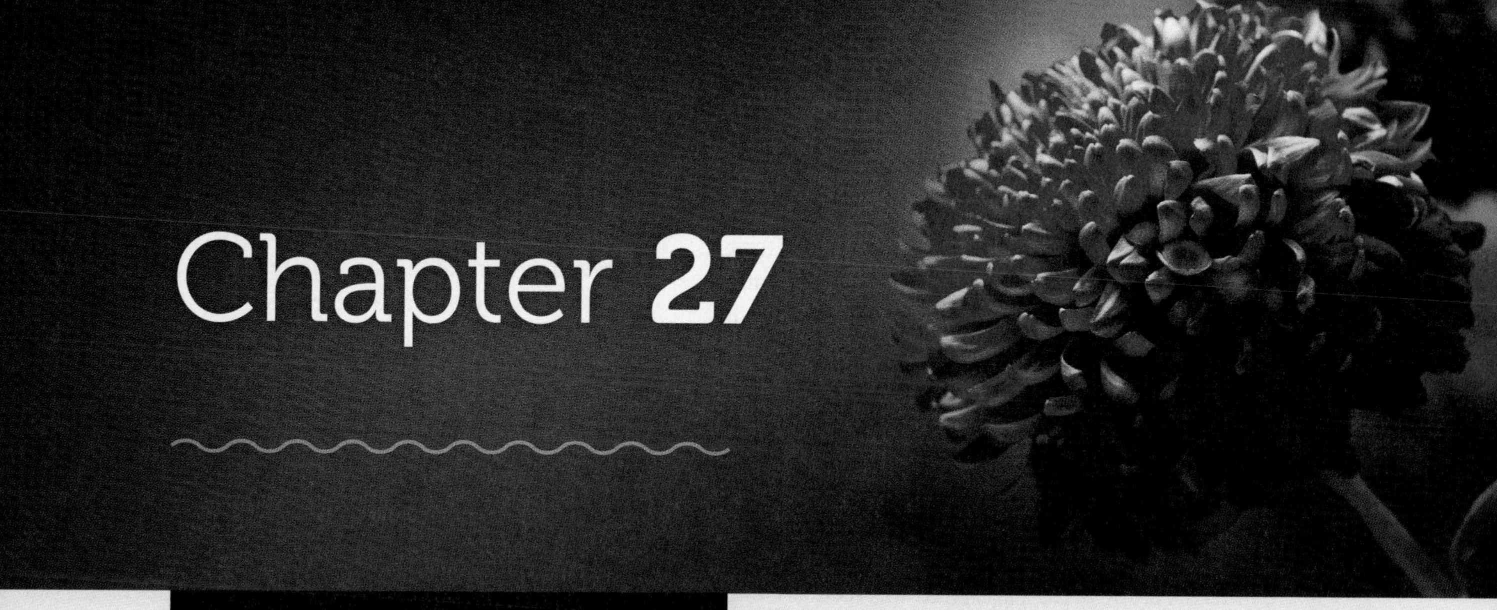

Children and Adolescents

Karen A. Ballard

http://go.jblearning.com/mentalhealth 

For a full suite of assignments and additional learning activities, use the access code located in the front of your book to visit this exclusive website: http://go.jblearning.com/mentalhealth. If you do not have an access code, you can obtain one at the site.

Introduction

Childhood is viewed by society in fairly idyllic terms. What worries, what problems can occur at such a carefree time? Just the problems and cares of growing up! Children have been viewed by previous generations as chattel, necessary evils, progeny, and insurance against want in parental old age. Interest in a child's developmental and psychological growth is fairly recent in comparison to centuries of child rearing. Even the first theorists who expressed interest in children as individuals often described the child in terms of the parent. The child was seen as a blank tablet upon which the parent wrote, a form molded and shaped by the parent into the parent's own image. Children were to be seen but most definitely not heard. William James, an early 19th-century writer, described the world of young children as a state of "buzzing, blooming confusion" (James, 1890 & 1981, p. 462). In today's society, there is a sincere interest in putting some order to this confusion.

Child's Bill of Rights

The Child's Bill of Rights states that children have the right to:
Be wanted
Be born healthy
Live in a healthy environment
Have basic needs met
Experience continuous, loving care
Acquire the cognitive skills needed for life

The President's Commission on Mental Health (1978) issued special recommendations for infants, children, and adolescents and sponsored the **Child's Bill of Rights**, which are applicable today and include the child's right to be wanted, to be born healthy, to live in a healthy environment, to have basic needs met, to experience continuous loving care, and to acquire the cognitive skills needed for life. At the Surgeon General's Conference on Children's Mental Health in 2000, it was reported that "growing numbers of children are suffering needlessly because their emotional, behavioral, and developmental needs are not being met by those very institutions which were explicitly created to take care of them ... It is time that we as a Nation took seriously the task of preventing mental health problems and treating mental illnesses in youth" (U.S. Department of Health and Human Services, 2000, para. 1.). In 2002, the Subcommittee on Children and Families of the President's New Freedom Commission on Mental Health noted that the "federal government should develop and implement a comprehensive approach for enhancing the well being of children and adolescents, based on a bio-psychosocial model, through preventive interventions prior to the onset of mental and behavioral disorders" (President's New Freedom Commission, 2002, para. 24). The implementation options that were cited included screening all children from 0 to 5 years for social and emotional development as part of primary care visits, providing mental health screening for children and their families in community health centers, and addressing the barriers to coverage of preventative mental health services in health insurance.

Critical Thinking Question

Is there evidence in today's society that children are undervalued, and, if so, what can be done to remedy the situation?

Mental Health and Emotional Problems of Childhood

Children and adolescents are not miniature adults. They are developing individuals whose focus is on coping with life as they reach maturity. It is not an easy journey. It is impossible to predict which children are vulnerable; however, nurses and other clinicians can learn to identify risk factors, contributing stresses, and the signs and symptoms of mental disorders in children and seek to intervene aggressively. Positive intervention with children and adolescents and their families and significant caretakers is critical; children with untreated emotional problems will become adults with mental health problems. Nurses should be particularly vigilant in assessing children for existing or potential emotional problems and be prepared to make the appropriate referrals to mental health agencies.

Nurses encounter children and adolescents as clients at many different points in the healthcare system—clinics, emergency rooms, schools, private physicians' offices, inpatient general pediatric or child psychiatric services, and special mental health agencies for children and adolescents. Some children are unfazed by their physical and mental experiences. These children are particularly resilient and appear protected from and invulnerable to the most extreme stresses, such as the death of a parent, divorce, abuse, and illness. Other children become stressed either as a direct result of a healthcare experience, because they have existing mental health problems that are exacerbated by current or past life events, or because they are living with mentally ill parents. During childhood, the rate of physical and mental development and the cognitive and emotional challenges faced by children make them uniquely vulnerable to multiple social, environmental, and developmental risks. Consequently, the health status of children is more at risk than that of adults for negative consequences from poor nutrition, violence, environmental pollutants, and social and economic stresses (Children's Defense Fund, 2005; Stein, 1997).

Family Structure

A family is a basic cultural group—a subsystem of society. It may include one or more adults of different generations and sexes and may or may not exist within the framework of marriage. A **nuclear family** is a subsystem consisting of one or more adults who undertake a parenting role for one or more children. A **family of orientation** is the nuclear family in which an individual has the status of a child. The **family of procreation** is a nuclear family in which the individual has or had the status of a parent; it can be a patriarchy or a matriarchy. An **extended family** is any family grouping that is related by descent, marriage, or adoption that is broader than the nuclear family and can include multiple generations (vertical extension) or aunts, uncles, and cousins (lateral extension).

When assessing the functioning of a family unit, the clinician examines the family's ability to do the following:

- To provide for the members' physical, emotional, and spiritual needs
- To be sensitive to the needs of family members
- To communicate with each other
- To provide support and security and to encourage growth and positive relationships and experiences within and outside the family
- To function in a responsible manner in the community
- To help themselves and to accept appropriate help from outside resources when needed
- To perform and complete family roles
- To respond to crises as a means of individual and family unit growth
- To create a sense of family unity and loyalty
- To demonstrate the presence of mutual respect for each individual in the family

The Task Force on the Family (Schor, 2003) identified that the power and importance of families arises out of the extended duration for which children are dependent on adults to meet their basic needs. It is important for nurses and other healthcare practitioners to understand that children's self-esteem grows from being cared for, loved, and valued and being part of a social unit that shares values, communicates openly, and provides companionship. Through nursing interventions that support the family unit and parents' functioning, nurses can directly improve children's health by identifying stressors such as financial difficulties, health problems, lack of social supports, work dissatisfaction, and unfortunate life events that cause parents emotional stress, interfering with their relationships with each other and their children and negatively disrupting their parenting and ability to emotionally support their children.

A family is a basic cultural group and a subsystem of society. Types of families include the nuclear family, family of orientation, family of procreation, and extended family. A family can be a patriarchy or matriarchy.

Critical Thinking Question

How does the type of family in which a child is a member help or hinder that child in learning to cope with the challenges and stressors in childhood?

Incidence and Prevalence

According to the U.S. Census Bureau, in 2010, 9.8 percent of children under 18 (7.3 million) were without health insurance with the family poverty rate at 11.7 million and the number of families living in poverty at 9.2 million (U.S. Census Bureau, 2011). Lack of insurance disproportionately affects minority children. While 1 in 14 white children is uninsured, the statistic jumps to nearly 1 in 9 for black children and 1 in 5 for Latino children (Children's Defense Fund, 2011). It is estimated that 6–8 million children either are currently dealing with mental health problems or will develop such difficulties.

One in every five children lives below the federal poverty level, and African American and Hispanic children and children living in female-headed households are disproportionately represented in those numbers.

Differential Diagnosis

The mental health conditions usually diagnosed in childhood and adolescence are mental retardation, learning disorders, motor skills disorders, communication disorders, pervasive developmental disorders, attention-deficit/hyperactivity disorder (ADHD), feeding and eating disorders, tics, elimination disorders, and separation anxiety disorder. The most commonly identified disorders in adolescence are conduct disorders, mood disorders, schizophrenia, eating disorders, and substance abuse. (See Chap-

A combination of factors contributes to the development of mental health problems in children and adolescents. These factors are genetic predisposition, neurobiologic factors, prenatal influences, maternal health during pregnancy, developmental stresses, concurrent physical problems or illnesses, family factors, siblings, environmental factors, and societal stressors.

ters 12, 15, 16, 17, 18, and 26 for discussion of these disorders.)

Etiology

It is unusual for there to be a single etiology for childhood emotional problems or actual mental disorders. A combination of factors, including genetic predisposition (heredity), neurobiologic factors, maternal health during pregnancy, developmental stresses, concurrent physical problems or illnesses, family factors, siblings, environmental factors, and societal stresses, is most likely. Some of the factors that put children and adolescents at risk include poverty, homelessness, illness or disability, child neglect or abuse, domestic violence, parents who are either younger or older than usual, parents with histories of mental illness, substance abuse, alcoholism, criminal behaviors, and being a member of a minority community (Burgess & Hartman, 1992). Other contributing factors that can be identified include acute or chronic illness in a family member, parental separation, poor parenting techniques (especially in the area of discipline), multiple substitute caretakers, and economic changes in the family (e.g., unemployment).

A complete mental health assessment includes assessing the identified presenting problem, general health history, developmental milestones, family problems, school performance and intellectual functioning, level of independence, peer relationships, and ability to play at an age-appropriate level.

Clinical Presentation

Children can be referred for single or multiple presenting problems. Depending on the circumstances and the developmental age of the child, some symptoms are not inappropriate, nor are they a sign of a mental health problem (e.g., temper tantrums); other symptoms should always be of concern to the nurse (e.g., hurting oneself, others, or animals; fire setting; inappropriate risk taking).

When children are identified as having mental health or emotional problems, they can be referred for treatment of single or multiple presenting problems. These problems are usually described as a more than normal inability to get along with parents, siblings, and peers; poor school performance and inability to concentrate; **temper tantrums**, impulsivity, and need for supervision; poor self-confidence; disobedience; lying; hurting oneself, animals, or others; developing somatic symptoms; unpredictable mood swings; regressive behaviors; and generally being described as sad, unhappy, or nervous (Mash & Barkley, 2003). Other problems can include inappropriate risk taking, acting-out behaviors and violence, participation in gangs or cults, running away, school delinquency, and sexual activity. It is important for the nurse to understand that, depending on the circumstances and developmental age of the child, some of these behaviors are not always inappropriate (e.g., temper tantrums), whereas others should always be of concern (e.g., hurting oneself, animals, or others).

Critical Thinking Question www

When working with children and adolescents, what behaviors might not always be inappropriate, and what types of behaviors would be of concern and require additional evaluation?

Assessing and Interviewing a Child or Adolescent

In assessing children and adolescents, nurses can observe the child interacting with others, when alone, or in play situations as well as receive reports from the family members, school teachers, other therapists, and social workers (see **Figure 27-1**). In addition to the identified presenting problem, there should be a clear understanding of the child's general health history, developmental milestones, family problems, school performance and intellectual functioning, level of independence, peer relationships, and ability to play at an age-appropriate level (House, 2002). Play and school are the work of childhood; the ability of the child or adolescent to function reasonably well

Figure 27-1 Observing a child playing can help the nurse assess the child's mental health.

in these areas is a good indicator of future mental health. When interviewing and assessing children, the nurse or clinician should explain briefly what behavior has resulted in referral and who you are (i.e., a person who helps children talk about their problems and helps them feel better). The nurse should be kind and nurturing and willing to let the child become comfortable. The interview should be conducted in a quiet, comfortable area that permits the child to move around and play with pencils, crayons, magic markers, paper, modeling dough, blocks, dolls (e.g., family figurines, action figures), trains, trucks, puppets, balls, jacks, and pickup sticks for younger children and more sophisticated and involved games and toys, including electronics, for older children. It may take a couple of visits before the child is comfortable sharing inner thoughts and concerns.

Child's Mental Status Examination

It was only with the development of **child psychiatry** as a subspecialty that clinicians began to appreciate that it was possible not only to test a child's intelligence, but also to consider the child's mental status, incorporating behavioral, neurologic, and developmental aspects. A **mental status examination** is a descriptive document that portrays a client's appearance, perception, affect, cognition, and general intellectual development. The components of a mental status examination (Goodman & Sours, 1994; House, 2002) for a child can be found in **Table 27-1**.

Tests used to evaluate a child's mental status are the Children's Apperceptive Test (CAT), Thematic Apperception Test (TAT), Rorschach Psychodiagnostic Battery, Mackover Sentence Completion, and Howells-Lickorish Family Relations Indicator. Standardized tests for evaluating expected developmental behaviors are the Denver Developmental Tests (versions DDST, DDST-R, and Denver II). Some of the abilities evaluated in the tests include the following:

- Responds to a bell (0–1 month)
- Follows objects to midline, coos, and gurgles (1 month)
- Displays social smile (2 months)
- Reaches for objects (4 months)
- Rolls over (5 months)
- Sits and crawls (6–8 months)
- Uses crude purposeful grasp (9 months)
- Uses pincer grasp (10 months)

Table 27-1 A Child's Mental Status Examination

Category	Description
Size and general appearance	Large or small for age Facial features Movements of hands, feet, and face General appearance (ill health, bruising, nail biting, thumb sucking, teeth grinding, hair pulling, tics, giggles) Clean clothes Dressing (age and sex appropriate)
Mobility	Hyperactive (episodic, patterned, random) Slowness, somnolence
Coordination: motor skills and abilities	Posture, gait, and balance Ability to manipulate play objects such as puzzle pieces and pick-up sticks and playing catch with and a ball
Speech	Receptive capacity (Can the child follow directions and hear the nurse?) Expressive ability and output (baby talk, mutism, stuttering, rhyming, echolalia)
Intellectual functioning	Knowledge of general information that is age appropriate Ability to name body parts and their functions Overall and specific school performance
Thinking and perception	Use of defense mechanisms Self-concept and body image Presence of hallucinations or paranoid ideation
Emotional reactions	Fearfulness, sadness, shame Anxiety, anger Apathy Oppositional behavior
Manner of relating	Ability to separate Level of friendliness Independence of behavior Adaptability
Fantasies and dreams	Type of dreams Stories Wishes and ambitions
Character of play	Type Family and gender constellations Content

A mental status examination is a descriptive document that portrays a client's appearance, perception, affect, cognition, and general intellectual development. A child's mental status examination includes an assessment of the child's size and general appearance, mobility, coordination, speech, intellectual functioning, thinking and perception, emotional reactions, manner of relating, fantasies and dreams, and character of play.

- Walks and uses three to four words (10–14 months)
- Scribbles with a crayon (12–18 months)
- Builds a six-cube tower (24 months)
- Uses three-word sentences and pronouns (2 1/2 years)
- Rides a tricycle, draws a circle (3 years)
- Throws overhand (4 years)
- Ties knots (5 years)
- Prints name and rides a two-wheeler (6 years)

There are three categories of attachment behaviors: signaling, approach, and following behaviors.

A complete evaluation of any child or adolescent should include an assessment of the child's family, school performance, **developmental history**, neurologic evaluation, psychologic testing results, and a complete history of the presenting problem. Clinicians need to be aware of that at various developmental stages, when confronted with specific stressors (family, peers, school, attachment losses, and illness), children and adolescents may seek to relieve themselves of overwhelming psychologic pain by engaging in self-injury or suicide. For additional information, see Chapter 17.

Theoretic Models

Maternal deprivation occurs when there is any significant separation of the infant between 3 and 15 months of age and the infant's mother figure, leading to serious emotional problems in the infant such as depression, eating disorders, and failure to thrive.

Many theorists have contributed to our understanding of how children, adolescents, and adults develop and learn to cope with multiple stresses and function in society. Previous chapters discussed psychoanalytic, interpersonal, behavioral, and neurobiologic theories. This chapter focuses on the **attachment model, psychosocial developmental model, cognitive model, sense of self model**, and **behavior modification model**.

Attachment Model

The establishment of trust is basic and critical to all future life interactions and achievements.

Bonding is an affectional feeling between mother or primary caretaker and child and is unidirectional. Attachment is a reciprocal affectional relationship between the mother or primary caretaker and child; it is bidirectional and develops throughout infancy.

According to John Bowlby (1994), the establishment of trust is essential to the survival of the human species. Bowlby notes that, within hours or days of a child's birth, bonding occurs between the mother and infant. **Bonding** is an affectional feeling that develops between the mother or primary caretaker and child; it is usually unidirectional, caretaker to child; occurs rapidly; and can be facilitated by physical contact. **Attachment** is a reciprocal affectional relationship between the mother or primary caretaker and child and develops throughout infancy. Once attachment occurs, one can note attachment behaviors between the caretaker and child; the child and primary caretaker produce behaviors that identify them to each other. This type of attachment and bonding sets the pattern for lifelong behaviors. There are three categories of behaviors: signaling behaviors (crying, smiling, babbling), approach behaviors (seeking, clinging, sucking), and following behaviors (crawling, walking with parent). There are identifiable phases in the mother–child relationship. First, the infant signals without discrimination at any figure; next, the infant directs signals toward a discriminated figure, usually the mother or main caretaker; third, the infant maintains proximity to the favored discriminated figure by crawling, crying, and motioning; and finally, the infant develops a goal-oriented partnership in which the child, usually around 2 years of age, predicts the caretaker's behavior and modifies his or her own behavior. This attachment to mother is the model for the child and adolescent in forming all future attachments (Bowlby, 1994). Although considerable attention is paid to encouraging early contact between mother and infant to develop attachment, mothers who cannot experience early contact should not be made to feel that they are damaging their infants. Once attachment is formed, it is believed that any significant separation of the infant and mother figure between 3 and 15 months of age can lead to serious emotional responses, depression, and failure to thrive. This is known as **maternal deprivation**.

Psychosocial Developmental Model

Erik Erikson's theory of psychosocial development (1964), although built on Freudian theory, is a developmental approach to human growth that stresses the importance of trust as a basic building block for normal psychologic development. He examines critical behaviors and challenges that are central to eight stages of development, which build upon each other. Each stage has a positive and negative component. Erikson postulates that the first stage, trust versus mistrust, is the initial critical challenge to the developing person. One can have problems with subsequent stages and still be fairly well integrated, but one cannot skip or incompletely finish the establishment of trust. It is basic to all future life interactions and achievements; it is critical to learn to trust (Hockenberry, 2008; Hockenberry & Wilson, 2010). Erikson's eight stages, also known as the Eight Stages of Man, are described in **Table 27-2**.

Table 27-2 **Erickson's Eight Stages of Development**

Stage	Description
Trust versus mistrust (infancy, 0–1 year)	Basic trust is the critical and most important building block. It develops from a consistent and caring relationship with a nurturing figure, usually the child's mother. Mistrust develops when basic needs are either not met or are met inconsistently. The outcomes of successful mastery of this stage are faith and optimism.
Autonomy versus shame and doubt (early childhood, 1–3 years)	This is the stage of holding on and letting go. Successful autonomy depends upon being able to positively experience activities such as walking, climbing, and toilet training. Shame and doubt develop from forced dependence, in which adults belittle the child's activities or the child is repeatedly unsuccessful in attempting new ones. The outcomes of successful mastery of this stage are self-control and willpower.
Initiative versus guilt (preschool, 3–6 years)	This is the stage of exploring the environment for all possible physical learning experiences. It is a period of heightened physical activity and imagination and the early development of conscience (right and wrong). Guilt develops when children are given the impression by others that their activities are wrong or unacceptable. The outcomes of successful mastery are direction and purpose.
Industry versus inferiority (school age, 6–12 years)	This is the stage when children apply themselves to engaging in and completing purposeful activities and tasks and to cooperating and competing with peers. Inferiority develops when expectations are too high or when children perceive that they cannot measure up to the standards of others. The outcome of successful mastery of this stage is competence.
Identity versus role confusion (adolescence, 12–18 years)	This stage is marked by rapid physical, emotional, and social changes in the child soon to be an adolescent and by a preoccupation with others', especially peers', perceptions of the self. Role confusion occurs when there are conflicts in the adolescent's ability to integrate these changes. The outcomes of successful mastery of this stage are devotion and fidelity.
Intimacy versus isolation (young adulthood, 18–25 years)	This is the stage in which one learns to form significant, loving, and intimate relationships with peers, colleagues, and, ultimately, lovers. Isolation occurs when one is unable to trust that it is safe to share oneself in a mutually giving relationship. The outcomes of successful mastery of this stage are affiliation and love.
Generativity versus stagnation (adulthood, 25–45 years)	This is the nourishing and nurturing stage. It focuses on caring for one's own or others' children or involvement in other creative productions. Stagnation occurs when one is so self-absorbed that focusing on creativity becomes impossible. The outcomes of successful mastery of this stage are production and caring.
Ego integrity versus despair (older adulthood, 45 years–to death)	This stage occurs as one perceives that one is moving toward the final years of life, and the individual is comfortable with the previous life stages, accepting what has been or has not occurred, and is able to feel a sense of satisfaction. Despair occurs when one focuses on what might have been. The outcome of successful mastery of this stage is wisdom.

Cognitive Model

Watching infants or children learn about themselves, their significant others, and their environment is exciting. The development of cognition is individual to each child but generally follows a pattern. Children often misinterpret adults, other children, or their environment because they simply do not have the cognitive skills or the knowledge to do otherwise. Watch an infant learn what the hand is and how to use it. The infant starts with a period of observing and moving, followed by learning to use the hand successfully to retrieve objects, which is usually accomplished by 5 months. Infants are interactive individuals who seek out stimuli and possess identifiable rhythms such as sucking, crying, sleeping, and wakefulness. They have a repertoire of behaviors such as looking, grasping, pushing, pulling, and moving. Cognitive development is cumulative; that is, the child's understanding of each new experience grows out of what was learned previously. *Adaptation* is the continuous process of using the environment to learn and learning

Learning and the development of cognition are individual to each child but generally follow a pattern. Cognitive development is cumulative, and the understanding of a new experience develops out of what was previously learned.

to adjust to changes in the environment. *Assimilation* is the process of taking new information and fitting it into a preconceived notion about objects, words, or other concepts. *Accommodation* is the process of adjusting to new experiences or objects by revising the previous plan to fit the new information. It is through the development of mental functioning that children learn about the world and all its objects, how these objects function, and the relationship between themselves and these objects. Through this cognitive or mental development children learn to reason abstractly, think logically, acquire language, develop morals and ethics, and acquire a sense of meaning, purpose, hope, and spirituality in their lives (Hockenberry & Wilson, 2010).

Three processes associated with cognitive development are adaptation, assimilation, and accommodation.

During childhood and culminating somewhere in adolescence, individuals develop a **self-concept**, an individual's awareness of self, beliefs, thoughts, and relationships. Inherent in self-concept are body image and self-esteem. Body image is how individuals perceive their own bodies while self-esteem reflects one's sense of worthiness and value, often influenced by others in the child's life.

Self-concept is an individual's awareness of self, beliefs, thoughts, and relationships. Body image and self-esteem are inherent in self-concept.

Jean Piaget developed a framework for understanding how children learn and adapt (Ginsberg & Opper, 1987). Although his studies have been challenged by some current theorists, his framework for understanding cognitive development is still worth considering. Piaget's stages of cognitive development are identified in **Table 27-3**.

Jean Piaget's stages of cognitive development are sensorimotor; preoperational, including preconceptual and intuitive; concrete operational; and formal operational.

To become fully functioning emotionally, one needs to develop the abilities to think, communicate, and understand. According to Piaget, the four factors that influence one's cognitive development are the following:

1. Emotions create the feelings that motivate learning.
2. The maturation of the nervous system promotes the development of the mental structures that permit a child to become capable of understanding.
3. The child needs to be exposed to a variety of experiences.
4. The child needs a variety of social interactions with others, such as parents, peers, and teachers.

Four different senses of self are described by Stern (2000):
Emergent self
Core self
Subjective self
Verbal self

Sense of Self Model

It is interesting to compare Bowlby's, Erikson's, and Piaget's theories with those of Daniel Stern, a child psychiatrist who has spent the last few decades describing the infant's changing concepts of self. Stern has a particular interest in the infant's preverbal understanding of self and subjective experience of life. Stern observes that all development occurs in leaps and bounds, and there are strategic leaps between 2 and 3 months, 9 and 12 months, and 15 and 18 months. These are periods of great change for the developing infant. Between 2 and 3 months, the infant smiles responsively, makes deliberate eye contact, and coos, and the parents experience a different relationship with the child. By 6 months of age, the infant has established a sense of core self—a separate, cohesive, physical being. Between the ages of 9 and 18 months, the infant is not only experiencing individu-

Table 27-3 Piaget's Stages of Cognition

Stage	Description
Sensorimotor (0–2 years)	This is preverbal intellectual development. The infant is in a world of self, learning first by repeating simple acts (*primary circular*) and then by repeating the acts and committing them to memory (*secondary circular*).
Preoperational (2–7 years)	This stage has two phases, preconceptual and intuitive. The world is seen from the child's point of view (egocentric thinking), including magical causation. The child is able to learn that actions have effects. Everything is literal and concrete to the child; that is, the world is either good or bad, right or wrong.
Concrete operational (7–12 years)	Thinking can still appear somewhat egocentric. The child knows past and present and is gaining understanding of future. The child is more flexible and is aware of the reversibility of acts.
Formal operational (12–16 years)	The child's conceptual organization becomes stable and coherent. The adolescent can think in abstract terms and make and test hypotheses. The child understands that death is final.

ation, but also seeking and creating an intersubjective union with another being. Stern describes four different senses of self: the *emergent self* (0–2 months), the *core self* (2–6 months), the *subjective self* (7–15 months), and the *verbal self* (after 15 months) (Stern, 1985, 2000).

Behavior Modification Model

Behavior modification teaches children how to establish controls from within themselves. It consists of teaching the consequences of behavior and involves such techniques as star charts and token systems, time-outs, and relaxation. Three types of consequences follow one's behavior:

- *Natural consequences:* Those behaviors that occur without any interventions, such as being late and missing dinner
- *Logical consequences:* Those behaviors that are directly related to a rule, such as not being allowed to play with another toy until the used ones are put away
- *Unrelated consequences:* Those that are imposed deliberately, such as no playing until homework is completed (Hockenberry, 2008)

Time-out is when the child is sent to be alone for a short period, and nothing progresses until the time-out is taken. For some children, 1 minute is a long time-out. Time-outs work only if they are planned, consistently used, and enforced.

It is believed that behavior that is rewarded will be repeated, and behavior that does not get a response or reward will be abandoned. One method that can be used is star charts. The child receives a star for each acceptable behavior or activity and, once a number of stars are earned, the child receives a reward. A similar system can be used with older children by substituting tokens. Contracts establishing certain behaviors and expectations can also be written simply and agreed to by the adult and the child. However, the verbal recognition given to the child by the adult is of primary importance. This positive reinforcement is ultimately sufficient reinforcement for the child as the star chart or token system is phased out.

Critical Thinking Question

Which theoretical model do you believe will be most helpful to you in caring for children, and how will you incorporate it into your nursing practice?

Parents and caregivers can learn to ignore certain unacceptable behavior as long as no one is in harm's way. Children are desperate for attention, and they will get it any way that they can, even if it means being physically disciplined or scolded by an adult. To the child, any attention means love. Studiously ignoring a child's unacceptable behavior is difficult to implement. When the adult does lose control and does not follow the behavior guidelines, it is helpful to verbalize an apology to the child for losing one's temper and leave the situation to regain control. Removing oneself from the child decreases the negative reinforcement of the behavior, gives the adult time to cool off, and teaches the child that adults can make mistakes and can be redeemed.

No adult will ever win a power struggle with a child; the adult has to demonstrate control and appropriate behavior. Verbalizing what we do, how we feel, and why we do things is good as long as we keep it simple. Children often have magical thoughts about adults, and the more they can learn to understand adult behaviors, the closer children are to learning adaptive behaviors for the rest of their lives.

Behavior modification teaches children how to establish controls from within. There are three consequences to behavior: natural, logical, and unrelated consequences.

Regardless of whether one focuses on a specific theorist—Freud (Sigmund and Anna), Mahler, Bowlby, Sullivan, Erikson, Fraiberg, Bowen, Yalom, or Stern—or adapts single or multiple theories—psychoanalytic, interpersonal, attachment, psychosocial, developmental, behavior, cognitive, or family systems—it is clear when working with children, that as developing individuals, they have critical needs to feel safe, to be able to trust others and the environment, to love, to play, and to learn. The establishment of trust in a child is absolutely essential for healthy development and the growth of a normal child into an adult. Trust is the cornerstone of a healthy personality. The child needs to feel that there is a guiding force (i.e., an adult) to help him or her distinguish between real and imagined dangers and fears. An example of how a child reacts negatively to a disorganized family life and the absence of a protective, caring parent is the story of Jamie in the next Case Study.

It appears clear that establishment of trust early in a child's life is absolutely essential for normal development and emotional and mental health.

Critical Thinking Question

What are some potential emotional outcomes in adolescence and adulthood for any child who has experienced significant emotional and physical abuse in early childhood?

CASE STUDIES Jamie

Jamie was a 7-year-old victim of child abuse who was admitted to a general pediatric unit with lethargy, mutism, bizarre screaming episodes, and extensive abrasions, welts, and festering sores over his lower extremities and buttocks. According to his social history, Jamie was born to a 15-year-old single mother who was addicted to heroin. She left him with his godparents when he was 7 months old so she could return to her boyfriend, who did not want the baby. Jamie lived with his godparents until he was 4 years old. He then went to live with his maternal grandmother, who kept him for a year until a neighbor's report of neglect resulted in foster care placement for a year. Jamie then returned to his grandmother for 6 months, when, in an alcoholic rage, she cut him across the arm with a butcher's knife. He spent 6 more months in foster care, and then he was placed again with his godparents. After 6 months, the godparents, without informing the child care agency, gave him to his mother, who was then married to a man who was not Jamie's father. This move occurred 4 months prior to the hospitalization.

When the mother and stepfather were asked how Jamie was hurt, they said that he was a "bad boy who needed to learn respect for adults and to stop teasing his younger sisters." A school report described a very quiet, nonverbal child who had almost no interactions with peers. He often was observed picking at his skin where he had healing sores. He had no real academic skills. He sought out the teacher for physical contact and frequently apologized for being stupid. In the hospital, Jamie was essentially nonverbal except for isolated words, sat on the floor or his bed rocking, continually picked and ate his skin, avoided eye contact, urinated anywhere, and screamed with no observable stimulus.

It was obvious to the nursing staff that Jamie would be a challenge. The key to Jamie's care was to establish a sense of trust between him and his environment. If this could be communicated, his own internal sense of basic trust might be stimulated. Jamie remained on the general pediatric unit for 6 weeks. During this time, his behavior dramatically improved but did not become entirely appropriate. At the time of discharge, he was transferred to an inpatient child psychiatric unit because of the continued bizarre screaming episodes and his inability to stop hurting himself by continuously picking at his skin and eating it. However, he had become more verbal, made eye contact, and related tentatively to peers.

Because of his screaming, Jamie initially had been given a private room. The nursing staff created a safe, predictable environment for Jamie. A radio was placed in his room, and pictures of his family were put on a tack board. The nursing staff tried to keep the same nurses involved in his care. Even with this effort, Jamie sometimes had six different nurses caring for him every 3 days, depending on the schedule. Communication regarding nursing care goals became essential, and one nurse assumed primary responsibility for the coordination of Jamie's daily care.

The sores on Jamie's buttocks had festered and become grossly infected; they looked like severe decubiti or burns. The resultant pain and need for treatment of the sores became an overwhelming problem. Jamie's pain was accompanied by significant anxiety. While his screaming during dressing changes reflected an appropriate affective response, Jamie soon began to anticipate the pain, and his anxiety clouded his perception of reality. His screaming assumed a constant, one-tone quality and began as soon as the nurses approached him. The nurses attempted to distract Jamie from his pain fantasy and help him perceive reality. This was very difficult; every time the nurses succeeded in preventing an autistic-like state was a small victory. Jamie slowly learned what was real and not real. By the time he was discharged, Jamie was demonstrating mastery over his anxiety by helping with the dressing changes; he prided himself on being able to open the dressing sets just like a nurse. He was not expected to like the procedure, but being able to master his anxiety was critical.

Children learn about reality from caring adults. Jamie's nurses helped fill this void in his life and helped to orient him. He was often confused as to the day or time and his whereabouts. As they went through the day, the nurses would comment on the external world in a normal conversational tone—"Good morning, Jamie. I am Marie, your nurse. It is breakfast time, and you have cereal and toast in front of you. Here is your schedule for the day. Let's put it on your tack board. What clothes do you want to wear today? Look, here are your choices."

Nurses and other caregivers should maintain a normal conversational tone when caring for children who are disoriented. Unfortunately, it is not unusual to observe caregivers shouting at disoriented children, as if shouting will break through the barrier. If the barrier is fear, the key is mutual trust, not shouting.

When Jamie was placed on psychotropic medication by the child psychiatrist to help control his extreme anxiety states, the nurses and staff were concerned. How could such a young child be given such strong medications? In a staff meeting, the pediatric-mental health clinical nurse specialist reviewed Jamie's chaotic life and periods of abuse and asked the nurses to imagine how Jamie was feeling. This helped the nurses to understand how serious Jamie's problems were and how the medication might actually provide him with some necessary relief.

During one visit with Jamie, the clinical nurse specialist observed an interesting event. These visits usually focused around reading a story. During the reading, Jamie reached over, picked up the nurse's finger, and slowly pulled her ring off. He rolled over onto his side, cupped the ring in his hand, and fell asleep. This was a perplexing dilemma for the clinical nurse specialist, who was frustrated with Jamie and angry at herself for having allowed him to take her ring. If she removed her ring from Jamie's hand and left, would he ever learn to trust her visits? If she left her ring with Jamie, what would he do with it when he awakened? What did Jamie's action mean, and how long would he sleep? Finally deciding that staying with Jamie was the better action, the clinical nurse specialist sat next to him and stroked his other hand. After 45 minutes, he abruptly awoke and dropped her ring on the bed. She thanked him for the ring and promised to return the same time the next day. When the clinical nurse specialist returned the next day, he looked directly at her, made deliberate eye contact and pointing to her ring, he reached out, turned it, and smiled. Obviously, the day before had been a significant breakthrough and Jamie's interaction with everyone became increasingly more deliberate and meaningful.

The next hurdle was to reintroduce Jamie to his peers. The nurses began a planned schedule of trips to the playroom where, at first, Jamie was an observer. Slowly, he was encouraged to be a participant. After 3 weeks, the decision was made to move Jamie from his single room into a room with two boys of a similar age. Initially, he seemed more withdrawn, but he soon became tentatively interactive. Within a month, Jamie was ambulating, more willing to interact with peers, and noticeably warm and responsive to his caregivers. However, there was never a period in which he was completely free of bizarre behavior; the incidence rate just decreased. He was able to play, attend the hospital school for 1 to 2 hours a day, watch and comprehend TV, and visit with his godparents and mother.

After Jamie's sores healed, the decision about where to send him had to be made. It was decided that he would be treated in an inpatient child psychiatric treatment setting where he could receive intensive therapy and continue with special schooling and play therapy. His mother, stepfather, and godparents would need to participate in family therapy before he could be returned to any of them. He was still too fragile. On the day of discharge, Jamie was accompanied to the other hospital by the clinical nurse specialist, his mother, and godparents. Although the other hospital had been discussed with Jamie, he became confused and thought that both he and the nurse were being transferred to the new hospital. When shown his new room, he wanted to know where the nurse would sleep. Jamie became appropriately tearful when it was time to separate. Both hospital staffs agreed that Jamie would be allowed to call the nurses in the first hospital twice a day for as long as he requested. His first call came before the clinical nurse specialist had returned to the hospital. He was pleased when she returned his telephone call, and he continued to call for almost two weeks with decreasing frequency as he became more integrated into the second hospital's routine.

Jamie remained hospitalized for an additional 3 months. During this time the godparents admitted to having physically abused him when he lived with them from the ages of 7 months to 4 years. Jamie's mother disappeared with her husband and two other children. During his continued hospitalization, Jamie's screaming episodes stopped, and he was eventually weaned from all medication. He became more overtly angry and would have more appropriate temper tantrums and angrily shout at staff. In group therapy, it was reported that he would often ask, "How can moms hurt kids?" and would ask staff, "What is wrong with me that mom and nanny hate me?" Jamie became a ward of the court and was placed in a small foster home with a court order forbidding any family members or previous caretakers from visiting him without a foster parent or child care agency representative present. For another case study describing child abuse, see Chapter 12.

Nursing Care Plan **An Abused Child**

Nursing Diagnosis 1: Impaired parenting related to lack of knowledge of parenting or the special needs of the child as evidenced by unrealistic expectations of the child.

Nursing Diagnosis 2: Chronic low self-esteem related to disturbances in self-concept formation as evidenced by expressions of shame, doubt, and/or guilt.

Expected Outcomes	Interventions	Evaluations
• The child will remain safe. • Episodes of physical, verbal, and emotional abuse and neglect will be eliminated.	• Supervise the child and family interactions. • Ensure that policies and procedures are followed to maintain the child's safety. • Notify hospital security that a child protection protocol is in effect. • All staff adopt a nonthreatening and nonjudgmental relationship with the child's caregivers. • Connect the child's feelings of ambivalence to realization that children love their parents and caregivers even when there are abusive episodes.	• Parental or caregiver visits are positive experiences. • There are no additional episodes of physical, verbal, or emotional abuse. • The child appears more comfortable when visited by parents or caregivers. • There is a decrease in the child's negative reactions to intrusive and painful procedures.
• The child will establish mastery over anxiety associated with dressing changes. • The child will develop trust and a more positive self-concept.	• Use play, family and action figures, art, and story-telling techniques with child to foster awareness of anxiety and understanding of intrusive and painful procedures. • Help the child to establish a comfort level in interacting with the nursing staff. • Help the child to engage with peers in play activities.	• The child is able to demonstrate, through play, mastery over anxiety and use of more appropriate coping behaviors. • The child begins to relate one to one with nurses, physicians, social workers, and therapists. • The child engages in parallel and shared play with peers in group and playroom activities.
• Contact will be established with other institutions or agencies for follow-up care.	• Have interdisciplinary team conferences to plan the child's return to the home or appropriate placement in another hospital or residential treatment center.	• The child is discharged to parental or foster home or an aftercare setting with appropriate oversight and protection.

Visit http://go.jblearning.com/mentalhealth for additional care plans and exercises.

Mental health services for children include outpatient treatment, in-home services, special education programs, respite care, foster care, day and partial hospitalization, group homes, residential treatment centers, and inpatient psychiatric hospitalization. Different types of therapy can be provided, such as individual counseling, group therapy, family therapy, special education, play therapy, and medication therapy.

Management and Treatment

In developing a method of treatment for children and adolescents, it is imperative that the nurse and other clinicians be skillful in a variety of treatment methods based on the different theories and models. Children and adolescents are too different in their individual emotional makeup, family, and cultural and societal constellations for any single method of intervention to be successful in all cases. Because adolescence is a particularly chaotic and unstable time for most individuals, some clinicians have raised the question as to whether adolescents who are hospitalized for mental health problems are truly mentally ill or just reacting differently to the many tumultuous biologic, hormonal, social, and environmental changes that they are experiencing (Smoyak, Pressler, Oppenheim, & Chapman, 1997).

A continuum of mental health services is available for the treatment of children and adolescents. These include outpatient treatment, in-home therapeutic services, special education programs, respite care, foster care, day and partial hospitalization, group homes, residential treatment centers, and inpatient psychiatric hospitalization. These treatment options, types of therapy, length of treatment, cost, and special characteristics are contrasted in **Table 27-4**.

Table 27-4 **Treatment Options for Children and Adolescents**

Treatment Option	Description	Types of Therapy	Usual Length of Treatment	Cost	Characteristics
Outpatient treatment	The goal is to maintain the child or adolescent in the family unit, school, and community. The child and family are seen once or twice a week for different types of therapy.	Individual counseling, group therapy, family therapy, play therapy, medication therapy	Can be short term (4–6 weeks) or long term (1–3 years)	One of the least expensive options	This treatment option is the least disruptive to the family unit. This allows the mental health practitioner to address ongoing problems related to family and school. It keeps the child or adolescent in contact with his or her peer group.
In-home treatment	The goal is to provide brief, intensive mental health services by one or more members of a multidisciplinary team to intervene in a specific crisis.	Family therapy (on site in the home), behavior modification therapy, parent education and training, medication therapy	Short term (4–6 weeks); used mainly for specific periods of crisis or stress	One of the least expensive options	This type of treatment may be slightly disruptive to family life because all members will be asked to attend therapy at specific times. It allows the mental health practitioner to observe how all family members are responding to the crisis. It is more intensive than simple outpatient treatment. It disrupts the normal school environment and possibly peer relationships.
Special education program	The goal is to provide the child or adolescent with a positive learning experience with specially trained teachers and to provide on-site mental health practitioners.	Special education, individual counseling, family therapy, play therapy, medication therapy	Long term (2–5 years)	One of the least expensive options	This treatment option is more intensive than simple outpatient treatment.
Day treatment or partial hospitalization	The goal is to provide the child or adolescent with the opportunity to receive treatment in a structured environment for a portion of the day.	Individual counseling, group therapy, family therapy, play therapy, medication therapy	Short term (a few months) or long term (a couple of years)	Moderately expensive; may be offset by insurance	This treatment option allows the child or adolescent to maintain family and peer group contact. It can be an after-school program or combined with a special education program. It may be associated with some stigmatization.
Respite care	The goal is to provide the parents or caretakers with time off from providing care.	Individual counseling, family therapy, parent education or training, medication therapy	Short term (2 weeks to 2 months)	Moderately expensive	This treatment option provides a break for the child or adolescent and parents or caretakers. It provides the mental health practitioner with an opportunity to use intensive individual therapy with the child or adolescent.

(Continues)

Table 27-4 **Treatment Options for Children and Adolescents *(Continued)***

Treatment Option	Description	Types of Therapy	Usual Length of Treatment	Cost	Characteristics
Foster care	The goal is to remove the child or adolescent from a dysfunctional home and to place the child or adolescent with foster parents who have been specially trained to work with children who have multiple emotional needs.	Individual counseling; group therapy; family therapy with foster parents, biologic parents, or both; medication therapy	Short term (a few months during crisis times) or long term (years)	Moderately expensive	Removal from even the most dysfunctional home can result in a major disruption in the child's life. The child or adolescent can continue to attend regular or similar school, or if necessary, a special education program can be incorporated into care. Provides the child or adolescent with a more normal, predictable family atmosphere. Mental health practitioners are available to support the foster parents and reduce burnout.
Group home care	The goal is to place the child or adolescent with 10–12 other children or adolescents who live in a structured, supervised residence, usually with specially trained house parents of both sexes.	Individual counseling, group therapy, family therapy, medication therapy	Long term (several years)	Moderately expensive	This type of care can result in a major disruption in the child's or adolescent's life from family and peers. It is less homelike than foster care. The child or adolescent must adapt to group home norms and follow rules established in the home. Most group homes have a treatment philosophy, such as behavior modification. The group home is usually operated by a child-care agency that is responsible for training the house parents, providing supervision, and providing a full range of mental health services as needed by the children or adolescents.
Residential treatment center	The goal is to place the child or adolescent in a center that functions like a therapeutic community in which a hundred or more children may be housed in a campus-like, multiple-residence setting.	Individual counseling, group therapy, family therapy, play therapy, medication therapy	Long term (several years)	Moderately to very expensive	Separation from family and peers can result in a major disruption in the child's or adolescent's life. A residential treatment center is less homelike than other options are. House parents and multidisciplinary teams are available 24 hours a day. Most centers use therapeutic milieu and behavior modification techniques to influence changes in behavior.

Table 27-4 Treatment Options for Children and Adolescents *(Continued)*

Treatment Option	Description	Types of Therapy	Usual Length of Treatment	Cost	Characteristics
Inpatient hospitalization	The goal is to provide safe mental health care under direct medical and nursing supervision in a secure setting.	Individual counseling and intensive psychotherapy, group therapy, family therapy, play therapy, medication therapy	Short term (a few weeks to a couple of months for inpatient crisis treatment or evaluation); long-term (years for children or adolescents who are placed)	Most expensive; may be offset by insurance	Children or adolescents who are placed in these centers usually have failed at other levels of treatment intervention and have chronic and multiple mental health problems. They are usually known to social services, mental health agencies, or juvenile justice agencies. Inpatient hospitalization results in the most direct disruption of the child's or adolescent's life. Many units are locked or geographically very distant from the family. Schooling is on site and is usually a special education program. Regimented schedule of daily activities assists in providing a structured environment. The usual treatment philosophy is a traditional medical model with behavior modification and therapeutic milieu techniques incorporated. Children or adolescents are placed in these settings when they are considered a potential harm to themselves or others or their behavior is chaotic. Contact with family members is structured and monitored. Passes may be provided for short visits to home.

Sources: Adapted from Hendren & Berlin, 1991, p. 62; Lyman & Campbell, 1996, pp. 1–24.

Group homes, residential centers, and some inpatient settings seek to establish a **therapeutic milieu** that provides "adaptive experiences that a child or adolescent presumably missed in the course of growing up. ... [It] also provides corrective experiences to offset some of the more damaging experiences; it is a safe place [that emphasizes] external structure and control" (Lyman & Campbell, 1996, p. 45). Such a community is a flexible environment that is able to meet the individual needs of the children while maintaining predictable standards of behavior (Lyman & Campbell, 1996).

It is generally accepted that children and adolescents should be treated in the least restrictive environment and removed from the family only when there are no other options. All alternatives should be explored first, including the provision of combined services, to keep the child in the family unit. Hospitalization allows for direct observation by clinicians of a child's problems and behaviors and the initiation and adjustment of medication regimens as appropriate (Lyman & Campbell, 1996).

Inpatient psychiatric hospitalization should be reserved for those children who are a danger to themselves or others, have significant bizarre behavior or a known psychiatric diagnosis, need to be on an established medication treatment regimen that must be closely monitored, or cannot be evaluated or kept safe without 24-hour skilled care and observation. Other criteria that can be used to determine the need for psychiatric hospitalization include significant emotional distress, the inability to function in school, and complete alienation from family and peers (Regan, 2006).

In group homes, residential treatment centers, and inpatient settings, programs usually use positive reinforcements with a privilege system (e.g., time-outs, debriefing, room restriction, loss of privileges). Negative responses to behavior, especially any aversion techniques, are used only when absolutely necessary (e.g., physically restraining a child). Staff members need to be trained in appropriate responses to acting out behaviors, self-injurious behaviors, suicidal thoughts or actions, intimidation, and sexual acting out. Other issues in treatment settings include the development of a coordinated multidisciplinary approach (i.e., psychiatry, psychology, nursing, social work, education, recreational and play therapy), the establishment of safety factors, the provision for **parenting education**, and planned **discipline** and limit setting.

The decision to place a child or adolescent in a treatment facility outside of the family structure should never be considered without due consideration, because such placement significantly changes the family dynamic.

The decision to remove a child from the family and familiar environment should never be made without due consideration. Removal is a drastic change for both the child and the family and can negatively impact on the child and family and result in stigmatization. It can lead to imitative institutionalized behaviors, and families can become disengaged from the child, while the child can become overly dependent on staff and the institution. On the positive side, removal provides the family and child with a respite from each other and the inherent conflict. It can provide everyone involved, including the clinicians on the team, the opportunity to view the problems from another perspective and provide an opportunity to maximize the therapeutic interventions. If legal assistance is requested in response to treatment suggestions, clinicians can refer children, adolescents, and their families and significant others to resources such as the American Bar Association's Center on Children and the Law (ABACCL), located in Washington, D.C., and the National Center on Women and Family Law (NCOWFL) in New York City.

Finally, there are not enough mental health services available for children. Most children cannot and should not be isolated from their families forever. Treatment services must focus on improving the functioning of the child or adolescent and providing supportive therapy and services for the family unit, which in most cases will be asked to continue raising the child or adolescent. It is imperative that there be a comprehensive and coordinated network of mental health and other services available to meet the changing needs of children and their families and caregivers, a **system of care** as advanced by the Child and Adolescent Service System Program in the National Institute of Health. Such a system provides services that are community based, child centered, family focused, and culturally appropriate (Arbuckle & Herrick, 2006).

Special Issues

In providing age-appropriate care for children, nurses may find themselves helping children deal with a variety of challenging life events. These include being hospitalized with medical conditions that often can be life threatening; facing intrusive and/or complicated procedures; coping with new and often frightening feelings; coping with pain and death; and surviving episodes of child abuse.

Children With Medical Conditions

Multiple factors affect a child's and family's abilities to adjust to a chronic illness or hospitalization, including the actual physical condition and its severity, whether the condition can be corrected, the ages of the child and the parents, sociocultural factors, financial status and availability of health insurance, accessibility of medical care, prior losses associated with illness in the family, and the parent–child and child–sibling relationships (Hayman, Mahon, & Turner, 2002).

Hospitalization is a potential trauma for all children (**Figure 27-2**). It includes elements of separation, strangeness of environment, pain, punishment, and threat to self, especially possible mutilation. Children react more to the fantasy aroused by medical procedures than to the procedure itself. Nurses are

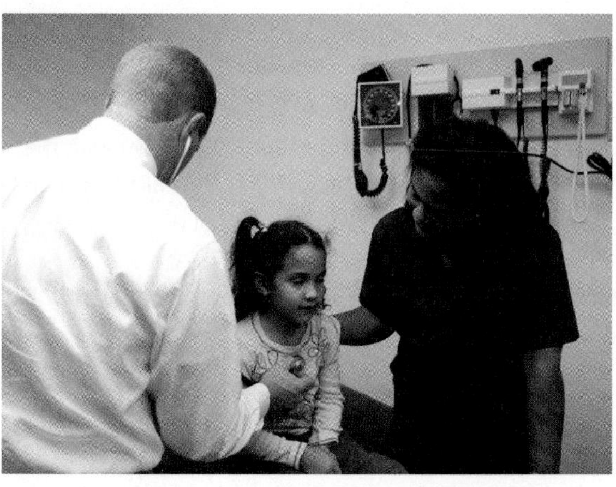

Figure 27-2 Being in a hospital can be traumatic for children.

in a unique position on the healthcare team because they often both prepare the child for an **intrusive procedure** and carry it out, either directly or by assisting the physician, and then comfort the child after the procedure. This is no simple task. There are three types of intrusive or invasive procedures: oral procedures, such as the administration of medication, suctioning, and tracheotomy care; anal procedures, such as suppositories and enemas; and cutaneous procedures, such as injections, blood tests, intravenous (IV) therapy, and dressing changes.

Critical Thinking Question

In addition to intrusive or invasive procedures, what other types of experiences during hospitalization can frighten a child, and how can nurses assist the child in feeling safe?

Children under 4 years of age tend to become more disturbed while in the hospital and to have more emotional sequelae afterward. Anxiety (e.g., crying, anorexia, bed wetting, nightmares) and regressive behaviors (e.g., loss of vocabulary, thumb sucking, masturbation, and demands to be fed) are common in hospitalized children. In younger children, imaginary companions may arise. However, these are not reasons to lie to children about what to expect. The hospitalized child is particularly at risk for problems that may not become apparent until later, even after discharge. Deception and overprotectiveness by the nurse can lead to a loss of trust and may influence the child's ability to form relationships. Adult personality patterns develop during childhood, and an early traumatic event can have lasting effects.

Hospitalized children need play outlets, established areas of control, and consistent caretaking from the same staff. There are five **play types** (social, explorative, imitative, group or gang, and competitive games) and four **play stages** (solitary, parallel, associative, and cooperative). Some examples of **play therapy** that are used with hospitalized children include structured play, mutual story telling, nondirective play, behavioral play, visualization, and guided imagery.

Play is the work of children. Some types of play therapy are structured play, mutual storytelling, nondirective play, behavioral play, visualization, and guided imagery.

Children have the basic right to know. This right is mediated by the child's cognitive ability, developmental stage, ethnic and cultural experiences, and the time frame for the medical or hospital experience. Children can refuse to listen, cry in protest, or cooperate. None of these reactions alters their right to know.

Children, adolescents, and their parents should be prepared for all procedures, medical treatments, and surgeries to diminish or prevent psychologic trauma. The parent or primary caretaker should always be involved in such preparation, facilitating communication between the multidisciplinary team and the parents, clearing up any misconceptions the parents may have, and giving the parents and child or adolescent a common point of reference regarding the

Clinical Example

Some examples of children's confusion about their bodies follow:

- A 4-year-old girl with a cyanotic heart condition was asked to draw her heart on a body outline. She put little hearts in her fingers and toes and a medium heart in the middle of her belly. The child had severe clubbing and cyanosis of her fingers and toes, and, of course, she associated her heart with these extremities.
- A 9-year-old boy confined to a wheelchair to allow healing of a graft on his burned leg correctly identified neutral, nonthreatening functions of his internal organs but claimed that muscles were important because "if you could not move, you would probably have a heart attack."
- A 12-year-old mentally retarded child repeatedly referred to his bone marrow tests as "bow and arrow" tests, which is how he probably heard and perceived the test.

Hospitalization is a potential trauma for children because it contains elements of separation, a strange environment, pain, punishment, threat to self, and possible mutilation.

Considerations for Client and Family Education

Both children and families benefit from appropriate education regarding the general hospital experience, tests and procedures, medical diseases, and specific surgical interventions. If at all possible, the nurse should first meet with the parents or caregivers to determine their understanding of the hospitalization and what, if anything, the child has been told. Parents sometimes want to avoid telling the child anything, based on a belief that the child cannot possibly understand and would be better off not knowing anything. Parents will respond positively to reassurances that any teaching will be done sensitively and based on the child's stage of development and age. The teaching should be reviewed with the parents, and parents should be included in the child's teaching sessions.

When teaching, nurses should try to use less emotional words such as fix, help, open, drain, and head instead of cut, bleed, or brain. Teaching children with orthopedic problems is uniquely difficult because many individuals, even adults, have faulty knowledge of the skeletal system. Special areas on which to focus when discussing orthopedic procedures are bone pain, bone healing, cast application or removal, maintenance of bodily integrity, and implications for future life activities. To help a child understand how something can be broken but look all right, put a tongue blade inside a gauze pad and break it, use x-rays of broken limbs, build a play traction apparatus, have model casts, or have the child apply casts to a doll.

Four general principles for teaching children about medical procedures are:

1. Children learn best when taught on a one-on-one basis. Although a group experience can reinforce learning, it is not a substitute for one-on-one teaching.
2. Children learn out of interest and curiosity.
3. Children learn only when ready.
4. Children learn at their own pace.

When teaching younger children, remember they often miss internal cues and rely on concrete external cues. If children displace their illnesses on a specific location, even if it is inaccurate, it should be incorporated into the child's perception to explain tests, procedures, and healing. Remember, children are visual and very literal. Therefore, it is important to teach the procedure in the order in which the child will experience it. For example, if the child is having surgery, describe the limitations on intake, preoperative medications, transportation, the attire of operating room personnel, the operating room, anesthesia, the recovery room and intensive care unit (ICU), tubes, machinery, bandages, postoperative pain, medications, and postoperative limitations on activity. The child does not need to know the details of the surgery, only what will be experienced or seen. The elements of the nursing process can be used in teaching children about healthcare experiences and hospitalization.

As an integral part of the teaching process, the nurse must assess:

- The child's chronologic age, development level, and cognitive skills
- The reasons for the hospitalization or other healthcare experience (planned versus emergency)
- Previous life experiences (prior hospitalizations, recent family or peer crises, and any handicaps)
- The effect the hospitalization or healthcare experience will have on future life goals (chronicity, prognosis, body changes)
- The availability of family and peer support systems (parents, siblings, and peer relationships; transcultural and economic factors)

The nurse needs to plan a teaching program that addresses the child's individual needs, including:

- Identification of the child's and family's current knowledge base and misconceptions
- Identification of content to be taught
- Choice of appropriate methods of teaching (one-to-one, group, demonstration, video)
- Establishment of a time frame (the younger the child, the closer to the event)
- Selection of teaching materials (hospital and play equipment, books, dolls, puppets, and body diagrams) before beginning the session

The nurse implements the teaching program by:

1. Demonstrating the procedure to the child and family
2. Having the child and family participate in the experience
3. Encouraging the child and family to demonstrate the learned content

The nurse evaluates the success of the teaching program either by using a formal evaluation tool or by observing the child's and family's reactions and responses to the teaching experience and the actual event. Remember to use **VIPP teaching**:

V = Visual aids are best.

I = Information is age appropriate.

PP = The child is Prepared for the event by Play (Ballard, 1985).

event. Parents can be particularly helpful in assisting the nursing staff in understanding any idiosyncratic language of a young child for the presenting problem (e.g., boo-boo, pimple, nasty thing), body parts (e.g., noggin, bum, peenie), and body functions (e.g., poo, pee, BM).

Feelings

Children have unique ways of conveying their feelings to caregivers. The following two poems illustrate this:

Sick Patient (by 12-year-old Chuck, with leukemia)

Part One

Come on doctor don't be slow
if I die you'll never know.
Come on doctor don't take so long
in a few minutes I may be gone.
Come on doctor don't stop to talk
at the rate I'm going I'll never walk.

Part Two

Come on social worker get off the elevator
'cause I know for a fact I won't see you later.
Come on social worker don't go to any meeting
in just a few minutes I may be leaving.
Come on social worker you're almost here
the longer you take the more I fear.

Part Three

Come on nurse don't delay
eat your Wheaties along the way.
Come on nurse don't waste time
'cause the life you save just might be mine.
Come on nurse just don't pass by
'cause in a few minutes I just may die.

The Victor (by 18-year-old Margaret, with an endocrine disorder)

When the doctors and nurses and others call me a
Stroke Victim, I say, "Wait a minute, I am
not a Stroke Victim. I am a Stroke Victor."
I can speak and walk and even write.
In life there are many things which can
claim us as their victim.
We make the decision what we will do about them.
Whether we let them victimize us or we fight
to be victorious over them. And I, for one,
with God's help will be victorious.

Remember that children need to know the order of events, so teach all the different elements of procedures and treatments in the order in which they occur

Teaching of children is "VIPP":
Visual aids are used.
Information is age appropriate.
Preparation is done by play.

Pain

How do children react to pain? Children experience pain as fear, abandonment, and not being able to get help. They think that the hurt will never end, and they fear losing control. They worry that pain can kill them. Children who cannot describe pain with words can use devices such as the Wong-Baker Faces Pain Rating Scale, a series of simple round faces progressing from happy to very sad and distressed (Hockenberry, 2008). Helping children cope with pain is a challenge. Children need to be encouraged to acknowledge, describe, and rate their pain and not to refuse medication because they fear getting an injection (the little hurt from the needle takes away the bigger pain).

Death

Children also have to learn to cope with death. Erikson noted that helping children to understand death is essential to support their ability to lead productive lives (Ginsberg & Opper, 1987). Children's perceptions of death are related to their developmental stages.

- For children 1–3 years old, death is seen as separation.
- For children 3–7 years old, death is both separation and punishment.
- For children 7–12 years old, death is something to be feared.
- For children over 13 years of age, death is seen as the end of life.

Helping children to understand death is essential to their ability to lead productive lives. Children respond to death based on their developmental levels. It is not until adolescence that one comprehends fully the reality of death.

Children's ability to comprehend death is quite limited until they reach adolescence. Children of different ages explain death differently. Death for younger children has no finality, because it is experienced as abandonment and separation. Children first learn that pets die, older people die, other people die, and then as adolescence approaches that they also will die. When children ask questions about death, nurses and other clinicians should listen carefully to the question and overcome the tendency to project their own fears and feelings. Seek clarification as to what is concerning or worrying the child.

The following poem was written by a 9-year-old girl for the nursing staff after her 14-year-old brother died from osteogenic sarcoma.

Paul

Paul was a very wonderful boy
But he isn't here for us to enjoy
The Nurses even cared for Paul
They really would give their all and all
They took care of Paul not because they were getting their pay
Just so they could see him live another day
The hospital was crying all that night
And they really gave up a terrible fight
They would care for Paul every day
And not turn their heads another way
They would cry all night or lose their pay
If Paul could see another day
But here we try to be very strong
Even though Paul has gone
If we could pray for him to come back
Even though we know he's on the right track
We know that Paul is in good hands with God.

Clinical Example 

A pediatric-mental health clinical nurse specialist has helped many children understand death. Each child's experience has been very different:

- A 3-year-old child talks about dog and cat heaven.
- A 5-year-old child wants to write letters to God and her grandparents in heaven.
- A 7-year-old child asks to always have flowers nearby if she dies.
- A 9-year-old asks for help in getting to the next year, which he knows will be better.
- A 12-year-old seeks reassurance that there is no pain after death and that it will not hurt to die.
- An adolescent with cancer expresses a desire to die as whole as possible—no more hair loss, no more disfiguring surgery.

In most states, nurses and other healthcare practitioners are mandatory reporters of child abuse and neglect. One need only suspect that abuse or neglect has occurred.

Child Abuse and Trauma

The phenomenon of **child abuse** occurs at all levels of society. Children are physically, psychologically, and sexually abused every day. Although society attempts to identify and help the abusing dysfunctional adult, the ills that lead to abuse and sustain it—poverty, substandard housing, substance abuse, poor education, and an inadequate child welfare system—are not addressed adequately. Victims of physical child abuse, maltreatment, and neglect change ambulatory care providers with greater frequency than nonabused children. Recognition of this characteristic may allow for earlier identification of children who are at risk for additional or future neglect or abuse (Friedlaender et al., 2005).

In most states, nurses are one of many mandatory reporters of child abuse and neglect. All nurses should be knowledgeable of their state's requirements. Usually, if anyone reports a suspicion of child abuse or neglect to the authorities and it is done in good faith and without malice, the reporting individual is protected from any legal action by the family. Violence in the family is covered in Chapter 11.

Signs and symptoms of child abuse or neglect include:

- Bruises, welts, lacerations, abrasions, burns, fractures, and head injuries
- Drug withdrawal
- Poor hygiene, unattended physical or medical needs
- Torn, stained, or bloody clothing
- Genital, vaginal, or anal injuries
- Sexually transmitted diseases and pregnancy in a minor

- Lack of supervision or abandonment
- Parentally induced or fabricated illnesses
- Extreme fear of parents or adults
- Frequent behavioral or mood changes
- Sucking, biting, rocking, and head banging
- Antisocial, destructive behavior
- Hysteria and phobias
- Sleep disorders and inhibited play
- Self-destructive or suicidal acts
- Delinquency, running away, and truancy
- No explanation for injuries by parents or caretakers
- Overreaction or underreaction to the injuries by parents or caretakers
- History of hospital shopping for the child's care

Trauma learning occurs when "the child's attempts to modify the sensory, perceptual, and cognitive alterations that occur during abuse (physical or sexual) emerge in overt behavioral patterns that specifically reflect the abuse itself" (Burgess & Hartman, 1992, p. 362). If this behavior is not interrupted, the child will begin to identify with the offender. Burgess recommends using the **TRIADS** abuse history for assessing trauma in children (Burgess & Hartman, p. 363):

- Type of abuse (physical, psychological, sexual)
- Role relationship (family member, stranger, friend, teacher)
- Intensity (frequently, single event)
- Autonomic response (hyperarousal, numbing)
- Duration (days, weeks, years)
- Style of abuse (repetitive, patterned, ritualistic)

Children are increasingly facing traumatic events in their lives, families, schools, communities, and world. These include child abuse; domestic violence; loss of loved ones; school violence (bullying, harassment, gangs, fatal shootings); catastrophic weather events (hurricanes, tornadoes, tsunamis); epidemics of contagious diseases; terrorism; bombings; drive-by shootings, and wars (Goldman, 2005). Traumatized children must be helped to feel safe with the mental health practitioners and others involved in their treatment and to learn to trust again in their caregivers, families, and communities.

Parenting Behaviors and Child Discipline

Children grow and develop based on the strength of the parenting behaviors of the main caregivers. Parenting, a critical and very serious task for adults, is often casually accepted by many members of society as something one automatically knows how to do upon the birth of a child. One need only look at the statistics for child abuse (almost 2 million children are abused annually) to know that this is not true. No parenting is perfect. We all tend to parent as we ourselves were parented. Becoming a parent, whether in a relationship and stable family unit, as a single parent, as a young parent with minimal support systems, or as an older, first-time parent, results in changes in the parent's lifestyle and relationships with others. Whether or not the parent views the birth of the child as stressful or fairly routine, the parent's self-image, family economics, and levels of responsibility will all change. One's life is not the same once a child has been born into it.

There is a general lack of appreciation of the role of the father figure in a child's development. Care of infants and children must be acknowledged as natural and appropriate male behavior. Many infants form primary attachments with the father, even when the father is not the primary caretaker, and almost all infants by 3 months of age can discriminate between maternal and paternal figures. A father's play and verbalizations have positive impact on developing infants. The mother figure's interactions with the child tend to involve caretaking activities, whereas the father figure's interactions are mostly play oriented.

If not successfully treated, children who have been victims of trauma will begin to identify with the offender.

The role of discipline in parental activities needs to be evaluated by pediatric and mental healthcare practitioners. All families use some form of discipline. Discipline that helps children learn to control their behaviors and keep themselves safe is appropriate; discipline that is harsh, unfocused, or physically, verbally, or psychologically abusive is never appropriate.

Caregiver Stress

Caregiver burden is "the presence of problems, difficulties, or adverse events that affect the lives of the psychiatric patient's significant others" (Angold et al., 1998, p. 75). Caring for children who are emotionally healthy is not easy, and caring for children with emotional problems is significantly difficult. Such care affects the caregiver's personal well-being, puts tremendous restrictions on personal activities, and can be a social stigma. Caregiver stress can be helped through counseling focused on the specific needs of the parents or caregivers and through respite care provided on a regular and scheduled basis.

People tend to parent the way they were parented. Parents need support through all stages of normal growth and development to understand their children and their own reactions to the child's various behaviors.

Sibling Rivalry

Sibling rivalry permits children to act out in the confines of a safe home environment many of the future challenges and competitions that will be faced in adulthood.

Children who are separated by more than 5 years in birth order seem to experience minimal **sibling rivalry**. Sibling rivalry can be constructive and is not necessarily harmful or destructive. It actually allows children to act out within the safe confines of the family many of the future challenges and competitions of adult life. Siblings' expectations of a new brother or sister must be realistic. They are not acquiring a new toy or playmate. They must be taught limitations of their interactions with the infant. They should be introduced to the reproductive process at an age-appropriate level (e.g., brothers and sisters are not delivered by storks but grow inside mommy). They must learn how everyone in the new family will fit together (e.g., sleeping arrangements, meals, family vacations). The older brother or sister can be encouraged to assist with specific, infant-directed activities; to play out feelings toward the new infant with dolls and other toys; to appreciate the specialness of older brother or older sister status; and to have their own private times with the mother and father.

Summary

American society sees childhood as an idyllic stage of development; however, it is a time of tremendous growth and challenge for the child and adolescent. A child's development is affected by numerous risk factors and contributing stresses. Children experience life in a family structure. The establishment of trust early in life is critical to the child's and adolescent's ability to function in the family, with peers, in school, and in adulthood.

Nurses can gain an understanding of the functioning of a child with mental health problems by interviewing and assessing the child and by conducting a mental status examination. Five theoretical models that assist in understanding how children develop and what influences their behavior are the attachment model, the psychosocial developmental model, the cognitive model, the behavioral modification model, and the sense of self model. In the case study of a young child, the effects of a long history of poor attachment behaviors and multiple instances of loss of trust through child abuse were examined.

Various methods of management and treatment, including outpatient treatment, in-home treatment, special education programs, respite care, foster care, day and partial hospitalization, group homes, residential treatment centers, and inpatient hospitalization were explored.

Special issues such as children with medical problems, child abuse and trauma, pain, death, self-injury and suicide, and nursing interventions such as play therapy, teaching children about medical procedures, and teaching about and administering medication therapy were discussed. Caregiver stress experienced by the parents and significant others of children with emotional problems can be significant. Caregivers can be helped by counseling and with the provision of respite services.

Evidence-Based Practice

When parents are not available to a child through death or mental illness, nurses need to be sensitive to how such life situations can affect a child. The death of a parent is a major stressful event for children and their families. Children who are not supported in the early phases of grieving can develop serious emotional and behavioral problems that can lead to the development of some major psychiatric disorders (Kirwin & Hamrin, 2005). Nurses should focus on assessing the child's self-care skills, deficits, and adaptive and maladaptive coping behaviors to plan individual interventions for assisting the child in coping with the loss of a parent or with the behaviors of a mentally ill parent(s).

Children with acute and chronic illnesses experience multiple major stressors. One in-depth exploratory study of children diagnosed with cancer revealed that the major stressors for these children were treatment procedures such as chemotherapy, loss of control, the hospital environment, relapses, and fear of dying. The children also identified body image issues, ongoing lack of self-esteem, and issues related to returning home and back to school as stressful (McCaffrey, 2006). These types of studies reinforce the important role of nurses in teaching both children and families about any hospital experience (inpatient or outpatient), tests and procedures, medical diseases, and specific surgical interventions.

Annotated References

Angold, A., Messer, S., Stangl, D., Farmer, E., Costello, E., & Burns, B. (1998). Perceived parental burden and service use for child and adolescent psychiatric disorders.

American Journal of Public Health, 88(1), 75–80.
This article reports on a study of the little-known area of caregiver and parental stress as experienced by those caring for emotionally disturbed children.

Arbuckle, M., & Herrick, C. (2006). *Child & adolescent mental health—Interdisciplinary systems of care*. Sudbury, MA: Jones and Bartlett.
This text discusses the integration of the systems of care philosophy and approach into providing mental health care to children and adolescents. It discusses the implications and impact of such a system on the patients, families, mental health professionals, and the behavioral healthcare community.

Ballard, K. (1985). *Preparing children for the hospital experience* [videotape]. New York, NY: American Journal of Nursing Company and Hospital Satellite Network.
This recorded presentation of teaching methods is a classic and can be used still in preparing children of all ages for hospitalization and medical and surgical procedures. It was chosen in 1986 by the American Association for the Advancement of Science as an exceptional film.

Bowlby, J. (1994). *Attachment*. New York, NY: Basic Books.
This is a late version of Bowlby's classic work on the formation of attachment behaviors between infants and mothers.

Burgess, A., & Hartman, C. (1992). Nursing interventions with children and adolescents experiencing sexually aggressive responses. In P. West (Ed.), *Psychiatric and mental health nursing with children and adolescents* (pp. 360–365). Gaithersburg, MD: Aspen.
This is an excellent review of trauma and its effects on children. It offers suggestions for assessment and interventions.

Children's Defense Fund. (2005). *The state of America's children—2004*. Washington, DC: Author.
This report discusses the impact of living in poverty in the United States upon children and their families and the implications of such status on their health, education, family structure, and criminal behavior.

Children's Defense Fund. (2011). Policy priorities: Uninsured children. Retrieved from http://www.childrensdefense.org/policy-priorities/childrens-health/uninsured-children/
This report examines state-by-state inequities in the insurance coverage and health disparities experienced by the nation's children.

Erikson, E. H. (1964). *Childhood and society* (2nd ed.). New York, NY: W. W. Norton and Company.
This book is appropriately identified by the publisher as the landmark book on the social significance of childhood.

Friedlaender, E. Y., Rubin, D. M., Alpern, E. R., Mandell, D. S., Christian, C. W., & Alessandrini, E. A. (2005). Patterns of health care that might identify young children who are at risk for maltreatment. *Pediatrics, 116*(6), 1303–1308.
This paper discusses how victims of physical child abuse, maltreatment, and neglect change ambulatory care providers with greater frequency than nonabused children and how recognizing this characteristic can lead to earlier identification of children who are at risk.

Ginsberg, H., & Opper, S. (1987). *Piaget's theory of intellectual development* (3rd ed.). Upper Saddle River, NJ: Prentice-Hall.
This book provides an excellent introduction to Piaget's life, work, and cognitive theories. It is a great introductory primer.

Goldman, L. (2005). *Raising our children to be resilient: A guide to helping children cope with trauma in today's world*. New York, NY: Brunner-Routledge.
This book offers sound practical advice for parents, teachers, and mental health practitioners on how to support children in adapting to a frightening world.

Goodman, J. D., & Sours, J. A. (1994). *The child mental status examination*. Northvale, NJ: Jason Aronson.
This is an excellent guide for understanding the processes involved in the developmental, emotional, mental, and neurologic examinations of children.

Hayman, L. L., Mahon, M. M., & Turner, J. R. (2002). *Chronic illness in children: An evidence-based approach*. New York, NY: Springer Publishing Company.
This book provides a research-based discussion of common childhood chronic illnesses and their etiology, diagnosis, treatment, and management. Special emphasis is placed on psychosocial management, family coping, and stress in the child.

Hendren, R., & Berlin, I. (1991). *Psychiatric inpatient care of children and adolescents: A multicultural approach.* New York, NY: Simon & Schuster.

The authors provide their uniques insights into providing mental health inpatient treatment to children and adolescents using a multicultural approach.

Hockenberry, M. (2008). *Wong's essentials of pediatric nursing* (8th ed.). St. Louis, MO: Mosby.

This is one of the premier pediatric textbooks. It provides an excellent presentation of child development, health promotion, and specific health problems organized by body systems.

Hockenberry, M., & Wilson, D. (2010). *Wong's nursing care of infants and children* (8th ed.). St. Louis, MO: Mosby.

This is an excellent pediatric nursing textbook for both nursing students and practicing nurses. It can serve as pediatric nursing guidelines, because it incorporates the latest information from many authoritative organizations.

House, A. E. (2002). *The first session with children and adolescents: Conducting a comprehensive mental health evaluation.* New York, NY: Guilford Press.

This book provides a comprehensive approach to evaluating the mental health status of children and adolescents. It includes instructional segments, case studies, and current applicable research.

James, W. (1981). *The principles of psychology.* Cambridge, MA: Harvard University Press, 1981. Originally published in 1890.

Kirwin, K. M., & Hamrin, V. (2005). Decreasing the risk of complicated bereavement and future psychiatric disorders in children. *Journal of Child and Adolescent Psychiatric Nursing, 18*(2), 62–78.

This is a discussion of the death of a parent as a major stressful event for children and their families and how to decrease its impact upon children's future mental health.

Lyman, R. D., & Campbell, N. R. (1996). *Treating children and adolescents in residential and inpatient settings.* Thousand Oaks, CA: Sage.

This reference provides useful guidelines for how and when to use inpatient and residential treatment in the care of children and adolescents.

Mash, E., & Barkley, R. (Eds.). (2003). *Child psychopathology* (2nd ed.). New York, NY: Guilford Press.

This book addresses a broad range of childhood and adolescent disorders. There is particular emphasis on developmental processes, current theories of etiology, research, and adaptive and maladaptive functioning.

McCaffrey, C. N. (2006). Major stressors and their effects on the well-being of children with cancer. *Pediatric Nursing, 21*(1), 59–66.

This is an in-depth, exploratory study of major stressors experienced by children diagnosed with cancer.

President's Commission on Mental Health. (1978). *Report to the president from the president's commission on mental health* (Vols. 1–4). Washington, DC: U.S. Government Printing Office.

Volume 1 contains the commission's report and recommendations; volumes 2, 3, and 4 contain the reports of the specialty panels.

President's New Freedom Commission on Mental Health. (2002). *Achieving the promise: Transforming mental health care in America.* Washington, DC: U.S. Government Printing Office.

This is a report on the commission's study of the U.S. mental health service delivery system, including both private and public sector providers. The commission provides advice to the president on methods to improve the system so that adults with serious mental illness and children with serious emotional disturbances can live, work, learn, and participate fully in their communities. This commission's report was the first comprehensive study of the nation's public and private mental health service delivery systems in nearly 25 years.

Regan, K. (2006). Paradigm shifts in inpatient psychiatric care of children: Approaching child- and family-centered care. *Journal of Child and Adolescent Psychiatric Nursing, 19*(1), 29–40.

This article describes the components of child- and family-centered care, focusing on an inpatient child psychiatric unit that has implemented an approach to care that embraces these principles.

Schor, E. L. (2003). Family pediatrics: Report of the Task Force on the Family. *Pediatrics, 111*(6 Pt 2), 1541–1571.

The task force found that stressors such as financial difficulties, health problems, lack of social supports, work dissatisfaction, and unfortunate life events can cause parents emotional stress interfering with their own relationship and disrupting their parenting.

Smoyak, S., Pressler, C., Oppenheim, J., & Chapman, V. (1997). Evaluating the decision to hospitalize SED youth using qualitative data. *Journal of Psychosocial Nursing, 35*(10), 244–249.
This article is an interesting exploration of whether seriously emotionally disturbed children are really mentally ill or simply troubled youth reacting to overwhelming factors. It is a study of a very small and limited sample group.

Stein, R. E. K. (1997). *Health care for children: What's right, what's wrong, what's next*. New York, NY: United Hospital Fund.
This practical resource describes innovative approaches and model programs for children's health care. It raises practical, ethical, and moral questions regarding the nation's commitment to the health of its children.

Stern, D. (1985). *The interpersonal world of the infant*. New York, NY: Basic Books.
This book is an interesting combination of psychoanalysis and developmental psychology. It discusses the importance of the first year and a half of life and the child's development of a sense of self.

Stern, D. (2000). *The interpersonal world of the infant: A view from psychoanalysis and developmental psychology*. New York, NY: Basic Books.
This book is an interesting exploration of the early experiences of an infant and how they do or do not impact upon later development.

U.S. Census Bureau. (2011, September). Income, poverty, and health insurance in the US: 2010. Retrieved from www.census.gov/pressreleases/archives/income_wealth/cb11-157.html
This reports data on income, poverty, and health insurance coverage in the United States based on information collected in 2010 and earlier American Social and Economic Supplements to the Current Population Survey conducted by the U.S. Census Bureau.

U.S. Department of Health and Human Services. (2000). *Report of the surgeon general's conference on children's mental health: A national action agenda*. Washington, DC: Author.
This report was a collaboration among the U.S. Departments of Health and Human Services, Education, and Justice. It contains a summary of the conference and presents sections on its vision, goals, and recommendations.

Additional Resources

Brazelton, T. B. (1992). *Touchpoints: The essential reference*. New York, NY: Addison-Wesley.
This is an excellent child care reference by an eminent pediatrician who addresses child development from a practical approach that incorporates physical, cognitive, emotional, and behavioral information.

Clark, C. D. (2003). *In sickness and in play: Children coping with chronic illness*. Piscataway, NJ: Rutgers University Press.
This book focuses on how children and their families cope with two common childhood illnesses, diabetes and asthma.

Fraiberg, S. (1996). *The magic years*. New York, NY: Simon & Schuster.
This later version of a classic is truly a wonderful book. If one wants to understand the mind of a child and how children confront and cope with the world, this magical book accomplishes the goal.

Johnson, B. (1995). *Child, adolescent and family psychiatric nursing*. Philadelphia, PA: J. B. Lippincott.
This comprehensive textbook addresses the knowledge and skill needs of nurses who provide care for children and adolescents with mental health problems and for their families.

Petrillo, M., & Sanger, S. (1980). *Emotional care of hospitalized children* (2nd ed.). Philadelphia, PA: J. B. Lippincott.
This multidisciplinary book is a classic in the specialty of pediatric health. It provides basic and practical knowledge in preparing children and their families for hospital experiences from a combined developmental and environmental approach.

Internet Resources

For a full suite of assignments and additional learning activities, use the access code located in the front of your book to visit this exclusive website: http://go.jblearning.com/mentalhealth. If you do not have an access code, you can obtain one at the site.

Learning Objectives

After reading this chapter, you will be able to:

- Describe the aging population in the United States.
- Discuss the most commonly used screening tools for older people exhibiting mental disorders.
- Discuss how nutrition, elimination, sleep problems, and pain can affect an elder's mental status.
- Determine the impact polypharmacy can have on an older individual's mental status.
- Examine the effect unrecognized and untreated depression and anxiety can have on the older adult.
- Differentiate the differences in suicide in the older population versus younger adults.
- Identify the differences in late-onset and early-onset substance abuse in the older adult.

Key Terms

Activities of daily living (ADLs)

Capacity

Competency

Confabulation

Dysphagia

Instrumental activities of daily living (IADLs)

Presbycusis

Presbyopia

Sundown syndrome

Tardive dyskinesia

Xerostomia

Chapter 28

The Aging Client

Beverley E. Holland

http://go.jblearning.com/mentalhealth 

For a full suite of assignments and additional learning activities, use the access code located in the front of your book to visit this exclusive website: http://go.jblearning.com/mentalhealth. If you do not have an access code, you can obtain one at the site.

Introduction

America is a youth-oriented society. No one wants to be old. In some cultures, the elderly are revered and hold a special place of honor within the society; but in highly industrialized countries such as the United States, status declines with age, a decrease in productivity, and participation in the mainstream of society.

Depression diagnosed after age 65 is considered late onset and is usually associated with medical illnesses.

Individuals experience many changes as they age. Physical changes occur in virtually every body system, but in the absence of pathology, older adults continue to function in their environment either independently or with assistance. Psychologically, there may be age-related change that could impact memory, particularly short-term memory, but again, in the absence of pathology the individual is able to function.

Unsuccessful resolution of Erikson's postulated final stage of personality development, integrity vs. despair, may be related to the depression observed in the elderly. Erikson's stages of development are discussed in Chapter 4.

Older adults can experience the same spectrum of mental disorders as younger adults. However, certain conditions are particularly notable in later life, because of either increased prevalence or high morbidity. Older people often do not receive the same amount or quality of services offered to younger adults (Administration on Aging, 2009). This may be due to limited reimbursement, limited access, and staffing patterns (Loge & Sorrell, 2010). Attitudes about aging, age-related conditions, and the limited geriatrics training of mental health professionals may also play roles in restricting the availability and quality of mental health care.

Psychiatric symptoms that develop later in life are often dismissed as normal manifestations of aging. Even psychotic symptoms may be dismissed as eccentricity or misdiagnosed as senility. Treatment can be planned only if the problem is acknowledged and identified.

Older people themselves often fail to report mental disorders such as depression or anxiety, thinking it is normal to feel sad and to worry. They often report physiologic complaints to the healthcare provider as opposed to psychological problems. For many there continues to be a stigma attached to having a mental disorder. It is important to be aware of the occurrence of mental disorders in the older adult, how they may present, and various age-appropriate assessment strategies.

There is an increasing number of elderly U.S. immigrants. They follow their children to the United States and assist in child care and home maintenance. Depression may be related to acculturation problems.

General Description

Life expectancy from birth has increased dramatically in the United States. Even those who are currently old can expect to live for many years. At age 65, men can expect to live more than 17 additional years, and for women it is an additional 20 years (AOA, 2009). The elderly population is the only segment of the general population that is expected to grow substantially in the next 50 years. Currently, individuals 65 and over make up 12.8% of the U.S. population (AOA, 2009). The baby boomers (those born between 1946 and 1964) began turning 65 in 2011, and we will see a shift in the population age by 2030. At that time, 72 million of the population will be 65 or older (AOA, 2009). Old-old people (those 85 years or older) constitute one of the fastest-growing subgroups.

Most people age 65 or older have at least one chronic medical illness and many have multiple conditions. Among the most frequently occurring chronic conditions in 2005 to 2007 were arthritis, hypertension and heart conditions, cancer, diabetes, and sinusitis (AOA, 2009). Each of these conditions can limit independent function and detract from quality of life.

Those with ongoing needs that cannot be met at home generally receive care in long-term care facilities. Although only about 5% of the elderly population is residing in nursing homes at a given time, the proportion of older persons requiring such care increases quite sharply with age (AOA, 2009).

Older people with mental disorders constitute a significant subgroup of the elderly population. Estimates indicate that about 12% of older, community-dwelling adults have diagnosable mental disorders. Approximately 30–50% of elderly clients seen in primary care or hospitalized for medical conditions have some type of mental disorder (Spar & LaRue, 2002). In long-term care, 70% or more of residents have been found to have mental disorders; overall, it is estimated that 15–25% of Americans over age 65 have significant mental health problems (Spar & LaRue, 2002).

Cognitive deficits in older clients have many different possible causes, and for as many as one client in five, treatment of underlying problems can reverse or substantially alleviate cognitive symptoms (Spar & LaRue, 2002). Even individuals with dementia of the Alzheimer type can gain in functional ability by treating coexisting medical or psychiatric illnesses.

Many older people without major mental disorders experience adjustment reactions to personal stresses, bereavement, pain syndromes, and sleep disturbance. Education and interventions directed at these problems may prevent more serious psychiatric or medical problems from developing.

The Normal Aging Process

The normal aging process is generally characterized by changes in physical appearance and functional decline. As a person ages, he or she may also have more chronic disease, which is due to pathologic changes. As we age, change occurring in a physiologic system can directly or indirectly influence other changes. Each individual ages differently, and aging is affected by the person's genetic makeup, health behaviors, environment, and availability of resources.

This section cannot provide a comprehensive overview of the normal aging process. **Table 28-1** gives a brief overview of normal biologic changes that occur with aging. If more information is needed, please refer to a health assessment text or a gerontological nursing text.

The ability to recognize the normal and the pathologic changes of aging and deal with the chronic conditions that may indicate impending illness or impair function is important in promoting quality of life. Many factors contribute to the onset of illness or result in a decline in function. Some of these factors include delirium and confusion, anxiety, depression, sleep disorders, and polypharmacy, any of which can be a key cause and contributory factor for many common health problems. Other changes such as **presbycusis**, or decreased auditory acuity, and **presbyopia**, or decreased visual accommodation, cam be part of the normal aging process.

Differentiating disease from normal changes of aging and the early recognition of health problems allow the early start of treatment while recovery is still possible (Amella, 2004).

Table 28-1 Normal Physiological and Functional Changes With Aging

Body Systems	Physiologic Changes	Functional Changes
Cardiovascular Heart, arteries	Enlargement, thickening, and stiffening of chambers. Arterial walls atrophy; thicken, twist, and stiffen; and show calcification and decreased elasticity	Increased blood pressure
Respiratory Lungs, musculoskeletal system	Decreased alveolar surface; decrease of lung elasticity; stiffening of chest wall due to loss of rib elasticity	Reduced vital capacity; poor gas exchange; increased residual volume
Gastrointestinal	Decreased saliva; impaired esophageal motility; atrophy of gastric mucosa; increase in gastric pH; decreased colon motility	Reduced elimination efficiency; reduced metabolism of drugs
Genitourinary	Loss of renal mass, loss of glomeruli; reduced bladder elasticity, especially in women; prostate enlargement in men	Reduced glomerular filtration rate; loss of bladder emptying capacity; decrease in clearance of some drugs
Endocrine	Atrophy and fibrosis; loss of vascularity	General decline in secretory rate
Nervous	Loss of brain weight and volume; loss of neurons; slowing of nerve conduction; decrease of secretion of most neurotransmitters	Thought processes, reasoning, and memory essentially unchanged; slower reaction time, decision making, and startle response
Musculoskeletal	Reduced muscle and bone mass; demineralization of bone; decreased number and size of muscle fibers; increased fat in muscles and calcium in cartilage; degeneration of cartilage; loss of elasticity in joints	Loss of muscular strength, endurance, and stamina; loss of bone strength; increased bone brittleness; loss of joint movement
Special senses Vision, hearing	Decreased visual acuity; decreased accommodation and focus; decreased ability to hear high-pitched sounds	Presbycusis (loss of auditory acuity) and decreased visual acuity, especially night vision; presbyopia (loss of visual accommodation)
Integumentary	Loss of subcutaneous fat and water; loss of elasticity; development of brown pigmented spots	Wrinkles, dry skin

Source: Adapted from Plahuta & Hamrick-King (2006).

Mental Health of the Older Adult

Almost 25% of adults older than age 55 experience specific mental disorders that are not part of normal aging (Flood & Buckwalter, 2009a; Substance Abuse and Mental Health Services Administration, 2008). Elders with mental health problems fall into one of two groups. One group consists of those with long-term mental illnesses who have aged with their mental illness. These individuals usually understand their disorders and treatments. Unfortunately, the changes associated with aging can affect a client's control of his or her chronic mental illness. Symptoms may reappear, and medications may need to be adjusted. The other group comprises individuals who are relatively free of mental health problems until their elder years. These individuals may already have other health problems and develop late-onset mental disorders, such as depression, schizophrenia, or dementia. For these individuals and their family members, the development of a mental disorder can be very traumatic.

Mental health problems in the elderly can be especially complex because of coexisting medical problems and treatments. Many symptoms of somatic disorders mimic or mask psychiatric disorders. For example, fatigue may be related to anemia, but it also may be symptomatic of depression. In addition, older individuals are more likely to report somatic symptoms, rather than psychological ones, making identification of a mental disorder even more difficult.

Geriatric Mental Health Assessment

A thorough geriatric mental health nursing assessment serves as a basis for care when psychiatric or mental health issues are identified or when clients with mental illnesses reach their later years (usually about age 65 years). The overall healthcare issues for the elderly can be very complex, so it follows that certain components of the mental health nursing assessment are unique. Thus the geriatric mental health assessment emphasizes some areas that are less critical to standard adult assessment.

Activities of daily living (ADLs) include self-care activities that people must accomplish to survive, such as eating, dressing, bathing, and toileting. **Instrumental activities of daily living (IADLs)** include performing housework, going on errands, managing finances, and making telephone calls.

Nursing Assessment

The nurse assesses the client using an interview format. The nurse may also rely on self-report standardized tests, such as depression and cognitive functioning tools. A wide variety of psychologic disorders may cause changes in the mental status of older adults; therefore, the results of laboratory tests often are significant. For example, urinalysis can detect a urinary tract infection that is affecting a client's cognitive status. Other changes that can affect mental status include acid-base imbalance, dehydration, drugs (prescribed and over the counter), electrolyte changes, hypothyroidism, hypo- and hyperthermia, hypoxia, infection, and sepsis. In addition, medical records from other healthcare practitioners are useful in developing a complete picture of the client's health status.

An important source of client data is family members. They often notice changes that the client overlooks, fails to recognize, or will not report. A client with memory impairment may be unable to give an accurate history. By interviewing family members, the nurse expands the scope of the client assessment. Moreover, the nurse has an opportunity to evaluate the caregivers themselves to determine whether they can care for the client adequately and how they are coping with the situation. For example, a husband whose wife has Alzheimer's disease may be the sole caregiver. He may be exhausted and unable to provide safe adequate care for her but be unwilling to admit it. If the nurse can establish rapport with the husband, he or she may use the assessment interview as an opportunity to help the husband realistically examine his wife's care requirements and his capabilities (**Figure 28-1**).

Testing and evaluating the older adult can be a challenge because of a number of factors such as visual and hearing impairments, memory problems, fatigability, and distrust of psychiatric personnel. Older adults often need special attention during the interview. Hearing impaired or visually impaired individuals may need to sit closer to and directly in front of the interviewer. It is important to speak clearly and at a volume the client does not find distorted. Using distinct enunciation will help lip-reading clients understand what is being said. Sometimes, deafness is mistaken for cognitive dysfunction. The elderly client may need more physical assistance than a younger client, and the pace of the interview may need to be slower than with younger populations.

Thought Processes

Evaluating the client's thought processes and content are critical in the assessment of elderly clients.

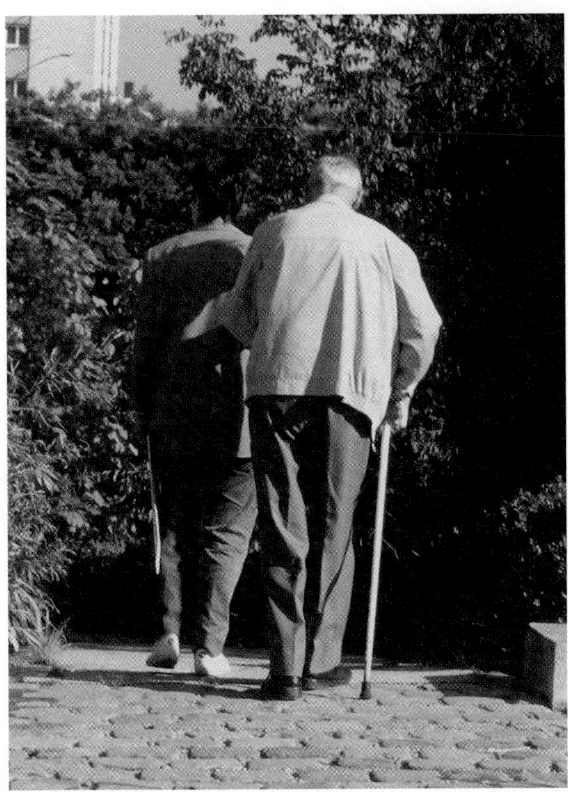

Figure 28-1 Caregivers can become exhausted from caring for a loved one and require care themselves.

Can the client express ideas and thoughts logically? Can the client understand questions and follow the conversation of others? If the client shows any indication of hallucinations or delusions, the nurse should explore the content of the hallucination or delusion. If the client has a history of mental illness, such as schizophrenia, these symptoms may be familiar to family members, who can validate whether they are old or new problems. If this is the first time the client has experienced these abnormal thought processes, the nurse should further evaluate the content. Suspicious and delusional thoughts that characterize dementia often include: my spouse is cheating on me; people are stealing my things; this house is not my home; my relative is an impostor. If a client shares any such thoughts, further assessment should be done.

Cognition and Intellectual Performance

Cognitive functioning includes such parameters as orientation, attention, short- and long-term memory, consciousness, and executive functioning. Intellectual functioning, also considered a cognitive measure, is rarely formally assessed with a standardized intelligence test in elderly people. Considerable variability among individuals depends on lifestyle and psychosocial factors. Some changes in cognitive capacity accompany aging, but important functions are spared. Normal cognitive changes during aging include a slowing of information processing and memory retrieval. Abnormalities of consciousness, orientation, judgment, speech, or language are not related to age but to underlying neuropathologic changes. Cognitive changes in elderly people are also associated with delirium, dementia, or schizophrenia. When assessing cognitive functioning, the Mini-Mental State Examination (MMSE) is a tool that can be used for baseline information and to evaluate treatment effectiveness over time.

Behavioral Changes

Behavior changes in elderly people can indicate neuropathologic processes. If such changes occur, it is likely that family members will notice them before the client does. Behavior problems including irritability, agitation, apathy, euphoria, wandering, and aggression are often noted in individuals with dementia and other neurologic and psychologic disorders. Underlying acute infectious processes can also cause behavior changes. It is important to do a physical work-up on individuals who present with sudden onset behavior changes.

Critical Thinking Question

The most common chronic health conditions in the elderly are arthritis, hypertension, heart disease, orthopedic problems, and cataracts. What are some of the symptoms of chronic conditions that may contribute to mental status problems? How do chronic conditions complicate mental status problems?

Memory is the ability of the mind to recall earlier events. The two types of memory are short-term, for events that happened within the past day or so, and long-term, for events that occurred from the first recollections of childhood and up to the current week.

The number one risk factor for Alzheimer's disease is age. The older you are, the greater the risk for developing Alzheimer's disease.

Mental Health Screening Tools

There are many mental health screening tools available. Not all are adaptable to the older population. Screening tests should be chosen with the specific population group in mind, and the choice should be based on the ability of the tool to provide valid results.

Cognitive assessment often requires a formal focused assessment. Individuals with advanced education or highly developed social skills may easily cover the signs of early impairment. A superficial social conversation will usually not reveal underlying disorientation to time and place or deficit in short-term memory. The most extensively used tool for assessment of mental status in geriatrics is the Mini-Mental State Examination (MMSE) (Folstein, Folstein, & McHugh, 1975). The 30-item test takes approximately 10–15 minutes to administer, and each section of the tool assesses a different aspect of cognitive function: orientation, registration, attention and calculation, recall, and language. Various studies suggest that an MMSE score below 23 has a reasonable sensitivity and specificity for discriminating between those with dementia and those without (Folstein, 1983) and should be followed up with a full diagnostic evaluation (Flood & Buckwalter, 2009b).

The four A's of Alzheimer's disease:
Amnesia: Loss of short- and/or long-term memory
Aphasia: Loss of the ability to send or receive messages using language
Agnosia: Inability to recognize objects, people, or things
Apraxia: Inability to carry out purposeful tasks

Another tool for cognitive assessment is the clock-drawing test (CDT). The CDT requires the client to draw a clock face, put the numbers on it, and indicate a specific time. This test evaluates a range of cognitive and executive functions and is a sensitive but nonspecific cognitive screening test (Sunderland et al., 1989). The MMSE and CDT are screening tools that can indicate impairment and dementia. If they indicate a problem, further testing must be done before a diagnosis is given. Dementia evaluation should include a complete history and examination, laboratory testing, and brain imaging.

Depression is a frequently overlooked problem in the geriatric population (National Institute of Mental Health [NIMH], 2008). Often the nonspecific somatic complaints may represent physical illnesses, but often are symptoms of depression. Use of the short form of the Geriatric Depression Screen (GDS) (Yesavage et al., 1983) has been found to have a high sensitivity for detecting depression in elderly adults (Kurlowicz & Greenberg, 1999). Depression and dementia can coexist. The Cornell Scale for Depression in Dementia (CSDD) (Alexopoulos, Abrams, Young, & Shamoian, 1998) is a reliable and valid instrument for assessing depression in older adults who also have dementia (Watson & Pignon, 2003).

A diagnostic workup for reversible causes of dementia and delirium consists of a complete physical and neurologic exam; medical history; laboratory testing (CBC, TSH, B_{12}, folate, chemistry panel, urinalysis [BUN, creatinine, bilirubin, and albumin/globulin if you suspect liver disease]); VDRL/HIV, depending on history; blood glucose (fasting); EKG; and MMSE. An EEG and a head CT scan are also useful.

The consumption of alcohol can affect different aspects of health, both physical and mental; it is important to accurately ascertain a client's alcohol intake. The CAGE (Mayfield, McLeod, & Hall, 1974) is a quick, effective screening tool for recognizing problematic drinking. CAGE is an acronym for the questions regarding cutting down on drinking, being annoyed when others criticize use, guilt regarding use, and use of an eye-opener. It is a self-report instrument given in oral or written form, is easy to administer, and it can be administered quickly.

Factors That Impact Mental Status

A variety of factors can impact the older adult's mental status. Simple things such as nutritional status, elimination problems, sleep disruption, pain issues, and polypharmacy can cause cognition changes and mental status disturbances.

Nutrition

Eating is frequently difficult for elderly individuals because they often experience a lack of appetite. Assessment of the type, amount, and frequency of food and fluids taken should be standard in any geriatric assessment. Unintentional weight loss of more than 10 pounds should be noted. Changes in eating habits and patterns and weight loss should be considered in light of mental health problems. For example, is a client's weight loss related to an underlying physical problem or is the client not eating due to a belief that she is being poisoned?

A common problem of elderly people is **dysphagia**, or difficulty swallowing. Dysphagia can lead to dehydration, malnutrition, pneumonia, or asphyxiation, all of which may be an underlying cause of delirium. People who have taken conventional antipsychotics (e.g., haloperidol, chlorpromazine) may have symptoms of **tardive dyskinesia**, which can also make swallowing difficult. **Xerostomia**, or dry mouth, which is common in elderly people, may also impair eating. Dry mouth is also a side effect of many other anticholinergic medications and drugs that have anticholinergic activities, such as cimetidine, digoxin, and furosemide. Many of the antipsychotic medications have anticholinergic properties also. Many psychiatric medications can affect digestion and may impair an already compromised gastrointestinal tract.

Elimination

Assessment of urinary and bowel function may show problems with constipation, urinary frequency, and incontinence. This can be a cause of embarrassment, isolation, and poor self-esteem leading to depression. Elderly clients are more likely to experience constipation because the peristaltic movement of the bowel slows as people get older, but poor diet, poor fluid intake, lack of activity, and medications with anticholinergic properties can also cause constipation. Many older adults think that they must have a bowel movement daily; this can lead to abuse of laxatives and cause electrolyte imbalance and dehydration.

Urinary incontinence occurs because the strength of the sphincter muscles decreases with aging. Because of the fear of having an accident, many older adults drink less fluids, refuse to leave their home, and become depressed. Bowel and bladder function is an important area to evaluate.

Sleep

The need for sleep is well established as affecting mental and physical health (Cole & Richards, 2006). Sleep changes become more prevalent with age. Age-related sleep disturbances are usually mild alterations in sleep that do not result in daytime sleepiness, but sleep disorders are distinctive, severe abnormalities of sleep associated with deterioration of daytime function (Cole & Richards, 2006). According to the National Sleep Foundation (NSF, 2003) Sleep in America Poll 2003, 26% of adults ages 44–65 and 21% of adults over the age of 65 rated their sleep as fair to poor.

Those with chronic illnesses, such as cardiovascular disease, stroke, endocrine disorders, depression, and Alzheimer's and Parkinson's diseases, tend to have a greater number of sleep disturbances. They sleep fewer hours, awaken more frequently, report difficulty falling asleep, awaken earlier, and report significant daytime sleepiness (NSF, 2003). Disruption in sleep can worsen chronic illness and exacerbate depression and lead to delirium in the older adult. Individuals with dementia show increasing sleep disruptions as the dementia progresses (Cole & Richards, 2006).

When working with an older person who complains of sleep disturbance and presents with daytime somnolence, disorientation, and decreased daytime functioning, it is important to conduct a good sleep assessment. Sleep assessment would include a sleep history, a sleep diary including the usual sleep pattern, and sleep hygiene or activities that enhance or deter sleep. A complete history including physical, medication, and alcohol history should also be obtained. Frequently the use of caffeinated medication, alcohol, and OTC medications contribute to sleep problems. A psychiatric history is necessary to assess for underlying stress or depression or affective disorder that may be impacting on sleep. This may need to be followed with a physiologic measure of sleep done in a sleep center or laboratory-controlled setting with polysomnography.

Interventions for sleep problems consist of reevaluating treatment plans for medical problems, environmental alterations, behavior modifications, and short-term use of sleep medications. If a physiologic problem is contributing to the sleep disturbance, treatment of the problem can make a difference. If chronic medical conditions are causing the nighttime waking, evaluation of treatment regimens can often reduce the sleep problems. For example, if the person has cardiovascular problems, evaluating medications so that diuretics are given early in the day to decrease nighttime enuresis, positioning upright, and using oxygen at night can help enhance sleep; individuals who become hypoglycemic at night related to diabetes may need a bedtime snack or adjustment of hypoglycemic medications; and gastrointestinal reflux may need treatment with a nightly medication or use of warm milk and positioning.

Confusion may be evident first at night, with associated insomnia, wandering, irritability, and combativeness, known as sundown syndrome. Confusion in the early morning due to the prolonged half-life of medications or substances of abuse is known as sunrise syndrome.

Environmental alterations and behavioral modifications, such as a cool, darkened bedroom; quiet time or soothing music before bed; a small snack with warm milk or herbal tea; and consistent bedtime routines and supportive reassurance can reduce sleep problems. Often planning daytime activities that keep the individual active and engaged will reduce daytime napping that can cause nighttime sleep problems. Medications such as benzodiazepines, hypnotics, or antidepressants are often used on a short-term trial (2 weeks or less) to help reestablish a sleep pattern. Long-term use of sleep medications has not been shown to maintain effectiveness (Spar & LaRue, 2002).

Diagnostic Criteria

Poor sleep is a common problem of the elderly, and elderly persons with problems sleeping make up a large proportion of hospitalized elders. Careful assessment including use of the Richards-Campbell Sleep Questionnaire is suggested. Nonpharmacologic nursing interventions such as providing a warm drink, back rub, progressive relaxation exercises, and relaxation audiotapes or music have proven effective in reducing sedative-hypnotic administration. Environmental interventions include noise reduction, light adjustment, minimizing client interruptions, and increasing meaningful daytime activity (Nagel, Markie, Richards, & Taylor, 2003).

Pain

Elders are more likely to experience chronic pain than younger adults (Herr, 2002). Multiple chronic medical conditions are sources of chronic pain. Most older persons report one chronic condition, and many report multiple conditions (AOA, 2009). Osteoarthritis may be a source of chronic pain in as much as 80% of the population older than age 65 (Herr, 2002). Studies of pain prevalence in older adults suggest that chronic pain occurs in 25–86% of community-dwelling older adults and in 45–80% of long-term care facility residents (Herr, 2002). Chronic pain often contributes to unexplained behavior and personality changes. Persistent pain has been associated with depression in community-dwelling older adults and in nursing home residents (Herr, 2002). Evidence indicates that pain is underreported, underassessed, and undertreated in older clients (Herr, 2002). Pain management in older adults can be a challenge. A major misconception is that pain is a consequence of older age and cannot be avoided. This misconception leads to a lack of effective pain assessment and intervention. Another challenge is the older person himself or herself. Many will not complain, thinking they want to be good patients, or they are fearful of the meaning of their pain. Finally, the healthcare provider, whether it is someone in an institution or a family member, may not be attuned to the older person's nonverbal pain expressions and may not be knowledgeable of appropriate pain assessment or pain treatment.

Pain assessment from individuals with cognitive impairment, language impairment, and dementia can be obtained. It may take patience and observation, but individuals with mild to moderate impairment can respond to pain scales with some adaptation (Herr, 2002). For others, observation of nonverbal pain behaviors (e.g., bracing, grimacing, guarding, restlessness, agitation), vocalizations (e.g., moaning, crying, verbal outbursts), and changes in behavior patterns (e.g., decreased activity level and interactions with others, new onset confusion, refusal to eat, resistance to care, difficulty sleeping) provide hints and information about the presence of pain from those unable to report it. Management of pain requires thorough assessment and a combination of pharmacologic and nonpharmacologic pain therapies.

Polypharmacy

Older adults take considerably more medications than younger people (**Figure 28-2**). They consume 34% of all prescription medications and 40% of all nonprescription medications (American Society of Consultant Pharmacists [ASCP], 2000). Normal age-related changes result in altered pharmacokinetics (i.e., absorption, distribution, metabolism, and excretion of a drug or what the body does to the drug) and pharmacodynamics (i.e., biochemical or physiological interactions of drugs or what the drug does to the body). See **Table 28-2**.

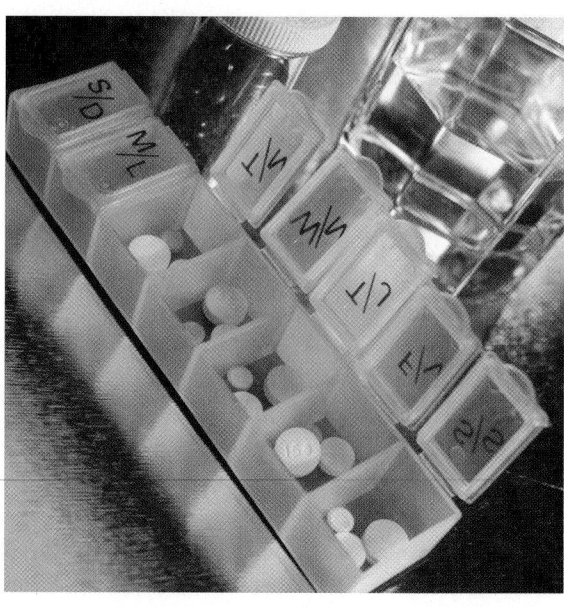

Figure 28-2 Older adults commonly take multiple prescription medications.

The use of multiple medications at the same time or the overprescribing of medications is called polypharmacy (Planton & Edlund, 2010). Adverse drug events were found to be responsible for 5–28% of acute geriatric hospital admissions (Planton & Edlund, 2010). Factors contributing to polypharmacy are numerous: multiple chronic illnesses, prescribing to treat side effects, multiple specialists treating complex problems, client stockpiling of medications, use of over-the-counter (OTC) medications, use of herbal medications, and failure of healthcare providers to periodically review all medications from all sources for appropriateness and continued need.

Herbals and OTC medications can interact with prescription drugs. Usually the individual does not think to consult with or tell his or her physician about nonprescription drugs he or she is taking. OTC medications are often perceived by individuals as harmless or not considered to be a drug. Difficulty reading the product inserts can lead to inappropri-

Table 28-2 Drug Response in the Older Adult

Pharmacokinetics	The body's absorption, distribution, metabolism, and excretion of drugs due to changes in normal aging. • Absorption is slightly decreased. • Distribution is affected by the shift to more body fat. • Metabolism is decreased. • Excretion is slowed. Some drugs (especially lipid-soluble drugs) may exhibit a longer half-life in older individuals as well as slower breakdown and elimination, thus becoming drug toxic. Example: Diazepam (Valium) will have a longer half-life in an older person than a younger person.
Pharmacodynamics	The physiologic response of the drug at its site of action. • Drug concentrations may result in greater or lesser effects at the site of action than expected. • The older person may show increased sensitivity to certain medications. Example: Older persons show increased sensitivity to the central nervous system depressant effects of benzodiazepines, anxiolytics, and hypnotics.

ate drug combinations and inaccurate dosing. Often older adults will swap drugs with others when they discuss their symptoms and treatments.

Some consequences of polypharmacy include adverse drug reactions, nonadherence to medical regimens, hospitalization resulting from confusion, delirium, electrolyte imbalance, gastrointestinal bleeding, exacerbation of chronic conditions, and falls. Recognizing that some drugs should be avoided in the elderly because their potential risk outweighs their potential benefit, the Beers criteria were developed in 1991 (Beers, 1997). It is updated annually and covers the elderly in all settings (Fick et al., 2003). There are many drugs on the list used in the treatment of mental health problems. Research has shown that following the Beers criteria, frequent medication monitoring, and decreasing and discontinuing inappropriate medications can make a difference in mental status for many elderly (Planton & Edlund, 2010).

Evidence-Based Practice

A review of hospital records of clients aged 65 years or older admitted to the emergency department with falls indicated that nearly half were 80 years old or older. After age, polypharmacy was the greatest risk factor, followed by a history of cognitive impairment and presence of more than one contributing medical factor. Elders older than 80 years old were more likely to have multiple risk factors such as polypharmacy, alcohol use, impairment of ADL, one or more medical conditions, cognitive impairment, use of an assistive device, or a gait/balance deficit. Careful assessment is needed to prevent undertreatment of potentially modifiable problems (Paniagua, Malphurs, & Phelan, 2006).

Stress and Coping

Identifying stressors and coping patterns is just as important for elderly clients as it is for younger adults. Unique stresses for elderly clients include living on a fixed income, handling declining health, losing partners and friends, and ultimately confronting death. Coping ability varies depending on each client's unique circumstances. Some people respond to stressful events with amazing adaptability, whereas others become depressed and suicidal.

Loss of a spouse is common in late life. Bereavement is a normal response. Bereavement symptoms include crying and sorrow, anxiety and agitation, insomnia, and loss of appetite. These symptoms, while overlapping with those of major depression, do not constitute a mental disorder. Only when these symptoms persist for 3 months or longer can a diagnosis of either adjustment disorder or major depressive disorder be made if it meets the *Diagnostic and Statistical Manual of Mental Disorders*, fourth edition, text revision (*DSM-IV-TR*) criteria (American Psychiatric Association, 2000). The nurse must identify normal bereavement and those at risk for prolonged grief reactions and develop interventions to help the individual successfully resolve the loss. At least 10% of widows and widowers experience symptoms of depression during the first year of bereavement (Spar & LaRue, 2002). Without interventions, depression can persist, becoming chronic and leading to further disability and other serious health problems.

Mnemonic for reversible causes for dementia:
D = Drugs or delirium
E = Ethanol (alcohol) or eyes and ears (visual or hearing deficits)
M = Metabolic changes
E = Endocrine disorders
N = Nutritional causes and normal pressure hydrocephalus
T = Trauma, tumor, toxins
I = Infections
A = Affective disorder, arteriosclerosis

Definitive diagnosis of Alzheimer's disease is done by autopsy of brain tissue or brain tissue biopsy to identify the hallmark brain atrophy with neurofibrillary tangles and neuritic plaques on microscopic examination.

Mental Disorders of Late Life

Some elders have had a history of mental disorders with symptoms that are in remission or stabilized by treatment. Many elders with new symptoms may not recognize these as related to psychiatric and mental health disorders that can be treated and underreport them to healthcare providers. They may fear that the symptoms may be indicative of an irreversible decline in functioning and loss of independence. Some nonspecific symptoms such as problems with memory are related to a variety of factors and may be reversible if the underlying reason for the symptoms is treated. Other symptoms may have a slow, insidious onset that is not noticed until there is marked impairment of functioning. Careful assessment may be needed to determine if problems are related to changes in health status or response to pharmaceuticals or substances of abuse.

Dementia

Dementing disorders are the most common causes of psychopathology in the elderly. Dementia is irreversible in 80–95% of cases, and 10% of individuals age 65 and older and 50% older than 85 are thought to have dementia (Flood & Buckwalter, 2009b; National Institute on Aging, 2008). Dementia is a chronic and progressive illness characterized by behavioral and cognitive changes that affect memory, problem solving, judgment, and speech and can cause deficits in functional abilities. Other types of dementia include multi-infarct dementia, Parkinson's dementia, and Huntington's dementia. No curative treatment is currently available for dementia. Symptomatic treatment, including pharmacologic interventions, attention to environment, and family support, can help to maximize the client's level of functioning.

Dementia is common in the elderly. The level of disability is determined by the progressive, static, or remitting course of the illness. Dementia often is confused with and coexists with depression and delirium. The five main domains involved in the clinical presentation of dementia are praxis (ability to function), memory (short- and long-term), calculation, concentration, and language.

Nurses must educate caregivers and family members to be alert to the varied presentations of dementia, because symptoms may have a sudden onset or a slow progression. Dementia often has a chronic, insidious, progressive course. Although long lasting, some types of dementia may be slowed or reversed. Clients with potentially reversible causes of dementia (e.g., myxedema, depression, pernicious anemia, adverse drug reaction) can improve remarkably in their cognitive function with the appropriate assessment and treatment. The history, especially information provided by family members or the identified caregiver, and medical workups are key to the evaluation and appropriate diagnosis.

In the elderly, the diagnosis of dementia requires a careful, accurate assessment of altered cognitive functioning that affects the client's daily functioning. Cognitive dysfunction may present during a hospitalization or treatment for another illness. It is important for nurses to understand that several causes of dementia are potentially reversible and may partially or totally respond to treatment (e.g., antipsychotic medications for agitation causes confusion).

The Mini-Mental State Examination (MMSE) augments the physical examination and laboratory data as part of the diagnostic workup for dementia (Luggen, Meiner, & National Gerontological Nursing Association, 2002). The nurse's assessment should contain a history of the memory disturbance and should include any medical and psychiatric illnesses (e.g., hypertension, stroke, alcohol abuse, depression), medications (e.g., benzodiazepines, narcotics, psychotropic agents), and changes in the environment (e.g., a move-in with adult children, assisted living). Some general clinical features of dementia include an insidious onset, **confabulation** when attempting to answer questions, struggling with tasks, getting lost in new surroundings, personality changes, and complaints of cognitive loss with concealment of problems.

Sundown Syndrome

Sundown syndrome is a commonly observed tendency for people with dementia to become more confused and agitated around late afternoon to nightfall. The term *sundown syndrome* can be interchanged with sundowning and nocturnal delirium; the characteristics resemble delirium, but there is no specific cause for the occurrence of sundown syndrome (Sharer, 2008). It has been hypothesized that sundowning may be the result of neurologic damage, making it impossible for the demented individual to clearly interpret environmental stimuli (Kazer, 2011). Individuals experiencing sundowning may show increased anxiety, increased confusion, or delusions or paranoia, or they may become restless, agitated, and aggressive (Sharer, 2008; Wick & Zanni, 2005). Individualized treatment is essential for the person exhibiting sundowning characteristics. It is important to identify and treat any physiologic factors that may be contributing to those behaviors (i.e., hunger, thirst, pain, elimination needs) and then develop nonpharmacologic management strategies for the sundown behaviors.

Delirium

Delirium, also referred to as acute confusional state, is a serious neuropsychiatric syndrome. It occurs in 4–53% of older clients in the hospital (Sendelbach & Guthrie, 2009). Although it occurs frequently, it often goes unrecognized. It is a temporary, reversible condition. The majority of individuals presenting with delirium show cognitive-perceptual difficulties and altered level of consciousness.

Causes of delirium in older adults may include medical problems, acute illness or infections, electrolyte imbalances, abuse of alcohol or drugs, and cognitive or memory disorders. Trauma, surgery, or

Mnemonic for delirium:
D = Dementia
E = Electrolyte imbalance
L = Lungs, liver, heart, kidney, brain dysfunction
I = Infection (especially pneumonia)
R = Rx (medications, polypharmacy)
I = Injury, pain, stress
U = Unfamiliar environment (nursing home, hospital)
M = Metabolic changes (endocrine)

Evidence-Based Practice

Rigney (2006) discusses the importance of nursing assessment for delirium in hospitalized elders due to the high mortality rate when the causes of delirium are unrecognized. Risk factors include underlying dementia, lethargy, age greater than 80 years, disruption of sleep, polypharmacy, common medical conditions, and extreme stress. Careful assessment for early recognition and treatment of the underlying causes of delirium are needed.

www

Mrs. A. CASE STUDIES

Mrs. A. is a 77-year-old widow who moved into her unmarried daughter's apartment 3 months earlier following a near fall at home. Shaken and slightly bruised, she did not sustain an injury but became increasingly fearful that a fall could place her in a wheelchair for good. Her medical history included long-standing mild hypertension and coronary artery disease, noninsulin-dependent diabetes for 15 years, and osteoarthritis for 10 years. Her medications included metoprolol (Lopressor, 100 mg orally daily), ibuprofen (Nuprin, 200 mg orally three times a day), glipizide (Glucotrol, 2.5 mg before breakfast), psyllium hydrophilic colloid (Metamucil, 1 packet in 8 oz of liquid twice a day), and calcium carbonate (Tums, 500 mg [2 tablets] daily with meals). Mrs. A. refused to have a home health aide and stated, "I can care for myself!"

Returning home after being away for the weekend, the daughter found Mrs. A. sitting on the floor next to her bed, diaphoretic, sedated, and unable to answer the daughter's questions clearly as to what happened. Mrs. A. was easily distracted and had a decreased attention span. Fearing that her mother was having a hypoglycemic episode, she gave her some orange juice and telephoned for an ambulance. While in the emergency room, Mrs. A. complained of having pleuritic chest pain, malaise, and weakness. A chest X-ray revealed left lower lobe consolidation. She scored 15 on the MMSE; a score consistent with cognitive impairment. A sputum sample was yellow and mucoid. Blood glucose (finger stick) was 40 mg/dl. Her sodium level was 117.

Mrs. A. was diagnosed with pneumonia. She was transferred to a subacute unit and later to a rehabilitation nursing home for medical treatment and rehabilitation evaluation. Arrangements were made for a visiting nurse to arrive the following day to make an evaluation and recommendations concerning ADLs and management. Mrs. A. was maintained at home with the assistance of a home healthcare aide 5 days a week, 6 hours a day. Mrs. A. has since been attending a senior citizen center three times a week at the assisted living complex, where she has made new friends. Mrs. A.'s delirium was the result of developing upper respiratory infection pneumonia. Her age, coexistent medical conditions, and lack of mobility facilitated the onset of illness. Mrs. A. had a change in living arrangements, a close-call injury that left her afraid to mobilize herself, and the onset of potential depression within a short period of time. Considering her medication regimen, noncompliance or misuse could lead to confusion and complications.

Nursing Care Plan **Cognitive Impairment**

Nursing Diagnosis 1: Risk for injury related to confusion as evidenced by wandering, cognitive impairment, and physiologic and neurologic dysfunction.

Nursing Diagnosis 2: Risk for self-care deficit-medication related to psychologic and neurologic dysfunction as evidenced by distraction and decreased attention span.

Expected Outcomes	Interventions	Evaluations
• Will experience decreased symptoms of confusion	• Monitor client behavior for disorientation, increased restlessness and agitation, communication problems, disturbed sensory perception, and problems interacting with her environment. • Implement interventions to reduce confusion (i.e., reorient, reduce excessive environmental stimuli, provide calm, one-to-one activities, and short walks to decrease restlessness). • Assess for dementia or delirium manifestations.	• Appropriate nursing assessment and early intervention for confusion. Assist in reorientation. Modify environment to enhance safety and provide cues such as calendars, clocks, and appropriate lighting to assist in orientation. • Client returns to baseline functioning. • Assist in establishing cues and methods to help in remembering essential things. Minimize excessive environmental stimuli to facilitate ability to focus and concentrate. • Evaluate for possible underlying dementia or delirium
• Will remain injury free	• Reduce environmental stimuli, provide regular contact with staff and family, reorient, and provide fall prevention plan.	• Minimization of use of physical and chemical restraints. Increase in client's ability to interact appropriately with her environment. Client is oriented and able to communicate with others. Discharge planning assessment and appropriate case management.
• Will monitor medications for effectiveness and adverse side effects.	• Administer medications as prescribed and monitor response to medications and possible side effects. • Assess the client's ability to self-administer medications. Provide education for the client and her family regarding medications and safe administration.	• Use of individualized packaged medications, medication box, or supervision of medication if indicated. Review of medication schedule to simplify administration and prevent errors. • Verify client's ability to self-administer medication. Client and her family understand medications and possible interactions. • Client takes medications as prescribed.

Visit http://go.jblearning.com/mentalhealth for additional care plans and exercises.

sudden environmental changes can also cause delirium. Medications, especially cholinergic drugs, are the most common medication cause of delirium in elderly people.

Schizophrenia

Schizophrenia and delusional disorders may accompany individuals as they age or may manifest themselves for the first time during old age (Leutwyler & Wallhagen, 2010). In most instances individuals who manifest psychotic disorders early in life show a decline in psychopathology as they age. Late-onset schizophrenia (after age 60) is not common, but when it does occur, it is often characterized by delusions or hallucinations of a persecutory nature. The disease is chronic and treatment is with neuroleptics and supportive psychotherapy.

Depression

Depression is the most common and most treatable of all mental disorders in older adults. It is not a consequence of normal aging. It is a major health concern that can be life threatening if unrecognized and untreated. In the community, the percentages of older people meeting strict diagnostic criteria for major depression or dysthymic disorder is low (Flood & Buckwalter, 2009a). What has been found is that traditional diagnostic criteria may not be appropriate to the prevalence of depressive symptoms among older people. Up to 15% of elderly community residents and up to 50% of institutionalized adults have depressive symptoms (Reed, 2010a). Patients diagnosed with general medical illnesses are at a significantly greater risk for developing depression and/or anxiety disorders (Flood & Buckwalter, 2009a). The presence of comorbid depression and anxiety greatly increases healthcare costs for clients in primary care.

Depression can often be difficult to recognize. Depression, dementia, and delirium can also occur simultaneously, further complicating diagnosis and treatment (Flood & Buckwalter, 2009b). Presenting symptoms of change in feeling or mood (i.e., feeling sad, hopeless, pessimistic, or blue; loss of interest in pleasurable activities) may be all that is shown, or the individual may also exhibit fatigue, decreased concentration and short-term memory, change in appetite, fluctuations in weight and sleep habits, irritability, and anxiety. Many older adults avoid complaining of sadness or depression; this along with societal expectations that older adults are more fatigued and less interested in activities can disguise symptoms of depression and deprive individuals of treatment.

After assessing cognition using the MMSE, the healthcare provider should then screen for depression. If the MMSE is 24 or higher, one should use the Geriatric Depression Scale. If the MMSE score is 23 or lower, one should use the Cornell Scale for Depression in Dementia. If the individual's scores indicate depression, use of antidepressants and counseling would be indicated. Older individuals often respond to lower doses of medications and take longer to show response to antidepressants, so careful monitoring is essential. Some of the newer antidepressants such as the SSRIs show a better response for the older individual with fewer side effects (Flood & Buckwalter, 2009a). Antidepressants such as citalopram hydrobromide (Celexa), escitalopram oxalate (Lexapro), and sertraline HCL (Zoloft) are often considered for use with the elderly. Medication selection is usually based upon symptoms and possible side effects with an attempt made to minimize the use of medications that can cause orthostatic hypotension, an anticholinergic response, or interact with other medications.

Psychiatric disorder is defined as having readily observable external symptoms that influence the mental state of the individual. Psychosocial integrity is related to both psychologic and social factors, such as family relationships, living environments, and enjoyment of life.

Critical Thinking Question

What are some signs of depression? What are some factors that may contribute to depression? What are some signs of passive suicidality? What are some factors that may be different in evaluating suicidality in an older person than in a younger client?

Clinical Example

Lewis, a 72-year-old man, was a successful businessman for 40 years. He had enjoyed good health, taken medication for hypertension that kept it under control, watched his diet, and exercised regularly. His wife died 5 years ago and he has a close relationship with his son and family. Lewis stopped visiting the family business and had decreased contact with his son. The son visited the family home and found his father sitting in the dark, unshaven and irritable. Lewis stated, "Leave me alone! I don't want to be bothered! Go away!" Lewis had lost weight, declared he had no appetite, and stated he was taking his medication when he remembered. He had ceased his social activities and stated he just wanted to sleep. Lewis told his longtime housekeeper to find other employment, stating, "I don't need to be a bother to anyone!"

Alarmed, his son supportively confronted his father and was able to get him to agree to see a psychiatrist the following day. The doctor diagnosed Lewis with a major depressive episode and started him on an antidepressant. He saw a psychiatric nurse practitioner for medication management and weekly group psychotherapy. The nurse practitioner's interventions and medication compliance enabled Lewis to attend and participate in weekly group psychotherapy sessions and resume his premorbid state of socialization, involving both family and business interests.

Evidence-Based Practice

Risk factors for depression in elders include being single or widowed and living alone, loss and grief reactions, pain, chronic illness and functional disabilities including incontinence, death anxiety, substance abuse, medication side effects, and a history of depression or suicide attempts. Butcher and McGonigal-Kennedy (2005) examined the concept of dispiritedness or being in low spirits as a functional aspect of depression in interviews with elders. Most clients expressed this as a sense that life had lost its meaning with themes around life transitions, disengagement, loss of vigor, bewilderment, fluctuations between engagement and disengagement, and ambivalence in continuing their day-to-day lives. Nursing interventions to deal with these feelings centered around helping the elder to facilitate hope and spirituality, encourage activity, and maintain connectedness with their support systems.

Anxiety

Anxiety is often conceptualized along a continuum from normal reactions to stress to maladaptive reactions to stress. Anxiety in later life may be reactive (i.e., a response to age-related losses and changes) or endogenous (i.e., a correlate of medical morbidity). Recurring and chronic anxiety can complicate many illnesses that are common to the elderly and can interfere with activities of daily living. The presence of anxiety in the older adult correlates with and predicts cognitive decline and impairment (Reed, 2010a). Anxiety has also been found to significantly elevate acute pain perception (Feeney, 2004).

Anxiety disorders include generalized anxiety disorder (GAD). GAD is characterized by persistent, excessive worry with fluctuating severity of symptoms that include restlessness, irritability, sleep disturbance, fatigue, and impaired concentration. This disorder typically manifests early in life, but can become a chronic condition that continues into the later adult years. Many individuals with GAD also have significant depression. Nonspecific complaints such as weakness, feeling light-headed, or a slight increase in heart and respiratory rate may signal anxiety. Older adults with chronic medical conditions are at a much higher risk for development of anxiety disorders compared to those without chronic illness (Mehta et al., 2003).

Treatment of anxiety can be complex and multidimensional. Assessment of symptoms and somatic complaints are essential. Once physiologic factors are ruled out, it may be necessary to incorporate cognitive-behavioral interventions and teach the older person coping skills for managing his or her anxiety. This may include recognition of triggers and cognitively reframing the stressor so they have some control of the situation. Short-term pharmacologic therapy may be necessary while working with the older individual to help him or her gain control over the situation.

Caregiver Issues

Families are often the first to be aware of the cognitive problems of their loved one. When the diagnosis of dementia or other mental disorder is confirmed, it can be devastating to the family. The diagnosis frequently means long-term care responsibilities. Most families want to keep their relative at home as long as possible to maintain contact and to avoid costly nursing home placement. Family caregivers provide the major percentage of informal, in-home care giving. Women in the family are generally the designated caregivers; this may be a wife, daughter, or other female relative (Mueth, 2010). Family caregivers are challenged often by lack of information, lack of practical skills training, and physical and emotional strain.

Caring for a family member with a mental disorder takes its toll. Caregivers' health is often compromised, and normal family function is threatened. Caregiver distress is a major health risk for the family and caregiver burnout is a common cause of institutionalization of clients with dementia.

Abuse and neglect of elderly individuals is a prevalent and serious form of family violence. It is difficult to estimate the prevalence of elder abuse and neglect in this country due to underreporting. It has been estimated that 10% of the community-dwelling elderly receiving family caregiving are abused (Mueth, 2010). However, it is also acknowledged that this number is low because abused elders will often minimize the abuse or deny that it occurred; they are often unwilling to disclose information because of fear of retaliation, fear of having to go to a nursing home, embarrassment about the existence of abuse in the family, protectiveness toward a family member, or unwillingness to institute legal action. The abuser often lives with the older person and may be the caregiver. Typically, caregivers who are likely to be abusers have been described as being under economic stress, substance abusers, themselves the victims of previous family violence, and exhausted and frustrated by the caregiver role (Mueth, 2010).

In addition to family and community settings, there is also a problem of elder abuse in institutional settings including sexual abuse. Staff screening, education, and staffing levels are an issue in care giving for these settings. Professional errors also include failure to assess client injuries and complaints, minimizing behaviors and incidents as well as misinterpreting client symptoms or disclosures due to assumptions about the client's cognitive and physical deficits (Teaster et al., 2006).

Critical Thinking Question

What are some of the factors that affect a caretaker's ability to take care of someone with Alzheimer's disease? What are some of the symptoms of Alzheimer's disease that may affect caretaking by others?

Evidence-Based Practice

Ramsey-Klawsnik et al. (2007) reviewed literature and data for sexual abuse in institutional settings, developed the Sexual Abuse Surveys (SASUs A and B) to help identify suspected cases, and collected information regarding alleged survivors of abuse for 6 months before and after the suspected abuse in order to identify effective methods of identification and response. While both male and female victims and perpetrators were identified, victims were found to be primarily female and perpetrators male. Perpetrators include family members, facility staff, and other residents. Practice implications include staff screening, education, careful client assessment, and the need for further research.

Capacity

The issue of **capacity** arises in many contexts involving cognitively impaired older adults. One of the basic human rights is that of autonomy to make decisions. **Competency** is a legal term and can only be determined by a court; it is often confused with capacity. Carroll (2010) indicates that capacity refers to the ability to make a single decision about an aspect of health care. It can be determined by three simple points in decision making. Does the person understand the medical issue in question? Can the person process the information cognitively? Can he or she understand the implications of the decision he or he has made? In situations of informed consent for medical procedures or participating in a research study, an additional component of voluntary consent is added.

Clinical Example

Stuart, a 72-year-old man, has devotedly taken care of his wife of 49 years, Ruth (they have no children), since she was diagnosed with Alzheimer's disease 5 years ago. She has a 4-year history of agitation and aggressiveness that is controlled by medication, and she is otherwise in generally good health. Stuart had been taking care of Ruth alone at home with minimal difficulty until 1 year ago, when Ruth had repeatedly misplaced things around the house, forgot to lock doors or close windows, paid less attention to her hygiene, and withdrew from socializing with friends and neighbors. Ruth sustained a wrist fracture after she tripped while wandering unsupervised in a neighbor's garden. While in the emergency room, Stuart confided to the nurse that he was overwhelmed. The social worker in the emergency room contacted the home healthcare agency and arranged a home visit the next day by a registered nurse for an assessment and evaluation. One month later, as a result of the home assessment, Stuart began regularly attending a community support group provided by the Alzheimer's Disease and Related Disorders Foundation; a home healthcare aide was put in place 12 hours per week; a physical therapist started to visit the house every week for mobilization and treatment; durable medical equipment was put in place (e.g., shower and bathroom rails) to assist with ADLs; and Stuart began to accept use of respite services from a nearby nursing home when needed.

Stuart now has more time to attend to his own needs. Since attending the support groups provided by the Alzheimer's Foundation and after meeting the director at the respite unit, Stuart has initiated the necessary legal and ethical decisions (e.g., advance directives, long-term care options) that he had avoided. Stuart anticipates celebrating their 50th wedding anniversary at home.

It must be emphasized that suicide is preventable and depression is treatable. Electroconvulsive therapy is often used for acutely suicidal, depressed elderly clients who cannot be treated with medication.

There may be a question about the individual's ability to give informed consent for medical treatment or to make end-of-life decisions regarding resuscitation and life support. Attorneys may become concerned about future challenges to wills, gifts, and trusts. Friends or relatives may recommend that durable power of attorney be executed or may contemplate guardianship or conservatorship. Statutory and governing case laws differ considerably from state to state; if you have specific questions, you need to gather further information specific to your state and situation.

End-of-Life Issues

Advance directives are legal instruments intended to ensure that appropriate decisions regarding medical care are made when a person becomes incompetent or unable to give informed consent. There are two types of advance directive. Proxy directives, such as the durable power of attorney for health care or healthcare proxy, allow an individual to authorize another person to give or withhold consent for medical care if a person should become incompetent or unable to make his or her own decisions. The second type of advance directive is the living will, which is a document created by the individual when he or she is of sound mind, specifying the limits of care to be given by healthcare providers if the individual cannot make or communicate a choice regarding a particular healthcare decision. The living will often allows the individual to specify particular treatments that he or she does not want as well as preferences regarding DNR (do not resuscitate) or DNI (do not intubate) orders.

Suicide

When attempting suicide, women tend to use passive methods from which they can be revived (e.g., drug overdoses), whereas men tend to use active, irreversible methods (e.g., gunshot).

Suicide is more prevalent in the elderly—16% of all suicides are committed by those 65 or older (Flood & Buckwalter, 2009a). The group especially at risk appears to be white men 85 years and older (Plawecki & Amrhein, 2010).

Suicide is a conscious, self-inflected injurious act that results in a fatal outcome. Older adults use more lethal means (e.g., guns, hanging, or jumping) to commit suicide and are more successful in their suicides (Reed, 2010a). Passive suicide or life-shortening behavior is often seen by people who refuse to follow medical treatment regimens, refuse to take medications, engage in stresses that could exacerbate a physical condition, or refuse fluids or food (Reed, 2010a).

Assessment of suicide risk is important when working with older individuals, especially those who present with warning signs or are at high risk. Suicidal ideation clues may be verbal and either direct (i.e., "I just want to end it all") or indirect (i.e., "What's the point of going on with life?"). Behavioral clues may also be direct (e.g., past suicide attempts) or indirect (e.g., giving away possessions). Situational clues may be events that trigger depression and lead to suicide (e.g., recent move; death of spouse, child, or friend; or diagnosis of a terminal disease). Symptomatic clues such as depression with anxiety, isolation, changes in sleeping and eating habits, or sudden recovery from a deep depression often are noted prior to suicide.

If it is suspected that a person is suicidal, ask direct questions to determine if he or she wishes to end his or her life and if so, whether there is a suicide plan. Asking these questions allows you to determine how specific the plan is, the lethality of the chosen method, and the availability or accessibility of the means to commit suicide. Asking why he or she has not carried out a plan thus far may bring out some supportive or protective factors that can be used to help the individual think about alternative options (Plawecki & Amrhein, 2010).

After assessment, crisis intervention is the next step, with the primary goal of maintaining the individual's safety. Often it is appropriate that a consultation with a mental health professional be done to determine if a hospital is the safest environment for the person. If it has been decided that the older adult does not need hospitalization, an ongoing program of treatment needs to be developed. The treatment can include treatment of presenting symptoms, referral for individual and/or group therapy, or referral for a support group or a community program. Ongoing monitoring is important and can show that the individual is overcoming a sense of despair and moving toward a healthier way of resolving his or her difficulties.

Substance Abuse

Experts suggest that substance abuse among adults 60 years and older is one of the fastest growing health problems in the United States (Reed, 2010b). It is estimated that 2–10% of community-dwelling older adults have alcohol problems and 21% of aging, hospitalized clients have a diagnosis of alcoholism.

These numbers and those for illicit drug abuse are projected to increase as the baby boom generation ages because this group has traditionally embraced more liberal attitudes related to substance use than previous generations (Reed, 2010b).

Often substance use is undetected by healthcare workers because the symptoms of weight loss, irritability, and sleeping problems are believed to be due to depression or other physical conditions. The *DSM-IV-TR* criteria for substance abuse indicate a problem if use results in failure to fulfill major role obligations at work, school, or home; in physically hazardous situations; or in substance-related legal problems or recurrent social or interpersonal problems (American Psychiatric Association [APA], 2000). Most older individuals do not work or go to school and have no role obligations in these areas. Many do not drive, so substance use in hazardous situations with resultant legal consequences may not be evident. Finally, it is not unusual for an older substance user to live alone, so substance-related interpersonal problems may not be readily apparent.

Older individuals who misuse alcohol are categorized as early- or late-onset problem drinkers. Early-onset alcohol abusers began abusing alcohol in their early adult years and have carried their drinking habits into old age with them. They are often well known to the medical and social service providers. They tend to drink more frequently and in greater quantities than younger drinkers, and they exhibit classic symptoms of long-term alcohol abuse, including physical withdrawal when they attempt to abstain (Reed, 2010b).

Late-onset alcohol abusers develop problems in their 50s or 60s. They are often seen as reactive drinkers because their problems stem from situational events, such as retirement or death of a spouse. They suffer from fewer medical and psychiatric complications, and they tend to have a greater overall life satisfaction than their early-onset counterparts (Reed, 2010b). Alcohol and benzodiazepines appear to be two of the most problematic drugs for older women (Reed, 2010b).

The initial treatment step in alcohol or substance abuse is to stop drinking, stop taking the drugs, or both.

As individuals age, the same amount of alcohol that had little effect at a younger age can cause inebriation. This is due to physiologic changes in liver and kidney function, metabolism, and elimination and decreases in body mass and water. The body responds to benzodiazepines in a similar way. Because of the physical changes and use of alcohol and benzodiazepines, an individual may become dependent without apparent abuse. He or she may be ingesting recommended amounts of the substance and using it as prescribed and become dependent and have withdrawal symptoms if the substance is abruptly discontinued.

Alcohol is the most common substance abused by the elderly, because it is readily available and not usually perceived as a drug.

Society has contributed to the problem with conflicting information about the benefits of alcohol consumption on cardiovascular health. We also see many pharmaceutical advertisements that promote the benefits of prescription drugs to induce sleep and diminish anxiety (Reed, 2010b). Unfortunately,

Clinical Example 

Oliver is a 66-year-old married man who has been a successful lawyer with a large international firm for 35 years. Much of his business is conducted over lunch or dinner and at countless social gatherings. Oliver's drinking has gradually increased without his being aware of it, until his wife commented on his ordering an alcoholic beverage at breakfast when she accompanied him on a recent trip. After drinking heavily at a social affair, Oliver fell asleep while driving and ran off the road. The car was badly damaged, but Oliver was not harmed. The police administered a Breathalyzer test that revealed a blood alcohol level of 0.3%. He was arrested and taken to the police station, where his wife, who was upset and overwhelmed, met him.

Upon returning home, Oliver expressed fear and concern about his behavior and his near death from the accident. He was uncertain of the response he would receive from his employer and the state of his marriage. Oliver decided to seek help from the employee assistance program at work and face his situation openly.

The client is expected to verbalize having a substance abuse problem, abstain from using alcohol, and overcome abuse and dependence with treatment. The nurse must confront the client with the substance-abusing behavior and its consequences, assist the client to identify the substance abuse problem, and constantly offer support and the expectation that the client has the strength to overcome the problem. The nurse also should encourage the client to participate in a treatment program, assist the client to identify and adopt healthier coping responses, and provide support to significant others.

many healthcare providers are reluctant to address the problem of substance abuse. Many providers do not recognize the early symptoms and do not ask about alcohol use. Treatment programs designed for older adults are rare and may not be covered by managed care or Medicare.

Experts recommend that alcohol abuse screening be a part of all older adult mental and physical examinations and a prerequisite to prescribing new medications (Barry, Oslin, & Bow, 2001). The MMSE can be used to rule out cognitive dysfunction and CAGE or another alcohol abuse assessment instrument also can be used. Studies have shown that the older drinker is more likely to honestly report his or her drinking to the healthcare provider and is more likely to comply with treatment strategies.

Management and Treatment

With few exceptions, geriatric clients require attention and care specific to individual needs and life changes. Psychiatric nursing contributes to the stabilization and ongoing improvement of quality of life for each client encountered in myriad settings and circumstances. The challenge of geriatric psychiatric nursing is to be proactive in caring for the elderly with a chronic or acute psychiatric illness. Assessment for the need for hospitalization (e.g., threatening suicide, increasing debilitation for self-care) must be performed and documented. Nurses should ask clients about how they see themselves by specific indicators such as sleeping, eating, weight loss or gain, interest in new things, energy level, concentration ability, and activities of daily living.

Use of medication is reserved for clients with psychotic behaviors such as agitation, anxiety, depression, and psychosis. Medication orders should always be questioned, especially when the dosage appears higher than standard. For the elderly, doses are typically one half the usual dosage. Neuroleptic, anticonvulsant, and antidepressant medications may cause delirium.

Specific short- and long-term goals should be based upon the client assessment including recognition of the client's situation and self-concept, physical status and stamina, support systems and stressors. Treatment of the elder community takes place in the community setting in outpatient clinics, mental health and community centers, and medical offices, as well as in the home and institutional setting. Treatment planning should involve everyone involved in care of the client.

Summary

Mental health problems in older adults are underrecognized and undertreated. The older client is less likely to receive treatment for mental health problems in either inpatient settings or by community-based healthcare practitioners (Leutwyler & Wallhagen, 2010).

As individuals age, they experience physical changes, and there may also be age-related psychologic changes. Because of these changes, the impact of sleep problems, pain issues, and polypharmacy may not be correlated with mental health problems. The frequency of chronic conditions makes older adults vulnerable to depression and anxiety. Dementia disorders are the most frequent cause of psychopathology in the elderly. The growing population of individuals age 65 and older suggests that the challenge of providing care will progress well into the 21st century. Nurses who work in the field of mental health need to be able to identify and work with the older person presenting with mental health problems.

Annotated References

Administration on Aging. (2009). *A profile of older Americans: 2009*. Washington, DC:

Considerations for Client and Family Education

- Monitor and, if necessary, modify activities to match physical and mental abilities.
- Utilize family and community support systems to maintain independence.
- When initiating communication, ensure that the client is able to pay attention to the communicator. Minimize environmental distracters.
- Due to normal changes in aging, it is important to assess speech/language, hearing, and visual acuity. If necessary, write things down; utilize large fonts in print. Ensure proper environmental lighting. For the hearing impaired, minimize background noise and use amplifiers or sign interpreters. If there are communication problems, utilize speech/language therapists.

U.S. Department of Health and Human Services.
This publication provides demographic information about the population age 65 and older.

Alexopoulos, G. S., Abrams, R. C., Young, R. C., & Shamoian, C. A. (1998). Cornell scale for depression in dementia. *Biological Psychiatry, 23*, 271–284.
This article provides information on the Cornell scale for depression for individuals with dementia.

Amella, E. J. (2004). Presentation of illness in older adults. *American Journal of Nursing, 104*(10), 40–51.
This article provides an overview of assessment, critical indicators of underlying conditions, and common diseases of the older adult.

American Psychiatric Association. (2000). *Diagnostic and statistical manual of mental disorders* (4th ed., text rev.). Washington, DC: Author.
This is the fourth edition, text revision, of the American Psychiatric Association's official nomenclature of psychiatric conditions and disorders. It provides a systematic listing of the official codes and categories, a description of the multiaxial system for diagnosis, and diagnostic criteria for each of the disorders. It is used by psychiatrists, physicians, psychologists, registered nurses, social workers, therapists, and other mental health workers in all clinical settings.

American Society of Consultant Pharmacists. (2000). Senior care pharmacy: The statistics. *Consultant Pharmacist, 15*, 310.
This article discusses the senior care pharmacy concept and provides information on the medication use of the senior population.

Barry, K. L., Oslin, D. W., & Bow, F. C. (2001). *Alcohol problems in older adults: Prevention and management*. New York, NY: Springer.
This book presents information on the prevention and management of alcohol abuse in older adults.

Beers, M. (1997). Explicit criteria for determining potentially inappropriate medication use by the elderly: An update. *Archives of Internal Medicine, 157*, 1531–1536.
This article presents criteria for determining the appropriateness of medications for use in the elderly. It also provides an update of inappropriate medications.

Butcher, H. K., & McGonigal-Kennedy, M. (2005). Depression and dispiritedness in later life. *American Journal of Nursing, 105*(12), 52–61.
This article discusses the difficulties in identifying depression in elders who might be less likely to describe typical depressive symptoms or report suicidal thoughts. Data obtained in interviews with clients was used to identify themes of dispiritedness in elders and three major coping mechanisms the elders utilized to deal with these feelings. Nursing interventions to inspire hope and encourage elders to keep active and maintain connections are based on this research.

Carroll, D. W. (2010). Assessment of capacity for medical decision making. *Journal of Gerontological Nursing, 36*(5), 47–52.
This article includes a discussion of competence and capacity issues for older adults.

Cole, C. S., & Richards, K. C. (2006). Sleep in persons with dementia: Increasing quality of life by managing sleep disorders. *Journal of Gerontological Nursing, 32*(3), 48–53.
This article discusses sleep disorders and management of disorders in older adults with dementia.

Feeney, S. L. (2004). The relationship between pain and negative affect in older adults: Anxiety as a predictor of pain. *Journal of Anxiety Disorder, 18*, 733–744.
This article looks at the relationship between pain and anxiety in the older adult and discusses some of the negative aspects resulting from it.

Fick, D. M., Cooper, J. W., Wade, W. E., Waller, J. L., Maclean, R. J., & Beers, M. H. (2003). Updating the Beers criteria for potentially inappropriate medication use in older adults: Results of a U.S. consensus panel of experts. *Archives of Internal Medicine, 163*(22), 2716–2724.
This is an update of the Beers criteria for inappropriate medication use in the older adult.

Flood, M., & Buckwalter, K. C. (2009a). Recommendations for mental health care of older adults: Part 1—An overview of depression and anxiety. *Journal of Gerontological Nursing 35*(2), 26–34.
This article provides a good overview of depression and anxiety assessment and treatment in older adults.

Flood, M., & Buckwalter, K. C. (2009b). Recommendations for mental health care of older adults: Part 2—An overview of dementia, delirium and substance abuse. *Journal of Gerontological Nursing 35*(2), 35–47.

This article provides a good overview of dementia, delirium, and substance abuse issues in the older adult.

Folstein, M. (1983). The Mini-Mental State Exam. In T. Cook, S. Ferris, & B.B. Bartus (Eds.), *Assessment in Geriatric Psychopharmacology* (pp. 47–51). New Canaan, CT: Mark Powley.
This chapter provides a copy of the MMSE and discussion of its use.

Folstein, M. F., Folstein, S. E., & McHugh, P. R. (1975). "Mini-mental state." A practical method for grading the cognitive state of clients for the clinician. *Journal of Psychiatric Research, 12*, 189–198.
This article discusses the Mini-Mental State Examination.

Herr, K. (2002). Chronic pain: Challenges and assessment strategies. *Journal of Gerontological Nursing, 28*(1), 20–27.
This article presents assessment and management strategies for working with older adults with chronic pain.

Kazer, M. W. (2011). Cognitive & neurologic function. In S. E. Meiner (Ed.), *Gerontological Nursing* (4th ed., pp. 564–595). St. Louis, MO: Elsevier Mosby.
This chapter presents the cognitive and neurologic changes seen in individuals with dementia and ways to intervene to maintain a safe environment for the individual and others.

Kurlowicz, L., & Greenberg, S. A. (1999). The Geriatric Depression Scale. *Hartford Institute for Geriatric Nursing*. Retrieved from http://www.consultgerirn.org/uploads/File/trythis/try_this_4.pdf
This document provides a copy of the Geriatric Depression Scale and a brief discussion of the strengths and limitations of the tool.

Leutwyler, H. C., & Wallhagen, M. I. (2010). Understanding physical health of older adults with schizophrenia, building and eroding trust. *Journal of Gerontological Nursing, 36*(5), 38–45.
This article discusses healthcare disparities and inequities for individuals with mental illness.

Loge, J., & Sorrell, J. M. (2010). Implications of an aging population for mental health nurses. *Journal of Psychosocial Nursing, 48*(9), 15–18.
This article provides a discussion of mental health issues for global aging.

Luggen, A. S., Meiner, S. E., & National Gerontological Nursing Association. (2002). *NGNA: Core curriculum for gerontological nursing*. St. Louis, MO: Mosby.
This is a comprehensive text for gerontological nursing that includes information on patient assessment.

Mayfield, D., McLeod, G., & Hall, P. (1974). The CAGE questionnaire: Validation of a new alcoholism screening instrument. *American Journal of Psychiatry, 131*, 1121–1123.
This article discusses the process the CAGE questionnaire underwent for validation.

Mehta, K. M., Simonsick, E. M., Penninx, B. W., Schultz, R., Rubin, S. M., Satterfield, S. & Yaffe, K. (2003). Prevalence and correlates of anxiety symptoms in well-functioning older adults: Findings from the health aging and body composition study. *Journal of the American Geriatrics Society, 51*(4), 499–504.
This article looks at anxiety symptoms in depressed and nondepressed older people.

Mueth, E. C. (2010). Family influences. In S. E. Meiner (Ed.), *Gerontological nursing* (4th ed., pp. 94–115). St. Louis, MO: Elsevier.
This article presents family dynamics in caring for the aging parent.

Nagel, C. L., Markie, M. B., Richards, K. C., & Taylor, J. (2003). Sleep promotion in hospitalized elders. *MedSurg Nursing, 12*(5), 279–290.
This article reviews sleep disturbances in hospitalized elders. It discusses the problems of pharmacologic interventions in elders that may increase the risk for falls, delirium, and functional decline as well as nonpharmacologic nursing interventions.

National Institute on Aging. (2008). *Alzheimer's information: General information*. Retrieved from http://www.nia.nih.gov/Alzheimers/AlzheimersInformation/GeneralInfo/
This site provides a general overview of Alzheimer's disease in the population.

National Institute of Mental Health. (2008). *Older adults and mental health*. Bethesda, MD: NIMH. Retrieved from http://www.nimh.nih.gov/health/topics/older-adults-and-mental-health/index.shtml
This site provides information regarding suicide in the older population.

National Sleep Foundation. (2003). Sleep in America poll 2003. *American Academy*

of Sleep Medicine. Retrieved from http://www.sleepfoundation.org/article/sleep-america-polls/2003-sleep-and-aging
This site provides information about the sleep habits of older Americans.

Paniagua, M. A., Malphurs, J. E., & Phelan, E. A. (2006). Older patients presenting to a county hospital ED after a fall: Missed opportunities for prevention. *American Journal of Emergency Medicine, 24*(4), 413–417.
This review of emergency department records of elders admitted with falls indicates that failure to assess clients for potentially reversible problems such as polypharmacy and alcohol abuse led to the release of clients without treatment or referral and inadequate discharge planning.

Plahuta, J. M., & Hamrick-King, J. (2006). Review of the aging of physiological systems. In K. L. Mauk (Ed.), *Gerontological nursing: Competencies for care* (pp. 143–264). Sudbury, MA: Jones and Bartlett.
This article reviews physiologic systems and effects of aging including skills in assessment of common functional and physical changes and allows for the individualization of nursing care according to the capabilities of the older adult.

Planton, J., & Edlund, B. J. (2010). Strategies for reducing polypharmacy in older adults. *Journal of Gerontological Nursing, 36*(1), 8–12.
This article provides a discussion of approaches to reduce problems resulting from polypharmacy in the older population.

Plawecki, L. H., & Amrhein, D. W. (2010). Someone to talk to: The nurse and the depressed or suicidal older patient. *Journal of Gerontological Nursing, 36*(5), 15–18.
This article discusses the responsibilities of healthcare providers working with depressed or suicidal older adults.

Ramsey-Klawsnik, H., Teaster, P. B., Mendiondo, M. S., Abner, E. L., Cecil, K. A., & Tooms, M. R. (2007). Sexual abuse of vulnerable adults in care facilities: Clinical findings and a research initiative. *American Psychiatric Nurses Association Journal, 12*(6), 332–339.
This article reviews literature and research on sexual abuse of elders and presents research on the first national survey of sexual abuse of elders in institutional settings.

Reed, M. J. (2010a). Mental health. In S. E. Meiner (Ed.), *Gerontological nursing* (4th ed., pp. 243–262). St. Louis, MO: Elsevier.
This chapter presents mental health issues in older adults.

Reed, M. J. (2010b). Substance abuse. In S. E. Meiner (Ed.), *Gerontological nursing* (4th ed., pp. 307–321). St. Louis, MO: Elsevier.
This article presents substance abuse issues in the older population.

Rigney, T. S. (2006). Delirium in the hospitalized elder and recommendations for practice. *Geriatric Nursing, 27*(3), 151–157.
This article emphasizes the need for identification and early intervention of symptoms of delirium because of the high mortality rate associated with delirium.

Sendelbach, S., & Guthrie, P. F. (2009). Evidence-based guideline: Acute confusional/delirium—identification, assessment, treatment, and prevention. *Journal of Gerontological Nursing, 35*(11), 11–18.
This article summarizes the guidelines for identifying risk factors and appropriate assessment and treatment for preventing delirium in hospitalized elderly patients.

Sharer, J. (2008). Tackling sundowning in a patient with Alzheimer's disease. *MEDSURG Nursing, 17*(1), 27–29.
This article discusses caring for the client with sundowning behaviors and nonpharmacologic interventions that can be effective.

Spar, J. E., & LaRue, A. (2002). *Geriatric psychiatry* (3rd ed.). Washington, DC: American Psychiatric.
This reference book discusses geriatric mental health care.

Substance Abuse and Mental Health Service Administration. (2008). Mental Health and mental disorders. In *Healthy People 2010—Conference edition*. Available from *Healthy People 2010, Conference Edition, January 2000 Chapter 18: Mental Health and Mental Disorders* pp. 4–18. http://www.healthypeople.gov/Document/HTML/Volume2/18Mental.htm
This publication presents information from Healthy People 2010 regarding the mental health of the population.

Suderland, T., Hill, J. L., Mellow, A. M., Lawlor, B. A., Gundersheimer, J., Newhouse, P.A. (1989). Clock drawing in Alzheimer's dis-

ease. A novel measure of dementia severity. *Journal of the American Geriatric Society, 7*(8), 725–729.
This article presents an alternative assessment of the severity of dementia.

Teaster, P. B., Otto, J. M., Dugar, T. D., Mendiondo, M. S., Abner, E. L., & Cecil, K. A. (2006). The 2004 survey of state adult protective services: Abuse of adults 60 years of age and older. *Report to the National Center on Elder Abuse, Administration on Aging*. Washington, DC: National Center on Elder Abuse, Administration on Aging.
A review of 565,747 Adult Protective Services (APS) reports of elder abuse found 5,797 allegations of sexual abuse. Estimates of sexual abuse of elders vary because APS is not responsible for investigating institutional settings in all states.

Watson, L., & Pignon, M. (2003). Screening accuracy for late-life depression in primary care: A systematic review. *The Journal of Family Practice, 52*(12), 956–964.
This article provides a review of tools to screen for depression in the older adult.

Wick, J., & Zanni, G. (2005). The consultant pharmacist. *The Journal of the American Society of Consultant Pharmacists, 20*(11), 947–950, 957–961.
This article discusses pharmacologic care of individuals with Alzheimer's disease and associated behaviors.

Yesavage, J. A., Brink, T. L., Rose, T. L., Lum, O., Huang, V., Adey, M., & Leirer, V. O. (1983). Development and validation of a geriatric depression screening scale. *Journal of Psychiatric Research, 17*, 37–49.
This article provides information on the development and validation of the geriatric depression screening scale.

Additional References

Haight, B., & Gibson, F. (2005). *Working with older adults: Group process & techniques* (4th ed.). Sudbury, MA: Jones and Bartlett.
This text discusses the psych-social-cultural aspects of working with elders in various settings (hospitals, nursing homes, residential facilities, day centers, and home care). It includes chapters on groups for clients with dementia, support and self-help groups, and reminiscence group work as well as other topics that are useful when working with older adults.

Schlossberg, N. K., Anderson, M. L., & Goodman, J. (2006). *Counseling adults in transition: Linking practice with theory* (3rd ed.). New York, NY: Springer.
Provides guidelines for assessing the client in transitional situations, whether planned (e.g., retirement) or unplanned (e.g., loss of spouse) and strategies for providing support and intervention.

Internet Resources

For a full suite of assignments and additional learning activities, use the access code located in the front of your book to visit this exclusive website: http://go.jblearning.com/mentalhealth. If you do not have an access code, you can obtain one at the site.

Appendix I

Psychiatric-Mental Health Standards of Nursing Practice[1]

Psychiatric-mental health nurses, like those in other nursing specialties, follow standards and guidelines in their practice. According to the American Nurses Association (ANA), standards of nursing practice, including the standards of practice and professional performance, are "authoritative statements by which the nursing profession describes the responsibilities for which its practitioners are accountable…standards reflect the values and priorities of the profession…provide direction for professional nursing practice and a framework for the evaluation of this practice…standards also define the nursing profession's accountability to the public and the outcomes for which registered nurses are responsible" (ANA, 2003, p. 1). Meanwhile, guidelines are based on "available scientific evidence and expert opinion" and describe "a process of patient care management, which has the potential for improving the quality of clinical and patient decision-making…practice guidelines address the care of specific patient populations or phenomena, whereas standards provide a broad framework for practice" (ANA, 2003, p. 5).

1 Reprinted with permission from American Nurses Association. (2007). *Psychiatric-mental health nursing: Scope and standards of practice.* Silver Spring, MD: Author.

http://go.jblearning.com/mentalhealth 

For a full suite of assignments and additional learning activities, use the access code located in the front of your book to visit this exclusive website: http://go.jblearning.com/mentalhealth. If you do not have an access code, you can obtain one at the site.

The ANA has been actively engaged in the development of nursing standards since the 1960s. The first generic standards of practice were developed in 1973, and the *Standards of Clinical Nursing Practice* were first published in 1991, with a revision in 1998. In 2003, ANA published *Nursing: Scope and Standards of Practice*. These generic standards are composed of standards of practice (assessment, diagnosis, outcomes identification, planning, implementation, evaluation) and standards of professional performance (quality of practice, education, professional practice evaluation, collegiality, collaboration, ethics, research, resource utilization, leadership). Specific measurement criteria are provided by ANA in their published documents for each of the standards. Most specialty nursing organizations have agreed to use these generic practice standards as the model for the development of specialty standards of practice.

Included in this appendix are ANA's *Psychiatric-Mental Health Nursing: Scope and Standards of Practice* (2007). Also available from American Nurses Publishing are standards for many different specialty areas including *Standards for Addictions Nursing Practice with Selected Diagnoses and Criteria* (1988) and *Intellectual and Developmental Disabilities Nursing: Scope and Standards of Practice* (2004).

Standards of Psychiatric–Mental Health Nursing Practice[1]

Standards of Practice*—These six standards "describe a competent level of nursing care as demonstrated by the critical thinking model known as the nursing process"(ANA, 2003, p. 4).*

Standard 1. Assessment

The psychiatric-mental health registered nurse collects comprehensive health data that is pertinent to the patient's health or situation.

Standard 2. Diagnosis

The psychiatric-mental health registered nurse analyzes the assessment data to determine diagnoses or problems, including level of risk.

Standard 3. Outcomes Identification

The psychiatric-mental health registered nurse identifies expected outcomes for a plan individualized to the patient or to the situation.

Standard 4. Planning

The psychiatric-mental health registered nurse develops a plan that prescribes strategies and alternatives to attain expected outcomes.

Standard 5. Implementation

The psychiatric-mental health registered nurse implements the identified plan.

Standard 5a. Coordination of Care

The psychiatric-mental health registered nurse coordinates care delivery.

Standard 5b. Health Teaching and Health Promotion

The psychiatric-mental health registered nurse employs strategies to promote health and a safe environment.

Standard 5c. Milieu Therapy

The psychiatric-mental health registered nurse provides, structures, and maintains a safe and therapeutic environment in collaboration with patients, families, and other healthcare clinicians.

Standard 5d. Pharmaceutical, Biological, Integrative Therapies

The psychiatric-mental health registered nurse incorporates knowledge of pharmacological, biological, and complementary interventions with applied clinical skills to restore the patient's health and prevent further disability.

Standard 5e. Prescriptive Authority and Treatment

The psychiatric-mental health advanced practice registered nurse uses prescriptive authority, procedures, referrals, treatments, and therapies in accordance with state and federal laws and regulations

Standard 5f. Psychotherapy

The psychiatric-mental health advanced practice registered nurse conducts individual, couples, group, and family psychotherapy using evidence-based psychotherapeutic frameworks and nurse-patient therapeutic relationships.

Standard 5g. Consultation

The psychiatric-mental health advanced practice registered nurse provides consultation to influence the identified plan, enhance the abilities of other clinicians to provide services for patients, and effect change.

Standard 6. Evaluation

The psychiatric-mental health registered nurse evaluates progress toward attainment of expected outcomes.

Standards of Professional Performance*—These nine standards "describe a competent level of behavior in the professional role" and all professional registered*

1 Reprinted with permission from American Nurses Association. (2007). *Psychiatric-mental health nursing: Scope and standards of practice.* Silver Spring, MD: Author.

nurses are "expected to engage in professional role activities...appropriate to their education and position" (ANA, 2003, p. 4).

Standard 7. Quality of Practice

The psychiatric-mental health registered nurse systematically enhances the quality and effectiveness of nursing practice.

Standard 8. Education

The psychiatric-mental health registered nurse attains knowledge and competency that reflect current nursing practice.

Standard 9. Professional Practice Evaluation

The psychiatric-mental health registered nurse evaluates one's own practice in relation to the professional practice standards and guidelines, relevant statutes, rules, and regulations.

Standard 10. Collegiality

The psychiatric-mental health registered nurse interacts with and contributes to the professional development of peers and colleagues.

Standard 11. Collaboration

The psychiatric-mental health registered nurse collaborates with patients, family, and others in the conduct of nursing practice.

Standard 12. Ethics

The psychiatric-mental health registered nurse integrates ethical provisions in all areas of practice.

Standard 13. Research

The psychiatric-mental health registered nurse integrates research findings into practice.

Standard 14. Resource Utilization

The psychiatric-mental health registered nurse considers factors related to safety, effectiveness, cost, and impact on practice in the planning and delivery of nursing services.

Standard 15. Leadership

The psychiatric-mental health registered nurse provides leadership in the professional practice setting and the profession.

References

American Nurses Association. (2003). *Nursing: Scope and standards of practice.* Washington, DC: Author.

American Nurses Association. (2007). *Psychiatric-mental health nursing: Scope and standards of practice.* Silver Spring, MD: Author.

Appendix II

NANDA-I Nursing Diagnoses II

In psychiatric-mental health nursing, the nurse should be familiar with two acceptable classification systems: NANDA-International (NANDA-I) Taxonomy II of nursing diagnoses, and the American Psychiatric Association's *Diagnostic and Statistical Manual of Mental Disorders*, 4th ed., Text Revision (*DSM-IV-TR*). The *DSM-IV-TR* classification system is the one most widely used by the four core mental health professions of psychiatry, psychology, nursing, and social work.

According to NANDA-I, "Nursing diagnosis is a clinical judgment about actual or potential individual, family, or community experiences/responses to health problems/life processes. A nursing diagnosis provides the basis for selection of nursing interventions to achieve outcomes for which the nurse has accountability" (NANDA.org).

It provides the basis for selection of nursing interventions to achieve outcomes for which the nurse can be held accountable. The NANDA-I Taxonomy II has three levels: domains, classes, and nursing diagnoses. The nursing diagnoses are organized into 13 domains: health promotion, nutrition, elimination and exchange, activity/rest, perception/cognition, self-perception, role relationships, sexuality, coping/stress tolerance, life principles, safety/protection, comfort, and growth/development.

The psychiatric-mental health nurse should understand how the classifications are used in formulating diagnoses and developing the nursing plan of care. The **Table II-1** compares the *DSM-IV-TR* diagnostic categories with select potential corresponding NANDA-I nursing diagnoses. A complete list of the NANDA-I *Taxonomy: domains, classes, and nursing diagnoses are found in Table II-2.*

http://go.jblearning.com/mentalhealth 

For a full suite of assignments and additional learning activities, use the access code located in the front of your book to visit this exclusive website: http://go.jblearning.com/mentalhealth. If you do not have an access code, you can obtain one at the site.

Table II-1 *DSM-IV-TR* Disorders and Examples of Select NANDA-I Nursing Diagnoses*

DSM-IV-TR **Disorders**	**NANDA-I Nursing Diagnoses**	
Disorders First Diagnosed in Infancy, Childhood, or Adolescence	*00111*	*Delayed growth & development*
	00058	*Risk for impaired attachment*
	00060	*Interrupted family processes*
	00016	*Disorganized infant behavior*
	00056	*Impaired parenting*
	00063	*Dysfunctional family processes*
	00075	*Readiness for enhanced family coping*
	00052	*Impaired social interaction*
	00051	*Impaired verbal communication*
	00121	*Disturbed personal identity*
	00140	*Risk for self-directed violence*
Dementia, Delirium, Amnesia, and Cognitive Disorders	*00127*	*Impaired environmental interpretation syndrome*
	00128	*Acute confusion*
	00129	*Chronic confusion*
	00131	*Impaired memory*
	00051	*Impaired verbal communication*
	00061	*Caregiver role strain*
	00073	*Disabled family coping*
	00075	*Readiness for enhanced family coping*
	00098	*Impaired home maintenance*
	00155	*Risk for falls*
	00154	*Wandering*
	00103	*Impaired swallowing*
Substance-Related Disorders	*00033*	*Impaired spontaneous ventilation*
	00055	*Ineffective role performance*
	00128	*Acute confusion*
	00188	*Risk-prone health behavior*
	0002	*Imbalanced nutrition: less than body requirements*
	00178	*Risk for impaired liver function*
	00174	*Risk for compromised human dignity*
	00063	*Dysfunctional family processes*
	00185	*Readiness for enhanced hope*
	00150	*Risk for suicide*
	00131	*Impaired memory*
	00138	*Risk for other-directed violence*
	00069	*Ineffective coping*
	00075	*Readiness for enhanced coping*
	00097	*Deficient diversional activity*
	00083	*Decisional conflict (re. sobriety)*
	00155	*Risk for falls*
	00162	*Readiness for enhanced self-health management*

Table II-1 *DSM-IV-TR* Disorders and Examples of Select NANDA-I Nursing Diagnoses *(Continued)*

DSM-IV-TR **Disorders**	**NANDA-I Nursing Diagnoses**	
Schizophrenia and Other Psychotic Disorders	*00130*	*Disturbed thought process***
	00051	*Impaired verbal communication*
	00108	*Bathing self-care deficit*
	00074	*Compromised family coping*
	00053	*Social isolation*
	00222	*Ineffective impulse control*
	00150	*Risk for suicide*
	00138	*Risk for other-directed violence*
	00097	*Deficient diversional activity*
	00122	*Disturbed sensory perception***
	00079	*Noncompliance (with medications)*
	00126	*Deficient knowledge*
	00025	*Risk for imbalanced fluid volume*
	0136	*Grieving*
Mood Disorders	*00198*	*Disturbed sleep pattern*
	00119	*Chronic low self esteem*
	00137	*Chronic sorrow*
	00150	*Risk for suicide*
	00138	*Risk for other-directed violence*
	00053	*Social isolation*
	00193	*Self-neglect*
	00051	*Impaired verbal communication*
	00066	*Spiritual distress*
	00002	*Imbalanced nutrition: less than body requirements*
	00003	*Risk for imbalanced nutrition: more than body requirements*
	00146	*Anxiety*
Anxiety Disorders	*00148*	*Fear*
	00146	*Anxiety*
	00141	*Post-trauma syndrome*
	00053	*Social isolation*
	00052	*Impaired social interaction*
	00124	*Hopelessness*
	00119	*Chronic low self-esteem*
	00173	*Risk for acute confusion*
	00078	*Ineffective self-health management*
Dissociative Disorders	*00141*	*Post-trauma syndrome*
	00131	*Impaired memory*
	00138	*Risk for other-directed violence*
	00121	*Disturbed personal identity*
	00119	*Chronic low self-esteem*
	00055	*Ineffective role performance*
	00069	*Ineffective coping*

(Continues)

Table II-1 *DSM-IV-TR* Disorders and Examples of Select NANDA-I Nursing Diagnoses *(Continued)*

DSM-IV-TR **Disorders**	**NANDA-I Nursing Diagnoses**	
Somatoform Disorders	00118	*Disturbed body image*
	00059	*Ineffective sexuality pattern*
	00146	*Anxiety*
	00147	*Death anxiety*
	00132	*Acute pain*
	00133	*Chronic pain*
	00069	*Ineffective coping*
	00075	*Readiness for enhanced coping*
	00099	*Ineffective health maintenance*
Factitious Disorders	00188	*Risk-prone health behavior*
	00146	*Anxiety*
	00148	*Fear*
	00125	*Powerlessness*
	00177	*Stress overload*
	00138	*Risk for other directed violence*
	00071	*Defensive coping*
Sexual and Gender Identity Disorders	00059	*Sexual dysfunction*
	00065	*Ineffective sexuality pattern*
	00126	*Deficient knowledge*
	00153	*Risk for situational low self-esteem*
	00146	*Anxiety*
	00069	*Ineffective coping*
	00060	*Interrupted family processes*
	00142	*Post-trauma syndrome*
	00066	*Spiritual distress*
Eating Disorders	00118	*Disturbed body image*
	00002	*Imbalanced nutrition: Less than body requirements*
	00001	*Imbalanced nutrition: More than body requirements*
	00196	*Risk for electrolyte imbalance*
	00093	*Fatigue*
	00125	*Powerlessness*
	00054	*Risk for loneliness*
	00069	*Ineffective coping*
	00060	*Interrupted family processes*
	00167	*Readiness for enhanced self-concept*
	00162	*Readiness for enhanced self-health management*
Sleep Disorders	00198	*Disturbed sleep pattern*
	00173	*Risk for acute confusion*
	00038	*Risk for falls*
	00093	*Fatigue*
	00032	*Ineffective breathing pattern*
	00095	*Insomnia*
	00165	*Readiness for enhanced sleep*
	00078	*Ineffective self-health management*

Table II-1 *DSM-IV-TR* Disorders and Examples of Select NANDA-I Nursing Diagnoses *(Continued)*

DSM-IV-TR Disorders	NANDA-I Nursing Diagnoses	
Impulse Disorders	*00167*	*Readiness for enhanced self-concept*
	00153	*Risk for situational low self-esteem*
	00069	*Ineffective coping*
	00067	*Risk for spiritual distress*
	00083	*Decisional conflict*
	00175	*Moral distress*
	00146	*Anxiety*
	00135	*Complicated grieving*
Personality Disorders	*00119*	*Chronic low self-esteem*
	00069	*Ineffective coping*
	00071	*Defensive coping*
	00139	*Risk for self-mutilation*
	00121	*Disturbed personal identity*
	00052	*Impaired social interaction*
	00167	*Readiness for enhanced self-concept*

* Other Nursing Diagnoses will also be relevant to individual patients depending on their individual needs.
** Not among currently approved NANDA-I nursing diagnoses
Source: Based on NANDA, (2012). NANDA nursing diagnoses: Definitions and classification, 2012–2014. Hoboken, NJ: Wiley-Blackwell.

Table II-2 Taxonomy II: Domains, Classes, and Diagnoses

DOMAIN 1 HEALTH PROMOTION

The awareness of well-being or normality of function and the strategies used to maintain control of and enhance that well-being or normality of function

Class 1 Health Awareness Recognition of normal function and well-being

Approved Diagnoses

00097	*Deficient diversional activity*
00168	*Sedentary lifestyle*

Class 2 Health Management Identifying, controlling, performing, and integrating activities to maintain health and well-being

Approved Diagnoses

00215	*Deficient community health*
00188	*Risk-prone health behavior*
00099	*Ineffective health maintenance*
00186	*Readiness for enhanced immunization status*
00043	*Ineffective protection*
00078	*Ineffective self-health management*
00162	*Readiness for enhanced self-health management*
00080	*Ineffective family therapeutic regimen management*

DOMAIN 2 NUTRITION

The activities of taking in, assimilating, and using nutrients for the purposes of tissue maintenance, tissue repair, and the production of energy

Class 1 Ingestion Taking food or nutrients into the body

Approved Diagnoses

00216	*Insufficient breast milk*
00107	*Ineffective infant feeding pattern*
00002	*Imbalanced nutrition: less than body requirements*
00001	*Imbalanced nutrition: more than body requirements*
00003	*Risk for imbalanced nutrition: more than body requirements*
00163	*Readiness for enhanced nutrition*
00103	*Impaired swallowing*

Class 2 Digestion The physical and chemical activities that convert foodstuffs into substances suitable for absorption and assimilation

Approved Diagnoses

None at present time

Class 3 Absorption The act of taking up nutrients through body tissues

Approved Diagnoses

None at present time

(Continues)

Table II-2 Taxonomy II: Domains, Classes, and Diagnoses *(Continued)*

Class 4 Metabolism The chemical and physical processes occurring in living organisms and cells for the development and use of protoplasm, the production of waste and energy, with the release of energy for all vital processes

Approved Diagnoses

00179	*Risk for unstable blood glucose level*
00194	*Neonatal jaundice*
00230	*Risk for neonatal jaundice*
00178	*Risk for impaired liver function*

Class 5 Hydration The taking in and absorption of fluids and electrolytes

Approved Diagnoses

00195	*Risk for electrolyte imbalance*
00160	*Readiness for enhanced fluid balance*
00027	*Deficient fluid volume*
00026	*Excess fluid volume*
00028	*Risk for deficient fluid volume*
00025	*Risk for imbalanced fluid volume*

DOMAIN 3 ELIMINATION AND EXCHANGE

Secretion and excretion of waste products from the body

Class 1 Urinary Function The process of secretion, reabsorption, and excretion of urine

Approved Diagnoses

00020	*Functional urinary incontinence*
00176	*Overflow urinary incontinence*
00018	*Reflex urinary incontinence*
00017	*Stress urinary incontinence*
00019	*Urge urinary incontinence*
00022	*Risk for urge urinary incontinence*
00016	*Impaired urinary elimination*
00166	*Readiness for enhanced urinary elimination*
00023	*Urinary retention*

Class 2 Gastrointestinal Function The process of absorption and excretion of the end products of digestion

Approved Diagnoses

00011	*Constipation*
00012	*Perceived constipation*
00015	*Risk for constipation*
00013	*Diarrhea*
00196	*Dysfunctional gastrointestinal motility*
00197	*Risk for dysfunctional gastrointestinal motility*
00014	*Bowel incontinence*

Class 3 Integumentary Function The process of secretion and excretion through the skin

Approved Diagnoses

None at present time

Class 4 Respiratory Function The process of exchange of gases and removal of the end products of metabolism

Approved Diagnoses

00030	*Impaired gas exchange*

DOMAIN 4 ACTIVITY/REST

The production, conservation, expenditure, or balance of energy resources

Class 1 Sleep/Rest Slumber, repose, ease, relaxation, or inactivity

Approved Diagnoses

00095	*Insomnia*
00096	*Sleep deprivation*
00165	*Readiness for enhanced sleep*
00198	*Disturbed sleep pattern*

Class 2 Activity/Exercise Moving parts of the body (mobility), doing work, or performing actions often (but not always) against resistance

Approved Diagnoses

00040	*Risk for disuse syndrome*
00091	*Impaired bed mobility*
00085	*Impaired physical mobility*
00089	*Impaired wheelchair mobility*
00090	*Impaired transfer ability*
00088	*Impaired walking*

Class 3 Energy Balance A dynamic state of harmony between intake and expenditure of resources

Approved Diagnoses

00050	*Disturbed energy field*
00093	*Fatigue*
00154	*Wandering*

Class 4 Cardiovascular/Pulmonary Responses Cardiopulmonary mechanisms that support activity/rest

Approved Diagnoses

00092	*Activity intolerance*
00094	*Risk for activity intolerance*
00032	*Ineffective breathing pattern*
00029	*Decreased cardiac output*
00202	*Risk for ineffective gastrointestinal perfusion*
00203	*Risk for ineffective renal perfusion*
00033	*Impaired spontaneous ventilation*
00204	*Ineffective peripheral tissue perfusion*
00200	*Risk for decreased cardiac tissue perfusion*

Table II-2 **Taxonomy II: Domains, Classes, and Diagnoses *(Continued)***

00201 *Risk for ineffective cerebral tissue perfusion*

00228 *Risk for ineffective peripheral tissue perfusion*

00034 *Dysfunctional ventilatory weaning response*

Class 5 Self-care Ability to perform activities to care for one's body and bodily functions

Approved Diagnoses

00098 *Impaired home maintenance*

00182 *Readiness for enhanced self-care*

00108 *Bathing self-care deficit*

00109 *Dressing self-care deficit*

00102 *Feeding self-care deficit*

00110 *Toileting self-care deficit*

00193 *Self-neglect*

DOMAIN 5 PERCEPTION/COGNITION

The human information processing system including attention, orientation, sensation, perception, cognition, and communication

Class 1 Attention Mental readiness to notice or observe

Approved Diagnoses

00123 *Unilateral neglect*

Class 2 Orientation Awareness of time, place, and person

Approved Diagnoses

00127 *Impaired environmental interpretation syndrome*

Class 3 Sensation/Perception Receiving information through the senses of touch, taste, smell, vision, hearing, and kinesthesia, and the comprehension of sensory data resulting in naming, associating, and/or pattern recognition

Approved Diagnoses

None at this time

Class 4 Cognition Use of memory, learning, thinking, problem-solving, abstraction, judgment, insight, intellectual capacity, calculation, and language

Approved Diagnoses

00128 *Acute confusion*

00129 *Chronic confusion*

00173 *Risk for acute confusion*

00222 *Ineffective impulse control*

00126 *Deficient knowledge*

00161 *Readiness for enhanced knowledge*

00131 *Impaired memory*

Class 5 Communication Sending and receiving verbal and nonverbal information

Approved Diagnoses

00157 *Readiness for enhanced communication*

00051 *Impaired verbal communication*

DOMAIN 6 SELF-PERCEPTION

Awareness about the self

Class 1 Self-concept The perception(s) about the total self

Approved Diagnoses

00124 *Hopelessness*

00174 *Risk for compromised human dignity*

00054 *Risk for loneliness*

00121 *Disturbed personal identity*

00225 *Risk for disturbed personal identity*

00167 *Readiness for enhanced self-concept*

Class 2 Self-esteem Assessment of one's own worth, capability, significance, and success

Approved Diagnoses

00119 *Chronic low self-esteem*

00224 *Risk for chronic low self-esteem*

00153 *Risk for situational low self-esteem*

00120 *Situational low self-esteem*

Class 3 Body Image A mental image of one's own body

Approved Diagnoses

00118 *Disturbed body image*

DOMAIN 7 ROLE RELATIONSHIPS

The positive and negative connections or associations between people or groups of people and the means by which those connections are demonstrated

Class 1 Caregiving Roles Socially expected behavior patterns by people providing care who are not healthcare professionals

Approved Diagnoses

00104 *Ineffective breastfeeding*

00105 *Interrupted breastfeeding*

00106 *Readiness for enhanced breastfeeding*

00061 *Caregiver role strain*

00062 *Risk for caregiver role strain*

00056 *Impaired parenting*

00164 *Readiness for enhanced parenting*

00057 *Risk for impaired parenting*

Class 2 Family Relationships Associations of people who are biologically related or related by choice

Approved Diagnoses

00058 *Risk for impaired attachment*

00063 *Dysfunctional family processes*

00060 *Interrupted family processes*

00159 *Readiness for enhanced family processes*

(Continues)

Table II-2 Taxonomy II: Domains, Classes, and Diagnoses *(Continued)*

Class 3 Role Performance Quality of functioning in socially expected behavior patterns

Approved Diagnoses

00223 *Ineffective relationship*
00207 *Readiness for enhanced relationship*
00229 *Risk for ineffective relationship*
00064 *Parental role conflict*
00055 *Ineffective role performance*
00052 *Impaired social interaction*

DOMAIN 8 SEXUALITY

Sexual identity, sexual function, and reproduction

Class 1 Sexual Identity The state of being a specific person in regard to sexuality and/or gender

Approved Diagnoses

None at present time

Class 2 Sexual Function The capacity or ability to participate in sexual activities

Approved Diagnoses

00059 *Sexual dysfunction*
00065 *Ineffective sexuality pattern*

Class 3 Reproduction Any process by which human beings are produced

Approved Diagnoses

00221 *Ineffective childbearing process*
00208 *Readiness for enhanced childbearing process*
00227 *Risk for ineffective childbearing process*
00209 *Risk for disturbed maternal–fetal dyad*

DOMAIN 9 COPING/STRESS TOLERANCE

Contending with life events/life processes

Class 1 Post-trauma Responses Reactions occurring after physical or psychological trauma

Approved Diagnoses

00141 *Post-trauma syndrome*
00145 *Risk for post-trauma syndrome*
00142 *Rape-trauma syndrome*
00114 *Relocation stress syndrome*
00149 *Risk for relocation stress syndrome*

Class 2 Coping Responses The process of managing environmental stress

Approved Diagnoses

00199 *Ineffective activity planning*
00226 *Risk for ineffective activity planning*
00146 *Anxiety*
00074 *Compromised family coping*
00071 *Defensive coping*
00073 *Disabled family coping*
00069 *Ineffective coping*
00077 *Ineffective community coping*
00158 *Readiness for enhanced coping*
00076 *Readiness for enhanced community coping*
00075 *Readiness for enhanced family coping*
00147 *Death anxiety*
00072 *Ineffective denial*
00101 *Adult failure to thrive*
00148 *Fear*
00136 *Grieving*
00135 *Complicated grieving*
00172 *Risk for complicated grieving*
00187 *Readiness for enhanced power*
00125 *Powerlessness*
00152 *Risk for powerlessness*
00210 *Impaired individual resilience*
00212 *Readiness for enhanced resilience*
00211 *Risk for compromised resilience*
00137 *Chronic sorrow*
00177 *Stress overload*

Class 3 Neurobehavioral Stress Behavioral responses reflecting nerve and brain function

Approved Diagnoses

00115 *Risk for disorganized infant behavior*
00009 *Autonomic dysreflexia*
00010 *Risk for autonomic dysreflexia*
00116 *Disorganized infant behavior*
00117 *Readiness for enhanced organized infant behavior*
00049 *Decreased intracranial adaptive capacity*

DOMAIN 10 LIFE PRINCIPLES

Principles underlying conduct, thought, and behavior about acts, customs, or institutions viewed as being true or having intrinsic worth

Class 1 Values The identification and ranking of preferred modes of conduct or end states

Approved Diagnoses

00185 *Readiness for enhanced hope*

Class 2 Beliefs Opinions, expectations, or judgments about acts, customs, or institutions viewed as being true or having intrinsic worth

Approved Diagnoses

00185 *Readiness for enhanced hope*

Table II-2 Taxonomy II: Domains, Classes, and Diagnoses *(Continued)*

00068	*Readiness for enhanced spiritual well-being*

Class 3 Value/Belief/Action Congruence The correspondence or balance achieved among values, beliefs, and actions

Approved Diagnoses

00184	*Readiness for enhanced decision-making*
00083	*Decisional conflict*
00175	*Moral distress*
00079	*Noncompliance*
00169	*Impaired religiosity*
00171	*Readiness for enhanced religiosity*
00170	*Risk for impaired religiosity*
00066	*Spiritual distress*
00067	*Risk for spiritual distress*

DOMAIN 11 SAFETY/PROTECTION

Freedom from danger, physical injury, or immune system damage; preservation from loss; and protection of safety and security

Class 1 Infection Host responses following pathogenic invasion

Approved Diagnoses

00004	*Risk for infection*

Class 2 Physical Injury Bodily harm or hurt

Approved Diagnoses

00031	*Ineffective airway clearance*
00039	*Risk for aspiration*
00206	*Risk for bleeding*
00048	*Impaired dentition*
00219	*Risk for dry eye*
00155	*Risk for falls*
00035	*Risk for injury*
00045	*Impaired oral mucous membrane*
00087	*Risk for perioperative positioning injury*
00086	*Risk for peripheral neurovascular dysfunction*
00205	*Risk for shock*
00046	*Impaired skin integrity*
00047	*Risk for impaired skin integrity*
00156	*Risk for sudden infant death syndrome*
00036	*Risk for suffocation*
00100	*Delayed surgical recovery*
00220	*Risk for thermal injury*
00044	*Impaired tissue integrity*
00038	*Risk for trauma*
00213	*Risk for vascular trauma*

Class 3 Violence The exertion of excessive force or power so as to cause injury or abuse

Approved Diagnoses

00138	*Risk for other-directed violence*
00140	*Risk for self-directed violence*
00151	*Self-mutilation*
00139	*Risk for self-mutilation*
00150	*Risk for suicide*

Class 4 Environmental Hazards Sources of danger in the surroundings

Approved Diagnoses

00181	*Contamination*
00180	*Risk for contamination*
00037	*Risk for poisoning*

Class 5 Defensive Processes The processes by which the self protects itself from the nonself

Approved Diagnoses

00218	*Risk for adverse reaction to iodinated contrast media*
00217	*Risk for allergy response*
00041	*Latex allergy response*
00042	*Risk for latex allergy response*

Class 6 Thermoregulation The physiological process of regulating heat and energy within the body for purposes of protecting the organism

Approved Diagnoses

00005	*Risk for imbalanced body temperature*
00007	*Hyperthermia*
00006	*Hypothermia*
00008	*Ineffective thermoregulation*

DOMAIN 12 COMFORT

Sense of mental, physical, or social well-being or ease

Class 1 Physical Comfort Sense of well-being or ease and/or freedom from pain

Approved Diagnoses

00214	*Impaired comfort*
00183	*Readiness for enhanced comfort*
00134	*Nausea*
00132	*Acute pain*
00133	*Chronic pain*

Class 2 Environmental Comfort Sense of well-being or ease in/with one's environment

Approved Diagnoses

00214	*Impaired comfort*
00183	*Readiness for enhanced comfort*

(Continues)

Table II-2 Taxonomy II: Domains, Classes, and Diagnoses *(Continued)*

Class 3 Social Comfort Sense of well-being or ease with one's social situations

Approved Diagnoses

00214	*Impaired comfort*
00053	*Social isolation*

DOMAIN 13 GROWTH/DEVELOPMENT

Age-appropriate increases in physical dimensions, maturation of organ systems, and/or progression through the developmental milestones

Class 1 Growth Increases in physical dimensions or maturity of organ systems

Approved Diagnoses

00113	*Risk for disproportionate growth*
00111	*Delayed growth and development*

Class 2 Development Progression or regression through a sequence of recognized milestones in life

Approved Diagnoses

00112	*Risk for delayed development*
00111	*Delayed growth and development*

In order to make safe and effective judgments using NANDA-I nursing diagnoses it is essential that nurses refer to the definitions and defining characteristics of the diagnoses listed in this work.

Other Nursing Diagnoses will also be relevant to individual patients depending on their individual needs.

Glossary

12-step approach: A self-help approach that encourages members to follow a program based on learning and applying 12 steps, which are usually adapted from the 12 steps of Alcoholics Anonymous.

12-step program: A self-help model that aids in recovery from various addictions, compulsions, and traumatic experiences and in preventing relapse. It provides structure and relies on the support of fellow persons in recovery. Alcoholics Anonymous and Narcotics Anonymous are examples of such programs.

Acetylcholine: A brain chemical or neurotransmitter affected by many psychotropic medications.

Active listening: An interactive process between the nurse and the client with the goal of understanding and being understood, involving hearing the message, understanding the message, and giving feedback about what was heard.

Active neglect: Intentional failure to fulfill the caregiving obligations, inflicting physical or emotional distress.

Activities of daily living (ADLs): Self-care activities that people must accomplish to survive, such as eating, dressing, bathing, and toileting.

Acupuncture: One of the ancient arts of traditional Chinese medicine, in which specific body areas are punctured with fine needles for the purposes of relieving pain, enhancing the immune system, and treating various conditions such as asthma, addictions, or stress-related illnesses.

Acute stress disorder: A psychiatric disorder occurring 2 days to 4 weeks after a threatened or actual event that involves a combination of affective, behavioral, cognitive, and physiologic symptoms significant enough to impair normal functioning.

Adaptive functioning: An individual's ability to meet standards of predetermined skills related to daily living in the context of the individual's community.

Advanced practice registered nurse (APRN): An umbrella classification used to describe the four major nurse specialist categories: certified registered nurse anesthetist (CRNA), certified nurse midwife (CNM), nurse practitioner (NP), and clinical nurse specialist (CNS). These individuals are educationally prepared to at least the master's degree level in the nursing specialty, have a significant depth of knowledge of theory and practice with validated clinical practice experience, and are competent in advanced clinical nursing skills.

Adventitious crisis: An accidental catastrophic event or disaster that causes disturbances affecting groups or communities.

Advocacy: Those efforts aimed at educational, political, or social change in the community or society.

Affect: The external, visible expression of emotion or mood state.

Affective flattening: A blunted or constricted facial expression making an individual appear immobile, masklike, and unresponsive. It is often seen in persons with schizophrenia.

Agnosia: The inability to recognize objects that cannot be explained by a reduced level of alertness.

Agonist: A medication that increases the activity of a neurotransmitter.

Agoraphobia: Anxiety about being in places or situations from which escape may be difficult or in which help may not be available should a panic attack occur.

Akathisia: A potential side effect of the antipsychotic agents consisting of physical restlessness and extreme difficulty remaining still.

Akinesia: A potential side effect of the antipsychotic agents consisting of slowing of movements.

Allostatic load: The wear and tear produced by the repeated activation of allostatic (adaptive) mechanisms as the result of excessive stress.

Alogia: Decreased thought content and use of language, often seen in persons with schizophrenia.

Alternative therapy: Therapy used in place of conventional treatment.

Alzheimer's disease: A degenerative cognitive disorder that involves the development of neurofibrils, neurofibrillary tangles, and beta-plated amyloid plaques, first in the cortex and hippocampus and later in the frontal, parietal, and temporal lobes. It is characterized by cortical atrophy, ventricular dilation, and decreased acetylcholine, norepinephrine, and other neurotransmitters.

Amine neurotransmitters: Acetylcholine, serotonin, dopamine, and norepinephrine.

Amnesia: A cognitive disorder associated with loss of memory.

Amygdala: An almond-shaped front portion of the brain's temporal lobe that plays a role in memory processing.

Anhedonia: The inability to feel pleasure.

Anorexia nervosa: The extreme pursuit of a thin body accompanied by a profoundly disturbed body image.

Anorexia nervosa, binge eating/purging type: In pursuit of a thin body, a person engages in binge eating and purging and perceives that he or she is out of control.

Anorexia nervosa, restricting type: Type of anorexia in which one restricts one's intake but does not regularly engage in binge eating or purging.

Anorgasmia: The inability to achieve orgasm.

Antagonist: A medication that blocks the activity of a neurotransmitter.

Anterograde amnesia: Problems learning and retaining new material due to a brain injury or intoxication; past learning or memory of past events may remain unimpaired but immediate and recent recall is impaired.

Antianxiety medication: A family of psychotropic medications used primarily to treat anxiety.

Anticholinergic side effects: A group of side effects of many psychotropic medications consisting of coexisting problems with blurred vision, dry mouth, constipation, dilated pupils, and delayed urination.

Anticipatory guidance: An educative process in which individuals and families are prepared for the normal life changes at each stage of development and are told about successful coping strategies.

Anticipatory molding: The movement of a child toward the mothering figure when being held.

Antidepressants: A family of medications used primarily to treat depression.

Antidyskinetics: A family of medications used primarily to treat muscular side effects of antipsychotics.

Antipsychotic medication: One of the psychotropic medications that treats psychotic symptoms.

Antisocial personality disorder: A pattern of disregard for, and violation of, the rights of others.

Anxiety: Apprehension or uneasiness in anticipation of danger; it is pathologic when it interferes with effectiveness in living.

Apathy: A defense against anxiety wherein a person appears indifferent in a situation expected to elicit a great deal of anxiety in most persons.

Aphasia: A speech or language disorder affecting expressive and/or receptive functioning.

Apoptosis: A phase of programmed demise of cells in an organism's life cycle that characterizes aging.

Applied behavior analysis (ABA): The use of behavioral analytic methods and research findings to change socially important behaviors in meaningful ways.

Apraxia: The loss of the ability to perform motor skills or purposeful acts.

Asperger's disorder: A pervasive developmental disorder similar to autistic disorder, characterized by impairment of social interactions and restricted interests and behaviors.

Assertiveness: A communication style that effectively expresses the person's thoughts and feelings in a way that respects the needs and rights of others and avoids passively submitting to the wishes of another.

Assertive community treatment (ACT): A team treatment approach designed to provide comprehensive, community-based psychiatric treatment, rehabilitation, and support to persons with serious and persistent mental illnesses.

Asterixis: Motor tremors in which the client is unable to maintain a posture or position without moving the involved body part. It usually refers to the inability of a client with a toxic-metabolic syndrome to maintain his or her hands in a flexed position without flapping.

Ataxia: Uncoordinated and inaccurate voluntary muscle movements as a result of cerebellar damage.

Attachment: A reciprocal affectional relationship between a mother or primary caretaker and a child.

Attachment model: A conceptual framework based upon the work of John Bowlby in which the establishment of trust, bonding, and attachment are essential to the survival of the human species.

Attention-deficit/hyperactivity disorder (ADHD): A persistent pattern of inattention and/or hyperactivity-impulsivity that is more frequent and more severe than typically observed in children of the same age and developmental level.

Autistic disorder: A pervasive developmental disorder with onset in infancy or early childhood characterized by a markedly abnormal or impaired development in social interaction and communication, typically with a restricted range of interests and activities and wide variability in one's intelligence and in the expression of the disorder.

Autocratic leader: A leader who usually takes an authoritative or directive role in determining the rules and conduct of a group and controlling the group's interactions.

Autogenic training: A popular relaxation technique that focuses on using self-statements suggesting heaviness and warmth.

Autonomic nervous system (ANS): The part of the nervous system that regulates involuntary body functions.

Autonomy: Self-determination, making decisions for oneself.

Avoidant personality disorder: A lifelong pattern characterized by experiences of extreme shyness, social inhibition, feelings of inadequacy, and hypersensitivity to rejection.

Avolition: The inability to initiate activity.

Axon: An extension of a neuron capable of self-propagating nervous impulses.

Bariatric surgical procedures: Different forms of surgical interventions designed to help a person lose weight.

Basal ganglia: The areas of gray matter composed of cell bodies in each cerebral hemisphere of the brain.

Battered child syndrome: Condition in which a child experiences multiple traumas and has been beaten repeatedly by a caregiver.

Battered partner syndrome: Condition that involves a victim who is exposed to multiple physical and/or emotional traumas; characterized by passive and socially isolated behavior and difficulty leaving the batterer.

Batterers: Abusive men or women who share certain characteristics. They deny responsibility for their actions, and they are unable to trust people; this is projected in all relationships.

Behavior modification model: An intervention based on teaching how to establish controls from within one's self and that there are consequences (natural, logical, and unrelated) to one's behavior.

Behavior therapy: A mode of treatment that focuses on modifying behavior.

Behavioral health: A term that encompasses treatment for mental health disorders and substance abuse as well as employee assistance programs.

Behavioral model: A model concerned with the here and now of behavior, not with how or why behavior developed.

Beneficence: To act in the client's welfare by preventing harm and doing no harm.

Benzodiazepine: A family of psychotropic medications used primarily to treat anxiety, agitation, and insomnia.

Bereavement: The usual response to loss and grief. The bereavement process may involve a sense of suffering and distress as an individual goes through the stages of grieving.

Binge eating: Eating large amounts of food while feeling out of control.

Binge eating disorder: A disorder in which people experience recurrent, rapid episodes of eating large amounts of food (binging) while feeling out of control. These individuals do not engage in purging behaviors and are usually overweight.

Biofeedback training: A process that uses technology to measure physiologic functions to feed information back to clients so that they can use the information to regulate or change an imbalance in their systems.

Biopsychosocial history: A comprehensive assessment of the client's lifetime biologic, psychologic, and social functioning.

Bipolar: A mood disorder in which both manic and depressive episodes occur.

Bipolar disorder of childhood: A pattern of severe mood instability in childhood or early adolescence that is characterized by typical or atypical mania, overactivity, a decreased need for sleep, affective storms, and in some cases hypersexuality and grandiosity.

Blackouts: Periods of amnesia during which a person appears to function normally but later does not recall the events that transpired.

Body dysmorphic disorder: A mental disorder in which the client believes his or her body is deformed in some manner that is not readily observed by others. This excessive preoccupation may lead to behaviors such as seeking constant reassurance or surgery and exercise or dieting to change the imagined defect.

Bonding: An affectional feeling between a mother or primary caretaker and a child.

Borderline personality disorder: A serious mental disorder characterized by pervasive instability in mood and affect, interpersonal relationships, and self-image, with marked impulsivity.

Boundaries: Limits that permit the client and mental health practitioner to have a therapeutic relationship based on the needs of the client.

Brain stem: The portion of the brain that contains the medulla oblongata, pons, and mesencephalon.

Breathing: In the context of complementary therapies, a simple practice for self-care offering increased calm, relaxation awareness, and reduction of stress and discomfort.

Breathing-related sleep disorders: Dyssomnias involving disruption of sleep as a result of ventilation abnormalities and neurologic or cardiac problems that can involve upper-airway structural abnormalities, periods of nonventilation, and obstructed respirations.

Briquet's syndrome: A disorder involving symptoms of overdramatization, exhibitionism, and seductiveness associated with multiple physical complaints attributed to hysteria.

Broca's area: An area of the brain involved in speech production.

Bulimia nervosa: A disorder where people experience recurrent, rapid episodes of eating large amounts of food (binging) while feeling out of control; these individuals also engage in purging, fasting, excessive exercise, or other compensatory behaviors.

Burnout: An individual's unproductive response to an overwhelming and chronically stressful work situation that limits his or her productivity on and off the job.

Case management: A method of assigning the coordination of a client's care; it may be a role, a technology, a process, a service, and a system. Its goal is to decrease fragmentation and ensure access to appropriate and cost-effective care.

Catalepsy: The ability to remain in postures associated with catatonia.

Cataplexy: A temporary, sudden loss of muscle tone often associated with narcolepsy.

Catatonia: A decreased reactivity to the environment that can be expressed as mutism, waxy flexibility, extreme negativism, echolalia, or echopraxia in an agitated or almost coma-like state.

Centering: A holistic nursing practice of calming, being in the present moment, and connecting with the intention to help and to heal.

Central nervous system: A major division of the brain consisting of the brain and spinal cord.

Cerebellum: The part of the brain located behind the brain stem consisting of two lobes and the vermis; it controls muscle coordination and body equilibrium.

Cerebrum: The largest and uppermost section of the brain consisting of a right and left hemisphere; location of higher level mental processes.

Chamomile: An herb that has been considered an effective antianxiety agent and, in tea form, is promoted to enhance relaxation and sleep.

Chief complaint: The reason for current contact with the mental health system, in the client's own words.

Child abuse: Causing physical, mental, or emotional injury to a child by action or neglect.

Child psychiatry: The study of medicine, psychiatry, and human development preparing one to address the mental health needs of infants, children, and adolescents.

Child's Bill of Rights: A document that establishes a child's right to be wanted, to be born healthy, to live in a healthy environment, to have basic needs met, to experience continuous loving care, and to acquire the cognitive skills needed for life.

Childhood disintegrative disorder: A pervasive developmental disorder characterized by a marked regression in language, social skills, and adaptive behaviors.

Chronic illness: All impairments or deviations from the norm that have one or more of the following characteristics: are permanent, leave residual disability, are caused by nonreversible pathologic alteration, require special training of the patient for rehabilitation, or may be expected to require a long period of supervision, observation, or care.

Chronic mental illness: Synonymous with both persistent mental illness and severe mental illness. Mental illness that tends to last for a long time, if not a lifetime, and may be characterized by periods of relapse or reoccurrence.

Circadian rhythm: The underlying biologic rhythms involved in sleep/wake cycles.

Classical conditioning: A behavioral model developed by Ivan Pavlov that focuses on a person's involuntary reaction to a neutral event because the reaction and the event have become associated.

Classification of mental retardation: The four categories are intermittent, limited, extensive, and pervasive.

Clubhouse model: A type of rehabilitation that demonstrates that people with mental illness can successfully live productive lives and work in the community, regardless of the nature or severity of their mental illness.

CODE-C: A mental health service model that includes consultation, outreach, debriefing and defusing, education, and crisis counseling to deal with psychologic reactions to traumatic stress over time. Also known as CODE-C Disaster Mental Health Service Model.

Codependence: A dynamic common among significant others of persons with substance dependence or abuse; characterized by behaviors that support or enable the substance use.

Cognitive behavioral therapy (CBT): A type of therapy that teaches the control of thought distortions and emphasizes the important role of thinking in how we feel and what we do.

Cognitive model: Model of development that examines the perceptual and intellectual growth of the individual.

Cognitive restructuring: A process of replacing negative, catastrophic thoughts that interfere with functioning with constructive thoughts.

Cognitive therapy: A treatment therapy that emphasizes the rearrangement of a person's maladaptive processes of thinking.

Collateral history: Information about a client obtained from the client's family, friends, colleagues, or mental health professionals.

Communication disorder: A disorder most often diagnosed in childhood that is characterized by severe difficulties in expressing oneself verbally or nonverbally and that is more frequent and severe than typically observed in individuals of the same age and developmental level.

Compassion fatigue: Secondary traumatic stress experienced by workers or volunteers dealing with stressful and traumatic situations related to the nature of the event, occupational and organizational support, and postevent recovery.

Competency: The capacity of an individual to manage his or her affairs and make appropriate self-care decisions on a consistent basis.

Complementary therapy: Therapy used together with a traditional treatment modality.

Compliance: Adherence to prescribed medications and other treatment protocols.

Complicated grief: A prolonged period of bereavement and impairment of normal functioning that may have many of the symptoms and characteristics of other mental disorders such as mood disorders or posttraumatic stress disorder.

Compulsion: Repetitive behaviors done in response to obsessions.

Computed tomography (CT): Diagnostic test in which images of thin "slices" (tomograms) of the brain are obtained by X-ray, reconstructed, and entered into a computer, revealing a variety of views of the brain.

Conceptual model: A framework of related concepts that address the bases for behavior in order to direct interventions; the most important conceptual models are the psychoanalytic, interpersonal, behavioral, cognitive, developmental, and neurobiologic models.

Concrete thought process: A thought process in which one is able to understand only the literal meaning of words, as opposed to abstract thought process.

Conduct disorder: Behavior that constitutes a repetitive and persistent pattern in which the basic rights of others, social norms, or rules are seriously violated.

Confidentiality: Ensuring that information shared is kept private.

Conversion disorder: A psychiatric disorder in which physical symptoms, usually associated with sensory or motor deficits or seizures, are related to unconscious psychologic conflicts.

Coping mechanisms: Conscious mental strategies or behaviors used to lower anxiety and adjust to demands in a purposeful manner.

Coping skills: Mechanisms people use to manage internal and external stressors; may be adaptive or maladaptive.

Countertransference: Displacement or projection of unconscious feelings that the mental health professional has toward a client.

Creutzfeldt-Jakob disease: A transmissible, rapidly degenerative cognitive disorder involving sponge-like vacuoles and damage to neurons by prions, characterized by changes in personality and functioning.

Crisis: A self-limited transitional period of disequilibrium and functional impairment experienced by an individual or family when confronted with a dangerous or threatening situation.

Crisis intervention: The use of cognitive and short-term psychotherapeutic techniques to help a client gain a realistic perception of events, become aware of feelings, develop active coping skills, and experience social support.

Critical incident stress management (CISM): A method of crisis intervention involving individual and group intervention that allows those involved in emergent and urgent disturbances to share thoughts and experiences, review events, give mutual support, normalize the experience, and provide meaning to their experiences.

Cross-tolerance: The increased tolerance that develops for drugs in the same category.

Cyclothymic disorder: A fluctuating mood disturbance ranging from hypomania to depressive symptoms.

Debriefing: An intervention used to deal with staff responses to traumatic events. It focuses on large-scale and time-limited, structured groups to provide for screening, support, and education.

Deep brain stimulation: Treatment originally developed for Parkinson's disease to reduce uncontrollable movements. It is being studied as a treatment for depression and obsessive compulsive disorder and is only available on an experimental basis.

Defusing: An intervention used to deal with staff responses to traumatic events. It is a brief, immediate intervention used with small groups that focuses upon gathering facts (who, what, when, where, and how), exploring thoughts, acknowledging feelings, and providing encouragement and anticipatory guidance.

Delirium: A temporary, potentially reversible cognitive disorder usually associated with acute changes in medical and surgical conditions or toxic metabolic syndromes.

Delusion: False belief not held by others in the same culture that can be nonbizarre and potentially possible, such as some jealous or persecutory false beliefs, or bizarre and not reality based, such as thought broadcasting or thought insertion. They may be paranoid, grandiose, somatic, erotic, nihilistic, guilty, bizarre, or referential in nature.

Dementia: Chronic, usually progressive, cognitive disorders associated with changes in brain structure and functioning.

Democratic leader: A leader who encourages a group to take responsibility for the group rules and decisions. The leader will seek to be less authoritative while facilitating the group.

Dendrites: A slender portion of a neuron's cell body that is capable of being stimulated by a neurotransmitter.

Denial: A defense mechanism that prevents an individual from recognizing reality; commonly used by individuals who are unable to recognize the destructive effects of substance use.

Dependent personality disorder: A condition characterized by submissive and clingy behaviors, an overreliance on others, an excessive need to be taken care of, and fears of separation.

Depersonalization: Feelings of unreality or strangeness concerning self-identity or body image.

Depolarization: The process that triggers the release of neurotransmitter into the synaptic cleft.

Derealization: A feeling of detachment from one's environment.

Detoxification: The process of gradual withdrawal from a substance on which the person is physiologically dependent. This process usually involves the administration of decreasing doses of a substitute medication.

Developmental crises: Crises that are predictable and occur in conjunction with normal developmental transitions.

Developmental disability: Severe chronic mental or physical disability that manifests before a person reaches 22 years of age, is likely to continue indefinitely, and results in substantial functional limitations in three or more of the following areas: self-care, receptive and expressive language, learning, mobility, self-direction, capacity for independent living, or economic self-sufficiency.

Developmental history: An assessment of a child's progress in attaining certain behaviors (e.g., sitting, walking, talking, playing) associated with a specific age.

***Diagnostic and Statistical Manual of Mental Disorders*, 4th ed., text revision (*DSM-IV-TR*):** A manual (in *DSM-IV-TR* edition as of this writing, soon to be the *DSM-5*) published by the American Psychiatric Association that identifies all mental health disorders for children and adults. It uses a multiaxial approach (Axis I to Axis V) and is intended for use by psychiatrists, psychologists, registered nurses, social workers, and other mental health therapists.

Dialectical behavior therapy (DBT): A broad-based cognitive-behavioral treatment developed specifically for the treatment of borderline personality disorder.

Differential diagnosis: The process of differentiating one disorder from another that presents similarly.

Diffusion tensor imaging (DTI): An MRI-based technology that enables visualization and characterization of the white matter pathways in the brain.

Disaster: An unpredicted, overpowering, and traumatic event that disrupts life circumstances and threatens survival and assumptions.

Discharge planning: The coordinated activities of the multidisciplinary team that facilitate a client's movement from one healthcare setting to another or to home.

Discipline: An intervention focused on helping children to learn appropriate ways to control their behaviors and to keep themselves safe.

Dissociation: An unconscious defense mechanism in which the person sustains an alteration in the integrative functions of consciousness or identity. Dissociative symptoms involve temporary changes in consciousness, identity, and motor function to protect and distance the individual from painful emotions or thoughts associated with anxiety, conflict, or trauma.

Dissociative state: An altered state of mental functioning characterized by a perception of distancing from one's emotions, body, and the environment in response to psychologic conflict or trauma.

Domestic violence: Type of violence in which an abuser acts violently toward an intimate partner.

Dopamine: A brain chemical or neurotransmitter affected by the antipsychotic medications.

Dopamine hypothesis: Theory that the mechanism for the positive symptoms of schizophrenia involves excessive amounts of dopamine in the limbic system. Support for this hypothesis comes from the efficacy of dopamine antagonists in reducing positive symptoms.

Down syndrome: A congenital condition characterized by mental retardation and multiple physical defects.

Dual diagnosis: The simultaneous existence of one or more substance use disorders and at least one other primary mental disorder.

Duty to protect: The legal requirement to inform authorities or others if there is evidence that a client needs to be protected from himself or herself due to the client's inability because of mental illness to distinguish between safe and dangerous situations.

Duty to warn: The legal requirement to inform authorities or others if there is evidence that a client may inflict danger on a specific person.

Dynamisms: A Sullivanian concept describing the methods used by persons to reduce the tension experienced by their perception of the needs for satisfaction and security.

Dyslexia: The inability to interpret written language.

Dyspareunia: Recurrent or persistent genital pain associated with sexual intercourse.

Dysphagia: Difficulty swallowing.

Dyssomnia: Disorders of initiating or maintaining sleep involving impaired amount, quality, and timing of sleep.

Dysthymic disorder: A mood disorder characterized by chronic mild depression.

Dystonia: A muscular side effect of the antipsychotics consisting of muscle spasms in any part of the body.

Echolalia: The automatic and meaningless mimicking or repetition of the words and phrases of another.

Echopraxia: The mimicking or repetition of the movements or actions of another.

Ego defense mechanisms: As formulated by Sigmund Freud, unconscious mental mechanisms derived from the ego that are designed to alleviate anxiety by effecting a compromise between the demands of the id and the superego.

Electroconvulsive therapy (ECT): The induction of a brief convulsion by passing an electric current through the brain, primarily for the treatment of affective disorders.

Electroencephalography (EEG): The measurement of electrical currents at the scalp that reflect events within the brain.

Emotional intelligence: The ability to control and manage personal emotions and respond appropriately to others. Also called *emotional competency*.

Empathy: The ability to mentally put oneself in someone else's place, viewing a person's world from his or her internal frame of reference, with the goal of gaining understanding of how he or she feels in a certain situation. This involves the nurse's sensitivity to the client's current feelings and the ability to communicate this to the client in a language that can be understood. This technique is most useful in establishing trust and expresses understanding and concern.

Empowerment: The process by which an individual gains the self-esteem and self-confidence to actively engage in and control the environment.

Encopresis: Repeated passage of feces into inappropriate places, such as clothing, closets, or floors, either involuntarily or intentionally, at least once a month for at least 3 months in a child who is mentally at least 4 years of age.

Enuresis: Repeated voiding or urinating during day or night into bed or clothing, either involuntarily or intentionally, for at least 3 months in a child who is mentally at least 5 years of age.

Erectile dysfunction: A persistent inability to achieve or maintain an erection.

Euphoria: An overexaggerated sense of physical and mental well-being.

Euthymia: A normal mood experience.

Evidence-based practice: A process founded on the collection, interpretation, and integration of valid, important, and applicable patient-reported, clinician-observed, and research-derived evidence.

Exposure: Used in therapy, it is the repeated experience or contact with a particular stress-provoking situation or stimulus.

Expressive language disorder: An impairment in expressive language development as demonstrated by scores on standardized measures of expressive language that are substantially below measures of both intellectual capacity and receptive language development.

Extended family: Any family grouping that is related by descent, marriage, or adoption that is broader than the nuclear family and can include multiple generations and aunts, uncles, and cousins.

Extinction: A behavioral model developed by B.F. Skinner that eliminates behavior by ignoring or not rewarding it.

Extrapyramidal pathways: Various relays of motor neurons between the cerebral cortex, basal nuclei, thalamus, cerebellum, and the brain stem.

Extrapyramidal symptoms (EPS): Muscular side effects usually associated with antipsychotic medications as a result of blocking the dopamine receptor sites in the brain. These symptoms include muscle cramps (dystonia), lack of movement (akinesia), tremors, motor restlessness (akathisia), twitching or overactivity of the tongue, changes in posture, and tic-like movements.

Factitious disorder: A mental disorder in which signs and symptoms of physical and/or psychiatric disorders are intentionally and consciously produced or feigned.

Family of orientation: The nuclear family in which an individual has the status of a child.

Family of procreation: The nuclear family in which the individual has or had the status of a parent.

Family systems therapy: A treatment approach based on the belief that families are systems in which change in one aspect of the system affects the entire system. Family therapy proposes that a client's symptoms emanate from problems within the family system.

Family violence: The use or threat of physical, emotional, sexual, or economic abuse to control a family member.

Fetal alcohol syndrome: Growth, physical, and mental problems that may result when a mother drinks alcohol during pregnancy. It is the severe end of the fetal alcohol spectrum disorders.

Flight of ideas: As seen in mania, involves pressured speech with rapid topic changes.

Flooding: Exposure to a stress-provoking stimulus for an extended period of time for the purpose of extinguishing the negative emotional response.

Frontal lobe: The largest of the five lobes constituting the two cerebral hemispheres of the brain.

Functional imaging: A category of brain imaging that gathers information about the functioning of the brain. Functional imaging tests include positron emission tomography (PET) and functional magnetic resonance imaging (fMRI).

Gender dysphoria: Excessive unhappiness or discomfort with one's natal gender. This discomfort may be focused on gender roles and expectations, physiognomic features, or a range of other issues.

Gender identity: The internal sense of oneself as male, female, or existing somewhere on a continuum.

General adaptation syndrome (GAS): The defense response of the body to stress as described by Hans Selye.

Generalized anxiety disorder (GAD): A pattern of persistent and excessive anxiety and worry about a wide range of subjects lasting at least 6 months.

Genes: The biologic units of inheritance.

Genogram: A diagram or map of multiple generations of a family indicating family relationships, life events, family functioning, and significant developmental events.

Genomics: The study of all of a person's genes (the genome), including how the genes are influenced by and interact with the environment.

Genuineness: A nurse's ability to be oneself, or to be real, when interacting with clients.

Ginkgo (*Ginkgo biloba*): An herbal remedy used to treat age-related memory impairment, dementia, and senility.

Glia: Nonneuronal cells in the brain (oligodendrocytes, microglia, and astrocytes) that serve supportive and nutritive roles for the neurons. Oligodendrocytes form the insulating myelin sheaths around the axons that control the speed of nerve impulse transmission through axons. Microglia and astrocytes defend the CNS from pathogens and help it to recover from stress and injury.

Global Assessment of Functioning scale: The fifth axis in a *DSM-IV-TR* diagnosis; a rating scale used by the mental health practitioner to gauge a client's total psychologic, social, and occupational or academic well-being on a scale of 1 to 100.

Grape seed extract (*Vitis vinifera*): Supplement produced from the seeds of grapes that may improve venous circulation.

Grief: Subjective feelings and affect that are experienced as a result of a loss or disappointment.

Group dynamics: The study of what happens in a group, including communication and interpersonal relationships.

Group therapy: An intervention in which three or more persons interact for the purpose of altering their behavior patterns and developing new and more effective ways of dealing with the stressors of daily living.

Habilitation: The process of developing new skills and abilities.

Hallucination: False sensory perceptions in the absence of an external stimulus. They may be auditory, visual, tactile, olfactory, or gustatory in nature.

Hierarchy of needs: Theory developed by Abraham Maslow that proposes that individuals must fulfill their basic needs before moving onto other, higher needs.

Hippocampus: A portion of the floor of the lateral ventricle of the brain involved in memory development.

History of present illness: A chronologic account of the events leading up to the current contact with the mental health professional, including a description of the precipitants, onset, duration, exacerbating and ameliorating factors, and change of symptoms over time.

Histrionic personality disorder: A condition characterized by pervasive and excessive emotionality and attention-seeking behaviors that become persistent and very disabling and distressing to the client.

Holistic nursing: A model of nursing practice that has the goal of healing the whole person.

Holistic psychiatric assessment: A comprehensive assessment of the client's physical, psychologic, cognitive, social, and spiritual dimensions.

Homelessness: A lack of a home or residence.

Homicidal thoughts: Thoughts to kill or harm others.

Huntington's disease: A genetic degenerative cognitive disorder involving destruction of neurons and causing movement disorder, personality changes, and emotional instability.

Hypersomnia: A dyssomnia characterized by prolonged or excessive sleep at night or during the day; can be related to depression or central nervous system dysfunction.

Hypertensive crisis: A life-threatening condition caused by eating foods that are high in the amino acid tyramine or taking restricted medications.

Hypnosis: The practice of working with an altered state of consciousness or trance for therapeutic benefit.

Hypnotic: A medication that induces sedation or sleep.

Hypochondriasis: An exaggerated, unrealistic preoccupation, based upon misinterpretations of physical sensations, of having a serious disease that persists despite medical evaluation and reassurance.

Hypomania: A mild form of mania.

Hypothalamic-pituitary-adrenal (HPA) axis: The part of the neuroendocrine system that regulates the secretion of cortisol from the adrenal gland and is activated in response to stress.

Hypothalamus: A portion of the brain that controls and integrates the peripheral autonomic nervous system.

Imagery: The practice of assisting clients to self-heal and self-regulate by bringing them into a state of relaxation through visualization, using any or all of their senses.

Impulse control: The ability to delay, modulate, or inhibit the expression of behaviors and feelings.

Impulse control disorders: Disorders that reflect an inability to resist impulsive acts that may be harmful to self or others, and include intermittent explosive disorder, kleptomania, pyromania, pathologic gambling, and trichotillomania.

Incest: Sexual intercourse or intimate sexual behavior with members of the same family.

Inclusion: The integration of all persons, regardless of special needs and disabilities or the environment (e.g., school, community), with typical peers in the least restrictive setting.

Individual therapy: Therapy that focuses on a person and includes other aspects of the person's life only as they relate to the individual.

Individualized Education Program (IEP): Program developed for a child based on standardized testing scores; it provides for modifications in work load, assignments, and testing or provides for specific behavioral techniques to be used in the classroom to aid in educating the child. It can also be referred to as an Individualized Education Plan.

Informed consent: The process of sharing information with the client regarding a proposed treatment; the client must be competent to understand the information provided, and the consent must be voluntary.

Inner reflection: A meditative process that explores our inner awareness, thoughts, images, beliefs, attitudes, expectations, and experiences in a quiet, centered state to cultivate a deeper understanding and awareness.

Insight: The extent of the client's awareness of illness and maladaptive behaviors.

Insomnia: A dyssomnia characterized by abnormal wakefulness such as an inability to fall or remain asleep, with impaired daytime performance.

Instrumental activities of daily living (IADL): Activities that include performing housework, going on errands, managing finances, and making telephone calls.

Intellectual disability: Disability that is characterized by a significantly below-average score on a test of mental ability or intelligence and by limitations in the ability to function in areas of daily life (communication, self-care, social situations, school activities); intellectual disability is also known as cognitive disability and/or mental retardation.

Intelligence quotient (IQ): A measure of relative intelligence determined through testing.

Intention: The conscious awareness of being in the present moment in order to help facilitate the healing process.

Interdependence: A method to accomplish inclusion; also known as mutual dependence.

Intermittent explosive disorder (IED): Discrete episodes of failure to resist aggressive impulses resulting in serious assaults or destruction of property.

Intersex condition: A condition in which a person has both male and female biologic characteristics.

Intimate partner violence: The use or threat of physical, emotional, sexual, or economic abuse between dating couples and current or former spouses in heterosexual or homosexual relationships.

Intoxication: A substance-specific syndrome that results from recent ingestion or exposure to a substance.

Intrusive procedures: Oral, anal, and cutaneous procedures that can be encountered during a hospitalization.

Journaling: A self-care practice that involves writing one's inner reflections, dreams, thoughts, and feelings for the purpose of reflection on one's own personal and professional processes.

Judgment: The capacity to identify possible courses of action, anticipate their consequences, and choose the appropriate behavior.

Justice: The concept that people should be treated equally and fairly.

Kindling: Describes the lowest threshold for setting off neuronal activity in seizure disorders.

Kleptomania: The recurrent failure to resist impulses to steal objects not needed for personal or monetary value.

Korsakoff syndrome: A cognitive disorder of anterograde amnesia (an inability to form new memories) and confabulation associated with a deficiency of thiamine, and usually found in chronic alcoholism. It follows the acute phase of Wernicke's encephalopathy.

La belle indifference: A characteristic of a response in which the client is calm and somewhat indifferent to problems or catastrophes; considered diagnostic in conversion disorder where the patient may experience a major loss of sensory or motor function.

Lag period: The period of time between taking the first dose of a medication and experiencing the therapeutic effect.

Laissez-faire leader: A leader whose hands-off approach may cause a group to be directionless or disorganized, losing productivity while it tries to determine its rules and decisions.

Latent: Underlying and often unconscious.

Learning disorder: Disorder identified when an individual's achievement on standardized tests in reading, mathematics, or written expression is substantially below that expected for age, intelligence, and educational background.

Least restrictive environment: Treatment provided in a setting that meets the client's needs with the least number of restrictions imposed.

Levels of consciousness: Psychoanalytic conceptual framework formulated by Sigmund Freud consisting of the conscious, preconscious, and unconscious mind.

Lewy body disease: A progressive cortical dementia that affects mainly memory and motor control functioning and involves symptoms of visual hallucinations, fluctuating levels of alertness, and motor symptoms similar to Parkinson's disease.

Limbic system: A group of interconnected brain structures that function together to regulate emotion, learning, and memory.

Lithium toxicity: Toxicity related to serum lithium levels indicated by nausea, vomiting, diarrhea, confusion, slurred speech, ataxia, poor coordination, hyperreflexia, tinnitus, nystagmus, seizures, coma, and death.

Loss: The disappearance of something cherished; it can be a relationship, job, health, mental faculties, or control over nature or various life events.

Magnetic resonance imagery (MRI): Diagnostic test that uses radio waves and magnets to obtain images of the white and gray matter in the brain.

Magnetic resonance spectroscopy (MRS): Diagnostic test used to detect chemical and metabolic information in certain brain areas.

Major depressive disorder: One or more episodes of depressed mood or irritability accompanied by a significant loss of interest in activities that is a change from baseline, and that persists for at least 2 weeks or is accompanied by suicidal thoughts.

Malingering: Intentional or exaggerated symptoms clearly associated with external factors such as the need to avoid work or school.

Managed care: Both a delivery and reimbursement system that aims to combine cost-effectiveness with quality care.

Mandatory outpatient treatment (MOT): Treatment mandated by the courts requiring clients to receive and attend outpatient psychiatric treatment.

MAOIs: *See* monoamine oxidase inhibitors.

Material exploitation: An example of economic abuse using resources inappropriate for one's own needs.

Maternal deprivation: Occurs when there is any significant separation from the mothering figure of an infant between 3 and 15 months of age, often leading to serious emotional problems in the infant such as depression, eating disorders, and failure to thrive.

Maturational disturbance: The adaptation and transition of normal developmental phases.

Maudsley approach: A treatment method for adolescents who are in the early stages of developing an eating disorder. It requires that the family, especially the parents, take responsibility for getting the adolescent to eat healthy again.

Medication adherence: Situation in which a client takes the correct medication, at the correct dose, according to the prescribed schedule and duration. It assumes a client's understanding and acceptance of the treatment protocol.

Meditation: An ancient mind-body spiritual practice found in traditions around the world.

Medulla: The area of the brain stem where the corticospinal tracts cross, resulting in the right motor cortex controlling the muscles on the left side of the body and the left motor cortex controlling the right side.

Melancholia: A loss of interest in activities and inability to find pleasure in activities or events that are usually pleasurable.

Membrane potential: The difference in the electrical charge between two sides of a cell wall.

Mental disorder or illness: A disturbance in thoughts or mood that causes maladaptive behavior, inability to cope with normal stresses, and impaired functioning; it meets diagnostic criteria established in *DSM-IV-TR*.

Mental health: Mental health is a state of well-being in which an individual realizes his or her own abilities, can cope with the normal stresses of life, can work productively, and is able to make a contribution to his or her community.

Mental health consumers: People who are receiving or have received mental health services.

Mental health parity: Equivalent benefits for medical and surgical benefits and mental health benefits in a health insurance plan.

Mental retardation: A disability that originates before 18 years of age and is characterized by significant limitation in both intellectual function and adaptive behavior as expressed in conceptual, social, and practical adaptive skills.

Mental status examination: An evaluation of a client's present state, including the client's behavior and general appearance, mood and affect, speech, thought process and content, perceptual disturbances, impulse control, cognition, knowledge, judgment, and insight.

Midbrain: The mesencephalon portion of the brain.

Milieu therapy: The use of the environment as a therapeutic tool.

Minor tranquilizers: Certain antianxiety medications or sedative/hypnotics, including barbiturates and benzodiazepines.

Monoamine oxidase inhibitors (MAOIs): A group of antidepressants that requires dietary restrictions and avoidance of certain other medications.

Mood: The internal feeling of emotion; a person's pervasive, subjective emotional state.

Mood stabilizer: A family of psychotropic medications used to prevent extreme ups and downs of mood.

Moral therapy: Therapy introduced by Philippe Pinel in 1792; attendants were required to treat patients kindly and keep them busy with various activities.

Motivational interviewing: A type of counseling in which interventions are delivered in a neutral and empathetic way, actively eliciting the client to identify the pros and cons of alternative problem solving approaches. It has been used effectively to change addictive behaviors that interfere with health.

Multiaxial *DSM-IV-TR diagnosis*: A comprehensive diagnostic system used widely in the United States; includes major psychiatric disorders, personality disorders/mental retardation, physical/medical conditions, psychosocial and environmental stressors, and a global assessment of functioning for each client.

Multidisciplinary treatment team: Treatment team that consists of the client and the family; psychiatric nurse; psychiatrist; clinical psychologist; psychiatric social worker; occupational, rehabilitation, and activities therapists; and ancillary staff.

Multiple sleep latency test (MSLT): A test of a client's daytime sleepiness; it measures sleep latency (the time it takes to fall asleep) and the amount of REM sleep.

Munchausen syndrome: Factitious disorders in which there is a manipulation or invention of symptoms; named after Baron Münchausen, who was known for telling wild, fantastic tales.

Myelin: A lipoprotein that constitutes the sheath of nerve fibers throughout the body and envelops the axis of myelinated nerves.

Narcissistic personality disorder: A pervasive pattern of grandiosity, an extremely exaggerated sense of self-importance, need for admiration, and lack of empathy for others.

Narcolepsy: A dyssomnia that involves uncontrollable, recurrent, brief episodes of sleep.

Need for satisfaction: A Sullivanian concept stemming from a person's biologic needs for food, air, water, shelter, sex, and so forth.

Need for security: A Sullivanian concept stemming from a person's emotional needs for feeling states such as interpersonal intimacy, status, and self-esteem.

Negative psychotic symptoms: *See negative symptoms.*

Negative reinforcement: A behavioral model developed by B.F. Skinner that increases the frequency of a behavior by removing an unpleasant stimulus when a desired response occurs.

Negative symptoms: Psychotic symptoms that represent a loss or restriction of normal functioning and expression and include affective flattening, alogia, anhedonia, attention problems, and avolition.

Neglect: A condition in which one fails to provide essential physical and/or emotional care to a dependent person.

Neurobiologic model: A model that postulates the relationship of the brain and the nervous system as basic to the understanding of the symptoms, processes, and treatment of mental illnesses and disorders.

Neurogenesis: The process of new cells being born across one's lifetime.

Neuroimaging: Various methods of brain imaging to expand the knowledge base of the structure, function, and neurochemistry of the CNS.

Neuroleptic malignant syndrome: A rare but potentially life-threatening side effect of antipsychotic medications that causes elevated creatinine phosphokinase levels, fever, diaphoresis, muscle rigidity, and autonomic instability.

Neuron: A highly specialized cell in the nervous system that can generate and transmit bioelectric signals. The neuron is characterized by three distinct parts: the cell body (soma), the dendrites, and the axon.

Neuroplasticity: The ability of the brain to respond to the environment. This includes the development of new synapses (synaptogenesis), the myelination of axons, the development of dendritic and axonal branches (arborization), the destruction or pruning of neurons, and even the birth of new neurons (neurogenesis).

Neurosis: A mental disorder usually characterized by anxiety and other uncomfortable and distressing symptoms for the individual while reality testing remains intact.

Neurotransmitter: Chemical that is released by presynaptic cells upon stimulation and activates postsynaptic receptors of other cells.

Neurotrophin: Brain growth factor that affects neuronal migration and cellular survival. Examples include brain-derived neurotrophic factor (BDNF) and glial-derived neurotrophic factor (GDNF).

Nightmare: Parasomnias involving intense, frightening dreams that can be recalled by the sleeper and may involve partial arousals from sleep.

Nonpurging: Compensatory behaviors, such as fasting or exercise, often observed in clients with bulimia.

Nonrapid eye movement (NREM): Slow-wave sleep that involves the three deepest and least active stages of sleep involving light sleep, sleep, and deep slow wave or delta sleep. It is measured by the relative absence of rapid eye movement and neuron activity.

Norepinephrine: A brain chemical or neurotransmitter affected by antidepressants and other psychotropic medications; a vasopressor and precursor of epinephrine.

Nuclear family: A grouping consisting of one or two adults who undertake a parenting role for one or more children.

Nurse–client relationship: A conceptual model developed by Hildegard Peplau as the nurse-patient relationship with four distinct yet overlapping phases: orientation, identification, exploitation, and resolution. As a type of therapeutic relationship, the nurse–client relationship also is defined by four stages: preinteraction, orientation, working stage, and termination.

Nurse–patient relationship: *See* nurse–client relationship.

Nurse practice acts: Laws in each state that direct nurses in both general and specialty practice and that establish the authority for professional nursing practice and the rules and regulations for the state. Most state nurse practice acts provide a general description of what constitutes the legally protected scope of practice in the state for registered professional nurses (RNs) and licensed practical nurses.

Nursing diagnosis: A diagnosis composed of the problem or unmet need, its etiology or cause (expressed as "related to"), and the objective and subjective supporting data (expressed as "evidenced by").

Nursing documentation: An accurate record of a client's care that psychiatric-mental health registered nurses are required to maintain with all information, plans, interventions, and outcomes in an understandable and retrievable manner that can be accessed as needed by all members of the healthcare team.

Nursing process: A systematic and interactive problem-solving approach that includes individualized client assessment, diagnosis, outcomes identification, planning, implementation, and evaluation.

Obesity: The state of being significantly above one's normal weight with a body mass index of 30 or above.

Object constancy: A psychoanalytic concept that refers to the recognition and tolerance of having loving and hostile feelings toward the same object or person.

Obsession: Unwanted, recurrent thoughts, ideas, or impulses.

Obsessive-compulsive disorder (OCD): A pattern of recurrent obsessions or compulsions, recognized by a person as excessive or unreasonable, that are severe enough to be time-consuming or cause significant impairment in relationships with others, education, or other important areas of functioning.

Obsessive-compulsive personality disorder: A condition characterized by an inordinate preoccupation with rules, orderliness, perfectionism, and mental and interpersonal control. The condition can become persistent and disabling resulting in a loss of flexibility, openness, and efficiency.

Oculogyric crisis: An acute dystonic reaction involving the eyes resulting in an involuntary upward, lateral gaze.

Omega-3 fatty acids: A group of polyunsaturated fatty acids that are important for a number of functions in the body, including brain development and functioning, blood clotting, and muscle contraction and relaxation.

Operant conditioning: A behavioral technique for shaping behavior; based on demonstration by B. F. Skinner that behaviors are influenced by their consequences; behaviors that have a positive consequence increase in strength and are likely to be repeated, and behaviors with negative consequences are weakened and decrease in frequency.

Opisthotonus: An extrapyramidal posturing manifested by severe spastic hyperextension of the neck that can be a side effect of antipsychotic medication.

Oppositional defiant disorder (ODD): A recurrent pattern of negative, defiant, disobedient, and hostile behavior in children toward adults that persists for at least 6 months.

Orgasm: A sudden, subjective experience of intense pleasure usually accompanied by rhythmic contractions in the pelvic area.

Outcomes of care: Measurable changes in the client's health status produced by nursing interventions.

Pain disorder: Mental disorders in response to pain that are influenced primarily by psychologic factors, cause significant impairment, and are considered to be out of proportion to physical symptoms.

Panic attack: Sudden overwhelming anxiety of such intensity that it produces terror and physiologic changes.

Paranoid personality disorder: A condition characterized by a pattern of pervasive and excessive distrust and suspiciousness of others, often interpreting others' motives as malevolent.

Paraphilias: Sexual attraction to objects, materials, or situations not commonly considered erotic.

Parasomnia: Sleep disorders involving abnormal physiologic and behavioral events related to sleep characterized by dysfunctions with sleep, sleep stages, or partial arousals and associated with disturbing physiologic and behavioral events.

Parasympathetic nervous system: System that regulates heart rate, increases intestinal peristalsis and gland activity, and relaxes sphincters.

Parataxic distortion: A distorted attitude toward a person based on an inaccurate perception often related to identification of the person or event with a past experience; described by Harry Stack Sullivan.

Parenting education: Education for adults structured to support them through all stages of child development and to understand their children and their own reactions to the various behaviors of childhood and adolescence.

Parkinson's disease: A chronic, progressive, cognitive disorder involving bradykinesia, tremor, and gait and posture problems.

Partial hospitalization program: An outpatient program of less than 24-hour daily care, usually provided by a hospital, specifically designed for the diagnosis or active treatment of a serious mental disorder when there is a reasonable expectation for improvement or when it is necessary to maintain a patient's functional level and prevent relapse or full hospitalization.

Passive neglect: An omission or unintentional failure to deliver caregiving obligations; inflicting distress without willful intent.

Pathologic gambling: Recurrent and persistent maladaptive gambling behavior.

Pediatric autoimmune neuropsychiatric disorder associated with group A *Streptococcus* (PANDAS): The rapid onset of either obsessive-compulsive symptoms or tic symptoms, directly following an infection with the group A *Streptococcus* bacterium in a child who had previously not demonstrated these symptoms.

Periodic limb movements (PLM): A disorder that involves twitching and/or uncontrolled movements of the limbs that occur at times of rest or sleep or both.

Peripheral nervous system (PNS): The motor and sensory nerves and ganglia outside of the brain and spinal cord.

Persistent mental illness: Synonymous with chronic mental illness and severe mental illness.

Personality disorder: An enduring pattern of inner experience and behavior that deviates markedly from cultural expectations, is pervasive and inflexible, begins in adolescence or young adulthood, and leads to distress and impairment.

Personality, structure of: *See* structure of personality.

Personality traits: Patterns enduring over a lifetime that correlate to how one perceives, relates to, and thinks of oneself and one's environment as revealed in both social and personal contexts.

Pervasive developmental disorder: Conditions characterized by severe and persistent impairment in several areas of development including social interaction skills, communication skills, restricted areas of interest or activities, intelligence, or other learning disorders in the presence of stereotypical behaviors.

Phobia: Irrational, involuntary, and inappropriate fear associated with certain objects or situations.

Physical assessment: A medical work-up (including physical examination, clinical laboratory tests, and specialized diagnostic procedures) used in psychiatry to determine if medical illness is contributing to psychiatric symptoms.

Pick's disease: A progressive cognitive disorder of the frontal and temporal lobes involving deterioration in social skills and behavior, emotional blunting, and language problems.

Play stages: Solitary, parallel, associative, and cooperative.

Play therapy: Methods such as structured play, mutual story telling, nondirective play, behavioral play, visualization, and guided imagery used in treating emotional distress in children.

Play types: Types of play that include social, explorative, imitative, group, and competitive play.

Polydipsia: Excessive water and fluid intake causing hyponatremia.

Polysomnography: A series of tests, often including an EEG, to measure sleep stages, usually done in a sleep lab.

Pons: A prominence on the ventral surface of the brain stem.

Positive psychotic symptoms: *See* positive symptoms.

Positive reinforcement: A behavioral model developed by B.F. Skinner that rewards the desired behavior.

Positive symptoms: Psychotic symptoms that reflect an exaggeration or distortion of normal functions and include hallucinations, delusions, and disorganized speech.

Positron emission tomography (PET): Scans that detect changes in regional blood flow and metabolism with the brain.

Postintervention treatment: Psychologic first aid in a crisis that focuses on providing voluntary access to short-term, cognitively based, pragmatic services.

Postpartum depression: A mood episode that occurs within 4 weeks after delivery.

Posttraumatic stress disorder (PTSD): A psychiatric disorder occurring at any point following a threatened or actual traumatic event that involves combinations of affective, behavioral, cognitive, physiologic, and relational symptoms as well as dissociative symptoms and traumatic flashbacks that impair normal functioning.

Premature ejaculation: Rapid ejaculation that occurs very early in sexual activity.

Preoccupation: A security operation that excludes the anxiety-producing reality by a consuming interest in a person, thought, or event.

Presbycusis: The hearing loss of aging.

Presbyopia: The loss of visual accommodation usually associated with aging.

Primary mental health care: Holistic health care that addresses the needs and strengths of the whole person.

Primary, secondary, and tertiary prevention: Levels of prevention that focus on reducing the incidence of mental disorders or the rates at which new cases develop, the prevalence of mental disorders by decreasing the number of existing cases, and the severity of a mental disorder and its associated disabilities.

Prion: Proteinaceous infectious particles or infectious agents made up of protein.

Privileged communication: Confidential information provided by a client that is shared with a person in a position of trust who has a legal duty not to disclose the shared information even in a court of law.

Progressive muscle relaxation: A sequential tensing and relaxing of each muscle group to help clients distinguish between tension and relaxation and to induce a state of relaxation.

Psychiatric advance directive (PAD): A document constructed by a client that provides information regarding the client's preferences for mental health treatment.

Psychiatric emergency: An unforeseen, acute, potentially serious and life-threatening event or situation in which a client is threatened or that may represent a danger to him- or herself or others.

Psychiatric nursing interview: A discussion between the nurse and client that is guided by the nurse with the intent of gathering the information necessary to understand and treat the client.

Psychiatric rehabilitation: The development of the necessary skills for a client with chronic mental illness to live independently.

Psychoanalytic model: A conceptual model developed by Sigmund Freud based primarily on his work with persons suffering from disabling anxiety; the treatment approach derived from this model is psychoanalysis.

Psychodynamic nursing: A theory developed by Hildegard Peplau that requires the nurse to understand his or her own behavior in order to help others to identify felt difficulties and to apply principles of human relations to the problems that arise at all levels of experience.

Psychoeducation: The teaching of clients and their families about mental diseases and disorders, treatment modalities, coping behaviors, and accessing community resources.

Psychological tests: Evaluation tools that objectively measure personality, intelligence, and symptoms of mental illness.

Psychoneuroimmunology: The field of study examining bidirectional interactions between the central nervous system and the immune system.

Psychopharmacologist: A psychiatrist who specializes in prescribing psychotropic medications.

Psychopharmacology: The study of the medications used in psychiatry.

Psychosexual theory of personality development: Formulated by Sigmund Freud, a theory of personality development that evolves from birth through young adulthood.

Psychosis: The gross impairment of reality testing usually associated with delusions, disorganized behavior and cognition, incoherent or disorganized speech, and hallucinations.

Psychosocial developmental model: An intervention based on the theories of Erik Erikson that stresses the importance of trust as a basic building block for normal psychologic development; it includes eight stages (trust vs. mistrust; autonomy vs. shame and doubt; initiative vs. guilt; industry vs. inferiority; identity vs. role confusion; intimacy vs. isolation; generativity vs. stagnation, and ego integrity vs. despair).

Psychosocial typology: The concepts of onset, course, outcome, and degree of incapacitation.

Psychosomatic: The relationship between the mind and the body, usually in reference to physiologic changes or physical symptoms that have mental or emotional origins.

Psychotropic medications: The drugs used to treat psychiatric illness.

Punishment: A behavioral model developed by B.F. Skinner that provides an aversive stimulus after a behavior and serves to decrease its future occurrence.

Purging: A destructive pattern of ridding one's body of excess calories (to control weight) by vomiting, abusing laxatives or diuretics, taking enemas, and/or exercising obsessively.

Pyromania: A pattern of fire setting for pleasure, gratification, or relief of tension.

Qi gong: Pronounced "chee gung." An ancient system of healing and energy medicine from China. It is the art and science of using movement, breathing techniques, and meditation to cleanse and strengthen the circulation of life energy (qi) around the body.

Rapid cycling: The occurrence of four or more mood disorders in a 1-year period.

Rapid eye movement (REM): The lightest and most active stage of sleep measured by neuron activity and rapid eye movements and characterized by dreaming.

Rational emotive behavioral therapy: A form of cognitive behavior therapy that is a comprehensive, active-directive, philosophically and empirically based psychotherapy, focusing on resolving emotional and behavioral problems.

Reactive attachment disorder (RAD): Markedly disturbed and inappropriate social relatedness that is associated with grossly pathological care; a person with RAD can be overly inhibited or overly uninhibited in interactions with others.

Recovery model: A treatment approach to mental illness based on the belief that the client has primary responsibility for care and treatment decisions. It builds on the client's strengths, with an emphasis upon self-care, mutual respect and responsibility; peer support; consumer empowerment; respect and social acceptance; and the instillation of hope.

Refeeding syndrome: A major, life-threatening risk that can occur during any nutritional rehabilitation regimen for anorexia, especially in severely malnourished clients. It is characterized by cardiac, hematologic, and neurologic complications, including sudden, unexpected death.

Referred pain: Pain that originates in one area of the body and is experienced in another that is not receiving the noxious stimuli directly.

Reframing: The process of facilitating change by developing or suggesting alternate options and interpretations.

Reiki: A form of Japanese spiritual healing with roots in Tibetan Buddhism. The aim of Reiki is to promote health, maintain well-being, and reduce anxiety.

Relaxation: A state of peaceful tranquility.

Repetitive transcranial magnetic stimulation (rTMS): A noninvasive, painless method to stimulate the cerebral cortex with the goal of treating depression, psychosis, and other disorders.

Residential treatment setting: A therapeutic community with varying levels of supportive care built into a client's daily life.

Resistance: A client's defense against the anxiety associated with acknowledging personal troubles and an unwillingness or ambivalence to change.

Response cost: A behavioral model developed by B.F. Skinner that exacts a loss or penalty as a consequence of a certain behavior.

Restless leg syndrome: A movement disorder that involves uncomfortable pulling or crawling sensations of the lower limbs that occur at times of rest or sleep.

Restraints: Pertains to both physical restraints and drugs that are used as a means to restrain a person.

Reticular activating system (RAS): A functional system in the brain essential for wakefulness, attention, concentration, and introspection.

Retrograde amnesia: The inability to recall previously retained material.

Rett's disorder: A pervasive developmental disorder that is progressive and characterized by autistic behavior, ataxia, dementia, and seizures.

Right to refuse medication: The client's right to decline to take prescribed medications as long as he or she does not represent a danger to himself, herself, or others.

Right to refuse treatment: The right to decline inpatient hospitalization or other mental health care unless one is a danger to self or others.

Right to treatment: The right to be cared for in facilities that are psychologically and physically humane, provide adequate number of staff, and use individualized treatment plans within a therapeutic setting.

Ritualistic behavior: A repetitive activity, usually a distorted or stereotyped elaboration of some routine of daily life.

Rumination: Obsessive pattern of thinking in which unwanted thoughts are repetitively forced into conscious awareness.

SAMe (S-adenosyl-L-methionine): A chemical that is found naturally in the body. SAMe is available as a dietary supplement with antidepressant properties.

Schizoid personality disorder: A condition characterized by a pervasive pattern of detachment from social relationships and a restricted range of expression of emotions in interpersonal settings that begins by early adulthood and occurs in a variety of contexts.

Schizotypal personality disorder: A condition, often disabling and extremely distressing, characterized by a pervasive pattern of social and interpersonal deficits resulting in acute discomfort and reduced capacity for close personal relationships; accompanied by cognitive or perceptual distortions and eccentric behavior; begins by early adulthood and occurs in a variety of contexts.

Seclusion: Situation in which a person is involuntarily confined in a room or an area and is physically not permitted to leave.

Second-generation antipsychotics: Also known as atypical antipsychotics, a group of antipsychotic medications acting as sertonergic-dopamine agonists that includes Abilify (aripiprazole), Clozaril (clozapine), Geodone (ziprasidone), Invega (paliperidone), Risperdal (risperdone), Seroquel (quetiapine) and Zyprexa (olanzapine).

Security operations: A Sullivanian concept for defenses against anxiety; common security operations include apathy, somnolent detachment, selective inattention, and preoccupation.

Sedative: A medication that produces generalized CNS depression and reduces anxiety and agitation.

Selective inattention: A common security operation in which anxiety-producing aspects of a situation are not allowed into awareness.

Selective mutism: A persistent failure to speak in social situations where speaking is expected that interferes with educational achievement or social communication and that lasts at least 1 month.

Selective serotonin reuptake inhibitors (SSRIs): A group of antidepressant medications that alter the serotonin system in the brain by blocking the reabsorption (reuptake) of serotonin.

Self-actualization: A psychological concept that refers to the fulfilling one's individual potential. In Maslow's hierarchy it refers to the attainment of the basic needs of physiological, safety and security, love and belonging, and self-esteem.

Self-care deficit theory: Nursing theory developed by Dorothea Orem; postulates that the actions of nurse and patient are determined by the patient's self-care agency, and nursing is seen as an interactive process based on the amount and kind of nursing agency needed.

Self-concept: A Sullivanian concept; a relatively enduring assessment of self that results from reflected appraisals of significant others. It is also an individual's awareness of self, beliefs, thoughts, relationships, body image, and self-esteem.

Self-disclosure: Revelation of personal information about oneself, with the goal of benefiting the client and the therapeutic process.

Self-esteem: A term that refers to a person's overall sense of self-worth or personal value.

Self-help clearinghouses: Nonprofit services that help people to find and form self-help groups within their service areas.

Self-help groups: Nonprofit, voluntary, community-based support groups, run by and for people who join together on the basis of their common experience, to help one another as peers. They are not professionally run, although professionals frequently serve them in supportive ancillary roles. They might best be described as mutual help groups, but their description as self-help has become the primary phrase used in the literature to distinguish them as member-run support groups.

Self-help networks: Mutual aid networks operating primarily on the Internet, wherein peers provide mutual help to one another via message boards, electronic mailing lists, chat rooms, and other interactive means. Networks can also operate through interactive newsletters, telephone, and correspondence networks.

Self-management training: Complementary therapies in which an individual learns to control thoughts and feelings by utilizing techniques such as breathing, meditation, or self-talk to manage symptoms.

Sense of self model: A theory advanced by child psychiatrist Daniel Stern in which four different senses of self are described (emergent self, core self, subjective self, and verbal self).

Sensitization: The tendency for initial mood episodes to be linked to identified stressors, but later episodes require less of a stressor or none at all.

Separation anxiety: Childhood-onset disorder characterized by excessive fear and apprehension when separated from home or from close attachment figures such as parents or the main caregiver.

Separation-individuation process: A developmental process, occurring in the first 3 years of life, consisting of a series of tasks critical to the development of effective interpersonal relationships and personal integration of positive and negative components in self and others.

Serotonin: A brain chemical or neurotransmitter affected by the atypical antipsychotic and antidepressant medications. It has been implicated in a number of disorders such as anxiety, depression, and migraine.

Serotonin syndrome: A potentially fatal syndrome caused by too much serotonin in the neuronal synapses in the brain stem and spinal cord, characterized by mental status changes, anxiety, fever, diaphoresis, diarrhea, tachycardia, uncoordination, myoclonus, and hyperreflexia.

Severe mental illness: Synonymous with chronic mental illness and persistent mental illness.

Sexual misconduct: The expression of any thoughts, feelings, or gestures that could be construed by the client as romantic or erotic in nature.

Sexual orientation: The gender to which one is erotically attracted. One can be androphilic (attracted to males), gynephilic (attracted to females), bisexual (attracted to both), asexual (attracted to neither), or undifferentiated.

Sexual response cycle: The physiological, cognitive, and emotional effects of sexual stimuli that occur in four phases, namely, desire, excitement, orgasm, and resolution.

Sibling rivalry: Children's interactions and experiences with brothers and sisters, often foreshadowing the many future challenges and competitions that they will encounter in adulthood.

Side effect: An unintended effect of a medication.

Situational crises: Crises that are precipitated by unpredictable events for which people cannot prepare.

Situational disturbance: Adaptation and transitions that can be accidental, planned, or imposed.

Sleep architecture: The patterns or five stages of REM (rapid eye movement) and NREM (nonrapid eye movement) representing the structure, continuity, and underlying physiologic mechanisms of sleep.

Sleep terror disorder: Parasomnias involving incomplete arousal from deep sleep and characterized by screaming and physical activity, unresponsiveness to others, and amnesia for the event.

Sleepwalking: Also known as somnambulism; the repeated action after the onset of sleep of rising from bed and ambulating.

Somatic motor system: Is responsible for voluntary control of skeletal muscle.

Somatic therapies: Physiologically based interventions designed to produce behavioral change.

Somatization: The process of expressing psychologic conflict through physical complaints or symptoms.

Somatoform disorder: A mental disorder in which physical symptoms or preoccupations present as a medical illness but are considered to be primarily psychiatric in origin.

Somnolent detachment: A primitive security operation wherein an individual falls asleep when confronted by a highly threatening, anxiety-producing experience.

Splitting: The inability to integrate positive and negative feelings, resulting in a tendency to view people and situations as all good or all bad; a primitive defense against a fear of abandonment.

SSRIs: *See* selective serotonin reuptake inhibitors.

St. John's wort (*Hypericum perforatum*): A plant whose flowers are used to produce teas, tablets, and capsules containing concentrated extracts to treat depression, anxiety, and insomnia.

Standards of practice: Authoritative statements that address the care that the mental health client receives; they are based on the nursing process.

Standards of professional performance: Authoritative statements that address the psychiatric-mental health registered nurse's professional functioning.

Stimulants: A family of psychotropic medications used primarily to treat attention-deficit disorder.

Stress-diathesis model: Theory that explains the development of psychiatric disorders as a combination of genetic predisposition (diathesis) and environmental stress.

Stressor: Any experience or stimulus that is experienced by an individual as a challenge, threat, or as potentially harmful.

Structural family therapy: Type of therapy developed by Salvador Minuchin; it stresses the importance of understanding a person within a social context, specifically the family's organization and the interactional patterns between members.

Structural imaging: A category of brain imaging that gathers information regarding the physical constitution of the brain at any point in time. Structural imaging tests include computed tomography (CT) and magnetic resonance imaging (MRI).

Structure of personality: Theory formulated by Sigmund Freud; it comprises the id, ego, and superego.

Stuttering: A disturbance in the normal fluency and time patterning of speech that is inappropriate for one's age or developmental stage.

Substance abuse: Brief or chronic episodes of substance use that result in failure to meet major role obligations, legal problems, or recurrent social or interpersonal problems. There is no evidence of physiologic or psychologic dependence.

Substance dependence: The excessive and continued use of a substance despite significant impairment to at least one aspect of life: physiologic, psychologic, behavioral, or social. Dependence includes additional symptoms that may include tolerance, withdrawal, preoccupation with the substance, compulsive behavior, or inability to stop or reduce the use of the substance.

Substance-induced disorders: Intoxication and withdrawal as well as other disorders induced by substances, including delirium, dementia, amnesia, paranoia, depression, anxiety, sexual dysfunction, and sleep disorders.

Suicidal thoughts: The thought, threat, plan, or intent for self-destruction.

Suicide: Intentional termination of one's own life.

Sundowning: The increased confusion experienced in dementia that occurs in the early evening.

Sympathetic nervous system: Part of the autonomic nervous system that responds to stress; prepares one to fight or flee in an emergency.

Synapse: The contact space between neurons or between neurons and muscles where a presynaptic neuron passes a chemical or electrical signal to a postsynaptic cell.

System of care: A comprehensive and coordinated system of mental health care and other services to meet the multiple and changing needs of those with mental health problems.

Systematic desensitization: Gradual exposure to an increasing hierarchy of stress-provoking stimuli for the purpose of extinguishing the negative emotional response.

Tai chi: A noncombative martial art that consists of slow, gentle movements, combined with breathing techniques and meditation, to improve the flow of qi, or life energy, thereby calming the mind and promoting health.

Tardive dyskinesia (TD): A late-occurring, irreversible side effect of antipsychotics that involves involuntary, unwanted, repetitious movements of the muscles of the face, limbs and trunk. The risk of this problem is greatly reduced with the newer atypical antipsychotics.

Temper tantrums: The physical way a young child lets out strong emotions and communicates feelings; these episodes of rage, stomping, screaming, and throwing himself or herself to the floor are a normal part of childhood development.

Temporal lobe: The lateral region of the cerebrum.

Thalamus: Part of the diencephalon of the brain; it conveys sensory information excluding smell to the cerebral cortex.

Therapeutic community: A type of participative, group-based milieu therapy that creates a microcosm of society in which persons with chronic mental illness or substance use disorders can learn and practice skills for daily living.

Therapeutic contract: The agreement between the nurse and client to work on mutually identified problems; may be written or oral in nature.

Therapeutic effect: The intended effect of a medication.

Therapeutic milieu: A nurturing environment that provides both adaptive and corrective experiences in a safe place with predictable standards for behavior.

Therapeutic touch: A form of energy healing derived from laying on of hands.

Third-party reimbursement: Services that are reimbursed through traditional indemnity insurance plans; self-insured plans constructed by employers and other groups; managed care plans, and state and federal government plans such as Medicare, Medicaid, and the Civilian Health and Medical Program of the Uniformed Services; and the Federal Employees Health Benefits Program.

Thought disorder: Disorganized cognition displayed by disorganized speech and use of language.

Tolerance: A person's need for increasing amounts of a substance to achieve the desired effects.

Tourette's syndrome (TS): A disorder involving multiple motor tics and one or more vocal tics occurring many times a day over a period of at least 1 year and during which there is never a period of more than 3 consecutive months tic free.

Trajectory model: The course of the chronic illness as an uncertain path that requires that those with the illness, their family members, and their healthcare providers work together to shape the illness; it is composed of seven key concepts.

Transdisciplinary team: A care model based on free-flowing communication and the transfer of knowledge and skills across discipline boundaries in the service of a common, client-centered goal.

Transference: A client's projection or displacement of unconscious feelings, desires, and actions from a person in his or her life onto the nurse or other therapist.

Transgendered: A social umbrella term commonly used to describe individuals whose gender identity, to different degrees, varies significantly from their chromosomal sex.

Transsexual: A popular term describing an individual whose cross-gender identification is so pervasive that he or she seeks to live in the gender role of the opposite sex.

Traumatic flashbacks: A transient, intense, intrusive, repeated reexperience in the present of thoughts, emotions, and physical sensations surrounding a past disturbance.

Treatment-resistant depression (TRD): A major depressive disorder that is severe, has lasted for at least 2 years, and has failed to respond to at least four different antidepressants.

TRIADS: A method for assessing trauma in children; it includes types of abuse, role relationship, intensity, autonomic response, duration, and style of abuse.

Triage: Derived from the French *trier* (to choose), triage is a classification process developed from battlefield techniques to rapidly assess acuity and attempt to balance needs and available resources, making certain that the right client, place, time, and care provider are identified.

Trichophagia: The act of eating one's hair, usually resulting in the development of hairballs and abdominal discomfort.

Trichotillomania: Recurrent pulling out of one's hair for pleasure, gratification, or relief of tension, resulting in noticeable hair loss.

Tricyclic antidepressant: Drug that works by blocking the reuptake of norepinephrine and serotonin at the nerve synapse.

Unipolar: A mood disorder of only depressive episodes.

Vaginismus: An involuntary contraction of the muscle around the vagina that prevents penile insertion.

Vagus nerve stimulation (VNS): A form of brain stimulation therapy used for the long-term therapy of clients with treatment-resistant depression (TRD).

Valerian root (*Valeriana officinalis*): Herb used for anxiety and insomnia. Valerian is believed to affect the amygdala, an area of the brain responsible for memory and emotions, and also to inhibit the breakdown of GABA, thereby inducing sedation.

Vascular dementia: A cognitive disorder, usually progressive, that is associated with cerebral vascular changes, sometimes causing speech problems and paresis.

Vicarious traumatization: A process in which traumatic damage is transferred to helpers or rescuers involved in crisis work by exposure to traumatic experiences through their work or through their intense involvement in the experiences of others.

Victim: Any person of any age who is violated by acts of disorderly conduct, harassment, reckless endangerment, entrapment, or assault, including attempted assault.

Violence: Any activity that demonstrates that one can be physically, emotionally, or sexually harmful to self or others.

VIPP teaching: When providing children with information, this method stresses the use of visual aids, information appropriate for age, and preparation done using play.

Wernicke's aphasia: A form of disordered language function affecting the comprehension of written and spoken words.

Wernicke's encephalopathy: A serious neurotoxic effect of alcohol abuse, related to thiamine deficiency; it is characterized by mental confusion, eye movement disturbances, and ataxia. It is the first stage of Wernicke-Korsakoff syndrome. (*see* Korsakoff syndrome)

Withdrawal: The process that occurs when a person who is physically addicted to a substance stops using or reduces the intake of that substance after heavy, prolonged consumption. The symptoms of withdrawal vary across substances.

Withdrawal delirium: Also known as delirium tremens (DTs), a life-threatening complication of alcohol withdrawal characterized by agitation, disorientation, visual hallucinations, elevated temperature, and cardiac arrhythmias.

Xerostomia: Dry mouth.

Yoga: A practice that involves gentle exercise combined with physical positions, breathing techniques, and meditation.

Index

Figures and tables are indicated by f and t following the page number.

A

C

D

J

K

L

M

O

P

Q

R

S

Photo Credits

Unless otherwise indicated, photographs and art are under copyright of Jones & Bartlett Learning.

Part and chapter openers © Subbotina Anna/ShutterStock, Inc.

Chapter 1

Figure 1-1 William Hogarth, *The Rake's Progress: 8. The Rake in Bedlam*, 1734. Oil on canvas, 625 x 752 mm. Sir John Sloane's Museum, London.

Figure 1-2 © David Buffington/Photodisc/Getty Images

Figure 1-3 © Markus Gann/ShutterStock, Inc.

Figure 1-4 © photobank.ch/ShutterStock, Inc.

Figure 1-5 Reprinted with permission from: Davis, C. (2006). Family History. In: Davis, C., (ed.), *Patient practitioner interaction: An experiential manual for developing the art of health care* (4th ed., p. 30). Thorofare, NJ: SLACK Incorporated.

Chapter 4

Figure 4-1 © AbleStock

Chapter 5

Figure 5-11 Courtesy of Lynn E. DeLisi, MD.

Chapter 6

Figure 6-1 Guy, W. (1976). ECDEU assessment manual for psychopharmacology. Washington, DC: U.S. Department of Health, Education and Welfare.

Chapter 7

Figure 7-1 Courtesy of Journalist 1st Class Mark D. Faram/U.S. Navy.

Figure 7-2 © Leah-Anne Thompson/ShutterStock, Inc.

Chapter 8

Figure 8-1 © Photos.com

Figure 8-2 © Renata Osinska/Shutterstock, Inc.

Chapter 10

Figure 10-2 ©AbleStock

Figure 10-4 © iofoto/ShutterStock, Inc.

Figure 10-5 © Cora Reed/ShutterStock, Inc.

Chapter 12

Figure 12-1 © Terrie L. Zeller/ShutterStock, Inc.

Figure 12-2 © Lorraine Swanson/ShutterStock, Inc.

Chapter 15

Figure 15-1 © Doug Menuez/ Photodisc/Getty Images

Chapter 16

Figure 16-1 © Modesty Girl/Shutterstock, Inc.

Figure 16-2 © iofoto/ShutterStock, Inc.

Chapter 17

Figure 17-1 © Isaac Brekken/AP Photo

Figure 17-2 © Karen Winton/ShutterStock, Inc.

Chapter 18

Figure 18-2 © Cameron Cross/Shutterstock, Inc.

Chapter 19

Figure 19-1 © Keith Brofsky/Photodisc/Getty Images

Chapter 21

Figure 21-2 © Ryan McVay/Photodisc/Getty Images

Chapter 22

Figure 22-1 (top) © Magdalena Szachowska/ShutterStock, Inc.
Figure 22-1 (bottom) © Doreen Salcher/ShutterStock, Inc.
Figure 22-2 © Photos.com

Chapter 23

Figure 23-1 © Photos.com

Chapter 25

Figure 25-1 © Ingram Publishing/Alamy Images

Chapter 26

Figure 26-1 © PhotoCreate/ShutterStock, Inc.
Figure 26-2 © Photos.com

Chapter 27

Figure 27-1 © PhotoCreate/ShutterStock, Inc.
Figure 27-2 © NorthGeorgiaMedia/ShutterStock, Inc.

Chapter 28

Figure 28-1 © Photos.com
Figure 28-2 © AbleStock